AP* Edition

BIOLOGY

Eighth Edition

Neil A. Campbell

Jane B. Reece
Berkeley, California

Lisa A. Urry
Mills College, Oakland, California

Michael L. Cain
Bowdoin College, Brunswick, Maine

Steven A. Wasserman
University of California, San Diego

Peter V. Minorsky
Mercy College, Dobbs Ferry, New York

Robert B. Jackson
Duke University, Durham, North Carolina

AP, Advanced Placement, and Advanced Placement Program are registered trademarks of The College Board, which was not involved in the production of, and does not endorse this product.

PEARSON

Benjamin Cummings

San Francisco   Boston   New York
Cape Town   Hong Kong   London   Madrid
Mexico City   Montreal   Munich   Paris
Singapore   Sydney   Tokyo   Toronto

Editor-in-Chief: *Beth Wilbur*

Executive Director of Development: *Deborah Gale*

Supervising Editors: *Pat Burner and Beth N. Winickoff*

Senior Editorial Manager: *Ginnie Simione Jutson*

Managing Editor: *Michael Early*

Marketing Managers: *Lauren Harp and Josh Frost*

Developmental Editors: *John Burner, Matt Lee, Alice E. Fugate, and Suzanne Olivier*

Developmental Artists: *Hilair Chism, Carla Simmons, Kelly Murphy, Andrew Recher, and Connie Balek*

Art Editors: *Laura Murray and Kelly Murphy*

Senior Photo Editor: *Donna Kalal*

Photo Researcher: *Maureen Spuhler*

Editorial Assistants: *Benjamin Pearson, Logan Triglia, and Julia Khait*

Production Management, Composition, and Prepress: *S4Carlisle Publishing Services*

Illustrations: *Precision Graphics*

Copy Editor: *Janet Greenblatt*

Design Director: *Mark Ong*

Art Director: *Marilyn Perry*

Text Design: *Mark Ong, Jennifer Dunn, Jana Anderson*

Cover Design: *Yvo Riezebos*

Text Printer: *Courier Kendallville*

Cover Printer: *Moore Langen/Courier*

Senior Supplements Project Editor: *Susan Berge*

Supplements Production Supervisor: *Jane Brundage*

Senior Media Producer: *Jonathan Ballard*

Media Project Editors: *Nora Lally-Graves and Brienn Buchanan*

Associate Web Developer: *Linda Young*

On the cover: Magnolia flower. Chris Fox/Corbis

Credits continue following the appendices.

Library of Congress Cataloging-in-Publication Data

Campbell, Neil A.

    Biology / Neil A. Campbell, Jane B. Reece. — 8th ed.
      p. cm.
    Includes index.
    ISBN-13: 978-0-8053-6844-4 (alk. paper)
    ISBN-10: 0-8053-6844-2 (alk. paper)
    1. Biology.   I. Reece, Jane B.   II. Title.

QH308.2.C34 2009
570--dc22   2007042662

AP Edition ISBN: 978-0-13-135691-7/0-13-135691-7

5 6 7 8 9 10—CRK—11 10 09

Benjamin Cummings
1301 Sansome Street
San Francisco, CA 94111
www.aw-bc.com

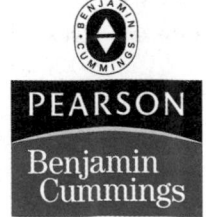

Brief Contents

About the Authors

Neil A. Campbell

Neil Campbell combined the investigative nature of a research scientist with the soul of an experienced and caring teacher. He earned his M.A. in Zoology from UCLA and his Ph.D. in Plant Biology from the University of California, Riverside, where he received the Distinguished Alumnus Award in 2001. Neil published numerous research articles on desert and coastal plants and how the sensitive plant (*Mimosa*) and other legumes move their leaves. His 30 years of teaching in diverse environments included general biology courses at Cornell University, Pomona College, and San Bernardino Valley College, where he received the college's first Outstanding Professor Award in 1986. Neil was a visiting scholar in the Department of Botany and Plant Sciences at the University of California, Riverside. In addition to his authorship of this book, he coauthored *Biology: Concepts & Connections* and *Essential Biology* with Jane Reece. Neil died shortly after the initial planning of this revision, but his legacy continues in *BIOLOGY*, Eighth Edition.

Jane B. Reece

Lead author Jane Reece, Neil Campbell's longtime collaborator, has participated in every edition of *BIOLOGY*—first as an editor and contributor, then as an author. Her education includes an A.B. in Biology from Harvard University, an M.S. in Microbiology from Rutgers University, and a Ph.D. in Bacteriology from the University of California, Berkeley. Before migrating to California from the Northeast, she taught biology at Middlesex County College and Queensborough Community College. At UC Berkeley, and later as a postdoctoral fellow in genetics at Stanford University, her research focused on genetic recombination in bacteria. Besides her work on *BIOLOGY*, she has been a coauthor on *Biology: Concepts & Connections*, *Essential Biology*, and *The World of the Cell*.

For the Eighth Edition, Jane Reece is joined by five coauthors whose contributions reflect their biological expertise as scientific researchers and their teaching sensibilities gained from years of experience as instructors.

Lisa A. Urry

Units 1–3 (Chapters 2–21) and Chapter 47
Lisa Urry is a professor at Mills College in Oakland, California, and was a major contributor to the Seventh Edition of *BIOLOGY*. After graduating from Tufts University with a double major in Biology and French, Lisa completed her Ph.D. in Molecular and Developmental Biology at MIT. Following postdoctoral appointments at Harvard Medical School, Tufts University, and UC Berkeley, she began teaching at Mills College, where she currently holds the Letts-Villard Professorship and serves as Chair of the Biology Department. She has published research articles on various topics involving gene expression during embryonic development. Her current research interest is in sea urchin development. Lisa is also deeply committed to promoting opportunities for women in science education and research.

Michael L. Cain

Units 4 and 5 (Chapters 22–34)
Michael Cain is an ecologist and evolutionary biologist currently at Bowdoin College. Michael earned a joint degree in Biology and Math from Bowdoin College, an M.Sc. from Brown University, and a Ph.D. in Ecology and Evolutionary Biology from Cornell University. After postdoctoral work in plant ecology at the University of Connecticut and molecular genetics at Washington University in St. Louis, Michael went on to teach general biology, ecology, and evolution in a diverse range of settings, including Carleton College, New Mexico State University, and Rose-Hulman Institute of Technology in Indiana. Michael is the author of dozens of scientific papers on topics that include foraging behavior in insects and plants, long-distance seed dispersal, and speciation in crickets.

Steven A. Wasserman

Unit 7 (Chapters 40–46, 48–51)
Steve Wasserman is a professor at the University of California, San Diego. He earned his A.B. in Biology from Harvard University and his Ph.D. in Biological Sciences from MIT. Since a postdoctoral sojourn at UC Berkeley, where he investigated topological transformations of DNA, he has focused on regulatory pathway mechanisms. Working with the fruit fly *Drosophila*, he has contributed to the fields of embryogenesis, reproduction, and immunity. As a faculty member at the University of Texas Southwestern Medical Center and UC San Diego, he has taught genetics, development, and physiology to undergraduate, graduate, and medical students. He has also served as the research mentor for more than a dozen doctoral students and nearly 40 aspiring scientists at the undergraduate and high school level. Steve has been the recipient of distinguished scholar awards from both the Markey Charitable Trust and the David and Lucille Packard Foundation. He recently received the 2007 Academic Senate Distinguished Teaching Award for undergraduate teaching at UC San Diego.

Peter V. Minorsky

Unit 6 (Chapters 35–39)
Peter Minorsky revised Unit 6 for the Sixth and Seventh Editions of *BIOLOGY* and is a professor at Mercy College in New York, where he teaches evolution, ecology, botany, and introductory biology. He is also the science writer for the journal *Plant Physiology*. He received his B.A. in Biology from Vassar College and his Ph.D. in Plant Physiology from Cornell University. After a postdoctoral fellowship at the University of Wisconsin at Madison, Peter taught at Kenyon College, Union College, Western Connecticut State University, and Vassar College. He is an electrophysiologist who studies plant responses to stress and is currently exploring the possible effects of geomagnetism on plant growth.

Robert B. Jackson

Unit 8 (Chapters 52–56)
Rob Jackson is a professor of biology and Nicholas Chair of Environmental Sciences at Duke University. He directed Duke's Program in Ecology for many years and is currently the Vice President of Science for the Ecological Society of America. Rob holds a B.S. in Chemical Engineering from Rice University, as well as M.S. degrees in Ecology and Statistics and a Ph.D. in Ecology from Utah State University. He was a postdoctoral scientist in Stanford University's Biology Department and an Assistant Professor at the University of Texas, Austin. Rob has received numerous awards, including being honored at the White House with a Presidential Early Career Award in Science and Engineering from the National Science Foundation. He has published a trade book about the environment, *The Earth Remains Forever*, and a children's book of poetry about biology and animals called *Animal Mischief*. His second children's book, *Not Again*, will be published in 2008.

About the *Biology* 8e AP* Edition Program

Welcome to the *BIOLOGY* 8e AP Edition Program. The publisher and the author team remain fully committed to ongoing support of the Advanced Placement biology community of teachers and students. In addition to the AP Edition of the textbook, the *BIOLOGY* 8e AP Edition Program includes a wealth of media and print supplements specifically designed for AP classrooms. Turn to pages xxvi-xxvii of this textbook's front section to read more about them. We look forward to hearing your thoughts and welcome your suggestions, which can be mailed to:

Campbell/Reece *BIOLOGY* 8e AP Program
Benjamin Cummings Publishing
1301 Sansome Street
San Francisco, CA 94111

About the AP* Edition Textbook

The *BIOLOGY* 8e AP Edition textbook is designed specifically for the Advanced Placement biology course. Although the biological content is the same, there are three differences between the AP and the college editions of this textbook:

- The AP Edition has a stronger, reinforced binding to withstand the rigors of high school use.
- There are references throughout the AP Edition textbook driving readers to the specially prepared website for AP teachers and students.
- The AP Edition textbook's front section includes material developed specifically for AP teachers and students. This front section includes a topic guide correlating the contents of the Eighth Edition to the AP curriculum; an essay to the AP student written by Fred and Theresa Holtzclaw (long-time AP instructors and graders); and a thematic study grid to help students connect the AP Biology themes to the course topics. Also on pages xxvi-xxvii is a list of all the materials and supplements particular to AP classroom needs, including customer access to websites.

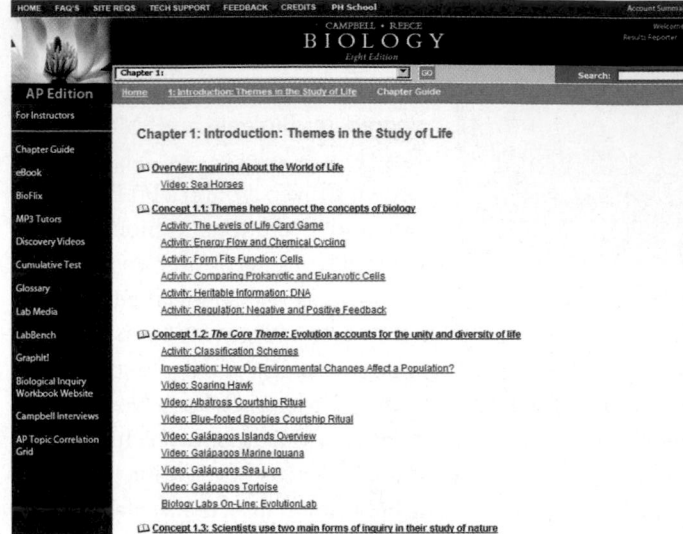

About the AP* Edition Technology

For the AP Edition, the publisher has prepared a complimentary version of the www.campbellbiology.com website for AP students and teachers adopting the textbook. The Student Media CD-ROM included with this textbook contains many of the assets and activities from the website. Turn to page xxvii for a detailed description of the site, access information, and the differences between the website and the CD-ROM.

Additional Technology Options

MasteringBiology™ (*For purchase only/12-month subscriptions.*)
See a description of this optional online homework, tutorial, and assessment system on page xxvii.

Biology Labs On-Line (*For purchase only.*)
See a description of this optional online lab program on page xxvii.

A Letter to the AP Student

Fred and Theresa Holtzclaw, co-authors of *Pearson Education AP* Test Prep Series: Biology*

Welcome to Advanced Placement Biology! We hope this will be a rewarding and exciting year for you. Your curiosity and enthusiasm about the natural world will make the task of studying biology a pleasure. As each topic unfolds, you will begin to see that, while some of your questions are answered, there will always be more that you wonder about.

We have been involved with AP Biology for many years. Besides teaching hundreds of students, we have worked on writing the AP exam, prepared rubrics to evaluate student responses to exam questions, graded exams, and edited the Advanced Placement laboratory manual. Through this letter, we hope to use our experiences to offer you encouragement and suggestions for success in your AP Biology journey.

The course you are about to begin is designed to provide high school students with a college-level course normally taken by life science majors. This is where future geneticists, ecologists, biology teachers, evolutionary biologists, and doctors all begin their studies. Students who do well on the AP exam in May generally receive 8 to 10 hours of college credit. To put that in perspective, a freshman becomes a sophomore at 30 credit hours.

One of the most valuable benefits of taking this course is to learn how to succeed in an academically challenging subject.

The skills you develop for success in AP Biology are applicable to all areas of study, and will provide a solid academic foundation regardless of your final occupation. At this challenging level, a course involves a two-way exchange of information. What will *you* bring to your class? Your teacher will organize the instruction, but any class is ultimately only as rewarding as the students make it. Your ideas, questions, and enthusiasm can make an ordinary class extraordinary!

There are myriad approaches to learning and you will need to develop your own strategies to master the concepts and content of this course. One requirement for success is to be an active learner. Reading your text in a semiconscious daze does not constitute time studying. Ask yourself, what do I know when the textbook is closed? Can I recreate key figures? Can I design a flow chart that simplifies complex ideas? Looking at your notes and looking at the book are just looking; learning requires that you understand.

You may find that study groups are an effective way to become an active learner. Meet with your study partners to reinforce the vocabulary, but more importantly to explain concepts to each other. Select key figures, and take turns sketching and explaining them. Do you wonder how your teacher can possibly know so much and explain it to you so easily? This ability comes from practicing the explanation over and over. Remember, *everyone* has to work to master the material in biology. Don't wait until exam time to meet your study group. The more you understand as the unit unfurls, the less you have to worry about as the exam approaches. If you keep up with your reading and study along the way, each day you will leave class with more information in your brain that you understand.

A word about the vocabulary in this course—it is extensive! The complex vocabulary of biology is required for biologists to communicate precisely, but it is not the end point of your studying. Try to put your work with the vocabulary into a larger, conceptual framework. As you become familiar with terms, be sure to try to hook each term to a larger idea. That is, use these terms to help you explain the concepts and connections between major biological themes in the course.

And then those exams! Your teacher may lump together several large chapters to test an entire unit. This is the way many college courses will work, so getting used to that will help prepare you for college. It is hard to achieve high scores on every single test. If a unit doesn't go well for you, revisit the material, review your errors, and strive to master the topic. Think about why you did well on one exam and not so well on another. Did you spend more time with one topic area? Was one subject more interesting than another? Relax, and use the exams to measure your progress and investigate your strengths and weaknesses. For example, if you are a person who can see details better than concepts, group the details into clusters that can be connected to concepts. If you work week to week and use each exam as another learning tool, you will be positioned to do well on the AP Biology Exam in May.

One resource that can help you focus on the most important concepts is the workbook *Pearson Education AP* Test Prep Series: Biology*. This workbook is intended as a review guide for the national AP exam, and it will help you to focus on the key concepts in the course. It follows the organization of this textbook and provides you with plenty of practice quizzes and tests. While a unit exam in your class may require more detail than this end-of-term guide provides, it will help you to identify the most important concepts and guide you in your study.

The AP Biology program includes 12 required labs. Each of these labs gives you the opportunity to participate in experiments that support important concepts from the text. In order to achieve this, you cannot merely show up for lab—you should arrive with a clear understanding of the purpose and procedure of the lab. Otherwise, you are likely to make procedural errors or leave without a conceptual understanding of the laboratory. It is very easy to fall into the trap of walking through the steps of a lab procedure without really knowing what they mean or why you are doing them. At our schools, we require students to preview the lab using LabBench, which is available on the textbook website (www.campbellbiology.com) or by visiting www.biology.com and selecting The Biology Place. The LabBench will help you visualize the apparatus used in the lab, see how to manipulate equipment and make measurements, and analyze your results.

AP Biology is a long journey, much like a long walk. To complete your journey you have to take many small steps every day. Consistently walking (or working!) every day allows you to cover a vast distance. The two of us are long-distance walkers. Over the years we have found many connections between what we learn on our walks and what we learn from our students. On a trek last summer we planned to walk across Switzerland before school resumed in the fall. About half way across the country we were faced with what seemed an impossibly hard day ahead. In order to reach our destination, we would hike 15 kilometers with a total elevation gain of just over 1350 meters. Scouting our route with binoculars the night before, we could just make out a small mountain hut perched on a snow-covered pass. We knew that we would pass that hut along the way and that our hike would continue beyond it! The trail ahead seemed so daunting that we barely slept that night. At dawn we started walking. The path took us up, and up, and up again, rising many hundreds of meters in elevation to reach the pass. The day was beautiful and we had a joyful walk—before we knew it, we were at the pass, looking back to the tiny village where we had started. The delight of being together and the accumulation of many small steps allowed us to conquer what seemed so difficult only the night before. And, in that summer, we completed the walk—from one end of Switzerland to the other.

Day by day, week by week, you will slowly accumulate knowledge, and at the end of your journey, you will look back and marvel at the progress you have made. And after you look back, take a look forward, much as we did from the top of the mountain pass in Switzerland. When you do, you will see the next steps ahead of you and feel the excitement of the continuing journey. Good luck!

Fred and Theresa Holtzclaw
Webb School of Knoxville and Oak Ridge High School, Tennessee

AP Biology Thematic Study Grid

The College Board has identified eight major themes that recur throughout the AP Biology course. You will find a discussion of these themes in Chapter 1 of your textbook. This study tool below connects the eight AP themes to the course topics.

The topics are in the left column and the themes are listed along the top. Some suggested examples of a theme applied to a topic are provided. Fill the empty grid cells in yourself and find additional examples to add to those already shown.

	Science as a Process	Evolution	Energy Transfer	Continuity and Change	Relationship of Structure to Function	Regulation	Inter-dependence in Nature	Science, Technology, and Society
Chemistry of Life	X-ray crystallography helps scientists determine the three-dimensional structure of proteins.	Chemical evolution of the young earth set the stage for the origin of life.				In feedback inhibition, a metabolic pathway is switched off by its end product.	Prokaryotes play essential roles in chemical cycling for plants and animals.	
Cells	The discovery and early study of cells progressed with the invention and improvement of microscopes.	The matching machinery of all eukaryotic cilia is evidence of an evolutionary connection between eukaryotes.			The mitochondrion's folded inner membrane allows cells to pack a large surface area into a very small container.			Advances in cancer research depend on progress in our understanding of how cells work.
Cellular Energetics			A proton gradient across membranes powers the synthesis of ATP in cells.		The folded organization of the mitochondrion's inner membrane enhances the productivity of cellular respiration.			
Heredity	Experiments with viruses that infect bacteria provided evidence that DNA is the genetic material.			DNA molecules carry biological information from one generation to the next.				DNA technology has provided new treatments for genetic diseases
Molecular Genetics		The continuity of life depends on the inheritance of information encoded in the nucleotide sequences of DNA molecules.				Mutations that cause deficiencies in signaling pathways that regulate the cell cycle can lead to cancer.		Automatic DNA-sequencing machines made the Human Genome Project possible.
Evolutionary Biology								
Diversity of Organisms	Evolutionary theory itself evolves as new methods and data refine our view of phylogenetic relationships among organisms.							Destruction of tropical rainforests has global consequences.
Structure and Function of Plants and Animals			Plants transform light energy into chemical energy.		The honeycombed construction of a bird's bones provides a lightweight skeleton of great strength that makes flight possible.		Consumers acquire their energy in chemical form by eating plants, by eating animals that ate plants, or by decomposing organic refuse.	
Ecology			Energy flows from sunlight to producers to consumers.		Morphological adaptations of parasites to hosts enhance their survival.		The energy that enters an ecosystem as sunlight exits as heat, which all organisms dissipate to their surroundings.	New technology may help us solve global problems.

AP Topic Correlation

This chart correlates the Advanced Placement Biology topics, as outlined by The College Board, with the corresponding chapters and Key Concept numbers in *BIOLOGY* 8e AP Edition.

AP BIOLOGY TOPICS	CORRELATION TO *BIOLOGY* 8E AP EDITION
I. Molecules and Cells	Units 1 and 2
A. Chemistry of Life	**Chapters 3, 4, 5, 8**
1. Water	Concepts 3.1–3.3
2. Organic molecules in organisms	Concepts 4.1–4.3, 5.1–5.5
3. Free energy changes	Concepts 8.1–8.3
4. Enzymes	Concepts 8.4–8.5
B. Cells	**Chapters 6, 7, 11, 12**
1. Prokaryotic and eukaryotic cells	Concepts 6.1–6.7, 27.1–27.6
2. Membranes	Concepts 6.2, 6.4, 7.1–7.5, 11.1–11.4
3. Subcellular organization	Concepts 6.2–6.7
4. Cell cycle and its regulation	Concepts 12.1–12.3
C. Cellular Energetics	**Chapters 8, 9, 10**
1. Coupled reactions	Concepts 8.3, 9.1–9.4
2. Fermentation and cellular respiration	Concepts 9.1–9.6
3. Photosynthesis	Concepts 10.1–10.4
II. Heredity and Evolution	Units 3, 4, and 5
A. Heredity	**Chapters 13–15**
1. Meiosis and gametogenesis	Concepts 13.1–13.4
2. Eukaryotic chromosomes	Concepts 15.1–15.3, 16.3
3. Inheritance patterns	Concepts 14.1–14.4, 15.2–15.5
B. Molecular Genetics	**Chapters 16–20**
1. RNA and DNA structure and function	Concepts 16.1–16.2, 17.1–17.4
2. Gene regulation	Concepts 18.1–18.5
3. Mutation	Concepts 15.4, 17.5, 18.5, 21.5
4. Viral structure and replication	Concepts 19.1–19.3
5. Nucleic acid technology and applications	Concepts 20.1–20.4, 21.1–21.2

C. Evolutionary Biology   **Chapters 22–26**

  1. Early evolution of life   Concepts 25.1–25.4

  2. Evidence for evolution   Concepts 22.2–22.3, 24.2–24.4, 25.2–25.5, 26.4–26.5

  3. Mechanisms of evolution   Concepts 22.1–22.3, 23.1–23.4, 24.1–24.4, 25.4–25.5, 26.4, 26.6

III. Organisms and Populations   **Units 4, 5, 6, 7, and 8**

A. Diversity of Organisms   **Chapters 25–34**

  1. Evolutionary patterns   Concepts 26.1, 26.3, 29.1–29.2, 32.1–32.4

  2. Survey of the diversity of life   Concepts 27.1–27.4, 28.1–28.6, 29.2–29.3, 30.1–30.3, 31.1–31.4, 32.1, 32.4, 33.1–33.5, 34.1–34.8

  3. Phylogenetic classification   Concepts 26.1–26.3, 26.6, 27.4, 28.1, 29.1–29.3, 30.2–30.3, 31.3–31.4, 32.4, 33.1–33.5, 34.1–34.8

  4. Evolutionary relationships   Concepts 26.1, 26.6

B. Structure and Function of Plants and Animals   **Chapters 29, 30, 35–39, 40–51**

  1. Reproduction, growth, and development (plants)   Concepts 29.2–29.3, 30.1–30.3, 35.1–35.5, 38.1–38.2

  2. Reproduction, growth, and development (animals)   Concepts 46.1–46.6, 47.1–47.3

  3. Structural, physiological, and behavioral adaptations (plants)   Concepts 29.1–29.3, 30.1–30.3, 35.1–35.2, 36.1–36.6, 37.1–37.3, 38.1–38.2, 39.1–39.5

  4. Structural, physiological, and behavioral adaptations (animals)   Concepts 40.1–40.4, 41.1–41.5, 42.1–42.7, 43.1–43.3, 44.1–44.6, 45.1–45.4, 46.1–46.6, 48.1–48.4, 49.1–49.3, 50.5–50.6, 51.2–51.5

  5. Response to the environment (plants)   Concepts 39.1–39.5

  6. Response to the environment (animals)   Concepts 40.3, 43.1–43.2, 44.1–44.2, 45.2–45.4, 48.1–48.4, 49.1–49.3, 50.1–50.4, 51.1–51.2

C. Ecology   **Chapters 52–56**

  1. Population dynamics   Concepts 53.1–53.6

  2. Communities and ecosystems   Concepts 52.3–52.4, 54.1–54.5, 55.1–55.5

  3. Global issues   Concepts 52.1–52.2, 53.6, 55.5, 56.1–56.5

Preface

Much has changed in the world since the completion of the previous edition of *BIOLOGY*. In the realm of the biological sciences, the sequencing of the genomes of many more species has had deep ramifications in diverse areas of research, providing new insights, for example, into the evolutionary histories of numerous species. There has been an explosion of discovery about small RNA molecules and their roles in gene regulation and, at the other end of the size spectrum, our knowledge of Earth's biodiversity has expanded to encompass hundreds of new species, including parrots, monkeys, and orchids. And during the same period, biology has become more prominent than ever in our daily lives. The news is filled with stories about the promise of personalized medicine, novel cancer treatments, the possibility of producing biofuels with the help of genetic engineering, and the use of genetic profiling in solving crimes. Other news stories report climate change and ecological disasters, new drug-resistant strains of the pathogens that cause tuberculosis and parasitic infections, and famine—crises in the world around us that are posing new challenges for biologists and their allies in the other sciences. On a personal level, many colleagues and I have missed our inspiring friend, the late Neil Campbell, even as our commitment to leadership in biological education has grown. Our changing world needs biologists and a scientifically literate citizenry as never before, and we are committed to working toward that goal.

The New Coauthors

The Seventh Edition of *BIOLOGY* has been used by more students and instructors than any previous edition, remaining the most widely used college textbook in the sciences. With the privilege of sharing biology with so many students comes the responsibility of improving the book to serve the biology community even better. For that reason, Neil would have been delighted to see that this Eighth Edition fulfills our decade-long goal of expanding the author team. As biological discoveries proliferated, Neil and I realized that it was becoming harder than ever to make judicious decisions about which biological concepts are most important to develop in depth in an introductory textbook. We needed an author team with first-hand expertise across the biological spectrum, and we wanted coauthors who had honed their teaching values in the classroom. Our new coauthors—Lisa Urry, Michael Cain, Steve Wasserman, Peter Minorsky, and Rob Jackson—represent the highest standards of scientific scholarship across a broad range of disciplines and a deep commitment to undergraduate teaching. As described on pages iv–v, their scientific expertise ranges from molecules to ecosystems, and the schools where they teach range from small liberal arts colleges to large universities. In addition, both Lisa and Peter, as major contributors to earlier editions, had prior experience working on the book. The six of us have collaborated unusually closely, starting with book-wide planning meetings and continuing with frequent exchanges of questions and advice as we worked on our chapters. For each chapter, the revising author, editors, and I together formulated a detailed plan; subsequently, my own role involved commenting on early drafts and polishing the final version. Together, we have strived to extend the book's effectiveness for today's students and instructors, while maintaining its core values.

Our Core Values

What are the core values of this book? They start with getting the science right but then focus on helping students make sense of the science. Below I highlight our longtime values and describe how they've been put into practice in the Eighth Edition. You can see examples of many of the book's features in "To the Student: How to Use This Book" (pp. xx-xxv).

Accuracy and Currency

Getting the science right goes beyond making sure that the facts are accurate and up-to-date. Equally important is ensuring that our chapters reflect how scientists in the various subdisciplines of biology, from cell biology to ecology, currently view their area. Changes in the basic paradigms in various biological fields may call for us to reorganize some chapters and even create new ones in a new edition. For example, a new Chapter 21 discusses genomes and their evolution, and neurobiology is now covered in two chapters (Chapters 48 and 49), one focused on the cellular level and one at the organ system level. On pages xv–xvi, you can read more about new content and organizational improvements in the Eighth Edition.

A Framework of Key Concepts

The explosion of discoveries that makes biology so exciting today also threatens to suffocate students under an avalanche of information. Our primary pedagogical goal is to help students build a framework for learning biology by organizing each chapter around a small number of "Key Concepts," typically three to six. Each chapter begins with a list of its Key Concepts, a photograph that raises an intriguing question, and an Overview section that addresses the question and introduces the chapter. In the body of the chapter, each Key Concept serves as a numbered heading for a major section, in which the prose and pictures tell a more detailed story. At the end of each concept section, Concept Check questions enable students to assess their understanding of that concept before going on to the next concept. Students encounter the Key Concepts one last time when they reach the Chapter Review at the end of the chapter; the Summary of Key Concepts restates them and offers succinct explanatory support in both words and summary diagrams—new to this edition.

Active Learning

Increasingly, instructors tell us that they want their students to take a more active role in learning biology and to think about biological questions at a higher level. In the Eighth Edition, we provide several new ways for students to engage in active learning. First, the Concept Check questions in this edition build in difficulty, and each set now ends with a new "What if?" question that challenges students to integrate what they have learned and to think analytically. There are also questions accompanying selected figures within the text; each of these questions encourages students to delve into the figure and assess their understanding of its underlying ideas. And new "Draw It" exercises in every chapter ask students to put pencil to paper and draw a structure, annotate a figure, or graph experimental data. In addition to appearing regularly in the Chapter Review, a "Draw It" question may show up in a Concept Check or figure legend. Finally, the website that accompanies the book features a new and exciting tool, BioFlix 3-D animations and tutorials, to help students focus on biology's toughest topics. It is described on page xxvii.

Evolution and Other Unifying Themes

Together with *BIOLOGY*'s emphasis on key concepts, a thematic approach has always distinguished our book from an encyclopedia of biology. In the Eighth Edition, as previously, the central theme is evolution. Evolution unifies all of biology by accounting for both the unity and diversity of life and for the remarkable adaptations of organisms to their environments. The evolutionary theme is woven into every chapter of *BIOLOGY*, and Unit Four, Mechanisms of Evolution, has undergone a major revision. In Chapter 1, the other unifying themes have been streamlined from ten to six. And throughout the book, these themes are now referenced more explicitly in Key Concepts and subheadings. The former themes of scientific inquiry and science, technology, and society continue to be highlighted throughout the book, not as biological themes but as aspects of how science is done and the role of science in our lives.

Integration of Text and Illustrations

We regard text and illustrations as equal in importance, and starting with the First Edition, have always developed them simultaneously. The Eighth Edition has a number of new and improved figures, with the increased use of a more three-dimensional art style where it can enhance understanding of biological structure. At the same time, we avoid excess detail, which can obscure the main point of the figure. We have also improved our popular "Exploring" Figures and have added more (see the list on p. xviii). Each of these large figures is a learning unit that brings together a set of related illustrations and the text that describes them. The Exploring Figures enable students to access dozens of complex topics very efficiently. They are core chapter content, not to be confused with some textbooks' "boxes," which have content peripheral to the flow of a chapter. Modern biology is challenging enough without diverting students' attention from a chapter's conceptual storyline.

Telling the Story at the Right Level

Whether in pictures or prose, we are committed to explaining biology at just the right level, and we've continued to use Neil's "quantum theory of teaching biology" as a touchstone. According to this idea, there are discrete levels at which a concept can be successfully explained, and a successful explanation must avoid getting "stuck between levels." Of course, most seasoned instructors have independently recognized this issue, also known as the "too much–too little" problem. The author team has drawn upon both scientific expertise and teaching experience to tell the story of biology at an appropriate level.

The Importance of Scientific Inquiry

Another of our core values is our belief in the importance of introducing students to the scientific way of thinking. In both lecture hall and laboratory, the authors and many of our colleagues are experimenting with diverse approaches for involving students in scientific inquiry, the process by which questions about nature are posed and explored. Special features in the textbook and in inquiry-based supplements make this edition of *BIOLOGY* more effective than ever in helping instructors convey the process of science in their courses.

Modeling Inquiry by Example

Every edition of *BIOLOGY* has traced the history of many research questions and scientific debates to help students appreciate not just "what we know," but "how we know," and "what we do not yet know." In *BIOLOGY*, Seventh Edition, we strengthened this aspect of the book by introducing "Inquiry" Figures, which showcase examples of experiments and field studies in a format that is consistent throughout the book. Each of these inquiry cases begins with a research question, followed by sections describing the experiment, results, and conclusion. Complementing the Inquiry Figures are "Research Method" Figures, which walk students through the techniques and tools of modern biology.

In the Eighth Edition, we have added many more Inquiry Figures; there is now at least one in every chapter and often more (see the list of Inquiry Figures on pp. xviii–xix). Each Inquiry Figure now ends with a "What if?" question that requires students to demonstrate their understanding of the experiment described. We have also expanded the usefulness of the Inquiry Figures in another important way: In response to feedback from many instructors, we now cite the journal article that is the source of the research, providing a gateway to the primary literature. And the full papers for nine of the Inquiry Figures are reprinted in *Inquiry in Action: Interpreting Scientific Papers*, by Ruth Buskirk and Christopher Gillen. This new supplement provides background information on how to read scientific papers plus specific questions that guide students through the nine featured articles.

Learning Inquiry by Practice

BIOLOGY, Eighth Edition, encourages students to practice thinking as scientists by tackling the "What if?" questions in the Concept Checks and Inquiry Figures (and occasional figure legends), as well as the "Scientific Inquiry" questions in the Chapter Review. Many of those in the Chapter Reviews ask students to analyze data or to design an experiment.

The Eighth Edition supplements build on the textbook to provide diverse opportunities for students to practice scientific inquiry in more depth. In addition to *Inquiry in Action: Interpreting Scientific Papers*, these include new editions of several other supplements. One is *Biological Inquiry: A Workbook of Investigative Cases*, Second Edition, by Margaret Waterman and Ethel Stanley; another is *Practicing Biology: A Student Workbook*, Third Edition, by Jean Heitz and Cynthia Giffen. You can find out more about these and other student supplements, both print and electronic, on pages xxvi–xxvii.

The BIOLOGY Interviews: A Continuing Tradition

Scientific inquiry is a social process catalyzed by communication among people who share a curiosity about nature. One of the many joys of authoring *BIOLOGY* is the privilege of interviewing some of the world's most influential biologists. Eight new interviews, one opening each unit of the textbook, introduce students to eight of the fascinating individuals who are driving progress in biology and connecting science to society. And in this edition, each unit of the text includes an Inquiry Figure based upon the research of the unit's interviewee; for example, see Inquiry Figure 2.2, on page 31. The interviewees for this edition are listed on page xvii.

A Versatile Book

Our book is intended to serve students as a textbook in their general biology course and also later as a useful tool for review and reference. *BIOLOGY*'s breadth, depth, and versatile organization enable the book to meet these dual goals. Even by limiting our scope to a few Key Concepts per chapter, *BIOLOGY* spans more biological territory than most introductory courses could or should attempt to cover. But given the great diversity of course syllabi, we have opted for a survey broad enough and deep enough to support each instructor's particular emphases. Students also seem to appreciate *BIOLOGY*'s breadth and depth. In fact, we are delighted to receive mail from undergraduate and graduate students, including medical students, expressing their appreciation for the long-term value of *BIOLOGY* as a general resource for their continuing education.

Just as we recognize that few courses will cover all 56 chapters of the textbook, we also understand that there is no single correct sequence of topics for a general biology course. Though a biology textbook's table of contents must be linear, biology itself is more like a web of related concepts without a fixed starting point or a prescribed path. Diverse courses can navigate this network of concepts starting with molecules and cells, or with evolution and the diversity of organisms, or with the big-picture ideas of ecology. We have built *BIOLOGY* to be versatile enough to support these different syllabi. The eight units of the book are largely self-contained, and, for most of the units, the chapters can be assigned in a different sequence without substantial loss of coherence. For example, instructors who integrate plant and animal physiology can merge chapters from Unit Six (Plant Form and Function) and Unit Seven (Animal Form and Function) to fit their courses. As another option, instructors who begin their course with ecology and continue with this top-down approach can assign Unit Eight (Ecology) right after Chapter 1, which introduces the unifying themes that provide students with a panoramic view of biology no matter what the topic order of the course syllabus.

Our Partnership with Instructors

A core value underlying all our work as authors is our belief in the importance of our partnership with instructors. Our primary way of serving instructors, of course, is providing a textbook that serves their students well. In addition, Benjamin Cummings makes available a wealth of instructor resources, in both print and electronic form (see pp. xxvi–xxvii). However, our relationship with instructors is not a one-way street. In our continuing efforts to improve the book and its supplements, we benefit tremendously from instructor feedback, not only in formal reviews from hundreds of scientists, but also via informal communication in person and by phone and e-mail. Neil Campbell built a vast network of colleagues throughout the world, and my new coauthors and I are fully committed to continuing that tradition.

The real test of any textbook is how well it helps instructors teach and students learn. We welcome comments from the students and instructors who use *BIOLOGY*. Please address your suggestions to me:

Jane Reece, Pearson Benjamin Cummings
1301 Sansome Street, San Francisco, CA 94111
E-mail address: JaneReece@cal.berkeley.edu

New to the Eighth Edition

This section provides just a few highlights of new content and organizational improvements in *BIOLOGY*, Eighth Edition.

UNIT ONE The Chemistry of Life

New examples make basic chemistry more engaging for students, including an explanation of why steam can burn your skin in Chapter 3, the structures of the enantiomeric medications ibuprofen and albuterol in Chapter 4, and information on trans fats in Chapter 5. A new Inquiry Figure in Chapter 3 relates acidity to the emerging global problem of ocean acidification and its effects on coral reefs. The new Inquiry Figure in Chapter 5 shows Roger Kornberg's 3-D model of the RNA polymerase–DNA–RNA complex, work for which he won the 2006 Nobel Prize in Chemistry.

UNIT TWO The Cell

The judicious addition of recent research includes updated coverage of the sensory roles of primary cilia in Chapter 6, new developments regarding the membrane model in Chapter 7, and Paul Nurse's Nobel Prize–winning work on the cell cycle in Chapter 12. Chapter 11 now ends with a section on apoptosis, formerly in Chapter 21. New Inquiry Figures in this unit describe research on the role of microtubules in orienting cellulose in cell walls (Chapter 6), allosteric regulators of enzymes (Chapter 8), ATP synthase (Chapter 9), yeast cell signaling (Chapter 11), and a cell cycle regulator (Chapter 12).

UNIT THREE Genetics

Chapter 14 now includes "Tips for Genetics Problems." In Chapter 15, sex linkage is discussed directly after the discussion of the white-eye trait in Morgan's fruit flies. Chapter 16 covers replication of the bacterial chromosome and the structure of the eukaryotic chromosome (including a new Exploring Figure), formerly in Chapters 18 and 19, respectively.

We have reorganized Chapters 18–21 with the dual aims of telling a more coherent story and facilitating instructors' coverage of molecular genetics. Regulation of gene expression for both bacteria and eukaryotes is now consolidated in Chapter 18, which also includes a concept section on the crucial role of small RNAs in eukaryotes. We have streamlined material on the genetic basis of development (formerly in Chapter 21), and included it in Chapter 18, where it provides the ultimate example of gene regulation. Chapter 18 ends with a section on the molecular basis of cancer (previously in Chapter 19), to demonstrate what happens when gene regu-

lation goes awry. Material on bacterial genetics in Seventh Edition Chapter 18 has been moved to other chapters within the genetics unit and to Chapter 27 on prokaryotes.

Chapter 19 now covers only viruses (from Seventh Edition Chapter 18), giving this chapter the flexibility to be assigned at any point in the course. Chapter 20 continues to cover biotechnology, but genome sequencing and analysis have been moved to Chapter 21. Cloning and stem cell production are now in Chapter 20. Newly explained techniques include the screening of an arrayed library, BAC clones, Northern blotting, RT-PCR, and *in situ* hybridization. The explosion of discoveries about genomes and their evolution led us to develop a chapter devoted to this subject, the new Chapter 21. This chapter consolidates new material with topics from Chapters 19–21 of the Seventh Edition.

UNIT FOUR Mechanisms of Evolution

Our revision emphasizes the centrality of evolution to biology and the breadth and depth of evidence for evolution. New examples and Inquiry Figures present data from field and laboratory studies and reveal how scientists study evolution.

Chapter 22 discusses how evolution can be viewed as both a pattern and a process, and introduces three key observations about life that are explained by evolution: the match between organisms and their environments (adaptation); the shared characteristics (unity) of life; and the diversity of life. This discussion serves as a conceptual anchor throughout Units Four and Five.

Chapters 24 and 25 have been significantly reorganized. Chapter 24 is now more tightly focused on speciation, enabling better pacing of this highly conceptual material. A new concept section explores hybrid zones as natural laboratories for studying speciation. Chapter 25 focuses on macroevolution, incorporating topics formerly in Chapters 24 and 26, such as the correlations between Earth's geologic and biological history. But the primary storyline concerns what we can learn from the fossil record about the evolutionary history of life. New text and figures explore how the rise and fall of dominant groups of organisms are linked to large-scale processes such as continental drift, mass extinctions, and adaptive radiations. Coverage of evo-devo has been expanded.

Phylogenetic trees are introduced earlier, in a new section on "tree-thinking" in Chapter 22. This material supports students in interpreting diagrams before studying phylogenetics more fully in Chapter 26.

UNIT FIVE The Evolutionary History of Biological Diversity

A new Chapter 26, Phylogeny and the Tree of Life, introduces the unit. Extending material formerly in Chapter 25, it describes how evolutionary trees are constructed and underscores their role as tools for understanding relationships, rather than facts to be memorized. New sections address common misconceptions in interpreting trees and help motivate students with practical applications.

Chapter 27 has a new concept section on prokaryotic reproduction, mutation, and recombination (formerly in Chapter 18). This unifies the coverage of prokaryote biology and supports students in developing a fuller understanding of these microorganisms.

Throughout Unit Five, along with updating the phylogenies of various groups of organisms—introducing, for example, the "supergroup" hypothesis of eukaryotic phylogeny (in Chapter 28)—we have found new opportunities to use the study of phylogeny as an opportunity to illustrate the iterative nature of the scientific process. We aim to help students stay focused on the big picture of why biologists study evolutionary relationships. Each chapter also now includes an Inquiry figure that models how researchers study organisms and their relationships. At the same time, in each chapter we highlight the key roles that various organisms play in the biosphere as well as their applied importance for humans.

UNIT SIX Plant Form and Function

Revisions to this unit draw more attention to the experimental basis of our understanding of plant biology. New examples include recent progress toward identifying the flowering "hormone" (Chapter 39). Featured in new Inquiry Figures are experiments demonstrating, for example, that trichomes affect insect feeding (Chapter 35) and that informational molecules transported through the symplast affect plant development (Chapter 36).

In Chapter 36, now titled Resource Acquisition and Transport in Vascular Plants, a new first concept section explores how architectural features of plants facilitate resource acquisition, helping students relate the transport of water and nutrients to what they learned in Chapter 35 about plant structure and growth. Another new concept section, on symplastic transport, discusses recent insights into changes in plasmodesmata shape and number and the transmission of electrical and molecular signals throughout the plant.

This unit now has more examples of practical applications of plant biotechnology. For instance, Chapter 37 discusses how genetic modification has increased the resistance of some plants to aluminum toxicity and has improved the flood tolerance of rice crops. Chapter 38 elaborates on the principles of plant breeding and incorporates a new section on genetic engineering of biofuels.

UNIT SEVEN Animal Form and Function

An evolutionary perspective more strongly pervades this unit, underscoring how environment and physical laws shape adaptations across animal groups. Each chapter now includes at least one Inquiry Figure; together, these figures highlight the wide range of methodologies used to study animal physiology, including several experiments using molecular biology techniques students studied earlier in the book.

Chapter 40 has been revised and reorganized to highlight functional relationships at all levels of organization in animal bodies; thermoregulation serves as an extended example throughout the chapter. Chapter 43, The Immune System, has been extensively revised. For instance, we now contrast recognition of pathogen class in innate immunity with antigen-specific recognition in adaptive immunity, helping overcome the common misconception that recognition is absent in innate immunity.

We have divided the former nervous system chapter into two, enabling us to better pace difficult material and highlight dynamic current research by focusing first on cellular processes in Chapter 48, and then on nervous system organization and function in Chapter 49. Chapter 50 rounds out the discussion of nervous system function by examining sensory and motor mechanisms. This sequence leads naturally into Chapter 51 on animal behavior (formerly in Unit Eight), which ties together aspects of genetics, natural selection, and physiology, and provides a bridge to the ecology unit.

UNIT EIGHT Ecology

This unit, which now includes Chapters 52-56, incorporates many new examples that demonstrate a range of methods and scales of study. For example, a new figure in Chapter 52 describes a large-scale field experiment in which researchers manipulated precipitation levels in forest plots, while new Research Method figures describe determining population size using the mark-recapture method (Chapter 53), using molecular tools to measure diversity of soil microorganisms (Chapter 54), and determining primary production with satellite data (Chapter 55). By building on earlier units, we hope to demonstrate how ecology represents a fitting capstone to the book.

We provide more microbial examples and more aquatic ones, from diverse locations around the globe. For instance, Chapter 52 now discusses the importance of salinity in determining the distribution of aquatic organisms, and Chapter 54's coverage of the intermediate disturbance hypothesis includes a new figure on a quantitative test of the hypothesis in New Zealand streams. The unit highlights the great relevance of ecology to society and to students' lives. A new concept section in Chapter 54, for example, discusses how community ecology helps us understand pathogen life cycles and control disease.

Interviews

Featured Figures

Exploring Figures

Inquiry Figures

Research Method Figures

Focus on the Key Concepts

Each chapter is organized around a framework of 3 to 6 Key Concepts that will help you stay focused on the big picture and give you a context for the supporting details.

Before you begin reading the chapter, get oriented by reading the list of Key Concepts, which introduces the big ideas covered in the chapter.

Each Key Concept serves as the heading for a major section of the chapter.

25 The History of Life on Earth

KEY CONCEPTS

25.1 **Conditions on early Earth made the origin of life possible**

25.2 **The fossil record documents the history of life**

25.3 **Key events in life's history include the origins of single-celled and multicelled organisms and the colonization of land**

25.4 **The rise and fall of dominant groups reflect continental drift, mass extinctions, and adaptive radiations**

25.5 **Major changes in body form can result from changes in the sequences and regulation of developmental genes**

25.6 **Evolution is not goal oriented**

OVERVIEW
Lost Worlds

Visitors to Antarctica today encounter one of Earth's harshest, most barren environments. In this land of extreme cold where there is almost no liquid water, life is sparse and small—the largest fully terrestrial animal is a fly 5 mm long. But even as early antarctic explorers struggled to survive, some of them made an astonishing discovery: fossil evidence that life once thrived where it now barely exists. Fossils reveal that 500 million years ago, the ocean waters surrounding Antarctica were warm and teeming with tropical invertebrates. Later, the continent was covered in forests for hundreds of millions of years. At various times, a wide range of animals stalked through these forests, including 3-meter-tall predatory "terror birds" and giant dinosaurs such as the voracious *Cryolophosaurus* (Figure 25.1), a 7-meter-long relative of *Tyrannosaurus rex*.

Fossils discovered in other parts of the world tell a similar, if not quite as surprising, story: Past organisms were very different from

▲ Figure 25.1 **What does fossil evidence say about wher these dinosaurs lived?**

▲ *Cryolophosaurus* skull

those now alive. The sweepir changes in life on Earth revealed l fossils illustrate **macroevolutio** the pattern of evolution over larg time scales. Specific examples c macroevolutionary change incluc the origin of key biochemic processes such as photosynthes the emergence of the first terrestri vertebrates, and the long-term in pact of a mass extinction on the c versity of life.

Taken together, such changes provide a grand view of th evolutionary history of life on Earth. We'll examine tha history in this chapter, beginning with hypotheses regarc ing the origin of life. The origin of life is the most specula tive topic of the entire unit, for no fossil evidence of tha seminal episode exists. We will then turn to the foss record and what it tells us about major events in the histor of life, paying particular attention to factors that hav helped to shape the rise and fall of different groups of or ganisms over time.

CONCEPT 25.1
Conditions on early Earth made the origin of life possible

The earliest evidence of life on Earth comes from fossils c microorganisms that are about 3.5 billion years old. Bu when and how did the first living cells appear? Observa tions and experiments in chemistry, geology, and physic have led scientists to propose one scenario that we'll exam ine here. They hypothesize that chemical and physica processes on early Earth, aided by the emerging force c

When you finish reading a concept section, check your understanding using the **Concept Check questions** at the end of the section. If you can answer them (see Appendix A to check your work), you're ready to move on.

CONCEPT CHECK 53.1

1. One species of forest bird is highly territorial, while a second lives in flocks. Predict each species' likely pattern of dispersion, and explain.
2. **DRAW IT** Each female of a particular fish species produces millions of eggs per year. Draw and label the most likely survivorship curve for this species, and explain your choice.
3. **WHAT IF?** As noted in Figure 53.2, an important assumption of the mark-recapture method is that marked individuals have the same probability of being recaptured as unmarked individuals. Describe a situation where this assumption might not be valid, and explain how the estimate of population size would be affected.

For suggested answers, see Appendix A.

Each set of Concept Check questions builds in difficulty, ending with a "What if?" question that asks you to apply what you've learned. Work through these questions on your own or in a study group—they're good practice for the kinds of questions you might be asked on an exam.

Practice thinking like a scientist

To succeed in biology, you need to do more than just memorize facts—you need to understand how scientists go about asking and investigating questions. In each chapter, you'll find one or more **Inquiry Figures** that highlight how researchers designed an experiment, interpreted their results, and drew conclusions.

Scientific Inquiry questions in the Chapter Review provide more opportunities to practice inquiry skills, including developing hypotheses, designing experiments, and analyzing real research data.

SCIENTIFIC INQUIRY

8. **DRAW IT** The nitrogen-fixing bacterium *Rhizobium* infects the roots of some plant species, forming a mutualism in which the bacterium provides the plant with nitrogen, and the plant provides the bacterium with carbohydrates. Scientists measured how well one such plant species (*Acacia irrorata*) grew when its roots were infected by six different *Rhizobium* strains.

(a) Graph the data. (b) Interpret your graph.

Rhizobium strain	Plant mass (g) after 12 weeks of growth
1	0.91
2	0.06
3	1.56
4	1.72
5	0.14
6	1.03

Source: J. J. Burdon, et al., Variation in the effectiveness of symbiotic associations between native rhizobia and temperate Australian *Acacia*: within species interactions, *Journal of Applied Ecology*, 36:398-408 (1999).

Note: In the absence of *Rhizobium*, after 12 weeks of growth, *Acacia* plants have a mass of about 0.1 g.

Some Inquiry Figures invite you to read and analyze the original research paper in its complete form. You can find the journal article, along with a worksheet guiding you through it, in the separate book *Inquiry in Action: Interpreting Scientific Papers* (ISBN 978-0-321-53659-4 | 0-321-53659-2). ▶

After exploring the featured experiment, test your analytical skills by answering the **"What if?" question.** Suggested answers are provided in Appendix A to help you gauge your understanding. ▶

▼ **Figure 2.2** **Inquiry**

What creates "devil's gardens" in the rain forest?

EXPERIMENT Working under Deborah Gordon and with Michael Greene, graduate student Megan Frederickson sought the cause of "devil's gardens," stands of a single species of tree, *Duroia hirsuta*. One hypothesis was that ants living in these trees, *Myrmelachista schumanni*, produce a poisonous chemical that kills trees of other species; another was that the *Duroia* trees themselves kill competing trees, perhaps by means of a chemical.

To test these hypotheses, Frederickson did field experiments in Peru. Two saplings of a local nonhost tree species, *Cedrela odorata*, were planted inside each of ten devil's gardens. At the base of one, a sticky insect barrier was applied; the other was unprotected. Two more *Cedrela* saplings, with and without barriers, were planted about 50 meters outside each garden.

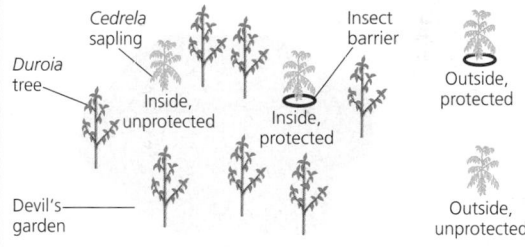

The researchers observed ant activity on the *Cedrela* leaves and measured areas of dead leaf tissue after one day. They also chemically analyzed contents of the ants' poison glands.

RESULTS The ants made injections from the tips of their abdomens into leaves of unprotected saplings in their gardens (see photo). Within one day, these leaves developed dead areas (see graph). The protected saplings were uninjured, as were the saplings planted outside the gardens. Formic acid was the only chemical detected in the poison glands of the ants.

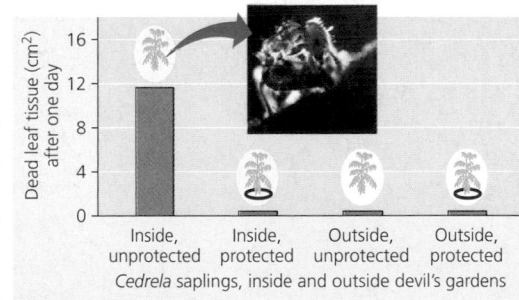

Cedrela saplings, inside and outside devil's gardens

CONCLUSION Ants of the species *Myrmelachista schumanni* kill nonhost trees by injecting the leaves with formic acid, thus creating hospitable habitats (devil's gardens) for the ant colony.

SOURCE M. E. Frederickson, M. J. Greene, and D. M. Gordon, "Devil's gardens" bedevilled by ants, *Nature* 437:495–496 (2005).

Inquiry in Action Read and analyze the original paper in *Inquiry in Action: Interpreting Scientific Papers.*

WHAT IF? What would be the results if the unprotected saplings' inability to grow in the devil's gardens was caused by a chemical released by the *Duroia* trees rather than by the ants?

As you read the text, study the art and photos

In selected illustrations, a **three-dimensional art style** helps you visualize biological structures.

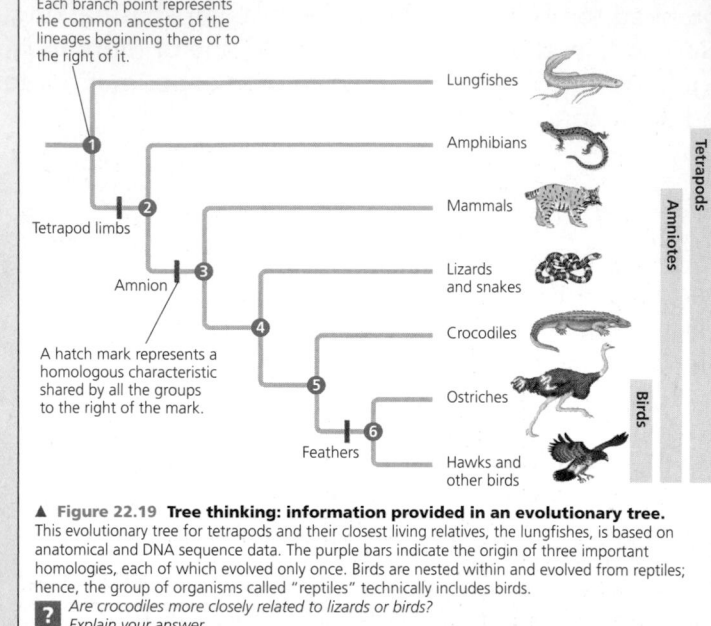

Each branch point represents the common ancestor of the lineages beginning there or to the right of it.

A hatch mark represents a homologous characteristic shared by all the groups to the right of the mark.

▲ **Figure 22.19 Tree thinking: information provided in an evolutionary tree.** This evolutionary tree for tetrapods and their closest living relatives, the lungfishes, is based on anatomical and DNA sequence data. The purple bars indicate the origin of three important homologies, each of which evolved only once. Birds are nested within and evolved from reptiles; hence, the group of organisms called "reptiles" technically includes birds.
? *Are crocodiles more closely related to lizards or birds? Explain your answer.*

▲ The book's **phylogenetic trees** will prepare you to analyze the evolutionary tree diagrams you may encounter in the scientific literature. This figure walks you through some of the conventions of the phylogenetic trees you will see throughout the evolution and diversity units.

"Guided Tour" figures include concise explanations that walk you through complicated diagrams. ▶

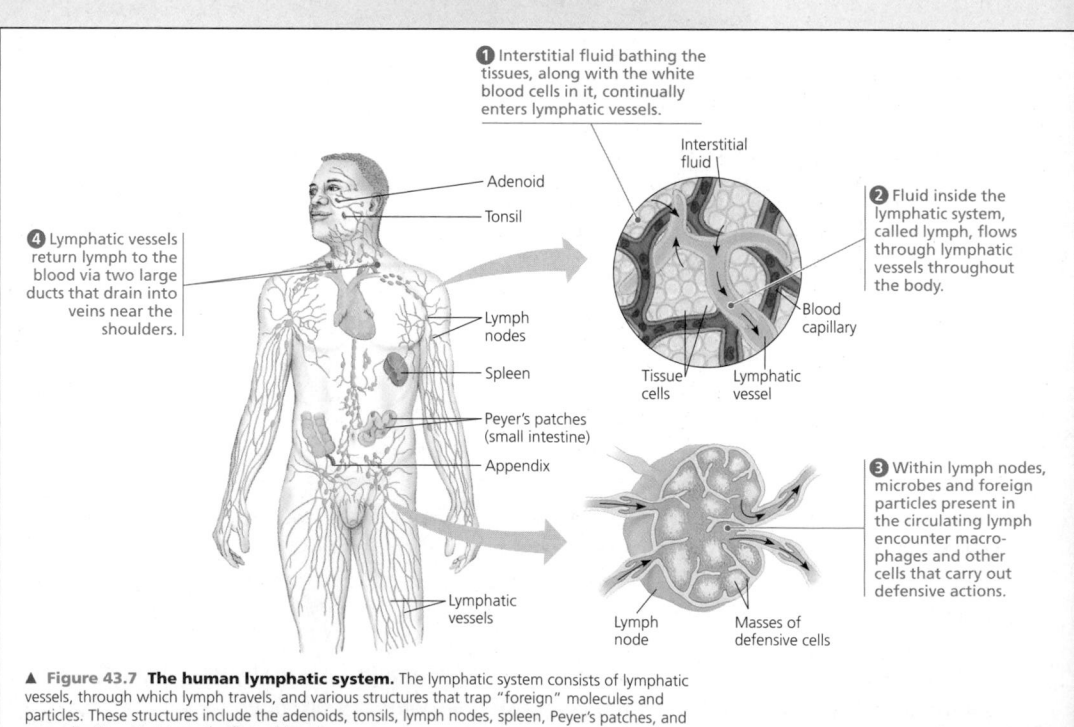

❶ Interstitial fluid bathing the tissues, along with the white blood cells in it, continually enters lymphatic vessels.

❷ Fluid inside the lymphatic system, called lymph, flows through lymphatic vessels throughout the body.

❸ Within lymph nodes, microbes and foreign particles present in the circulating lymph encounter macrophages and other cells that carry out defensive actions.

❹ Lymphatic vessels return lymph to the blood via two large ducts that drain into veins near the shoulders.

▲ **Figure 43.7 The human lymphatic system.** The lymphatic system consists of lymphatic vessels, through which lymph travels, and various structures that trap "foreign" molecules and particles. These structures include the adenoids, tonsils, lymph nodes, spleen, Peyer's patches, and appendix. Steps 1–4 trace the flow of lymph.

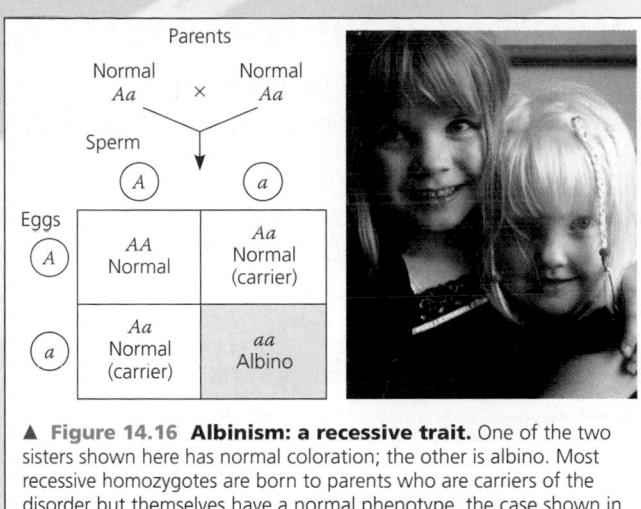

▲ **Figure 14.16 Albinism: a recessive trait.** One of the two sisters shown here has normal coloration; the other is albino. Most recessive homozygotes are born to parents who are carriers of the disorder but themselves have a normal phenotype, the case shown in the Punnett square.

? *What is the probability that the sister with normal coloration is a carrier of the albinism allele?*

Figure Legend questions prompt you to delve into a figure's content to make sure you understand it.

● By integrating text and visuals, **Exploring Figures** help you learn more efficiently.

▼ Figure 24.4

Exploring **Reproductive Barriers**

◄·········· Prezygotic barriers impede mating or hinder fertilization if mating does occur ·········· ► | ◄·········· Postzygotic barriers prevent a hybrid zygote from developing into a viable, fertile adult ·········· ►

| Habitat Isolation | Temporal Isolation | Behavioral Isolation | Mechanical Isolation | Gametic Isolation | Reduced Hybrid Viability | Reduced Hybrid Fertility | Hybrid Breakdown |

Individuals of different species → [Mating attempt] → [Fertilization] → Viable, fertile offspring

Habitat Isolation
Two species that occupy different habitats within the same area may encounter each other rarely, if at all, even though they are not isolated by obvious physical barriers, such as mountain ranges.

Example: Two species of garter snakes in the genus *Thamnophis* occur in the same geographic areas, but one lives mainly in water (a) while the other is primarily terrestrial (b).

Temporal Isolation
Species that breed during different times of the day, different seasons, or different years cannot mix their gametes.

Example: In North America, the geographic ranges of the eastern spotted skunk (*Spilogale putorius*) (c) and the western spotted skunk (*Spilogale gracilis*) (d) overlap, but *S. putorius* mates in late winter and *S. gracilis* mates in late summer.

Behavioral Isolation
Courtship rituals that attract mates and other behaviors unique to a species are effective reproductive barriers, even between closely related species. Such behavioral rituals enable *mate recognition*—a way to identify potential mates of the same species.

Example: Blue-footed boobies, inhabitants of the Galápagos, mate only after a courtship display unique to their species. Part of the "script" calls for the male to high-step (e), a behavior that calls the female's attention to his bright blue feet.

Mechanical Isolation
Mating is attempted, but morphological differences prevent its successful completion.

Example: The shells of two species of snails in the genus *Bradybaena* spiral in different directions: Moving inward to the center, one spirals in a counterclockwise direction (f, left), the other in a clockwise direction (f, right). As a result, the snails' genital openings (indicated by arrows) are not aligned, and mating cannot be completed.

Gametic Isolation
Sperm of one species may not be able to fertilize the eggs of another species. For instance, sperm may not be able to survive in the reproductive tract of females of the other species, or biochemical mechanisms may prevent the sperm from penetrating the membrane surrounding the other species' eggs.

Example: Gametic isolation separates certain closely related species of aquatic animals, such as sea urchins (g). Sea urchins release their sperm and eggs into the surrounding water, where they fuse and form zygotes. Gametes of different species, such as the red and purple urchins shown here, are unable to fuse because proteins on the surfaces of the eggs and sperm cannot bind to each other.

Reduced Hybrid Viability
The genes of different parent species may interact in ways that impair the hybrid's development or survival in its environment.

Example: Some salamander subspecies of the genus *Ensatina* live in the same regions and habitats, where they may occasionally hybridize. But most of the hybrids do not complete development, and those that do are frail (h).

Reduced Hybrid Fertility
Even if hybrids are vigorous, they may be sterile. If the chromosomes of the two parent species differ in number or structure, meiosis in the hybrids may fail to produce normal gametes. Since the infertile hybrids cannot produce offspring when they mate with either parent species, genes cannot flow freely between the species.

Example: The hybrid offspring of a donkey (i) and a horse (j) is a mule (k), which is robust but sterile.

Hybrid Breakdown
Some first-generation hybrids are viable and fertile, but when they mate with one another or with either parent species, offspring of the next generation are feeble or sterile.

Example: Strains of cultivated rice have accumulated different mutant recessive alleles at two loci in the course of their divergence from a common ancestor. Hybrids between them are vigorous and fertile (l, left and right), but plants in the next generation that carry too many of these recessive alleles are small and sterile (l, center). Although these rice strains are not yet considered different species, they have begun to be separated by postzygotic barriers.

Review what you've learned

At the end of the chapter, the **Chapter Review** focuses you again on the main points of the chapter, with a Summary of Key Concepts, practice questions, and references to other study tools.

● Go to **www.campbellbiology.com** for BioFlix 3-D animations and student tools plus MP3 Tutors, Discovery Channel Videos, Practice Tests, Activities, Investigations, an eBook, and more.

Chapter 9 Review

MEDIA Go to www.campbellbiology.com for BioFlix 3-D Animations, MP3 Tutors, Videos, Practice Tests, an eBook, and more.

SUMMARY OF KEY CONCEPTS

CONCEPT 9.1
Catabolic pathways yield energy by oxidizing organic fuels (pp. 162–167)

▶ **Catabolic Pathways and Production of ATP** To keep working, a cell must regenerate the ATP it uses. The breakdown of glucose and other organic fuels is exergonic. Starting with glucose or another organic molecule and using O_2, aerobic respiration yields H_2O, CO_2, and energy in the form of ATP and heat. Cellular respiration includes both aerobic and anaerobic respiration; the latter uses another electron acceptor instead of O_2, but also yields ATP.

▶ **Redox Reactions: Oxidation and Reduction** The cell taps the energy stored in food molecules through redox reactions, in which one substance partially or totally shifts electrons to another. The substance receiving electrons is reduced; the substance losing electrons is oxidized. During cellular respiration, glucose ($C_6H_{12}O_6$) is oxidized to CO_2, and O_2 is reduced to H_2O. Electrons lose potential energy during their transfer from organic compounds to oxygen. Electrons from organic compounds are usually passed first to NAD^+, reducing it to NADH. NADH passes the electrons to an electron transport chain, which conducts them to O_2 in energy-releasing steps. The energy released is used to make ATP.

▶ **The Stages of Cellular Respiration: *A Preview*** Glycolysis and the citric acid cycle supply electrons (via NADH or $FADH_2$) to the electron transport chain, which drives oxidative phosphorylation. Oxidative phosphorylation generates ATP.

MEDIA
BioFlix 3-D Animation Cellular Respiration
Activity Build a Chemical Cycling System
Activity Overview of Cellular Respiration

CONCEPT 9.2
Glycolysis harvests chemical energy by oxidizing glucose to pyruvate (pp. 167–169)

MEDIA
MP3 Tutor Cellular Respiration Part 1—Glycolysis
Activity Glycolysis

CONCEPT 9.3
The citric acid cycle completes the energy-yielding oxidation of organic molecules (pp. 170–172)

▶ In eukaryotic cells, the import of pyruvate into the mitochondrion and its conversion to acetyl CoA links glycolysis to the citric acid cycle. (In prokaryotic cells, the citric acid cycle occurs in the cytosol.)

MEDIA
Activity The Citric Acid Cycle

◀ **Summary Figures** present key information in a visual way, serving as "one-stop shopping" study tools.

● **MP3 Tutors** explain some of the most difficult biological concepts in simple terms. A tutor that goes anywhere you go, anytime.

● **BioFlix animations and student tools** review the most difficult biology topics with 3-D, movie-quality animations, labeled slide shows, carefully constructed student tutorials, study sheets, and quizzes that support all types of learners.

SELF-QUIZ

1. What is the reducing agent in the following reaction?

    Pyruvate + NADH + H^+ → Lactate + NAD^+

    a. oxygen
    b. NADH
    c. NAD^+
    d. lactate
    e. pyruvate

2. The *immediate* energy source that drives ATP synthesis by ATP synthase during oxidative phosphorylation is
    a. the oxidation of glucose and other organic compounds.
    b. the flow of electrons down the electron transport chain.
    c. the affinity of oxygen for electrons.
    d. the H^+ concentration gradient across the inner mitochondrial membrane.
    e. the transfer of phosphate to ADP.

3. Which metabolic pathway is common to both fermentation and cellular respiration of a glucose molecule?
    a. the citric acid cycle
    b. the electron transport chain
    c. glycolysis
    d. synthesis of acetyl CoA from pyruvate
    e. reduction of pyruvate to lactate

4. In mitochondria, exergonic redox reactions
    a. are the source of energy driving prokaryotic ATP synthesis.
    b. are directly coupled to substrate-level phosphorylation.
    c. provide the energy that establishes the proton gradient.
    d. reduce carbon atoms to carbon dioxide.
    e. are coupled via phosphorylated intermediates to endergonic processes.

◀ To start preparing for a test, take the **end-of-chapter Self-Quiz.**

● **"Draw It" exercises** ask you to put pencil to paper and draw a structure, annotate a figure, or graph experimental data. Check your work by turning to the suggested answers in Appendix A.

▼

11. **DRAW IT** Trace the uptake of water and minerals from root hairs to the vessels in a root, following a symplastic route and an apoplastic route. Label the routes.

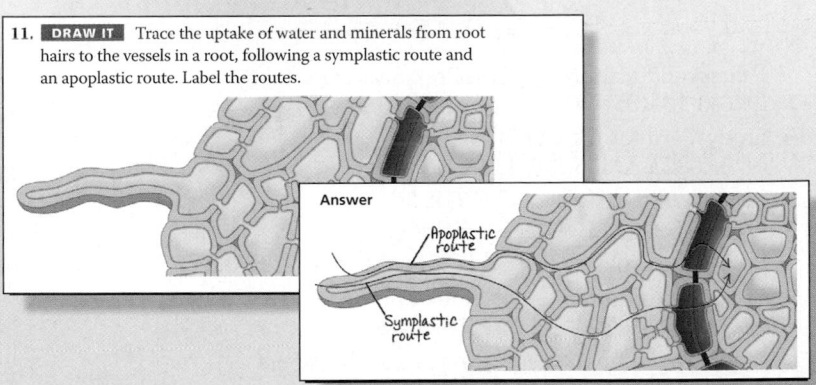

10. **DRAW IT** The graph here shows the pH difference across the inner mitochondrial membrane over time in an actively respiring cell. At the time indicated by the vertical arrow, a metabolic poison is added that specifically and completely inhibits all function of mitochondrial ATP synthase. Draw what you would expect to see for the rest of the graphed line.

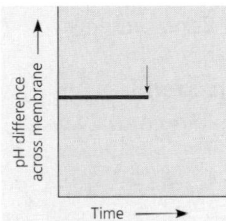

For Self-Quiz answers, see Appendix A.

MEDIA Visit **www.campbellbiology.com** for a Practice Test.

For more **practice test questions** visit **www.campbellbiology.com** ▶

EVOLUTION CONNECTION

11. ATP synthases are found in the prokaryotic plasma membrane and in mitochondria and chloroplasts. What does this suggest about the evolutionary relationship of these eukaryotic organelles to prokaryotes? How might the amino acid sequences of the ATP synthases from the different sources support or refute your hypothesis?

SCIENTIFIC INQUIRY

12. In the 1940s, some physicians prescribed low doses of a drug called dinitrophenol (DNP) to help patients lose weight. This unsafe method was abandoned after a few patients died. DNP uncouples the chemiosmotic machinery by making the lipid bilayer of the inner mitochondrial membrane leaky to H^+. Explain how this causes weight loss.

SCIENCE, TECHNOLOGY, AND SOCIETY

13. Nearly all human societies use fermentation to produce alcoholic drinks such as beer and wine. The practice dates back to the earliest days of agriculture. How do you suppose this use of fermentation was first discovered? Why did wine prove to be a more useful beverage, especially to a preindustrial culture, than the grape juice from which it was made?

Biological Inquiry: A Workbook of Investigative Cases Explore fermentation further in the case "Bean Brew."

◀ The **essay questions** in the Chapter Review give you practice writing about biological topics and making connections between the content of different chapters, as you may be asked to do in class discussions or on exams.

Supplements

Items displayed in red are specifically for the AP course.

For the AP Student

Print

- Pearson Education AP* Test Prep Series: Biology (978-0-13-135749-5/0-13-135749-2)
- Study Card for *BIOLOGY*, 8e (978-0-321-49436-8/0-321-49436-9)
- Spanish Glossary for *BIOLOGY*, 8e (978-0-321-49434-4/0-321-49434-2)
- Practicing Biology, 3e (978-0-321-52293-1/0-321-52293-1)
- Biological Inquiry: A Workbook of Investigative Cases, 2e (978-0-321-51320-5/0-321-51320-7)
- Inquiry in Action: Interpreting Scientific Papers (978-0-321-53659-4/0-321-53659-2)
- Student Study Guide for *BIOLOGY*, 8e (978-0-321-50156-1/0-321-50156-X)
- Get Ready for Biology (978-0-321-50057-1/0-321-50057-1)
- An Introduction to Chemistry for Biology Students, 9e (978-0-8053-9571-6/0-8053-9571-7)

Media

- *BIOLOGY* 8e AP* Edition website (www.campbellbiology.com)
- Student Media for *BIOLOGY* 8e AP* Edition Replacement CD-ROM (978-0-13-713620-9/0-13-713620-X)
- Biology Labs On-Line (www.biologylabsonline.com)
- Classic Edition of the Biology Place (www.biology.com)
- MasteringBiology™ (www.masteringbio.com)

For the AP Teacher

- Transparency Acetates (978-0-321-52328-0/0-321-52328-8)
- Instructor Guide for Biological Inquiry: A Workbook of Investigative Cases, 2e (978-0-321-49435-1/0-321-49435-0)
- Printed Test Bank (978-0-321-49431-3/0-321-49431-8)

- Computerized Test Bank (TestGen) (available for download from the Instructor Resource Center)
- AP* ExamView Test Bank (978-0-13-235764-7/0-13-235764-X)
- Instructor Resource CD/DVD-ROM Set (978-0-321-52292-4/0-321-52292-3)
- *BIOLOGY* 8e AP* Edition website (www.campbellbiology.com)
- PowerPoint® Lectures (available on www.campbellbiology.com and on the Instructor Resource CD/DVD-ROM Set)
- Instructor Guide for Practicing Biology, 3e (available on www.campbellbiology.com)
- Instructor Guide for Inquiry in Action: Interpreting Scientific Papers (available on www.campbellbiology.com)

Most of the teacher supplements and resources are available electronically for preview and download from the Instructor Resource Center (IRC). Please go to www.pearsonschool.com/access_request. You will be required to complete a one-time registration, subject to verification, before being emailed access information to download materials. The media resources also are available on www.campbellbiology.com.

Descriptions

Pearson Education AP* Test Prep Series: Biology
Fred Holtzclaw, Webb School of Knoxville, and Theresa Holtzclaw, Oak Ridge High School
For purchase only. Fred and Theresa Holtzclaw bring over 40 years of AP Biology teaching experience to this student preparation manual. The workbook includes a chapter-by-chapter topic review correlated to *BIOLOGY* 8e AP Edition; new "Must Know" sections; study tips and organization ideas; misconception warnings; practice quizzes for each chapter with answers and explanations; practice exams; and a new section reviewing the 12 required AP laboratories.

Study Card for *BIOLOGY*, Eighth Edition
For purchase only. This quick reference card provides an overview of the entire field of biology.

Spanish Glossary for *BIOLOGY*, Eighth Edition
Laura P. Zanello, University of California, Riverside
For purchase only.

Practicing Biology, Third Edition
Jean Heitz and Cynthia Giffen, University of Wisconsin, Madison
For purchase only. This workbook offers a variety of activities for different learning styles. The Instructor Guide is available to teachers registered for access on www.campbellbiology.com.

Biological Inquiry: A Workbook of Investigative Cases, Second Edition
Margaret Waterman, Southeast Missouri State University, and Ethel Stanley, BioQUEST and Beloit College
For purchase only. This workbook offers ten investigative cases, including new cases on avian influenza and hedgehog developmental pathways. Online resources are provided to teachers registered for access on www.campbellbiology.com. The printed instructor guide provides coaching on how to teach using a case-based approach, as well as suggested answers.

Inquiry in Action: Interpreting Scientific Papers

Ruth Buskirk, University of Texas, Austin, and Christopher M. Gillen, Kenyan College

For purchase only. In this new supplement, articles referenced in selected Inquiry Figures in the Eighth Edition are reprinted and accompanied by questions that help students analyze the articles. The Instructor Guide is available to teachers registered for access on www.campbellbiology.com.

Student Study Guide for *BIOLOGY*, Eighth Edition

Martha R. Taylor, Cornell University

For purchase only. This printed study guide helps students extract key ideas from the textbook and organize their knowledge of biology.

Get Ready for Biology

For purchase only. This workbook helps students brush up on math and study skills and get up to speed on biological terminology and the basics of chemistry and cell biology.

An Introduction to Chemistry for Biology Students, Ninth Edition

George I. Sackheim, University of Illinois, Chicago

For purchase only. This text/workbook helps students master chemistry they need for their life science course.

Campbell *BIOLOGY* 8e AP* Edition Website (www.campbellbiology.com) and CD-ROM

Benjamin Cummings offers two delivery methods for media—website and CD-ROM. Both the website and CD-ROM include over 230 interactive activities, 85 videos, 55 investigations, LabBench, graphing exercises, and quizzes for each chapter. The CD-ROM is included with each AP Edition textbook and can be reused year after year. If a CD-ROM is lost or destroyed, replacements can be purchased from the publisher (replacement CD ISBN 978-0-13-713620-9/0-13-713620-X).

The website includes additional items not found on the CD-ROM: the gradebook function, an electronic version of the textbook (eBook), Discovery Channel Videos, art from the textbook, self-quizzes, a cumulative test-builder, web links for AP teachers, and the Campbell *BIOLOGY* interviews from all editions. Students can also access word roots and a glossary, key terms, and flashcards with audio pronunciations for every term.

BioFlix New BioFlix animations, available only on the website, help students learn the most challenging biological topics with 3-D animations plus labeled slideshows, basic tutorials, study sheets, and quizzes.

Also available only on the website are MP3 audio tutorials that can be played from the website or downloaded onto personal MP3 players for studying anytime.

The website also provides a number of AP teacher tools (only accessible by teachers) including: lecture outlines, common misconceptions, active lecture questions, and answers to selected Eighth Edition essay questions.

Student access to the site is available through their teacher. Instructor access is provided upon textbook adoption. A 6" x 9" folded access card should be included with a school's textbook shipment. The access card contains registration instructions and access codes for teachers and students. A single set of website access codes can be used by two teachers and up to 50 students for one year. During registration, instructors and students create a personal login name and password, which they then use to log into the site each time they visit. Individual login-password information is required for students to view the results of their own work.

If for some reason the access card is not included with the first shipment of texts, or an instructor inherits a set of texts, new access codes can be requested by emailing phwebaccess@pearsoned.com. In subsequent out-years of the adoption, registered teachers will be sent an email in the summer with information for setting up website access for a new set of students.

Teachers who are considering this text for adoption and who also wish to review the website can request a "preview access" card (ISBN 0-13-111589-8), contact their local Pearson representative, or send an e-mail request to phwebaccess@pearsoned.com.

Biology Labs On-Line (www.biologylabsonline.com)

For purchase only. These 12 optional, online labs enable students to go beyond the traditional wet lab setting and perform potentially dangerous, lengthy, or expensive experiments in a safe electronic environment. For more information or to purchase, visit www.biologylabsonline.com.

Classic Edition of The Biology Place (www.biology.com)

This open-access website provides students and teachers with a comprehensive online glossary, BioCoach activities, and LabBench with pre- and post-lab reviews that correspond to the prescribed AP Biology labs.

MasteringBiology™

For purchase only/12-month subscriptions.

MasteringBiology™ is an optional online homework, tutorial, and assessment system. Students work through in-depth tutorials and are provided with hints, feedback, and guidance in real time. Teachers can assign quizzes and homework to students and then view student progress through the gradebook function. For more information, speak to your sales representative or visit www.masteringbio.com.

Transparency Acetates

The transparencies include all the art and tables from the text; many incorporate photos. In addition, selected figures are broken down for step-by-step lecture presentation.

Printed Test Bank, Computerized Test Bank (TestGen), and AP* ExamView Test Bank

These print and computerized assessment materials include more than 4,500 questions that have been refined through class testing. Over 30 percent of the questions are new. The Test Bank is available in print and on a cross-platform CD-ROM in the Instructor Resource CD/DVD-ROM Set.

Instructor Resource CD/DVD-ROM Set

The instructor media for Campbell/Reece *BIOLOGY* 8e AP Edition is combined into one chapter-by-chapter resource with a Quick Reference Guide. The DVDs provide convenient one-stop access to all the visual media for each chapter: new BioFlix 3-D Animations; Discovery Channel Videos; new cell biology videos; all the art, tables, and photos from the text; extra photos; and customizable PowerPoint resources.

Reviewers

Advanced Placement Biology Advisory Group

The authors and the publisher would like to thank the biology educators who reviewed and provided helpful advice for the Eighth Edition.

Barbara Beitch, Quinnipiac University
Suzanne Black, Inglemoor High School
Jean DeSaix, University of North Carolina
Tricia Glidewell, Marist School
Fred Holtzclaw, Webb School of Knoxville
Theresa Holtzclaw, Oak Ridge High School
Jack C. Kay, Iolani School
Nancy Monson, West Linn High School
Richard Patterson, Athens Academy
Nancy Ramos, Northside Health Careers High School
Peggy O'Neill Skinner, The Bush School
Diane Sweeney, Punahou Academy
Brad Williamson, Biology Educator

Eighth Edition Reviewers

Dominique Adriaens, Ghent University
George R. Aliaga, Tarrant County College
J. David Archibald, San Diego State University
David M. Armstrong, University of Colorado-Boulder
Angela S. Aspbury, Texas State University
Ellen Baker, Santa Monica College
Rebecca A. Bartow, Western Kentucky University
Tim Beagley, Salt Lake Community College
Kenneth Birnbaum, New York University
Michael W. Black, California Polytechnic State University, San Luis Obispo
Edward Blumenthal, Marquette University
Jason E. Bond, East Carolina University
Cornelius Bondzi, Hampton University
Oliver Bossdorf, State University of New York, Stony Book
Edward Braun, Iowa State University
Chad Brommer, Emory University
Judith L. Bronstein, University of Arizona
Robb T. Brumfield, Louisiana State University
Richard C. Brusca, University of Arizona, Arizona-Sonora Desert Museum
Jorge Busciglio, University of California, Irvine
Guy A. Caldwell, University of Alabama
Jane Caldwell, West Virginia University
Kim A. Caldwell, University of Alabama
R. Andrew Cameron, California Institute of Technology
W. Zacheus Cande, University of California, Berkeley
Frank R. Cantelmo, St. John's University
Jeffrey Carmichael, University of North Dakota
Laura L. Carruth, Georgia State University
J. Aaron Cassill, University of Texas at San Antonio
P. Bryant Chase, Florida State University
Jung H. Choi, Georgia Institute of Technology
Geoffrey Church, Fairfield University
Patricia J. Clark, Indiana University-Purdue University, Indianapolis
Janice J. Clymer, San Diego Mesa College

Jan Colpaert, Hasselt University
Jay Comeaux, McNeese State University
Gregory Copenhaver, University of North Carolina, Chapel Hill
Karen Curto, University of Pittsburgh
Marymegan Daly, The Ohio State University
Cynthia Dassler, The Ohio State University
Michael A. Davis, Central Connecticut State University
Maria E. de Bellard, California State University, Northridge
Patricia A. DeLeon, University of Delaware
Charles F. Delwiche, University of Maryland
William L. Dentler, University of Kansas
Jean DeSaix, University of North Carolina
Michael Dini, Texas Tech University
Douglas J. Eernisse, California State University, Fullerton
Brad Elder, Doane College
Michelle Elekonich, University of Nevada, Las Vegas
Mary Ellard-Ivey, Pacific Lutheran University
Johnny El-Rady, University of South Florida
John A. Endler, University of California, Santa Barbara
Frederick B. Essig, University of South Florida
Olukemi Fadayomi, Ferris State University
Ellen H. Fanning, Vanderbilt University
Lewis Feldman, University of California, Berkeley
Rebecca Ferrell, Metropolitan State College of Denver
Jonathan S. Fisher, St. Louis University
Kirk Fitzhugh, Natural History Museum of Los Angeles County
Norma Fowler, University of Texas, Austin
Robert Gilbert Fowler, San Jose State University
Jed Fuhrman, University of Southern California
Zofia E. Gagnon, Marist College
Michael Gaines, University of Miami
Stephen Gammie, University of Wisconsin, Madison
Andrea Gargas, University of Wisconsin, Madison
Lauren Garner, California Polytechnic State University, San Luis Obispo
Simon Gilroy, Pennsylvania State University
Alan D. Gishlick, Gustavus Adolphus College
Jessica Gleffe, University of California, Irvine
Tricia Glidewell, Marist School
Elizabeth Godrick, Boston University
Ken Halanych, Auburn University
E. William Hamilton, Washington and Lee University
William F. Hanna, Massasoit Community College
Laszlo Hanzely, Northern Illinois University
Lisa Harper, University of California, Berkeley
Bernard A. Hauser, University of Florida
Evan B. Hazard, Bemidji State University (Emeritus)
S. Blair Hedges, Pennsylvania State University
Brian Hedlund, University of Nevada, Las Vegas
Jean Heitz, University of Wisconsin, Madison
Susan Hengeveld, Indiana University
Albert Herrera, University of Southern California
Kenneth Hillers, California Polytechnic State University, San Luis Obispo
A. Scott Holaday, Texas Tech University
N. Michele Holbrook, Harvard University
Alan R. Holyoak, Brigham Young University, Idaho
Sandra M. Horikami, Daytona Beach Community College
Becky Houck, University of Portland
Daniel J. Howard, New Mexico State University
Cristin Hulslander, University of Oregon
Linda L. Hyde, Gordon College

Jeffrey Ihara, Mira Costa College
Lee Johnson, The Ohio State University
Chad Jordan, North Carolina State University
Walter S. Judd, University of Florida
Thomas W. Jurik, Iowa State University
Caroline M. Kane, University of California, Berkeley
Jennifer Katcher, Pima Community College
Laura A. Katz, Smith College
Maureen Kearney, Field Museum of Natural History
Patrick Keeling, University of British Columbia
Elizabeth A. Kellogg, University of Missouri-St. Louis
Chris Kennedy, Simon Fraser University
Rebecca T. Kimball, University of Florida
Jennifer Knight, University of Colorado
Margareta Krabbe, Uppsala University
Anselm Kratochwil, Universität Osnabrück
Deborah M. Kristan, California State University at San Marcos
William Kroll, Loyola University, Chicago
Justin P. Kumar, Indiana University
Marc-André Lachance, University of Western Ontario
Mohamed Lakrim, Kingsborough Community College
John Latto, University of California, Santa Barbara
Daewoo Lee, Ohio University
Michael R. Leonardo, Coe College
John J. Lepri, University of North Carolina at Greensboro
Graeme Lindbeck, Valencia Community College
Diana Lipscomb, George Washington University
Christopher Little, The University of Texas-Pan American
Kevin D. Livingstone, Trinity University
Andrea Lloyd, Middlebury College
Christopher A. Loretz, State University of New York at Buffalo
Douglas B. Luckie, Michigan State University
Christine R. Maher, University of Southern Maine
Keith Malmos, Valencia Community College – East Campus
Cindy Malone, California State University, Northridge
Carol Mapes, Kutztown University of Pennsylvania
Kathleen A. Marrs, Indiana University-Purdue University, Indianapolis
Diane L. Marshall, University of New Mexico
Andrew McCubbin, Washington State University
Lisa Marie Meffert, Rice University
Scott Meissner, Cornell University
John Merrill, Michigan State University
Michael J. Misamore, Texas Christian University
Alan Molumby, University of Illinois, Chicago
Joseph P. Montoya, Georgia Institute of Technology
Janice Moore, Colorado State University
Jeanette Mowery, Madison Area Technical College
Tom Neils, Grand Rapids Community College
Ray Neubauer, University of Texas, Austin
James Newcomb, New England College
Anders Nilsson, University of Umeå
Mohamed A. F. Noor, Duke University
Shawn Nordell, St. Louis University
Richard S. Norman, University of Michigan, Dearborn (Emeritus)
Gretchen North, Occidental College
Mark P. Oemke, Alma College
Nathan O. Okia, Auburn University, Montgomery
John Oross, University of California, Riverside
Charissa Osborne, Butler University
Thomas G. Owens, Cornell University
Kevin Padian, University of California, Berkeley
Anthony T. Paganini, Michigan State University
Michael A. Palladino, Monmouth University
Imara Y. Perera, North Carolina State University
David S. Pilliod, California Polytechnic State University, San Luis Obispo
J. Chris Pires, University of Missouri-Columbia
Angela R. Porta, Kean University

Daniel Potter, University of California, Davis
Mary V. Price, University of California, Riverside
Mitch Price, Pennsylvania State University
Peter Quinby, University of Pittsburgh
Robert H. Reaves, Glendale Community College
Erin Rempala, San Diego Mesa College
Eric Ribbens, Western Illinois University
Christina Richards, New York University
Loren Rieseberg, University of British Columbia
Bruce B. Riley, Texas A&M University
Laurel Roberts, University of Pittsburgh
Mike Rosenzweig, Virginia Polytechnic Institute and State University
Tyson Sacco, Cornell University
Rowan F. Sage, University of Toronto
Tammy Lynn Sage, University of Toronto
Thomas R. Sawicki, Spartanburg Community College
Inder Saxena, University of Texas, Austin
Maynard H. Schaus, Virginia Wesleyan College
Renate Scheibe, University of Osnabrück
Mark Schlissel, University of California, Berkeley
Christopher J. Schneider, Boston University
Thomas W. Schoener, University of California, Davis
Patricia M. Schulte, University of British Columbia
Karen S. Schumaker, University of Arizona
David J. Schwartz, Houston Community College
Robert W. Seagull, Hofstra University
Duane Sears, University of California, Santa Barbara
Joan Sharp, Simon Fraser University
Timothy E. Shannon, Francis Marion University
Richard M. Showman, University of South Carolina
Rebecca Simmons, University of North Dakota
Anne Simon, University of Maryland, College Park
Robert Simons, University of California, Los Angeles
Julio G. Soto, San Jose State University
John Stachowicz, University of California, Davis
Gail A. Stewart, Camden County College
Michael A. Sypes, Pennsylvania State University
Emily Taylor, California Polytechnic State University, San Luis Obispo
John W. Taylor, University of California, Berkeley
William Thwaites, Tillamook Bay Community College
Eric Toolson, University of New Mexico
Paul Q. Trombley, Florida State University
Nancy J. Trun, Duquesne University
Claudia Uhde-Stone, California State University, East Bay
Saba Valadkhan, Case Western Reserve University School of Medicine
Steven D. Verhey, Central Washington University
Kathleen Verville, Washington College
Sara Via, University of Maryland
Leif Asbjørn Vøllestad, University of Oslo
Linda Walters, University of Central Florida
Nickolas M. Waser, University of California, Riverside
Andrea Weeks, George Mason University
Richard Wetts, University of California, Irvine
Susan Whittemore, Keene State College
Ernest H. Williams, Hamilton College
Kathy Williams, San Diego State University
Paul Wilson, California State University, Northridge
Peter Wimberger, University of Puget Sound
Robert Winning, Eastern Michigan University
E. William Wischusen, Louisiana State University
Vickie L. Wolfe, Marshall University
Denise Woodward, Pennsylvania State University
Sarah E. Wyatt, Ohio University
Ramin Yadegari, University of Arizona
Paul Yancey, Whitman College
Gina M. Zainelli, Loyola University, Chicago
Miriam Zolan, Indiana University

Acknowledgments

The authors wish to express their gratitude to the global community of instructors, researchers, students, and publishing professionals who have contributed to this edition.

As authors of this text, we are mindful of the daunting challenge of keeping up to date in all areas of our rapidly expanding subject. We are grateful to the numerous scientists who helped shape this edition by discussing their research fields with us, answering specific questions in their areas of expertise, and, often, sharing their ideas about biology education.

For advice in updating the phylogeny of Galápagos finches in Chapter 1, we are indebted to Kevin Burns and Peter Grant. For assistance with the chapters of Units 1 through 3 (chemistry, cell biology, and genetics), we first wish to thank the members of the Mills College Biology and Chemistry/Physics Department, notably Barbara Bowman and Elisabeth Wade. We are also grateful to Tom Owens and Mimi Zolan, who were each exceptionally generous with their time and knowledge, and to Michael Black, Laurie Heyer, and Ed Blake, for noteworthy contributions to figures. And we thank the individuals who took the time to share their expertise on early atmospheric conditions (Laura Schaefer), cell biology (Pat Zambryski, Steve King, Jeremy Reiter, and Jeff Hardin), gene regulation (Phil Zamore, Dave Bartel, Tom Gingeras, Steve Bell, Saba Valadkhan, Joe Heilig, Lorraine Pillus, and Mike Levine), current cloning approaches (Caroline Kane and Andy Cameron), genomics (Nikos Krypides, Emir Khatipov, and Rebekah Rasooly), and homeobox genes (Bill McGinnis). In addition, we thank Lisa Weasel for her feedback on the new "Tips for Genetics Problems."

For the chapters of Units 4 and 5, on evolution and the diversity of life, researchers who generously shared their expertise with us included Richard Anthony, Nick Barton, Toby Bradshaw, Keith Clay, Kevin de Queiroz, Peter and Rosemary Grant, Daniel J. Howard, Patrick Keeling, Andrew H. Knoll, Jon Mallatt, Amy McCune, Axel Meyer, Kevin J. Peterson, Loren Rieseberg, Ole Seehausen, and Mark Webster.

For Units 6 through 8, the units on plant and animal form and function, and ecology, we benefited greatly from the expertise of Charles Michel, Eric Britt, Don Boyer, and Alan French. In addition, Tom Deerinck, Peter Gillespie, Mark Chappell, and Doug DeSimone provided important assistance with figures. We also thank Eric Simon, a coauthor of the Campbell nonmajors texts, for helping us think through some terminology and presentation dilemmas in Unit 7.

And finally, for her many contributions throughout the book, we sincerely thank Marty Taylor, the author of the *Student Study Guide* and a coauthor of *Biology: Concepts & Connections*.

More than 230 biologists, listed on pages xxviii–xxix, provided detailed reviews of one or more chapters for this edition, helping us ensure the book's scientific accuracy and improve its pedagogical effectiveness. Special thanks for exceptional contributions go to Johnny El-Rady, Graeme Lindbeck, Bruce Riley, Robert Fowler, Alan Gishlick, Alastair Simpson, Ken Halanych, Kevin Padian, John Taylor, Jay Comeaux, Grace Wyngaard, Lauren Garner, Missy Holbrook, Toby Kellogg, Eduardo Zeiger, Richard Norman, Albert Herrera, and Patricia Schulte. Thanks also to the numerous other professors and students, from all over the world, who offered suggestions directly to the authors. Of course, we alone bear the responsibility for any errors that remain in the text, but the dedication of our consultants, reviewers, and other correspondents makes us especially confident in the accuracy and effectiveness of this edition.

Conducting the unit-opening interviews was again one of the great pleasures of revising *BIOLOGY*. For the Eighth Edition, we are proud to include interviews with Deborah Gordon, Paul Nurse, Terry Orr-Weaver, Scott Edwards, Sean Carroll, Pat Zambryski, Masashi Yanagisawa, and Diana Wall (see p. xvii). We thank these busy people for generously sharing their experiences with us.

The value of *BIOLOGY* as a learning tool is greatly enhanced by the supplementary materials that have been created for instructors and students. We recognize that the dedicated authors of these materials are essentially writing mini (and not so mini) books. We much appreciate the hard work and creativity of the following: Ruth Buskirk and Christopher Gillen (authors of the new *Inquiry in Action: Interpreting Scientific Papers*); Judith Morgan and Eloise Brown Carter (*Investigating Biology*, 6th Edition); Jean Heitz and Cynthia Giffen (*Practicing Biology*, 3rd Edition); Margaret Waterman and Ethel Stanley (*Biological Inquiry: A Workbook of Investigative Cases*, 2nd Edition); Bill Barstow, Louise Paquin, Michael Dini, John Lepri, John Zarnetske, C. O. Patterson, and Jean DeSaix (*Test Bank*); Ed Zalisko, Margaret Ricci, Lauren Garner, Jung Choi, and Virginia White (*Media Quizzes*); Joan Sharp (*Lecture Outlines, PowerPoint Lectures,* and *Student Misconceptions*); Erin Barley (*PowerPoint Lectures*); Bill Wischusen, Ruth Buskirk, Jung Choi, John Merrill, Melissa Michael, Randy Phillis, Mark Lyford, and Chris Gregg (*Active Learning Questions*); and Laura Zanello (*Spanish Glossary*). Once again, we thank our long-time colleague Marty Taylor for her excellent work on the *Student Study Guide*; she has now completed eight editions of this popular student aid. Special thanks go to Tom Owens for his visionary work on the *BioFlix* animations and his creative, collaborative work as lead author on our new *MasteringBiology* tutorials. We also thank Brad Williamson, Jennifer Yeh, Dawn Keller, and Scott Bowling for their excellent work on the *BioFlix* animations and the accompanying student tools. In addition, we are grateful to the many other people—biology instructors, editors, artists, production experts, and narrators—who are listed in the credits for these and other elements of the electronic media that accompany the book. Finally, we thank the class testers and reviewers of *BioFlix* and *MasteringBiology*.

BIOLOGY, Eighth Edition, results from an unusually strong synergy between a team of scientists and a team of publishing professionals. The expansion of the author team and major revision of many chapters, the creation of new pedagogical features and the improvement of old ones, and the exceptionally rich package of supplements created unprecedented challenges for the publishing team.

The members of our core editorial team at Benjamin Cummings—our Fab Five—brought unmatched talents, commitment, and pedagogical insights to this revision, and working with this team over the past three years has been a great pleasure. Our Editor-in-Chief, Beth Wilbur, continues to be a full colleague in the book's ongoing evolution and a respected advocate for biology education in the academic community. Our extraordinary Supervising Editors, Pat Burner and Beth Winickoff, once again had the awesome responsibility of overseeing in detail the work of all the authors, developmental editors, and developmental artists. Together, Beth and Pat ensured that every page of every chapter has the text, figures, and pedagogy to make this edition the most effective biology textbook ever. Deborah Gale, Executive Director of Development, and our Senior Editorial Manager, the incomparable Ginnie Simione Jutson, oversaw the entire project on a day-by-day basis, a feat equivalent to running a three-ring circus. Ginnie's patience and resourcefulness and Deborah's oversight of the project as a whole have enabled the entire book team to operate at a level of sanity that would not have been possible without their guidance.

We were fortunate to have on our team some of college publishing's top developmental editors. In addition to Beth Winickoff and Pat Burner (who did important hands-on editing themselves, as well as their many other tasks), the primary developmental editors for this edition were John Burner and Matt Lee, joined as the project progressed by Alice Fugate and Suzanne Olivier. We are deeply grateful to all our editors for making us better writers, teachers, and biologists.

Biology is a visual subject, and we are indebted to our developmental artists Hilair Chism, Carla Simmons, Andrew Recher, Connie Balek, and Kelly Murphy for helping us make all our figures better tools for teaching and learning—as well as visually appealing. In addition, the support of our bright, efficient, and good-natured Editorial Assistants—Julia Khait, Ben Pearson, and Logan Triglia—is much appreciated. We couldn't have finished the book without them!

We also want to thank Robin Heyden for organizing the annual Benjamin Cummings Biology Leadership Conferences, which always bring us closer to the teaching community and offer a fresh supply of creative teaching ideas from outstanding biology educators. In addition, Robin is our invaluable liaison with high school teachers of Advanced Placement Biology, most of whom use our book in their courses.

You would not have a book in your hands today if not for the herculean efforts of the book production team, which has the crucial responsibility of converting the text manuscript and illustrations to pages ready for the printer. For the Eighth Edition, these efforts were headed up by Managing Editor Mike Early. We thank him, as well as our longtime copyeditor Janet Greenblatt, proofreaders Joanna Dinsmore and Marie Dartman, Permissions Editors Sue Ewing and Marcy Lunetta, and indexers Lynn Armstrong and Charlotte Shane. Handling the illustrations were Art Editors Laura Murray and Kelly Murphy; the final rendering of the new and revised illustrations was carried out by the artists of Precision Graphics, working under Kristina Seymour. Senior Photo Editor Donna Kalal and photo researcher Maureen Spuhler obtained a large number of handsome and informative photos for this edition. We are indebted to the entire art and photo team. For the beautiful design of the book's interior, we want to thank Art and Design Director Mark Ong and Design Manager Marilyn Perry for their design of text and art styles that show off the words and pictures in a way that will appeal to readers and help them learn. (And thanks to both of them for their endless patience with all our concerns!) For the user-friendly page layouts, we are grateful to Jennifer Dunn and Jana Anderson. And many thanks to Yvo Riezebos for designing the striking cover. Putting together all the pieces of this complicated book were the staff at S4Carlisle Publishing Services, led by Production Manager Lori Dalberg and Composition Supervisor Holly Paige. Thank you, Lori and Holly!

We are pleased to thank the topnotch publishing professionals who worked on the book's printed supplements: Senior Supplements Project Editor Susan Berge, who coordinated the entire print supplements package; Production Supervisor Jane Brundage; Developmental Editor Susan Weisberg; and Project Editors Mary Douglas, Kim Wimpsett, Elizabeth Campbell, and Melanie Field.

With regard to the wonderful package of electronic media that accompanies the book, we offer special thanks to Senior Media Producer Jon Ballard, Project Editors Nora Lally-Graves and Brienn Buchanan, media correlators Nina Lewallen Hufford and Sarah Kaminker, and

proofreader Pete Shanks for their work on the website. We also are grateful to Associate Web Developer Linda Young and Web Technologies Manager Steve Wright. For their work on the *Instructor Resource CD/DVD-ROM*, we thank Project Manager James Bruce; Developmental Artist Hilair Chism; Developmental Editors John Burner, Pat Burner, Matt Lee, and Beth Winickoff; copyeditor John Hammett (*PPT Lectures*); proofreader Pete Shanks (*PPT Lectures*); and Donna King, Production Project Manager at Progressive Information Technologies.

We are especially grateful to the team of publishing professionals whose combined talents are evident in the *BioFlix* animations and student tools: Pat Burner, Russell Chun (storyboard artist extraordinaire), Ginnie Simione Jutson, Jon Ballard, Karen Gulliver (developmental editor), Animated Biomedical Productions (animation production); and Groove 11 (tutorial production). For their work on *MasteringBiology*, we thank the aforementioned Pat Burner, Ginnie Simione Jutson, and Jon Ballard, plus Tania Mlawer, Director of Content Development and Project Management; Mary Catherine Hager, Developmental Editor; Deb Greco, Media Producer; Kristen Sutton, Content Lead; and Developmental Artist Jay McElroy and the artists at Pearson Production Solutions. For their hard work and support, our appreciation goes to the MasteringX Team (in alphabetical order): Ruth Berry, Lewis Costas, Katherine Foley, Julia Henderson, Joseph Ignazi, Jeff King, David Kokorowski, Mary Lee, Claire Masson, Nissi Mathews, Adam Morton, Fred Mueller, Ian Nordby, Maria Panos, Andrea Pascarella, Mary Ann Perry, Caroline Power, Sarah Smith, Margaret Trombley, and Rasil Warnakulasooriya. Last, but not least, we thank Lauren Fogel, Director of Media Development at Benjamin Cummings, for her continued leadership on all things media.

For their important roles in marketing the book, we are very grateful to Director of Marketing Christy Lawrence, Executive Marketing Manager Lauren Harp, and Market Development Manager Josh Frost. For the creation of visually stunning print and electronic promotional materials, we thank Creative Director Lillian Carr; Marketing Communication Specialists Jane Campbell, Kristi Hlaing, and Jessica Perry; Designer Laurie Campbell; Web Designer Mansour Bethoney, who led the creation of the e-brochure; and Webmaster Anna Molodtsova.

Linda Davis, President of Pearson Math, Economics, and Science, has shared our commitment to excellence and provided strong support for four editions now, and we are happy to thank her once again. We also want to thank Paul Corey, now President of Pearson Science, for his enthusiasm, encouragement, and support.

The Pearson Science sales team, which represents *BIOLOGY* on campus, is our living link to the students and professors who use the text. The field representatives tell us what you like and don't like about the book, and they provide prompt service to biology departments. They are strong allies in biology education, and we thank them for their professionalism in communicating the features of our book. For representing our book and its teaching values to our wider international audience, we thank the sustained work of our sales and marketing partners throughout the world, including (but by no means only) Marlene Olsavsky, Ann Oravetz, and Pablo Rendina.

Finally, we wish to thank our families and friends for their encouragement and patience throughout this long project. Our special thanks to: Paul, Dan, Maria, Armelle, and Sean (J.R.); Lily, Grant, Ross, Lilytoo, and Alex (L.U.); Debra and Hannah (M.C.); Harry, Elga, Aaron, Sophie, Noah, and Gabriele (S.W.); Natalie (P.M.); and Sally, Robert, David, and Will (R.J.). And as always, Rochelle and Allison.

Jane Reece, Lisa Urry, Michael Cain,
Steve Wasserman, Peter Minorsky, and Rob Jackson

Detailed Contents

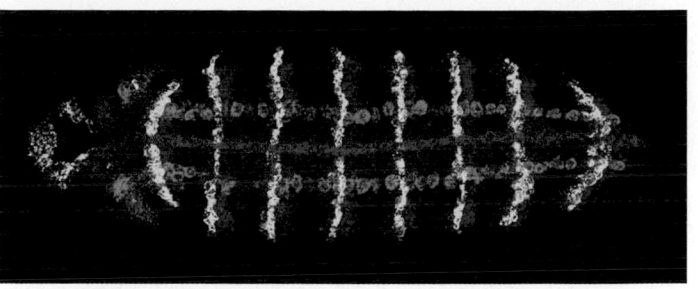

UNIT THREE

Genetics   246

UNIT FOUR

Mechanisms of Evolution   450

UNIT EIGHT

Ecology 1146

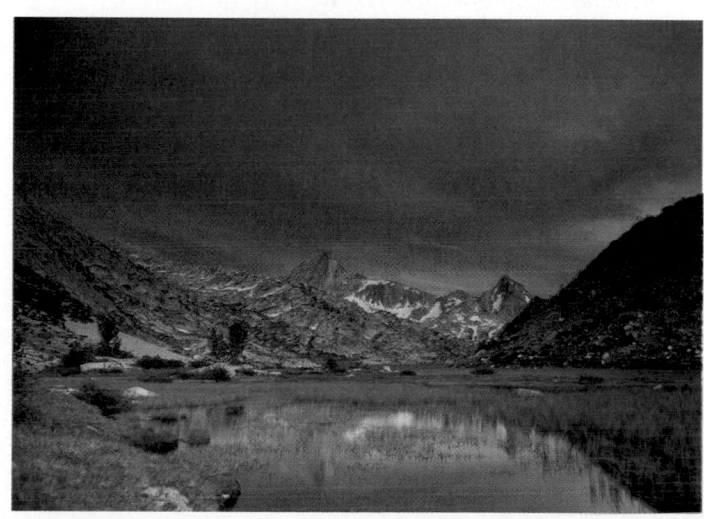

Introduction: Themes in the Study of Life

1

▲ **Figure 1.1 What properties of life are demonstrated by this flower?**

OVERVIEW

Inquiring About the World of Life

The flower featured on the cover of this book and in **Figure 1.1** is from a magnolia, a tree of ancient lineage that is native to Asian and American forests. The magnolia blossom is a sign of the plant's status as a living organism, for flowers contain organs of sexual reproduction, and reproduction is a key property of life, as you will learn later.

Like all organisms, the magnolia tree in **Figure 1.2** is living in close association with other organisms, though it is a lone specimen far from its ancestral forest. For example, it depends on beetles to carry pollen from one flower to another, and the beetles, in turn, eat from its flowers. The flowers are adapted to the beetles in several ways: Their bowl shape allows easy access, and their multiple reproductive organs and tough petals (see Figure 1.1) help ensure that some survive the voracious beetles. Such adaptations are the result of **evolution**, the process of change that has transformed life on Earth from its earliest beginnings to the diversity of organisms living today. As discussed later in this chapter, evolution is the fundamental organizing principle of biology and the main theme of this book.

Although biologists know a great deal about magnolias and other plants, many mysteries remain. For instance, what exactly led to the origin of flowering plants? Posing questions about the living world and seeking science-based answers—scientific inquiry—are the central activities of **biology**, the sci-

entific study of life. Biologists' questions can be ambitious. They may ask how a single tiny cell becomes a tree or a dog, how the human mind works, or how the different forms of life in a forest interact. Can you think of some questions about living organisms that interest you? When you do, you are already starting to think like a biologist. More than anything else, biology is a quest, an ongoing inquiry about the nature of life.

Perhaps some of your questions relate to health or to societal or environmental issues. Biology is woven into the fabric of our culture more than ever before and can help answer many questions that affect our lives. Research breakthroughs in genetics and cell biology are transforming medicine and agriculture. Neuroscience and evolutionary biology are reshaping psychology and sociology. New models in ecology are helping societies evaluate environmental issues, such as global warming. There has never been a more important time to embark on a study of life.

▲ **Figure 1.2 A magnolia tree in early spring.**

▼ **Order.** This close-up of a sunflower illustrates the highly ordered structure that characterizes life.

▲ **Evolutionary adaptation.** The appearance of this pygmy sea horse camouflages the animal in its environment. Such adaptations evolve over many generations by the reproductive success of those individuals with heritable traits that are best suited to their environments.

▲ **Response to the environment.** This Venus flytrap closed its trap rapidly in response to the environmental stimulus of a damselfly landing on the open trap.

▼ **Growth and development.** Inherited information carried by genes controls the pattern of growth and development of organisms, such as this Nile crocodile.

▲ **Regulation.** The regulation of blood flow through the blood vessels of this jackrabbit's ears helps maintain a constant body temperature by adjusting heat exchange with the surrounding air.

▲ **Energy processing.** This hummingbird obtains fuel in the form of nectar from flowers. The hummingbird will use chemical energy stored in its food to power flight and other work.

▲ **Reproduction.** Organisms (living things) reproduce their own kind. Here an emperor penguin protects its baby.

▲ **Figure 1.3 Some properties of life.**
? *Is a gasoline-powered lawn mower alive? Which of these properties does it have? Which properties does it lack?*

But what is life? Even a small child realizes that a dog or a plant is alive, while a rock is not. Yet the phenomenon we call life defies a simple, one-sentence definition. We recognize life by what living things do. **Figure 1.3** highlights some of the properties and processes we associate with life.

While limited to a handful of images, Figure 1.3 reminds us that the living world is wondrously varied. How do biologists make sense of this diversity and complexity? This opening chapter sets up a framework for answering this question. The first part of the chapter provides a panoramic view of the biological "landscape," organized around some unifying themes. We then focus on biology's overarching theme, evolution, with an introduction to the reasoning that led Charles Darwin to his explanatory theory. Finally, we look at scientific inquiry—how scientists raise and attempt to answer questions about the natural world.

CONCEPT 1.1

Themes connect the concepts of biology

Biology is a subject of enormous scope, and anyone who follows the news knows that biological knowledge is expanding at an ever-increasing rate. Simply memorizing the factual details of this huge subject is not a reasonable option. How, then, can you, as a student, go beyond the facts to develop a coherent view of life? One approach is to fit the many things you learn into a set of themes that pervade all of biology—ways of thinking about life that will still apply decades from now. Focusing on a few big ideas will help you organize and make sense of all the information you'll encounter as you study biology. To help you, we have selected seven unifying themes to serve as touchstones as you proceed through this book.

Evolution, the Overarching Theme of Biology

Evolution is biology's core theme—the one idea that makes sense of everything we know about living organisms. Life has been evolving on Earth for billions of years, resulting in a vast diversity of past and present organisms. But along with the diversity we find many shared features. For example, while the sea horse, jackrabbit, hummingbird, crocodile, and penguins in Figure 1.3 look very different, their skeletons are basically similar. The scientific explanation for this unity and diversity—and for the suitability of organisms to their environments—is evolution: the idea that the organisms living on Earth today are the modified descendants of common ancestors. In other words, we can explain traits shared by two organisms with the idea that they have descended from a common ancestor, and we can account for differences with the idea that heritable changes have occurred along the way. Many kinds of evidence support the occurrence of evolution and the theory that describes how it takes place. We'll return to evolution later in the chapter, after surveying some other themes and painting a fuller picture of the scope of biology.

Theme: New properties emerge at each level in the biological hierarchy

The study of life extends from the microscopic scale of the molecules and cells that make up organisms to the global scale of the entire living planet. We can divide this enormous range into different levels of biological organization.

Imagine zooming in from space to take a closer and closer look at life on Earth. It is spring, and our destination is a forest in Ontario, Canada, where we will eventually explore a maple leaf right down to the molecular level. **Figure 1.4** (on the next two pages) narrates this journey into life, with the circled numbers leading you through the levels of biological organization illustrated by the photographs.

Emergent Properties

If we now zoom back out from the molecular level in Figure 1.4, we can see that novel properties emerge at each step, properties that are not present at the preceding level. These **emergent properties** are due to the arrangement and interactions of parts as complexity increases. For example, if you make a test-tube mixture of chlorophyll and all the other kinds of molecules found in a chloroplast, photosynthesis will not occur. Photosynthesis can take place only when the molecules are arranged in a specific way in an intact chloroplast. To take another example, if a serious head injury disrupts the intricate architecture of a human brain, the mind may cease to function properly even though all of the brain parts are still present. Our thoughts and memories are emergent properties of a complex network of nerve cells. At a much higher level of biological organization—at the ecosystem level—the recycling of chemical elements essential to life, such as carbon, depends on a network of diverse organisms interacting with each other and with the soil, water, and air.

Emergent properties are not unique to life. We can see the importance of arrangement in the distinction between a box of bicycle parts and a working bicycle. And while graphite and diamonds are both pure carbon, they have very different properties because their carbon atoms are arranged differently. But compared to such nonliving examples, the unrivaled complexity of biological systems makes the emergent properties of life especially challenging to study.

The Power and Limitations of Reductionism

Because the properties of life emerge from complex organization, scientists seeking to understand biological systems confront a dilemma. On the one hand, we cannot fully explain a higher level of order by breaking it down into its parts. A dissected animal no longer functions; a cell reduced to its chemical ingredients is no longer a cell. Disrupting a living system interferes with its functioning. On the other hand, something as complex as an organism or a cell cannot be analyzed without taking it apart.

Reductionism—the reduction of complex systems to simpler components that are more manageable to study—is a powerful strategy in biology. For example, by studying the molecular structure of DNA that had been extracted from cells, James Watson and Francis Crick inferred, in 1953, how this molecule could serve as the chemical basis of inheritance. The central role of DNA in cells and organisms became better understood, however, when scientists were able to study the interactions of DNA with other molecules. Biologists must balance the reductionist strategy with the larger-scale, holistic objective of understanding emergent properties—how the parts of cells, organisms, and higher levels of order, such as ecosystems, work together. At the cutting edge of research today is the approach called systems biology.

Exploring Levels of Biological Organization

◀ 1 The Biosphere

As soon as we are near enough to Earth to make out its continents and oceans, we begin to see signs of life—in the green mosaic of the planet's forests, for example. This is our first view of the biosphere, which consists of all the environments on Earth that are inhabited by life. The biosphere includes most regions of land, most bodies of water, and the atmosphere to an altitude of several kilometers.

◀ 2 Ecosystems

As we approach Earth's surface for an imaginary landing in Ontario, we can begin to make out a forest with an abundance of deciduous trees (trees that lose their leaves in one season and grow new ones in another). Such a deciduous forest is an example of an ecosystem. Grasslands, deserts, and the ocean's coral reefs are other types of ecosystems. An ecosystem consists of all the living things in a particular area, along with all the nonliving components of the environment with which life interacts, such as soil, water, atmospheric gases, and light. All of Earth's ecosystems combined make up the biosphere.

▶ 3 Communities

The entire array of organisms inhabiting a particular ecosystem is called a biological community. The community in our forest ecosystem includes many kinds of trees and other plants, a diversity of animals, various mushrooms and other fungi, and enormous numbers of diverse microorganisms, which are living forms, such as bacteria, that are too small to see without a microscope. Each of these forms of life is called a *species*.

▶ 4 Populations

A population consists of all the individuals of a species living within the bounds of a specified area. For example, our Ontario forest includes a population of sugar maple trees and a population of white-tailed deer. We can now refine our definition of a community as the set of populations that inhabit a particular area.

▲ 5 Organisms

Individual living things are called organisms. Each of the maple trees and other plants in the forest is an organism, and so is each forest animal, such as a frog, squirrel, deer, and beetle. The soil teems with microorganisms such as bacteria.

▼ 6 Organs and Organ Systems

The structural hierarchy of life continues to unfold as we explore the architecture of the more complex organisms. A maple leaf is an example of an organ, a body part consisting of two or more tissues (which we'll see upon our next scale change). An organ carries out a particular function in the body. Stems and roots are the other major organs of plants. Examples of human organs are the brain, heart, and kidney. The organs of humans, other complex animals, and plants are organized into organ systems, each a team of organs that cooperate in a specific function. For example, the human digestive system includes such organs as the tongue, stomach, and intestines.

▶ 7 Tissues

Our next scale change—to see a leaf's tissues—requires a microscope. The leaf shown here has been cut on an angle. The honeycombed tissue in the interior of the leaf (left portion of photo) is the main location of photosynthesis, the process that converts light energy to the chemical energy of sugar and other food. We are viewing the sliced leaf from a perspective that also enables us to see the jigsaw puzzle–like tissue called epidermis, the "skin" on the surface of the leaf (right part of photo). The pores through the epidermis allow the gas carbon dioxide, a raw material for sugar production, to reach the photosynthetic tissue inside the leaf. At this scale, we can also see that each tissue has a cellular structure. In fact, each kind of tissue is a group of similar cells.

▼ 8 Cells

The cell is life's fundamental unit of structure and function. Some organisms, such as amoebas and most bacteria, are single cells. Other organisms, including plants and animals, are multicellular. Instead of a single cell performing all the functions of life, a multicellular organism has a division of labor among specialized cells. A human body consists of trillions of microscopic cells of many different kinds, such as muscle cells and nerve cells, which are organized into the various specialized tissues. For example, muscle tissue consists of bundles of muscle cells. In the photo below, we see a more highly magnified view of some of the cells in a leaf tissue. Each of the cells is only about 25 micrometers (µm) across. It would take more than 700 of these cells to reach across a penny. As small as these cells are, you can see that each contains numerous green structures called chloroplasts, which are responsible for photosynthesis.

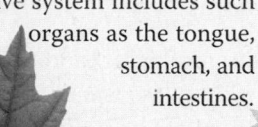

10 µm   Cell

50 µm

▼ 9 Organelles

Chloroplasts are examples of organelles, the various functional components that make up cells. In this image, a very powerful tool called an electron microscope brings a single chloroplast into sharp focus.

1 µm

▶ 10 Molecules

Our last scale change vaults us into a chloroplast for a view of life at the molecular level. A molecule is a chemical structure consisting of two or more small chemical units called *atoms*, which are represented as balls in this computer graphic of a chlorophyll molecule. Chlorophyll is the pigment molecule that makes a maple leaf green. One of the most important molecules on Earth, chlorophyll absorbs sunlight during the first step of photosynthesis. Within each chloroplast, millions of chlorophylls and other molecules are organized into the equipment that converts light energy to the chemical energy of food.

Atoms

Systems Biology

A system is simply a combination of components that function together. A biologist can study a system at any level of organization. A single leaf cell can be considered a system, as can a frog, an ant colony, or a desert ecosytem. To understand how such systems work, it is not enough to have a "parts list," even a complete one. Realizing this, many researchers are now complementing the reductionist approach with new strategies for studying whole systems. This changing perspective is analogous to moving from ground level on a street corner to a helicopter high above a city, from which you can see how variables such as time of day, construction projects, accidents, and traffic-signal malfunctions affect traffic throughout the city.

The goal of **systems biology** is to construct models for the dynamic behavior of whole biological systems. Successful models enable biologists to predict how a change in one or more variables will affect other components and the whole system. Thus, the systems approach enables us to pose new kinds of questions. How might a drug that lowers blood pressure affect the functions of organs throughout the human body? How might increasing a crop's water supply affect processes in the plants, such as the storage of molecules essential for human nutrition? How might a gradual increase in atmospheric carbon dioxide alter ecosystems and the entire biosphere? The ultimate aim of systems biology is to answer big questions like the last one.

Systems biology is relevant to the study of life at all levels. During the early years of the 20th century, biologists studying animal physiology (functioning) began integrating data on how multiple organs coordinate processes such as the regulation of sugar concentration in the blood. And in the 1960s, scientists investigating ecosystems pioneered a more mathematically sophisticated systems approach with elaborate models diagramming the network of interactions between organisms and nonliving components of ecosystems such as salt marshes. Such models have already been useful for predicting the responses of these systems to changing variables. More recently, systems biology has taken hold at the cellular and molecular levels, as we'll describe later when we discuss DNA.

Theme: Organisms interact with their environments, exchanging matter and energy

Turn back again to Figure 1.4, this time focusing on the forest. In this or any other ecosystem, each organism interacts continuously with its environment, which includes both nonliving factors and other organisms. A tree, for example, absorbs water and minerals from the soil, through its roots. At the same time, its leaves take in carbon dioxide from the air and use sunlight absorbed by chlorophyll to drive photosynthesis, converting water and carbon dioxide to sugar and oxygen. The tree releases oxygen to the air, and its roots help form soil by breaking up rocks. Both organism and environment are affected by the interactions between them. The tree also interacts with other organisms, such as soil microorganisms associated with its roots and animals that eat its leaves and fruit.

Ecosystem Dynamics

The operation of any ecosystem involves two major processes. One process is the cycling of nutrients. For example, minerals acquired by a tree will eventually be returned to the soil by organisms that decompose leaf litter, dead roots, and other organic debris. The second major process in an ecosystem is the one-way flow of energy from sunlight to producers to consumers. Producers are plants and other photosynthetic organisms, which use light energy to make sugar. Consumers are organisms, such as animals, that feed on producers and other consumers. The diagram in **Figure 1.5** outlines the two processes acting in an African ecosystem.

Energy Conversion

Moving, growing, reproducing, and the other activities of life are work, and work requires energy. The exchange of energy between an organism and its surroundings often involves the transformation of one form of energy to another. For example, the leaves of a plant absorb light energy and convert it to chemical energy stored in sugar molecules. When an animal's muscle cells use sugar as fuel to power movements, they convert chemical energy to kinetic energy, the energy of motion. And

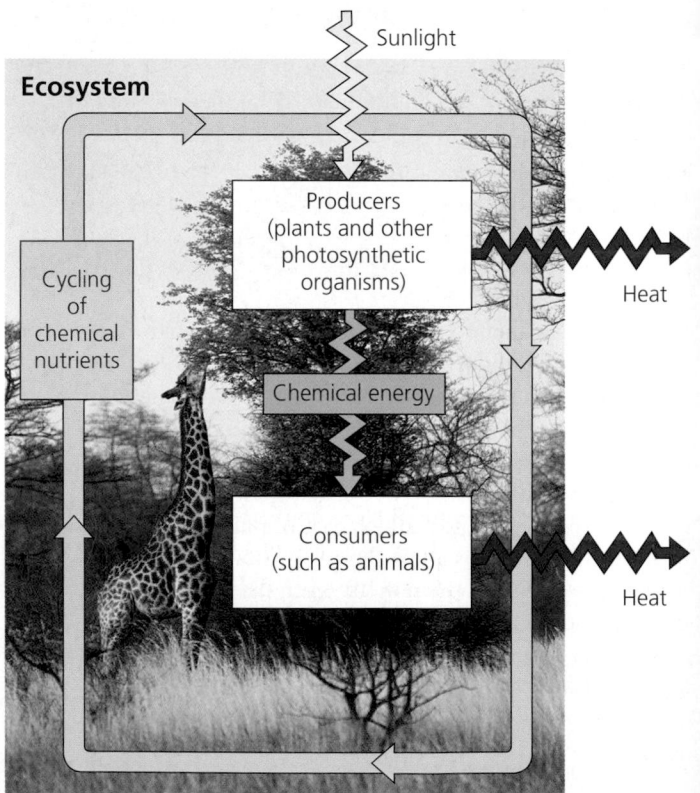

▲ Figure 1.5 **Nutrient cycling and energy flow in an ecosystem.**

(a) A bird's wings have an aerodynamically efficient shape.

(b) Wing bones have a honeycombed internal structure that is strong but lightweight.

100 μm

(c) The flight muscles are controlled by neurons (nerve cells), which transmit signals. With long extensions, neurons are especially well structured for communication within the body.

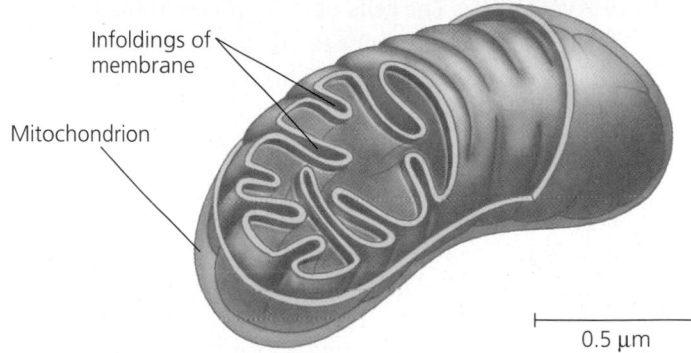

Infoldings of membrane

Mitochondrion

0.5 μm

(d) The flight muscles obtain energy in a usable form from organelles called mitochondria. A mitochondrion has an inner membrane with many infoldings. Molecules embedded in the inner membrane carry out many of the steps in energy production, and the infoldings pack a large amount of this membrane into a small container.

▲ **Figure 1.6 Form fits function in a gull's wing.** A bird's build and the structures of its components make flight possible.
? *How does form fit function in a human hand?*

in all these energy conversions, some of the energy is converted to thermal energy, which dissipates to the surroundings as heat. In contrast to chemical nutrients, which recycle within an ecosystem, energy flows through an ecosystem, usually entering as light and exiting as heat (see Figure 1.5).

Theme: Structure and function are correlated at all levels of biological organization

Another theme evident in Figure 1.4 is the idea that form fits function, which you'll recognize from everyday life. For example, a screwdriver is suited to tighten or loosen screws, a hammer to pound nails. How a device works is correlated with its structure. Applied to biology, this theme is a guide to the anatomy of life at all its structural levels. An example from Figure 1.4 is seen in the leaf: Its thin, flat shape maximizes the amount of sunlight that can be captured by its chloroplasts. Analyzing a biological structure gives us clues about what it does and how it works. Conversely, knowing the function of something provides insight into its construction. An example from the animal kingdom, the wing of a bird, provides additional instances of the structure-function theme **(Figure 1.6)**. In exploring life on its different structural levels, we discover functional beauty at every turn.

Theme: Cells are an organism's basic units of structure and function

In life's structural hierarchy, the cell has a special place as the lowest level of organization that can perform all activities required for life. Moreover, the activities of organisms are all based on the activities of cells. For instance, the division of cells to form new cells is the basis for all reproduction and for the growth and repair of multicellular organisms **(Figure 1.7)**. To

25 μm

▲ **Figure 1.7 A lung cell from a newt divides into two smaller cells that will grow and divide again.**

cite another example, the movement of your eyes as you read this line is based on activities of muscle and nerve cells. Even a global process such as the recycling of carbon is the cumulative product of cellular activities, including the photosynthesis that occurs in the chloroplasts of leaf cells. Understanding how cells work is a major focus of biological research.

All cells share certain characteristics. For example, every cell is enclosed by a membrane that regulates the passage of materials between the cell and its surroundings. And every cell uses DNA as its genetic information. However, we can distinguish between two main forms of cells: prokaryotic cells and eukaryotic cells. The cells of two groups of microorganisms called bacteria and archaea are prokaryotic. All other forms of life, including plants and animals, are composed of eukaryotic cells.

A **eukaryotic cell** is subdivided by internal membranes into various membrane-enclosed organelles, such as the ones you see in **Figure 1.8** and the chloroplast you saw in Figure 1.4. In most eukaryotic cells, the largest organelle is the nucleus, which contains the cell's DNA. The other organelles are located in the cytoplasm, the entire region between the nucleus and outer membrane of the cell. As Figure 1.8 also shows, prokaryotic cells are much simpler and generally smaller than eukaryotic cells. In a **prokaryotic cell**, the DNA is not separated from the rest of the cell by enclosure in a membrane-bounded nucleus. Prokaryotic cells also lack the other kinds of membrane-enclosed organelles that characterize eukaryotic cells. But whether an organism has prokaryotic or eukaryotic cells, its structure and function depend on cells.

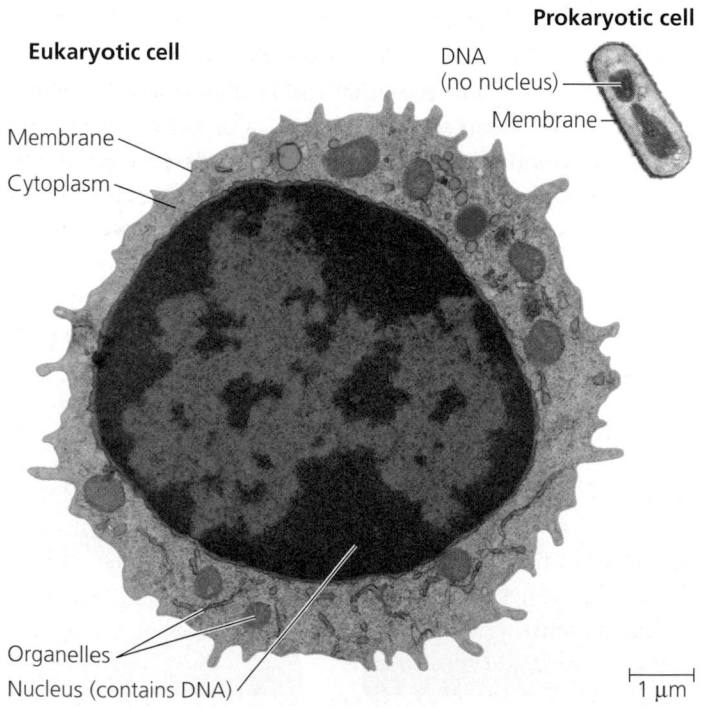

Eukaryotic cell

Membrane

Cytoplasm

Prokaryotic cell

DNA (no nucleus)

Membrane

Organelles

Nucleus (contains DNA)

1 μm

▲ **Figure 1.8 Contrasting eukaryotic and prokaryotic cells in size and complexity.**

Theme: The continuity of life is based on heritable information in the form of DNA

Inside the dividing cell in Figure 1.7 (on the previous page), you can see structures called chromosomes, which are stained with a blue-glowing dye. The chromosomes have almost all of the cell's genetic material, its **DNA** (short for deoxyribonucleic acid). DNA is the substance of **genes**, the units of inheritance that transmit information from parents to offspring. Your blood group (A, B, AB, or O), for example, is the result of certain genes that you inherited from your parents.

DNA Structure and Function

Each chromosome has one very long DNA molecule, with hundreds or thousands of genes arranged along its length. The DNA of chromosomes replicates as a cell prepares to divide, and each of the two cellular offspring inherits a complete set of genes.

Each of us began life as a single cell stocked with DNA inherited from our parents. Replication of that DNA with each round of cell division transmitted copies of it to our trillions of cells. In each cell, the genes along the length of the DNA molecules encode the information for building the cell's other molecules. In this way, DNA controls the development and maintenance of the entire organism and, indirectly, everything it does **(Figure 1.9)**. The DNA serves as a central database.

The molecular structure of DNA accounts for its ability to store information. Each DNA molecule is made up of two long chains arranged in a double helix. Each chain link is one of four kinds of chemical building blocks called nucleotides **(Figure 1.10)**. The way DNA encodes information is analogous to the way we arrange the letters of the alphabet into precise sequences with specific meanings. The word *rat*, for example, evokes a rodent; the words *tar* and *art*, which contain the same letters, mean very different things. Libraries are filled with books containing information encoded in varying sequences of only 26 letters. We can think of nucleotides as the alphabet of inheritance. Specific sequential arrangements of these four chemical letters encode the precise information in genes, which are typically hundreds or thousands of nucleotides long. One gene in a bacterial cell may be translated as "Build a certain component of the cell membrane." A particular human gene may mean "Make growth hormone."

More generally, genes like those just mentioned program the cell's production of large molecules called proteins. Other human proteins include a muscle cell's contraction proteins and the defensive proteins called antibodies. A class of proteins crucial to all cells are enzymes, which catalyze (speed up) specific chemical reactions. Thus, DNA provides the blueprints, and proteins serve as the tools that actually build and maintain the cell and carry out its activities.

The DNA of genes controls protein production indirectly, using a related kind of molecule called RNA as an intermediary.

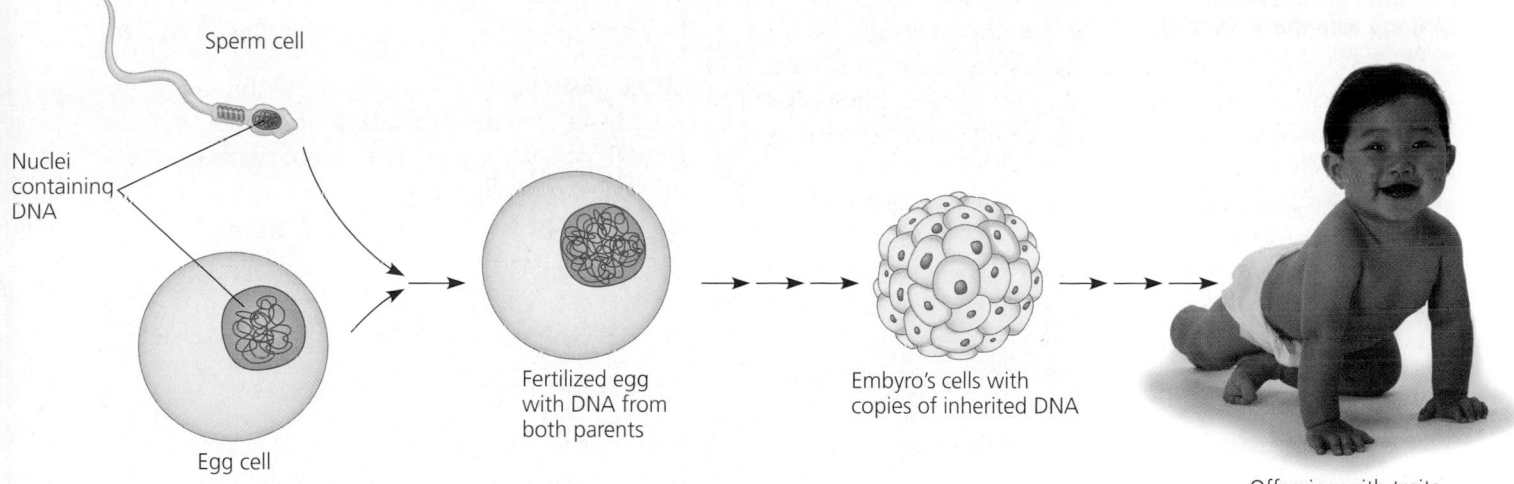

▲ **Figure 1.9 Inherited DNA directs development of an organism.**

Sperm cell

Nuclei containing DNA

Egg cell

Fertilized egg with DNA from both parents

Embyro's cells with copies of inherited DNA

Offspring with traits inherited from both parents

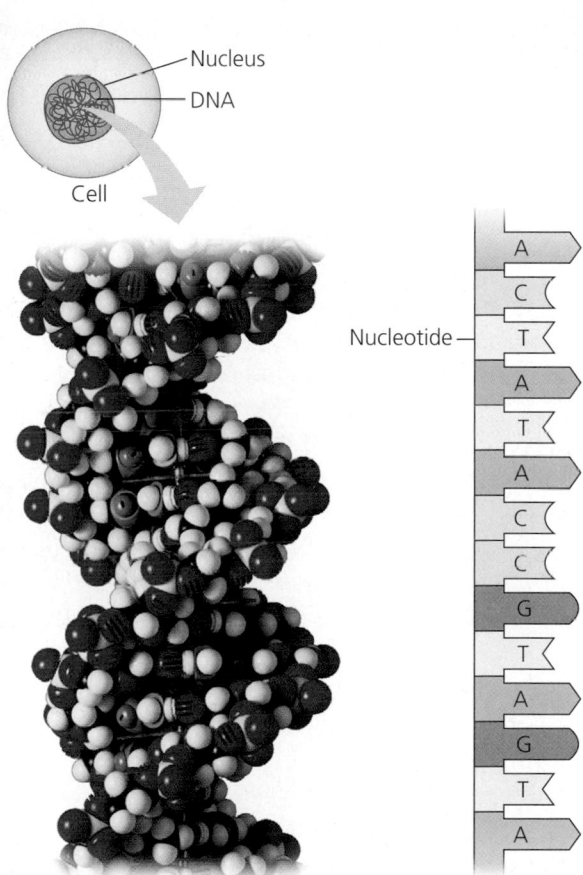

Nucleus

DNA

Cell

Nucleotide

A
C
T
A
T
A
C
C
G
T
A
G
T
A

(a) DNA double helix. This model shows each atom in a segment of DNA. Made up of two long chains of building blocks called nucleotides, a DNA molecule takes the three-dimensional form of a double helix.

(b) Single strand of DNA. These geometric shapes and letters are simple symbols for the nucleotides in a small section of one chain of a DNA molecule. Genetic information is encoded in specific sequences of the four types of nucleotides. (Their names are abbreviated here as A, T, C, and G.)

▲ **Figure 1.10 DNA: The genetic material.**

The sequence of nucleotides along a gene is transcribed into RNA, which is then translated into a specific protein with a unique shape and function. In the translation process, all forms of life employ essentially the same genetic code. A particular sequence of nucleotides says the same thing to one organism as it does to another. Differences between organisms reflect differences between their nucleotide sequences.

Not all RNA in the cell is translated into protein. We have known for decades that some types of RNA molecules are actually components of the cellular machinery that manufactures proteins. Recently, scientists have discovered whole new classes of RNA that play other roles in the cell, such as regulating the functioning of protein-coding genes.

The entire "library" of genetic instructions that an organism inherits is called its **genome**. A typical human cell has two similar sets of chromosomes, and each set has DNA totaling about 3 billion nucleotides. If the one-letter symbols for these nucleotides were written in letters the size of those you are now reading, the genetic text would fill about 600 books the size of this one. Within this genomic library of nucleotide sequences are genes for about 75,000 kinds of proteins and an as yet unknown number of RNA molecules.

Systems Biology at the Levels of Cells and Molecules

The entire sequence of nucleotides in the human genome is now known, along with the genome sequences of many other organisms, including bacteria, archaea, fungi, plants, and animals. These accomplishments have been made possible by the development of new methods and DNA-sequencing machines, such as those shown in **Figure 1.11,** on the next page.

The sequencing of the human genome is a scientific and technological achievement comparable to landing the *Apollo* astronauts on the moon in 1969. But it is only the beginning of an even bigger research endeavor, an effort to learn how the activities of the myriad proteins encoded by the DNA are coordinated in cells and whole organisms.

The best way to make sense of the deluge of data from genome-sequencing projects and the growing catalog of known protein functions is to apply a systems approach at the cellular and molecular levels. **Figure 1.12** illustrates the results of a large study that mapped a network of protein interactions within a cell of a fruit fly, a popular research organism. The model is based on a database of thousands of known proteins and their known interactions with other proteins. For example, protein A may attach to and alter the activities of proteins B, C, and D, which then go on to interact with still other proteins. The figure maps these protein partnerships to their cellular locales.

The basics of the systems strategy are straightforward. First, it is necessary to inventory as many parts of the system as possible, such as all the known genes and proteins in a cell (an application of reductionism). Then it is necessary to investigate how each part behaves in relation to others in the working system—all the protein-protein interactions, in the case of our fly cell example. Finally, with the help of computers and specialized software, it is possible to pool all the data into the kind of system network pictured in Figure 1.12.

Though the basic idea of systems biology is simple, the practice is not, as you would expect from the complexity of biological systems. It has taken three key research developments to bring systems biology within reach. One is "high-throughput" technology, tools that can analyze biological materials very rapidly and produce enormous amounts of data. The automatic DNA-sequencing machines that made the sequencing of

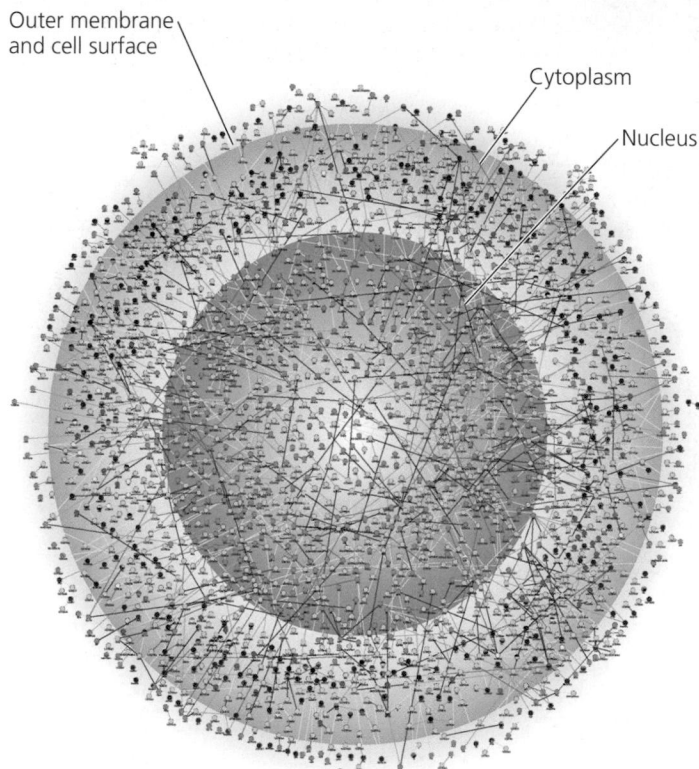

▲ **Figure 1.12 A systems map of interactions among proteins in a cell.** This diagram maps 2,346 proteins (dots) and their network of interactions (lines connecting the proteins) in a fruit fly cell. Systems biologists develop such models from huge databases of information about molecules and their interactions in the cell. A major goal of this systems approach is to use the models to predict how one change, such as an increase in the activity of a particular protein, can ripple through the cell's molecular circuitry to cause other changes. The total number of proteins in this type of cell is probably in the range of 4,000 to 7,000.

the human genome possible are examples of high-throughput devices (see Figure 1.11). The second is **bioinformatics**, which is the use of computational tools to store, organize, and analyze the huge volume of data that result from high-throughput methods. The third key development is the formation of inter-disciplinary research teams—melting pots of diverse special-ists that may include computer scientists, mathematicians, engineers, chemists, physicists, and, of course, biologists from a variety of fields.

Theme: Feedback mechanisms regulate biological systems

A kind of supply-and-demand economy applies to many bio-logical systems. Consider your muscles, for instance. When your muscle cells require more energy during exercise, they increase their consumption of the sugar molecules that pro-vide fuel. In contrast, when you rest, a different set of chemi-cal reactions converts surplus sugar to storage molecules.

Like most of the cell's chemical processes, those that de-compose or store sugar are accelerated, or catalyzed, by the specialized proteins called enzymes. Each type of enzyme cat-alyzes a specific chemical reaction. In many cases, these reac-tions are linked into chemical pathways, each step with its own enzyme. How does the cell coordinate its various chemical pathways? In our example of sugar management, how does the cell match fuel supply to demand, regulating its opposing pathways of sugar consumption and storage? The key is the ability of many biological processes to self-regulate by a mech-anism called feedback.

In feedback regulation, the output, or product, of a process regulates that very process. In life, the most common form of regulation is **negative feedback**, in which accumu-lation of an end product of a process slows that process. For example, the cell's breakdown of sugar generates chemical energy in the form of a substance called ATP. When a cell makes more ATP than it can use, the excess ATP "feeds back" and inhibits an enzyme near the beginning of the pathway **(Figure 1.13a)**.

Though less common than processes regulated by nega-tive feedback, there are also many biological processes reg-ulated by **positive feedback**, in which an end product *speeds up* its production **(Figure 1.13b)**. The clotting of your blood in response to injury is an example. When a blood vessel is damaged, structures in the blood called platelets begin to aggregate at the site. Positive feedback oc-curs as chemicals released by the platelets attract *more* platelets. The platelet pile then initiates a complex process that seals the wound with a clot.

Feedback is a regulatory motif common to life at all levels, from the molecular level to ecosystems and the biosphere. Such regulation is an example of the integration that makes living systems much greater than the sum of their parts.

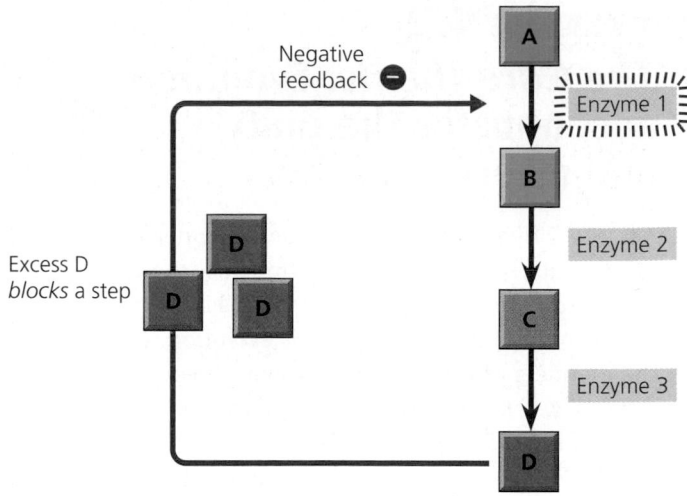

(a) Negative feedback. This three-step chemical pathway converts substance A to substance D. A specific enzyme catalyzes each chemical reaction. Accumulation of the final product (D) inhibits the first enzyme in the sequence, thus slowing down production of more D.

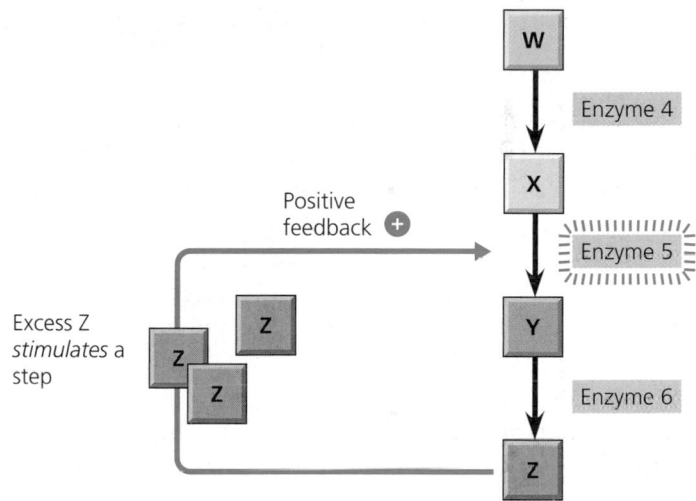

(b) Positive feedback. In a biochemical pathway regulated by positive feedback, a product stimulates an enzyme in the reaction sequence, increasing the rate of production of the product.

▲ **Figure 1.13 Regulation by feedback mechanisms.**
? *What would happen if enzyme 2 were missing?*

CONCEPT CHECK 1.1

1. For each biological level in Figure 1.4, write a sentence that includes the next "lower" level. Example: "A com-munity consists of *populations* of the various species inhabiting a specific area."
2. What theme or themes are exemplified by (a) the sharp spines of a porcupine, (b) the cloning of a plant from a single cell, and (c) a hummingbird using sugar to power its flight?
3. **WHAT IF?** For each theme discussed in this sec-tion, give an example not mentioned in the book.

For suggested answers, see Appendix A.

CONCEPT 1.2

The Core Theme: Evolution accounts for the unity and diversity of life

The list of biological themes discussed under Concept 1.1 is not absolute; some people might find a shorter or longer list more useful. There is consensus among biologists, however, as to the core theme of biology: It is evolution. To quote one of the founders of modern evolutionary theory, Theodosius Dobzhansky, "Nothing in biology makes sense except in the light of evolution."

In addition to encompassing a hierarchy of size scales from molecules to the biosphere, biology extends across the great diversity of species that have ever lived on Earth. To under-stand Dobzhansky's statement, we need to discuss how biologists think about this vast diversity.

Organizing the Diversity of Life

Diversity is a hallmark of life. Biologists have so far identified and named about 1.8 million species. To date, this diversity of life is known to include at least 6,300 species of prokaryotes (organisms with prokaryotic cells), 100,000 fungi, 290,000 plants, 52,000 vertebrates (animals with backbones), and 1 million insects (more than half of all known forms of life). Researchers identify thousands of additional species each year. Estimates of the total number of species range from about 10 million to over 100 million. Whatever the actual number, the enormous variety of life gives biology a very broad scope. Biologists face a major challenge in attempting to make sense of this variety **(Figure 1.14)**.

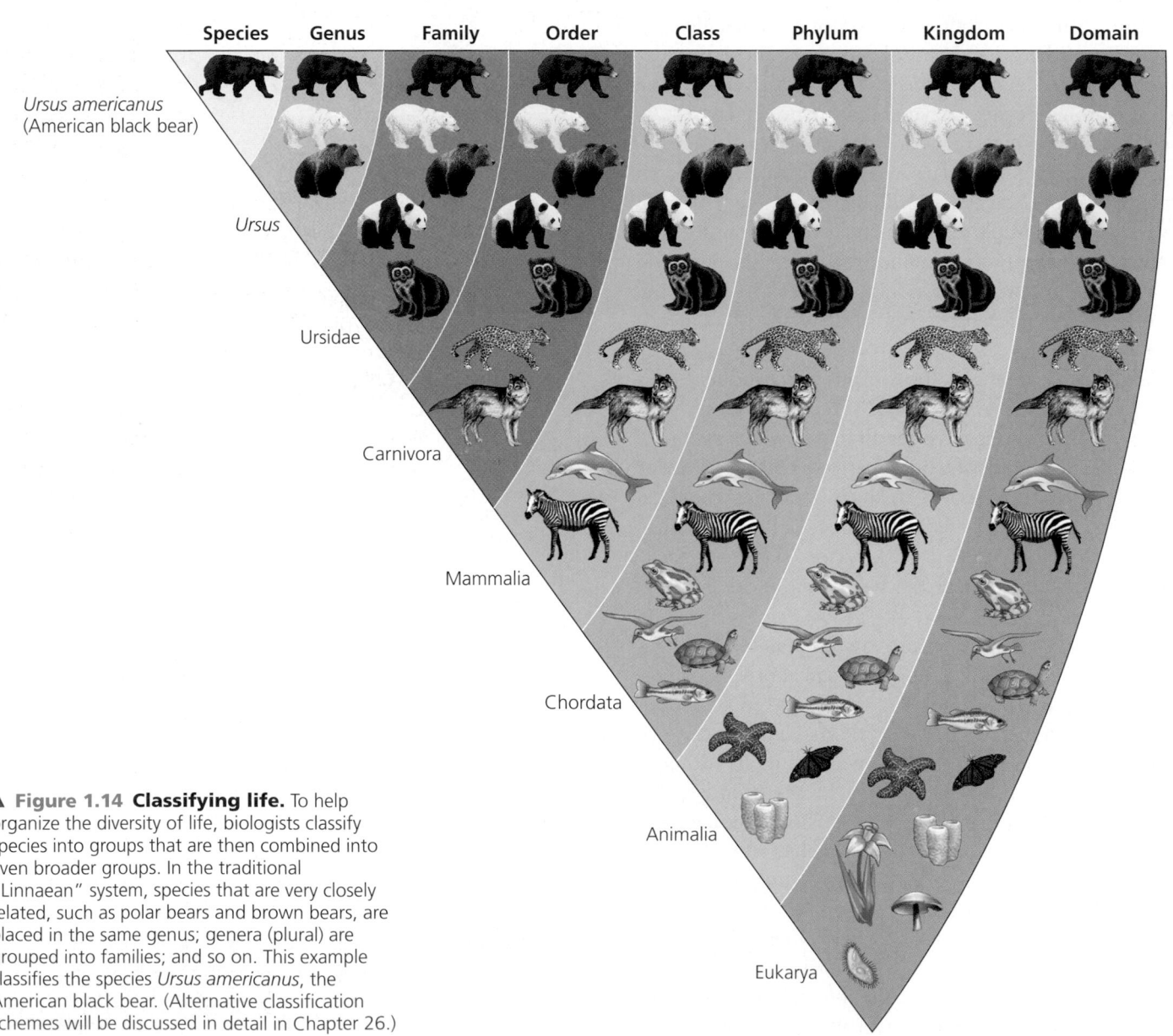

| Species | Genus | Family | Order | Class | Phylum | Kingdom | Domain |

Ursus americanus
(American black bear)

Ursus

Ursidae

Carnivora

Mammalia

Chordata

Animalia

Eukarya

▲ **Figure 1.14 Classifying life.** To help organize the diversity of life, biologists classify species into groups that are then combined into even broader groups. In the traditional "Linnaean" system, species that are very closely related, such as polar bears and brown bears, are placed in the same genus; genera (plural) are grouped into families; and so on. This example classifies the species *Ursus americanus*, the American black bear. (Alternative classification schemes will be discussed in detail in Chapter 26.)

(a) DOMAIN BACTERIA

▼ **Bacteria** are the most diverse and widespread prokaryotes and are now divided among multiple kingdoms. Each of the rod-shaped structures in this photo is a bacterial cell.

2 μm

(b) DOMAIN ARCHAEA

▼ Many of the prokaryotes known as **archaea** live in Earth's extreme environments, such as salty lakes and boiling hot springs. Domain Archaea includes multiple kingdoms. The photo shows a colony composed of many cells.

0.5 μm

(c) DOMAIN EUKARYA

100 μm

▲ **Protists** (multiple kingdoms) are unicellular eukaryotes and their relatively simple multicellular relatives. Pictured here is an assortment of protists inhabiting pond water. Scientists are currently debating how to assign the protists to kingdoms that accurately reflect their evolutionary relationships.

▶ **Kingdom Fungi** is defined in part by the nutritional mode of its members, such as this mushroom, which absorb nutrients from their surroundings.

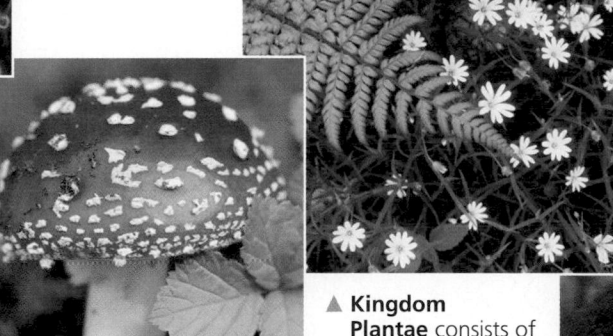

▲ **Kingdom Plantae** consists of multicellular eukaryotes that carry out photosynthesis, the conversion of light energy to the chemical energy in food.

▼ **Kingdom Animalia** consists of multicellular eukaryotes that ingest other organisms.

▲ **Figure 1.15 The three domains of life.**

Grouping Species: The Basic Idea

There is a human tendency to group diverse items according to similarities. For instance, perhaps you organize your music collection by artist. And then maybe you group the various artists into broader categories, such as rock, jazz, and classical. In the same way, grouping species that are similar is natural for us. We may speak of squirrels and butterflies, though we recognize that many different species belong to each group. We may even sort groups into broader categories, such as rodents (which include squirrels) and insects (which include butterflies). Taxonomy, the branch of biology that names and classifies species, formalizes this ordering of species into groups of increasing breadth (see Figure 1.14). You will learn more about this taxonomic scheme in Chapter 26. For now, we will focus on kingdoms and domains, the broadest units of classification.

The Three Domains of Life

Until a few decades ago, most biologists adopted a taxonomic scheme that divided the diversity of life into five kingdoms: plants, animals, fungi, single-celled eukaryotic organisms, and prokaryotes. Since then, new methods, such as comparisons of DNA sequences from different species, have led to an ongoing reevaluation of the number and boundaries of kingdoms. Researchers have proposed anywhere from six kingdoms to dozens of kingdoms. But as debate continues at the kingdom level, there is a consensus that the kingdoms of life can now be grouped into three even higher levels of classification called domains. The three domains are named Bacteria, Archaea, and Eukarya (**Figure 1.15**).

The organisms making up **domain Bacteria** and **domain Archaea** are all prokaryotic. Most prokaryotes are single-celled and microscopic. In the five-kingdom system, bacteria and archaea were combined in a single kingdom because they shared the prokaryotic form of cell structure. But much evidence now supports the view that bacteria and archaea represent two very distinct branches of prokaryotic life, different in key ways that you'll learn about in Chapter 27. There is also evidence that archaea are at least as closely related to eukaryotic organisms as they are to bacteria.

All the eukaryotes (organisms with eukaryotic cells) are now grouped in **domain Eukarya**. In the era of the five-kingdom scheme, most single-celled eukaryotes, such as the microorganisms known as protozoans, were placed in a single kingdom, "Protista." Many biologists extended the boundaries of kingdom Protista to include some multicellular forms, such as seaweeds, that are closely related to certain unicellular protists. The recent taxonomic trend has been to split the protists into several groups at the kingdom level. In addition to these protistan groups, domain Eukarya includes three kingdoms of multicellular eukaryotes: kingdoms Plantae, Fungi, and Animalia. These three kingdoms are distinguished partly by their modes of nutrition. Plants produce their own sugars and other foods by photosynthesis. Fungi absorb dissolved nutrients from their surroundings; many decompose dead organisms and organic wastes (such as leaf litter and animal feces) and absorb nutrients from these sources. Animals obtain food by ingestion, which is the eating and digesting of other organisms. Animalia is, of course, the kingdom to which we belong.

Unity in the Diversity of Life

As diverse as life is, it also displays remarkable unity. Earlier we mentioned the similar skeletons of different vertebrate animals, but similarities are even more striking at the molecular and cellular levels. For example, the universal genetic language of DNA is common to organisms as different as bacteria and animals. Unity is also evident in many features of cell structure **(Figure 1.16)**.

How can we account for life's dual nature of unity and diversity? The process of evolution, explained next, illuminates both the similarities and differences in the world of life and introduces another dimension of biology: historical time.

Charles Darwin and the Theory of Natural Selection

The history of life, as documented by fossils and other evidence, is a saga of a changing Earth billions of years old, inhabited by an evolving cast of living forms **(Figure 1.17)**. This evolutionary view of life came into sharp focus in November 1859, when Charles Robert Darwin published one of the most important and influential books ever written. Entitled *On the Origin of Species by Means of Natural Selection*, Darwin's book was an immediate bestseller and soon made "Darwinism" almost synonymous with the concept of evolution **(Figure 1.18)**.

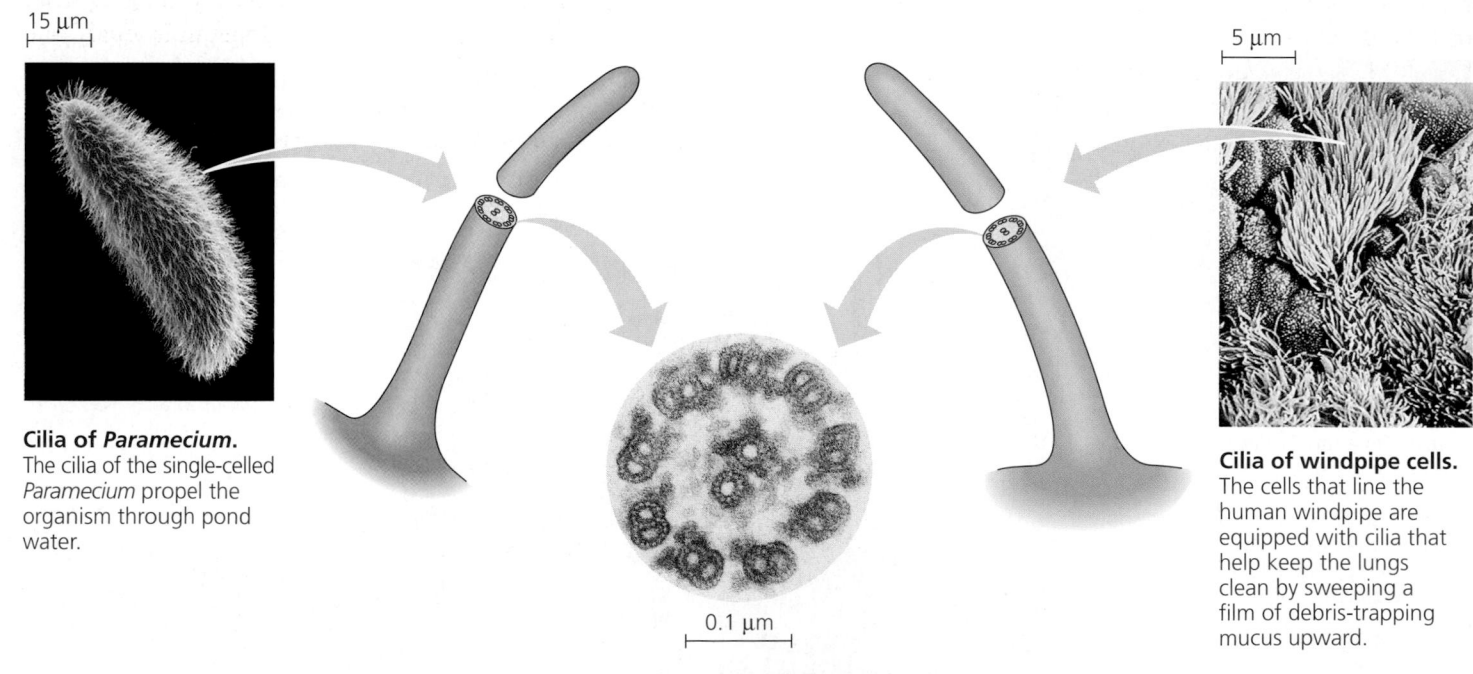

15 μm

Cilia of *Paramecium*.
The cilia of the single-celled *Paramecium* propel the organism through pond water.

0.1 μm

Cross section of a cilium, as viewed with an electron microscope

5 μm

Cilia of windpipe cells.
The cells that line the human windpipe are equipped with cilia that help keep the lungs clean by sweeping a film of debris-trapping mucus upward.

▲ **Figure 1.16 An example of unity underlying the diversity of life: the architecture of cilia in eukaryotes.** Cilia (singular, *cilium*) are extensions of cells that function in locomotion. They occur in eukaryotes as diverse as paramecia and humans. Even organisms so different share a common architecture for their cilia, which have an elaborate system of tubules that is striking in cross-sectional views.

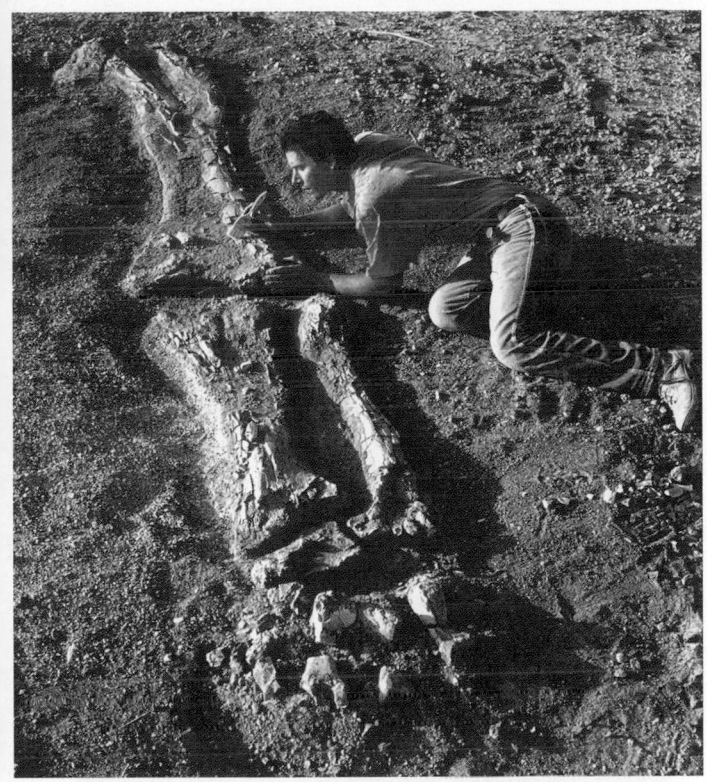

▲ **Figure 1.17 Digging into the past.** Paleontologist Paul Sereno, of the University of Chicago, gingerly excavates the leg bones of a dinosaur fossil in Niger.

The Origin of Species articulated two main points. First, Darwin presented evidence to support his view that contemporary species arose from a succession of ancestors. (We will discuss the evidence for evolution in detail in Chapter 22.) Darwin called this evolutionary history of species "descent with modification." It was an insightful phrase, as it captured the duality of life's unity and diversity—unity in the kinship among species that descended from common ancestors; diversity in the modifications that evolved as species branched from their common ancestors (**Figure 1.19**). Darwin's second main point was to propose a mechanism for descent with modification. He called this evolutionary mechanism natural selection.

Darwin synthesized his theory of natural selection from observations that by themselves were neither new nor profound. Others had the pieces of the puzzle, but Darwin saw how they fit together. He started with the following observations from

▲ Figure 1.18 **Charles Darwin as a young man.**

nature: Individuals in a population vary in their traits, many of which seem to be heritable (passed on from parents to offspring). Also, a population can produce far more offspring than can survive to produce offspring of their own. With more individuals than the environment can support, competition is inevitable. Lastly, species generally suit their environments. For instance, birds living where tough seeds are a good food source may have especially strong beaks.

Darwin made inferences from these observations to arrive at his theory of evolution. He reasoned that individuals with inherited traits that are best suited to the local environment are more likely to survive and reproduce than less fit individuals. Over many generations, a higher and higher proportion

▲ Figure 1.19 **Unity and diversity in the orchid family.** These three rain forest orchids are variations on a common floral theme. For example, each of these flowers has a liplike petal that helps attract pollinating insects and provides a landing platform for the pollinators.

① Population with varied inherited traits.

② Elimination of individuals with certain traits.

③ Reproduction of survivors.

④ Increasing frequency of traits that enhance survival and reproductive success.

▲ **Figure 1.20 Natural selection.** This imaginary beetle population has colonized a locale where the soil has been blackened by a recent brush fire. Initially, the population varies extensively in the inherited coloration of the individuals, from very light gray to charcoal. For hungry birds that prey on the beetles, it is easiest to spot the beetles that are lightest in color.

of individuals in a population will have the advantageous traits. Evolution occurs as the unequal reproductive success of individuals adapts the population to its environment.

Darwin called this mechanism of evolutionary adaptation "natural selection" because the natural environment "selects" for the propagation of certain traits. The example in **Figure 1.20** illustrates the ability of natural selection to "edit" a population's heritable variations in color. We see the products of natural selection in the exquisite adaptations of various organisms to the special circumstances of their way of life and their environment (**Figure 1.21**).

The Tree of Life

Take another look at the skeletal architecture of the bat's wings in Figure 1.21. These forelimbs, though adapted for flight, actually have all the same bones, joints, nerves, and blood vessels found in other limbs as diverse as the human arm, the horse's foreleg, and the whale's flipper. Indeed, all mammalian forelimbs are anatomical variations of a common architecture, much as the flowers in Figure 1.19 are variations on an underlying "orchid" theme. Such examples of kinship connect life's unity in diversity to the Darwinian concept of descent with modification. In this view, the unity of mammalian limb anatomy reflects inheritance of that structure from a common ancestor—the "prototype" mammal from which all other mammals descended. The diversity of mammalian forelimbs results from modification by natural selection operating over millions of generations in different environmental contexts. Fossils and other evidence corroborate anatomical unity in supporting this view of mammalian descent from a common ancestor.

Darwin proposed that natural selection, by its cumulative effects over long periods of time, could cause an ancestral species to give rise to two or more descendant species. This could occur, for example, if one population fragmented into

▲ **Figure 1.21 Evolutionary adaptation.** Bats, the only mammals capable of active flight, have wings with webbing between extended "fingers." In the Darwinian view of life, such adaptations are refined by natural selection.

several subpopulations isolated in different environments. In these separate arenas of natural selection, one species could gradually radiate into multiple species as the geographically isolated populations adapted over many generations to different sets of environmental factors.

The "family tree" of 14 finches in **Figure 1.22** illustrates a famous example of adaptive radiation of new species from a common ancestor. Darwin collected specimens of these birds during his 1835 visit to the remote Galápagos Islands, 900 kilometers (km) off the Pacific coast of South America. These relatively young, volcanic islands are home to many species of plants and animals found nowhere else in the world, though most Galápagos organisms are clearly related to species on the South American mainland. After volcanism built the Galápagos several million years ago, finches probably diversified on the various islands from an ancestral finch species that by chance reached the archipelago from elsewhere. (Once

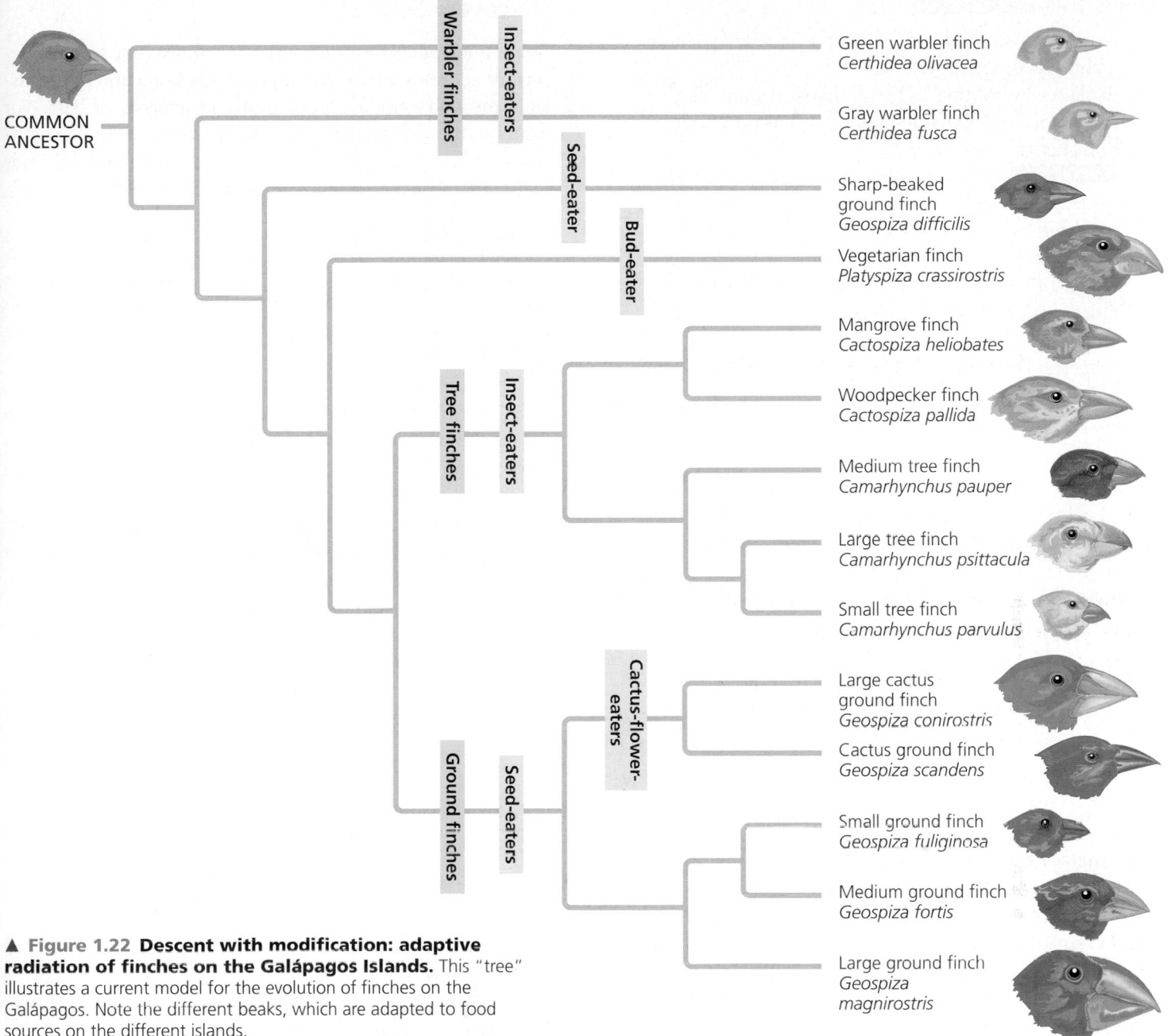

▲ Figure 1.22 Descent with modification: adaptive radiation of finches on the Galápagos Islands. This "tree" illustrates a current model for the evolution of finches on the Galápagos. Note the different beaks, which are adapted to food sources on the different islands.

Tree labels (top to bottom):

Warbler finches — Insect-eaters
- Green warbler finch *Certhidea olivacea*
- Gray warbler finch *Certhidea fusca*

Seed-eater
- Sharp-beaked ground finch *Geospiza difficilis*

Bud-eater
- Vegetarian finch *Platyspiza crassirostris*

Tree finches — Insect-eaters
- Mangrove finch *Cactospiza heliobates*
- Woodpecker finch *Cactospiza pallida*
- Medium tree finch *Camarhynchus pauper*
- Large tree finch *Camarhynchus psittacula*
- Small tree finch *Camarhynchus parvulus*

Ground finches — Seed-eaters — Cactus-flower-eaters
- Large cactus ground finch *Geospiza conirostris*
- Cactus ground finch *Geospiza scandens*
- Small ground finch *Geospiza fuliginosa*
- Medium ground finch *Geospiza fortis*
- Large ground finch *Geospiza magnirostris*

COMMON ANCESTOR

---

thought to have originated on the mainland of South America like many Galápagos organisms, the ancestral finches are now thought to have come from islands of the Carribean.) Years after Darwin's collection of Galápagos finches, researchers began to sort out the relationships among the finch species, first from anatomical and geographic data and more recently with the help of DNA sequence comparisons.

Biologists' diagrams of evolutionary relationships generally take treelike forms, though today biologists usually turn the trees sideways as in Figure 1.22. Tree diagrams make sense: Just as an individual has a genealogy that can be diagrammed as a family tree, each species of organism is one twig of a branching tree of life extending back in time through ancestral species

more and more remote. Species that are very similar, such as the Galápagos finches, share a common ancestor at a relatively recent branch point on the tree of life. But through an ancestor that lived much farther back in time, finches are related to sparrows, hawks, penguins, and all other birds. And birds, mammals, and all other vertebrates share a common ancestor even more ancient. We find evidence of still broader relationships in such similarities as the identical construction of all eukaryotic cilia (see Figure 1.16). Trace life back far enough, and there are only fossils of the primeval prokaryotes that inhabited Earth over 3.5 billion years ago. We can recognize their vestiges in our own cells—in the universal genetic code, for example. All of life is connected through its long evolutionary history.

1. How is a mailing address analogous to biology's hierarchical taxonomic system?

2. Explain why "editing" is better than "creating" as a metaphor for how natural selection acts on a population's heritable variation.

3. **WHAT IF?** The three domains you learned about in Concept 1.2 can be represented in the tree of life as the three main branches. On the eukaryotic branch, three of the subbranches are the kingdoms Plantae, Fungi, and Animalia. What if fungi and animals are more closely related to each other than either of these kingdoms is to plants—as recent evidence strongly suggests? Draw a simple branching pattern that symbolizes the proposed relationship between these three eukaryotic kingdoms.

For suggested answers, see Appendix A.

CONCEPT 1.3

Scientists use two main forms of inquiry in their study of nature

The word *science* is derived from a Latin verb meaning "to know." Science is a way of knowing about the natural world. It developed out of our curiosity about ourselves, other lifeforms, our planet, and the universe. Striving to understand seems to be one of our basic urges.

At the heart of science is **inquiry**, a search for information and explanation, often focusing on specific questions. Inquiry drove Darwin to seek answers in nature for how species adapt to their environments. And today inquiry drives the genome analyses that are helping us understand biological unity and diversity at the molecular level. In fact, the inquisitive mind is the engine that drives all progress in biology.

There is no formula for successful scientific inquiry, no single scientific method with a rule book that researchers must rigidly follow. As in all quests, science includes elements of challenge, adventure, and luck, along with careful planning, reasoning, creativity, cooperation, competition, patience, and the persistence to overcome setbacks. Such diverse elements of inquiry make science far less structured than most people realize. That said, it is possible to distill certain characteristics that help to distinguish science from other ways of describing and explaining nature.

Biologists use two main types of scientific inquiry: discovery science and hypothesis-based science. Discovery science is mostly about *describing* nature. Hypothesis-based science is mostly about *explaining* nature. Most scientific inquiries combine these two research approaches.

Discovery Science

Sometimes called descriptive science, **discovery science** describes natural structures and processes as accurately as possible through careful observation and analysis of data. For example, it is discovery science that has built our understanding of cell structure, and it is discovery science that is expanding our databases of genomes of diverse species.

Types of Data

Observation is the use of the senses to gather information, either directly or indirectly with the help of tools such as microscopes that extend our senses. Recorded observations are called **data**. Put another way, data are items of information on which scientific inquiry is based.

The term *data* implies numbers to many people. But some data are *qualitative*, often in the form of recorded descriptions rather than numerical measurements. For example, Jane Goodall spent decades recording her observations of chimpanzee behavior during field research in a jungle in Tanzania **(Figure 1.23)**. She also documented her observations with photographs and movies. Along with these qualitative data, Goodall also enriched the field of animal behavior with volumes of *quantitative* data, which are generally recorded as measurements. Skim through any of the scientific journals in your college library, and you'll see many examples of quantitative data organized into tables and graphs.

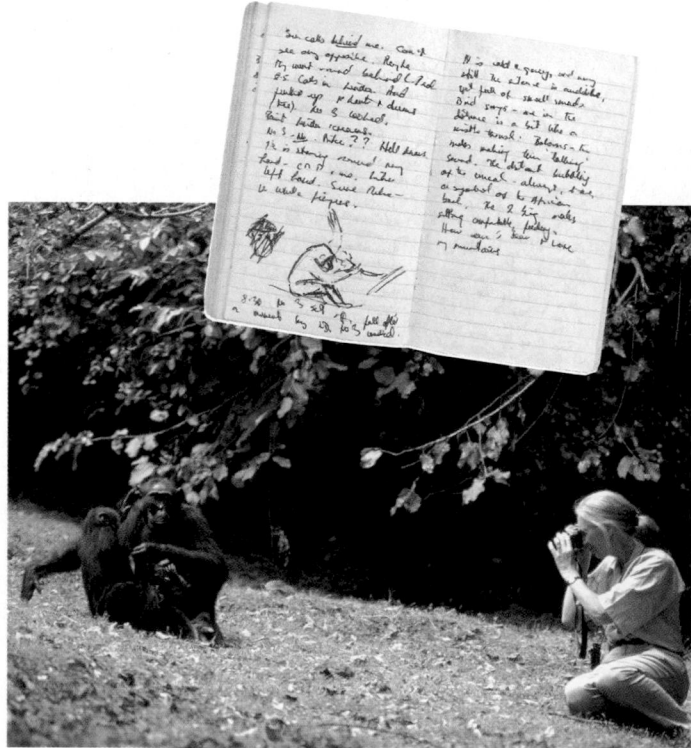

▲ Figure 1.23 **Jane Goodall collecting qualitative data on chimpanzee behavior.** Goodall recorded her observations in field notebooks, often with sketches of the animals' behavior.

Induction in Discovery Science

Discovery science can lead to important conclusions based on a type of logic called induction, or **inductive reasoning**. Through induction, we derive generalizations from a large number of specific observations. "The sun always rises in the east" is an example. And so is "All organisms are made of cells." The latter generalization, part of the so-called cell theory, was based on two centuries of biologists discovering cells in the diverse biological specimens they observed with microscopes. The careful observations and data analyses of discovery science, along with the generalizations reached by induction, are fundamental to our understanding of nature.

Hypothesis-Based Science

The observations and inductions of discovery science stimulate us to seek natural causes and explanations for those observations. What *caused* the diversification of finches on the Galápagos Islands? What *causes* the roots of a plant seedling to grow downward and the leaf-bearing shoot to grow upward? What *explains* the generalization that the sun always rises in the east? In science, such inquiry usually involves the proposing and testing of hypothetical explanations—that is, hypotheses.

The Role of Hypotheses in Inquiry

In science, a **hypothesis** is a tentative answer to a well-framed question—an explanation on trial. It is usually an educated guess, based on experience and on the data available from discovery science. A scientific hypothesis leads to predictions that can be tested by making additional observations or by performing experiments.

We all use hypotheses in solving everyday problems. Let's say, for example, that your flashlight fails during a camp-out. That's an observation. The question is obvious: Why doesn't the flashlight work? Two reasonable hypotheses based on your experience are that (1) the batteries in the flashlight are dead or (2) the bulb is burnt out. Each of these alternative hypotheses leads to predictions you can test with experiments. For example, the dead-battery hypothesis predicts that replacing the batteries will fix the problem. **Figure 1.24** diagrams this campground inquiry. Of course, we rarely dissect our thought processes this way when we are solving a problem using hypotheses, predictions, and experiments. But hypothesis-based science clearly has its origins in the human tendency to figure things out by trial and error.

Deduction: The "If . . . Then" Logic of Hypothesis-Based Science

A type of logic called deduction is built into hypothesis-based science. Deduction contrasts with induction, which, remember, is reasoning from a set of specific observations to reach a general conclusion. In **deductive reasoning**, the logic flows in the opposite direction, from the general to the specific.

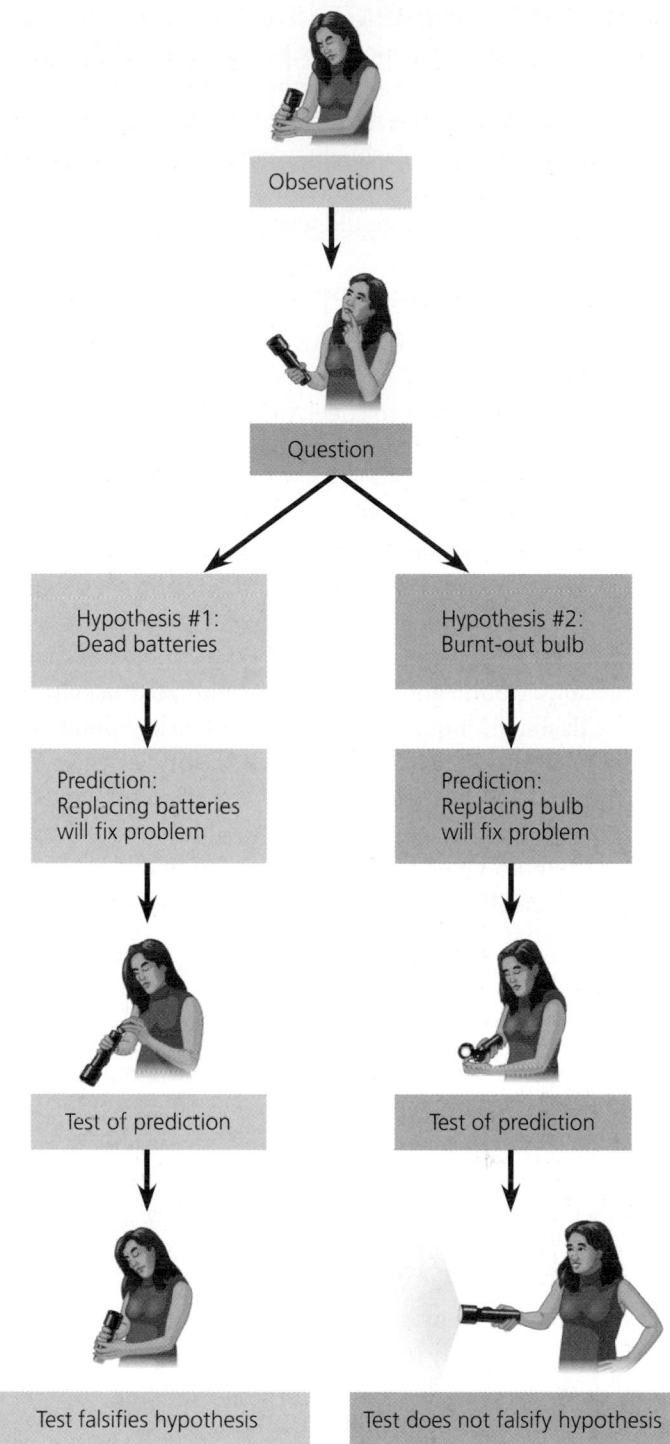

▲ Figure 1.24 **A campground example of hypothesis-based inquiry.**

From general premises, we extrapolate to the specific results we should expect if the premises are true. If all organisms are made of cells (premise 1), and humans are organisms (premise 2), then humans are composed of cells (deductive prediction about a specific case).

In hypothesis-based science, deductions usually take the form of predictions of experimental or observational results that will be found if a particular hypothesis (premise) is correct. We then test the hypothesis by carrying out the experiments or observations to see whether or not the results are as predicted. This deductive testing takes the form of "*If . . . then*" logic. In the case of the flashlight example: *If* the dead-battery hypothesis is correct, and you replace the batteries with new ones, *then* the flashlight should work.

A Closer Look at Hypotheses in Scientific Inquiry

The flashlight example illustrates two important qualities of scientific hypotheses. First, a hypothesis must be *testable*; there must be some way to check the validity of the idea. Second, a hypothesis must be *falsifiable*; there must be some observation or experiment that could reveal if such an idea is actually *not* true. The hypothesis that dead batteries are the sole cause of the broken flashlight could be falsified by replacing the old batteries with new ones and finding that the flashlight still doesn't work. Not all hypotheses meet the criteria of science: Try to devise a test to falsify the hypothesis that invisible campground ghosts are fooling with your flashlight!

The flashlight inquiry illustrates another key point about hypothesis-based science. The ideal is to frame two or more alternative hypotheses and design experiments to falsify those candidate explanations. In addition to the two explanations tested in Figure 1.24, another of the many possible alternative hypotheses is that *both* the batteries *and* the bulb are bad. What does this hypothesis predict about the outcome of the experiments in Figure 1.24? What additional experiment would you design to test this hypothesis of multiple malfunction?

We can mine the flashlight scenario for still one more important lesson about hypothesis-based science. Although the burnt-out bulb hypothesis stands up as the most likely explanation, notice that the testing supports that hypothesis *not* by proving that it is correct, but by not eliminating it through falsification. Perhaps the bulb was simply loose and the new bulb was inserted correctly. We could attempt to falsify the burnt-out bulb hypothesis by trying another experiment—removing the bulb and carefully reinstalling it. But no amount of experimental testing can *prove* a hypothesis beyond a shadow of doubt, because it is impossible to test *all* alternative hypotheses. A hypothesis gains credibility by surviving attempts to falsify it while testing eliminates (falsifies) alternative hypotheses.

The Myth of the Scientific Method

The flashlight example of Figure 1.24 traces an idealized process of inquiry called *the scientific method*. We can recognize the elements of this process in most of the research articles published by scientists, but rarely in such structured form. Very few scientific inquiries adhere rigidly to the sequence of steps prescribed by the "textbook" scientific method. For example, a scientist may start to design an experiment, but then backtrack upon realizing that more observations are necessary. In other cases, puzzling observations simply don't prompt well-defined questions until other research places those observations in a new context. For example, Darwin collected specimens of the Galápagos finches, but it wasn't until years later, as the idea of natural selection began to gel, that biologists began asking key questions about the history of those birds.

Moreover, scientists sometimes redirect their research when they realize they have been asking the wrong question. For example, in the early 20th century, much research on schizophrenia and manic-depressive disorder (now called bipolar disorder) got sidetracked by focusing too much on the question of how life experiences might cause these serious maladies. Research on the causes and potential treatments became more productive when it was refocused on questions of how certain chemical imbalances in the brain contribute to mental illness. To be fair, we acknowledge that such twists and turns in scientific inquiry become more evident with the advantage of historical perspective.

There is still another reason that good science need not conform exactly to any one method of inquiry: Discovery science has contributed much to our understanding of nature without most of the steps of the so-called scientific method.

It is important for you to get some experience with the power of the scientific method—by using it for some of the laboratory inquiries in your biology course, for example. But it is also important to avoid stereotyping science as lock-step adherence to this method.

A Case Study in Scientific Inquiry: Investigating Mimicry in Snake Populations

Now that we have highlighted the key features of discovery science and hypothesis-based science, you should be able to recognize these forms of inquiry in a case study of actual scientific research.

The story begins with a set of observations and generalizations from discovery science. Many poisonous animals are brightly colored, often with distinctive patterns that stand out against the background. This is called warning coloration because it apparently signals "dangerous species" to potential predators. But there are also mimics. These imposters look like poisonous species but are actually harmless. A question that follows from these observations is: What is the function of such mimicry? A reasonable hypothesis is that such "deception" is an evolutionary adaptation that reduces the harmless animal's risk of being eaten because predators mistake it for the poisonous species. This hypothesis was first formulated by British scientist Henry Bates in 1862.

As obvious as this hypothesis may seem, it has been relatively difficult to test, especially with field experiments. But in

2001, biologists David and Karin Pfennig, of the University of North Carolina, along with William Harcombe, an undergraduate, designed a simple but elegant set of field experiments to test Bates's mimicry hypothesis.

The team investigated a case of mimicry among snakes that live in North and South Carolina **(Figure 1.25)**. A poisonous snake called the eastern coral snake has warning coloration: bold, alternating rings of red, yellow (or white), and black. Predators rarely attack these snakes. It is unlikely that the predators learn this avoidance behavior by trial and error, as a first encounter with a coral snake is usually deadly. In areas where coral snakes live, natural selection has apparently increased the frequency of predators that have inherited an instinctive avoidance of the coral snake's coloration. A nonpoisonous snake named the scarlet kingsnake mimics the ringed coloration of the coral snake.

Both types of snakes live in the Carolinas, but the kingsnakes' geographic range also extends into regions where no coral snakes are found (see Figure 1.25). The geographic distribution of the snakes made it possible to test the key prediction of the mimicry hypothesis. Avoiding snakes with warning coloration is an adaptation we expect to be present only in predator populations that evolved in areas where the poisonous coral snakes are present. Therefore, mimicry should help protect kingsnakes from predators, but *only* in regions where coral snakes also live. The mimicry hypothesis predicts that predators adapted to the warning coloration of coral snakes will attack kingsnakes less frequently than will predators in areas where coral snakes are absent.

Field Experiments with Artificial Snakes

To test the prediction, Harcombe made hundreds of artificial snakes out of wire covered with plasticine. He fashioned two versions of fake snakes: an *experimental group* with the red, black, and white ring pattern of kingsnakes; and a *control group* of plain brown artificial snakes as a basis of comparison **(Figure 1.26)**.

The researchers placed equal numbers of the two types of artificial snakes in field sites throughout North and South Carolina, including the region where coral snakes are absent. After four weeks, the scientists retrieved the fake snakes and recorded how many had been attacked by looking for bite or claw marks. The most common predators were foxes, coyotes, and raccoons, but black bears also attacked some of the artificial snakes (see Figure 1.26b).

The data fit the key prediction of the mimicry hypothesis. Compared to the brown artificial snakes, the ringed artificial snakes were attacked by predators less frequently *only* in field sites within the geographic range of the poisonous coral

Scarlet kingsnake (nonpoisonous)

Key
Range of scarlet kingsnake only
Overlapping ranges of scarlet kingsnake and eastern coral snake

North Carolina

South Carolina

Eastern coral snake (poisonous)

Scarlet kingsnake (nonpoisonous)

▲ **Figure 1.25 The geographic ranges of a poisonous snake and its mimic.** The scarlet kingsnake (*Lampropeltis triangulum*) mimics the warning coloration of the poisonous eastern coral snake (*Micrurus fulvius*).

(a) Artificial kingsnake

(b) Brown artificial snake that has been attacked

▲ **Figure 1.26 Artificial snakes used in field experiments to test the mimicry hypothesis.** You can see where a bear chomped on the brown artificial snake in (b).

snakes. **Figure 1.27** summarizes the field experiments that the researchers carried out. This figure also introduces a format we will use throughout the book for other examples of biological inquiry.

Designing Controlled Experiments

The snake mimicry experiment is an example of a **controlled experiment**, one that is designed to compare an experimental group (the artificial kingsnakes, in this case) with a control group (the brown artificial snakes). Ideally, the experimental and control groups differ only in the one factor the experiment is designed to test—in our example, the effect of the snakes' coloration on the behavior of predators. Without the control group, the researchers would not have been able to rule out other factors as causes of the more frequent attacks on the artificial kingsnakes—such as different numbers of predators or different temperatures in the different test areas. The clever experimental design left coloration as the only factor that could account for the low predation rate on the artificial kingsnakes placed within the range of coral snakes. It was not the absolute number of attacks on the artificial kingsnakes that counted, but the difference between that number and the number of attacks on the brown snakes.

A common misconception is that the term *controlled experiment* means that scientists control the experimental environment to keep everything constant except the one variable being tested. But that's impossible in field research and not realistic even in highly regulated laboratory environments. Researchers usually "control" unwanted variables not by *eliminating* them through environmental regulation, but by *canceling* their effects by using control groups.

Limitations of Science

Scientific inquiry is a powerful way to learn about nature, but there are limitations to the kinds of questions it can answer. These limits are set by science's requirements that hypotheses be testable and falsifiable and that observations and experimental results be repeatable.

Observations that can't be verified may be interesting or even entertaining, but they cannot count as evidence in scientific inquiry. The headlines of supermarket tabloids would have you believe that humans are occasionally born with the head of a dog and that some of your classmates are extraterrestrials. The unconfirmed eyewitness accounts and the computer-rigged photos are amusing but unconvincing. In science, evidence from observations and experiments is only convincing if it stands up to the criterion of repeatability. The scientists who investigated snake mimicry in the Carolinas obtained similar data when they repeated their experiments with different species of coral snakes and kingsnakes in Arizona. And *you* should be able to obtain similar results if you were to repeat the snake experiments.

▼ Figure 1.27 **Inquiry**

Does the presence of poisonous coral snakes affect predation rates on their mimics, kingsnakes?

EXPERIMENT David Pfennig and his colleagues made artificial snakes to test a prediction of the mimicry hypothesis: that kingsnakes benefit from mimicking the warning coloration of poisonous coral snakes *only* in regions where coral snakes are present. The researchers placed equal numbers of artificial kingsnakes (experimental group) and brown artificial snakes (control group) at 14 field sites, half in the area the two snakes cohabit and half in the area where coral snakes were absent. The researchers recovered the artificial snakes after four weeks and tabulated predation data based on teeth and claw marks on the snakes.

RESULTS In field sites where coral snakes were present, most attacks were on brown artificial snakes. Where coral snakes were absent, most attacks were on artificial kingsnakes.

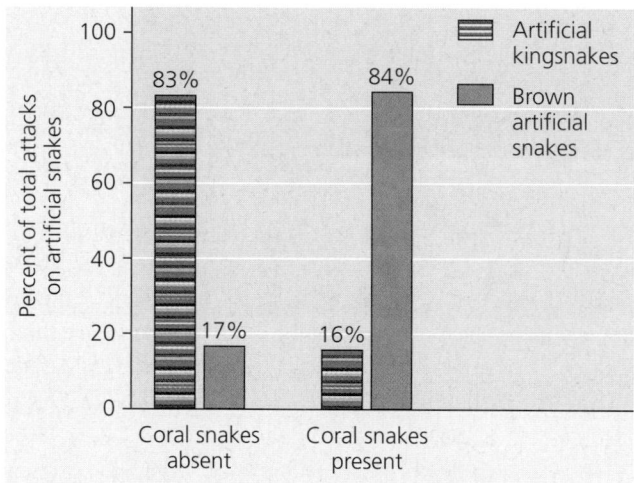

CONCLUSION The field experiments support the mimicry hypothesis by not falsifying the prediction that imitation of coral snakes is only effective where coral snakes are present. The experiments also tested an alternative hypothesis: that predators generally avoid all snakes with brightly colored rings. That hypothesis was falsified by the data showing that the ringed coloration failed to repel predators where coral snakes were absent. (The fake kingsnakes may have been attacked more often in those areas because their bright pattern made them easier to spot than the brown fakes.)

SOURCE D. W. Pfennig, W. R. Harcombe, and K. S. Pfennig, Frequency-dependent Batesian mimicry, *Nature* 410:323 (2001).

Inquiry in Action Read and analyze the original paper in *Inquiry in Action: Interpreting Scientific Papers.*

WHAT IF? What experimental results would you predict if predators throughout the Carolinas avoid all snakes with brightly colored ring patterns?

Because science requires natural explanations for natural phenomena, it can neither support nor falsify hypotheses that angels, ghosts, or spirits, whether benevolent or evil, cause storms, rainbows, illnesses, and cures. Such supernatural explanations are simply outside the bounds of science.

Theories in Science

"It's just a theory!" Our everyday use of the term *theory* often implies an untested speculation. But the term *theory* has a different meaning in science. What is a scientific theory, and how is it different from a hypothesis or from mere speculation?

First, a scientific **theory** is much broader in scope than a hypothesis. *This* is a hypothesis: "Mimicking the coloration of poisonous snakes is an adaptation that protects nonpoisonous snakes from predators." But *this* is a theory: "Evolutionary adaptations arise by natural selection." Darwin's theory of natural selection accounts for an enormous diversity of adaptations, including mimicry.

Second, a theory is general enough to spin off many new, specific hypotheses that can be tested. For example, two researchers at Princeton University, Peter and Rosemary Grant, were motivated by the theory of natural selection to test the specific hypothesis that the beaks of Galápagos finches evolve in response to changes in the types of available food. (Their results supported their hypothesis; see p. 468.)

And third, compared to any one hypothesis, a theory is generally supported by a much greater body of evidence. Those theories that become widely adopted in science (such as the theory of natural selection) explain a great diversity of observations and are supported by a vast accumulation of evidence. In fact, scrutiny of theories continues through testing of the specific, falsifiable hypotheses they spawn.

In spite of the body of evidence supporting a widely accepted theory, scientists must sometimes modify or even reject theories when new research methods produce results that don't fit. For example, the five-kingdom theory of biological diversity began to erode when new methods for comparing cells and molecules made it possible to test some of the hypothetical relationships between organisms that were based on the theory. If there is "truth" in science, it is conditional, based on the preponderance of available evidence.

Model Building in Science

You may work with many models in your biology course this year. Perhaps you'll model cell division by using pipe cleaners as chromosomes. Or maybe you'll practice using mathematical models to predict the growth of a bacterial population. Scientists often construct models as representations of natural phenomena. Scientific **models** can take many forms, including diagrams (such as the evolutionary tree in Figure 1.22), graphs, three-dimensional objects, computer programs, or mathematical equations.

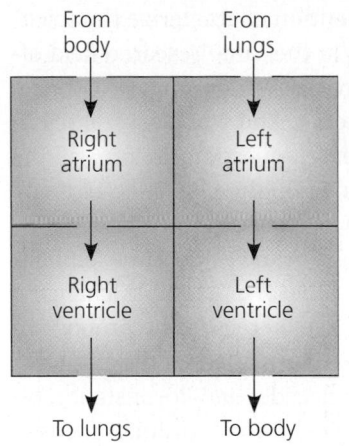

From body   From lungs

| Right atrium | Left atrium |
| Right ventricle | Left ventricle |

To lungs   To body

◄ **Figure 1.28 A model of the blood flow through the four chambers of a human heart.**

? *The blood picks up oxygen (and releases carbon dioxide) in the lungs and releases oxygen (and picks up carbon dioxide) in the rest of the body. From the model shown here, predict what would happen if there were a small hole between the two ventricles.*

Choosing the most appropriate type of model depends on what needs to be communicated and explained about the object, idea, or process the model is to represent. Some models need to be as lifelike as possible. Other models are more useful if they are simple schematics. For example, the simple diagram in **Figure 1.28** does a good job of modeling blood flow through the chambers of a human heart without looking anything like a real heart. A heart model designed to help train a physician to perform heart surgery would look very different. Whatever the design of a model, the test of its success is how well it fits the available data, how comfortably it accommodates new observations, how accurately it predicts the outcomes of new experiments or observations, and how effectively it communicates.

The Culture of Science

Movies and cartoons sometimes portray scientists as loners working in isolated labs. In reality, science is an intensely social activity. Most scientists work in teams, which often include both graduate and undergraduate students **(Figure 1.29)**. And to succeed in science, it helps to be a good communicator. Research results have no impact until shared with a community of peers through seminars, publications, and websites.

◄ **Figure 1.29 Science as a social process.** In her New York University laboratory, plant biologist Gloria Coruzzi mentors one of her students in the methods of molecular biology.

Both cooperation and competition characterize the scientific culture. Scientists working in the same research field often check one another's claims by attempting to confirm observations or repeat experiments. And when several scientists converge on the same research question, there is all the excitement of a race. Scientists enjoy the challenge of being first with an important discovery or key experiment.

The biology community is part of society at large, embedded in the cultural milieu of the times. For example, changing attitudes about career choices have increased the proportion of women in biology, which has in turn affected the emphasis in certain research fields. A few decades ago, for instance, biologists who studied the mating behavior of animals focused mostly on competition among males for access to females. More recent research, however, emphasizes the important role that females play in choosing mates. For example, in many bird species, females prefer the bright coloration that "advertises" a male's vigorous health, a behavior that enhances the female's probability of having healthy offspring.

Some philosophers of science argue that scientists are so influenced by cultural and political values that science is no more objective than other ways of understanding nature. At the other extreme are people who speak of scientific theories as though they were natural laws instead of human interpretations of nature. The reality of science is probably somewhere in between—rarely perfectly objective, but continuously vetted through the expectation that observations and experiments be repeatable and hypotheses be testable and falsifiable.

Science, Technology, and Society

The relationship of science to society becomes clearer when we add technology to the picture. Though science and technology sometimes employ similar inquiry patterns, their basic goals differ. The goal of science is to understand natural phenomena. In contrast, **technology** generally *applies* scientific knowledge for some specific purpose. Biologists and other scientists often speak of "discoveries," while engineers and other technologists more often speak of "inventions." And the beneficiaries of those inventions include scientists, who put new technology to work in their research; the impact of information technology on systems biology is just one example. Thus, science and technology are interdependent.

The potent combination of science and technology has dramatic effects on society. For example, discovery of the structure of DNA by Watson and Crick half a century ago and subsequent achievements in DNA science led to the technologies of DNA engineering that are transforming many applied fields, including medicine, agriculture, and forensics **(Figure 1.30)**. Perhaps Watson and Crick envisioned that their discovery would someday produce important applications, but it is unlikely that they could have predicted exactly what all those applications would be.

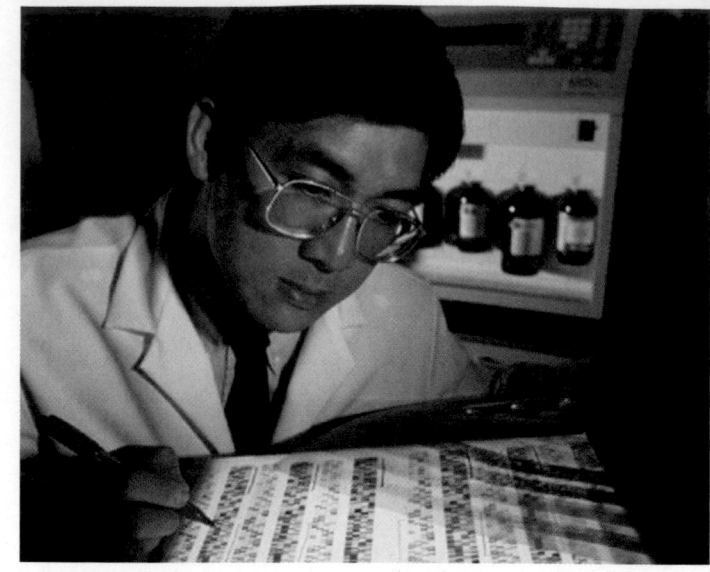

▲ **Figure 1.30 DNA technology and crime scene investigation.** Forensic technicians can use traces of DNA extracted from a blood sample or other body tissue collected at a crime scene to produce molecular "fingerprints." The stained bands you see in this photograph represent fragments of DNA, and the pattern of bands varies from person to person.

The directions that technology takes depend less on the curiosity that drives basic science than on the current needs and wants of people and on the social environment of the times. Debates about technology center more on "*should* we do it" than "*can* we do it." With advances in technology come difficult choices. For example, under what circumstances is it acceptable to use DNA technology to find out if particular people have genes for hereditary diseases? Should such tests always be voluntary, or are there circumstances when genetic testing should be mandatory? Should insurance companies or employers have access to the information, as they do for many other types of personal health data?

Such ethical issues have as much to do with politics, economics, and cultural values as with science and technology. All citizens—not only professional scientists—have a responsibility to be informed about how science works and about the potential benefits and risks of technology. The relationship between science, technology, and society increases the significance and value of any biology course.

CONCEPT CHECK **1.3**

1. Contrast inductive reasoning with deductive reasoning.
2. Why is natural selection called a theory?
3. **WHAT IF?** Suppose you extended the snake mimicry experiment to an area of Virginia where neither type of snake is known to live. What results would you predict at your field site?

For suggested answers, see Appendix A.

Chapter 1 Review

MEDIA Go to **www.campbellbiology.com** for BioFlix 3-D Animations, MP3 Tutors, Videos, Practice Tests, an eBook, and more.

SUMMARY OF KEY CONCEPTS

CONCEPT 1.1

Themes connect the concepts of biology (pp. 3–11)

▶ **Evolution, the Overarching Theme of Biology** Evolution accounts for the unity and diversity of life, and also for the match of organisms to their environments.

▶ *Theme:* **New properties emerge at each level in the biological hierarchy** The hierarchy of life unfolds as follows: biosphere > ecosystem > community > population > organism > organ system > organ > tissue > cell > organelle > molecule > atom. With each step "upward" from atoms, new properties emerge as a result of interactions among components at the lower levels. In an approach called reductionism, complex systems are broken down to simpler components that are more manageable to study. In systems biology, scientists make models of complex biological systems.

▶ *Theme:* **Organisms interact with their environments, exchanging matter and energy** An organism's environment includes other organisms as well as nonliving factors. Whereas chemical nutrients recycle within an ecosystem, energy flows through an ecosystem. All organisms must perform work, which requires energy. Energy flows from sunlight to producers to consumers.

▶ *Theme:* **Structure and function are correlated at all levels of biological organization** The form of a biological structure suits its function and vice versa.

▶ *Theme:* **Cells are an organism's basic units of structure and function** The cell is the lowest level of organization that can perform all activities required for life. Cells are either prokaryotic or eukaryotic. Eukaryotic cells contain membrane-enclosed organelles, including a DNA-containing nucleus. Prokaryotic cells lack such organelles.

▶ *Theme:* **The continuity of life is based on heritable information in the form of DNA** Genetic information is encoded in the nucleotide sequences of DNA. It is DNA that transmits heritable information from parents to offspring. DNA sequences program a cell's protein production by being transcribed into RNA and then translated into specific proteins. RNA that is not translated into protein serves other important functions.

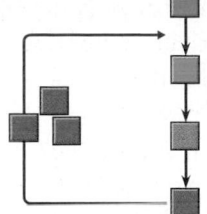

▶ *Theme:* **Feedback mechanisms regulate biological systems** In negative feedback, accumulation of an end product slows the process that makes that product. In positive feedback, the end product stimulates the production of more product. Feedback is a type of regulation common to life at all levels, from molecules to ecosystems.

MEDIA

Activity The Levels of Life Card Game
Activity Energy Flow and Chemical Cycling
Activity Form Fits Function: Cells
Activity Comparing Prokaryotic and Eukaryotic Cells
Activity Heritable Information: DNA
Activity Regulation: Negative and Positive Feedback

CONCEPT 1.2

The Core Theme: Evolution accounts for the unity and diversity of life (pp. 12–18)

▶ **Organizing the Diversity of Life** Biologists classify species according to a system of broader and broader groups. Domain Bacteria and domain Archaea consist of prokaryotes. Domain Eukarya, the eukaryotes, includes various groups of protists and the kingdoms Plantae, Fungi, and Animalia. As diverse as life is, there is also evidence of remarkable unity, which is revealed in the similarities between different kinds of organisms.

▶ **Charles Darwin and the Theory of Natural Selection** Darwin proposed natural selection as the mechanism for evolutionary adaptation of populations to their environments.

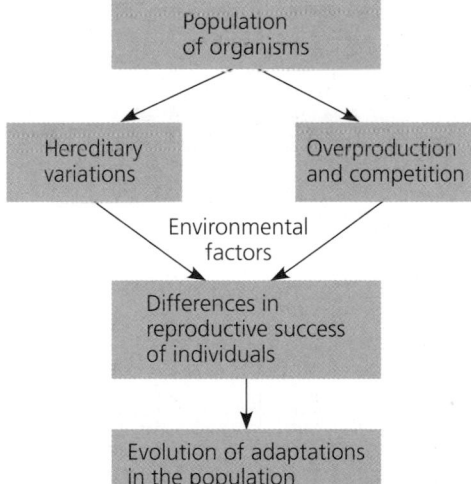

▶ **The Tree of Life** Each species is one twig of a branching tree of life extending back in time through ancestral species more and more remote. All of life is connected through its long evolutionary history.

MEDIA

Activity Classification Schemes
Investigation How Do Environmental Changes Affect a Population?
Biology Labs On-Line EvolutionLab

Scientists use two main forms of inquiry in their study of nature (pp. 18–24)

▶ **Discovery Science** In discovery science, scientists observe and describe some aspect of the world and use inductive reasoning to draw general conclusions.

▶ **Hypothesis-Based Science** Based on observations, scientists propose hypotheses that lead to predictions and then test the hypotheses by seeing if the predictions come true. Deductive reasoning is used in testing hypotheses: If a hypothesis is correct, and we test it, then we can expect a particular outcome. Hypotheses must be testable and falsifiable.

▶ **A Case Study in Scientific Inquiry: Investigating Mimicry in Snake Populations** Experiments must be designed to demonstrate the effect of one variable by testing control groups and experimental groups that differ in only that one variable.

▶ **Limitations of Science** Science cannot address the possibility of supernatural phenomena because hypotheses must be testable and falsifiable, and observations and experimental results must be repeatable.

▶ **Theories in Science** A scientific theory is broad in scope, generates new hypotheses, and is supported by a large body of evidence.

▶ **Model Building in Science** Models of ideas, structures, and processes help us understand scientific phenomena and make predictions.

▶ **The Culture of Science** Science is a social activity characterized by both cooperation and competition.

▶ **Science, Technology, and Society** Technology is a method or device that applies scientific knowledge for some specific purpose.

MEDIA

GraphIt! An Introduction to Graphing
Investigation How Does Acid Precipitation Affect Trees?
Activity Science, Technology, and Society: DDT

TESTING YOUR KNOWLEDGE

SELF-QUIZ

1. All the organisms on your campus make up
   a. an ecosystem.
   b. a community.
   c. a population.
   d. an experimental group.
   e. a taxonomic domain.

2. Which of the following is a correct sequence of levels in life's hierarchy, proceeding downward from an individual animal?
   a. brain, organ system, nerve cell, nervous tissue
   b. organ system, nervous tissue, brain
   c. organism, organ system, tissue, cell, organ
   d. nervous system, brain, nervous tissue, nerve cell
   e. organ system, tissue, molecule, cell

3. Which of the following is *not* an observation or inference on which Darwin's theory of natural selection is based?
   a. Poorly adapted individuals never produce offspring.

   b. There is heritable variation among individuals.
   c. Because of overproduction of offspring, there is competition for limited resources.
   d. Individuals whose inherited characteristics best fit them to the environment will generally produce more offspring.
   e. A population can become adapted to its environment over time.

4. Systems biology is mainly an attempt to
   a. understand the integration of all levels of biological organization from molecules to the biosphere.
   b. simplify complex problems by reducing the system into smaller, less complex units.
   c. construct models of the behavior of entire biological systems.
   d. build high-throughput machines for the rapid acquisition of biological data.
   e. speed up the technological application of scientific knowledge.

5. Protists and bacteria are grouped into different domains because
   a. protists eat bacteria.
   b. bacteria are not made of cells.
   c. protists have a membrane-bounded nucleus, which bacterial cells lack.
   d. bacteria decompose protists.
   e. protists are photosynthetic.

6. Which of the following best demonstrates the unity among all organisms?
   a. matching DNA nucleotide sequences
   b. descent with modification
   c. the structure and function of DNA
   d. natural selection
   e. emergent properties

7. Which of the following is an example of qualitative data?
   a. The temperature decreased from 20°C to 15°C.
   b. The plant's height is 25 centimeters (cm).
   c. The fish swam in a zig-zag motion.
   d. The six pairs of robins hatched an average of three chicks.
   e. The contents of the stomach are mixed every 20 seconds.

8. Which of the following best describes the logic of hypothesis-based science?
   a. If I generate a testable hypothesis, tests and observations will support it.
   b. If my prediction is correct, it will lead to a testable hypothesis.
   c. If my observations are accurate, they will support my hypothesis.
   d. If my hypothesis is correct, I can expect certain test results.
   e. If my experiments are set up right, they will lead to a testable hypothesis.

9. A controlled experiment is one that
   a. proceeds slowly enough that a scientist can make careful records of the results.
   b. may include experimental groups and control groups tested in parallel.

c. is repeated many times to make sure the results are accurate.

d. keeps all environmental variables constant.

e. is supervised by an experienced scientist.

10. Which of the following statements best distinguishes hypotheses from theories in science?

a. Theories are hypotheses that have been proved.

b. Hypotheses are guesses; theories are correct answers.

c. Hypotheses usually are relatively narrow in scope; theories have broad explanatory power.

d. Hypotheses and theories are essentially the same thing.

e. Theories are proved true in all cases; hypotheses are usually falsified by tests.

11. **DRAW IT** With rough sketches, draw a biological hierarchy similar to the one in Figure 1.4 but using a coral reef as the ecosystem, a fish as the organism, its stomach as the organ, and DNA as the molecule. Include all levels in the hierarchy.

For Self-Quiz answers, see Appendix A.

MEDIA Visit **www.campbellbiology.com** for a Practice Test.

EVOLUTION CONNECTION

12. A typical prokaryotic cell has about 3,000 genes in its DNA, while a human cell has about 20,500 genes. About 1,000 of these genes are present in both types of cells. Based on your understanding of evolution, explain how such different organisms could have this same subset of genes. What sorts of functions might these shared genes have?

SCIENTIFIC INQUIRY

13. Based on the results of the snake mimicry case study, suggest another hypothesis researchers might use to extend the investigation.

SCIENCE, TECHNOLOGY, AND SOCIETY

14. The fruits of wild species of tomato are tiny compared to the giant beefsteak tomatoes available today. This difference in fruit size is almost entirely due to the larger number of cells in the domesticated fruits. Plant molecular biologists have recently discovered genes that are responsible for controlling cell division in tomatoes. Why would such a discovery be important to producers of other kinds of fruits and vegetables? To the study of human development and disease? To our basic understanding of biology?

The Chemistry of Life

AN INTERVIEW WITH

Deborah M. Gordon

What does an ant sense as it goes about its daily chores? Mainly chemicals— because these are the cues ants use to navigate their environment. The interactions of ants with each other and their surroundings are the research focus of Deborah M. Gordon, a professor of biological sciences at Stanford University. While at Stanford, Dr. Gordon has won several awards for excellence in teaching, as well as recognition for her research in the Arizona desert and the tropics of South America. And through appearances on radio, TV nature shows, and her book *Ants at Work: How an Insect Society Is Organized* (Free Press, 1999), Dr. Gordon has shared her fascination with ant society with people around the world.

How did you get interested in biology?

In my first year in college, thinking of a career in medicine as a possibility, I took introductory chemistry and biology. But those courses just gave me a lot of information that I couldn't really put together. I ended up majoring in French. But I was also very interested in math and in music theory, because I like looking at patterns and understanding how they change over time. Then, in my senior year, I took a course in comparative anatomy, which completely changed my view of biology. That course showed me that evolution is a process that changes patterns in interesting ways.

After graduation, curious about the human body and health, I came to Stanford to take the medical school course in human anatomy. I stayed to complete a master's degree in biology. Then, although I still wasn't sure what I wanted to do with my life, I entered a Ph.D. program at Duke. It was there that I began research on ant behavior—and I loved it.

Students of biology have to study chemistry as well. How is chemistry relevant to ant behavior?

Ants don't see very well; they operate mostly by chemical communication. If you work on ants, you have to think about chemistry because chemicals are critically important in the ant's world. For example, the ants I study in Arizona use long-lasting chemical cues to identify themselves and to mark their nest area. Ants also use many short-term chemical cues called pheromones, which they secrete in certain situations. The best known are alarm pheromones, which are what make ants run around in circles when they're disturbed. Some ants secrete a pheromone from the tip of the abdomen that marks where they walk and creates a trail that other ants can follow. Ants have 12 or 14 different glands that secrete different substances. We really don't know what they're all for, or how many chemical combinations an ant can respond to. In addition to chemicals used in communication, some ants produce antibiotics or chemical defenses against predators. Other ants use chemicals to kill certain plants [see Chapter 2, pp. 30–31].

Why do you study ants?

What interests me about ants is that ants live in societies without any central control. Yet individual ants are very limited in what they can do; each can take in only local information. No ant can figure out what needs to be done for the good of the colony. The big question for me is: How can an ant colony function when nobody's in charge and each ant can only perceive what's right around it?

What about the queens? Please tell us more about how ants live.

There are 10,000 to 12,000 species of ants. They all live in colonies, each with one or a few reproductive females, called queens. The queens lay eggs, using sperm stored from a mating that preceded her establishment of the colony. The rest of the colony—all the ants you see walking around—are her daughters, sterile female workers. These workers do all the work, and they do it without any direction from the queen. Males,

born from unfertilized eggs, are produced only once a year, just in time to join virgin queens in a mating flight. Soon after mating, they die.

What exactly do worker ants do?

The ants I study in Arizona, called harvester ants, perform four kinds of tasks. Some workers forage for food. Some patrol; that is, they go out early in the morning and decide where the foragers should go that day. Others do nest-maintenance work, building chambers underground and then carrying out the excess sand. And still others work on the refuse pile, or midden, which they mark with the colony's specific odor. Different groups of ants perform each of the four tasks.

Tell us about your research in Arizona.

At my research site in Arizona, where I've been working for more than 20 years, I study a population of about 300 colonies of harvester ants. Each year my students and I map the locations of the colonies that make up this population. We identify all the colonies that were there the year before, figure out which ones have died, and map the new ones. In this way I can follow the same colonies year after year. I get to know them quite well. I have found that colonies last 15 to 20 years.

In addition to observing the ant colonies, we do simple experiments where we change the ants' environment in some way and observe how the ants respond. For example, in the last few years we've been studying how a colony regulates the number of ants that go out to forage. We've learned that each ant uses its recent history of interactions with other ants to decide what to do next. An ant uses odors to identify the task of the ants it meets. Each ant is coated with a layer of grease, made of chemicals called hydrocarbons. Each task group—the foragers, the patrollers, the nest maintenance workers, and the midden workers—has a unique mixture of hydrocarbons, which the ants secrete and spread on each other by grooming. We've found that, as an ant spends time outside, the proportions of different hydrocarbons on its body changes.

What causes this change?

The heat of the sun. We learned this from an experiment in which we took ants that had been working inside the nest and exposed them to different conditions. After exposure to high temperatures and low humidity for long enough times, these ants came to smell like foragers. So it's not that foragers secrete something different as they do their task but that doing the task changes them. Just as a carpenter gets calluses from holding tools, an ant comes to smell different from the work it does. The ants of a colony all secrete the same mixture of hydrocarbons, but each ant's chemical profile changes depending on what it does.

What tells an ant what to do? For example, what tells an ant to forage?

We've learned that ants use their recent experience of quick antennal contacts with each other to decide what to do. The antennae are their organs of chemical perception. Anyone who has watched ants has seen them meet and touch antennae, and when they do that, they smell each other, detecting the chemicals on each other's body. But a single interaction is not an instruction; a forager meeting another ant is not saying, "Go forage." It's the *pattern* of encounters that conveys the message.

How did you figure that out?

Working with Michael Greene, who's now at the University of Colorado at Denver, we've been able to extract the hydrocarbons from the ants' bodies and put them on little glass beads, and we've found that the ants respond to a bead coated with ant hydrocarbons as if it were an ant. So by dropping these coated beads into the nest, we can figure out how the ants react to encounters with an ant of a particular task group.

Recently we've been working on how foragers use the rate at which other foragers come in with food to decide whether to go out again. This rate gives feedback about how much food is out there. A forager looking for food won't come back until it finds something; if it has to stay out for 45 minutes, it will. But when there's an abundance of food near the nest, the foragers return quickly. The returning ants provide positive feedback: The faster ants come back, the more ants go out.

We've found that harvester ants respond surprisingly quickly to changes in the frequency of encounters with other ants. This rapid response is probably driven by the ants' short memories—only about 10 seconds.

So the answer to the question of what controls a colony is the aggregate of "decisions" made in the simple interactions between individual ants. Are there analogies in other areas of biology?

A system without central control, built from simple, interacting components, is called a "complex system," and scientists in many areas of biology are interested in such systems. One obvious analog to an ant colony is a brain. Your brain is composed of neurons (nerve cells), but no single neuron knows how to think about, for example, the subject of ants—although your brain as a whole can think about ants. The brain operates without central control, in the sense that there isn't a master neuron in there that says, "OK, you guys, you do ants." Yet somehow all of the simple interactions among the neurons add up to the brain's very complex functioning. Another analogy is the growth of an embryo: The cells of an embryo all have the same DNA, but as the embryo grows, its cells take on different forms and functions. Nobody says, "OK, you become liver, you become bone." Instead, as a result of molecular interactions among cells, the embryo develops tissues of different types.

In your book, the colony is spoken of as if it were an organism. Does evolution operate on the level of the colony?

Yes, because the whole colony cooperates to make more queens and males that go out and start new colonies. A colony's behavior can determine how many offspring colonies it makes. In the long term, I'd like to understand how natural selection is acting on ant behavior (if it is). Why does it matter to the colony that it behaves in a certain way?

Now for a practical question: How can we deal with ant invasions in our homes?

It depends on where you live. In Northern California, the invading ants are usually Argentine ants, whose activity is clearly connected to the weather. The ants come into everybody's houses at the same time—when it rains or is very hot and dry—and they go out at the same time. The most important thing to remember is that putting out pesticide, especially when you don't have ants, sends pesticide into the groundwater but doesn't have much effect on the numbers of ants. I don't like having ants in my kitchen—I always take it personally—but I know that when I do, everybody else does, too. And covering or washing away a trail works only briefly—about 20 minutes for Argentine ants, as I found out in an experiment. Blocking off the places where ants are coming in is the best approach.

Ant-bait devices, from which foraging ants are supposed to carry poison to their nest, can work for ants that have one queen in a central nest. Such ants include carpenter ants, which enter houses in many parts of the United States. These ants nest in decaying wood, though contrary to their reputation, they don't eat wood. Ant baits don't work at all for the Argentine ants because these ants have many queens and many nests and you are unlikely to reach all the queens with the poison.

What advice do you have for undergraduates interested in a research career?

Students should try to experience several kinds of research, involving different kinds of activities. The best way to find out if you like doing research—whether it's working in the field or in the lab—is to try it.

How can an ant colony function when nobody's in charge and each ant can only perceive what's right around it?

Inquiry in Action

Learn about an experiment by Deborah Gordon and her graduate student Megan Frederickson in Inquiry Figure 2.2 on page 31. Read and analyze the original paper in *Inquiry in Action: Interpreting Scientific Papers.*

Left to right: Deborah Gordon, Megan Frederickson, Lisa Urry, and Jane Reece

The Chemical Context of Life

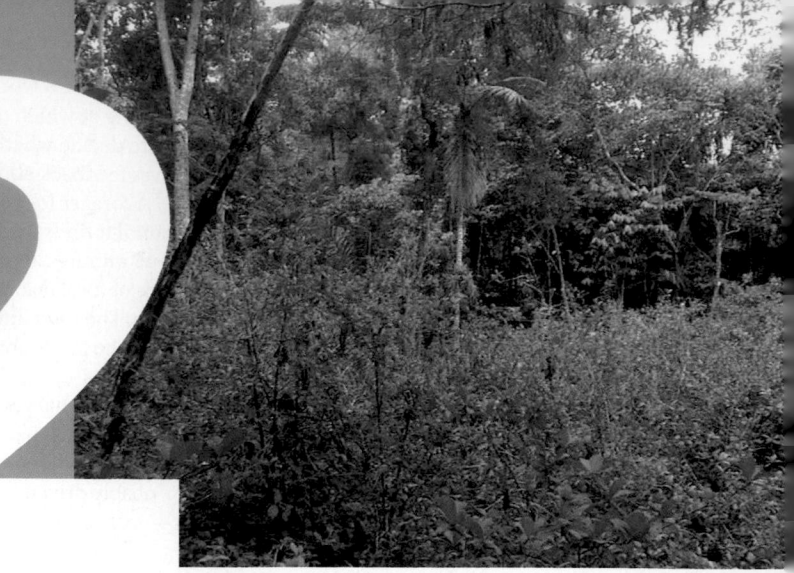

▲ Figure 2.1 **Who tends this garden?**

OVERVIEW

A Chemical Connection to Biology

The Amazon rain forest in South America is a showcase for the diversity of life on Earth. Colorful birds, insects, and other animals live among a myriad of trees, shrubs, vines, and wildflowers, and an excursion along a waterway or a forest path typically reveals a lush variety of plant life. Visitors traveling near the Amazon's headwaters in Peru are therefore surprised to come across tracts of forest like that seen in the foreground of the photo in **Figure 2.1**. This patch is almost completely dominated by a single plant species—a willowy flowering tree called *Duroia hirsuta*. Travelers may wonder if the garden is planted and maintained by local people, but the indigenous people are as mystified as the visitors. They call these stands of *Duroia* trees "devil's gardens," from a legend attributing them to an evil forest spirit.

Seeking a scientific explanation, a research team working under Deborah Gordon, who is interviewed on pages 28–29, recently solved the "devil's garden" mystery. **Figure 2.2** describes their main experiment. The researchers showed that the "farmers" who create and maintain these gardens are actually ants that live in the hollow stems of the *Duroia* trees. The ants do not plant the *Duroia* trees, but they prevent other plant species

from growing in the garden by injecting intruders with a poisonous chemical. In this way, the ants create space for the growth of the *Duroia* trees that serve as their home. With the ability to maintain and expand its habitat, a single colony of devil's garden ants can live for hundreds of years.

The chemical the ants use to weed their garden turns out to be formic acid. This substance is produced by many species of ants and in fact got its name from the Latin word for ant, *formica*. In many cases, the formic acid probably serves as a disinfectant that protects the ants against microbial parasites. The devil's garden ant is the first ant species found to use formic acid as a herbicide. This use of a chemical is an important addition to the list of functions mediated by chemicals in the insect world. Scientists already know that chemicals play an important role in insect communication, attraction of mates, and defense against predators.

Research on devil's gardens is only one example of the relevance of chemistry to the study of life. Unlike a list of college courses, nature is not neatly packaged into the individual natural sciences—biology, chemistry, physics, and so forth. Biologists specialize in the study of life, but organisms and their environments are natural systems to which the concepts of chemistry and physics apply. Biology is a multidisciplinary science.

This unit of chapters introduces basic concepts of chemistry that will apply throughout our study of life. We will make many connections to the themes introduced in Chapter 1. One of these themes is the organization of life into a hierarchy of structural levels, with additional properties emerging at each successive level. In this unit, we will see how emergent properties are apparent at the lowest levels of biological organization—such as the ordering of atoms into molecules and the interactions of those molecules within cells. Somewhere in the transition from molecules to cells, we will cross the blurry boundary between nonlife and life. This chapter focuses on the chemical components that make up all matter.

What creates "devil's gardens" in the rain forest?

EXPERIMENT   Working under Deborah Gordon and with Michael Greene, graduate student Megan Frederickson sought the cause of "devil's gardens," stands of a single species of tree, *Duroia hirsuta*. One hypothesis was that ants living in these trees, *Myrmelachista schumanni*, produce a poisonous chemical that kills trees of other species; another was that the *Duroia* trees themselves kill competing trees, perhaps by means of a chemical.

To test these hypotheses, Frederickson did field experiments in Peru. Two saplings of a local nonhost tree species, *Cedrela odorata*, were planted inside each of ten devil's gardens. At the base of one, a sticky insect barrier was applied; the other was unprotected. Two more *Cedrela* saplings, with and without barriers, were planted about 50 meters outside each garden.

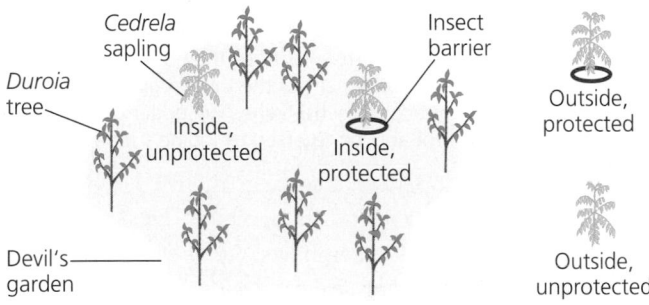

The researchers observed ant activity on the *Cedrela* leaves and measured areas of dead leaf tissue after one day. They also chemically analyzed contents of the ants' poison glands.

RESULTS   The ants made injections from the tips of their abdomens into leaves of unprotected saplings in their gardens (see photo). Within one day, these leaves developed dead areas (see graph). The protected saplings were uninjured, as were the saplings planted outside the gardens. Formic acid was the only chemical detected in the poison glands of the ants.

Cedrela saplings, inside and outside devil's gardens

CONCLUSION   Ants of the species *Myrmelachista schumanni* kill nonhost trees by injecting the leaves with formic acid, thus creating hospitable habitats (devil's gardens) for the ant colony.

SOURCE   M. E. Frederickson, M. J. Greene, and D. M. Gordon, "Devil's gardens" bedevilled by ants, *Nature* 437:495–496 (2005).

Inquiry in Action   Read and analyze the original paper in *Inquiry in Action: Interpreting Scientific Papers.*

WHAT IF?   What would be the results if the unprotected saplings' inability to grow in the devil's gardens was caused by a chemical released by the *Duroia* trees rather than by the ants?

Matter consists of chemical elements in pure form and in combinations called compounds

Organisms are composed of **matter**, which is anything that takes up space and has mass.* Matter exists in many diverse forms. Rocks, metals, oils, gases, and humans are just a few examples of what seems an endless assortment of matter.

Elements and Compounds

Matter is made up of elements. An **element** is a substance that cannot be broken down to other substances by chemical reactions. Today, chemists recognize 92 elements occurring in nature; gold, copper, carbon, and oxygen are examples. Each element has a symbol, usually the first letter or two of its name. Some symbols are derived from Latin or German; for instance, the symbol for sodium is Na, from the Latin word *natrium.*

A **compound** is a substance consisting of two or more different elements combined in a fixed ratio. Table salt, for example, is sodium chloride (NaCl), a compound composed of the elements sodium (Na) and chlorine (Cl) in a 1:1 ratio. Pure sodium is a metal, and pure chlorine is a poisonous gas. When chemically combined, however, sodium and chlorine form an edible compound. Water (H_2O), another compound, consists of the elements hydrogen (H) and oxygen (O) in a 2:1 ratio. These are simple examples of organized matter having emergent properties: A compound has characteristics different from those of its elements **(Figure 2.3)**.

Sodium   **Chlorine**   **Sodium chloride**

▲ **Figure 2.3 The emergent properties of a compound.** The metal sodium combines with the poisonous gas chlorine, forming the edible compound sodium chloride, or table salt.

---

* Sometimes we substitute the term *weight* for mass, although the two are not identical. Mass is the amount of matter in an object, whereas the weight of an object is how strongly that mass is pulled by gravity. The weight of an astronaut walking on the moon is approximately ⅙ that of the astronaut's weight on Earth, but his or her mass is the same. However, as long as we are earthbound, the weight of an object is a measure of its mass; in everyday language, therefore, we tend to use the terms interchangeably.

Essential Elements of Life

About 25 of the 92 natural elements are known to be essential to life. Just four of these—carbon (C), oxygen (O), hydrogen (H), and nitrogen (N)—make up 96% of living matter. Phosphorus (P), sulfur (S), calcium (Ca), potassium (K), and a few other elements account for most of the remaining 4% of an organism's weight. **Table 2.1** lists by percentage the elements that make up the human body; the percentages for other organisms are similar. **Figure 2.4a** illustrates the effect of a deficiency of nitrogen, an essential element, in a plant.

Trace elements are those required by an organism in only minute quantities. Some trace elements, such as iron (Fe), are needed by all forms of life; others are required only by certain species. For example, in vertebrates (animals with backbones), the element iodine (I) is an essential ingredient of a hormone produced by the thyroid gland. A daily intake of only 0.15 milligram (mg) of iodine is adequate for normal activity of the human thyroid. An iodine deficiency in the diet causes the thyroid gland to grow to abnormal size, a condition called goiter **(Figure 2.4b)**. Where it is available, iodized salt has reduced the incidence of goiter.

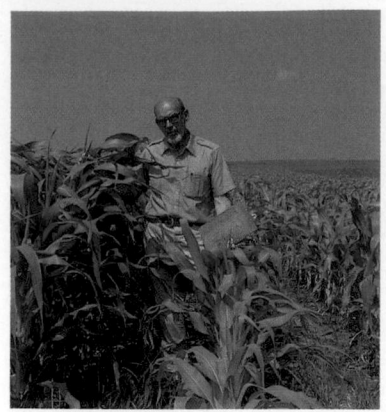

(a) Nitrogen deficiency　　　　**(b) Iodine deficiency**

▲ **Figure 2.4 The effects of essential-element deficiencies. (a)** This photo shows the effect of nitrogen deficiency in corn (maize). In this controlled experiment, the taller plants on the left are growing in nitrogen-rich soil, and the shorter plants on the right in nitrogen-poor soil. **(b)** Goiter is an enlargement of the thyroid gland, resulting from a deficiency of the trace element iodine. The goiter of this Malaysian woman can probably be reversed by iodine supplements.

Table 2.1	**Naturally Occurring Elements in the Human Body**		
Symbol	Element	Atomic Number (see p. 33)	Percentage of Human Body Weight
Elements making up about 96% of human body weight			
O	Oxygen	8	65.0
C	Carbon	6	18.5
H	Hydrogen	1	9.5
N	Nitrogen	7	3.3
Elements making up about 4% of human body weight			
Ca	Calcium	20	1.5
P	Phosphorus	15	1.0
K	Potassium	19	0.4
S	Sulfur	16	0.3
Na	Sodium	11	0.2
Cl	Chlorine	17	0.2
Mg	Magnesium	12	0.1

Elements making up less than 0.01% of human body weight (trace elements)

Boron (B), chromium (Cr), cobalt (Co), copper (Cu), fluorine (F), iodine (I), iron (Fe), manganese (Mn), molybdenum (Mo), selenium (Se), silicon (Si), tin (Sn), vanadium (V), zinc (Zn)

CONCEPT CHECK 2.1

1. Explain how table salt has emergent properties.
2. Is a trace element an essential element? Explain.
3. **WHAT IF?** Iron (Fe) is a trace element required for the proper functioning of hemoglobin, the molecule that carries oxygen in red blood cells. What might be the effects of an iron deficiency?

For suggested answers, see Appendix A.

CONCEPT 2.2

An element's properties depend on the structure of its atoms

Each element consists of a certain kind of atom that is different from the atoms of any other element. An **atom** is the smallest unit of matter that still retains the properties of an element. Atoms are so small that it would take about a million of them to stretch across the period printed at the end of this sentence. We symbolize atoms with the same abbreviation used for the element that is made up of those atoms. For example, the symbol C stands for both the element carbon and a single carbon atom.

Subatomic Particles

Although the atom is the smallest unit having the properties of its element, these tiny bits of matter are composed of even smaller parts, called *subatomic particles*. Physicists have split the atom into more than a hundred types of particles, but only

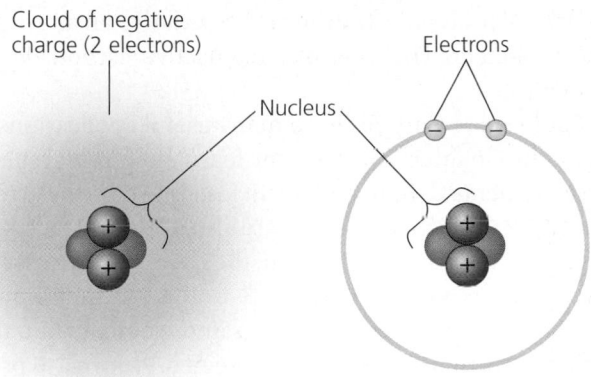

Cloud of negative
charge (2 electrons)

Nucleus

Electrons

(a) This model represents the electrons as a cloud of negative charge.

(b) In this even more simplified model, the electrons are shown as two small yellow spheres on a circle around the nucleus.

▲ **Figure 2.5 Simplified models of a helium (He) atom.** The helium nucleus consists of 2 neutrons (brown) and 2 protons (pink). Two electrons (yellow) exist outside the nucleus. These models are not to scale; they greatly overestimate the size of the nucleus in relation to the electron cloud.

three kinds of particles are relevant here: **neutrons, protons**, and **electrons**. Protons and electrons are electrically charged. Each proton has one unit of positive charge, and each electron has one unit of negative charge. A neutron, as its name implies, is electrically neutral.

Protons and neutrons are packed together tightly in a dense core, or **atomic nucleus**, at the center of an atom; protons give the nucleus a positive charge. The electrons form a sort of cloud of negative charge around the nucleus, and it is the attraction between opposite charges that keeps the electrons in the vicinity of the nucleus. **Figure 2.5** shows two models of the structure of the helium atom as an example.

The neutron and proton are almost identical in mass, each about 1.7×10^{-24} gram (g). Grams and other conventional units are not very useful for describing the mass of objects so minuscule. Thus, for atoms and subatomic particles (and for molecules, too), we use a unit of measurement called the **dalton**, in honor of John Dalton, the British scientist who helped develop atomic theory around 1800. (The dalton is the same as the *atomic mass unit*, or *amu*, a unit you may have encountered elsewhere.) Neutrons and protons have masses close to 1 dalton. Because the mass of an electron is only about $\frac{1}{2,000}$ that of a neutron or proton, we can ignore electrons when computing the total mass of an atom.

Atomic Number and Atomic Mass

Atoms of the various elements differ in their number of subatomic particles. All atoms of a particular element have the same number of protons in their nuclei. This number of protons, which is unique to that element, is called the **atomic number** and is written as a subscript to the left of the symbol

for the element. The abbreviation $_2$He, for example, tells us that an atom of the element helium has 2 protons in its nucleus. Unless otherwise indicated, an atom is neutral in electrical charge, which means that its protons must be balanced by an equal number of electrons. Therefore, the atomic number tells us the number of protons and also the number of electrons in an electrically neutral atom.

We can deduce the number of neutrons from a second quantity, the **mass number**, which is the sum of protons plus neutrons in the nucleus of an atom. The mass number is written as a superscript to the left of an element's symbol. For example, we can use this shorthand to write an atom of helium as $_2^4$He. Because the atomic number indicates how many protons there are, we can determine the number of neutrons by subtracting the atomic number from the mass number: The helium atom, $_2^4$He, has 2 neutrons. An atom of sodium, $_{11}^{23}$Na, has 11 protons, 11 electrons, and 12 neutrons. The simplest atom is hydrogen, $_1^1$H, which has no neutrons; it consists of a single proton with a single electron.

As mentioned earlier, the contribution of electrons to mass is negligible. Therefore, almost all of an atom's mass is concentrated in its nucleus. Because neutrons and protons each have a mass very close to 1 dalton, the mass number is an approximation of the total mass of an atom, called its **atomic mass**. So we might say that the atomic mass of sodium ($_{11}^{23}$Na) is 23 daltons, although more precisely it is 22.9898 daltons.

Isotopes

All atoms of a given element have the same number of protons, but some atoms have more neutrons than other atoms of the same element and therefore have greater mass. These different atomic forms are called **isotopes** of the element. In nature, an element occurs as a mixture of its isotopes. For example, consider the three isotopes of the element carbon, which has the atomic number 6. The most common isotope is carbon-12, $_6^{12}$C, which accounts for about 99% of the carbon in nature. The isotope $_6^{12}$C has 6 neutrons. Most of the remaining 1% of carbon consists of atoms of the isotope $_6^{13}$C, with 7 neutrons. A third, even rarer isotope, $_6^{14}$C, has 8 neutrons. Notice that all three isotopes of carbon have 6 protons; otherwise, they would not be carbon. Although the isotopes of an element have slightly different masses, they behave identically in chemical reactions. (The number usually given as the atomic mass of an element, such as 22.9898 daltons for sodium, is actually an average of the atomic masses of all the element's naturally occurring isotopes.)

Both ^{12}C and ^{13}C are stable isotopes, meaning that their nuclei do not have a tendency to lose particles. The isotope ^{14}C, however, is unstable, or radioactive. A **radioactive isotope** is one in which the nucleus decays spontaneously, giving off particles and energy. When the decay leads to a change in the

▼ Figure 2.6 Research Method

Radioactive Tracers

APPLICATION Scientists use radioactive isotopes to label certain chemical compounds, creating tracers that can be used to follow a metabolic process or locate the compound within an organism. In this example, radioactive tracers are being used to determine the effect of temperature on the rate at which cells make copies of their DNA.

TECHNIQUE

Compounds including radioactive tracer (bright blue)

Human cells

Incubators

1 10°C	2 15°C	3 20°C
4 25°C	5 30°C	6 35°C
7 40°C	8 45°C	9 50°C

❶ Compounds used by cells to make DNA are added to human cells. One ingredient is labeled with ^3H, a radioactive isotope of hydrogen. Nine dishes of cells are incubated at different temperatures. The cells make new DNA, incorporating the radioactive tracer with ^3H.

❷ The cells are placed in test tubes; their DNA is isolated; and unused labeled compounds are removed.

DNA (old and new)

❸ A solution called scintillation fluid is added to the test tubes and they are placed in a scintillation counter. As the ^3H in the newly made DNA decays, it emits radiation that excites chemicals in the scintillation fluid, causing them to give off light. Flashes of light are recorded by the scintillation counter.

RESULTS The frequency of flashes, which is recorded as counts per minute, is proportional to the amount of the radioactive tracer present, indicating the amount of new DNA. In this experiment, when the counts per minute are plotted against temperature, it is clear that temperature affects the rate of DNA synthesis; the most DNA was made at 35°C.

Graph: Counts per minute (× 1,000) vs. Temperature (°C); Optimum temperature for DNA synthesis; peak at 35°C.

number of protons, it transforms the atom to an atom of a different element. For example, radioactive carbon decays to form nitrogen.

Radioactive isotopes have many useful applications in biology. In Chapter 25, you will learn how researchers use measurements of radioactivity in fossils to date these relics of past life. Radioactive isotopes are also useful as tracers to follow atoms through metabolism, the chemical processes of an organism. Cells use the radioactive atoms as they would use nonradioactive isotopes of the same element, but the radioactive tracers can be readily detected. **Figure 2.6** presents an example of how biologists use radioactive tracers to monitor biological processes, in this case the synthesis of DNA by human cells.

Radioactive tracers are important diagnostic tools in medicine. For example, certain kidney disorders can be diagnosed by injecting small doses of substances containing radioactive isotopes into the blood and then measuring the amount of tracer excreted in the urine. Radioactive tracers are also used in combination with sophisticated imaging instruments, such as PET scanners, which can monitor chemical processes, such as those involved in cancerous growth, as they actually occur in the body **(Figure 2.7)**.

Cancerous throat tissue

▲ **Figure 2.7 A PET scan, a medical use for radioactive isotopes.** PET, an acronym for positron-emission tomography, detects locations of intense chemical activity in the body. The patient is first injected with a nutrient such as glucose labeled with a radioactive isotope that emits subatomic particles. These particles collide with electrons made available by chemical reactions in the body. A PET scanner detects the energy released in these collisions and maps "hot spots," the regions of an organ that are most chemically active at the time. The color of the image varies with the amount of the isotope present, with the bright yellow color here identifying a region of cancerous throat tissue.

Although radioactive isotopes are very useful in biological research and medicine, radiation from decaying isotopes also poses a hazard to life by damaging cellular molecules. The severity of this damage depends on the type and amount of radiation an organism absorbs. One of the most serious environmental threats is radioactive fallout from nuclear accidents. The doses of most isotopes used in medical diagnosis, however, are relatively safe.

The Energy Levels of Electrons

The simplified models of the atom in Figure 2.5 greatly exaggerate the size of the nucleus relative to the volume of the whole atom. If an atom of helium were the size of Yankee Stadium, the nucleus would be only the size of a pencil eraser in the center of the field. Moreover, the electrons would be like two tiny gnats buzzing around the stadium. Atoms are mostly empty space.

When two atoms approach each other during a chemical reaction, their nuclei do not come close enough to interact. Of the three kinds of subatomic particles we have discussed, only electrons are directly involved in the chemical reactions between atoms.

An atom's electrons vary in the amount of energy they possess. **Energy** is defined as the capacity to cause change—for instance, by doing work. **Potential energy** is the energy that matter possesses because of its location or structure. For example, water in a reservoir on a hill has potential energy because of its altitude. When the gates of the reservoir's dam are opened and the water runs downhill, the energy can be used to do work, such as turning generators. Because energy has been expended, the water has less energy at the bottom of the hill than it did in the reservoir. Matter has a natural tendency to move to the lowest possible state of potential energy; in this example, the water runs downhill. To restore the potential energy of a reservoir, work must be done to elevate the water against gravity.

The electrons of an atom have potential energy because of how they are arranged in relation to the nucleus. The negatively charged electrons are attracted to the positively charged nucleus. It takes work to move a given electron farther away from the nucleus, so the more distant an electron is from the nucleus, the greater its potential energy. Unlike the continuous flow of water downhill, changes in the potential energy of electrons can occur only in steps of fixed amounts. An electron having a certain amount of energy is something like a ball on a staircase **(Figure 2.8a)**. The ball can have different amounts of potential energy, depending on which step it is on, but it cannot spend much time between the steps. Similarly, an electron's potential energy is determined by its energy level. An electron cannot exist in between energy levels.

An electron's energy level is correlated with its average distance from the nucleus. Electrons are found in different

(a) A ball bouncing down a flight of stairs provides an analogy for energy levels of electrons, because the ball can come to rest only on each step, not between steps.

Third shell (highest energy level)

Second shell (higher energy level)

First shell (lowest energy level)

Energy absorbed

Energy lost

Atomic nucleus

(b) An electron can move from one shell to another only if the energy it gains or loses is exactly equal to the difference in energy between the energy levels of the two shells. Arrows indicate some of the stepwise changes in potential energy that are possible.

▲ **Figure 2.8 Energy levels of an atom's electrons.** Electrons exist only at fixed levels of potential energy called electron shells.

electron shells, each with a characteristic average distance and energy level. In diagrams, shells can be represented by concentric circles **(Figure 2.8b)**. The first shell is closest to the nucleus, and electrons in this shell have the lowest potential energy. Electrons in the second shell have more energy, and electrons in the third shell even more energy. An electron can change the shell it occupies, but only by absorbing or losing an amount of energy equal to the difference in potential energy between its position in the old shell and that in the new shell. When an electron absorbs energy, it moves to a shell farther out from the nucleus. For example, light energy can excite an electron to a higher energy level. (Indeed, this is the first step taken when plants harness the energy of sunlight for photosynthesis, the process that produces food from carbon dioxide and water.) When an electron loses energy, it "falls back" to a shell closer to the nucleus, and the lost energy is usually released to the environment as heat. For example, sunlight excites electrons in the surface of a car to higher energy levels. When the electrons fall back to their original levels, the car's surface heats up. This thermal energy can be transferred to the air or to your hand if you touch the car.

Electron Distribution and Chemical Properties

The chemical behavior of an atom is determined by the distribution of electrons in the atom's electron shells. Beginning with hydrogen, the simplest atom, we can imagine building the atoms of the other elements by adding 1 proton and 1 electron

▲ **Figure 2.9 Electron-distribution diagrams for the first 18 elements in the periodic table.** In a standard periodic table (see Appendix B), information for each element is presented as shown for helium in the inset. In the diagrams in this table, electrons are represented as yellow dots and electron shells as concentric circles. These diagrams are a convenient way to picture the distribution of an atom's electrons among its electron shells, but these simplified models do not accurately represent the shape of the atom or the location of its electrons. The elements are arranged in rows, each representing the filling of an electron shell. As electrons are added, they occupy the lowest available shell.

? *What is the atomic number of magnesium? How many protons and electrons does it have? How many electron shells? How many valence electrons?*

at a time (along with an appropriate number of neutrons). **Figure 2.9**, an abbreviated version of what is called the *periodic table of the elements*, shows this distribution of electrons for the first 18 elements, from hydrogen ($_1$H) to argon ($_{18}$Ar). The elements are arranged in three rows, or periods, corresponding to the number of electron shells in their atoms. The left-to-right sequence of elements in each row corresponds to the sequential addition of electrons and protons. (See Appendix B for the complete periodic table.)

Hydrogen's 1 electron and helium's 2 electrons are located in the first shell. Electrons, like all matter, tend to exist in the lowest available state of potential energy. In an atom, this state is in the first shell. However, the first shell can hold no more than 2 electrons; thus, hydrogen and helium are the only elements in the first row of the table. An atom with more than 2 electrons must use higher shells because the first shell is full. The next element, lithium, has 3 electrons. Two of these electrons fill the first shell, while the third electron occupies the second shell. The second shell holds a maximum of 8 electrons. Neon, at the end of the second row, has 8 electrons in the second shell, giving it a total of 10 electrons.

The chemical behavior of an atom depends mostly on the number of electrons in its *outermost* shell. We call those outer

electrons **valence electrons** and the outermost electron shell the **valence shell**. In the case of lithium, there is only 1 valence electron, and the second shell is the valence shell. Atoms with the same number of electrons in their valence shells exhibit similar chemical behavior. For example, fluorine (F) and chlorine (Cl) both have 7 valence electrons, and both form compounds when combined with the element sodium (see Figure 2.3). An atom with a completed valence shell is unreactive; that is, it will not interact readily with other atoms. At the far right of the periodic table are helium, neon, and argon, the only three elements shown in Figure 2.9 that have full valence shells. These elements are said to be *inert*, meaning chemically unreactive. All the other atoms in Figure 2.9 are chemically reactive because they have incomplete valence shells.

Electron Orbitals

In the early 1900s, the electron shells of an atom were visualized as concentric paths of electrons orbiting the nucleus, somewhat like planets orbiting the sun. It is still convenient to use two-dimensional concentric-circle diagrams to symbolize electron shells, as in Figure 2.9. However, you need to remember that each concentric circle represents only the

(a) Electron-distribution diagram. An electron-distribution diagram is shown here for a neon atom, which has a total of 10 electrons. Each concentric circle represents an electron shell, which can be subdivided into electron orbitals.

Neon, with two filled shells (10 electrons)

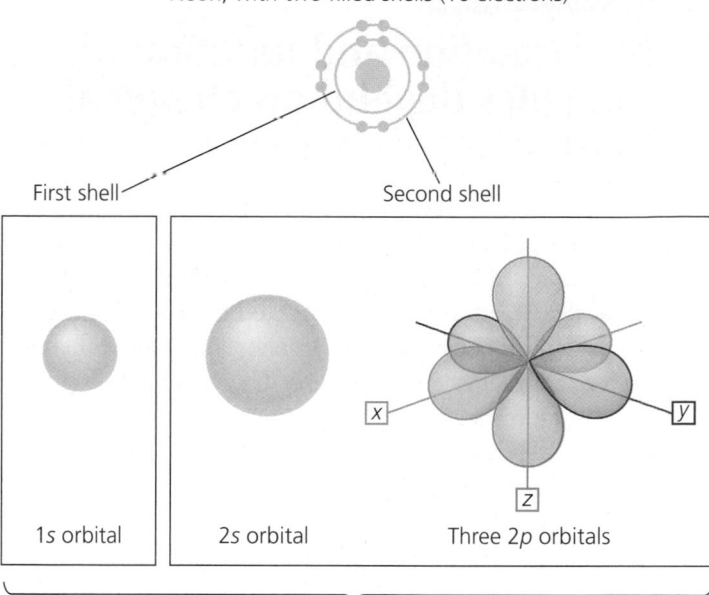

First shell   Second shell

(b) Separate electron orbitals. The three-dimensional shapes represent electron orbitals—the volumes of space where the electrons of an atom are most likely to be found. Each orbital holds a maximum of 2 electrons. The first electron shell, on the left, has one spherical (*s*) orbital, designated 1*s*. The second shell, on the right, has one larger *s* orbital (designated 2*s* for the second shell) plus three dumbbell-shaped orbitals called *p* orbitals (2*p* for the second shell). The three 2*p* orbitals lie at right angles to one another along imaginary *x*-, *y*-, and *z*-axes of the atom. Each 2*p* orbital is outlined here in a different color.

1*s* orbital   2*s* orbital   Three 2*p* orbitals

(c) Superimposed electron orbitals. To show the complete picture of the electron orbitals of neon, we superimpose the 1*s* orbital of the first shell and the 2*s* and three 2*p* orbitals of the second shell.

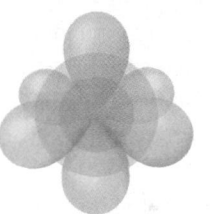

▲ **Figure 2.10 Electron orbitals.**

1*s*, 2*s*, and 2*p* orbitals

average distance between an electron in that shell and the nucleus. Accordingly, the concentric-circle diagrams do not give a real picture of an atom. In reality, we can never know the exact location of an electron. What we can do instead is describe the space in which an electron spends most of its time. The three-dimensional space where an electron is found 90% of the time is called an **orbital**.

Each electron shell contains electrons at a particular energy level, distributed among a specific number of orbitals of distinctive shapes and orientations. **Figure 2.10** shows the orbitals of neon as an example. You can think of an orbital as a component of an electron shell. The first electron shell has only one spherical *s* orbital (called 1*s*), but the second shell has four orbitals: one large spherical *s* orbital (called 2*s*) and three dumbbell-shaped *p* orbitals (called 2*p* orbitals). (The third shell and other higher electron shells also have *s* and *p* orbitals, as well as orbitals of more complex shapes.)

No more than 2 electrons can occupy a single orbital. The first electron shell can therefore accommodate up to 2 electrons in its *s* orbital. The lone electron of a hydrogen atom occupies the 1*s* orbital, as do the 2 electrons of a helium atom. The four orbitals of the second electron shell can hold up to 8 electrons. Electrons in each of the four orbitals have nearly the same energy, but they move in different volumes of space.

The reactivity of atoms arises from the presence of unpaired electrons in one or more orbitals of their valence shells. As you will see in the next section, atoms interact in a way that completes their valence shells. When they do so, it is the *unpaired* electrons that are involved.

CONCEPT CHECK 2.2

1. A lithium atom has 3 protons and 4 neutrons. What is its atomic mass in daltons?
2. A nitrogen atom has 7 protons, and the most common isotope of nitrogen has 7 neutrons. A radioactive isotope of nitrogen has 8 neutrons. Write the atomic number and mass number of this radioactive nitrogen as a chemical symbol with a subscript and superscript.
3. How many electrons does fluorine have? How many electron shells? Name the orbitals that are occupied. How many electrons are needed to fill the valence shell?
4. **WHAT IF?** In Figure 2.9, if two or more elements are in the same row, what do they have in common? If two or more elements are in the same column, what do they have in common?

For suggested answers, see Appendix A.

The formation and function of molecules depend on chemical bonding between atoms

Now that we have looked at the structure of atoms, we can move up the hierarchy of organization and see how atoms combine to form molecules and ionic compounds. Atoms with incomplete valence shells can interact with certain other atoms in such a way that each partner completes its valence shell: The atoms either share or transfer valence electrons. These interactions usually result in atoms staying close together, held by attractions called **chemical bonds**. The strongest kinds of chemical bonds are covalent bonds and ionic bonds.

Covalent Bonds

A **covalent bond** is the sharing of a pair of valence electrons by two atoms. For example, let's consider what happens when two hydrogen atoms approach each other. Recall that hydrogen has 1 valence electron in the first shell, but the shell's capacity is 2 electrons. When the two hydrogen atoms come close enough for their 1s orbitals to overlap, they can share their electrons (**Figure 2.11**). Each hydrogen atom now has 2 electrons associated with it in what amounts to a completed valence shell. Two or more atoms held together by covalent bonds constitute a **molecule**. In this case, the example is a hydrogen molecule.

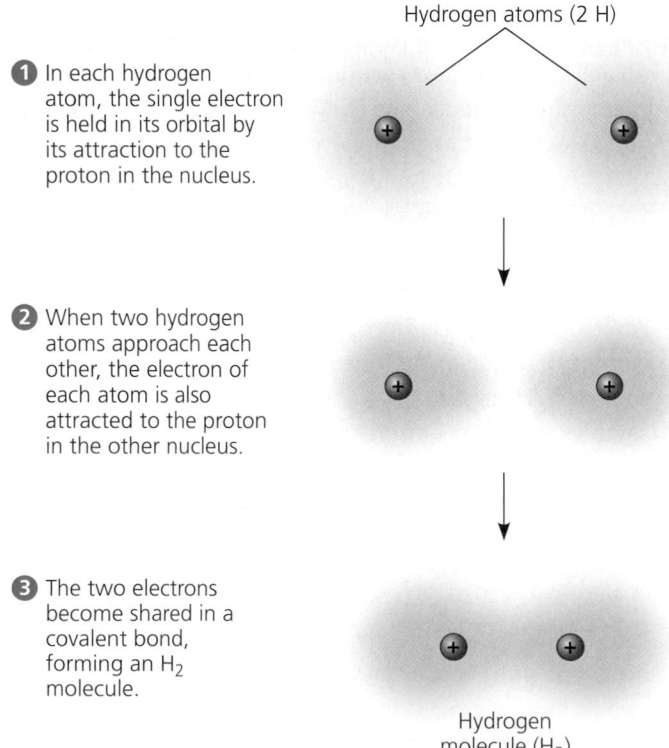

Hydrogen atoms (2 H)

1 In each hydrogen atom, the single electron is held in its orbital by its attraction to the proton in the nucleus.

2 When two hydrogen atoms approach each other, the electron of each atom is also attracted to the proton in the other nucleus.

3 The two electrons become shared in a covalent bond, forming an H$_2$ molecule.

Hydrogen molecule (H$_2$)

▲ **Figure 2.11 Formation of a covalent bond.**

Electron sharing can be depicted using element symbols, with dots representing the outermost electrons. You have probably seen such diagrams, called Lewis dot structures, in your chemistry book. The Lewis dot structure for a hydrogen molecule, H:H, is shown in **Figure 2.12a**. We can abbreviate the structure of this molecule as H—H, where the line represents a single covalent bond, or simply a **single bond**—that is, a pair of shared electrons. This notation, which represents both atoms and bonding, is called a **structural formula**. We can abbreviate even further by writing H$_2$, a **molecular formula** indicating simply that the molecule consists of two atoms of hydrogen.

Oxygen has 6 electrons in its second electron shell and therefore needs 2 more electrons to complete its valence shell. Two oxygen atoms form a molecule by sharing *two* pairs of valence electrons (**Figure 2.12b**). The atoms are thus joined by what is called a double covalent bond, or **double bond**.

Name and Molecular Formula	Electron-distribution Diagram	Lewis Dot Structure and Structural Formula	Space-filling Model
(a) Hydrogen (H$_2$). Two hydrogen atoms can form a single bond.		H:H H—H	
(b) Oxygen (O$_2$). Two oxygen atoms share two pairs of electrons to form a double bond.		Ö::Ö O=O	
(c) Water (H$_2$O). Two hydrogen atoms and one oxygen atom are joined by covalent bonds to produce a molecule of water.		:Ö:H H O—H H	
(d) Methane (CH$_4$). Four hydrogen atoms can satisfy the valence of one carbon atom, forming methane.		H:C:H H H H—C—H H	

▲ **Figure 2.12 Covalent bonding in four molecules.** A single covalent bond consists of a pair of shared electrons. The number of electrons required to complete an atom's valence shell generally determines how many bonds that atom will form. Four ways of indicating bonds are shown; the space-filling model comes closest to representing the actual shape of the molecule (see also Figure 2.17).

Each atom that can share valence electrons has a bonding capacity corresponding to the number of covalent bonds the atom can form. When the bonds form, they give the atom a full complement of electrons in the valence shell. The bonding capacity of oxygen, for example, is 2. This bonding capacity is called the atom's **valence** and usually equals the number of unpaired electrons required to complete the atom's outermost (valence) shell. See if you can determine the valences of hydrogen, oxygen, nitrogen, and carbon by studying the electron distribution diagrams in Figure 2.9. You can see that the valence of hydrogen is 1; oxygen, 2; nitrogen, 3; and carbon, 4. However, there are more complicated cases, such as phosphorus (P), another element important to life. Phosphorus can have a valence of 3, as we would predict from the presence of 3 unpaired electrons in its valence shell. In biologically important molecules, however, phosphorus can form three single bonds and one double bond. Therefore, it can also have a valence of 5.

The molecules H_2 and O_2 are pure elements rather than compounds because a compound is a combination of two or more *different* elements. Water, with the molecular formula H_2O, is a compound. Two atoms of hydrogen are needed to satisfy the valence of one oxygen atom. **Figure 2.12c** shows the structure of a water molecule. Water is so important to life that Chapter 3 is devoted entirely to its structure and behavior.

Another molecule that is a compound is methane, the main component of natural gas, with the molecular formula CH_4 **(Figure 2.12d)**. It takes four hydrogen atoms, each with a valence of 1, to complement one atom of carbon, with its valence of 4. We will look at many other compounds of carbon in Chapter 4.

The attraction of a particular kind of atom for the electrons of a covalent bond is called its **electronegativity**. The more electronegative an atom, the more strongly it pulls shared electrons toward itself. In a covalent bond between two atoms of the same element, the outcome of the tug-of-war for common electrons is a standoff; the two atoms are equally electronegative. Such a bond, in which the electrons are shared equally, is a **nonpolar covalent bond**. For example, the covalent bond of H_2 is nonpolar, as is the double bond of O_2. In other compounds, however, where one atom is bonded to a more electronegative atom, the electrons of the bond are not shared equally. This type of bond is called a **polar covalent bond**. Such bonds vary in their polarity, depending on the relative electronegativity of the two atoms. For example, the bonds between the oxygen and hydrogen atoms of a water mol-

Because oxygen (O) is more electronegative than hydrogen (H), shared electrons are pulled more toward oxygen.

This results in a partial negative charge on the oxygen and a partial positive charge on the hydrogens.

▲ **Figure 2.13 Polar covalent bonds in a water molecule.**

ecule are quite polar **(Figure 2.13)**. Oxygen is one of the most electronegative of all the elements, attracting shared electrons much more strongly than hydrogen does. In a covalent bond between oxygen and hydrogen, the electrons spend more time near the oxygen nucleus than they do near the hydrogen nucleus. Because electrons have a negative charge, the unequal sharing of electrons in water causes the oxygen atom to have a partial negative charge (indicated by the Greek letter δ with a minus sign, δ−, or "delta minus") and each hydrogen atom to have a partial positive charge (δ+, or "delta plus"). In contrast, the individual bonds of methane (CH_4) are much less polar because carbon and hydrogen differ much less in electronegativity than do oxygen and hydrogen.

Ionic Bonds

In some cases, two atoms are so unequal in their attraction for valence electrons that the more electronegative atom strips an electron completely away from its partner. This is what happens when an atom of sodium ($_{11}Na$) encounters an atom of chlorine ($_{17}Cl$) **(Figure 2.14)**. A sodium atom has a total of 11 electrons,

❶ The lone valence electron of a sodium atom is transferred to join the 7 valence electrons of a chlorine atom.

❷ Each resulting ion has a completed valence shell. An ionic bond can form between the oppositely charged ions.

Na Sodium atom

Cl Chlorine atom

Na⁺ Sodium ion (a cation)

Cl⁻ Chloride ion (an anion)

Sodium chloride (NaCl)

▲ **Figure 2.14 Electron transfer and ionic bonding.** The attraction between oppositely charged atoms, or ions, is an ionic bond. An ionic bond can form between any two oppositely charged ions, even if they have not been formed by transfer of an electron from one to the other.

with its single valence electron in the third electron shell. A chlorine atom has a total of 17 electrons, with 7 electrons in its valence shell. When these two atoms meet, the lone valence electron of sodium is transferred to the chlorine atom, and both atoms end up with their valence shells complete. (Because sodium no longer has an electron in the third shell, the second shell is now the valence shell.)

The electron transfer between the two atoms moves one unit of negative charge from sodium to chlorine. Sodium, now with 11 protons but only 10 electrons, has a net electrical charge of 1+. A charged atom (or molecule) is called an **ion**. When the charge is positive, the ion is specifically called a **cation**; the sodium atom has become a cation. Conversely, the chlorine atom, having gained an extra electron, now has 17 protons and 18 electrons, giving it a net electrical charge of 1−. It has become a chloride ion—an **anion**, or negatively charged ion. Because of their opposite charges, cations and anions attract each other; this attraction is called an **ionic bond**. The transfer of an electron is not the formation of a bond; rather, it allows a bond to form because it results in two ions. Any two ions of opposite charge can form an ionic bond. The ions do not need to have acquired their charge by an electron transfer with each other.

Compounds formed by ionic bonds are called **ionic compounds**, or **salts**. We know the ionic compound sodium chloride (NaCl) as table salt **(Figure 2.15)**. Salts are often found in nature as crystals of various sizes and shapes. Each salt crystal is an aggregate of vast numbers of cations and anions bonded by their electrical attraction and arranged in a three-dimensional lattice. Unlike a covalent compound, which consists of molecules having a definite size and number of atoms, an ionic compound does not consist of molecules in the same sense. The formula for an ionic compound, such as NaCl, indicates only the ratio of elements in a crystal of the salt. "NaCl" by itself is not a molecule.

Not all salts have equal numbers of cations and anions. For example, the ionic compound magnesium chloride ($MgCl_2$) has two chloride ions for each magnesium ion. Magnesium ($_{12}Mg$) must lose 2 outer electrons if the atom is to have a complete valence shell, so it tends to become a cation with a net charge of 2+ (Mg^{2+}). One magnesium cation can therefore form ionic bonds with two chloride anions.

The term *ion* also applies to entire molecules that are electrically charged. In the salt ammonium chloride (NH_4Cl), for instance, the anion is a single chloride ion (Cl^-), but the cation is ammonium (NH_4^+), a nitrogen atom with four covalently bonded hydrogen atoms. The whole ammonium ion has an electrical charge of 1+ because it is 1 electron short.

Environment affects the strength of ionic bonds. In a dry salt crystal, the bonds are so strong that it takes a hammer and chisel to break enough of them to crack the crystal in two. If the same salt crystal is dissolved in water, however, the ionic bonds are much weaker because each ion is partially shielded by its interactions with water molecules. Most drugs are manufactured as salts because they are quite stable when dry but can dissociate easily in water. In the next chapter, you will learn how water dissolves salts.

Weak Chemical Bonds

In organisms, most of the strongest chemical bonds are covalent bonds, which link atoms to form a cell's molecules. But weaker bonding within and between molecules is also indispensable in the cell, contributing greatly to the emergent properties of life. Most important large biological molecules are held in their functional form by weak bonds. In addition, when two molecules in the cell make contact, they may adhere temporarily by weak bonds. The reversibility of weak bonding can be an advantage: Two molecules can come together, respond to one another in some way, and then separate.

Certain types of weak chemical bonds are important in organisms. One is the ionic bond as it exists between ions dissociated in water, which we just discussed. Another type of weak bond, known as a hydrogen bond, is also crucial to life.

Hydrogen Bonds

Among the various kinds of weak chemical bonds, hydrogen bonds are so important in the chemistry of life that they deserve special attention. A **hydrogen bond** forms when a hydrogen atom covalently bonded to one electronegative atom is also attracted to another electronegative atom. In living cells, the electronegative partners are usually oxygen or nitrogen atoms. Refer to **Figure 2.16** to examine the simple case of hydrogen bonding between water (H_2O) and ammonia (NH_3). In the next chapter, we'll see how the hydrogen bonds between water molecules allow some insects to walk on water.

Van der Waals Interactions

Even a molecule with nonpolar covalent bonds may have positively and negatively charged regions. Electrons are not always symmetrically distributed in such a molecule; at any

▲ **Figure 2.15 A sodium chloride crystal.** The sodium ions (Na^+) and chloride ions (Cl^-) are held together by ionic bonds. The formula NaCl tells us that the ratio of Na^+ to Cl^- is 1:1.

— Na$^+$
— Cl$^-$

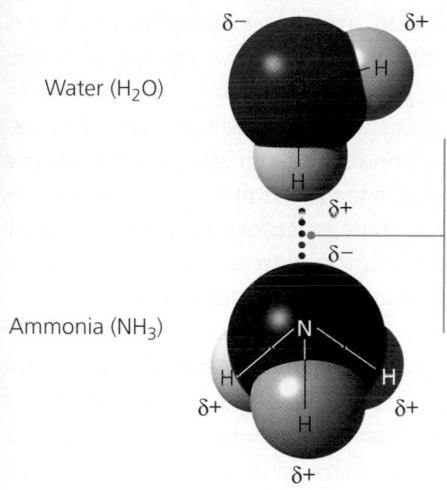

Water (H₂O)

Ammonia (NH₃)

A hydrogen bond results from the attraction between the partial positive charge on the hydrogen atom of water and the partial negative charge on the nitrogen atom of ammonia.

▲ **Figure 2.16 A hydrogen bond.**

DRAW IT *Draw five water molecules using structural formulas and indicating partial charges, and show how they can make hydrogen bonds with each other.*

instant, they may accumulate by chance in one part of the molecule or another. The results are ever-changing regions of positive and negative charge that enable all atoms and molecules to stick to one another. These **van der Waals interactions** are weak and occur only when atoms and molecules are very close together. In spite of their weakness, van der Waals interactions were recently shown to be responsible for the ability of a gecko lizard (left) to walk up a wall. Each gecko toe has hundreds of thousands of tiny hairs, with multiple projections at the hair's tip that increase surface area. Apparently, the van der Waals interactions between the hair tip molecules and the molecules of the wall's surface are so numerous that despite their individual weakness, together they can support the gecko's body weight.

Van der Waals interactions, hydrogen bonds, ionic bonds in water, and other weak bonds may form not only between molecules but also between different regions of a single large molecule, such as a protein. Although these bonds are individually weak, their cumulative effect is to reinforce the three-dimensional shape of a large molecule. You will learn more about the very important biological roles of weak bonds in Chapter 5.

Molecular Shape and Function

A molecule has a characteristic size and shape. The precise shape of a molecule is usually very important to its function in the living cell.

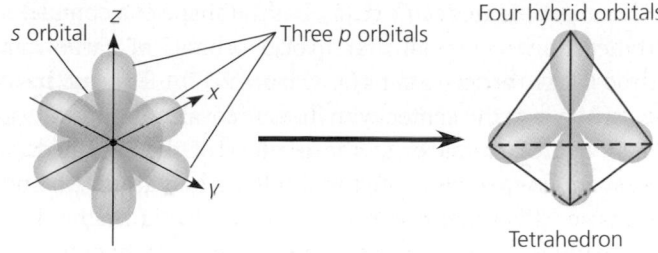

(a) Hybridization of orbitals. The single *s* and three *p* orbitals of a valence shell involved in covalent bonding combine to form four teardrop-shaped hybrid orbitals. These orbitals extend to the four corners of an imaginary tetrahedron (outlined in red).

Space-filling Model	Ball-and-stick Model	Hybrid-orbital Model (with ball-and-stick model superimposed)

Water (H₂O)

104.5°

Unbonded electron pair

Methane (CH₄)

(b) Molecular-shape models. Three models representing molecular shape are shown for water and methane. The positions of the hybrid orbitals determine the shapes of the molecules.

▲ **Figure 2.17 Molecular shapes due to hybrid orbitals.**

A molecule consisting of two atoms, such as H_2 or O_2, is always linear, but molecules with more than two atoms have more complicated shapes. These shapes are determined by the positions of the atoms' orbitals. When an atom forms covalent bonds, the orbitals in its valence shell rearrange. For atoms with valence electrons in both *s* and *p* orbitals (review Figure 2.10), the single *s* and three *p* orbitals hybridize to form four new hybrid orbitals shaped like identical teardrops extending from the region of the atomic nucleus **(Figure 2.17a)**. If we connect the larger ends of the teardrops with lines, we have the outline of a geometric shape called a tetrahedron, similar to a pyramid.

For the water molecule (H_2O), two of the hybrid orbitals in the oxygen atom's valence shell are shared with hydrogen atoms **(Figure 2.17b)**. The result is a molecule shaped roughly like a V, with its two covalent bonds spread apart at an angle of 104.5°.

The methane molecule (CH_4) has the shape of a completed tetrahedron because all four hybrid orbitals of carbon are shared with hydrogen atoms (see Figure 2.17b). The nucleus of the carbon is at the center, with its four covalent bonds radiating to hydrogen nuclei at the corners of the tetrahedron. Larger molecules containing multiple carbon atoms, including many of the molecules that make up living matter, have more complex overall shapes. However, the tetrahedral shape of a carbon atom bonded to four other atoms is often a repeating motif within such molecules.

Molecular shape is crucial in biology because it determines how biological molecules recognize and respond to one another with specificity. Only molecules with complementary shapes can form weak bonds with each other. We can see this specificity in the effects of opiates, drugs derived from opium. Opium's narcotic effects have been known since ancient times. During the 1800s, morphine was isolated from opium,

and heroin was synthesized from morphine. These opiates relieve pain and alter mood by binding to specific receptor molecules on the surface of brain cells. Why would brain cells carry receptors for opiates, compounds not made by our bodies? The discovery of endorphins in 1975 answered this question. Endorphins are signaling molecules made by the pituitary gland that bind to the receptors, relieving pain and producing euphoria during times of stress, such as intense exercise. It turns out that opiates have shapes similar to endorphins and mimic them by binding to endorphin receptors in the brain. That is why opiates and endorphins have similar effects **(Figure 2.18)**. The role of molecular shape in brain chemistry illustrates the relationship between structure and function, one of biology's unifying themes.

CONCEPT CHECK 2.3

1. Why does the following structure fail to make sense chemically?

$$H—C≡C—H$$

2. Explain what holds together the atoms in a crystal of magnesium chloride ($MgCl_2$).

3. **WHAT IF?** If you were a pharmaceutical researcher, why would you want to learn the three-dimensional shapes of naturally occurring signaling molecules?

For suggested answers, see Appendix A.

Key

- ■ Carbon
- ■ Hydrogen
- ■ Nitrogen
- ■ Sulfur
- ■ Oxygen

Natural endorphin

Morphine

(a) Structures of endorphin and morphine. The boxed portion of the endorphin molecule (left) binds to receptor molecules on target cells in the brain. The boxed portion of the morphine molecule (right) is a close match.

Natural endorphin

Morphine

Endorphin receptors

Brain cell

(b) Binding to endorphin receptors. Both endorphin and morphine can bind to endorphin receptors on the surface of a brain cell.

▲ **Figure 2.18 A molecular mimic.** Morphine affects pain perception and emotional state by mimicking the brain's natural endorphins.

CONCEPT 2.4

Chemical reactions make and break chemical bonds

The making and breaking of chemical bonds, leading to changes in the composition of matter, are called **chemical reactions**. An example is the reaction between hydrogen and oxygen that forms water:

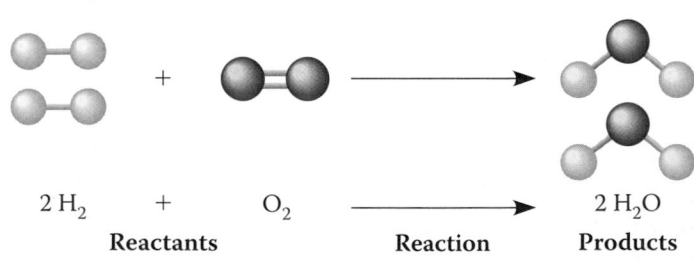

$$2\,H_2 \quad + \quad O_2 \quad \longrightarrow \quad 2\,H_2O$$

Reactants   **Reaction**   **Products**

This reaction breaks the covalent bonds of H_2 and O_2 and forms the new bonds of H_2O. When we write a chemical reaction, we use an arrow to indicate the conversion of the starting materials, called the **reactants**, to the **products**. The coefficients indicate the number of molecules involved; for example, the coefficient 2 in front of the H_2 means that the reaction starts with two molecules of hydrogen. Notice that all atoms of the reactants must be accounted for in the products. Matter is conserved in a chemical reaction: Reactions cannot create or destroy matter but can only rearrange it.

Photosynthesis, which takes place within the cells of green plant tissues, is a particularly important example of how chemical reactions rearrange matter. Humans and other animals ultimately depend on photosynthesis for food and oxygen, and this process is at the foundation of almost all ecosystems. The following chemical shorthand summarizes the process of photosynthesis:

$$6 CO_2 + 6 H_2O \longrightarrow C_6H_{12}O_6 + 6 O_2$$

The raw materials of photosynthesis are carbon dioxide (CO_2), which is taken from the air, and water (H_2O), which is absorbed from the soil. Within the plant cells, sunlight powers the conversion of these ingredients to a sugar called glucose ($C_6H_{12}O_6$) and oxygen molecules (O_2), a by-product that the plant releases into the surroundings (Figure 2.19). Although photosynthesis is actually a sequence of many chemical reactions, we still end up with the same number and kinds of atoms we had when we started. Matter has simply been rearranged, with an input of energy provided by sunlight.

All chemical reactions are reversible, with the products of the forward reaction becoming the reactants for the reverse reaction. For example, hydrogen and nitrogen molecules can combine to form ammonia, but ammonia can also decompose to regenerate hydrogen and nitrogen:

$$3 H_2 + N_2 \rightleftharpoons 2 NH_3$$

The two opposite-headed arrows indicate that the reaction is reversible.

One of the factors affecting the rate of a reaction is the concentration of reactants. The greater the concentration of reactant molecules, the more frequently they collide with one another and have an opportunity to react and form products. The same holds true for products. As products accumulate, collisions resulting in the reverse reaction become more frequent. Eventually, the forward and reverse reactions occur at the same rate, and the relative concentrations of products and reactants stop changing. The point at which the reactions offset one another exactly is called **chemical equilibrium**. This is a dynamic equilibrium; reactions are still going on, but with no net effect on the concentrations of reactants and products. Equilibrium does *not* mean that the reactants and products are equal in concentration, but only that their concentrations have stabilized at a particular ratio. The reaction involving ammonia reaches equilibrium when ammonia decomposes as rapidly as it forms. In some chemical reactions, the equilibrium point may lie so far to the right that these reactions go essentially to completion; that is, virtually all the reactants are converted to products.

We will return to the subject of chemical reactions after more detailed study of the various types of molecules that are important to life. In the next chapter, we focus on water, the substance in which all the chemical processes of organisms occur.

▲ Figure 2.19 **Photosynthesis: a solar-powered rearrangement of matter.** *Elodea*, a freshwater plant, produces sugar by rearranging the atoms of carbon dioxide and water in the chemical process known as photosynthesis, which is powered by sunlight. Much of the sugar is then converted to other food molecules. Oxygen gas (O_2) is a by-product of photosynthesis; notice the bubbles of oxygen escaping from the leaves in the photo.

? *Explain how this photo relates to the reactants and products in the equation for photosynthesis given in the above text. (You will learn more about photosynthesis in Chapter 10.)*

CONCEPT CHECK **2.4**

1. Refer to the reaction between hydrogen and oxygen that forms water, shown with ball-and-stick models on page 42. Draw the Lewis dot structures representing this reaction.
2. Which types of chemical reactions occur faster at equilibrium, the formation of products from reactants, or reactants from products?
3. **WHAT IF?** Write an equation that uses the products of photosynthesis as reactants and uses the reactants as products. Add energy as another product. This new equation describes a process that occurs in your cells. Describe this equation in words. How does this equation relate to breathing?

For suggested answers, see Appendix A.

Chapter 2 Review

MEDIA Go to www.campbellbiology.com for BioFlix 3-D Animations, MP3 Tutors, Videos, Practice Tests, an eBook, and more.

SUMMARY OF KEY CONCEPTS

CONCEPT 2.1

Matter consists of chemical elements in pure form and in combinations called compounds (pp. 31–32)

▶ **Elements and Compounds** Elements cannot be broken down chemically to other substances. A compound contains two or more different elements in a fixed ratio.

▶ **Essential Elements of Life** Carbon, oxygen, hydrogen, and nitrogen make up approximately 96% of living matter.

> **MEDIA**
>
> **Investigation** How Are Space Rocks Analyzed for Signs of Life?

CONCEPT 2.2

An element's properties depend on the structure of its atoms (pp. 32–37)

▶ **Subatomic Particles** An atom, the smallest unit of an element, has the following components:

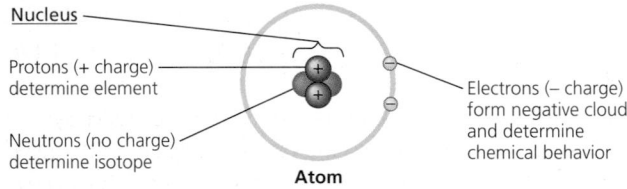

Nucleus

Protons (+ charge) determine element

Neutrons (no charge) determine isotope

Electrons (− charge) form negative cloud and determine chemical behavior

Atom

▶ **Atomic Number and Atomic Mass** An electrically neutral atom has equal numbers of electrons and protons; the number of protons determines the atomic number. The atomic mass is measured in daltons and is roughly equal to the sum of protons plus neutrons.

▶ **Isotopes** Isotopes of an element differ from each other in neutron number and therefore mass. Unstable isotopes give off particles and energy as radioactivity.

▶ **The Energy Levels of Electrons** In an atom, electrons occupy specific energy shells; the electrons in a shell have a characteristic energy level.

▶ **Electron Distribution and Chemical Properties** Electron distribution in shells determines the chemical behavior of an atom. An atom that has an incomplete valence shell is reactive.

▶ **Electron Orbitals** Electrons exist in orbitals, three-dimensional spaces with specific shapes that are components of electron shells.

> **MEDIA**
>
> **Activity** Structure of the Atomic Nucleus
> **Activity** Electron Arrangement
> **Activity** Build an Atom

CONCEPT 2.3

The formation and function of molecules depend on chemical bonding between atoms (pp. 38–42)

▶ **Covalent Bonds** Chemical bonds form when atoms interact and complete their valence shells. Covalent bonds form when pairs of electrons are shared.

$$H\cdot + H\cdot \longrightarrow H{:}H \qquad\qquad {:}\overset{..}{O}\cdot + \cdot\overset{..}{O}{:} \longrightarrow \overset{..}{O}{::}\overset{..}{O}$$

Single covalent bond   Double covalent bond

Molecules consist of two or more covalently bonded atoms. Electrons of a polar covalent bond are pulled closer to the more electronegative atom. If both atoms are the same, they have the same electronegativity, and the covalent bond is nonpolar.

▶ **Ionic Bonds**

Ionic bond

Electron transfer forms ions

Na
Sodium atom

Cl
Chlorine atom

Na⁺
Sodium ion
(a cation)

Cl⁻
Chloride ion
(an anion)

▶ **Weak Chemical Bonds** A hydrogen bond is an attraction between a hydrogen atom carrying a partial positive charge $(\delta+)$ and an electronegative atom $(\delta-)$. Van der Waals interactions occur between transiently positive and negative regions of molecules. Weak bonds reinforce the shapes of large molecules and help molecules adhere to each other.

▶ **Molecular Shape and Function** A molecule's shape is determined by the positions of its atoms' valence orbitals. Covalent bonds result in hybrid orbitals, which are responsible for the shapes of H_2O, CH_4, and many more complex biological molecules. Shape is usually the basis for the recognition of one biological molecule by another.

> **MEDIA**
>
> **Activity** Covalent Bonds
> **Activity** Nonpolar and Polar Molecules
> **Activity** Ionic Bonds
> **Activity** Hydrogen Bonds

CONCEPT 2.4

Chemical reactions make and break chemical bonds (pp. 42–43)

▶ Chemical reactions change reactants into products while conserving matter. All chemical reactions are theoretically reversible. Chemical equilibrium is reached when the forward and reverse reaction rates are equal.

SELF-QUIZ

1. In the term *trace element*, the modifier *trace* means
   a. the element is required in very small amounts.
   b. the element can be used as a label to trace atoms through an organism's metabolism.
   c. the element is very rare on Earth.
   d. the element enhances health but is not essential for the organism's long-term survival.
   e. the element passes rapidly through the organism.

2. Compared with ^{31}P, the radioactive isotope ^{32}P has
   a. a different atomic number.
   b. one more neutron.
   c. one more proton.
   d. one more electron.
   e. a different charge.

3. Atoms can be represented by simply listing the number of protons, neutrons, and electrons—for example, $2p^+$; $2n^0$; $2e^-$ for helium. Which one of the following lists represents the ^{18}O isotope of oxygen?
   a. $6p^+$; $8n^0$; $6e^-$
   b. $8p^+$; $10n^0$; $8e^-$
   c. $9p^+$; $9n^0$; $9e^-$
   d. $7p^+$; $2n^0$; $9e^-$
   e. $10p^+$; $8n^0$; $9e^-$

4. The atomic number of sulfur is 16. Sulfur combines with hydrogen by covalent bonding to form a compound, hydrogen sulfide. Based on the number of valence electrons in a sulfur atom, predict the molecular formula of the compound:
   a. HS   b. HS_2 c. H_2S d. H_3S_2 e. H_4S

5. The reactivity of an atom arises from
   a. the average distance of the outermost electron shell from the nucleus.
   b. the existence of unpaired electrons in the valence shell.
   c. the sum of the potential energies of all the electron shells.
   d. the potential energy of the valence shell.
   e. the energy difference between the *s* and *p* orbitals.

6. Which statement is true of all atoms that are anions?
   a. The atom has more electrons than protons.
   b. The atom has more protons than electrons.
   c. The atom has fewer protons than does a neutral atom of the same element.
   d. The atom has more neutrons than protons.
   e. The net charge is 1−.

7. What coefficients must be placed in the following blanks so that all atoms are accounted for in the products?

   $$C_6H_{12}O_6 \longrightarrow \underline{\quad}C_2H_6O + \underline{\quad}CO_2$$

   a. 1; 2   b. 2; 2   c. 1; 3   d. 1; 1   e. 3; 1

8. Which of the following statements correctly describes any chemical reaction that has reached equilibrium?
   a. The concentrations of products and reactants are equal.
   b. The rates of the forward and reverse reactions are equal.
   c. Both forward and reverse reactions have halted.
   d. The reaction is now irreversible.
   e. No reactants remain.

9. **DRAW IT** Draw Lewis structures for each hypothetical molecule shown below, using the correct number of valence electrons for each atom. Determine which molecule makes sense because each atom has a complete valence shell and each bond has the correct number of electrons. Explain what makes the other molecules nonsensical, considering the number of bonds each type of atom can make.

   a. O=C—H

   b.
   ```
        H   H
        |   |
   H—O—C—C=O
        |
        H
   ```

   c.
   ```
        H       H
        |       |
   H—C—H—C=O
        |
        H
   ```

   d. H—N=H   (with O double-bonded: $\overset{O}{\underset{\|}{}}$)

   For Self-Quiz answers, see Appendix A.

   MEDIA Visit **www.campbellbiology.com** for a Practice Test.

EVOLUTION CONNECTION

10. The percentages of naturally occurring elements making up the human body (see Table 2.1) are similar to the percentages of these elements found in other organisms. How could you account for this similarity among organisms?

SCIENTIFIC INQUIRY

11. Female silkworm moths (*Bombyx mori*) attract males by emitting chemical signals that spread through the air. A male hundreds of meters away can detect these molecules and fly toward their source. The sensory organs responsible for this behavior are the comblike antennae visible in the photograph here. Each filament of an antenna is equipped with thousands of receptor cells that detect the sex attractant. Based on what you learned in this chapter, propose a hypothesis to account for the ability of the male moth to detect a specific molecule in the presence of many other molecules in the air. What predictions does your hypothesis make? Design an experiment to test one of these predictions.

SCIENCE, TECHNOLOGY, AND SOCIETY

12. While waiting at an airport, Neil Campbell once overheard this claim: "It's paranoid and ignorant to worry about industry or agriculture contaminating the environment with their chemical wastes. After all, this stuff is just made of the same atoms that were already present in our environment." How would you counter this argument?

Water and the Fitness of the Environment

3

KEY CONCEPTS

3.1 **The polarity of water molecules results in hydrogen bonding**

3.2 **Four emergent properties of water contribute to Earth's fitness for life**

3.3 **Acidic and basic conditions affect living organisms**

OVERVIEW
The Molecule That Supports All of Life

As astronomers study newly discovered planets orbiting distant stars, they hope to find evidence of water on these far-off celestial bodies, for water is the substance that makes possible life as we know it here on Earth. All organisms familiar to us are made mostly of water and live in an environment dominated by water. Water is the biological medium here on Earth, and possibly on other planets as well.

Three-quarters of Earth's surface is submerged in water **(Figure 3.1)**. Although most of this water is in liquid form, water is also present on Earth as ice and vapor. Water is the only common substance to exist in the natural environment in all three physical states of matter: solid, liquid, and gas. The abundance of water is a major reason Earth is habitable. In a classic book called *The Fitness of the Environment*, ecologist Lawrence Henderson highlights the importance of water to life. While acknowledging that life adapts to its environment through natural selection, Henderson emphasizes that for life to exist at all, the environment must first be a suitable abode.

Life on Earth began in water and evolved there for 3 billion years before spreading onto land. Modern life, even terrestrial (land-dwelling) life, remains tied to water. All living organisms require water more than any other substance. Human beings, for example, can survive for quite a few weeks without food, but only a week or so without water. Molecules of water par-

▲ Figure 3.1 **Why does the abundance of water allow life to exist on the planet Earth?**

ticipate in many chemical reactions necessary to sustain life. Most cells are surrounded by water, and cells themselves are about 70–95% water.

What properties of the simple water molecule allow it to function as a support to all living organisms? In this chapter, you will learn how the structure of a water molecule allows it to interact with other molecules, including other water molecules. This ability leads to unique emergent properties that support and maintain living systems on our planet. Your objective in this chapter is to develop a conceptual understanding of how water contributes to the fitness of Earth for life.

CONCEPT 3.1
The polarity of water molecules results in hydrogen bonding

Water is so common that it is easy to overlook the fact that it is an exceptional substance with many extraordinary qualities. Following the theme of emergent properties, we can trace water's unique behavior to the structure and interactions of its molecules.

Studied in isolation, the water molecule is deceptively simple. It is shaped something like a wide V, with its two hydrogen atoms joined to the oxygen atom by single covalent bonds. Because oxygen is more electronegative than hydrogen, the electrons of the covalent bonds spend more time closer to oxygen than to hydrogen; in other words, they are polar covalent bonds (see Figure 2.13). This unequal distribution of electrons makes water a **polar molecule**, meaning that the two ends of the molecule have opposite charges: The oxygen region of the molecule has a partial negative charge ($\delta-$), and the hydrogens have a partial positive charge ($\delta+$).

The anomalous properties of water arise from attractions between its polar molecules: The slightly positive hydrogen of

▲ **Figure 3.2 Hydrogen bonds between water molecules.** The charged regions of a polar water molecule are attracted to oppositely charged parts of neighboring molecules. Each molecule can hydrogen-bond to multiple partners, and these associations are constantly changing.

one molecule is attracted to the slightly negative oxygen of a nearby molecule. The two molecules are thus held together by a hydrogen bond **(Figure 3.2)**. When water is in its liquid form, its hydrogen bonds are very fragile, each about $\frac{1}{20}$ as strong as a covalent bond. The hydrogen bonds form, break, and re-form with great frequency. Each lasts only a few trillionths of a second, but the molecules are constantly forming new hydrogen bonds with a succession of partners. Therefore, at any instant, a substantial percentage of all the water molecules are hydrogen-bonded to their neighbors. The extraordinary qualities of water are emergent properties resulting from the hydrogen bonding that orders molecules into a higher level of structural organization.

Four emergent properties of water contribute to Earth's fitness for life

We will examine four emergent properties of water that contribute to Earth's suitability as an environment for life: cohesive behavior, ability to moderate temperature, expansion upon freezing, and versatility as a solvent.

Cohesion

Water molecules stay close to each other as a result of hydrogen bonding. Although the arrangement of molecules in a sample of liquid water is constantly changing, at any given moment many of the molecules are linked by multiple hydrogen bonds. These linkages make water more structured than most other liquids. Collectively, the hydrogen bonds hold the substance together, a phenomenon called **cohesion**.

Cohesion due to hydrogen bonding contributes to the transport of water and dissolved nutrients against gravity in plants **(Figure 3.3)**. Water from the roots reaches the leaves through a network of water-conducting cells. As water evaporates from a leaf, hydrogen bonds cause water molecules leaving the veins to tug on molecules farther down, and the upward pull is transmitted through the water-conducting cells all the way to the roots. **Adhesion**, the clinging of one substance to

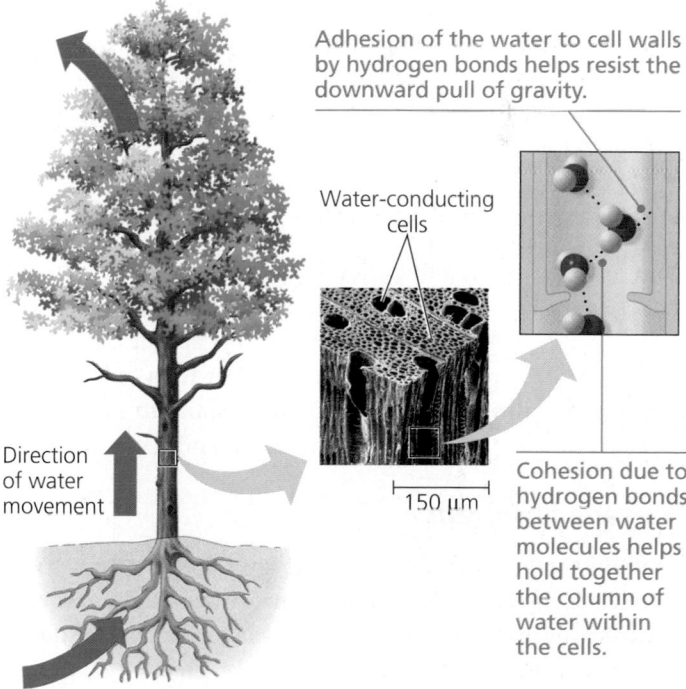

Adhesion of the water to cell walls by hydrogen bonds helps resist the downward pull of gravity.

Water-conducting cells

Direction of water movement

150 μm

Cohesion due to hydrogen bonds between water molecules helps hold together the column of water within the cells.

▲ **Figure 3.3 Water transport in plants.** Evaporation from leaves pulls water upward from the roots through water-conducting cells. Because of the properties of cohesion and adhesion, the tallest trees can transport water more than 100 m upward—approximately one-quarter the height of the Empire State Building in New York City.

▲ **Figure 3.4 Walking on water.** The high surface tension of water, resulting from the collective strength of its hydrogen bonds, allows the water strider to walk on the surface of a pond.

another, also plays a role. Adhesion of water to cell walls by hydrogen bonds helps counter the downward pull of gravity (see Figure 3.3).

Related to cohesion is **surface tension**, a measure of how difficult it is to stretch or break the surface of a liquid. Water has a greater surface tension than most other liquids. At the interface between water and air is an ordered arrangement of water molecules, hydrogen-bonded to one another and to the water below. This makes the water behave as though coated with an invisible film. You can observe the surface tension of water by slightly overfilling a drinking glass; the water will stand above the rim. In a more biological example, some animals can stand, walk, or run on water without breaking the surface **(Figure 3.4)**.

Moderation of Temperature

Water moderates air temperature by absorbing heat from air that is warmer and releasing the stored heat to air that is cooler. Water is effective as a heat bank because it can absorb or release a relatively large amount of heat with only a slight change in its own temperature. To understand this capability of water, we must first look briefly at heat and temperature.

Heat and Temperature

Anything that moves has **kinetic energy**, the energy of motion. Atoms and molecules have kinetic energy because they are always moving, although not necessarily in any particular direction. The faster a molecule moves, the greater its kinetic energy. **Heat** is a form of energy. For a given body of matter, the amount of heat is a measure of the matter's *total* kinetic energy due to motion of its molecules; thus, heat depends in part on the matter's volume. Although heat is related to temperature,

they are not the same thing. **Temperature** is a measure of heat intensity that represents the *average* kinetic energy of the molecules, regardless of volume. When water is heated in a coffeemaker, the average speed of the molecules increases, and the thermometer records this as a rise in temperature of the liquid. The amount of heat also increases in this case. Note, however, that although the pot of coffee has a much higher temperature than, say, the water in a swimming pool, the swimming pool contains more heat because of its much greater volume.

Whenever two objects of different temperature are brought together, heat passes from the warmer to the cooler object until the two are the same temperature. Molecules in the cooler object speed up at the expense of the kinetic energy of the warmer object. An ice cube cools a drink not by adding coldness to the liquid, but by absorbing heat from the liquid as the ice itself melts.

Throughout this book, we will use the **Celsius scale** to indicate temperature (Celsius degrees are abbreviated °C). At sea level, water freezes at 0°C and boils at 100°C. The temperature of the human body averages 37°C, and comfortable room temperature is about 20–25°C.

One convenient unit of heat used in this book is the **calorie (cal)**. A calorie is the amount of heat it takes to raise the temperature of 1 g of water by 1°C. Conversely, a calorie is also the amount of heat that 1 g of water releases when it cools by 1°C. A **kilocalorie (kcal)**, 1,000 cal, is the quantity of heat required to raise the temperature of 1 kilogram (kg) of water by 1°C. (The "calories" on food packages are actually kilocalories.) Another energy unit used in this book is the **joule (J)**. One joule equals 0.239 cal; one calorie equals 4.184 J.

Water's High Specific Heat

The ability of water to stabilize temperature stems from its relatively high specific heat. The **specific heat** of a substance is defined as the amount of heat that must be absorbed or lost for 1 g of that substance to change its temperature by 1°C. We already know water's specific heat because we have defined a calorie as the amount of heat that causes 1 g of water to change its temperature by 1°C. Therefore, the specific heat of water is 1 calorie per gram per degree Celsius, abbreviated as 1 cal/g/°C. Compared with most other substances, water has an unusually high specific heat. For example, ethyl alcohol, the type of alcohol in alcoholic beverages, has a specific heat of 0.6 cal/g/°C; that is, only 0.6 cal is required to raise the temperature of 1 g of ethyl alcohol 1°C.

Because of the high specific heat of water relative to other materials, water will change its temperature less when it absorbs or loses a given amount of heat. The reason you can burn your fingers by touching the side of a metal pot on the stove when the water in the pot is still lukewarm is that the specific heat of water is ten times greater than that of iron. In other words, the same amount of heat will raise the temperature of

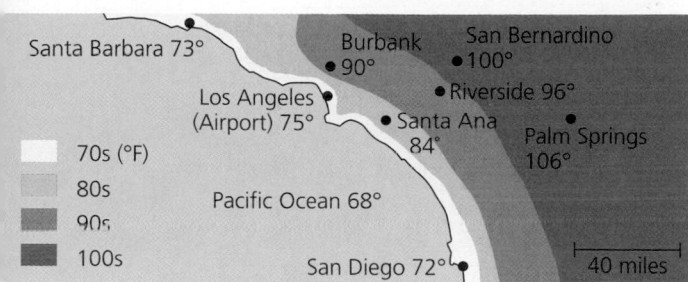

▲ Figure 3.5 Effect of a large body of water on climate. By absorbing or releasing heat, oceans moderate coastal climates. In this example from an August day in Southern California, the relatively cool ocean reduces coastal air temperatures by absorbing heat.

1 g of the iron much faster than the temperature of 1 g of the water. Specific heat can be thought of as a measure of how well a substance resists changing its temperature when it absorbs or releases heat. Water resists changing its temperature; when it does change its temperature, it absorbs or loses a relatively large quantity of heat for each degree of change.

We can trace water's high specific heat, like many of its other properties, to hydrogen bonding. Heat must be absorbed in order to break hydrogen bonds, and heat is released when hydrogen bonds form. A calorie of heat causes a relatively small change in the temperature of water because much of the heat is used to disrupt hydrogen bonds before the water molecules can begin moving faster. And when the temperature of water drops slightly, many additional hydrogen bonds form, releasing a considerable amount of energy in the form of heat.

What is the relevance of water's high specific heat to life on Earth? A large body of water can absorb and store a huge amount of heat from the sun in the daytime and during summer while warming up only a few degrees. And at night and during winter, the gradually cooling water can warm the air. This is the reason coastal areas generally have milder climates than inland regions (Figure 3.5). The high specific heat of water also tends to stabilize ocean temperatures, creating a favorable environment for marine life. Thus, because of its high specific heat, the water that covers most of Earth keeps temperature fluctuations on land and in water within limits that permit life. Also, because organisms are made primarily of water, they are more able to resist changes in their own temperature than if they were made of a liquid with a lower specific heat.

Evaporative Cooling

Molecules of any liquid stay close together because they are attracted to one another. Molecules moving fast enough to overcome these attractions can depart the liquid and enter the air as gas. This transformation from a liquid to a gas is called vaporization, or *evaporation*. Recall that the speed of molecular movement varies and that temperature is the *average* kinetic energy of molecules. Even at low temperatures, the speediest molecules can escape into the air. Some evaporation occurs at any temperature; a glass of water at room temperature, for example, will eventually evaporate. If a liquid is heated, the average kinetic energy of molecules increases and the liquid evaporates more rapidly.

Heat of vaporization is the quantity of heat a liquid must absorb for 1 g of it to be converted from the liquid to the gaseous state. For the same reason that water has a high specific heat, it also has a high heat of vaporization relative to most other liquids. To evaporate 1 g of water at 25°C, about 580 cal of heat is needed—nearly double the amount needed to vaporize a gram of alcohol or ammonia. Water's high heat of vaporization is another emergent property caused by hydrogen bonds, which must be broken before the molecules can make their exodus from the liquid.

The high amount of energy required to vaporize water has a wide range of effects. On a global scale, for example, it helps moderate Earth's climate. A considerable amount of solar heat absorbed by tropical seas is consumed during the evaporation of surface water. Then, as moist tropical air circulates poleward, it releases heat as it condenses and forms rain. On an organismal level, water's high heat of vaporization accounts for the severity of steam burns. These burns are caused by the heat energy released when steam condenses into liquid on the skin.

As a liquid evaporates, the surface of the liquid that remains behind cools down. This **evaporative cooling** occurs because the "hottest" molecules, those with the greatest kinetic energy, are the most likely to leave as gas. It is as if the hundred fastest runners at a college transferred to another school; the average speed of the remaining students would decline.

Evaporative cooling of water contributes to the stability of temperature in lakes and ponds and also provides a mechanism that prevents terrestrial organisms from overheating. For example, evaporation of water from the leaves of a plant helps keep the tissues in the leaves from becoming too warm in the sunlight. Evaporation of sweat from human skin dissipates body heat and helps prevent overheating on a hot day or when excess heat is generated by strenuous activity. High humidity on a hot day increases discomfort because the high concentration of water vapor in the air inhibits the evaporation of sweat from the body.

Insulation of Bodies of Water by Floating Ice

Water is one of the few substances that are less dense as a solid than as a liquid. In other words, ice floats in liquid water. While other materials contract when they solidify, water expands. The cause of this exotic behavior is, once again, hydrogen bonding. At temperatures above 4°C, water behaves like other liquids, expanding as it warms and contracting as it cools. Water begins to freeze when its molecules are no longer moving vigorously enough to break their hydrogen bonds. As the temperature falls to 0°C, the water becomes locked into a crystalline lattice, each water molecule hydrogen-bonded to

Ice
Hydrogen bonds are stable

Liquid water
Hydrogen bonds break and re-form

▲ **Figure 3.6 Ice: crystalline structure and floating barrier.** In ice, each molecule is hydrogen-bonded to four neighbors in a three-dimensional crystal. Because the crystal is spacious, ice has fewer molecules than an equal volume of liquid water. In other words, ice is less dense than liquid water. Floating ice becomes a barrier that protects the liquid water below from the colder air. The marine organism shown here is a type of shrimp called krill; it was photographed beneath floating ice in the Antarctic Ocean.

? *If water did not form hydrogen bonds, what would happen to the shrimp's environment?*

four partners **(Figure 3.6)**. The hydrogen bonds keep the molecules at "arm's length," far enough apart to make ice about 10% less dense (10% fewer molecules for the same volume) than liquid water at 4°C. When ice absorbs enough heat for its temperature to rise above 0°C, hydrogen bonds between molecules are disrupted. As the crystal collapses, the ice melts, and molecules are free to slip closer together. Water reaches its greatest density at 4°C and then begins to expand as the molecules move faster. Keep in mind, however, that even in liquid water, many of the molecules are connected by hydrogen bonds, though only transiently: The hydrogen bonds are constantly breaking and re-forming.

The ability of ice to float because of the expansion of water as it solidifies is an important factor in the fitness of the environment. If ice sank, then eventually all ponds, lakes, and even oceans would freeze solid, making life as we know it impossible on Earth. During summer, only the upper few inches of the ocean would thaw. Instead, when a deep body of water cools, the floating ice insulates the liquid water below, preventing it from freezing and allowing life to exist under the frozen surface, as shown in the photo in Figure 3.6.

The Solvent of Life

A sugar cube placed in a glass of water will dissolve. The glass will then contain a uniform mixture of sugar and water; the concentration of dissolved sugar will be the same everywhere in the mixture. A liquid that is a completely homogeneous mixture of two or more substances is called a **solution**. The dissolving agent of a solution is the **solvent**, and the substance that is dissolved is the **solute**. In this case, water is the solvent and sugar is the solute. An **aqueous solution** is one in which water is the solvent.

The medieval alchemists tried to find a universal solvent, one that would dissolve anything. They learned that nothing works better than water. However, water is not a universal solvent; if it were, it would dissolve any container in which it was stored, including our cells. But water is a very versatile solvent, a quality we can trace to the polarity of the water molecule.

Suppose, for example, that a spoonful of table salt, the ionic compound sodium chloride (NaCl), is placed in water **(Figure 3.7)**. At the surface of each grain, or crystal, of salt, the sodium and chloride ions are exposed to the solvent. These ions and the water molecules have a mutual affinity owing to the attraction between opposite charges. The oxygen

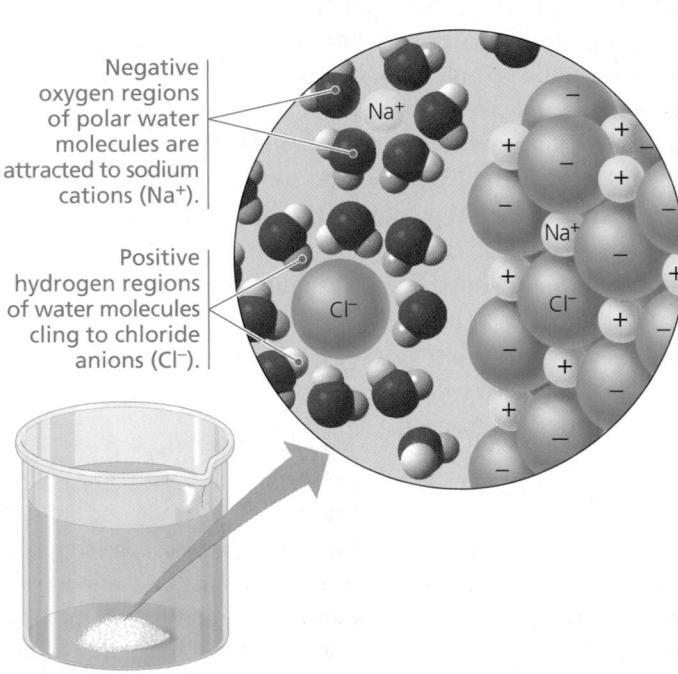

Negative oxygen regions of polar water molecules are attracted to sodium cations (Na^+).

Positive hydrogen regions of water molecules cling to chloride anions (Cl^-).

▲ **Figure 3.7 Table salt dissolving in water.** A sphere of water molecules, called a hydration shell, surrounds each solute ion.

? *What would happen if you heated this solution for a long time?*

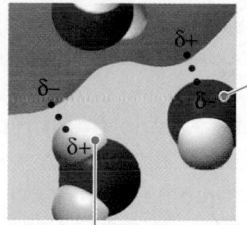

This oxygen is attracted to a slight positive charge on the lysozyme molecule.

This hydrogen is attracted to a slight negative charge on the lysozyme molecule.

(a) Lysozyme molecule in a nonaqueous environment

(b) Lysozyme molecule (purple) in an aqueous environment such as tears or saliva

(c) Ionic and polar regions on the protein's surface attract water molecules.

▲ **Figure 3.8 A water-soluble protein.** This figure shows human lysozyme, a protein found in tears and saliva that has antibacterial action.

regions of the water molecules are negatively charged and cling to sodium cations. The hydrogen regions are positively charged and are attracted to chloride anions. As a result, water molecules surround the individual sodium and chloride ions, separating and shielding them from one another. The sphere of water molecules around each dissolved ion is called a **hydration shell**. Working inward from the surface of each salt crystal, water eventually dissolves all the ions. The result is a solution of two solutes, sodium cations and chloride anions, homogeneously mixed with water, the solvent. Other ionic compounds also dissolve in water. Seawater, for instance, contains a great variety of dissolved ions, as do living cells.

A compound does not need to be ionic to dissolve in water; many compounds made up of nonionic polar molecules, such as sugars, are also water-soluble. Such compounds dissolve when water molecules surround each of the solute molecules, forming hydrogen bonds with them. Even molecules as large as proteins can dissolve in water if they have ionic and polar regions on their surface **(Figure 3.8)**. Many different kinds of polar compounds are dissolved (along with ions) in the water of such biological fluids as blood, the sap of plants, and the liquid within all cells. Water is the solvent of life.

Hydrophilic and Hydrophobic Substances

Any substance that has an affinity for water is said to be **hydrophilic** (from the Greek *hydro*, water, and *philios*, loving). In some cases, substances can be hydrophilic without actually dissolving. For example, some molecules in cells are so large that they do not dissolve. Instead, they remain suspended in the aqueous liquid of the cell. Such a mixture is an example of a **colloid**, a stable suspension of fine particles in a liquid. Another example of a hydrophilic substance that does not dissolve is cotton, a plant product. Cotton consists of giant molecules of cellulose, a compound with numerous

regions of partial positive and partial negative charges that can form hydrogen bonds with water. Water adheres to the cellulose fibers. Thus, a cotton towel does a great job of drying the body, yet does not dissolve in the washing machine. Cellulose is also present in the walls of water-conducting cells in a plant; you read earlier how the adhesion of water to these hydrophilic walls allows water transport to occur.

There are, of course, substances that do not have an affinity for water. Substances that are nonionic and nonpolar (or for some other reason cannot form hydrogen bonds) actually seem to repel water; these substances are said to be **hydrophobic** (from the Greek *phobos*, fearing). An example from the kitchen is vegetable oil, which, as you know, does not mix stably with water-based substances such as vinegar. The hydrophobic behavior of the oil molecules results from a prevalence of relatively nonpolar bonds, in this case bonds between carbon and hydrogen, which share electrons almost equally. Hydrophobic molecules related to oils are major ingredients of cell membranes. (Imagine what would happen to a cell if its membrane dissolved!)

Solute Concentration in Aqueous Solutions

Biological chemistry is "wet" chemistry. Most of the chemical reactions in organisms involve solutes dissolved in water. To understand such reactions, we must know how many atoms and molecules are involved and be able to calculate the concentration of solutes in an aqueous solution (the number of solute molecules in a volume of solution).

When carrying out experiments, we use mass to calculate the number of molecules. We know the mass of each atom in a given molecule, so we can calculate its **molecular mass**, which is simply the sum of the masses of all the atoms in a molecule. As an example, let's calculate the molecular mass of table sugar (sucrose), which has the molecular formula

$C_{12}H_{22}O_{11}$. In round numbers of daltons, the mass of a carbon atom is 12, the mass of a hydrogen atom is 1, and the mass of an oxygen atom is 16. Thus, sucrose has a molecular mass of 342 daltons. Of course, weighing out small numbers of molecules is not practical. For this reason, we usually measure substances in units called moles. Just as a dozen always means 12 objects, a **mole (mol)** represents an exact number of objects—6.02×10^{23}, which is called Avogadro's number. Because of the way in which Avogadro's number and the unit *dalton* were originally defined, there are 6.02×10^{23} daltons in 1 g. This is significant because once we determine the molecular mass of a molecule such as sucrose, we can use the same number (342), but with the unit *gram*, to represent the mass of 6.02×10^{23} molecules of sucrose, or 1 mol of sucrose (this is sometimes called the *molar mass*). To obtain 1 mol of sucrose in the lab, therefore, we weigh out 342 g.

The practical advantage of measuring a quantity of chemicals in moles is that a mole of one substance has exactly the same number of molecules as a mole of any other substance. If the molecular mass of substance A is 342 daltons and that of substance B is 10 daltons, then 342 g of A will have the same number of molecules as 10 g of B. A mole of ethyl alcohol (C_2H_6O) also contains 6.02×10^{23} molecules, but its mass is only 46 g because the mass of a molecule of ethyl alcohol is less than that of a molecule of sucrose. Measuring in moles makes it convenient for scientists working in the laboratory to combine substances in fixed ratios of molecules.

How would we make a liter (L) of solution consisting of 1 mol of sucrose dissolved in water? We would measure out 342 g of sucrose and then gradually add water, while stirring, until the sugar was completely dissolved. We would then add enough water to bring the total volume of the solution up to 1 L. At that point, we would have a 1-molar ($1 M$) solution of sucrose. **Molarity**—the number of moles of solute per liter of solution—is the unit of concentration most often used by biologists for aqueous solutions.

CONCEPT CHECK 3.2

1. Describe how properties of water contribute to the upward movement of water in a tree.
2. Explain the saying "It's not the heat; it's the humidity."
3. How can the freezing of water crack boulders?
4. If you were a pharmacist, how would you make a 0.5-molar ($0.5 M$) solution of sodium chloride (NaCl)? (The atomic mass of Na is 23 daltons and that of Cl is 35.5 daltons.)
5. **WHAT IF?** A water strider's legs (see Figure 3.4) are coated with a hydrophobic substance. What might be the benefit? What would happen if the substance were hydrophilic?

For suggested answers, see Appendix A.

CONCEPT 3.3
Acidic and basic conditions affect living organisms

Occasionally, a hydrogen atom participating in a hydrogen bond between two water molecules shifts from one molecule to the other. When this happens, the hydrogen atom leaves its electron behind, and what is actually transferred is a **hydrogen ion** (H^+), a single proton with a charge of $1+$. The water molecule that lost a proton is now a **hydroxide ion** (OH^-), which has a charge of $1-$. The proton binds to the other water molecule, making that molecule a **hydronium ion** (H_3O^+). We can picture the chemical reaction this way:

2H_2O Hydronium ion (H_3O^+)   Hydroxide ion (OH^-)

By convention, H^+ (the hydrogen ion) is used to represent H_3O^+ (the hydronium ion), and we follow that practice here. Keep in mind, though, that H^+ does not exist on its own in an aqueous solution. It is always associated with another water molecule in the form of H_3O^+.

As indicated by the double arrows, this is a reversible reaction that reaches a state of dynamic equilibrium when water molecules dissociate at the same rate that they are being re-formed from H^+ and OH^-. At this equilibrium point, the concentration of water molecules greatly exceeds the concentrations of H^+ and OH^-. In pure water, only one water molecule in every 554 million is dissociated. The concentration of each ion in pure water is $10^{-7} M$ (at 25°C). This means there is only one ten-millionth of a mole of hydrogen ions per liter of pure water and an equal number of hydroxide ions.

Although the dissociation of water is reversible and statistically rare, it is exceedingly important in the chemistry of life. H^+ and OH^- are very reactive. Changes in their concentrations can drastically affect a cell's proteins and other complex molecules. As we have seen, the concentrations of H^+ and OH^- are equal in pure water, but adding certain kinds of solutes, called acids and bases, disrupts this balance. Biologists use something called the pH scale to describe how acidic or basic (the opposite of acidic) a solution is. In the remainder of this chapter, you will learn about acids, bases, and pH and why changes in pH can adversely affect organisms.

Effects of Changes in pH

Before discussing the pH scale, let's see what acids and bases are and how they interact with water.

Acids and Bases

What would cause an aqueous solution to have an imbalance in H^+ and OH^- concentrations? When acids dissolve in water, they donate additional H^+ to the solution. An **acid** is a substance that increases the hydrogen ion concentration of a solution. For example, when hydrochloric acid (HCl) is added to water, hydrogen ions dissociate from chloride ions:

$$HCl \longrightarrow H^+ + Cl^-$$

This source of H^+ (dissociation of water is the other source) results in an acidic solution—one having more H^+ than OH^-.

A substance that reduces the hydrogen ion concentration of a solution is called a **base**. Some bases reduce the H^+ concentration directly by accepting hydrogen ions. Ammonia (NH_3), for instance, acts as a base when the unshared electron pair in nitrogen's valence shell attracts a hydrogen ion from the solution, resulting in an ammonium ion (NH_4^+):

$$NH_3 + H^+ \rightleftharpoons NH_4^+$$

Other bases reduce the H^+ concentration indirectly by dissociating to form hydroxide ions, which combine with hydrogen ions and form water. One such base is sodium hydroxide (NaOH), which in water dissociates into its ions:

$$NaOH \longrightarrow Na^+ + OH^-$$

In either case, the base reduces the H^+ concentration. Solutions with a higher concentration of OH^- than H^+ are known as basic solutions. A solution in which the H^+ and OH^- concentrations are equal is said to be neutral.

Notice that single arrows were used in the reactions for HCl and NaOH. These compounds dissociate completely when mixed with water, and so hydrochloric acid is called a strong acid and sodium hydroxide a strong base. In contrast, ammonia is a relatively weak base. The double arrows in the reaction for ammonia indicate that the binding and release of hydrogen ions are reversible reactions, although at equilibrium there will be a fixed ratio of NH_4^+ to NH_3.

There are also weak acids, which reversibly release and accept back hydrogen ions. An example is carbonic acid:

$$\underset{\substack{\text{Carbonic} \\ \text{acid}}}{H_2CO_3} \rightleftharpoons \underset{\substack{\text{Bicarbonate} \\ \text{ion}}}{HCO_3^-} + \underset{\substack{\text{Hydrogen} \\ \text{ion}}}{H^+}$$

Here the equilibrium so favors the reaction in the left direction that when carbonic acid is added to water, only 1% of the molecules are dissociated at any particular time. Still, that is enough to shift the balance of H^+ and OH^- from neutrality.

The pH Scale

In any aqueous solution at 25°C, the *product* of the H^+ and OH^- concentrations is constant at 10^{-14}. This can be written

$$[H^+][OH^-] = 10^{-14}$$

In such an equation, brackets indicate molar concentration. In a neutral solution at room temperature (25°C), $[H^+] = 10^{-7}$ and $[OH^-] = 10^{-7}$, so in this case, 10^{-14} is the product of $10^{-7} \times 10^{-7}$. If enough acid is added to a solution to increase $[H^+]$ to 10^{-5} M, then $[OH^-]$ will decline by an equivalent amount to 10^{-9} M (note that $10^{-5} \times 10^{-9} = 10^{-14}$). This constant relationship expresses the behavior of acids and bases in an aqueous solution. An acid not only adds hydrogen ions to a solution, but also removes hydroxide ions because of the tendency for H^+ to combine with OH^-, forming water. A base has the opposite effect, increasing OH^- concentration but also reducing H^+ concentration by the formation of water. If enough of a base is added to raise the OH^- concentration to 10^{-4} M, it will cause the H^+ concentration to drop to 10^{-10} M. Whenever we know the concentration of either H^+ or OH^- in an aqueous solution, we can deduce the concentration of the other ion.

Because the H^+ and OH^- concentrations of solutions can vary by a factor of 100 trillion or more, scientists have developed a way to express this variation more conveniently than in moles per liter. The pH scale (**Figure 3.9**) compresses the

▲ **Figure 3.9 The pH scale and pH values of some aqueous solutions.**

range of H^+ and OH^- concentrations by employing logarithms. The **pH** of a solution is defined as the negative logarithm (base 10) of the hydrogen ion concentration:

$$pH = -\log [H^+]$$

For a neutral aqueous solution, $[H^+]$ is $10^{-7} M$, giving us

$$-\log 10^{-7} = -(-7) = 7$$

Notice that pH *declines* as H^+ concentration *increases*. Notice, too, that although the pH scale is based on H^+ concentration, it also implies OH^- concentration. A solution of pH 10 has a hydrogen ion concentration of $10^{-10} M$ and a hydroxide ion concentration of $10^{-4} M$.

The pH of a neutral aqueous solution at 25°C is 7, the midpoint of the scale. A pH value less than 7 denotes an acidic solution; the lower the number, the more acidic the solution. The pH for basic solutions is above 7. Most biological fluids are within the range pH 6–8. There are a few exceptions, however, including the strongly acidic digestive juice of the human stomach, which has a pH of about 2.

Remember that each pH unit represents a tenfold difference in H^+ and OH^- concentrations. It is this mathematical feature that makes the pH scale so compact. A solution of pH 3 is not twice as acidic as a solution of pH 6, but a thousand times more acidic. When the pH of a solution changes slightly, the actual concentrations of H^+ and OH^- in the solution change substantially.

Buffers

The internal pH of most living cells is close to 7. Even a slight change in pH can be harmful, because the chemical processes of the cell are very sensitive to the concentrations of hydrogen and hydroxide ions.

The pH of human blood is very close to 7.4, which is slightly basic. A person cannot survive for more than a few minutes if the blood pH drops to 7 or rises to 7.8, and a chemical system exists in the blood that maintains a stable pH. If you add 0.01 mol of a strong acid to a liter of pure water, the pH drops from 7.0 to 2.0. If the same amount of acid is added to a liter of blood, however, the pH decrease is only from 7.4 to 7.3. Why does the addition of acid have so much less of an effect on the pH of blood than it does on the pH of water? The presence of substances called buffers allows for a relatively constant pH in biological fluids despite the addition of acids or bases. **Buffers** are substances that minimize changes in the concentrations of H^+ and OH^- in a solution. They do so by accepting hydrogen ions from the solution when they are in excess and donating hydrogen ions to the solution when they have been depleted. Most buffer solutions contain a weak acid and its corresponding base, which combine reversibly with hydrogen ions. There are several buffers that contribute to pH stability in human blood and many other biological solutions. One of these is carbonic

acid (H_2CO_3), formed when CO_2 reacts with water in blood plasma. As mentioned earlier, carbonic acid dissociates to yield a bicarbonate ion (HCO_3^-) and a hydrogen ion (H^+):

$$
\begin{array}{ccccc}
 & \text{Response} & & & \\
 & \text{to a rise in pH} & & & \\
H_2CO_3 & \rightleftharpoons & HCO_3^- & + & H^+ \\
H^+ \text{ donor} & \text{Response to} & H^+ \text{ acceptor} & & \text{Hydrogen} \\
\text{(acid)} & \text{a drop in pH} & \text{(base)} & & \text{ion}
\end{array}
$$

The chemical equilibrium between carbonic acid and bicarbonate acts as a pH regulator, the reaction shifting left or right as other processes in the solution add or remove hydrogen ions. If the H^+ concentration in blood begins to fall (that is, if pH rises), the reaction proceeds to the right and more carbonic acid dissociates, replenishing hydrogen ions. But when H^+ concentration in blood begins to rise (when pH drops), the reaction proceeds to the left, with HCO_3^- (the base) removing the hydrogen ions from the solution and forming H_2CO_3. Thus, the carbonic acid–bicarbonate buffering system consists of an acid and a base in equilibrium with each other. Most other buffers are also acid-base pairs.

Threats to Water Quality on Earth

Considering the dependence of all life on water, contamination of rivers, lakes, seas, and rain is a dire environmental problem. Many threats to water quality have been posed by human activities. Consider, for example, the burning of fossil fuels (coal, oil, and gas). This practice, which has been increasing since the Industrial Revolution in the 1800s, releases gaseous compounds into the atmosphere, including prodigious amounts of CO_2. The chemical reactions of these compounds with water alter the delicate balance of conditions for life on Earth by affecting water pH and temperature.

The burning of fossil fuels is a major source of sulfur oxides and nitrous oxides. These react with water in the air to form strong acids, which fall to Earth with rain or snow. **Acid precipitation** refers to rain, snow, or fog with a pH lower (more acidic) than pH 5.2. (Uncontaminated rain has a pH of about 5.6, slightly acidic, owing to the formation of carbonic acid from carbon dioxide and water.) Electric power plants that burn coal produce more of these oxides than any other single source. Winds carry the pollutants away, and acid rain may fall hundreds of kilometers away from industrial centers. In certain sites in Pennsylvania and New York, the pH of rainfall in December 2001 averaged 4.3, about 20 times more acidic than normal rain. Acid precipitation falls on many other regions, including eastern Canada, the Cascade Mountains of the Pacific Northwest, and certain parts of Europe and Asia (**Figure 3.10**).

Acid precipitation can damage life in lakes and streams. Also, acid precipitation falling on land adversely affects soil chemistry and has taken a toll on some North American and European forests (see Figure 3.10). Nevertheless, studies indicate that the majority of North American forests are not

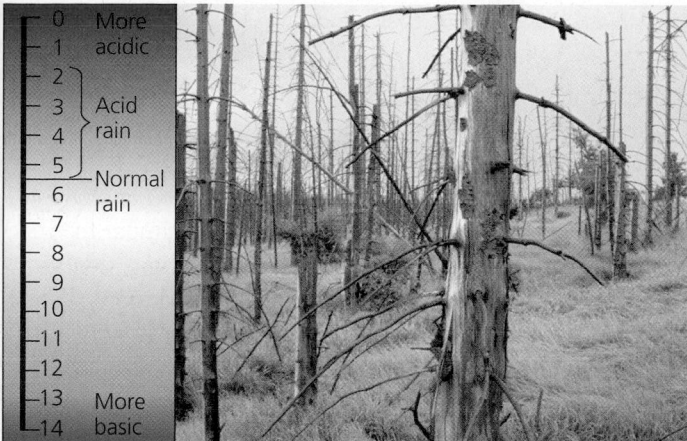

▲ Figure 3.10 Acid precipitation and its effects on a forest. Acid rain is thought to be responsible for killing trees in many forests, including the fir forest shown here in the Czech Republic.

currently suffering substantially from acid precipitation, in large part due to amendments made in 1990 to the Clean Air Act.

Carbon dioxide, the main product of fossil fuel combustion, causes other problems. Its release into the atmosphere has been increasing steadily and is expected to double by the year 2065, relative to 1880 levels. About half of the CO_2 stays in the atmosphere, acting like a reflective blanket over the planet that prevents heat from radiating into outer space. This "greenhouse" effect and the problems associated with it will be discussed in Chapter 55. A portion of the CO_2 is taken up by trees and other organisms during photosynthesis, as mentioned in Chapter 2. The remainder—about 30% or so—is absorbed by the oceans. In spite of the huge volume of water in the oceans, scientists worry that this absorption of so much CO_2 will harm marine life and ecosystems.

When CO_2 dissolves in seawater, it reacts with water (H_2O) to form carbonic acid (H_2CO_3). Almost all of the carbonic acid in turn dissociates, producing protons and a balance between two ions, bicarbonate (HCO_3^-) and carbonate (CO_3^{2-}). As seawater acidifies due to the extra protons, the balance shifts toward HCO_3^-, lowering the concentration of CO_3^{2-}. Many studies have shown that calcification, the production of calcium carbonate ($CaCO_3$) by corals and other organisms, is directly affected by the concentration of CO_3^{2-}. Any decrease in CO_3^{2-} is therefore of great concern because calcification accounts for the formation of coral reefs in our tropical seas. These sensitive ecosystems act as havens for a great diversity of organisms.

Perhaps one of the best-known and longest studies on coral reef calcification was carried out by scientists at the ecosystem center in Arizona known as Biosphere-2. The center includes an artificial coral reef system in which the temperature and chemistry of the seawater can be controlled and manipulated. Chris Langdon and colleagues used this system to test the effects of varying the concentration of CO_3^{2-} on the rate of calcification in the coral reef **(Figure 3.11)**. Together with

▼ Figure 3.11 **Inquiry**

What is the effect of carbonate ion concentration on coral reef calcification?

EXPERIMENT Chris Langdon and colleagues at Columbia University wondered how the increase in CO_2 emissions due to burning of fossil fuels and the resulting decrease in CO_3^{2-} concentration in the oceans affect coral reefs. They took advantage of the artificial coral reef system at Biosphere-2. This 2,650-cubic-meter (m^3) aquarium behaves like a natural coral reef community. For almost four years, these researchers varied the carbonate concentration in the seawater under controlled conditions and measured the rate of calcification by reef organisms.

RESULTS The calcification rate was observed to be lower at lower concentrations of carbonate ion ($[CO_3^{2-}]$).

CONCLUSION Coral reefs could be endangered by reduced $[CO_3^{2-}]$. Other studies have predicted a doubling of CO_2 emissions from 1880 to 2065 and a resulting decrease in carbonate ion concentration. Combining those predictions with the results of this study, the authors predict that by 2065 the rate of coral reef calcification may decrease by 40% relative to preindustrial levels.

SOURCE C. Langdon et al., Effect of calcium carbonate saturation state on the calcification rate of an experimental coral reef, *Global Biogeochemical Cycles* 14:639–654 (2000).

WHAT IF? The data above were for a particular concentration of calcium (Ca^{2+}). The series of experiments included measurements at two higher concentrations of Ca^{2+}. Given that the following reaction represents calcification, predict how the $[Ca^{2+}]$ would affect the results and explain why.

$$Ca^{2+} + CO_3^{2-} \longrightarrow CaCO_3$$

conclusions from other studies, their results led them to predict that the expected doubling of CO_2 emissions by the year 2065 could lead to a 40% decrease in coral reef calcification. Although scientists may not agree on the exact percentage, most concur that this and other studies provide cause for grave concern.

If there is reason for optimism about the future quality of water resources on our planet, it is that we have made progress in learning about the delicate chemical balances in oceans and other bodies of water. Continued progress can come only from the actions of people who are concerned about environmental quality. This requires understanding the crucial role that water plays in the environment's fitness for continued life on Earth.

Chapter 3 Review

SUMMARY OF KEY CONCEPTS

CONCEPT 3.1

The polarity of water molecules results in hydrogen bonding (pp. 46–47)

▶ A hydrogen bond forms when the slightly negatively charged oxygen of one water molecule is attracted to the slightly positively charged hydrogen of a nearby molecule. Hydrogen bonding between water molecules is the basis for water's unusual properties.

Hydrogen bond

MEDIA

Activity The Polarity of Water

CONCEPT 3.2

Four emergent properties of water contribute to Earth's fitness for life (pp. 47–52)

▶ **Cohesion** Hydrogen bonding keeps water molecules close to each other, and this cohesion helps pull water upward in the microscopic water-conducting cells of plants. Hydrogen bonding is also responsible for water's surface tension.

▶ **Moderation of Temperature** Water has a high specific heat: Heat is absorbed when hydrogen bonds break and is released when hydrogen bonds form. This helps keep temperatures relatively steady, within limits that permit life. Evaporative cooling is based on water's high heat of vaporization. The evaporative loss of the most energetic water molecules cools a surface.

▶ **Insulation of Bodies of Water by Floating Ice** Ice floats because it is less dense than liquid water. This allows life to exist under the frozen surfaces of lakes and polar seas.

Ice: stable hydrogen bonds **Liquid water:** transient hydrogen bonds

▶ **The Solvent of Life** Water is an unusually versatile solvent because its polar molecules are attracted to charged and polar substances capable of forming hydrogen bonds. Hydrophilic substances have an affinity for water; hydrophobic substances do not. Molarity, the number of moles of solute per liter of solution, is used as a measure of solute concentration in solutions. A mole is a certain number of molecules of a substance. The mass of a mole of the substance in grams is the same as the molecular mass in daltons.

MEDIA

MP3 Tutor The Properties of Water

Activity Cohesion of Water

CONCEPT 3.3

Acidic and basic conditions affect living organisms (pp. 52–56)

▶ A water molecule can transfer an H^+ to another water molecule to form H_3O^+ (represented simply by H^+) and OH^-.

▶ **Effects of Changes in pH** The concentration of H^+ is expressed as pH, where $pH = -\log [H^+]$. Buffers in biological fluids resist changes in pH. A buffer consists of an acid-base pair that combines reversibly with hydrogen ions.

▶ **Threats to Water Quality on Earth** The burning of fossil fuels results in emission of oxides (leading to acid precipitation) and increasing amounts of CO_2. Some CO_2 becomes dissolved in the oceans, lowering pH and potentially affecting the rate of calcification on coral reefs.

MEDIA

Activity Dissociation of Water Molecules
Activity Acids, Bases, and pH
Investigation How Does Acid Precipitation Affect Trees?

TESTING YOUR KNOWLEDGE

SELF-QUIZ

1. Many mammals control their body temperature by sweating. Which property of water is most directly responsible for the ability of sweat to lower body temperature?
   a. water's change in density when it condenses
   b. water's ability to dissolve molecules in the air
   c. the release of heat by the formation of hydrogen bonds
   d. the absorption of heat by the breaking of hydrogen bonds
   e. water's high surface tension

2. A slice of pizza has 500 kcal. If we could burn the pizza and use all the heat to warm a 50-L container of cold water, what would be the approximate increase in the temperature of the water? (*Note:* A liter of cold water weighs about 1 kg.)
   a. 50°C
   b. 5°C
   c. 10°C
   d. 100°C
   e. 1°C

3. The bonds that are broken when water vaporizes are
   a. ionic bonds.
   b. hydrogen bonds between water molecules.
   c. covalent bonds between atoms within water molecules.
   d. polar covalent bonds.
   e. nonpolar covalent bonds.

4. Which of the following is a hydrophobic material?
   a. paper
   b. table salt
   c. wax
   d. sugar
   e. pasta

5. We can be sure that a mole of table sugar and a mole of vitamin C are equal in their
   a. mass in daltons.
   b. mass in grams.
   c. number of molecules.
   d. number of atoms.
   e. volume.

6. How many grams of acetic acid ($C_2H_4O_2$) would you use to make 10 L of a 0.1 M aqueous solution of acetic acid? (*Note:* The atomic masses, in daltons, are approximately 12 for carbon, 1 for hydrogen, and 16 for oxygen.)
   a. 10.0 g
   b. 0.1 g
   c. 6.0 g
   d. 60.0 g
   e. 0.6 g

7. Measurements show that the pH of a particular lake is 4.0. What is the hydrogen ion concentration of the lake?
   a. 4.0 M
   b. $10^{-10} M$
   c. $10^{-4} M$
   d. $10^4 M$
   e. 4%

8. What is the *hydroxide* ion concentration of the lake described in question 7?
   a. $10^{-7} M$
   b. $10^{-4} M$
   c. $10^{-10} M$
   d. $10^{-14} M$
   e. 10 M

9. **DRAW IT** Draw three water molecules, using space filling models, and label the atoms. Draw solid lines to indicate covalent bonds and dotted lines for hydrogen bonds. Add partial-charge labels as appropriate.

For Self-Quiz answers, see Appendix A.

MEDIA Visit the Study Area at **www.masteringbio.com** for a Practice Test.

EVOLUTION CONNECTION

10. The surface of the planet Mars has many landscape features reminiscent of those formed by flowing water on Earth, including what appear to be meandering channels and outwash areas. In 2004, images of Meridiani Planum

Surface of Mars   Surface of Earth

on Mars taken by NASA's *Opportunity* rover suggested that liquid water was once present on its surface. For example, one image (left, above) shows polygonal fractures in the rock. Similar fracture patterns in rocks on Earth's surface (above, right) correlate with the earlier presence of water. Ice exists at the Martian poles today, and some scientists suspect a great deal more water may be present beneath the Martian surface. Why has there been so much interest in the presence of water on Mars? Does the presence of water make it more likely that life arose there? What other physical factors might also be important?

SCIENTIFIC INQUIRY

11. Design a controlled experiment to test the hypothesis that acid precipitation inhibits the growth of *Elodea*, a common freshwater plant (see Figure 2.19).

12. In agricultural areas, farmers pay close attention to the weather forecast. Right before a predicted overnight freeze, farmers spray water on crops to protect the plants. Use the properties of water to explain how this method works. Be sure to mention why hydrogen bonds are responsible for this phenomenon.

SCIENCE, TECHNOLOGY, AND SOCIETY

13. Agriculture, industry, and the growing populations of cities all compete, through political influence, for water. If you were in charge of water resources in an arid region, what would your priorities be for allocating the limited water supply for various uses? How would you try to build consensus among the different special-interest groups?

Carbon and the Molecular Diversity of Life

▲ Figure 4.1 **What properties of carbon underlie its role as the molecular basis of life?**

OVERVIEW

Carbon: The Backbone of Life

Although water is the universal medium for life on Earth, living organisms, such as the plants and trilobite beetle in **Figure 4.1**, are made up of chemicals that are based mostly on the element carbon. Carbon enters the biosphere through the action of plants, which use solar energy to transform atmospheric CO_2 into the molecules of life. These molecules are passed along to animals that feed on plants.

Of all chemical elements, carbon is unparalleled in its ability to form molecules that are large, complex, and diverse, and this molecular diversity has made possible the diversity of organisms that have evolved on Earth. Proteins, DNA, carbohydrates, and other molecules that distinguish living matter from inanimate material are all composed of carbon atoms bonded to one another and to atoms of other elements. Hydrogen (H), oxygen (O), nitrogen (N), sulfur (S), and phosphorus (P) are other common ingredients of these compounds, but it is the element carbon (C) that accounts for the large diversity of biological molecules.

Proteins and other very large molecules are the main focus of Chapter 5. Here we investigate the properties of smaller molecules. We will use these molecules to illustrate concepts of molecular architecture that will help explain why carbon is so important to life, at the same time highlighting the theme that emergent properties arise from the organization of matter in living organisms.

CONCEPT 4.1
Organic chemistry is the study of carbon compounds

For historical reasons, compounds containing carbon are said to be organic, and the branch of chemistry that specializes in the study of carbon compounds is called **organic chemistry**. Organic compounds range from simple molecules, such as methane (CH_4), to colossal ones, such as proteins, with thousands of atoms. Most organic compounds contain hydrogen atoms in addition to carbon atoms.

The overall percentages of the major elements of life—C, H, O, N, S, and P—are quite uniform from one organism to another. Because of carbon's versatility, however, this limited assortment of atomic building blocks, taken in roughly the same proportions, can be used to build an inexhaustible variety of organic molecules. Different species of organisms, and different individuals within a species, are distinguished by variations in their organic molecules.

Since the dawn of human history, people have used other organisms as sources of valued substances—from foods and medicines to fabrics. The science of organic chemistry originated in attempts to purify and improve the yield of such products. By the early 1800s, chemists had learned to make many simple compounds in the laboratory by combining elements under the right conditions. Artificial synthesis of the complex molecules extracted from living matter seemed impossible, however. At that time, the Swedish chemist Jöns Jakob Berzelius made the distinction between organic compounds, those thought to arise only in living organisms, and inorganic compounds, those found only in the nonliving world. *Vitalism*, the belief in a life force outside the jurisdiction of physical and chemical laws, provided the foundation for the new discipline of organic chemistry.

Chemists began to chip away at the foundation of vitalism when they finally learned to synthesize organic compounds in laboratories. In 1828, Friedrich Wöhler, a German chemist who had studied with Berzelius, attempted to make an "inorganic" salt, ammonium cyanate, by mixing solutions of ammonium ions (NH_4^+) and cyanate ions (CNO^-). Wöhler was astonished to find that instead he had made urea, an organic compound present in the urine of animals. Wöhler challenged the vitalists when he wrote, "I must tell you that I can prepare urea without requiring a kidney or an animal, either man or dog." However, one of the ingredients used in the synthesis, the cyanate, had been extracted from animal blood, and the vitalists were not swayed by Wöhler's discovery. A few years later, however, Hermann Kolbe, a student of Wöhler's, made the organic compound acetic acid from inorganic substances that could be prepared directly from pure elements.

Vitalism crumbled completely after several decades of laboratory synthesis of some increasingly complex organic compounds. In 1953, Stanley Miller, a graduate student of Harold Urey at the University of Chicago, helped bring this abiotic (nonliving) synthesis of organic compounds into the context of evolution in a classic experiment described in **Figure 4.2**. Miller's experiment, testing whether complex organic molecules could arise spontaneously under conditions thought to have existed on the early Earth, stimulated interest and further research on the origin of organic compounds. Some scientists have questioned whether the gases Miller used as starting materials were really present in the primitive Earth's atmosphere. Recent work supports a slightly different recipe for early Earth's conditions; when used in the experiment, it led to the compounds Miller found. Although the jury is still out, these experiments support the idea that abiotic synthesis of organic compounds could have been an early stage in the origin of life.

The pioneers of organic chemistry helped shift the mainstream of biological thought from vitalism to *mechanism*, the view that physical and chemical laws govern all natural phenomena, including the processes of life. Organic chemistry was redefined as the study of carbon compounds, regardless of origin. Organisms produce most of the naturally occurring organic compounds, and these molecules represent a diversity and range of complexity unrivaled by inorganic compounds. However, the rules of chemistry apply to all molecules. The foundation of organic chemistry is not some intangible life force, but the unique chemical versatility of the element carbon.

<hr/>

CONCEPT CHECK **4.1**

1. What conclusion did Stanley Miller draw when he found amino acids in the products of his experiment?
2. **WHAT IF?** When Miller tried the experiment in Figure 4.2 without the electrical discharge, no organic compounds were found. What might explain this result?

For suggested answers, see Appendix A.

▼ Figure 4.2 **Inquiry**

Can organic molecules form under conditions believed to simulate those on the early Earth?

EXPERIMENT In 1953, Stanley Miller set up a closed system to simulate conditions thought to have existed on the early Earth. A flask of water simulated the primeval sea. The water was heated so that some vaporized and moved into a second, higher flask containing the "atmosphere"—a mixture of gases. Sparks were discharged in the synthetic atmosphere to mimic lightning.

2 The "atmosphere" contained a mixture of hydrogen gas (H_2), methane (CH_4), ammonia (NH_3), and water vapor.

3 Sparks were discharged to mimic lightning.

"Atmosphere"

CH_4

Water vapor →

1 The water mixture in the "sea" flask was heated; vapor entered the "atmosphere" flask.

Electrode

NH_3 H_2

Condenser

Cooled water containing organic molecules

Cold water

H_2O "sea"

Sample for chemical analysis

5 As material cycled through the apparatus, Miller periodically collected samples for analysis.

4 A condenser cooled the atmosphere, raining water and any dissolved molecules down into the sea flask.

RESULTS Miller identified a variety of organic molecules that are common in organisms. These included simple compounds such as formaldehyde (CH_2O) and hydrogen cyanide (HCN) and more complex molecules such as amino acids and long chains of carbon and hydrogen known as hydrocarbons.

CONCLUSION Organic molecules, a first step in the origin of life, may have been synthesized abiotically on the early Earth. (We will explore this hypothesis in more detail in Chapter 25.)

SOURCE S. Miller, A production of amino acids under possible primitive Earth conditions, *Science* 117:528–529 (1953).

WHAT IF? If Miller had increased the concentration of NH_3 in his experiment, how might the relative amounts of the products HCN and CH_2O have differed?

CONCEPT 4.2

Carbon atoms can form diverse molecules by bonding to four other atoms

The key to an atom's chemical characteristics is its electron configuration. This configuration determines the kinds and number of bonds an atom will form with other atoms.

The Formation of Bonds with Carbon

Carbon has 6 electrons, with 2 in the first electron shell and 4 in the second shell. Having 4 valence electrons in a shell that holds 8, carbon would have to donate or accept 4 electrons to complete its valence shell and become an ion. Instead, a carbon atom usually completes its valence shell by sharing its 4 electrons with other atoms in covalent bonds so that 8 electrons are present. These bonds may include single and double covalent bonds. Each carbon atom thus acts as an intersection point from which a molecule can branch off in as many as four directions. This *tetravalence* is one facet of carbon's versatility that makes large, complex molecules possible.

When a carbon atom forms four single covalent bonds, the arrangement of its four hybrid orbitals causes the bonds to angle toward the corners of an imaginary tetrahedron (see Figure 2.17b). The bond angles in methane (CH_4) are 109.5° **(Figure 4.3a)**, and they are roughly the same in any group of atoms where carbon has four single bonds. For example, ethane (C_2H_6) is shaped like two overlapping tetrahedrons

(Figure 4.3b). In molecules with more carbons, every grouping of a carbon bonded to four other atoms has a tetrahedral shape. But when two carbon atoms are joined by a double bond, all bonds around those carbons are in the same plane. For example, ethene (C_2H_4) is a flat molecule; its atoms all lie in the same plane **(Figure 4.3c)**. We find it convenient to write all structural formulas as though the molecules represented were flat, but keep in mind that molecules are three-dimensional and that the shape of a molecule often determines its function.

The electron configuration of carbon gives it covalent compatibility with many different elements. **Figure 4.4** shows the valences of carbon and its most frequent partners—oxygen, hydrogen, and nitrogen. These are the four major atomic components of organic molecules. These valences are the basis for the rules of covalent bonding in organic chemistry—the building code for the architecture of organic molecules.

Let's consider how the rules of covalent bonding apply to carbon atoms with partners other than hydrogen. We'll look at two examples, the simple molecules carbon dioxide and urea.

In the carbon dioxide molecule (CO_2), a single carbon atom is joined to two atoms of oxygen by double covalent bonds. The structural formula for CO_2 is shown here:

$$O=C=O$$

Each line in a structural formula represents a pair of shared electrons. The two double bonds formed by the carbon atom are the equivalent of four single covalent bonds. The arrangement completes the valence shells of all atoms in the molecule. Because CO_2 is a very simple molecule and lacks hydrogen, it is often considered inorganic, even though it contains carbon.

Name and Comment	Molecular Formula	Structural Formula	Ball-and-Stick Model	Space-Filling Model
(a) Methane. When a carbon atom has four single bonds to other atoms, the molecule is tetrahedral.	CH_4			
(b) Ethane. A molecule may have more than one tetrahedral group of single-bonded atoms. (Ethane consists of two such groups.)	C_2H_6			
(c) Ethene (ethylene). When two carbon atoms are joined by a double bond, all atoms attached to those carbons are in the same plane; the molecule is flat.	C_2H_4			

▲ **Figure 4.3 The shapes of three simple organic molecules.**

| Hydrogen (valence = 1) | Oxygen (valence = 2) | Nitrogen (valence = 3) | Carbon (valence = 4) |

▲ **Figure 4.4 Valences of the major elements of organic molecules.** Valence is the number of covalent bonds an atom can form. It is generally equal to the number of electrons required to complete the valence (outermost) shell (see Figure 2.9). All the electrons are shown for each atom in the electron distribution diagrams (top). Only the electrons in the valence shell are presented in the Lewis dot structures.

DRAW IT *Refer to Figure 2.9 and draw the Lewis dot structures for sodium, phosphorus, sulfur, and chlorine.*

Whether we call CO_2 organic or inorganic, however, it is clearly important to the living world as the source of carbon for all organic molecules in organisms.

Urea, $CO(NH_2)_2$, is the organic compound found in urine that Wöhler synthesized in the early 1800s. The structural formula for urea is shown at the right. Again, each atom has the required number of covalent bonds. In this case, one carbon atom is involved in both single and double bonds.

Urea and carbon dioxide are molecules with one carbon atom. But as Figure 4.3 shows, a carbon atom can also use one or more valence electrons to form covalent bonds to other carbon atoms, linking the atoms into chains of seemingly infinite variety.

Molecular Diversity Arising from Carbon Skeleton Variation

Carbon chains form the skeletons of most organic molecules (**Figure 4.5**). The skeletons vary in length and may be straight, branched, or arranged in closed rings. Some carbon skeletons have double bonds, which vary in number and location. Such variation in carbon skeletons is one important source of the molecular complexity and diversity that characterize living matter. In addition, atoms of other elements can be bonded to the skeletons at available sites.

Hydrocarbons

All of the molecules that are shown in Figures 4.3 and 4.5 are **hydrocarbons**, organic molecules consisting of only carbon and hydrogen. Atoms of hydrogen are attached to the carbon skeleton wherever electrons are available for covalent bonding. Hydrocarbons are the major components of petroleum, which is called a fossil fuel because it consists of the partially decomposed remains of organisms that lived millions of years ago.

Although hydrocarbons are not prevalent in living organisms, many of a cell's organic molecules have regions consisting of only carbon and hydrogen. For example, the molecules known as fats have long hydrocarbon tails attached to a non-hydrocarbon component (**Figure 4.6**, on next page). Neither petroleum nor fat dissolves in water; both are hydrophobic compounds because the great majority of their bonds are relatively nonpolar carbon-to-hydrogen linkages. Another characteristic of hydrocarbons is that they can undergo reactions that release a relatively large amount of energy. The gasoline that fuels a car consists of hydrocarbons, and the hydrocarbon tails of fat molecules serve as stored fuel for animal bodies.

(a) **Length.** Carbon skeletons vary in length.

(b) **Branching.** Skeletons may be unbranched or branched.

(c) **Double bonds.** The skeleton may have double bonds, which can vary in location.

(d) **Rings.** Some carbon skeletons are arranged in rings. In the abbreviated structural formula for each compound (at the right), each corner represents a carbon and its attached hydrogens.

▲ **Figure 4.5 Variations in carbon skeletons.** Hydrocarbons, organic molecules consisting only of carbon and hydrogen, illustrate the diversity of the carbon skeletons of organic molecules.

(a) Mammalian adipose cells   (b) A fat molecule

▲ **Figure 4.6 The role of hydrocarbons in fats. (a)** Mammalian adipose cells stockpile fat molecules as a fuel reserve. Each adipose cell in this micrograph is almost filled by a large fat droplet, which contains a huge number of fat molecules. **(b)** A fat molecule consists of a small, nonhydrocarbon component joined to three hydrocarbon tails. The tails can be broken down to provide energy. They also account for the hydrophobic behavior of fats. (Black = carbon; gray = hydrogen; red = oxygen.)

Isomers

Variation in the architecture of organic molecules can be seen in **isomers**, compounds that have the same numbers of atoms of the same elements but different structures and hence different properties. Compare, for example, the two five-carbon compounds in **Figure 4.7a**. Both have the molecular formula C_5H_{12}, but they differ in the covalent arrangement of their carbon skeletons. The skeleton is straight in one compound but branched in the other. We will examine three types of isomers: structural isomers, geometric isomers, and enantiomers.

Structural isomers differ in the covalent arrangements of their atoms. The number of possible isomers increases tremendously as carbon skeletons increase in size. There are only 3 forms of C_5H_{12} (2 are shown in Figure 4.7a), but there are 18 variations of C_8H_{18} and 366,319 possible structural isomers of $C_{20}H_{42}$. Structural isomers may also differ in the location of double bonds.

Geometric isomers have the same covalent partnerships, but they differ in their spatial arrangements. The differences arise from the inflexibility of double bonds. Single bonds allow the atoms they join to rotate freely about the bond axis without changing the compound. In contrast, double bonds do not permit such rotation, resulting in the possibility of geometric isomers. If a double bond joins two carbon atoms, and each C also has two different atoms (or groups of atoms) attached to it, then two distinct geometric isomers are possible. Consider a simple molecule with two double-bonded carbons, each of which has an H and an X attached to it **(Figure 4.7b)**. The arrangement with both Xs on the same side of the double bond is called a *cis* isomer, and the arrangement with the Xs on opposite sides is called a *trans* isomer. The subtle difference in shape between geometric isomers can dramatically affect the biological activities of organic molecules. For example, the biochemistry of vision involves a light-induced

(a) Structural isomers differ in covalent partners, as shown in this example of two isomers of C_5H_{12}: pentane (left) and 2-methyl butane (right).

cis isomer: The two Xs are on the same side.

trans isomer: The two Xs are on opposite sides.

(b) Geometric isomers differ in arrangement about a double bond. In these diagrams, X represents an atom or group of atoms attached to a double-bonded carbon.

CO$_2$H   CO$_2$H

H   NH$_2$ NH$_2$ H

CH$_3$ CH$_3$

L isomer   D isomer

(c) Enantiomers differ in spatial arrangement around an asymmetric carbon, resulting in molecules that are mirror images, like left and right hands. The two isomers are designated the L and D isomers from the Latin for left and right (*levo* and *dextro*). Enantiomers cannot be superimposed on each other.

▲ **Figure 4.7 Three types of isomers.** Compounds with the same molecular formula but different structures, isomers are a source of diversity in organic molecules.

DRAW IT *There are three structural isomers of C_5H_{12}; draw the one not shown in (a).*

change of rhodopsin, a chemical compound in the eye, from the *cis* isomer to the *trans* isomer (see Chapter 50).

Enantiomers are isomers that are mirror images of each other. In the ball-and-stick models shown in **Figure 4.7c**, the middle carbon is called an *asymmetric carbon* because it is attached to four different atoms or groups of atoms. The four groups can be arranged in space around the asymmetric carbon in two different ways that are mirror images. Enantiomers are, in a way, left-handed and right-handed versions of the molecule. Just as your right hand won't fit into a left-handed glove, the working molecules in a cell can distinguish the two versions by shape. Usually, one isomer is biologically active, and the other is inactive.

The concept of enantiomers is important in the pharmaceutical industry because the two enantiomers of a drug may not be equally

Drug	Condition	Effective Enantiomer	Ineffective Enantiomer
Ibuprofen	Pain; inflammation	*S* Ibuprofen	*R* Ibuprofen
Albuterol	Asthma	*R*-Albuterol	*S*-Albuterol

▲ **Figure 4.8 The pharmacological importance of enantiomers.** Ibuprofen and albuterol are examples of drugs whose enantiomers have different effects. (*S* and *R* are letters used in one system to distinguish two enantiomers.) Ibuprofen reduces inflammation and pain. It is commonly sold as a mixture of the two enantiomers. The *S* enantiomer is 100 times more effective than the other. Albuterol is used to relax bronchial muscles, improving airflow in asthma patients. Only *R*-albuterol is synthesized and sold as a drug; the *S* form counteracts the active *R* form.

effective **(Figure 4.8)**. In some cases, one of the isomers may even produce harmful effects. This was the case with thalidomide, a drug prescribed for thousands of pregnant women in the late 1950s and early 1960s. The drug was a mixture of two enantiomers. One enantiomer reduced morning sickness, the desired effect, but the other caused severe birth defects. (Unfortunately, even if the "good" thalidomide enantiomer is used in purified form, some of it soon converts to the "bad" enantiomer in the patient's body.) The differing effects of enantiomers in the body demonstrate that organisms are sensitive to even the most subtle variations in molecular architecture. Once again, we see that molecules have emergent properties that depend on the specific arrangement of their atoms.

CONCEPT CHECK 4.2

1. Draw a structural formula for C_2H_4.
2. Which molecules in Figure 4.5 are isomers? For each pair, identify the type of isomer.
3. How are gasoline and fat chemically similar?
4. **WHAT IF?** Can propane (C_3H_8) form isomers?

For suggested answers, see Appendix A.

CONCEPT 4.3

A small number of chemical groups are key to the functioning of biological molecules

The distinctive properties of an organic molecule depend not only on the arrangement of its carbon skeleton but also on the molecular components attached to that skeleton. We can think of hydrocarbons, the simplest organic molecules, as the

▲ **Figure 4.9 A comparison of chemical groups of female (estradiol) and male (testosterone) sex hormones.** The two molecules differ only in the chemical groups attached to a common carbon skeleton of four fused rings, shown here in abbreviated form. These subtle variations in molecular architecture (shaded in blue) influence the development of the anatomical and physiological differences between female and male vertebrates.

underlying framework for more complex organic molecules. A number of chemical groups can replace one or more of the hydrogens bonded to the carbon skeleton of the hydrocarbon. (Some groups include atoms of the carbon skeleton, as we will see.) These groups may participate in chemical reactions or may contribute to function indirectly by their effects on molecular shape. The number and arrangement of the groups help give each molecule its unique properties.

The Chemical Groups Most Important in the Processes of Life

Consider the differences between testosterone and estradiol (a type of estrogen). These compounds are male and female sex hormones, respectively, in humans and other vertebrates **(Figure 4.9)**. Both are steroids, organic molecules with a common carbon skeleton in the form of four fused rings. These sex hormones differ only in the chemical groups attached to the rings. The different actions of these two molecules on many targets throughout the body help produce the contrasting features of males and females. Thus, even our sexuality has its biological basis in variations of molecular architecture.

In the example of sex hormones, different chemical groups contribute to function by affecting the molecule's shape. In other cases, the chemical groups affect molecular function by being directly involved in chemical reactions; these important chemical groups are known as **functional groups**. Each functional group participates in chemical reactions in a characteristic way, from one organic molecule to another.

The seven chemical groups most important in biological processes are the hydroxyl, carbonyl, carboxyl, amino, sulfhydryl, phosphate, and methyl groups. The first six groups can act as functional groups; they are also hydrophilic and thus increase the solubility of organic compounds in water. The methyl group is not reactive, but instead often acts as a recognizable tag on biological molecules. Before reading further, study **Figure 4.10** on the next two pages to familiarize yourself with these biologically important chemical groups.

Exploring Some Biologically Important Chemical Groups

CHEMICAL GROUP	Hydroxyl	Carbonyl	Carboxyl
STRUCTURE	 (may be written HO—) In a **hydroxyl group** (—OH), a hydrogen atom is bonded to an oxygen atom, which in turn is bonded to the carbon skeleton of the organic molecule. (Do not confuse this functional group with the hydroxide ion, OH⁻.)	 The **carbonyl group** (>CO) consists of a carbon atom joined to an oxygen atom by a double bond.	 When an oxygen atom is double-bonded to a carbon atom that is also bonded to an —OH group, the entire assembly of atoms is called a **carboxyl group** (—COOH).
NAME OF COMPOUND	**Alcohols** (their specific names usually end in -*ol*)	**Ketones** if the carbonyl group is within a carbon skeleton **Aldehydes** if the carbonyl group is at the end of the carbon skeleton	**Carboxylic acids,** or organic acids
EXAMPLE	 **Ethanol,** the alcohol present in alcoholic beverages	 **Acetone,** the simplest ketone **Propanal,** an aldehyde	 **Acetic acid,** which gives vinegar its sour taste
FUNCTIONAL PROPERTIES	● Is polar as a result of the electrons spending more time near the electronegative oxygen atom. ● Can form hydrogen bonds with water molecules, helping dissolve organic compounds such as sugars (see Figure 5.3).	● A ketone and an aldehyde may be structural isomers with different properties, as is the case for acetone and propanal. ● These two groups are also found in sugars, giving rise to two major groups of sugars: aldoses (containing an aldehyde) and ketoses (containing a ketone).	● Has acidic properties (is a source of hydrogen ions) because the covalent bond between oxygen and hydrogen is so polar; for example, Acetic acid ⇌ Acetate ion + H⁺ ● Found in cells in the ionized form with a charge of 1– and called a carboxylate ion (here, specifically, the acetate ion).

Amino

The **amino group** (—NH₂) consists of a nitrogen atom bonded to two hydrogen atoms and to the carbon skeleton.

Amines

Glycine

Because it also has a carboxyl group, glycine is both an amine and a carboxylic acid; compounds with both groups are called **amino acids**.

- Acts as a base; can pick up an H⁺ from the surrounding solution (water, in living organisms).

—N〈H H〉   —⁺N—H〈H H〉

(nonionized)   (ionized)

- Ionized, with a charge of 1+, under cellular conditions.

Sulfhydryl

—SH
(may be written HS —)

The **sulfhydryl group** consists of a sulfur atom bonded to an atom of hydrogen; resembles a hydroxyl group in shape.

Thiols

O=C—OH
H—C—CH₂—SH
N〈H H〉

Cysteine

Cysteine is an important sulfur-containing amino acid.

- Two sulfhydryl groups can react, forming a covalent bond. This "cross-linking" helps stabilize protein structure (see Figure 5.21).
- Cross-linking of cysteines in hair proteins maintains the curliness or straightness of hair. Straight hair can be "permanently" curled by shaping it around curlers, then breaking and re-forming the cross-linking bonds.

Phosphate

$-O-\overset{\displaystyle O}{\underset{\displaystyle O^-}{P}}-O^-$

In a **phosphate group**, a phosphorus atom is bonded to four oxygen atoms; one oxygen is bonded to the carbon skeleton; two oxygens carry negative charges. The phosphate group (—OPO₃²⁻, abbreviated Ⓟ) is an ionized form of a phosphoric acid group (—OPO₃H₂; note the two hydrogens).

Organic phosphates

OH OH H   O
H—C—C—C—O—P—O⁻
   H H H   O⁻

Glycerol phosphate

In addition to taking part in many important chemical reactions in cells, glycerol phosphate provides the backbone for phospholipids, the most prevalent molecules in cell membranes.

- Contributes negative charge to the molecule of which it is a part (2− when at the end of a molecule, as above; 1− when located internally in a chain of phosphates).
- Has the potential to react with water, releasing energy.

Methyl

H
H—C—H
H

A **methyl group** consists of a carbon bonded to three hydrogen atoms. The methyl group may be attached to a carbon or to a different atom.

Methylated compounds

NH₂
H—N=C—C—CH₃
O=C—N—C—H
       H

5-Methyl cytidine

5-Methyl cytidine is a component of DNA that has been modified by addition of the methyl group.

- Addition of a methyl group to DNA, or to molecules bound to DNA, affects expression of genes.
- Arrangement of methyl groups in male and female sex hormones affects their shape and function (see Figure 4.9).

? *Given the information in this figure and what you know about the electronegativity of oxygen, predict which of the following molecules would be the stronger acid. Explain your answer.*

a.
H—C—C—C〈O OH〉
   H H
   H H

b.
H—C—C—C〈O OH〉
   H   O

ATP: An Important Source of Energy for Cellular Processes

The "Phosphate" column in Figure 4.10 shows a simple example of an organic phosphate molecule. A more complicated organic phosphate, **adenosine triphosphate**, or **ATP**, is worth mentioning because its function in the cell is so important. ATP consists of an organic molecule called adenosine attached to a string of three phosphate groups:

Where three phosphates are present in series, as in ATP, one phosphate may be split off as a result of a reaction with water. This inorganic phosphate ion, $HOPO_3^{2-}$, is often abbreviated P_i in this book. Having lost one phosphate, ATP becomes adenosine *di*phosphate, or ADP. Although ATP is sometimes said to "store" energy, it is more accurate to think of it as "storing" the potential to react with water. This reaction releases energy that can be used by the cell. You will learn about this in more detail in Chapter 8.

CONCEPT CHECK 4.3

1. What does the term *amino acid* signify about the structure of such a molecule?
2. What chemical change occurs when ATP reacts with water and releases energy?
3. **WHAT IF?** Suppose you had an organic molecule such as glycine (see Figure 4.10, amino group example), and you chemically removed the —NH₂ group and replaced it with —COOH. Draw the structural formula for this molecule and speculate about its chemical properties.

For suggested answers, see Appendix A.

The Chemical Elements of Life: *A Review*

Living matter, as you have learned, consists mainly of carbon, oxygen, hydrogen, and nitrogen, with smaller amounts of sulfur and phosphorus. These elements all form strong covalent bonds, an essential characteristic in the architecture of complex organic molecules. Of all these elements, carbon is the virtuoso of the covalent bond. The versatility of carbon makes possible the great diversity of organic molecules, each with particular properties that emerge from the unique arrangement of its carbon skeleton and the chemical groups appended to that skeleton. At the foundation of all biological diversity lies this variation at the molecular level.

Chapter 4 Review

MEDIA Go to www.campbellbiology.com for BioFlix 3-D Animations, MP3 Tutors, Videos, Practice Tests, an eBook, and more.

SUMMARY OF KEY CONCEPTS

CONCEPT 4.1
Organic chemistry is the study of carbon compounds (pp. 58–59)

▶ Organic compounds were once thought to arise only within living organisms, but this idea (vitalism) was disproved when chemists were able to synthesize organic compounds in the laboratory.

CONCEPT 4.2
Carbon atoms can form diverse molecules by bonding to four other atoms (pp. 60–63)

▶ **The Formation of Bonds with Carbon** Carbon, with a valence of 4, can bond to various other atoms, including O, H,

and N. Carbon can also bond to other carbon atoms, forming the carbon skeletons of organic compounds.

▶ **Molecular Diversity Arising from Carbon Skeleton Variation** The carbon skeletons of organic molecules vary in length and shape and have bonding sites for atoms of other elements. Hydrocarbons consist only of carbon and hydrogen. Isomers are compounds with the same molecular formula but different structures and properties. Three types of isomers are structural isomers, geometric isomers, and enantiomers.

MEDIA
Activity Diversity of Carbon-Based Molecules
Activity Isomers
Investigation What Factors Determine the Effectiveness of Drugs?

CONCEPT 4.3
A small number of chemical groups are key to the functioning of biological molecules (pp. 63–66)

▶ **The Chemical Groups Most Important in the Processes of Life** Chemical groups attached to the carbon skeletons of organic molecules participate in chemical reactions (functional groups) or contribute to function by affecting molecular shape.

▶ ATP: An Important Source of Energy for Cellular Processes

Reacts with H₂O

(P)-(P)-(P)-[Adenosine] ⟶ P_i + (P)-(P)-[Adenosine] + Energy

ATP   Inorganic phosphate   ADP

MEDIA
Activity Functional Groups

▶ **The Chemical Elements of Life:** *A Review* Living matter is made mostly of carbon, oxygen, hydrogen, and nitrogen, with some sulfur and phosphorus. Biological diversity has its molecular basis in carbon's ability to form a huge number of molecules with particular shapes and chemical properties.

TESTING YOUR KNOWLEDGE

SELF-QUIZ

1. Organic chemistry is currently defined as
   a. the study of compounds made only by living cells.
   b. the study of carbon compounds.
   c. the study of vital forces.
   d. the study of natural (as opposed to synthetic) compounds.
   e. the study of hydrocarbons.

2. Which of the following hydrocarbons has a double bond in its carbon skeleton?
   a. C_3H_8 d. C_2H_4
   b. C_2H_6 e. C_2H_2
   c. CH_4

3. Choose the term that correctly describes the relationship between these two sugar molecules:

```
    H                    H   O
    |                     \ //
 H—C—OH              H—C
    |                     |
    C=O              H—C—OH
    |                     |
 H—C—OH              H—C—OH
    |                     |
    H                     H
```

   a. structural isomers   c. enantiomers
   b. geometric isomers   d. isotopes

4. Identify the asymmetric carbon in this molecule:

```
  O   OH H  H  H
  \\  |a |b|c|d|e
   C—C—C—C—C—H
  /   |  |  |  |
 H    H  H  H  H
```

5. Which functional group is *not* present in this molecule?

```
  HO   O
    \ //
     C   H
     |   |
  H—C—C—OH
     |
     N   H
    / \
   H   H
```

   a. carboxyl   b. sulfhydryl   c. hydroxyl   d. amino

6. Which action could produce a carbonyl group?
   a. the replacement of the —OH of a carboxyl group with hydrogen
   b. the addition of a thiol to a hydroxyl
   c. the addition of a hydroxyl to a phosphate
   d. the replacement of the nitrogen of an amine with oxygen
   e. the addition of a sulfhydryl to a carboxyl

7. Which chemical group is most likely to be responsible for an organic molecule behaving as a base?
   a. hydroxyl   d. amino
   b. carbonyl   e. phosphate
   c. carboxyl

For Self-Quiz answers, see Appendix A.

MEDIA Visit **www.campbellbiology.com** for a Practice Test.

EVOLUTION CONNECTION

8. **DRAW IT** Some scientists believe that life elsewhere in the universe might be based on the element silicon, rather than on carbon, as on Earth. Look at the electron distribution diagram for silicon in Figure 2.9 and draw the Lewis dot structure for silicon. What properties does silicon share with carbon that would make silicon-based life more likely than, say, neon-based life or aluminum-based life?

SCIENTIFIC INQUIRY

9. In 1918, an epidemic of sleeping sickness caused an unusual rigid paralysis in some survivors, similar to symptoms of advanced Parkinson's disease. Years later, L-dopa (below, left), a chemical used to treat Parkinson's disease, was given to some of these patients, as dramatized in the movie *Awakenings*. L-dopa was remarkably effective at eliminating the paralysis, at least temporarily. However, its enantiomer, D-dopa (right), was subsequently shown to have no effect at all, as is the case for Parkinson's disease. Suggest a hypothesis to explain why, for both diseases, one enantiomer is effective and the other is not.

L-dopa   **D-dopa**

SCIENCE, TECHNOLOGY, AND SOCIETY

10. Thalidomide achieved notoriety 50 years ago because of a wave of birth defects among children born to women who took thalidomide during pregnancy as a treatment for morning sickness. However, in 1998 the U.S. Food and Drug Administration (FDA) approved this drug for the treatment of certain conditions associated with Hansen's disease (leprosy). In clinical trials, thalidomide also shows promise for use in treating patients suffering from AIDS, tuberculosis, and some types of cancer. Do you think approval of this drug is appropriate? If so, under what conditions? What criteria do you think the FDA should use in weighing a drug's benefits against its dangers?

The Structure and Function of Large Biological Molecules

5

▲ Figure 5.1 **Why do scientists study the structures of macromolecules?**

OVERVIEW

The Molecules of Life

Given the rich complexity of life on Earth, we might expect organisms to have an enormous diversity of molecules. Remarkably, however, the critically important large molecules of all living things—from bacteria to elephants—fall into just four main classes: carbohydrates, lipids, proteins, and nucleic acids. On the molecular scale, members of three of these classes—carbohydrates, proteins, and nucleic acids—are huge and are thus called **macromolecules**. For example, a protein may consist of thousands of atoms that form a molecular colossus with a mass well over 100,000 daltons. Considering the size and complexity of macromolecules, it is noteworthy that biochemists have determined the detailed structures of so many of them **(Figure 5.1)**.

The architecture of a large biological molecule helps explain how that molecule works. Like water and simple organic molecules, large biological molecules exhibit unique emergent properties arising from the orderly arrangement of their atoms. In this chapter, we'll first consider how macromolecules are built. Then we'll examine the structure and function of all four classes of large biological molecules: carbohydrates, lipids, proteins, and nucleic acids.

CONCEPT 5.1

Macromolecules are polymers, built from monomers

The macromolecules in three of the four classes of life's organic compounds—carbohydrates, proteins, and nucleic acids—are chain-like molecules called polymers (from the Greek *polys*, many, and *meris*, part). A **polymer** is a long molecule consisting of many similar or identical building blocks linked by covalent bonds, much as a train consists of a chain of cars. The repeating units that serve as the building blocks of a polymer are smaller molecules called **monomers**. Some of the molecules that serve as monomers also have other functions of their own.

The Synthesis and Breakdown of Polymers

The classes of polymers differ in the nature of their monomers, but the chemical mechanisms by which cells make and break down polymers are basically the same in all cases **(Figure 5.2)**. Monomers are connected by a reaction in which two molecules are covalently bonded to each other through loss of a water molecule; this is known as a **condensation reaction**, specifically a **dehydration reaction**, because water is the molecule that is lost **(Figure 5.2a)**. When a bond forms between two monomers, each monomer contributes part of the water molecule that is lost: One molecule provides a hydroxyl group (—OH), while the other provides a hydrogen (—H). This reaction can be repeated as monomers are added to the chain one by one, making a polymer. The dehydration process is facilitated by **enzymes**, specialized macromolecules that speed up chemical reactions in cells.

Polymers are disassembled to monomers by **hydrolysis**, a process that is essentially the reverse of the dehydration

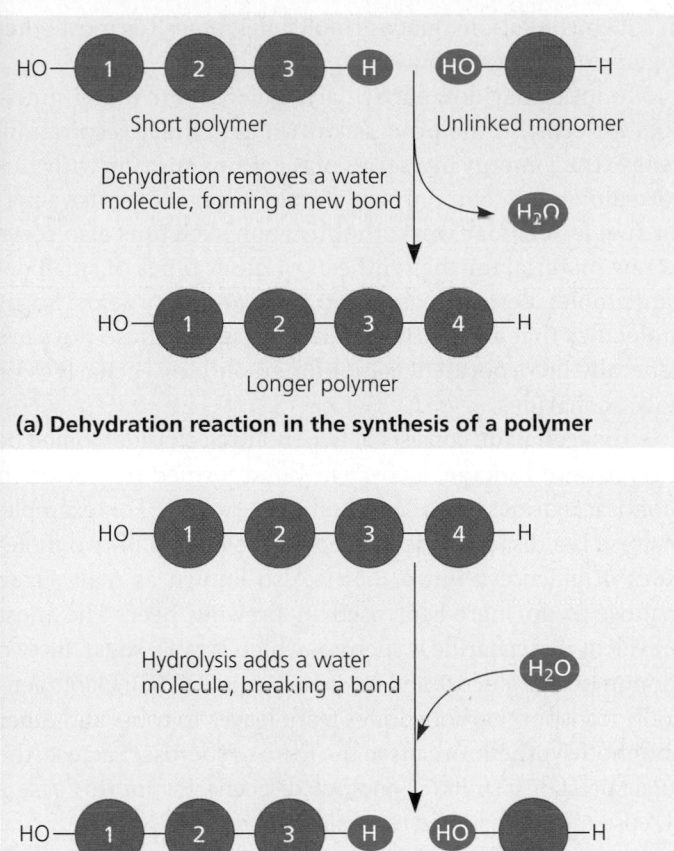

(a) Dehydration reaction in the synthesis of a polymer

HO—1—2—3—H   HO—H   Unlinked monomer

Short polymer

Dehydration removes a water molecule, forming a new bond

H_2O

HO—1—2—3—4—H

Longer polymer

HO—1—2—3—4—H

Hydrolysis adds a water molecule, breaking a bond

H_2O

HO—1—2—3—H   HO—H

(b) Hydrolysis of a polymer

▲ **Figure 5.2 The synthesis and breakdown of polymers.**

reaction **(Figure 5.2b)**. Hydrolysis means to break using water (from the Greek *hydro*, water, and *lysis*, break). Bonds between the monomers are broken by the addition of water molecules, with a hydrogen from the water attaching to one monomer and a hydroxyl group attaching to the adjacent monomer. An example of hydrolysis working within our bodies is the process of digestion. The bulk of the organic material in our food is in the form of polymers that are much too large to enter our cells. Within the digestive tract, various enzymes attack the polymers, speeding up hydrolysis. The released monomers are then absorbed into the bloodstream for distribution to all body cells. Those cells can then use dehydration reactions to assemble the monomers into new, different polymers that can perform specific functions required by the cell.

The Diversity of Polymers

Each cell has thousands of different kinds of macromolecules; the collection varies from one type of cell to another even in the same organism. The inherent differences between human siblings reflect variations in polymers, particularly DNA and proteins. Molecular differences between unrelated individu-

als are more extensive and those between species greater still. The diversity of macromolecules in the living world is vast, and the possible variety is effectively limitless.

What is the basis for such diversity in life's polymers? These molecules are constructed from only 40 to 50 common monomers and some others that occur rarely. Building a huge variety of polymers from such a limited number of monomers is analogous to constructing hundreds of thousands of words from only 26 letters of the alphabet. The key is arrangement—the particular linear sequence that the units follow. However, this analogy falls far short of describing the great diversity of macromolecules because most biological polymers have many more monomers than the number of letters in the longest word. Proteins, for example, are built from 20 kinds of amino acids arranged in chains that are typically hundreds of amino acids long. The molecular logic of life is simple but elegant: Small molecules common to all organisms are ordered into unique macromolecules.

Despite this immense diversity, molecular structure and function can still be grouped roughly by class. Let's look at each of the four major classes of large biological molecules. For each class, the large molecules have emergent properties not found in their individual building blocks.

CONCEPT 5.2

Carbohydrates serve as fuel and building material

Carbohydrates include both sugars and polymers of sugars. The simplest carbohydrates are the monosaccharides, also known as simple sugars. Disaccharides are double sugars, consisting of two monosaccharides joined by a covalent bond. Carbohydrates also include macromolecules called polysaccharides, polymers composed of many sugar building blocks.

Sugars

Monosaccharides (from the Greek *monos*, single, and *sacchar*, sugar) generally have molecular formulas that are some multiple of the unit CH_2O (**Figure 5.3**). Glucose ($C_6H_{12}O_6$), the most common monosaccharide, is of central importance in the chemistry of life. In the structure of glucose, we can see the trademarks of a sugar: The molecule has a carbonyl group ($>C=O$) and multiple hydroxyl groups (—OH). Depending on the location of the carbonyl group, a sugar is either an aldose (aldehyde sugar) or a ketose (ketone sugar). Glucose, for example, is an aldose; fructose, a structural isomer of glucose, is a ketose. (Most names for sugars end in -ose.) Another criterion for classifying sugars is the size of the carbon skeleton, which ranges from three to seven carbons long. Glucose, fructose, and other sugars that have six carbons are called hexoses. Trioses (three-carbon sugars) and pentoses (five-carbon sugars) are also common.

Still another source of diversity for simple sugars is in the spatial arrangement of their parts around asymmetric carbons. (Recall that an asymmetric carbon is a carbon attached to four different atoms or groups of atoms.) Glucose and galactose, for example, differ only in the placement of parts around one asymmetric carbon (see the purple boxes in Figure 5.3). What seems like a small difference is significant enough to give the two sugars distinctive shapes and behaviors.

Although it is convenient to draw glucose with a linear carbon skeleton, this representation is not completely accurate.

In aqueous solutions, glucose molecules, as well as most other sugars, form rings (**Figure 5.4**).

Monosaccharides, particularly glucose, are major nutrients for cells. In the process known as cellular respiration, cells extract energy in a series of reactions starting with glucose molecules. Not only are simple-sugar molecules a major fuel for cellular work; their carbon skeletons also serve as raw material for the synthesis of other types of small organic molecules, such as amino acids and fatty acids. Sugar molecules that are not immediately used in these ways are generally incorporated as monomers into disaccharides or polysaccharides.

A **disaccharide** consists of two monosaccharides joined by a **glycosidic linkage**, a covalent bond formed between two monosaccharides by a dehydration reaction. For example, maltose is a disaccharide formed by the linking of two molecules of glucose (**Figure 5.5a**). Also known as malt sugar, maltose is an ingredient used in brewing beer. The most prevalent disaccharide is sucrose, which is table sugar. Its two monomers are glucose and fructose (**Figure 5.5b**). Plants generally transport carbohydrates from leaves to roots and other nonphotosynthetic organs in the form of sucrose. Lactose, the sugar present in milk, is another disaccharide, in this case a glucose molecule joined to a galactose molecule.

▶ **Figure 5.3 The structure and classification of some monosaccharides.** Sugars may be aldoses (aldehyde sugars, top row) or ketoses (ketone sugars, bottom row), depending on the location of the carbonyl group (dark orange). Sugars are also classified according to the length of their carbon skeletons. A third point of variation is the spatial arrangement around asymmetric carbons (compare, for example, the purple portions of glucose and galactose).

	Trioses ($C_3H_6O_3$)	Pentoses ($C_5H_{10}O_5$)	Hexoses ($C_6H_{12}O_6$)	
Aldoses	**Glyceraldehyde** An initial breakdown product of glucose	**Ribose** A component of RNA	**Glucose** An energy source for organisms	**Galactose** An energy source for organisms
Ketoses	**Dihydroxyacetone** An initial breakdown product of glucose	**Ribulose** An intermediate in photosynthesis	**Fructose** An energy source for organisms	

(a) **Linear and ring forms.** Chemical equilibrium between the linear and ring structures greatly favors the formation of rings. The carbons of the sugar are numbered 1 to 6, as shown. To form the glucose ring, carbon 1 bonds to the oxygen attached to carbon 5.

(b) **Abbreviated ring structure.** Each corner represents a carbon. The ring's thicker edge indicates that you are looking at the ring edge-on; the components attached to the ring lie above or below the plane of the ring.

▲ **Figure 5.4 Linear and ring forms of glucose.**

DRAW IT *Start with the linear form of fructose (see Figure 5.3) and draw the formation of the fructose ring in two steps. Number the carbons. Attach carbon 5 via oxygen to carbon 2. Compare the number of carbons in the fructose and glucose rings.*

(a) **Dehydration reaction in the synthesis of maltose.** The bonding of two glucose units forms maltose. The glycosidic linkage joins the number 1 carbon of one glucose to the number 4 carbon of the second glucose. Joining the glucose monomers in a different way would result in a different disaccharide.

Glucose   Glucose   Maltose

(b) **Dehydration reaction in the synthesis of sucrose.** Sucrose is a disaccharide formed from glucose and fructose. Notice that fructose, though a hexose like glucose, forms a five-sided ring.

Glucose   Fructose   Sucrose

▲ **Figure 5.5 Examples of disaccharide synthesis.**

Polysaccharides

Polysaccharides are macromolecules, polymers with a few hundred to a few thousand monosaccharides joined by glycosidic linkages. Some polysaccharides serve as storage material, hydrolyzed as needed to provide sugar for cells. Other polysaccharides serve as building material for structures that protect the cell or the whole organism. The architecture and function of a polysaccharide are determined by its sugar monomers and by the positions of its glycosidic linkages.

Storage Polysaccharides

Both plants and animals store sugars for later use in the form of storage polysaccharides. Plants store **starch**, a polymer of glucose monomers, as granules within cellular structures known as plastids, which include chloroplasts. Synthesizing starch enables the plant to stockpile surplus glucose. Because glucose is a major cellular fuel, starch represents stored energy. The sugar can later be withdrawn from this carbohydrate "bank" by hydrolysis, which breaks the bonds between the glucose monomers. Most animals, including humans, also have enzymes that can hydrolyze plant starch, making glucose available as a nutrient for cells. Potato tubers and grains—the fruits of wheat, maize (corn), rice, and other grasses—are the major sources of starch in the human diet.

Most of the glucose monomers in starch are joined by 1–4 linkages (number 1 carbon to number 4 carbon), like the glucose units in maltose (see Figure 5.5a). The angle of these

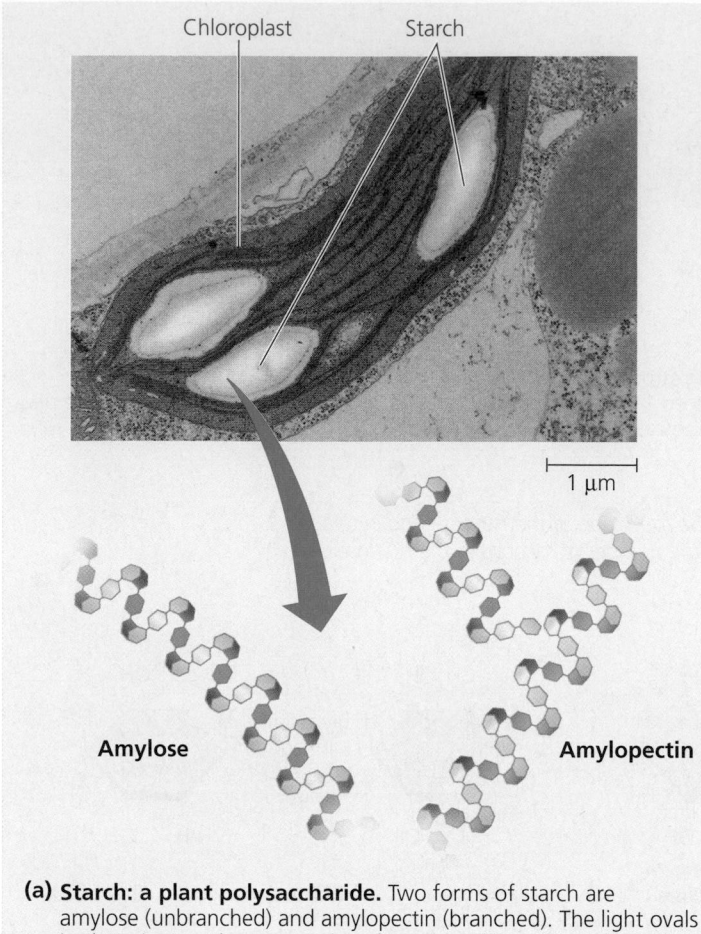

(a) Starch: a plant polysaccharide. Two forms of starch are amylose (unbranched) and amylopectin (branched). The light ovals in the micrograph are granules of starch within a chloroplast of a plant cell.

Chloroplast   Starch

1 μm

Amylose

Amylopectin

(b) Glycogen: an animal polysaccharide. Glycogen is more branched than amylopectin. Animal cells stockpile glycogen as dense clusters of granules within liver and muscle cells. (The micrograph shows part of a liver cell; mitochondria are organelles that help break down sugars.)

Mitochondria   Glycogen granules

0.5 μm

Glycogen

▲ **Figure 5.6 Storage polysaccharides of plants and animals.** These examples, starch and glycogen, are composed entirely of glucose monomers, represented here by hexagons. Because of their molecular structure, the polymer chains tend to form helices.

bonds makes the polymer helical. The simplest form of starch, amylose, is unbranched **(Figure 5.6a)**. Amylopectin, a more complex starch, is a branched polymer with 1–6 linkages at the branch points.

Animals store a polysaccharide called **glycogen**, a polymer of glucose that is like amylopectin but more extensively branched **(Figure 5.6b)**. Humans and other vertebrates store glycogen mainly in liver and muscle cells. Hydrolysis of glycogen in these cells releases glucose when the demand for sugar increases. This stored fuel cannot sustain an animal for long, however. In humans, for example, glycogen stores are depleted in about a day unless they are replenished by consumption of food. This is an issue of concern in low-carbohydrate diets.

Structural Polysaccharides

Organisms build strong materials from structural polysaccharides. For example, the polysaccharide called **cellulose** is a major component of the tough walls that enclose plant cells. On a global scale, plants produce almost 10^{14} kg (100 billion tons) of cellulose per year; it is the most abundant organic compound on Earth. Like starch, cellulose is a polymer of glucose, but the glycosidic linkages in these two polymers differ. The difference is based on the fact that there are actually two slightly different ring structures for glucose **(Figure 5.7a)**. When glucose forms a ring, the hydroxyl group attached to the number 1 carbon is positioned either below or above the plane of the ring. These two ring forms for glucose are called alpha (α) and beta (β), respectively. In starch, all the glucose monomers are in the α configuration **(Figure 5.7b)**, the arrangement we saw in Figures 5.4 and 5.5. In contrast, the glucose monomers of cellulose are all in the β configuration, making every other glucose monomer upside down with respect to its neighbors **(Figure 5.7c)**.

The differing glycosidic linkages in starch and cellulose give the two molecules distinct three-dimensional shapes. Whereas a starch molecule is mostly helical, a cellulose molecule is straight. Cellulose is never branched, and some hydroxyl groups on its glucose monomers are free to hydrogen-bond with the hydroxyls of other cellulose molecules lying parallel to it. In plant cell walls, parallel cellulose molecules held together in this way are grouped into units called microfibrils **(Figure 5.8)**. These cable-like

(a) α and β glucose ring structures. These two interconvertible forms of glucose differ in the placement of the hydroxyl group (highlighted in blue) attached to the number 1 carbon.

α Glucose

β Glucose

(b) Starch: 1–4 linkage of α glucose monomers. All monomers are in the same orientation. Compare the positions of the —OH groups highlighted in yellow with those in cellulose (c).

(c) Cellulose: 1–4 linkage of β glucose monomers. In cellulose, every other β glucose monomer is upside down with respect to its neighbors.

▲ Figure 5.7 **Starch and cellulose structures.**

Cell walls

Cellulose microfibrils in a plant cell wall

Microfibril

About 80 cellulose molecules associate to form a microfibril, the main architectural unit of the plant cell wall.

10 μm

0.5 μm

Cellulose molecules

Parallel cellulose molecules are held together by hydrogen bonds between hydroxyl groups attached to carbon atoms 3 and 6.

A cellulose molecule is an unbranched β glucose polymer.

β Glucose monomer

▲ Figure 5.8 **The arrangement of cellulose in plant cell walls.**

▲ **Figure 5.9 Cellulose-digesting prokaryotes are found in grazing animals such as this cow.**

microfibrils are a strong building material for plants and an important substance for humans because cellulose is the major constituent of paper and the only component of cotton.

Enzymes that digest starch by hydrolyzing its α linkages are unable to hydrolyze the β linkages of cellulose because of the distinctly different shapes of these two molecules. In fact, few organisms possess enzymes that can digest cellulose. Humans do not; the cellulose in our food passes through the digestive tract and is eliminated with the feces. Along the way, the cellulose abrades the wall of the digestive tract and stimulates the lining to secrete mucus, which aids in the smooth passage of food through the tract. Thus, although cellulose is not a nutrient for humans, it is an important part of a healthful diet. Most fresh fruits, vegetables, and whole grains are rich in cellulose. On food packages, "insoluble fiber" refers mainly to cellulose.

Some prokaryotes can digest cellulose, breaking it down into glucose monomers. A cow harbors cellulose-digesting prokaryotes in its rumen, the first compartment in its stomach (**Figure 5.9**). The prokaryotes hydrolyze the cellulose of hay and grass and convert the glucose to other nutrients that nourish the cow. Similarly, a termite, which is unable to digest cellulose by itself, has prokaryotes living in its gut that can make a meal of wood. Some fungi can also digest cellulose, thereby helping recycle chemical elements within Earth's ecosystems.

Another important structural polysaccharide is **chitin**, the carbohydrate used by arthropods (insects, spiders, crustaceans, and related animals) to build their exoskeletons (**Figure 5.10**). An exoskeleton is a hard case that surrounds the soft parts of an animal. Pure chitin is leathery and flexible, but it becomes hardened when encrusted with calcium carbonate, a salt. Chitin is also found in many fungi, which use this polysaccharide rather than cellulose as the building material for their cell walls. Chitin is similar to cellulose, except that the glucose monomer of chitin has a nitrogen-containing appendage (see Figure 5.10a).

CONCEPT CHECK 5.2

1. Write the formula for a monosaccharide that has three carbons.
2. A dehydration reaction joins two glucose molecules to form maltose. The formula for glucose is $C_6H_{12}O_6$. What is the formula for maltose?
3. **WHAT IF?** What would happen if a cow were given antibiotics that killed all the prokaryotes in its stomach?

For suggested answers, see Appendix A.

CONCEPT 5.3

Lipids are a diverse group of hydrophobic molecules

Lipids are the one class of large biological molecules that does not include true polymers, and they are generally not big enough to be considered macromolecules. The compounds called **lipids** are grouped together because they share one important trait: They mix poorly, if at all, with water. The hydrophobic behavior of lipids is based on their molecular structure. Although they may have some polar bonds associated with oxygen, lipids consist mostly of hydrocarbon regions.

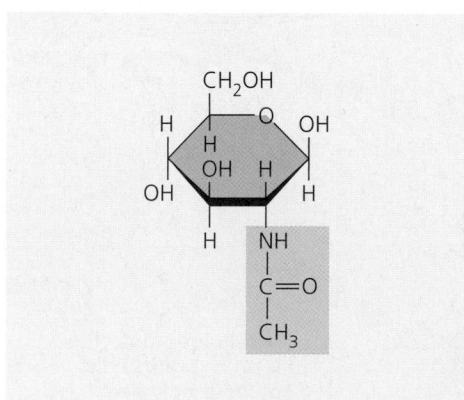

(a) The structure of the chitin monomer.

(b) Chitin forms the exoskeleton of arthropods. This cicada is molting, shedding its old exoskeleton and emerging in adult form.

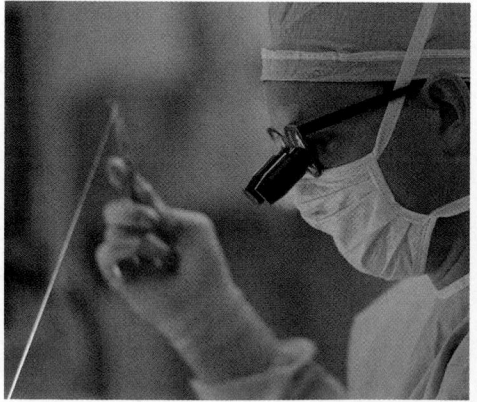

(c) Chitin is used to make a strong and flexible surgical thread that decomposes after the wound or incision heals.

▲ **Figure 5.10 Chitin, a structural polysaccharide.**

Lipids are varied in form and function. They include waxes and certain pigments, but we will focus on the most biologically important types of lipids: fats, phospholipids, and steroids.

Fats

Although fats are not polymers, they are large molecules assembled from a few smaller molecules by dehydration reactions. A **fat** is constructed from two kinds of smaller molecules: glycerol and fatty acids (**Figure 5.11a**). Glycerol is an alcohol with three carbons, each bearing a hydroxyl group. A **fatty acid** has a long carbon skeleton, usually 16 or 18 carbon atoms in length. The carbon at one end of the fatty acid is part of a carboxyl group, the functional group that gives these molecules the name fatty *acid*. Attached to the carboxyl group is a long hydrocarbon chain. The relatively nonpolar C—H bonds in the hydrocarbon chains of fatty acids are the reason fats are hydrophobic. Fats separate from water because the water molecules hydrogen-bond to one another and exclude the fats. This is the reason that vegetable oil (a liquid fat) separates from the aqueous vinegar solution in a bottle of salad dressing.

In making a fat, three fatty acid molecules each join to glycerol by an ester linkage, a bond between a hydroxyl group and a carboxyl group. The resulting fat, also called a **triacylglycerol**, thus consists of three fatty acids linked to one glycerol molecule. (Still another name for a fat is *triglyceride*, a word often found in the list of ingredients on packaged foods.) The fatty acids in a fat can be the same, as in **Figure 5.11b**, or they can be of two or three different kinds.

Fatty acids vary in length and in the number and locations of double bonds. The terms *saturated fats* and *unsaturated fats* are commonly used in the context of nutrition (**Figure 5.12**).

Structural formula of a saturated fat molecule

Stearic acid, a saturated fatty acid

(a) Saturated fat. At room temperature, the molecules of a saturated fat such as this butter are packed closely together, forming a solid.

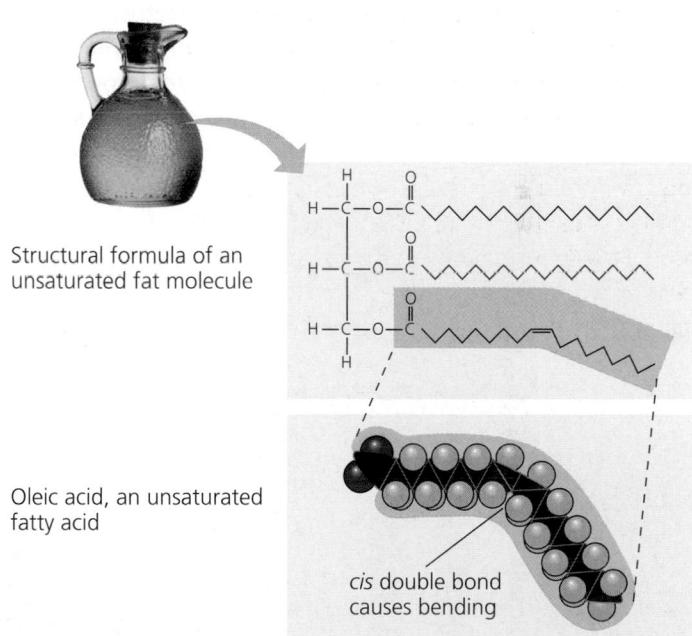

Structural formula of an unsaturated fat molecule

Oleic acid, an unsaturated fatty acid

cis double bond causes bending

(b) Unsaturated fat. At room temperature, the molecules of an unsaturated fat such as this olive oil cannot pack together closely enough to solidify because of the kinks in some of their fatty acid hydrocarbon chains.

▲ **Figure 5.12 Examples of saturated and unsaturated fats and fatty acids.** The structural formula for each fat follows a common chemical convention of omitting the carbons and attached hydrogens of the hydrocarbon regions. In the space-filling models of the fatty acids, black = carbon, gray = hydrogen, and red = oxygen.

Glycerol

(a) Dehydration reaction in the synthesis of a fat

Fatty acid
(palmitic acid)

Ester linkage

(b) Fat molecule (triacylglycerol)

▲ **Figure 5.11 The synthesis and structure of a fat, or triacylglycerol.** The molecular building blocks of a fat are one molecule of glycerol and three molecules of fatty acids. **(a)** One water molecule is removed for each fatty acid joined to the glycerol. **(b)** A fat molecule with three identical fatty acid units. The carbons of the fatty acids are arranged zig-zag to suggest the actual orientations of the four single bonds extending from each carbon (see Figure 4.3a).

These terms refer to the structure of the hydrocarbon chains of the fatty acids. If there are no double bonds between carbon atoms composing the chain, then as many hydrogen atoms as possible are bonded to the carbon skeleton. Such a structure is described as being *saturated* with hydrogen, so the resulting fatty acid is called a **saturated fatty acid (Figure 5.12a)**. An **unsaturated fatty acid** has one or more double bonds, formed by the removal of hydrogen atoms from the carbon skeleton. The fatty acid will have a kink in its hydrocarbon chain wherever a *cis* double bond occurs **(Figure 5.12b)**.

A fat made from saturated fatty acids is called a saturated fat. Most animal fats are saturated: The hydrocarbon chains of their fatty acids—the "tails" of the fat molecules—lack double bonds, and their flexibility allows the fat molecules to pack together tightly. Saturated animal fats—such as lard and butter—are solid at room temperature. In contrast, the fats of plants and fishes are generally unsaturated, meaning that they are built of one or more types of unsaturated fatty acids. Usually liquid at room temperature, plant and fish fats are referred to as oils—olive oil and cod liver oil are examples. The kinks where the *cis* double bonds are located prevent the molecules from packing together closely enough to solidify at room temperature. The phrase "hydrogenated vegetable oils" on food labels means that unsaturated fats have been synthetically converted to saturated fats by adding hydrogen. Peanut butter, margarine, and many other products are hydrogenated to prevent lipids from separating out in liquid (oil) form.

A diet rich in saturated fats is one of several factors that may contribute to the cardiovascular disease known as atherosclerosis. In this condition, deposits called plaques develop within the walls of blood vessels, causing inward bulges that impede blood flow and reduce the resilience of the vessels. Recent studies have shown that the process of hydrogenating vegetable oils produces not only saturated fats but also unsaturated fats with *trans* double bonds. These **trans fats** may contribute more than saturated fats to atherosclerosis (see Chapter 42) and other problems. Because trans fats are especially common in baked goods and processed foods, the USDA requires trans fat content information on nutritional labels.

Fat has come to have such a negative connotation in our culture that you might wonder what useful purpose fats serve. The major function of fats is energy storage. The hydrocarbon chains of fats are similar to gasoline molecules and just as rich in energy. A gram of fat stores more than twice as much energy as a gram of a polysaccharide, such as starch. Because plants are relatively immobile, they can function with bulky energy storage in the form of starch. (Vegetable oils are generally obtained from seeds, where more compact storage is an asset to the plant.) Animals, however, must carry their energy stores with them, so there is an advantage to having a more compact reservoir of fuel—fat. Humans and other mammals stock their long-term food reserves in adipose cells (see Figure 4.6a), which swell and shrink as fat is deposited and withdrawn from storage. In addition to storing energy, adipose tissue also cushions such vital organs as the kidneys, and a layer of fat beneath the skin insulates the body. This subcutaneous layer is especially thick in whales, seals, and most other marine mammals, protecting them from cold ocean water.

Phospholipids

Cells could not exist without another type of lipid—**phospholipids (Figure 5.13)**. Phospholipids are essential

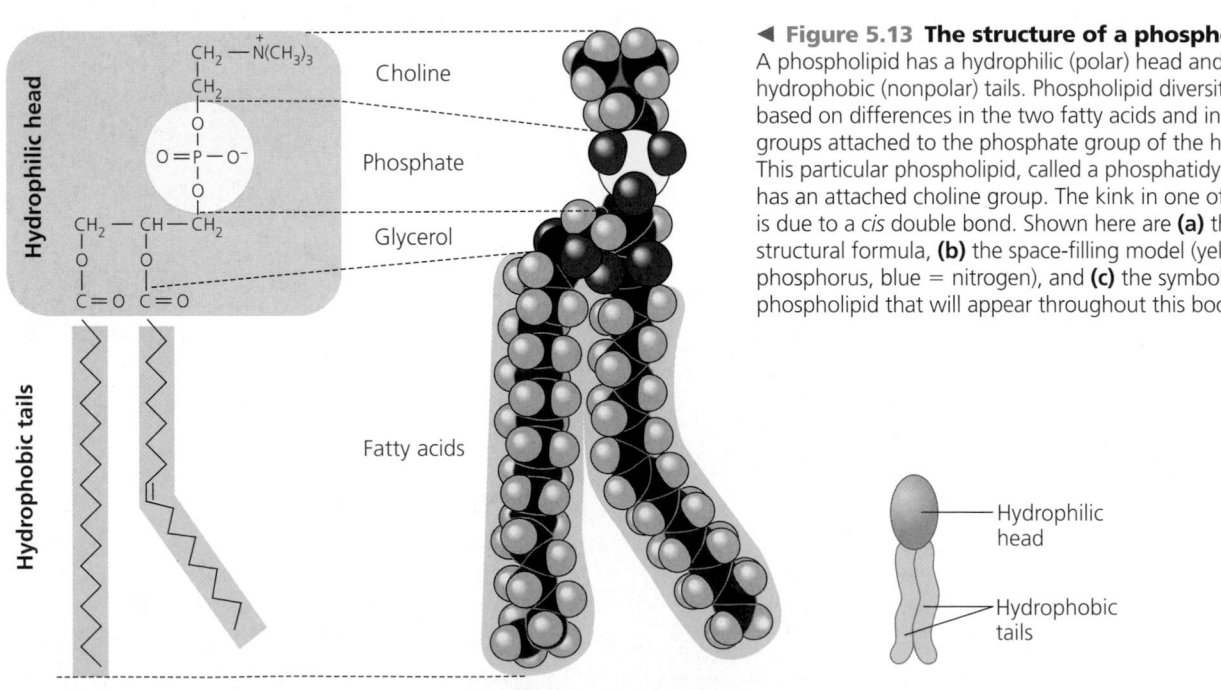

◀ **Figure 5.13 The structure of a phospholipid.** A phospholipid has a hydrophilic (polar) head and two hydrophobic (nonpolar) tails. Phospholipid diversity is based on differences in the two fatty acids and in the groups attached to the phosphate group of the head. This particular phospholipid, called a phosphatidylcholine, has an attached choline group. The kink in one of its tails is due to a *cis* double bond. Shown here are **(a)** the structural formula, **(b)** the space-filling model (yellow = phosphorus, blue = nitrogen), and **(c)** the symbol for a phospholipid that will appear throughout this book.

(a) Structural formula

(b) Space-filling model

(c) Phospholipid symbol

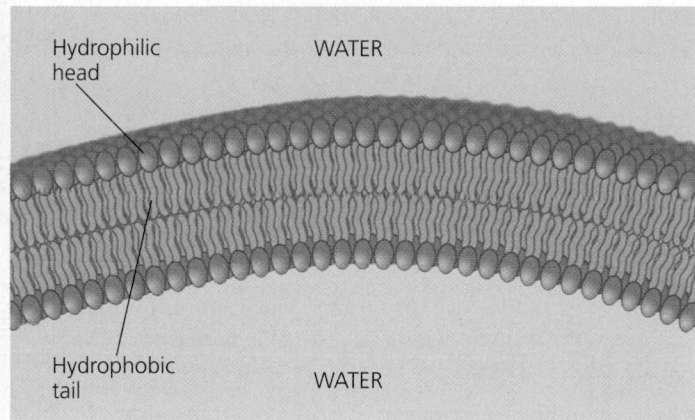

▲ Figure 5.14 **Bilayer structure formed by self-assembly of phospholipids in an aqueous environment.** The phospholipid bilayer shown here is the main fabric of biological membranes. Note that the hydrophilic heads of the phospholipids are in contact with water in this structure, whereas the hydrophobic tails are in contact with each other and remote from water.

▲ Figure 5.15 **Cholesterol, a steroid.** Cholesterol is the molecule from which other steroids, including the sex hormones, are synthesized. Steroids vary in the chemical groups attached to their four interconnected rings (shown in gold).

for cells because they make up cell membranes. Their structure provides a classic example of how form fits function at the molecular level. As shown in Figure 5.13, a phospholipid is similar to a fat molecule but has only two fatty acids attached to glycerol rather than three. The third hydroxyl group of glycerol is joined to a phosphate group, which has a negative electrical charge. Additional small molecules, which are usually charged or polar, can be linked to the phosphate group to form a variety of phospholipids.

The two ends of phospholipids show different behavior toward water. The hydrocarbon tails are hydrophobic and are excluded from water. However, the phosphate group and its attachments form a hydrophilic head that has an affinity for water. When phospholipids are added to water, they self-assemble into double-layered aggregates—bilayers—that shield their hydrophobic portions from water (**Figure 5.14**).

At the surface of a cell, phospholipids are arranged in a similar bilayer. The hydrophilic heads of the molecules are on the outside of the bilayer, in contact with the aqueous solutions inside and outside of the cell. The hydrophobic tails point toward the interior of the bilayer, away from the water. The phospholipid bilayer forms a boundary between the cell and its external environment; in fact, cells could not exist without phospholipids.

Steroids

Many hormones, as well as cholesterol, are **steroids**, which are lipids characterized by a carbon skeleton consisting of four fused rings (**Figure 5.15**). Different steroids vary in the chemical groups attached to this ensemble of rings. **Cholesterol** is a common component of animal cell membranes and is also the precursor from which other steroids are synthesized. In vertebrates, cholesterol is synthesized in the liver. Many hormones, including vertebrate sex hormones, are steroids produced from cholesterol (see Figure 4.9). Thus, cholesterol is a crucial molecule in animals, although a high level of it in the blood may contribute to atherosclerosis. Both saturated fats and trans fats exert their negative impact on health by affecting cholesterol levels.

<hr>

CONCEPT CHECK **5.3**

1. Compare the structure of a fat (triglyceride) with that of a phospholipid.
2. Why are human sex hormones considered lipids?
3. **WHAT IF?** Suppose a membrane surrounded an oil droplet, as it does in the cells of plant seeds. Describe and explain the form it might take.

For suggested answers, see Appendix A.

<hr>

CONCEPT **5.4**

Proteins have many structures, resulting in a wide range of functions

Nearly every dynamic function of a living being depends on proteins. In fact, the importance of proteins is underscored by their name, which comes from the Greek word *proteios*, meaning "first place." Proteins account for more than 50% of the dry mass of most cells, and they are instrumental in almost everything organisms do. Some proteins speed up chemical reactions, while others play a role in structural support,

Table 5.1 An Overview of Protein Functions

Type of Protein	Function	Examples
Enzymatic proteins	Selective acceleration of chemical reactions	Digestive enzymes catalyze the hydrolysis of the polymers in food.
Structural proteins	Support	Insects and spiders use silk fibers to make their cocoons and webs, respectively. Collagen and elastin provide a fibrous framework in animal connective tissues. Keratin is the protein of hair, horns, feathers, and other skin appendages.
Storage proteins	Storage of amino acids	Ovalbumin is the protein of egg white, used as an amino acid source for the developing embryo. Casein, the protein of milk, is the major source of amino acids for baby mammals. Plants have storage proteins in their seeds.
Transport proteins	Transport of other substances	Hemoglobin, the iron-containing protein of vertebrate blood, transports oxygen from the lungs to other parts of the body. Other proteins transport molecules across cell membranes.
Hormonal proteins	Coordination of an organism's activities	Insulin, a hormone secreted by the pancreas, helps regulate the concentration of sugar in the blood of vertebrates.
Receptor proteins	Response of cell to chemical stimuli	Receptors built into the membrane of a nerve cell detect chemical signals released by other nerve cells.
Contractile and motor proteins	Movement	Actin and myosin are responsible for the contraction of muscles. Other proteins are responsible for the undulations of the organelles called cilia and flagella.
Defensive proteins	Protection against disease	Antibodies combat bacteria and viruses.

storage, transport, cellular communication, movement, and defense against foreign substances **(Table 5.1)**.

Life would not be possible without **enzymes**, most of which are proteins. Enzymatic proteins regulate metabolism by acting as **catalysts**, chemical agents that selectively speed up chemical reactions without being consumed by the reaction **(Figure 5.16)**.

Because an enzyme can perform its function over and over again, these molecules can be thought of as workhorses that keep cells running by carrying out the processes of life.

A human has tens of thousands of different proteins, each with a specific structure and function; proteins, in fact, are the most structurally sophisticated molecules known. Consistent with their diverse functions, they vary extensively in structure, each type of protein having a unique three-dimensional shape.

Polypeptides

Diverse as proteins are, they are all polymers constructed from the same set of 20 amino acids. Polymers of amino acids are called **polypeptides**. A **protein** consists of one or more polypeptides, each folded and coiled into a specific three-dimensional structure.

Amino Acid Monomers

All amino acids share a common structure. **Amino acids** are organic molecules possessing both carboxyl and amino groups (see Chapter 4). The illustration at the right shows the general formula for an amino acid. At the center of the amino acid is an asymmetric carbon atom called the *alpha* (α) *carbon*. Its

four different partners are an amino group, a carboxyl group, a hydrogen atom, and a variable group symbolized by R. The R group, also called the side chain, differs with each amino acid.

Figure 5.17 shows the 20 amino acids that cells use to build their thousands of proteins. Here the amino and carboxyl

① Active site is available for a molecule of substrate, the reactant on which the enzyme acts.

② Substrate binds to enzyme.

Substrate (sucrose)

Glucose

OH

Enzyme (sucrase)

Fructose

HO

H_2O

④ Products are released.

③ Substrate is converted to products.

▲ **Figure 5.16 The catalytic cycle of an enzyme.** The enzyme sucrase accelerates hydrolysis of sucrose into glucose and fructose. Acting as a catalyst, the sucrase protein is not consumed during the cycle, but remains available for further catalysis.

▲ Figure 5.17 The 20 amino acids of proteins. The amino acids are grouped here according to the properties of their side chains (R groups), highlighted in white. The amino acids are shown in their prevailing ionic forms at pH 7.2, the pH within a cell. The three-letter and more commonly used one-letter abbreviations for the amino acids are in parentheses. All the amino acids used in proteins are the same enantiomer, called the L form, as shown here (see Figure 4.7).

Nonpolar

Glycine (Gly or G)

Alanine (Ala or A)

Valine (Val or V)

Leucine (Leu or L)

Isoleucine (Ile or I)

Methionine (Met or M)

Phenylalanine (Phe or F)

Tryptophan (Trp or W)

Proline (Pro or P)

Polar

Serine (Ser or S)

Threonine (Thr or T)

Cysteine (Cys or C)

Tyrosine (Tyr or Y)

Asparagine (Asn or N)

Glutamine (Gln or Q)

Electrically charged

Acidic

Aspartic acid (Asp or D)

Glutamic acid (Glu or E)

Basic

Lysine (Lys or K)

Arginine (Arg or R)

Histidine (His or H)

groups are all depicted in ionized form, the way they usually exist at the pH in a cell. The R group may be as simple as a hydrogen atom, as in the amino acid glycine (the one amino acid lacking an asymmetric carbon, since two of its α carbon's partners are hydrogen atoms), or it may be a carbon skeleton with various functional groups attached, as in glutamine. (Organisms do have other amino acids, some of which are occasionally found in proteins. Because these are relatively rare, they are not shown in Figure 5.17.)

The physical and chemical properties of the side chain determine the unique characteristics of a particular amino acid, thus affecting its functional role in a polypeptide. In Figure 5.17, the amino acids are grouped according to the properties of their side chains. One group consists of amino acids with nonpolar side chains, which are hydrophobic. Another group consists of amino acids with polar side chains, which are hydrophilic. Acidic amino acids are those with side chains that are generally negative in charge owing to the presence of a carboxyl group, which is usually dissociated (ionized) at cellular pH. Basic amino acids have amino groups in their side chains that are generally positive in charge. (Notice that *all* amino acids have carboxyl groups and amino groups; the terms *acidic* and *basic* in this context refer only to groups on the side chains.) Because they are charged, acidic and basic side chains are also hydrophilic.

Amino Acid Polymers

Now that we have examined amino acids, let's see how they are linked to form polymers **(Figure 5.18)**. When two amino acids are positioned so that the carboxyl group of one is adjacent to the amino group of the other, they can become joined by a dehydration reaction, with the removal of a water molecule. The resulting covalent bond is called a **peptide bond**. Repeated over and over, this process yields a polypeptide, a polymer of many amino acids linked by peptide bonds. At one end of the polypeptide chain is a free amino group; at the opposite end is a free carboxyl group. Thus, the chain has an amino end (N-terminus) and a carboxyl end (C-terminus). The repeating sequence of atoms highlighted in purple in Figure 5.18b is called the polypeptide backbone. Extending from this backbone are different kinds of appendages, the side chains of the amino acids. Polypeptides range in length from a few monomers to a thousand or more. Each specific polypeptide has a unique linear sequence of amino acids. The immense variety of polypeptides in nature illustrates an important concept introduced earlier—that cells can make many different polymers by linking a limited set of monomers into diverse sequences.

Protein Structure and Function

The specific activities of proteins result from their intricate three-dimensional architecture, the simplest level of which is

(a)

(b)

Amino end (N-terminus)

Carboxyl end (C-terminus)

▲ **Figure 5.18 Making a polypeptide chain. (a)** Peptide bonds formed by dehydration reactions link the carboxyl group of one amino acid to the amino group of the next. **(b)** The peptide bonds are formed one at a time, starting with the amino acid at the amino end (N-terminus). The polypeptide has a repetitive backbone (purple) to which the amino acid side chains are attached.

DRAW IT *In (a), circle and label the carboxyl and amino groups that will form the peptide bond shown in (b).*

the sequence of their amino acids. The pioneer in determining the amino acid sequence of proteins was Frederick Sanger, who, with his colleagues at Cambridge University in England, worked on the hormone insulin in the late 1940s and early 1950s. He used agents that break polypeptides at specific places, followed by chemical methods to determine the amino acid sequence in these small fragments. Sanger and his co-workers were able, after years of effort, to reconstruct the complete amino acid sequence of insulin. Since then, most of the steps involved in sequencing a polypeptide have been automated.

Once we have learned the amino acid sequence of a polypeptide, what can it tell us about the three-dimensional structure (commonly referred to simply as the "structure") of the protein and its function? The term *polypeptide* is not synonymous with the term *protein*. Even for a protein consisting of a single polypeptide, the relationship is somewhat analogous to that between a long strand of yarn and a sweater of particular size and shape that can be knit from the yarn. A functional protein is not *just* a polypeptide chain, but one or more polypeptides precisely twisted, folded, and coiled into a molecule of unique shape **(Figure 5.19)**. And it

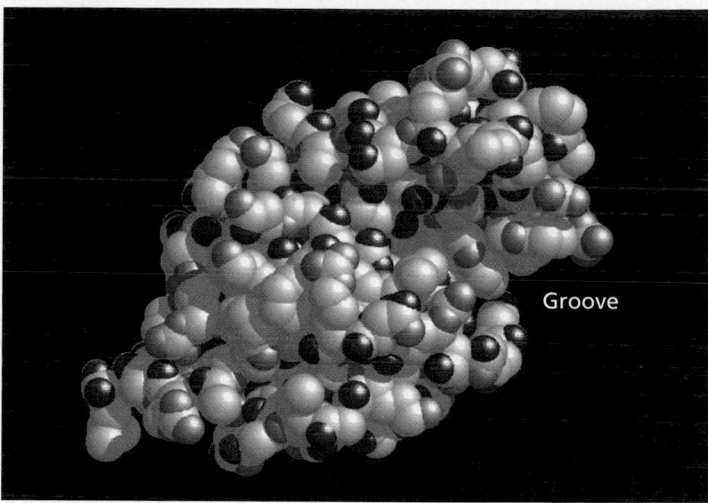

(a) A **ribbon model** shows how the single polypeptide chain folds and coils to form the functional protein. (The yellow lines represent cross-linking bonds between cysteines that stabilize the protein's shape.)

(b) A **space-filling model** shows more clearly the globular shape seen in many proteins, as well as the specific three-dimensional structure unique to lysozyme.

▲ **Figure 5.19 Structure of a protein, the enzyme lysozyme.** Present in our sweat, tears, and saliva, lysozyme is an enzyme that helps prevent infection by binding to and destroying specific molecules on the surface of many kinds of bacteria. The groove is the part of the protein that recognizes and binds to the target molecules on bacterial walls.

is the amino acid sequence of each polypeptide that determines what three-dimensional structure the protein will have.

When a cell synthesizes a polypeptide, the chain generally folds spontaneously, assuming the functional structure for that protein. This folding is driven and reinforced by the formation of a variety of bonds between parts of the chain, which in turn depends on the sequence of amino acids. Many proteins are roughly spherical (*globular proteins*), while others are shaped like long fibers (*fibrous proteins*). Even within these broad categories, countless variations exist.

A protein's specific structure determines how it works. In almost every case, the function of a protein depends on its ability to recognize and bind to some other molecule. In an especially striking example of the marriage of form and function, **Figure 5.20** shows the exact match of shape between an antibody (a protein in the body) and the particular foreign substance on a flu virus that the antibody binds to and marks for destruction. A second example is an enzyme, which must recognize and bind closely to its substrate, the substance the enzyme works on (see Figure 5.16). Also, you learned in Chapter 2 that natural signaling molecules called endorphins bind to specific receptor proteins on the surface of brain cells in humans, producing euphoria and relieving pain. Morphine, heroin, and other opiate drugs are able to mimic endorphins because they all share a similar shape with endorphins and can thus fit into and bind to endorphin receptors in the brain. This fit is very specific, something like a lock and key (see Figure 2.18). Thus, the function of a protein—for instance, the ability of a receptor protein to bind to a particular pain-relieving signaling molecule—is an emergent property resulting from exquisite molecular order.

Four Levels of Protein Structure

With the goal of understanding the function of a protein, learning about its structure is often productive. In spite of their great diversity, all proteins share three superimposed levels of structure, known as primary, secondary, and tertiary structure. A fourth level, quaternary structure, arises when a protein consists of two or more polypeptide chains. **Figure 5.21**, on the following two pages, describes these four levels of protein structure. Be sure to study this figure thoroughly before going on to the next section.

▲ **Figure 5.20 An antibody binding to a protein from a flu virus.** A technique called X-ray crystallography was used to generate a computer model of an antibody protein (blue and orange, left) bound to a flu virus protein (green and yellow, right). Computer software was then used to back the images away from each other, revealing the exact complementarity of shape between the two protein surfaces.

Exploring **Levels of Protein Structure**

Primary Structure

Examples of amino acid subunits

The **primary structure** of a protein is its unique sequence of amino acids. As an example, let's consider transthyretin, a globular protein found in the blood that transports vitamin A and one of the thyroid hormones throughout the body. Each of the four identical polypeptide chains that together make up transthyretin is composed of 127 amino acids. Shown here is one of these chains unraveled for a closer look at its primary structure. Each of the 127 positions along the chain is occupied by one of the 20 amino acids, indicated here by its three-letter abbreviation. The primary structure is like the order of letters in a very long word. If left to chance, there would be 20^{127} different ways of making a polypeptide chain 127 amino acids long. However, the precise primary structure of a protein is determined not by the random linking of amino acids, but by inherited genetic information.

Secondary Structure

β pleated sheet

α helix

Most proteins have segments of their polypeptide chains repeatedly coiled or folded in patterns that contribute to the protein's overall shape. These coils and folds, collectively referred to as **secondary structure**, are the result of hydrogen bonds between the repeating constituents of the polypeptide backbone (not the amino acid side chains). Both the oxygen and the nitrogen atoms of the backbone are electronegative, with partial negative charges (see Figure 2.16). The weakly positive hydrogen atom attached to the nitrogen atom has an affinity for the oxygen atom of a nearby peptide bond. Individually, these hydrogen bonds are weak, but because they are repeated many times over a relatively long region of the polypeptide chain, they can support a particular shape for that part of the protein.

One such secondary structure is the **α helix**, a delicate coil held together by hydrogen bonding between every fourth amino acid, shown above. Although transthyretin has only one α helix region (see tertiary structure), other globular proteins have multiple stretches of α helix separated by nonhelical regions. Some fibrous proteins, such as α-keratin, the structural protein of hair, have the α helix formation over most of their length.

The other main type of secondary structure is the **β pleated sheet**. As shown above, in this structure two or more regions of the polypeptide chain lying side by side are connected by hydrogen bonds between parts of the two parallel polypeptide backbones. Pleated sheets make up the core of many globular proteins, as is the case for transthyretin, and dominate some fibrous proteins, including the silk protein of a spider's web. The teamwork of so many hydrogen bonds makes each spider silk fiber stronger than a steel strand of the same weight.

Abdominal glands of the spider secrete silk fibers made of a structural protein containing β pleated sheets.

The radiating strands, made of dry silk fibers, maintain the shape of the web.

The spiral strands (capture strands) are elastic, stretching in response to wind, rain, and the touch of insects.

Superimposed on the patterns of secondary structure is a protein's **tertiary structure**, shown above for the transthyretin polypeptide. While secondary structure involves interactions between backbone constituents, tertiary structure is the overall shape of a polypeptide resulting from interactions between the side chains (R groups) of the various amino acids. One type of interaction that contributes to tertiary structure is—somewhat misleadingly—called a **hydrophobic interaction**. As a polypeptide folds into its functional shape, amino acids with hydrophobic (nonpolar) side chains usually end up in clusters at the core of the protein, out of contact with water. Thus, what we call a hydrophobic interaction is actually caused by the action of water molecules, which exclude nonpolar substances as they form hydrogen bonds with each other and with hydrophilic parts of the protein. Once nonpolar amino acid side chains are close together, van der Waals interactions help hold them together. Meanwhile, hydrogen bonds between polar side chains and ionic bonds between positively and negatively charged side chains also help stabilize tertiary structure. These are all weak interactions, but their cumulative effect helps give the protein a unique shape.

The shape of a protein may be reinforced further by covalent bonds called **disulfide bridges**. Disulfide bridges form where two cysteine monomers, amino acids with sulfhydryl groups (—SH) on their side chains (see Figure 4.10), are brought close together by the folding of the protein. The sulfur of one cysteine bonds to the sulfur of the second, and the disulfide bridge (—S—S—) rivets parts of the protein together (see yellow lines in Figure 5.19a). All of these different kinds of bonds can occur in one protein, as shown here in a small part of a hypothetical protein.

Some proteins consist of two or more polypeptide chains aggregated into one functional macromolecule. **Quaternary structure** is the overall protein structure that results from the aggregation of these polypeptide subunits. For example, shown above is the complete, globular transthyretin protein, made up of its four polypeptides. Another example is collagen, shown below left, which is a fibrous protein that has helical subunits intertwined into a larger triple helix, giving the long fibers great strength. This suits collagen fibers to their function as the girders of connective tissue in skin, bone, tendons, ligaments, and other body parts (collagen accounts for 40% of the protein in a human body). Hemoglobin, the oxygen-binding protein of red blood cells shown below right, is another example of a globular protein with quaternary structure. It consists of four polypeptide subunits, two of one kind ("α chains") and two of another kind ("β chains"). Both α and β subunits consist primarily of α-helical secondary structure. Each subunit has a nonpolypeptide component, called heme, with an iron atom that binds oxygen.

Hydrophobic interactions and van der Waals interactions

Polypeptide backbone

Hydrogen bond

Disulfide bridge

Ionic bond

Polypeptide chain

Collagen

β Chains

Iron
Heme

α Chains

Hemoglobin

Sickle-Cell Disease: A Change in Primary Structure

Even a slight change in primary structure can affect a protein's shape and ability to function. For instance, *sickle-cell disease*, an inherited blood disorder, is caused by the substitution of one amino acid (valine) for the normal one (glutamic acid) at a particular position in the primary structure of hemoglobin, the protein that carries oxygen in red blood cells. Normal red blood cells are disk-shaped, but in sickle-cell disease, the abnormal hemoglobin molecules tend to crystallize, deforming some of the cells into a sickle shape (Figure 5.22). The life of someone with the disease is punctuated by "sickle-cell crises," which occur when the angular cells clog tiny blood vessels, impeding blood flow. The toll taken on such patients is a dramatic example of how a simple change in protein structure can have devastating effects on protein function.

What Determines Protein Structure?

You've learned that a unique shape endows each protein with a specific function. But what are the key factors determining protein structure? You already know most of the answer: A polypeptide chain of a given amino acid sequence can spontaneously arrange itself into a three-dimensional shape determined and maintained by the interactions responsible for secondary and tertiary structure. This folding normally occurs as the protein is being synthesized within the cell. However, protein structure also depends on the physical and chemical conditions of the protein's environment. If the pH, salt concentration, temperature, or other aspects of its environment are altered, the protein may unravel and lose its native shape, a change called **denaturation (Figure 5.23)**. Because it is misshapen, the denatured protein is biologically inactive.

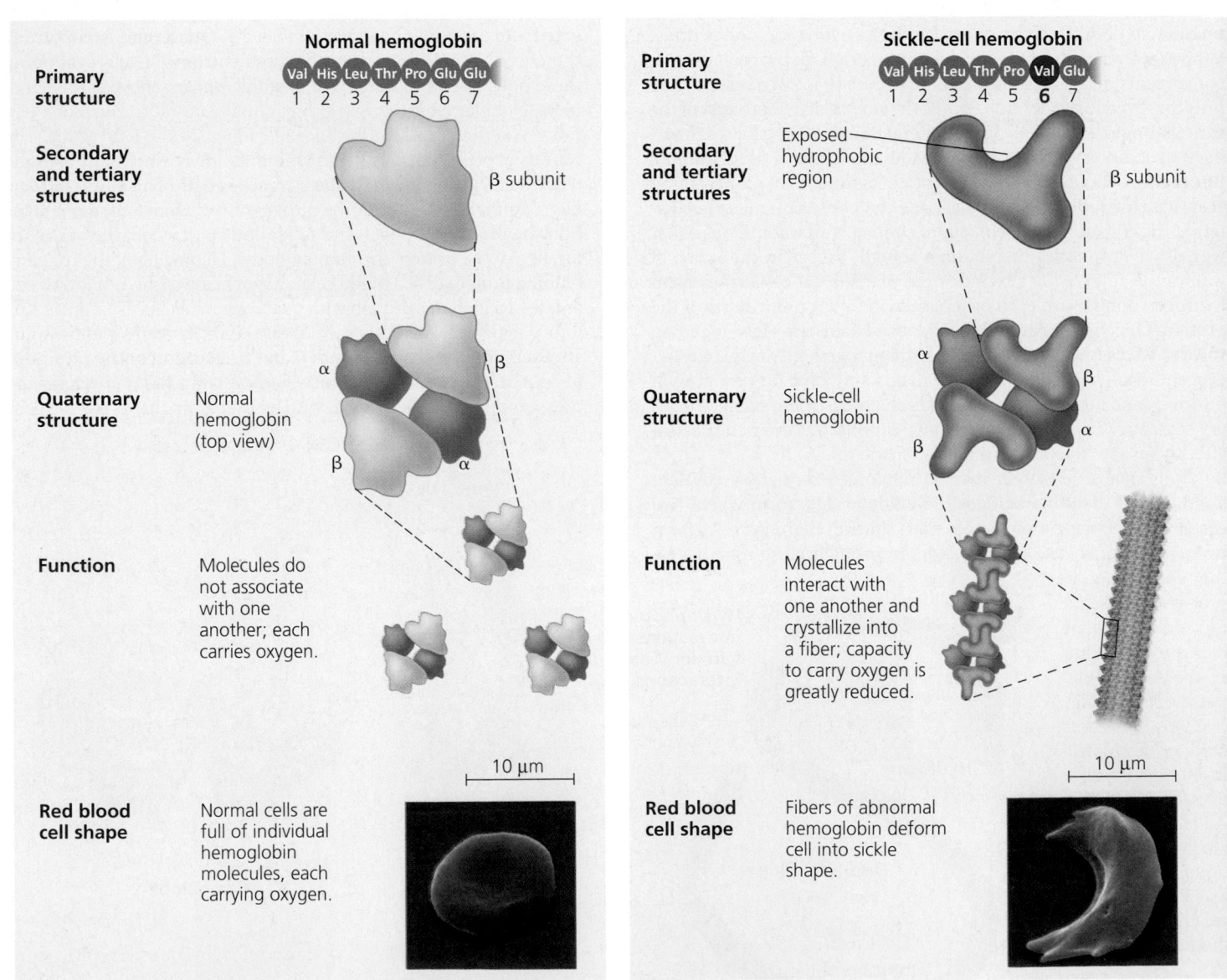

▲ **Figure 5.22 A single amino acid substitution in a protein causes sickle-cell disease.** To show fiber formation clearly, the orientation of the hemoglobin molecule here is different from that in Figure 5.21.

▲ Figure 5.23 Denaturation and renaturation of a protein.
High temperatures or various chemical treatments will denature a
protein, causing it to lose its shape and hence its ability to function. If
the denatured protein remains dissolved, it can often renature when the
chemical and physical aspects of its environment are restored to normal.

Most proteins become denatured if they are transferred
from an aqueous environment to an organic solvent, such as
ether or chloroform; the polypeptide chain refolds so that its
hydrophobic regions face outward toward the solvent. Other
denaturation agents include chemicals that disrupt the hydrogen bonds, ionic bonds, and disulfide bridges that maintain a
protein's shape. Denaturation can also result from excessive
heat, which agitates the polypeptide chain enough to over-
power the weak interactions that stabilize the structure. The
white of an egg becomes opaque during cooking because the
denatured proteins are insoluble and solidify. This also explains why excessively high fevers can be fatal: Proteins in the
blood can denature at very high body temperatures.

When a protein in a test-tube solution has been denatured
by heat or chemicals, it can sometimes return to its functional
shape when the denaturing agent is removed. We can conclude that the information for building specific shape is intrinsic to the protein's primary structure. The sequence of
amino acids determines the protein's shape—where an α helix
can form, where β pleated sheets can occur, where disulfide
bridges are located, where ionic bonds can form, and so on. In
the crowded environment inside a cell, there are also specific
proteins that aid in the folding of other proteins.

Protein Folding in the Cell

Biochemists now know the amino acid sequences of more
than 1.2 million proteins and the three-dimensional shapes of
about 8,500. One would think that by correlating the primary
structures of many proteins with their three-dimensional
structures, it would be relatively easy to discover the rules of
protein folding. Unfortunately, the protein-folding process is
not that simple. Most proteins probably go through several intermediate structures on their way to a stable shape, and looking at the mature structure does not reveal the stages of folding
required to achieve that form. However, biochemists have developed methods for tracking a protein through such stages.
Researchers have also discovered **chaperonins** (also called
chaperone proteins), protein molecules that assist in the
proper folding of other proteins **(Figure 5.24)**. Chaperonins do
not specify the final structure of a polypeptide. Instead, they
keep the new polypeptide segregated from "bad influences" in
the cytoplasmic environment while it folds spontaneously. The
chaperonin shown in Figure 5.24, from the bacterium *E. coli*, is
a giant multiprotein complex shaped like a hollow cylinder.
The cavity provides a shelter for folding polypeptides.

Misfolding of polypeptides is a serious problem in cells.
Many diseases, such as Alzheimer's and Parkinson's, are associated with an accumulation of misfolded proteins. Recently,
researchers have begun to shed light on molecular systems in
the cell that interact with chaperonins and check whether
proper folding has occurred. Such systems either refold the
misfolded proteins correctly or mark them for destruction.

Even when scientists have a correctly folded protein in hand,
determining its exact three-dimensional structure is not simple,
for a single protein molecule has thousands of atoms. The first
3-D structures were worked out in 1959, for hemoglobin and a
related protein. The method that made these feats possible was
X-ray crystallography, which has since been used to determine
the 3-D structures of many other proteins. In a recent example, Roger Kornberg and his colleagues at Stanford University
used this method in order to elucidate the structure of RNA
polymerase, an enzyme that plays a crucial role in the expression

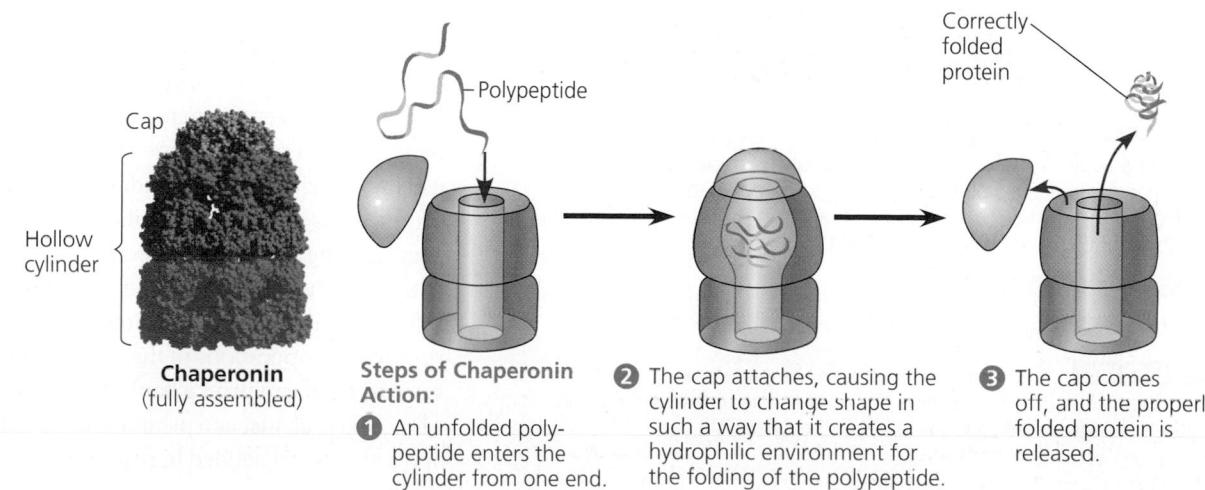

**▶ Figure 5.24 A
chaperonin in
action.** The computer
graphic (left) shows a
large chaperonin protein
complex. It has an
interior space that
provides a shelter for the
proper folding of newly
made polypeptides. The
complex consists of two
proteins: One protein is
a hollow cylinder; the
other is a cap that can fit
on either end.

Cap

Hollow
cylinder

Chaperonin
(fully assembled)

Polypeptide

Correctly
folded
protein

**Steps of Chaperonin
Action:**
❶ An unfolded poly-
peptide enters the
cylinder from one end.

❷ The cap attaches, causing the
cylinder to change shape in
such a way that it creates a
hydrophilic environment for
the folding of the polypeptide.

❸ The cap comes
off, and the properly
folded protein is
released.

of genes (**Figure 5.25**). Another method now in use is nuclear magnetic resonance (NMR) spectroscopy, which does not require protein crystallization.

A still newer approach uses bioinformatics (see Chapter 1) to predict the 3-D structures of polypeptides from their amino acid sequences. In 2005, researchers in Austria used comput-

ers to analyze the sequences and structures of 129 common plant protein allergens. They were able to classify all of these allergens into 20 families of proteins out of 3,849 families and 65% into just 4 families. This result suggests that the shared structures in these protein families may play a role in generating allergic reactions. These structures may provide targets for new allergy medications.

X-ray crystallography, NMR spectroscopy, and bioinformatics are complementary approaches to understanding protein structure. Together they have also given us valuable hints about protein function.

CONCEPT CHECK 5.4

1. Why does a denatured protein no longer function normally?
2. What parts of a polypeptide chain participate in the bonds that hold together secondary structure? What parts participate in tertiary structure?
3. **WHAT IF?** If a genetic mutation changes primary structure, how might it destroy the protein's function?

For suggested answers, see Appendix A.

▼ Figure 5.25 Inquiry

What can the 3-D shape of the enzyme RNA polymerase II tell us about its function?

EXPERIMENT In 2006, Roger Kornberg was awarded the Nobel Prize in Chemistry for using X-ray crystallography to determine the 3-D shape of RNA polymerase II, which binds to the DNA double helix and synthesizes RNA. After crystallizing a complex of all three components, Kornberg and his colleagues aimed an X-ray beam through the crystal. The atoms of the crystal diffracted (bent) the X-rays into an orderly array that a digital detector recorded as a pattern of spots called an X-ray diffraction pattern.

RESULTS Using data from X-ray diffraction patterns, as well as the amino acid sequence determined by chemical methods, Kornberg and colleagues built a 3-D model of the complex with the help of computer software.

CONCLUSION By analyzing their model, the researchers developed a hypothesis about the functions of different regions of RNA polymerase II. For example, the region above the DNA may act as a clamp that holds the nucleic acids in place. (You'll learn more about this enzyme in Chapter 17.)

SOURCE A. L. Gnatt et al., Structural basis of transcription: an RNA polymerase II elongation complex at 3.3Å, *Science* 292:1876–1882 (2001).

WHAT IF? If you were an author of the paper and were describing the model, what type of protein structure would you call the small green polypeptide spiral in the center?

CONCEPT 5.5
Nucleic acids store and transmit hereditary information

If the primary structure of polypeptides determines a protein's shape, what determines primary structure? The amino acid sequence of a polypeptide is programmed by a unit of inheritance known as a **gene**. Genes consist of DNA, a polymer belonging to the class of compounds known as **nucleic acids**.

The Roles of Nucleic Acids

The two types of nucleic acids, **deoxyribonucleic acid (DNA)** and **ribonucleic acid (RNA)**, enable living organisms to reproduce their complex components from one generation to the next. Unique among molecules, DNA provides directions for its own replication. DNA also directs RNA synthesis and, through RNA, controls protein synthesis (**Figure 5.26**).

DNA is the genetic material that organisms inherit from their parents. Each chromosome contains one long DNA molecule, usually carrying several hundred or more genes. When a cell reproduces itself by dividing, its DNA molecules are copied and passed along from one generation of cells to the next. Encoded in the structure of DNA is the information that programs all the cell's activities. The DNA, however, is not directly involved in running the operations of the cell, any more than computer software by itself can print a bank statement or read the bar code on a box of cereal. Just as a printer is needed to print out a statement and a scanner is needed to read a bar code, proteins are required

1 Synthesis of mRNA in the nucleus

DNA

mRNA

NUCLEUS

CYTOPLASM

2 Movement of mRNA into cytoplasm via nuclear pore

mRNA

Ribosome

3 Synthesis of protein

Polypeptide

Amino acids

▲ **Figure 5.26 DNA → RNA → protein.** In a eukaryotic cell, DNA in the nucleus programs protein production in the cytoplasm by dictating synthesis of messenger RNA (mRNA). (The cell nucleus is actually much larger relative to the other elements of this figure.)

to implement genetic programs. The molecular hardware of the cell—the tools for biological functions—consists mostly of proteins. For example, the oxygen carrier in red blood cells is the protein hemoglobin, not the DNA that specifies its structure.

How does RNA, the other type of nucleic acid, fit into the flow of genetic information from DNA to proteins? Each gene along a DNA molecule directs synthesis of a type of RNA called *messenger RNA* (*mRNA*). The mRNA molecule interacts with the cell's protein-synthesizing machinery to direct production of a polypeptide, which folds into all or part of a protein. We can summarize the flow of genetic information as DNA → RNA → protein (see Figure 5.26). The sites of protein synthesis are tiny structures called ribosomes. In a eukaryotic cell, ribosomes are in the cytoplasm, but DNA resides in the nucleus. Messenger RNA conveys genetic instructions for building proteins from the nucleus to the cytoplasm. Prokaryotic cells lack nuclei but still use RNA to convey a message from the DNA to ribosomes and other cellular equipment that translate the coded information into amino acid sequences. RNA also plays many other roles in the cell.

The Structure of Nucleic Acids

Nucleic acids are macromolecules that exist as polymers called **polynucleotides (Figure 5.27a)**. As indicated by the

5′ end

5′C

3′C

5′C

3′C

5′C

3′C

OH

3′ end

(a) Polynucleotide, or nucleic acid

Nucleoside

Nitrogenous base

$-O-P-O-$ 5′C

CH_2

Phosphate group

3′C

Sugar (pentose)

(b) Nucleotide

▲ **Figure 5.27 Components of nucleic acids. (a)** A polynucleotide has a sugar-phosphate backbone with variable appendages, the nitrogenous bases. **(b)** A nucleotide monomer includes a nitrogenous base, a sugar, and a phosphate group. Without the phosphate group, the structure is called a nucleoside. **(c)** A nucleoside includes a nitrogenous base (purine or pyrimidine) and a five-carbon sugar (deoxyribose or ribose).

Nitrogenous bases

Pyrimidines

Cytosine (C)   Thymine (T, in DNA)   Uracil (U, in RNA)

Purines

Adenine (A)   Guanine (G)

Sugars

$HOCH_2$

Deoxyribose (in DNA)   Ribose (in RNA)

(c) Nucleoside components

name, each polynucleotide consists of monomers called **nucleotides**. A nucleotide is itself composed of three parts: a nitrogenous base, a five-carbon sugar (a pentose), and a phosphate group **(Figure 5.27b)**. The portion of this unit without the phosphate group is called a *nucleoside*.

Nucleotide Monomers

To build a nucleotide, let's first consider the two components of the nucleoside: the nitrogenous base and the sugar **(Figure 5.27c)**. There are two families of nitrogenous bases: pyrimidines and purines. A **pyrimidine** has a six-membered ring of carbon and nitrogen atoms. (The nitrogen atoms tend to take up H^+ from solution, which explains why it's called a nitrogenous *base.*) The members of the pyrimidine family are cytosine (C), thymine (T), and uracil (U). **Purines** are larger, with a six-membered ring fused to a five-membered ring. The purines are adenine (A) and guanine (G). The specific pyrimidines and purines differ in the chemical groups attached to the rings. Adenine, guanine, and cytosine are found in both types of nucleic acid; thymine is found only in DNA and uracil only in RNA.

The sugar connected to the nitrogenous base is **ribose** in the nucleotides of RNA and **deoxyribose** in DNA (see Figure 5.27c). The only difference between these two sugars is that deoxyribose lacks an oxygen atom on the second carbon in the ring; hence the name *deoxy*ribose. Because the atoms in both the nitrogenous base and the sugar are numbered, the sugar atoms have a prime (′) after the number to distinguish them. Thus, the second carbon in the sugar ring is the 2′ ("2 prime") carbon, and the carbon that sticks up from the ring is called the 5′ carbon.

So far, we have built a nucleoside. To complete the construction of a nucleotide, we attach a phosphate group to the 5′ carbon of the sugar (see Figure 5.27b). The molecule is now a nucleoside monophosphate, better known as a nucleotide.

Nucleotide Polymers

Now we can see how these nucleotides are linked together to build a polynucleotide. Adjacent nucleotides are joined by a phosphodiester linkage, which consists of a phosphate group that links the sugars of two nucleotides. This bonding results in a backbone with a repeating pattern of sugar-phosphate units (see Figure 5.27a). The two free ends of the polymer are distinctly different from each other. One end has a phosphate attached to a 5′ carbon, and the other end has a hydroxyl group on a 3′ carbon; we refer to these as the 5′ end and the 3′ end, respectively. We can say that the DNA strand has a built-in directionality along its sugar-phosphate backbone, from 5′ to 3′, somewhat like a one-way street. All along this sugar-phosphate backbone are appendages consisting of the nitrogenous bases.

The sequence of bases along a DNA (or mRNA) polymer is unique for each gene and provides very specific information to the cell. Because genes are hundreds to thousands of nucleotides long, the number of possible base sequences is effectively limitless. A gene's meaning to the cell is encoded in its specific sequence of the four DNA bases. For example, the sequence AGGTAACTT means one thing, whereas the sequence CGCTTTAAC has a different meaning. (Entire genes, of course, are much longer.) The linear order of bases in a gene specifies the amino acid sequence—the primary structure—of a protein, which in turn specifies that protein's three-dimensional structure and function in the cell.

The DNA Double Helix

The RNA molecules of cells consist of a single polynucleotide chain like the one shown in Figure 5.27. In contrast, cellular DNA molecules have two polynucleotides that spiral around an imaginary axis, forming a **double helix** **(Figure 5.28)**. James Watson and Francis Crick, working at Cambridge University, first proposed the double helix as the three-dimensional structure of DNA in 1953. The two sugar-phosphate backbones run in opposite 5′ → 3′ directions from each other, an arrangement referred to as **antiparallel**, somewhat like a divided highway. The sugar-phosphate backbones are on the outside of the helix, and the nitrogenous bases are paired in the interior of the helix. The two polynucleotides, or strands, as they are called, are held together by hydrogen bonds between the paired bases and by van der Waals interactions between the stacked bases. Most DNA molecules are very long, with thousands or even millions of base pairs connecting the two chains. One long DNA double helix includes many genes, each one a particular segment of the molecule.

Only certain bases in the double helix are compatible with each other. Adenine (A) always pairs with thymine (T), and guanine (G) always pairs with cytosine (C). If we were to read the sequence of bases along one strand as we traveled the length of the double helix, we would know the sequence of bases along the other strand. If a stretch of one strand has the base sequence 5′-AGGTCCG-3′, then the base-pairing rules tell us that the same stretch of the other strand must have the sequence 3′-TCCAGGC-5′. The two strands of the double helix are *complementary,* each the predictable counterpart of the other. It is this feature of DNA that makes possible the precise copying of genes that is responsible for inheritance (see Figure 5.28). In preparation for cell division, each of the two strands of a DNA molecule serves as a template to order nucleotides into a new complementary strand. The result is two identical copies of the original double-stranded DNA molecule, which are then distributed to the two daughter cells. Thus, the structure of DNA accounts for its function in transmitting genetic information whenever a cell reproduces.

DNA and Proteins as Tape Measures of Evolution

We are accustomed to thinking of shared traits, such as hair and milk production in mammals, as evidence of shared ancestors. Because we now understand that DNA carries heritable information in the form of genes, we can see that genes and their products (proteins) document the hereditary background of an organism. The linear sequences of nucleotides in DNA molecules are passed from parents to offspring; these sequences determine the amino acid sequences of proteins. Siblings have greater similarity in their DNA and proteins than do unrelated individuals of the same species. If the evolutionary view of life is valid, we should be able to extend this concept of "molecular genealogy" to relationships *between* species: We should expect two species that appear to be closely related based on fossil and anatomical evidence to also share a greater proportion of their DNA and protein sequences than do more distantly related species. In fact, that is the case. An example is the comparison of a polypeptide chain of human hemoglobin with the corresponding hemoglobin polypeptide in five other vertebrates. In this chain of 146 amino acids, humans and gorillas differ in just 1 amino acid, while humans and frogs differ in 67 amino acids. (Clearly, these changes do not make the protein nonfunctional.)

Molecular biology has added a new tape measure to the toolkit biologists use to assess evolutionary kinship.

CONCEPT CHECK 5.5

1. Go to Figure 5.27a and number all the carbons in the sugars for the top three nucleotides; circle the nitrogenous bases and star the phosphates.
2. In a DNA double helix, a region along one DNA strand has this sequence of nitrogenous bases: 5'-TAGGCCT-3'. Write down this strand and its complementary strand, clearly indicating the 5' and 3' ends of the complementary strand.
3. **WHAT IF?** (a) Suppose a substitution occurred in one DNA strand of the double helix in question 2, resulting in:

   5'-TAAGCCT-3'
   3'-ATCCGGA-5'

   Draw the two strands; circle and label the mismatched bases. (b) If the modified top strand is replicated, what would its matching strand be?

For suggested answers, see Appendix A.

▶ **Figure 5.28 The DNA double helix and its replication.** The DNA molecule is usually double-stranded, with the sugar-phosphate backbone of the antiparallel polynucleotide strands (symbolized here by blue ribbons) on the outside of the helix. Holding the two strands together are pairs of nitrogenous bases attached to each other by hydrogen bonds. As illustrated here with symbolic shapes for the bases, adenine (A) can pair only with thymine (T), and guanine (G) can pair only with cytosine (C). When a cell prepares to divide, the two strands of the double helix separate, and each serves as a template for the precise ordering of nucleotides into new complementary strands (orange). Each DNA strand in this figure is the structural equivalent of the polynucleotide diagrammed in Figure 5.27a.

The Theme of Emergent Properties in the Chemistry of Life: *A Review*

Recall that life is organized along a hierarchy of structural levels (see Figure 1.4). With each increasing level of order, new properties emerge. In Chapters 2–5, we have dissected the chemistry of life. But we have also begun to develop a more integrated view of life, exploring how properties emerge with increasing order.

We have seen that water's behavior results from interactions of its molecules, each an ordered arrangement of hydrogen and oxygen atoms. We reduced the complexity and diversity of organic compounds to carbon skeletons and appended chemical groups. We saw that macromolecules are assembled from small organic molecules, taking on new properties. By completing our overview with an introduction to macromolecules and lipids, we have built a bridge to Unit Two, where we will study cell structure and function. We will keep a balance between the need to reduce life to simpler processes and the ultimate satisfaction of viewing those processes in their integrated context.

Chapter 5 Review

MEDIA Go to www.campbellbiology.com for BioFlix 3-D Animations, MP3 Tutors, Videos, Practice Tests, an eBook, and more.

SUMMARY OF KEY CONCEPTS

CONCEPT 5.1

Macromolecules are polymers, built from monomers (pp. 68–69)

▶ **The Synthesis and Breakdown of Polymers** Carbohydrates, proteins, and nucleic acids are polymers, chains of monomers. The components of lipids vary. Monomers form larger molecules by dehydration reactions, in which water molecules are released. Polymers can disassemble by the reverse process, hydrolysis.

▶ **The Diversity of Polymers** An immense variety of polymers can be built from a small set of monomers.

MEDIA

Activity Making and Breaking Polymers

Large Biological Molecules	Components	Examples	Functions
Concept 5.2 **Carbohydrates serve as fuel and building material (pp. 69–74)** **MEDIA** Activity Models of Glucose Activity Carbohydrates	 Monosaccharide monomer	Monosaccharides: glucose, fructose	Fuel; carbon sources that can be converted to other molecules or combined into polymers
		Disaccharides: lactose, sucrose	
		Polysaccharides: • Cellulose (plants) • Starch (plants) • Glycogen (animals) • Chitin (animals and fungi)	• Strengthens plant cell walls • Stores glucose for energy • Stores glucose for energy • Strengthens exoskeletons and fungal cell walls
Concept 5.3 **Lipids are a diverse group of hydrophobic molecules (pp. 74–77)** **MEDIA** Activity Lipids	 Glycerol 3 fatty acids	Triacylglycerols (fats or oils): glycerol + 3 fatty acids	Important energy source
	 Head with P 2 fatty acids	Phospholipids: phosphate group + 2 fatty acids	Lipid bilayers of membranes Hydrophobic tails Hydrophilic heads
	 Steroid backbone	Steroids: four fused rings with attached chemical groups	• Component of cell membranes (cholesterol) • Signaling molecules that travel through the body (hormones)
Concept 5.4 **Proteins have many structures, resulting in a wide range of functions (pp. 77–86)** **MEDIA** MP3 Tutor Protein Structure and Function Activity Protein Functions Activity Protein Structure Biology Labs On-Line HemoglobinLab	 Amino acid monomer (20 types)	• Enzymes • Structural proteins • Storage proteins • Transport proteins • Hormones • Receptor proteins • Motor proteins • Defensive proteins	• Catalyze chemical reactions • Provide structural support • Store amino acids • Transport substances • Coordinate organismal responses • Receive signals from outside cell • Function in cell movement • Protect against disease
Concept 5.5 **Nucleic acids store and transmit hereditary information (pp. 86–89)** **MEDIA** Activity Nucleic Acid Functions Activity Nucleic Acid Structure	 Nitrogenous base Phosphate group Sugar Nucleotide monomer	DNA: • Sugar = deoxyribose • Nitrogenous bases = C, G, A, T • Usually double-stranded	Stores all hereditary information
		RNA: • Sugar = ribose • Nitrogenous bases = C, G, A, U • Usually single-stranded	Carries protein-coding instructions from DNA to protein-synthesizing machinery

TESTING YOUR KNOWLEDGE

SELF-QUIZ

1. Which term includes all others in the list?
   - a. monosaccharide
   - b. disaccharide
   - c. starch
   - d. carbohydrate
   - e. polysaccharide

2. The molecular formula for glucose is $C_6H_{12}O_6$. What would be the molecular formula for a polymer made by linking ten glucose molecules together by dehydration reactions?
   - a. $C_{60}H_{120}O_{60}$
   - b. $C_6H_{12}O_6$
   - c. $C_{60}H_{102}O_{51}$
   - d. $C_{60}H_{100}O_{50}$
   - e. $C_{60}H_{111}O_{51}$

3. The enzyme amylase can break glycosidic linkages between glucose monomers only if the monomers are the α form. Which of the following could amylase break down?
   - a. glycogen, starch, and amylopectin
   - b. glycogen and cellulose
   - c. cellulose and chitin
   - d. starch and chitin
   - e. starch, amylopectin, and cellulose

4. Which of the following statements concerning *unsaturated* fats is true?
   - a. They are more common in animals than in plants.
   - b. They have double bonds in the carbon chains of their fatty acids.
   - c. They generally solidify at room temperature.
   - d. They contain more hydrogen than saturated fats having the same number of carbon atoms.
   - e. They have fewer fatty acid molecules per fat molecule.

5. The structural level of a protein least affected by a disruption in hydrogen bonding is the
   - a. primary level.
   - b. secondary level.
   - c. tertiary level.
   - d. quaternary level.
   - e. All structural levels are equally affected.

6. Which of the following pairs of base sequences could form a short stretch of a normal double helix of DNA?
   - a. 5'-purine-pyrimidine-purine-pyrimidine-3' with 3'-purine-pyrimidine-purine-pyrimidine-5'
   - b. 5'-AGCT-3' with 5'-TCGA-3'
   - c. 5'-GCGC-3' with 5'-TATA-3'
   - d. 5'-ATGC-3' with 5'-GCAT-3'
   - e. All of these pairs are correct.

7. Enzymes that break down DNA catalyze the hydrolysis of the covalent bonds that join nucleotides together. What would happen to DNA molecules treated with these enzymes?
   - a. The two strands of the double helix would separate.
   - b. The phosphodiester linkages between deoxyribose sugars would be broken.
   - c. The purines would be separated from the deoxyribose sugars.
   - d. The pyrimidines would be separated from the deoxyribose sugars.
   - e. All bases would be separated from the deoxyribose sugars.

8. Construct a table that organizes the following terms, and label the columns and rows.

phosphodiester linkages	polypeptides	monosaccharides
peptide bonds	triacylglycerols	nucleotides
glycosidic linkages	polynucleotides	amino acids
ester linkages	polysaccharides	fatty acids

9. **DRAW IT** Draw the polynucleotide strand in Figure 5.27a and label the bases G, T, C, and T, starting from the 5' end. Now draw the complementary strand of the double helix, using the same symbols for phosphates (circles), sugars (pentagons), and bases. Label the bases. Draw arrows showing the 5' → 3' direction of each strand. Use the arrows to make sure the second strand is antiparallel to the first. *Hint:* After you draw the first strand vertically, turn the paper upside down; it is easier to draw the second strand from the 5' toward the 3' direction as you go from top to bottom.

For Self-Quiz answers, see Appendix A.

MEDIA Visit **www.campbellbiology.com** for a Practice Test.

EVOLUTION CONNECTION

10. Comparisons of amino acid sequences can shed light on the evolutionary divergence of related species. Would you expect all the proteins of a given set of living species to show the same degree of divergence? Why or why not?

SCIENTIFIC INQUIRY

11. During the Napoleonic Wars in the early 1800s, there was a sugar shortage in Europe because supply ships could not enter blockaded harbors. To create artificial sweeteners, German scientists hydrolyzed wheat starch. They did this by adding hydrochloric acid to heated starch solutions, breaking some of the glycosidic linkages between the glucose monomers. The graph here shows the percentage of glycosidic linkages broken over time. Why do you think consumers found the sweetener to be less sweet than sugar? Sketch a glycosidic linkage in starch using Figures 5.5a and 5.7b for reference. Show how the acid was able to break this bond. Why do you think the acid broke only 50% of the linkages in the wheat starch?

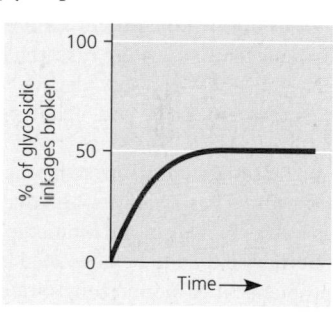

Biological Inquiry: A Workbook of Investigative Cases Explore large biological molecules further with the case "Picture Perfect."

SCIENCE, TECHNOLOGY, AND SOCIETY

12. Some amateur and professional athletes take anabolic steroids to help them "bulk up" or build strength. The health risks of this practice are extensively documented. Apart from health considerations, how do you feel about the use of chemicals to enhance athletic performance? Is an athlete who takes anabolic steroids cheating, or is such use part of the preparation that is required to succeed in competition? Explain.

The Cell

AN INTERVIEW WITH

Paul Nurse

British biologist Sir Paul Nurse shared a Nobel Prize in 2001 with Leland H. Hartwell and R. Timothy Hunt for groundbreaking discoveries about how the eukaryotic cell controls its reproduction. Educated at the Universities of Birmingham and East Anglia, Dr. Nurse was a professor at the University of Oxford and a researcher at the Imperial Cancer Research Fund (now called Cancer Research UK), eventually heading up the latter organization. In 2003, he left the United Kingdom for Rockefeller University in New York City, where he serves as president while also running an active research laboratory.

Tell us about Rockefeller University.
Rockefeller is basically a research institute that gives Ph.D.'s. We have no departments; instead, we have between 70 and 80 independent laboratories. Our sole purpose is to do the highest-quality research relevant to biomedicine. We have physicists, chemists, and mathematicians, as well as biologists and biomedical scientists, but they all tend to be interested in biological problems. It's a wonderfully stimulating environment— and rather anarchic, but I'm happy with that. In my role as president, I focus very much on having the best people around, and then just letting them loose to investigate what they want. I'm very privileged to be here.

How did you first become interested in science, and biology in particular?
When I was a child, I had a long walk to my school through a couple of parks, and I liked to look at the plants, the birds, and the insects. I remember wondering why certain plants seemed to have big leaves when they grew in the shade and small leaves when they grew in sunlight. I also had an interest in astronomy, which I still have. So the origin of my interest in science was really through natural history.

I wasn't the greatest of students at school. My parents were working class, and we didn't have many books at home. It took me quite a while to get up to speed. But I had a tremendous curiosity to learn about the world around me. Then, as a teenager, I had a science teacher who really encouraged me, named Keith Neil. I did a number of biology projects with him—a fruit fly project, censuses of butterflies and beetles, and a trout egg-laying project in the lab. After I got the Nobel Prize, I nominated him for a mentoring award and did a TV program with him. I think my interest in biology was also influenced by a sense that there were so many unanswered questions in biology that even an ordinary mortal could contribute to the field in some way!

At university, I was at first going to concentrate on ecology and evolution, but I ended up going for subjects that seemed easier to study in a laboratory—cell biology and genetics.

What led you to study the cell cycle?
As a graduate student, I asked myself, "What's really important in biology?" I thought it would be important to focus on the features that distinguish life from nonlife, and a key one of those is the ability of an organism to reproduce itself. You see reproduction in its simplest form in the division of a cell because the cell is the simplest unit of life.

What did you want to find out about cell division?
The cell cycle is a series of events from the "birth" of a cell to its later division into two cells. I wanted to understand how the different events in the cell cycle were coordinated—what controlled the progression of cell-cycle events. In fact, I have ended up spending most of my life trying to answer that question!

There were two alternative ideas about how the cell cycle works: One was that the cell simply proceeds automatically through the events in the pathway, from A to B to C to D, and so forth. Another was that a smaller number of rate-limiting steps within the pathway serve as control points. These control points would determine how rapidly the cell cycle progressed.

How did you proceed to figure out which hypothesis was correct?
My inspiration came from Lee Hartwell, who had used genetics in budding yeast (the yeast used by bakers and brewers) to find mutants with defects in the cell cycle. This is the classical genetic approach. You look for what stops a system from working to tell you how it should be working. I used Lee's work as a template, but I used a different sort of yeast, called fission yeast, which is actually not closely related to budding yeast. Like Lee, I isolated mutants with defects in genes that defined particular steps in the cell-cycle process. We called them *cdc* genes—*cdc* for *c*ell *d*ivision *c*ycle.

In reproducing, a cell of fission yeast first grows to twice its starting size and then divides in two. I looked for mutants that couldn't divide, where the cells just got bigger and bigger. Finding such mutants told us that the genes defective in these cells were necessary for the cells to divide. And when you find a number of different kinds of mutants that are defective in a process, the obvious interpretation is that the process is a pathway of events, each of which is controlled by one or more genes. So the cell cycle could have worked like a straightforward pathway, with each step simply leading to the next.

But one day I happened to notice a different sort of mutant under the microscope: yeast cells that were dividing but at an unusually small size. I realized that if a cell went through the cell cycle faster than normal, it would reach the end of the cell cycle before it had doubled in size. The mutant I'd spotted had only a single mutation, in a single gene, but it was sufficient to make the whole cell cycle go faster. That meant there had to be at least some major rate-limiting steps in the cell cycle, because if they didn't exist you couldn't make the cell cycle go faster. So the second hypothesis seemed to be correct.

All of that came out of just looking at those small mutant cells for five minutes. I could say that most of the next twenty years of my career was based on those five minutes!

It's essential to add that many other scientists have contributed to the field of cell cycle regulation, working in many different places. In addition to Lee Hartwell, who is in Seattle, these people included Yoshio Masui in Toronto and Jim Maller in Colorado, who both worked with frog eggs, and my longtime friend Tim Hunt, in England, who studied the eggs of sea urchins.

You focused in on a mutant with a defect in a gene you called *cdc2*. What does this gene do?
It turned out that the *cdc2* gene codes for an enzyme called a protein kinase. Protein kinases are heavily used by cells as a means of regulating what other proteins do. There are hundreds of different kinds of these enzymes—over 500 in human cells, for example. What they do is phosphorylate other proteins: They take phosphates from ATP molecules and transfer them to proteins. Phosphate groups are big lumps of negative charge, and they can change the shape of a protein and therefore its properties. So showing that *cdc2* coded for a protein kinase was important in identifying protein phosphorylation as a key regulatory mechanism in the cell cycle. Eventually we showed that, in fission yeast, the *cdc2* protein kinase is used fairly early in the cell cycle, where it controls the replication of DNA, and then again later in the cycle, when the replicated chromosomes are ready to separate from each other in mitosis. This is soon before the cell divides in two.

Do similar enzymes control the cell cycle in other kinds of organisms?
A postdoc in my lab, Melanie Lee, was able to track down the human equivalent of the yeast *cdc2* gene, by showing that it was able to substitute for a defective *cdc2* gene in a yeast cell. After we put the human gene in a yeast cell that had a defective *cdc2* gene, the yeast cell was able to divide normally!

It turns out that the Cdc2 protein and many others involved in cell-cycle regulation are very similar in all eukaryotic organisms. What this has to mean is that this system of controlling cell division must have evolved very soon after eukaryotic cells first appeared on the planet, and that it was so crucial to cell survival that it remained unchanged. We have found the *cdc2* gene, for example, in every eukaryotic organism we've looked at.

What is the medical relevance of research on the cell cycle?
The main medical relevance is to cancer, because cancer occurs when cells grow and divide out of control. Now, growth and division is a good thing in the right place at the right time; it's how a fertilized human egg develops into a baby and how wounds in the body are repaired. But if you start getting growth and division in the wrong place at the wrong time, then you can get tumors that destroy the function of the organs or tissue in which they are located.

But maybe, in the end, the more important connection to cancer has to do with what's called genome stability. You have to precisely replicate all your genes in every cell cycle and then separate them precisely into the two progeny cells—that's what the cell cycle is all about. If there are mistakes, if the DNA does not replicate properly or the chromosomes don't separate properly, you end up generating genome instability, in which the number of chromosomes may be altered and parts of chromosomes rearranged. Such changes can lead to cancer. So understanding how genome stability is maintained is crucial for understanding how cancer arises.

What is your approach to mentoring young scientists in your lab? And what about collaboration with other labs?
I've always run a pretty disorganized lab. With students and postdocs, I look upon my job as not so much directing them as helping them follow their own interests, although I do try to keep them from falling into too many elephant traps. The lab is a bit inefficient, to be honest, because we're constantly starting new projects. But since people take these projects away with them when they leave, this practice helps the field expand very fast.

My collaboration with people outside my own lab is mostly in the form of talking. I find I think much better when I can bounce around ideas with other people. This sort of conversation is especially useful when there is a very honest and open relationship—it's good to be sufficiently comfortable with someone to be able to say, "What you just said was stupid." I've benefited from such frank discussions for decades with Tim Hunt, for example, but we've never published a paper together. Tim discovered another kind of cell-cycle control protein, called cyclin, which works in partnership with protein kinases like Cdc2. The protein kinases we've been talking about in this interview are therefore called cyclin-dependent kinases, or CDKs.

What responsibilities do scientists have toward society?
I always say that scientists need to have a "license to operate." We have to earn that license; we cannot assume society will be pro-science. When I was younger, I used to think: Well, I'm doing this because I'm curious, and science should be supported because it's an important cultural endeavor, something like art or music. But we have to realize that if we can justify science only in cultural terms, science budgets will plummet. The public and their governmental representatives want to use scientific discoveries to benefit humankind, and that's completely reasonable. I think it's critical that scientists communicate effectively with the public so that we can influence policymakers in government. Most importantly, we scientists have to listen to the public and understand how they see the issues; we need to have a dialogue with the public. Without that dialogue, we just don't know what misunderstandings are out there. I think we need more grassroots involvement by scientists.

. . . this system of controlling cell division must have evolved very soon after eukaryotic cells first appeared on the planet.

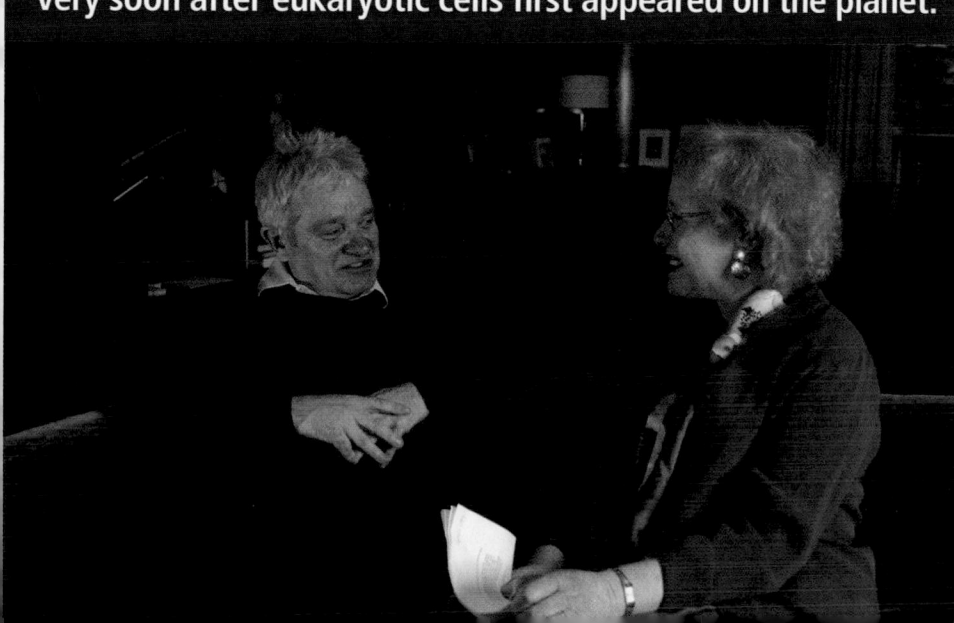

Inquiry in Action

Learn about an experiment by Paul Nurse and colleagues in Inquiry Figure 12.16 on page 240.

Paul Nurse and Jane Reece

A Tour of the Cell

6

▲ **Figure 6.1 How do cellular components cooperate to help the cell function?**

OVERVIEW

The Fundamental Units of Life

What do a small compartment in a honeycomb, a prison room, and the area covered by a mobile phone tower have in common with a microscopic part of your body? Each is the simplest unit of function in a larger system, and each is described by the word *cell*. The cell is as fundamental to the living systems of biology as the atom is to chemistry: All organisms are made of cells.

In the hierarchy of biological organization, the cell is the simplest collection of matter that can live. Indeed, there are diverse forms of life existing as single-celled organisms. More complex organisms, including plants and animals, are multicellular; their bodies are cooperatives of many kinds of specialized cells that could not survive for long on their own. However, even when they are arranged into higher levels of organization, such as tissues and organs, cells are an organism's

basic units of structure and function. The contraction of muscle cells moves your eyes as you read this sentence; when you decide to turn the next page, nerve cells will transmit that decision from your brain to the muscle cells of your hand. Each action of an organism begins at the cellular level.

The cell is a microcosm that demonstrates most of the themes introduced in Chapter 1. Life at the cellular level arises from structural order, reflecting emergent properties and the correlation between structure and function. For example, the movement of an animal cell depends on an intricate interplay of the structures that make up a cellular skeleton (the colored fibers in the micrograph in **Figure 6.1**). Another recurring theme in biology is the interaction of organisms with their environment. Cells sense and respond to environmental fluctuations. And keep in mind the one biological theme that unifies all others: evolution. All cells are related by their descent from earlier cells. However, they have been modified in many different ways during the long evolutionary history of life on Earth.

Although cells can differ substantially from one another, they share certain common characteristics. In this chapter, we'll first examine the tools and experimental approaches that allow us to understand subcellular details; then we'll tour the cell and become acquainted with its components.

CONCEPT 6.1

To study cells, biologists use microscopes and the tools of biochemistry

It can be difficult to understand how a cell, usually too small to be seen by the unaided eye, can be so complex. How can cell biologists possibly investigate the inner workings of such tiny entities? Before we tour the cell, it will be helpful to learn how cells are studied.

Microscopy

The development of instruments that extend the human senses has gone hand in hand with the advance of science. The discovery and early study of cells progressed with the invention of microscopes in 1590 and their refinement during the 1600s. Microscopes are still indispensable for the study of cells.

The microscopes first used by Renaissance scientists, as well as the microscopes you are likely to use in the laboratory, are all light microscopes. In a **light microscope (LM)**, visible light is passed through the specimen and then through glass lenses. The lenses refract (bend) the light in such a way that the image of the specimen is magnified as it is projected into the eye, onto photographic film or a digital sensor, or onto a video screen. (See the diagram of microscope structure in Appendix D.)

Two important parameters in microscopy are magnification and resolving power, or resolution. *Magnification* is the ratio of an object's image size to its real size. *Resolution* is a measure of the clarity of the image; it is the minimum distance two points can be separated and still be distinguished as two points. For example, what appears to the unaided eye as one star in the sky may be resolved as twin stars with a telescope.

Just as the resolving power of the human eye is limited, the light microscope cannot resolve detail finer than about 0.2 micrometer (μm), or 200 nanometers (nm), the size of a small bacterium, regardless of the magnification factor **(Figure 6.2)**. This resolution is limited by the shortest wavelength of light used to illuminate the specimen. Light microscopes can magnify effectively to about 1,000 times the actual size of the specimen; at greater magnifications, additional details cannot be seen clearly. A third important parameter in microscopy is *contrast*, which accentuates differences in parts of the sample. In fact, most improvements in light microscopy in the last hundred years have involved new methods for enhancing contrast, such as staining or labeling cell components to stand out visually **(Figure 6.3**, on the next page).

Cell walls were first seen by Robert Hooke in 1665 as he looked through a microscope at dead cells from the bark of an oak tree. But it took the wonderfully crafted lenses of Antoni van Leeuwenhoek to visualize living cells. Imagine Hooke's awe when he visited van Leeuwenhoek in 1674 and the world of microorganisms—what his host called "very little animalcules"—was revealed to him. In spite of these early observations, the cell's geography remained largely uncharted for some time. Most subcellular structures—including **organelles**, which are membrane-enclosed compartments—are simply too small to be resolved by the light microscope.

Cell biology advanced rapidly in the 1950s with the introduction of the electron microscope. Instead of using light, the **electron microscope (EM)** focuses a beam of electrons through the specimen or onto its surface (see Appendix D). Resolution is inversely related to the wavelength of the radiation a microscope uses for imaging, and electron beams have much shorter wavelengths than visible light. Modern electron

microscopes can theoretically achieve a resolution of about 0.002 nm, although for practical purposes they usually cannot resolve biological structures smaller than about 2 nm. Still, this resolution is a hundredfold improvement over the light

1 centimeter (cm) = 10^{-2} meter (m) = 0.4 inch
1 millimeter (mm) = 10^{-3} m
1 micrometer (μm) = 10^{-3} mm = 10^{-6} m
1 nanometer (nm) = 10^{-3} μm = 10^{-9} m

▲ **Figure 6.2 The size range of cells.** Most cells are between 1 and 100 μm in diameter (yellow region of chart) and are therefore visible only under a microscope. Notice that the scale along the left side is logarithmic to accommodate the range of sizes shown. Starting at the top of the scale with 10 m and going down, each reference measurement marks a tenfold decrease in diameter or length. For a complete table of the metric system, see Appendix C.

Research Method

Light Microscopy

TECHNIQUE	RESULTS

(a) Brightfield (unstained specimen). Passes light directly through specimen. Unless cell is naturally pigmented or artificially stained, image has little contrast. [Parts (a)–(d) show a human cheek epithelial cell.]

50 μm

(b) Brightfield (stained specimen). Staining with various dyes enhances contrast. Most staining procedures require that cells be fixed (preserved).

(c) Phase-contrast. Enhances contrast in unstained cells by amplifying variations in density within specimen; especially useful for examining living, unpigmented cells.

(d) Differential-interference-contrast (Nomarski). Like phase-contrast microscopy, uses optical modifications to exaggerate differences in density, making the image appear almost 3-D.

(e) Fluorescence. Shows the locations of specific molecules in the cell by tagging the molecules with fluorescent dyes or antibodies. These fluorescent substances absorb ultraviolet radiation and emit visible light, as shown here in a cell from an artery.

50 μm

(f) Confocal. A fluorescent "optical sectioning" technique that uses a pinhole aperture to eliminate out-of-focus light from a thick sample, creating a single plane of fluorescence in the image. By capturing sharp images at many different planes, a 3-D reconstruction can be created. At the right are confocal (top) and standard fluorescent micrographs of stained nervous tissue, where nerve cells are green, support cells are red, and regions of overlap are yellow. The standard image is blurry because the out-of-focus light is not excluded.

50 μm

microscope. The term *cell ultrastructure* refers to the cellular anatomy revealed by an electron microscope.

The **scanning electron microscope (SEM)** is especially useful for detailed study of the surface of a specimen **(Figure 6.4a)**. The electron beam scans the surface of the sample, which is usually coated with a thin film of gold. The beam excites electrons on the surface, and these secondary electrons are detected by a device that translates the pattern of electrons into an electronic signal to a video screen. The result is an image of the specimen's topography. The SEM has great depth of field, resulting in an image that appears three-dimensional.

The **transmission electron microscope (TEM)** is used to study the internal ultrastructure of cells **(Figure 6.4b)**. The TEM aims an electron beam through a very thin section of the specimen, similar to the way a light microscope transmits light through a slide. The specimen has been stained with atoms of heavy metals, which attach to certain cellular structures, thus enhancing the electron density of some parts of the cell more than others. The electrons passing through the specimen are scattered more in the denser regions, so fewer are transmitted. The image displays the pattern of transmitted electrons. Instead of using glass lenses, the TEM uses electromagnets as lenses to bend the paths of the electrons, ultimately focusing the image onto a screen for viewing or onto photographic film. Some microscopes are equipped with a digital camera to photograph the image on the screen; others have a digital detector in place of both screen and camera.

Research Method

Electron Microscopy

TECHNIQUE	RESULTS

(a) Scanning electron microscopy (SEM). Micrographs taken with a scanning electron microscope show a 3-D image of the surface of a specimen. This SEM shows the surface of a cell from a rabbit trachea (windpipe) covered with motile organelles called cilia. Beating of the cilia helps move inhaled debris upward toward the throat.

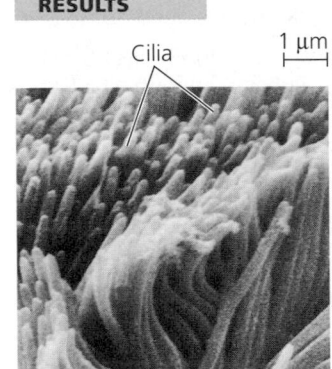

Cilia

1 μm

(b) Transmission electron microscopy (TEM). A transmission electron microscope profiles a thin section of a specimen. Here we see a section through a tracheal cell, revealing its ultrastructure. In preparing the TEM, some cilia were cut along their lengths, creating longitudinal sections, while other cilia were cut straight across, creating cross sections.

Longitudinal section of cilium   Cross section of cilium

1 μm

Electron microscopes reveal many organelles and other subcellular structures that are impossible to resolve with the light microscope. But the light microscope offers advantages, especially in studying living cells. A disadvantage of electron microscopy is that the methods used to prepare the specimen kill the cells. Also, specimen preparation can introduce artifacts, structural features seen in micrographs that do not exist in the living cell (as is true for all microscopy techniques). From this point on in the book, micrographs are identified by the type of microscopy: LM for a light micrograph, SEM for a scanning electron micrograph, and TEM for a transmission electron micrograph. Also, micrograph images may be artificially "colorized" to highlight particular structures.

Microscopes are the most important tools of *cytology*, the study of cell structure. But simply describing the diverse organelles and other structures within the cell reveals little about their function. Modern cell biology developed from an integration of cytology with *biochemistry*, the study of the molecules and chemical processes (metabolism) of cells.

Cell Fractionation

A useful technique for studying cell structure and function is **cell fractionation**, which takes cells apart and separates the major organelles and other subcellular structures from one another **(Figure 6.5)**. The instrument used is the centrifuge, which spins test tubes holding mixtures of disrupted cells at various speeds. The resulting forces cause a fraction of the cell components to settle to the bottom of the tube, forming a pellet. At lower speeds, the pellet consists of larger components, and higher speeds yield a pellet with smaller components. The most powerful machines, called *ultracentrifuges*, spin up to 130,000 revolutions per minute (rpm) and apply forces on particles of more than 1 million times the force of gravity (1,000,000 *g*).

Cell fractionation enables researchers to prepare specific cell components in bulk and identify their functions, a task that would be far more difficult with intact cells. For example, biochemical tests showed that one of the cell fractions produced by centrifugation included enzymes involved in cellular respiration. Electron microscopy revealed that this fraction contained large numbers of the organelles called mitochondria. Together, these data helped biologists determine that mitochondria are the sites of cellular respiration. Biochemistry and cytology thus complement each other in correlating cell function with structure.

CONCEPT CHECK 6.1

1. How do stains used for light microscopy compare with those used for electron microscopy?
2. **WHAT IF?** Which type of microscope would you use to study (a) the changes in shape of a living white blood cell, (b) the details of surface texture of a hair, and (c) the detailed structure of an organelle?

For suggested answers, see Appendix A.

▼ **Figure 6.5** **Research Method**

Cell Fractionation

APPLICATION Cell fractionation is used to isolate (fractionate) cell components based on size and density.

TECHNIQUE First, cells are homogenized in a blender to break them up. The resulting mixture (cell homogenate) is then centrifuged at various speeds and durations to fractionate the cell components, forming a series of pellets, overlaid by the remaining homogenate (supernatant).

Tissue cells

Homogenization

Homogenate

1,000 *g*
(1,000 times the force of gravity)
10 min

Differential centrifugation

Supernatant poured into next tube

20,000 *g*
20 min

Pellet rich in nuclei and cellular debris

80,000 *g*
60 min

Pellet rich in mitochondria (and chloroplasts if cells are from a plant)

150,000 *g*
3 hr

Pellet rich in "microsomes" (pieces of plasma membranes and cells' internal membranes)

Pellet rich in ribosomes

RESULTS In early experiments, researchers used microscopy to identify the organelles in each pellet and biochemical methods to determine their metabolic functions. These identifications established a baseline for this method, enabling today's researchers to know which cell fraction they should collect in order to isolate and study particular organelles.

Eukaryotic cells have internal membranes that compartmentalize their functions

The basic structural and functional unit of every organism is one of two types of cells—prokaryotic or eukaryotic. Only organisms of the domains Bacteria and Archaea consist of prokaryotic cells. Protists, fungi, animals, and plants all consist of eukaryotic cells. This chapter focuses on generalized animal and plant cells after first comparing them with prokaryotic cells.

Comparing Prokaryotic and Eukaryotic Cells

All cells have several basic features in common: They are all bounded by a selective barrier, called the *plasma membrane*. Enclosed by the membrane is a semifluid, jellylike substance called **cytosol**, in which organelles and other components are found. All cells contain *chromosomes*, which carry genes in the form of DNA. And all cells have *ribosomes*, tiny complexes that make proteins according to instructions from the genes.

A major difference between prokaryotic and eukaryotic cells is the location of their DNA, as reflected in their names. In a **eukaryotic cell**, most of the DNA is in an organelle called the *nucleus*, which is bounded by a double membrane (see Figure 6.9, on pp. 100–101). (The word *eukaryotic* is from the Greek *eu*, true, and *karyon*, kernel, here referring to the nucleus.) In a **prokaryotic cell** (from the Greek *pro*, before, and *karyon*), the DNA is concentrated in a region that is not membrane-enclosed, called the **nucleoid (Figure 6.6)**. The interior of a prokaryotic cell is called the **cytoplasm**; this term is also used for the region between the nucleus and the plasma membrane of a eukaryotic cell. Within the cytoplasm of a eukaryotic cell, suspended in cytosol, are a variety of organelles of specialized form and function. These membrane-bounded structures are absent in prokaryotic cells. Thus, the presence or absence of a true nucleus is just one example of the disparity in structural complexity between the two types of cells.

Eukaryotic cells are generally much larger than prokaryotic cells (see Figure 6.2). Size is a general aspect of cell structure that relates to function. The logistics of carrying out cellular metabolism sets limits on cell size. At the lower limit, the smallest cells known are bacteria called mycoplasmas, which have diameters between 0.1 and 1.0 μm. These are perhaps the smallest packages with enough DNA to program metabolism and enough enzymes and other cellular equipment to carry out the activities necessary for a cell to sustain itself and reproduce. Typical bacteria are 1–5 μm in diameter, a dimension about ten times greater than that of mycoplasmas. Eukaryotic cells are typically 10–100 μm in diameter.

Metabolic requirements also impose theoretical upper limits on the size that is practical for a single cell. At the boundary of every cell, the **plasma membrane** functions as a selective barrier that allows sufficient passage of oxygen, nutrients, and wastes to

Fimbriae: attachment structures on the surface of some prokaryotes

Nucleoid: region where the cell's DNA is located (not enclosed by a membrane)

Ribosomes: complexes that synthesize proteins

Plasma membrane: membrane enclosing the cytoplasm

Cell wall: rigid structure outside the plasma membrane

Capsule: jellylike outer coating of many prokaryotes

Bacterial chromosome

Flagella: locomotion organelles of some bacteria

(a) A typical rod-shaped bacterium

0.5 μm

(b) A thin section through the bacterium *Bacillus coagulans* **(TEM)**

▲ **Figure 6.6 A prokaryotic cell.** Lacking a true nucleus and the other membrane-enclosed organelles of the eukaryotic cell, the prokaryotic cell is much simpler in structure. Only bacteria and archaea are prokaryotes.

(a) TEM of a plasma membrane. The plasma membrane, here in a red blood cell, appears as a pair of dark bands separated by a light band.

Outside of cell

Inside of cell
0.1 µm

Carbohydrate side chain

Hydrophilic region

Hydrophobic region

Hydrophilic region

Phospholipid   Proteins

(b) Structure of the plasma membrane

▲ **Figure 6.7 The plasma membrane.** The plasma membrane and the membranes of organelles consist of a double layer (bilayer) of phospholipids with various proteins attached to or embedded in it. In the interior of a membrane, the phospholipid tails are hydrophobic, as are the interior portions of membrane proteins in contact with them. The phospholipid heads are hydrophilic, as are proteins or parts of proteins in contact with the aqueous solution on either side of the membrane. (Channels through certain proteins are also hydrophilic.) Carbohydrate side chains are found only attached to proteins or lipids on the outer surface of the plasma membrane.

? *Describe the components of a phospholipid (see Figure 5.13) that allow it to function as the major element in the plasma membrane.*

service the entire cell (**Figure 6.7**). For each square micrometer of membrane, only a limited amount of a particular substance can cross per second, so the ratio of surface area to volume is critical. As a cell (or any other object) increases in size, its volume grows proportionately more than its surface area. (Area is proportional to a linear dimension squared, whereas volume is proportional to the linear dimension cubed.) Thus, a smaller object has a greater ratio of surface area to volume (**Figure 6.8**).

The need for a surface area sufficiently large to accommodate the volume helps explain the microscopic size of most cells and the narrow, elongated shapes of others, such as nerve cells. Larger organisms do not generally have *larger* cells than smaller organisms—simply *more* cells (see Figure 6.8). A sufficiently high ratio of surface area to volume is especially important in cells that exchange a lot of material with their surroundings, such as intestinal cells. Such cells may have many long, thin projections from their surface called microvilli, which increase surface area without an appreciable increase in volume.

The possible evolutionary relationships between prokaryotic and eukaryotic cells will be discussed in Chapter 25, and prokaryotic cells will be described in detail in Chapter 27. Most of the discussion of cell structure that follows in this chapter applies to eukaryotic cells.

Surface area increases while total volume remains constant

	1	5	1
Total surface area [Sum of the surface areas (height × width) of all box sides × number of boxes]	6	150	750
Total volume [height × width × length × number of boxes]	1	125	125
Surface-to-volume (S-to-V) ratio [surface area ÷ volume]	6	1.2	6

▲ **Figure 6.8 Geometric relationships between surface area and volume.** In this diagram, cells are represented as boxes. Using arbitrary units of length, we can calculate the cell's surface area (in square units, or units^2), volume (in cubic units, or units^3), and ratio of surface area to volume. A high surface-to-volume ratio facilitates the exchange of materials between a cell and its environment.

A Panoramic View of the Eukaryotic Cell

In addition to the plasma membrane at its outer surface, a eukaryotic cell has extensive and elaborately arranged internal membranes, which divide the cell into compartments—the organelles mentioned earlier. The cell's compartments provide different local environments that facilitate specific metabolic functions, so incompatible processes can go on simultaneously inside a single cell. The plasma and organelle membranes also participate directly in the cell's metabolism, because many enzymes are built right into the membranes.

Because membranes are fundamental to the organization of the cell, Chapter 7 will discuss them in detail. In general, biological membranes consist of a double layer of phospholipids and other lipids. Embedded in this lipid bilayer or attached to its surfaces are diverse proteins (see Figure 6.7). However, each type of membrane has a unique composition of lipids and proteins suited to that membrane's specific functions. For example, enzymes embedded in the membranes of the organelles called mitochondria function in cellular respiration.

Before continuing with this chapter, examine the overviews of eukaryotic cells in **Figure 6.9**, on the next two pages. These generalized cell diagrams introduce the various organelles and provide a map of the cell for the detailed tour upon which we will now embark. Figure 6.9 also contrasts animal and plant cells. As eukaryotic cells, they have much more in common than either has with any prokaryotic cell. As you will see, however, there are important differences between animal and plant cells.

Exploring Animal and Plant Cells

Animal Cell

This drawing of a generalized animal cell incorporates the most common structures of animal cells (no cell actually looks just like this). As shown by this cutaway view, the cell has a variety of components, including organelles ("little organs"), which are bounded by membranes. The most prominent organelle in an animal cell is usually the nucleus. Most of the cell's metabolic activities occur in the cytoplasm, the entire region between the nucleus and the plasma membrane. The cytoplasm contains many organelles and other cell components suspended in a semifluid medium, the cytosol. Pervading much of the cytoplasm is a labyrinth of membranes called the endoplasmic reticulum (ER).

Flagellum: locomotion organelle present in some animal cells; composed of a cluster of microtubules within an extension of the plasma membrane

ENDOPLASMIC RETICULUM (ER): network of membranous sacs and tubes; active in membrane synthesis and other synthetic and metabolic processes; has rough (ribosome-studded) and smooth regions

Rough ER   Smooth ER

Nuclear envelope: double membrane enclosing the nucleus; perforated by pores; continuous with ER

Nucleolus: structure involved in production of ribosomes; a nucleus has one or more nucleoli

Chromatin: material consisting of DNA and proteins; visible as individual chromosomes in a dividing cell

NUCLEUS

Centrosome: region where the cell's microtubules are initiated; contains a pair of centrioles (function unknown)

Plasma membrane: membrane enclosing the cell

CYTOSKELETON: reinforces cell's shape, functions in cell movement; components are made of protein. Includes:

Microfilaments

Intermediate filaments

Microtubules

Ribosomes: complexes (small brown dots) that make proteins; free in cytosol or bound to rough ER or nuclear envelope

Microvilli: projections that increase the cell's surface area

Golgi apparatus: organelle active in synthesis, modification, sorting, and secretion of cell products

Peroxisome: organelle with various specialized metabolic functions; produces hydrogen peroxide as a by-product, then converts it to water

Mitochondrion: organelle where cellular respiration occurs and most ATP is generated

Lysosome: digestive organelle where macromolecules are hydrolyzed

In animal cells but not plant cells:
Lysosomes
Centrosomes, with centrioles
Flagella (but present in some plant sperm)

Plant Cell

This drawing of a generalized plant cell reveals the similarities and differences between an animal cell and a plant cell. In addition to most of the features seen in an animal cell, a plant cell has organelles called plastids. The most important type of plastid is the chloroplast, which carries out photosynthesis. Many plant cells have a large central vacuole; some may have one or more smaller vacuoles. Among other tasks, vacuoles carry out functions performed by lysosomes in animal cells. Outside a plant cell's plasma membrane is a thick cell wall, perforated by channels called plasmodesmata.

 MEDIA *BioFlix* Visit **www.campbellbiology.com** for the BioFlix 3-D Animations called Tour of an Animal Cell and Tour of a Plant Cell.

If you preview the rest of the chapter now, you'll see Figure 6.9 repeated in miniature as orientation diagrams. In each case, a particular organelle is highlighted, color-coded to its appearance in Figure 6.9. As we take a closer look at individual organelles, the orientation diagrams will help you place those structures in the context of the whole cell.

NUCLEUS
Nuclear envelope
Nucleolus
Chromatin

Rough endoplasmic reticulum

Smooth endoplasmic reticulum

Ribosomes (small brown dots)

Central vacuole: prominent organelle in older plant cells; functions include storage, breakdown of waste products, hydrolysis of macromolecules; enlargement of vacuole is a major mechanism of plant growth

Golgi apparatus

Microfilaments
Intermediate filaments
Microtubules
CYTOSKELETON

Mitochondrion

Peroxisome

Plasma membrane

Cell wall: outer layer that maintains cell's shape and protects cell from mechanical damage; made of cellulose, other polysaccharides, and protein

Wall of adjacent cell

Chloroplast: photosynthetic organelle; converts energy of sunlight to chemical energy stored in sugar molecules

Plasmodesmata: channels through cell walls that connect the cytoplasms of adjacent cells

In plant cells but not animal cells:
Chloroplasts
Central vacuole
Cell wall
Plasmodesmata

1. After carefully reviewing Figure 6.9, briefly describe the structure and function of the nucleus, the mitochondrion, the chloroplast, and the endoplasmic reticulum.

2. **WHAT IF?** Imagine an elongated cell (such as a nerve cell) that is $125 \times 1 \times 1$, using arbitrary units similar to the ones in Figure 6.8. Predict where its surface-to-volume ratio would lie in Figure 6.8. Then calculate and check your prediction.

For suggested answers, see Appendix A.

CONCEPT 6.3

The eukaryotic cell's genetic instructions are housed in the nucleus and carried out by the ribosomes

On the first stop of our detailed tour of the cell, let's look at two cellular components involved in the genetic control of the cell: the nucleus, which houses most of the cell's DNA, and the ribosomes, which use information from the DNA to make proteins.

The Nucleus: Information Central

The **nucleus** contains most of the genes in the eukaryotic cell (some genes are located in mitochondria and chloroplasts). It is generally the most conspicuous organelle in a eukaryotic cell, averaging about 5 μm in diameter. The **nuclear envelope** encloses the nucleus **(Figure 6.10)**, separating its contents from the cytoplasm.

The nuclear envelope is a *double* membrane. The two membranes, each a lipid bilayer with associated proteins, are separated by a space of 20–40 nm. The envelope is perforated by pore structures that are about 100 nm in diameter. At the lip of each pore, the inner and outer membranes of the nuclear envelope are continuous. An intricate protein structure called a *pore complex* lines each pore and plays an important role in the cell by regulating the entry and exit of most proteins and RNAs, as well as large complexes of macromolecules. Except at the pores, the nuclear side of the envelope is lined by the **nuclear lamina**, a netlike array of protein filaments that maintains the shape of the nucleus by mechanically supporting the nuclear envelope. There is also much evidence for a *nuclear matrix*, a framework of fibers extending throughout the nuclear interior. (On page 322, we will touch on possible functions of the nuclear lamina and matrix in organizing the genetic material.)

Within the nucleus, the DNA is organized into discrete units called **chromosomes**, structures that carry the genetic information. Each chromosome is made up of a material called **chromatin**, a complex of proteins and DNA. Stained chromatin usually appears as a diffuse mass through both light microscopes and electron microscopes. As a cell prepares to divide, however, the thin chromatin fibers coil up (condense), becoming thick enough to be distinguished as the familiar separate structures we know as chromosomes. Each eukaryotic species has a characteristic number of chromosomes. A typical human cell, for example, has 46 chromosomes in its nucleus; the exceptions are the sex cells (eggs and sperm), which have only 23 chromosomes in humans. A fruit fly cell has 8 chromosomes in most cells and 4 in the sex cells.

A prominent structure within the nondividing nucleus is the **nucleolus** (plural, *nucleoli*), which appears through the electron microscope as a mass of densely stained granules and fibers adjoining part of the chromatin. Here a type of RNA called *ribosomal RNA* (rRNA) is synthesized from instructions in the DNA. Also in the nucleolus, proteins imported from the cytoplasm are assembled with rRNA into large and small ribosomal subunits. These subunits then exit the nucleus through the nuclear pores to the cytoplasm, where a large and a small subunit can assemble into a ribosome. Sometimes there are two or more nucleoli; the number depends on the species and the stage in the cell's reproductive cycle. Recent studies suggest that the nucleolus also functions in regulation of some cellular processes, such as cell division.

As we saw in Figure 5.26, the nucleus directs protein synthesis by synthesizing messenger RNA (mRNA) according to instructions provided by the DNA. The mRNA is then transported to the cytoplasm via the nuclear pores. Once an mRNA molecule reaches the cytoplasm, ribosomes translate the mRNA's genetic message into the primary structure of a specific polypeptide. This process of transcribing and translating genetic information is described in detail in Chapter 17.

Ribosomes: Protein Factories

Ribosomes, which are complexes made of ribosomal RNA and protein, are the cellular components that carry out protein synthesis **(Figure 6.11)**. Cells that have high rates of protein synthesis have particularly large numbers of ribosomes. For example, a human pancreas cell has a few million ribosomes. Not surprisingly, cells active in protein synthesis also have prominent nucleoli.

Ribosomes build proteins in two cytoplasmic locales (see Figure 6.11). At any given time, *free ribosomes* are suspended in the cytosol, while *bound ribosomes* are attached to the outside of the endoplasmic reticulum or nuclear envelope. Bound and free ribosomes are structurally identical, and ribosomes can alternate between the two roles. Most of the proteins

1 µm

Nucleus

Nucleus

Nucleolus

Chromatin

Nuclear envelope:
Inner membrane
Outer membrane

Nuclear pore

Surface of nuclear envelope.
TEM of a specimen prepared by
a technique known as
freeze-fracture.

0.25 µm

Pore
complex

Ribosome

Rough ER

1 µm

**Close-up of nuclear
envelope**

Pore complexes (TEM). Each pore is
ringed by protein particles.

Nuclear lamina (TEM). The netlike lamina
lines the inner surface of the nuclear envelope.

▲ **Figure 6.10 The nucleus and its
envelope.** Within the nucleus are the
chromosomes, which appear as a mass of chromatin (DNA and associated proteins), and one or more nucleoli (singular, *nucleolus*), which function in ribosome synthesis. The nuclear envelope, which consists of two membranes separated by a narrow space, is perforated with pores and lined by the nuclear lamina.

▶ **Figure 6.11 Ribosomes.** This electron
micrograph of part of a pancreas cell shows
many ribosomes, both free (in the cytosol) and
bound (to the endoplasmic reticulum). The
simplified diagram of a ribosome shows its two
subunits.

Ribosomes

ER

Cytosol

Endoplasmic reticulum (ER)

Free ribosomes

Bound ribosomes

Large
subunit

Small
subunit

0.5 µm

TEM showing ER and ribosomes

Diagram of a ribosome

made on free ribosomes function within the cytosol; examples are enzymes that catalyze the first steps of sugar breakdown. Bound ribosomes generally make proteins that are destined for insertion into membranes, for packaging within certain organelles such as lysosomes (see Figure 6.9), or for export from the cell (secretion). Cells that specialize in protein secretion—for instance, the cells of the pancreas that secrete digestive enzymes—frequently have a high proportion of bound ribosomes. You will learn more about ribosome structure and function in Chapter 17.

CONCEPT CHECK 6.3

1. What role do the ribosomes play in carrying out genetic instructions?
2. Describe the molecular composition of nucleoli and explain their function.
3. **WHAT IF?** If the function of a particular protein in a eukaryotic cell is to make up part of the chromatin, describe the process of its synthesis. Include the cellular locations of all relevant molecules.

For suggested answers, see Appendix A.

CONCEPT 6.4

The endomembrane system regulates protein traffic and performs metabolic functions in the cell

Many of the different membranes of the eukaryotic cell are part of an **endomembrane system**, which carries out a variety of tasks in the cell. These tasks include synthesis of proteins and their transport into membranes and organelles or out of the cell, metabolism and movement of lipids, and detoxification of poisons. The membranes of this system are related either through direct physical continuity or by the transfer of membrane segments as tiny **vesicles** (sacs made of membrane). Despite these relationships, the various membranes are not identical in structure and function. Moreover, the thickness, molecular composition, and types of chemical reactions carried out in a given membrane are not fixed, but may be modified several times during the membrane's life. The endomembrane system includes the nuclear envelope, the endoplasmic reticulum, the Golgi apparatus, lysosomes, various kinds of vacuoles, and the plasma membrane (not actually an *endo*membrane in physical location, but nevertheless related to the endoplasmic reticulum and other internal membranes). Having already discussed the nuclear envelope, we will now focus on the endoplasmic reticulum and the other endomembranes to which the endoplasmic reticulum gives rise.

The Endoplasmic Reticulum: Biosynthetic Factory

The **endoplasmic reticulum (ER)** is such an extensive network of membranes that it accounts for more than half the total membrane in many eukaryotic cells. (The word *endoplasmic* means "within the cytoplasm," and *reticulum* is Latin for "little net.") The ER consists of a network of membranous tubules and sacs called cisternae (from the Latin *cisterna*, a reservoir for a liquid). The ER membrane separates the internal compartment of the ER, called the ER lumen (cavity) or cisternal space, from the cytosol. And because the ER membrane is continuous with the nuclear envelope, the space between the two membranes of the envelope is continuous with the lumen of the ER (**Figure 6.12**).

There are two distinct, though connected, regions of the ER that differ in structure and function: smooth ER and rough ER. **Smooth ER** is so named because its outer surface lacks ribosomes. **Rough ER** has ribosomes on the outer surface of the membrane and thus appears rough through the electron microscope. As already mentioned, ribosomes are also attached to the cytoplasmic side of the nuclear envelope's outer membrane, which is continuous with rough ER.

Functions of Smooth ER

The smooth ER functions in diverse metabolic processes, which vary with cell type. These processes include synthesis of lipids, metabolism of carbohydrates, and detoxification of drugs and poisons.

Enzymes of the smooth ER are important in the synthesis of lipids, including oils, phospholipids, and steroids. Among the steroids produced by the smooth ER in animal cells are the sex hormones of vertebrates and the various steroid hormones secreted by the adrenal glands. The cells that synthesize and secrete these hormones—in the testes and ovaries, for example—are rich in smooth ER, a structural feature that fits the function of these cells.

Other enzymes of the smooth ER help detoxify drugs and poisons, especially in liver cells. Detoxification usually involves adding hydroxyl groups to drug molecules, making them more soluble and easier to flush from the body. The sedative phenobarbital and other barbiturates are examples of drugs metabolized in this manner by smooth ER in liver cells. In fact, barbiturates, alcohol, and many other drugs induce the proliferation of smooth ER and its associated detoxification enzymes, thus increasing the rate of detoxification. This, in turn, increases tolerance to the drugs, meaning that higher doses are required to achieve a particular effect, such as sedation. Also, because some of the detoxification enzymes have relatively broad action, the proliferation of smooth ER in response to one drug can increase tolerance to other drugs as well. Barbiturate abuse, for example, can decrease the effectiveness of certain antibiotics and other useful drugs.

trigger contraction of the muscle cell. In other cell types, calcium ion release from the smooth ER triggers different responses.

Functions of Rough ER

Many types of cells secrete proteins produced by ribosomes attached to rough ER. For example, certain pancreatic cells synthesize the protein insulin on the ER and secrete this hormone into the bloodstream. As a polypeptide chain grows from a bound ribosome, it is threaded into the ER lumen through a pore formed by a protein complex in the ER membrane. As the new protein enters the ER lumen, it folds into its native shape. Most secretory proteins are **glycoproteins**, proteins that have carbohydrates covalently bonded to them. The carbohydrates are attached to the proteins in the ER by specialized molecules built into the ER membrane.

After secretory proteins are formed, the ER membrane keeps them separate from proteins that are produced by free ribosomes and will remain in the cytosol. Secretory proteins depart from the ER wrapped in the membranes of vesicles that bud like bubbles from a specialized region called transitional ER (see Figure 6.12). Vesicles in transit from one part of the cell to another are called **transport vesicles**; we will discuss their fate shortly.

In addition to making secretory proteins, rough ER is a membrane factory for the cell; it grows in place by adding membrane proteins and phospholipids to its own membrane. As polypeptides destined to be membrane proteins grow from the ribosomes, they are inserted into the ER membrane itself and are anchored there by their hydrophobic portions. The rough ER also makes its own membrane phospholipids; enzymes built into the ER membrane assemble phospholipids from precursors in the cytosol. The ER membrane expands and is transferred in the form of transport vesicles to other components of the endomembrane system.

The Golgi Apparatus: Shipping and Receiving Center

After leaving the ER, many transport vesicles travel to the **Golgi apparatus**. We can think of the Golgi as a center of manufacturing, warehousing, sorting, and shipping. Here, products of the ER, such as proteins, are modified and stored and then sent to other destinations. Not surprisingly, the Golgi apparatus is especially extensive in cells specialized for secretion.

The Golgi apparatus consists of flattened membranous sacs—cisternae—looking like a stack of pita bread (**Figure 6.13**, on the next page). A cell may have many, even hundreds, of these stacks. The membrane of each cisterna in a stack separates its internal space from the cytosol. Vesicles concentrated in the vicinity of the Golgi apparatus are engaged in the transfer of material between parts of the Golgi and other structures.

▲ Figure 6.12 **Endoplasmic reticulum (ER).** A membranous system of interconnected tubules and flattened sacs called cisternae, the ER is also continuous with the nuclear envelope. (The drawing is a cutaway view.) The membrane of the ER encloses a continuous compartment called the ER lumen (or cisternal space). Rough ER, which is studded on its outer surface with ribosomes, can be distinguished from smooth ER in the electron micrograph (TEM). Transport vesicles bud off from a region of the rough ER called transitional ER and travel to the Golgi apparatus and other destinations.

The smooth ER also stores calcium ions. In muscle cells, for example, a specialized smooth ER membrane pumps calcium ions from the cytosol into the ER lumen. When a muscle cell is stimulated by a nerve impulse, calcium ions rush back across the ER membrane into the cytosol and

Golgi apparatus

cis face ("receiving" side of Golgi apparatus)

6 Vesicles also transport certain proteins back to ER, their site of function.

1 Vesicles move from ER to Golgi.

2 Vesicles coalesce to form new *cis* Golgi cisternae.

Cisternae

3 Cisternal maturation: Golgi cisternae move in a *cis*-to-*trans* direction.

4 Vesicles form and leave Golgi, carrying specific proteins to other locations or to the plasma membrane for secretion.

5 Vesicles transport some proteins backward to less mature Golgi cisternae, where they function.

trans face ("shipping" side of Golgi apparatus)

0.1 μm

TEM of Golgi apparatus

▲ **Figure 6.13 The Golgi apparatus.** The Golgi apparatus consists of stacks of flattened sacs, or cisternae, which, unlike ER cisternae, are not physically connected. (The drawing is a cutaway view.) A Golgi stack receives and dispatches transport vesicles and the products they contain. A Golgi stack has a structural and functional polarity, with a *cis* face that receives vesicles containing ER products and a *trans* face that dispatches vesicles. The cisternal maturation model proposes that the Golgi cisternae themselves "mature," moving from the *cis* to the *trans* face while carrying some proteins along. In addition, some vesicles recycle enzymes that had been carried forward in moving cisternae, transporting them "backward" to a less mature region where their functions are needed.

A Golgi stack has a distinct structural polarity, with the membranes of cisternae on opposite sides of the stack differing in thickness and molecular composition. The two poles of a Golgi stack are referred to as the *cis* face and the *trans* face; these act, respectively, as the receiving and shipping departments of the Golgi apparatus. The *cis* face is usually located near the ER. Transport vesicles move material from the ER to the Golgi apparatus. A vesicle that buds from the ER can add its membrane and the contents of its lumen to the *cis* face by fusing with a Golgi membrane. The *trans* face gives rise to vesicles, which pinch off and travel to other sites.

Products of the ER are usually modified during their transit from the *cis* region to the *trans* region of the Golgi. For example, various Golgi enzymes modify the carbohydrate portions of glycoproteins. Carbohydrates are first added to proteins in the rough ER, often during the process of polypeptide synthesis. The carbohydrate on the resulting glycoprotein is then modified as it passes through the rest of the ER and the Golgi. The Golgi removes some sugar monomers and substitutes others, producing a large variety of carbohydrates. Membrane phospholipids may also be altered in the Golgi.

In addition to its finishing work, the Golgi apparatus manufactures certain macromolecules by itself. Many polysaccharides secreted by cells are Golgi products, including pectins and certain other noncellulose polysaccharides made by plant cells and incorporated along with cellulose into their cell walls. (Cellulose is made by enzymes located within the plasma membrane, which directly deposit this polysaccharide on the outside surface.) Like secretory proteins, non-protein Golgi products that will be secreted depart from the *trans* face of the Golgi inside transport vesicles that eventually fuse with the plasma membrane.

The Golgi manufactures and refines its products in stages, with different cisternae containing unique teams of enzymes. Until recently, biologists viewed the Golgi as a static structure, with products in various stages of processing transferred from one cisterna to the next by vesicles. While this may occur, recent research has given rise to a new model of the Golgi as a more dynamic structure. According to the model called the *cisternal maturation model*, the cisternae of the Golgi actually progress forward from the *cis* to the *trans* face of the Golgi, carrying and modifying their cargo as they move. Figure 6.13 shows the details of this model.

Before a Golgi stack dispatches its products by budding vesicles from the *trans* face, it sorts these products and targets them for various parts of the cell. Molecular identification tags, such as phosphate groups added to the Golgi products, aid in sorting by acting like ZIP codes on mailing labels. Finally, transport vesicles budded from the Golgi may have external molecules on their membranes that recognize "docking sites" on the surface of specific organelles or on the plasma membrane, thus targeting the vesicles appropriately.

Lysosomes: Digestive Compartments

A **lysosome** is a membranous sac of hydrolytic enzymes that an animal cell uses to digest macromolecules. Lysosomal enzymes work best in the acidic environment found in lysosomes. If a lysosome breaks open or leaks its contents, the released enzymes are not very active because the cytosol has a neutral pH. However, excessive leakage from a large number of lysosomes can destroy a cell by autodigestion.

Hydrolytic enzymes and lysosomal membrane are made by rough ER and then transferred to the Golgi apparatus for further processing. At least some lysosomes probably arise by budding from the *trans* face of the Golgi apparatus (see Figure 6.13). Proteins of the inner surface of the lysosomal membrane and the digestive enzymes themselves are thought to be spared from destruction by having three-dimensional shapes that protect vulnerable bonds from enzymatic attack.

Lysosomes carry out intracellular digestion in a variety of circumstances. Amoebas and many other protists eat by engulfing smaller organisms or other food particles, a process called **phagocytosis** (from the Greek *phagein*, to eat, and *kytos*, vessel, referring here to the cell). The *food vacuole* formed in this way then fuses with a lysosome, whose enzymes digest the food (**Figure 6.14a**, bottom). Digestion products, including simple sugars, amino acids, and other monomers, pass into the cytosol and become nutrients for the cell. Some human cells also carry out phagocytosis. Among them are macrophages, a type of white blood cell that helps defend the body by engulfing and destroying bacteria and other invaders (see Figure 6.14a, top, and Figure 6.33).

(a) Phagocytosis: lysosome digesting food

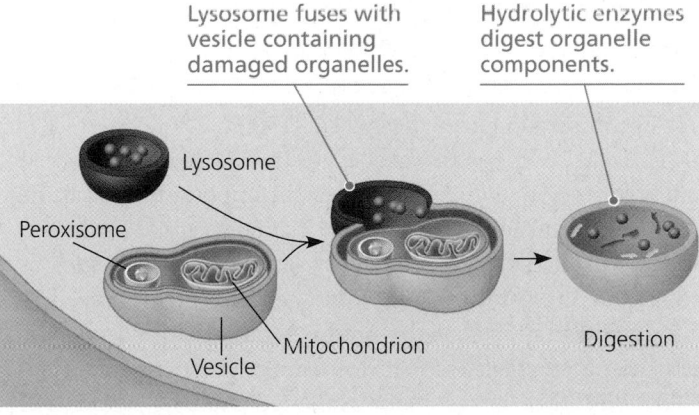

(b) Autophagy: lysosome breaking down damaged organelles

▲ **Figure 6.14 Lysosomes.** Lysosomes digest (hydrolyze) materials taken into the cell and recycle intracellular materials. **(a)** *Top:* In this macrophage (a type of white blood cell) from a rat, the lysosomes are very dark because of a stain that reacts with one of the products of digestion within the lysosome (TEM). Macrophages ingest bacteria and viruses and destroy them using lysosomes. *Bottom:* This diagram shows one lysosome fusing with a food vacuole during the process of phagocytosis by a protist. **(b)** *Top:* In the cytoplasm of this rat liver cell is a vesicle containing two disabled organelles; the vesicle will fuse with a lysosome in the process of autophagy (TEM). *Bottom:* This diagram shows fusion of such a vesicle with a lysosome. This type of vesicle has a double membrane of unknown origin. The outer membrane fuses with the lysosome, and the inner membrane is degraded along with the damaged organelles.

Lysosomes also use their hydrolytic enzymes to recycle the cell's own organic material, a process called *autophagy*. During autophagy, a damaged organelle or small amount of cytosol becomes surrounded by a double membrane, which is of unknown origin, and a lysosome fuses with the outer membrane of this vesicle **(Figure 6.14b)**. The lysosomal enzymes dismantle the enclosed material, and the organic monomers are returned to the cytosol for reuse. With the help of lysosomes, the cell continually renews itself. A human liver cell, for example, recycles half of its macromolecules each week.

The cells of people with inherited lysosomal storage diseases lack a functioning hydrolytic enzyme normally present in lysosomes. The lysosomes become engorged with indigestible substrates, which begin to interfere with other cellular activities. In Tay-Sachs disease, for example, a lipid-digesting enzyme is missing or inactive, and the brain becomes impaired by an accumulation of lipids in the cells. Fortunately, lysosomal storage diseases are rare in the general population.

Vacuoles: Diverse Maintenance Compartments

Vacuoles are membrane-bounded vesicles whose functions vary in different kinds of cells. **Food vacuoles**, formed by phagocytosis, have already been mentioned (see Figure 6.14a). Many freshwater protists have **contractile vacuoles** that pump excess water out of the cell, thereby maintaining a suitable concentration of ions and molecules inside the cell (see Figure 7.14). In plants and fungi, which lack lysosomes, vacuoles carry out hydrolysis; however, they play other roles as well. Mature plant cells generally contain a large **central vacuole** **(Figure 6.15)**. The central vacuole develops by the coalescence of smaller vacuoles, themselves derived from the endoplasmic reticulum and Golgi apparatus. The vacuole is thus an integral part of a plant cell's endomembrane system. Like all cellular membranes, the vacuolar membrane is selective in transporting solutes; as a result, the solution inside the central vacuole, called cell sap, differs in composition from the cytosol.

The plant cell's central vacuole is a versatile compartment. It can hold reserves of important organic compounds, such as the proteins stockpiled in the vacuoles of storage cells in seeds. It is also the plant cell's main repository of inorganic ions, such as potassium and chloride. Many plant cells use their vacuoles as disposal sites for metabolic by-products that would endanger the cell if they accumulated in the cytosol. Some vacuoles contain pigments that color the cells, such as the red and blue pigments of petals that help attract pollinating insects to flowers. Vacuoles may also help protect the plant against predators by containing compounds that are poisonous or unpalatable to animals. The vacuole has a major role in the growth of plant cells, which enlarge as their vacuoles absorb water, enabling the cell to become larger with a minimal investment in new cytoplasm. The cytosol often occupies only a thin layer between the central vacuole and the

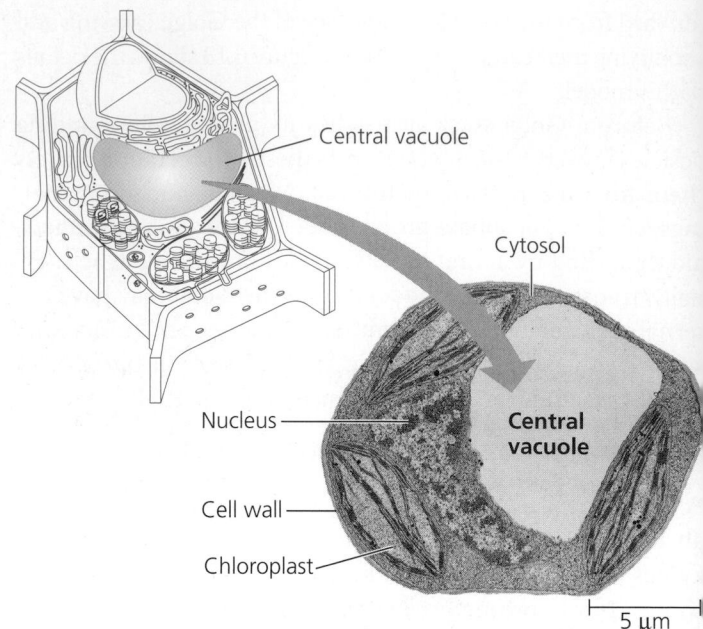

▲ **Figure 6.15 The plant cell vacuole.** The central vacuole is usually the largest compartment in a plant cell; the rest of the cytoplasm is generally confined to a narrow zone between the vacuolar membrane and the plasma membrane (TEM).

plasma membrane, so the ratio of plasma membrane surface to cytosolic volume is great, even for a large plant cell.

The Endomembrane System: *A Review*

Figure 6.16 reviews the endomembrane system, which shows the flow of membrane lipids and proteins through the various organelles. As the membrane moves from the ER to the Golgi and then elsewhere, its molecular composition and metabolic functions are modified, along with those of its contents. The endomembrane system is a complex and dynamic player in the cell's compartmental organization.

We'll continue our tour of the cell with some membranous organelles that are *not* closely related to the endomembrane system but play crucial roles in the energy transformations carried out by cells.

CONCEPT CHECK **6.4**

1. Describe the structural and functional distinctions between rough and smooth ER.
2. Describe how transport vesicles integrate the endomembrane system.
3. **WHAT IF?** Imagine a protein that functions in the ER but requires modification in the Golgi apparatus before it can achieve that function. Describe the protein's path through the cell, starting with the mRNA molecule that specifies the protein.

For suggested answers, see Appendix A.

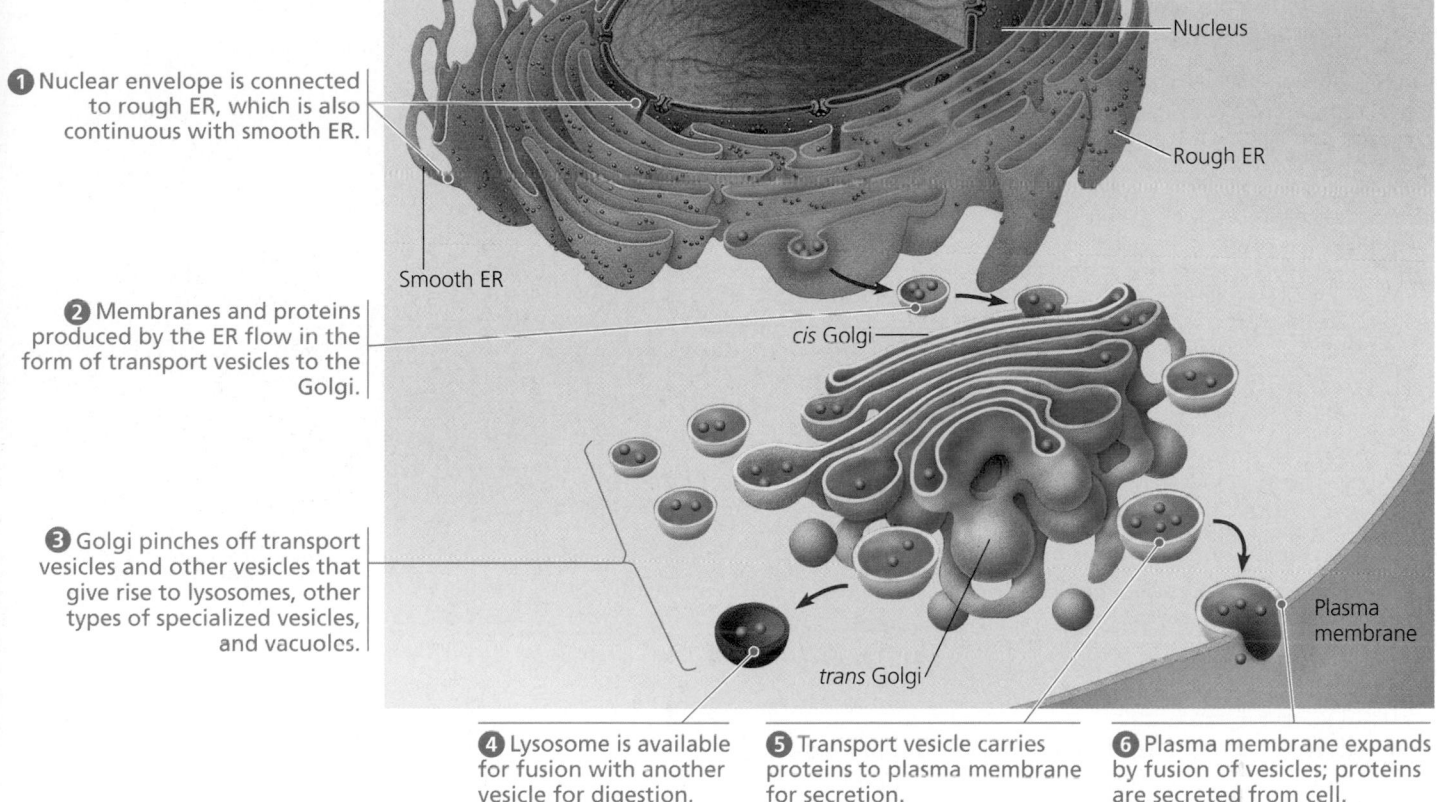

1 Nuclear envelope is connected to rough ER, which is also continuous with smooth ER.

Smooth ER

2 Membranes and proteins produced by the ER flow in the form of transport vesicles to the Golgi.

3 Golgi pinches off transport vesicles and other vesicles that give rise to lysosomes, other types of specialized vesicles, and vacuoles.

Nucleus

Rough ER

cis Golgi

trans Golgi

Plasma membrane

4 Lysosome is available for fusion with another vesicle for digestion.

5 Transport vesicle carries proteins to plasma membrane for secretion.

6 Plasma membrane expands by fusion of vesicles; proteins are secreted from cell.

▲ **Figure 6.16 Review: relationships among organelles of the endomembrane system.** The red arrows show some of the migration pathways for membranes and the materials they enclose.

Mitochondria and chloroplasts change energy from one form to another

Organisms transform the energy they acquire from their surroundings. In eukaryotic cells, mitochondria and chloroplasts are the organelles that convert energy to forms that cells can use for work. **Mitochondria** (singular, *mitochondrion*) are the sites of cellular respiration, the metabolic process that generates ATP by extracting energy from sugars, fats, and other fuels with the help of oxygen. **Chloroplasts**, found in plants and algae, are the sites of photosynthesis. They convert solar energy to chemical energy by absorbing sunlight and using it to drive the synthesis of organic compounds such as sugars from carbon dioxide and water.

Although mitochondria and chloroplasts are enclosed by membranes, they are not part of the endomembrane system. In contrast to organelles of the endomembrane system, mitochondria have two membranes separating their innermost space from the cytosol, and chloroplasts typically have three. (Chloroplasts and related organelles in some algae have *four* membranes.) The membrane proteins of mitochondria and

chloroplasts are made not by ribosomes bound to the ER, but by free ribosomes in the cytosol and by ribosomes contained within these organelles themselves. These organelles also contain a small amount of DNA. It is this DNA that programs the synthesis of the proteins made on the organelle's ribosomes. (Proteins imported from the cytosol—most of the organelle's proteins—are programmed by nuclear DNA.) Mitochondria and chloroplasts are semiautonomous organelles that grow and reproduce within the cell. In Chapters 9 and 10, we will focus on how mitochondria and chloroplasts function. We will consider the evolution of these organelles in Chapter 25. Here we are concerned mainly with the structure of these energy transformers.

In this section, we will also consider the **peroxisome**, an oxidative organelle that is not part of the endomembrane system. Like mitochondria and chloroplasts, the peroxisome imports its proteins primarily from the cytosol.

Mitochondria: Chemical Energy Conversion

Mitochondria are found in nearly all eukaryotic cells, including those of plants, animals, fungi, and most protists. Even in exceptions, such as the human intestinal parasite *Giardia* and some other protists, recent studies have identified closely related organelles that probably evolved from mitochondria.

▶ **Figure 6.17 The mitochondrion, site of cellular respiration.** The inner and outer membranes of the mitochondrion are evident in the drawing and micrograph (TEM). The cristae are infoldings of the inner membrane, which increase its surface area. The cutaway drawing shows the two compartments bounded by the membranes: the intermembrane space and the mitochondrial matrix. Many respiratory enzymes are found in the inner membrane and the matrix. Free ribosomes are also present in the matrix. The DNA molecules, too small to be seen here, are usually circular and are attached to the inner mitochondrial membrane.

Some cells have a single large mitochondrion, but more often a cell has hundreds or even thousands of mitochondria; the number correlates with the cell's level of metabolic activity. For example, motile or contractile cells have proportionally more mitochondria per volume than less active cells. Mitochondria are about 1–10 μm long. Time-lapse films of living cells reveal mitochondria moving around, changing their shapes, and fusing or dividing in two, unlike the static cylinders seen in electron micrographs of dead cells.

The mitochondrion is enclosed by two membranes, each a phospholipid bilayer with a unique collection of embedded proteins (**Figure 6.17**). The outer membrane is smooth, but the inner membrane is convoluted, with infoldings called **cristae**. The inner membrane divides the mitochondrion into two internal compartments. The first is the intermembrane space, the narrow region between the inner and outer membranes. The second compartment, the **mitochondrial matrix**, is enclosed by the inner membrane. The matrix contains many different enzymes as well as the mitochondrial DNA and ribosomes. Enzymes in the matrix catalyze some steps of cellular respiration. Other proteins that function in respiration, including the enzyme that makes ATP, are built into the inner membrane. As highly folded surfaces, the cristae give the inner mitochondrial membrane a large surface area, thus enhancing the productivity of cellular respiration. This is another example of structure fitting function.

Chloroplasts: Capture of Light Energy

The chloroplast is a specialized member of a family of closely related plant organelles called **plastids**. Some others are amyloplasts, colorless plastids that store starch (amylose),

particularly in roots and tubers, and chromoplasts, which have pigments that give fruits and flowers their orange and yellow hues. Chloroplasts contain the green pigment chlorophyll, along with enzymes and other molecules that function in the photosynthetic production of sugar. These lens-shaped organelles, measuring about 2 μm by 5 μm, are found in leaves and other green organs of plants and in algae (**Figure 6.18**).

The contents of a chloroplast are partitioned from the cytosol by an envelope consisting of two membranes separated by a very narrow intermembrane space. Inside the chloroplast is another membranous system in the form of flattened, interconnected sacs called **thylakoids**. In some regions, thylakoids are stacked like poker chips; each stack is called a **granum** (plural, *grana*). The fluid outside the thylakoids is the **stroma**, which contains the chloroplast DNA and ribosomes as well as many enzymes. The membranes of the chloroplast divide the chloroplast space into three compartments: the intermembrane space, the stroma, and the thylakoid space. In Chapter 10, you will learn how this compartmental organization enables the chloroplast to convert light energy to chemical energy during photosynthesis.

As with mitochondria, the static and rigid appearance of chloroplasts in micrographs or schematic diagrams is not true to their dynamic behavior in the living cell. Their shapes are changeable, and they grow and occasionally pinch in two, reproducing themselves. They are mobile and, with mitochondria and other organelles, move around the cell along tracks of the cytoskeleton, a structural network we will consider later in this chapter.

Peroxisomes: Oxidation

The peroxisome is a specialized metabolic compartment that is bounded by a single membrane (**Figure 6.19**). Peroxisomes

◄ **Figure 6.18 The chloroplast, site of photosynthesis.** A typical chloroplast is enclosed by two membranes separated by a narrow intermembrane space that constitutes an outer compartment. The inner membrane encloses a second compartment containing the fluid called stroma. The stroma surrounds a third compartment, the thylakoid space, delineated by the thylakoid membrane. Interconnected thylakoid sacs (thylakoids) are stacked to form structures called grana (singular, *granum*), which are further connected by thin tubules between individual thylakoids. Photosynthetic enzymes are embedded in the thylakoid membranes. Free ribosomes are present in the stroma, along with copies of the chloroplast genome (DNA), too small to be seen here (TEM).

contain enzymes that transfer hydrogen from various substrates to oxygen (O_2), producing hydrogen peroxide (H_2O_2) as a by-product, from which the organelle derives its name. These reactions may have many different functions. Some peroxisomes use oxygen to break fatty acids down into smaller molecules that can then be transported to mitochondria, where they are used as fuel for cellular respiration. Peroxisomes in the liver detoxify alcohol and other harmful compounds by transferring hydrogen from the poisons to oxygen. The H_2O_2 formed by peroxisomes is itself toxic, but the organelle also contains an enzyme that converts H_2O_2 to water. This is an excellent example of how the cell's compartmental structure is crucial to its functions: The enzymes that produce hydrogen peroxide and those that dispose of this toxic compound are sequestered in the same space, away from other cellular components that could otherwise be damaged.

Specialized peroxisomes called *glyoxysomes* are found in the fat-storing tissues of plant seeds. These organelles contain enzymes that initiate the conversion of fatty acids to sugar, which the emerging seedling uses as a source of energy and carbon until it can produce its own sugar by photosynthesis.

Unlike lysosomes, peroxisomes do not bud from the endomembrane system. They grow larger by incorporating proteins made primarily in the cytosol, lipids made in the ER, and lipids synthesized within the peroxisome itself. Peroxisomes may increase in number by splitting in two when they reach a certain size.

CONCEPT CHECK 6.5

1. Describe two common characteristics of chloroplasts and mitochondria. Consider both function and membrane structure.
2. **WHAT IF?** A classmate proposes that mitochondria, chloroplasts, and peroxisomes should be classified in the endomembrane system. Argue against the proposal.

For suggested answers, see Appendix A.

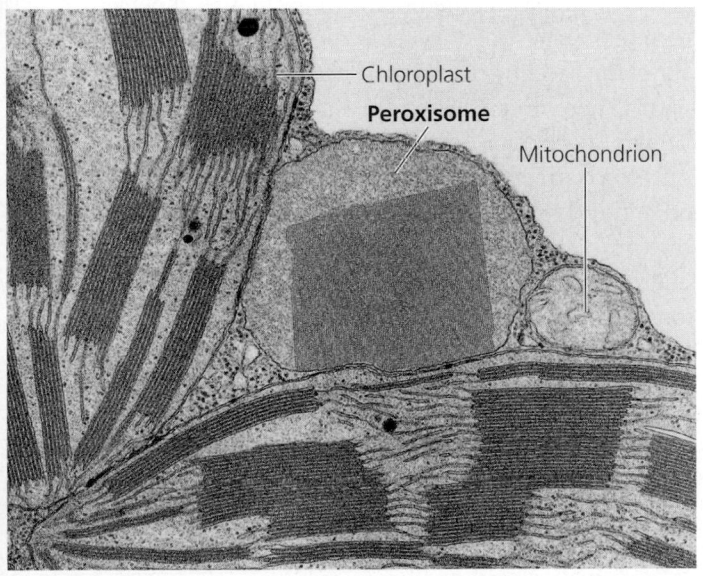

▲ **Figure 6.19 A peroxisome.** Peroxisomes are roughly spherical and often have a granular or crystalline core that is thought to be a dense collection of enzyme molecules. This peroxisome is in a leaf cell (TEM). Notice its proximity to two chloroplasts and a mitochondrion. These organelles cooperate with peroxisomes in certain metabolic functions.

CONCEPT 6.6

The cytoskeleton is a network of fibers that organizes structures and activities in the cell

In the early days of electron microscopy, biologists thought that the organelles of a eukaryotic cell floated freely in the cytosol. But improvements in both light microscopy and electron microscopy have revealed the **cytoskeleton**, a network of fibers extending throughout the cytoplasm **(Figure 6.20)**. The cytoskeleton, which plays a major role in organizing the structures and activities of the cell, is composed of three types of molecular structures: microtubules, microfilaments, and intermediate filaments.

Roles of the Cytoskeleton: Support, Motility, and Regulation

The most obvious function of the cytoskeleton is to give mechanical support to the cell and maintain its shape. This is especially important for animal cells, which lack walls. The remarkable strength and resilience of the cytoskeleton as a whole is based on its architecture. Like a geodesic dome, the cytoskeleton is stabilized by a balance between opposing forces exerted by its elements. And just as the skeleton of an animal helps fix the positions of other body parts, the cytoskeleton provides anchorage for many organelles and even cytosolic enzyme molecules. The cytoskeleton is more dynamic than an animal skeleton, however. It can be quickly dismantled in one part of the cell and reassembled in a new location, changing the shape of the cell.

Several types of cell motility (movement) also involve the cytoskeleton. The term *cell motility* encompasses both changes in cell location and more limited movements of parts of the cell. Cell motility generally requires the interaction of the cytoskeleton with **motor proteins**. Examples of such cell motility

(a) Motor proteins that attach to receptors on vesicles can "walk" the vesicles along microtubules or, in some cases, microfilaments.

(b) Vesicles containing neurotransmitters migrate to the tips of nerve cell axons via the mechanism in (a). In this SEM of a squid giant axon, two vesicles can be seen moving along a microtubule. (A separate part of the experiment provided the evidence that they were in fact moving.)

▲ **Figure 6.21 Motor proteins and the cytoskeleton.**

abound. Cytoskeletal elements and motor proteins work together with plasma membrane molecules to allow whole cells to move along fibers outside the cell. Motor proteins bring about the bending of cilia and flagella by gripping microtubules within those organelles and sliding them against each other. A similar mechanism involving microfilaments causes muscle cells to contract. Inside the cell, vesicles and other organelles often travel to their destinations along "monorails" provided by the cytoskeleton. For example, this is how vesicles containing neurotransmitter molecules migrate to the tips of axons, the long extensions of nerve cells that release these molecules as chemical signals to adjacent nerve cells **(Figure 6.21)**. The vesicles that bud off from the ER travel to the Golgi along cytoskeletal tracks. The cytoskeleton also manipulates the plasma membrane in a way that forms food vacuoles or other phagocytic vesicles. And the streaming of cytoplasm that circulates materials within many large plant cells is yet another kind of cellular movement brought about by the cytoskeleton.

The cytoskeleton is also involved in regulating biochemical activities in the cell in response to mechanical stimulation. Forces exerted by extracellular molecules via cell-surface proteins are apparently transmitted into the cell by cytoskeletal elements, and the forces may even reach the nucleus. In one experiment, investigators used a micromanipulation device to

▲ **Figure 6.20 The cytoskeleton.** In this TEM, prepared by a method known as deep-etching, the thicker, hollow microtubules and the thinner, solid microfilaments are visible. A third component of the cytoskeleton, intermediate filaments, is not evident here.

Table 6.1 The Structure and Function of the Cytoskeleton

Property	Microtubules (Tubulin Polymers)	Microfilaments (Actin Filaments)	Intermediate Filaments
Structure	Hollow tubes; wall consists of 13 columns of tubulin molecules	Two intertwined strands of actin, each a polymer of actin subunits	Fibrous proteins supercoiled into thicker cables
Diameter	25 nm with 15-nm lumen	7 nm	8–12 nm
Protein subunits	Tubulin, a dimer consisting of α-tubulin and β-tubulin	Actin	One of several different proteins of the keratin family, depending on cell type
Main functions	Maintenance of cell shape (compression-resisting "girders") Cell motility (as in cilia or flagella) Chromosome movements in cell division Organelle movements	Maintenance of cell shape (tension-bearing elements) Changes in cell shape Muscle contraction Cytoplasmic streaming Cell motility (as in pseudopodia) Cell division (cleavage furrow formation)	Maintenance of cell shape (tension-bearing elements) Anchorage of nucleus and certain other organelles Formation of nuclear lamina

Micrographs of fibroblasts, a favorite cell type for cell biology studies. Each has been experimentally treated to fluorescently tag the structure of interest.

pull on certain plasma membrane proteins attached to the cytoskeleton. A video microscope captured the almost instantaneous rearrangements of nucleoli and other structures in the nucleus. In this way, cytoskeletal transmission of naturally occurring mechanical signals may help regulate and coordinate the cell's response.

Components of the Cytoskeleton

Now let's look more closely at the three main types of fibers that make up the cytoskeleton **(Table 6.1)**. *Microtubules* are the thickest of the three types; *microfilaments* (also called actin filaments) are the thinnest; and *intermediate filaments* are fibers with diameters in a middle range.

Microtubules

All eukaryotic cells have **microtubules**, hollow rods measuring about 25 nm in diameter and from 200 nm to 25 μm in length. The wall of the hollow tube is constructed from a globular protein called tubulin. Each tubulin protein is a *dimer*, a molecule made up of two subunits. A tubulin dimer consists of two slightly different polypeptides, α-tubulin and β-tubulin. Microtubules grow in length by adding tubulin dimers; they can also be disassembled and their tubulin used to build microtubules elsewhere in the cell. Because of the architecture of a microtubule, its two ends are slightly different. One end can accumulate or release tubulin dimers at a much higher rate than the other, thus growing and shrinking significantly during cellular activities. (This is called the "plus end," not because it can only add tubulin proteins but because it's the end where both "on" and "off" rates are much higher.)

Microtubules shape and support the cell and also serve as tracks along which organelles equipped with motor proteins can move. To mention an example different from the one in Figure 6.21, microtubules guide secretory vesicles from the Golgi apparatus to the plasma membrane. Microtubules also separate chromosomes during cell division (see Chapter 12).

Centrosomes and Centrioles In animal cells, microtubules grow out from a **centrosome**, a region that is often located near the nucleus and is considered a "microtubule-organizing center." These microtubules function as compression-resisting girders of the cytoskeleton. Within the centrosome are a pair of **centrioles**, each composed of nine sets of triplet microtubules arranged in a ring **(Figure 6.22)**. Before an animal cell divides, the centrioles replicate. Although centrosomes with centrioles may help organize microtubule assembly in animal cells, they are not essential for this function in all eukaryotes; yeast cells and plant cells lack centrosomes with centrioles but have well-organized microtubules. Clearly, other microtubule-organizing centers must play the role of centrosomes in these cells.

Cilia and Flagella In eukaryotes, a specialized arrangement of microtubules is responsible for the beating of **flagella** (singular, *flagellum*) and **cilia** (singular, *cilium*), microtubule-containing extensions that project from some cells. Many unicellular eukaryotes are propelled through water by cilia or flagella that act as locomotor appendages, and the sperm of animals, algae, and some plants have flagella. When cilia or flagella extend from cells that are held in place as part of a tissue layer, they can move fluid over the surface of the tissue. For example, the ciliated lining of the trachea (windpipe) sweeps mucus containing trapped debris out of the lungs (see Figure 6.4). In a woman's reproductive tract, the cilia lining the oviducts help move an egg toward the uterus.

Motile cilia usually occur in large numbers on the cell surface. They are about 0.25 µm in diameter and about 2–20 µm long. Flagella are the same diameter but longer, 10–200 µm. Also, flagella are usually limited to just one or a few per cell.

Flagella and cilia differ in their beating patterns **(Figure 6.23)**. A flagellum has an undulating motion that generates force in the same direction as the flagellum's axis. In contrast, cilia work more like oars, with alternating power and recovery strokes generating force in a direction perpendicular to the cilium's axis, much as the oars of a crew boat extend outward at right angles to the boat's forward movement.

Centrosome

Microtubule

Centrioles

0.25 µm

Longitudinal section of one centriole   Microtubules   Cross section of the other centriole

▲ **Figure 6.22 Centrosome containing a pair of centrioles.** Most animal cells have a centrosome, a region near the nucleus where the cell's microtubules are initiated. Within the centrosome is a pair of centrioles, each about 250 nm (0.25 µm) in diameter. The two centrioles are at right angles to each other, and each is made up of nine sets of three microtubules. The blue portions of the drawing represent nontubulin proteins that connect the microtubule triplets (TEM).

? *How many microtubules are in a centrosome? In the drawing, circle and label one microtubule and describe its structure.*

A cilium may also act as a signal-receiving "antenna" for the cell. Cilia that have this function are generally nonmotile, and there is only one per cell. (In fact, in vertebrate animals, almost all cells seem to have such a cilium, which is called a *primary cilium*.) Membrane proteins on this kind of cilium transmit molecular signals from the cell's environment to its interior, triggering signaling pathways that may lead to changes in the cell's activities. Cilia-based signaling appears to be crucial to brain function and to embryonic development.

Though different in length, number per cell, and beating pattern, motile cilia and flagella share a common ultrastructure. Each has a core of microtubules sheathed in an extension of the plasma membrane **(Figure 6.24)**. Nine doublets of microtubules, the members of each pair sharing part of their walls, are arranged in a ring. In the center of the ring are two single microtubules. This arrangement, referred to as the "9 + 2" pattern, is found in nearly all eukaryotic flagella and motile cilia. (Nonmotile primary cilia have a "9 + 0" pattern, lacking the central pair of microtubules.) The microtubule assembly of a cilium or

► **Figure 6.23**
A comparison of the beating of flagella and cilia.

(a) Motion of flagella. A flagellum usually undulates, its snakelike motion driving a cell in the same direction as the axis of the flagellum. Propulsion of a human sperm cell is an example of flagellate locomotion (LM).

Direction of swimming

5 μm

(b) Motion of cilia. Cilia have a back-and-forth motion. The rapid power stroke moves the cell in a direction perpendicular to the axis of the cilium. Then, during the slower recovery stroke, the cilium bends and sweeps sideways, closer to the surface. A dense nap of cilia, beating at a rate of about 40 to 60 strokes a second, covers this *Colpidium*, a freshwater protozoan (colorized SEM).

Direction of organism's movement

Power stroke   Recovery stroke

15 μm

Microtubules

Plasma membrane

Basal body

0.5 μm

(a) A longitudinal section of a motile cilium shows microtubules running the length of the structure (TEM).

0.1 μm

Outer microtubule doublet

Dynein proteins

Central microtubule

Radial spoke

Protein cross-linking outer doublets

Plasma membrane

(b) A cross section through a motile cilium shows the "9 + 2" arrangement of microtubules (TEM). The outer microtubule doublets and the two central microtubules are held together by flexible cross-linking proteins (blue in art), including the radial spokes. The doublets also have attached motor proteins called dyneins (red in art). In the drawing, the plasma membrane has been peeled away to reveal a longitudinal view of two of the doublets.

0.1 μm

Triplet

(c) Basal body: The nine outer doublets of a cilium or flagellum extend into the basal body, where each doublet joins another microtubule to form a ring of nine triplets. Each triplet is connected to the next triplet and to the center by nontubulin proteins (the blue lines in diagram). The two central microtubules are not shown because they terminate above the basal body (TEM).

Cross section of basal body

▲ **Figure 6.24 Ultrastructure of a eukaryotic flagellum or motile cilium.**

flagellum is anchored in the cell by a **basal body**, which is structurally very similar to a centriole. In fact, in many animals (including humans), the basal body of the fertilizing sperm's flagellum enters the egg and becomes a centriole.

In flagella and motile cilia, flexible cross-linking proteins, evenly spaced along the length of the cilium or flagellum, connect the outer doublets to each other and to the two central microtubules. Each outer doublet also has pairs of protruding proteins spaced along its length and reaching toward the neighboring doublet; these are large motor proteins called **dyneins**, each composed of several polypeptides. Dyneins are responsible for the bending movements of the organelle. A dynein molecule performs a complex cycle of movements caused by changes in the shape of the protein, with ATP providing the energy for these changes **(Figure 6.25)**.

The mechanics of dynein-based bending involve a process that resembles walking. A typical dynein protein has two "feet" that "walk" along the microtubule of the adjacent doublet, one foot maintaining contact while the other releases and reattaches one step further along the microtubule. Without any restraints on the movement of the microtubule doublets, one doublet would continue to "walk" along and slide past the surface of the other, elongating the cilium or flagellum rather than bending it (see Figure 6.25a). For lateral movement of a cilium or flagellum, the dynein "walking" must have something to pull against, as when the muscles in your leg pull against your bones to move your knee. In cilia and flagella, the microtubule doublets seem to be held in place by the cross-linking proteins just inside the outer doublets and by the radial spokes and other structural elements. Thus, neighboring doublets cannot slide past each other very far. Instead, the forces exerted by dynein "walking" cause the doublets to curve, bending the cilium or flagellum (see Figure 6.25b and c).

Microfilaments (Actin Filaments)

Microfilaments are solid rods about 7 nm in diameter. They are also called actin filaments because they are built from molecules of **actin**, a globular protein. A microfilament is a twisted double chain of actin subunits (see Table 6.1). Besides occurring as linear filaments, microfilaments can form structural networks, due to the presence of proteins that bind along the side of an actin filament and allow a new filament to extend as a branch. Microfilaments seem to be present in all eukaryotic cells.

In contrast to the compression-resisting role of microtubules, the structural role of microfilaments in the cytoskeleton is to bear tension (pulling forces). A three-dimensional network formed by microfilaments just inside the plasma membrane (*cortical microfilaments*) helps support the cell's shape. This network gives the outer cytoplasmic layer of a cell, called the **cortex**, the semisolid consistency of a gel, in contrast with the more fluid (sol) state of the interior cytoplasm.

(a) Effect of unrestrained dynein movement. If a cilium or flagellum had no cross-linking proteins, the two feet of each dynein along one doublet (powered by ATP) would alternately grip and release the adjacent doublet. This "walking" motion would push the adjacent doublet up. Instead of bending, the doublets would slide past each other.

(b) Effect of cross-linking proteins. In a cilium or flagellum, two adjacent doublets cannot slide far because they are physically restrained by proteins, so they bend. (Only two of the nine outer doublets in Figure 6.24b are shown here.)

(c) Wavelike motion. Synchronized cycles of movement of many dyneins probably cause a bend to begin at the base of the cilium or flagellum and move outward toward the tip. Many successive bends, such as the ones shown here to the left and right, result in a wavelike motion. In this diagram, the two central microtubules and the cross-linking proteins are not shown.

▲ **Figure 6.25 How dynein "walking" moves flagella and cilia.**

Microvillus

Plasma membrane

Microfilaments (actin filaments)

Intermediate filaments

0.25 µm

▲ **Figure 6.26 A structural role of microfilaments.** The surface area of this nutrient-absorbing intestinal cell is increased by its many microvilli (singular, *microvillus*), cellular extensions reinforced by bundles of microfilaments. These actin filaments are anchored to a network of intermediate filaments (TEM).

Muscle cell

Actin filament

Myosin filament
Myosin arm

(a) Myosin motors in muscle cell contraction. The "walking" of myosin arms drives the parallel myosin and actin filaments past each other so that the actin filaments approach each other in the middle (red arrows). This shortens the muscle cell. Muscle contraction involves the shortening of many muscle cells at the same time.

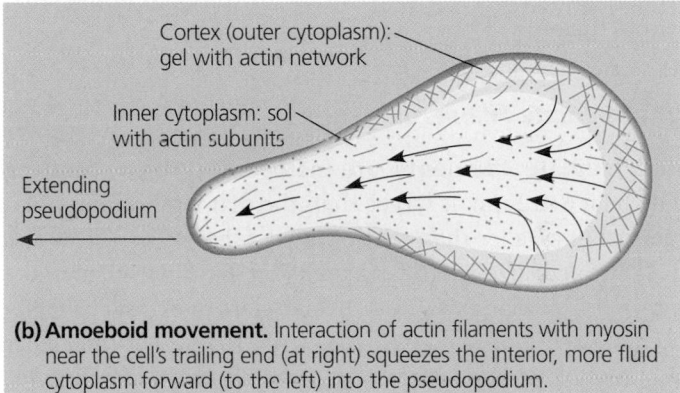

Cortex (outer cytoplasm): gel with actin network

Inner cytoplasm: sol with actin subunits

Extending pseudopodium

(b) Amoeboid movement. Interaction of actin filaments with myosin near the cell's trailing end (at right) squeezes the interior, more fluid cytoplasm forward (to the left) into the pseudopodium.

Nonmoving cortical cytoplasm (gel)

Chloroplast

Streaming cytoplasm (sol)

Vacuole

Parallel actin filaments

Cell wall

(c) Cytoplasmic streaming in plant cells. A layer of cytoplasm cycles around the cell, moving over a carpet of parallel actin filaments. Myosin motors attached to organelles in the fluid cytosol may drive the streaming by interacting with the actin.

▲ **Figure 6.27 Microfilaments and motility.** In the three examples shown in this figure, cell nuclei and most other organelles have been omitted for clarity.

In animal cells specialized for transporting materials across the plasma membrane, such as intestinal cells, bundles of microfilaments make up the core of microvilli, the previously mentioned delicate projections that increase the cell surface area there **(Figure 6.26)**.

Microfilaments are well known for their role in cell motility, particularly as part of the contractile apparatus of muscle cells. Thousands of actin filaments are arranged parallel to one another along the length of a muscle cell, interdigitated with thicker filaments made of a protein called **myosin** **(Figure 6.27a)**. Like dynein when it interacts with microtubules, myosin acts as a microfilament-based motor protein by means of projections that "walk" along the actin filaments. Contraction of the muscle cell results from the actin and myosin filaments sliding past one another in this way, shortening the cell. In other kinds of cells, actin filaments are associated with myosin in miniature and less elaborate versions of the arrangement in muscle cells. These actin-myosin aggregates are responsible for localized contractions of cells. For example, a contracting belt of microfilaments forms a cleavage furrow that pinches a dividing animal cell into two daughter cells.

Localized contraction brought about by actin and myosin also plays a role in amoeboid movement **(Figure 6.27b)**, in which a cell such as an amoeba crawls along a surface by extending and flowing into cellular extensions called **pseudopodia** (from the Greek *pseudes*, false, and *pod*, foot).

Pseudopodia extend and contract through the reversible assembly of actin subunits into microfilaments and of microfilaments into networks that convert cytoplasm from a sol to a gel. According to a widely accepted model, filaments near the cell's trailing end interact with myosin, causing contraction. Like squeezing on a toothpaste tube, this contraction forces the interior, more fluid cytoplasm into the pseudopodium, where the actin network has been weakened. The pseudopodium extends until the actin reassembles into a network. Amoebas are not the only cells that move by crawling; so do many cells in the animal body, including some white blood cells.

In plant cells, both actin-myosin interactions and sol-gel transformations brought about by actin may be involved in **cytoplasmic streaming**, a circular flow of cytoplasm within cells **(Figure 6.27c)**. This movement, which is especially common in large plant cells, speeds the distribution of materials within the cell.

Intermediate Filaments

Intermediate filaments are named for their diameter, which, at 8–12 nm, is larger than the diameter of microfilaments but smaller than that of microtubules (see Table 6.1, p. 113). Specialized for bearing tension (like microfilaments), intermediate filaments are a diverse class of cytoskeletal elements. Each type is constructed from a different molecular subunit belonging to a family of proteins whose members include the keratins. Microtubules and microfilaments, in contrast, are consistent in diameter and composition in all eukaryotic cells.

Intermediate filaments are more permanent fixtures of cells than are microfilaments and microtubules, which are often disassembled and reassembled in various parts of a cell. Even after cells die, intermediate filament networks often persist; for example, the outer layer of our skin consists of dead skin cells full of keratin proteins. Chemical treatments that remove microfilaments and microtubules from the cytoplasm of living cells leave a web of intermediate filaments that retains its original shape. Such experiments suggest that intermediate filaments are especially important in reinforcing the shape of a cell and fixing the position of certain organelles. For instance, the nucleus commonly sits within a cage made of intermediate filaments, fixed in location by branches of the filaments that extend into the cytoplasm. Other intermediate filaments make up the nuclear lamina that lines the interior of the nuclear envelope (see Figure 6.10). In cases where the shape of the entire cell is correlated with function, intermediate filaments support that shape. A case in point is the long extensions (axons) of nerve cells that transmit impulses, which are strengthened by one class of intermediate filament. Thus, the various kinds of intermediate filaments may function as the framework of the entire cytoskeleton.

1. Describe shared features of microtubule-based motion of flagella and microfilament-based muscle contraction.
2. How do cilia and flagella bend?
3. **WHAT IF?** Males afflicted with Kartagener's syndrome are sterile because of immotile sperm, tend to suffer lung infections, and frequently have internal organs, such as the heart, on the wrong side of the body. This disorder has a genetic basis. Suggest what the underlying defect might be.

For suggested answers, see Appendix A.

CONCEPT **6.7**

Extracellular components and connections between cells help coordinate cellular activities

Having crisscrossed the interior of the cell to explore its interior components, we complete our tour of the cell by returning to the surface of this microscopic world, where there are additional structures with important functions. The plasma membrane is usually regarded as the boundary of the living cell, but most cells synthesize and secrete materials that are external to the plasma membrane. Although these materials and the structures they form are outside the cell, their study is central to cell biology because they are involved in a great many cellular functions.

Cell Walls of Plants

The **cell wall** is an extracellular structure of plant cells that distinguishes them from animal cells. The wall protects the plant cell, maintains its shape, and prevents excessive uptake of water. On the level of the whole plant, the strong walls of specialized cells hold the plant up against the force of gravity. Prokaryotes, fungi, and some protists also have cell walls, but we will postpone discussion of them until Unit Five.

Plant cell walls are much thicker than the plasma membrane, ranging from 0.1 μm to several micrometers. The exact chemical composition of the wall varies from species to species and even from one cell type to another in the same plant, but the basic design of the wall is consistent. Microfibrils made of the polysaccharide cellulose (see Figure 5.8) are synthesized by an enzyme called cellulose synthase and secreted to the extracellular space, where they become embedded in a matrix of other polysaccharides and proteins. This combination of materials, strong fibers in a "ground substance" (matrix), is the same basic architectural design found in steel-reinforced concrete and in fiberglass.

Secondary cell wall

Primary cell wall

Middle lamella

1 μm

Central vacuole

Cytosol

Plasma membrane

Plant cell walls

Plasmodesmata

▲ **Figure 6.28 Plant cell walls.** The drawing shows several cells, each with a large vacuole, a nucleus, and several chloroplasts and mitochondria. The transmission electron micrograph (TEM) shows the cell walls where two cells come together. The multilayered partition between plant cells consists of adjoining walls individually secreted by the cells.

A young plant cell first secretes a relatively thin and flexible wall called the **primary cell wall (Figure 6.28)**. In actively growing cells, the cellulose fibrils are oriented at right angles to the direction of cell expansion, possibly affecting the growth pattern. David Ehrhardt and colleagues investigated the role of microtubules in orienting these fibrils **(Figure 6.29)**. Their observations strongly supported the idea that microtubules in the cell cortex guide cellulose synthase as it synthesizes and deposits the fibrils. By orienting cellulose deposition, microtubules thus affect the growth pattern of the cells.

Between primary walls of adjacent cells is the **middle lamella**, a thin layer rich in sticky polysaccharides called pectins. The middle lamella glues adjacent cells together (pectin is used as a thickening agent in jams and jellies). When the cell matures and stops growing, it strengthens its wall. Some plant cells do this simply by secreting hardening substances into the primary wall. Other cells add a **secondary cell wall** between the plasma membrane and the primary wall. The secondary wall, often deposited in several laminated layers, has a strong and durable matrix that affords the cell protection and support. Wood, for example, consists mainly of secondary walls. Plant cell walls are commonly perforated by channels be-

▼ **Figure 6.29** **Inquiry**

What role do microtubules play in orienting deposition of cellulose in cell walls?

EXPERIMENT   Previous experiments on preserved plant tissues had shown alignment of microtubules in the cell cortex with cellulose fibrils in the cell wall. Also, drugs that disrupted microtubules were observed to cause disoriented cellulose fibrils. To further investigate the possible role of cortical microtubules in guiding fibril deposition, David Ehrhardt and colleagues at Stanford University used a type of confocal microscopy to study cell wall deposition in living cells. In these cells, they labeled both cellulose synthase and microtubules with fluorescent markers and observed them over time.

RESULTS   The path of cellulose synthase movement and the positions of existing microtubules coincided highly over time. The fluorescent micrographs below represent an average of five images, taken 10 seconds apart. The labeling molecules caused cellulose synthase to fluoresce green and the microtubules to fluoresce red. The arrowheads indicate prominent areas where the two are seen to align.

10 μm

Distribution of cellulose synthase over time

Distribution of microtubules over time

CONCLUSION   The organization of microtubules appears to directly guide the path of cellulose synthase as it lays down cellulose, thus determining the orientation of cellulose fibrils.

SOURCE   A. R. Paradez et al., Visualization of cellulose synthase demonstrates functional association with microtubules, *Science* 312:1491–1495 (2006).

WHAT IF?   In a second experiment, the researchers exposed the plant cells to blue light, previously shown to cause reorientation of microtubules. What events would you predict would follow blue light exposure?

tween adjacent cells called plasmodesmata (see Figure 6.28), which will be discussed shortly.

The Extracellular Matrix (ECM) of Animal Cells

Although animal cells lack walls akin to those of plant cells, they do have an elaborate **extracellular matrix (ECM) (Figure 6.30,** on the next page). The main ingredients of the ECM are glycoproteins secreted by the cells. (Recall that glycoproteins are proteins with covalently bonded carbohydrate, usually short chains of sugars.) The most abundant glycoprotein in the ECM of most animal cells is **collagen**, which forms strong fibers outside the

Collagen fibers are embedded in a web of proteoglycan complexes.

Fibronectin attaches the ECM to integrins embedded in the plasma membrane.

Plasma membrane

EXTRACELLULAR FLUID

A **proteoglycan complex** consists of hundreds of proteoglycan molecules attached noncovalently to a single long polysaccharide molecule.

Integrins, membrane proteins with two subunits, bind to the ECM on one side and to associated proteins attached to microfilaments on the other. This linkage can transmit signals between the cell's external environment and its interior and can result in changes in cell behavior.

Micro-filaments

CYTOPLASM

Polysaccharide molecule

Carbo-hydrates

Core protein

Proteoglycan molecule

Proteoglycan complex

▲ **Figure 6.30 Extracellular matrix (ECM) of an animal cell.** The molecular composition and structure of the ECM varies from one cell type to another. In this example, three different types of glycoproteins are present: proteoglycans, collagen, and fibronectin.

cells (see Figure 5.21). In fact, collagen accounts for about 40% of the total protein in the human body. The collagen fibers are embedded in a network woven from **proteoglycans**. A proteoglycan molecule consists of a small core protein with many carbohydrate chains covalently attached, so that it may be up to 95% carbohydrate. Large proteoglycan complexes can form when hundreds of proteoglycans become noncovalently attached to a single long polysaccharide molecule, as shown in Figure 6.30. Some cells are attached to the ECM by still other ECM glycoproteins, such as **fibronectin**. Fibronectin and other ECM proteins bind to cell surface receptor proteins called **integrins** that are built into the plasma membrane. Integrins span the membrane and bind on their cytoplasmic side to associated proteins attached to microfilaments of the cytoskeleton. The name *integrin* is based on the word *integrate*: Integrins are in a position to transmit signals between the ECM and the cytoskeleton and thus to integrate changes occurring outside and inside the cell.

Current research on fibronectin, other ECM molecules, and integrins is revealing the influential role of the extracellular matrix in the lives of cells. By communicating with a cell through integrins, the ECM can regulate a cell's behavior. For example, some cells in a developing embryo migrate along specific pathways by matching the orientation of their microfilaments to the "grain" of fibers in the extracellular matrix. Researchers are also learning that the extracellular matrix around a cell can influence the activity of genes in the nucleus. Information about the ECM probably reaches the nucleus by a combination of mechanical and chemical signaling pathways. Mechanical signaling involves fibronectin, integrins, and microfilaments of the cytoskeleton. Changes in the cytoskeleton may in turn trigger

chemical signaling pathways inside the cell, leading to changes in the set of proteins being made by the cell and therefore changes in the cell's function. In this way, the extracellular matrix of a particular tissue may help coordinate the behavior of all the cells within that tissue. Direct connections between cells also function in this coordination, as we discuss next.

Intercellular Junctions

Cells in an animal or plant are organized into tissues, organs, and organ systems. Cells often adhere, interact, and communicate through direct physical contact.

Plasmodesmata in Plant Cells

It might seem that the nonliving cell walls of plants would isolate cells from one another. But in fact, as shown in **Figure 6.31**, cell walls are perforated with channels called **plasmodesmata**

Cell walls

Interior of cell

Interior of cell

0.5 μm

Plasmodesmata   Plasma membranes

▲ **Figure 6.31 Plasmodesmata between plant cells.** The cytoplasm of one plant cell is continuous with the cytoplasm of its neighbors via plasmodesmata, channels through the cell walls (TEM).

(singular, *plasmodesma*; from the Greek *desmos*, to bind). Cytosol passes through the plasmodesmata and connects the chemical environments of adjacent cells. These connections unify most of the plant into one living continuum. The plasma membranes of adjacent cells line the channel of each plasmodesma and thus are continuous. Water and small solutes can pass freely from cell to cell, and recent experiments have shown that in some circumstances, certain proteins and RNA molecules can also do this (see Concept 36.6). The macromolecules transported to neighboring cells seem to reach the plasmodesmata by moving along fibers of the cytoskeleton.

Tight Junctions, Desmosomes, and Gap Junctions in Animal Cells

In animals, there are three main types of intercellular junctions: *tight junctions*, *desmosomes*, and *gap junctions* (the latter of which are most like the plasmodesmata of plants). All three types of intercellular junctions are especially common in epithelial tissue, which lines the external and internal surfaces of the body. **Figure 6.32** uses epithelial cells of the intestinal lining to illustrate these junctions; you should study this figure before moving on.

▼ **Figure 6.32**

Exploring Intercellular Junctions in Animal Tissues

Tight junctions prevent fluid from moving across a layer of cells

Tight junction

Intermediate filaments

Desmosome

Gap junction

Space between cells

Plasma membranes of adjacent cells

Extracellular matrix

Tight junction

0.5 μm

1 μm

0.1 μm

Tight Junctions

At **tight junctions**, the plasma membranes of neighboring cells are very tightly pressed against each other, bound together by specific proteins (purple). Forming continuous seals around the cells, tight junctions prevent leakage of extracellular fluid across a layer of epithelial cells. For example, tight junctions between skin cells make us watertight by preventing leakage between cells in our sweat glands.

Desmosomes

Desmosomes (also called *anchoring junctions*) function like rivets, fastening cells together into strong sheets. Intermediate filaments made of sturdy keratin proteins anchor desmosomes in the cytoplasm. Desmosomes attach muscle cells to each other in a muscle. Some "muscle tears" involve the rupture of desmosomes.

Gap Junctions

Gap junctions (also called *communicating junctions*) provide cytoplasmic channels from one cell to an adjacent cell and in this way are similar in their function to the plasmodesmata in plants. Gap junctions consist of membrane proteins that surround a pore through which ions, sugars, amino acids, and other small molecules may pass. Gap junctions are necessary for communication between cells in many types of tissues, including heart muscle, and in animal embryos.

1. In what way are the cells of plants and animals structurally different from single-celled eukaryotes?
2. **WHAT IF?** If the plant cell wall or the animal extracellular matrix were impermeable, what effect would this have on cell function?

For suggested answers, see Appendix A.

▲ **Figure 6.33 The emergence of cellular functions.** The ability of this macrophage (brown) to recognize, apprehend, and destroy bacteria (yellow) is a coordinated activity of the whole cell. Its cytoskeleton, lysosomes, and plasma membrane are among the components that function in phagocytosis (colorized SEM).

The Cell: A Living Unit Greater Than the Sum of Its Parts

From our panoramic view of the cell's overall compartmental organization to our close-up inspection of each organelle's architecture, this tour of the cell has provided many opportunities to correlate structure with function. (This would be a good time to review cell structure by returning to Figure 6.9, on pp. 100 and 101.) But even as we dissect the cell, remember that none of its components works alone. As an example of cellular integration, consider the microscopic scene in **Figure 6.33**. The large cell is a macrophage (see Figure 6.14a). It helps defend the mammalian body against infections by ingesting bacteria (the smaller cells) into phagocytic vesicles. The macrophage crawls along a surface and reaches out to the bacteria with thin pseudopodia (called filopodia). Actin filaments interact with other elements of the cytoskeleton in these movements. After the macrophage engulfs the bacteria, they are destroyed by lysosomes. The elaborate endomembrane system produces the lysosomes. The digestive enzymes of the lysosomes and the proteins of the cytoskeleton are all made on ribosomes. And the synthesis of these proteins is programmed by genetic messages dispatched from the DNA in the nucleus. All these processes require energy, which mitochondria supply in the form of ATP. Cellular functions arise from cellular order: The cell is a living unit greater than the sum of its parts.

Chapter 6 Review

SUMMARY OF KEY CONCEPTS

CONCEPT 6.1

To study cells, biologists use microscopes and the tools of biochemistry (pp. 94–97)

▶ **Microscopy** Improvements in microscopy that affect the parameters of magnification, resolution, and contrast have catalyzed progress in the study of cell structure. Light and electron microscopy (LM and EM) remain important tools.

▶ **Cell Fractionation** Cell biologists can obtain pellets enriched in particular cellular components by centrifuging disrupted cells at sequential speeds. Larger components are in the pellet after lower speed centrifugation, and smaller components after higher speed centrifugation.

CONCEPT 6.2

Eukaryotic cells have internal membranes that compartmentalize their functions (pp. 98–102)

▶ **Comparing Prokaryotic and Eukaryotic Cells** All cells are bounded by a plasma membrane. Unlike eukaryotic cells, prokaryotic cells lack nuclei and other membrane-enclosed organelles. The surface-to-volume ratio is an important parameter affecting cell size and shape.

▶ **A Panoramic View of the Eukaryotic Cell** Plant and animal cells have most of the same organelles.

	Cell Component	Structure	Function
Concept 6.3 **The eukaryotic cell's genetic instructions are housed in the nucleus and carried out by the ribosomes** (pp. 102–104) **MEDIA** **Activity** Role of the Nucleus and Ribosomes in Protein Synthesis	Nucleus 	Surrounded by nuclear envelope (double membrane) perforated by nuclear pores. The nuclear envelope is continuous with the endoplasmic reticulum (ER).	Houses chromosomes, made of chromatin (DNA, the genetic material, and proteins); contains nucleoli, where ribosomal subunits are made. Pores regulate entry and exit of materials.
	Ribosome 	Two subunits made of ribosomal RNA and proteins; can be free in cytosol or bound to ER	Protein synthesis
Concept 6.4 **The endomembrane system regulates protein traffic and performs metabolic functions in the cell** (pp. 104–108) **MEDIA** **Activity** The Endomembrane System	Endoplasmic reticulum 	Extensive network of membrane-bounded tubules and sacs; membrane separates lumen from cytosol; continuous with the nuclear envelope	Smooth ER: synthesis of lipids, metabolism of carbohydrates, Ca^{2+} storage, detoxification of drugs and poisons Rough ER: Aids in synthesis of secretory and other proteins from bound ribosomes; adds carbohydrates to glycoproteins; produces new membrane
	Golgi apparatus 	Stacks of flattened membranous sacs; has polarity (*cis* and *trans* faces)	Modification of proteins, carbohydrates on proteins, and phospholipids; synthesis of many polysaccharides; sorting of Golgi products, which are then released in vesicles
	Lysosome 	Membranous sac of hydrolytic enzymes (in animal cells)	Breakdown of ingested substances, cell macromolecules, and damaged organelles for recycling
	Vacuole 	Large membrane-bounded vesicle in plants	Digestion, storage, waste disposal, water balance, cell growth, and protection
Concept 6.5 **Mitochondria and chloroplasts change energy from one form to another** (pp. 109–111) **MEDIA** **Activity** Build a Chloroplast and a Mitochondrion	Mitochondrion 	Bounded by double membrane; inner membrane has infoldings (cristae)	Cellular respiration
	Chloroplast 	Typically two membranes around fluid stroma, which contains membranous thylakoids stacked into grana (in plants)	Photosynthesis
	Peroxisome 	Specialized metabolic compartment bounded by a single membrane	Contains enzymes that transfer hydrogen to water, producing hydrogen peroxide (H_2O_2) as a by-product, which is converted to water by other enzymes in the peroxisome

CONCEPT 6.6

The cytoskeleton is a network of fibers that organizes structures and activities in the cell (pp. 112–118)

▶ **Roles of the Cytoskeleton: Support, Motility, and Regulation** The cytoskeleton functions in structural support for the cell and in motility and signal transmission.

▶ **Components of the Cytoskeleton** Microtubules shape the cell, guide organelle movement, and separate chromosomes in dividing cells. Cilia and flagella are motile appendages containing microtubules. Primary cilia also play sensory and signaling roles. Microfilaments are thin rods functioning in muscle contraction, amoeboid movement, cytoplasmic streaming, and microvillus support. Intermediate filaments support cell shape and fix organelles in place.

MEDIA

Activity Cilia and Flagella

CONCEPT 6.7

Extracellular components and connections between cells help coordinate cellular activities (pp. 118–122)

▶ **Cell Walls of Plants** Plant cell walls are made of cellulose fibers embedded in other polysaccharides and proteins. Cellulose deposition is oriented along microtubules.

▶ **The Extracellular Matrix (ECM) of Animal Cells** Animal cells secrete glycoproteins that form the ECM, which functions in support, adhesion, movement, and regulation.

▶ **Intercellular Junctions** Plants have plasmodesmata that pass through adjoining cell walls. Animal cells have tight junctions, desmosomes, and gap junctions.

▶ **The Cell: A Living Unit Greater Than the Sum of Its Parts**

MEDIA

Activity Cell Junctions
Activity Review: Animal Cell Structure and Function
Activity Review: Plant Cell Structure and Function

TESTING YOUR KNOWLEDGE

SELF-QUIZ

1. Which statement correctly characterizes bound ribosomes?
   a. Bound ribosomes are enclosed in their own membrane.
   b. Bound and free ribosomes are structurally different.
   c. Bound ribosomes generally synthesize membrane proteins and secretory proteins.
   d. The most common location for bound ribosomes is the cytoplasmic surface of the plasma membrane.
   e. All of the above.

2. Which structure is *not* part of the endomembrane system?
   a. nuclear envelope   d. plasma membrane
   b. chloroplast   e. ER
   c. Golgi apparatus

3. Cells of the pancreas will incorporate radioactively labeled amino acids into proteins. This "tagging" of newly synthesized proteins enables a researcher to track their location. In this case, we are tracking an enzyme secreted by pancreatic cells. What is its most likely pathway?
   a. ER→Golgi→nucleus
   b. Golgi→ER→lysosome
   c. nucleus→ER→Golgi
   d. ER→Golgi→vesicles that fuse with plasma membrane
   e. ER→lysosomes→vesicles that fuse with plasma membrane

4. Which structure is common to plant *and* animal cells?
   a. chloroplast   d. mitochondrion
   b. wall made of cellulose e. centriole
   c. central vacuole

5. Which of the following is present in a prokaryotic cell?
   a. mitochondrion   d. chloroplast
   b. ribosome   e. ER
   c. nuclear envelope

6. Which cell would be best for studying lysosomes?
   a. muscle cell   d. leaf cell of a plant
   b. nerve cell   e. bacterial cell
   c. phagocytic white blood cell

7. Which structure-function pair is *mismatched*?
   a. nucleolus; production of ribosomal subunits
   b. lysosome; intracellular digestion
   c. ribosome; protein synthesis
   d. Golgi; protein trafficking
   e. microtubule; muscle contraction

8. Cyanide binds with at least one molecule involved in producing ATP. If a cell is exposed to cyanide, most of the cyanide would be found within the
   a. mitochondria.   d. lysosomes.
   b. ribosomes.   e. endoplasmic reticulum.
   c. peroxisomes.

9. **DRAW IT** From memory, draw two cells, showing the structures below and any connections between them.

   nucleus, rough ER, smooth ER, mitochondrion, centrosome, chloroplast, vacuole, lysosome, microtubule, cell wall, ECM, microfilament, Golgi apparatus, intermediate filament, plasma membrane, peroxisome, ribosome, nucleolus, nuclear pore, vesicle, flagellum, microvilli, plasmodesma

For Self-Quiz Answers, see Appendix A.

MEDIA Visit www.campbellbiology.com for a Practice Test.

EVOLUTION CONNECTION

10. Which aspects of cell structure best reveal evolutionary unity? What are some examples of specialized modifications?

SCIENTIFIC INQUIRY

11. Imagine protein X, destined to go to the plasma membrane. Assume that the mRNA carrying the genetic message for protein X has already been translated by ribosomes in a cell culture. If you fractionate the cell (see Figure 6.5), in which fraction would you find protein X? Explain by describing its transit.

Membrane Structure and Function

7

▲ **Figure 7.1 How do cell membrane proteins help regulate chemical traffic?**

OVERVIEW

Life at the Edge

The plasma membrane is the edge of life, the boundary that separates the living cell from its surroundings. A remarkable film only about 8 nm thick—it would take over 8,000 to equal the thickness of this page—the plasma membrane controls traffic into and out of the cell it surrounds. Like all biological membranes, the plasma membrane exhibits **selective permeability**; that is, it allows some substances to cross it more easily than others. One of the earliest episodes in the evolution of life may have been the formation of a membrane that enclosed a solution different from the surrounding solution while still permitting the uptake of nutrients and elimination of waste products. The ability of the cell to discriminate in its chemical exchanges with its environment is fundamental to life, and it is the plasma membrane and its component molecules that make this selectivity possible.

In this chapter, you will learn how cellular membranes control the passage of substances. The image in **Figure 7.1** shows the elegant structure of a eukaryotic plasma membrane protein that plays a crucial role in nerve cell signaling. This protein restores the ability of the nerve cell to fire again by providing a channel for a stream of potassium ions (K^+) to exit the cell at a precise moment after nerve stimulation. (The green ball in the center represents one K^+ moving through the channel.) In this case, the plasma membrane and its proteins not only act as an outer boundary but also enable the cell to carry out its functions. The same applies to the many varieties of internal membranes that partition the eukaryotic cell: The molecular makeup of each membrane allows compartmentalized specialization in cells. To understand how membranes work, we'll begin by examining their architecture.

CONCEPT 7.1

Cellular membranes are fluid mosaics of lipids and proteins

Lipids and proteins are the staple ingredients of membranes, although carbohydrates are also important. The most abundant lipids in most membranes are phospholipids. The ability of phospholipids to form membranes is inherent in their molecular structure. A phospholipid is an **amphipathic** molecule, meaning it has both a hydrophilic region and a hydrophobic region (see Figure 5.13). Other types of membrane lipids are also amphipathic. Furthermore, most of the proteins within membranes have both hydrophobic and hydrophilic regions.

How are phospholipids and proteins arranged in the membranes of cells? You encountered the currently accepted model for the arrangement of these molecules in Chapter 6 (see Figure 6.7). In this **fluid mosaic model**, the membrane is a fluid structure with a "mosaic" of various proteins embedded in or attached to a double layer (bilayer) of phospholipids. Scientists propose models as hypotheses, ways of organizing and explaining existing information. We'll discuss the fluid mosaic model in detail, starting with the story of how it was developed.

Membrane Models: *Scientific Inquiry*

Scientists began building molecular models of the membrane decades before membranes were first seen with the electron microscope in the 1950s. In 1915, membranes isolated from red blood cells were chemically analyzed and found to be composed of lipids and proteins. Ten years later, two Dutch scientists, E. Gorter and F. Grendel, reasoned that cell membranes must be phospholipid bilayers. Such a double layer of molecules could exist as a stable boundary between two aqueous compartments because the molecular arrangement shelters the hydrophobic tails of the phospholipids from water while exposing the hydrophilic heads to water (**Figure 7.2**).

Building on the idea that a phospholipid bilayer was the main fabric of a membrane, the next question was where the proteins were located. Although the heads of phospholipids are hydrophilic, the surface of a membrane consisting of a pure phospholipid bilayer adheres less strongly to water than does the surface of a biological membrane. Given these data, Hugh Davson and James Danielli suggested in 1935 that this difference could be accounted for if the membrane were coated on both sides with hydrophilic proteins. They proposed a sandwich model: a phospholipid bilayer between two layers of proteins.

When researchers first used electron microscopes to study cells in the 1950s, the pictures seemed to support the Davson-Danielli model. By the 1960s, the Davson-Danielli sandwich had become widely accepted as the structure not only of the plasma membrane but also of all the cell's internal membranes. By the end of that decade, however, many cell biologists recognized two problems with the model. The first problem was the generalization that all membranes of the cell are identical. Whereas the plasma membrane is 7–8 nm thick and has a three-layered structure in electron micrographs, the inner membrane of the mitochondrion is only 6 nm thick and looks like a row of beads. Mitochondrial membranes also have a higher percentage of proteins and different kinds of phospholipids and other lipids. In short, membranes with different functions differ in chemical composition and structure.

A second, more serious problem with the sandwich model was the protein placement. Unlike proteins dissolved in the cytosol, membrane proteins are not very soluble in water, because they are amphipathic; that is,

they have hydrophobic regions as well as hydrophilic regions. If such proteins were layered on the surface of the membrane, their hydrophobic parts would be in aqueous surroundings.

In 1972, S. J. Singer and G. Nicolson proposed that membrane proteins are dispersed, individually inserted into the phospholipid bilayer with their hydrophilic regions protruding (**Figure 7.3**). This molecular arrangement would maximize contact of hydrophilic regions of proteins and phospholipids with water in the cytosol and extracellular fluid, while providing their hydrophobic parts with a nonaqueous environment. In this fluid mosaic model, the membrane is a mosaic of protein molecules bobbing in a fluid bilayer of phospholipids.

A method of preparing cells for electron microscopy called freeze-fracture has demonstrated visually that proteins are indeed embedded in the phospholipid bilayer of the membrane. Freeze-fracture splits a membrane along the middle of the phospholipid bilayer, somewhat like pulling apart a chunky peanut butter sandwich. When the membrane layers are viewed in the electron microscope, the interior of the bilayer appears cobblestoned, with protein particles interspersed in a smooth matrix, as in the fluid mosaic model (**Figure 7.4**). Some proteins travel with one layer or the other, like the peanut chunks in the sandwich.

Because models are hypotheses, replacing one model of membrane structure with another does not imply that the original model was worthless. The acceptance or rejection of a model depends on how well it fits observations and explains experimental results. A good model also makes predictions that shape future research. Models inspire experiments, and few models survive these tests without modification. New findings may make a model obsolete; even then, it may not be totally scrapped, but revised to incorporate the new observations. The fluid mosaic model is continually being refined. For example, recent research suggests that membranes may be "more mosaic than fluid." Often, multiple proteins semipermanently associate in specialized patches, where they carry out common functions. Also, the membrane may be much more packed with proteins than imagined in the classic fluid mosaic model. Let's now take a closer look at membrane structure.

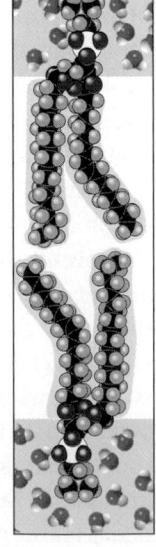

▲ **Figure 7.2** **Phospholipid bilayer (cross section).**

▲ Figure 7.3 **The fluid mosaic model for membranes.**

▼ Figure 7.4 Research Method

Freeze-Fracture

APPLICATION A cell membrane can be split into its two layers, revealing the ultrastructure of the membrane's interior.

TECHNIQUE A cell is frozen and fractured with a knife. The fracture plane often follows the hydrophobic interior of a membrane, splitting the phospholipid bilayer into two separated layers. The membrane proteins go wholly with one of the layers.

RESULTS These SEMs show membrane proteins (the "bumps") in the two layers, demonstrating that proteins are embedded in the phospholipid bilayer.

Inside of extracellular layer

Inside of cytoplasmic layer

The Fluidity of Membranes

Membranes are not static sheets of molecules locked rigidly in place. A membrane is held together primarily by hydrophobic interactions, which are much weaker than covalent bonds (see Figure 5.21). Most of the lipids and some of the proteins can shift about laterally—that is, in the plane of the membrane, like partygoers elbowing their way through a crowded room (Figure 7.5a). It is quite rare, however, for a molecule to flip-flop transversely across the membrane, switching from one phospholipid layer to the other; to do so, the hydrophilic part of the molecule must cross the hydrophobic core of the membrane.

The lateral movement of phospholipids within the membrane is rapid. Adjacent phospholipids switch positions about 10^7 times per second, which means that a phospholipid can travel about 2 μm—the length of many bacterial cells—in 1 second. Proteins are much larger than lipids and move more slowly, but some membrane proteins do drift, as shown in a classic experiment by David Frye and Michael Edidin (Figure 7.6, on the next page). And some membrane proteins seem to move in a highly directed manner, perhaps driven along cytoskeletal fibers by motor proteins connected to the membrane proteins' cytoplasmic regions. However, many other membrane proteins seem to be held virtually immobile by their attachment to the cytoskeleton.

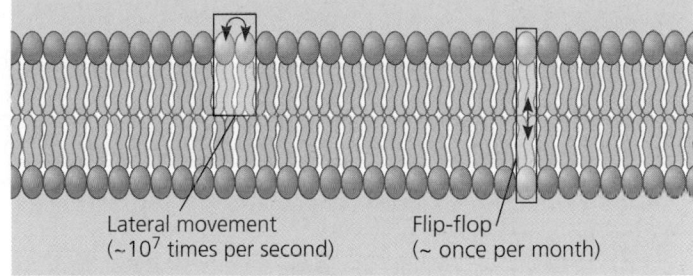

(a) Movement of phospholipids. Lipids move laterally in a membrane, but flip-flopping across the membrane is quite rare.

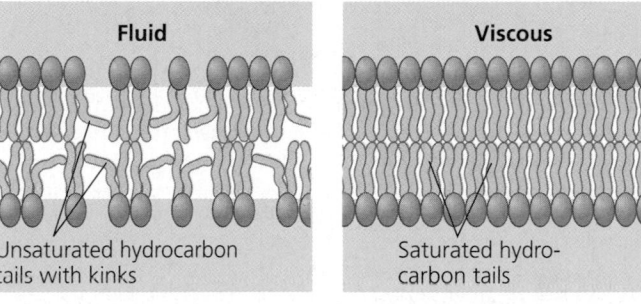

(b) Membrane fluidity. Unsaturated hydrocarbon tails of phospholipids have kinks that keep the molecules from packing together, enhancing membrane fluidity.

(c) Cholesterol within the animal cell membrane. Cholesterol reduces membrane fluidity at moderate temperatures by reducing phospholipid movement, but at low temperatures it hinders solidification by disrupting the regular packing of phospholipids.

▲ **Figure 7.5 The fluidity of membranes.**

A membrane remains fluid as temperature decreases until finally the phospholipids settle into a closely packed arrangement and the membrane solidifies, much as bacon grease forms lard when it cools. The temperature at which a membrane solidifies depends on the types of lipids it is made of. The membrane remains fluid to a lower temperature if it is rich in phospholipids with unsaturated hydrocarbon tails (see Figures 5.12 and 5.13). Because of kinks in the tails where double bonds are located, unsaturated hydrocarbon tails cannot pack together as closely as saturated hydrocarbon tails, and this makes the membrane more fluid (Figure 7.5b).

The steroid cholesterol, which is wedged between phospholipid molecules in the plasma membranes of animal cells, has different effects on membrane fluidity at different temperatures (Figure 7.5c). At relatively higher temperatures—at 37°C, the

▼ Figure 7.6 **Inquiry**

Do membrane proteins move?

EXPERIMENT David Frye and Michael Edidin, at Johns Hopkins University, labeled the plasma membrane proteins of a mouse cell and a human cell with two different markers and fused the cells. Using a microscope, they observed the markers on the hybrid cell.

RESULTS

Membrane proteins

Mouse cell + Human cell → Hybrid cell → Mixed proteins after 1 hour

CONCLUSION The mixing of the mouse and human membrane proteins indicates that at least some membrane proteins move sideways within the plane of the plasma membrane.

SOURCE L. D. Frye and M. Edidin, The rapid intermixing of cell surface antigens after formation of mouse-human heterokaryons, *J. Cell Sci.* 7:319 (1970).

WHAT IF? If, after many hours, the protein distribution still looked like that in the third image above, would you be able to conclude that proteins don't move within the membrane? What other explanation could there be?

body temperature of humans, for example—cholesterol makes the membrane less fluid by restraining phospholipid movement. However, because cholesterol also hinders the close packing of phospholipids, it lowers the temperature required for the membrane to solidify. Thus, cholesterol can be thought of as a "temperature buffer" for the membrane, resisting changes in membrane fluidity that can be caused by changes in temperature.

Membranes must be fluid to work properly; they are usually about as fluid as salad oil. When a membrane solidifies, its permeability changes, and enzymatic proteins in the membrane may become inactive—for example, if their activity requires them to be able to move laterally in the membrane. The lipid composition of cell membranes can change as an adjustment to changing temperature. For instance, in many plants that tolerate extreme cold, such as winter wheat, the percentage of unsaturated phospholipids increases in autumn, an adaptation that keeps the membranes from solidifying during winter.

Membrane Proteins and Their Functions

Now we come to the *mosaic* aspect of the fluid mosaic model. A membrane is a collage of different proteins embedded in the fluid matrix of the lipid bilayer **(Figure 7.7)**. More than 50 kinds of proteins have been found so far in the plasma mem-

Fibers of extracellular matrix (ECM)

Glyco-protein

Carbohydrate

Glycolipid

EXTRACELLULAR SIDE OF MEMBRANE

Cholesterol

Microfilaments of cytoskeleton

Peripheral proteins

Integral protein

CYTOPLASMIC SIDE OF MEMBRANE

▲ Figure 7.7 **The detailed structure of an animal cell's plasma membrane, in a cutaway view.**

brane of red blood cells, for example. Phospholipids form the main fabric of the membrane, but proteins determine most of the membrane's functions. Different types of cells contain different sets of membrane proteins, and the various membranes within a cell each have a unique collection of proteins.

Notice in Figure 7.7 that there are two major populations of membrane proteins: integral proteins and peripheral proteins. **Integral proteins** penetrate the hydrophobic core of the lipid bilayer. Many are *transmembrane proteins*, which span the membrane; other integral proteins extend only partway into the hydrophobic core. The hydrophobic regions of an integral protein consist of one or more stretches of nonpolar amino acids (see Figure 5.17), usually coiled into α helices (Figure 7.8). The hydrophilic parts of the molecule are exposed to the aqueous solutions on either side of the membrane. Some proteins also have a hydrophilic channel through their center that allows passage of hydrophilic substances (see Figure 7.1). **Peripheral proteins** are not embedded in the lipid bilayer at all; they are appendages loosely bound to the surface of the membrane, often to exposed parts of integral proteins (see Figure 7.7).

On the cytoplasmic side of the plasma membrane, some membrane proteins are held in place by attachment to the cytoskeleton. And on the extracellular side, certain membrane proteins are attached to fibers of the extracellular matrix (see Figure 6.30; *integrins* are one type of integral protein). These attachments combine to give animal cells a stronger framework than the plasma membrane alone could provide.

Figure 7.9 gives an overview of six major functions performed by proteins of the plasma membrane. A single cell may

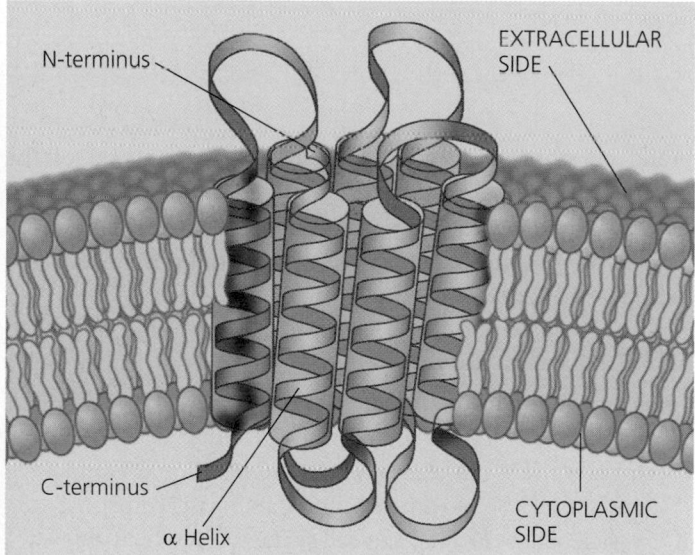

▲ **Figure 7.8 The structure of a transmembrane protein.** This protein, bacteriorhodopsin (a bacterial transport protein), has a distinct orientation in the membrane, with the N-terminus outside the cell and the C-terminus inside. This ribbon model highlights the α-helical secondary structure of the hydrophobic parts, which lie mostly within the hydrophobic core of the membrane. The protein includes seven transmembrane helices (outlined with cylinders for emphasis). The nonhelical hydrophilic segments are in contact with the aqueous solutions on the extracellular and cytoplasmic sides of the membrane.

(a) Transport. *Left:* A protein that spans the membrane may provide a hydrophilic channel across the membrane that is selective for a particular solute. *Right:* Other transport proteins shuttle a substance from one side to the other by changing shape. Some of these proteins hydrolyze ATP as an energy source to actively pump substances across the membrane.

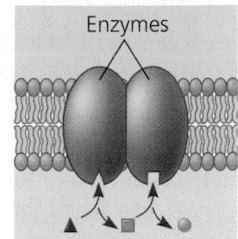

(b) Enzymatic activity. A protein built into the membrane may be an enzyme with its active site exposed to substances in the adjacent solution. In some cases, several enzymes in a membrane are organized as a team that carries out sequential steps of a metabolic pathway.

(c) Signal transduction. A membrane protein (receptor) may have a binding site with a specific shape that fits the shape of a chemical messenger, such as a hormone. The external messenger (signaling molecule) may cause a shape change in the protein that relays the message to the inside of the cell, usually by binding to a cytoplasmic protein. (See Figure 11.6.)

(d) Cell-cell recognition. Some glycoproteins serve as identification tags that are specifically recognized by membrane proteins of other cells.

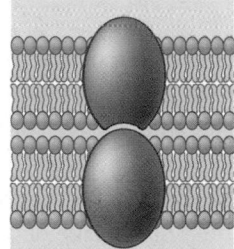

(e) Intercellular joining. Membrane proteins of adjacent cells may hook together in various kinds of junctions, such as gap junctions or tight junctions (see Figure 6.32).

(f) Attachment to the cytoskeleton and extracellular matrix (ECM). Microfilaments or other elements of the cytoskeleton may be noncovalently bound to membrane proteins, a function that helps maintain cell shape and stabilizes the location of certain membrane proteins. Proteins that can bind to ECM molecules can coordinate extracellular and intracellular changes (see Figure 6.30).

▲ **Figure 7.9 Some functions of membrane proteins.** In many cases, a single protein performs multiple tasks.

? *Some transmembrane proteins can bind to a particular ECM molecule and, when bound, transmit a signal into the cell. Use the proteins shown here to explain how this might occur.*

have membrane proteins carrying out several of these functions, and a single membrane protein may have multiple functions. In this way, the membrane is a functional mosaic as well as a structural one.

The Role of Membrane Carbohydrates in Cell-Cell Recognition

Cell-cell recognition, a cell's ability to distinguish one type of neighboring cell from another, is crucial to the functioning of an organism. It is important, for example, in the sorting of cells into tissues and organs in an animal embryo. It is also the basis for the rejection of foreign cells (including those of transplanted organs) by the immune system, an important line of defense in vertebrate animals (see Chapter 43). Cells recognize other cells by binding to surface molecules, often to carbohydrates, on the plasma membrane (see Figure 7.9d).

Membrane carbohydrates are usually short, branched chains of fewer than 15 sugar units. Some are covalently bonded to lipids, forming molecules called **glycolipids**. (Recall that *glyco* refers to the presence of carbohydrate.) However, most are covalently bonded to proteins, which are thereby **glycoproteins** (see Figure 7.7).

The carbohydrates on the extracellular side of the plasma membrane vary from species to species, among individuals of the same species, and even from one cell type to another in a single individual. The diversity of the molecules and their location on the cell's surface enable membrane carbohydrates to function as markers that distinguish one cell from another. For example, the four human blood types designated A, B, AB, and O reflect variation in the carbohydrates on the surface of red blood cells.

Synthesis and Sidedness of Membranes

Membranes have distinct inside and outside faces. The two lipid layers may differ in specific lipid composition, and each protein has directional orientation in the membrane (see Figure 7.8). When a vesicle fuses with the plasma membrane, the outside layer of the vesicle becomes continuous with the cytoplasmic (inner) layer of the plasma membrane. Therefore, molecules that start out on the *inside* face of the ER end up on the *outside* face of the plasma membrane.

The process, shown in **Figure 7.10**, starts with ❶ the synthesis of membrane proteins and lipids in the endoplasmic reticulum. Carbohydrates (green) are added to the proteins (purple), making them glycoproteins. The carbohydrate portions may then be modified. ❷ Inside the Golgi apparatus, the glycoproteins undergo further carbohydrate modification, and lipids acquire carbohydrates, becoming glycolipids. ❸ The transmembrane proteins (purple dumbbells), membrane glycolipids, and secretory proteins (purple spheres) are transported in vesicles to the plasma membrane. ❹ There the vesicles fuse with the membrane, releasing secretory proteins from the cell. Vesicle fusion positions the carbohydrates of mem-

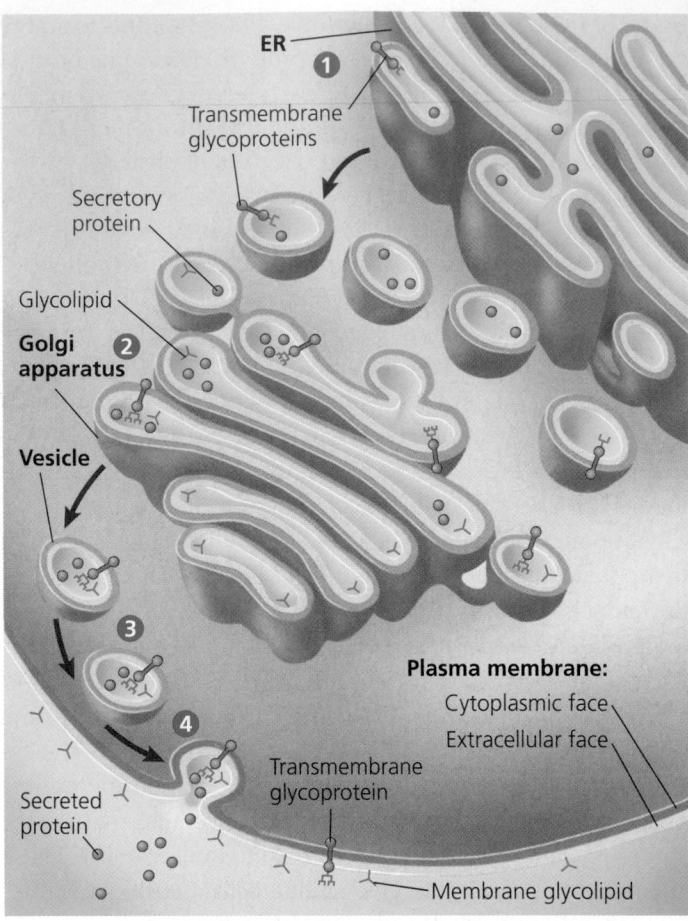

▲ Figure 7.10 **Synthesis of membrane components and their orientation on the resulting membrane.** The plasma membrane has distinct cytoplasmic (orange) and extracellular (aqua) faces, with the extracellular face arising from the inside face of ER, Golgi, and vesicle membranes.

brane glycoproteins and glycolipids on the outside of the plasma membrane. Thus, the asymmetrical arrangement of proteins, lipids, and their associated carbohydrates in the plasma membrane is determined as the membrane is being built by the ER and Golgi apparatus.

CONCEPT CHECK 7.1

1. The carbohydrates attached to some proteins and lipids of the plasma membrane are added as the membrane is made and refined in the ER and Golgi apparatus; the new membrane then forms transport vesicles that travel to the cell surface. On which side of the vesicle membrane are the carbohydrates?

2. **WHAT IF?** How would you expect the saturation levels of membrane phospholipid fatty acids to differ in plants adapted to cold environments and plants adapted to hot environments?

For suggested answers, see Appendix A.

Membrane structure results in selective permeability

The biological membrane is an exquisite example of a supramolecular structure—many molecules ordered into a higher level of organization—with emergent properties beyond those of the individual molecules. The remainder of this chapter focuses on one of the most important of those properties: the ability to regulate transport across cellular boundaries, a function essential to the cell's existence. We will see once again that form fits function: The fluid mosaic model helps explain how membranes regulate the cell's molecular traffic.

A steady traffic of small molecules and ions moves across the plasma membrane in both directions. Consider the chemical exchanges between a muscle cell and the extracellular fluid that bathes it. Sugars, amino acids, and other nutrients enter the cell, and metabolic waste products leave it. The cell takes in oxygen for use in cellular respiration and expels carbon dioxide. Also, the cell regulates its concentrations of inorganic ions, such as Na^+, K^+, Ca^{2+}, and Cl^-, by shuttling them one way or the other across the plasma membrane. Although traffic through the membrane is extensive, cell membranes are selectively permeable, and substances do not cross the barrier indiscriminately. The cell is able to take up many varieties of small molecules and ions and exclude others. Moreover, substances that move through the membrane do so at different rates.

The Permeability of the Lipid Bilayer

Nonpolar molecules, such as hydrocarbons, carbon dioxide, and oxygen, are hydrophobic and can therefore dissolve in the lipid bilayer of the membrane and cross it easily, without the aid of membrane proteins. However, the hydrophobic core of the membrane impedes the direct passage of ions and polar molecules, which are hydrophilic, through the membrane. Polar molecules such as glucose and other sugars pass only slowly through a lipid bilayer, and even water, an extremely small polar molecule, does not cross very rapidly. A charged atom or molecule and its surrounding shell of water (see Figure 3.7) find the hydrophobic layer of the membrane even more difficult to penetrate. Furthermore, the lipid bilayer is only one aspect of the gatekeeper system responsible for the selective permeability of a cell. Proteins built into the membrane play key roles in regulating transport.

Transport Proteins

Cell membranes *are* permeable to specific ions and a variety of polar molecules. These hydrophilic substances can avoid contact with the lipid bilayer by passing through **transport proteins** that span the membrane.

Some transport proteins, called *channel proteins*, function by having a hydrophilic channel that certain molecules or atomic ions use as a tunnel through the membrane (see Figure 7.9a, left). For example, the passage of water molecules through the membrane in certain cells is greatly facilitated by channel proteins known as **aquaporins**. Each aquaporin allows entry of up to 3 *billion* (3×10^9) water molecules per second, passing single file through its central channel, which fits ten at a time. Without aquaporins, only a tiny fraction of these water molecules would diffuse through the same area of the cell membrane in a second, so the channel protein brings about a tremendous increase in rate. Other transport proteins, called *carrier proteins*, hold onto their passengers and change shape in a way that shuttles them across the membrane (see Figure 7.9a, right). A transport protein is specific for the substance it translocates (moves), allowing only a certain substance (or substances) to cross the membrane. For example, glucose, carried in the blood and needed by red blood cells for cellular activities, enters the red blood cells rapidly via specific carrier proteins in the plasma membrane. The glucose passes through the membrane 50,000 times faster than if diffusing through on its own. This "glucose transporter" is so selective as a carrier protein that it even rejects fructose, a structural isomer of glucose.

Thus, the selective permeability of a membrane depends on both the discriminating barrier of the lipid bilayer and the specific transport proteins built into the membrane. But what establishes the *direction* of traffic across a membrane? At a given time, what determines whether a particular substance will enter the cell or leave the cell? And what mechanisms actually drive molecules across membranes? We will address these questions next as we explore two modes of membrane traffic: passive transport and active transport.

CONCEPT CHECK 7.2

1. Two molecules that can cross a lipid bilayer without help from membrane proteins are O_2 and CO_2. What properties allow this to occur?
2. Why would water molecules need a transport protein to move rapidly and in large quantities across a membrane?
3. **WHAT IF?** Aquaporins exclude passage of hydronium ions (H_3O^+). But recent research has revealed a role for some aquaporins in fat metabolism, in which they allow passage of glycerol, a three-carbon alcohol (see Figure 5.11), as well as H_2O. Since H_3O^+ is much closer in size to water than is glycerol, what do you suppose is the basis of this selectivity?

For suggested answers, see Appendix A.

Passive transport is diffusion of a substance across a membrane with no energy investment

Molecules have a type of energy called thermal motion (heat). One result of thermal motion is **diffusion**, the movement of molecules of any substance so that they spread out evenly into the available space. Each molecule moves randomly, yet diffusion of a *population* of molecules may be directional. To understand this process, let's imagine a synthetic membrane separating pure water from a solution of a dye in water. Assume that this membrane has microscopic pores and is permeable to the dye molecules (**Figure 7.11a**). Each dye molecule wanders randomly, but there will be a *net* movement of the dye molecules across the membrane to the side that began as pure water. The dye molecules will continue to spread across the membrane until both solutions have equal concentrations of the dye. Once that point is reached, there will be a dynamic equilibrium, with as many dye molecules crossing the membrane each second in one direction as in the other.

We can now state a simple rule of diffusion: In the absence of other forces, a substance will diffuse from where it is more concentrated to where it is less concentrated. Put another way, any substance will diffuse down its **concentration gradient**, the region along which the density of a chemical substance decreases.

No work must be done in order to make this happen; diffusion is a spontaneous process, needing no input of energy. Note that each substance diffuses down its *own* concentration gradient, unaffected by the concentration differences of other substances (**Figure 7.11b**).

Much of the traffic across cell membranes occurs by diffusion. When a substance is more concentrated on one side of a membrane than on the other, there is a tendency for the substance to diffuse across the membrane down its concentration gradient (assuming that the membrane is permeable to that substance). One important example is the uptake of oxygen by a cell performing cellular respiration. Dissolved oxygen diffuses into the cell across the plasma membrane. As long as cellular respiration consumes the O_2 as it enters, diffusion into the cell will continue because the concentration gradient favors movement in that direction.

The diffusion of a substance across a biological membrane is called **passive transport** because the cell does not have to expend energy to make it happen. The concentration gradient itself represents potential energy (see Chapter 2, p. 35) and drives diffusion. Remember, however, that membranes are selectively permeable and therefore have different effects on the rates of diffusion of various molecules. In the case of water, aquaporins allow water to diffuse very rapidly across the membranes of certain cells. As we'll see next, the movement of water across the plasma membrane has important consequences for cells.

(a) Diffusion of one solute. The membrane has pores large enough for molecules of dye to pass through. Random movement of dye molecules will cause some to pass through the pores; this will happen more often on the side with more molecules. The dye diffuses from where it is more concentrated to where it is less concentrated (called diffusing down a concentration gradient). This leads to a dynamic equilibrium: The solute molecules continue to cross the membrane, but at equal rates in both directions.

Molecules of dye — Membrane (cross section)

WATER

Net diffusion — Net diffusion — Equilibrium

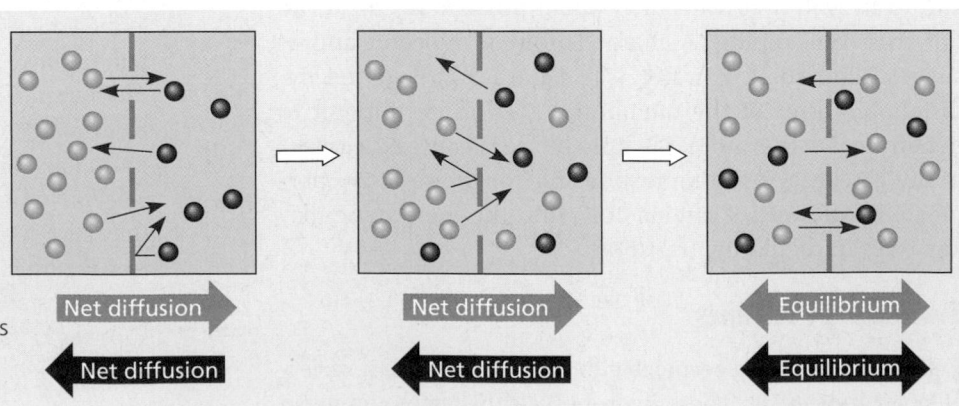

(b) Diffusion of two solutes. Solutions of two different dyes are separated by a membrane that is permeable to both. Each dye diffuses down its own concentration gradient. There will be a net diffusion of the purple dye toward the left, even though the *total* solute concentration was initially greater on the left side.

▲ **Figure 7.11 The diffusion of solutes across a membrane.** Each of the large arrows under the diagrams shows the net diffusion of the dye molecules of that color.

Net diffusion — Net diffusion — Equilibrium
Net diffusion — Net diffusion — Equilibrium

Effects of Osmosis on Water Balance

To see how two solutions with different solute concentrations interact, picture a U-shaped glass tube with a selectively permeable membrane separating two sugar solutions (**Figure 7.12**). Pores in this synthetic membrane are too small for sugar molecules to pass through but large enough for water molecules. How does this affect the *water* concentration? It seems logical that the solution with the higher concentration of solute would have the lower concentration of water and that water would diffuse into it from the other side for that reason. However, for a dilute solution like most biological fluids, solutes do not affect the water concentration significantly. Instead, tight clustering of water molecules around the hydrophilic solute molecules makes some of the water unavailable to cross the membrane. It is the difference in *free* water concentration that is important. In the end, the effect is the same: Water diffuses across the membrane from the region of lower solute concentration to that of higher solute concentration until the solute concentrations on both sides of the membrane are equal. The diffusion of water across a selectively permeable membrane is called **osmosis**. The movement of water across cell membranes and the balance of water between the cell and its environment are crucial to organisms. Let's now apply to living cells what we have learned about osmosis in artificial systems.

Water Balance of Cells Without Walls

When considering the behavior of a cell in a solution, both solute concentration and membrane permeability must be considered. Both factors are taken into account in the concept of **tonicity**, the ability of a solution to cause a cell to gain or lose water. The tonicity of a solution depends in part on its concentration of solutes that cannot cross the membrane (nonpenetrating solutes), relative to that inside the cell. If there is a higher concentration of nonpenetrating solutes in the surrounding solution, water will tend to leave the cell, and vice versa.

If a cell without a wall, such as an animal cell, is immersed in an environment that is **isotonic** to the cell (*iso* means "same"), there will be no *net* movement of water across the plasma membrane. Water flows across the membrane, but at the same rate in both directions. In an isotonic environment, the volume of an animal cell is stable (**Figure 7.13a**).

Now let's transfer the cell to a solution that is **hypertonic** to the cell (*hyper* means "more," in this case referring to nonpenetrating solutes). The cell will lose water to its environment, shrivel, and probably die. This is one way an

▲ Figure 7.12 Osmosis. Two sugar solutions of different concentrations are separated by a membrane, which the solvent (water) can pass through but the solute (sugar) cannot. Water molecules move randomly and may cross in either direction, but overall, water diffuses from the solution with less concentrated solute to that with more concentrated solute. This transport of water, or osmosis, equalizes the sugar concentrations on both sides.

WHAT IF? *If an orange dye capable of passing through the membrane was added to the left side of the tube above, how would it be distributed at the end of the process? (See Figure 7.11.) Would the solution levels in the tube on the right be affected?*

(a) Animal cell. An animal cell fares best in an isotonic environment unless it has special adaptations that offset the osmotic uptake or loss of water.

(b) Plant cell. Plant cells are turgid (firm) and generally healthiest in a hypotonic environment, where the uptake of water is eventually balanced by the wall pushing back on the cell.

Hypotonic solution	Isotonic solution	Hypertonic solution

▲ Figure 7.13 The water balance of living cells. How living cells react to changes in the solute concentration of their environment depends on whether or not they have cell walls. **(a)** Animal cells, such as this red blood cell, do not have cell walls. **(b)** Plant cells do. (Arrows indicate net water movement after the cells were first placed in these solutions.)

increase in the salinity (saltiness) of a lake can kill animals there; if the lake water becomes hypertonic to the animals' cells, the cells might shrivel and die. However, taking up too much water can be just as hazardous to an animal cell as losing water. If we place the cell in a solution that is **hypotonic** to the cell (*hypo* means "less"), water will enter the cell faster than it leaves, and the cell will swell and lyse (burst) like an overfilled water balloon.

A cell without rigid walls can tolerate neither excessive uptake nor excessive loss of water. This problem of water balance is automatically solved if such a cell lives in isotonic surroundings. Seawater is isotonic to many marine invertebrates. The cells of most terrestrial (land-dwelling) animals are bathed in an extracellular fluid that is isotonic to the cells. Animals and other organisms without rigid cell walls living in hypertonic or hypotonic environments must have special adaptations for **osmoregulation**, the control of water balance. For example, the protist *Paramecium* lives in pond water, which is hypotonic to the cell. *Paramecium* has a plasma membrane that is much less permeable to water than the membranes of most other cells, but this only slows the uptake of water, which continually enters the cell. The *Paramecium* cell doesn't burst because it is also equipped with a contractile vacuole, an organelle that functions as a bilge pump to force water out of the cell as fast as it enters by osmosis **(Figure 7.14)**. We will examine other evolutionary adaptations for osmoregulation in Chapter 44.

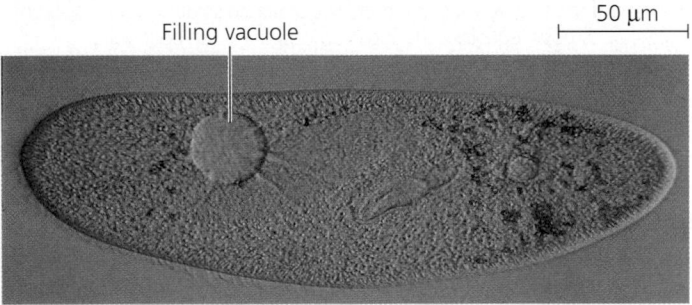

Filling vacuole

50 μm

(a) A contractile vacuole fills with fluid that enters from a system of canals radiating throughout the cytoplasm.

Contracting vacuole

(b) When full, the vacuole and canals contract, expelling fluid from the cell.

▲ **Figure 7.14 The contractile vacuole of *Paramecium*: an evolutionary adaptation for osmoregulation.** The contractile vacuole of this freshwater protist offsets osmosis by pumping water out of the cell (LM).

Water Balance of Cells with Walls

The cells of plants, prokaryotes, fungi, and some protists have walls (see Figure 6.28). When such a cell is immersed in a hypotonic solution—bathed in rainwater, for example—the wall helps maintain the cell's water balance. Consider a plant cell. Like an animal cell, the plant cell swells as water enters by osmosis **(Figure 7.13b)**. However, the relatively inelastic wall will expand only so much before it exerts a back pressure on the cell that opposes further water uptake. At this point, the cell is **turgid** (very firm), which is the healthy state for most plant cells. Plants that are not woody, such as most houseplants, depend for mechanical support on cells kept turgid by a surrounding hypotonic solution. If a plant's cells and their surroundings are isotonic, there is no net tendency for water to enter, and the cells become **flaccid** (limp).

However, a wall is of no advantage if the cell is immersed in a hypertonic environment. In this case, a plant cell, like an animal cell, will lose water to its surroundings and shrink. As the plant cell shrivels, its plasma membrane pulls away from the wall. This phenomenon, called **plasmolysis**, causes the plant to wilt and can lead to plant death. The walled cells of bacteria and fungi also plasmolyze in hypertonic environments.

Facilitated Diffusion: Passive Transport Aided by Proteins

Let's look more closely at how water and certain hydrophilic solutes cross a membrane. As mentioned earlier, many polar molecules and ions impeded by the lipid bilayer of the membrane diffuse passively with the help of transport proteins that span the membrane. This phenomenon is called **facilitated diffusion**. Cell biologists are still trying to learn exactly how various transport proteins facilitate diffusion. Most transport proteins are very specific: They transport some substances but not others.

As described earlier, the two types of transport proteins are channel proteins and carrier proteins. Channel proteins simply provide corridors that allow a specific molecule or ion to cross the membrane **(Figure 7.15a)**. The hydrophilic passageways provided by these proteins can allow water molecules or small ions to flow very quickly from one side of the membrane to the other. Although water molecules are small enough to cross through the phospholipid bilayer, the rate of water movement by this route is relatively slow because of the polarity of the water molecules. Aquaporins, the water channel proteins, facilitate the massive amounts of diffusion that occur in plant cells and in animal cells such as red blood cells (see Figure 7.13). Kidney cells also have a high number of aquaporins, allowing them to reclaim water from urine before it is excreted. It has been estimated that a person would have to drink 50 gallons of water a day and excrete the same volume if the kidneys did not perform this function.

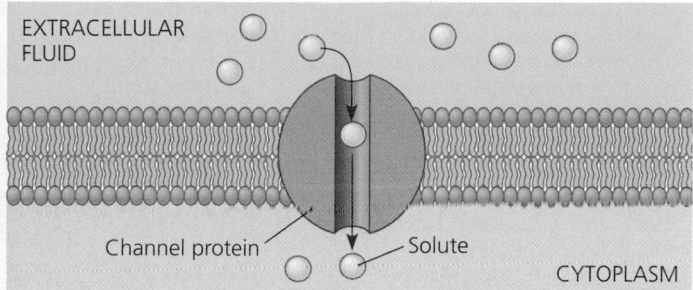

EXTRACELLULAR FLUID

Channel protein   Solute

CYTOPLASM

(a) A channel protein (purple) has a channel through which water molecules or a specific solute can pass.

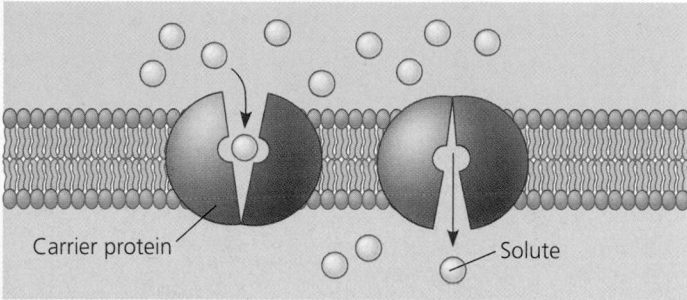

Carrier protein   Solute

(b) A carrier protein alternates between two shapes, moving a solute across the membrane during the shape change.

▲ **Figure 7.15 Two types of transport proteins that carry out facilitated diffusion.** In both cases, the protein can transport the solute in either direction, but the net movement is down the concentration gradient of the solute.

Another group of channel proteins are **ion channels**, many of which function as **gated channels**, which open or close in response to a stimulus. The stimulus may be electrical or chemical; if chemical, the stimulus is a substance other than the one to be transported. For example, stimulation of a nerve cell by certain neurotransmitter molecules opens gated channels that allow sodium ions into the cell. Later, an electrical stimulus activates the ion channel protein shown in Figure 7.1, and potassium ions rush out of the cell.

Carrier proteins, such as the glucose transporter mentioned earlier, seem to undergo a subtle change in shape that somehow translocates the solute-binding site across the membrane **(Figure 7.15b)**. These changes in shape may be triggered by the binding and release of the transported molecule.

In certain inherited diseases, specific transport systems are either defective or missing altogether. An example is cystinuria, a human disease characterized by the absence of a carrier protein that transports cysteine and some other amino acids across the membranes of kidney cells. Kidney cells normally reabsorb these amino acids from the urine and return them to the blood, but an individual afflicted with cystinuria develops painful stones from amino acids that accumulate and crystallize in the kidneys.

CONCEPT CHECK 7.3

1. How do you think a cell performing cellular respiration rids itself of the resulting CO_2?
2. In the supermarket, produce is often sprayed with water. Explain why this makes vegetables look crisp.
3. **WHAT IF?** If a *Paramecium* swims from a hypotonic environment to an isotonic one, will its contractile vacuole become more active or less? Why?

For suggested answers, see Appendix A.

CONCEPT 7.4
Active transport uses energy to move solutes against their gradients

Despite the help of transport proteins, facilitated diffusion is considered passive transport because the solute is moving down its concentration gradient. Facilitated diffusion speeds transport of a solute by providing efficient passage through the membrane, but it does not alter the direction of transport. Some transport proteins, however, can move solutes against their concentration gradients, across the plasma membrane from the side where they are less concentrated (whether inside or outside) to the side where they are more concentrated.

The Need for Energy in Active Transport

To pump a solute across a membrane against its gradient requires work; the cell must expend energy. Therefore, this type of membrane traffic is called **active transport**. The transport proteins that move solutes against a concentration gradient are all carrier proteins, rather than channel proteins. This makes sense because when channel proteins are open, they merely allow solutes to flow down their concentration gradient, rather than picking them up and transporting them against their gradient.

Active transport enables a cell to maintain internal concentrations of small solutes that differ from concentrations in its environment. For example, compared with its surroundings, an animal cell has a much higher concentration of potassium ions and a much lower concentration of sodium ions. The plasma membrane helps maintain these steep gradients by pumping sodium out of the cell and potassium into the cell.

As in other types of cellular work, ATP supplies the energy for most active transport. One way ATP can power active transport is by transferring its terminal phosphate group directly to the transport protein. This can induce the protein to change its shape in a manner that translocates a solute bound to the protein across the membrane. One transport system that works this way is the **sodium-potassium pump**, which exchanges sodium (Na^+) for

1 Cytoplasmic Na⁺ binds to the sodium-potassium pump. The affinity for Na⁺ is high when the protein has this shape.

2 Na⁺ binding stimulates phosphorylation (addition of a phosphate group) of the protein by ATP.

6 K⁺ is released; affinity for Na⁺ is high again, and the cycle repeats.

3 Phosphorylation causes the protein to change its shape, decreasing its affinity for Na⁺, which is expelled to the outside.

5 Loss of the phosphate restores the protein's original shape, which has a lower affinity for K⁺.

4 The new shape has a high affinity for K⁺, which binds on the extracellular side and triggers release of the phosphate group.

▲ **Figure 7.16 The sodium-potassium pump: a specific case of active transport.** This transport system pumps ions against steep concentration gradients: Sodium ion concentration (represented as [Na⁺]) is high outside the cell and low inside, while potassium ion concentration ([K⁺]) is low outside the cell and high inside. The pump oscillates between two shapes in a pumping cycle that translocates three sodium ions out of the cell for every two potassium ions pumped into the cell. The two shapes have different affinities for the two types of ions. ATP powers the shape change by phosphorylating the transport protein (that is, by transferring a phosphate group to the protein).

potassium (K^+) across the plasma membrane of animal cells **(Figure 7.16)**. The distinction between passive transport and active transport is reviewed in **Figure 7.17**.

Passive transport. Substances diffuse spontaneously down their concentration gradients, crossing a membrane with no expenditure of energy by the cell. The rate of diffusion can be greatly increased by transport proteins in the membrane.

Active transport. Some transport proteins act as pumps, moving substances across a membrane against their concentration (or electro-chemical) gradients. Energy for this work is usually supplied by ATP.

Diffusion. Hydrophobic molecules and (at a slow rate) very small un-charged polar molecules can diffuse through the lipid bilayer.

Facilitated diffusion. Many hydrophilic substances diffuse through membranes with the assistance of transport proteins, either channel or carrier proteins.

▲ **Figure 7.17 Review: passive and active transport.**

How Ion Pumps Maintain Membrane Potential

All cells have voltages across their plasma membranes. Voltage is electrical potential energy—a separation of opposite charges. The cytoplasm is negative in charge relative to the extracellular fluid because of an unequal distribution of anions and cations on opposite sides of the membrane. The voltage across a membrane, called a **membrane potential**, ranges from about -50 to -200 millivolts (mV). (The minus sign indicates that the inside of the cell is negative relative to the outside.)

The membrane potential acts like a battery, an energy source that affects the traffic of all charged substances across the membrane. Because the inside of the cell is negative compared with the outside, the membrane potential favors the passive transport of cations into the cell and anions out of the cell. Thus, *two* forces drive the diffusion of ions across a membrane: a chemical force (the ion's concentration gradient) and an electrical force (the effect of the membrane potential on the ion's movement). This combination of forces acting on an ion is called the **electrochemical gradient**.

In the case of ions, then, we must refine our concept of passive transport: An ion diffuses not simply down its *concentration* gradient but, more exactly, down its *electrochemical* gradient. For example, the concentration of sodium ions (Na^+) inside a resting nerve cell is much lower than outside it. When the cell is stimulated, gated channels open that facilitate Na$^+$ diffusion. Sodium ions then "fall" down their electrochemical gradient, driven by the concentration gradient of Na$^+$ and by the attraction of these cations to the negative side of the membrane. In this example, both electrical and chemical contributions to the electrochemical gradient act in the same direction across the membrane, but this is not always so. In cases where electrical forces due to the membrane potential oppose the simple diffusion of an ion down its concentration gradient, active transport may be necessary. In Chapter 48, you'll learn about the importance of electrochemical gradients and membrane potentials in the transmission of nerve impulses.

Some membrane proteins that actively transport ions contribute to the membrane potential. An example is the sodium-potassium pump. Notice in Figure 7.16 that the pump does not translocate Na$^+$ and K$^+$ one for one, but pumps three sodium ions out of the cell for every two potassium ions it pumps into the cell. With each "crank" of the pump, there is a net transfer of one positive charge from the cytoplasm to the extracellular fluid, a process that stores energy as voltage. A transport protein that generates voltage across a membrane is called an **electrogenic pump**. The sodium-potassium pump seems to be the major electrogenic pump of animal cells. The main electrogenic pump of plants, fungi, and bacteria is a **proton pump**, which actively transports hydrogen ions (protons) out of the cell. The pumping of H$^+$ transfers positive charge from the cytoplasm to the extracellular solution **(Figure 7.18)**. By generating voltage across membranes, electrogenic pumps store energy that can be tapped for cellular work. One important use of proton gradients in the cell is for ATP synthesis during cellular respiration, as you will see in Chapter 9. Another is a type of membrane traffic called cotransport.

Cotransport: Coupled Transport by a Membrane Protein

A single ATP-powered pump that transports a specific solute can indirectly drive the active transport of several other solutes in a mechanism called **cotransport**. A substance that has been pumped across a membrane can do work as it moves back across the membrane by diffusion, analogous to water that has been pumped uphill and performs work as it flows back down. Another transport protein, a cotransporter separate from the pump, can couple the "downhill" diffusion of this substance to the "uphill" transport of a second substance against its own concentration gradient. For example, a plant cell uses the gradient of hydrogen ions generated by its proton pumps to drive the active transport of amino acids, sugars, and several other nutrients into the cell. One transport protein couples the return of hydrogen ions to the transport of sucrose into the cell **(Figure 7.19)**. This protein can translocate sucrose into the cell against a concentration gradient, but only if the sucrose molecule travels in the company of a hydrogen ion. The hydrogen ion uses the

transport protein as an avenue to diffuse down the electrochemical gradient maintained by the proton pump. Plants use sucrose-H$^+$ cotransport to load sucrose produced by photosynthesis into cells in the veins of leaves. The vascular tissue of the plant can then distribute the sugar to nonphotosynthetic organs, such as roots.

What we know about cotransport proteins, osmosis, and water balance in animal cells has helped us find more effective treat-

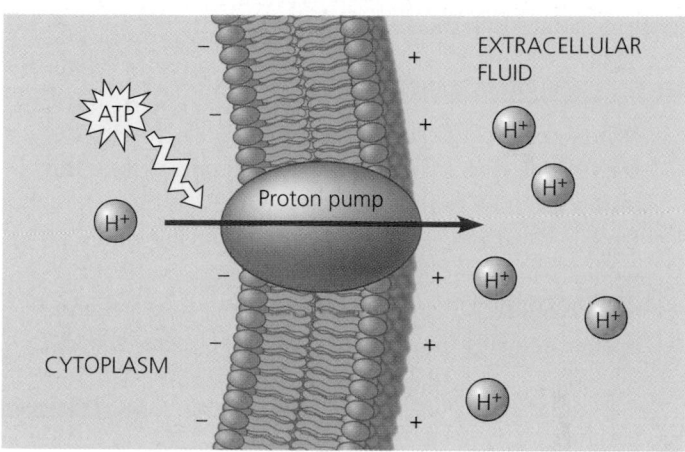

▲ **Figure 7.18 An electrogenic pump.** Proton pumps, the main electrogenic pumps of plants, fungi, and bacteria, are membrane proteins that store energy by generating voltage (charge separation) across membranes. Using ATP for power, a proton pump translocates positive charge in the form of hydrogen ions. The voltage and H$^+$ concentration gradient represent a dual energy source that can drive other processes, such as the uptake of nutrients.

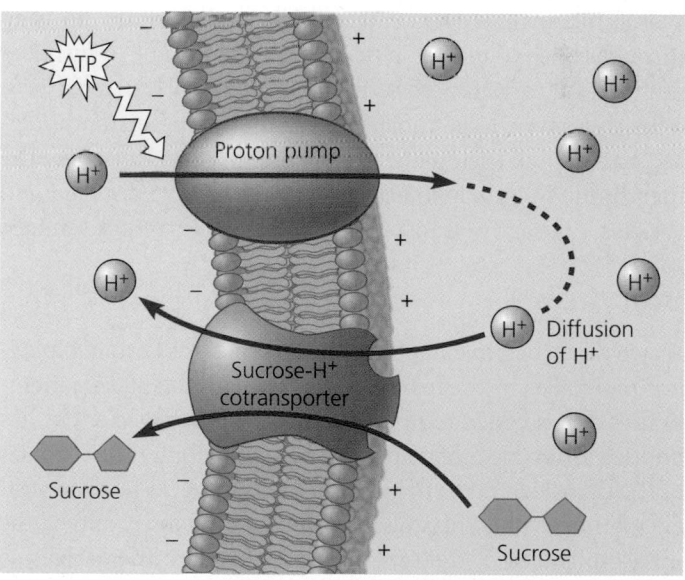

▲ **Figure 7.19 Cotransport: active transport driven by a concentration gradient.** A carrier protein such as this sucrose-H$^+$ cotransporter is able to use the diffusion of H$^+$ down its electrochemical gradient into the cell to drive the uptake of sucrose. The H$^+$ gradient is maintained by an ATP-driven proton pump that concentrates H$^+$ outside the cell, thus storing potential energy that can be used for active transport, in this case of sucrose. Thus, ATP is indirectly providing the energy necessary for cotransport.

ments for the dehydration resulting from diarrhea, a serious problem in developing countries where intestinal parasites are prevalent. Patients are given a solution to drink containing a high concentration of glucose and salt. The solutes are taken up by transport proteins on the surface of intestinal cells and passed through the cells into the blood. The increase in the blood's solute concentration causes a flow of water from the intestine through the intestinal cells into the blood, rehydrating the patient. Because of the transport proteins involved, both glucose *and* sodium ions from salt must be present. This is why athletes consume solute-rich sports drinks.

CONCEPT 7.5

Bulk transport across the plasma membrane occurs by exocytosis and endocytosis

Water and small solutes enter and leave the cell by diffusing through the lipid bilayer of the plasma membrane or by being pumped or carried across the membrane by transport proteins. However, large molecules, such as proteins and polysaccharides, as well as larger particles, generally cross the membrane in bulk by mechanisms that involve packaging in vesicles. Like active transport, these processes require energy.

Exocytosis

As we described in Chapter 6, the cell secretes certain biological molecules by the fusion of vesicles with the plasma membrane; this is called **exocytosis**. A transport vesicle that has budded from the Golgi apparatus moves along microtubules of the cytoskeleton to the plasma membrane. When the vesicle membrane and plasma membrane come into contact, the lipid molecules of the two bilayers rearrange themselves so that the two membranes fuse. The contents of the vesicle then spill to the outside of the cell, and the vesicle membrane becomes part of the plasma membrane (see Figure 7.10).

Many secretory cells use exocytosis to export products. For example, some cells in the pancreas make insulin and secrete it into the extracellular fluid by exocytosis. Another example is the neuron (nerve cell), which uses exocytosis to release neurotransmitters that signal other neurons or muscle cells.

When plant cells are making walls, exocytosis delivers proteins and carbohydrates from Golgi vesicles to the outside of the cell.

Endocytosis

In **endocytosis**, the cell takes in biological molecules and particulate matter by forming new vesicles from the plasma membrane. Although the proteins involved in the processes are different, the events of endocytosis look like the reverse of exocytosis. A small area of the plasma membrane sinks inward to form a pocket. As the pocket deepens, it pinches in, forming a vesicle containing material that had been outside the cell. There are three types of endocytosis: **phagocytosis** ("cellular eating"), **pinocytosis** ("cellular drinking"), and **receptor-mediated endocytosis**. (Study **Figure 7.20**.)

Human cells use receptor-mediated endocytosis to take in cholesterol for use in the synthesis of membranes and other steroids. Cholesterol travels in the blood in particles called low-density lipoproteins (LDLs), complexes of lipids and proteins. LDLs act as **ligands** (a term for any molecule that binds specifically to a receptor site of another molecule) by binding to LDL receptors on plasma membranes and then entering the cells by endocytosis. In humans with familial hypercholesterolemia, an inherited disease characterized by a very high level of cholesterol in the blood, the LDL receptor proteins are defective or missing, and the LDL particles cannot enter cells. Instead, cholesterol accumulates in the blood, where it contributes to early atherosclerosis, the buildup of lipid deposits within the walls of blood vessels. This buildup causes the walls to bulge inward, thereby narrowing the vessel and impeding blood flow.

Vesicles not only transport substances between the cell and its surroundings but also provide a mechanism for rejuvenating or remodeling the plasma membrane. Endocytosis and exocytosis occur continually in most eukaryotic cells, yet the amount of plasma membrane in a nongrowing cell remains fairly constant. Apparently, the addition of membrane by one process offsets the loss of membrane by the other.

Energy and cellular work have figured prominently in our study of membranes. We have seen, for example, that active transport is powered by ATP. In the next three chapters, you will learn more about how cells acquire chemical energy to do the work of life.

Exploring Endocytosis in Animal Cells

Phagocytosis

In **phagocytosis**, a cell engulfs a particle by wrapping pseudopodia (singular, *pseudopodium*) around it and packaging it within a membrane-enclosed sac that can be large enough to be classified as a vacuole. The particle is digested after the vacuole fuses with a lysosome containing hydrolytic enzymes.

EXTRACELLULAR FLUID
CYTOPLASM
Pseudopodium
"Food" or other particle
Food vacuole

1 µm

Pseudopodium of amoeba
Bacterium
Food vacuole

An amoeba engulfing a bacterium via phagocytosis (TEM)

Pinocytosis

In **pinocytosis**, the cell "gulps" droplets of extracellular fluid into tiny vesicles. It is not the fluid itself that is needed by the cell, but the molecules dissolved in the droplets. Because any and all included solutes are taken into the cell, pinocytosis is nonspecific in the substances it transports.

Plasma membrane
Vesicle

0.5 µm

Pinocytosis vesicles forming (arrows) in a cell lining a small blood vessel (TEM)

Receptor-Mediated Endocytosis

Receptor-mediated endocytosis enables the cell to acquire bulk quantities of specific substances, even though those substances may not be very concentrated in the extracellular fluid. Embedded in the membrane are proteins with specific receptor sites exposed to the extracellular fluid. The receptor proteins are usually already clustered in regions of the membrane called coated pits, which are lined on their cytoplasmic side by a fuzzy layer of coat proteins. The specific substances (ligands) bind to these receptors. When binding occurs, the coated pit forms a vesicle containing the ligand molecules. Notice that there are relatively more bound molecules (purple) inside the vesicle, but other molecules (green) are also present. After this ingested material is liberated from the vesicle, the receptors are recycled to the plasma membrane by the same vesicle.

Coat protein
Receptor
Coated vesicle
Coated pit
Ligand

Coat protein
Plasma membrane
0.25 µm

A coated pit and a coated vesicle formed during receptor-mediated endocytosis (TEMs)

SUMMARY OF KEY CONCEPTS

CONCEPT 7.1

Cellular membranes are fluid mosaics of lipids and proteins (pp. 125–130)

▶ **Membrane Models: *Scientific Inquiry*** The Davson-Danielli sandwich model of the membrane has been replaced by the fluid mosaic model, in which amphipathic proteins are embedded in the phospholipid bilayer.

▶ **The Fluidity of Membranes** Phospholipids and, to a lesser extent, proteins move laterally within the membrane. The unsaturated hydrocarbon tails of some phospholipids keep membranes fluid at lower temperatures, while cholesterol acts as a temperature buffer, resisting changes in fluidity caused by temperature changes.

▶ **Membrane Proteins and Their Functions** Integral proteins are embedded in the lipid bilayer; peripheral proteins are attached to the surfaces. The functions of membrane proteins include transport, enzymatic activity, signal transduction, cell-cell recognition, intercellular joining, and attachment to the cytoskeleton and extracellular matrix.

▶ **The Role of Membrane Carbohydrates in Cell-Cell Recognition** Short chains of sugars are linked to proteins and lipids on the exterior side of the plasma membrane, where they interact with surface molecules of other cells.

▶ **Synthesis and Sidedness of Membranes** Membrane proteins and lipids are synthesized in the ER and modified in the ER and Golgi apparatus. The inside and outside faces of the membrane differ in molecular composition.

MEDIA Activity Membrane Structure

CONCEPT 7.2

Membrane structure results in selective permeability (p. 131)

▶ A cell must exchange molecules and ions with its surroundings, a process controlled by the plasma membrane.

▶ **The Permeability of the Lipid Bilayer** Hydrophobic substances are soluble in lipid and pass through membranes rapidly.

▶ **Transport Proteins** To cross the membrane, polar molecules and ions generally require specific transport proteins.

MEDIA Activity Selective Permeability of Membranes

CONCEPT 7.3

Passive transport is diffusion of a substance across a membrane with no energy investment (pp. 132–135)

▶ Diffusion is the spontaneous movement of a substance down its concentration gradient.

▶ **Effects of Osmosis on Water Balance** Water diffuses out of a cell if the solution outside has a higher solute concentration (hypertonic) than the cytosol and enters the cell if the solution has a lower solute concentration (hypotonic). If the concentrations are equal (isotonic), no net osmosis occurs. Cell survival depends on balancing water uptake and loss. Cells lacking walls (as in animals and some protists) are isotonic with their environments or have adaptations for osmoregulation. Plants, prokaryotes, fungi, and some protists have relatively inelastic cell walls, so the cells don't burst when in a hypotonic environment.

▶ **Facilitated Diffusion: Passive Transport Aided by Proteins** In facilitated diffusion, a transport protein speeds the movement of water or a solute across a membrane down its concentration gradient.

Passive transport: Facilitated diffusion

Channel protein — Carrier protein

MEDIA
Activity Diffusion
Activity Osmosis and Water Balance in Cells
Investigation How Do Salt Concentrations Affect Cells?
Activity Facilitated Diffusion

CONCEPT 7.4

Active transport uses energy to move solutes against their gradients (pp. 135–138)

Active transport:

▶ **The Need for Energy in Active Transport** Specific membrane proteins use energy, usually in the form of ATP, to do the work of active transport.

▶ **How Ion Pumps Maintain Membrane Potential** Ions can have both a concentration (chemical) gradient and an electrical gradient (voltage). These forces combine in the electrochemical gradient, which determines the net direction of ionic diffusion. Electrogenic pumps, such as sodium-potassium pumps and proton pumps, are transport proteins that contribute to electrochemical gradients.

▶ **Cotransport: Coupled Transport by a Membrane Protein** One solute's "downhill" diffusion drives the other's "uphill" transport.

MEDIA Activity Active Transport

CONCEPT 7.5

Bulk transport across the plasma membrane occurs by exocytosis and endocytosis (pp. 138–139)

▶ **Exocytosis** In exocytosis, transport vesicles migrate to the plasma membrane, fuse with it, and release their contents.

► **Endocytosis** In endocytosis, molecules enter cells within vesicles that pinch inward from the plasma membrane. The three types of endocytosis are phagocytosis, pinocytosis, and receptor-mediated endocytosis.

MEDIA
Activity Exocytosis and Endocytosis

TESTING YOUR KNOWLEDGE

SELF-QUIZ

1. In what way do the membranes of a eukaryotic cell vary?
   a. Phospholipids are found only in certain membranes.
   b. Certain proteins are unique to each membrane.
   c. Only certain membranes of the cell are selectively permeable.
   d. Only certain membranes are constructed from amphipathic molecules.
   e. Some membranes have hydrophobic surfaces exposed to the cytoplasm, while others have hydrophilic surfaces facing the cytoplasm.

2. According to the fluid mosaic model of membrane structure, proteins of the membrane are mostly
   a. spread in a continuous layer over the inner and outer surfaces of the membrane.
   b. confined to the hydrophobic core of the membrane.
   c. embedded in a lipid bilayer.
   d. randomly oriented in the membrane, with no fixed inside-outside polarity.
   e. free to depart from the fluid membrane and dissolve in the surrounding solution.

3. Which of the following factors would tend to increase membrane fluidity?
   a. a greater proportion of unsaturated phospholipids
   b. a greater proportion of saturated phospholipids
   c. a lower temperature
   d. a relatively high protein content in the membrane
   e. a greater proportion of relatively large glycolipids compared with lipids having smaller molecular masses

4. Which of the following processes includes all others?
   a. osmosis
   b. diffusion of a solute across a membrane
   c. facilitated diffusion
   d. passive transport
   e. transport of an ion down its electrochemical gradient

5. Based on Figure 7.19, which of these experimental treatments would increase the rate of sucrose transport into the cell?
   a. decreasing extracellular sucrose concentration
   b. decreasing extracellular pH
   c. decreasing cytoplasmic pH
   d. adding an inhibitor that blocks the regeneration of ATP
   e. adding a substance that makes the membrane more permeable to hydrogen ions

6. **DRAW IT** An artificial cell consisting of an aqueous solution enclosed in a selectively permeable membrane is immersed in a beaker containing a different solution. The membrane is permeable to water and to the simple sugars glucose and fructose but impermeable to the disaccharide sucrose.

   a. Draw solid arrows to indicate the net movement of solutes into and/or out of the cell.

   "Cell" 0.03 M sucrose 0.02 M glucose

   Environment: 0.01 M sucrose 0.01 M glucose 0.01 M fructose

   b. Is the solution outside the cell isotonic, hypotonic, or hypertonic?
   c. Draw a dashed arrow to show the net osmotic movement of water, if any.
   d. Will the artificial cell become more flaccid, more turgid, or stay the same?
   e. Eventually, will the two solutions have the same or different solute concentrations?

For Self-Quiz answers, see Appendix A.

MEDIA Visit the Study Area at **www.masteringbio.com** for a Practice Test.

EVOLUTION CONNECTION

7. *Paramecium* and other protists that live in hypotonic environments have cell membranes that slow osmotic water uptake, while those living in isotonic environments have more permeable cell membranes. What water regulation adaptations might have evolved in protists in hypertonic habitats such as Great Salt Lake? In habitats with changing salt concentration?

SCIENTIFIC INQUIRY

8. An experiment is designed to study the mechanism of sucrose uptake by plant cells. Cells are immersed in a sucrose solution, and the pH of the solution is monitored. Samples of the cells are taken at intervals, and their sucrose concentration is measured. Their sucrose uptake correlates with a rise in the solution's pH. This rise is proportional to the starting concentration of sucrose in the solution. A metabolic poison that blocks the ability of cells to regenerate ATP is found to inhibit the pH changes in the solution. Propose a hypothesis accounting for these results. Suggest an experiment to test it.

SCIENCE, TECHNOLOGY, AND SOCIETY

9. Extensive irrigation in arid regions causes salts to accumulate in the soil. (When water evaporates, salts are left behind to concentrate in the soil.) Based on what you learned about water balance in plant cells, why might increased soil salinity (saltiness) be harmful to crops? Suggest ways to minimize damage. What costs are attached to your solutions?

An Introduction to Metabolism

8

KEY CONCEPTS

8.1 An organism's metabolism transforms matter and energy, subject to the laws of thermodynamics

8.2 The free-energy change of a reaction tells us whether or not the reaction occurs spontaneously

8.3 ATP powers cellular work by coupling exergonic reactions to endergonic reactions

8.4 Enzymes speed up metabolic reactions by lowering energy barriers

8.5 Regulation of enzyme activity helps control metabolism

OVERVIEW

The Energy of Life

The living cell is a chemical factory in miniature, where thousands of reactions occur within a microscopic space. Sugars can be converted to amino acids that are linked together into proteins when needed, and proteins are dismantled into amino acids that can be converted to sugars when food is digested. Small molecules are assembled into polymers, which may be hydrolyzed later as the needs of the cell change. In multicellular organisms, many cells export chemical products that are used in other parts of the organism. The process known as cellular respiration drives the cellular economy by extracting the energy stored in sugars and other fuels. Cells apply this energy to perform various types of work, such as the transport of solutes across the plasma membrane, which we discussed in Chapter 7. In a more exotic example, cells of the fungus in **Figure 8.1** convert the energy stored in certain organic molecules to light, a process called bioluminescence. (The glow may attract insects that benefit the fungus by dispersing its spores.) Bioluminescence and all other metabolic activities carried out by a cell are precisely coordinated and controlled. In its complexity, its efficiency, its integration, and its responsiveness to subtle changes, the cell is peerless as a chemical factory. The concepts of metabolism that you learn in this chapter will help you understand how matter and energy flow during life's processes and how that flow is regulated.

CONCEPT 8.1

An organism's metabolism transforms matter and energy, subject to the laws of thermodynamics

The totality of an organism's chemical reactions is called **metabolism** (from the Greek *metabole*, change). Metabolism is an emergent property of life that arises from interactions between molecules within the orderly environment of the cell.

Organization of the Chemistry of Life into Metabolic Pathways

We can picture a cell's metabolism as an elaborate road map of the thousands of chemical reactions that occur in a cell, arranged as intersecting metabolic pathways. A **metabolic pathway** begins with a specific molecule, which is then altered in a series of defined steps, resulting in a certain product. Each step of the pathway is catalyzed by a specific enzyme:

Analogous to the red, yellow, and green stoplights that control the flow of automobile traffic, mechanisms that regulate enzymes balance metabolic supply and demand, averting deficits or surpluses of important cellular molecules.

Metabolism as a whole manages the material and energy resources of the cell. Some metabolic pathways release energy by breaking down complex molecules to simpler compounds. These degradative processes are called **catabolic pathways**, or breakdown pathways. A major pathway of catabolism is cellular respiration, in which the sugar glucose and other organic fuels are broken down in the presence of oxygen to carbon dioxide and water. (Pathways can have more than one starting molecule and/or product.) Energy that was stored in the organic molecules becomes available to do the work of the cell, such as ciliary beating or membrane transport. **Anabolic pathways**, in contrast, consume energy to build complicated molecules from simpler ones; they are sometimes called biosynthetic pathways. An example of anabolism is the synthesis of a protein from amino acids. Catabolic and anabolic pathways are the "downhill" and "uphill" avenues of the metabolic map. Energy released from the downhill reactions of catabolic pathways can be stored and then used to drive the uphill reactions of anabolic pathways.

In this chapter, we will focus on mechanisms common to metabolic pathways. Because energy is fundamental to all metabolic processes, a basic knowledge of energy is necessary to understand how the living cell works. Although we will use some nonliving examples to study energy, the concepts demonstrated by these examples also apply to **bioenergetics**, the study of how energy flows through living organisms.

Forms of Energy

Energy is the capacity to cause change. In everyday life, energy is important because some forms of energy can be used to do work—that is, to move matter against opposing forces, such as gravity and friction. Put another way, energy is the ability to rearrange a collection of matter. For example, you expend energy to turn the pages of this book, and your cells expend energy in transporting certain substances across membranes. Energy exists in various forms, and the work of life depends on the ability of cells to transform energy from one form into another.

Energy can be associated with the relative motion of objects; this energy is called **kinetic energy**. Moving objects can perform work by imparting motion to other matter: A pool player uses the motion of the cue stick to push the cue ball, which in turn moves the other balls; water gushing through a dam turns turbines; and the contraction of leg muscles pushes bicycle pedals. **Heat**, or **thermal energy**, is kinetic energy associated with the random movement of atoms or molecules. Light is also a type of energy that can be harnessed to perform work, such as powering photosynthesis in green plants.

An object not presently moving may still possess energy. Energy that is not kinetic is called **potential energy**; it is energy that matter possesses because of its location or structure. Water behind a dam, for instance, possesses energy because of its altitude above sea level. Molecules possess energy because of the arrangement of their atoms. **Chemical energy** is a term used by biologists to refer to the potential energy available for release in a chemical reaction. Recall that catabolic pathways release energy by breaking down complex molecules. Biologists say that these complex molecules, such as glucose, are high in chemical energy. During a catabolic reaction, atoms are rearranged and energy is released, resulting in lower-energy breakdown products. This transformation also occurs, for example, in the engine of a car when the hydrocarbons of gasoline react explosively with oxygen, releasing the energy that pushes the pistons and producing exhaust. Although less explosive, a similar reaction of food molecules with oxygen provides chemical energy in biological systems, producing carbon dioxide and water as waste products. It is the structures and biochemical pathways of cells that enable them to release chemical energy from food molecules, powering life processes.

How is energy converted from one form to another? Consider the divers in **Figure 8.2**. The young man climbing the steps to the diving platform is releasing chemical energy from the food he ate for lunch and using some of that energy to perform the work

A diver has more potential energy on the platform than in the water.

Diving converts potential energy to kinetic energy.

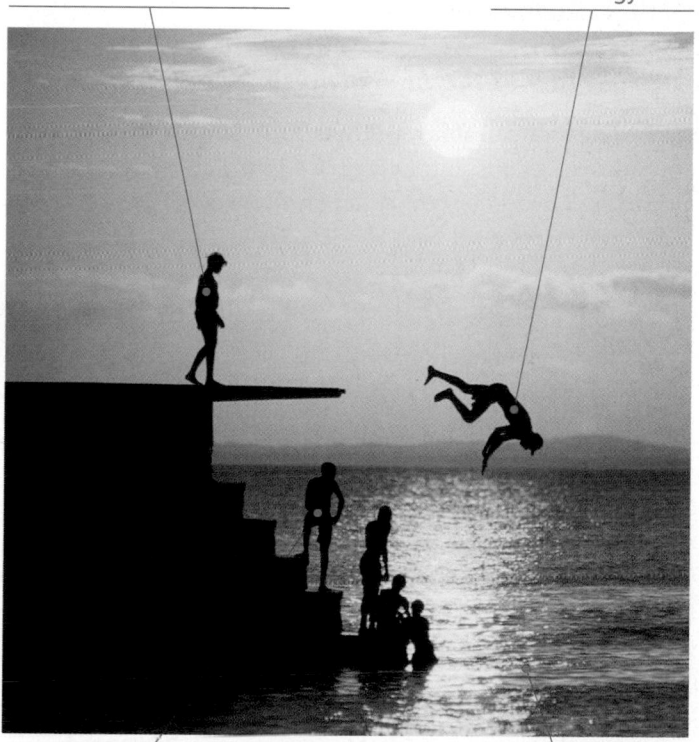

Climbing up converts the kinetic energy of muscle movement to potential energy.

A diver has less potential energy in the water than on the platform.

▲ **Figure 8.2 Transformations between potential and kinetic energy.**

of climbing. The kinetic energy of muscle movement is thus being transformed into potential energy due to his increasing height above the water. The young man diving is converting his potential energy to kinetic energy, which is then transferred to the water as he enters it. A small amount of energy is lost as heat due to friction.

Now let's go back one step and consider the original source of the organic food molecules that provided the necessary chemical energy for the diver to climb the steps. This chemical energy was itself derived from light energy by plants during photosynthesis. Organisms are energy transformers.

The Laws of Energy Transformation

The study of the energy transformations that occur in a collection of matter is called **thermodynamics**. Scientists use the word *system* to denote the matter under study; they refer to the rest of the universe—everything outside the system—as the *surroundings*. An *isolated system*, such as that approximated by liquid in a thermos bottle, is unable to exchange either energy or matter with its surroundings. In an *open system*, energy and matter can be transferred between the system and its surroundings. Organisms are open systems. They absorb energy—for instance, light energy or chemical energy in the form of organic molecules—and release heat and metabolic waste products, such as carbon dioxide, to the surroundings. Two laws of thermodynamics govern energy transformations in organisms and all other collections of matter.

The First Law of Thermodynamics

According to the **first law of thermodynamics**, the energy of the universe is constant. *Energy can be transferred and transformed, but it cannot be created or destroyed.* The first law is also known as the *principle of conservation of energy.* The electric company does not make energy, but merely converts it to a form that is convenient for us to use. By converting sunlight to chemical energy, a plant acts as an energy transformer, not an energy producer.

The cheetah in **Figure 8.3a** will convert the chemical energy of the organic molecules in its food to kinetic and other forms of energy as it carries out biological processes. What happens to this energy after it has performed work? The second law helps to answer this question.

The Second Law of Thermodynamics

If energy cannot be destroyed, why can't organisms simply recycle their energy over and over again? It turns out that during every energy transfer or transformation, some energy becomes unusable energy, unavailable to do work. In most energy transformations, more usable forms of energy are at least partly converted to heat, which is the energy associated with the random motion of atoms or molecules. Only a small fraction of the chemical energy from the food in Figure 8.3a is transformed into the motion of the cheetah shown in **Figure 8.3b**; most is lost as heat, which dissipates rapidly through the surroundings.

In the process of carrying out chemical reactions that perform various kinds of work, living cells unavoidably convert other forms of energy to heat. A system can put heat to work only when there is a temperature difference that results in the heat flowing from a warmer location to a cooler one. If temperature is uniform, as it is in a living cell, then the only use for heat energy generated during a chemical reaction is to warm a body of matter, such as the organism. (This can make a room crowded with people uncomfortably warm, as each person is carrying out a multitude of chemical reactions!)

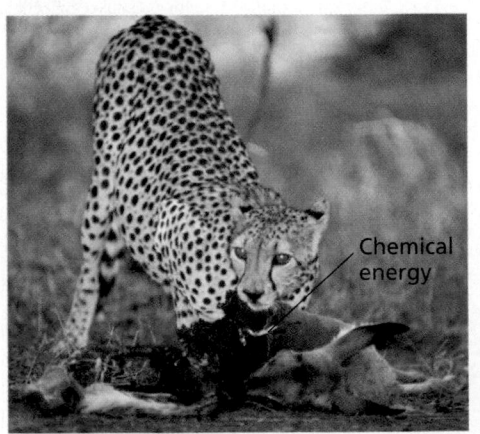

(a) First law of thermodynamics: Energy can be transferred or transformed but neither created nor destroyed. For example, the chemical (potential) energy in food will be converted to the kinetic energy of the cheetah's movement in (b).

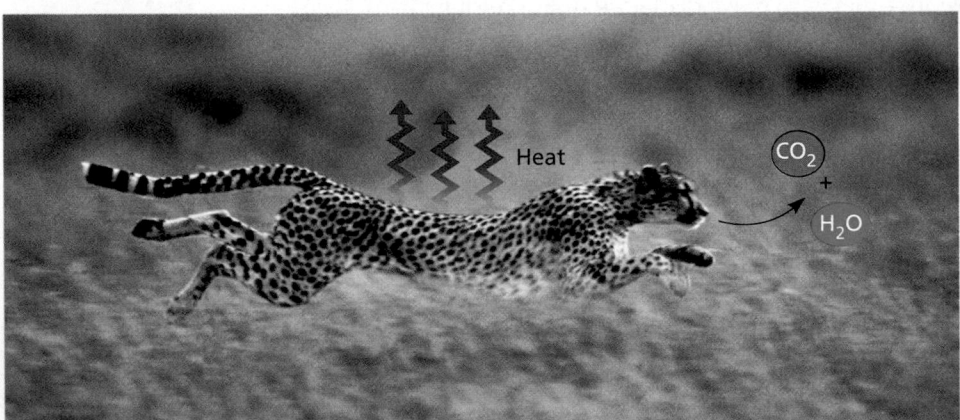

(b) Second law of thermodynamics: Every energy transfer or transformation increases the disorder (entropy) of the universe. For example, disorder is added to the cheetah's surroundings in the form of heat and the small molecules that are the by-products of metabolism.

▲ Figure 8.3 **The two laws of thermodynamics.**

A logical consequence of the loss of usable energy during energy transfer or transformation is that each such event makes the universe more disordered. Scientists use a quantity called **entropy** as a measure of disorder, or randomness. The more randomly arranged a collection of matter is, the greater its entropy. We can now state the **second law of thermodynamics** as follows: *Every energy transfer or transformation increases the entropy of the universe.* Although order can increase locally, there is an unstoppable trend toward randomization of the universe as a whole.

In many cases, increased entropy is evident in the physical disintegration of a system's organized structure. For example, you can observe increasing entropy in the gradual decay of an unmaintained building. Much of the increasing entropy of the universe is less apparent, however, because it appears as increasing amounts of heat and less ordered forms of matter. As the cheetah in Figure 8.3b converts chemical energy to kinetic energy, it is also increasing the disorder of its surroundings by producing heat and the small molecules, such as the CO_2 it exhales, that are the breakdown products of food.

The concept of entropy helps us understand why certain processes occur. It turns out that for a process to occur on its own, without outside help (an input of energy), it must increase the entropy of the universe. Let's first agree to use the word *spontaneous* for a process that can occur without an input of energy. Note that as we're using it here, the word *spontaneous* does not imply that such a process would occur quickly. Some spontaneous processes may be virtually instantaneous, such as an explosion, while others may be much slower, such as the rusting of an old car over time. A process that cannot occur on its own is said to be nonspontaneous; it will happen only if energy is added to the system. We know from experience that certain events occur spontaneously and others do not. For instance, we know that water flows downhill spontaneously, but moves uphill only with an input of energy, such as when a machine pumps the water against gravity. In fact, another way to state the second law is: *For a process to occur spontaneously, it must increase the entropy of the universe.*

Biological Order and Disorder

Living systems increase the entropy of their surroundings, as predicted by thermodynamic law. It is true that cells create ordered structures from less organized starting materials. For example, amino acids are ordered into the specific sequences of polypeptide chains. At the organismal level, **Figure 8.4** shows the extremely symmetrical anatomy of a plant's root, formed by biological processes from simpler starting materials. However, an organism also takes in organized forms of matter and energy from the surroundings and replaces them with less ordered forms. For example, an animal obtains starch, proteins, and other complex molecules from the food it eats. As catabolic pathways break these molecules down, the animal releases car-

50 μm

▲ **Figure 8.4 Order as a characteristic of life.** Order is evident in the detailed anatomy of this root tissue from a buttercup plant (LM, cross section). As open systems, organisms can increase their order as long as the order of their surroundings decreases.

bon dioxide and water—small molecules that possess less chemical energy than the food did. The depletion of chemical energy is accounted for by heat generated during metabolism. On a larger scale, energy flows into an ecosystem in the form of light and exits in the form of heat (see Figure 1.5).

During the early history of life, complex organisms evolved from simpler ancestors. For example, we can trace the ancestry of the plant kingdom from much simpler organisms called green algae to more complex flowering plants. However, this increase in organization over time in no way violates the second law. The entropy of a particular system, such as an organism, may actually decrease as long as the total entropy of the *universe*—the system plus its surroundings—increases. Thus, organisms are islands of low entropy in an increasingly random universe. The evolution of biological order is perfectly consistent with the laws of thermodynamics.

CONCEPT CHECK 8.1

1. How does the second law of thermodynamics help explain the diffusion of a substance across a membrane?
2. Describe the forms of energy found in an apple as it grows on a tree, then falls and is digested by someone who eats it.
3. **WHAT IF?** If you place a teaspoon of sugar in the bottom of a glass of water, it will dissolve completely over time. Left longer, eventually the water will disappear and the sugar crystals will reappear. Explain these observations in terms of entropy.

For suggested answers, see Appendix A.

The free-energy change of a reaction tells us whether or not the reaction occurs spontaneously

The laws of thermodynamics that we've just discussed apply to the universe as a whole. As biologists, we want to understand the chemical reactions of life—for example, which reactions occur spontaneously and which ones require some input of energy from outside. But how can we know this without assessing the energy and entropy changes in the entire universe for each separate reaction?

Free-Energy Change, ΔG

Recall that the universe is really equivalent to "the system" plus "the surroundings." In 1878, J. Willard Gibbs, a professor at Yale, defined a very useful function called the Gibbs free energy of a system (without considering its surroundings), symbolized by the letter G. We'll refer to the Gibbs free energy simply as free energy. **Free energy** is the portion of a system's energy that can perform work when temperature and pressure are uniform throughout the system, as in a living cell. Let's consider how we determine the free-energy change that occurs when a system changes—for example, during a chemical reaction.

The change in free energy, ΔG, can be calculated for a chemical reaction with the following formula:

$$\Delta G = \Delta H - T\Delta S$$

This formula uses only properties of the system (the reaction) itself: ΔH symbolizes the change in the system's *enthalpy* (in biological systems, equivalent to total energy); ΔS is the change in the system's entropy; and T is the absolute temperature in Kelvin (K) units (K = °C + 273; see Appendix C).

Once we know the value of ΔG for a process, we can use it to predict whether the process will be spontaneous (that is, whether it will occur without an input of energy from outside). More than a century of experiments has shown that only processes with a negative ΔG are spontaneous. For a process to occur spontaneously, therefore, the system must either give up enthalpy (H must decrease), give up order (TS must increase), or both: When the changes in H and TS are tallied, ΔG must have a negative value ($\Delta G < 0$) for a process to be spontaneous. This means that every spontaneous process decreases the system's free energy. Processes that have a positive or zero ΔG are never spontaneous.

This information is immensely interesting to biologists, for it gives us the power to predict which kinds of change can happen without help. Such spontaneous changes can be harnessed to perform work. This principle is very important in the study of metabolism, where a major goal is to determine which reactions can supply energy for cellular work.

Free Energy, Stability, and Equilibrium

As we saw in the previous section, when a process occurs spontaneously in a system, we can be sure that ΔG is negative. Another way to think of ΔG is to realize that it represents the difference between the free energy of the final state and the free energy of the initial state:

$$\Delta G = G_{\text{final state}} - G_{\text{initial state}}$$

Thus, ΔG can be negative only when the process involves a loss of free energy during the change from initial state to final state. Because it has less free energy, the system in its final state is less likely to change and is therefore more stable than it was previously.

We can think of free energy as a measure of a system's instability—its tendency to change to a more stable state. Unstable systems (higher G) tend to change in such a way that they become more stable (lower G). For example, a diver on top of a platform is less stable (more likely to fall) than when floating in the water, a drop of concentrated dye is less stable (more likely to disperse) than when the dye is spread randomly through the liquid, and a sugar molecule is less stable (more likely to break down) than the simpler molecules into which it can be split **(Figure 8.5)**. Unless something prevents it, each of these systems will move toward greater stability: The diver falls, the solution becomes uniformly colored, and the sugar molecule is broken down.

Another term that describes a state of maximum stability is *equilibrium*, which you learned about in Chapter 2 in connection with chemical reactions. There is an important relationship between free energy and equilibrium, including chemical equilibrium. Recall that most chemical reactions are reversible and proceed to a point at which the forward and backward reactions occur at the same rate. The reaction is then said to be at chemical equilibrium, and there is no further net change in the relative concentration of products and reactants.

As a reaction proceeds toward equilibrium, the free energy of the mixture of reactants and products decreases. Free energy increases when a reaction is somehow pushed away from equilibrium, perhaps by removing some of the products (and thus changing their concentration relative to that of the reactants). For a system at equilibrium, G is at its lowest possible value in that system. We can think of the equilibrium state as a free-energy valley. Any change from the equilibrium position will have a positive ΔG and will not be spontaneous. For this reason, systems never spontaneously move away from equilibrium. Because a system at equilibrium cannot spontaneously change, it can do no work. A process is spontaneous and can perform work only when it is moving toward equilibrium.

- More free energy (higher *G*)
- Less stable
- Greater work capacity

In a **spontaneous change**
- The free energy of the system decreases ($\Delta G < 0$)
- The system becomes more stable
- The released free energy can be harnessed to do work

- Less free energy (lower *G*)
- More stable
- Less work capacity

(a) Gravitational motion. Objects move spontaneously from a higher altitude to a lower one.

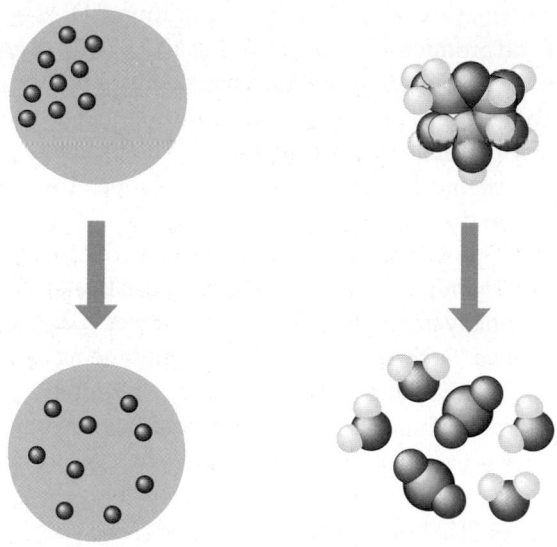

(b) Diffusion. Molecules in a drop of dye diffuse until they are randomly dispersed.

(c) Chemical reaction. In a cell, a sugar molecule is broken down into simpler molecules.

▲ **Figure 8.5 The relationship of free energy to stability, work capacity, and spontaneous change.** Unstable systems (top diagrams) are rich in free energy, *G*. They have a tendency to change spontaneously to a more stable state (bottom), and it is possible to harness this "downhill" change to perform work.

Free Energy and Metabolism

We can now apply the free-energy concept more specifically to the chemistry of life's processes.

Exergonic and Endergonic Reactions in Metabolism

Based on their free-energy changes, chemical reactions can be classified as either exergonic ("energy outward") or endergonic ("energy inward"). An **exergonic reaction** proceeds with a net release of free energy **(Figure 8.6a)**. Because the chemical mixture loses free energy (*G* decreases), ΔG is negative for an exergonic reaction. Using ΔG as a standard for spontaneity, exergonic reactions are those that occur spontaneously. (Remember, the word *spontaneous* does not imply that a reaction will occur instantaneously or even rapidly.) The magnitude of ΔG for an exergonic reaction represents the maximum amount of work the reaction can perform.* The greater the decrease in free energy, the greater the amount of work that can be done.

We can use the overall reaction for cellular respiration as an example:

$$C_6H_{12}O_6 + 6\ O_2 \rightarrow 6\ CO_2 + 6\ H_2O$$
$$\Delta G = -686 \text{ kcal/mol } (-2,870 \text{ kJ/mol})$$

---

* The word *maximum* qualifies this statement, because some of the free energy is released as heat and cannot do work. Therefore, ΔG represents a theoretical upper limit of available energy.

(a) Exergonic reaction: energy released

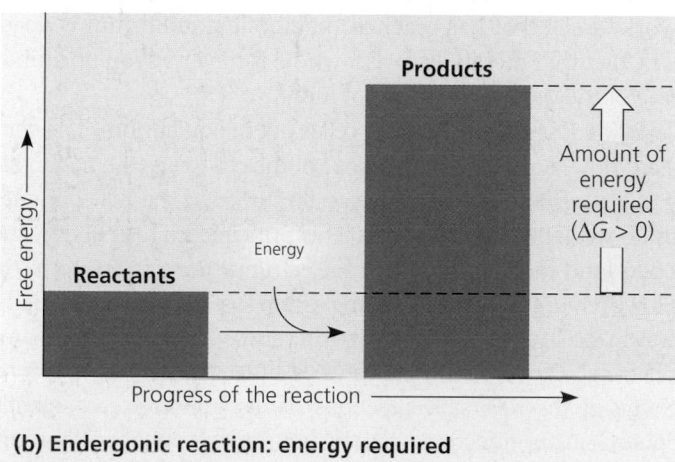

(b) Endergonic reaction: energy required

▲ **Figure 8.6 Free energy changes (ΔG) in exergonic and endergonic reactions.**

For each mole (180 g) of glucose broken down by respiration under what are called "standard conditions" (1 *M* of each reactant and product, 25°C, pH 7), 686 kcal (2,870 kJ) of energy are made available for work. Because energy must be conserved, the chemical products of respiration store 686 kcal less free energy per mole than the reactants. The products are, in a sense, the spent exhaust of a process that tapped the free energy stored in the sugar molecules.

An **endergonic reaction** is one that absorbs free energy from its surroundings **(Figure 8.6b)**. Because this kind of reaction essentially *stores* free energy in molecules (*G* increases), Δ*G* is positive. Such reactions are nonspontaneous, and the magnitude of Δ*G* is the quantity of energy required to drive the reaction. If a chemical process is exergonic (downhill), releasing energy in one direction, then the reverse process must be endergonic (uphill), using energy. A reversible process cannot be downhill in both directions. If Δ*G* = −686 kcal/mol for respiration, which converts sugar and oxygen to carbon dioxide and water, then the reverse process—the conversion of carbon dioxide and water to sugar and oxygen—must be strongly endergonic, with Δ*G* = +686 kcal/mol. Such a reaction would never happen by itself.

How, then, do plants make the sugar that organisms use for energy? They get the required energy—686 kcal to make a mole of sugar—from the environment by capturing light and converting its energy to chemical energy. Next, in a long series of exergonic steps, they gradually spend that chemical energy to assemble sugar molecules.

Equilibrium and Metabolism

Reactions in an isolated system eventually reach equilibrium and can then do no work, as illustrated by the isolated hydroelectric system in **Figure 8.7a**. The chemical reactions of metabolism are reversible, and they, too, would reach equilibrium if they occurred in the isolation of a test tube. Because systems at equilibrium are at a minimum of *G* and can do no work, a cell that has reached metabolic equilibrium is dead! The fact that metabolism as a whole is never at equilibrium is one of the defining features of life.

Like most systems, a living cell is not in equilibrium. The constant flow of materials in and out of the cell keeps the metabolic pathways from ever reaching equilibrium, and the cell continues to do work throughout its life. This principle is illustrated by the open (and more realistic) hydroelectric system in **Figure 8.7b**. However, unlike this simple single-step system, a catabolic pathway in a cell releases free energy in a series of reactions. An example is cellular respiration, illustrated by analogy in **Figure 8.7c**. Some of the reversible reactions of respiration are constantly "pulled" in one direction—that is, they are kept out of equilibrium. The key to maintaining this lack of equilibrium is that the product of a reaction does not accumulate, but instead becomes a reactant in the next step; finally, waste products are expelled from the cell.

(a) An isolated hydroelectric system. Water flowing downhill turns a turbine that drives a generator providing electricity to a light bulb, but only until the system reaches equilibrium.

(b) An open hydroelectric system. Flowing water keeps driving the generator because intake and outflow of water keep the system from reaching equilibrium.

(c) A multistep open hydroelectric system. Cellular respiration is analogous to this system: Glucose is broken down in a series of exergonic reactions that power the work of the cell. The product of each reaction becomes the reactant for the next, so no reaction reaches equilibrium.

▲ **Figure 8.7 Equilibrium and work in isolated and open systems.**

The overall sequence of reactions is kept going by the huge free-energy difference between glucose and oxygen at the top of the energy "hill" and carbon dioxide and water at the "downhill" end. As long as our cells have a steady supply of glucose or other fuels and oxygen and are able to expel waste products to the surroundings, their metabolic pathways never reach equilibrium and can continue to do the work of life.

We see once again how important it is to think of organisms as open systems. Sunlight provides a daily source of free energy for an ecosystem's plants and other photosynthetic organisms. Animals and other nonphotosynthetic organisms in an ecosystem must have a source of free energy in the form of the organic products of photosynthesis. Now that we have applied the free-energy concept to metabolism, we are ready to see how a cell actually performs the work of life.

1. Cellular respiration uses glucose and oxygen, which have high levels of free energy, and releases CO_2 and water, which have low levels of free energy. Is respiration spontaneous or not? Is it exergonic or endergonic? What happens to the energy released from glucose?

2. A key process in metabolism is the transport of hydrogen ions (H^+) across a membrane to create a concentration gradient. Other processes can result in an equal concentration of hydrogen ions on each side. Which arrangement of hydrogen ions allows the H^+ to perform work in this system?

3. **WHAT IF?** At nighttime celebrations, revelers can sometimes be seen wearing glow-in-the-dark necklaces. The necklaces start glowing once they are "activated," which usually involves snapping the necklace in a way that allows two chemicals to react and emit light in the form of "chemiluminescence." Is the chemical reaction exergonic or endergonic? Explain your answer.

For suggested answers, see Appendix A.

CONCEPT 8.3

ATP powers cellular work by coupling exergonic reactions to endergonic reactions

A cell does three main kinds of work:

▶ *Chemical work*, the pushing of endergonic reactions, which would not occur spontaneously, such as the synthesis of polymers from monomers (chemical work will be discussed further here and will come up again in Chapters 9 and 10)

▶ *Transport work*, the pumping of substances across membranes against the direction of spontaneous movement (see Chapter 7)

▶ *Mechanical work*, such as the beating of cilia (see Chapter 6), the contraction of muscle cells, and the movement of chromosomes during cellular reproduction

A key feature in the way cells manage their energy resources to do this work is **energy coupling**, the use of an exergonic process to drive an endergonic one. ATP is responsible for mediating most energy coupling in cells, and in most cases it acts as the immediate source of energy that powers cellular work.

The Structure and Hydrolysis of ATP

ATP (adenosine triphosphate) was introduced in Chapter 4 when we discussed the phosphate group as a functional group. ATP contains the sugar ribose, with the nitrogenous base ade-

nine and a chain of three phosphate groups bonded to it (**Figure 8.8**). In addition to its role in energy coupling, ATP is also one of the nucleoside triphosphates used to make RNA (see Figure 5.27).

The bonds between the phosphate groups of ATP can be broken by hydrolysis. When the terminal phosphate bond is broken, a molecule of inorganic phosphate ($HOPO_3^{2-}$, abbreviated ⓟ$_i$ throughout this book) leaves the ATP, which becomes adenosine diphosphate, or ADP (**Figure 8.9**). The reaction is exergonic and releases 7.3 kcal of energy per mole of ATP hydrolyzed:

$$ATP + H_2O \rightarrow ADP + ⓟ_i$$
$$\Delta G = -7.3 \text{ kcal/mol } (-30.5 \text{ kJ/mol})$$

This is the free-energy change measured under standard conditions. In the cell, conditions do not conform to standard conditions, primarily because reactant and product concentrations differ from 1 M. For example, when ATP hydrolysis occurs under cellular conditions, the actual ΔG is about −13 kcal/mol, 78% greater than the energy released by ATP hydrolysis under standard conditions.

Because their hydrolysis releases energy, the phosphate bonds of ATP are sometimes referred to as high-energy phosphate bonds, but the term is misleading. The phosphate bonds of ATP

▲ **Figure 8.8 The structure of adenosine triphosphate (ATP).** In the cell, most hydroxyl groups of phosphates are ionized (—O^-).

▲ **Figure 8.9 The hydrolysis of ATP.** The reaction of ATP and water yields inorganic phosphate (ⓟ$_i$) and ADP and releases energy.

are not unusually strong bonds, as "high-energy" may imply; rather, the reactants (ATP and water) themselves have high energy relative to the energy of the products (ADP and $\textcircled{P}_i$). The release of energy during the hydrolysis of ATP comes from the chemical change to a state of lower free energy, not from the phosphate bonds themselves.

ATP is useful to the cell because the energy it releases on losing a phosphate group is somewhat greater than the energy most other molecules could deliver. But why does this hydrolysis release so much energy? If we reexamine the ATP molecule in Figure 8.8, we can see that all three phosphate groups are negatively charged. These like charges are crowded together, and their mutual repulsion contributes to the instability of this region of the ATP molecule. The triphosphate tail of ATP is the chemical equivalent of a compressed spring.

How ATP Performs Work

When ATP is hydrolyzed in a test tube, the release of free energy merely heats the surrounding water. In an organism, this same generation of heat can sometimes be beneficial. For instance, the process of shivering uses ATP hydrolysis during muscle contraction to generate heat and warm the body. In most cases in the cell, however, the generation of heat alone would be an inefficient (and potentially dangerous) use of a valuable energy resource. Instead, the cell's proteins harness the energy released during ATP hydrolysis in several ways to perform the three types of cellular work—chemical, transport, and mechanical.

For example, with the help of specific enzymes, the cell is able to use the energy released by ATP hydrolysis directly to drive chemical reactions that, by themselves, are endergonic. If the ΔG of an endergonic reaction is less than the amount of energy released by ATP hydrolysis, then the two reactions can be coupled so that, overall, the coupled reactions are exergonic (Figure 8.10). This usually involves the transfer of a phosphate group from ATP to some other molecule, such as the reactant. The recipient of the phosphate group is then said to be **phosphorylated**. The key to coupling exergonic and endergonic reactions is the formation of this phosphorylated intermediate, which is more reactive (less stable) than the original unphosphorylated molecule.

Transport and mechanical work in the cell are also nearly always powered by the hydrolysis of ATP. In these cases, ATP hydrolysis leads to a change in a protein's shape and often its ability to bind another molecule. Sometimes this occurs via a phosphorylated intermediate, as seen for the transport protein in Figure 8.11a. In most instances of mechanical work involving motor proteins "walking" along cytoskeletal elements (Figure 8.11b), a cycle occurs in which ATP is first bound noncovalently to the motor protein. Next, ATP is hydrolyzed, releasing ADP and $\textcircled{P}_i$; another ATP molecule can then bind. At each stage, the motor protein changes its shape and ability

(a) Endergonic reaction. Amino acid conversion by itself is endergonic (ΔG is positive), so it is not spontaneous.

(b) Coupled with ATP hydrolysis, an exergonic reaction. In the cell, glutamine synthesis occurs in two steps, coupled by a phosphorylated intermediate. ❶ ATP phosphorylates glutamic acid, making the amino acid less stable. ❷ Ammonia displaces the phosphate group, forming glutamine.

Glu + NH$_3$	$\longrightarrow$	Glu—NH$_2$	ΔG = +3.4 kcal/mol
ATP	$\longrightarrow$	ADP + $\textcircled{P}_i$	ΔG = −7.3 kcal/mol
			Net ΔG = −3.9 kcal/mol

(c) Overall free-energy change. Adding the ΔG (under standard conditions) for the amino acid conversion to the ΔG for ATP hydrolysis gives the free-energy change for the overall reaction. Because the overall process is exergonic (ΔG is negative), it occurs spontaneously.

▲ **Figure 8.10 How ATP drives chemical work: Energy coupling using ATP hydrolysis.** In this example, the exergonic process of ATP hydrolysis is used to drive an endergonic process—the cellular synthesis of the amino acid glutamine from glutamic acid and ammonia.

to bind the cytoskeleton, resulting in movement of the protein along the cytoskeletal track.

The Regeneration of ATP

An organism at work uses ATP continuously, but ATP is a renewable resource that can be regenerated by the addition of phosphate to ADP (Figure 8.12). The free energy required to phosphorylate ADP comes from exergonic breakdown reactions (catabolism) in the cell. This shuttling of inorganic phosphate and energy is called the ATP cycle, and it couples the cell's energy-yielding (exergonic) processes to the energy-consuming (endergonic) ones. The ATP cycle moves at an astonishing pace. For example, a working muscle cell recycles its entire pool of ATP in less than a minute. That turnover represents 10 million molecules of ATP consumed and regenerated per second per cell. If ATP could not be regenerated by the phosphorylation of ADP, humans would use up nearly their body weight in ATP each day.

(a) Transport work: ATP phosphorylates transport proteins

(b) Mechanical work: ATP binds noncovalently to motor proteins, then is hydrolyzed

▲ **Figure 8.11 How ATP drives transport and mechanical work.** ATP hydrolysis causes changes in the shapes and binding affinities of proteins. This can occur either **(a)** directly, by phosphorylation, as shown for membrane proteins involved in active transport of solutes, or **(b)** indirectly, via noncovalent binding of ATP and its hydrolytic products, as is the case for motor proteins that move vesicles (and organelles) along cytoskeletal "tracks" in the cell.

ATP synthesis from ADP + Ⓟᵢ requires energy

ATP hydrolysis to ADP + Ⓟᵢ yields energy

Energy from catabolism (exergonic, energy-releasing processes)

Energy for cellular work (endergonic, energy-consuming processes)

▲ **Figure 8.12 The ATP cycle.** Energy released by breakdown reactions (catabolism) in the cell is used to phosphorylate ADP, regenerating ATP. Chemical potential energy stored in ATP drives most cellular work.

Because both directions of a reversible process cannot go downhill, the regeneration of ATP from ADP and Ⓟᵢ is necessarily endergonic:

$$ADP + Ⓟᵢ \rightarrow ATP + H_2O$$

$\Delta G = +7.3$ kcal/mol (+30.5 kJ/mol) (standard conditions)

Because ATP formation from ADP and Ⓟᵢ is not spontaneous, free energy must be spent to make it occur. Catabolic (exergonic) pathways, especially cellular respiration, provide the energy for the endergonic process of making ATP. Plants also use light energy to produce ATP.

Thus, the ATP cycle is a turnstile through which energy passes during its transfer from catabolic to anabolic pathways. In fact, the chemical potential energy temporarily stored in ATP drives most cellular work.

CONCEPT CHECK 8.3

1. In most cases, how does ATP transfer energy from exergonic to endergonic reactions in the cell?
2. **WHAT IF?** Which of the following combinations has more free energy: glutamic acid + ammonia + ATP, or glutamine + ADP + Ⓟᵢ? Explain your answer.

For suggested answers, see Appendix A.

CONCEPT 8.4

Enzymes speed up metabolic reactions by lowering energy barriers

The laws of thermodynamics tell us what will and will not happen under given conditions but say nothing about the rate of these processes. A spontaneous chemical reaction occurs without any requirement for outside energy, but it may occur so slowly that it is imperceptible. For example, even though the hydrolysis of sucrose (table sugar) to glucose and fructose is exergonic, occurring spontaneously with a release of free energy ($\Delta G = -7$ kcal/mol), a solution of sucrose dissolved in sterile water will sit for years at room temperature with no appreciable hydrolysis. However, if we add a small amount of the enzyme sucrase to the solution, then all the sucrose may be hydrolyzed within seconds **(Figure 8.13)**. How does the enzyme do this?

Sucrose ($C_{12}H_{22}O_{11}$)

Sucrase

Glucose ($C_6H_{12}O_6$)   +   Fructose ($C_6H_{12}O_6$)

▲ **Figure 8.13 Example of an enzyme-catalyzed reaction: hydrolysis of sucrose by sucrase.**

An **enzyme** is a macromolecule that acts as a **catalyst**, a chemical agent that speeds up a reaction without being consumed by the reaction. In this chapter, we are focusing on enzymes that are proteins. (RNA enzymes, also called ribozymes, are discussed in Chapters 17 and 25.) In the absence of regulation by enzymes, chemical traffic through the pathways of metabolism would become terribly congested because many chemical reactions would take such a long time. In the next two sections, we will see what impedes a spontaneous reaction from occurring faster and how an enzyme changes the situation.

The Activation Energy Barrier

Every chemical reaction between molecules involves both bond breaking and bond forming. For example, the hydrolysis of sucrose involves breaking the bond between glucose and fructose and one of the bonds of a water molecule and then forming two new bonds, as shown in Figure 8.13. Changing one molecule into another generally involves contorting the starting molecule into a highly unstable state before the reaction can proceed. This contortion can be compared to the bending of a metal key ring when you pry it open to add a new key. The key ring is highly unstable in its opened form but returns to a stable state once the key is threaded all the way onto the ring. To reach the contorted state where bonds can change, reactant molecules must absorb energy from their surroundings. When the new bonds of the product molecules form, energy is released as heat, and the molecules return to stable shapes with lower energy than the contorted state.

The initial investment of energy for starting a reaction—the energy required to contort the reactant molecules so the bonds can break—is known as the *free energy of activation*, or **activation energy**, abbreviated E_A in this book. We can think of activation energy as the amount of energy needed to push the reactants over an energy barrier, or hill, so that the "downhill" part of the reaction can begin. **Figure 8.14** graphs the energy changes for a hypothetical exergonic reaction that swaps portions of two reactant molecules:

$$AB + CD \rightarrow AC + BD$$

The energizing, or activation, of the reactants is represented by the uphill portion of the graph, in which the free-energy content of the reactant molecules is increasing. At the summit, the reactants are in an unstable condition known as the *transition state*: They are activated, and their bonds can be broken. The subsequent bond-forming phase of the reaction corresponds to the downhill part of the curve, which shows the loss of free energy by the molecules.

Activation energy is often supplied in the form of heat that the reactant molecules absorb from the surroundings. The bonds of the reactants break only when the molecules have absorbed enough energy to become unstable—to enter the transition state. The absorption of thermal energy increases the speed of

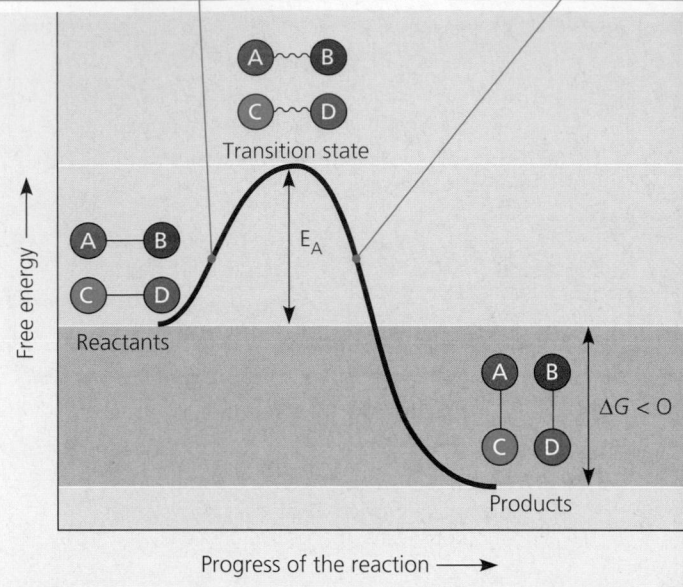

▲ **Figure 8.14 Energy profile of an exergonic reaction.** The "molecules" are hypothetical, with A, B, C, and D representing portions of the molecules. Thermodynamically, this is an exergonic reaction, with a negative ΔG, and the reaction occurs spontaneously. However, the activation energy (E_A) provides a barrier that determines the rate of the reaction.

DRAW IT *Graph the progress of an endergonic reaction in which EF and GH form products EG and FH, assuming that the reactants must pass through a transition state.*

the reactant molecules, so they collide more often and more forcefully. Also, thermal agitation of the atoms within the molecules makes the bonds more likely to break. As the atoms settle into their new, more stable bonding arrangements, energy is released to the surroundings. If the reaction is exergonic, E_A will be repaid with interest, as the formation of new bonds releases more energy than was invested in the breaking of old bonds.

The reaction shown in Figure 8.14 is exergonic and occurs spontaneously. However, the activation energy provides a barrier that determines the rate of the reaction. The reactants must absorb enough energy to reach the top of the activation energy barrier before the reaction can occur. For some reactions, E_A is modest enough that even at room temperature there is sufficient thermal energy for many of the reactants to reach the transition state in a short time. In most cases, however, E_A is so high and the transition state is reached so rarely that the reaction will hardly proceed at all. In these cases, the reaction will occur at a noticeable rate only if the reactants are heated. For example, the reaction of gasoline and oxygen is exergonic and will occur spontaneously, but energy is required for the molecules to reach the transition state and react. Only when the spark plugs fire in an automobile engine can there be the explosive release of energy that pushes the pistons. Without a spark, a mixture of gasoline

▲ **Figure 8.15 The effect of an enzyme on activation energy.** Without affecting the free-energy change (ΔG) for a reaction, an enzyme speeds the reaction by reducing its activation energy (E_A).

hydrocarbons and oxygen will not react because the E_A barrier is too high.

How Enzymes Lower the E_A Barrier

Proteins, DNA, and other complex molecules of the cell are rich in free energy and have the potential to decompose spontaneously; that is, the laws of thermodynamics favor their breakdown. These molecules persist only because at temperatures typical for cells, few molecules can make it over the hump of activation energy. However, the barriers for selected reactions must occasionally be surmounted for cells to carry out the processes needed for life. Heat speeds a reaction by allowing reactants to attain the transition state more often, but this solution would be inappropriate for biological systems. First, high temperature denatures proteins and kills cells. Second, heat would speed up *all* reactions, not just those that are needed. Organisms therefore use an alternative: catalysis.

An enzyme catalyzes a reaction by lowering the E_A barrier **(Figure 8.15)**, enabling the reactant molecules to absorb enough energy to reach the transition state even at moderate temperatures. An enzyme cannot change the ΔG for a reaction; it cannot make an endergonic reaction exergonic. Enzymes can only hasten reactions that would occur eventually anyway, but this function makes it possible for the cell to have a dynamic metabolism, routing chemicals smoothly through the cell's metabolic pathways. And because enzymes are very specific for the reactions they catalyze, they determine which chemical processes will be going on in the cell at any particular time.

Substrate Specificity of Enzymes

The reactant an enzyme acts on is referred to as the enzyme's **substrate**. The enzyme binds to its substrate (or substrates, when there are two or more reactants), forming an **enzyme-substrate complex.** While enzyme and substrate are joined, the catalytic action of the enzyme converts the substrate to the product (or products) of the reaction. The overall process can be summarized as follows:

$$\text{Enzyme} + \text{Substrate(s)} \rightleftharpoons \begin{array}{c}\text{Enzyme-}\\\text{substrate}\\\text{complex}\end{array} \rightleftharpoons \text{Enzyme} + \text{Product(s)}$$

For example, the enzyme sucrase (most enzyme names end in *-ase*) catalyzes the hydrolysis of the disaccharide sucrose into its two monosaccharides, glucose and fructose (see Figure 8.13):

$$\begin{array}{c}\text{Sucrase} +\\\text{Sucrose} +\\\text{H}_2\text{O}\end{array} \rightleftharpoons \begin{array}{c}\text{Sucrase-}\\\text{sucrose-H}_2\text{O}\\\text{complex}\end{array} \rightleftharpoons \begin{array}{c}\text{Sucrase} +\\\text{Glucose} +\\\text{Fructose}\end{array}$$

The reaction catalyzed by each enzyme is very specific; an enzyme can recognize its specific substrate even among closely related compounds, such as isomers. For instance, sucrase will act only on sucrose and will not bind to other disaccharides, such as maltose. What accounts for this molecular recognition? Recall that most enzymes are proteins, and proteins are macromolecules with unique three-dimensional configurations. The specificity of an enzyme results from its shape, which is a consequence of its amino acid sequence.

Only a restricted region of the enzyme molecule actually binds to the substrate. This region, called the **active site**, is typically a pocket or groove on the surface of the protein where catalysis occurs **(Figure 8.16a)**. Usually, the active site is formed by

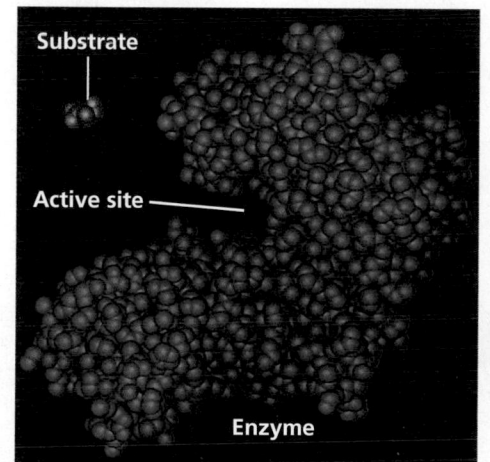

(a) In this computer graphic model, the active site of this enzyme (hexokinase, shown in blue) forms a groove on its surface. Its substrate is glucose (red).

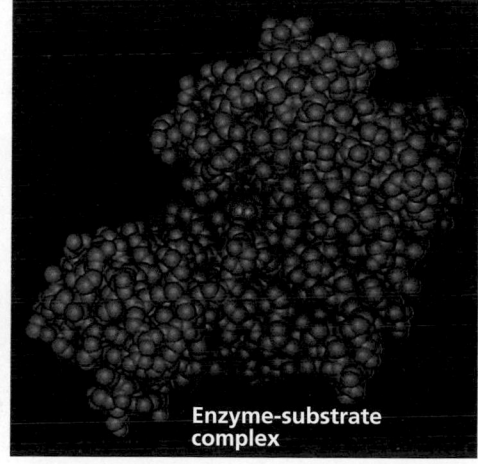

(b) When the substrate enters the active site, it induces a change in the shape of the protein. This change allows more weak bonds to form, causing the active site to enfold the substrate and hold it in place.

▲ **Figure 8.16 Induced fit between an enzyme and its substrate.**

only a few of the enzyme's amino acids, with the rest of the protein molecule providing a framework that determines the configuration of the active site. The specificity of an enzyme is attributed to a compatible fit between the shape of its active site and the shape of the substrate. The active site, however, is not a rigid receptacle for the substrate. As the substrate enters the active site, interactions between its chemical groups and those on the R groups (side chains) of the amino acids that form the active site of the protein cause the enzyme to change its shape slightly so that the active site fits even more snugly around the substrate (Figure 8.16b). This **induced fit** is like a clasping handshake. Induced fit brings chemical groups of the active site into positions that enhance their ability to catalyze the chemical reaction.

Catalysis in the Enzyme's Active Site

In most enzymatic reactions, the substrate is held in the active site by so-called weak interactions, such as hydrogen bonds and ionic bonds. R groups of a few of the amino acids that make up the active site catalyze the conversion of substrate to product, and the product departs from the active site. The enzyme is then free to take another substrate molecule into its active site. The entire cycle happens so fast that a single enzyme molecule typically acts on about a thousand substrate

molecules per second. Some enzymes are much faster. Enzymes, like other catalysts, emerge from the reaction in their original form. Therefore, very small amounts of enzyme can have a huge metabolic impact by functioning over and over again in catalytic cycles. **Figure 8.17** shows a catalytic cycle involving two substrates and two products.

Most metabolic reactions are reversible, and an enzyme can catalyze either the forward or the reverse reaction, depending on which direction has a negative ΔG. This in turn depends mainly on the relative concentrations of reactants and products. The net effect is always in the direction of equilibrium.

Enzymes use a variety of mechanisms that lower activation energy and speed up a reaction (see Figure 8.17, step ❸). First, in reactions involving two or more reactants, the active site provides a template on which the substrates can come together in the proper orientation for a reaction to occur between them. Second, as the active site of an enzyme clutches the bound substrates, the enzyme may stretch the substrate molecules toward their transition-state form, stressing and bending critical chemical bonds that must be broken during the reaction. Because E_A is proportional to the difficulty of breaking the bonds, distorting the substrate helps it approach the transition state and thus reduces the amount of free energy that must be absorbed to achieve that state.

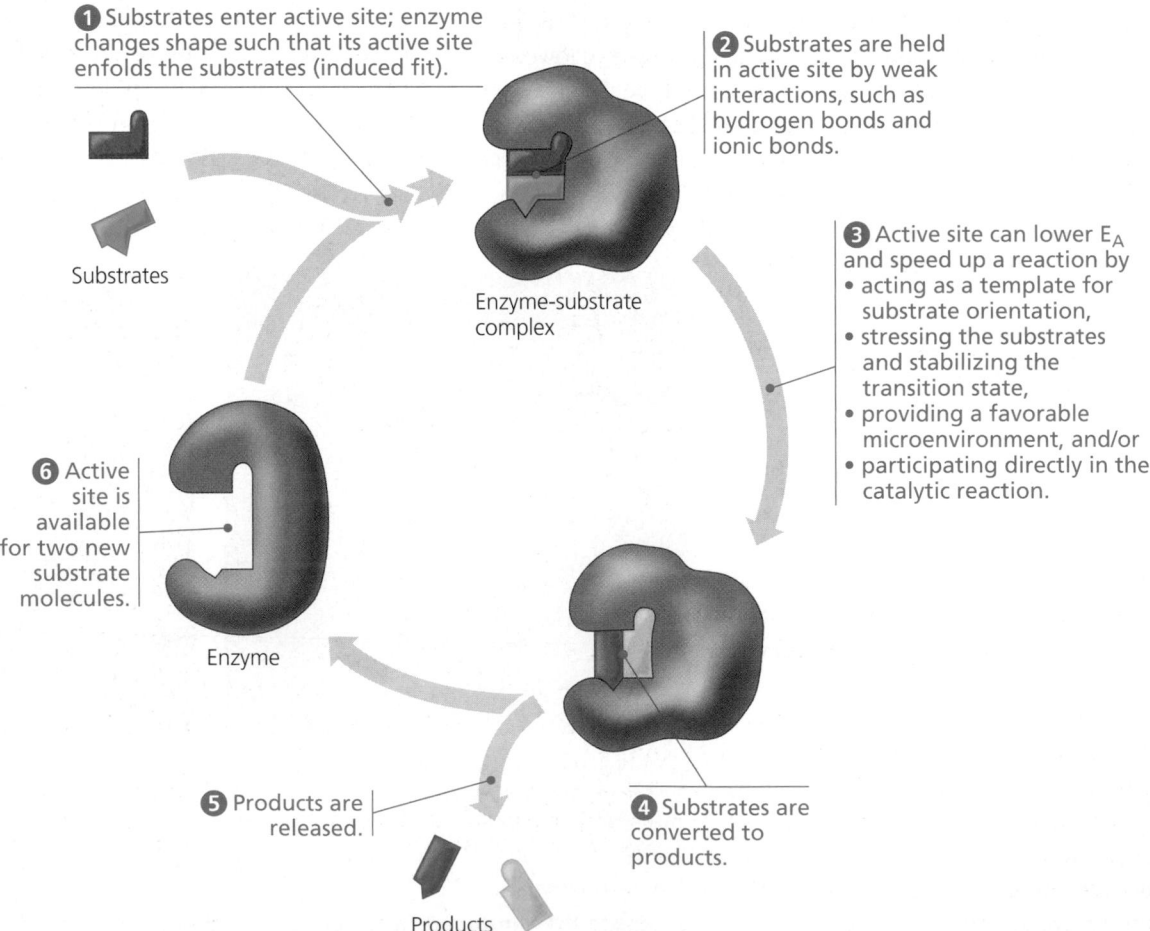

▶ **Figure 8.17 The active site and catalytic cycle of an enzyme.** An enzyme can convert one or more reactant molecules to one or more product molecules. The enzyme shown here converts two substrate molecules to two product molecules.

❶ Substrates enter active site; enzyme changes shape such that its active site enfolds the substrates (induced fit).

Substrates

❷ Substrates are held in active site by weak interactions, such as hydrogen bonds and ionic bonds.

Enzyme-substrate complex

❸ Active site can lower E_A and speed up a reaction by
• acting as a template for substrate orientation,
• stressing the substrates and stabilizing the transition state,
• providing a favorable microenvironment, and/or
• participating directly in the catalytic reaction.

❻ Active site is available for two new substrate molecules.

Enzyme

❺ Products are released.

❹ Substrates are converted to products.

Products

Third, the active site may also provide a microenvironment that is more conducive to a particular type of reaction than the solution itself would be without the enzyme. For example, if the active site has amino acids with acidic R groups, the active site may be a pocket of low pH in an otherwise neutral cell. In such cases, an acidic amino acid may facilitate H^+ transfer to the substrate as a key step in catalyzing the reaction.

A fourth mechanism of catalysis is the direct participation of the active site in the chemical reaction. Sometimes this process even involves brief covalent bonding between the substrate and an R group of an amino acid of the enzyme. Subsequent steps of the reaction restore the R groups to their original states, so that the active site is the same after the reaction as it was before.

The rate at which a particular amount of enzyme converts substrate to product is partly a function of the initial concentration of the substrate: The more substrate molecules that are available, the more frequently they access the active sites of the enzyme molecules. However, there is a limit to how fast the reaction can be pushed by adding more substrate to a fixed concentration of enzyme. At some point, the concentration of substrate will be high enough that all enzyme molecules have their active sites engaged. As soon as the product exits an active site, another substrate molecule enters. At this substrate concentration, the enzyme is said to be *saturated*, and the rate of the reaction is determined by the speed at which the active site converts substrate to product. When an enzyme population is saturated, the only way to increase the rate of product formation is to add more enzyme. Cells sometimes increase the rate of a reaction by producing more enzyme molecules.

Effects of Local Conditions on Enzyme Activity

The activity of an enzyme—how efficiently the enzyme functions—is affected by general environmental factors, such as temperature and pH. It can also be affected by chemicals that specifically influence that enzyme. In fact, researchers have learned much about enzyme function by employing such chemicals.

Effects of Temperature and pH

Recall from Chapter 5 that the three-dimensional structures of proteins are sensitive to their environment. As a consequence, each enzyme works better under some conditions than under others, because these *optimal conditions* favor the most active shape for the enzyme molecule.

Temperature and pH are environmental factors important in the activity of an enzyme. Up to a point, the rate of an enzymatic reaction increases with increasing temperature, partly because substrates collide with active sites more frequently when the molecules move rapidly. Above that temperature, however, the speed of the enzymatic reaction drops sharply.

The thermal agitation of the enzyme molecule disrupts the hydrogen bonds, ionic bonds, and other weak interactions that stabilize the active shape of the enzyme, and the protein molecule eventually denatures. Each enzyme has an optimal temperature at which its reaction rate is greatest. Without denaturing the enzyme, this temperature allows the greatest number of molecular collisions and the fastest conversion of the reactants to product molecules. Most human enzymes have optimal temperatures of about 35–40°C (close to human body temperature). The thermophilic bacteria that live in hot springs contain enzymes with optimal temperatures of 70°C or higher (**Figure 8.18a**).

Just as each enzyme has an optimal temperature, it also has a pH at which it is most active. The optimal pH values for most enzymes fall in the range of pH 6–8, but there are exceptions. For example, pepsin, a digestive enzyme in the human stomach, works best at pH 2. Such an acidic environment denatures most enzymes, but pepsin is adapted to maintain its functional three-dimensional structure in the acidic environment of the stomach. In contrast, trypsin, a digestive enzyme residing in the alkaline environment of the human intestine, has an optimal pH of 8 and would be denatured in the stomach (**Figure 8.18b**).

(a) Optimal temperature for two enzymes

(b) Optimal pH for two enzymes

▲ **Figure 8.18 Environmental factors affecting enzyme activity.** Each enzyme has an optimal **(a)** temperature and **(b)** pH that favor the most active shape of the protein molecule.
DRAW IT *Given that a mature lysosome has an internal pH of around 4.5, draw a curve in (b) showing what you would predict for a lysosomal enzyme, labeling its optimal pH.*

Cofactors

Many enzymes require nonprotein helpers for catalytic activity. These adjuncts, called **cofactors**, may be bound tightly to the enzyme as permanent residents, or they may bind loosely and reversibly along with the substrate. The cofactors of some enzymes are inorganic, such as the metal atoms zinc, iron, and copper in ionic form. If the cofactor is an organic molecule, it is more specifically called a **coenzyme**. Most vitamins are important in nutrition because they act as coenzymes or raw materials from which coenzymes are made. Cofactors function in various ways, but in all cases where they are used, they perform a crucial function in catalysis. You'll encounter examples of cofactors later in the book.

Enzyme Inhibitors

Certain chemicals selectively inhibit the action of specific enzymes, and we have learned a lot about enzyme function by studying the effects of these molecules. If the inhibitor attaches to the enzyme by covalent bonds, inhibition is usually irreversible.

Many enzyme inhibitors, however, bind to the enzyme by weak interactions, in which case inhibition is reversible. Some reversible inhibitors resemble the normal substrate molecule and compete for admission into the active site **(Figure 8.19a and b)**. These mimics, called **competitive inhibitors**, reduce the productivity of enzymes by blocking substrates from entering active sites. This kind of inhibition can be overcome by increasing the concentration of substrate so that as active sites become available, more substrate molecules than inhibitor molecules are around to gain entry to the sites.

In contrast, **noncompetitive inhibitors** do not directly compete with the substrate to bind to the enzyme at the active site **(Figure 8.19c)**. Instead, they impede enzymatic reactions by binding to another part of the enzyme. This interaction causes the enzyme molecule to change its shape in such a way that the active site becomes less effective at catalyzing the conversion of substrate to product.

Toxins and poisons are often irreversible enzyme inhibitors. An example is sarin, a nerve gas that caused the death of several people and injury to many others when it was released by terrorists in the Tokyo subway in 1995. This small molecule binds covalently to the R group on the amino acid serine, which is found in the active site of acetylcholinesterase, an enzyme important in the nervous system. Other examples include the pesticides DDT and parathion, inhibitors of key enzymes in the nervous system. Finally, many antibiotics are inhibitors of specific enzymes in bacteria. For instance, penicillin blocks the active site of an enzyme that many bacteria use to make their cell walls.

Citing enzyme inhibitors that are metabolic poisons may give the impression that enzyme inhibition is generally abnormal and harmful. In fact, molecules naturally present in the

A substrate can bind normally to the active site of an enzyme.

Substrate
Active site
Enzyme

(a) Normal binding

A competitive inhibitor mimics the substrate, competing for the active site.

Competitive inhibitor

(b) Competitive inhibition

A noncompetitive inhibitor binds to the enzyme away from the active site, altering the shape of the enzyme so that even if the substrate can bind, the active site functions less effectively.

Noncompetitive inhibitor

(c) Noncompetitive inhibition

▲ **Figure 8.19 Inhibition of enzyme activity.**

cell often regulate enzyme activity by acting as inhibitors. Such regulation—selective inhibition—is essential to the control of cellular metabolism, as we discuss next.

CONCEPT CHECK 8.4

1. Many spontaneous reactions occur very slowly. Why don't all spontaneous reactions occur instantly?
2. Why do enzymes act only on very specific substrates?
3. **WHAT IF?** Malonate is an inhibitor of the enzyme succinate dehydrogenase. How would you determine whether malonate is a competitive or noncompetitive inhibitor?

For suggested answers, see Appendix A.

Regulation of enzyme activity helps control metabolism

Chemical chaos would result if all of a cell's metabolic pathways were operating simultaneously. Intrinsic to the process of life is a cell's ability to tightly regulate its metabolic pathways by controlling when and where its various enzymes are active. It does this either by switching on and off the genes that encode specific enzymes (as we will discuss in Unit Three) or, as we discuss here, by regulating the activity of enzymes once they are made.

Allosteric Regulation of Enzymes

In many cases, the molecules that naturally regulate enzyme activity in a cell behave something like reversible noncompetitive inhibitors (see Figure 8.19c): These regulatory molecules change an enzyme's shape and the functioning of its active site by binding to a site elsewhere on the molecule, via noncovalent interactions. **Allosteric regulation** is the term used to describe any case in which a protein's function at one site is affected by the binding of a regulatory molecule to a separate site. It may result in either inhibition or stimulation of an enzyme's activity.

Allosteric Activation and Inhibition

Most enzymes known to be allosterically regulated are constructed from two or more subunits, each composed of a polypeptide chain and having its own active site (Figure 8.20). Each subunit has its own active site. The entire complex oscillates between two different shapes, one catalytically active and the other inactive (Figure 8.20a). In the simplest case of allosteric regulation, an activating or inhibiting regulatory molecule binds to a regulatory site (sometimes called an allosteric site), often located where subunits join. The binding of an *activator* to a regulatory site stabilizes the shape that has functional active sites, whereas the binding of an *inhibitor* stabilizes the inactive form of the enzyme. The subunits of an allosteric enzyme fit together in such a way that a shape change in one subunit is transmitted to all others. Through this interaction of subunits, a single activator or inhibitor molecule that binds to one regulatory site will affect the active sites of all subunits.

Fluctuating concentrations of regulators can cause a sophisticated pattern of response in the activity of cellular enzymes. The products of ATP hydrolysis (ADP and P_i), for example, play a complex role in balancing the flow of traffic between anabolic and catabolic pathways by their effects on key enzymes. ATP binds to several catabolic enzymes allosterically, lowering their affinity for substrate and thus inhibiting their activity. ADP, however, functions as an activator of the same enzymes. This is logical because a major function of catabolism is to regenerate ATP. If ATP production lags behind its use, ADP ac-

cumulates and activates the enzymes that speed up catabolism, producing more ATP. If the supply of ATP exceeds demand, then catabolism slows down as ATP molecules accumulate and bind these same enzymes, inhibiting them. (You'll see specific examples of this type of regulation when you learn about cellular respiration in the next chapter.) ATP, ADP, and other related

(a) **Allosteric activators and inhibitors.** In the cell, activators and inhibitors dissociate when at low concentrations. The enzyme can then oscillate again.

(b) **Cooperativity: another type of allosteric activation.** The inactive form shown on the left oscillates back and forth with the active form when the active form is not stabilized by substrate.

▲ Figure 8.20 **Allosteric regulation of enzyme activity.**

molecules also affect key enzymes in anabolic pathways. In this way, allosteric enzymes control the rates of key reactions in both sorts of metabolic pathways.

In another kind of allosteric activation, a *substrate* molecule binding to one active site may stimulate the catalytic powers of a multisubunit enzyme by affecting the other active sites **(Figure 8.20b)**. If an enzyme has two or more subunits, a substrate molecule causing induced fit in one subunit can trigger the same favorable shape change in all the other subunits of the enzyme. Called **cooperativity**, this mechanism amplifies the response of enzymes to substrates: One substrate molecule primes an enzyme to accept additional substrate molecules more readily.

The vertebrate oxygen transport protein hemoglobin is a classic example of cooperativity. Although hemoglobin is not an enzyme, the study of how cooperative binding works in this protein has elucidated the principle of cooperativity. Hemoglobin is made up of four subunits, each of which has an oxygen-binding site (see Figure 5.21). The binding of an oxygen molecule to each binding site increases the affinity for oxygen of the remaining binding sites. Thus, in oxygen-deprived tissues, hemoglobin will be less likely to bind oxygen and will release it where it is needed. Where oxygen is at higher levels, such as in the lungs or gills, the protein will have a greater affinity for oxygen as more binding sites are filled. An example of an enzyme that exhibits cooperativity is the first enzyme in the pathway for pyrimidine biosynthesis in bacteria (this enzyme is called aspartyl transcarbamoylase).

Identification of Allosteric Regulators

Although allosteric regulation is probably quite widespread, relatively few of the many known metabolic enzymes have been shown to be regulated in this way. Allosteric regulatory molecules are hard to characterize, in part because they tend to bind the enzyme at low affinity and are thus hard to isolate. Recently, however, pharmaceutical companies have turned their attention to allosteric regulators. These molecules are attractive drug candidates for enzyme regulation because they exhibit higher specificity for particular enzymes than do inhibitors that bind to the active site. (An active site may be similar to the active site in another, related enzyme, whereas allosteric regulatory sites appear to be quite distinct between enzymes.)

Figure 8.21 describes a search for allosteric regulators, carried out as a collaboration between researchers at the University of California at San Francisco and a company called Sunesis Pharmaceuticals. The study was designed to find allosteric inhibitors of *caspases*, protein-digesting enzymes that play an active role in inflammation and cell death. (You'll learn more about caspases and cell death in Chapter 11.) By specifically regulating these enzymes, we may be able to better manage inappropriate inflammatory responses, such as those commonly seen in vascular and neurodegenerative diseases.

▼ Figure 8.21 **Inquiry**

Are there allosteric inhibitors of caspase enzymes?

EXPERIMENT   In an effort to identify allosteric inhibitors of caspases, Justin Scheer and co-workers screened close to 8,000 compounds for their ability to bind to a possible allosteric binding site in caspase 1 and inhibit the enzyme's activity. Each compound was designed to form a disulfide bond with a cysteine near the site in order to stabilize the low-affinity interaction that is expected of an allosteric inhibitor. As the caspases are known to exist in both active and inactive forms, the researchers hypothesized that this linkage might lock the enzyme in the inactive form.

To test this model, X-ray diffraction analysis was used to determine the structure of caspase 1 when bound to one of the inhibitors and to compare it with the active and inactive structures.

RESULTS   Fourteen compounds were identified that could bind to the proposed allosteric site (red) of caspase 1 and block enzymatic activity. The enzyme's shape when one such inhibitor was bound resembled the inactive caspase 1 more than the active form.

Active form   **Allosterically inhibited form**   **Inactive form**

CONCLUSION   The inhibitory compound that was studied apparently locks the enzyme in its inactive form, as expected for a true allosteric regulator. The data therefore support the existence of an allosteric inhibitory site on caspase 1, which can be used to control enzymatic activity.

SOURCE   J. M. Scheer et al., A common allosteric site and mechanism in caspases, *PNAS* 103:7595–7600 (2006).

WHAT IF?   As a control, the researchers broke the disulfide linkage between one of the inhibitors and the caspase. Assuming that the experimental solution contains no other inhibitors, how would you expect the resulting caspase 1 activity to be affected?

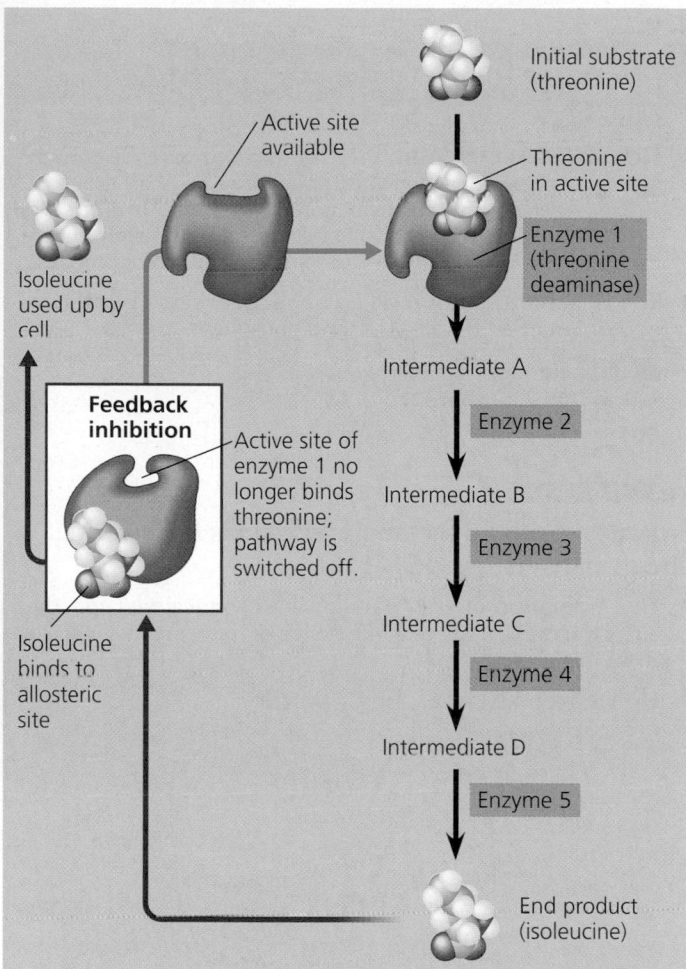

▲ **Figure 8.22 Feedback inhibition in isoleucine synthesis.**

Labels in figure 8.22:
- Initial substrate (threonine)
- Active site available
- Threonine in active site
- Enzyme 1 (threonine deaminase)
- Isoleucine used up by cell
- Intermediate A
- Feedback inhibition
- Enzyme 2
- Active site of enzyme 1 no longer binds threonine; pathway is switched off.
- Intermediate B
- Enzyme 3
- Isoleucine binds to allosteric site
- Intermediate C
- Enzyme 4
- Intermediate D
- Enzyme 5
- End product (isoleucine)

Feedback Inhibition

When ATP allosterically inhibits an enzyme in an ATP-generating pathway, as we discussed earlier, the result is feedback inhibition, a common method of metabolic control. In **feedback inhibition**, a metabolic pathway is switched off by the inhibitory binding of its end product to an enzyme that acts early in the pathway. **Figure 8.22** shows an example of this control mechanism operating on an anabolic pathway. Some cells use this five-step pathway to synthesize the amino acid isoleucine from threonine, another amino acid. As isoleucine accumulates, it slows down its own synthesis by allosterically inhibiting the enzyme for the first step of the pathway. Feedback inhibition thereby prevents the cell from wasting chemical resources by making more isoleucine than is necessary.

Specific Localization of Enzymes Within the Cell

The cell is not just a bag of chemicals with thousands of different kinds of enzymes and substrates in a random mix. The cell is compartmentalized, and cellular structures help bring order to metabolic pathways. In some cases, a team of enzymes for several steps of a metabolic pathway are assembled

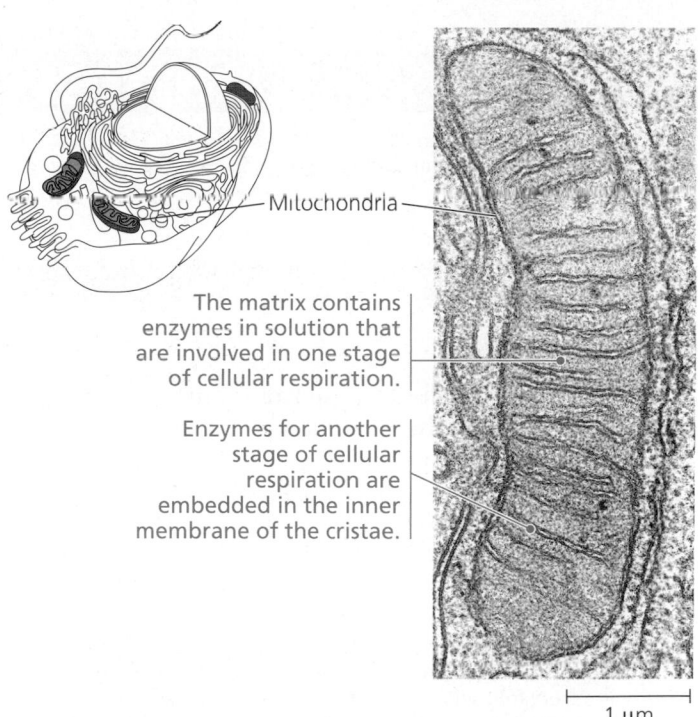

Labels in figure 8.23:
- Mitochondria
- The matrix contains enzymes in solution that are involved in one stage of cellular respiration.
- Enzymes for another stage of cellular respiration are embedded in the inner membrane of the cristae.
- 1 μm

▲ **Figure 8.23 Organelles and structural order in metabolism.** Organelles such as these mitochondria (TEM) contain enzymes that carry out specific functions, in this case cellular respiration.

into a multienzyme complex. The arrangement facilitates the sequence of reactions, with the product from the first enzyme becoming the substrate for an adjacent enzyme in the complex, and so on, until the end product is released. Some enzymes and enzyme complexes have fixed locations within the cell and act as structural components of particular membranes. Others are in solution within specific membrane-enclosed eukaryotic organelles, each with its own internal chemical environment. For example, in eukaryotic cells, the enzymes for cellular respiration reside in specific locations within mitochondria **(Figure 8.23)**.

In this chapter, you have learned that metabolism, the intersecting set of chemical pathways characteristic of life, is a choreographed interplay of thousands of different kinds of cellular molecules. In the next chapter, we explore cellular respiration, the major catabolic pathway that breaks down organic molecules, releasing energy for the crucial processes of life.

CONCEPT CHECK 8.5

1. How can an activator and an inhibitor have different effects on an allosterically regulated enzyme?
2. **WHAT IF?** Imagine you are a pharmacological researcher who wants to design a drug that inhibits a particular enzyme. Upon reading the scientific literature, you find that the enzyme's active site is similar to that of several other enzymes. What might be the best approach to developing your inhibitor drug?

For suggested answers, see Appendix A.

SUMMARY OF KEY CONCEPTS

CONCEPT 8.1

An organism's metabolism transforms matter and energy, subject to the laws of thermodynamics (pp. 142–145)

▶ **Organization of the Chemistry of Life into Metabolic Pathways** Metabolism is the collection of chemical reactions that occur in an organism. Aided by enzymes, it follows intersecting pathways, which may be catabolic (breaking down molecules, releasing energy) or anabolic (building molecules, consuming energy).

▶ **Forms of Energy** Energy is the capacity to cause change; some forms of energy do work by moving matter. Kinetic energy is associated with motion. Potential energy is related to the location or structure of matter and includes chemical energy possessed by a molecule due to its structure.

▶ **The Laws of Energy Transformation** The first law, conservation of energy, states that energy cannot be created or destroyed, only transferred or transformed. The second law states that spontaneous changes, those requiring no outside input of energy, increase the entropy (disorder) of the universe.

MEDIA
MP3 Tutor Basic Energy Concepts
Activity Energy Transformations

CONCEPT 8.2

The free-energy change of a reaction tells us whether or not the reaction occurs spontaneously (pp. 146–149)

▶ **Free-Energy Change, ΔG** A living system's free energy is energy that can do work under cellular conditions. The change in free energy (ΔG) during a biological process is related directly to enthalpy change (ΔH) and to the change in entropy (ΔS): $\Delta G = \Delta H - T\Delta S$.

▶ **Free Energy, Stability, and Equilibrium** Organisms live at the expense of free energy. During a spontaneous change, free energy decreases and the stability of a system increases. At maximum stability, the system is at equilibrium and can do no work.

▶ **Free Energy and Metabolism** In an exergonic (spontaneous) chemical reaction, the products have less free energy than the reactants ($-\Delta G$). Endergonic (nonspontaneous) reactions require an input of energy ($+\Delta G$). The addition of starting materials and the removal of end products prevent metabolism from reaching equilibrium.

CONCEPT 8.3

ATP powers cellular work by coupling exergonic reactions to endergonic reactions (pp. 149–151)

▶ **The Structure and Hydrolysis of ATP** ATP is the cell's energy shuttle. Hydrolysis at its terminal phosphate group produces ADP and phosphate and releases free energy.

▶ **How ATP Performs Work** ATP hydrolysis drives endergonic reactions by phosphorylation, the transfer of a phosphate group to specific reactants, making them more reactive. ATP hydrolysis (sometimes with protein phosphorylation) also causes changes in the shape and binding affinities of transport and motor proteins.

▶ **The Regeneration of ATP** Catabolic pathways drive the regeneration of ATP from ADP and phosphate.

MEDIA
Activity The Structure of ATP
Activity Chemical Reactions and ATP

CONCEPT 8.4

Enzymes speed up metabolic reactions by lowering energy barriers (pp. 151–156)

▶ **The Activation Energy Barrier** In a chemical reaction, the energy necessary to break the bonds of the reactants is the activation energy, E_A.

▶ **How Enzymes Lower the E_A Barrier**

▶ **Substrate Specificity of Enzymes** Each type of enzyme has a unique active site that combines specifically with its substrate, the reactant molecule on which it acts. The enzyme changes shape slightly when it binds the substrate (induced fit).

▶ **Catalysis in the Enzyme's Active Site** The active site can lower an E_A barrier by orienting substrates correctly, straining their bonds, providing a favorable microenvironment, and even covalently bonding with the substrate.

▶ **Effects of Local Conditions on Enzyme Activity** Each enzyme has an optimal temperature and pH. Inhibitors reduce enzyme function. A competitive inhibitor binds to the active site, while a noncompetitive inhibitor binds to a different site on the enzyme.

MEDIA
Activity How Enzymes Work
Investigation How Is the Rate of Enzyme Catalysis Measured?
Biology Labs On-Line EnzymeLab

CONCEPT 8.5

Regulation of enzyme activity helps control metabolism (pp. 157–159)

▶ **Allosteric Regulation of Enzymes** Many enzymes are allosterically regulated: Regulatory molecules, either activators or inhibitors, bind to specific regulatory sites, affecting the shape and function of the enzyme. In cooperativity, binding of one substrate molecule can stimulate binding or activity at other active sites. In feedback inhibition, the end product of a metabolic pathway allosterically inhibits the enzyme for a previous step in the pathway.

▶ **Specific Localization of Enzymes Within the Cell** Some enzymes are grouped into complexes, some are incorporated into membranes, and some are contained inside organelles, increasing the efficiency of metabolic processes.

TESTING YOUR KNOWLEDGE

SELF-QUIZ

1. Choose the pair of terms that correctly completes this sentence: Catabolism is to anabolism as _____ is to _____.
   a. exergonic; spontaneous
   b. exergonic; endergonic
   c. free energy; entropy
   d. work; energy
   e. entropy; enthalpy

2. Most cells cannot harness heat to perform work because
   a. heat is not a form of energy.
   b. cells do not have much heat; they are relatively cool.
   c. temperature is usually uniform throughout a cell.
   d. heat can never be used to do work.
   e. heat must remain constant during work.

3. Which of the following metabolic processes can occur without a net influx of energy from some other process?
   a. $ADP + \textcircled{P}_i \rightarrow ATP + H_2O$
   b. $C_6H_{12}O_6 + 6\,O_2 \rightarrow 6\,CO_2 + 6\,H_2O$
   c. $6\,CO_2 + 6\,H_2O \rightarrow C_6H_{12}O_6 + 6\,O_2$
   d. amino acids → protein
   e. glucose + fructose → sucrose

4. If an enzyme in solution is saturated with substrate, the most effective way to obtain a faster yield of products is to
   a. add more of the enzyme.
   b. heat the solution to 90°C.
   c. add more substrate.
   d. add an allosteric inhibitor.
   e. add a noncompetitive inhibitor.

5. If an enzyme is added to a solution where its substrate and product are in equilibrium, what would occur?
   a. Additional product would be formed.
   b. Additional substrate would be formed.
   c. The reaction would change from endergonic to exergonic.
   d. The free energy of the system would change.
   e. Nothing; the reaction would stay at equilibrium.

6. Some bacteria are metabolically active in hot springs because
   a. they are able to maintain a lower internal temperature.
   b. high temperatures make catalysis unnecessary.
   c. their enzymes have high optimal temperatures.
   d. their enzymes are completely insensitive to temperature.
   e. they use molecules other than proteins or RNAs as their main catalysts.

7. **DRAW IT** Using a series of arrows, draw the branched metabolic reaction pathway described by the following statements, and then answer the question at the end. Use red arrows and minus signs to indicate inhibition.
   L can form either M or N.
   M can form O.
   O can form either P or R.
   P can form Q.
   R can form S.
   O inhibits the reaction of L to form M.
   Q inhibits the reaction of O to form P.
   S inhibits the reaction of O to form R.

   Which reaction would prevail if both Q and S were present in the cell in high concentrations?
   a. L → M
   b. M → O
   c. L → N
   d. O → P
   e. R → S

For Self-Quiz answers, see Appendix A.

MEDIA Visit www.campbellbiology.com for a Practice Test.

EVOLUTION CONNECTION

8. A recent revival of the antievolutionary "intelligent design" argument holds that biochemical pathways are too complex to have evolved, because all intermediate steps in a given pathway must be present to produce the final product. Critique this argument. How could you use the diversity of metabolic pathways that produce the same or similar products to support your case?

SCIENTIFIC INQUIRY

9. **DRAW IT** A researcher has developed an assay to measure the activity of an important enzyme present in liver cells being grown in culture. She adds the enzyme's substrate to a dish of cells and then measures the appearance of reaction products. The results are graphed as the amount of product on the y-axis versus time on the x-axis. The researcher notes four sections of the graph. For a short period of time, no products appear (section A). Then (section B) the reaction rate is quite high (the slope of the line is steep). Next, the reaction gradually slows down (section C). Finally, the graph line becomes flat (section D). Draw and label the graph, and propose a model to explain the molecular events occurring at each stage of this reaction profile.

SCIENCE, TECHNOLOGY, AND SOCIETY

10. The EPA is evaluating the safety of the most commonly used organophosphate insecticides (organic compounds containing phosphate groups). Organophosphates typically interfere with nerve transmission by inhibiting the enzymes that degrade transmitter molecules diffusing from one neuron to another. Noxious insects are not uniquely susceptible; humans and other vertebrates can be affected as well. Thus, the use of organophosphate pesticides creates some health risks. As a consumer, what level of risk are you willing to accept in exchange for an abundant and affordable food supply?

Cellular Respiration
Harvesting Chemical Energy

9

KEY CONCEPTS

9.1 Catabolic pathways yield energy by oxidizing organic fuels

9.2 Glycolysis harvests chemical energy by oxidizing glucose to pyruvate

9.3 The citric acid cycle completes the energy-yielding oxidation of organic molecules

9.4 During oxidative phosphorylation, chemiosmosis couples electron transport to ATP synthesis

9.5 Fermentation and anaerobic respiration enable cells to produce ATP without the use of oxygen

9.6 Glycolysis and the citric acid cycle connect to many other metabolic pathways

OVERVIEW

Life Is Work

Living cells require transfusions of energy from outside sources to perform their many tasks—for example, assembling polymers, pumping substances across membranes, moving, and reproducing. The giant panda in **Figure 9.1** obtains energy for its cells by eating plants; some animals feed on other organisms that eat plants. The energy stored in the organic molecules of food ultimately comes from the sun. Energy flows into an ecosystem as sunlight and leaves as heat **(Figure 9.2)**. In contrast, the chemical elements essential to life are recycled. Photosynthesis generates oxygen and organic molecules used by the mitochondria of eukaryotes (including plants and algae) as fuel for cellular respiration. Respiration breaks this fuel down, generating ATP. The waste products of this type of respiration, carbon dioxide and water, are the raw materials for photosynthesis. In this chapter, we consider how cells harvest the chemical energy stored in organic molecules and use it to generate ATP, the molecule that drives most cellular work. After presenting some basics about respiration, we will focus on the three key pathways of respiration: glycolysis, the citric acid cycle, and oxidative phosphorylation.

▲ **Figure 9.2 Energy flow and chemical recycling in ecosystems.** Energy flows into an ecosystem as sunlight and ultimately leaves as heat, while the chemical elements essential to life are recycled.

CONCEPT 9.1
Catabolic pathways yield energy by oxidizing organic fuels

As you learned in Chapter 8, metabolic pathways that release stored energy by breaking down complex molecules are called catabolic pathways. Electron transfer plays a major role in these pathways. In this section, we consider these processes, which are central to cellular respiration.

Catabolic Pathways and Production of ATP

Organic compounds possess potential energy as a result of their arrangement of atoms. Compounds that can participate in exergonic reactions can act as fuels. With the help of enzymes, a cell systematically degrades complex organic molecules that are rich in potential energy to simpler waste products that have less energy. Some of the energy taken out of chemical storage can be used to do work; the rest is dissipated as heat.

One catabolic process, **fermentation**, is a partial degradation of sugars that occurs without the use of oxygen. However, the most prevalent and efficient catabolic pathway is **aerobic respiration**, in which oxygen is consumed as a reactant along with the organic fuel (*aerobic* is from the Greek *aer*, air, and *bios*, life). The cells of most eukaryotic and many prokaryotic organisms can carry out aerobic respiration. Some prokaryotes use substances other than oxygen as reactants in a similar process that harvests chemical energy without using any oxygen at all; this process is called *anaerobic respiration* (the prefix *an-* means "without"). Technically, the term **cellular respiration** includes both aerobic and anaerobic processes. However, it originated as a synonym for aerobic respiration because of the relationship of that process to organismal respiration, in which an animal breathes in oxygen. Thus, *cellular respiration* is often used to refer to the aerobic process, a practice we follow in most of this chapter.

Although very different in mechanism, aerobic respiration is in principle similar to the combustion of gasoline in an automobile engine after oxygen is mixed with the fuel (hydrocarbons). Food provides the fuel for respiration, and the exhaust is carbon dioxide and water. The overall process can be summarized as follows:

$$\text{Organic compounds} + \text{Oxygen} \longrightarrow \text{Carbon dioxide} + \text{Water} + \text{Energy}$$

Although carbohydrates, fats, and proteins can all be processed and consumed as fuel, it is helpful to learn the steps of cellular respiration by tracking the degradation of the sugar glucose ($C_6H_{12}O_6$):

$$C_6H_{12}O_6 + 6\,O_2 \longrightarrow 6\,CO_2 + 6\,H_2O + \text{Energy (ATP + heat)}$$

Glucose is the fuel that cells most often use; we will discuss other organic molecules contained in foods later in the chapter.

This breakdown of glucose is exergonic, having a free-energy change of −686 kcal (2,870 kJ) per mole of glucose decomposed ($\Delta G = -686$ kcal/mol). Recall that a negative ΔG indicates that the products of the chemical process store less energy than the reactants and that the reaction can happen spontaneously—in other words, without an input of energy.

Catabolic pathways do not directly move flagella, pump solutes across membranes, polymerize monomers, or perform other cellular work. Catabolism is linked to work by a chemical drive shaft—ATP, which you learned about in Chapter 8. To keep working, the cell must regenerate its supply of ATP from ADP and $\circledP_i$ (see Figure 8.12). To understand how cellular respiration accomplishes this, let's examine the fundamental chemical processes known as oxidation and reduction.

Redox Reactions: Oxidation and Reduction

How do the catabolic pathways that decompose glucose and other organic fuels yield energy? The answer is based on the transfer of electrons during the chemical reactions. The relocation of electrons releases energy stored in organic molecules, and this energy ultimately is used to synthesize ATP.

The Principle of Redox

In many chemical reactions, there is a transfer of one or more electrons (e^-) from one reactant to another. These electron transfers are called oxidation-reduction reactions, or **redox reactions** for short. In a redox reaction, the loss of electrons from one substance is called **oxidation**, and the addition of electrons to another substance is known as **reduction**. (Note that *adding* electrons is called *reduction*; negatively charged electrons added to an atom *reduce* the amount of positive charge of that atom.) To take a simple, nonbiological example, consider the reaction between the elements sodium (Na) and chlorine (Cl) that forms table salt:

$$\overset{\overbrace{\text{becomes oxidized}}^{\text{(loses electron)}}}{\text{Na}} \quad + \quad \text{Cl} \quad \longrightarrow \quad \underset{\underbrace{\text{becomes reduced}}_{\text{(gains electron)}}}{\text{Na}^+ \quad + \quad \text{Cl}^-}$$

We could generalize a redox reaction this way:

$$\overset{\overbrace{\text{becomes oxidized}}}{Xe^-} \quad + \quad Y \quad \longrightarrow \quad \underset{\underbrace{\text{becomes reduced}}}{X \quad + \quad Ye^-}$$

In the generalized reaction, substance Xe^-, the electron donor, is called the **reducing agent**; it reduces Y, which accepts the donated electron. Substance Y, the electron acceptor, is the **oxidizing agent**; it oxidizes Xe^- by removing its electron. Because an electron transfer requires both a donor and an acceptor, oxidation and reduction always go together.

Not all redox reactions involve the complete transfer of electrons from one substance to another; some change the degree of electron sharing in covalent bonds. The reaction between methane and oxygen, shown in **Figure 9.3** on the next page, is an example. As explained in Chapter 2, the covalent electrons in methane are shared nearly equally between the bonded atoms because carbon and hydrogen have about the same affinity for valence electrons; they are about equally electronegative. But when methane reacts with oxygen, forming carbon dioxide, electrons end up shared less equally between the carbon atom and its new covalent partners, the oxygen atoms, which are very electronegative. In effect, the carbon atom has partially "lost" its shared electrons; thus, methane has been oxidized.

▲ Figure 9.3 Methane combustion as an energy-yielding redox reaction. The reaction releases energy to the surroundings because the electrons lose potential energy when they end up being shared unequally, spending more time near electronegative atoms such as oxygen.

Now let's examine the fate of the reactant O_2. The two atoms of the oxygen molecule (O_2) share their electrons equally. But when oxygen reacts with the hydrogen from methane, forming water, the electrons of the covalent bonds spend more time near the oxygen (see Figure 9.3). In effect, each oxygen atom has partially "gained" electrons, so the oxygen molecule has been reduced. Because oxygen is so electronegative, it is one of the most potent of all oxidizing agents.

Energy must be added to pull an electron away from an atom, just as energy is required to push a ball uphill. The more electronegative the atom (the stronger its pull on electrons), the more energy is required to take an electron away from it. An electron loses potential energy when it shifts from a less electronegative atom toward a more electronegative one, just as a ball loses potential energy when it rolls downhill. A redox reaction that moves electrons closer to oxygen, such as the burning (oxidation) of methane, therefore releases chemical energy that can be put to work.

Oxidation of Organic Fuel Molecules During Cellular Respiration

The oxidation of methane by oxygen is the main combustion reaction that occurs at the burner of a gas stove. The combustion of gasoline in an automobile engine is also a redox reaction; the energy released pushes the pistons. But the energy-yielding redox process of greatest interest to biologists is respiration: the oxidation of glucose and other molecules in food. Examine again the summary equation for cellular respiration, but this time think of it as a redox process:

$$\overbrace{C_6H_{12}O_6 \;+\; 6\,O_2}^{\text{becomes oxidized}} \longrightarrow 6\,CO_2 \;+\; 6\,H_2O \;+\; \text{Energy}$$

As in the combustion of methane or gasoline, the fuel (glucose) is oxidized and oxygen is reduced. The electrons lose potential energy along the way, and energy is released.

In general, organic molecules that have an abundance of hydrogen are excellent fuels because their bonds are a source of "hilltop" electrons, whose energy may be released as these electrons "fall" down an energy gradient when they are transferred to oxygen. The summary equation for respiration indicates that hydrogen is transferred from glucose to oxygen. But the important point, not visible in the summary equation, is that the energy state of the electron changes as hydrogen (with its electron) is transferred to oxygen. In respiration, the oxidation of glucose transfers electrons to a lower energy state, liberating energy that becomes available for ATP synthesis.

The main energy foods, carbohydrates and fats, are reservoirs of electrons associated with hydrogen. Only the barrier of activation energy holds back the flood of electrons to a lower energy state (see Figure 8.14). Without this barrier, a food substance like glucose would combine almost instantaneously with O_2. When we supply the activation energy by igniting glucose, it burns in air, releasing 686 kcal (2,870 kJ) of heat per mole of glucose (about 180 g). Body temperature is not high enough to initiate burning, of course. Instead, if you swallow some glucose, enzymes in your cells will lower the barrier of activation energy, allowing the sugar to be oxidized in a series of steps.

Stepwise Energy Harvest via NAD^+ and the Electron Transport Chain

If energy is released from a fuel all at once, it cannot be harnessed efficiently for constructive work. For example, if a gasoline tank explodes, it cannot drive a car very far. Cellular respiration does not oxidize glucose in a single explosive step either. Rather, glucose and other organic fuels are broken down in a series of steps, each one catalyzed by an enzyme. At key steps, electrons are stripped from the glucose. As is often the case in oxidation reactions, each electron travels with a proton—thus, as a hydrogen atom. The hydrogen atoms are not transferred directly to oxygen, but instead are usually passed first to an electron carrier, a coenzyme called **NAD^+** (nicotinamide adenine dinucleotide, a derivative of the vitamin niacin). As an electron acceptor, NAD^+ functions as an oxidizing agent during respiration.

How does NAD^+ trap electrons from glucose and other organic molecules? Enzymes called dehydrogenases remove a pair of hydrogen atoms (2 electrons and 2 protons) from the substrate (glucose, in this example), thereby oxidizing it. The enzyme delivers the 2 electrons along with 1 proton to its coenzyme, NAD^+ **(Figure 9.4)**. The other proton is released as a hydrogen ion (H^+) into the surrounding solution:

$$H{-}\overset{|}{\underset{|}{C}}{-}OH + NAD^+ \xrightarrow{\text{Dehydrogenase}} \overset{|}{C}{=}O + NADH + H^+$$

By receiving 2 negatively charged electrons but only 1 positively charged proton, NAD^+ has its charge neutralized when it is reduced to NADH. The name NADH shows the hydrogen that has been received in the reaction. NAD^+ is the most versatile electron

NAD⁺

Nicotinamide
(oxidized form)

2 e⁻ + 2 H⁺

2 e⁻ + H⁺

Dehydrogenase

Reduction of NAD⁺

Oxidation of NADH

+ 2[H]
(from food)

NADH

H⁺

Nicotinamide
(reduced form)

+ H⁺

▲ **Figure 9.4 NAD⁺ as an electron shuttle.** The full name for NAD⁺, nicotinamide adenine dinucleotide, describes its structure: the molecule consists of two nucleotides joined together at their phosphate groups (shown in yellow). (Nicotinamide is a nitrogenous base, although not one that is present in DNA or RNA.) The enzymatic transfer of 2 electrons and 1 proton (H⁺) from an organic molecule in food to NAD⁺ reduces the NAD⁺ to NADH; the second proton (H⁺) is released. Most of the electrons removed from food are transferred initially to NAD⁺.

acceptor in cellular respiration and functions in several of the redox steps during the breakdown of glucose.

Electrons lose very little of their potential energy when they are transferred from glucose to NAD⁺. Each NADH molecule formed during respiration represents stored energy that can be tapped to make ATP when the electrons complete their "fall" down an energy gradient from NADH to oxygen.

How do electrons that are extracted from glucose and stored as potential energy in NADH finally reach oxygen? It will help to compare the redox chemistry of cellular respiration to a much simpler reaction: the reaction between hydrogen and oxygen to form water (**Figure 9.5a**). Mix H_2 and O_2, provide a spark for activation energy, and the gases combine explosively. In fact, combustion of liquid H_2 and O_2 is harnessed to power the main engines of the space shuttle after it is launched, boosting it into orbit. The explosion represents a release of energy as the electrons of hydrogen "fall" closer to the electronegative oxygen atoms. Cellular respiration also brings hydrogen and oxygen together to form water, but there are two important differences. First, in cellular respiration, the hydrogen that reacts with oxygen is derived from organic molecules rather than H_2. Second, instead of occurring in one explosive reaction, respiration uses an **electron transport chain** to break the fall of electrons to oxygen into several energy-releasing steps (**Figure 9.5b**). An electron transport chain consists of a number of

molecules, mostly proteins, built into the inner membrane of mitochondria of eukaryotic cells and the plasma membrane of aerobically respiring prokaryotes. Electrons removed from glucose are shuttled by NADH to the "top," higher-energy end of the chain. At the "bottom," lower-energy end, O_2 captures these electrons along with hydrogen nuclei (H⁺), forming water.

Electron transfer from NADH to oxygen is an exergonic reaction with a free-energy change of −53 kcal/mol (−222 kJ/mol). Instead of this energy being released and wasted in a single explosive step, electrons cascade down the chain from

(a) Uncontrolled reaction

$H_2 + \frac{1}{2} O_2$

Free energy, G

Explosive release of heat and light energy

H_2O

(b) Cellular respiration

2 H + $\frac{1}{2} O_2$
(from food via NADH)

Free energy, G

2 H⁺ + 2 e⁻

Controlled release of energy for synthesis of ATP

Electron transport chain

ATP
ATP
ATP

2 e⁻

$\frac{1}{2} O_2$

2 H⁺

H_2O

▲ **Figure 9.5 An introduction to electron transport chains. (a)** The one-step exergonic reaction of hydrogen with oxygen to form water releases a large amount of energy in the form of heat and light: an explosion. **(b)** In cellular respiration, the same reaction occurs in stages: An electron transport chain breaks the "fall" of electrons in this reaction into a series of smaller steps and stores some of the released energy in a form that can be used to make ATP. (The rest of the energy is released as heat.)

one carrier molecule to the next in a series of redox reactions, losing a small amount of energy with each step until they finally reach oxygen, the terminal electron acceptor, which has a very great affinity for electrons. Each "downhill" carrier is more electronegative than, and thus capable of oxidizing, its "uphill" neighbor, with oxygen at the bottom of the chain. Therefore, the electrons removed from glucose by NAD^+ fall down an energy gradient in the electron transport chain to a far more stable location in the electronegative oxygen atom. Put another way, oxygen pulls electrons down the chain in an energy-yielding tumble analogous to gravity pulling objects downhill.

In summary, during cellular respiration, most electrons travel the following "downhill" route: glucose → NADH → electron transport chain → oxygen. Later in this chapter, you will learn more about how the cell uses the energy released from this exergonic electron fall to regenerate its supply of ATP. For now, having covered the basic redox mechanisms of cellular respiration, let's look at the entire process.

The Stages of Cellular Respiration: *A Preview*

Respiration is a cumulative function of three metabolic stages:
1. **Glycolysis (color-coded teal throughout the chapter)**
2. **The citric acid cycle (color-coded salmon)**
3. **Oxidative phosphorylation: electron transport and chemiosmosis (color-coded violet)**

Cellular respiration is sometimes defined as including only the citric acid cycle and oxidative phosphorylation. We include glycolysis, however, because most respiring cells deriving energy from glucose use this process to produce starting material for the citric acid cycle.

As diagrammed in **Figure 9.6**, the first two stages of cellular respiration, glycolysis and the citric acid cycle, are the catabolic pathways that break down glucose and other organic fuels. **Glycolysis**, which occurs in the cytosol, begins the degradation process by breaking glucose into two molecules of a compound called pyruvate. The **citric acid cycle**, which takes place within the mitochondrial matrix of eukaryotic cells or simply in the cytosol of prokaryotes, completes the breakdown of glucose by oxidizing a derivative of pyruvate to carbon dioxide. Thus, the carbon dioxide produced by respiration represents fragments of oxidized organic molecules.

Some of the steps of glycolysis and the citric acid cycle are redox reactions in which dehydrogenases transfer electrons from substrates to NAD^+, forming NADH. In the third stage of respiration, the electron transport chain accepts electrons from the breakdown products of the first two stages (most often via NADH) and passes these electrons from one molecule to another. At the end of the chain, the electrons are combined with molecular oxygen and hydrogen ions (H^+), forming water (see Figure 9.5b). The energy released at each step of the chain is stored in a form the mitochondrion (or prokaryotic cell) can use to make ATP. This mode of ATP synthesis is called **oxidative phosphorylation** because it is powered by the redox reactions of the electron transport chain.

In eukaryotic cells, the inner membrane of the mitochondrion is the site of electron transport and chemiosmosis, the processes that together constitute oxidative phosphorylation. In prokaryotes, these processes take place in the plasma membrane. Oxidative phosphorylation accounts for almost 90% of the ATP generated by respiration. A smaller amount of ATP is formed directly in a few reactions of glycolysis and the citric acid cycle by a mechanism called **substrate-level phosphorylation** (**Figure 9.7**). This mode of ATP synthesis occurs when an enzyme transfers a phosphate group from a substrate molecule to ADP, rather than adding an inorganic phosphate to ADP as in oxidative phosphorylation.

▶ **Figure 9.6 An overview of cellular respiration.** During glycolysis, each glucose molecule is broken down into two molecules of the compound pyruvate. In eukaryotic cells, as shown here, the pyruvate enters the mitochondrion, where the citric acid cycle oxidizes it to carbon dioxide. NADH and a similar electron carrier, a coenzyme called FADH₂, transfer electrons derived from glucose to electron transport chains, which are built into the inner mitochondrial membrane. (In prokaryotes, the electron transport chains are located in the plasma membrane.) During oxidative phosphorylation, electron transport chains convert the chemical energy to a form used for ATP synthesis in the process called chemiosmosis.

▲ **Figure 9.7 Substrate-level phosphorylation.** Some ATP is made by direct transfer of a phosphate group from an organic substrate to ADP by an enzyme. (For examples in glycolysis, see Figure 9.9, steps 7 and 10.)

? *Do you think the potential energy is higher for the reactants or the products? Explain.*

"Substrate molecule" here refers to an organic molecule generated as an intermediate during the catabolism of glucose.

For each molecule of glucose degraded to carbon dioxide and water by respiration, the cell makes up to about 38 molecules of ATP, each with 7.3 kcal/mol of free energy. Respiration cashes in the large denomination of energy banked in a single molecule of glucose (686 kcal/mol) for the small change of many molecules of ATP, which is more practical for the cell to spend on its work.

This preview has introduced you to how glycolysis, the citric acid cycle, and oxidative phosphorylation fit into the process of cellular respiration. We are now ready to take a closer look at each of these three stages of respiration.

CONCEPT CHECK 9.1

1. Compare and contrast aerobic and anaerobic respiration.
2. **WHAT IF?** If the following redox reaction occurred, which compound would be oxidized and which reduced?

$$C_4H_6O_5 + NAD^+ \longrightarrow C_4H_4O_5 + NADH + H^+$$

For suggested answers, see Appendix A.

CONCEPT 9.2

Glycolysis harvests chemical energy by oxidizing glucose to pyruvate

The word *glycolysis* means "sugar splitting," and that is exactly what happens during this pathway. Glucose, a six-carbon sugar, is split into two three-carbon sugars. These smaller sugars are then oxidized and their remaining atoms rearranged to form two molecules of pyruvate. (Pyruvate is the ionized form of pyruvic acid.)

As summarized in **Figure 9.8**, glycolysis can be divided into two phases: energy investment and energy payoff. During the energy investment phase, the cell actually spends ATP. This investment is repaid with interest during the energy payoff phase, when ATP is produced by substrate-level phosphorylation and NAD$^+$ is reduced to NADH by electrons released

Energy investment phase

Energy payoff phase

Net

▲ **Figure 9.8 The energy input and output of glycolysis.**

from the oxidation of glucose. The net energy yield from glycolysis, per glucose molecule, is 2 ATP plus 2 NADH. The ten steps of the glycolytic pathway are described in more detail in **Figure 9.9**, on the next two pages, which you should study carefully before continuing.

In the end, all of the carbon originally present in glucose is accounted for in the two molecules of pyruvate; no CO_2 is released during glycolysis. Glycolysis occurs whether or not O_2 is present. However, if O_2 *is* present, the chemical energy stored in pyruvate and NADH can be extracted by the citric acid cycle and oxidative phosphorylation.

CONCEPT CHECK 9.2

1. During the redox reaction in glycolysis (step 6 in Figure 9.9), which molecule acts as the oxidizing agent? The reducing agent?
2. **WHAT IF?** Step 3 in Figure 9.9 is a major point of regulation of glycolysis. The enzyme phosphofructokinase is allosterically regulated by ATP and related molecules. Considering the overall result of glycolysis, would you expect ATP to inhibit or stimulate activity of this enzyme? (*Hint:* Make sure you consider the role of ATP as an allosteric regulator, not as a substrate of the enzyme.)

For suggested answers, see Appendix A.

Glucose

CH₂OH
H
H
OH
H
HO
OH
H
H
OH

ATP
❶
Hexokinase
ADP

Glucose-6-phosphate

CH₂O—Ⓟ
H
H
OH
H
HO
OH
H
H
OH

❷
Phosphoglucoisomerase

Fructose-6-phosphate

CH₂O—Ⓟ
CH₂OH
H
HO
H
OH
HO
H

ATP
❸
Phosphofructokinase
ADP

Fructose-1, 6-bisphosphate

Ⓟ—O—CH₂
CH₂—O—Ⓟ
H
HO
OH
HO
H

❹
Aldolase

❺
Isomerase

Dihydroxyacetone phosphate

Ⓟ—O—CH₂
C=O
CH₂OH

Glyceraldehyde-3-phosphate

H—C=O
CHOH
CH₂—O—Ⓟ

▼ **Figure 9.9 A closer look at glycolysis.** The orientation diagram at the right relates glycolysis to the entire process of respiration. Do not let the chemical detail in the main diagram block your view of glycolysis as a source of ATP and NADH.

ENERGY INVESTMENT PHASE

❶ Glucose enters the cell and is phosphorylated by the enzyme hexokinase, which transfers a phosphate group from ATP to the sugar. The charge of the phosphate group traps the sugar in the cell because the plasma membrane is impermeable to large ions. Phosphorylation also makes glucose more chemically reactive. In this diagram, the transfer of a phosphate group or pair of electrons from one reactant to another is indicated by coupled arrows: ⤵

❷ Glucose-6-phosphate is converted to its isomer, fructose-6-phosphate.

❸ This enzyme transfers a phosphate group from ATP to the sugar, investing another molecule of ATP in glycolysis. So far, 2 ATP have been used. With phosphate groups on its opposite ends, the sugar is now ready to be split in half. This is a key step for regulation of glycolysis; phosphofructokinase is allosterically regulated by ATP and its products.

❹ This is the reaction from which glycolysis gets its name. The enzyme cleaves the sugar molecule into two different three-carbon sugars: dihydroxyacetone phosphate and glyceraldehyde-3-phosphate. These two sugars are isomers of each other.

❺ Isomerase catalyzes the reversible conversion between the two three-carbon sugars. This reaction never reaches equilibrium in the cell because the next enzyme in glycolysis uses only glyceraldehyde-3-phosphate as its substrate (and not dihydroxyacetone phosphate). This pulls the equilibrium in the direction of glyceraldehyde-3-phosphate, which is removed as fast as it forms. Thus, the net result of steps 4 and 5 is cleavage of a six-carbon sugar into two molecules of glyceraldehyde-3-phosphate; each will progress through the remaining steps of glycolysis.

WHAT IF? *What would happen if you removed dihydroxyacetone phosphate as fast as it was produced?*

2 NAD⁺

6 Triose phosphate dehydrogenase

2 NADH + 2 H⁺

2 Pᵢ

P—O—C=O
|
CHOH
|
CH₂—O—P

2 **1, 3-Bisphosphoglycerate**

2 ADP

7 Phosphoglycerokinase

2 ATP

O⁻
|
C=O
|
CHOH
|
CH₂—O—P

2 **3-Phosphoglycerate**

8 Phosphoglyceromutase

O⁻
|
C=O
|
H—C—O—P
|
CH₂OH

2 **2-Phosphoglycerate**

2 H₂O

9 Enolase

O⁻
|
C=O
|
C—O—P
‖
CH₂

2 **Phosphoenolpyruvate**

2 ADP

10 Pyruvate kinase

2 ATP

O⁻
|
C=O
|
C=O
|
CH₃

2 **Pyruvate**

ENERGY PAYOFF PHASE

6 This enzyme catalyzes two sequential reactions while it holds glyceraldehyde-3-phosphate in its active site. First, the sugar is oxidized by the transfer of electrons and H⁺ to NAD⁺, forming NADH (a redox reaction). This reaction is very exergonic, and the enzyme uses the released energy to attach a phosphate group to the oxidized substrate, making a product of very high potential energy. The source of the phosphates is the pool of inorganic phosphate ions that are always present in the cytosol. Notice that the coefficient 2 precedes all molecules in the energy payoff phase; these steps occur after glucose has been split into two three-carbon sugars (step 4).

7 Glycolysis produces some ATP by substrate-level phosphorylation. The phosphate group added in the previous step is transferred to ADP in an exergonic reaction. For each glucose molecule that began glycolysis, step 7 produces 2 ATP, since every product after the sugar-splitting step (step 4) is doubled. Recall that 2 ATP were invested to get sugar ready for splitting; this ATP debt has now been repaid. Glucose has been converted to two molecules of 3-phosphoglycerate, which is not a sugar. The carbonyl group that characterizes a sugar has been oxidized to a carboxyl group (— COO⁻), the hallmark of an organic acid. The sugar was oxidized in step 6, and now the energy made available by that oxidation has been used to make ATP.

8 This enzyme relocates the remaining phosphate group, preparing the substrate for the next reaction.

9 This enzyme causes a double bond to form in the substrate by extracting a water molecule, yielding phosphoenolpyruvate (PEP). The electrons of the substrate are rearranged in such a way that the resulting phosphorylated compound has a very high potential energy, allowing step 10 to occur.

10 The last reaction of glycolysis produces more ATP by transferring the phosphate group from PEP to ADP, a second instance of substrate-level phosphorylation. Since this step occurs twice for each glucose molecule, 2 ATP are produced. Overall, glycolysis has used 2 ATP in the energy investment phase (steps 1 and 3) and produced 4 ATP in the energy payoff phase (steps 7 and 10), for a net gain of 2 ATP. Glycolysis has repaid the ATP investment with 100% interest. Additional energy was stored by step 6 in NADH, which can be used to make ATP by oxidative phosphorylation if oxygen is present. Glucose has been broken down and oxidized to two molecules of pyruvate, the end product of the glycolytic pathway. If oxygen is present, the chemical energy in pyruvate can be extracted by the citric acid cycle. If oxygen is not present, fermentation may occur; this will be described later.

CONCEPT 9.3

The citric acid cycle completes the energy-yielding oxidation of organic molecules

Glycolysis releases less than a quarter of the chemical energy stored in glucose; most of the energy remains stockpiled in the two molecules of pyruvate. If molecular oxygen is present, the pyruvate enters a mitochondrion (in eukaryotic cells), where the enzymes of the citric acid cycle complete the oxidation of glucose. (In prokaryotic cells, this process occurs in the cytosol.)

Upon entering the mitochondrion via active transport, pyruvate is first converted to a compound called acetyl coenzyme A, or **acetyl CoA (Figure 9.10)**. This step, the junction between glycolysis and the citric acid cycle, is accomplished by a multi-enzyme complex that catalyzes three reactions: ❶ Pyruvate's carboxyl group ($-COO^-$), which is already fully oxidized and thus has little chemical energy, is removed and given off as a molecule of CO_2. (This is the first step in which CO_2 is released during respiration.) ❷ The remaining two-carbon fragment is oxidized, forming a compound named acetate (the ionized form of acetic acid). An enzyme transfers the extracted electrons to NAD^+, storing energy in the form of NADH. ❸ Finally, coenzyme A (CoA), a sulfur-containing compound derived from a B vitamin, is attached to the acetate by an unstable bond (the wavy line in Figure 9.10) that makes the acetyl group (the attached acetate) very reactive. Because of the chemical nature of the CoA group, the product of this chemical grooming, acetyl CoA, has a high potential energy; in other words, the reaction of acetyl CoA to yield lower-energy products is highly exergonic. This molecule is now ready to feed its acetyl group into the citric acid cycle for further oxidation.

The citric acid cycle is also called the tricarboxylic acid cycle or the Krebs cycle, the latter honoring Hans Krebs, the German-British scientist who was largely responsible for working out the pathway in the 1930s. The cycle functions as a metabolic furnace that oxidizes organic fuel derived from pyruvate. **Figure 9.11** summarizes the inputs and outputs as pyruvate is broken down to three CO_2 molecules, including the molecule of CO_2 released during the conversion of pyruvate to acetyl CoA. The cycle generates 1 ATP per turn by substrate-level phosphorylation, but most of the chemical energy is transferred to NAD^+ and a related electron carrier, the coenzyme FAD (flavin adenine dinucleotide, derived from riboflavin, a B vitamin), during the redox reactions. The reduced coenzymes, NADH and $FADH_2$, shuttle their cargo of high-energy electrons to the electron transport chain.

Now let's look at the citric acid cycle in more detail. The cycle has eight steps, each catalyzed by a specific enzyme. You can see in **Figure 9.12** that for each turn of the citric acid cycle, two

▲ **Figure 9.11 An overview of the citric acid cycle.** To calculate the inputs and outputs on a per-glucose basis, multiply by 2, because each glucose molecule is split during glycolysis into two pyruvate molecules.

▲ **Figure 9.10 Conversion of pyruvate to acetyl CoA, the junction between glycolysis and the citric acid cycle.** Pyruvate is a charged molecule, so in eukaryotic cells it must enter the mitochondrion via active transport, with the help of a transport protein. Next, a complex of several enzymes (the pyruvate dehydrogenase complex) catalyzes the three numbered steps, which are described in the text. The acetyl group of acetyl CoA will enter the citric acid cycle. The CO_2 molecule will diffuse out of the cell.

① Acetyl CoA adds its two-carbon acetyl group to oxaloacetate, producing citrate.

② Citrate is converted to its isomer, isocitrate, by removal of one water molecule and addition of another.

③ Isocitrate is oxidized, reducing NAD⁺ to NADH. Then the resulting compound loses a CO_2 molecule.

④ Another CO_2 is lost, and the resulting compound is oxidized, reducing NAD⁺ to NADH. The remaining molecule is then attached to coenzyme A by an unstable bond.

⑤ CoA is displaced by a phosphate group, which is transferred to GDP, forming GTP, a molecule with functions similar to ATP that, in some cases, is used to generate ATP.

⑥ Two hydrogens are transferred to FAD, forming FADH₂ and oxidizing succinate.

⑦ Addition of a water molecule rearranges bonds in the substrate.

⑧ The substrate is oxidized, reducing NAD⁺ to NADH and regenerating oxaloacetate.

Citric acid cycle

Glycolysis — Citric acid cycle — Oxidative phosphorylation

Acetyl CoA
Oxaloacetate
Citrate
Isocitrate
α-Ketoglutarate
Succinyl CoA
Succinate
Fumarate
Malate

▲ **Figure 9.12 A closer look at the citric acid cycle.** In the chemical structures, red type traces the fate of the two carbon atoms that enter the cycle via acetyl CoA (step 1), and blue type indicates the two carbons that exit the cycle as CO_2 in steps 3 and 4. (The red labeling goes only through step 5 because the succinate molecule is symmetrical; the two ends cannot be distinguished from each other.) Notice that the carbon atoms that enter the cycle from acetyl CoA do not leave the cycle in the same turn. They remain in the cycle, occupying a different location in the molecules on their next turn, after another acetyl group is added. As a consequence, the oxaloacetate that is regenerated at step 8 is composed of different carbon atoms each time around. In eukaryotic cells, all the citric acid cycle enzymes are located in the mitochondrial matrix except for the enzyme that catalyzes step 6, which resides in the inner mitochondrial membrane. Carboxylic acids are represented in their ionized forms, as —COO⁻, because the ionized forms prevail at the pH within the mitochondrion. For example, citrate is the ionized form of citric acid.

carbons (red) enter in the relatively reduced form of an acetyl group (step 1), and two different carbons (blue) leave in the completely oxidized form of CO_2 molecules (steps 3 and 4). The acetyl group of acetyl CoA joins the cycle by combining with the compound oxaloacetate, forming citrate (step 1). (Citrate is the ionized form of citric acid, for which the cycle is named.) The next seven steps decompose the citrate back to oxaloacetate. It is this regeneration of oxaloacetate that makes this process a *cycle*.

Now let's tally the energy-rich molecules produced by the citric acid cycle. For each acetyl group entering the cycle, 3 NAD^+ are reduced to NADH (steps 3, 4, and 8). In step 6, electrons are transferred not to NAD^+, but to FAD, which accepts 2 electrons and 2 protons to become $FADH_2$. In many animal tissue cells, step 5 produces a guanosine triphosphate (GTP) molecule by substrate-level phosphorylation as shown in Figure 9.12. GTP is a molecule similar to ATP in its structure and cellular function. This GTP may be used to make an ATP molecule (as shown) or directly power work in the cell. In the cells of plants, bacteria, and some animal tissues, step 5 forms an ATP molecule directly by substrate-level phosphorylation. The output from step 5 represents the only ATP generated directly by the citric acid cycle.

Most of the ATP produced by respiration results from oxidative phosphorylation, when the NADH and $FADH_2$ produced by the citric acid cycle relay the electrons extracted from food to the electron transport chain. In the process, they supply the necessary energy for the phosphorylation of ADP to ATP. We will explore this process in the next section.

CONCEPT CHECK 9.3

1. Name the molecules that conserve most of the energy from the citric acid cycle's redox reactions. How is this energy converted to a form that can be used to make ATP?
2. What cellular processes produce the CO_2 that you exhale?
3. **WHAT IF?** The conversions shown in Figure 9.10 and step 4 of Figure 9.12 are each catalyzed by a large multienzyme complex. What similarities are there in the reactions that occur in these two cases?

For suggested answers, see Appendix A.

CONCEPT 9.4
During oxidative phosphorylation, chemiosmosis couples electron transport to ATP synthesis

Our main objective in this chapter is to learn how cells harvest the energy of glucose and other nutrients in food to make ATP. But the metabolic components of respiration we have dissected so far, glycolysis and the citric acid cycle, produce only 4 ATP molecules per glucose molecule, all by substrate-level phosphorylation: 2 net ATP from glycolysis and 2 ATP from the citric acid cycle. At this point, molecules of NADH (and $FADH_2$) account for most of the energy extracted from the glucose. These electron escorts link glycolysis and the citric acid cycle to the machinery of oxidative phosphorylation, which uses energy released by the electron transport chain to power ATP synthesis. In this section, you will learn first how the electron transport chain works, then how electron flow down the chain is coupled to ATP synthesis.

The Pathway of Electron Transport

The electron transport chain is a collection of molecules embedded in the inner membrane of the mitochondrion in eukaryotic cells (in prokaryotes, they reside in the plasma membrane). The folding of the inner membrane to form cristae increases its surface area, providing space for thousands of copies of the chain in each mitochondrion. (Once again, we see that structure fits function.) Most components of the chain are proteins, which exist in multiprotein complexes numbered I through IV. Tightly bound to these proteins are *prosthetic groups*, nonprotein components essential for the catalytic functions of certain enzymes.

Figure 9.13 shows the sequence of electron carriers in the electron transport chain and the drop in free energy as electrons travel down the chain. During electron transport along the chain, electron carriers alternate between reduced and oxidized states as they accept and donate electrons. Each component of the chain becomes reduced when it accepts electrons from its "uphill" neighbor, which has a lower affinity for electrons (is less electronegative). It then returns to its oxidized form as it passes electrons to its "downhill," more electronegative neighbor.

Now let's take a closer look at the electron transport chain in Figure 9.13. We'll first describe the passage of electrons through complex I in some detail, as an illustration of the general principles involved in electron transport. Electrons removed from glucose by NAD^+, during glycolysis and the citric acid cycle, are transferred from NADH to the first molecule of the electron transport chain in complex I. This molecule is a flavoprotein, so named because it has a prosthetic group called flavin mononucleotide (FMN). In the next redox reaction, the flavoprotein returns to its oxidized form as it passes electrons to an iron-sulfur protein (Fe·S in complex I), one of a family of proteins with both iron and sulfur tightly bound. The iron-sulfur protein then passes the electrons to a compound called ubiquinone (Q in Figure 9.13). This electron carrier is a small hydrophobic molecule, the only member of the electron transport chain that is not a protein. Ubiquinone is individually mobile within the membrane rather than residing in a particular complex. (Another name for ubiquinone is coenzyme Q, or CoQ; you may have seen it sold as a nutritional supplement.)

Most of the remaining electron carriers between ubiquinone and oxygen are proteins called **cytochromes**. Their prosthetic

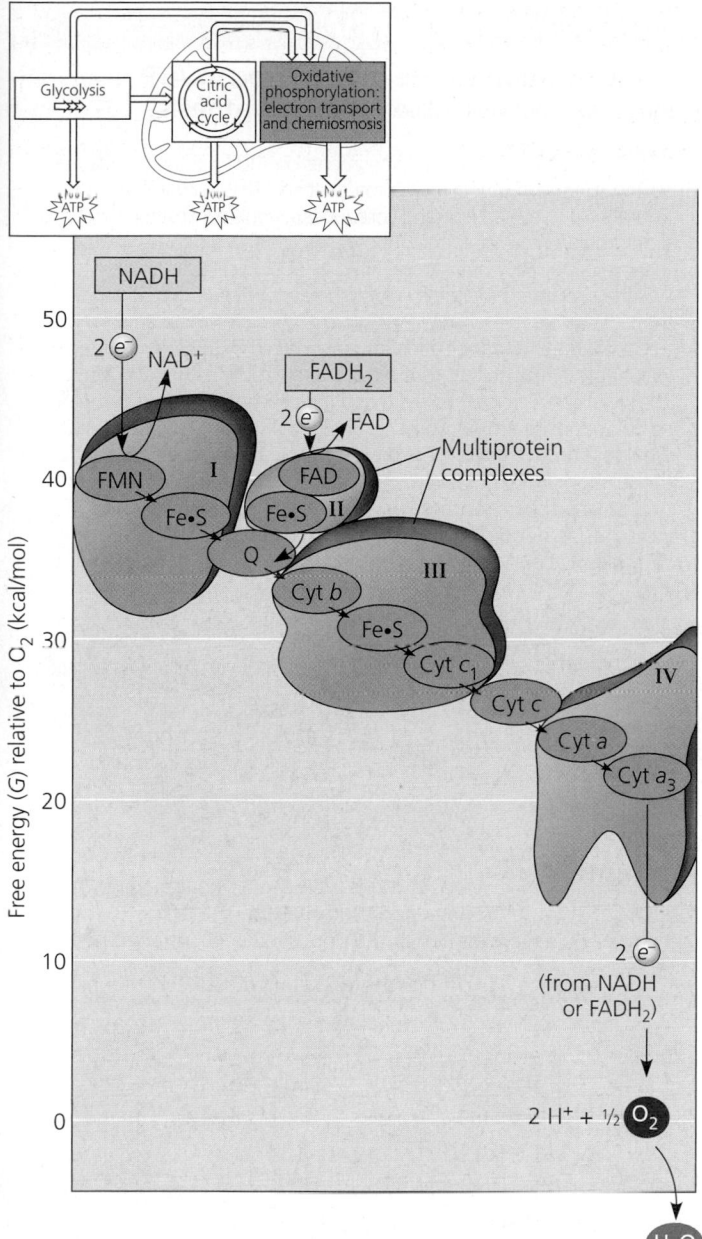

▲ **Figure 9.13 Free-energy change during electron transport.** The overall energy drop (ΔG) for electrons traveling from NADH to oxygen is 53 kcal/mol, but this "fall" is broken up into a series of smaller steps by the electron transport chain. (An oxygen atom is represented here as ½ O_2 to emphasize that the electron transport chain reduces molecular oxygen, O_2, not individual oxygen atoms.)

group, called a heme group, has an iron atom that accepts and donates electrons. (It is similar to the heme group in hemoglobin, the protein of red blood cells, except that the iron in hemoglobin carries oxygen, not electrons.) The electron transport chain has several types of cytochromes, each a different protein with a slightly different electron-carrying heme group. The last cytochrome of the chain, cyt a_3, passes its electrons to oxygen,

which is *very* electronegative. Each oxygen atom also picks up a pair of hydrogen ions from the aqueous solution, forming water.

Another source of electrons for the transport chain is $FADH_2$, the other reduced product of the citric acid cycle. Notice in Figure 9.13 that $FADH_2$ adds its electrons to the electron transport chain at complex II, at a lower energy level than NADH does. Consequently, although NADH and $FADH_2$ each donate an equivalent number of electrons (2) for oxygen reduction, the electron transport chain provides about one-third less energy for ATP synthesis when the electron donor is $FADH_2$ rather than NADH. We'll see why in the next section.

The electron transport chain makes no ATP directly. Instead, it eases the fall of electrons from food to oxygen, breaking a large free-energy drop into a series of smaller steps that release energy in manageable amounts. How does the mitochondrion (or the prokaryotic plasma membrane) couple this electron transport and energy release to ATP synthesis? The answer is a mechanism called chemiosmosis.

Chemiosmosis: The Energy-Coupling Mechanism

Populating the inner membrane of the mitochondrion or the prokaryotic plasma membrane are many copies of a protein complex called **ATP synthase**, the enzyme that actually makes ATP from ADP and inorganic phosphate. ATP synthase works like an ion pump running in reverse. Recall from Chapter 7 that ion pumps usually use ATP as an energy source to transport ions against their gradients. In fact, the proton pump shown in Figure 7.19 is an ATP synthase. As we mentioned in Chapter 8, enzymes can catalyze a reaction in either direction, depending on the ΔG for the reaction, which is affected by the local concentrations of reactants and products. Rather than hydrolyzing ATP to pump protons against their concentration gradient, under the conditions of cellular respiration, ATP synthase uses the energy of an existing ion gradient to power ATP synthesis. The power source for the ATP synthase is a difference in the concentration of H^+ on opposite sides of the inner mitochondrial membrane. (We can also think of this gradient as a difference in pH, since pH is a measure of H^+ concentration.) This process, in which energy stored in the form of a hydrogen ion gradient across a membrane is used to drive cellular work such as the synthesis of ATP, is called **chemiosmosis** (from the Greek *osmos*, push). We have previously used the word *osmosis* in discussing water transport, but here it refers to the flow of H^+ across a membrane.

From studying the structure of ATP synthase, scientists have learned how the flow of H^+ through this large enzyme powers ATP generation. ATP synthase is a multisubunit complex with four main parts, each made up of multiple polypeptides. Protons move one by one into binding sites on one of the parts (the rotor), causing it to spin in a way that catalyzes ATP production from ADP and inorganic phosphate. The flow of

INTERMEMBRANE SPACE

H⁺

Rotor

Stator

Internal rod

Catalytic knob

ADP + Pᵢ

ATP

MITOCHONDRIAL MATRIX

① H⁺ ions flowing down their gradient enter a half channel in a **stator**, which is anchored in the membrane.

② H⁺ ions enter binding sites within a **rotor**, changing the shape of each subunit so that the rotor spins within the membrane.

③ Each H⁺ ion makes one complete turn before leaving the rotor and passing through a second half channel in the stator into the mitochondrial matrix.

④ Spinning of the rotor causes an internal **rod** to spin as well. This rod extends like a stalk into the **knob** below it, which is held stationary by part of the stator.

⑤ Turning of the rod activates catalytic sites in the knob that produce ATP from ADP and Pᵢ.

▲ **Figure 9.14 ATP synthase, a molecular mill.** The ATP synthase protein complex functions as a mill, powered by the flow of hydrogen ions. This complex resides in mitochondrial and chloroplast membranes of eukaryotes and in the plasma membranes of prokaryotes. Each of the four parts of ATP synthase consists of a number of polypeptide subunits.

protons thus behaves somewhat like a rushing stream that turns a waterwheel **(Figure 9.14).**

ATP synthase is the smallest molecular rotary motor known in nature. The research that led to a detailed description of this enzyme's activity first showed that part of the complex actually spun around in the membrane when the reaction proceeded in the direction of ATP *hydrolysis.* Although biochemists assumed that the same rotational mechanism was responsible for ATP *synthesis,* there was no definitive support for this model until 2004, when several research institutions in collaboration with a private company were able to tackle this issue using *nanotechnology* (techniques involving control of matter on the molecular scale; from the Greek *nanos,* meaning "dwarf"). **Figure 9.15** describes the elegant experiment performed by these investigators to demonstrate that the direction of rotation of one part of

▼ **Figure 9.15** **Inquiry**

Is the rotation of the internal rod in ATP synthase responsible for ATP synthesis?

EXPERIMENT Previous experiments on ATP synthase had demonstrated that the "internal rod" rotated when ATP was hydrolyzed (see Figure 9.14). Hiroyasu Itoh and colleagues set out to investigate whether simply rotating the rod in the opposite direction would cause ATP synthesis to occur. They isolated the internal rod and catalytic knob, which was then anchored to a nickel plate. A magnetic bead was bound to the rod. This complex was placed in a chamber containing an array of electromagnets, and the bead was manipulated by the sequential activation of the magnets to rotate the internal rod in either direction. The investigators hypothesized that if the bead were rotated in the direction opposite to that observed during hydrolysis, ATP synthesis would occur. ATP levels were monitored by a "reporter enzyme" in the solution that emits a discrete amount of light (a photon) when it cleaves ATP. Their hypothesis was that rotation in one direction would result in more photons than rotation in the other direction or no rotation at all.

Electromagnet

Sample

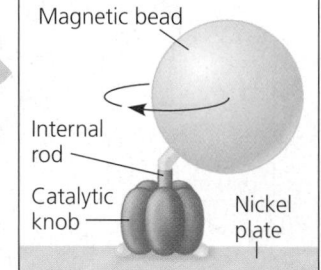

Magnetic bead

Internal rod

Catalytic knob

Nickel plate

RESULTS More photons were emitted by spinning the rod for 5 minutes in one direction (yellow bars) than by no rotation (gray bars) or rotation in the opposite direction (blue bars).

Rotation in one direction
Rotation in opposite direction
No rotation

Number of photons detected (×10³)

Sequential trials

CONCLUSION The researchers concluded that the mechanical rotation of the internal rod in a particular direction within ATP synthase appears to be all that is required for generating ATP. As ATP synthase is the smallest rotary motor known, one of the goals in this type of research is to learn how to use its activity in artificial ways.

SOURCE H. Itoh et al., Mechanically driven ATP synthesis by F₁-ATPase, *Nature* 427:465–468 (2004).

Inquiry in Action Read and analyze the original paper in *Inquiry in Action: Interpreting Scientific Papers.*

WHAT IF? The "no rotation" (gray) bars represent the background level of ATP in the experiment. When the enzyme is rotated one way (yellow bars), the increase in ATP level suggests synthesis is occurring. For enzymes rotating the other way (blue bars), what level of ATP would you expect compared to the gray bars? (Note: this may not be what is observed.)

the protein complex in relation to another is solely responsible for either ATP synthesis or ATP hydrolysis.

How does the inner mitochondrial membrane or the prokaryotic plasma membrane generate and maintain the H^+ gradient that drives ATP synthesis by the ATP synthase protein complex? Establishing the H^+ gradient is a major function of the electron transport chain, which is shown in its mitochondrial location in **Figure 9.16**. The chain is an energy converter that uses the exergonic flow of electrons from NADH and $FADH_2$ to pump H^+ across the membrane, from the mitochondrial matrix into the intermembrane space. The H^+ has a tendency to move back across the membrane, diffusing down its gradient. And the ATP synthases are the only sites that pro-

vide a route through the membrane for H^+. As we described previously, their passage through ATP synthase uses the exergonic flow of H^+ to drive the phosphorylation of ADP. Thus, the energy stored in an H^+ gradient across a membrane couples the redox reactions of the electron transport chain to ATP synthesis, an example of chemiosmosis.

At this point, you may be wondering how the electron transport chain pumps hydrogen ions. Researchers have found that certain members of the electron transport chain accept and release protons (H^+) along with electrons. (The aqueous solutions inside and surrounding the cell are a ready source of H^+.) At certain steps along the chain, electron transfers cause H^+ to be taken up and released into the

▲ **Figure 9.16 Chemiosmosis couples the electron transport chain to ATP synthesis.** ❶ NADH and $FADH_2$ shuttle high-energy electrons extracted from food during glycolysis and the citric acid cycle to an electron transport chain built into the inner mitochondrial membrane. The gold arrows trace the transport of electrons, which finally pass to oxygen at the "downhill" end of the chain, forming water. As Figure 9.13 showed, most of the electron carriers of the chain are grouped into four complexes. Two mobile

carriers, ubiquinone (Q) and cytochrome c (Cyt c), move rapidly, ferrying electrons between the large complexes. As complexes I, III, and IV accept and then donate electrons, they pump protons from the mitochondrial matrix into the intermembrane space. (In prokaryotes, protons are pumped outside the plasma membrane.) Note that $FADH_2$ deposits its electrons via complex II and so results in fewer protons being pumped into the intermembrane space than occurs with NADH. Chemical energy originally harvested from food is transformed into a

proton-motive force, a gradient of H^+ across the membrane. ❷ During chemiosmosis, the protons flow back down their gradient via ATP synthase, which is built into the membrane nearby. The ATP synthase harnesses the proton-motive force to phosphorylate ADP, forming ATP. Together, electron transport and chemiosmosis make up oxidative phosphorylation.

WHAT IF? *If complex IV were nonfunctional, could chemiosmosis produce any ATP, and if so, how would the rate of synthesis differ?*

surrounding solution. In eukaryotic cells, the electron carriers are spatially arranged in the membrane in such a way that H^+ is accepted from the mitochondrial matrix and deposited in the intermembrane space (see Figure 9.16). The H^+ gradient that results is referred to as a **proton-motive force**, emphasizing the capacity of the gradient to perform work. The force drives H^+ back across the membrane through the H^+ channels provided by ATP synthases.

In general terms, *chemiosmosis is an energy-coupling mechanism that uses energy stored in the form of an H^+ gradient across a membrane to drive cellular work.* In mitochondria, the energy for gradient formation comes from exergonic redox reactions, and ATP synthesis is the work performed. But chemiosmosis also occurs elsewhere and in other variations. Chloroplasts use chemiosmosis to generate ATP during photosynthesis; in these organelles, light (rather than chemical energy) drives both electron flow down an electron transport chain and the resulting H^+ gradient formation. Prokaryotes, as already mentioned, generate H^+ gradients across their plasma membranes. They then tap the proton-motive force not only to make ATP inside the cell but also to rotate their flagella and to pump nutrients and waste products across the membrane. Because of its central importance to energy conversions in prokaryotes and eukaryotes, chemiosmosis has helped unify the study of bioenergetics. Peter Mitchell was awarded the Nobel Prize in 1978 for originally proposing the chemiosmotic model.

An Accounting of ATP Production by Cellular Respiration

In the last few sections, we have looked more closely at the key processes of cellular respiration. Now, let's take a step back and remind ourselves of its overall function: harvesting the energy of glucose for ATP synthesis.

During respiration, most energy flows in this sequence: glucose → NADH → electron transport chain → proton-motive force → ATP. We can do some bookkeeping to calculate the ATP profit when cellular respiration oxidizes a molecule of glucose to six molecules of carbon dioxide. The three main departments of this metabolic enterprise are glycolysis, the citric acid cycle, and the electron transport chain, which drives oxidative phosphorylation. **Figure 9.17** gives a detailed accounting of the ATP yield per glucose molecule oxidized. The tally adds the 4 ATP produced directly by substrate-level phosphorylation during glycolysis and the citric acid cycle to the many more molecules of ATP generated by oxidative phosphorylation. Each NADH that transfers a pair of electrons from glucose to the electron transport chain contributes enough to the proton-motive force to generate a maximum of about 3 ATP.

Why are the numbers in Figure 9.17 inexact? There are three reasons we cannot state an exact number of ATP molecules generated by the breakdown of one molecule of glucose. First, phosphorylation and the redox reactions are not directly coupled to

▲ Figure 9.17 **ATP yield per molecule of glucose at each stage of cellular respiration.**

each other, so the ratio of number of NADH molecules to number of ATP molecules is not a whole number. We know that 1 NADH results in 10 H^+ being transported out across the inner mitochondrial membrane, and we also know that somewhere between 3 and 4 H^+ must reenter the mitochondrial matrix via ATP synthase to generate 1 ATP. Therefore, a single molecule of NADH generates enough proton-motive force for synthesis of 2.5 to 3.3 ATP; generally, we round off and say that 1 NADH can generate about 3 ATP. The citric acid cycle also supplies electrons to the electron transport chain via $FADH_2$, but since it enters later in the chain, each molecule of this electron carrier is responsible for transport of only enough H^+ for the synthesis of 1.5 to 2 ATP. These numbers also take into account the slight energetic cost of moving the ATP formed in the mitochondrion out into the rest of the cytoplasm where it will be used.

Second, the ATP yield varies slightly depending on the type of shuttle used to transport electrons from the cytosol into the mitochondrion. The mitochondrial inner membrane is impermeable to NADH, so NADH in the cytosol is segregated from the machinery of oxidative phosphorylation. The two electrons of NADH captured in glycolysis must be conveyed into the mitochondrion by one of several electron shuttle systems. Depending on the type of shuttle in a particular cell type, the electrons are passed either to NAD^+ or to FAD in the mitochondrial matrix (see Figure 9.17). If the electrons are passed to FAD, as in brain cells, only about 2 ATP can result from each cytosolic NADH. If the electrons are passed to mitochondrial NAD^+, as in liver cells and heart cells, the yield is about 3 ATP.

A third variable that reduces the yield of ATP is the use of the proton-motive force generated by the redox reactions of respiration to drive other kinds of work. For example, the proton-motive force powers the mitochondrion's uptake of pyruvate from the cytosol. However, if *all* the proton-motive force generated by the electron transport chain were used to drive ATP synthesis, one glucose molecule could generate a maximum of 34 ATP produced by oxidative phosphorylation plus 4 ATP (net) from substrate-level phosphorylation to give a total yield of about 38 ATP (or only about 36 ATP if the less efficient shuttle were functioning).

We can now make a rough estimate of the efficiency of respiration—that is, the percentage of chemical energy possessed by glucose that has been transferred to ATP. Recall that the complete oxidation of a mole of glucose releases 686 kcal of energy under standard conditions ($\Delta G = -686$ kcal/mol). Phosphorylation of ADP to form ATP stores at least 7.3 kcal per mole of ATP. Therefore, the efficiency of respiration is 7.3 kcal per mole of ATP times 38 moles of ATP per mole of glucose divided by 686 kcal per mole of glucose, which equals 0.4. Thus, about 40% of the potential chemical energy in glucose has been transferred to ATP; the actual percentage is probably higher because ΔG is lower under cellular conditions. The rest of the stored energy is lost as heat. We humans use some of this heat to maintain our relatively high body temperature (37°C), and we dissipate the rest through sweating and other cooling mechanisms. Cellular respiration is remarkably efficient in its energy conversion. By comparison, the most efficient automobile converts only about 25% of the energy stored in gasoline to energy that moves the car.

CONCEPT CHECK 9.4

1. What effect would an absence of O_2 have on the process shown in Figure 9.16?
2. **WHAT IF?** In the absence of O_2, as in question 1, what do you think would happen if you decreased the pH of the intermembrane space of the mitochondrion? Explain your answer.

For suggested answers, see Appendix A.

CONCEPT 9.5
Fermentation and anaerobic respiration enable cells to produce ATP without the use of oxygen

Because most of the ATP generated by cellular respiration is due to the work of oxidative phosphorylation, our estimate of ATP yield from aerobic respiration is contingent on an adequate supply of oxygen to the cell. Without the electronegative oxygen to pull electrons down the transport chain, oxidative phosphorylation ceases. However, there are two general mechanisms by which certain cells can oxidize organic fuel and generate ATP *without* the use of oxygen: anaerobic respiration and fermentation. The distinction between these two is based on whether an electron transport chain is present. (The electron transport chain is also called the respiratory chain because of its role in cellular respiration.)

We have already mentioned anaerobic respiration, which takes place in certain prokaryotic organisms that live in environments without oxygen. These organisms have an electron transport chain but do not use oxygen as a final electron acceptor at the end of the chain. Oxygen performs this function very well because it is extremely electronegative, but other, less electronegative substances can also serve as final electron acceptors. Some "sulfate-reducing" marine bacteria, for instance, use the sulfate ion (SO_4^{2-}) at the end of their respiratory chain. Operation of the chain builds up a proton-motive force used to produce ATP, but H_2S (hydrogen sulfide) is produced as a by-product rather than water.

Fermentation is a way of harvesting chemical energy without using either oxygen or any electron transport chain—in other words, without cellular respiration. How can food be oxidized without cellular respiration? Remember, oxidation simply refers to the loss of electrons to an electron acceptor, so it does not need to involve oxygen. Glycolysis oxidizes glucose to two molecules of pyruvate. The oxidizing agent of glycolysis is NAD⁺, and neither oxygen nor any electron transfer chain is involved. Overall, glycolysis is exergonic, and some of the energy made available is used to produce 2 ATP (net) by substrate-level phosphorylation. If oxygen *is* present, then additional ATP is made by oxidative phosphorylation when NADH passes electrons removed from glucose to the electron transport chain. But glycolysis generates 2 ATP whether oxygen is present or not—that is, whether conditions are aerobic or anaerobic.

As an alternative to respiratory oxidation of organic nutrients, fermentation is an expansion of glycolysis that allows continuous generation of ATP by the substrate-level phosphorylation of glycolysis. For this to occur, there must be a sufficient supply of NAD⁺ to accept electrons during the oxidation step of glycolysis. Without some mechanism to recycle NAD⁺ from NADH, glycolysis would soon deplete the cell's pool of NAD⁺ by reducing it all to NADH and would shut itself down for lack of an oxidizing agent. Under aerobic conditions, NAD⁺ is recycled from NADH by the transfer of electrons to the electron transport chain. An anaerobic alternative is to transfer electrons from NADH to pyruvate, the end product of glycolysis.

Types of Fermentation

Fermentation consists of glycolysis plus reactions that regenerate NAD⁺ by transferring electrons from NADH to pyruvate or derivatives of pyruvate. The NAD⁺ can then be reused to oxidize sugar by glycolysis, which nets two molecules of ATP by substrate-level phosphorylation. There are many types of fermentation, differing in the end products formed from pyruvate. Two common types are alcohol fermentation and lactic acid fermentation.

In **alcohol fermentation (Figure 9.18a)**, pyruvate is converted to ethanol (ethyl alcohol) in two steps. The first step releases carbon dioxide from the pyruvate, which is converted to the two-carbon compound acetaldehyde. In the second step, acetaldehyde is reduced by NADH to ethanol. This regenerates the supply of NAD⁺ needed for the continuation of glycolysis. Many bacteria carry out alcohol fermentation under anaerobic conditions. Yeast (a fungus) also carries out alcohol fermentation. For thousands of years, humans have used yeast in brewing, winemaking, and baking. The CO_2 bubbles generated by baker's yeast during alcohol fermentation allow bread to rise.

During **lactic acid fermentation (Figure 9.18b)**, pyruvate is reduced directly by NADH to form lactate as an end product, with no release of CO_2. (Lactate is the ionized form of lactic acid.) Lactic acid fermentation by certain fungi and bacteria is used in the dairy industry to make cheese and yogurt.

(a) Alcohol fermentation

(b) Lactic acid fermentation

▲ **Figure 9.18 Fermentation.** In the absence of oxygen, many cells use fermentation to produce ATP by substrate-level phosphorylation. Pyruvate, the end product of glycolysis, serves as an electron acceptor for oxidizing NADH back to NAD⁺, which can then be reused in glycolysis. Two of the common end products formed from fermentation are **(a)** ethanol and **(b)** lactate, the ionized form of lactic acid.

Human muscle cells make ATP by lactic acid fermentation when oxygen is scarce. This occurs during the early stages of strenuous exercise, when sugar catabolism for ATP production outpaces the muscle's supply of oxygen from the blood. Under these conditions, the cells switch from aerobic respiration to fermentation. The lactate that accumulates was previously thought to cause muscle fatigue and pain, but recent research suggests instead that increased levels of potassium ions (K⁺) may be to blame, while lactate appears to enhance muscle performance. In any case, the excess lactate is gradually carried away by the blood to the liver. Lactate is converted back to pyruvate by liver cells.

Fermentation and Aerobic Respiration Compared

Fermentation and aerobic cellular respiration are anaerobic and aerobic alternatives, respectively, for producing ATP by harvesting the chemical energy of food. Both pathways use glycolysis to oxidize glucose and other organic fuels to pyruvate, with a net production of 2 ATP by substrate-level phosphorylation. And in both fermentation and respiration, NAD^+ is the oxidizing agent that accepts electrons from food during glycolysis. A key difference is the contrasting mechanisms for oxidizing NADH back to NAD^+, which is required to sustain glycolysis. In fermentation, the final electron acceptor is an organic molecule such as pyruvate (lactic acid fermentation) or acetaldehyde (alcohol fermentation). In aerobic respiration, by contrast, the final acceptor for electrons from NADH is oxygen. This process not only regenerates the NAD^+ required for glycolysis but pays an ATP bonus when the stepwise electron transport from this NADH to oxygen drives oxidative phosphorylation. An even bigger ATP payoff comes from the oxidation of pyruvate in the citric acid cycle, which is unique to respiration. Without oxygen, the energy still stored in pyruvate is unavailable to the cell. Thus, cellular respiration harvests much more energy from each sugar molecule than fermentation can. In fact, respiration yields up to 19 times as much ATP per glucose molecule as does fermentation—up to 38 molecules of ATP for respiration, compared with 2 molecules of ATP produced by substrate-level phosphorylation in fermentation.

Some organisms, called **obligate anaerobes**, carry out only fermentation or anaerobic respiration and in fact cannot survive in the presence of oxygen. A few cell types, such as cells of the vertebrate brain, can carry out only aerobic oxidation of pyruvate, but not fermentation. Other organisms, including yeasts and many bacteria, can make enough ATP to survive using either fermentation or respiration. Such species are called **facultative anaerobes**. On the cellular level, our muscle cells behave as facultative anaerobes. In such cells, pyruvate is a fork in the metabolic road that leads to two alternative catabolic routes **(Figure 9.19)**. Under aerobic conditions, pyruvate can be converted to acetyl CoA, and oxidation continues in the citric acid cycle. Under anaerobic conditions, pyruvate is diverted from the citric acid cycle, serving instead as an electron acceptor to recycle NAD^+. To make the same amount of ATP, a facultative anaerobe would have to consume sugar at a much faster rate when fermenting than when respiring.

The Evolutionary Significance of Glycolysis

The role of glycolysis in both fermentation and respiration has an evolutionary basis. Ancient prokaryotes probably used glycolysis to make ATP long before oxygen was present in Earth's atmosphere. The oldest known fossils of bacteria date back 3.5 billion years, but appreciable quantities of oxygen probably did not begin to accumulate in the atmosphere until about 2.7 billion years ago. Cyanobacteria produced this O_2 as a by-product of photosynthesis. Therefore, early prokaryotes may have generated ATP exclusively from glycolysis. The fact that glycolysis is today the most widespread metabolic pathway among Earth's organisms suggests that it evolved very early in the history of life. The cytosolic location of glycolysis also implies great antiquity; the pathway does not require any of the membrane-bounded organelles of the eukaryotic cell, which evolved approximately 1 billion years after the prokaryotic cell. Glycolysis is a metabolic heirloom from early cells that continues to function in fermentation and as the first stage in the breakdown of organic molecules by respiration.

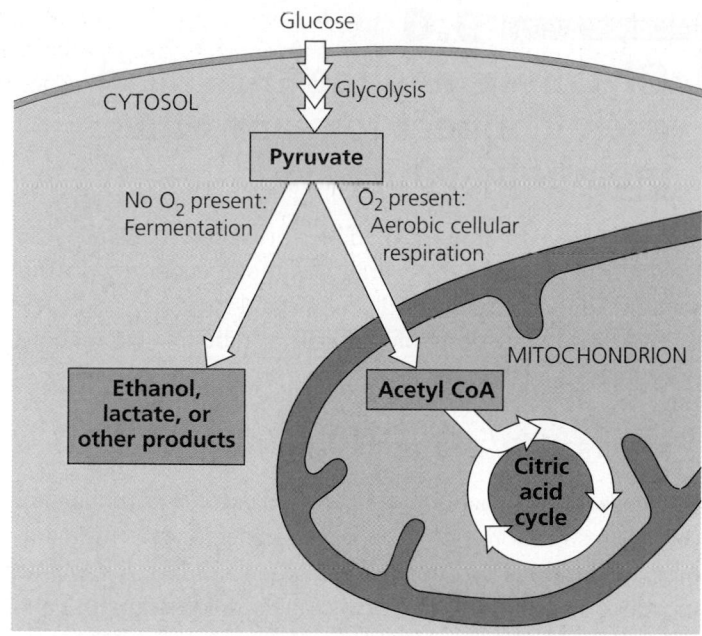

▲ **Figure 9.19 Pyruvate as a key juncture in catabolism.** Glycolysis is common to fermentation and cellular respiration. The end product of glycolysis, pyruvate, represents a fork in the catabolic pathways of glucose oxidation. In a facultative anaerobe, which is capable of both aerobic cellular respiration and fermentation, pyruvate is committed to one of those two pathways, usually depending on whether or not oxygen is present.

CONCEPT CHECK 9.5

1. Consider the NADH formed during glycolysis. What is the final acceptor for its electrons during fermentation? What is the final acceptor for its electrons during aerobic respiration?
2. **WHAT IF?** A glucose-fed yeast cell is moved from an aerobic environment to an anaerobic one. For the cell to continue generating ATP at the same rate, how would its rate of glucose consumption need to change?

For suggested answers, see Appendix A.

CONCEPT 9.6

Glycolysis and the citric acid cycle connect to many other metabolic pathways

So far, we have treated the oxidative breakdown of glucose in isolation from the cell's overall metabolic economy. In this section, you will learn that glycolysis and the citric acid cycle are major intersections of the cell's catabolic and anabolic (biosynthetic) pathways.

The Versatility of Catabolism

Throughout this chapter, we have used glucose as the fuel for cellular respiration. But free glucose molecules are not common in the diets of humans and other animals. We obtain most of our calories in the form of fats, proteins, sucrose and other disaccharides, and starch, a polysaccharide. All these organic molecules in food can be used by cellular respiration to make ATP (Figure 9.20).

Glycolysis can accept a wide range of carbohydrates for catabolism. In the digestive tract, starch is hydrolyzed to glucose, which can then be broken down in the cells by glycolysis and the citric acid cycle. Similarly, glycogen, the polysaccharide that humans and many other animals store in their liver and muscle cells, can be hydrolyzed to glucose between meals as fuel for respiration. The digestion of disaccharides, including sucrose, provides glucose and other monosaccharides as fuel for respiration.

Proteins can also be used for fuel, but first they must be digested to their constituent amino acids. Many of the amino acids, of course, are used by the organism to build new proteins. Amino acids present in excess are converted by enzymes to intermediates of glycolysis and the citric acid cycle. Before amino acids can feed into glycolysis or the citric acid cycle, their amino groups must be removed, a process called deamination. The nitrogenous refuse is excreted from the animal in the form of ammonia, urea, or other waste products.

Catabolism can also harvest energy stored in fats obtained either from food or from storage cells in the body. After fats are digested to glycerol and fatty acids, the glycerol is converted to glyceraldehyde-3-phosphate, an intermediate of glycolysis. Most of the energy of a fat is stored in the fatty acids. A metabolic sequence called **beta oxidation** breaks the fatty acids down to two-carbon fragments, which enter the citric acid cycle as acetyl CoA. NADH and $FADH_2$ are also generated during beta oxidation; they can enter the electron transport chain, leading to further ATP production. Fats make excellent fuel, in large part due to their chemical structure and the high energy level of their electrons compared to those of carbohydrates. A gram of fat oxidized by

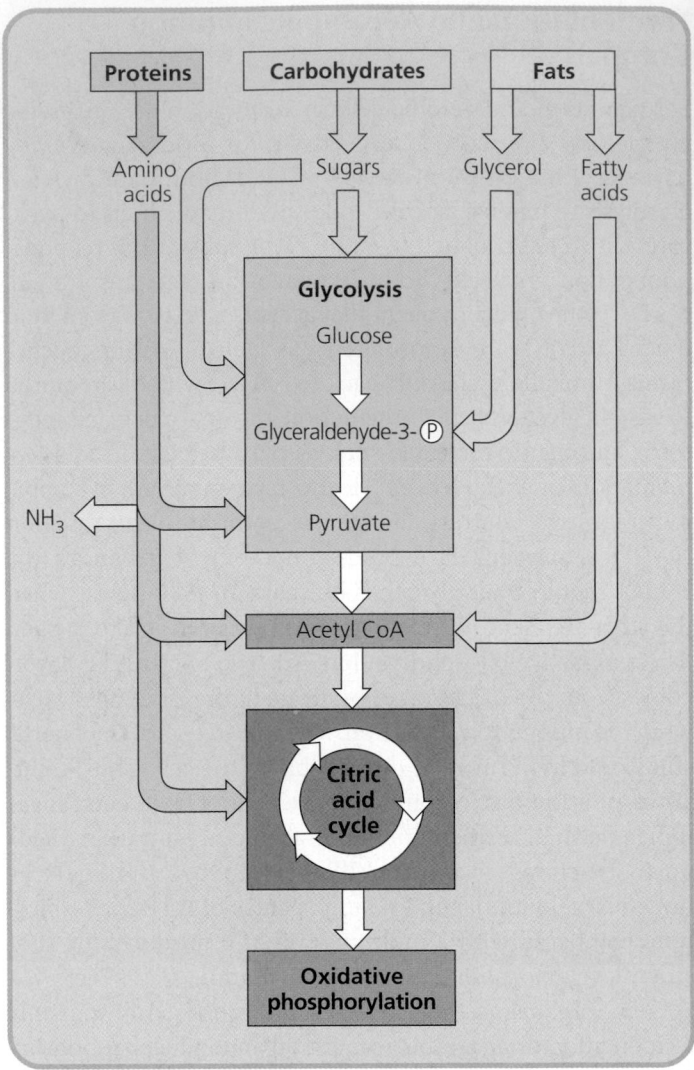

▲ **Figure 9.20 The catabolism of various molecules from food.** Carbohydrates, fats, and proteins can all be used as fuel for cellular respiration. Monomers of these molecules enter glycolysis or the citric acid cycle at various points. Glycolysis and the citric acid cycle are catabolic funnels through which electrons from all kinds of organic molecules flow on their exergonic fall to oxygen.

respiration produces more than twice as much ATP as a gram of carbohydrate. Unfortunately, this also means that a person trying to lose weight must work hard to use up fat stored in the body because so many calories are stockpiled in each gram of fat.

Biosynthesis (Anabolic Pathways)

Cells need substance as well as energy. Not all the organic molecules of food are destined to be oxidized as fuel to make ATP. In addition to calories, food must also provide the carbon skeletons that cells require to make their own molecules. Some organic monomers obtained from digestion can be used directly. For example, as previously mentioned, amino acids from the hydrolysis of proteins in food can be incorporated into the organism's own proteins. Often, however, the body needs specific molecules that are not present as such in food. Compounds formed as intermediates of glycolysis and the citric acid cycle can be diverted into anabolic pathways as precursors from which the cell can synthesize the molecules it requires. For example, humans can make about half of the 20 amino acids in proteins by modifying compounds siphoned away from the citric acid cycle; the rest are "essential amino acids" that must be obtained in the diet. Also, glucose can be made from pyruvate, and fatty acids can be synthesized from acetyl CoA. Of course, these anabolic, or biosynthetic, pathways do not generate ATP, but instead consume it.

In addition, glycolysis and the citric acid cycle function as metabolic interchanges that enable our cells to convert some kinds of molecules to others as we need them. For example, an intermediate compound generated during glycolysis, dihydroxyacetone phosphate (see Figure 9.9, step 5), can be converted to one of the major precursors of fats. If we eat more food than we need, we store fat even if our diet is fat-free. Metabolism is remarkably versatile and adaptable.

Regulation of Cellular Respiration via Feedback Mechanisms

Basic principles of supply and demand regulate the metabolic economy. The cell does not waste energy making more of a particular substance than it needs. If there is a glut of a certain amino acid, for example, the anabolic pathway that synthesizes that amino acid from an intermediate of the citric acid cycle is switched off. The most common mechanism for this control is feedback inhibition: The end product of the anabolic pathway inhibits the enzyme that catalyzes an early step of the pathway (see Figure 8.22). This prevents the needless diversion of key metabolic intermediates from uses that are more urgent.

The cell also controls its catabolism. If the cell is working hard and its ATP concentration begins to drop, respiration speeds up. When there is plenty of ATP to meet demand, respiration slows down, sparing valuable organic molecules for other functions. Again, control is based mainly on regulating the activity of enzymes at strategic points in the catabolic pathway. As shown in **Figure 9.21**, one important switch is phosphofructokinase, the enzyme that catalyzes step 3 of glycolysis (see Figure 9.9). That is the first step that commits substrate irreversibly to the glycolytic pathway. By controlling the rate of this step, the cell can speed up or slow down the entire catabolic process. Phosphofructokinase can thus be considered the pacemaker of respiration.

Phosphofructokinase is an allosteric enzyme with receptor sites for specific inhibitors and activators. It is inhibited by ATP and stimulated by AMP (adenosine monophosphate), which the cell derives from ADP. As

▲ **Figure 9.21 The control of cellular respiration.** Allosteric enzymes at certain points in the respiratory pathway respond to inhibitors and activators that help set the pace of glycolysis and the citric acid cycle. Phosphofructokinase, which catalyzes an early step in glycolysis (see Figure 9.9), is one such enzyme. It is stimulated by AMP (derived from ADP) but is inhibited by ATP and by citrate. This feedback regulation adjusts the rate of respiration as the cell's catabolic and anabolic demands change.

ATP accumulates, inhibition of the enzyme slows down glycolysis. The enzyme becomes active again as cellular work converts ATP to ADP (and AMP) faster than ATP is being regenerated. Phosphofructokinase is also sensitive to citrate, the first product of the citric acid cycle. If citrate accumulates in mitochondria, some of it passes into the cytosol and inhibits phosphofructokinase. This mechanism helps synchronize the rates of glycolysis and the citric acid cycle. As citrate accumulates, glycolysis slows down, and the supply of acetyl groups to the citric acid cycle decreases. If citrate consumption increases, either because of a demand for more ATP or because anabolic pathways are draining off intermediates of the citric acid cycle, glycolysis accelerates and meets the demand.

Metabolic balance is augmented by the control of enzymes that catalyze other key steps of glycolysis and the citric acid cycle. Cells are thrifty, expedient, and responsive in their metabolism.

Examine Figure 9.2 again to put cellular respiration into the broader context of energy flow and chemical cycling in ecosystems. The energy that keeps us alive is *released*, but not *produced*, by cellular respiration. We are tapping energy that was stored in food by photosynthesis. In the next chapter, you will learn how photosynthesis captures light and converts it to chemical energy.

CONCEPT CHECK 9.6

1. Compare the structure of a fat (see Figure 5.11) with that of a carbohydrate (see Figure 5.3). What features of their structures make fat a much better fuel?
2. Under what circumstances might your body synthesize fat molecules?
3. **WHAT IF?** What will happen in a muscle cell that has used up its supply of oxygen and ATP? (See Figures 9.19 and 9.21.)

For suggested answers, see Appendix A.

Chapter 9 Review

MEDIA Go to **www.campbellbiology.com** for BioFlix 3-D Animations, MP3 Tutors, Videos, Practice Tests, an eBook, and more.

SUMMARY OF KEY CONCEPTS

CONCEPT 9.1

Catabolic pathways yield energy by oxidizing organic fuels (pp. 162–167)

▶ **Catabolic Pathways and Production of ATP** To keep working, a cell must regenerate the ATP it uses. The breakdown of glucose and other organic fuels is exergonic. Starting with glucose or another organic molecule and using O_2, aerobic respiration yields H_2O, CO_2, and energy in the form of ATP and heat. Cellular respiration includes both aerobic and anaerobic respiration; the latter uses another electron acceptor at the end of the electron transport chain instead of O_2, but also yields ATP.

▶ **Redox Reactions: Oxidation and Reduction** The cell taps the energy stored in food molecules through redox reactions, in which one substance partially or totally shifts electrons to another. The substance receiving electrons is reduced; the substance losing electrons is oxidized. During cellular respiration, glucose ($C_6H_{12}O_6$) is oxidized to CO_2, and O_2 is reduced to H_2O. Electrons lose potential energy during their transfer from organic compounds to oxygen. Electrons from organic compounds are usually passed first to NAD^+, reducing it to NADH. NADH passes the electrons to an electron transport chain, which conducts them to O_2 in energy-releasing steps. The energy is used to make ATP.

▶ **The Stages of Cellular Respiration: *A Preview*** Glycolysis and the citric acid cycle supply electrons (via NADH or $FADH_2$) to the electron transport chain, which drives oxidative phosphorylation. Oxidative phosphorylation generates ATP.

MEDIA
BioFlix 3-D Animation Cellular Respiration
Activity Build a Chemical Cycling System
Activity Overview of Cellular Respiration

CONCEPT 9.2

Glycolysis harvests chemical energy by oxidizing glucose to pyruvate (pp. 167–169)

MEDIA
MP3 Tutor Cellular Respiration Part 1—Glycolysis
Activity Glycolysis

CONCEPT 9.3

The citric acid cycle completes the energy-yielding oxidation of organic molecules (pp. 170–172)

▶ In eukaryotic cells, the import of pyruvate into the mitochondrion and its conversion to acetyl CoA links glycolysis to the citric acid cycle. (In prokaryotic cells, the citric acid cycle occurs in the cytosol.)

MEDIA
Activity The Citric Acid Cycle

CONCEPT 9.4

During oxidative phosphorylation, chemiosmosis couples electron transport to ATP synthesis (pp. 172–177)

▶ NADH and FADH$_2$ donate electrons to the electron transport chain, which powers ATP synthesis via oxidative phosphorylation.

▶ **The Pathway of Electron Transport** In the electron transport chain, electrons from NADH and FADH$_2$ lose energy in several energy-releasing steps. At the end of the chain, electrons are passed to O$_2$, reducing it to H$_2$O.

▶ **Chemiosmosis: The Energy-Coupling Mechanism** At certain steps along the electron transport chain, electron transfer causes protein complexes in eukaryotes to move H$^+$ from the mitochondrial matrix to the intermembrane space, storing energy as a proton-motive force (H$^+$ gradient). As H$^+$ diffuses back into the matrix through ATP synthase, its passage drives the phosphorylation of ADP. Prokaryotes generate an H$^+$ gradient across their plasma membrane and use this gradient to synthesize ATP in the cell.

INTER-MEMBRANE SPACE

H$^+$

ATP synthase

ADP + $\textcircled{P}_i$

ATP

MITO-CHONDRIAL MATRIX

H$^+$

▶ **An Accounting of ATP Production by Cellular Respiration** About 40% of the energy stored in a glucose molecule is transferred to ATP during cellular respiration, producing a maximum of about 38 ATP.

MEDIA

MP3 Tutor Cellular Respiration Part 2—Citric Acid Cycle and Electron Transport
Activity Electron Transport
Biology Labs On-Line MitochondriaLab
Investigation How Is the Rate of Cellular Respiration Measured?

CONCEPT 9.5

Fermentation and anaerobic respiration enable cells to produce ATP without the use of oxygen (pp. 177–179)

▶ **Types of Fermentation** Glycolysis nets 2 ATP by substrate-level phosphorylation, whether oxygen is present or not. Under anaerobic conditions, either anaerobic respiration or fermentation can take place. In anaerobic respiration, an electron transport chain is present with a final electron acceptor other than oxygen. In fermentation, the electrons from NADH are passed to pyruvate or a derivative of pyruvate, regenerating the NAD$^+$ required to oxidize more glucose. Two common types of fermentation are alcohol fermentation and lactic acid fermentation.

▶ **Fermentation and Aerobic Respiration Compared** Both use glycolysis to oxidize glucose but differ in their final electron acceptor. Respiration yields more ATP.

▶ **The Evolutionary Significance of Glycolysis** Glycolysis occurs in nearly all organisms and probably evolved in ancient prokaryotes before there was O$_2$ in the atmosphere.

MEDIA

Activity Fermentation

CONCEPT 9.6

Glycolysis and the citric acid cycle connect to many other metabolic pathways (pp. 180–182)

▶ **The Versatility of Catabolism** Catabolic pathways funnel electrons from many kinds of organic molecules into cellular respiration.

▶ **Biosynthesis (Anabolic Pathways)** Cells can use small molecules from food directly or use them to build other substances through glycolysis or the citric acid cycle.

▶ **Regulation of Cellular Respiration via Feedback Mechanisms** Cellular respiration is controlled by allosteric enzymes at key points in glycolysis and the citric acid cycle.

TESTING YOUR KNOWLEDGE

SELF-QUIZ

1. What is the reducing agent in the following reaction?

Pyruvate + NADH + H$^+$ → Lactate + NAD$^+$

a. oxygen
b. NADH
c. NAD$^+$
d. lactate
e. pyruvate

2. The *immediate* energy source that drives ATP synthesis by ATP synthase during oxidative phosphorylation is the
a. oxidation of glucose and other organic compounds.
b. flow of electrons down the electron transport chain.
c. affinity of oxygen for electrons.
d. H$^+$ concentration across the membrane holding ATP synthase.
e. transfer of phosphate to ADP.

3. Which metabolic pathway is common to both fermentation and cellular respiration of a glucose molecule?
a. the citric acid cycle
b. the electron transport chain
c. glycolysis
d. synthesis of acetyl CoA from pyruvate
e. reduction of pyruvate to lactate

4. In mitochondria, exergonic redox reactions
a. are the source of energy driving prokaryotic ATP synthesis.
b. are directly coupled to substrate-level phosphorylation.
c. provide the energy that establishes the proton gradient.
d. reduce carbon atoms to carbon dioxide.
e. are coupled via phosphorylated intermediates to endergonic processes.

5. The final electron acceptor of the electron transport chain that functions in aerobic oxidative phosphorylation is
   a. oxygen.
   b. water.
   c. NAD$^+$.
   d. pyruvate.
   e. ADP.

6. When electrons flow along the electron transport chains of mitochondria, which of the following changes occurs?
   a. The pH of the matrix increases.
   b. ATP synthase pumps protons by active transport.
   c. The electrons gain free energy.
   d. The cytochromes phosphorylate ADP to form ATP.
   e. NAD$^+$ is oxidized.

7. Cells do not catabolize carbon dioxide because
   a. its double bonds are too stable to be broken.
   b. CO$_2$ has fewer bonding electrons than other organic compounds.
   c. CO$_2$ is already completely reduced.
   d. CO$_2$ is already completely oxidized.
   e. the molecule has too few atoms.

8. Which of the following is a true distinction between fermentation and cellular respiration?
   a. Only respiration oxidizes glucose.
   b. NADH is oxidized by the electron transport chain in respiration only.
   c. Fermentation, but not respiration, is an example of a catabolic pathway.
   d. Substrate-level phosphorylation is unique to fermentation.
   e. NAD$^+$ functions as an oxidizing agent only in respiration.

9. Most CO$_2$ from catabolism is released during
   a. glycolysis.
   b. the citric acid cycle.
   c. lactate fermentation.
   d. electron transport.
   e. oxidative phosphorylation.

10. **DRAW IT** The graph here shows the pH difference across the inner mitochondrial membrane over time in an actively respiring cell. At the time indicated by the vertical arrow, a metabolic poison is added that specifically and completely inhibits all function of mitochondrial ATP synthase. Draw what you would expect to see for the rest of the graphed line.

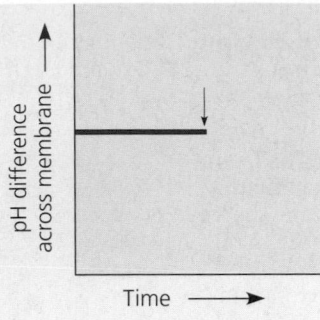

For Self-Quiz answers, see Appendix A.

MEDIA Visit **www.campbellbiology.com** for a Practice Test.

EVOLUTION CONNECTION

11. ATP synthases are found in the prokaryotic plasma membrane and in mitochondria and chloroplasts. What does this suggest about the evolutionary relationship of these eukaryotic organelles to prokaryotes? How might the amino acid sequences of the ATP synthases from the different sources support or refute your hypothesis?

SCIENTIFIC INQUIRY

12. In the 1940s, some physicians prescribed low doses of a drug called dinitrophenol (DNP) to help patients lose weight. This unsafe method was abandoned after a few patients died. DNP uncouples the chemiosmotic machinery by making the lipid bilayer of the inner mitochondrial membrane leaky to H$^+$. Explain how this causes weight loss.

SCIENCE, TECHNOLOGY, AND SOCIETY

13. Nearly all human societies use fermentation to produce alcoholic drinks such as beer and wine. The practice dates back to the earliest days of agriculture. How do you suppose this use of fermentation was first discovered? Why did wine prove to be a more useful beverage, especially to a preindustrial culture, than the grape juice from which it was made?

Biological Inquiry: A Workbook of Investigative Cases Explore fermentation further in the case "Bean Brew."

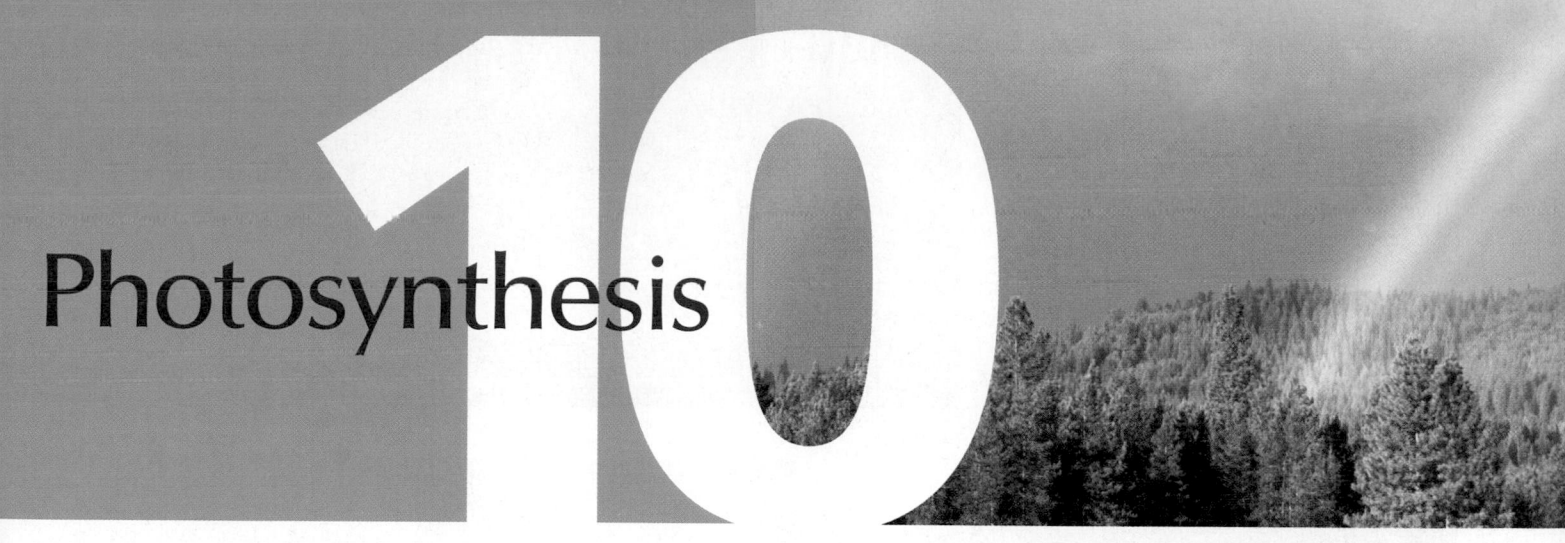

Photosynthesis

KEY CONCEPTS

10.1 Photosynthesis converts light energy to the chemical energy of food

10.2 The light reactions convert solar energy to the chemical energy of ATP and NADPH

10.3 The Calvin cycle uses ATP and NADPH to convert CO_2 to sugar

10.4 Alternative mechanisms of carbon fixation have evolved in hot, arid climates

OVERVIEW

The Process That Feeds the Biosphere

Life on Earth is solar powered. The chloroplasts of plants capture light energy that has traveled 150 million kilometers from the sun and convert it to chemical energy stored in sugar and other organic molecules. This conversion process is called **photosynthesis**. Let's begin by placing photosynthesis in its ecological context.

Photosynthesis nourishes almost the entire living world directly or indirectly. An organism acquires the organic compounds it uses for energy and carbon skeletons by one of two major modes: autotrophic nutrition or heterotrophic nutrition. **Autotrophs** are "self-feeders" (*auto* means "self," and *trophos* means "feed"); they sustain themselves without eating anything derived from other living beings. Autotrophs produce their organic molecules from CO_2 and other inorganic raw materials obtained from the environment. They are the ultimate sources of organic compounds for all nonautotrophic organisms, and for this reason, biologists refer to autotrophs as the *producers* of the biosphere.

▲ Figure 10.1 **How can sunlight, seen here as a spectrum of colors in a rainbow, power the synthesis of organic substances?**

Almost all plants are autotrophs; the only nutrients they require are water and minerals from the soil and carbon dioxide from the air. Specifically, plants are *photo*autotrophs, organisms that use light as a source of energy to synthesize organic substances (**Figure 10.1**). Photosynthesis also occurs in algae, certain other protists, and some prokaryotes (**Figure 10.2**, on the next page). In this chapter, we will touch on these other groups in passing, but our emphasis will be on plants. Variations in autotrophic nutrition that occur in prokaryotes and algae will be detailed in Chapters 27 and 28.

Heterotrophs obtain their organic material by the second major mode of nutrition. Unable to make their own food, they live on compounds produced by other organisms (*hetero* means "other"). Heterotrophs are the biosphere's *consumers.* The most obvious form of this "other-feeding" occurs when an animal eats plants or other animals. But heterotrophic nutrition may be more subtle. Some heterotrophs consume the remains of dead organisms by decomposing and feeding on organic litter such as carcasses, feces, and fallen leaves; they are known as decomposers. Most fungi and many types of prokaryotes get their nourishment this way. Almost all heterotrophs, including humans, are completely dependent, either directly or indirectly, on photoautotrophs for food—and also for oxygen, a by-product of photosynthesis.

In this chapter, you will learn how photosynthesis works. After a discussion of the general principles of photosynthesis, we will consider the two stages of photosynthesis: the light reactions, in which solar energy is captured and transformed into chemical energy; and the Calvin cycle, in which the chemical energy is used to make organic molecules of food. Finally, we will consider a few aspects of photosynthesis from an evolutionary perspective.

▼ **Figure 10.2 Photoautotrophs.** These organisms use light energy to drive the synthesis of organic molecules from carbon dioxide and (in most cases) water. They feed not only themselves, but the entire living world. **(a)** On land, plants are the predominant producers of food. In aquatic environments, photosynthetic organisms include **(b)** multicellular algae, such as this kelp; **(c)** some unicellular protists, such as *Euglena*; **(d)** the prokaryotes called cyanobacteria; and **(e)** other photosynthetic prokaryotes, such as these purple sulfur bacteria, which produce sulfur (spherical globules) (c, d, e: LMs).

(a) Plants

(c) Unicellular protist 10 μm

(e) Purple sulfur bacteria 1.5 μm

(b) Multicellular alga

(d) Cyanobacteria 40 μm

CONCEPT **10.1**

Photosynthesis converts light energy to the chemical energy of food

The remarkable ability of an organism to harness light energy and use it to drive the synthesis of organic compounds emerges from structural organization in the cell: Photosynthetic enzymes and other molecules are grouped together in a biological membrane, enabling the necessary series of chemical reactions to be carried out efficiently. The process of photosynthesis most likely originated in a group of bacteria that had infolded regions of the plasma membrane containing clusters of such molecules. In existing photosynthetic bacteria, infolded photosynthetic membranes function similarly to the internal membranes of the chloroplast, a eukaryotic organelle you learned about in Chapter 6. In fact, the original chloroplast is believed to have been a photosynthetic prokaryote that lived inside a eukaryotic cell. (You'll learn more about this hypothesis in Chapter 25.) Chloroplasts are present in a variety of photosynthesizing organisms (see Figure 10.2), but here we will focus on plants.

Chloroplasts: The Sites of Photosynthesis in Plants

All green parts of a plant, including green stems and unripened fruit, have chloroplasts, but the leaves are the major sites of photosynthesis in most plants **(Figure 10.3)**. There are about half a million chloroplasts per square millimeter of leaf surface. The color of the leaf is from **chlorophyll**, the green pigment located within chloroplasts. It is the light energy absorbed by chlorophyll that drives the synthesis of organic molecules in the chloroplast. Chloroplasts are found mainly in the cells of the **mesophyll**, the tissue in the interior of the leaf.

Carbon dioxide enters the leaf, and oxygen exits, by way of microscopic pores called **stomata** (singular, *stoma*; from the Greek, meaning "mouth"). Water absorbed by the roots is delivered to the leaves in veins. Leaves also use veins to export sugar to roots and other nonphotosynthetic parts of the plant.

A typical mesophyll cell has about 30 to 40 chloroplasts, each organelle measuring about 2–4 μm by 4–7 μm. An envelope of two membranes encloses the **stroma**, the dense fluid within the chloroplast. An elaborate system of interconnected membranous sacs called **thylakoids** segregates the stroma from another compartment, the interior of the thylakoids, or *thylakoid space*. In some places, thylakoid sacs are stacked in columns called *grana* (singular, *granum*). Chlorophyll resides in the thylakoid membranes. (The infolded photosynthetic membranes of prokaryotes are also called thylakoid membranes; see Figure 27.7b.) Now that we have looked at the sites of photosynthesis in plants, we are ready to look more closely at the process of photosynthesis.

Tracking Atoms Through Photosynthesis: *Scientific Inquiry*

Scientists have tried for centuries to piece together the process by which plants make food. Although some of the steps are still not completely understood, the overall photosynthetic equation has been known since the 1800s: In the presence of light, the green parts of plants produce organic compounds and oxygen from carbon dioxide and water. Using molecular formulas, we can summarize the complex series of chemical reactions in photosynthesis with this chemical equation:

$$6\,CO_2 + 12\,H_2O + \text{Light energy} \rightarrow C_6H_{12}O_6 + 6\,O_2 + 6\,H_2O$$

We use glucose ($C_6H_{12}O_6$) here to simplify the relationship between photosynthesis and respiration, but the direct product of photosynthesis is actually a three-carbon sugar that can be used to make glucose. Water appears on both sides of the equation because 12 molecules are consumed and 6 molecules are newly formed during photosynthesis. We can simplify the equation by indicating only the net consumption of water:

$$6\,CO_2 + 6\,H_2O + \text{Light energy} \rightarrow C_6H_{12}O_6 + 6\,O_2$$

Writing the equation in this form, we can see that the overall chemical change during photosynthesis is the reverse of the one that occurs during cellular respiration. Both of these metabolic processes occur in plant cells. However, as you will soon learn, chloroplasts do not synthesize sugars by simply reversing the steps of respiration.

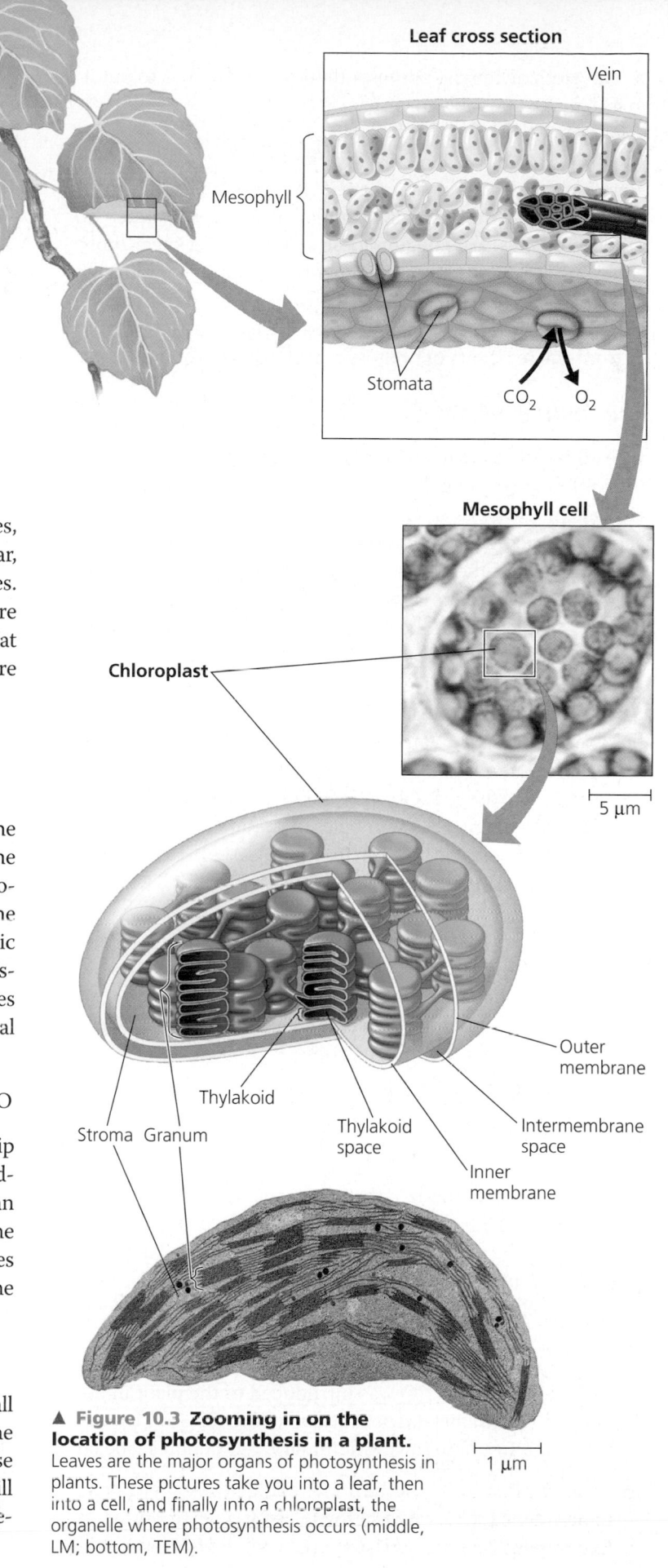

▲ **Figure 10.3 Zooming in on the location of photosynthesis in a plant.** Leaves are the major organs of photosynthesis in plants. These pictures take you into a leaf, then into a cell, and finally into a chloroplast, the organelle where photosynthesis occurs (middle, LM; bottom, TEM).

Now let's divide the photosynthetic equation by 6 to put it in its simplest possible form:

$$CO_2 + H_2O \rightarrow [CH_2O] + O_2$$

Here, the brackets indicate that CH_2O is not an actual sugar but represents the general formula for a carbohydrate. In other words, we are imagining the synthesis of a sugar molecule one carbon at a time. Six repetitions would theoretically produce a glucose molecule. Let's now use this simplified formula to see how researchers tracked the elements C, H, and O from the reactants of photosynthesis to the products.

The Splitting of Water

One of the first clues to the mechanism of photosynthesis came from the discovery that the O_2 given off by plants is derived from H_2O and not from CO_2. The chloroplast splits water into hydrogen and oxygen. Before this discovery, the prevailing hypothesis was that photosynthesis split carbon dioxide ($CO_2 \rightarrow C + O_2$) and then added water to the carbon ($C + H_2O \rightarrow [CH_2O]$). This hypothesis predicted that the O_2 released during photosynthesis came from CO_2. This idea was challenged in the 1930s by C. B. van Niel, of Stanford University. Van Niel was investigating photosynthesis in bacteria that make their carbohydrate from CO_2 but do not release O_2. Van Niel concluded that, at least in these bacteria, CO_2 is not split into carbon and oxygen. One group of bacteria used hydrogen sulfide (H_2S) rather than water for photosynthesis, forming yellow globules of sulfur as a waste product (these globules are visible in Figure 10.2e). Here is the chemical equation for photosynthesis in these sulfur bacteria:

$$CO_2 + 2\,H_2S \rightarrow [CH_2O] + H_2O + 2\,S$$

Van Niel reasoned that the bacteria split H_2S and used the hydrogen atoms to make sugar. He then generalized that idea, proposing that all photosynthetic organisms require a hydrogen source but that the source varies:

Sulfur bacteria: $CO_2 + 2\,H_2S \rightarrow [CH_2O] + H_2O + 2\,S$
Plants: $CO_2 + 2\,H_2O \rightarrow [CH_2O] + H_2O + O_2$
General: $CO_2 + 2\,H_2X \rightarrow [CH_2O] + H_2O + 2\,X$

Thus, van Niel hypothesized that plants split H_2O as a source of electrons from hydrogen atoms, releasing O_2 as a by-product.

Nearly 20 years later, scientists confirmed van Niel's hypothesis by using oxygen-18 (^{18}O), a heavy isotope, as a tracer to follow the fate of oxygen atoms during photosynthesis. The experiments showed that the O_2 from plants was labeled with ^{18}O *only* if water was the source of the tracer (experiment 1). If the ^{18}O was introduced to the plant in the form of CO_2, the label did not turn up in the released O_2 (experiment 2). In the following summary, red denotes labeled atoms of oxygen (^{18}O):

Experiment 1: $CO_2 + 2\,H_2O \rightarrow [CH_2O] + H_2O + O_2$
Experiment 2: $CO_2 + 2\,H_2O \rightarrow [CH_2O] + H_2O + O_2$

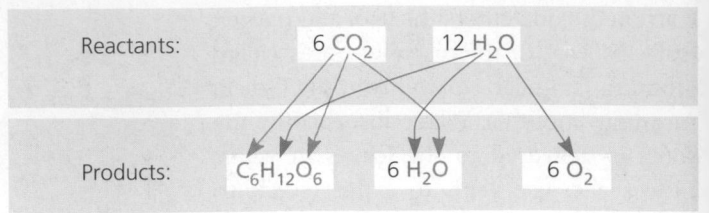

▲ **Figure 10.4 Tracking atoms through photosynthesis.** The atoms from CO_2 are shown in orange, and the atoms from H_2O are shown in blue.

A significant result of the shuffling of atoms during photosynthesis is the extraction of hydrogen from water and its incorporation into sugar. The waste product of photosynthesis, O_2, is released to the atmosphere. **Figure 10.4** shows the fates of all atoms in photosynthesis.

Photosynthesis as a Redox Process

Let's briefly compare photosynthesis with cellular respiration. Both processes involve redox reactions. During cellular respiration, energy is released from sugar when electrons associated with hydrogen are transported by carriers to oxygen, forming water as a by-product. The electrons lose potential energy as they "fall" down the electron transport chain toward electronegative oxygen, and the mitochondrion harnesses that energy to synthesize ATP (see Figure 9.16). Photosynthesis reverses the direction of electron flow. Water is split, and electrons are transferred along with hydrogen ions from the water to carbon dioxide, reducing it to sugar. Because the electrons increase in potential energy as they move from water to sugar, this process requires energy, in other words is endergonic. This energy boost is provided by light.

The Two Stages of Photosynthesis: *A Preview*

The equation for photosynthesis is a deceptively simple summary of a very complex process. Actually, photosynthesis is not a single process, but two processes, each with multiple steps. These two stages of photosynthesis are known as the **light reactions** (the *photo* part of photosynthesis) and the **Calvin cycle** (the *synthesis* part) **(Figure 10.5)**.

The light reactions are the steps of photosynthesis that convert solar energy to chemical energy. Water is split, providing a source of electrons and protons (hydrogen ions, H^+) and giving off O_2 as a by-product. Light absorbed by chlorophyll drives a transfer of the electrons and hydrogen ions from water to an acceptor called **NADP+** (nicotinamide adenine dinucleotide phosphate), where they are temporarily stored. The electron acceptor $NADP^+$ is first cousin to NAD^+, which functions as an electron carrier in cellular respiration; the two molecules differ only by the presence of an extra phosphate group in the $NADP^+$ molecule. The light reactions use solar power to reduce $NADP^+$ to NADPH by adding a

► **Figure 10.5 An overview of photosynthesis: cooperation of the light reactions and the Calvin cycle.** In the chloroplast, the thylakoid membranes are the sites of the light reactions, whereas the Calvin cycle occurs in the stroma. The light reactions use solar energy to make ATP and NADPH, which supply chemical energy and reducing power, respectively, to the Calvin cycle. The Calvin cycle incorporates CO_2 into organic molecules, which are converted to sugar. (Recall that most simple sugars have formulas that are some multiple of CH_2O.)

A smaller version of this diagram will reappear in several subsequent figures as a reminder of whether the events being described occur in the light reactions or in the Calvin cycle.

MEDIA **BioFlix** Visit **www.campbellbiology.com** for the BioFlix 3-D Animation on Photosynthesis.

pair of electrons along with an H^+. The light reactions also generate ATP, using chemiosmosis to power the addition of a phosphate group to ADP, a process called **photophosphorylation**. Thus, light energy is initially converted to chemical energy in the form of two compounds: NADPH, a source of electrons as "reducing power" that can be passed along to an electron acceptor, reducing it, and ATP, the versatile energy currency of cells. Notice that the light reactions produce no sugar; that happens in the second stage of photosynthesis, the Calvin cycle.

The Calvin cycle is named for Melvin Calvin, who, along with his colleagues, began to elucidate its steps in the late 1940s. The cycle begins by incorporating CO_2 from the air into organic molecules already present in the chloroplast. This initial incorporation of carbon into organic compounds is known as **carbon fixation**. The Calvin cycle then reduces the fixed carbon to carbohydrate by the addition of electrons. The reducing power is provided by NADPH, which acquired its cargo of electrons in the light reactions. To convert CO_2 to carbohydrate, the Calvin cycle also requires chemical energy in the form of ATP, which is also generated by the light reactions. Thus, it is the Calvin cycle that makes sugar, but it can do so only with the help of the NADPH and ATP produced by the light reactions. The metabolic steps of the Calvin cycle are sometimes referred to as the dark reactions, or light-independent reactions, because none of the steps requires light *directly*. Nevertheless, the Calvin cycle in most plants occurs during daylight, for only then can the light reactions

provide the NADPH and ATP that the Calvin cycle requires. In essence, the chloroplast uses light energy to make sugar by coordinating the two stages of photosynthesis.

As Figure 10.5 indicates, the thylakoids of the chloroplast are the sites of the light reactions, while the Calvin cycle occurs in the stroma. In the thylakoids, molecules of $NADP^+$ and ADP pick up electrons and phosphate, respectively, and NADPH and ATP are then released to the stroma, where they play crucial roles in the Calvin cycle. The two stages of photosynthesis are treated in this figure as metabolic modules that take in ingredients and crank out products. Our next step toward understanding photosynthesis is to look more closely at how the two stages work, beginning with the light reactions.

CONCEPT CHECK 10.1

1. How do the reactant molecules of photosynthesis reach the chloroplasts in leaves?
2. How did the use of an oxygen isotope help elucidate the chemistry of photosynthesis?
3. **WHAT IF?** The Calvin cycle clearly requires the products of the light reactions, ATP and NADPH. Suppose a classmate asserts that the converse is not true—that the light reactions don't depend on the Calvin cycle and, with continual light, could just keep on producing ATP and NADPH. Do you agree or disagree? Explain.

For suggested answers, see Appendix A.

The light reactions convert solar energy to the chemical energy of ATP and NADPH

Chloroplasts are chemical factories powered by the sun. Their thylakoids transform light energy into the chemical energy of ATP and NADPH. To understand this conversion better, we need to know about some important properties of light.

The Nature of Sunlight

Light is a form of energy known as electromagnetic energy, also called electromagnetic radiation. Electromagnetic energy travels in rhythmic waves analogous to those created by dropping a pebble into a pond. Electromagnetic waves, however, are disturbances of electric and magnetic fields rather than disturbances of a material medium such as water.

The distance between the crests of electromagnetic waves is called the **wavelength**. Wavelengths range from less than a nanometer (for gamma rays) to more than a kilometer (for radio waves). This entire range of radiation is known as the **electromagnetic spectrum (Figure 10.6)**. The segment most important to life is the narrow band from about 380 nm to 750 nm in wavelength. This radiation is known as **visible light** because it can be detected as various colors by the human eye.

The model of light as waves explains many of light's properties, but in certain respects light behaves as though it consists of discrete particles, called **photons**. Photons are not tangible objects, but they act like objects in that each of them has a fixed quantity of energy. The amount of energy is in-versely related to the wavelength of the light: the shorter the wavelength, the greater the energy of each photon of that light. Thus, a photon of violet light packs nearly twice as much energy as a photon of red light.

Although the sun radiates the full spectrum of electromagnetic energy, the atmosphere acts like a selective window, allowing visible light to pass through while screening out a substantial fraction of other radiation. The part of the spectrum we can see—visible light—is also the radiation that drives photosynthesis.

Photosynthetic Pigments: The Light Receptors

When light meets matter, it may be reflected, transmitted, or absorbed. Substances that absorb visible light are known as *pigments*. Different pigments absorb light of different wavelengths, and the wavelengths that are absorbed disappear. If a pigment is illuminated with white light, the color we see is the color most reflected or transmitted by the pigment. (If a pigment absorbs all wavelengths, it appears black.) We see green when we look at a leaf because chlorophyll absorbs violet-blue and red light while transmitting and reflecting green light **(Figure 10.7)**. The ability of a pigment to absorb various wavelengths of light can be measured with an instrument called a **spectrophotometer**. This machine directs beams of light of different wavelengths through a solution of the pigment and measures the fraction of the light transmitted at each wavelength. A graph plotting

▲ **Figure 10.6 The electromagnetic spectrum.** White light is a mixture of all wavelengths of visible light. A prism can sort white light into its component colors by bending light of different wavelengths at different angles. (Droplets of water in the atmosphere can act as prisms, forming a rainbow; see Figure 10.1.) Visible light drives photosynthesis.

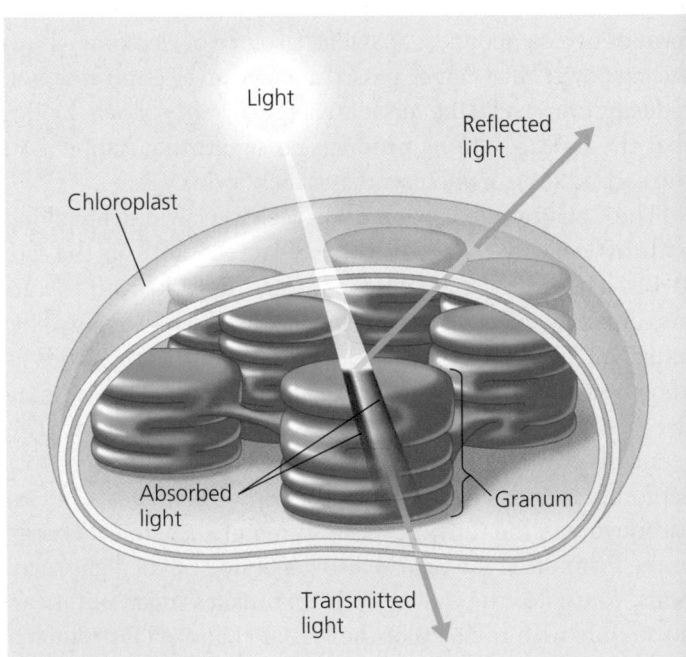

▲ **Figure 10.7 Why leaves are green: interaction of light with chloroplasts.** The chlorophyll molecules of chloroplasts absorb violet-blue and red light (the colors most effective in driving photosynthesis) and reflect or transmit green light. This is why leaves appear green.

a pigment's light absorption versus wavelength is called an **absorption spectrum (Figure 10.8)**.

The absorption spectra of chloroplast pigments provide clues to the relative effectiveness of different wavelengths for driving photosynthesis, since light can perform work in chloroplasts only if it is absorbed. **Figure 10.9a** shows the absorption spectra of three types of pigments in chloroplasts: **chlorophyll *a***, which participates directly in the light reactions; the accessory pigment *chlorophyll b*; and a group of accessory pigments called carotenoids. The spectrum of chlorophyll *a* suggests that

▼ Figure 10.8 Research Method

Determining an Absorption Spectrum

APPLICATION An absorption spectrum is a visual representation of how well a particular pigment absorbs different wavelengths of visible light. Absorption spectra of various chloroplast pigments help scientists decipher each pigment's role in a plant.

TECHNIQUE A spectrophotometer measures the relative amounts of light of different wavelengths absorbed and transmitted by a pigment solution.

① White light is separated into colors (wavelengths) by a prism.

② One by one, the different colors of light are passed through the sample (chlorophyll in this example). Green light and blue light are shown here.

③ The transmitted light strikes a photoelectric tube, which converts the light energy to electricity.

④ The electrical current is measured by a galvanometer. The meter indicates the fraction of light transmitted through the sample, from which we can determine the amount of light absorbed.

White light / Refracting prism / Chlorophyll solution / Photoelectric tube / Galvanometer

Slit moves to pass light of selected wavelength

Green light

The high transmittance (low absorption) reading indicates that chlorophyll absorbs very little green light.

Blue light

The low transmittance (high absorption) reading indicates that chlorophyll absorbs most blue light.

RESULTS See Figure 10.9a for absorption spectra of three types of chloroplast pigments.

▼ Figure 10.9 Inquiry

Which wavelengths of light are most effective in driving photosynthesis?

EXPERIMENT Absorption and action spectra, along with a classic experiment by Theodor W. Engelmann, reveal which wavelengths of light are photosynthetically important.

RESULTS

Chlorophyll a / Chlorophyll b / Carotenoids

Absorption of light by chloroplast pigments

Wavelength of light (nm)

(a) Absorption spectra. The three curves show the wavelengths of light best absorbed by three types of chloroplast pigments.

Rate of photosynthesis (measured by O₂ release)

(b) Action spectrum. This graph plots the rate of photosynthesis versus wavelength. The resulting action spectrum resembles the absorption spectrum for chlorophyll *a* but does not match exactly (see part a). This is partly due to the absorption of light by accessory pigments such as chlorophyll *b* and carotenoids.

Aerobic bacteria / Filament of alga

(c) Engelmann's experiment. In 1883, Theodor W. Engelmann illuminated a filamentous alga with light that had been passed through a prism, exposing different segments of the alga to different wavelengths. He used aerobic bacteria, which concentrate near an oxygen source, to determine which segments of the alga were releasing the most O₂ and thus photosynthesizing most. Bacteria congregated in greatest numbers around the parts of the alga illuminated with violet-blue or red light.

CONCLUSION Light in the violet-blue and red portions of the spectrum is most effective in driving photosynthesis.

SOURCE T. W. Engelmann, *Bacterium photometricum. Ein Betrag zur vergleichenden Physiologie des Licht- und farbensinnes, Archiv. für Physiologie.* 30:95–124 (1883).

WHAT IF? If Engelmann had placed a red-colored filter between the prism and the alga, how would the results have differed?

violet-blue and red light work best for photosynthesis, since they are absorbed, while green is the least effective color. This is confirmed by an **action spectrum** for photosynthesis (**Figure 10.9b**), which profiles the relative effectiveness of different wavelengths of radiation in driving the process. An action spectrum is prepared by illuminating chloroplasts with light of different colors and then plotting wavelength against some measure of photosynthetic rate, such as CO_2 consumption or O_2 release. The action spectrum for photosynthesis was first demonstrated by a German botanist in 1883. Before equipment for measuring O_2 levels had even been invented, Theodor W. Engelmann performed a clever experiment in which he used bacteria to measure rates of photosynthesis in filamentous algae (**Figure 10.9c**). His results are a striking match to the modern action spectrum shown in Figure 10.9b.

Notice by comparing Figures 10.9a and 10.9b that the action spectrum for photosynthesis does not exactly match the absorption spectrum of chlorophyll *a*. The absorption spectrum of chlorophyll *a* alone underestimates the effectiveness of certain wavelengths in driving photosynthesis. This is partly because accessory pigments with different absorption spectra are also photosynthetically important in chloroplasts and broaden the spectrum of colors that can be used for photosynthesis. **Figure 10.10** shows chlorophyll *a* compared to one of these accessory pigments, **chlorophyll *b***. A slight structural difference between them is enough to cause the two pigments to absorb at slightly different wavelengths in the red and blue parts of the spectrum (see Figure 10.9a). As a result, chlorophyll *a* is blue green and chlorophyll *b* is olive green.

Other accessory pigments include **carotenoids**, hydrocarbons that are various shades of yellow and orange because they absorb violet and blue-green light (see Figure 10.9a). Carotenoids may broaden the spectrum of colors that can drive photosynthesis. However, a more important function of at least some carotenoids seems to be *photoprotection*: These compounds absorb and dissipate excessive light energy that would otherwise damage chlorophyll or interact with oxygen, forming reactive oxidative molecules that are dangerous to the cell. Interestingly, carotenoids similar to the photoprotective ones in chloroplasts have a photoprotective role in the human eye. These and related molecules, often found in health food products, are valued as "phytochemicals" (from the Greek *phyton*, plant), compounds with antioxidant properties. Plants can synthesize all the antioxidants they require, but humans and other animals must obtain some of them from their diets.

Excitation of Chlorophyll by Light

What exactly happens when chlorophyll and other pigments absorb light? The colors corresponding to the absorbed wavelengths disappear from the spectrum of the transmitted and reflected light, but energy cannot disappear. When a molecule absorbs a photon of light, one of the molecule's electrons is elevated to an orbital where it has more potential energy. When the electron is in its normal orbital, the pigment molecule is said to be in its ground state. Absorption of a photon boosts an electron to an orbital of higher energy, and the pigment molecule is then said to be in an excited state. The only photons absorbed are those whose energy is exactly equal to the energy difference between the ground state and an excited state, and this energy difference varies from one kind of molecule to another. Thus, a particular compound absorbs only photons corresponding to specific wavelengths, which is why each pigment has a unique absorption spectrum.

Once absorption of a photon raises an electron from the ground state to an excited state, the electron cannot remain there long. The excited state, like all high-energy states, is unstable. Generally, when isolated pigment molecules absorb light, their excited electrons drop back down to the ground-state orbital in a billionth of a second, releasing their excess energy as heat. This conversion of light energy to heat is what makes the top of an automobile so hot on a sunny day. (White cars are coolest because their paint reflects all wavelengths of visible light, although it may absorb ultraviolet and other invisible radiation.) In isolation, some pigments, including chlorophyll, emit light as well as heat after absorbing photons. As excited electrons fall back to the ground state, photons are given off. This afterglow is called

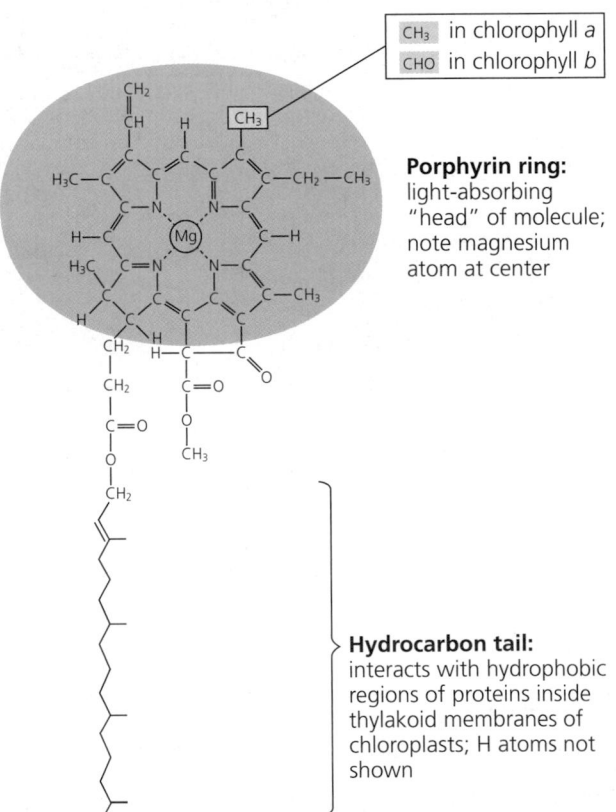

CH₃ in chlorophyll *a*
CHO in chlorophyll *b*

Porphyrin ring: light-absorbing "head" of molecule; note magnesium atom at center

Hydrocarbon tail: interacts with hydrophobic regions of proteins inside thylakoid membranes of chloroplasts; H atoms not shown

▲ **Figure 10.10 Structure of chlorophyll molecules in chloroplasts of plants.** Chlorophyll *a* and chlorophyll *b* differ only in one of the functional groups bonded to the organic structure called a porphyrin ring.

(a) Excitation of isolated chlorophyll molecule

(b) Fluorescence

◀ **Figure 10.11 Excitation of isolated chlorophyll by light. (a)** Absorption of a photon causes a transition of the chlorophyll molecule from its ground state to its excited state. The photon boosts an electron to an orbital where it has more potential energy. If the illuminated molecule exists in isolation, its excited electron immediately drops back down to the ground-state orbital, and its excess energy is given off as heat and fluorescence (light). **(b)** A chlorophyll solution excited with ultraviolet light fluoresces with a red-orange glow.

WHAT IF? *If a leaf containing a similar concentration of chlorophyll as the solution was exposed to the same ultraviolet light, no fluorescence would be seen. Explain the difference in fluorescence emission between the solution and the leaf.*

fluorescence. If a solution of chlorophyll isolated from chloroplasts is illuminated, it will fluoresce in the red-orange part of the spectrum and also give off heat **(Figure 10.11)**.

A Photosystem: A Reaction-Center Complex Associated with Light-Harvesting Complexes

Chlorophyll molecules excited by the absorption of light energy produce very different results in an intact chloroplast than they do in isolation (see Figure 10.11). In their native environment of the thylakoid membrane, chlorophyll molecules are organized along with other small organic molecules and proteins into photosystems.

A **photosystem** is composed of a protein complex called a **reaction-center complex** surrounded by several light-harvesting complexes **(Figure 10.12)**. The reaction-center complex includes a special pair of chlorophyll *a* molecules. Each **light-harvesting complex** consists of various pigment molecules (which may include chlorophyll *a*, chlorophyll *b*, and carotenoids) bound to proteins. The number and variety of pigment molecules enable a photosystem to harvest light over a larger surface and a larger portion of the spectrum than any single pigment molecule alone could. Together, these light-harvesting complexes act as an antenna for the reaction-center complex. When a pigment molecule absorbs a photon, the energy is transferred from pigment molecule to pigment molecule within a light-harvesting complex, somewhat like a human "wave" at a sports arena, until it is passed into the reaction-center complex. The reaction-center complex contains a molecule capable of accepting electrons and becoming reduced; it is called the **primary electron acceptor**. The pair of chlorophyll *a* molecules in the reaction-center complex are special because their molecular environment—their location and the other molecules with which they are associated—enables

▲ **Figure 10.12 How a photosystem harvests light.** When a photon strikes a pigment molecule in a light-harvesting complex, the energy is passed from molecule to molecule until it reaches the reaction-center complex. Here, an excited electron from the special pair of chlorophyll *a* molecules is transferred to the primary electron acceptor.

them to use the energy from light not only to boost one of their electrons to a higher energy level, but also to transfer it to a different molecule—the primary electron acceptor.

The solar-powered transfer of an electron from the reaction-center chlorophyll *a* pair to the primary electron acceptor is the first step of the light reactions. As soon as the chlorophyll electron is excited to a higher energy level, the primary electron acceptor captures it; this is a redox reaction. Isolated chlorophyll fluoresces because there is no electron acceptor, so electrons of photoexcited chlorophyll drop right back to the ground state. In a chloroplast, the potential energy represented by the excited electron is not lost. Thus, each photosystem—a reaction-center complex surrounded by light-harvesting complexes—functions in the chloroplast as a unit. It converts light energy to chemical energy, which will ultimately be used for the synthesis of sugar.

The thylakoid membrane is populated by two types of photosystems that cooperate in the light reactions of photosynthesis. They are called **photosystem II (PS II)** and **photosystem I (PS I)**. (They were named in order of their discovery, but photosystem II functions first in the light reactions.) Each has a characteristic reaction-center complex—a particular kind of primary electron acceptor next to a special pair of chlorophyll *a* molecules associated with specific proteins. The reaction-center chlorophyll *a* of photosystem II is known as P680 because this pigment is best at absorbing light having a wavelength of 680 nm (in the red part of the spectrum). The chlorophyll *a* at the reaction-center complex of photosystem I is called P700 because it most effectively absorbs light of wavelength 700 nm (in the far-red part of the spectrum). These two pigments, P680 and P700, are nearly identical chlorophyll *a* molecules. However, their association with different proteins in the thylakoid membrane affects the electron distribution in the two pigments and accounts for the slight differences in their light-absorbing properties. Now let's see how the two photosystems work together in using light energy to generate ATP and NADPH, the two main products of the light reactions.

Linear Electron Flow

Light drives the synthesis of ATP and NADPH by energizing the two photosystems embedded in the thylakoid membranes of chloroplasts. The key to this energy transformation is a flow of electrons through the photosystems and other molecular components built into the thylakoid membrane. This is called **linear electron flow**, and it occurs during the light reactions of photosynthesis, as shown in **Figure 10.13**. The numbers in the text description correspond to the numbered steps in the figure.

❶ A photon of light strikes a pigment molecule in a light-harvesting complex, boosting one of its electrons to a higher energy level. As this electron falls back to its ground state, an electron in a nearby pigment molecule is simultaneously raised to an excited state. The process continues, with the energy being relayed to other pigment molecules until it reaches the P680 pair of chlorophyll *a* molecules in the PS II reaction-center complex. It excites an electron in this pair of chlorophylls to a higher energy state.

❷ This electron is transferred from the excited P680 to the primary electron acceptor. We can refer to the resulting form of P680, missing an electron, as P680$^+$.

❸ An enzyme catalyzes the splitting of a water molecule into two electrons, two hydrogen ions, and an oxygen atom. The electrons are supplied one by one to the P680$^+$ pair, each electron replacing one transferred to the primary electron acceptor. (P680$^+$ is the strongest biological oxidizing agent known; its electron "hole" must be filled. This greatly facilitates the transfer of electrons from the split water molecule.) The oxygen atom immediately combines with an oxygen atom generated by the splitting of another water molecule, forming O_2.

❹ Each photoexcited electron passes from the primary electron acceptor of PS II to PS I via an electron transport chain, the components of which are similar to those of the electron transport chain that functions in cellular respiration. The electron transport chain between PS II and PS I is made up of the electron carrier plastoquinone (Pq), a cytochrome complex, and a protein called plastocyanin (Pc).

❺ The exergonic "fall" of electrons to a lower energy level provides energy for the synthesis of ATP. As electrons pass through the cytochrome complex, the pumping of protons builds a proton gradient that is subsequently used in chemiosmosis.

❻ Meanwhile, light energy was transferred via light-harvesting complex pigments to the PS I reaction-center complex, exciting an electron of the P700 pair of chlorophyll *a* molecules located there. The photoexcited electron was then transferred to PS I's primary electron acceptor, creating an electron "hole" in the P700—which we now can call P700$^+$. In other words, P700$^+$ can now act as an electron acceptor, accepting an electron that reaches the bottom of the electron transport chain from PS II.

❼ Photoexcited electrons are passed in a series of redox reactions from the primary electron acceptor of PS I down a second electron transport chain through the protein ferredoxin (Fd). (This chain does not create a proton gradient and thus does not produce ATP.)

❽ The enzyme NADP$^+$ reductase catalyzes the transfer of electrons from Fd to NADP$^+$. Two electrons are required for its reduction to NADPH. This molecule is at a higher energy level than water, and its electrons are more readily available for the reactions of the Calvin cycle than were those of water.

As complicated as the scheme shown in Figure 10.13 is, do not lose track of its functions. The light reactions use solar power to generate ATP and NADPH, which provide chemical energy and reducing power, respectively, to the carbohydrate-synthesizing reactions of the Calvin cycle. The energy changes of electrons as they flow through the light reactions are shown in a mechanical analogy in **Figure 10.14**.

H₂O CO₂

Light

NADP⁺
ADP

Light Reactions — Calvin Cycle

ATP
NADPH

O₂ [CH₂O] (sugar)

Photosystem II (PS II)

Primary acceptor

Electron transport chain ④

2 H⁺ + ½ O₂

H₂O ③

① Light

e⁻ e⁻

P680

Pq ②

Cytochrome complex

Pc

⑤

ATP

Pigment molecules

Photosystem I (PS I)

Primary acceptor

Electron transport chain ⑦

Fd

e⁻ e⁻ ⑧

NADP⁺ reductase

NADP⁺ + H⁺

NADPH

P700

Light ⑥

▲ **Figure 10.14 A mechanical analogy for the light reactions.**

ATP

NADPH

Mill makes ATP

Photon

Photosystem II

Photon

Photosystem I

Cyclic Electron Flow

In certain cases, photoexcited electrons can take an alternative path called **cyclic electron flow**, which uses photosystem I but not photosystem II. You can see in **Figure 10.15**, on the next page, that cyclic flow is a short circuit: The electrons cycle back from ferredoxin (Fd) to the cytochrome complex and from there continue on to a P700 chlorophyll in the PS I reaction-center complex. There is no production of NADPH and no release of oxygen. Cyclic flow does, however, generate ATP.

Several of the currently existing groups of photosynthetic bacteria are known to have photosystem I but not photosystem II; for these species, which include the purple sulfur bacteria (see Figure 10.2e), cyclic electron flow is the sole means of generating ATP in photosynthesis. Evolutionary biologists believe that these bacterial groups are descendants of the bacteria in which photosynthesis first evolved, in a form similar to cyclic electron flow.

Cyclic electron flow can also occur in photosynthetic species that possess both photosystems; this includes some prokaryotes, such as the cyanobacteria shown in Figure 10.2d, as well as the eukaryotic photosynthetic species that have been tested to

► **Figure 10.15 Cyclic electron flow.**
Photoexcited electrons from PS I are occasionally shunted back from ferredoxin (Fd) to chlorophyll via the cytochrome complex and plastocyanin (Pc). This electron shunt supplements the supply of ATP (via chemiosmosis) but produces no NADPH. The "shadow" of linear electron flow is included in the diagram for comparison with the cyclic route. The two ferredoxin molecules shown in this diagram are actually one and the same—the final electron carrier in the electron transport chain of PS I.

date. Although the process is probably in part an "evolutionary leftover," it clearly plays at least one beneficial role for these organisms. Mutant plants that are not able to carry out cyclic electron flow are capable of growing well in low light, but do not grow well where light is intense. This is evidence for the idea that cyclic electron flow may be photoprotective, protecting cells from light-induced damage. Later you'll learn more about cyclic electron flow as it relates to a particular adaptation of photosynthesis (C_4 plants; see Concept 10.4).

Whether ATP synthesis is driven by linear or cyclic electron flow, the actual mechanism is the same. Before we move on to consider the Calvin cycle, let's review chemiosmosis, the process that uses membranes to couple redox reactions to ATP production.

A Comparison of Chemiosmosis in Chloroplasts and Mitochondria

Chloroplasts and mitochondria generate ATP by the same basic mechanism: chemiosmosis. An electron transport chain assembled in a membrane pumps protons across the membrane as electrons are passed through a series of carriers that are progressively more electronegative. In this way, electron transport chains transform redox energy to a proton-motive force, potential energy stored in the form of an H^+ gradient across a membrane. Built into the same membrane is an ATP synthase complex that couples the diffusion of hydrogen ions down their gradient to the phosphorylation of ADP. Some of the electron carriers, including the iron-containing proteins called cytochromes, are very similar in chloroplasts and mitochondria. The ATP synthase complexes of the two organelles are also very much alike. But there are noteworthy differences between oxidative phosphorylation in mitochondria and photophosphorylation in chloroplasts. In mitochondria, the high-energy electrons dropped down the transport chain are extracted from organic molecules (which are thus oxidized), while in chloroplasts, the source of electrons is water. Chloroplasts do not need molecules from food to make ATP; their

photosystems capture light energy and use it to drive the electrons from water to the top of the transport chain. In other words, mitochondria use chemiosmosis to transfer chemical energy from food molecules to ATP, whereas chloroplasts transform light energy into chemical energy in ATP.

Although the spatial organization of chemiosmosis differs slightly between chloroplasts and mitochondria, it is easy to see similarities in the two **(Figure 10.16)**. The inner membrane of

▲ **Figure 10.16 Comparison of chemiosmosis in mitochondria and chloroplasts.** In both kinds of organelles, electron transport chains pump protons (H^+) across a membrane from a region of low H^+ concentration (light gray in this diagram) to one of high H^+ concentration (dark gray). The protons then diffuse back across the membrane through ATP synthase, driving the synthesis of ATP.

the mitochondrion pumps protons from the mitochondrial matrix out to the intermembrane space, which then serves as a reservoir of hydrogen ions. The thylakoid membrane of the chloroplast pumps protons from the stroma into the thylakoid space (interior of the thylakoid), which functions as the H$^+$ reservoir. If you imagine the cristae of mitochondria pinching off from the inner membrane, this may help you see how the thylakoid space and the intermembrane space are comparable spaces in the two organelles, while the mitochondrial matrix is analogous to the stroma of the chloroplast. In the mitochondrion, protons diffuse down their concentration gradient from the intermembrane space through ATP synthase to the matrix,

driving ATP synthesis. In the chloroplast, ATP is synthesized as the hydrogen ions diffuse from the thylakoid space back to the stroma through ATP synthase complexes, whose catalytic knobs are on the stroma side of the membrane. Thus, ATP forms in the stroma, where it is used to help drive sugar synthesis during the Calvin cycle (Figure 10.17).

The proton (H$^+$) gradient, or pH gradient, across the thylakoid membrane is substantial. When chloroplasts in an experimental setting are illuminated, the pH in the thylakoid space drops to about 5 (the H$^+$ concentration increases), and the pH in the stroma increases to about 8 (the H$^+$ concentration decreases). This gradient of three pH units corresponds to a thousandfold

▲ **Figure 10.17 The light reactions and chemiosmosis: the organization of the thylakoid membrane.** This diagram shows a current model for the organization of the thylakoid membrane. The gold arrows track the linear electron flow outlined in Figure 10.13. As electrons pass from carrier to carrier in redox reactions, hydrogen ions removed from the stroma are deposited in the thylakoid space, storing energy as a proton-motive force (H$^+$ gradient). At least three steps in the light reactions contribute to the proton gradient: ❶ Water is split by photosystem II on the side of the membrane facing the thylakoid space; ❷ as plastoquinone (Pq), a mobile carrier, transfers electrons to the cytochrome complex, four protons are translocated across the membrane into the thylakoid space; and ❸ a hydrogen ion is removed from the stroma when it is taken up by NADP$^+$. Notice how, as in Figure 10.16, hydrogen ions are being pumped from the stroma into the thylakoid space. The diffusion of H$^+$ from the thylakoid space back to the stroma (along the H$^+$ concentration gradient) powers the ATP synthase. These light-driven reactions store chemical energy in NADPH and ATP, which shuttle the energy to the carbohydrate-producing Calvin cycle.

difference in H^+ concentration. If in the laboratory the lights are turned off, the pH gradient is abolished, but it can quickly be restored by turning the lights back on. Experiments such as this provided strong evidence in support of the chemiosmotic model.

Based on studies in several laboratories, Figure 10.17 shows a current model for the organization of the light-reaction "machinery" within the thylakoid membrane. Each of the molecules and molecular complexes in the figure is present in numerous copies in each thylakoid. Notice that NADPH, like ATP, is produced on the side of the membrane facing the stroma, where the Calvin cycle reactions take place.

Let's summarize the light reactions. Electron flow pushes electrons from water, where they are at a low state of potential energy, ultimately to NADPH, where they are stored at a high state of potential energy. The light-driven electron current also generates ATP. Thus, the equipment of the thylakoid membrane converts light energy to chemical energy stored in ATP and NADPH. (Oxygen is a by-product.) Let's now see how the Calvin cycle uses the products of the light reactions to synthesize sugar from CO_2.

CONCEPT CHECK **10.2**

1. What color of light is *least* effective in driving photosynthesis? Explain.
2. Compared to a solution of isolated chlorophyll, why do intact chloroplasts release less heat and fluorescence when illuminated?
3. In the light reactions, what is the initial electron donor? Where do the electrons end up?
4. **WHAT IF?** In an experiment, isolated chloroplasts placed in a solution with the appropriate components can carry out ATP synthesis. Predict what would happen to the rate of synthesis if a compound is added to the solution that makes membranes freely permeable to hydrogen ions.

For suggested answers, see Appendix A.

CONCEPT **10.3**

The Calvin cycle uses ATP and NADPH to convert CO_2 to sugar

The Calvin cycle is similar to the citric acid cycle in that a starting material is regenerated after molecules enter and leave the cycle. However, while the citric acid cycle is catabolic, oxidizing glucose and using the energy to synthesize ATP, the Calvin cycle is anabolic, building carbohydrates from smaller molecules and consuming energy. Carbon enters the Calvin cycle in the form of CO_2 and leaves in the form of sugar. The cycle spends ATP as an energy source and consumes NADPH as reducing power for adding high-energy electrons to make the sugar.

As we mentioned previously, the carbohydrate produced directly from the Calvin cycle is actually not glucose, but a three-carbon sugar; the name of this sugar is **glyceraldehyde-3-phosphate (G3P)**. For the net synthesis of one molecule of G3P, the cycle must take place three times, fixing three molecules of CO_2. (Recall that carbon fixation refers to the initial incorporation of CO_2 into organic material.) As we trace the steps of the cycle, keep in mind that we are following three molecules of CO_2 through the reactions. **Figure 10.18** divides the Calvin cycle into three phases: carbon fixation, reduction, and regeneration of the CO_2 acceptor.

Phase 1: Carbon fixation. The Calvin cycle incorporates each CO_2 molecule, one at a time, by attaching it to a five-carbon sugar named ribulose bisphosphate (abbreviated RuBP). The enzyme that catalyzes this first step is RuBP carboxylase, or **rubisco**. (This is the most abundant protein in chloroplasts and is also said to be the most abundant protein on Earth.) The product of the reaction is a six-carbon intermediate so unstable that it immediately splits in half, forming two molecules of 3-phosphoglycerate (for each CO_2 fixed).

Phase 2: Reduction. Each molecule of 3-phosphoglycerate receives an additional phosphate group from ATP, becoming 1,3-bisphosphoglycerate. Next, a pair of electrons donated from NADPH reduces 1,3-bisphosphoglycerate, which also loses a phosphate group, becoming G3P. Specifically, the electrons from NADPH reduce a carboyxl group on 1,3-bisphosphoglycerate to the aldehyde group of G3P, which stores more potential energy. G3P is a sugar—the same three-carbon sugar formed in glycolysis by the splitting of glucose (see Figure 9.9). Notice in Figure 10.18 that for every *three* molecules of CO_2 that enter the cycle, there are *six* molecules of G3P formed. But only one molecule of this three-carbon sugar can be counted as a net gain of carbohydrate. The cycle began with 15 carbons' worth of carbohydrate in the form of three molecules of the five-carbon sugar RuBP. Now there are 18 carbons' worth of carbohydrate in the form of six molecules of G3P. One molecule exits the cycle to be used by the plant cell, but the other five molecules must be recycled to regenerate the three molecules of RuBP.

Phase 3: Regeneration of the CO_2 acceptor (RuBP). In a complex series of reactions, the carbon skeletons of five molecules of G3P are rearranged by the last steps of the Calvin cycle into three molecules of RuBP. To accomplish this, the cycle spends three more molecules of ATP. The RuBP is now prepared to receive CO_2 again, and the cycle continues.

For the net synthesis of one G3P molecule, the Calvin cycle consumes a total of nine molecules of ATP and six molecules

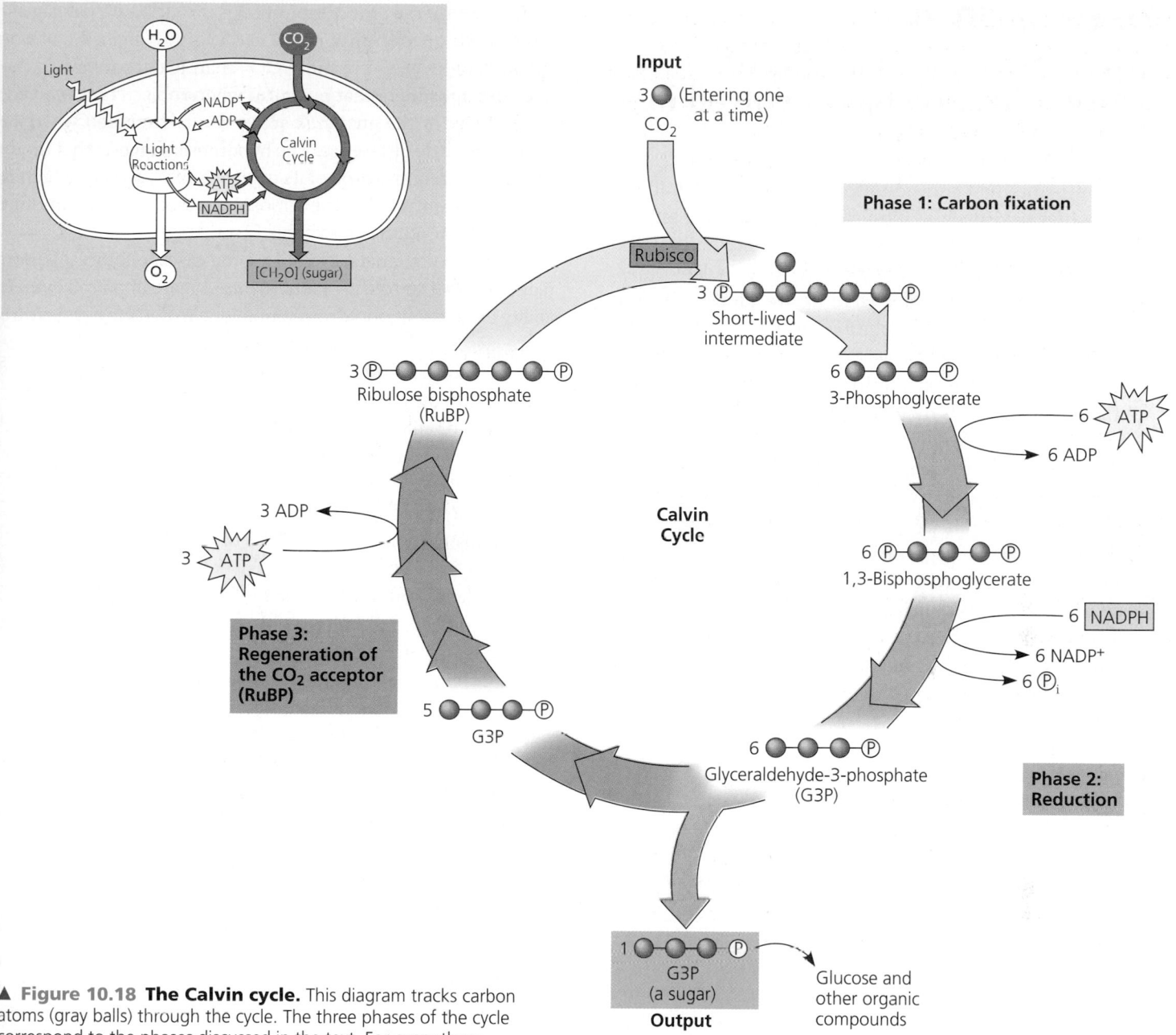

Input

3 ● (Entering one at a time)
CO₂

Phase 1: Carbon fixation

Rubisco

3 Ⓟ●●●●●Ⓟ
Short-lived intermediate

6 ●●●Ⓟ
3-Phosphoglycerate

3 Ⓟ●●●●Ⓟ
Ribulose bisphosphate
(RuBP)

6 ATP
6 ADP

Calvin Cycle

6 Ⓟ●●●Ⓟ
1,3-Bisphosphoglycerate

3 ADP

3 ATP

Phase 3: Regeneration of the CO₂ acceptor (RuBP)

6 NADPH
6 NADP⁺
6 Ⓟ$_i$

5 ●●●Ⓟ
G3P

6 ●●●Ⓟ
Glyceraldehyde-3-phosphate
(G3P)

Phase 2: Reduction

1 ●●●Ⓟ
G3P
(a sugar)
Output

Glucose and other organic compounds

▲ **Figure 10.18 The Calvin cycle.** This diagram tracks carbon atoms (gray balls) through the cycle. The three phases of the cycle correspond to the phases discussed in the text. For every three molecules of CO₂ that enter the cycle, the net output is one molecule of glyceraldehyde-3-phosphate (G3P), a three-carbon sugar. The light reactions sustain the Calvin cycle by regenerating ATP and NADPH.
DRAW IT *Redraw this cycle using numerals to indicate the numbers of carbons instead of gray balls, multiplying at each step to ensure that you have accounted for all carbons. In what forms do the carbon atoms enter and leave the cycle?*

of NADPH. The light reactions regenerate the ATP and NADPH. The G3P spun off from the Calvin cycle becomes the starting material for metabolic pathways that synthesize other organic compounds, including glucose and other carbohydrates. Neither the light reactions nor the Calvin cycle alone can make sugar from CO₂. Photosynthesis is an emergent property of the intact chloroplast, which integrates the two stages of photosynthesis.

CONCEPT CHECK 10.3

1. To synthesize one glucose molecule, the Calvin cycle uses _____ molecules of CO₂, _____ molecules of ATP, and _____ molecules of NADPH.
2. Explain why the large numbers of ATP and NADPH molecules used during the Calvin cycle are consistent with the high value of glucose as an energy source.
3. **WHAT IF?** Explain why a poison that inhibits an enzyme of the Calvin cycle will also inhibit the light reactions.

For suggested answers, see Appendix A.

CONCEPT 10.4

Alternative mechanisms of carbon fixation have evolved in hot, arid climates

Ever since plants first moved onto land about 475 million years ago, they have been adapting to the problems of terrestrial life, particularly the problem of dehydration. In Chapters 29 and 36, we will consider anatomical adaptations that help plants conserve water. Here we are concerned with metabolic adaptations. The solutions often involve trade-offs. An important example is the compromise between photosynthesis and the prevention of excessive water loss from the plant. The CO_2 required for photosynthesis enters a leaf via stomata, the pores through the leaf surface (see Figure 10.3). However, stomata are also the main avenues of transpiration, the evaporative loss of water from leaves. On a hot, dry day, most plants close their stomata, a response that conserves water. This response also reduces photosynthetic yield by limiting access to CO_2. With stomata even partially closed, CO_2 concentrations begin to decrease in the air spaces within the leaf, and the concentration of O_2 released from the light reactions begins to increase. These conditions within the leaf favor an apparently wasteful process called photorespiration.

Photorespiration: An Evolutionary Relic?

In most plants, initial fixation of carbon occurs via rubisco, the Calvin cycle enzyme that adds CO_2 to ribulose bisphosphate. Such plants are called **C_3 plants** because the first organic product of carbon fixation is a three-carbon compound, 3-phosphoglycerate (see Figure 10.18). Rice, wheat, and soybeans are C_3 plants that are important in agriculture. When their stomata partially close on hot, dry days, C_3 plants produce less sugar because the declining level of CO_2 in the leaf starves the Calvin cycle. In addition, rubisco can bind O_2 in place of CO_2. As CO_2 becomes scarce within the air spaces of the leaf, rubisco adds O_2 to the Calvin cycle instead of CO_2. The product splits, and a two-carbon compound leaves the chloroplast. Peroxisomes and mitochondria rearrange and split this compound, releasing CO_2. The process is called **photorespiration** because it occurs in the light (*photo*) and consumes O_2 while producing CO_2 (*respiration*). However, unlike normal cellular respiration, photorespiration generates no ATP; in fact, photorespiration consumes ATP. And unlike photosynthesis, photorespiration produces no sugar. In fact, photorespiration *decreases* photosynthetic output by siphoning organic material from the Calvin cycle and releasing CO_2 that would otherwise be fixed.

How can we explain the existence of a metabolic process that seems to be counterproductive for the plant? According to one hypothesis, photorespiration is evolutionary baggage—a metabolic relic from a much earlier time when the atmosphere had less O_2 and more CO_2 than it does today. In the ancient atmosphere that prevailed when rubisco first evolved, the inability of the enzyme's active site to exclude O_2 would have made little difference. The hypothesis suggests that modern rubisco retains some of its chance affinity for O_2, which is now so concentrated in the atmosphere that a certain amount of photorespiration is inevitable.

We now know that, at least in some cases, photorespiration plays a protective role in plants. Plants that are impaired in their ability to carry out photorespiration (due to defective genes) are more susceptible to damage induced by excess light. Researchers consider this clear evidence that photorespiration acts to neutralize the otherwise damaging products of the light reactions, which build up when a low CO_2 concentration limits the progress of the Calvin cycle. Whether there are other benefits of photorespiration is still unknown. In many types of plants—including a significant number of crop plants—photorespiration drains away as much as 50% of the carbon fixed by the Calvin cycle. As heterotrophs that depend on carbon fixation in chloroplasts for our food, we naturally view photorespiration as wasteful. Indeed, if photorespiration could be reduced in certain plant species without otherwise affecting photosynthetic productivity, crop yields and food supplies might increase.

In some plant species, alternate modes of carbon fixation have evolved that minimize photorespiration and optimize the Calvin cycle—even in hot, arid climates. The two most important of these photosynthetic adaptations are C_4 photosynthesis and CAM.

C_4 Plants

The **C_4 plants** are so named because they preface the Calvin cycle with an alternate mode of carbon fixation that forms a four-carbon compound as its first product. Several thousand species in at least 19 plant families use the C_4 pathway. Among the C_4 plants important to agriculture are sugarcane and corn, members of the grass family.

A unique leaf anatomy is correlated with the mechanism of C_4 photosynthesis (**Figure 10.19**; compare with Figure 10.3). In C_4 plants, there are two distinct types of photosynthetic cells: bundle-sheath cells and mesophyll cells. **Bundle-sheath cells** are arranged into tightly packed sheaths around the veins of the leaf. Between the bundle sheath and the leaf surface are the more loosely arranged **mesophyll cells**. The Calvin cycle is confined to the chloroplasts of the bundle-sheath cells. However, the cycle is preceded by incorporation of CO_2 into organic compounds in the mesophyll cells (see the numbered steps in Figure 10.19). ❶ The first step is carried out by an enzyme present only in mesophyll cells called **PEP carboxylase**. This enzyme adds CO_2 to phosphoenolpyruvate (PEP), forming the four-carbon product oxaloacetate. PEP carboxylase

Photosynthetic cells of C₄ plant leaf {
Mesophyll cell
Bundle-sheath cell

Vein (vascular tissue)

C₄ leaf anatomy

Stoma

Mesophyll cell

PEP carboxylase

CO_2

The C₄ pathway

Oxaloacetate (4C)   PEP (3C)

Malate (4C)

ADP
ATP

Pyruvate (3C)

Bundle-sheath cell

CO_2

Calvin Cycle

Sugar

Vascular tissue

❶ In mesophyll cells, the enzyme PEP carboxylase adds carbon dioxide to PEP.

❷ A four-carbon compound conveys the atoms of the CO_2 into a bundle-sheath cell via plasmodesmata.

❸ In bundle-sheath cells, CO_2 is released and enters the Calvin cycle.

▲ **Figure 10.19 C₄ leaf anatomy and the C₄ pathway.** The structure and biochemical functions of the leaves of C₄ plants are an evolutionary adaptation to hot, dry climates. This adaptation maintains a CO_2 concentration in the bundle sheath that favors photosynthesis over photorespiration.

has a much higher affinity for CO_2 than does rubisco and no affinity for O_2. Therefore, PEP carboxylase can fix carbon efficiently when rubisco cannot—that is, when it is hot and dry and stomata are partially closed, causing CO_2 concentration in the leaf to fall and O_2 concentration to rise. ❷ After the C₄ plant fixes carbon from CO_2, the mesophyll cells export their four-carbon products (malate in the example shown in Figure 10.19) to bundle-sheath cells through plasmodesmata (see Figure 6.31). ❸ Within the bundle-sheath cells, the four-carbon compounds release CO_2, which is reassimilated into organic material by rubisco and the Calvin cycle. The same reaction regenerates pyruvate, which is transported to mesophyll cells. There, ATP is used to convert pyruvate to PEP, allowing the reaction cycle to continue; this ATP can be thought of as the "price" of concentrating CO_2 in the bundle-sheath cells. To generate this extra ATP, bundle-sheath cells carry out cyclic electron flow, the process described earlier in this chapter (see Figure 10.15). In fact, these cells contain PS I but no PS II, so cyclic electron flow is their only photosynthetic mode of generating ATP.

In effect, the mesophyll cells of a C₄ plant pump CO_2 into the bundle sheath, keeping the CO_2 concentration in the bundle-sheath cells high enough for rubisco to bind carbon dioxide rather than oxygen. The cyclic series of reactions involving PEP carboxylase and the regeneration of PEP can be thought of as a CO_2-concentrating pump that is powered by ATP. In

this way, C₄ photosynthesis minimizes photorespiration and enhances sugar production. This adaptation is especially advantageous in hot regions with intense sunlight, where stomata partially close during the day, and it is in such environments that C₄ plants evolved and thrive today.

CAM Plants

A second photosynthetic adaptation to arid conditions has evolved in many succulent (water-storing) plants, numerous cacti, pineapples, and representatives of several other plant families. These plants open their stomata during the night and close them during the day, just the reverse of how other plants behave. Closing stomata during the day helps desert plants conserve water, but it also prevents CO_2 from entering the leaves. During the night, when their stomata are open, these plants take up CO_2 and incorporate it into a variety of organic acids. This mode of carbon fixation is called **crassulacean acid metabolism**, or **CAM**, after the plant family Crassulaceae, the succulents in which the process was first discovered. The mesophyll cells of **CAM plants** store the organic acids they make during the night in their vacuoles until morning, when the stomata close. During the day, when the light reactions can supply ATP and NADPH for the Calvin cycle, CO_2 is released from the organic acids made the night before to become incorporated into sugar in the chloroplasts.

▶ **Figure 10.20 C₄ and CAM photosynthesis compared.** Both adaptations are characterized by ❶ preliminary incorporation of CO_2 into organic acids, followed by ❷ transfer of CO_2 to the Calvin cycle. The C₄ and CAM pathways are two evolutionary solutions to the problem of maintaining photosynthesis with stomata partially or completely closed on hot, dry days.

Sugarcane

Pineapple

C₄

Mesophyll cell

Bundle-sheath cell

CO_2

Organic acid

CO_2

Calvin Cycle

Sugar

❶ CO_2 incorporated into four-carbon organic acids (carbon fixation)

❷ Organic acids release CO_2 to Calvin cycle

CAM

Night

Day

CO_2

Organic acid

CO_2

Calvin Cycle

Sugar

(a) Spatial separation of steps. In C₄ plants, carbon fixation and the Calvin cycle occur in different types of cells.

(b) Temporal separation of steps. In CAM plants, carbon fixation and the Calvin cycle occur in the same cells at different times.

Notice in **Figure 10.20** that the CAM pathway is similar to the C₄ pathway in that carbon dioxide is first incorporated into organic intermediates before it enters the Calvin cycle. The difference is that in C₄ plants, the initial steps of carbon fixation are separated structurally from the Calvin cycle, whereas in CAM plants, the two steps occur at separate times but within the same cell. (Keep in mind that CAM, C₄, and C₃ plants all eventually use the Calvin cycle to make sugar from carbon dioxide.)

CONCEPT CHECK 10.4

1. Explain why photorespiration lowers photosynthetic output for plants.
2. The presence of only PS I, not PS II, in the bundle-sheath cells of C₄ plants has an effect on O_2 concentration. What is that effect, and how might that benefit the plant?
3. **WHAT IF?** How would you expect the relative abundance of C₃ versus C₄ and CAM species to change in a geographic region whose climate becomes much hotter and drier?

For suggested answers, see Appendix A.

The Importance of Photosynthesis: *A Review*

In this chapter, we have followed photosynthesis from photons to food. The light reactions capture solar energy and use it to make ATP and transfer electrons from water to $NADP^+$, forming NADPH. The Calvin cycle uses the ATP and NADPH to produce sugar from carbon dioxide. The energy that enters the chloroplasts as sunlight becomes stored as chemical energy in organic compounds. See **Figure 10.21** for a review of the entire process.

What are the fates of photosynthetic products? The sugar made in the chloroplasts supplies the entire plant with chemical energy and carbon skeletons for the synthesis of all the major organic molecules of plant cells. About 50% of the organic material made by photosynthesis is consumed as fuel for cellular respiration in the mitochondria of the plant cells. Sometimes there is a loss of photosynthetic products to photorespiration.

Technically, green cells are the only autotrophic parts of the plant. The rest of the plant depends on organic molecules exported from leaves via veins. In most plants, carbohydrate is transported out of the leaves in the form of

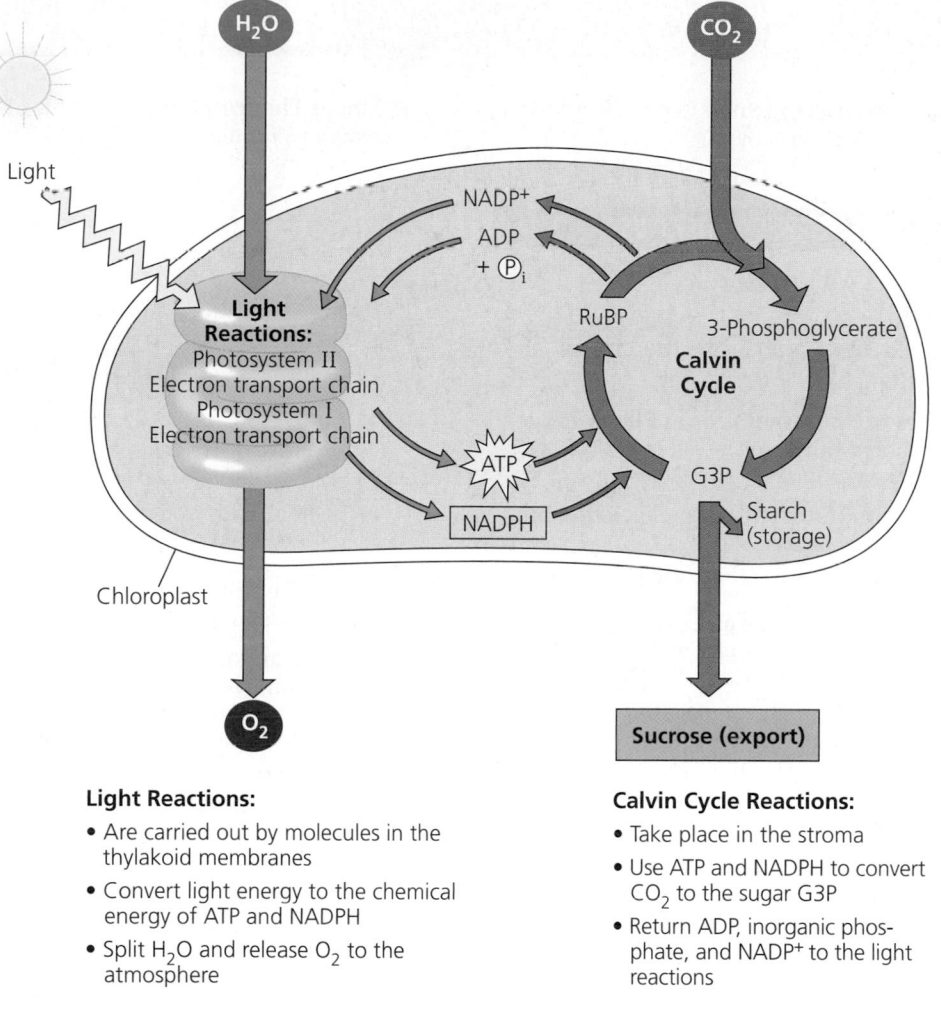

Light Reactions:

- Are carried out by molecules in the thylakoid membranes
- Convert light energy to the chemical energy of ATP and NADPH
- Split H_2O and release O_2 to the atmosphere

Calvin Cycle Reactions:

- Take place in the stroma
- Use ATP and NADPH to convert CO_2 to the sugar G3P
- Return ADP, inorganic phosphate, and $NADP^+$ to the light reactions

▲ **Figure 10.21 A review of photosynthesis.** This diagram outlines the main reactants and products of the light reactions and the Calvin cycle as they occur in the chloroplasts of plant cells. The entire ordered operation depends on the structural integrity of the chloroplast and its membranes. Enzymes in the chloroplast and cytosol convert glyceraldehyde-3-phosphate (G3P), the direct product of the Calvin cycle, to many other organic compounds.

sucrose, a disaccharide. After arriving at nonphotosynthetic cells, the sucrose provides raw material for cellular respiration and a multitude of anabolic pathways that synthesize proteins, lipids, and other products. A considerable amount of sugar in the form of glucose is linked together to make the polysaccharide cellulose, especially in plant cells that are still growing and maturing. Cellulose, the main ingredient of cell walls, is the most abundant organic molecule in the plant—and probably on the surface of the planet.

Most plants manage to make more organic material each day than they need to use as respiratory fuel and precursors for biosynthesis. They stockpile the extra sugar by synthesizing starch, storing some in the chloroplasts themselves and some in storage cells of roots, tubers, seeds, and fruits. In accounting for the consumption of the food mol-

ecules produced by photosynthesis, let's not forget that most plants lose leaves, roots, stems, fruits, and sometimes their entire bodies to heterotrophs, including humans.

On a global scale, photosynthesis is the process responsible for the presence of oxygen in our atmosphere. Furthermore, in terms of food production, the collective productivity of the minuscule chloroplasts is prodigious: Photosynthesis makes an estimated 160 billion metric tons of carbohydrate per year (a metric ton is 1,000 kg, about 1.1 tons). That's organic matter equivalent in mass to a stack of about 60 trillion copies of this textbook—17 stacks of books reaching from Earth to the sun! No other chemical process on the planet can match the output of photosynthesis. And no process is more important than photosynthesis to the welfare of life on Earth.

MEDIA Go to **www.campbellbiology.com** for BioFlix 3-D Animations, MP3 Tutors, Videos, Practice Tests, an eBook, and more.

SUMMARY OF KEY CONCEPTS

CONCEPT 10.1

Photosynthesis converts light energy to the chemical energy of food (pp. 186–189)

▶ **Chloroplasts: The Sites of Photosynthesis in Plants** In autotrophic eukaryotes, photosynthesis occurs in chloroplasts, organelles containing thylakoids. Stacks of thylakoids form grana.

▶ **Tracking Atoms Through Photosynthesis:** *Scientific Inquiry* Photosynthesis is summarized as

$$6\ CO_2 + 12\ H_2O + Light\ energy \rightarrow C_6H_{12}O_6 + 6\ O_2 + 6\ H_2O$$

Chloroplasts split water into hydrogen and oxygen, incorporating the electrons of hydrogen into sugar molecules. Photosynthesis is a redox process: H_2O is oxidized, CO_2 is reduced.

▶ **The Two Stages of Photosynthesis:** *A Preview* The light reactions in the thylakoid membranes split water, releasing O_2, producing ATP, and forming NADPH. The Calvin cycle in the stroma forms sugar from CO_2, using ATP for energy and NADPH for reducing power.

> **MEDIA**
>
> **BioFlix 3-D Animation** Photosynthesis
> **MP3 Tutor** Photosynthesis
> **Activity** The Sites of Photosynthesis
> **Activity** Overview of Photosynthesis

CONCEPT 10.2

The light reactions convert solar energy to the chemical energy of ATP and NADPH (pp. 190–198)

▶ **The Nature of Sunlight** Light is a form of electromagnetic energy. The colors we see as visible light include those wavelengths that drive photosynthesis.

▶ **Photosynthetic Pigments: The Light Receptors** A pigment absorbs visible light of specific wavelengths. Chlorophyll *a* is the main photosynthetic pigment in plants. Other accessory pigments absorb different wavelengths of light and pass the energy on to chlorophyll *a*.

▶ **Excitation of Chlorophyll by Light** A pigment goes from a ground state to an excited state when a photon boosts one of its electrons to a higher-energy orbital. This excited state is unstable. Electrons from isolated pigments tend to fall back to the ground state, giving off heat and/or light.

▶ **A Photosystem: A Reaction-Center Complex Associated with Light-Harvesting Complexes** A photosystem is composed of a reaction-center complex surrounded by light-harvesting complexes that funnel the energy of photons to the reaction-center complex. When a special pair of reaction-center chlorophyll *a* molecules absorbs energy, one of its electrons is boosted to a higher energy level and transferred to the primary electron acceptor. Photosystem II contains P680 chlorophyll *a* molecules in the reaction-center complex; photosystem I contains P700 molecules.

▶ **Linear Electron Flow** The flow of electrons during the light reactions produces NADPH, ATP, and oxygen:

▶ **Cyclic Electron Flow** Cyclic electron flow employs only photosystem I, producing ATP but no NADPH or O_2.

▶ **A Comparison of Chemiosmosis in Chloroplasts and Mitochondria** In both organelles, redox reactions of electron transport chains generate an H^+ gradient across a membrane. ATP synthase uses this proton-motive force to make ATP.

> **MEDIA**
>
> **Activity** Light Energy and Pigments
> **Investigation** How Does Paper Chromatography Separate Plant Pigments?
> **Activity** The Light Reactions

CONCEPT 10.3

The Calvin cycle uses ATP and NADPH to convert CO_2 to sugar (pp. 198–199)

▶ The Calvin cycle occurs in the stroma, using electrons from NADPH and energy from ATP. One molecule of G3P exits the cycle per three CO_2 molecules fixed and is converted to glucose and other organic molecules.

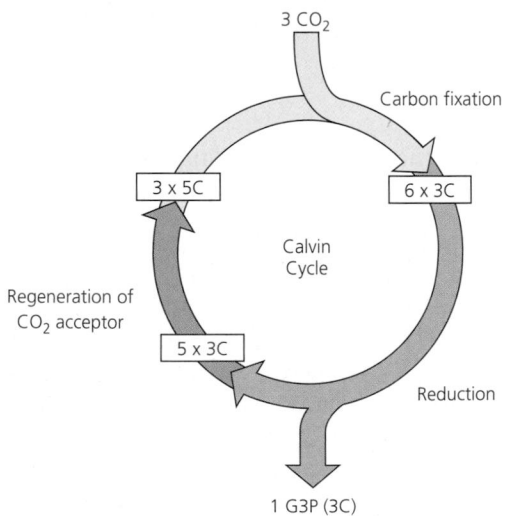

> **MEDIA**
>
> **Activity** The Calvin Cycle
> **Investigation** How Is the Rate of Photosynthesis Measured?
> **Biology Labs On-Line** LeafLab

Alternative mechanisms of carbon fixation have evolved in hot, arid climates (pp. 200–202)

▶ **Photorespiration: An Evolutionary Relic?** On dry, hot days, C_3 plants close their stomata, conserving water. Oxygen from the light reactions builds up. In photorespiration, O_2 substitutes for CO_2 in the active site of rubisco. This process consumes organic fuel and releases CO_2 without producing ATP or carbohydrate.

▶ **C_4 Plants** C_4 plants minimize the cost of photorespiration by incorporating CO_2 into four-carbon compounds in mesophyll cells. These compounds are exported to bundle-sheath cells, where they release carbon dioxide for use in the Calvin cycle.

▶ **CAM Plants** CAM plants open their stomata at night, incorporating CO_2 into organic acids, which are stored in mesophyll cells. During the day, the stomata close, and the CO_2 is released from the organic acids for use in the Calvin cycle.

MEDIA Activity Photosynthesis in Dry Climates

▶ **The Importance of Photosynthesis:** *A Review* Organic compounds produced by photosynthesis provide the energy and building material for ecosystems.

TESTING YOUR KNOWLEDGE

SELF-QUIZ

1. The light reactions of photosynthesis supply the Calvin cycle with
  a. light energy.
  b. CO_2 and ATP.
  c. H_2O and NADPH.
  d. ATP and NADPH.
  e. sugar and O_2.

2. Which of the following sequences correctly represents the flow of electrons during photosynthesis?
  a. NADPH → O_2 → CO_2
  b. H_2O → NADPH → Calvin cycle
  c. NADPH → chlorophyll → Calvin cycle
  d. H_2O → photosystem I → photosystem II
  e. NADPH → electron transport chain → O_2

3. In *mechanism*, photophosphorylation is most similar to
  a. substrate-level phosphorylation in glycolysis.
  b. oxidative phosphorylation in cellular respiration.
  c. the Calvin cycle.
  d. carbon fixation.
  e. reduction of $NADP^+$.

4. How is photosynthesis similar in C_4 plants and CAM plants?
  a. In both cases, only photosystem I is used.
  b. Both types of plants make sugar without the Calvin cycle.
  c. In both cases, rubisco is not used to fix carbon initially.
  d. Both types of plants make most of their sugar in the dark.
  e. In both cases, thylakoids are not involved in photosynthesis.

5. Which process is most directly driven by light energy?
  a. creation of a pH gradient by pumping protons across the thylakoid membrane
  b. carbon fixation in the stroma
  c. reduction of $NADP^+$ molecules
  d. removal of electrons from chlorophyll molecules
  e. ATP synthesis

6. Which of the following statements is a correct distinction between autotrophs and heterotrophs?
  a. Only heterotrophs require chemical compounds from the environment.
  b. Cellular respiration is unique to heterotrophs.
  c. Only heterotrophs have mitochondria.
  d. Autotrophs, but not heterotrophs, can nourish themselves beginning with CO_2 and other nutrients that are inorganic.
  e. Only heterotrophs require oxygen.

7. Which of the following does *not* occur during the Calvin cycle?
  a. carbon fixation
  b. oxidation of NADPH
  c. release of oxygen
  d. regeneration of the CO_2 acceptor
  e. consumption of ATP

For Self-Quiz answers, see Appendix A.

MEDIA Visit **www.campbellbiology.com** for a Practice Test.

EVOLUTION CONNECTION

8. Photorespiration can decrease soybeans' photosynthetic output by about 50%. Would you expect this figure to be higher or lower in wild relatives of soybeans? Why?

SCIENTIFIC INQUIRY

9. **DRAW IT** The following diagram represents an experiment with isolated chloroplasts. The chloroplasts were first made acidic by soaking them in a solution at pH 4. After the thylakoid space reached pH 4, the chloroplasts were transferred to a basic solution at pH 8. The chloroplasts then made ATP in the dark.

Draw an enlargement of part of the thylakoid membrane in the beaker with the solution at pH 8. Draw ATP synthase. Label the areas of high H^+ concentration and low H^+ concentration. Show the direction protons flow through the enzyme, and show the reaction where ATP is synthesized. Would ATP end up in the thylakoid or outside of it? Explain why the chloroplasts in the experiment were able to make ATP in the dark.

SCIENCE, TECHNOLOGY, AND SOCIETY

10. Scientific evidence indicates that the CO_2 added to the air by the burning of wood and fossil fuels is contributing to "global warming," a rise in global temperature. Tropical rain forests are estimated to be responsible for more than 20% of global photosynthesis, yet their consumption of large amounts of CO_2 is thought to make little or no *net* contribution to reduction of global warming. Why might this be? (*Hint:* What happens to the food produced by a rain forest tree when it is eaten by animals or the tree dies?)

Cell Communication

KEY CONCEPTS

11.1 External signals are converted to responses within the cell

11.2 Reception: A signaling molecule binds to a receptor protein, causing it to change shape

11.3 Transduction: Cascades of molecular interactions relay signals from receptors to target molecules in the cell

11.4 Response: Cell signaling leads to regulation of transcription or cytoplasmic activities

11.5 Apoptosis (programmed cell death) integrates multiple cell-signaling pathways

OVERVIEW

The Cellular Internet

A hiker slips and falls down a steep ravine, injuring her leg in the fall. Tragedy is averted when she is able to pull out a cell phone and call for help. Cell phones, the Internet, e-mail, instant messaging—no one would deny the importance of communication in our lives. The role of communication in life at the cellular level is equally critical. Cell-to-cell communication is absolutely essential for multicellular organisms such as humans and oak trees. The trillions of cells in a multicellular organism must communicate with each other to coordinate their activities in a way that enables the organism to develop from a fertilized egg, then survive and reproduce in turn. Communication between cells is also important for many unicellular organisms. Networks of communication between cells can be even more complicated than the World Wide Web.

In studying how cells signal to each other and how they interpret the signals they receive, biologists have discovered some universal mechanisms of cellular regulation, additional evidence for the evolutionary relatedness of all life. The same small set of cell-signaling mechanisms shows up again and again in many

▲ **Figure 11.1 How do the effects of Viagra (multicolored) result from its inhibition of a signaling-pathway enzyme (purple)?**

lines of biological research—from embryonic development to hormone action to cancer. In one example, a common cell-to-cell signaling pathway leads to dilation of blood vessels. Once the signal subsides, the response is shut down by the enzyme shown in purple in **Figure 11.1**. Also shown is a multicolored molecule that blocks the action of this enzyme and keeps blood vessels dilated. Enzyme-inhibiting compounds like this one are often prescribed for treatment of medical conditions. The action of the multicolored compound, known as Viagra, will be discussed later in the chapter. The signals received by cells, whether originating from other cells or from changes in the physical environment, take various forms, including light and touch. However, cells most often communicate with each other by chemical signals. In this chapter, we focus on the main mechanisms by which cells receive, process, and respond to chemical signals sent from other cells. At the end, we will take a look at *apoptosis*, a type of programmed cell death that integrates input from multiple signaling pathways.

CONCEPT 11.1

External signals are converted to responses within the cell

What does a "talking" cell say to a "listening" cell, and how does the latter cell respond to the message? Let's approach these questions by first looking at communication among microorganisms, for modern microbes are a window on the role of cell signaling in the evolution of life on Earth.

Evolution of Cell Signaling

One topic of cell "conversation" is sex—at least for the yeast *Saccharomyces cerevisiae*, which people have used for millennia to make bread, wine, and beer. Researchers have learned that cells of this yeast identify their mates by chemical signaling. There are two sexes, or mating types, called **a** and **α** (**Figure 11.2**). Cells of mating type **a** secrete a signaling molecule called **a** factor, which can bind to specific receptor proteins on nearby **α** cells. At the same time, **α** cells secrete **α** factor, which binds to receptors on **a** cells. Without actually entering the cells, the two mating factors cause the cells to grow toward each other and also bring about other cellular changes. The result is the fusion, or mating, of two cells of opposite type. The new **a/α** cell contains all the genes of both original cells, a combination of genetic resources that provides advantages to the cell's descendants, which arise by subsequent cell divisions.

How is the mating signal at the yeast cell surface changed, or *transduced*, into a form that brings about the cellular response of mating? The process by which a signal on a cell's surface is converted to a specific cellular response is a series of steps called a **signal transduction pathway**. Many such pathways have been extensively studied in both yeast and animal cells. Amazingly, the molecular details of signal transduction in yeast and mammals are strikingly similar, even though the last common ancestor of these two groups of organisms lived over a billion years ago. These similarities—

and others more recently uncovered between signaling systems in bacteria and plants—suggest that early versions of the cell-signaling mechanisms used today evolved well before the first multicellular creatures appeared on Earth.

Scientists think that signaling mechanisms first evolved in ancient prokaryotes and single-celled eukaryotes and then were adopted for new uses by their multicellular descendants. Meanwhile, cell signaling has remained important in the microbial world. Cells of many bacterial species secrete small molecules that can be detected by other bacterial cells. The concentration of such signaling molecules allows bacteria to sense the local density of bacterial cells, a phenomenon called *quorum sensing*. Furthermore, signaling among members of a bacterial population can lead to coordination of their activities. In response to the signal, bacterial cells are able to come together and form *biofilms*, aggregations of bacteria that often form recognizable structures containing regions of specialized function. **Figure 11.3** shows an aggregation response characteristic of one type of bacterium.

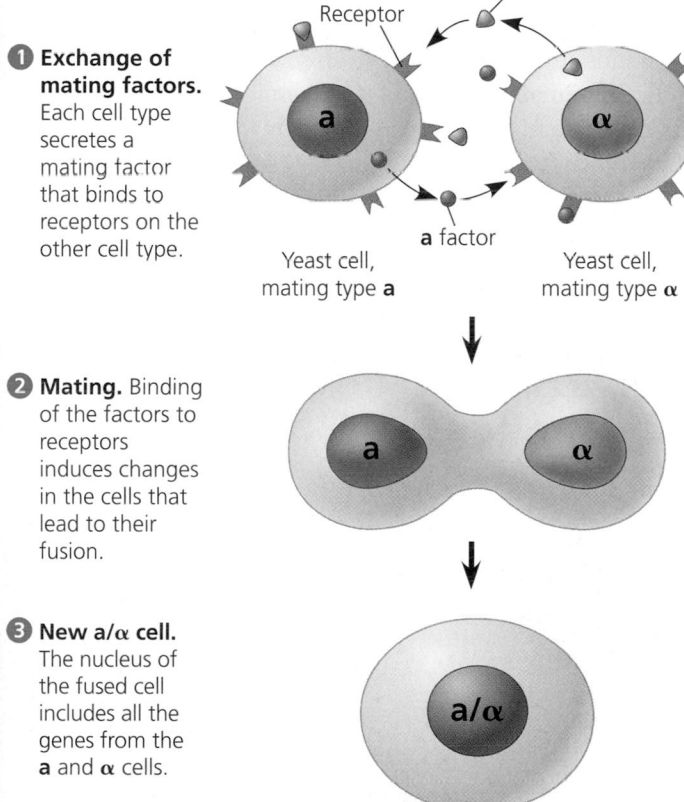

① Exchange of mating factors. Each cell type secretes a mating factor that binds to receptors on the other cell type.

② Mating. Binding of the factors to receptors induces changes in the cells that lead to their fusion.

③ New a/α cell. The nucleus of the fused cell includes all the genes from the **a** and **α** cells.

▲ **Figure 11.2 Communication between mating yeast cells.** *Saccharomyces cerevisiae* cells use chemical signaling to identify cells of opposite mating type and initiate the mating process. The two mating types and their corresponding chemical signaling molecules, or mating factors, are called **a** and **α**.

① Individual rod-shaped cells

0.5 mm

② Aggregation in process

③ Spore-forming structure (fruiting body)

Fruiting bodies

▲ **Figure 11.3 Communication among bacteria.** Soil-dwelling bacteria called myxobacteria ("slime bacteria") use chemical signals to share information about nutrient availability. When food is scarce, starving cells secrete a molecule that reaches neighboring cells and stimulates them to aggregate. The cells form a structure, called a fruiting body, that produces thick-walled spores capable of surviving until the environment improves. The bacteria shown here are *Myxococcus xanthus* (steps 1–3, SEMs; lower photo, LM).

Local and Long-Distance Signaling

Like yeast cells, cells in a multicellular organism usually communicate via chemical messengers targeted for cells that may or may not be immediately adjacent. As we saw in Chapters 6 and 7, cells may communicate by direct contact (**Figure 11.4**). Both animals and plants have cell junctions that, where present, directly connect the cytoplasms of adjacent cells (**Figure 11.4a**). In these cases, signaling substances dissolved in the cytosol can pass freely between adjacent cells. Moreover, animal cells may communicate via direct contact between membrane-bound cell-surface molecules, which occurs during a process called cell-cell recognition (**Figure 11.4b**). This sort of signaling is important in such processes as embryonic development and the immune response.

In many other cases, messenger molecules are secreted by the signaling cell. Some of these travel only short distances; such **local regulators** influence cells in the vicinity. One class of local regulators in animals, *growth factors*, consists of compounds that stimulate nearby target cells to grow and divide. Numerous cells can simultaneously receive and respond to the molecules of growth factor produced by a single cell in their vicinity. This type of local signaling in animals is called *paracrine signaling* (**Figure 11.5a**).

Another, more specialized type of local signaling called *synaptic signaling* occurs in the animal nervous system (**Figure 11.5b**). An electrical signal along a nerve cell triggers the secretion of a chemical signal carried by neurotransmitter molecules. These diffuse across the synapse, the narrow space between the nerve cell and its target cell (often another nerve cell). The neurotransmitter stimulates the target cell.

Local signaling in plants is not as well understood. Because of their cell walls, plants use mechanisms somewhat different from those operating locally in animals.

Both animals and plants use chemicals called **hormones** for long-distance signaling. In hormonal signaling in animals, also known as endocrine signaling, specialized cells release

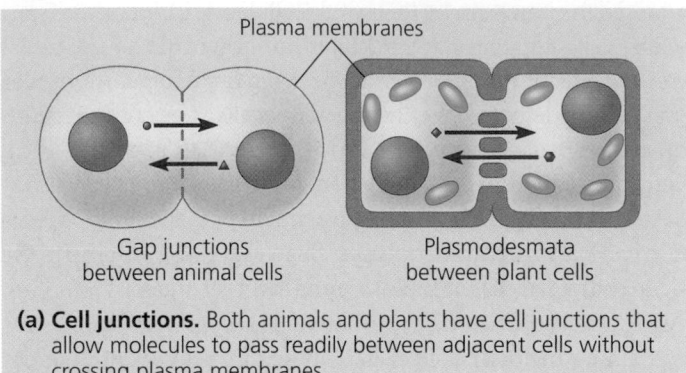

Plasma membranes

Gap junctions between animal cells

Plasmodesmata between plant cells

(a) Cell junctions. Both animals and plants have cell junctions that allow molecules to pass readily between adjacent cells without crossing plasma membranes.

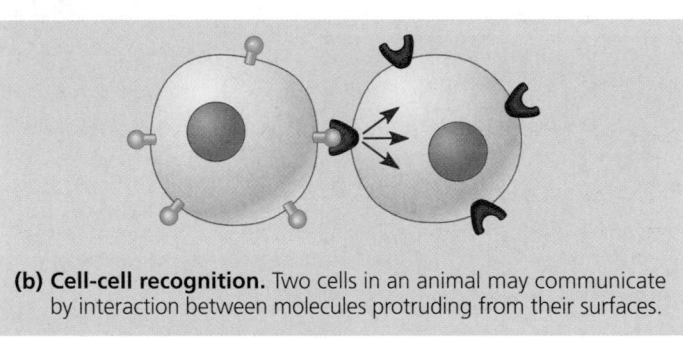

(b) Cell-cell recognition. Two cells in an animal may communicate by interaction between molecules protruding from their surfaces.

▲ **Figure 11.4 Communication by direct contact between cells.**

Local signaling

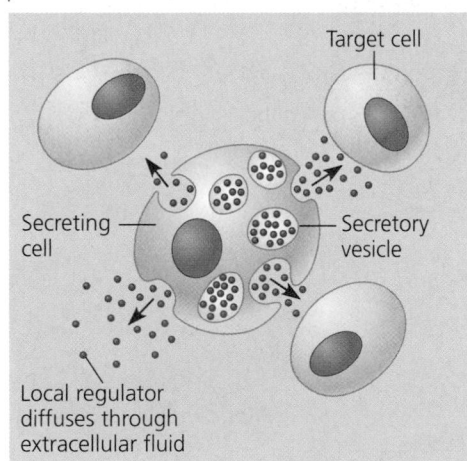

Target cell

Secreting cell

Secretory vesicle

Local regulator diffuses through extracellular fluid

(a) Paracrine signaling. A secreting cell acts on nearby target cells by discharging molecules of a local regulator (a growth factor, for example) into the extracellular fluid.

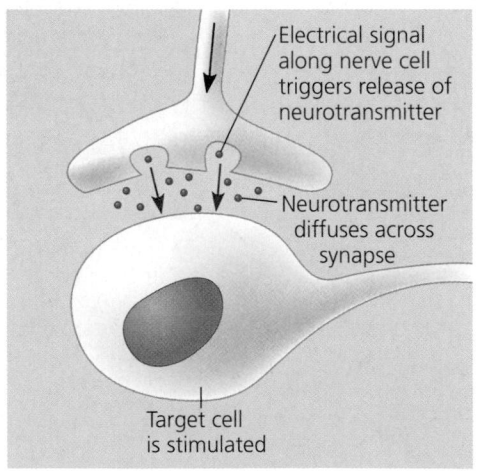

Electrical signal along nerve cell triggers release of neurotransmitter

Neurotransmitter diffuses across synapse

Target cell is stimulated

(b) Synaptic signaling. A nerve cell releases neurotransmitter molecules into a synapse, stimulating the target cell.

Long-distance signaling

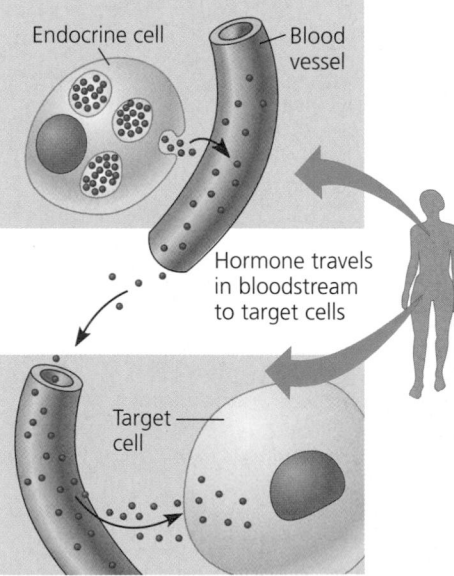

Endocrine cell

Blood vessel

Hormone travels in bloodstream to target cells

Target cell

(c) Hormonal signaling. Specialized endocrine cells secrete hormones into body fluids, often the blood. Hormones may reach virtually all body cells.

▲ **Figure 11.5 Local and long-distance cell communication in animals.** In both local and long-distance signaling, only specific target cells recognize and respond to a given signaling molecule.

hormone molecules, which travel via the circulatory system to target cells in other parts of the body **(Figure 11.5c)**. Plant hormones (often called *plant growth regulators*) sometimes travel in vessels but more often reach their targets by moving through cells or by diffusing through the air as a gas (see Chapter 39). Hormones vary widely in molecular size and type, as do local regulators. For instance, the plant hormone ethylene, a gas that promotes fruit ripening and helps regulate growth, is a hydrocarbon of only six atoms (C_2H_4), small enough to pass through cell walls. In contrast, the mammalian hormone insulin, which regulates sugar levels in the blood, is a protein with thousands of atoms.

The transmission of a signal through the nervous system can also be considered an example of long-distance signaling. An electrical signal travels the length of a nerve cell and is then converted back to a chemical signal when a signaling molecule is released and crosses the synapse to another nerve cell. Here it is converted back to an electrical signal. In this way, a nerve signal can travel along a series of nerve cells. Because some nerve cells are quite long, the nerve signal can quickly travel great distances—from your brain to your big toe, for example. This type of long-distance signaling will be covered in detail in Chapter 48.

What happens when a cell encounters a signaling molecule? The molecule must be recognized by a specific receptor molecule, and the information it carries, the signal, must be changed into another form—transduced—inside the cell before the cell can respond. The remainder of the chapter discusses this process, primarily as it occurs in animal cells.

The Three Stages of Cell Signaling: *A Preview*

Our current understanding of how chemical messengers act via signal transduction pathways had its origins in the pioneering work of Earl W. Sutherland, whose research led to a Nobel Prize in 1971. Sutherland and his colleagues at Vanderbilt University were investigating how the animal hormone epinephrine stimulates the breakdown of the storage polysaccharide glycogen within liver cells and skeletal muscle cells. Glycogen breakdown releases the sugar glucose-1-phosphate, which the cell converts to glucose-6-phosphate. The cell (a liver cell, for example) can then use this compound, an early intermediate in glycolysis, for energy production. Alternatively, the compound can be stripped of phosphate and released from the liver cell into the blood as glucose, which can fuel cells throughout the body. Thus, one effect of epinephrine, which is secreted from the adrenal gland during times of physical or mental stress, is the mobilization of fuel reserves.

Sutherland's research team discovered that epinephrine stimulates glycogen breakdown by somehow activating a cytosolic enzyme, glycogen phosphorylase. However, when epinephrine was added to a test-tube mixture containing the enzyme and its substrate, glycogen, no breakdown occurred. Epinephrine could activate glycogen phosphorylase only when the hormone was added to a solution containing *intact* cells. This result told Sutherland two things. First, epinephrine does not interact directly with the enzyme responsible for glycogen breakdown; an intermediate step or series of steps must be occurring inside the cell. Second, the plasma membrane is somehow involved in transmitting the epinephrine signal.

Sutherland's early work suggested that the process going on at the receiving end of a cellular conversation can be dissected into three stages: reception, transduction, and response **(Figure 11.6)**:

❶ **Reception.** Reception is the target cell's detection of a signaling molecule coming from outside the cell. A chemical signal is "detected" when the signaling molecule binds to a receptor protein located at the cell's surface or inside the cell.

❷ **Transduction.** The binding of the signaling molecule changes the receptor protein in some way, initiating the process of transduction. The transduction stage converts the signal to a form that can bring about a specific

▶ **Figure 11.6 Overview of cell signaling.** From the perspective of the cell receiving the message, cell signaling can be divided into three stages: signal reception, signal transduction, and cellular response. When reception occurs at the plasma membrane, as shown here, the transduction stage is usually a pathway of several steps, with each relay molecule in the pathway bringing about a change in the next molecule. The final molecule in the pathway triggers the cell's response. The three stages are explained in more detail in the text.

? *How does the epinephrine in Sutherland's experiment fit into this diagram of cell signaling?*

cellular response. In Sutherland's system, the binding of epinephrine to a receptor protein in a liver cell's plasma membrane leads to activation of glycogen phosphorylase. Transduction sometimes occurs in a single step but more often requires a sequence of changes in a series of different molecules—a *signal transduction pathway*. The molecules in the pathway are often called relay molecules.

❸ **Response.** In the third stage of cell signaling, the transduced signal finally triggers a specific cellular response. The response may be almost any imaginable cellular activity—such as catalysis by an enzyme (for example, glycogen phosphorylase), rearrangement of the cytoskeleton, or activation of specific genes in the nucleus. The cell-signaling process helps ensure that crucial activities like these occur in the right cells, at the right time, and in proper coordination with the other cells of the organism. We'll now explore the mechanisms of cell signaling in more detail.

CONCEPT CHECK 11.1

1. Explain how signaling is involved in ensuring that yeast cells only fuse with cells of the opposite mating type.
2. Explain how nerve cells provide examples of both local and long-distance signaling.
3. When epinephrine is mixed with glycogen phosphorylase and glycogen in a test tube, is glucose-1-phosphate generated? Why or why not?
4. **WHAT IF?** In liver cells, glycogen phosphorylase acts in which of the three stages of the signaling pathway associated with an epinephrine-initiated signal?

For suggested answers, see Appendix A.

CONCEPT 11.2

Reception: A signaling molecule binds to a receptor protein, causing it to change shape

When we speak to someone, others nearby may inadvertently hear our message, sometimes with unfortunate consequences. However, errors of this kind rarely occur among cells. The signals emitted by an **a** yeast cell are "heard" only by its prospective mates, **α** cells. Similarly, although epinephrine encounters many types of cells as it circulates in the blood, only certain target cells detect and react to the hormone. A receptor protein on or in the target cell allows the cell to "hear" the signal and respond to it. The signaling molecule is complementary in shape to a specific site on the receptor and attaches there, like a key in a lock or a substrate in the catalytic site of an enzyme. The signaling molecule behaves as a **ligand**, the term for a molecule that specifically binds to another molecule, often a larger one. Ligand binding generally causes a receptor protein to undergo a change in shape. For many receptors, this shape change directly activates the receptor, enabling it to interact with other cellular molecules. For other kinds of receptors, the immediate effect of ligand binding is to cause the aggregation of two or more receptor molecules, which leads to further molecular events inside the cell.

In a general way, ligand binding is similar to the binding of an allosteric regulator to an enzyme, causing a shape change that either promotes or inhibits enzyme activity. In the case of signal transduction, binding of the ligand alters the ability of the receptor to transmit the signal.

Most signal receptors are plasma membrane proteins. Their ligands are water-soluble and generally too large to pass freely through the plasma membrane. Other signal receptors, however, are located inside the cell. We discuss both of these next.

Receptors in the Plasma Membrane

Most water-soluble signaling molecules bind to specific sites on receptor proteins embedded in the cell's plasma membrane. Such a receptor transmits information from the extracellular environment to the inside of the cell by changing shape or aggregating when a specific ligand binds to it. We can see how membrane receptors work by looking at three major types: G protein-coupled receptors, receptor tyrosine kinases, and ion channel receptors. These receptors are discussed and illustrated in **Figure 11.7**, on the next three pages; study this figure before going on.

Intracellular Receptors

Intracellular receptor proteins are found in either the cytoplasm or nucleus of target cells. To reach such a receptor, a chemical messenger passes through the target cell's plasma membrane. A number of important signaling molecules can do this because they are either hydrophobic enough or small enough to cross the phospholipid interior of the membrane. Such hydrophobic chemical messengers include the steroid hormones and thyroid hormones of animals. Another chemical signaling molecule with an intracellular receptor is nitric oxide (NO), a gas; its very small molecules readily pass between the membrane phospholipids.

The behavior of testosterone is representative of steroid hormones. Secreted by cells of the testis, the hormone travels through the blood and enters cells all over the body. In the cytoplasm of target cells, the only cells that contain receptor molecules for testosterone, the hormone binds to the receptor

Exploring Membrane Receptors

G Protein-Coupled Receptors

Signaling-molecule binding site

Segment that interacts with G proteins

G protein-coupled receptor

A **G protein-coupled receptor** is a plasma membrane receptor that works with the help of a **G protein**, a protein that binds the energy-rich molecule GTP. Many different signaling molecules, including yeast mating factors, epinephrine and many other hormones, and neurotransmitters, use G protein-coupled receptors. These receptors vary in the binding sites for both their signaling molecules (also called their ligands) and for different G proteins inside the cell. Nevertheless, G protein-coupled receptor proteins are all remarkably similar in structure. They each have seven α helices spanning the membrane, as shown above.

A large family of eukaryotic receptor proteins has this secondary structure, where the single polypeptide, represented here as a ribbon, has seven transmembrane α helices, represented as cylinders and depicted in a row for clarity. Specific loops between the helices form binding sites for signaling and G-protein molecules.

G protein-coupled receptor systems are extremely widespread and diverse in their functions, including roles in embryonic development and sensory reception. In humans, for example, both vision and smell depend on such proteins. Similarities in structure among G proteins and G protein-coupled receptors in diverse organisms suggest that G proteins and associated receptors evolved very early.

G-protein systems are involved in many human diseases, including bacterial infections. The bacteria that cause cholera, pertussis (whooping cough), and botulism, among others, make their victims ill by producing toxins that interfere with G-protein function. Pharmacologists now realize that up to 60% of all medicines used today exert their effects by influencing G-protein pathways.

G protein-coupled receptor

Plasma membrane

GDP

G protein (inactive)

Enzyme

CYTOPLASM

1 Loosely attached to the cytoplasmic side of the membrane, the G protein functions as a molecular switch that is either on or off, depending on which of two guanine nucleotides is attached, GDP or GTP—hence the term *G protein*. (GTP, or guanosine triphosphate, is similar to ATP.) When GDP is bound to the G protein, as shown above, the G protein is inactive. The receptor and G protein work together with another protein, usually an enzyme.

Activated receptor

Signaling molecule

Inactive enzyme

GDP

GTP

2 When the appropriate signaling molecule binds to the extracellular side of the receptor, the receptor is activated and changes shape. Its cytoplasmic side then binds an inactive G protein, causing a GTP to displace the GDP. This activates the G protein.

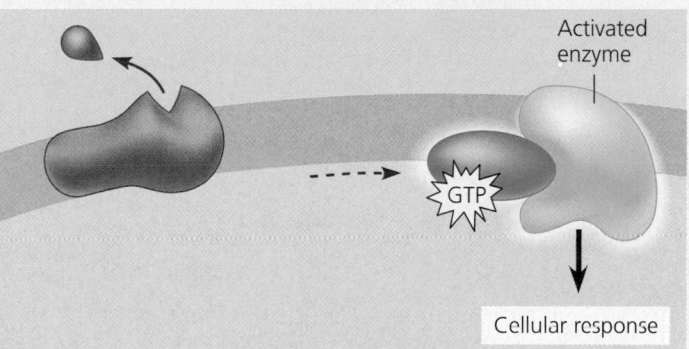

Activated enzyme

GTP

Cellular response

3 The activated G protein dissociates from the receptor, diffuses along the membrane, and then binds to an enzyme, altering the enzyme's shape and activity. When the enzyme is activated, it can trigger the next step in a pathway leading to a cellular response.

GDP

P$_i$

4 The changes in the enzyme and G protein are only temporary because the G protein also functions as a GTPase enzyme—in other words, it then hydrolyzes its bound GTP to GDP. Now inactive again, the G protein leaves the enzyme, which returns to its original state. The G protein is now available for reuse. The GTPase function of the G protein allows the pathway to shut down rapidly when the signaling molecule is no longer present.

Continued on next page

Exploring Membrane Receptors

Receptor Tyrosine Kinases

Receptor tyrosine kinases belong to a major class of plasma membrane receptors characterized by having enzymatic activity. A *kinase* is an enzyme that catalyzes the transfer of phosphate groups. The part of the receptor protein extending into the cytoplasm functions as a tyrosine kinase, an enzyme that catalyzes the transfer of a phosphate group from ATP to the amino acid tyrosine on a substrate protein. Thus, receptor tyrosine kinases are membrane receptors that attach phosphates to tyrosines.

One receptor tyrosine kinase complex may activate ten or more different transduction pathways and cellular responses. Often, more than one signal transduction pathway can be triggered at once, helping the cell regulate and coordinate many aspects of cell growth and cell reproduction. The ability of a single ligand-binding event to trigger so many pathways is a key difference between receptor tyrosine kinases and G protein-coupled receptors. Abnormal receptor tyrosine kinases that function even in the absence of signaling molecules may contribute to some kinds of cancer.

1 Many receptor tyrosine kinases have the structure depicted schematically here. Before the signaling molecule binds, the receptors exist as individual polypeptides. Notice that each has an extracellular ligand-binding site, an α helix spanning the membrane, and an intracellular tail containing multiple tyrosines.

2 The binding of a signaling molecule (such as a growth factor) causes two receptor polypeptides to associate closely with each other, forming a dimer (dimerization).

3 Dimerization activates the tyrosine kinase region of each polypeptide; each tyrosine kinase adds a phosphate from an ATP molecule to a tyrosine on the tail of the other polypeptide.

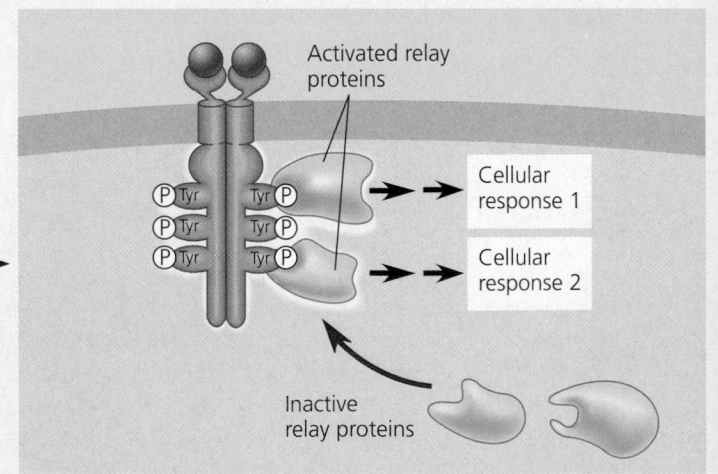

4 Now that the receptor protein is fully activated, it is recognized by specific relay proteins inside the cell. Each such protein binds to a specific phosphorylated tyrosine, undergoing a resulting structural change that activates the bound protein. Each activated protein triggers a transduction pathway, leading to a cellular response.

Ion Channel Receptors

A **ligand-gated ion channel** is a type of membrane receptor containing a region that can act as a "gate" when the receptor changes shape. When a signaling molecule binds as a ligand to the receptor protein, the gate opens or closes, allowing or blocking the flow of specific ions, such as Na$^+$ or Ca^{2+}, through a channel in the receptor. Like the other receptors we have discussed, these proteins bind the ligand at a specific site on their extracellular sides.

❶ Here we show a ligand-gated ion channel receptor in which the gate remains closed until a ligand binds to the receptor.

Signaling molecule (ligand)
Gate closed
Ions
Plasma membrane
Ligand-gated ion channel receptor

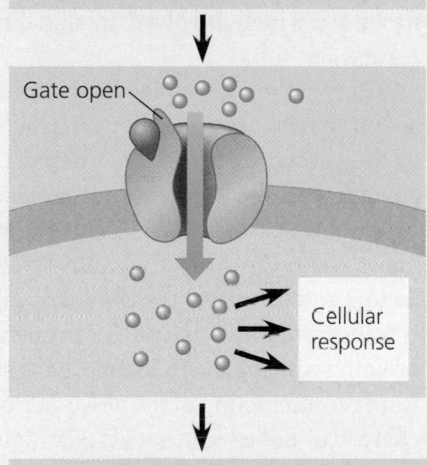

❷ When the ligand binds to the receptor and the gate opens, specific ions can flow through the channel and rapidly change the concentration of that particular ion inside the cell. This change may directly affect the activity of the cell in some way.

Gate open
Cellular response

❸ When the ligand dissociates from this receptor, the gate closes and ions no longer enter the cell.

Gate closed

Ligand-gated ion channels are very important in the nervous system. For example, the neurotransmitter molecules released at a synapse between two nerve cells (see Figure 11.5b) bind as ligands to ion channels on the receiving cell, causing the channels to open. Ions flow in (or, in some cases, out), triggering an electrical signal that propagates down the length of the receiving cell. Some gated ion channels are controlled by electrical signals instead of ligands; these *voltage-gated ion channels* are also crucial to the functioning of the nervous system, as we will discuss in Chapter 48.

protein, activating it **(Figure 11.8)**. With the hormone attached, the active form of the receptor protein then enters the nucleus and turns on specific genes that control male sex characteristics.

How does the activated hormone-receptor complex turn on genes? Recall that the genes in a cell's DNA function by being transcribed and processed into messenger RNA (mRNA), which leaves the nucleus and is translated into a specific protein by ribosomes in the cytoplasm (see Figure 5.26). Special proteins called *transcription factors* control which genes are turned on—that is, which genes are transcribed into mRNA—in a particular cell at a particular time. The testosterone receptor, when activated, acts as a transcription factor that turns on specific genes.

By acting as a transcription factor, the testosterone receptor itself carries out the complete transduction of the signal. Most other intracellular receptors function in the same way, although many of them are already in the nucleus before the signaling molecule reaches them (an example is the thyroid hormone receptor). Interestingly, many of these intracellular receptor proteins are structurally similar, suggesting an evolutionary

Hormone (testosterone)
EXTRACELLULAR FLUID
❶ The steroid hormone testosterone passes through the plasma membrane.

Receptor protein
Plasma membrane
❷ Testosterone binds to a receptor protein in the cytoplasm, activating it.

Hormone-receptor complex

❸ The hormone-receptor complex enters the nucleus and binds to specific genes.

DNA

mRNA

❹ The bound protein acts as a transcription factor, stimulating the transcription of the gene into mRNA.

NUCLEUS
New protein

❺ The mRNA is translated into a specific protein.

CYTOPLASM

▲ **Figure 11.8 Steroid hormone interacting with an intracellular receptor.**

? *Why is a cell-surface receptor protein not required for this steroid hormone to enter the cell?*

kinship. We will look more closely at hormones with intracellular receptors in Chapter 45.

CONCEPT 11.3
Transduction: Cascades of molecular interactions relay signals from receptors to target molecules in the cell

When receptors for signaling molecules are plasma membrane proteins, like most of those we have discussed, the transduction stage of cell signaling is usually a multistep pathway. Steps often include activation of proteins by addition or removal of phosphate groups, or release of other small molecules or ions that act as messengers. One benefit of multiple steps is the possibility of greatly amplifying a signal. If some of the molecules in a pathway transmit the signal to numerous molecules at the next step in the series, the result can be a large number of activated molecules at the end of the pathway. Moreover, multistep pathways provide more opportunities for coordination and regulation than simpler systems do. This allows fine-tuning of the response, in both unicellular and multicellular organisms, as we'll discuss later in the chapter.

Signal Transduction Pathways

The binding of a specific signaling molecule to a receptor in the plasma membrane triggers the first step in the chain of molecular interactions—the signal transduction pathway—that leads to a particular response within the cell. Like falling dominoes, the signal-activated receptor activates another molecule, which activates yet another molecule, and so on, until the protein that produces the final cellular response is activated. The molecules that relay a signal from receptor to response, which we call relay molecules in this book, are often proteins. The interaction of proteins is a major theme of cell signaling. Indeed, protein interaction is a unifying theme of all regulation at the cellular level.

Keep in mind that the original signaling molecule is not physically passed along a signaling pathway; in most cases, it never even enters the cell. When we say that the signal is re-

layed along a pathway, we mean that certain information is passed on. At each step, the signal is transduced into a different form, commonly a shape change in a protein. Very often, the shape change is brought about by phosphorylation.

Protein Phosphorylation and Dephosphorylation

Previous chapters introduced the concept of activating a protein by adding one or more phosphate groups to it (see Figure 8.11a). In Figure 11.7, we have already seen how phosphorylation is involved in the activation of receptor tyrosine kinases. In fact, the phosphorylation and dephosphorylation of proteins is a widespread cellular mechanism for regulating protein activity. The general name for an enzyme that transfers phosphate groups from ATP to a protein is **protein kinase**. Recall that a receptor tyrosine kinase phosphorylates tyrosines on the other receptor tyrosine kinase in a dimer. Most cytoplasmic protein kinases, however, act on proteins different from themselves. Another distinction is that most cytoplasmic protein kinases phosphorylate either the amino acid serine or threonine, rather than tyrosine. Such serine/threonine kinases are widely involved in signaling pathways in animals, plants, and fungi.

Many of the relay molecules in signal transduction pathways are protein kinases, and they often act on other protein kinases in the pathway. **Figure 11.9** depicts a hypothetical pathway containing three different protein kinases that create a "phosphorylation cascade." The sequence shown is similar to many known pathways, including those triggered in yeast by mating factors and in animal cells by many growth factors. The signal is transmitted by a cascade of protein phosphorylations, each bringing with it a shape change. Each such shape change results from the interaction of the newly added phosphate groups with charged or polar amino acids (see Figure 5.17). The addition of phosphate groups often changes a protein from an inactive form to an active form (although in other cases phosphorylation *decreases* the activity of the protein).

The importance of protein kinases can hardly be overstated. About 2% of our own genes are thought to code for protein kinases. A single cell may have hundreds of different kinds, each specific for a different substrate protein. Together, they probably regulate a large proportion of the thousands of proteins in a cell. Among these are most of the proteins that, in turn, regulate cell reproduction. Abnormal activity of such a kinase can cause abnormal cell growth and contribute to the development of cancer.

Equally important in the phosphorylation cascade are the **protein phosphatases**, enzymes that can rapidly remove phosphate groups from proteins, a process called dephosphorylation. By dephosphorylating and thus inactivating protein kinases, phosphatases provide the mechanism for turning off the signal transduction pathway when the initial signal is no

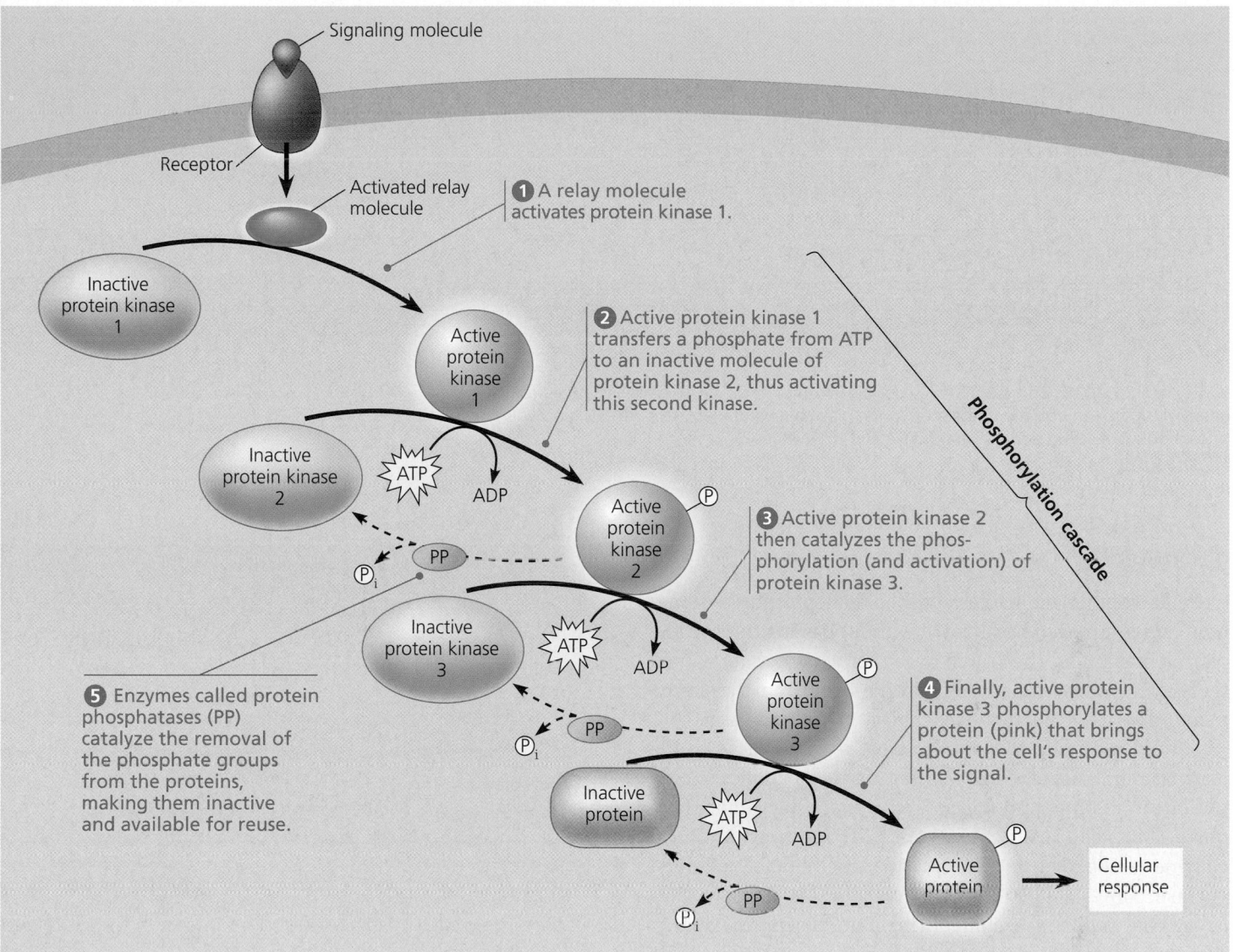

Figure 11.9 A phosphorylation cascade. In a phosphorylation cascade, a series of different molecules in a pathway are phosphorylated in turn, each molecule adding a phosphate group to the next one in line. In this example, phosphorylation activates each molecule, and dephosphorylation returns it to its inactive form. The active and inactive forms of each protein are represented by different shapes to remind you that activation is usually associated with a change in molecular shape.

? *Which protein is responsible for activation of protein kinase 3?*

Inside the figure:
- Signaling molecule
- Receptor
- Activated relay molecule
- Inactive protein kinase 1
- **1** A relay molecule activates protein kinase 1.
- Active protein kinase 1
- ATP
- ADP
- Inactive protein kinase 2
- **2** Active protein kinase 1 transfers a phosphate from ATP to an inactive molecule of protein kinase 2, thus activating this second kinase.
- Active protein kinase 2
- PP
- Inactive protein kinase 3
- ATP
- ADP
- **3** Active protein kinase 2 then catalyzes the phosphorylation (and activation) of protein kinase 3.
- Active protein kinase 3
- PP
- **4** Finally, active protein kinase 3 phosphorylates a protein (pink) that brings about the cell's response to the signal.
- Inactive protein
- ATP
- ADP
- **5** Enzymes called protein phosphatases (PP) catalyze the removal of the phosphate groups from the proteins, making them inactive and available for reuse.
- PP
- Active protein
- Cellular response
- Phosphorylation cascade

longer present. Phosphatases also make the protein kinases available for reuse, enabling the cell to respond again to an extracellular signal. At any given moment, the activity of a protein regulated by phosphorylation depends on the balance in the cell between active kinase molecules and active phosphatase molecules. The phosphorylation/dephosphorylation system acts as a molecular switch in the cell, turning activities on or off as required.

Small Molecules and Ions as Second Messengers

Not all components of signal transduction pathways are proteins. Many signaling pathways also involve small, nonprotein, water-soluble molecules or ions called **second messengers**. (The extracellular signaling molecule that binds to the membrane receptor is a pathway's "first messenger.") Because second messengers are both small and water-soluble, they can readily spread throughout the cell by diffusion. For example, as we'll see shortly, it is a second messenger called cyclic AMP that carries the signal initiated by epinephrine from the plasma membrane of a liver or muscle cell into the cell's interior, where it brings about glycogen breakdown. Second messengers participate in pathways initiated by both G protein-coupled receptors and receptor tyrosine kinases. The two most widely used second messengers are cyclic AMP and calcium ions, Ca^{2+}. A large variety of relay proteins are sensitive to the cytosolic concentration of one or the other of these second messengers.

▲ **Figure 11.10 Cyclic AMP.** The second messenger cyclic AMP (cAMP) is made from ATP by adenylyl cyclase, an enzyme embedded in the plasma membrane. Cyclic AMP is inactivated by phosphodiesterase, an enzyme that converts it to AMP.

WHAT IF? *What would happen if a molecule that inactivated phosphodiesterase were introduced into the cell?*

Cyclic AMP

Once Earl Sutherland had established that epinephrine somehow causes glycogen breakdown without passing through the plasma membrane, the search began for what he later named the *second messenger* that transmits the signal from the plasma membrane to the metabolic machinery in the cytoplasm.

Sutherland found that the binding of epinephrine to the plasma membrane of a liver cell elevates the cytosolic concentration of a compound called cyclic adenosine monophosphate, abbreviated **cyclic AMP** or **cAMP** (**Figure 11.10**). An enzyme embedded in the plasma membrane, **adenylyl cyclase**, converts ATP to cAMP in response to an extracellular signal—in this case, epinephrine. But epinephrine doesn't stimulate adenylyl cyclase directly. When epinephrine outside the cell binds to a specific receptor protein, the protein activates adenylyl cyclase, which in turn can catalyze the synthesis of many molecules of cAMP. In this way, the normal cellular concentration of cAMP can be boosted 20-fold in a matter of seconds. The cAMP broadcasts the signal to the cytoplasm. It does not persist for long in the absence of the hormone because another enzyme, called phosphodiesterase, converts cAMP to AMP. Another surge of epinephrine is needed to boost the cytosolic concentration of cAMP again.

Subsequent research has revealed that epinephrine is only one of many hormones and other signaling molecules that trigger the formation of cAMP. It has also brought to light the other components of cAMP pathways, including G proteins, G protein-coupled receptors, and protein kinases (**Figure 11.11**). The immediate effect of cAMP is usually the activation of a serine/threonine kinase called *protein kinase A.* The activated kinase then phosphorylates various other proteins, depending on the cell type. (The complete pathway for epinephrine's stimulation of glycogen breakdown is shown later, in Figure 11.15.)

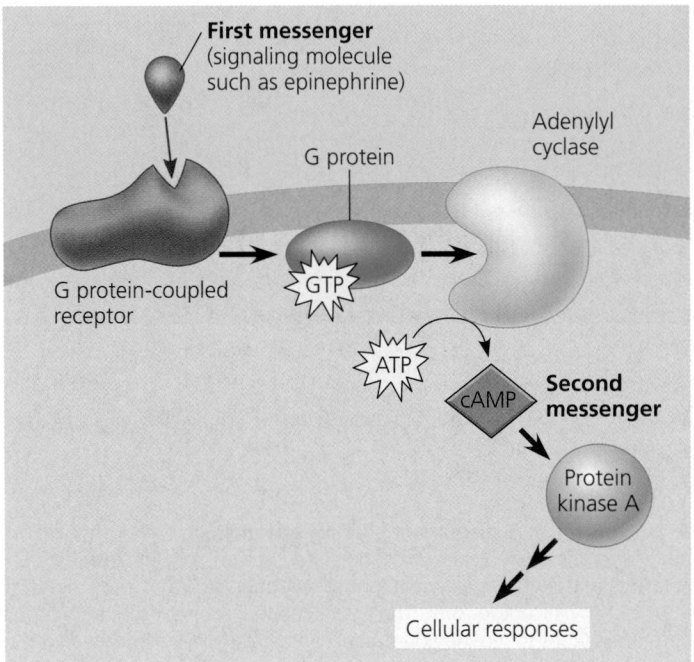

▲ **Figure 11.11 cAMP as a second messenger in a G-protein-signaling pathway.** The first messenger activates a G protein-coupled receptor, which activates a specific G protein. In turn, the G protein activates adenylyl cyclase, which catalyzes the conversion of ATP to cAMP. The cAMP then acts as a second messenger and activates another protein, usually protein kinase A, leading to cellular responses.

Further regulation of cell metabolism is provided by other G-protein systems that *inhibit* adenylyl cyclase. In these systems, a different signaling molecule activates a different receptor, which activates an *inhibitory* G protein.

Now that we know about the role of cAMP in G-protein-signaling pathways, we can explain in molecular detail how certain microbes cause disease. Consider cholera, a disease that is frequently epidemic in places where the water supply is contaminated with human feces. People acquire the cholera bacterium, *Vibrio cholerae*, by drinking contaminated water. The bacteria colonize the lining of the small intestine and produce a toxin. The cholera toxin is an enzyme that chemically modifies a G protein involved in regulating salt and water secretion. Because the modified G protein is unable to hydrolyze GTP to GDP, it remains stuck in its active form, continuously stimulating adenylyl cyclase to make cAMP. The resulting high concentration of cAMP causes the intestinal cells to secrete large amounts of salts, with water following by osmosis, into the intestines. An infected person quickly develops profuse diarrhea and if left untreated can soon die from the loss of water and salts.

Our understanding of signaling pathways involving cyclic AMP or related messengers has allowed us to develop treatments for certain conditions in humans. In one pathway *cyclic GMP*, or *cGMP*, acts as a signaling molecule whose effects include relaxation of smooth muscle cells in artery walls. A compound that inhibits the hydrolysis of cGMP to GMP, thus prolonging the signal, was originally prescribed for chest pains because it increased blood flow to the heart muscle. Under the trade name Viagra (see Figure 11.1), this compound is now widely used as a treatment for erectile dysfunction in human males. Because Viagra leads to dilation of blood vessels, it also allows increased blood flow to the penis, optimizing physiological conditions for penile erections. The similarities between external reproductive structures in males and females (see Chapter 46) have motivated medical researchers to initiate clinical studies exploring whether Viagra might also be used to treat sexual dysfunction in females; these studies are currently under way.

Calcium Ions and Inositol Trisphosphate (IP₃)

Many signaling molecules in animals, including neurotransmitters, growth factors, and some hormones, induce responses in their target cells via signal transduction pathways that increase the cytosolic concentration of calcium ions (Ca^{2+}). Calcium is even more widely used than cAMP as a second messenger. Increasing the cytosolic concentration of Ca^{2+} causes many responses in animal cells, including muscle cell contraction, secretion of certain substances, and cell division. In plant cells, a wide range of hormonal and environmental stimuli can cause brief increases in cytosolic Ca^{2+} concentration, triggering various signaling pathways, such as the pathway for greening in response to light (see Figure 39.4). Cells use Ca^{2+} as a second messenger in both G-protein and receptor tyrosine kinase pathways.

Although cells always contain some Ca^{2+}, this ion can function as a second messenger because its concentration in the cytosol is normally much lower than the concentration outside the cell (**Figure 11.12**). In fact, the level of Ca^{2+} in the blood and extracellular fluid of an animal often exceeds that in the cytosol by more than 10,000 times. Calcium ions are actively transported out of the cell and are actively imported from the cytosol into the endoplasmic reticulum (and, under some conditions, into mitochondria and chloroplasts) by various protein pumps (see Figure 11.12). As a result, the calcium concentration in the ER is usually much higher than that in the cytosol. Because the cytosolic calcium level is low, a small change in absolute numbers of ions represents a relatively large percentage change in calcium concentration.

In response to a signal relayed by a signal transduction pathway, the cytosolic calcium level may rise, usually by a mechanism that releases Ca^{2+} from the cell's ER. The pathways leading to calcium release involve still other second messengers, **inositol trisphosphate (IP₃)** and **diacylglycerol (DAG)**. These two messengers are produced by cleavage of a certain kind of phospholipid in the plasma membrane.

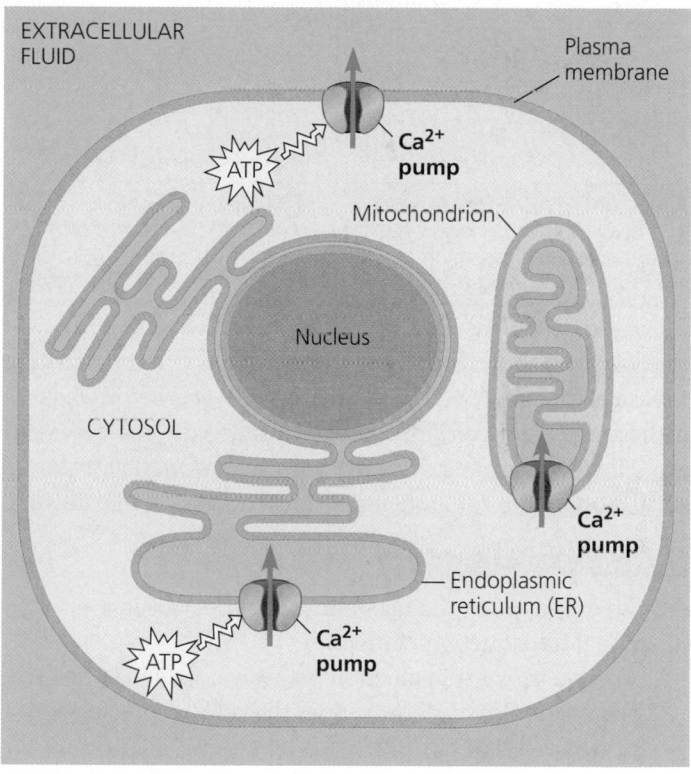

Key
▨ High [Ca²⁺]
▨ Low [Ca²⁺]

▲ Figure 11.12 **The maintenance of calcium ion concentrations in an animal cell.** The Ca^{2+} concentration in the cytosol is usually much lower (light blue) than that in the extracellular fluid and ER (darker blue). Protein pumps in the plasma membrane and the ER membrane, driven by ATP, move Ca^{2+} from the cytosol into the extracellular fluid and into the lumen of the ER. Mitochondrial pumps, driven by chemiosmosis (see Chapter 9), move Ca^{2+} into mitochondria when the calcium level in the cytosol rises significantly.

① A signaling molecule binds to a receptor, leading to activation of phospholipase C.

② Phospholipase C cleaves a plasma membrane phospholipid called PIP_2 into DAG and IP_3.

③ DAG functions as a second messenger in other pathways.

◄ **Figure 11.13 Calcium and IP_3 in signaling pathways.** Calcium ions (Ca^{2+}) and inositol trisphosphate (IP_3) function as second messengers in many signal transduction pathways. In this figure, the process is initiated by the binding of a signaling molecule to a G protein-coupled receptor. A receptor tyrosine kinase could also initiate this pathway by activating phospholipase C.

④ IP_3 quickly diffuses through the cytosol and binds to an IP_3-gated calcium channel in the ER membrane, causing it to open.

⑤ Calcium ions flow out of the ER (down their concentration gradient), raising the Ca^{2+} level in the cytosol.

⑥ The calcium ions activate the next protein in one or more signaling pathways.

Figure 11.13 shows how this occurs and how IP_3 stimulates the release of calcium from the ER. Because IP_3 acts before calcium in these pathways, calcium could be considered a "*third* messenger." However, scientists use the term *second messenger* for all small, nonprotein components of signal transduction pathways.

CONCEPT CHECK **11.3**

1. What is a protein kinase, and what is its role in a signal transduction pathway?
2. When a signal transduction pathway involves a phosphorylation cascade, how does the cell's response get turned off?
3. What is the actual "signal" that is being transduced in any signal transduction pathway, such as those shown in Figures 11.6 and 11.9? In other words, in what way is information being passed from the exterior to the interior of the cell?
4. **WHAT IF?** Upon activation of phospholipase C by ligand binding to a receptor, what effect does the IP_3-gated calcium channel have on Ca^{2+} concentration in the cytosol?

For suggested answers, see Appendix A.

CONCEPT **11.4**

Response: Cell signaling leads to regulation of transcription or cytoplasmic activities

We now take a closer look at the cell's subsequent response to an extracellular signal—what some researchers call the "output response." What is the nature of the final step in a signaling pathway?

Nuclear and Cytoplasmic Responses

Ultimately, a signal transduction pathway leads to the regulation of one or more cellular activities. The response at the end of the pathway may occur in the nucleus of the cell or in the cytoplasm.

Many signaling pathways ultimately regulate protein synthesis, usually by turning specific genes on or off in the nucleus. Like an activated steroid receptor (see Figure 11.8), the final activated molecule in a signaling pathway may function as a transcription factor. **Figure 11.14** shows an example in which a signaling pathway activates a transcription factor

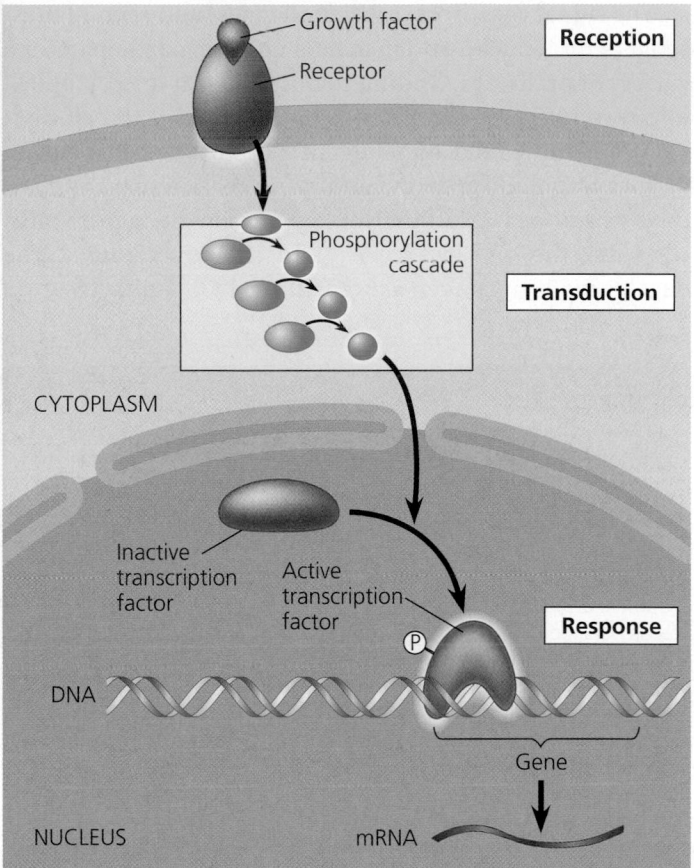

▲ **Figure 11.14 Nuclear responses to a signal: the activation of a specific gene by a growth factor.** This diagram is a simplified representation of a typical signaling pathway that leads to the regulation of gene activity in the cell nucleus. The initial signaling molecule, a local regulator called a growth factor, triggers a phosphorylation cascade. (The ATP molecules that serve as sources of phosphate are not shown.) Once phosphorylated, the last kinase in the sequence enters the nucleus and there activates a gene-regulating protein, a transcription factor. This protein stimulates a specific gene so that an mRNA is synthesized, which then directs the synthesis of a particular protein in the cytoplasm.

▲ **Figure 11.15 Cytoplasmic response to a signal: the stimulation of glycogen breakdown by epinephrine.** In this signaling system, the hormone epinephrine acts through a G protein-coupled receptor to activate a succession of relay molecules, including cAMP and two protein kinases (see also Figure 11.11). The final protein to be activated is the enzyme glycogen phosphorylase, which uses inorganic phosphate to release glucose monomers from glycogen in the form of glucose-1-phosphate molecules. This pathway amplifies the hormonal signal, because one receptor protein can activate about 100 molecules of G protein, and each enzyme in the pathway, once activated, can act on many molecules of its substrate, the next molecule in the cascade. The number of activated molecules given for each step is approximate.

that turns a gene on: The response to the growth factor signal is the synthesis of mRNA, which will be translated in the cytoplasm into a specific protein. In other cases, the transcription factor might regulate a gene by turning it off. Often a transcription factor regulates several different genes.

Sometimes a signaling pathway may regulate the *activity* of proteins rather than their *synthesis*, directly affecting proteins that function outside the nucleus. For example, a signal may cause the opening or closing of an ion channel in the plasma membrane or a change in cell metabolism. As we have discussed already, the response of liver cells to signaling by the hormone epinephrine helps regulate cellular energy metabolism by affecting the activity of an enzyme. The final step in the signaling pathway that begins with epinephrine binding acti-

vates the enzyme that catalyzes the breakdown of glycogen. **Figure 11.15** shows the complete pathway leading to the release of glucose-1-phosphate molecules from glycogen. Note that as each molecule is activated, the response is amplified, as we will discuss later.

In addition to the regulation of enzymes, signaling events may also affect other cellular attributes, such as overall cell shape. An example of this regulation can be found in the activities leading to the mating of yeast cells (see Figure 11.2). Yeast cells are not motile; their mating process depends on the growth of localized projections in one cell toward a cell of the opposite mating type. As shown in **Figure 11.16**, binding of the mating factor causes this directional growth. When the mating factor binds, it activates signaling-pathway kinases that affect the orientation of growth of cytoskeletal microfilaments. Because activation of signaling kinases is coupled in this way to cytoskeletal dynamics, cell projections emerge from regions of the plasma membrane exposed to the highest concentration of the mating factor. As a result, these projections are oriented toward the cell of the opposite mating type, which is the source of the signaling molecule.

The signal receptors, relay molecules, and second messengers introduced so far in this chapter participate in a variety of pathways, leading to both nuclear and cytoplasmic responses. Some of these pathways lead to cell division. The molecular messengers that initiate cell-division pathways include growth factors and certain plant and animal hormones. Malfunctioning of growth factor pathways like the one in Figure 11.14 can contribute to the development of cancer, as we will see in Chapter 18.

▼ **Figure 11.16** **Inquiry**

How do signals induce directional cell growth in yeast?

EXPERIMENT   When a yeast cell binds mating factor molecules from a cell of the opposite mating type, a signaling pathway causes it to grow a projection toward the potential mate. The cell with the projection is called a "shmoo" because it resembles a 1950s cartoon character by that name. Dina Matheos and colleagues in Mark Rose's lab at Princeton University sought to determine how mating factor signaling is linked to this asymmetrical growth. Previous work had shown that activation of one of the kinases in the signaling cascade (Fus3) caused it to move to the membrane near where the factor bound. Preliminary experiments by these researchers identified formin, a protein that directs the construction of microfilaments, as a phosphorylation target of Fus3 kinase. To examine the role of Fus3 and formin in shmoo formation, the researchers generated two mutant yeast strains: one that no longer had the kinase (this strain is called ΔFus3) and one that lacked the formin (Δformin). To observe the effects of these mutations on cell growth induced by the mating factor, the cell walls of each strain were first stained with a green fluorescent dye. These green-stained cells were then exposed to mating factor and stained with a red fluorescent dye that labeled new cell wall growth. Images taken of the cells after the staining procedure were then compared with a similarly treated strain that expressed Fus3 and formin (the wild type).

RESULTS   The cells of the wild-type strain showed shmoo projections, whose walls were stained red, while the rest of their cell walls were green, indicating asymmetrical growth. Cells of both the ΔFus3 and Δformin strains showed no shmoo formation, and their cell walls were stained almost uniformly yellow. This color resulted from merged green and red stains, indicating symmetrical growth, characteristic of cells not exposed to mating factor.

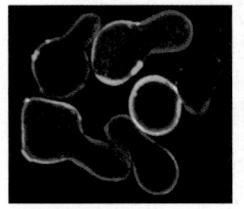

Wild-type (shmoos)   ΔFus3   Δformin

CONCLUSION   The similar defect (lack of ability to form shmoos) in strains lacking either Fus3 or formin suggests that both proteins are required for shmoo formation. These results led the investigators to propose the model shown here for the induction of directed asymmetrical growth in the receiving cell toward the cell of the opposite mating type.

① Mating factor activates receptor.

Mating factor

G protein-coupled receptor

GDP

② G protein binds GTP and becomes activated.

GTP

Phosphorylation cascade

Fus3

③ Phosphorylation cascade activates Fus3, which moves to plasma membrane.

Fus3 (P)

④ Fus3 phosphorylates formin, activating it.

Fus3 (P)

Formin   Formin (P)

Microfilament

Shmoo projection forming

Formin (P)

Actin subunit

⑤ Formin initiates growth of microfilaments that form the shmoo projections.

SOURCE   D. Matheos et al., Pheromone-induced polarization is dependent on the Fus3p MAPK acting through the formin Bni1p, *Journal of Cell Biology* 165:99–109 (2004).

WHAT IF?   Based on these results and the proposed model from this work, what would happen to a cell if its Fus3 kinase were not able to associate with the membrane upon activation?

Fine-Tuning of the Response

Regardless of whether the response occurs in the nucleus or in the cytoplasm, it is fine-tuned at multiple points. As mentioned earlier, signaling pathways with numerous steps between a signaling event at the cell surface and the cell's response have two important benefits: They amplify the signal (and thus the response), and they provide different points at which a cell's response can be regulated. This allows coordination of signaling pathways and also contributes to the specificity of the response. The overall efficiency of the response is also enhanced by scaffolding proteins. Finally, a crucial point in fine-tuning the response is the termination of the signal.

Signal Amplification

Elaborate enzyme cascades amplify the cell's response to a signal. At each catalytic step in the cascade, the number of activated products is much greater than in the preceding step. For example, in the epinephrine-triggered pathway in Figure 11.15, each adenylyl cyclase molecule catalyzes the formation of many cAMP molecules, each molecule of protein kinase A phosphorylates many molecules of the next kinase in the pathway, and so on. The amplification effect stems from the fact that these proteins persist in the active form long enough to process numerous molecules of substrate before they become inactive again. As a result of the signal's amplification, a small number of epinephrine molecules binding to receptors on the surface of a liver cell or muscle cell can lead to the release of hundreds of millions of glucose molecules from glycogen.

The Specificity of Cell Signaling and Coordination of the Response

Consider two different cells in your body—a liver cell and a heart muscle cell, for example. Both are in contact with your bloodstream and are therefore constantly exposed to many different hormone molecules, as well as to local regulators secreted by nearby cells. Yet the liver cell responds to some signals but ignores others, and the same is true for the heart cell. And some kinds of signals trigger responses in both cells—but different responses. For instance, epinephrine stimulates the liver cell to break down glycogen, but the main response of the heart cell to epinephrine is contraction, leading to a more rapid heartbeat. How do we account for this difference?

The explanation for the specificity exhibited in cellular responses to signals is the same as the basic explanation for virtually all differences between cells: *Different kinds of cells have different collections of proteins* **(Figure 11.17)**. (This is because different kinds of cells turn on different sets of genes.) The response of a particular cell to a signal depends on its particular collection of signal receptor proteins, relay proteins, and proteins needed to carry out the response. A liver cell, for example, is poised to respond appropriately to epinephrine by having the proteins listed in Figure 11.15 as well as those needed to manufacture glycogen.

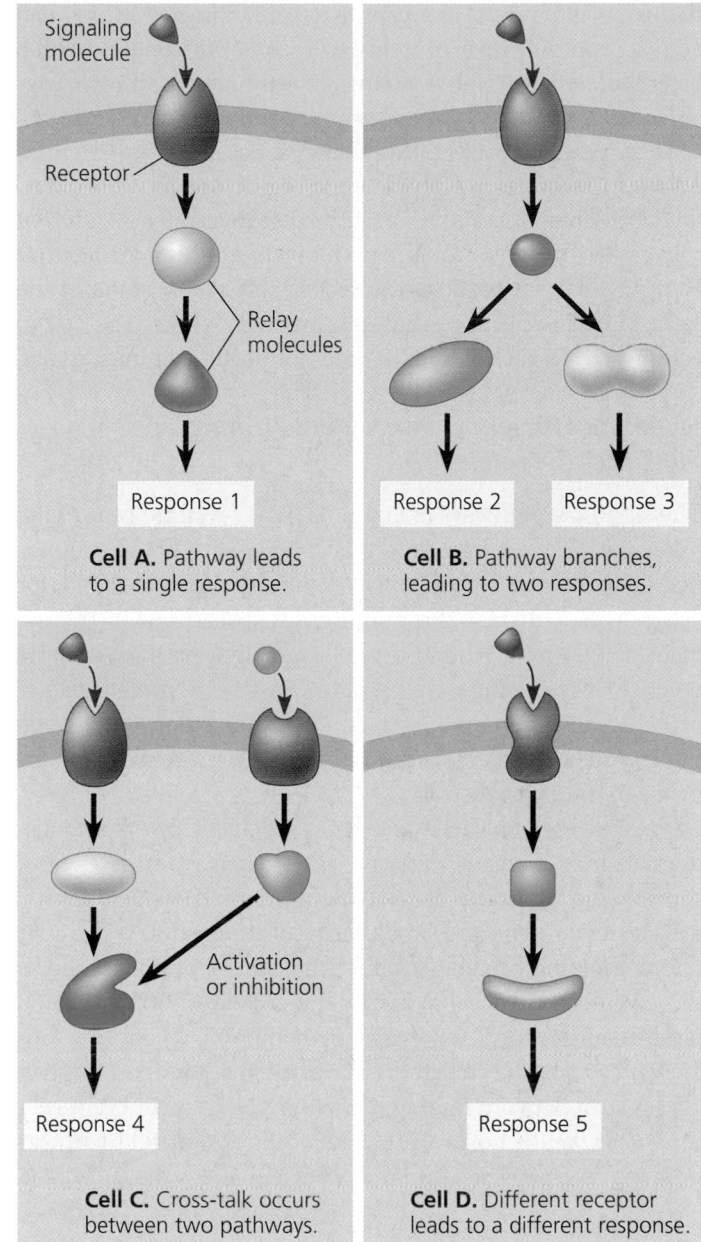

▲ **Figure 11.17 The specificity of cell signaling.** The particular proteins a cell possesses determine what signaling molecules it responds to and the nature of the response. The four cells in these diagrams respond to the same signaling molecule (red) in different ways because each has a different set of proteins (purple and teal shapes). Note, however, that the same kinds of molecules can participate in more than one pathway.

Thus, two cells that respond differently to the same signal differ in one or more of the proteins that handle and respond to the signal. Notice in Figure 11.17 that different pathways may have some molecules in common. For example, cells A, B, and C all use the same receptor protein for the red signaling molecule; differences in other proteins account for their differing responses. In cell D, a different receptor protein is used for the same signaling molecule, leading to yet another response. In cell B, a pathway that is triggered by a single kind of signal diverges to produce two responses; such branched pathways often involve receptor tyrosine kinases (which can activate multiple relay proteins) or second messengers (which can regulate numerous proteins). In cell C, two pathways triggered by separate signals converge to modulate a single response. Branching of pathways and "cross-talk" (interaction) between pathways are important in regulating and coordinating a cell's responses to information coming in from different sources in the body. (You'll learn more about this coordination later, in the next section.) Moreover, the use of some of the same proteins in more than one pathway allows the cell to economize on the number of different proteins it must make.

Signaling Efficiency: Scaffolding Proteins and Signaling Complexes

The signaling pathways in Figure 11.17 (as well as some of the other pathway depictions in this chapter) are greatly simplified. The diagrams show only a few relay molecules and, for clarity's sake, display these molecules spread out in the cytosol. If this were true in the cell, signaling pathways would operate very inefficiently because most relay molecules are proteins, and proteins are too large to diffuse quickly through the viscous cytosol. How does a particular protein kinase, for instance, find its substrate?

Recent research suggests that the efficiency of signal transduction may in many cases be increased by the presence of **scaffolding proteins**, large relay proteins to which several other relay proteins are simultaneously attached. For example, one scaffolding protein isolated from mouse brain cells holds three protein kinases and carries these kinases with it when it binds to an appropriately activated membrane receptor; it thus facilitates a specific phosphorylation cascade (**Figure 11.18**). In fact, researchers are finding scaffolding proteins in brain cells that *permanently* hold together networks of signaling-pathway proteins at synapses. This hardwiring enhances the speed and

accuracy of signal transfer between cells, because the rate of protein-protein interaction is not limited by diffusion.

When signaling pathways were first discovered, they were thought to be linear, independent pathways. Our understanding of the processes of cellular communication has benefited from the realization that things are not that simple. In fact, as seen in Figure 11.17, some proteins may participate in more than one pathway, either in different cell types or in the same cell at different times or under different conditions. This view underscores the importance of permanent or transient protein complexes in the functioning of a cell.

The importance of the relay proteins that serve as points of branching or intersection in signaling pathways is highlighted by the problems arising when these proteins are defective or missing. For instance, in an inherited disorder called Wiskott-Aldrich syndrome (WAS), the absence of a single relay protein leads to such diverse effects as abnormal bleeding, eczema, and a predisposition to infections and leukemia. These symptoms are thought to arise primarily from the absence of the protein in cells of the immune system. By studying normal cells, scientists found that the WAS protein is located just beneath the cell surface. The protein interacts both with microfilaments of the cytoskeleton and with several different components of signaling pathways that relay information from the cell surface, including pathways regulating immune cell proliferation. This multifunctional relay protein is thus both a branch point and an important intersection point in a complex signal transduction network that controls immune cell behavior. When the WAS protein is absent, the cytoskeleton is not properly organized and signaling pathways are disrupted, leading to the WAS symptoms.

Termination of the Signal

To keep Figure 11.17 simple, we did not indicate the *inactivation* mechanisms that are an essential aspect of cell signaling. For a cell of a multicellular organism to remain alert and capable of responding to incoming signals, each molecular change in its signaling pathways must last only a short time. As we saw in the cholera example, if a signaling pathway component becomes locked into one state, whether active or inactive, the consequences for the organism can be dire.

Thus, a key to a cell's continuing receptiveness to regulation by signaling is the reversibility of the changes that signals produce. The binding of signaling molecules to receptors is reversible; the lower the concentration of signaling molecules is, the fewer will be bound at any given moment. When signaling molecules leave the receptor, the receptor reverts to its inactive form. Then, by a variety of means, the relay molecules return to their inactive forms:

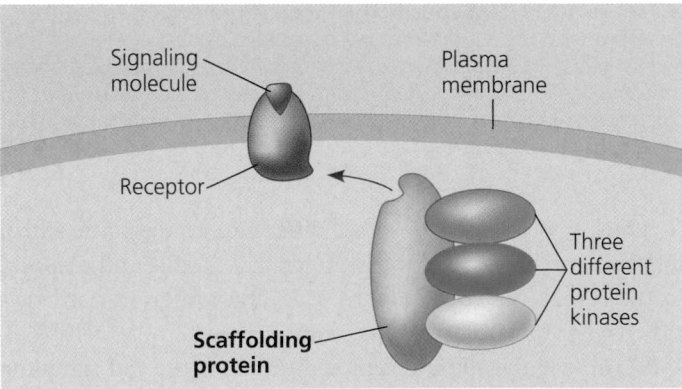

▲ **Figure 11.18 A scaffolding protein.** The scaffolding protein shown here (pink) simultaneously binds to a specific activated membrane receptor and three different protein kinases. This physical arrangement facilitates signal transduction by these molecules.

The GTPase activity intrinsic to a G protein hydrolyzes its bound GTP; the enzyme phosphodiesterase converts cAMP to AMP; protein phosphatases inactivate phosphorylated kinases and other proteins; and so forth. As a result, the cell is soon ready to respond to a fresh signal.

In this section, we explored the complexity of signaling initiation and termination in a single pathway, and we saw the potential for pathways to intersect with each other. In the next section, we'll consider an important network of interacting pathways in the cell.

CONCEPT **11.5**
Apoptosis (programmed cell death) integrates multiple cell-signaling pathways

One of the most elaborate networks of signaling pathways in the cell seems to ask and answer the basic question posed by Hamlet: To be or not to be? Cells that are infected or damaged or that have simply reached the end of their functional life span often enter a program of controlled cell suicide called **apoptosis** (from the Greek, meaning "falling off," and used in a classic Greek poem to refer to leaves falling from a tree). During this process, cellular agents chop up the DNA and fragment the organelles and other cytoplasmic components. The cell shrinks and becomes lobed (called "blebbing") **(Figure 11.19)**, and the cell's parts are packaged up in vesicles that are engulfed and digested by specialized scavenger cells, leaving no trace. Apoptosis protects neighboring cells from damage that they would otherwise suffer if a dying cell merely leaked out all its contents, including its many digestive and other enzymes.

Apoptosis in the Soil Worm *Caenorhabditis elegans*

Embryonic development is a period during which apoptosis is widespread and plays a crucial role. The molecular mechanisms underlying apoptosis were worked out in detail by researchers studying embryonic development of a small soil worm, a nematode called *Caenorhabditis elegans*. Because the adult worm has only about a thousand cells, the researchers were able to work out the entire ancestry of each cell. The timely suicide of cells occurs exactly 131 times during normal development of *C. elegans*, at precisely the same points in the cell lineage of each worm. In worms and other species, apoptosis is triggered by signals that activate a cascade of "suicide" proteins in the cells destined to die.

Genetic research on *C. elegans* has revealed two key apoptosis genes, called *ced-3* and *ced-4* (*ced* stands for "cell death"), which encode proteins essential for apoptosis. (The proteins are called Ced-3 and Ced-4, respectively.) These and most other proteins involved in apoptosis are continually present in cells, but in inactive form; thus, protein activity is regulated rather than protein synthesis (by way of gene activity).

▶ Figure 11.19 **Apoptosis of a human white blood cell.** We can compare a normal white blood cell (left) with a white blood cell undergoing apoptosis (right). The apoptotic cell is shrinking and forming lobes ("blebs"), which eventually are shed as membrane-bounded cell fragments (colorized SEMs).

2 μm

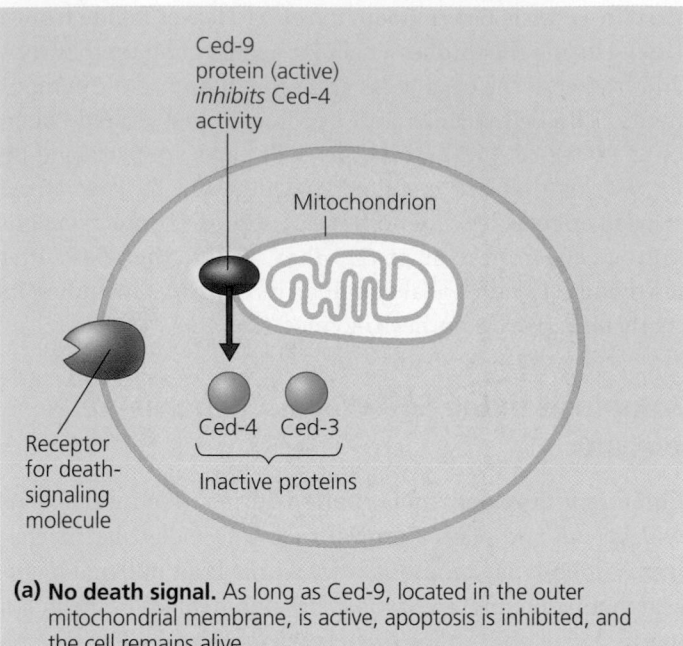

(a) No death signal. As long as Ced-9, located in the outer mitochondrial membrane, is active, apoptosis is inhibited, and the cell remains alive.

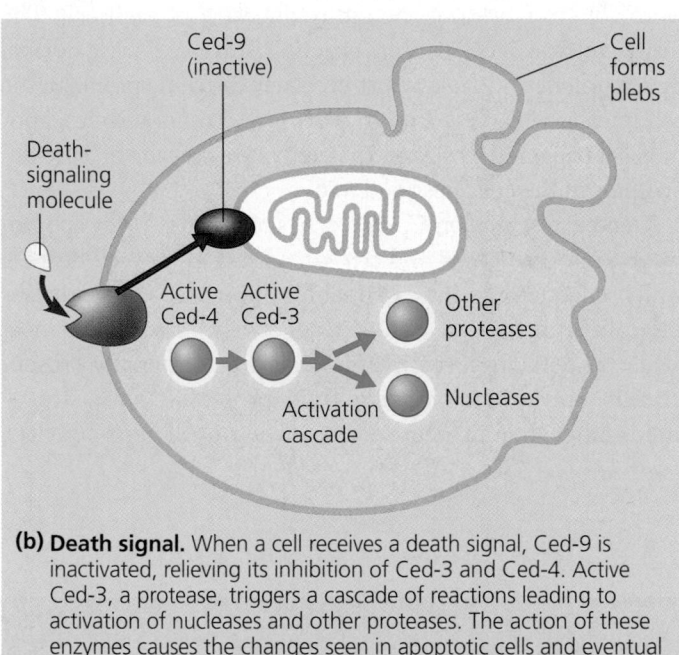

(b) Death signal. When a cell receives a death signal, Ced-9 is inactivated, relieving its inhibition of Ced-3 and Ced-4. Active Ced-3, a protease, triggers a cascade of reactions leading to activation of nucleases and other proteases. The action of these enzymes causes the changes seen in apoptotic cells and eventual cell death.

▲ **Figure 11.20 Molecular basis of apoptosis in *C. elegans.*** Three proteins, Ced-3, Ced-4, and Ced-9, are critical to apoptosis and its regulation in the nematode. Apoptosis is more complicated in mammals but involves proteins similar to those in the nematode.

In *C. elegans*, a protein in the outer mitochondrial membrane, called Ced-9 (the product of the *ced-9* gene), serves as a master regulator of apoptosis, acting as a brake in the absence of a signal promoting apoptosis **(Figure 11.20)**. When a death signal is received by the cell, it overrides the brake, and the apoptotic pathway activates proteases and nucleases, enzymes that cut up the proteins and DNA of the cell. The main pro-

teases of apoptosis are called *caspases*; in the nematode, the chief caspase is Ced-3.

Apoptotic Pathways and the Signals That Trigger Them

In humans and other mammals, several different pathways, involving about 15 different caspases, can carry out apoptosis. The pathway that is used depends on the type of cell and on the particular signal that triggers apoptosis. One major pathway involves mitochondrial proteins. Apoptotic proteins can form molecular pores in the mitochondrial outer membrane, causing it to leak and release proteins that promote apoptosis. Surprisingly, these include cytochrome *c*, which functions in mitochondrial electron transport in healthy cells (see Figure 9.16) but acts as a cell death factor when released from mitochondria. The process of mitochondrial apoptosis in mammals uses proteins similar to the nematode proteins Ced-3, Ced-4, and Ced-9.

At key points in the apoptotic program, proteins integrate signals from several different sources and can send a cell down an apoptotic pathway. Often, the signal originates outside the cell, like the death-signaling molecule depicted in Figure 11.20, which presumably was released by a neighboring cell. When a death-signaling ligand occupies a cell-surface receptor, this binding leads to activation of caspases and other enzymes that carry out apoptosis, without involving the mitochondrial pathway. Two other types of alarm signals originate from *inside* the cell. One comes from the nucleus, generated when the DNA has suffered irreparable damage, and a second comes from the endoplasmic reticulum when excessive protein misfolding occurs. Mammalian cells make life-or-death "decisions" by somehow integrating the death signals and life signals they receive from these external and internal sources.

A built-in cell suicide mechanism is essential to development and maintenance in all animals. The similarities between apoptosis genes in nematodes and mammals, as well as the observation that apoptosis occurs in multicellular fungi and even in single-celled yeasts, indicate that the basic mechanism evolved early in animal evolution. In vertebrates, apoptosis is essential for normal development of the nervous system, for normal operation of the immune system, and for normal morphogenesis of hands and feet in humans and paws in other mammals **(Figure 11.21)**. A lower level of apoptosis in developing limbs accounts for the webbed feet of ducks and other water birds, in contrast to chickens and other land birds with nonwebbed feet. In the case of humans, the failure of appropriate apoptosis can result in webbed fingers and toes.

Significant evidence points to the involvement of apoptosis in certain degenerative diseases of the nervous system, such as Parkinson's disease and Alzheimer's disease. Also, cancer can result from a failure of cell suicide; some cases of human melanoma, for example, have been linked to faulty forms of

Interdigital tissue

1 mm

▲ **Figure 11.21 Effect of apoptosis during paw development in the mouse.** In mice, humans, and other mammals, as well as in land birds, the embryonic region that develops into feet or hands initially has a solid, platelike structure. Apoptosis eliminates the cells in the interdigital regions, thus forming the digits. The embryonic mouse paws shown in these fluorescence light micrographs are stained so that cells undergoing apoptosis appear bright yellow. Apoptosis of cells begins at the margin of each interdigital region (left), peaks as the tissue in these regions is reduced (middle), and is no longer visible when the interdigital tissue has been eliminated (right).

the human version of the *C. elegans* Ced-4 protein. It is not surprising, therefore, that the signaling pathways feeding into apoptosis are quite elaborate. After all, the life-or-death question is the most fundamental one imaginable for a cell.

This chapter has introduced you to many of the general mechanisms of cell communication, such as ligand binding, protein-protein interactions and shape changes, cascades of interactions, and protein phosphorylation. As you continue through the text, you will encounter numerous examples of cell signaling.

CONCEPT CHECK 11.5

1. Give an example of apoptosis during embryonic development, and explain its function in the developing embryo.
2. **WHAT IF?** What type of protein defects could result in apoptosis occurring when it should not? What type could result in apoptosis not occurring when it should?

For suggested answers, see Appendix A.

Chapter 11 Review

SUMMARY OF KEY CONCEPTS

CONCEPT 11.1

External signals are converted to responses within the cell (pp. 206–210)

▶ **Evolution of Cell Signaling** Signaling in microbes has much in common with processes in multicellular organisms, suggesting an early origin of signaling mechanisms. Bacterial cells can sense the local density of bacterial cells (quorum sensing) by binding molecules secreted by other cells. In some cases, such signals lead to aggregation of these cells into biofilms.

▶ **Local and Long-Distance Signaling** In local signaling, animal cells may communicate by direct contact or by secreting local regulators, such as growth factors or neurotransmitters. For signaling over long distances, both animals and plants use hormones; animals also signal along nerve cells.

▶ **The Three Stages of Cell Signaling: *A Preview*** Earl Sutherland discovered how the hormone epinephrine acts on cells, shown here as an example of a cell-signaling pathway:

| ❶ Reception | ❷ Transduction | ❸ Response |

As discussed in Sections 11.2 and 11.3, the signal is transmitted by successive shape changes in the receptor and relay molecules.

MEDIA
Investigation How Do Cells Communicate with Each Other?
Activity Overview of Cell Signaling

CONCEPT 11.2

Reception: A signaling molecule binds to a receptor protein, causing it to change shape (pp. 210–214)

▶ The binding between signaling molecule (ligand) and receptor is highly specific. A shape change in a receptor is often the initial transduction of the signal.

▶ **Receptors in the Plasma Membrane** A G protein-coupled receptor is a membrane receptor that works with the help of a cytoplasmic G protein. Ligand binding activates the receptor, which then activates a specific G protein, which activates yet another protein, thus propagating the signal along a signal transduction pathway.

Receptor tyrosine kinases react to the binding of signaling molecules by forming dimers and then adding phosphate groups to tyrosines on the cytoplasmic part of the other subunit of the dimer. Relay proteins in the cell can then be activated by binding to different phosphorylated tyrosines, allowing this receptor to trigger several pathways at once.

Specific signaling molecules cause ligand-gated ion channels in a membrane to open or close, regulating the flow of specific ions.

▶ **Intracellular Receptors** Intracellular receptors are cytoplasmic or nuclear proteins. Signaling molecules that are small or hydrophobic and can readily cross the plasma membrane use these receptors.

MEDIA

Activity Reception

CONCEPT 11.3

Transduction: Cascades of molecular interactions relay signals from receptors to target molecules in the cell (pp. 214–218)

▶ **Signal Transduction Pathways** At each step in a pathway, the signal is transduced into a different form, commonly a shape change in a protein.

▶ **Protein Phosphorylation and Dephosphorylation** Many signal transduction pathways include phosphorylation cascades, in which a series of protein kinases each add a phosphate group to the next one in line, activating it. Phosphatase enzymes soon remove the phosphates.

▶ **Small Molecules and Ions as Second Messengers** Second messengers, such as cyclic AMP (cAMP) and Ca^{2+}, diffuse readily through the cytosol and thus help broadcast signals quickly. Many G proteins activate adenylyl cyclase, which makes cAMP from ATP. Cells use Ca^{2+} as a second messenger in both G-protein and tyrosine kinase pathways. The tyrosine kinase pathways can also involve two other second messengers, DAG and IP_3. IP_3 can trigger a subsequent increase in Ca^{2+} levels.

MEDIA

Activity Signal Transduction Pathways

CONCEPT 11.4

Response: Cell signaling leads to regulation of transcription or cytoplasmic activities (pp. 218–223)

▶ **Nuclear and Cytoplasmic Responses** Some pathways regulate genes by activating transcription factors, proteins that turn specific genes on or off. In the cytoplasm, signaling pathways regulate, for example, enzyme activity and cytoskeleton rearrangement, which can lead to cell shape changes.

▶ **Fine-Tuning of the Response** Each catalytic protein in a signaling pathway amplifies the signal by activating multiple copies of the next component of the pathway; for long pathways, the total amplification may be a millionfold or more. The particular combination of proteins in a cell gives the cell great specificity in both the signals it detects and the re-

sponses it carries out. Scaffolding proteins can increase signal transduction efficiency. Pathway branching and cross-talk further help the cell coordinate incoming signals. Signal response is terminated quickly by the reversal of ligand binding.

MEDIA

Activity Cellular Responses
Activity Build a Signaling Pathway

CONCEPT 11.5

Apoptosis (programmed cell death) integrates multiple cell-signaling pathways (pp. 223–225)

▶ Apoptosis is a type of programmed cell death in which cell components are disposed of in an orderly fashion, without damage to neighboring cells.

▶ **Apoptosis in the Soil Worm** *Caenorhabditis elegans* Apoptosis occurs at defined times during embryonic development of *C. elegans*. A protein (Ced-9) in the mitochondrial membrane acts as a brake; when released by a death signal, it allows activation of caspases that carry out apoptosis.

▶ **Apoptotic Pathways and the Signals That Trigger Them** Several apoptotic pathways exist in the cells of humans and other mammals, and these pathways may be triggered in different ways. A major pathway involves pore formation in the outer mitochondrial membrane, which leads to release of factors that activate caspases. Signals can originate from outside or inside the cell.

TESTING YOUR KNOWLEDGE

SELF-QUIZ

1. Phosphorylation cascades involving a series of protein kinases are useful for cellular signal transduction because
   a. they are species specific.
   b. they always lead to the same cellular response.
   c. they amplify the original signal manyfold.
   d. they counter the harmful effects of phosphatases.
   e. the number of molecules used is small and fixed.

2. Binding of a signaling molecule to which type of receptor leads directly to a change in the distribution of ions on opposite sides of the membrane?
   a. receptor tyrosine kinase
   b. G protein-coupled receptor
   c. phosphorylated receptor tyrosine kinase dimer
   d. ligand-gated ion channel
   e. intracellular receptor

3. The activation of receptor tyrosine kinases is characterized by
   a. dimerization and phosphorylation.
   b. IP_3 binding.
   c. a phosphorylation cascade.
   d. GTP hydrolysis.
   e. channel protein shape change.

4. Which observation suggested to Sutherland the involvement of a second messenger in epinephrine's effect on liver cells?
   a. Enzymatic activity was proportional to the amount of calcium added to a cell-free extract.
   b. Receptor studies indicated that epinephrine was a ligand.

c. Glycogen breakdown was observed only when epinephrine was administered to intact cells.

d. Glycogen breakdown was observed when epinephrine and glycogen phosphorylase were combined.

e. Epinephrine was known to have different effects on different types of cells.

5. Protein phosphorylation is commonly involved with all of the following *except*

a. regulation of transcription by extracellular signaling molecules.

b. enzyme activation.

c. activation of G protein-coupled receptors.

d. activation of receptor tyrosine kinases.

e. activation of protein kinase molecules.

6. Lipid-soluble signaling molecules, such as testosterone, cross the membranes of all cells but affect only target cells because

a. only target cells retain the appropriate DNA segments.

b. intracellular receptors are present only in target cells.

c. most cells lack the Y chromosome required.

d. only target cells possess the cytosolic enzymes that transduce the testosterone.

e. only in target cells is testosterone able to initiate the phosphorylation cascade leading to activated transcription factor.

7. Consider this pathway: epinephrine → G protein-coupled receptor → G protein → adenylyl cyclase → cAMP. Identify the second messenger.

a. cAMP

b. G protein

c. GTP

d. adenylyl cyclase

e. G protein-coupled receptor

8. Apoptosis involves all but the following:

a. fragmentation of the DNA

b. cell-signaling pathways

c. activation of cellular enzymes

d. lysis of the cell

e. digestion of cellular contents by scavenger cells

9. **DRAW IT** Draw the following apoptotic pathway, which operates in human immune cells. A death signal is received when a molecule called Fas binds its cell-surface receptor. The binding of many Fas molecules to receptors causes receptor clustering. The intracellular regions of the receptors, when together, bind adapter proteins. These in turn bind to inactive forms of caspase-8, which become activated and activate caspase-3, in turn. Once activated, caspase-3 initiates apoptosis.

For Self-Quiz answers, see Appendix A.

MEDIA Visit **www.campbellbiology.com** for a Practice Test.

EVOLUTION CONNECTION

10. What evolutionary mechanisms might account for the origin and persistence of cell-to-cell signaling systems in unicellular prokaryotes?

SCIENTIFIC INQUIRY

11. Epinephrine initiates a signal transduction pathway that involves production of cyclic AMP (cAMP) and leads to the breakdown of glycogen to glucose, a major energy source for cells. But glycogen breakdown is actually only part of a "fight-or-flight response" that epinephrine brings about; the overall effect on the body includes increased heart rate and alertness, as well as a burst of energy. Given that caffeine blocks the activity of cAMP phosphodiesterase, propose a mechanism by which caffeine ingestion leads to heightened alertness and sleeplessness.

Biological Inquiry: A Workbook of Investigative Cases Explore cell signaling processes in the hedgehog signaling pathway with the case "Shh: Silencing the Hedgehog Pathway."

SCIENCE, TECHNOLOGY, AND SOCIETY

12. The aging process is thought to be initiated at the cellular level. Among the changes that can occur after a certain number of cell divisions is the loss of a cell's ability to respond to growth factors and other chemical signals. Much research into aging is aimed at understanding such losses, with the ultimate goal of significantly extending the human life span. Not everyone, however, agrees that this is a desirable goal. If life expectancy were greatly increased, what might be the social and ecological consequences? How might we cope with them?

The Cell Cycle

12

KEY CONCEPTS

12.1 **Cell division results in genetically identical daughter cells**

12.2 **The mitotic phase alternates with interphase in the cell cycle**

12.3 **The eukaryotic cell cycle is regulated by a molecular control system**

OVERVIEW

The Key Roles of Cell Division

The ability of organisms to reproduce their own kind is the one characteristic that best distinguishes living things from nonliving matter. This unique capacity to procreate, like all biological functions, has a cellular basis. Rudolf Virchow, a German physician, put it this way in 1855: "Where a cell exists, there must have been a preexisting cell, just as the animal arises only from an animal and the plant only from a plant." He summarized this concept with the Latin axiom "*Omnis cellula e cellula*," meaning "Every cell from a

▲ **Figure 12.1 How do a cell's chromosomes change during cell division?**

cell." The continuity of life is based on the reproduction of cells, or **cell division**. The series of fluorescence micrographs in **Figure 12.1** follows an animal cell's chromosomes, from lower left to lower right, as one cell divides into two.

Cell division plays several important roles in the life of an organism. When a unicellular organism, such as an amoeba, divides and forms duplicate offspring, the division of one cell reproduces an entire organism (**Figure 12.2a**). Cell division on a larger scale can produce progeny from some multicellular organisms (such as plants that grow from cuttings). Cell division also enables sexually reproducing organisms to develop from a single cell—the fertilized egg, or zygote (**Figure 12.2b**). And after an organism is fully grown, cell division continues to function in renewal and repair, replacing cells that die from normal wear and tear or accidents. For example, dividing cells in your bone marrow continuously make new blood cells (**Figure 12.2c**).

The cell division process is an integral part of the **cell cycle**, the life of a cell from the time it is first formed from a dividing parent cell until its own division into two cells. Passing identical genetic material to cellular offspring is a crucial function of cell

(a) Reproduction. An amoeba, a single-celled eukaryote, is dividing into two cells. Each new cell will be an individual organism (LM).

(b) Growth and development. This micrograph shows a sand dollar embryo shortly after the fertilized egg divided, forming two cells (LM).

(c) Tissue renewal. These dividing bone marrow cells (arrow) will give rise to new blood cells (LM).

▲ **Figure 12.2 The functions of cell division.**

division. In this chapter, you will learn how cell division distributes identical genetic material to daughter cells.* After studying the cellular mechanics of cell division in eukaryotes and bacteria, you will learn about the molecular control system that regulates progress through the eukaryotic cell cycle and what happens when the control system malfunctions. Because cell cycle regulation, or a lack thereof, plays a major role in cancer development, this aspect of cell biology is an active area of research.

▲ **Figure 12.3 Eukaryotic chromosomes.** Chromosomes (stained purple) are visible within the nucleus of this cell from an African blood lily. The thinner red threads in the surrounding cytoplasm are the cytoskeleton. The cell is preparing to divide (LM).

CONCEPT 12.1
Cell division results in genetically identical daughter cells

The reproduction of an ensemble as complex as a cell cannot occur by a mere pinching in half; a cell is not like a soap bubble that simply enlarges and splits in two. Most cell division involves the distribution of identical genetic material—DNA—to two daughter cells. (The special type of cell division that produces sperm and eggs results in daughter cells that are *not* genetically identical.) What is most remarkable about cell division is the fidelity with which the DNA is passed along from one generation of cells to the next. A dividing cell duplicates its DNA, allocates the two copies to opposite ends of the cell, and only then splits into daughter cells.

Cellular Organization of the Genetic Material

A cell's endowment of DNA, its genetic information, is called its **genome**. Although a prokaryotic genome is often a single long DNA molecule, eukaryotic genomes usually consist of a number of DNA molecules. The overall length of DNA in a eukaryotic cell is enormous. A typical human cell, for example, has about 2 m of DNA—a length about 250,000 times greater than the cell's diameter. Yet before the cell can divide to form genetically identical daughter cells, all of this DNA must be copied and then the two copies separated so that each daughter cell ends up with a complete genome.

The replication and distribution of so much DNA is manageable because the DNA molecules are packaged into **chromosomes**, so named because they take up certain dyes used in microscopy (from the Greek *chroma*, color, and *soma*, body) **(Figure 12.3)**. Every eukaryotic species has a characteristic number of chromosomes in each cell nucleus. For example, the nuclei of human **somatic cells** (all body cells except the reproductive cells) each contain 46 chromosomes made up of two sets of 23, one set inherited from each parent. Reproductive cells, or **gametes**—sperm and eggs—have half as many chromosomes as somatic cells, or one set of 23 chromo-

somes in humans. The number of chromosomes in somatic cells varies widely among species: 18 in cabbage plants, 56 in elephants, 90 in hedgehogs, and 148 in one species of alga.

Eukaryotic chromosomes are made of **chromatin**, a complex of DNA and associated protein molecules. Each single chromosome contains one very long, linear DNA molecule that carries several hundred to a few thousand genes, the units that specify an organism's inherited traits. The associated proteins maintain the structure of the chromosome and help control the activity of the genes.

Distribution of Chromosomes During Eukaryotic Cell Division

When a cell is not dividing, and even as it duplicates its DNA in preparation for cell division, each chromosome is in the form of a long, thin chromatin fiber. After DNA duplication, however, the chromosomes condense: Each chromatin fiber becomes densely coiled and folded, making the chromosomes much shorter and so thick that we can see them with a light microscope.

Each duplicated chromosome has two **sister chromatids**. The two chromatids, each containing an identical DNA molecule, are initially attached all along their lengths by adhesive protein complexes called *cohesins*; this attachment is known as *sister chromatid cohesion*. In its condensed form, the duplicated chromosome has a narrow "waist" at the **centromere**, a specialized region where the two chromatids are most closely attached. The part of a chromatid on either side of the centromere is referred to as an *arm* of the chromatid. Later in the cell division process, the two sister chromatids of each duplicated chromosome separate and move into two new nuclei, one forming at each end of the cell. Once the sister chromatids separate, they are considered individual chromosomes. Thus, each new nucleus receives a collection of chromosomes identical to that of

---
* Although the terms *daughter cells* and *sister chromatids* (a term you will encounter later in the chapter) are traditional and will be used throughout this book, the structures they refer to have no gender.

Chromosomes | DNA molecules

0.5 µm

Chromo-
some arm

Centromere

Chromosome
duplication
(including DNA
synthesis)

Sister
chromatids

Separation
of sister
chromatids

Sister chromatids

Centromeres

1 A eukaryotic cell has multiple chromosomes, one of which is represented here. Before duplication, each chromosome has a single DNA molecule.

2 Once replicated, a chromosome consists of two sister chromatids connected along their entire lengths by sister chromatid cohesion. Each chromatid contains a copy of the DNA molecule.

3 Mechanical processes separate the sister chromatids into two chromosomes and distribute them to two daughter cells.

◄ **Figure 12.4 Chromosome duplication and distribution during cell division.** A eukaryotic cell preparing to divide duplicates each of its chromosomes. Next to each chromosome drawing is a simplified double helix representing each DNA molecule. (In an actual chromosome, each DNA molecule would be tightly folded and coiled, complexed with proteins.) The micrograph shows a highly condensed duplicated human chromosome (SEM). The sister chromatids of each duplicated chromosome are distributed to two daughter cells during cell division. (Chromosomes normally exist in the highly condensed state shown here only during the process of cell division; the chromosomes in the top and bottom cells are shown in condensed form for illustration purposes only.)

? *Circle one chromatid in the chromosome in the micrograph. How many arms does the chromosome have?*

the parent cell **(Figure 12.4)**. **Mitosis**, the division of the nucleus, is usually followed immediately by **cytokinesis**, the division of the cytoplasm. Where there was one cell, there are now two, each the genetic equivalent of the parent cell.

What happens to the chromosome number as we follow the human life cycle through the generations? You inherited 46 chromosomes, one set of 23 from each parent. They were combined in the nucleus of a single cell when a sperm from your father united with an egg from your mother, forming a fertilized egg, or zygote. Mitosis and cytokinesis produced the 200 trillion somatic cells that now make up your body, and the same processes continue to generate new cells to replace dead and damaged ones. In contrast, you produce gametes—eggs or sperm—by a variation of cell division called **meiosis**, which yields nonidentical daughter cells that have only one set of chromosomes, thus half as many chromosomes as the parent cell. Meiosis occurs only in your gonads (ovaries or testes). In each generation of humans, meiosis reduces the chromosome number from 46 (two sets of chromosomes) to 23 (one set). Fertilization fuses two gametes together and returns the chromosome number to 46, and mitosis conserves that number in every somatic cell nucleus of the new individual. In Chapter 13, we will examine the role of meiosis in reproduction and inheritance in more detail. In the remainder of this chapter, we focus on mitosis and the rest of the cell cycle in eukaryotes.

CONCEPT CHECK 12.1

1. Starting with a fertilized egg (zygote), a series of five cell divisions would produce an early embryo with how many cells?

2. How many chromatids are in a duplicated chromosome?

3. **WHAT IF?** A chicken has 78 chromosomes in its somatic cells. How many chromosomes did the chicken inherit from each parent? How many chromosomes are in each of the chicken's gametes? How many chromosomes will be in each somatic cell of the chicken's offspring?

For suggested answers, see Appendix A.

CONCEPT 12.2

The mitotic phase alternates with interphase in the cell cycle

In 1882, a German anatomist named Walther Flemming developed dyes that allowed him to observe, for the first time, the behavior of chromosomes during mitosis and cytokinesis. (In fact, Flemming coined the terms *mitosis* and *chromatin*.) During the period between one cell division and the next, it appeared to Flemming that the cell was simply growing larger. But we now know that many critical events occur during this stage in the life of a cell.

Phases of the Cell Cycle

Mitosis is just one part of the cell cycle (**Figure 12.5**). In fact, the **mitotic (M) phase**, which includes both mitosis and cytokinesis, is usually the shortest part of the cell cycle. Mitotic cell division alternates with a much longer stage called **interphase**, which often accounts for about 90% of the cycle. It is during interphase that the cell grows and copies its chromosomes in preparation for cell division. Interphase can be divided into subphases: the **G_1 phase** ("first gap"), the **S phase** ("synthesis"), and the **G_2 phase** ("second gap"). During all three subphases, the cell grows by producing proteins and cytoplasmic organelles such as mitochondria and endoplasmic reticulum. However, chromosomes are duplicated only during the S phase (we will discuss synthesis of DNA in Chapter 16). Thus, a cell grows (G_1), continues to grow as it copies its chromosomes (S), grows more as it completes preparations for cell division (G_2), and divides (M). The daughter cells may then repeat the cycle.

A particular human cell might undergo one division in 24 hours. Of this time, the M phase would occupy less than 1 hour, while the S phase might occupy about 10–12 hours, or about half the cycle. The rest of the time would be apportioned between the G_1 and G_2 phases. The G_2 phase usually takes 4–6 hours; in our example, G_1 would occupy about 5–6 hours. G_1 is the most variable in length in different types of cells.

Mitosis is conventionally broken down into five stages: **prophase, prometaphase, metaphase, anaphase,** and **telophase**. Overlapping with the latter stages of mitosis, cytokinesis completes the mitotic phase. **Figure 12.6**, on the next two pages, describes these stages in an animal cell. Be sure to study this figure thoroughly before progressing to the next two sections, which examine mitosis and cytokinesis more closely.

The Mitotic Spindle: *A Closer Look*

Many of the events of mitosis depend on the **mitotic spindle**, which begins to form in the cytoplasm during prophase. This structure consists of fibers made of microtubules and associated proteins. While the mitotic spindle assembles, the other microtubules of the cytoskeleton partially disassemble, probably providing the material used to construct the spindle. The spindle microtubules elongate (polymerize) by incorporating more subunits of the protein tubulin and shorten (depolymerize) by losing subunits (see Table 6.1).

In animal cells, the assembly of spindle microtubules starts at the **centrosome**, a subcellular region containing material that functions throughout the cell cycle to organize the cell's microtubules (it is also called the *microtubule-organizing center*). A pair of centrioles is located at the center of the centrosome, but they are not essential for cell division: If the centrioles are destroyed with a laser microbeam, a spindle nevertheless forms during mitosis. In fact, centrioles are not even present in plant cells, which do form mitotic spindles.

During interphase in animal cells, the single centrosome replicates, forming two centrosomes, which remain together near the nucleus. The two centrosomes move apart during prophase and prometaphase of mitosis as spindle microtubules grow out from them. By the end of prometaphase, the two centrosomes, one at each pole of the spindle, are at opposite ends of the cell. An **aster**, a radial array of short microtubules, extends from each centrosome. The spindle includes the centrosomes, the spindle microtubules, and the asters.

Each of the two sister chromatids of a replicated chromosome has a **kinetochore**, a structure of proteins associated with specific sections of chromosomal DNA at the centromere. The chromosome's two kinetochores face in opposite directions. During prometaphase, some of the spindle microtubules attach to the kinetochores; these are called kinetochore microtubules. (The number of microtubules attached to a kinetochore varies among species, from one microtubule in yeast cells to 40 or so in some mammalian cells.) When one of a chromosome's kinetochores is "captured" by microtubules, the chromosome begins to move toward the pole from which those microtubules extend. However, this movement is checked as soon as microtubules from the opposite pole attach to the other kinetochore. What happens next is like a tug-of-war that ends in a draw. The chromosome moves first in one direction, then the other, back and forth, finally settling midway between the two ends of the cell. At metaphase, the centromeres of all the duplicated chromosomes are on a plane midway between the spindle's two poles. This imaginary plane is called the **metaphase plate** of the cell

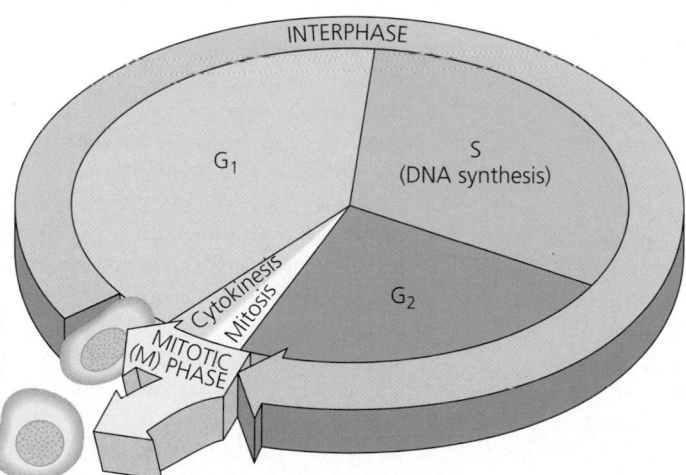

▲ **Figure 12.5 The cell cycle.** In a dividing cell, the mitotic (M) phase alternates with interphase, a growth period. The first part of interphase (G_1) is followed by the S phase, when the chromosomes replicate; G_2 is the last part of interphase. In the M phase, mitosis divides the nucleus and distributes its chromosomes to the daughter nuclei, and cytokinesis divides the cytoplasm, producing two daughter cells. The relative durations of G_1, S, and G_2 may vary.

▼ Figure 12.6

Exploring The Mitotic Division of an Animal Cell

G₂ of Interphase

Prophase

Prometaphase

Centrosomes (with centriole pairs) — Chromatin (duplicated)

Nucleolus — Nuclear envelope — Plasma membrane

Early mitotic spindle — Aster — Centromere

Chromosome, consisting of two sister chromatids

Fragments of nuclear envelope — Nonkinetochore microtubules

Kinetochore — Kinetochore microtubule

G₂ of Interphase

- A nuclear envelope bounds the nucleus.
- The nucleus contains one or more nucleoli (singular, *nucleolus*).
- Two centrosomes have formed by replication of a single centrosome.
- In animal cells, each centrosome features two centrioles.
- Chromosomes, duplicated during S phase, cannot be seen individually because they have not yet condensed.

The light micrographs show dividing lung cells from a newt, which has 22 chromosomes in its somatic cells (chromosomes appear blue, microtubules green, and intermediate filaments red). For simplicity, the drawings show only six chromosomes.

Prophase

- The chromatin fibers become more tightly coiled, condensing into discrete chromosomes observable with a light microscope.
- The nucleoli disappear.
- Each duplicated chromosome appears as two identical sister chromatids joined together at their centromeres and all along their arms by cohesins (sister chromatid cohesion).
- The mitotic spindle (named for its shape) begins to form. It is composed of the centrosomes and the microtubules that extend from them. The radial arrays of shorter microtubules that extend from the centrosomes are called asters ("stars").
- The centrosomes move away from each other, apparently propelled by the lengthening microtubules between them.

Prometaphase

- The nuclear envelope fragments.
- The microtubules extending from each centrosome can now invade the nuclear area.
- The chromosomes have become even more condensed.
- Each of the two chromatids of each chromosome now has a kinetochore, a specialized protein structure located at the centromere.
- Some of the microtubules attach to the kinetochores, becoming "kinetochore microtubules"; these jerk the chromosomes back and forth.
- Nonkinetochore microtubules interact with those from the opposite pole of the spindle.

? *How many molecules of DNA are in the prometaphase drawing? How many molecules per chromosome? How many double helices are there per chromosome? Per chromatid?*

Metaphase   **Anaphase**   **Telophase and Cytokinesis**

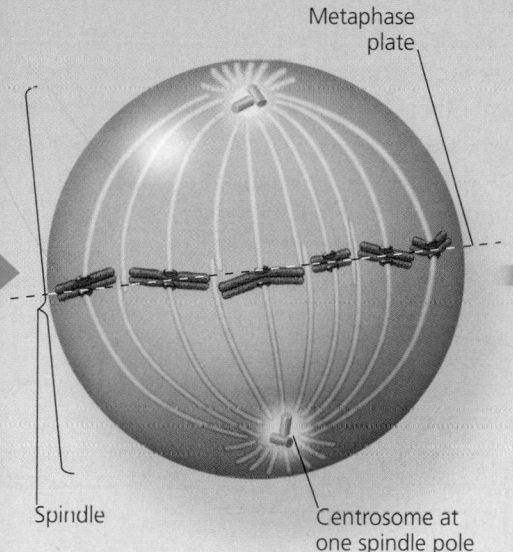

Metaphase plate

Spindle

Centrosome at one spindle pole

Daughter chromosomes

Cleavage furrow

Nucleolus forming

Nuclear envelope forming

Metaphase

- Metaphase is the longest stage of mitosis, often lasting about 20 minutes.
- The centrosomes are now at opposite poles of the cell.
- The chromosomes convene on the metaphase plate, an imaginary plane that is equidistant between the spindle's two poles. The chromosomes' centromeres lie on the metaphase plate.
- For each chromosome, the kinetochores of the sister chromatids are attached to kinetochore microtubules coming from opposite poles.

Anaphase

- Anaphase is the shortest stage of mitosis, often lasting only a few minutes.
- Anaphase begins when the cohesin proteins are cleaved. This allows the two sister chromatids of each pair to part suddenly. Each chromatid thus becomes a full-fledged chromosome.
- The two liberated daughter chromosomes begin moving toward opposite ends of the cell as their kinetochore microtubules shorten. Because these microtubules are attached at the centromere region, the chromosomes move centromere first (at about 1 μm/min).
- The cell elongates as the nonkinetochore microtubules lengthen.
- By the end of anaphase, the two ends of the cell have equivalent—and complete—collections of chromosomes.

Telophase

- Two daughter nuclei form in the cell.
- Nuclear envelopes arise from the fragments of the parent cell's nuclear envelope and other portions of the endomembrane system.
- Nucleoli reappear.
- The chromosomes become less condensed.
- Mitosis, the division of one nucleus into two genetically identical nuclei, is now complete.

Cytokinesis

- The division of the cytoplasm is usually well under way by late telophase, so the two daughter cells appear shortly after the end of mitosis.
- In animal cells, cytokinesis involves the formation of a cleavage furrow, which pinches the cell in two.

(Figure 12.7). Meanwhile, microtubules that do not attach to kinetochores have been elongating, and by metaphase they overlap and interact with other nonkinetochore microtubules from the opposite pole of the spindle. (These are sometimes called "polar" microtubules.) By metaphase, the microtubules of the asters have also grown and are in contact with the plasma membrane. The spindle is now complete.

▲ **Figure 12.7 The mitotic spindle at metaphase.** The kinetochores of each chromosome's two sister chromatids face in opposite directions. Here, each kinetochore is attached to a *cluster* of kinetochore microtubules extending from the nearest centrosome. Nonkinetochore microtubules overlap at the metaphase plate (TEMs).

DRAW IT *On the lower micrograph, draw a line indicating the metaphase plate. Circle an aster. Draw arrows indicating the directions of chromosome movement once anaphase begins.*

Let's now see how the structure of the completed spindle correlates with its function during anaphase. Anaphase commences suddenly when the cohesins holding together the sister chromatids of each chromosome are cleaved by enzymes. Once the chromatids become separate, full-fledged chromosomes, they move toward opposite ends of the cell.

How do the kinetochore microtubules function in this pole-ward movement of chromosomes? Apparently, two mechanisms are in play, both involving motor proteins. (To review how motor proteins move an object along a microtubule, see Figure 6.21.) A clever experiment carried out in Gary Borisy's lab at the University of Wisconsin in 1987 suggested that motor proteins on the kinetochores "walk" the chromosomes along the microtubules, which depolymerize at their kinetochore ends after the motor proteins have passed (**Figure 12.8**). (This is referred to as the "Pacman" mechanism because of its resemblance to the arcade game character that moves by eating all the dots in its path.) However, other researchers, working with different cell types or cells from other species, have shown that chromosomes are "reeled in" by motor proteins at the spindle poles and that the microtubules depolymerize after they pass by these motor proteins. The general consensus now is that the relative contributions of these two mechanisms vary among cell types.

What is the function of the *non*kinetochore microtubules? In a dividing animal cell, these microtubules are responsible for elongating the whole cell during anaphase. Nonkinetochore microtubules from opposite poles overlap each other extensively during metaphase (see Figure 12.7). During anaphase, the region of overlap is reduced as motor proteins attached to the microtubules walk them away from one another, using energy from ATP. As the microtubules push apart from each other, their spindle poles are pushed apart, elongating the cell. At the same time, the microtubules lengthen somewhat by the addition of tubulin subunits to their overlapping ends. As a result, the microtubules continue to overlap.

At the end of anaphase, duplicate groups of chromosomes have arrived at opposite ends of the elongated parent cell. Nuclei re-form during telophase. Cytokinesis generally begins during anaphase or telophase, and the spindle eventually disassembles.

Cytokinesis: *A Closer Look*

In animal cells, cytokinesis occurs by a process known as **cleavage**. The first sign of cleavage is the appearance of a **cleavage furrow**, a shallow groove in the cell surface near the old metaphase plate (**Figure 12.9a**). On the cytoplasmic side of the furrow is a contractile ring of actin microfilaments associated with molecules of the protein myosin. (Actin and myosin are also responsible for muscle contraction and many other kinds of cell movement.) The actin microfilaments interact with the myosin molecules, causing the ring to contract. The contraction of the dividing cell's ring of microfilaments is like the pulling of drawstrings. The cleavage furrow deepens

At which end do kinetochore microtubules shorten during anaphase?

EXPERIMENT   Gary Borisy and colleagues wanted to determine whether kinetochore microtubules depolymerize at the kinetochore end or the pole end as chromosomes move toward the poles during mitosis. First, they labeled the microtubules of a pig kidney cell in early anaphase with a yellow fluorescent dye.

Then they marked a region of the kinetochore microtubules between one spindle pole and the chromosomes by using a laser to eliminate the fluorescence from that region. (The microtubules remained intact.) As anaphase proceeded, they monitored the changes in microtubule length on either side of the mark.

RESULTS   As the chromosomes moved poleward, the microtubule segments on the kinetochore side of the mark shortened, while those on the spindle pole side stayed the same length.

CONCLUSION   During anaphase in this cell type, chromosome movement is correlated with kinetochore microtubules shortening at their kinetochore ends and not at their spindle pole ends. This experiment supports the hypothesis that during anaphase, a chromosome is walked along a microtubule as the microtubule depolymerizes at its kinetochore end, releasing tubulin subunits.

SOURCE   G. J. Gorbsky, P. J. Sammak, and G. G. Borisy, *Chromosomes move poleward in anaphase along stationary microtubules that coordinately disassemble from their kinetochore ends, Journal of Cell Biology* 104:9–18 (1987).

WHAT IF?   If this experiment had been done on a cell type in which "reeling in" at the poles was the main cause of chromosome movement, how would the mark have moved relative to the poles? How would the microtubule lengths have changed?

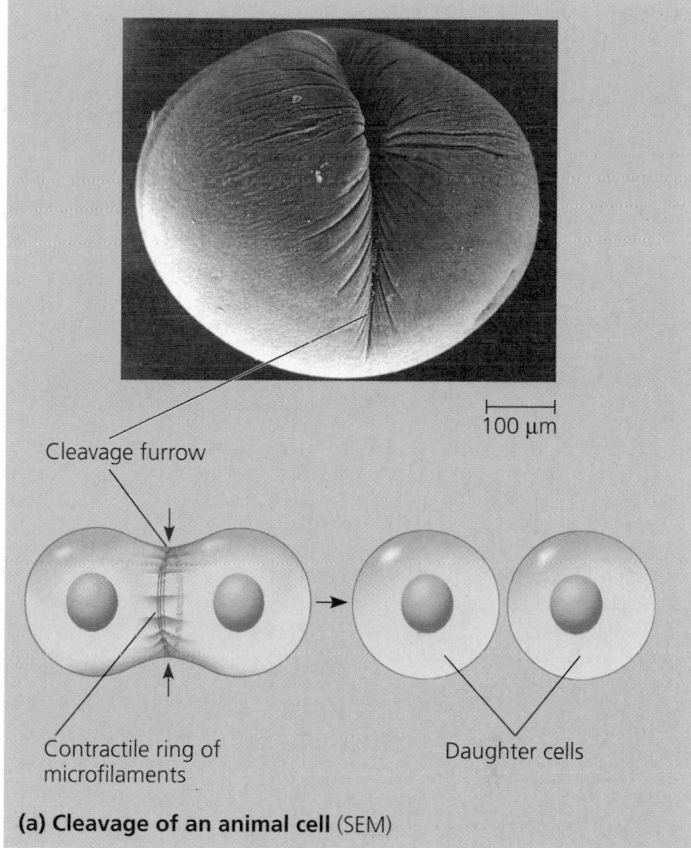

Cleavage furrow

Contractile ring of microfilaments

Daughter cells

100 μm

(a) Cleavage of an animal cell (SEM)

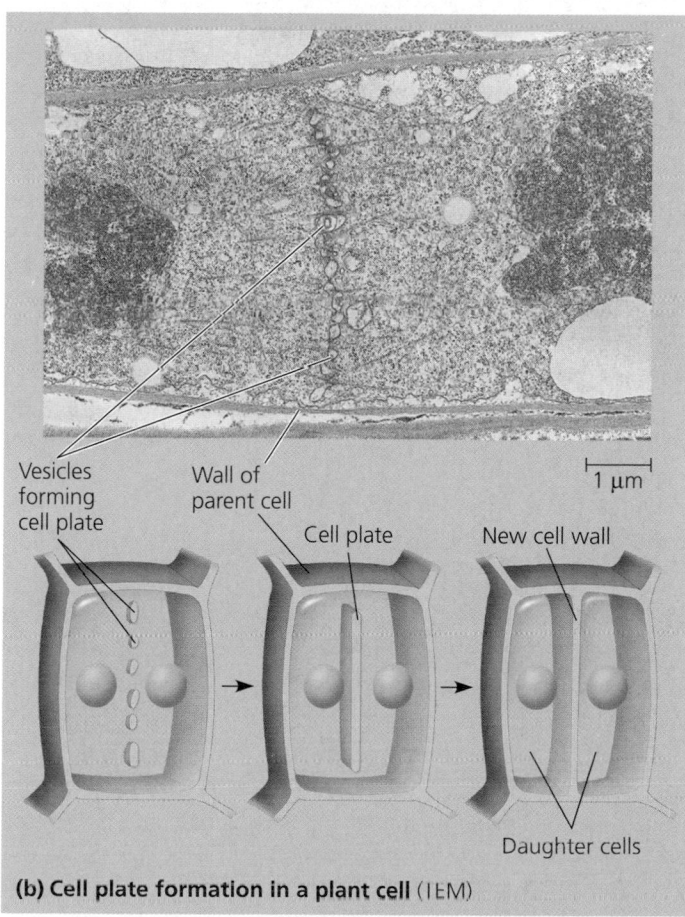

Vesicles forming cell plate

Wall of parent cell

Cell plate

New cell wall

Daughter cells

1 μm

(b) Cell plate formation in a plant cell (TEM)

▲ Figure 12.9 **Cytokinesis in animal and plant cells.**

Nucleus Chromatin Chromosomes Cell plate 10 μm
Nucleolus condensing

❶ Prophase. The chromatin is condensing and the nucleolus is beginning to disappear. Although not yet visible in the micrograph, the mitotic spindle is starting to form.

❷ Prometaphase. Discrete chromosomes are now visible; each consists of two aligned, identical sister chromatids. Later in prometaphase, the nuclear envelope will fragment.

❸ Metaphase. The spindle is complete, and the chromosomes, attached to microtubules at their kinetochores, are all at the metaphase plate.

❹ Anaphase. The chromatids of each chromosome have separated, and the daughter chromosomes are moving to the ends of the cell as their kinetochore microtubules shorten.

❺ Telophase. Daughter nuclei are forming. Meanwhile, cytokinesis has started: The cell plate, which will divide the cytoplasm in two, is growing toward the perimeter of the parent cell.

▲ **Figure 12.10 Mitosis in a plant cell.** These light micrographs show mitosis in cells of an onion root.

until the parent cell is pinched in two, producing two completely separated cells, each with its own nucleus and share of cytosol, organelles, and other subcellular structures.

Cytokinesis in plant cells, which have cell walls, is markedly different. There is no cleavage furrow. Instead, during telophase, vesicles derived from the Golgi apparatus move along microtubules to the middle of the cell, where they coalesce, producing a **cell plate** (**Figure 12.9b**). Cell wall materials carried in the vesicles collect in the cell plate as it grows. The cell plate enlarges until its surrounding membrane fuses with the plasma membrane along the perimeter of the cell. Two daughter cells result, each with its own plasma membrane. Meanwhile, a new cell wall arising from the contents of the cell plate has formed between the daughter cells.

Figure 12.10 is a series of micrographs of a dividing plant cell. Examining this figure will help you review mitosis and cytokinesis.

Binary Fission

The asexual reproduction of single-celled eukaryotes, such as the amoeba in Figure 12.2a, includes mitosis and occurs by a type of cell division called **binary fission**, meaning "division in half." Prokaryotes (bacteria and archaea) also reproduce by binary fission, but the prokaryotic process does not involve mitosis. In bacteria, most genes are carried on a single *bacterial chromosome* that consists of a circular DNA molecule and associated proteins. Although bacteria are smaller and simpler than eukaryotic cells, the challenge of replicating their genomes in an orderly fashion and distributing the copies equally to two daughter cells is still formidable. The chromosome of the bacterium

Escherichia coli, for example, when it is fully stretched out, is about 500 times as long as the cell. For such a long chromosome to fit within the cell requires that it be highly coiled and folded.

In *E. coli*, the process of cell division is initiated when the DNA of the bacterial chromosome begins to replicate at a specific place on the chromosome called the **origin of replication**, producing two origins. As the chromosome continues to replicate, one origin moves rapidly toward the opposite end of the cell (**Figure 12.11**). While the chromosome is replicating, the cell elongates. When replication is complete and the bacterium has reached about twice its initial size, its plasma membrane grows inward, dividing the parent *E. coli* cell into two daughter cells. Each cell inherits a complete genome.

Using the techniques of modern DNA technology to tag the origins of replication with molecules that glow green in fluorescence microscopy (see Figure 6.3), researchers have directly observed the movement of bacterial chromosomes. This movement is reminiscent of the poleward movements of the centromere regions of eukaryotic chromosomes during anaphase of mitosis, but bacteria don't have visible mitotic spindles or even microtubules. In most bacterial species studied, the two origins of replication end up at opposite ends of the cell or in some other very specific location, possibly anchored there by one or more proteins. How bacterial chromosomes move and how their specific location is established and maintained are still not fully understood. However, several proteins have been identified that play important roles: One resembling eukaryotic actin may function in bacterial chromosome movement during cell division, and another that is related to tubulin may help separate the two bacterial daughter cells.

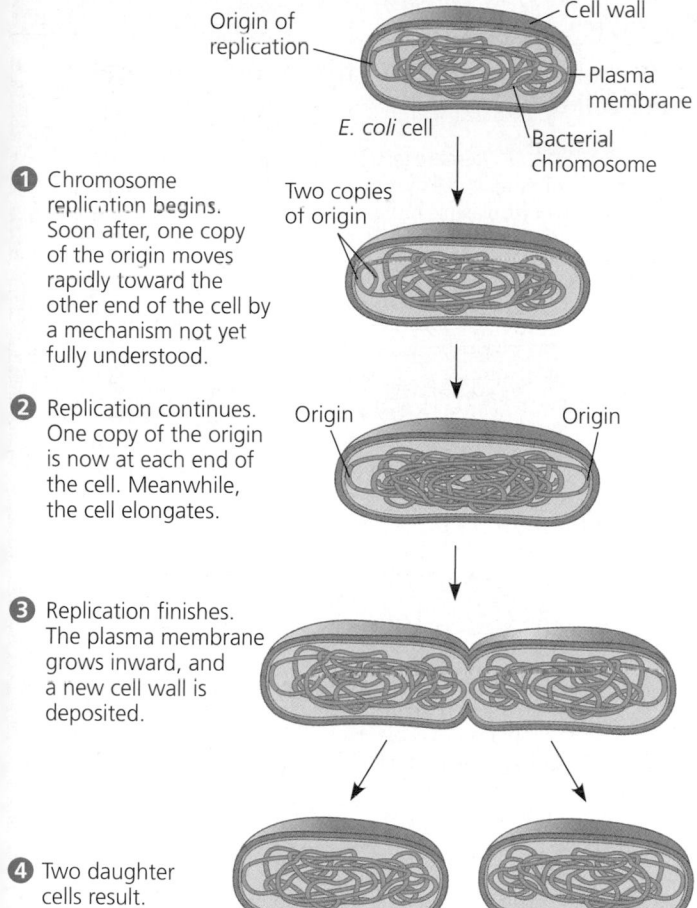

① Chromosome replication begins. Soon after, one copy of the origin moves rapidly toward the other end of the cell by a mechanism not yet fully understood.

② Replication continues. One copy of the origin is now at each end of the cell. Meanwhile, the cell elongates.

③ Replication finishes. The plasma membrane grows inward, and a new cell wall is deposited.

④ Two daughter cells result.

▲ **Figure 12.11 Bacterial cell division by binary fission.** The example shown here is the bacterium *E. coli*, which has a single, circular chromosome.

The Evolution of Mitosis

How did mitosis evolve? Given that prokaryotes preceded eukaryotes on Earth by more than a billion years, we might hypothesize that mitosis had its origins in simpler prokaryotic mechanisms of cell reproduction. The fact that some of the proteins involved in bacterial binary fission are related to eukaryotic proteins that function in mitosis supports that hypothesis.

As eukaryotes evolved, along with their larger genomes and nuclear envelopes, the ancestral process of binary fission, seen today in bacteria, somehow gave rise to mitosis. **Figure 12.12** traces a hypothesis for the stepwise evolution of mitosis. Possible intermediate stages are represented by two unusual types of nuclear division found today in certain unicellular eukaryotes. These two examples of nuclear division are thought to be cases where ancestral mechanisms have remained relatively unchanged over evolutionary time. In both types, the nuclear envelope remains intact. In dinoflagellates, replicated chromosomes are attached to the nuclear envelope and separate as the nucleus elongates prior to dividing. In diatoms and yeasts, a spindle *within* the nucleus separates the chromosomes. In most eukaryotic cells, the nuclear envelope breaks down and a spindle separates the chromosomes.

(a) Bacteria. During binary fission in bacteria, the origins of the daughter chromosomes move to opposite ends of the cell. The mechanism is not fully understood, but proteins may anchor the daughter chromosomes to specific sites on the plasma membrane.

(b) Dinoflagellates. In unicellular protists called dinoflagellates, the chromosomes attach to the nuclear envelope, which remains intact during cell division. Microtubules pass through the nucleus inside cytoplasmic tunnels, reinforcing the spatial orientation of the nucleus, which then divides in a process reminiscent of bacterial binary fission.

(c) Diatoms and yeasts. In two other groups of unicellular protists, diatoms and yeasts, the nuclear envelope also remains intact during cell division. But in these organisms, the microtubules form a spindle *within* the nucleus. Microtubules separate the chromosomes, and the nucleus splits into two daughter nuclei.

(d) Most eukaryotes. In most other eukaryotes, including plants and animals, the spindle forms outside the nucleus, and the nuclear envelope breaks down during mitosis. Microtubules separate the chromosomes, and the nuclear envelope then re-forms.

▲ **Figure 12.12 A hypothetical sequence for the evolution of mitosis.** Some unicellular eukaryotes existing today have mechanisms of cell division that appear to be intermediate between the binary fission of bacteria (a) and mitosis as it occurs in most other eukaryotes (d). Except for (a), these schematic diagrams do not show cell walls.

1. How many chromosomes are shown in the diagram in Figure 12.7? How many chromatids are shown?
2. Compare cytokinesis in animal cells and plant cells.
3. What is a function of nonkinetochore microtubules?
4. Identify three similarities between bacterial chromosomes and eukaryotic chromosomes, considering both structure and behavior during cell division.
5. Compare the roles of tubulin and actin during eukaryotic cell division with the roles of tubulin-like and actin-like proteins during bacterial binary fission.
6. **WHAT IF?** During which stages of the cell cycle does a chromosome consist of two identical chromatids?

For suggested answers, see Appendix A.

CONCEPT **12.3**
The eukaryotic cell cycle is regulated by a molecular control system

The timing and rate of cell division in different parts of a plant or animal are crucial to normal growth, development, and maintenance. The frequency of cell division varies with the type of cell. For example, human skin cells divide frequently throughout life, whereas liver cells maintain the ability to divide but keep it in reserve until an appropriate need arises—say, to repair a wound. Some of the most specialized cells, such as fully formed nerve cells and muscle cells, do not divide at all in a mature human. These cell cycle differences result from regulation at the molecular level. The mechanisms of this regulation are of intense interest, not only for understanding the life cycles of normal cells but also for understanding how cancer cells manage to escape the usual controls.

Evidence for Cytoplasmic Signals

What controls the cell cycle? As Paul Nurse mentions in the interview opening this unit, one reasonable hypothesis might be that each event in the cell cycle merely leads to the next, as in a simple metabolic pathway. According to this hypothesis, the replication of chromosomes in the S phase, for example, might cause cell growth during the G_2 phase, which might in turn lead inevitably to the onset of mitosis. However, this hypothesis, which proposes a pathway that is not subject to either internal or external regulation, turns out to be incorrect.

In the early 1970s, a variety of experiments led to an alternative hypothesis: that the cell cycle is driven by specific signaling molecules present in the cytoplasm. Some of the first strong evidence for this hypothesis came from experiments with mammalian cells grown in culture. In these experiments,

▼ **Figure 12.13** **Inquiry**

Do molecular signals in the cytoplasm regulate the cell cycle?

EXPERIMENT Researchers at the University of Colorado wondered whether a cell's progression through the cell cycle is controlled by cytoplasmic molecules. To investigate this, they induced cultured mammalian cells at different phases of the cell cycle to fuse. Two such experiments are shown here.

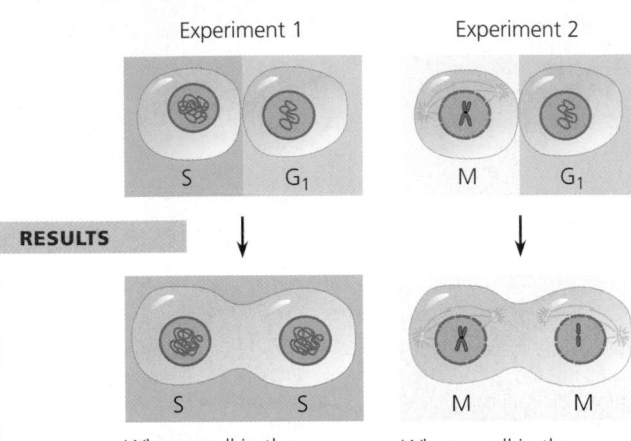

RESULTS

When a cell in the S phase was fused with a cell in G_1, the G_1 nucleus immediately entered the S phase—DNA was synthesized.

When a cell in the M phase was fused with a cell in G_1, the G_1 nucleus immediately began mitosis—a spindle formed and chromatin condensed, even though the chromosome had not been duplicated.

CONCLUSION The results of fusing a G_1 cell with a cell in the S or M phase of the cell cycle suggest that molecules present in the cytoplasm during the S or M phase control the progression to those phases.

SOURCE R. T. Johnson and P. N. Rao, Mammalian cell fusion: Induction of premature chromosome condensation in interphase nuclei, *Nature* 226:717–722 (1970).

WHAT IF? If the progression of phases did not depend on cytoplasmic molecules and each phase began when the previous one was complete, how would the results have differed?

two cells in different phases of the cell cycle were fused to form a single cell with two nuclei. If one of the original cells was in the S phase and the other was in G_1, the G_1 nucleus immediately entered the S phase, as though stimulated by chemicals present in the cytoplasm of the first cell. Similarly, if a cell undergoing mitosis (M phase) was fused with another cell in any stage of its cell cycle, even G_1, the second nucleus immediately entered mitosis, with condensation of the chromatin and formation of a mitotic spindle **(Figure 12.13)**.

The Cell Cycle Control System

The experiment shown in Figure 12.13 and other experiments on animal cells and yeasts demonstrated that the sequential events of the cell cycle are directed by a distinct **cell cycle control system**, a cyclically operating set of molecules in the cell that both triggers and coordinates key events in the cell cycle. The cell cycle control system has been compared to the control device of an automatic washing machine **(Figure 12.14)**. Like the washer's timing device, the cell cycle control system proceeds on its own, according to a built-in clock. However, just as a washer's cycle is subject to both internal control (such as the sensor that detects when the tub is filled with water) and external adjustment (such as activation of the start mechanism), the cell cycle is regulated at certain checkpoints by both internal and external signals.

A **checkpoint** in the cell cycle is a control point where stop and go-ahead signals can regulate the cycle. (The signals are transmitted within the cell by the kinds of signal transduction pathways discussed in Chapter 11.) Animal cells generally have built-in stop signals that halt the cell cycle at checkpoints until overridden by go-ahead signals. Many signals registered at checkpoints come from cellular surveillance mechanisms inside the cell; the signals report whether crucial cellular processes that should have occurred by that point have in fact been completed correctly and thus whether or not the cell cycle should proceed. Checkpoints also register signals from outside the cell, as we will discuss later. Three major checkpoints are found in the G_1, G_2, and M phases (see Figure 12.14).

For many cells, the G_1 checkpoint—dubbed the "restriction point" in mammalian cells—seems to be the most important. If a cell receives a go-ahead signal at the G_1 checkpoint, it will usually complete the G_1, S, G_2, and M phases and divide. If it does not receive a go-ahead signal at that point, it will exit the cycle, switching into a nondividing state called the G_0 **phase**

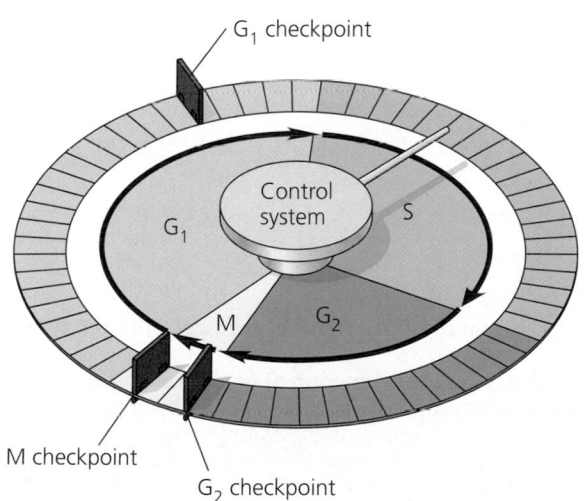

▲ **Figure 12.14 Mechanical analogy for the cell cycle control system.** In this diagram of the cell cycle, the flat "stepping stones" around the perimeter represent sequential events. Like the control device of an automatic washer, the cell cycle control system proceeds on its own, driven by a built-in clock. However, the system is subject to internal and external regulation at various checkpoints, of which three are shown (red).

(a) If a cell receives a go-ahead signal at the G_1 checkpoint, the cell continues on in the cell cycle.

(b) If a cell does not receive a go-ahead signal at the G_1 checkpoint, the cell exits the cell cycle and goes into G_0, a nondividing state.

▲ **Figure 12.15 The G_1 checkpoint.**

WHAT IF? *What might be the result if the cell ignored the checkpoint and progressed through the cell cycle?*

(Figure 12.15). Most cells of the human body are actually in the G_0 phase. As mentioned earlier, mature nerve cells and muscle cells never divide. Other cells, such as liver cells, can be "called back" from the G_0 phase to the cell cycle by external cues, such as growth factors released during injury.

To understand how cell cycle checkpoints work, we first need to see what kinds of molecules make up the cell cycle control system (the molecular basis for the cell cycle clock) and how a cell progresses through the cycle. Then we will consider the internal and external checkpoint signals that can make the clock pause or continue.

The Cell Cycle Clock: Cyclins and Cyclin-Dependent Kinases

Rhythmic fluctuations in the abundance and activity of cell cycle control molecules pace the sequential events of the cell cycle. These regulatory molecules are mainly proteins of two types: protein kinases and cyclins. Protein kinases are enzymes that activate or inactivate other proteins by phosphorylating them (see Chapter 11). Particular protein kinases give the go-ahead signals at the G_1 and G_2 checkpoints. **Figure 12.16**, on the next page, describes an experiment from Paul Nurse's laboratory that demonstrates the crucial function of the protein kinase Cdc2 in triggering mitosis at the G_2 checkpoint in one type of yeast. Studies by other researchers have shown that this enzyme plays the same role in sea star eggs and cultured human cells, suggesting that the function of this protein has been conserved during the evolution of eukaryotes and is likely the same in many species.

Many of the kinases that drive the cell cycle are actually present at a constant concentration in the growing cell, but much of the time they are in an inactive form. To be active, such a kinase must be attached to a **cyclin**, a protein that gets its name from its cyclically fluctuating concentration in the cell. Because of this requirement, these kinases are called **cyclin-dependent kinases**, or **Cdks**. The activity of a Cdk

▼ Figure 12.16 Inquiry

How does the activity of a protein kinase essential for mitosis vary during the cell cycle?

EXPERIMENT   Working with the fission yeast *Schizosaccharomyces pombe*, Paul Nurse and colleagues identified a gene, *cdc2*, whose normal functioning is necessary for cell division. They first showed that its product was a protein kinase (see the Unit Two interview, pp. 92–93). As part of a large study on how the *cdc2* protein kinase is regulated during the cell cycle, they measured its activity as the cell cycle progressed. In a culture of yeast cells synchronized so that they divided simultaneously, the researchers removed samples at intervals over a period of time sufficient for two cycles of cell division.

They submitted each sample to two kinds of analysis: (1) microscopic examination to determine the percentage of cells dividing (as shown by the presence of the cell plate formed during yeast cytokinesis) and (2) measurement of kinase activity in an extract of the cells (as indicated by phosphorylation of a standard protein). Control experiments established that the kinase activity they measured was due primarily to the *cdc2* protein kinase. In this way, they were able to see if an increase in enzymatic activity correlated with cell division.

RESULTS   The activity of the *cdc2* protein kinase varied during the cell cycle in a periodic way, rising to a peak just before mitosis and then falling.

CONCLUSION   The correlation between enzyme activity and the onset of mitosis, combined with evidence from other experiments that mitosis does not occur in the absence of *cdc2* kinase activity, supports the hypothesis that the *cdc2* kinase plays an essential role in triggering mitosis.

SOURCE   S. Moreno, J. Hayles, and P. Nurse, Regulation of p34^{cdc2} protein kinase during mitosis, *Cell* 58:361–372 (1989).

WHAT IF?   What results would you expect—for both kinase activity and percentage of cells dividing—if the cells tested were mutants completely deficient in the *cdc2* protein kinase?

Time

(a) Fluctuation of MPF activity and cyclin concentration during the cell cycle

5 During G$_1$, conditions in the cell favor degradation of cyclin, and the Cdk component of MPF is recycled.

1 Synthesis of cyclin begins in late S phase and continues through G$_2$. Because cyclin is protected from degradation during this stage, it accumulates.

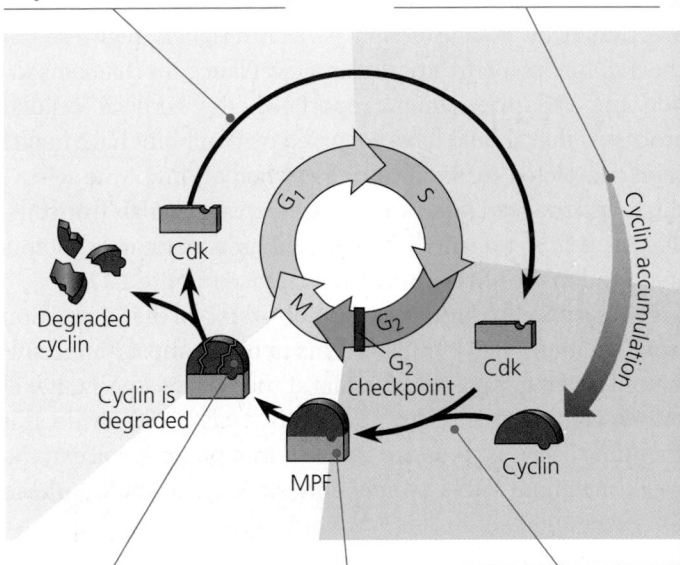

4 During anaphase, the cyclin component of MPF is degraded, terminating the M phase. The cell enters the G$_1$ phase.

3 MPF promotes mitosis by phosphorylating various proteins. MPF's activity peaks during metaphase.

2 Accumulated cyclin molecules combine with recycled Cdk molecules, producing enough molecules of MPF for the cell to pass the G$_2$ checkpoint and initiate the events of mitosis.

(b) Molecular mechanisms that help regulate the cell cycle

▲ **Figure 12.17 Molecular control of the cell cycle at the G$_2$ checkpoint.** The steps of the cell cycle are timed by rhythmic fluctuations in the activity of cyclin-dependent kinases (Cdks). Here we focus on a cyclin-Cdk complex in animal cells called MPF, which acts at the G$_2$ checkpoint as a go-ahead signal, triggering the events of mitosis. (The Cdk of MPF is the same as the *cdc2* protein kinase of fission yeast featured in Figure 12.16.)

---

rises and falls with changes in the concentration of its cyclin partner. **Figure 12.17a** shows the fluctuating activity of **MPF**, the cyclin-Cdk complex that was discovered first (in frog eggs). Note that the peaks of MPF activity correspond to the peaks of cyclin concentration. The cyclin level rises during the S and G$_2$ phases and then falls abruptly during M phase. (The red curve in Figure 12.16 shows the cyclic activity of the MPF in fission yeast.)

The initials MPF stand for "maturation-promoting factor," but we can think of MPF as "M-phase-promoting factor" be-

cause it triggers the cell's passage past the G$_2$ checkpoint into M phase **(Figure 12.17b)**. When cyclins that accumulate during G$_2$ associate with Cdk molecules, the resulting MPF complex phosphorylates a variety of proteins, initiating mitosis.

MPF acts both directly as a kinase and indirectly by activating other kinases. For example, MPF causes phosphorylation of various proteins of the nuclear lamina (see Figure 6.10), which promotes fragmentation of the nuclear envelope during prometaphase of mitosis. There is also evidence that MPF contributes to molecular events required for chromosome condensation and spindle formation during prophase.

During anaphase, MPF helps switch itself off by initiating a process that leads to the destruction of its own cyclin. The noncyclin part of MPF, the Cdk, persists in the cell in inactive form until it associates with new cyclin molecules synthesized during the S and G_2 phases of the next round of the cycle.

What controls cell behavior at the G_1 checkpoint? Animal cells appear to have at least three Cdk proteins and several different cyclins that operate at this checkpoint. The fluctuating activities of different cyclin-Cdk complexes are of major importance in controlling all the stages of the cell cycle.

Stop and Go Signs: Internal and External Signals at the Checkpoints

Research scientists are currently working out the pathways that link signals originating inside and outside the cell with the responses by cyclin-dependent kinases and other proteins. An example of an internal signal occurs at the M phase checkpoint. Anaphase, the separation of sister chromatids, does not begin until all the chromosomes are properly attached to the spindle at the metaphase plate. Researchers have learned that as long as some kinetochores are unattached to spindle microtubules, the sister chromatids remain together, delaying anaphase. Only when the kinetochores of all the chromosomes are attached to the spindle does the appropriate regulatory protein become activated. (In this case, the regulatory protein is not a Cdk.) Once activated, the protein sets off a chain of molecular events that ultimately results in the enzymatic cleavage of cohesins, allowing the sister chromatids to separate. This mechanism ensures that daughter cells do not end up with missing or extra chromosomes.

Studies using animal cells in culture have led to the identification of many external factors, both chemical and physical, that can influence cell division. For example, cells fail to divide if an essential nutrient is lacking in the culture medium. (This is analogous to trying to run an automatic washing machine without the water supply hooked up.) And even if all other conditions are favorable, most types of mammalian cells divide in culture only if the growth medium includes specific growth factors. As mentioned in Chapter 11, a **growth factor** is a protein released by certain cells that stimulates other cells to divide. Researchers have discovered more than 50 growth factors. Different cell types respond specifically to different growth factors or combinations of growth factors.

Consider, for example, *platelet-derived growth factor* (*PDGF*), which is made by blood cell fragments called platelets.

① A sample of human connective tissue is cut up into small pieces.

Scalpels

Petri plate

② Enzymes are used to digest the extracellular matrix in the tissue pieces, resulting in a suspension of free fibroblasts.

③ Cells are transferred to sterile culture vessels containing a basic growth medium consisting of glucose, amino acids, salts, and antibiotics (as a precaution against bacterial growth). PDGF is added to half the vessels. The culture vessels are incubated at 37°C.

Without PDGF

In the basic growth medium without PDGF (the control), the cells fail to divide.

With PDGF

In the basic growth medium plus PDGF, the cells proliferate. The SEM shows cultured fibroblasts.

10 µm

▲ Figure 12.18 **The effect of a growth factor on cell division.** As this experiment shows, adding platelet-derived growth factor (PDGF) to human fibroblasts in culture causes the cells to proliferate.

? *PDGF is known to signal cells by binding to a cell-surface receptor that is a receptor tyrosine kinase. If you added a chemical that prevented phosphorylation of this receptor, how would the results differ?*

The experiment illustrated in **Figure 12.18** demonstrates that PDGF is required for the division of fibroblasts in culture. Fibroblasts, a type of connective tissue cell, have PDGF receptors on their plasma membranes. The binding of PDGF molecules to these receptors (which are receptor tyrosine kinases; see Chapter 11) triggers a signal transduction pathway that allows the cells to pass the G_1 checkpoint and divide. PDGF stimulates fibroblast division not only in the artificial conditions of cell culture, but in an animal's body as well. When an injury occurs, platelets release PDGF in the vicinity. The resulting proliferation of fibroblasts helps heal the wound.

The effect of an external physical factor on cell division is clearly seen in **density-dependent inhibition**, a phenomenon in which crowded cells stop dividing (Figure 12.19a). As first observed many years ago, cultured cells normally divide until they form a single layer of cells on the inner surface of the culture container, at which point the cells stop dividing. If some cells are removed, those bordering the open space begin dividing again and continue until the vacancy is filled. Recent studies have revealed that the binding of a cell-surface protein to its counterpart on an adjoining cell sends a growth-inhibiting signal to both cells, preventing them from moving forward in the cell cycle, even in the presence of growth factors.

Most animal cells also exhibit **anchorage dependence** (see Figure 12.19a). To divide, they must be attached to a substratum, such as the inside of a culture jar or the extracellular matrix of a tissue. Experiments suggest that like cell density, anchorage is signaled to the cell cycle control system via pathways involving plasma membrane proteins and elements of the cytoskeleton linked to them.

Density-dependent inhibition and anchorage dependence appear to function in the body's tissues as well as in cell culture, checking the growth of cells at some optimal density and location. Cancer cells, which we discuss next, exhibit neither density-dependent inhibition nor anchorage dependence (Figure 12.19b).

Loss of Cell Cycle Controls in Cancer Cells

Cancer cells do not heed the normal signals that regulate the cell cycle. They divide excessively and invade other tissues. If unchecked, they can kill the organism.

In addition to their lack of density-dependent inhibition and anchorage dependence, cancer cells do not stop dividing when growth factors are depleted. A logical hypothesis is that cancer cells do not need growth factors in their culture medium to grow and divide. They may make a required growth factor themselves, or they may have an abnormality in the signaling pathway that conveys the growth factor's signal to the cell cycle control system even in the absence of that factor. Another possibility is an abnormal cell cycle control system. In fact, as you will learn in Chapter 18, these are all conditions that may lead to cancer.

There are other important differences between normal cells and cancer cells that reflect derangements of the cell cycle. If and when they stop dividing, cancer cells do so at random points in the cycle, rather than at the normal checkpoints. Moreover, can-

Cells anchor to dish surface and divide (anchorage dependence).

When cells have formed a complete single layer, they stop dividing (density-dependent inhibition).

If some cells are scraped away, the remaining cells divide to fill the gap and then stop once they contact each other (density-dependent inhibition).

├─── 25 μm ───┤

(a) Normal mammalian cells. Contact with neighboring cells and the availability of nutrients, growth factors, and a substratum for attachment limit cell density to a single layer.

├─── 25 μm ───┤

(b) Cancer cells. Cancer cells usually continue to divide well beyond a single layer, forming a clump of overlapping cells. They do not exhibit anchorage dependence or density-dependent inhibition.

▲ **Figure 12.19 Density-dependent inhibition and anchorage dependence of cell division.** Individual cells are shown disproportionately large in the drawings.

cer cells can go on dividing indefinitely in culture if they are given a continual supply of nutrients; in essence, they are "immortal." A striking example is a cell line that has been reproducing in culture since 1951. Cells of this line are called HeLa cells because their original source was a tumor removed from a woman named Henrietta Lacks. By contrast, nearly all normal mammalian cells growing in culture divide only about 20 to 50 times before they stop dividing, age, and die. (We'll see a possible reason for this phenomenon when we discuss chromosome replication in Chapter 16.)

The abnormal behavior of cancer cells can be catastrophic when it occurs in the body. The problem begins when a single cell in a tissue undergoes **transformation**, the process that converts a normal cell to a cancer cell. The body's immune system normally recognizes a transformed cell as an insurgent and destroys it. However, if the cell evades destruction, it may proliferate and form a tumor, a mass of abnormal cells within otherwise normal tissue. If the abnormal cells remain at the original site, the lump is called a **benign tumor**. Most benign tumors do not cause serious problems and can be completely removed by surgery. In contrast, a **malignant tumor** becomes invasive enough to impair the functions of one or more organs **(Figure 12.20)**. An individual with a malignant tumor is said to have cancer.

The cells of malignant tumors are abnormal in many ways besides their excessive proliferation. They may have unusual numbers of chromosomes (whether this is a cause or an effect of transformation is a current topic of debate). Their metabolism may be disabled, and they may cease to function in any constructive way. Abnormal changes on the cell surface cause cancer cells to lose attachments to neighboring cells and the extracellular matrix, which allows them to spread into nearby tissues. Cancer cells may also secrete signal molecules that cause blood vessels to grow toward the tumor. A few tumor cells may separate from the original tumor, enter blood vessels and lymph vessels, and travel to other parts of the body. There, they may proliferate and form a new tumor. This spread of cancer cells to locations distant from their original site is called **metastasis** (see Figure 12.20).

A tumor that appears to be localized may be treated with high-energy radiation, which damages DNA in cancer cells much more than it does in normal cells, apparently because the majority of cancer cells have lost the ability to repair such damage. To treat known or suspected metastatic tumors, chemotherapy is used, in which drugs that are toxic to actively dividing cells are administered through the circulatory system. As you might expect, chemotherapeutic drugs interfere with specific steps in the cell cycle. For example, the drug Taxol freezes the mitotic spindle by preventing microtubule depolymerization, which stops actively dividing cells from proceeding past metaphase. The side effects of chemotherapy are due to the drugs' effects on normal cells that divide often. For example, nausea results from chemotherapy's effects on intestinal cells, hair loss from effects on hair follicle cells, and susceptibility to infection from effects on immune system cells.

Researchers are beginning to understand how a normal cell is transformed into a cancer cell. You will learn more about the molecular biology of cancer in Chapter 18. Though the causes of cancer are diverse, cellular transformation always involves the alteration of genes that somehow influence the cell cycle control system. Our knowledge of how changes in the genome lead to the various abnormalities of cancer cells remains rudimentary, however.

Perhaps the reason we have so many unanswered questions about cancer cells is that there is still so much to learn about how normal cells function. The cell, life's basic unit of structure and function, holds enough secrets to engage researchers well into the future.

CONCEPT CHECK   12.3

1. In Figure 12.13, why do the nuclei resulting from experiment 2 contain different amounts of DNA?
2. What is the go-ahead signal for a cell to pass the G_2 phase checkpoint and enter mitosis? (See Figure 12.17.)
3. What phase are most of your body cells in?
4. Compare and contrast a benign tumor and a malignant tumor.
5. **WHAT IF?**   What would happen if you performed the experiment in Figure 12.18 with cancer cells?

For suggested answers, see Appendix A.

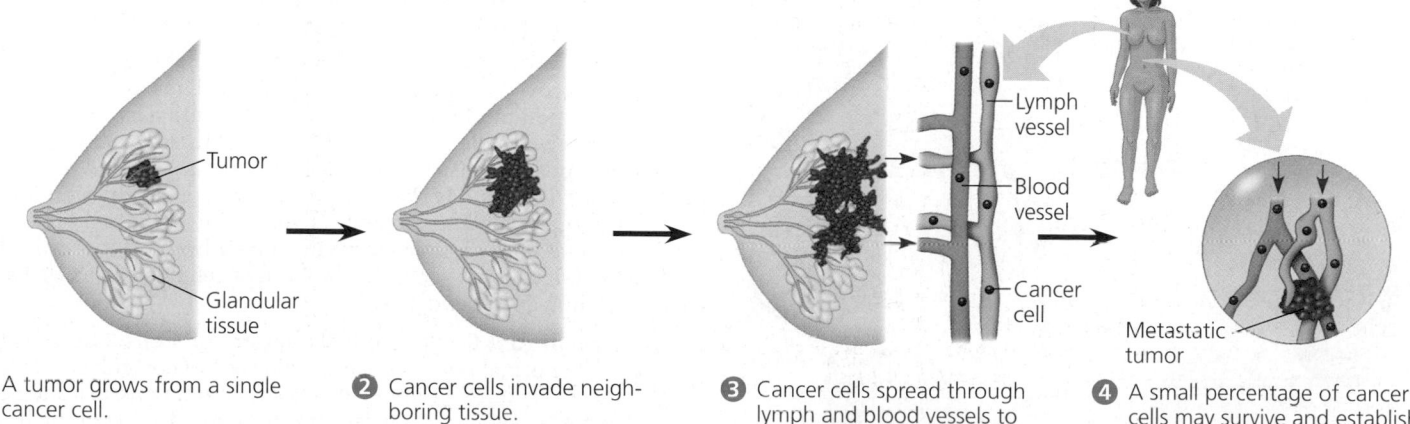

❶ A tumor grows from a single cancer cell.

❷ Cancer cells invade neighboring tissue.

❸ Cancer cells spread through lymph and blood vessels to other parts of the body.

❹ A small percentage of cancer cells may survive and establish a new tumor in another part of the body.

▲ **Figure 12.20 The growth and metastasis of a malignant breast tumor.** The cells of malignant (cancerous) tumors grow in an uncontrolled way and can spread to neighboring tissues and, via lymph and blood vessels, to other parts of the body. The spread of cancer cells beyond their original site is called metastasis.

SUMMARY OF KEY CONCEPTS

▶ Unicellular organisms reproduce by cell division; multicellular organisms depend on cell division for their development from a fertilized egg and for growth and repair.

> **MEDIA**
>
> **Activity** Roles of Cell Division

CONCEPT **12.1**

Cell division results in genetically identical daughter cells (pp. 229–230)

▶ Cells duplicate their genetic material before they divide, ensuring that each daughter cell receives an exact copy of the genetic material, DNA.

▶ **Cellular Organization of the Genetic Material** DNA is partitioned among chromosomes. Eukaryotic chromosomes consist of chromatin, a complex of DNA and protein that condenses during mitosis. In animals, gametes have one set of chromosomes and somatic cells have two sets.

▶ **Distribution of Chromosomes During Eukaryotic Cell Division** In preparation for cell division, chromosomes replicate, each one then consisting of two identical sister chromatids joined along their lengths by sister chromatid cohesion. When this cohesion is broken, the chromatids separate during cell division, becoming the chromosomes of the new daughter cells. Eukaryotic cell division consists of mitosis (division of the nucleus) and cytokinesis (division of the cytoplasm).

CONCEPT **12.2**

The mitotic phase alternates with interphase in the cell cycle (pp. 230–238)

▶ **Phases of the Cell Cycle** Between divisions, cells are in interphase: the G_1, S, and G_2 phases. The cell grows throughout interphase, but DNA is replicated only during the synthesis (S) phase. Mitosis and cytokinesis make up the mitotic (M) phase of the cell cycle.

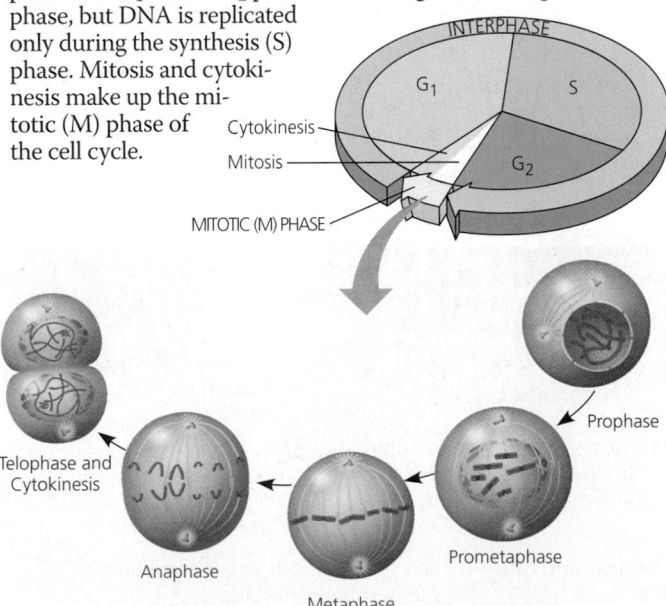

▶ **The Mitotic Spindle: *A Closer Look*** The mitotic spindle is an apparatus of microtubules that controls chromosome movement during mitosis. In animal cells, the spindle arises from the centrosomes and includes spindle microtubules and asters. Some spindle microtubules attach to the kinetochores of chromosomes and move the chromosomes to the metaphase plate. In anaphase, sister chromatids separate, and motor proteins move them along the kinetochore microtubules toward opposite ends of the cell. Meanwhile, motor proteins push nonkinetochore microtubules from opposite poles away from each other, elongating the cell. In telophase, genetically identical daughter nuclei form at opposite ends of the cell.

▶ **Cytokinesis: *A Closer Look*** Mitosis is usually followed by cytokinesis. Animal cells carry out cytokinesis by cleavage, and plant cells form a cell plate.

▶ **Binary Fission** During binary fission in bacteria, the chromosome replicates and the two daughter chromosomes actively move apart. The specific proteins involved in this movement are a subject of current research.

▶ **The Evolution of Mitosis** Since prokaryotes preceded eukaryotes by more than a billion years, it is likely that mitosis evolved from prokaryotic cell division. Certain protists exhibit types of cell division that seem intermediate between bacterial binary fission and the process of mitosis carried out by most eukaryotic cells.

> **MEDIA**
>
> **BioFlix 3-D Animation** Mitosis
> **MP3 Tutor** Mitosis
> **Activity** The Cell Cycle
> **Activity** Mitosis and Cytokinesis Animation
> **Activity** Mitosis and Cytokinesis Video
> **Investigation** How Much Time Do Cells Spend in Each Phase of Mitosis?

CONCEPT **12.3**

The eukaryotic cell cycle is regulated by a molecular control system (pp. 238–243)

▶ **Evidence for Cytoplasmic Signals** Molecules present in the cytoplasm regulate progress through the cell cycle.

▶ **The Cell Cycle Control System** Cyclic changes in regulatory proteins work as a cell cycle clock. The clock has specific checkpoints where the cell cycle stops until a go-ahead signal is received. The key molecules are cyclins and cyclin-dependent kinases (Cdks). Cell culture has enabled researchers to study the molecular details of cell division. Both internal signals and external signals control the cell cycle checkpoints via signal transduction pathways. Most cells exhibit density-dependent inhibition of cell division as well as anchorage dependence.

▶ **Loss of Cell Cycle Controls in Cancer Cells** Cancer cells elude normal regulation and divide out of control, forming tumors. Malignant tumors invade surrounding tissues and can metastasize, exporting cancer cells to other parts of the body, where they may form secondary tumors.

> **MEDIA**
>
> **Activity** Causes of Cancer

SELF-QUIZ

1. Through a microscope, you can see a cell plate beginning to develop across the middle of a cell and nuclei re-forming on either side of the cell plate. This cell is most likely
   a. an animal cell in the process of cytokinesis.
   b. a plant cell in the process of cytokinesis.
   c. an animal cell in the S phase of the cell cycle.
   d. a bacterial cell dividing.
   e. a plant cell in metaphase.

2. Vinblastine is a standard chemotherapeutic drug used to treat cancer. Because it interferes with the assembly of microtubules, its effectiveness must be related to
   a. disruption of mitotic spindle formation.
   b. inhibition of regulatory protein phosphorylation.
   c. suppression of cyclin production.
   d. myosin denaturation and inhibition of cleavage furrow formation.
   e. inhibition of DNA synthesis.

3. A particular cell has half as much DNA as some other cells in a mitotically active tissue. The cell in question is most likely in
   a. G_1.
   b. G_2.
   c. prophase.
   d. metaphase.
   e. anaphase.

4. One difference between cancer cells and normal cells is that cancer cells
   a. are unable to synthesize DNA.
   b. are arrested at the S phase of the cell cycle.
   c. continue to divide even when they are tightly packed together.
   d. cannot function properly because they are affected by density-dependent inhibition.
   e. are always in the M phase of the cell cycle.

5. The decline of MPF activity at the end of mitosis is due to
   a. the destruction of the protein kinase Cdk.
   b. decreased synthesis of cyclin.
   c. the degradation of cyclin.
   d. synthesis of DNA.
   e. an increase in the cell's volume-to-genome ratio.

6. The drug cytochalasin B blocks the function of actin. Which of the following aspects of the cell cycle would be most disrupted by cytochalasin B?
   a. spindle formation
   b. spindle attachment to kinetochores
   c. DNA synthesis
   d. cell elongation during anaphase
   e. cleavage furrow formation

7. In the cells of some organisms, mitosis occurs without cytokinesis. This will result in
   a. cells with more than one nucleus.
   b. cells that are unusually small.
   c. cells lacking nuclei.
   d. destruction of chromosomes.
   e. cell cycles lacking an S phase.

8. Which of the following does *not* occur during mitosis?
   a. condensation of the chromosomes
   b. replication of the DNA
   c. separation of sister chromatids
   d. spindle formation
   e. separation of the spindle poles

9. In the light micrograph below of dividing cells near the tip of an onion root, identify a cell in each of the following stages: prophase, prometaphase, metaphase, anaphase, and telophase. Describe the major events occurring at each stage.

10. **DRAW IT**   Draw one eukaryotic chromosome as it would appear during interphase, during each of the stages of mitosis, and during cytokinesis. Also draw and label the nuclear envelope and any microtubules attached to the chromosome(s).

For Self-Quiz answers, see Appendix A.

MEDIA   Visit **www.campbellbiology.com** for a Practice Test.

EVOLUTION CONNECTION

11. The result of mitosis is that the daughter cells end up with the same number of chromosomes that the parent cell had. Another way to maintain the number of chromosomes would be to carry out cell division first and then duplicate the chromosomes in each daughter cell. Do you think this would be an equally good way of organizing the cell cycle? Why do you suppose that evolution has not led to this alternative?

SCIENTIFIC INQUIRY

12. Although both ends of a microtubule can gain or lose subunits, one end (called the plus end) polymerizes and depolymerizes at a higher rate than the other end (the minus end). For spindle microtubules, the plus ends are in the center of the spindle, and the minus ends are at the poles. Motor proteins that move on microtubules specialize in walking either toward the plus end or toward the minus end; the two types are called plus end–directed and minus end–directed motor proteins, respectively. Given what you know about chromosome movement and spindle changes during anaphase, predict which type of motor proteins would be present on (a) kinetochore microtubules and (b) nonkinetochore microtubules.

UNIT 3

Genetics

Terry L. Orr-Weaver

How the daughter cells resulting from cell division end up with equal numbers of chromosomes is the focus of much of Terry Orr-Weaver's research; she also studies how cells control the DNA replication that precedes cell division. Her research group has identified a number of proteins involved in these processes. A professor of biology at MIT and the first woman to become a member of the Whitehead Institute for Biomedical Research, Dr. Orr-Weaver has an undergraduate degree in chemistry from UC San Diego and a Ph.D. in biological chemistry from Harvard. She is a member of the U.S. National Academy of Sciences and a past president of the Genetics Society of America.

After receiving your Ph.D., you switched from using single-celled yeast as your model organism to the multicelled fruit fly *Drosophila melanogaster*. Why?

I was excited by the possibility of working at the interface of two fields. At that time, the cell cycle field was exploding from work with single cells—mainly yeasts and mammalian cells grown in culture—and biochemical experiments using extracts. Meanwhile, developmental biology was entering a new era with the discovery of pattern formation genes. I realized there was a key question at the interface of these two fields that was being ignored: If an organism starts as a single cell and ends up as a multicellular entity, how are pattern and cell divisions coordinated? And I realized there had to be intrinsic regulation from the cell cycle components but also extrinsic developmental control feeding into that. This was clearly going to be an important area of study.

In choosing a multicellular model organism, why use *Drosophila*?

A lot of fundamental discoveries in biology have been made with fruit flies. For example, it was research with *Drosophila* that established in 1916 that chromosomes were the physical basis of inheritance, the structures that carried the genes. Decades later, the master regulatory genes that set up the animal body plan in embryonic development were discovered in *Drosophila*. These genes determine, for example, where the fly's head is and where its legs are. Then, to the amazement of biologists, it turned out that exactly the same genes control how the human body plan is set up! So *Drosophila* has a really rich heritage. When I started working on *Drosophila*, it had a 70-year-long history of use in genetics, providing an incredible array of knowledge and methods.

How do geneticists approach biological questions?

Geneticists want to discover the genes that are involved in a biological process and then figure out what the genes do. First, you decide what process you're interested in—in our case, how chromosomes get partitioned during cell division. Next, you figure out what you would see if you had a mutant in which that process was perturbed—how would you recognize it? Then you generate mutations, usually with the help of high-energy radiation or a chemical, hoping that one or more of the resulting mutants are affected in the process of interest. What you're doing by making a mutation is generating a disease state in your organism. When you've found a mutant you're interested in, you can find out what gene has been made defective, and you know that that gene has to play an important role in the process you're interested in.

Now that we have the genome sequences of many organisms, including the fruit fly and the human, you might think that all their genes are known—so what's to discover? But it turned out that we didn't know the functions of many of the genes that showed up in genome sequences. Even in an organism as simple and well-studied as yeast, at the publication of the genome sequence we didn't know what 70% of the genes did. And we still don't have a clue about half of the human genes. So having genome sequences provides a foundation, but we must still find out what all the genes do, and we geneticists feel the best way to go about this is to use genetics.

A big and useful surprise in this gene-discovery enterprise has been how many genes have been "conserved" through evolutionary history and are still very similar in organisms as distantly related as fruit flies and humans. It's very hard to figure out directly what human genes do. But when we discover a new gene in *Drosophila*, invariably it turns out that there's a similar gene in humans that does the same thing. So *Drosophila* turns out to be an even better model organism than we had guessed.

Besides genetics, what other approaches and methods do you use?

A combination of genetics, biochemistry, and cell biology turns out to be incredibly powerful for our research. For instance, with the microscope, a tool of cell biology, we can literally watch the chromosomes as they undergo mitosis or meiosis. If we have a mutation causing a defect in one of those processes, we can look directly at how the chromosomes behave in mutant cells. And in our research on DNA replication, we can look directly at proteins that attach to the DNA during DNA replication. In this lab, we try to do things as directly as possible!

Here's an example from our work on DNA replication in *Drosophila*. Using a genetic approach, we discovered a mutant that couldn't carry out DNA replication—although such a mutant can live and grow for a while by using proteins its mother stockpiled in the egg. It looked like the gene affected might code for a really important protein. But we wanted to find out if it was a protein that played a *direct* role in DNA replication, and we couldn't tell that from the genetics alone. However, by labeling the normal version of the protein with a fluorescent tag, we could use the microscope to see where the protein was located in cells, and we saw that the protein got on the DNA right at a place where DNA synthesis starts. That established that this protein was directly involved.

How is meiosis different from mitosis?

Let me first review mitosis. After a cell duplicates its DNA, mitosis ensures that each duplicated chromosome gets partitioned to the daughter cells so that you end up with two cells that have exactly the same DNA content and chromosome number. That's what happens in normal cell division.

But what about making a sperm or an egg? In fertilization, a sperm and egg are going to fuse and give rise to a new progeny. If the organism is diploid—that is, has two similar copies of each chromosome, as flies and humans do—and the progeny is going to be diploid, then you've got to make sperm and eggs that have only one copy of each chromosome, so that when those sperm and egg come together you restore the right chromosome number. And to produce sperm and eggs with only half the diploid chromosome number, you need a special kind of cell division—meiosis. There has to be a way to bring together the two similar copies of each chromosome and then pull them apart, with each going to a different daughter cell. In meiosis, there is an extra round of chromosome partitioning where what we call the homologous pairs of chromosomes—the chromosome that initially came from dad and the similar chromosome that came from mom—get separated from each other. To sum up, in mitosis you're separating identical copies of each chromosome, whereas in meiosis you have an extra round of division stuck in there, where the copy of each chromosome from dad and the copy from mom get separated from each other.

What important questions about meiosis still need to be answered?

What we don't understand at all is how the chromosomes of a homologous pair find each other. That pairing is unique to meiosis; it doesn't happen in mitosis. The two strands of the DNA don't come apart, so although the homologous chromosomes have very similar DNA sequences, it's not base-pairing that brings the homologous chromosomes together. Given the relatively gigantic volume of the nucleus and the huge mass of chromatin in a eukaryotic cell, how do the right chromosomes find each other? That's the number one mystery about meiosis. And I would say the second big mystery is why humans are so unbelievably bad at carrying out meiosis.

What makes you say that? Are we worse than fruit flies?

We're about a thousand times worse. Here are some amazing statistics: Twenty percent of recognized pregnancies end in spontaneous miscarriage, and out of those at least half are due to a mistake during meiosis. And for every pregnancy that proceeds far enough to be recognized, there have been many that ended without being recognized. So about 10–20% of the time meiosis doesn't work properly in humans. In fruit flies, meiosis seems to occur inaccurately only 0.01–0.05% of the time. Even mice, which are mammals like ourselves, do much better than humans. So I would call this the second big mystery regarding meiosis: Why are humans so bad at it?

Tell us more about what happens when meiosis doesn't work correctly.

Most of the time the result is early death of the embryo. In humans, if any chromosome other than X or Y is present in only one copy or more than two copies, the embryo dies very early. The only exceptions are for chromosomes number 13, 18, and 21: When one of these is present in three copies, the embryo usually dies at an early stage, but it may survive. Even in the case of Down syndrome, a relatively common condition where a person has three copies of chromosome 21, only a minority of fetuses survive to term. And when the individual does survive, there are serious effects.

In fact, errors in meiosis are the leading cause of mental retardation in the United States. Some scientists argue that, in evolutionary terms, the human species is able to cope with such a high rate of meiotic errors because most of the pregnancies are lost very early.

What do you like best about research?

What's so great about research is that you get to unwrap presents all the time! When you find an interesting mutant, it's like a beautifully wrapped present. And then you unwrap it, and it can be a big surprise to learn which gene is affected and what its protein product is. Sometimes you unwrap it and it's beautiful and satisfying and completely makes sense; other times you don't at first understand what the gift is, and then you have to figure that out. I want to tell students how wonderful it is getting these presents to unwrap. But they also need to realize that it might take three years to get the ribbon and all the tape off. It can take some real patience to unwrap the present!

In your view, how important is it for scientists to reach out beyond the scientific community?

I think scientists do have an obligation to educate the public. It's especially critical for people to understand the importance of basic research and the study of model organisms. Because if we shortchange basic research, in the long run we won't be able to benefit from medical applications. The reason we've done so well in this country is our willingness to invest in basic research science.

The challenge is figuring out how to convey a message like this in an era of soundbites. The media and the public want to hear that a piece of research is directly going to cure a disease. So how can we get a message across that requires an explanation more complex than a catchphrase? There are many stories we can tell where discoveries in basic research have led to very important applications, but these stories take at least a couple of paragraphs to communicate. Also, there's a real need for scientists to try to build a bridge between science and the public.

It's especially important to educate our representatives in government. A coalition of several biology societies, including the Genetics Society of America, has a Joint Steering Committee for Public Policy, which has been terrific in educating members of Congress and their staffs. They bring in scientists to explain their research and why investing in research is important. Maybe that's a good starting point.

When you find an interesting mutant, it's like a beautifully wrapped present . . . and it can be a big surprise . . .

Inquiry in Action

Learn about an experiment by Terry Orr-Weaver in Inquiry Figure 16.22 on page 322.

Jane Reece and Terry Orr-Weaver

Meiosis and Sexual Life Cycles

13

13.1 Offspring acquire genes from parents by inheriting chromosomes

13.2 Fertilization and meiosis alternate in sexual life cycles

13.3 Meiosis reduces the number of chromosome sets from diploid to haploid

13.4 Genetic variation produced in sexual life cycles contributes to evolution

OVERVIEW

Variations on a Theme

Most people who send out birth announcements mention the sex of the baby, but they don't feel the need to specify that their offspring is a human being! One of the characteristics of life is the ability of organisms to reproduce their own kind—elephants produce little elephants, and oak trees generate oak saplings. Exceptions to this rule show up only as sensational but highly suspect stories in tabloid newspapers.

Another rule often taken for granted is that offspring resemble their parents more than they do unrelated individuals. If you examine the family members shown in **Figure 13.1**—Sissy Spacek and Jack Fisk with daughters Madison and Schuyler Fisk—you can pick out some similar features among them. The transmission of traits from one generation to the next is called inheritance, or **heredity** (from the Latin *heres*, heir). However, sons and daughters are not identical copies of either parent or of their siblings. Along with inherited similarity, there is also **variation**. Farmers have exploited the principles of heredity and variation for thousands of years, breeding plants and animals for desired traits. But what are the biological mechanisms leading to the hereditary similarity and variation that we call a "family resemblance"? This question eluded biologists until the development of genetics in the 20th century.

▲ **Figure 13.1 What accounts for family resemblance?**

Genetics is the scientific study of heredity and hereditary variation. In this unit, you will learn about genetics at multiple levels, from organisms to cells to molecules. On the practical side, you will see how genetics continues to revolutionize medicine and agriculture, and you will be asked to consider some social and ethical questions raised by our ability to manipulate DNA, the genetic material. At the end of the unit, you will be able to stand back and consider the whole genome, an organism's entire complement of DNA. The rapid accumulation of the genome sequences of many species, including our own, has taught us a great deal about evolution on the molecular level—in other words, evolution of the genome itself. In fact, genetic methods and discoveries are catalyzing progress in all areas of biology, from cell biology to physiology, developmental biology, behavior, and even ecology.

We begin our study of genetics in this chapter by examining how chromosomes pass from parents to offspring in sexually reproducing organisms. The processes of meiosis (a special type of cell division) and fertilization (the fusion of sperm and egg) maintain a species' chromosome count during the sexual life cycle. We will describe the cellular mechanics of meiosis and how this process differs from mitosis. Finally, we will consider how both meiosis and fertilization contribute to genetic variation, such as the variation obvious in the family shown in Figure 13.1.

CONCEPT 13.1

Offspring acquire genes from parents by inheriting chromosomes

Family friends may tell you that you have your mother's freckles or your father's eyes. However, parents do not, in any literal sense, give their children freckles, eyes, hair, or any other traits. What, then, *is* actually inherited?

Inheritance of Genes

Parents endow their offspring with coded information in the form of hereditary units called **genes**. The genes we inherit from our mothers and fathers are our genetic link to our parents, and they account for family resemblances such as shared eye color or freckles. Our genes program the specific traits that emerge as we develop from fertilized eggs into adults.

The genetic program is written in the language of DNA, the polymer of four different nucleotides you learned about in Chapters 1 and 5. Inherited information is passed on in the form of each gene's specific sequence of DNA nucleotides, much as printed information is communicated in the form of meaningful sequences of letters. In both cases, the language is symbolic. Just as your brain translates the word *apple* into a mental image of the fruit, cells translate genes into freckles and other features. Most genes program cells to synthesize specific enzymes and other proteins, whose cumulative action produces an organism's inherited traits. The programming of these traits in the form of DNA is one of the unifying themes of biology.

The transmission of hereditary traits has its molecular basis in the precise replication of DNA, which produces copies of genes that can be passed along from parents to offspring. In animals and plants, reproductive cells called **gametes** are the vehicles that transmit genes from one generation to the next. During fertilization, male and female gametes (sperm and eggs) unite, thereby passing on genes of both parents to their offspring.

Except for small amounts of DNA in mitochondria and chloroplasts, the DNA of a eukaryotic cell is packaged into chromosomes within the nucleus. Every living species has a characteristic number of chromosomes. For example, humans have 46 chromosomes in almost all of their cells. Each chromosome consists of a single long DNA molecule elaborately coiled in association with various proteins. One chromosome includes several hundred to a few thousand genes, each of which is a specific sequence of nucleotides within the DNA molecule. A gene's specific location along the length of a chromosome is called the gene's **locus** (from the Latin, meaning "place"; plural, *loci*). Our genetic endowment consists of the genes carried on the chromosomes we inherited from our parents.

Comparison of Asexual and Sexual Reproduction

Only organisms that reproduce asexually produce offspring that are exact copies of themselves. In **asexual reproduction**, a single individual is the sole parent and passes copies of all its genes to its offspring. For example, single-celled eukaryotic organisms can reproduce asexually by mitotic cell division, in which DNA is copied and allocated equally to two daughter cells. The genomes of the offspring are virtually exact copies of the parent's genome. Some multicellular organisms are also

(a) Hydra   **(b) Redwoods**

▲ **Figure 13.2 Asexual reproduction in two multicellular organisms. (a)** This relatively simple animal, a hydra, reproduces by budding. The bud, a localized mass of mitotically dividing cells, develops into a small hydra, which detaches from the parent (LM). **(b)** Each tree in this circle of redwoods grew from a single parent tree, whose stump is in the center of the circle.

capable of reproducing asexually **(Figure 13.2)**. Because the cells of the offspring are derived by mitosis in the parent, the "chip off the old block" is usually genetically identical to its parent. An individual that reproduces asexually gives rise to a **clone**, a group of genetically identical individuals. Genetic differences occasionally arise in asexually reproducing organisms as a result of changes in the DNA called mutations, which we will discuss in Chapter 17.

In **sexual reproduction**, two parents give rise to offspring that have unique combinations of genes inherited from the two parents. In contrast to a clone, offspring of sexual reproduction vary genetically from their siblings and both parents: They are variations on a common theme of family resemblance, not exact replicas. Genetic variation like that shown in Figure 13.1 is an important consequence of sexual reproduction. What mechanisms generate this genetic variation? The key is the behavior of chromosomes during the sexual life cycle.

CONCEPT CHECK 13.1

1. How are the traits of parents (such as hair color) transmitted to their offspring?
2. Explain how asexually reproducing organisms produce offspring that are genetically identical to each other and to their parents.
3. **WHAT IF?** A horticulturalist breeds orchids, trying to obtain a plant with a unique combination of desirable traits. After many years, she finally succeeds. To produce more plants like this one, should she breed it or clone it? Why?

For suggested answers, see Appendix A.

CONCEPT 13.2

Fertilization and meiosis alternate in sexual life cycles

A **life cycle** is the generation-to-generation sequence of stages in the reproductive history of an organism, from conception to production of its own offspring. In this section, we use humans as an example to track the behavior of chromosomes through sexual life cycles. We begin by considering the chromosome count in human somatic cells and gametes; we will then explore how the behavior of chromosomes relates to the human life cycle and other types of sexual life cycles.

Sets of Chromosomes in Human Cells

In humans, each **somatic cell**—any cell other than those involved in gamete formation—has 46 chromosomes. During mitosis, the chromosomes become condensed enough to be visible in a light microscope. Because chromosomes differ in size, in the positions of their centromeres, and in the pattern of colored bands produced by certain stains, they can be distinguished from one another by microscopic examination when sufficiently condensed.

Careful examination of a micrograph of the 46 human chromosomes from a single cell in mitosis reveals that there are two chromosomes of each of 23 types. This becomes clear when images of the chromosomes are arranged in pairs, starting with the longest chromosomes. The resulting ordered display is called a **karyotype (Figure 13.3)**. The two chromosomes composing a pair have the same length, centromere position, and staining pattern: These are called **homologous chromosomes**, or homologs. Both chromosomes of each pair carry genes controlling the same inherited characters. For example, if a gene for eye color is situated at a particular locus on a certain chromosome, then the homolog of that chromosome will also have a gene specifying eye color at the equivalent locus.

The two distinct chromosomes referred to as X and Y are an important exception to the general pattern of homologous chromosomes in human somatic cells. Human females have a homologous pair of X chromosomes (XX), but males have one X and one Y chromosome (XY). Only small parts of the X and Y are homologous. Most of the genes carried on the X chromosome do not have counterparts on the tiny Y, and the Y chromosome has genes lacking on the X. Because they determine an individual's sex, the X and Y chromosomes are called **sex chromosomes**. The other chromosomes are called **autosomes**.

The occurrence of homologous pairs of chromosomes in each human somatic cell is a consequence of our sexual origins. We inherit one chromosome of each pair from each parent. Thus, the 46 chromosomes in our somatic cells are actually two sets of 23 chromosomes—a maternal set (from our mother)

▼ Figure 13.3 Research Method

Preparing a karyotype

APPLICATION A karyotype is a display of condensed chromosomes arranged in pairs. Karyotyping can be used to screen for abnormal numbers of chromosomes or defective chromosomes associated with certain congenital disorders, such as Down syndrome.

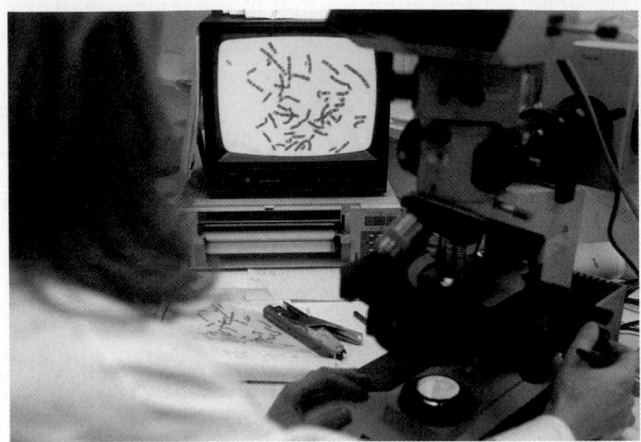

TECHNIQUE Karyotypes are prepared from isolated somatic cells, which are treated with a drug to stimulate mitosis and then grown in culture for several days. Cells arrested in metaphase are stained and then viewed with a microscope equipped with a digital camera. A photograph of the chromosomes is displayed on a computer monitor, and the images of the chromosomes are arranged into pairs according to size and shape.

RESULTS This karyotype shows the chromosomes from a normal human male. The size of the chromosome, position of the centromere, and pattern of stained bands help identify specific chromosomes. Although difficult to discern in the karyotype, each metaphase chromosome consists of two closely attached sister chromatids (see the diagram of a pair of homologous replicated chromosomes).

and a paternal set (from our father). The number of chromosomes in a single set is represented by n. Any cell with two chromosome sets is called a **diploid cell** and has a diploid number of chromosomes, abbreviated $2n$. For humans, the diploid number is 46 ($2n = 46$), the number of chromosomes in our somatic cells. In a cell in which DNA synthesis has occurred, all the chromosomes are replicated, and therefore each consists of two identical sister chromatids, associated closely at the centromere and along the arms. **Figure 13.4** helps clarify the various terms that we use in describing replicated chromosomes in a diploid cell. Study this figure so that you understand the differences between homologous chromosomes, sister chromatids, nonsister chromatids, and chromosome sets.

Unlike somatic cells, gametes (sperm and eggs) contain a single chromosome set. Such cells are called **haploid cells**, and each has a haploid number of chromosomes (n). For humans, the haploid number is 23 ($n = 23$). The set of 23 consists of the 22 autosomes plus a single sex chromosome. An unfertilized egg contains an X chromosome, but a sperm may contain an X or a Y chromosome.

Note that each sexually reproducing species has a characteristic diploid number and haploid number. For example, the fruit fly, *Drosophila melanogaster*, has a diploid number of 8 and a haploid number of 4, while dogs have a diploid number of 78 and a haploid number of 39.

Now that you have learned the concepts of diploid and haploid numbers of chromosomes, let's consider chromosome behavior during sexual life cycles. We'll use the human life cycle as an example.

Behavior of Chromosome Sets in the Human Life Cycle

The human life cycle begins when a haploid sperm from the father fuses with a haploid egg from the mother. This union of gametes, culminating in fusion of their nuclei, is called **fertilization**. The resulting fertilized egg, or **zygote**, is diploid because it contains two haploid sets of chromosomes bearing genes representing the maternal and paternal family lines. As a human develops into a sexually mature adult, mitosis of the zygote and its descendants generates all the somatic cells of the body. Both chromosome sets in the zygote and all the genes they carry are passed with precision to the somatic cells.

The only cells of the human body not produced by mitosis are the gametes, which develop from specialized cells called *germ cells* in the gonads—ovaries in females and testes in males **(Figure 13.5)**. Imagine what would happen if human gametes were made by mitosis: They would be diploid like the somatic cells. At the next round of fertilization, when two gametes fused, the normal chromosome number of 46 would double to 92, and each subsequent generation would double the

Key

$2n = 6$ {
■ Maternal set of chromosomes ($n = 3$)
■ Paternal set of chromosomes ($n = 3$)
}

Two sister chromatids of one replicated chromosome

Centromere

Two nonsister chromatids in a homologous pair

Pair of homologous chromosomes (one from each set)

▲ **Figure 13.4 Describing chromosomes.** A cell with a diploid number of 6 ($2n = 6$) is depicted here following chromosome replication and condensation. Each of the six replicated chromosomes consists of two sister chromatids associated closely along their lengths. Each homologous pair is composed of one chromosome from the maternal set (red) and one from the paternal set (blue). Each set is made up of three chromosomes in this example. Nonsister chromatids are any two chromatids in a pair of homologous chromosomes that are not sister chromatids.

? *What is the haploid number of this cell? Is a "set" of chromosomes haploid or diploid?*

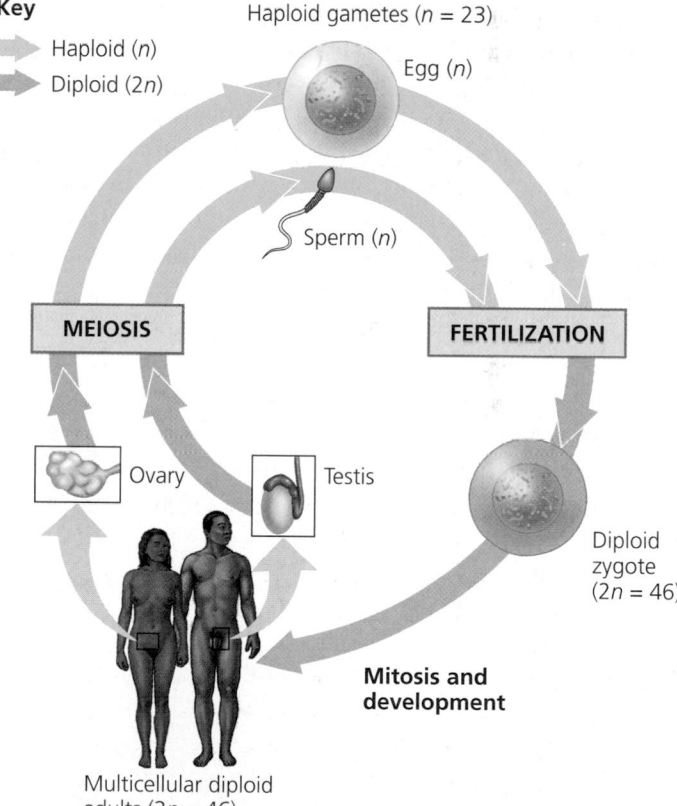

Key

→ Haploid (n)
→ Diploid ($2n$)

Haploid gametes ($n = 23$)

Egg (n)

Sperm (n)

MEIOSIS

FERTILIZATION

Ovary

Testis

Diploid zygote ($2n = 46$)

Mitosis and development

Multicellular diploid adults ($2n = 46$)

▲ **Figure 13.5 The human life cycle.** In each generation, the number of chromosome sets doubles at fertilization, but is halved during meiosis. For humans, the number of chromosomes in a haploid cell is 23, consisting of one set ($n = 23$); the number of chromosomes in the diploid zygote and all somatic cells arising from it is 46, consisting of two sets ($2n = 46$).

This figure introduces a color code that will be used for other life cycles later in this book. The teal arrows highlight haploid stages of a life cycle, and the beige arrows highlight diploid stages.

number of chromosomes yet again. This does not happen, however, because in sexually reproducing organisms, the gametes are formed by a modified type of cell division called **meiosis**. This type of cell division reduces the number of sets of chromosomes from two to one in the gametes, counterbalancing the doubling that occurs at fertilization. In animals, meiosis occurs only in the ovaries or testes. As a result of meiosis, each human sperm and egg is haploid ($n = 23$). Fertilization restores the diploid condition by combining two haploid sets of chromosomes, and the human life cycle is repeated, generation after generation (see Figure 13.5). You will learn more about the production of sperm and eggs in Chapter 46.

In general, the steps of the human life cycle are typical of many sexually reproducing animals. Indeed, the processes of fertilization and meiosis are the unique trademarks of sexual reproduction, in plants as well as animals. Fertilization and meiosis alternate in sexual life cycles, maintaining a constant number of chromosomes in each species from one generation to the next.

The Variety of Sexual Life Cycles

Although the alternation of meiosis and fertilization is common to all organisms that reproduce sexually, the timing of these two events in the life cycle varies, depending on the species. These variations can be grouped into three main types of life cycles. In the type that occurs in humans and most other animals, gametes are the only haploid cells. Meiosis occurs in germ cells during the production of gametes, which undergo no further cell division prior to fertilization. After fertilization, the diploid zygote divides by mitosis, producing a multicellular organism that is diploid (**Figure 13.6a**).

Plants and some species of algae exhibit a second type of life cycle called **alternation of generations**. This type includes both diploid and haploid stages that are multicellular. The multicellular diploid stage is called the **sporophyte**. Meiosis in the sporophyte produces haploid cells called **spores**. Unlike a gamete, a haploid spore doesn't fuse with another cell but divides mitotically, generating a multicellular haploid stage called the **gametophyte**. Cells of the gametophyte give rise to gametes by mitosis. Fusion of two haploid gametes at fertilization results in a diploid zygote, which develops into the next sporophyte generation. Therefore, in this type of life cycle, the sporophyte generation produces a gametophyte as its offspring, and the gametophyte generation produces the next sporophyte generation (**Figure 13.6b**). Clearly, the term *alternation of generations* is a fitting name for this type of life cycle.

A third type of life cycle occurs in most fungi and some protists, including some algae. After gametes fuse and form a diploid zygote, meiosis occurs without a multicellular diploid offspring developing. Meiosis produces not gametes but haploid cells that then divide by mitosis and give rise to either unicellular descendants or a haploid multicellular adult organism. Subsequently, the haploid organism carries out further mitoses, producing the cells that develop into gametes. The only diploid stage found in these species is the single-celled zygote (**Figure 13.6c**).

Note that *either* haploid or diploid cells can divide by mitosis, depending on the type of life cycle. Only diploid cells, however, can undergo meiosis because haploid cells have a single set of chromosomes that cannot be further reduced. Though the three types of sexual life cycles differ in the timing of meiosis and fertilization, they share a fundamental result: genetic

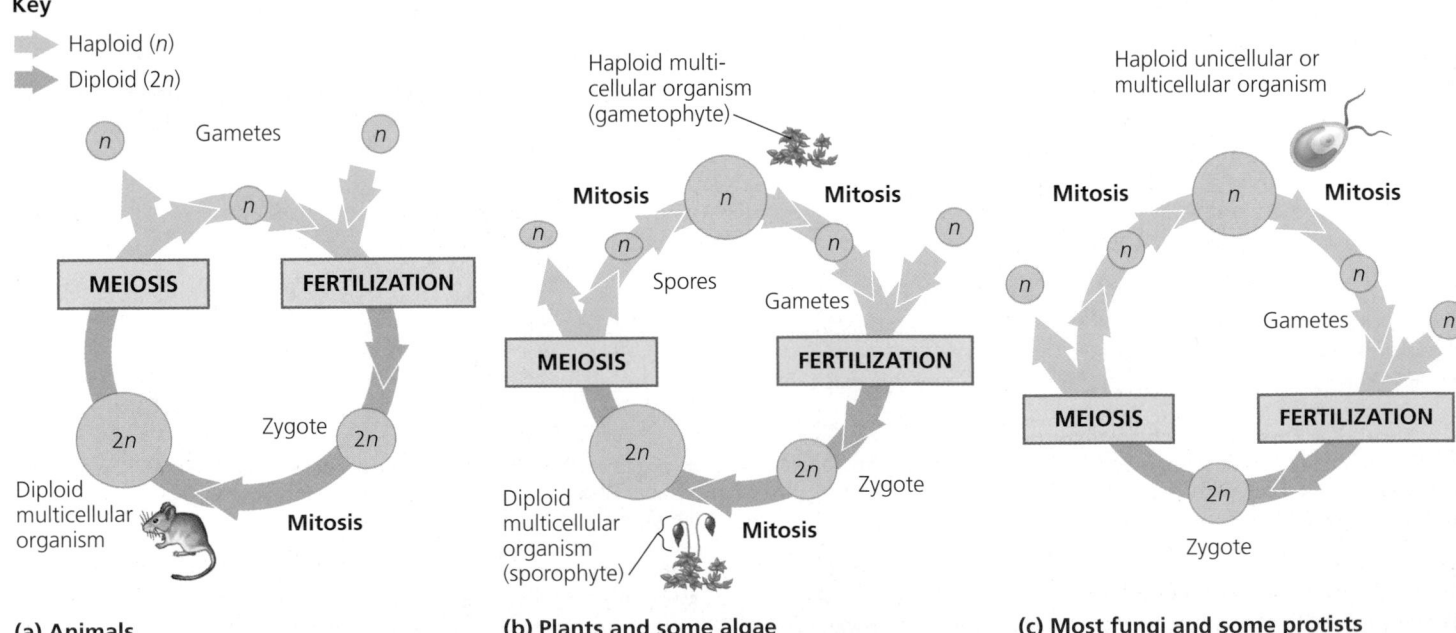

Key

- Haploid (n)
- Diploid ($2n$)

(a) Animals

(b) Plants and some algae

(c) Most fungi and some protists

▲ **Figure 13.6 Three types of sexual life cycles.** The common feature of all three cycles is the alternation of meiosis and fertilization, key events that contribute to genetic variation among offspring. The cycles differ in the timing of these two key events.

variation among offspring. A closer look at meiosis will reveal the sources of this variation.

▲ **Figure 13.7 Overview of meiosis: how meiosis reduces chromosome number.** After the chromosomes replicate in interphase, the diploid cell divides *twice*, yielding four haploid daughter cells. This overview tracks just one pair of homologous chromosomes, which for the sake of simplicity are drawn in the condensed state throughout (they would not normally be condensed during interphase). The red chromosome was inherited from the female parent, the blue chromosome from the male parent.

DRAW IT *Redraw the cells in this figure using a simple DNA double helix to represent each DNA molecule.*

CONCEPT 13.3
Meiosis reduces the number of chromosome sets from diploid to haploid

Many of the steps of meiosis closely resemble corresponding steps in mitosis. Meiosis, like mitosis, is preceded by the replication of chromosomes. However, this single replication is followed by not one but two consecutive cell divisions, called **meiosis I** and **meiosis II**. These two divisions result in four daughter cells (rather than the two daughter cells of mitosis), each with only half as many chromosomes as the parent cell.

The Stages of Meiosis

The overview of meiosis in **Figure 13.7** shows that both members of a single homologous pair of chromosomes in a diploid cell are replicated and that the copies are then sorted into four haploid daughter cells. Recall that sister chromatids are two copies of *one* chromosome, closely associated all along their lengths; this association is called *sister chromatid cohesion*. Together, the sister chromatids make up one replicated chromosome (see Figure 13.4). In contrast, the two chromosomes of a homologous pair are individual chromosomes that were inherited from different parents. Homologs appear alike in the microscope, but they may have different versions of genes, called *alleles*, at corresponding loci (for example, an allele for freckles on one chromosome and an allele for the absence of freckles at the same locus on the homolog). Homologs are not associated with each other except during meiosis, as you will soon see.

Figure 13.8, on the next two pages, describes in detail the stages of the two divisions of meiosis for an animal cell whose diploid number is 6. Meiosis halves the total number of chromosomes in a very specific way, reducing the number of sets from two to one, with each daughter cell receiving one set of chromosomes. Study Figure 13.8 thoroughly before going on.

Exploring The Meiotic Division of an Animal Cell

MEIOSIS I: Separates homologous chromosomes

Prophase I	Metaphase I	Anaphase I	Telophase I and Cytokinesis

Centrosome (with centriole pair)

Sister chromatids

Chiasmata

Spindle

Homologous chromosomes

Fragments of nuclear envelope

Replicated homologous chromosomes (red and blue) pair and exchange segments; $2n = 6$ in this example

Centromere (with kinetochore)

Metaphase plate

Microtubule attached to kinetochore

Chromosomes line up by homologous pairs

Sister chromatids remain attached

Homologous chromosomes separate

Each pair of homologous chromosomes separates

Cleavage furrow

Two haploid cells form; each chromosome still consists of two sister chromatids

Prophase I

- Chromosomes begin to condense, and homologs loosely pair along their lengths, aligned gene by gene.

- Crossing over (the exchange of corresponding segments of DNA molecules by nonsister chromatids) is completed while homologs are in *synapsis*, held tightly together by proteins along their lengths (before the stage shown).

- Synapsis ends in mid-prophase, and the chromosomes in each pair move apart slightly, as shown above.

- Each homologous pair has one or more chiasmata, points where crossing over has occurred and the homologs are still associated due to cohesion between sister chromatids (*sister chromatid cohesion*).

- Centrosome movement, spindle formation, and nuclear envelope breakdown occur as in mitosis.

- In late prophase I (after the stage shown), microtubules from one pole or the other attach to the two kinetochores, protein structures at the centromeres of the two homologs. The homologous pairs then move toward the metaphase plate.

Metaphase I

- Pairs of homologous chromosomes are now arranged on the metaphase plate, with one chromosome in each pair facing each pole.

- Both chromatids of one homolog are attached to kinetochore microtubules from one pole; those of the other homolog are attached to microtubules from the opposite pole.

Anaphase I

- Breakdown of proteins responsible for sister chromatid cohesion along chromatid arms allows homologs to separate.

- The homologs move toward opposite poles, guided by the spindle apparatus.

- Sister chromatid cohesion persists at the centromere, causing chromatids to move as a unit toward the same pole.

Telophase I and Cytokinesis

- At the beginning of telophase I, each half of the cell has a complete haploid set of replicated chromosomes. Each chromosome is composed of two sister chromatids; one or both chromatids include regions of nonsister chromatid DNA.

- Cytokinesis (division of the cytoplasm) usually occurs simultaneously with telophase I, forming two haploid daughter cells.

- In animal cells, a cleavage furrow forms. (In plant cells, a cell plate forms.)

- In some species, chromosomes decondense and the nuclear envelope re-forms.

- No replication occurs between meiosis I and meiosis II.

Prophase II	Metaphase II	Anaphase II	Telophase II and Cytokinesis

During another round of cell division, the sister chromatids finally separate; four haploid daughter cells result, containing unreplicated chromosomes

Sister chromatids separate

Haploid daughter cells forming

Prophase II
- A spindle apparatus forms.
- In late prophase II (not shown here), chromosomes, each still composed of two chromatids associated at the centromere, move toward the metaphase II plate.

Metaphase II
- The chromosomes are positioned on the metaphase plate as in mitosis.
- Because of crossing over in meiosis I, the two sister chromatids of each chromosome are *not* genetically identical.
- The kinetochores of sister chromatids are attached to microtubules extending from opposite poles.

Anaphase II
- Breakdown of proteins holding the sister chromatids together at the centromere allows the chromatids to separate. The chromatids move toward opposite poles as individual chromosomes.

Telophase II and Cytokinesis
- Nuclei form, the chromosomes begin decondensing, and cytokinesis occurs.
- The meiotic division of one parent cell produces four daughter cells, each with a haploid set of (unreplicated) chromosomes.
- Each of the four daughter cells is genetically distinct from the other daughter cells and from the parent cell.

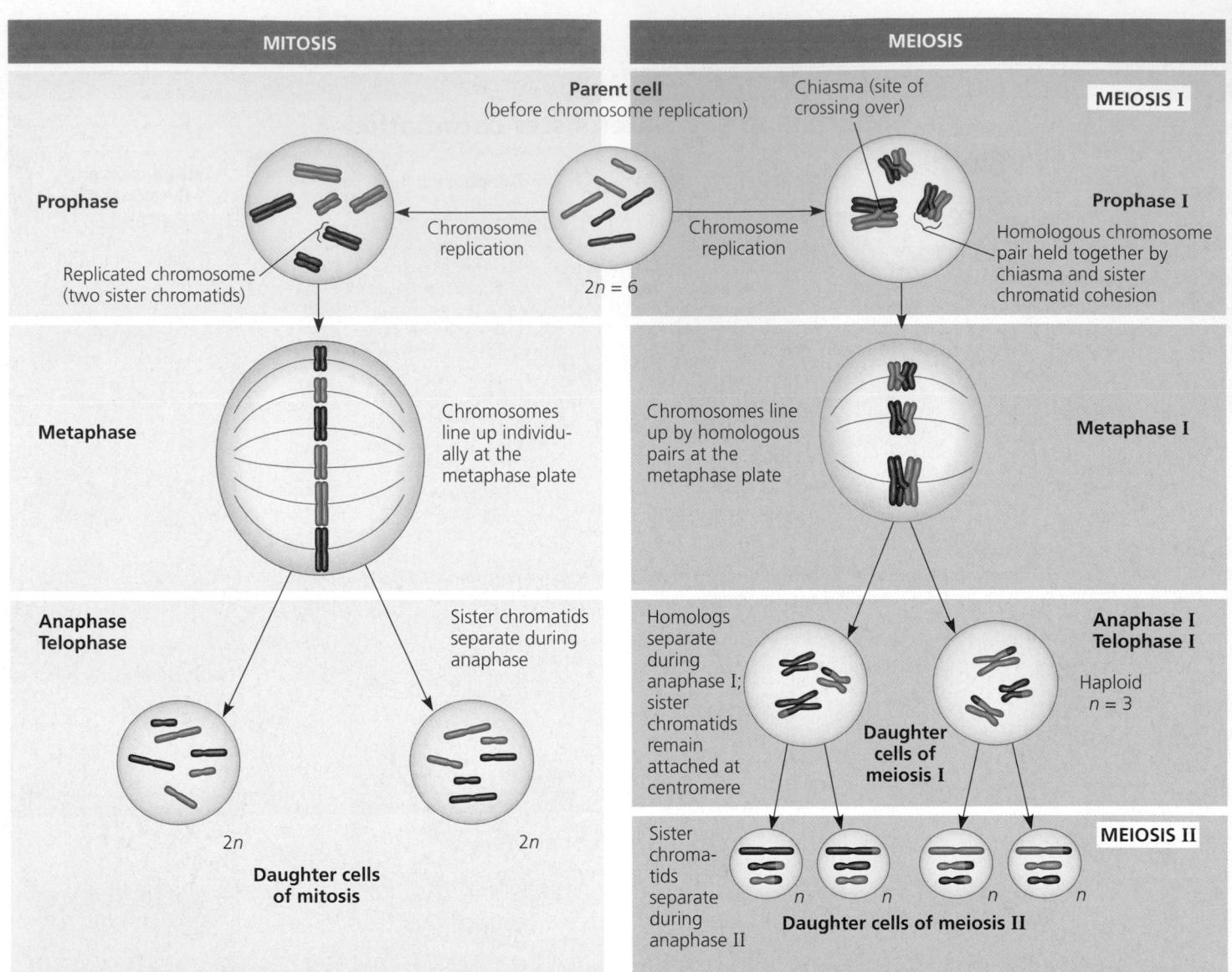

Property	Mitosis	Meiosis
DNA replication	Occurs during interphase before mitosis begins	Occurs during interphase before meiosis I begins
Number of divisions	One, including prophase, metaphase, anaphase, and telophase	Two, each including prophase, metaphase, anaphase, and telophase
Synapsis of homologous chromosomes	Does not occur	Occurs during prophase I along with crossing over between nonsister chromatids; resulting chiasmata hold pairs together due to sister chromatid cohesion
Number of daughter cells and genetic composition	Two, each diploid ($2n$) and genetically identical to the parent cell	Four, each haploid (n), containing half as many chromosomes as the parent cell; genetically different from the parent cell and from each other
Role in the animal body	Enables multicellular adult to arise from zygote; produces cells for growth, repair, and, in some species, asexual reproduction	Produces gametes; reduces number of chromosomes by half and introduces genetic variability among the gametes

▲ **Figure 13.9 A comparison of mitosis and meiosis in diploid cells.**

DRAW IT *Could any other combinations of chromosomes be generated during meiosis II from the specific cells shown in telophase I? Explain.* (Hint: *Draw the cells as they would appear in metaphase II.*)

A Comparison of Mitosis and Meiosis

Figure 13.9 summarizes the key differences between meiosis and mitosis in diploid cells. Basically, meiosis reduces the number of chromosome sets from two (diploid) to one (haploid), whereas mitosis conserves the number of chromosome sets. Therefore, meiosis produces cells that differ genetically from their parent cell and from each other, whereas mitosis produces daughter cells that are genetically identical to their parent cell and to each other.

Three events unique to meiosis occur during meiosis I:

1. **Synapsis and crossing over.** During prophase I, replicated homologs pair up and become physically connected along their lengths by a zipper-like protein structure, the *synaptonemal complex*; this process is called **synapsis**. Genetic rearrangement between nonsister chromatids, known as **crossing over**, is completed during this stage. Following disassembly of the synaptonemal complex in late prophase, the two homologs pull apart slightly but remain connected by at least one X-shaped region called a **chiasma** (plural, *chiasmata*). A chiasma is the physical manifestation of crossing over; it appears as a cross because sister chromatid cohesion still holds the two original sister chromatids together, even in regions where one of them is now part of the other homolog. Synapsis and crossing over normally do not occur during mitosis.

2. **Homologs on the metaphase plate.** At metaphase I of meiosis, chromosomes are positioned on the metaphase plate as pairs of homologs, rather than individual chromosomes, as in metaphase of mitosis.

3. **Separation of homologs.** At anaphase I of meiosis, the replicated chromosomes of each homologous pair move toward opposite poles, but the sister chromatids of each replicated chromosome remain attached. In anaphase of mitosis, by contrast, sister chromatids separate.

How do sister chromatids stay together through meiosis I but separate from each other in meiosis II and mitosis? Sister chromatids are attached along their lengths by protein complexes called *cohesins*. In mitosis, this attachment lasts until the end of metaphase, when enzymes cleave the cohesins, freeing the sister chromatids to move to opposite poles of the cell. In meiosis, sister chromatid cohesion is released in two steps. In metaphase I, homologs are held together by cohesion between sister chromatid arms in regions where DNA has been exchanged. At anaphase I, cohesins are cleaved along the arms, allowing homologs to separate. At anaphase II, cohesins are cleaved at the centromeres, allowing chromatids to separate.

Figure 13.10 shows one of a series of experiments carried out by Yoshinori Watanabe and colleagues at the University of Tokyo. They knew that similar proteins were present in cohesin complexes during mitosis and meiosis, and they wondered what was responsible for preventing cohesin cleavage at the centromere while it was occurring along sister chromatid

---

▼ **Figure 13.10** **Inquiry**

What prevents the separation of sister chromatids at anaphase I of meiosis?

EXPERIMENT Yoshinori Watanabe and colleagues knew that during anaphase I, the protein shugoshin is present only around centromeres. They wondered whether it protects cohesins there from degradation in meiosis I, ensuring that chromatids stay together while homologs separate. To test this hypothesis, they used a species of yeast in which meiosis produces haploid spores lined up in a specific order inside a spore case. To follow the movement of chromosomes, they fluorescently labeled a region near the centromere of both chromatids in one homolog, leaving the other homolog unlabeled. They then disabled the gene coding for shugoshin and compared this yeast strain (shugoshin⁻) with normal yeast cells (shugoshin⁺). The researchers expected that the two labeled chromosomes arising from the labeled chromatids in normal cells would end up in separate spores at one end of the spore case. They further predicted that if shugoshin does protect cohesins from cleavage at the centromere at anaphase I, then the labeled chromosomes in shugoshin⁻ cells would separate randomly in meiosis II, sometimes ending up in the same spore.

Two of three possible arrangements of labeled chromosomes

RESULTS In shugoshin⁺ cells, the two labeled chromosomes ended up in different spores in almost all cases. In shugoshin⁻ cells, they were in the same spore in about half the cases.

CONCLUSION The researchers concluded that shugoshin protects cohesins at the centromere at anaphase I, thus maintaining the attachment between sister chromatids and ensuring that they separate properly during meiosis II.

SOURCE T. S. Kitajima, S. A. Kawashima, and Y. Watanabe, The conserved kinetochore protein shugoshin protects centromeric cohesion during meiosis, *Nature* 427:510–517 (2004).

WHAT IF? Draw a graph showing what you expect happened to the chromatids of the *unlabeled* chromosome in both strains of cells.

arms at the end of metaphase I. They found a protein they named shugoshin (Japanese for "guardian spirit") that protects cohesins from cleavage at the centromere during meiosis I. Shugoshin is similar to a fruit fly protein identified 10 years earlier by Terry Orr-Weaver, this unit's interviewee.

Meiosis I is called the *reductional division* because it halves the number of chromosome sets per cell—a reduction from two sets (the diploid state) to one set (the haploid state). During the second meiotic division, meiosis II (sometimes called the *equational division*), the sister chromatids separate, producing haploid daughter cells. The mechanism for separating sister chromatids is virtually identical in meiosis II and mitosis. The molecular basis of chromosome behavior during meiosis continues to be a focus of intense research interest.

CONCEPT CHECK 13.3

1. How are the chromosomes in a cell at metaphase of mitosis similar to and different from the chromosomes in a cell at metaphase of meiosis II?
2. **WHAT IF?** Given that the synaptonemal complex disappears by the end of prophase, how would the two homologs be associated if crossing over did not occur? What effect might this ultimately have on gamete formation?

For suggested answers, see Appendix A.

CONCEPT 13.4

Genetic variation produced in sexual life cycles contributes to evolution

How do we account for the genetic variation illustrated in Figure 13.1? As you will learn in more detail in later chapters, mutations are the original source of genetic diversity. These changes in an organism's DNA create the different versions of genes known as *alleles*. Once these differences arise, reshuffling of the alleles during sexual reproduction produces the variation that results in each member of a species having its own unique combination of traits.

Origins of Genetic Variation Among Offspring

In species that reproduce sexually, the behavior of chromosomes during meiosis and fertilization is responsible for most of the variation that arises each generation. Let's examine three mechanisms that contribute to the genetic variation arising from sexual reproduction: independent assortment of chromosomes, crossing over, and random fertilization.

Independent Assortment of Chromosomes

One aspect of sexual reproduction that generates genetic variation is the random orientation of homologous pairs of chromosomes at metaphase of meiosis I. At metaphase I, the homologous pairs, each consisting of one maternal and one paternal chromosome, are situated on the metaphase plate. (Note that the terms *maternal* and *paternal* refer, respectively, to the mother and father of the individual whose cells are undergoing meiosis.) Each pair may orient with either its maternal or paternal homolog closer to a given pole—its orientation is as random as the flip of a coin. Thus, there is a 50% chance that a particular daughter cell of meiosis I will get the maternal chromosome of a certain homologous pair and a 50% chance that it will get the paternal chromosome.

Because each homologous pair of chromosomes is positioned independently of the other pairs at metaphase I, the first meiotic division results in each pair sorting its maternal and paternal homologs into daughter cells independently of every other pair. This is called *independent assortment*. Each daughter cell represents one outcome of all possible combinations of maternal and paternal chromosomes. As shown in **Figure 13.11**, the number of combinations possible for daughter cells formed by meiosis of a diploid cell with two homologous pairs of chromosomes is four (two possible arrangements for the first pair times two possible arrangements for the second pair). Note that only two of the four

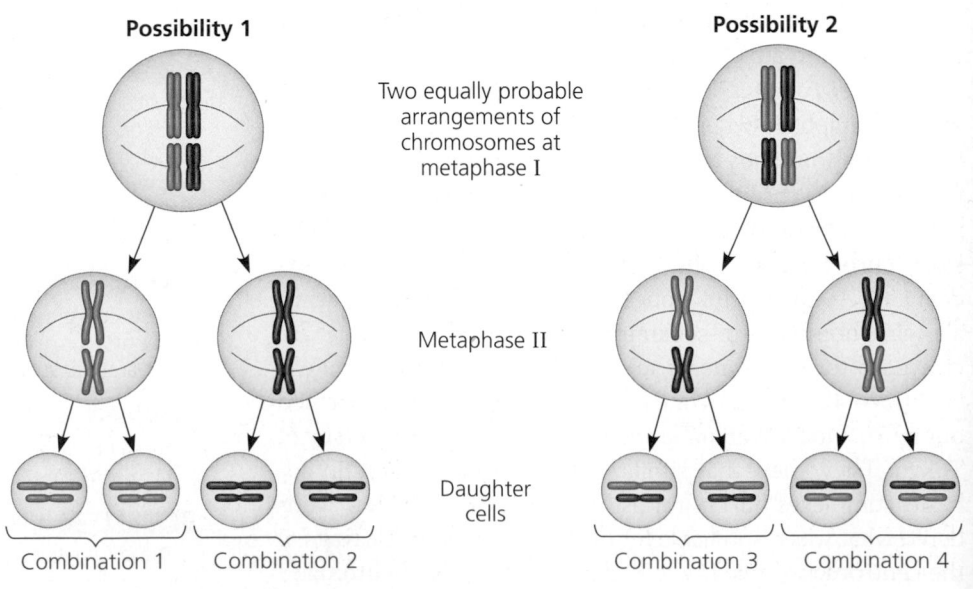

▶ **Figure 13.11 The independent assortment of homologous chromosomes in meiosis.**

Possibility 1

Possibility 2

Two equally probable arrangements of chromosomes at metaphase I

Metaphase II

Daughter cells

Combination 1   Combination 2

Combination 3   Combination 4

combinations of daughter cells shown in the figure would result from meiosis of a *single* diploid cell, because a single parent cell would have one or the other possible chromosomal arrangement at metaphase I, but not both. However, the population of daughter cells resulting from meiosis of a large number of diploid cells contains all four types in approximately equal numbers. In the case of $n = 3$, eight combinations of chromosomes are possible for daughter cells. More generally, the number of possible combinations when chromosomes sort independently during meiosis is 2^n, where n is the haploid number of the organism.

In the case of humans ($n = 23$), the number of possible combinations of maternal and paternal chromosomes in the resulting gametes is 2^{23}, or about 8.4 million. Each gamete that you produce in your lifetime contains one of roughly 8.4 million possible combinations of chromosomes.

Crossing Over

As a consequence of the independent assortment of chromosomes during meiosis, each of us produces a collection of gametes differing greatly in their combinations of the chromosomes we inherited from our two parents. Figure 13.11 suggests that each individual chromosome in a gamete is exclusively maternal or paternal in origin. In fact, this is *not* the case, because crossing over produces **recombinant chromosomes**, individual chromosomes that carry genes (DNA) derived from two different parents (**Figure 13.12**). In meiosis in humans, an average of one to three crossover events occur per chromosome pair, depending on the size of the chromosomes and the position of their centromeres.

Crossing over begins very early in prophase I, as homologous chromosomes pair loosely along their lengths. Each gene on one homolog is aligned precisely with the corresponding gene on the other homolog. In a single crossover event, specific proteins orchestrate an exchange of corresponding segments of two *nonsister* chromatids—one maternal and one paternal chromatid of a homologous pair. In this way, crossing over produces chromosomes with new combinations of maternal and paternal alleles (see Figure 13.12).

In humans and most other organisms studied so far, crossing over also plays an essential role in the lining up of homologous chromosomes during metaphase I. As seen in Figure 13.8, a chiasma forms as the result of a crossover occurring while sister chromatid cohesion is present along the arms. Chiasmata hold homologs together as the spindle forms for the first meiotic division. During anaphase I, the release of cohesion along sister chromatid arms allows homologs to separate. During anaphase II, the release of sister chromatid cohesion at the centromeres allows the sister chromatids to separate. The different possible arrangements of nonidentical sister chromatids dur-

ing meiosis II further increases the number of genetic types of daughter cells that can result from meiosis.

You will learn more about crossing over in Chapter 15. The important point for now is that crossing over, by combining DNA inherited from two parents into a single chromosome, is an important source of genetic variation in sexual life cycles.

Random Fertilization

The random nature of fertilization adds to the genetic variation arising from meiosis. In humans, each male and female gamete represents one of about 8.4 million (2^{23}) possible chromosome combinations due to independent assortment. The fusion of a male gamete with a female gamete during fertilization will produce a zygote with any of about 70 trillion ($2^{23} \times 2^{23}$) diploid combinations. If we factor in the variation brought about by crossing over, the number of possibilities is truly astronomical. It may sound trite, but you really *are* unique.

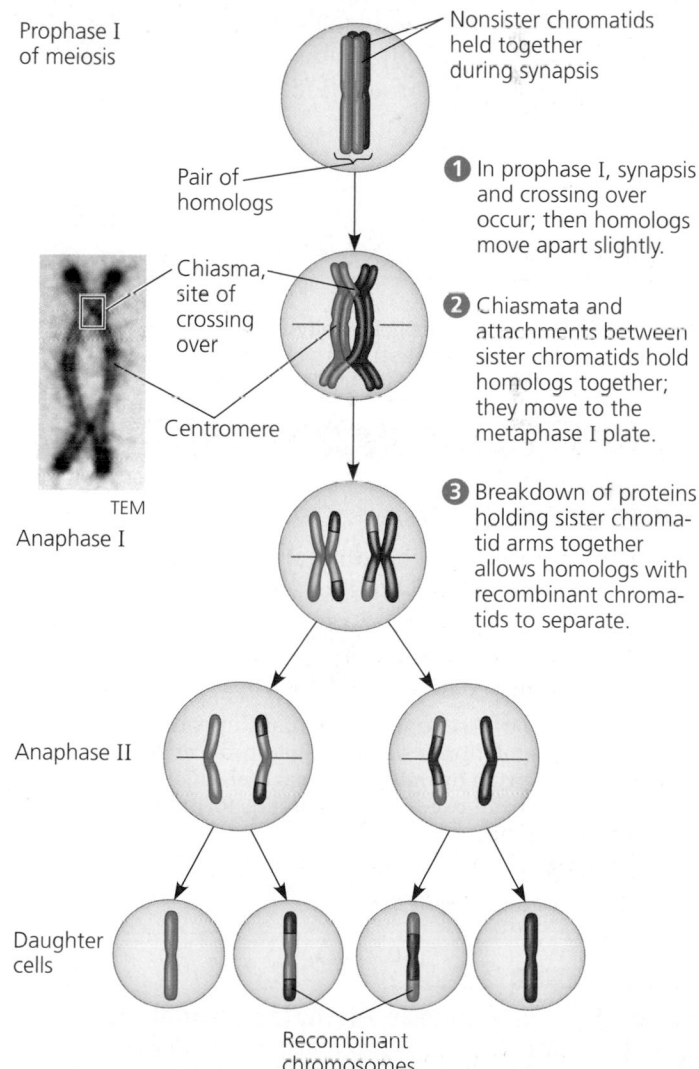

▲ **Figure 13.12 The results of crossing over during meiosis.**

Prophase I of meiosis

Pair of homologs

Chiasma, site of crossing over

Centromere

TEM

Anaphase I

Anaphase II

Daughter cells

Nonsister chromatids held together during synapsis

❶ In prophase I, synapsis and crossing over occur; then homologs move apart slightly.

❷ Chiasmata and attachments between sister chromatids hold homologs together; they move to the metaphase I plate.

❸ Breakdown of proteins holding sister chromatid arms together allows homologs with recombinant chromatids to separate.

Recombinant chromosomes

The Evolutionary Significance of Genetic Variation Within Populations

Now that you've learned how new combinations of genes arise among offspring in a sexually reproducing population, let's see how the genetic variation in a population relates to evolution. Darwin recognized that a population evolves through the differential reproductive success of its variant members. On average, those individuals best suited to the local environment leave the most offspring, thus transmitting their genes. This natural selection results in the accumulation of those genetic variations favored by the environment. As the environment changes, the population may survive if, in each generation, at least some of its members can cope effectively with the new conditions. Different combinations of alleles may work better than those that previously prevailed. Mutations are the original source of different alleles, which are then mixed and matched during meiosis. In this chapter, we have seen how sexual reproduction greatly increases the genetic variation present in a population. In fact, the ability of sexual reproduction to generate genetic variation is one of the most commonly proposed explanations for the persistence of sexual reproduction.

Although Darwin realized that heritable variation is what makes evolution possible, he could not explain why offspring resemble—but are not identical to—their parents. Ironically, Gregor Mendel, a contemporary of Darwin, published a theory of inheritance that helps explain genetic variation, but his discoveries had no impact on biologists until 1900, more than 15 years after Darwin (1809–1882) and Mendel (1822–1884) had died. In the next chapter, you will learn how Mendel discovered the basic rules governing the inheritance of specific traits.

CONCEPT CHECK 13.4

1. What is the original source of all the different alleles of a gene?
2. The diploid number for fruit flies is 8, while that for grasshoppers is 46. If no crossing over took place, would the genetic variation among offspring from a given pair of parents be greater in fruit flies or grasshoppers? Explain.
3. **WHAT IF?** Under what circumstances would crossing over during meiosis *not* contribute to genetic variation among daughter cells?

For suggested answers, see Appendix A.

Chapter 13 Review

MEDIA Go to www.campbellbiology.com for BioFlix 3-D Animations, MP3 Tutors, Videos, Practice Tests, an eBook, and more.

SUMMARY OF KEY CONCEPTS

CONCEPT 13.1

Offspring acquire genes from parents by inheriting chromosomes (pp. 248–249)

▶ **Inheritance of Genes** Each gene in an organism's DNA exists at a specific locus on a certain chromosome. We inherit one set of chromosomes from our mother and one set from our father.

▶ **Comparison of Asexual and Sexual Reproduction** In asexual reproduction, a single parent produces genetically identical offspring by mitosis. Sexual reproduction combines sets of genes from two different parents, forming genetically diverse offspring.

MEDIA

Activity Asexual and Sexual Life Cycles

CONCEPT 13.2

Fertilization and meiosis alternate in sexual life cycles (pp. 250–253)

▶ **Sets of Chromosomes in Human Cells** Normal human somatic cells are diploid. They have 46 chromosomes made up of two sets of 23—one set from each parent. In human diploid cells, there are 22 homologous pairs of autosomes, each with a maternal and a paternal homolog. The 23rd pair, the sex chromosomes, determines whether the person is female (XX) or male (XY).

▶ **Behavior of Chromosome Sets in the Human Life Cycle** At sexual maturity, ovaries and testes (the gonads) produce haploid gametes by meiosis, each gamete containing a single set of 23 chromosomes ($n = 23$). During fertilization, an egg and sperm unite, forming a diploid ($2n = 46$) single-celled zygote, which develops into a multicellular organism by mitosis.

▶ **The Variety of Sexual Life Cycles** Sexual life cycles differ in the timing of meiosis relative to fertilization and in the point(s) of the cycle at which a multicellular organism is produced by mitosis.

CONCEPT 13.3

Meiosis reduces the number of chromosome sets from diploid to haploid (pp. 253–258)

▶ **The Stages of Meiosis** The two cell divisions of meiosis produce four haploid daughter cells. The number of chromosome sets is reduced from two (diploid) to one (haploid) during meiosis I, the reductional division.

▶ **A Comparison of Mitosis and Meiosis** Meiosis is distinguished from mitosis by three events of meiosis I, as shown on the next page:

Prophase I: Each homologous pair undergoes synapsis and crossing over between nonsister chromatids.

Metaphase I: Chromosomes line up as homologous pairs on the metaphase plate.

Anaphase I: Homologs separate from each other; sister chromatids remain joined at the centromere.

Meiosis II separates the sister chromatids.

> **MEDIA**
>
> **BioFlix 3-D Animation** Meiosis
> **MP3 Tutor** Meiosis
> **MP3 Tutor** Mitosis-Meiosis Comparison
> **Activity** Meiosis Animation

CONCEPT 13.4

Genetic variation produced in sexual life cycles contributes to evolution (pp. 258–260)

▶ **Origins of Genetic Variation Among Offspring** Three events in sexual reproduction contribute to genetic variation in a population: independent assortment of chromosomes during meiosis, crossing over during meiosis I, and random fertilization of egg cells by sperm. Due to sister chromatid cohesion, crossing over leads to chiasmata, which hold homologs together until anaphase I.

▶ **The Evolutionary Significance of Genetic Variation Within Populations** Genetic variation is the raw material for evolution by natural selection. Mutations are the original source of this variation; the production of new combinations of variant genes in sexual reproduction generates additional genetic diversity.

> **MEDIA**
>
> **Activity** Origins of Genetic Variation
> **Investigation** How Can the Frequency of Crossing Over Be Estimated?

TESTING YOUR KNOWLEDGE

SELF-QUIZ

1. A human cell containing 22 autosomes and a Y chromosome is
   a. a sperm.
   b. an egg.
   c. a zygote.
   d. a somatic cell of a male.
   e. a somatic cell of a female.

2. Which life cycle stage is found in plants but not animals?
   a. gamete
   b. zygote
   c. multicellular diploid
   d. multicellular haploid
   e. unicellular diploid

3. Homologous chromosomes move toward opposite poles of a dividing cell during
   a. mitosis.
   b. meiosis I.
   c. meiosis II.
   d. fertilization.
   e. binary fission.

4. Meiosis II is similar to mitosis in that
   a. sister chromatids separate during anaphase.
   b. DNA replicates before the division.

c. the daughter cells are diploid.
d. homologous chromosomes synapse.
e. the chromosome number is reduced.

5. If the DNA content of a diploid cell in the G_1 phase of the cell cycle is x, then the DNA content of the same cell at metaphase of meiosis I would be
   a. $0.25x$.   b. $0.5x$.   c. x.   d. $2x$.   e. $4x$.

6. If we continued to follow the cell lineage from question 5, then the DNA content of a single cell at metaphase of meiosis II would be
   a. $0.25x$.   b. $0.5x$.   c. x.   d. $2x$.   e. $4x$.

7. How many different combinations of maternal and paternal chromosomes can be packaged in gametes made by an organism with a diploid number of 8 ($2n = 8$)?
   a. 2   b. 4   c. 8   d. 16   e. 32

Use the diagram of a cell below to answer questions 8–10.

8. How can you tell this cell is undergoing meiosis, not mitosis?

9. Identify the stage of meiosis shown.

10. **DRAW IT** Copy the drawing to a separate sheet of paper and label appropriate structures with these terms, drawing lines or brackets as needed: chromosome (label as replicated or unreplicated), centromere, kinetochore, sister chromatids, nonsister chromatids, homologous pair, homologs, chiasma, sister chromatid cohesion. Describe the makeup of a haploid set and a diploid set.

For Self-Quiz answers, see Appendix A.

> **MEDIA** Visit the Study Area at **www.masteringbio.com** for a Practice Test.

EVOLUTION CONNECTION

11. Many species can reproduce either asexually or sexually. What might be the evolutionary significance of the switch from asexual to sexual reproduction that occurs in some organisms when the environment becomes unfavorable?

SCIENTIFIC INQUIRY

12. The diagram accompanying questions 8–10 represents a meiotic cell in a certain individual. A previous study has shown that the freckles gene is located at the locus marked F, and the hair color gene is located at the locus marked H, both on the long chromosome. The individual from whom this cell was taken has inherited different alleles for each gene ("freckles" and "black hair" from one parent, and "no freckles" and "blond hair" from the other). Predict allele combinations in the gametes resulting from this meiotic event. (It will help if you draw out the rest of meiosis, labeling alleles by name.) List other possible combinations of these alleles in this individual's gametes.

14

Mendel and the Gene Idea

▲ Figure 14.1 **What principles of inheritance did Gregor Mendel discover by breeding garden pea plants?**

OVERVIEW

Drawing from the Deck of Genes

If you happened to see a woman with bright purple hair walking down the street, you would probably conclude that she hadn't inherited her striking hair color from either parent. Consciously or not, you have transformed a lifetime of observations of hair color and other features into a list of possible variations that occur naturally among people. Eyes of brown, blue, green, or gray; hair of black, brown, blond, or red—these are just a few examples of heritable variations that we may observe among individuals in a population. What are the genetic principles that account for the transmission of such traits from parents to offspring in humans and other organisms?

The explanation of heredity most widely in favor during the 1800s was the "blending" hypothesis, the idea that genetic material contributed by the two parents mixes in a manner analogous to the way blue and yellow paints blend to make green. This hypothesis predicts that over many generations, a freely mating population will give rise to a uniform population of individuals. However, our everyday observations and the results of breeding experiments with animals and plants contradict that prediction. The blending hypothesis also fails to explain other phenomena of inheritance, such as traits reappearing after skipping a generation.

An alternative to the blending model is a "particulate" hypothesis of inheritance: the gene idea. According to this model, parents pass on discrete heritable units—genes—that retain their separate identities in offspring. An organism's collection of genes is more like a deck of cards than a pail of paint. Like playing cards, genes can be shuffled and passed along, generation after generation, in undiluted form.

Modern genetics had its genesis in an abbey garden, where a monk named Gregor Mendel documented a particulate mechanism for inheritance. **Figure 14.1** shows Mendel (back row, holding a sprig of fuchsia) with his fellow monks. Mendel developed his theory of inheritance several decades before chromosomes were observed in the microscope and the significance of their behavior was understood. In this chapter, we will step into Mendel's garden to re-create his experiments and explain how he arrived at his theory of inheritance. We will also explore inheritance patterns more complex than those observed by Mendel in garden peas. Finally, we will see how the Mendelian model applies to the inheritance of human variations, including hereditary disorders such as sickle-cell disease.

CONCEPT 14.1
Mendel used the scientific approach to identify two laws of inheritance

Mendel discovered the basic principles of heredity by breeding garden peas in carefully planned experiments. As we retrace his work, you will recognize the key elements of the scientific process that were introduced in Chapter 1.

Mendel's Experimental, Quantitative Approach

Mendel grew up on his parents' small farm in a region of Austria that is now part of the Czech Republic. In this agricultural area, Mendel and the other children received agricultural training in school along with their basic education. As an adolescent, Mendel overcame financial hardship and illness to excel in high school and, later, at the Olmutz Philosophical Institute.

In 1843, at the age of 21, Mendel entered an Augustinian monastery, a reasonable choice at that time for someone who valued the life of the mind. He considered becoming a teacher but failed the necessary examination. In 1851, he left the monastery to pursue two years of study in physics and chemistry at the University of Vienna. These were very important years for Mendel's development as a scientist, in large part due to the strong influence of two professors. One was the physicist Christian Doppler, who encouraged his students to learn science through experimentation and trained Mendel to use mathematics to help explain natural phenomena. The other was a botanist named Franz Unger, who aroused Mendel's interest in the causes of variation in plants. The instruction Mendel received from these two mentors later played a critical role in his experiments with garden peas.

After attending the university, Mendel returned to the monastery and was assigned to teach at a local school, where several other instructors were enthusiastic about scientific research. In addition, his fellow monks shared a long-standing fascination with the breeding of plants. The monastery therefore provided fertile soil in more ways than one for Mendel's scientific endeavors. Around 1857, Mendel began breeding garden peas in the abbey garden to study inheritance. Although the question of heredity had long been a focus of curiosity at the monastery, Mendel's fresh approach allowed him to deduce principles that had remained elusive to others.

One reason Mendel probably chose to work with peas is that they are available in many varieties. For example, one variety has purple flowers, while another variety has white flowers. A heritable feature that varies among individuals, such as flower color, is called a **character**. Each variant for a character, such as purple or white color for flowers, is termed a **trait.**[*]

Other advantages of using peas are their short generation time and the large number of offspring from each mating. Furthermore, Mendel could strictly control mating between plants. The reproductive organs of a pea plant are in its flowers, and each pea flower has both pollen-producing organs (stamens) and an egg-bearing organ (carpel). In nature, pea plants usually self-fertilize: Pollen grains from the stamens land on the carpel of the same flower, and sperm released from the pollen grains fertilize eggs present in the carpel. To achieve cross-pollination (fertilization between different plants), Mendel removed the immature stamens of a plant before they produced pollen and then dusted pollen from another plant onto the altered flowers **(Figure 14.2)**. Each resulting zygote then developed into a plant embryo encased in a seed (pea).

---

[*] Some geneticists use the terms *character* and *trait* synonymously, but in this book we distinguish between them.

Whether forcing self-pollination or executing artificial cross-pollination, Mendel could always be sure of the parentage of new seeds.

Mendel chose to track only those characters that varied between two distinct alternatives. For example, his plants had either purple flowers or white flowers; there was nothing intermediate between these two varieties. Had Mendel focused instead on characters that varied in a continuum among individuals— seed weight, for example—he would not have discovered the particulate nature of inheritance. (You'll learn why later.)

Mendel also made sure that he started his experiments with varieties that, over many generations of self-pollination,

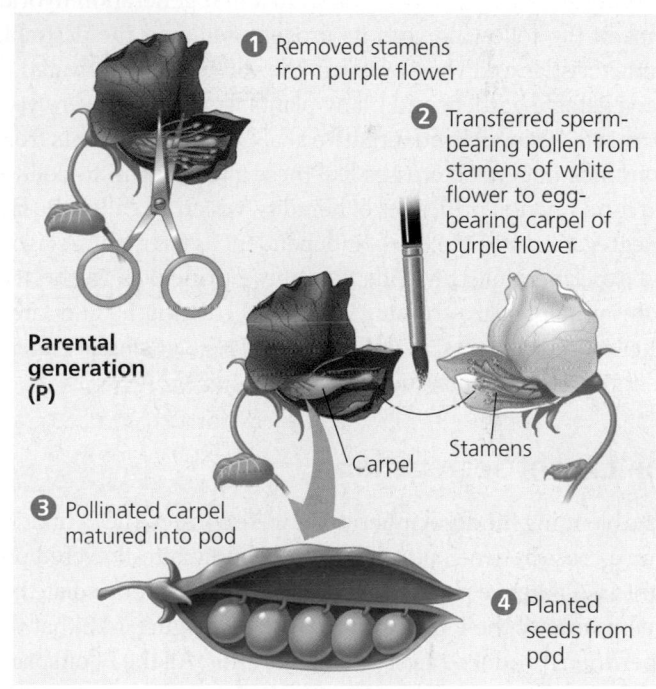

▼ **Figure 14.2** **Research Method**

Crossing Pea Plants

APPLICATION   By crossing (mating) two true-breeding varieties of an organism, scientists can study patterns of inheritance. In this example, Mendel crossed pea plants that varied in flower color.

TECHNIQUE

❶ Removed stamens from purple flower

❷ Transferred sperm-bearing pollen from stamens of white flower to egg-bearing carpel of purple flower

Parental generation (P)

Carpel   Stamens

❸ Pollinated carpel matured into pod

❹ Planted seeds from pod

RESULTS   When pollen from a white flower was transferred to a purple flower, the first-generation hybrids all had purple flowers. The result was the same for the reciprocal cross, which involved the transfer of pollen from purple flowers to white flowers.

First filial generation offspring (F_1)

❺ Examined offspring: all purple flowers

had produced only the same variety as the parent plant. Such plants are said to be **true-breeding**. For example, a plant with purple flowers is true-breeding if the seeds produced by self-pollination in successive generations all give rise to plants that also have purple flowers.

In a typical breeding experiment, Mendel cross-pollinated two contrasting, true-breeding pea varieties—for example, purple-flowered plants and white-flowered plants (see Figure 14.2). This mating, or *crossing*, of two true-breeding varieties is called **hybridization**. The true-breeding parents are referred to as the **P generation** (parental generation), and their hybrid offspring are the **F₁ generation** (first filial generation, the word *filial* from the Latin word for "son"). Allowing these F_1 hybrids to self-pollinate produces an **F_2 generation** (second filial generation). Mendel usually followed traits for at least the P, F_1, and F_2 generations. Had Mendel stopped his experiments with the F_1 generation, the basic patterns of inheritance would have escaped him.

Mendel was a thorough and enthusiastic researcher. In a letter dated 1867, he wrote, "In 1859 I obtained a very fertile descendant with large, tasty seeds from a first generation hybrid. Since in the following year, its progeny retained the desirable characteristics and were uniform, the variety was cultivated in our vegetable garden, and many plants were raised every year up to 1865." Mendel's quantitative analysis of the F_2 plants from thousands of genetic crosses like these allowed him to deduce two fundamental principles of heredity, which he called the law of segregation and the law of independent assortment. A rigorous experimentalist, Mendel put these principles to the test again and again by crossing and self-fertilizing F_2 and later-generation pea plants, as well as by carrying out similar experiments on other plants, such as beans.

The Law of Segregation

If the blending model of inheritance were correct, the F_1 hybrids from a cross between purple-flowered and white-flowered pea plants would have pale purple flowers, a trait intermediate between those of the P generation. Notice in Figure 14.2 that the experiment produced a very different result: All the F_1 offspring had flowers just as purple as the purple-flowered parents. What happened to the white-flowered plants' genetic contribution to the hybrids? If it were lost, then the F_1 plants could produce only purple-flowered offspring in the F_2 generation. But when Mendel allowed the F_1 plants to self-pollinate and planted their seeds, the white-flower trait reappeared in the F_2 generation.

Mendel used very large sample sizes and kept accurate records of his results: 705 of the F_2 plants had purple flowers, and 224 had white flowers. These data fit a ratio of approximately three purple to one white **(Figure 14.3)**. Mendel reasoned that the heritable factor for white flowers did not disappear in the F_1 plants, but was somehow hidden or masked when the purple-flower factor was present. In Mendel's termi-

nology, purple flower color is a *dominant* trait and white flower color is a *recessive* trait. The reappearance of white-flowered plants in the F_2 generation was evidence that the heritable factor causing white flowers had not been diluted or destroyed by coexisting with the purple-flower factor in the F_1 hybrids.

Mendel observed the same pattern of inheritance in six other characters, each represented by two distinctly different

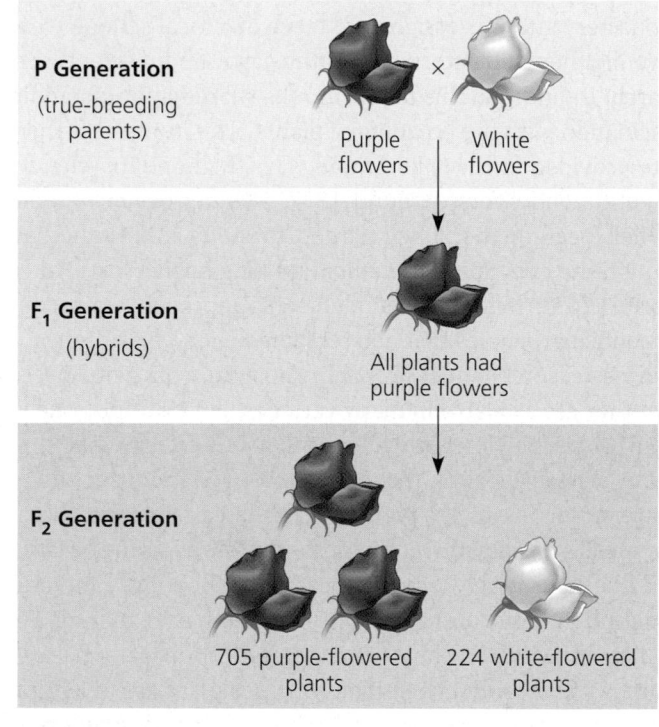

▼ Figure 14.3 **Inquiry**

When F₁ hybrid pea plants are allowed to self-pollinate, which traits appear in the F₂ generation?

EXPERIMENT   Around 1860, in a monastery garden in Brünn, Austria, Gregor Mendel used the character of flower color in pea plants to follow traits through two generations. He crossed true-breeding purple-flowered plants and white-flowered plants (crosses are symbolized by ×). The resulting F₁ hybrids were allowed to self-pollinate or were cross-pollinated with other F₁ hybrids. The F₂ generation plants were then observed for flower color.

P Generation
(true-breeding parents)

Purple flowers × White flowers

F₁ Generation
(hybrids)

All plants had purple flowers

F₂ Generation

705 purple-flowered plants   224 white-flowered plants

RESULTS   Both purple-flowered and white-flowered plants appeared in the F₂ generation, in a ratio of approximately 3:1.

CONCLUSION   The "heritable factor" for the recessive trait (white flowers) had not been destroyed or deleted in the F₁ generation, but merely masked by the presence of the factor for purple flowers, which is the dominant trait.

SOURCE   G. Mendel, Experiments in plant hybridization, *Proceedings of the Natural History Society of Brünn* 4:3–47 (1866).

WHAT IF?   If you mated two purple-flowered plants from the P generation, what ratio of traits would you expect to observe in the offspring? Explain.

traits **(Table 14.1)**. For example, when Mendel crossed a true-breeding variety that produced smooth, round pea seeds with one that produced wrinkled seeds, all the F_1 hybrids produced round seeds; this is the dominant trait for seed shape. In the F_2 generation, 75% of the seeds were round and 25% were wrinkled—a 3:1 ratio, as in Figure 14.3. Now let's see how Mendel deduced the law of segregation from his experimental results. In the discussion that follows, we will use modern terms instead of some of the terms used by Mendel. (For example, we'll use "gene" instead of Mendel's "heritable factor.")

Mendel's Model

Mendel developed a model to explain the 3:1 inheritance pattern that he consistently observed among the F_2 offspring in his pea experiments. We describe four related concepts making up this model, the fourth of which is the law of segregation.

First, *alternative versions of genes account for variations in inherited characters.* The gene for flower color in pea plants, for example, exists in two versions, one for purple flowers and the other for white flowers. These alternative versions of a gene are called **alleles** **(Figure 14.4)**. Today, we can relate this concept to chromosomes and DNA. As noted in Chapter 13, each gene is a sequence of nucleotides at a specific place, or locus, along a particular chromosome. The DNA at that locus, however, can vary slightly in its nucleotide sequence and hence in its information content. The purple-flower allele and the white-flower allele are two DNA variations possible at the flower-color locus on one of a pea plant's chromosomes.

Second, *for each character, an organism inherits two alleles, one from each parent.* Remarkably, Mendel made this deduction without knowing about the role of chromosomes. Recall from Chapter 13 that each somatic cell in a diploid organism has two sets of chromosomes, one set inherited from each parent. Thus, a genetic locus is actually represented twice in a diploid cell, once on each homolog of a specific pair of chromosomes. The two alleles at a particular locus may be identical, as in the true-breeding plants of Mendel's P generation. Or the alleles may differ, as in the F_1 hybrids (see Figure 14.4).

Table 14.1 The Results of Mendel's F_1 Crosses for Seven Characters in Pea Plants

Character	Dominant Trait	x	Recessive Trait	F_2 Generation Dominant:Recessive	Ratio
Flower color	Purple	×	White	705:224	3.15:1
Flower position	Axial	×	Terminal	651:207	3.14:1
Seed color	Yellow	×	Green	6,022:2,001	3.01:1
Seed shape	Round	×	Wrinkled	5,474:1,850	2.96:1
Pod shape	Inflated	×	Constricted	882:299	2.95:1
Pod color	Green	×	Yellow	428:152	2.82:1
Stem length	Tall	×	Dwarf	787:277	2.84:1

▲ **Figure 14.4 Alleles, alternative versions of a gene.** A somatic cell has two copies of each chromosome (forming a homologous pair) and thus two alleles of each gene, which may be identical or different. This figure depicts a homologous pair of chromosomes in an F_1 hybrid pea plant. The chromosome with an allele for purple flowers was inherited from one parent, and that with an allele for white flowers from the other parent.

Third, *if the two alleles at a locus differ, then one, the* **dominant allele**, *determines the organism's appearance; the other, the* **recessive allele**, *has no noticeable effect on the organism's appearance.* Accordingly, Mendel's F₁ plants had purple flowers because the allele for that trait is dominant and the allele for white flowers is recessive.

The fourth and final part of Mendel's model, the **law of segregation**, states that *the two alleles for a heritable character segregate (separate) during gamete formation and end up in different gametes.* Thus, an egg or a sperm gets only one of the two alleles that are present in the somatic cells of the organism making the gamete. In terms of chromosomes, this segregation corresponds to the distribution of the two members of a homologous pair of chromosomes to different gametes in meiosis (see Figure 13.7). Note that if an organism has identical alleles for a particular character—that is, the organism is true-breeding for that character—then that allele is present in all gametes. But if different alleles are present, as in the F₁ hybrids, then 50% of the gametes receive the dominant allele and 50% receive the recessive allele.

Does Mendel's segregation model account for the 3:1 ratio he observed in the F₂ generation of his numerous crosses? For the flower-color character, the model predicts that the two different alleles present in an F₁ individual will segregate into gametes such that half the gametes will have the purple-flower allele and half will have the white-flower allele. During self-pollination, gametes of each class unite randomly. An egg with a purple-flower allele has an equal chance of being fertilized by a sperm with a purple-flower allele or one with a white-flower allele. Since the same is true for an egg with a white-flower allele, there are four equally likely combinations of sperm and egg. **Figure 14.5** illustrates these combinations using a **Punnett square**, a handy diagrammatic device for predicting the allele composition of offspring from a cross between individuals of known genetic makeup. Notice that we use a capital letter to symbolize a dominant allele and a lowercase letter for a recessive allele. In our example, *P* is the purple-flower allele, and *p* is the white-flower allele; the gene itself may be referred to as the *P/p* gene.

In the F₂ offspring, what color will the flowers be? One-fourth of the plants have inherited two purple-flower alleles; clearly, these plants will have purple flowers. One-half of the F₂ offspring have inherited one purple-flower allele and one white-flower allele; these plants will also have purple flowers, the dominant trait. Finally, one-fourth of the F₂ plants have inherited two white-flower alleles and will express the recessive trait. Thus, Mendel's model accounts for the 3:1 ratio of traits that he observed in the F₂ generation.

Useful Genetic Vocabulary

An organism that has a pair of identical alleles for a character is said to be **homozygous** for the gene controlling that character. In the parental generation in Figure 14.5, the purple pea plant is homozygous for the dominant allele (*PP*), while the white plant is homozygous for the recessive allele (*pp*). Homozygous plants "breed true" because all of their gametes contain the same allele—either *P* or *p* in this example. If we

Each true-breeding plant of the parental generation has identical alleles, *PP* or *pp*.

Gametes (circles) each contain only one allele for the flower-color gene. In this case, every gamete produced by one parent has the same allele.

Union of parental gametes produces F₁ hybrids having a *Pp* combination. Because the purple-flower allele is dominant, all these hybrids have purple flowers.

When the hybrid plants produce gametes, the two alleles segregate. Half of the gametes receive the *P* allele and the other half the *p* allele.

This box, a Punnett square, shows all possible combinations of alleles in offspring that result from an F₁ × F₁ (*Pp* × *Pp*) cross. Each square represents an equally probable product of fertilization. For example, the bottom left box shows the genetic combination resulting from a *p* egg fertilized by a *P* sperm.

Random combination of the gametes results in the 3:1 ratio that Mendel observed in the F₂ generation.

P Generation

Appearance: Purple flowers   White flowers
Genetic makeup: *PP*   *pp*
Gametes: *P*   *p*

F₁ Generation

Appearance: Purple flowers
Genetic makeup: *Pp*
Gametes: ½ *P*   ½ *p*

F₂ Generation

Sperm from F₁ (*Pp*) plant
P   *p*

Eggs from F₁ (*Pp*) plant
P | *PP* | *Pp*
p | *Pp* | *pp*

3 : 1

▲ **Figure 14.5 Mendel's law of segregation.** This diagram shows the genetic makeup of the generations in Figure 14.3. It illustrates Mendel's model for inheritance of the alleles of a single gene. Each plant has two alleles for the gene controlling flower color, one allele inherited from each parent. To construct a Punnett square that predicts the F₂ generation offspring, we list all the possible gametes from one parent (here, the F₁ female) along the left side of the square and all the possible gametes from the other parent (here, the F₁ male) along the top. The boxes represent the offspring resulting from all the possible unions of male and female gametes.

Phenotype		Genotype	
Purple		PP (homozygous)	1
Purple		Pp (heterozygous)	2
Purple		Pp (heterozygous)	
White		pp (homozygous)	1

Ratio 3:1   Ratio 1:2:1

▲ **Figure 14.6 Phenotype versus genotype.** Grouping F_2 offspring from a cross for flower color according to phenotype results in the typical 3:1 phenotypic ratio. In terms of genotype, however, there are actually two categories of purple-flowered plants, PP (homozygous) and Pp (heterozygous), giving a 1:2:1 genotypic ratio.

cross dominant homozygotes with recessive homozygotes, every offspring will have two different alleles—Pp in the case of the F_1 hybrids of our flower-color experiment (see Figure 14.5). An organism that has two different alleles for a gene is said to be **heterozygous** for that gene. Unlike homozygotes, heterozygotes are not true-breeding because they produce gametes with different alleles; for example, P- and p-containing gametes are both produced by the F_1 hybrids of Figure 14.5. As a result, self-pollination of those F_1 hybrids produces both purple-flowered and white-flowered offspring.

Because of the different effects of dominant and recessive alleles, an organism's traits do not always reveal its genetic composition. Therefore, we distinguish between an organism's appearance or observable traits, called its **phenotype**, and its genetic makeup, its **genotype**. In the case of flower color in pea plants, PP and Pp plants have the same phenotype (purple) but different genotypes. **Figure 14.6** reviews these terms. Note that "phenotype" refers to physiological traits as well as traits that relate directly to appearance. For example, there is a pea variety that lacks the normal ability to self-pollinate. This physiological variation (non-self-pollination) is a phenotypic trait.

The Testcross

Suppose we have a "mystery" pea plant that has purple flowers. We cannot tell from its flower color if this plant is homozygous (PP) or heterozygous (Pp) because both genotypes result in the same purple phenotype. To determine the genotype, we can cross this plant with a white-flowered plant (pp), which will

▼ **Figure 14.7** **Research Method**

The Testcross

APPLICATION An organism that exhibits a dominant trait, such as purple flowers in pea plants, can be either homozygous for the dominant allele or heterozygous. To determine the organism's genotype, geneticists can perform a testcross.

TECHNIQUE In a testcross, the individual with the unknown genotype is crossed with a homozygous individual expressing the recessive trait (white flowers in this example), and Punnett squares are used to predict the possible outcomes.

RESULTS Matching the results to either prediction identifies the unknown parental genotype (either PP or Pp in this example). In this testcross, we transferred pollen from a white-flowered plant to the carpels of a purple-flowered plant; the opposite (reciprocal) cross would have led to the same results.

make only gametes with the recessive allele (p). The allele in the gamete contributed by the mystery plant will therefore determine the appearance of the offspring **(Figure 14.7)**. If all the offspring of the cross have purple flowers, then the purple-flowered mystery plant must be homozygous for the dominant allele, because a $PP \times pp$ cross produces all Pp offspring. But if both the purple and the white phenotypes appear among the offspring, then the purple-flowered parent must be heterozygous. The offspring of a $Pp \times pp$ cross will have a 1:1 phenotypic ratio. Breeding an organism of unknown genotype with a recessive homozygote is called a **testcross** because it can reveal the genotype of that organism. The testcross was devised by Mendel and continues to be an important tool of geneticists.

The Law of Independent Assortment

Mendel derived the law of segregation from experiments in which he followed only a *single* character, such as flower color. All the F₁ progeny produced in his crosses of true-breeding parents were **monohybrids**, meaning that they were heterozygous for one character. We refer to a cross between such heterozygotes as a *monohybrid cross.*

Mendel identified his second law of inheritance by following *two* characters at the same time, such as seed color and seed shape. Seeds (peas) may be either yellow or green. They also may be either round (smooth) or wrinkled. From single-character crosses, Mendel knew that the allele for yellow seeds is dominant (*Y*) and the allele for green seeds is recessive (*y*). For the seed-shape character, the allele for round is dominant (*R*), and the allele for wrinkled is recessive (*r*).

Imagine crossing two true-breeding pea varieties that differ in *both* of these characters—a cross between a plant with yellow-round seeds (*YYRR*) and a plant with green-wrinkled seeds (*yyrr*). The F₁ plants will be **dihybrids**, individuals heterozygous for two characters (*YyRr*). But are these two characters transmitted from parents to offspring as a package? That is, will the *Y* and *R* alleles always stay together, generation after generation? Or are seed color and seed shape inherited independently? **Figure 14.8** illustrates how a *dihybrid cross,* a cross between F₁ dihybrids, can determine which of these two hypotheses is correct.

The F₁ plants, of genotype *YyRr*, exhibit both dominant phenotypes, yellow seeds with round shapes, no matter which hypothesis is correct. The key step in the experiment is to see what happens when F₁ plants self-pollinate and produce F₂ offspring. If the hybrids must transmit their alleles in the same combinations in which the alleles were inherited from the P generation, then the F₁ hybrids will produce only two classes of gametes: *YR* and *yr*. This "dependent assortment" hypothesis predicts that the phenotypic ratio of the F₂ generation will be 3:1, just as in a monohybrid cross (Figure 14.8, left side).

The alternative hypothesis is that the two pairs of alleles segregate independently of each other. In other words, genes are packaged into gametes in all possible allelic combinations, as long as each gamete has one allele for each gene. In our example, an F₁ plant will produce four classes of gametes in equal quantities: *YR*,

▼ **Figure 14.8** **Inquiry**

Do the alleles for one character assort into gametes dependently or independently of the alleles for a different character?

EXPERIMENT   Gregor Mendel followed the characters of seed color and seed shape through the F₂ generation. He crossed a true-breeding plant with yellow-round seeds with a true-breeding plant with green-wrinkled seeds, producing dihybrid F₁ plants. Self-pollination of the F₁ dihybrids produced the F₂ generation. The two hypotheses (dependent and independent assortment) predict different phenotypic ratios.

P Generation   *YYRR*   *yyrr*

Gametes *YR* × *yr*

F₁ Generation   *YyRr*

Predictions   Hypothesis of dependent assortment   Hypothesis of independent assortment

Predicted offspring of F₂ generation   or

Sperm   ½ *YR*   ½ *yr*

Eggs   ½ *YR*   ½ *yr*

	YR	*yr*
YR	*YYRR*	*YyRr*
yr	*YyRr*	*yyrr*

¾   ¼

Phenotypic ratio 3:1

Sperm   ¼ *YR*   ¼ *Yr*   ¼ *yR*   ¼ *yr*

Eggs   ¼ *YR*   ¼ *Yr*   ¼ *yR*   ¼ *yr*

	YR	*Yr*	*yR*	*yr*
YR	*YYRR*	*YYRr*	*YyRR*	*YyRr*
Yr	*YYRr*	*YYrr*	*YyRr*	*Yyrr*
yR	*YyRR*	*YyRr*	*yyRR*	*yyRr*
yr	*YyRr*	*Yyrr*	*yyRr*	*yyrr*

⁹/₁₆   ³/₁₆   ³/₁₆   ¹/₁₆

Phenotypic ratio 9:3:3:1

RESULTS

315   108   101   32   Phenotypic ratio approximately 9:3:3:1

CONCLUSION   Only the hypothesis of independent assortment predicts the appearance of two of the observed phenotypes: green-round seeds and yellow-wrinkled seeds (see the right-hand Punnett square). The alleles for seed color and seed shape sort into gametes independently of each other.

SOURCE   G. Mendel, Experiments in plant hybridization, *Proceedings of the Natural History Society of Brünn* 4:3–47 (1866).

WHAT IF?   Suppose Mendel had transferred pollen from an F₁ plant to the carpel of a plant that was homozygous recessive for both genes. Set up the cross and draw Punnett squares that predict the offspring for both hypotheses. Would this cross have supported the hypothesis of independent assortment equally well?

Yr, yR, and *yr.* If sperm of the four classes fertilize eggs of the four classes, there will be 16 (4 × 4) equally probable ways in which the alleles can combine in the F₂ generation, as shown in Figure 14.8, right side. These combinations make up four phenotypic categories with a ratio of 9:3:3:1 (nine yellow-round to three green-round to three yellow-wrinkled to one green-wrinkled). When Mendel did the experiment and classified the F₂ offspring, his results were close to the predicted 9:3:3:1 phenotypic ratio, supporting the hypothesis that the alleles for one gene—controlling seed color or seed shape, in this example—are sorted into gametes independently of the alleles of other genes.

Mendel tested his seven pea characters in various dihybrid combinations and always observed a 9:3:3:1 phenotypic ratio in the F₂ generation. However, notice in Figure 14.8 that there is a 3:1 phenotypic ratio for each of the two characters if you consider them separately: three yellow to one green, and three round to one wrinkled. As far as a single character is concerned, the alleles segregate as if this were a monohybrid cross. The results of Mendel's dihybrid experiments are the basis for what we now call the **law of independent assortment**, which states that *each pair of alleles segregates independently of each other pair of alleles during gamete formation.*

Strictly speaking, this law applies only to genes (allele pairs) located on different chromosomes—that is, on chromosomes that are not homologous. Genes located near each other on the same chromosome tend to be inherited together and have more complex inheritance patterns than predicted by the law of independent assortment (see Chapter 15). All the pea characters Mendel chose for analysis were controlled by genes on different chromosomes (or behaved as though they were); this situation greatly simplified interpretation of his multicharacter pea crosses. All the examples we consider in the rest of this chapter involve genes located on different chromosomes.

CONCEPT CHECK 14.1

1. **DRAW IT** A pea plant heterozygous for inflated pods (*Ii*) is crossed with a plant homozygous for constricted pods (*ii*). Draw a Punnett square for this cross. Assume pollen comes from the *ii* plant.
2. **DRAW IT** Pea plants heterozygous for flower position and stem length (*AaTt*) are allowed to self-pollinate, and 400 of the resulting seeds are planted. Draw a Punnett square for this cross. How many offspring would be predicted to have terminal flowers and be dwarf? (See Table 14.1.)
3. **WHAT IF?** List the different gametes that could be made by a pea plant heterozygous for seed color, seed shape, and pod shape (*YyRrIi*; see Table 14.1). How large a Punnett square would you need to predict the offspring of a self-pollination of this "trihybrid"?

For suggested answers, see Appendix A.

The laws of probability govern Mendelian inheritance

Mendel's laws of segregation and independent assortment reflect the same rules of probability that apply to tossing coins, rolling dice, and drawing cards from a deck. The probability scale ranges from 0 to 1. An event that is certain to occur has a probability of 1, while an event that is certain *not* to occur has a probability of 0. With a coin that has heads on both sides, the probability of tossing heads is 1, and the probability of tossing tails is 0. With a normal coin, the chance of tossing heads is ½, and the chance of tossing tails is ½. The probability of drawing the ace of spades from a 52-card deck is 1/52. The probabilities of all possible outcomes for an event must add up to 1. With a deck of cards, the chance of picking a card other than the ace of spades is 51/52.

Tossing a coin illustrates an important lesson about probability. For every toss, the probability of heads is ½. The outcome of any particular toss is unaffected by what has happened on previous trials. We refer to phenomena such as coin tosses as independent events. Each toss of a coin, whether done sequentially with one coin or simultaneously with many, is independent of every other toss. And like two separate coin tosses, the alleles of one gene segregate into gametes independently of another gene's alleles (the law of independent assortment). Two basic rules of probability can help us predict the outcome of the fusion of such gametes in simple monohybrid crosses and more complicated crosses.

The Multiplication and Addition Rules Applied to Monohybrid Crosses

How do we determine the probability that two or more independent events will occur together in some specific combination? For example, what is the chance that two coins tossed simultaneously will both land heads up? The *multiplication rule* states that to determine this probability, we multiply the probability of one event (one coin coming up heads) by the probability of the other event (the other coin coming up heads). By the multiplication rule, then, the probability that both coins will land heads up is ½ × ½ = ¼.

We can apply the same reasoning to an F₁ monohybrid cross. With seed shape in pea plants as the heritable character, the genotype of F₁ plants is *Rr.* Segregation in a heterozygous plant is like flipping a coin: Each egg produced has a ½ chance of carrying the dominant allele (*R*) and a ½ chance of carrying the recessive allele (*r*). The same odds apply to each sperm cell produced. For a particular F₂ plant to have wrinkled seeds, the recessive trait, both the egg and the sperm that come together must carry the *r* allele. The probability that two *r* alleles will be present in gametes at fertilization is found by multiplying ½ (the

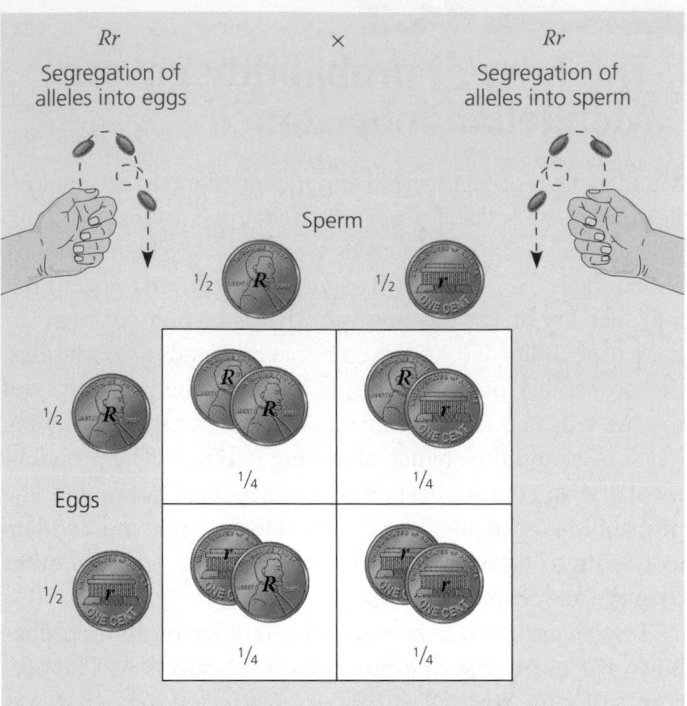

▲ **Figure 14.9 Segregation of alleles and fertilization as chance events.** When a heterozygote (*Rr*) forms gametes, whether a particular gamete ends up with an *R* or an *r* is like the toss of a coin. We can determine the probability for any genotype among the offspring of two heterozygotes by multiplying together the individual probabilities of an egg and sperm having a particular allele (*R* or *r* in this example).

probability that the egg will have an *r*) × ½ (the probability that the sperm will have an *r*). Thus, the multiplication rule tells us that the probability of an F_2 plant with wrinkled seeds (*rr*) is ¼ (**Figure 14.9**). Likewise, the probability of an F_2 plant carrying both dominant alleles for seed shape (*RR*) is ¼.

To figure out the probability that an F_2 plant from a monohybrid cross will be heterozygous rather than homozygous, we need to invoke a second rule. Notice in Figure 14.9 that the dominant allele can come from the egg and the recessive allele from the sperm, or vice versa. That is, F_1 gametes can combine to produce *Rr* offspring in two independent and mutually exclusive ways: For any particular heterozygous F_2 plant, the dominant allele can come from the egg *or* the sperm, but not from both. According to the *addition rule*, the probability that any one of two or more mutually exclusive events will occur is calculated by adding their individual probabilities. As we have just seen, the multiplication rule gives us the individual probabilities that we will now add together. The probability for one possible way of obtaining an F_2 heterozygote—the dominant allele from the egg and the recessive allele from the sperm—is ¼. The probability for the other possible way—the recessive allele from the egg and the dominant allele from the sperm—is also ¼ (see Figure 14.9). Using the rule of addition, then, we can calculate the probability of an F_2 heterozygote as ¼ + ¼ = ½.

Solving Complex Genetics Problems with the Rules of Probability

We can also apply the rules of probability to predict the outcome of crosses involving multiple characters. Recall that each allelic pair segregates independently during gamete formation (the law of independent assortment). Thus, a dihybrid or other multicharacter cross is equivalent to two or more independent monohybrid crosses occurring simultaneously. By applying what we have learned about monohybrid crosses, we can determine the probability of specific genotypes occurring in the F_2 generation without having to construct unwieldy Punnett squares.

Consider the dihybrid cross between *YyRr* heterozygotes shown in Figure 14.8. We will focus first on the seed-color character. For a monohybrid cross of *Yy* plants, the probabilities of the offspring genotypes are ¼ for *YY*, ½ for *Yy*, and ¼ for *yy*. The same probabilities apply to the offspring genotypes for seed shape: ¼ *RR*, ½ *Rr*, and ¼ *rr*. Knowing these probabilities, we can simply use the multiplication rule to determine the probability of each of the genotypes in the F_2 generation. For example, the probability of an F_2 plant having the *YYRR* genotype is ¼ (*YY*) × ¼ (*RR*) = ¹⁄₁₆. This corresponds to the upper left box in the larger Punnett square in Figure 14.8. To give another example, the probability of an F_2 plant with the *YyRR* genotype is ½ (*Yy*) × ¼ (*RR*) = ⅛. If you look closely at the larger Punnett square in Figure 14.8, you will see that 2 of the 16 boxes (⅛) correspond to the *YyRR* genotype.

Now let's see how we can combine the multiplication and addition rules to solve even more complex problems in Mendelian genetics. For instance, imagine a cross of two pea varieties in which we track the inheritance of three characters. Suppose we cross a trihybrid with purple flowers and yellow, round seeds (heterozygous for all three genes) with a plant with purple flowers and green, wrinkled seeds (heterozygous for flower color but homozygous recessive for the other two characters). Using Mendelian symbols, our cross is *PpYyRr* × *Ppyyrr*. What fraction of offspring from this cross would be predicted to exhibit the recessive phenotypes for *at least two* of the three characters?

To answer this question, we can start by listing all genotypes that fulfill this condition: *ppyyRr*, *ppYyrr*, *Ppyyrr*, *PPyyrr*, and *ppyyrr*. (Because the condition is *at least two* recessive traits, it includes the last genotype, which produces all three recessive traits.) Next, we calculate the probability for each of these genotypes resulting from our *PpYyRr* × *Ppyyrr* cross by multiplying together the individual probabilities for the allele pairs, just as we did in our dihybrid example. Note that in a cross involving heterozygous and homozygous allele pairs (for example, *Yy* × *yy*), the probability of heterozygous offspring is ½ and the probability of homozygous offspring is ½. Finally, we use the addition rule to add the probabilities for all the different genotypes that fulfill the condition of at least two recessive traits, as shown below.

$ppyyRr$	$\frac{1}{4}$ (probability of pp) $\times \frac{1}{2}$ (yy) $\times \frac{1}{2}$ (Rr)	$= \frac{1}{16}$
$ppYyrr$	$\frac{1}{4} \times \frac{1}{2} \times \frac{1}{2}$	$= \frac{1}{16}$
$Ppyyrr$	$\frac{1}{2} \times \frac{1}{2} \times \frac{1}{2}$	$= \frac{2}{16}$
$PPyyrr$	$\frac{1}{4} \times \frac{1}{2} \times \frac{1}{2}$	$= \frac{1}{16}$
$ppyyrr$	$\frac{1}{4} \times \frac{1}{2} \times \frac{1}{2}$	$= \frac{1}{16}$
Chance of *at least two* recessive traits		$= \frac{6}{16}$ or $\frac{3}{8}$

With practice, you'll be able to solve genetics problems faster by using the rules of probability than by filling in Punnett squares.

We cannot predict with certainty the exact numbers of progeny of different genotypes resulting from a genetic cross. But the rules of probability give us the *chance* of various outcomes. Usually, the larger the sample size, the closer the results will conform to our predictions. The reason Mendel counted so many offspring from his crosses is that he understood this statistical feature of inheritance and had a keen sense of the rules of chance.

CONCEPT CHECK 14.2

1. For any gene with a dominant allele C and recessive allele c, what proportions of the offspring from a $CC \times Cc$ cross are expected to be homozygous dominant, homozygous recessive, and heterozygous?
2. An organism with the genotype $BbDD$ is mated to one with the genotype $BBDd$. Assuming independent assortment of these two genes, write the genotypes of all possible offspring from this cross and use the rules of probability to calculate the chance of each genotype occurring.
3. **WHAT IF?** Three characters (flower color, seed color, and pod shape) are considered in a cross between two pea plants ($PpYyIi \times ppYyii$). What fraction of offspring would be predicted to be homozygous recessive for at least two of the three characters?

For suggested answers, see Appendix A.

CONCEPT 14.3
Inheritance patterns are often more complex than predicted by simple Mendelian genetics

In the 20th century, geneticists extended Mendelian principles not only to diverse organisms, but also to patterns of inheritance more complex than those described by Mendel. For the work that led to his two laws of inheritance, Mendel chose pea plant characters that turn out to have a relatively simple genetic basis: Each character is determined by one gene, for which there are only two alleles, one completely dominant and the other completely recessive.* But these conditions are not met by all heritable characters, and the relationship between genotype and phenotype is rarely so simple. Mendel himself realized that he could not explain the more complicated patterns he observed in crosses involving other pea characters or other plant species. This does not diminish the utility of Mendelian genetics (also called Mendelism), however, because the basic principles of segregation and independent assortment apply even to more complex patterns of inheritance. In this section, we will extend Mendelian genetics to hereditary patterns that were not reported by Mendel.

Extending Mendelian Genetics for a Single Gene

The inheritance of characters determined by a single gene deviates from simple Mendelian patterns when alleles are not completely dominant or recessive, when a particular gene has more than two alleles, or when a single gene produces multiple phenotypes. We will describe examples of each of these situations in this section.

Degrees of Dominance

Alleles can show different degrees of dominance and recessiveness in relation to each other. In Mendel's classic pea crosses, the F_1 offspring always looked like one of the two parental varieties because one allele in a pair showed **complete dominance** over the other. In such situations, the phenotypes of the heterozygote and the dominant homozygote are indistinguishable.

For some genes, however, neither allele is completely dominant, and the F_1 hybrids have a phenotype somewhere between those of the two parental varieties. This phenomenon, called **incomplete dominance**, is seen when red snapdragons are crossed with white snapdragons: All the F_1 hybrids have pink flowers, as shown in **Figure 14.10** on the next page. This third phenotype results from flowers of the heterozygotes having less red pigment than the red homozygotes (unlike the situation in Mendel's pea plants, where the Pp heterozygotes make enough pigment for the flowers to be a purple color indistinguishable from that of PP plants).

At first glance, incomplete dominance of either allele seems to provide evidence for the blending hypothesis of inheritance, which would predict that the red or white trait could never be retrieved from the pink hybrids. In fact, interbreeding F_1 hybrids produces F_2 offspring with a phenotypic ratio of one red to two pink to one white. (Because heterozygotes have a separate phenotype, the genotypic and phenotypic ratios for the F_2 generation are the same, 1:2:1.) The segregation of the red-flower and white-flower alleles in the

---

* There is one exception: Geneticists have found that Mendel's pod-shape character is actually determined by two genes.

P Generation

Red
$C^R C^R$

×

White
$C^W C^W$

Gametes C^R C^W

F₁ Generation

Pink
$C^R C^W$

Gametes $\frac{1}{2}\ C^R$ $\frac{1}{2}\ C^W$

F₂ Generation

Sperm

$\frac{1}{2}\ C^R$ $\frac{1}{2}\ C^W$

Eggs

$\frac{1}{2}\ C^R$

$\frac{1}{2}\ C^W$

$C^R C^R$	$C^R C^W$
$C^R C^W$	$C^W C^W$

▲ **Figure 14.10 Incomplete dominance in snapdragon color.** When red snapdragons are crossed with white ones, the F₁ hybrids have pink flowers. Segregation of alleles into gametes of the F₁ plants results in an F₂ generation with a 1:2:1 ratio for both genotype and phenotype. The letter *C* with a superscript indicates an allele for flower color: C^R for red and C^W for white.

? *Suppose a classmate argues that this figure supports the blending hypothesis for inheritance. What might your classmate say, and how would you respond?*

gametes produced by the pink-flowered plants confirms that the alleles for flower color are heritable factors that maintain their identity in the hybrids; that is, inheritance is particulate.

Another variation on dominance relationships between alleles is called **codominance**; in this variation, the two alleles both affect the phenotype in separate, distinguishable ways. For example, the human MN blood group is determined by codominant alleles for two specific molecules located on the surface of red blood cells, the M and N molecules. A single gene locus, at which two allelic variations are possible, determines the phenotype of this blood group. Individuals homozygous for the *M* allele (*MM*) have red blood cells with only M molecules; individuals homozygous for the *N* allele (*NN*) have red blood cells with only N molecules. But *both* M and N molecules are present on the red blood cells of individuals heterozygous for the *M* and *N* alleles (*MN*). Note that the MN phenotype is *not* intermediate between the M and N phenotypes, which distinguishes codominance from incomplete

dominance. Rather, *both* M and N phenotypes are exhibited by heterozygotes, since both molecules are present.

The Relationship Between Dominance and Phenotype

We've now seen that the relative effects of two alleles range from complete dominance of one allele, through incomplete dominance of either allele, to codominance of both alleles. It is important to understand that an allele is not termed *dominant* because it somehow subdues a recessive allele. Recall that alleles are simply variations in a gene's nucleotide sequence. When a dominant allele coexists with a recessive allele in a heterozygote, they do not actually interact at all. It is in the pathway from genotype to phenotype that dominance and recessiveness come into play.

To illustrate the relationship between dominance and phenotype, we can use one of the characters Mendel studied—round versus wrinkled pea seed shape. The dominant allele (round) codes for an enzyme that helps convert an unbranched form of starch to a branched form in the seed. The recessive allele (wrinkled) codes for a defective form of this enzyme, leading to an accumulation of unbranched starch, which causes excess water to enter the seed by osmosis. Later, when the seed dries, it wrinkles. If a dominant allele is present, no excess water enters the seed and it does not wrinkle when it dries. One dominant allele results in enough of the enzyme to synthesize adequate amounts of branched starch, which means dominant homozygotes and heterozygotes have the same phenotype: round seeds.

A closer look at the relationship between dominance and phenotype reveals an intriguing fact: For any character, the observed dominant/recessive relationship of alleles depends on the level at which we examine phenotype. **Tay-Sachs disease**, an inherited disorder in humans, provides an example. The brain cells of a child with Tay-Sachs disease cannot metabolize certain lipids because a crucial enzyme does not work properly. As these lipids accumulate in brain cells, the child begins to suffer seizures, blindness, and degeneration of motor and mental performance and dies within a few years.

Only children who inherit two copies of the Tay-Sachs allele (homozygotes) have the disease. Thus, at the *organismal* level, the Tay-Sachs allele qualifies as recessive. However, the activity level of the lipid-metabolizing enzyme in heterozygotes is intermediate between that in individuals homozygous for the normal allele and that in individuals with Tay-Sachs disease. The intermediate phenotype observed at the *biochemical* level is characteristic of incomplete dominance of either allele. Fortunately, the heterozygote condition does not lead to disease symptoms, apparently because half the normal enzyme activity is sufficient to prevent lipid accumulation in the brain. Extending our analysis to yet another level, we find that heterozygous individuals produce equal numbers of normal and dysfunctional enzyme molecules. Thus, at the *molecular* level, the normal allele and the Tay-Sachs allele are codominant. As you can see, whether alleles appear to be completely dominant, incompletely dominant, or codominant depends on the level at which the phenotype is analyzed.

Frequency of Dominant Alleles Although you might assume that the dominant allele for a particular character would be more common in a population than the recessive allele for that character, this is not necessarily the case. For example, about one baby out of 400 in the United States is born with extra fingers or toes, a condition known as polydactyly. Some cases of polydactyly are caused by the presence of a dominant allele. The low frequency of polydactyly indicates that the recessive allele, which results in five digits per appendage, is far more prevalent than the dominant allele in the population. In Chapter 23, you will learn how the relative frequencies of alleles in a population are affected by natural selection.

Multiple Alleles

Only two alleles exist for the pea characters that Mendel studied, but most genes exist in more than two allelic forms. The ABO blood groups in humans, for instance, are determined by three alleles of a single gene: I^A, I^B, and i. A person's blood group (phenotype) may be one of four types: A, B, AB, or O. These letters refer to two carbohydrates—A and B—that may be found on the surface of red blood cells. A person's blood cells may have carbohydrate A (type A blood), carbohydrate B (type B), both (type AB), or neither (type O), as shown schematically in **Figure 14.11**. Matching compatible blood groups is critical for safe blood transfusions (see Chapter 43).

Pleiotropy

So far, we have treated Mendelian inheritance as though each gene affects only one phenotypic character. Most genes, however, have multiple phenotypic effects, a property called **pleiotropy** (from the Greek *pleion*, more). In humans, for example, pleiotropic alleles are responsible for the multiple symptoms associated with certain hereditary diseases, such as cystic fibrosis and sickle-cell disease, discussed later in this chapter. In the garden pea, the gene that determines flower color also affects the color of the coating on the outer surface of the seed, which can be gray or white. Given the intricate molecular and cellular interactions responsible for an organism's development and physiology, it isn't surprising that a single gene can affect a number of characteristics in an organism.

Extending Mendelian Genetics for Two or More Genes

Dominance relationships, multiple alleles, and pleiotropy all have to do with the effects of the alleles of a single gene. We now consider two situations in which two or more genes are involved in determining a particular phenotype.

Epistasis

In **epistasis** (from the Greek for "standing upon"), a gene at one locus alters the phenotypic expression of a gene at a second lo-

(a) The three alleles for the ABO blood groups and their associated carbohydrates. Each allele codes for an enzyme that may add a specific carbohydrate (designated by the superscript on the allele and shown as a triangle or circle) to the red blood cell.

Allele	Carbohydrate
I^A	A △
I^B	B ○
i	none

Genotype	Red blood cell appearance	Phenotype (blood group)
$I^A I^A$ or $I^A i$		A
$I^B I^B$ or $I^B i$		B
$I^A I^B$		AB
ii		O

(b) Blood group genotypes and phenotypes. There are six possible genotypes, resulting in four different phenotypes.

▲ **Figure 14.11 Multiple alleles for the ABO blood groups.** The four blood groups result from different combinations of three alleles.

? *Based on the surface carbohydrate phenotype in (b), what are the dominance relationships among the alleles?*

cus. An example will help clarify this concept. In mice and many other mammals, black coat color is dominant to brown. Let's designate B and b as the two alleles for this character. For a mouse to have brown fur, its genotype must be bb. But there is more to the story. A second gene determines whether or not pigment will be deposited in the hair. The dominant allele, symbolized by C (for color), results in the deposition of either black or brown pigment, depending on the genotype at the first locus. But if the mouse is homozygous recessive for the second locus (cc), then the coat is white (albino), regardless of the genotype at the black/brown locus. In this case, the gene for pigment deposition (C/c) is said to be epistatic to the gene that codes for black or brown pigment (B/b).

What happens if we mate black mice that are heterozygous for both genes ($BbCc$)? Although the two genes affect the same phenotypic character (coat color), they follow the law of independent assortment. Thus, our breeding experiment represents an F_1 dihybrid cross, like those that produced a 9:3:3:1

▲ **Figure 14.12 An example of epistasis.** This Punnett square illustrates the genotypes and phenotypes predicted for offspring of matings between two black mice of genotype *BbCc*. The *C/c* gene, which is epistatic to the *B/b* gene coding for hair pigment, controls whether or not pigment of any color will be deposited in the hair.

Phenotypes: $\frac{1}{64}$ $\frac{6}{64}$ $\frac{15}{64}$ $\frac{20}{64}$ $\frac{15}{64}$ $\frac{6}{64}$ $\frac{1}{64}$

Number of dark-skin alleles: 0 1 2 3 4 5 6

▲ **Figure 14.13 A simplified model for polygenic inheritance of skin color.** According to this model, three separately inherited genes affect the darkness of skin. The heterozygous individuals (*AaBbCc*) represented by the two rectangles at the top of this figure each carry three dark-skin alleles (black circles, which represent *A*, *B*, or *C*) and three light-skin alleles (white circles, which represent *a*, *b*, or *c*). The Punnett square shows all the possible genetic combinations in gametes and in offspring of a large number of hypothetical matings between these heterozygotes. The results are summarized by the phenotypic ratios under the Punnett square.

DRAW IT *Make a bar graph of the results, with skin color (number of dark-skin alleles) along the x-axis and fraction of offspring along the y-axis. Draw a rough curve corresponding to the results and discuss what it shows about the relative proportions of different phenotypes among the offspring.*

ratio in Mendel's experiments. We can use a Punnett square to represent the genotypes of the F_2 offspring (**Figure 14.12**). As a result of epistasis, the phenotypic ratio among the F_2 offspring is 9 black to 3 brown to 4 white. Other types of epistatic interactions produce different ratios, but all are modified versions of 9:3:3:1.

Polygenic Inheritance

Mendel studied characters that could be classified on an either-or basis, such as purple versus white flower color. But for many characters, such as human skin color and height, an either-or classification is impossible because the characters vary in the population along a continuum (in gradations). These are called **quantitative characters**. Quantitative variation usually indicates **polygenic inheritance**, an additive effect of two or more genes on a single phenotypic character (the converse of pleiotropy, where a single gene affects several phenotypic characters).

There is evidence, for instance, that skin pigmentation in humans is controlled by at least three separately inherited genes (probably more, but we will simplify). Let's consider three genes, with a dark-skin allele for each gene (*A*, *B*, or *C*) contributing one "unit" of darkness to the phenotype and be-

ing incompletely dominant to the other allele (*a*, *b*, or *c*). An *AABBCC* person would be very dark, while an *aabbcc* individual would be very light. An *AaBbCc* person would have skin of an intermediate shade. Because the alleles have a cumulative effect, the genotypes *AaBbCc* and *AABbcc* would make the same genetic contribution (three units) to skin darkness. The Punnett square in **Figure 14.13** shows all possible genotypes of offspring from a mating between individuals heterozygous for all three genes. As indicated by the row of squares below the Punnett square, there are seven skin-color phenotypes that could result from this mating. Environmental factors, such as exposure to the sun, also affect the skin-color phenotype.

Nature and Nurture: The Environmental Impact on Phenotype

Another departure from simple Mendelian genetics arises when the phenotype for a character depends on environment

▲ **Figure 14.14 The effect of environment on phenotype.**
The outcome of a genotype lies within its norm of reaction, a phenotypic range that depends on the environment in which the genotype is expressed. For example, hydrangea flowers of the same genetic variety range in color from blue-violet to pink, with the shade and intensity of color depending on the acidity and aluminum content of the soil.

as well as genotype. A single tree, locked into its inherited genotype, has leaves that vary in size, shape, and greenness, depending on exposure to wind and sun. For humans, nutrition influences height, exercise alters build, sun-tanning darkens the skin, and experience improves performance on intelligence tests. Even identical twins, who are genetic equals, accumulate phenotypic differences as a result of their unique experiences.

Whether human characteristics are more influenced by genes or the environment—nature or nurture—is a very old and hotly contested debate that we will not attempt to settle here. We can say, however, that a genotype generally is not associated with a rigidly defined phenotype, but rather with a range of phenotypic possibilities due to environmental influences. This phenotypic range is called the **norm of reaction** for a genotype (**Figure 14.14**). For some characters, such as the ABO blood group system, the norm of reaction has no breadth whatsoever; that is, a given genotype mandates a very specific phenotype. Other characteristics, such as a person's blood count of red and white cells, vary quite a bit, depending on such factors as the altitude, the customary level of physical activity, and the presence of infectious agents.

Generally, norms of reaction are broadest for polygenic characters. Environment contributes to the quantitative nature of these characters, as we have seen in the continuous variation of skin color. Geneticists refer to such characters as **multifactorial**, meaning that many factors, both genetic and environmental, collectively influence phenotype.

Integrating a Mendelian View of Heredity and Variation

Over the past several pages, we have broadened our view of Mendelian inheritance by exploring degrees of dominance as well as multiple alleles, pleiotropy, epistasis, polygenic inheritance, and the phenotypic impact of the environment. How can we integrate these refinements into a comprehensive theory of Mendelian genetics? The key is to make the transition from the reductionist emphasis on single genes and phenotypic characters to the emergent properties of the organism as a whole, one of the themes of this book.

The term *phenotype* can refer not only to specific characters, such as flower color and blood group, but also to an organism in its entirety—*all* aspects of its physical appearance, internal anatomy, physiology, and behavior. Similarly, the term *genotype* can refer to an organism's entire genetic makeup, not just its alleles for a single genetic locus. In most cases, a gene's impact on phenotype is affected by other genes and by the environment. In this integrated view of heredity and variation, an organism's phenotype reflects its overall genotype and unique environmental history.

Considering all that can occur in the pathway from genotype to phenotype, it is indeed impressive that Mendel could uncover the fundamental principles governing the transmission of individual genes from parents to offspring. Mendel's two laws, segregation and independent assortment, explain heritable variations in terms of alternative forms of genes (hereditary "particles," now known as the alleles of genes) that are passed along, generation after generation, according to simple rules of probability. This theory of inheritance is equally valid for peas, flies, fishes, birds, and human beings—indeed for any organism with a sexual life cycle. Furthermore, by extending the principles of segregation and independent assortment to help explain such hereditary patterns as epistasis and quantitative characters, we begin to see how broadly Mendelism applies. From Mendel's abbey garden came a theory of particulate inheritance that anchors modern genetics. In the last section of this chapter, we will apply Mendelian genetics to human inheritance, with emphasis on the transmission of hereditary diseases.

CONCEPT CHECK 14.3

1. *Incomplete dominance* and *epistasis* are both terms that define genetic relationships. What is the most basic distinction between these terms?
2. If a man with type AB blood marries a woman with type O blood, what blood types would you expect in their children?
3. **WHAT IF?** A rooster with gray feathers is mated with a hen of the same phenotype. Among their offspring, 15 chicks are gray, 6 are black, and 8 are white. What is the simplest explanation for the inheritance of these colors in chickens? What phenotypes would you expect in the offspring of a cross between a gray rooster and a black hen?

For suggested answers, see Appendix A.

Many human traits follow Mendelian patterns of inheritance

Whereas peas are convenient subjects for genetic research, humans are not. The human generation span is about 20 years, and human parents produce relatively few offspring compared to peas and most other species. Even more important, no one would consider it ethical to ask pairs of humans to breed so that the phenotypes of their offspring could be analyzed! In spite of these constraints, the study of human genetics continues to advance, spurred on by the desire to understand our own inheritance. New techniques in molecular biology have led to many breakthrough discoveries, as we will see in Chapter 20, but basic Mendelism endures as the foundation of human genetics.

Pedigree Analysis

Unable to manipulate the mating patterns of people, geneticists must analyze the results of matings that have already occurred. They do so by collecting information about a family's history for a particular trait and assembling this information into a family tree describing the traits of parents and children across the generations—the family **pedigree**.

Figure 14.15a shows a three-generation pedigree that traces the occurrence of a pointed contour of the hairline on the forehead. This trait, called a widow's peak, is due to a dominant allele, *W*. Because the widow's-peak allele is dominant, all individuals who lack a widow's peak must be homozygous recessive (*ww*). The two grandparents with widow's peaks must have the *Ww* genotype, since some of their offspring are homozygous recessive. The offspring in the second generation who *do* have widow's peaks must also be heterozygous, because they are the products of *Ww* × *ww* matings. The third generation in this pedigree consists of two sisters. The one who has a widow's peak could be either homozygous (*WW*) or heterozygous (*Ww*), given what we know about the genotypes of her parents (both *Ww*).

Figure 14.15b is a pedigree of the same family, but this time we focus on a recessive trait, attached earlobes. We'll use *f* for the recessive allele and *F* for the dominant allele, which results in free earlobes. As you work your way through the pedigree, notice once again that you can apply what you have learned about Mendelian inheritance to understand the genotypes shown for the family members.

An important application of a pedigree is to help us calculate the probability that a child will have a particular genotype and phenotype. Suppose that the couple represented in the second generation of Figure 14.15 decides to have one more child. What is the probability that the child will have a widow's

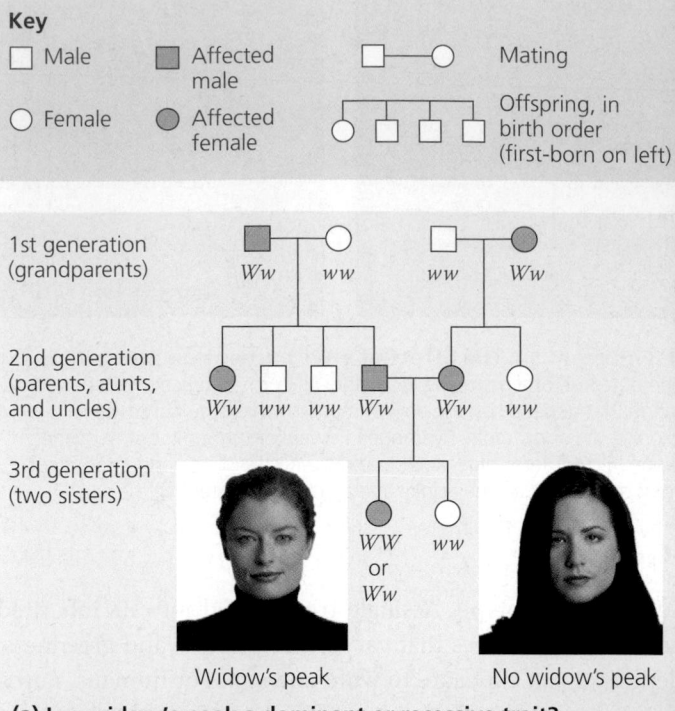

(a) Is a widow's peak a dominant or recessive trait?
Tips for pedigree analysis: Notice in the third generation that the second-born daughter lacks a widow's peak, although both of her parents had the trait. Such a pattern of inheritance supports the hypothesis that the trait is due to a dominant allele. If the trait were due to a *recessive* allele, and both parents had the recessive phenotype, then *all* of their offspring would also have the recessive phenotype.

(b) Is an attached earlobe a dominant or recessive trait?
Tips for pedigree analysis: Notice that the first-born daughter in the third generation has attached earlobes, although both of her parents lack that trait (they have free earlobes). Such a pattern is easily explained if the attached-lobe phenotype is due to a recessive allele. If it were due to a *dominant* allele, then at least one parent would also have had the trait.

▲ **Figure 14.15 Pedigree analysis.** Each of these pedigrees traces a trait through three generations of the same family. The two traits have different inheritance patterns, as seen by analysis of the pedigrees.

peak? This is equivalent to a Mendelian F_1 monohybrid cross ($Ww \times Ww$), and thus the probability that a child will inherit a dominant allele and have a widow's peak is ¾ (¼ WW + ½ Ww). What is the probability that the child will have attached earlobes? Again, we can treat this as a monohybrid cross ($Ff \times Ff$), but this time we want to know the chance that the offspring will be homozygous recessive (ff). That probability is ¼. Finally, what is the chance that the child will have a widow's peak *and* attached earlobes? Assuming that the genes for these two characters are on different chromosomes, the two pairs of alleles will assort independently in this dihybrid cross ($WwFf \times WwFf$). Thus, we can use the multiplication rule: ¾ (chance of widow's peak) × ¼ (chance of attached earlobes) = ³⁄₁₆ (chance of widow's peak and attached earlobes).

Pedigrees are a more serious matter when the alleles in question cause disabling or deadly diseases instead of innocuous human variations such as hairline or earlobe configuration. However, for disorders inherited as simple Mendelian traits, the same techniques of pedigree analysis apply.

Recessively Inherited Disorders

Thousands of genetic disorders are known to be inherited as simple recessive traits. These disorders range in severity from relatively mild, such as albinism (lack of pigmentation, which results in susceptibility to skin cancers and vision problems), to life-threatening, such as cystic fibrosis.

The Behavior of Recessive Alleles

How can we account for the behavior of alleles that cause recessively inherited disorders? Recall that genes code for proteins of specific function. An allele that causes a genetic disorder (let's call it allele *a*) codes either for a malfunctioning protein or for no protein at all. In the case of disorders classified as recessive, heterozygotes (Aa) are normal in phenotype because one copy of the normal allele (A) produces a sufficient amount of the specific protein. Thus, a recessively inherited disorder shows up only in the homozygous individuals (aa) who inherit one recessive allele from each parent. Although phenotypically normal with regard to the disorder, heterozygotes may transmit the recessive allele to their offspring and thus are called **carriers**. **Figure 14.16** illustrates these ideas using albinism as an example.

Most people who have recessive disorders are born to parents who are carriers of the disorder but themselves have a normal phenotype, as is the case shown in the Punnett square in Figure 14.16. A mating between two carriers corresponds to a Mendelian F_1 monohybrid cross, so the predicted genotypic ratio for the offspring is 1 AA : 2 Aa : 1 aa. Thus, each child has a ¼ chance of inheriting a double dose of the recessive allele; in the case of albinism, such a child will be albino. From the genotypic ratio, we also can see that out of three offspring with the *normal* phenotype (one AA plus two Aa), two are pre-

dicted to be heterozygous carriers, a ⅔ chance. Recessive homozygotes could also result from $Aa \times aa$ and $aa \times aa$ matings, but if the disorder is lethal before reproductive age or results in sterility (neither of which is true for albinism), no aa individuals will reproduce. Even if recessive homozygotes are able to reproduce, such individuals will still account for a much smaller percentage of the population than heterozygous carriers (for reasons we will examine in Chapter 23).

In general, genetic disorders are not evenly distributed among all groups of people. For example, the incidence of Tay-Sachs disease, which we described earlier in this chapter, is disproportionately high among Ashkenazic Jews, Jewish people whose ancestors lived in central Europe. In that population, Tay-Sachs disease occurs in one out of 3,600 births, an incidence about 100 times greater than that among non-Jews or Mediterranean (Sephardic) Jews. This uneven distribution results from the different genetic histories of the world's peoples during less technological times, when populations were more geographically (and hence genetically) isolated.

When a disease-causing recessive allele is rare, it is relatively unlikely that two carriers of the same harmful allele will meet and mate. However, if the man and woman are close relatives (for example, siblings or first cousins), the probability of passing on recessive traits increases greatly. These are called consanguineous ("same blood") matings, and they are indicated in pedigrees by double lines. Because people with recent common ancestors are more likely to carry the same recessive alleles than are unrelated people, it is more likely that a mating of close relatives will produce offspring homozygous for recessive traits—including harmful ones. Such effects can be observed in many types of domesticated and zoo animals that have become inbred.

There is debate among geneticists about the extent to which human consanguinity increases the risk of inherited

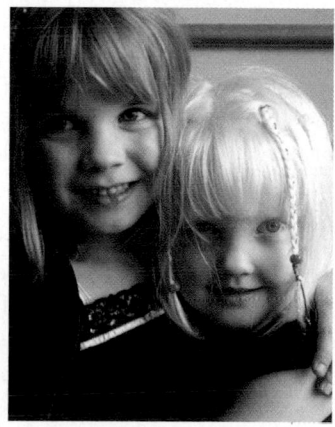

▲ **Figure 14.16 Albinism: a recessive trait.** One of the two sisters shown here has normal coloration; the other is albino. Most recessive homozygotes are born to parents who are carriers of the disorder but themselves have a normal phenotype, the case shown in the Punnett square.

? *What is the probability that the sister with normal coloration is a carrier of the albinism allele?*

diseases. Many deleterious alleles have such severe effects that a homozygous embryo spontaneously aborts long before birth. Still, most societies and cultures have laws or taboos forbidding marriages between close relatives. These rules may have evolved out of empirical observation that in most populations, stillbirths and birth defects are more common when parents are closely related. Social and economic factors have also influenced the development of customs and laws against consanguineous marriages.

Cystic Fibrosis

The most common lethal genetic disease in the United States is **cystic fibrosis**, which strikes one out of every 2,500 people of European descent, though it is much rarer in other groups. Among people of European descent, one out of 25 (4%) are carriers of the cystic fibrosis allele. The normal allele for this gene codes for a membrane protein that functions in the transport of chloride ions between certain cells and the extracellular fluid. These chloride transport channels are defective or absent in the plasma membranes of children who inherit two recessive alleles for cystic fibrosis. The result is an abnormally high concentration of extracellular chloride, which causes the mucus that coats certain cells to become thicker and stickier than normal. The mucus builds up in the pancreas, lungs, digestive tract, and other organs, leading to multiple (pleiotropic) effects, including poor absorption of nutrients from the intestines, chronic bronchitis, and recurrent bacterial infections. Recent research indicates that the high concentration of extracellular chloride also contributes to infection by disabling a natural antibiotic made by some body cells. When immune cells come to the rescue, their remains add to the mucus, creating a vicious cycle.

If untreated, most children with cystic fibrosis die before their 5th birthday. But daily doses of antibiotics to prevent infection, gentle pounding on the chest to clear mucus from clogged airways, and other preventive treatments can prolong life. In the United States, more than half of those with cystic fibrosis now survive into their late 20s or even 30s and beyond.

Sickle-Cell Disease

The most common inherited disorder among people of African descent is **sickle-cell disease**, which affects one out of 400 African-Americans. Sickle-cell disease is caused by the substitution of a single amino acid in the hemoglobin protein of red blood cells. When the oxygen content of an affected individual's blood is low (at high altitudes or under physical stress, for instance), the sickle-cell hemoglobin molecules aggregate into long rods that deform the red cells into a sickle shape (see Figure 5.22). Sickled cells may clump and clog small blood vessels, often leading to other symptoms throughout the body, including physical weakness, pain, organ damage,

and even paralysis. The multiple effects of a double dose of the sickle-cell allele are another example of pleiotropy. Regular blood transfusions can ward off brain damage in children with sickle-cell disease, and new drugs can help prevent or treat other problems, but there is no cure.

Although two sickle-cell alleles are necessary for an individual to manifest full-blown sickle-cell disease, the presence of one sickle-cell allele can affect the phenotype. Thus, at the organismal level, the normal allele is incompletely dominant to the sickle-cell allele. Heterozygotes, said to have *sickle-cell trait*, are usually healthy, but they may suffer some sickle-cell symptoms during prolonged periods of reduced blood oxygen content. At the molecular level, the two alleles are codominant; both normal and abnormal (sickle-cell) hemoglobins are made in heterozygotes.

About one out of ten African-Americans have sickle-cell trait, an unusually high frequency of heterozygotes for an allele with severe detrimental effects in homozygotes. One explanation for this is that a single copy of the sickle-cell allele reduces the frequency and severity of malaria attacks, especially among young children. The malaria parasite spends part of its life cycle in red blood cells (see Figure 28.10), and the presence of even heterozygous amounts of sickle-cell hemoglobin results in lower parasite densities and hence reduced malaria symptoms. Thus, in tropical Africa, where infection with the malaria parasite is common, the sickle-cell allele is both boon and bane. The relatively high frequency of African-Americans with sickle-cell trait is a vestige of their African roots.

Dominantly Inherited Disorders

Although many harmful alleles are recessive, a number of human disorders are due to dominant alleles. One example is *achondroplasia*, a form of dwarfism that occurs in one of every 25,000 people. Heterozygous individuals have the dwarf phenotype (**Figure 14.17**). Therefore, all people who are not achondroplastic dwarfs—99.99% of the population—are homozygous for the recessive allele. Like the presence of extra fingers or toes mentioned earlier, achondroplasia is a trait for which the recessive allele is much more prevalent than the corresponding dominant allele.

Dominant alleles that cause a lethal disease are much less common than recessive alleles that do so. All lethal alleles arise by mutations (changes to the DNA) in cells that produce sperm or eggs; presumably, such mutations occur equally often whether the mutant allele is dominant or recessive. However, if a lethal dominant allele causes the death of offspring before they mature and can reproduce, the allele will not be passed on to future generations. (In contrast, a lethal recessive allele can be perpetuated from generation to generation by heterozygous carriers who have normal phenotypes, since only homozygous recessive offspring will have the lethal disease.)

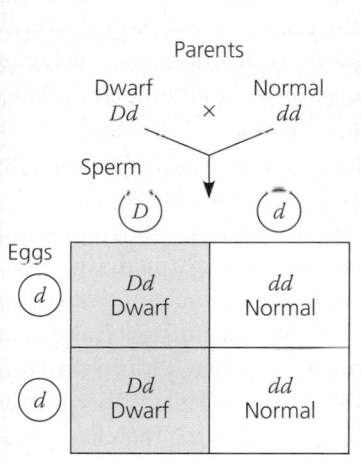

Parents

Dwarf   Normal
Dd   ×   *dd*

Sperm

▲ **Figure 14.17 Achondroplasia: a dominant trait.** The late actor David Rappaport had achondroplasia, a form of dwarfism caused by a dominant allele (*D*). The allele might have arisen as a mutation in the egg or sperm of a parent or could have been inherited from an affected parent, as shown for an affected father in the Punnett square.

Huntington's Disease

A lethal dominant allele can escape elimination if it causes death only after an individual who carries the allele has reached a relatively advanced age. By the time the symptoms become evident, the individual may have already transmitted the lethal allele to his or her children. For example, **Huntington's disease**, a degenerative disease of the nervous system, is caused by a lethal dominant allele that has no obvious phenotypic effect until the individual is about 35 to 45 years old. Once the deterioration of the nervous system begins, it is irreversible and inevitably fatal. Any child born to a parent who has the allele for Huntington's disease has a 50% chance of inheriting the allele and the disorder (see the Punnett square in Figure 14.17). In the United States, this devastating disease afflicts about one in 10,000 people.

Until relatively recently, the onset of symptoms was the only way to know if a person had inherited the Huntington's allele. This is no longer the case. By analyzing DNA samples from a large family with a high incidence of the disorder, geneticists tracked the Huntington's allele to a locus near the tip of chromosome 4, and the gene has now been sequenced. This information led to development of a test that can detect the presence of the Huntington's allele in an individual's genome. (The methods that make such tests possible are discussed in Chapter 20.) The availability of this test poses an agonizing dilemma for those with a family history of Huntington's disease, such as relatives of the folk singer Woody Guthrie, who died of the disease. Does a person currently in good health benefit by finding out whether he or she has inherited a fatal and not yet curable disease? Some individuals may want to be tested for the disease before planning a family, whereas others may decide it would be too stressful to find out. Clearly, this is a personal decision.

Multifactorial Disorders

The hereditary diseases we have discussed so far are sometimes described as simple Mendelian disorders because they result from abnormality of one or both alleles at a single genetic locus. Many more people are susceptible to diseases that have a multifactorial basis—a genetic component plus a significant environmental influence. Heart disease, diabetes, cancer, alcoholism, certain mental illnesses such as schizophrenia and bipolar disorder, and many other diseases are multifactorial. In many cases, the hereditary component is polygenic. For example, many genes affect cardiovascular health, making some of us more prone than others to heart attacks and strokes. No matter what our genotype, however, our lifestyle has a tremendous effect on phenotype for cardiovascular health and other multifactorial characters. Exercise, a healthful diet, abstinence from smoking, and an ability to handle stressful situations all reduce our risk of heart disease and some types of cancer.

At present, so little is understood about the genetic contributions to most multifactorial diseases that the best public health strategy is to educate people about the importance of environmental factors and to promote healthful behavior.

Genetic Testing and Counseling

A preventive approach to simple Mendelian disorders is possible when the risk of a particular genetic disorder can be assessed before a child is conceived or during the early stages of the pregnancy. Many hospitals have genetic counselors who can provide information to prospective parents concerned about a family history for a specific disease.

Counseling Based on Mendelian Genetics and Probability Rules

Consider the case of a hypothetical couple, John and Carol. Both had a brother who died from the same recessively inherited lethal disease. Before conceiving their first child, John and Carol seek genetic counseling to determine the risk of having a child with the disease. From the information about their brothers, we know that both parents of John and both parents of Carol must have been carriers of the recessive allele. Thus, John and Carol are both products of *Aa* × *Aa* crosses, where *a* symbolizes the allele that causes this particular disease. We also know that John and Carol are not homozygous recessive (*aa*), because they do not have the disease. Therefore, their genotypes are either *AA* or *Aa*.

Given a genotypic ratio of 1 *AA* : 2 *Aa* : 1 *aa* for offspring of an *Aa* × *Aa* cross, John and Carol each have a ⅔ chance of being carriers (*Aa*). According to the rule of multiplication, the overall probability of their firstborn having the disorder is ⅔ (the chance that John is a carrier) times ⅔ (the chance that Carol is a carrier) times ¼ (the chance of two carriers having a child with the disease), which equals ⅑. Suppose that Carol and John decide to have a child—after all, there is an ⅛ chance that their baby will not have the disorder. If, despite these odds, their child is born with the disease, then we would know that *both* John and Carol are, in fact, carriers (*Aa* genotype). If both John and Carol are carriers, there is a ¼ chance that any subsequent child this couple has will have the disease.

When we use Mendel's laws to predict possible outcomes of matings, it is important to remember that each child represents an independent event in the sense that its genotype is unaffected by the genotypes of older siblings. Suppose that John and Carol have three more children, and *all three* have the hypothetical hereditary disease. There is only one chance in 64 (¼ × ¼ × ¼) that such an outcome will occur. Despite this run of misfortune, the chance that still another child of this couple will have the disease remains ¼.

Tests for Identifying Carriers

Because most children with recessive disorders are born to parents with normal phenotypes, the key to accurately assessing the genetic risk for a particular disease is determining whether the prospective parents are heterozygous carriers of the recessive allele. For an increasing number of heritable disorders, tests are available that can distinguish individuals of normal phenotype who are dominant homozygotes from those who are heterozygotes. There are now tests that can identify carriers of the alleles for Tay-Sachs disease, sickle-cell disease, and the most common form of cystic fibrosis.

These tests for identifying carriers enable people with family histories of genetic disorders to make informed decisions about having children. But these new methods for genetic screening pose potential problems. If confidentiality is breached, will carriers be stigmatized? Will they be denied health or life insurance, even though they themselves are healthy? Will misinformed employers equate "carrier" with disease? And will sufficient genetic counseling be available to help a large number of individuals understand their test results? Advances in biotechnology offer possibilities for reducing human suffering, but not before key ethical issues are resolved.

Fetal Testing

Suppose a couple learns that they are both carriers of the Tay-Sachs allele, but they decide to have a child anyway. Tests performed in conjunction with a technique known as **amniocentesis** can determine, beginning at the 14th–16th week of pregnancy, whether the developing fetus has Tay-Sachs disease (**Figure 14.18a**). To perform this procedure, a physician inserts a needle into the uterus and extracts about 10 mL of amniotic fluid, the liquid that bathes the fetus. Some genetic disorders can be detected from the presence of certain chemicals in the amniotic fluid itself. Tests for other disorders, including Tay-Sachs disease, are performed on cells cultured in the laboratory, descendants of the fetal cells sloughed off into the amniotic fluid. These cultured cells can also be used for karyotyping to identify certain chromosomal defects (see Figure 13.3).

In an alternative technique called **chorionic villus sampling (CVS)**, a physician inserts a narrow tube through the cervix into the uterus and suctions out a tiny sample of tissue from the placenta, the organ that transmits nutrients and fetal wastes between the fetus and the mother (**Figure 14.18b**). The cells of the chorionic villi of the placenta, the portion sampled, are derived from the fetus and have the same genotype as the new individual. These cells are proliferating rapidly enough to allow karyotyping to be carried out immediately. This rapid analysis is an advantage over amniocentesis, in which the cells must be cultured for several weeks before karyotyping. Another advantage of CVS is that it can be performed as early as the 8th–10th week of pregnancy. However, CVS is not suitable for tests requiring amniotic fluid. Recently, medical scientists have developed methods for isolating fetal cells that have escaped into the mother's blood. Although very few in number, these cells can be cultured and then tested.

Imaging techniques allow a physician to examine a fetus directly for major anatomical abnormalities. In the *ultrasound* technique, sound waves are used to produce an image of the fetus by a simple noninvasive procedure. In *fetoscopy*, a needle-thin tube containing a viewing scope and fiber optics (to transmit light) is inserted into the uterus.

Ultrasound has no known risk to either mother or fetus, while the other procedures can cause complications in a small percentage of cases. Previously, amniocentesis or CVS for diagnostic testing was generally offered only to women over age 35, due to their increased risk of bearing a child with Down syndrome. In 2007, however, reassessment of the risks and possible benefits led to a change in the recommended practice, and now such testing is offered to all pregnant women. If the fetal tests reveal a serious disorder, the parents face the difficult choice of terminating the pregnancy or preparing to care for a child with a genetic disorder.

Newborn Screening

Some genetic disorders can be detected at birth by simple tests that are now routinely performed in most hospitals in the United States. One common screening program is for phenylketonuria (PKU), a recessively inherited disorder that occurs in about one out of every 10,000 to 15,000 births in the United States. Children with this disease cannot properly metabolize the amino acid phenylalanine. This compound and its by-product, phenylpyruvate, can accumulate to toxic levels in the blood, causing mental retardation. However, if the deficiency is detected in the newborn, a special diet low in phenylalanine will usually allow normal development and prevent retardation. Unfortunately, very few other genetic disorders are treatable at the present time.

Screening of newborns and fetuses for serious inherited diseases, tests for identifying carriers, and genetic counseling all rely on the Mendelian model of inheritance. We owe the "gene idea"—the concept of particulate heritable factors transmitted according to simple rules of chance—to the elegant quantitative experiments of Gregor Mendel. The importance of his discoveries was overlooked by most biologists until early in the 20th century, several decades after his findings were reported. In the next chapter, you will learn how Mendel's laws have their physical basis in the behavior of chromosomes during sexual life cycles and how the synthesis of Mendelism and a chromosome theory of inheritance catalyzed progress in genetics.

CONCEPT CHECK **14.4**

1. Beth and Tom each have a sibling with cystic fibrosis, but neither Beth nor Tom nor any of their parents have the disease. Calculate the probability that if this couple has a child, the child will have cystic fibrosis. What would be the probability if a test revealed that Tom is a carrier but Beth is not?
2. Joan was born with six toes on each foot, a dominant trait called polydactyly. Two of her five siblings and her mother, but not her father, also have extra digits. What is Joan's genotype for the number-of-digits character? Explain your answer. Use *D* and *d* to symbolize the alleles for this character.
3. **WHAT IF?** What would you suspect if Peter was born with polydactyly, but neither of his biological parents had extra digits?

For suggested answers, see Appendix A.

(a) Amniocentesis

(b) Chorionic villus sampling (CVS)

① A sample of amniotic fluid can be taken starting at the 14th to 16th week of pregnancy.

② Biochemical tests can be performed immediately on the amniotic fluid or later on the cultured cells.

③ Fetal cells must be cultured for several weeks to obtain sufficient numbers for karyotyping.

① A sample of chorionic villus tissue can be taken as early as the 8th to 10th week of pregnancy.

② Karyotyping and biochemical tests can be performed on the fetal cells immediately, providing results within a day or so.

▲ **Figure 14.18 Testing a fetus for genetic disorders.** Biochemical tests may detect substances associated with particular disorders. Karyotyping shows whether the chromosomes of the fetus are normal in number and appearance.

SUMMARY OF KEY CONCEPTS

CONCEPT 14.1

Mendel used the scientific approach to identify two laws of inheritance (pp. 262–269)

▶ **Mendel's Experimental, Quantitative Approach** In the 1860s, Gregor Mendel formulated a theory of inheritance based on experiments with garden peas, proposing that parents pass on to their offspring discrete genes that retain their identity through generations.

▶ **The Law of Segregation** Genes have alternative forms, or alleles. In a diploid organism, the two alleles of a gene segregate (separate) during gamete formation; each sperm or egg carries only one allele of each pair. This law explains the 3:1 ratio of F_2 phenotypes observed when monohybrids self-pollinate. Each organism inherits one allele for each gene from each parent. In heterozygotes, the two alleles are different, and expression of one (the dominant allele) masks the phenotypic effect of the other (the recessive allele). Homozygotes have identical alleles of a given gene and are true-breeding.

▶ **The Law of Independent Assortment** Each pair of alleles (for one gene) segregates into gametes independently of the pair of alleles for any other gene. In a cross between dihybrids (individuals heterozygous for two genes), the offspring have four phenotypes in a 9:3:3:1 ratio.

CONCEPT 14.2

The laws of probability govern Mendelian inheritance (pp. 269–271)

▶ **The Multiplication and Addition Rules Applied to Monohybrid Crosses** The multiplication rule states that the probability of a compound event is equal to the product of the individual probabilities of the independent single events. The addition rule states that the probability of an event that can occur in two or more independent, mutually exclusive ways is the sum of the individual probabilities.

▶ **Solving Complex Genetics Problems with the Rules of Probability** A dihybrid or other multicharacter cross is equivalent to two or more independent monohybrid crosses occurring simultaneously. In calculating the chances of the various offspring genotypes from such crosses, each character first is considered separately and then the individual probabilities are multiplied.

CONCEPT 14.3

Inheritance patterns are often more complex than predicted by simple Mendelian genetics (pp. 271–275)

▶ **Extending Mendelian Genetics for a Single Gene**

Degree of dominance	Description	Example
Complete dominance of one allele	Heterozygous phenotype same as that of homozygous dominant	PP Pp
Incomplete dominance of either allele	Heterozygous phenotype intermediate between the two homozygous phenotypes	$C^R C^R$ $C^R C^W$ $C^W C^W$
Codominance	Heterozygotes: Both phenotypes expressed	$I^A I^B$
Multiple alleles	In the whole population, some genes have more than two alleles	ABO blood group alleles I^A, I^B, i
Pleiotropy	One gene is able to affect multiple phenotypic characters	Sickle-cell disease

▶ **Extending Mendelian Genetics for Two or More Genes**

Relationship among genes	Description	Example
Epistasis	One gene affects the expression of another	$BbCc$ × $BbCc$ 9 : 3 : 4
Polygenic inheritance	A single phenotypic character is affected by two or more genes	$AaBbCc$ × $AaBbCc$

▶ **Nature and Nurture: The Environmental Impact on Phenotype** The expression of a genotype can be affected by environmental influences. The phenotypic range of a particular genotype is called its norm of reaction. Polygenic characters that are also influenced by the environment are called multifactorial characters.

▶ **Integrating a Mendelian View of Heredity and Variation** An organism's overall phenotype, including its physical appearance, internal anatomy, physiology, and behavior, reflects its overall genotype and unique environmental history. Even in more complex inheritance patterns, Mendel's fundamental laws of segregation and independent assortment still apply.

MEDIA

Activity Incomplete Dominance

CONCEPT **14.4**

Many human traits follow Mendelian patterns of inheritance (pp. 276–281)

▶ **Pedigree Analysis** Family pedigrees can be used to deduce the possible genotypes of individuals and make predictions about future offspring. Predictions are usually statistical probabilities rather than certainties.

▶ **Recessively Inherited Disorders** Many genetic disorders are inherited as simple recessive traits. Most affected (ho-mozygous recessive) individuals are children of phenotypically normal, heterozygous carriers.

▶ **Dominantly Inherited Disorders** Lethal dominant alleles are eliminated from the population if affected people die before reproducing. Nonlethal dominant alleles and lethal ones that strike relatively late in life are inherited in a Mendelian way.

▶ **Multifactorial Disorders** Many human diseases have both genetic and environmental components and do not follow simple Mendelian inheritance patterns.

▶ **Genetic Testing and Counseling** Using family histories, genetic counselors help couples determine the odds that their children will have genetic disorders. Amniocentesis and chorionic villus sampling can indicate whether a suspected genetic disorder is present in a fetus. Other genetic tests can be performed after birth.

MEDIA

Investigation How Do You Diagnose a Genetic Disorder?

TESTING YOUR KNOWLEDGE

TIPS FOR GENETICS PROBLEMS

1. Write down symbols for the alleles. (These may be given in the problem.) When represented by single letters, the dominant allele is uppercase and the recessive is lowercase.

2. Write down the possible genotypes, as determined by the phenotype.
   a. If the phenotype is that of the dominant trait (for example, purple flowers), then the genotype is either homozygous dominant or heterozygous (PP or Pp, in this example).
   b. If the phenotype is that of the recessive trait, the genotype must be homozygous recessive (for example, pp).
   c. If the problem says "true-breeding," the genotype is homozygous.

3. Determine what the problem is asking for. If asked to do a cross, write it out in the form [Genotype] × [Genotype], using the alleles you've decided on.

4. To figure out the outcome of a cross, set up a Punnett square.
   a. Put the gametes of one parent at the top and those of the other on the left. To determine the allele(s) in each gamete for a given genotype, set up a systematic way to list all the possibilities. (Remember, each gamete has one allele of each gene.) Note that there are 2^n possible types of gametes, where n is the number of gene loci that are heterozygous. For example, an individual with genotype $AaBbCc$ would produce $2^3 = 8$ types of gametes. Write the genotypes of the gametes in circles above the columns and to the left of the rows.
   b. Fill in the Punnett square as if each possible sperm were fertilizing each possible egg, making all of the possible offspring. In a cross of $AaBbCc \times AaBbCc$, for example, the Punnett square would have 8 columns and 8 rows, so there are 64 different offspring; you would know the genotype of each and thus the phenotype. Count genotypes and phenotypes to obtain the genotypic and phenotypic ratios.

5. You can use the rules of probability if the Punnett square would be too big. (For example, see Genetics Problem 4.) You can consider each gene separately (see pp. 270–271).

6. If, instead, the problem gives you the phenotypic ratios of offspring, but not the genotypes of the parents in a given cross, the phenotypes can help you deduce the parents' unknown genotypes.
   a. For example, if ½ the offspring have the recessive phenotype and ½ the dominant, you know that the cross was between a heterozygote and a homozygous recessive.
   b. If the ratio is 3:1, the cross was between two heterozygotes.
   c. If two genes are involved and you see a 9:3:3:1 ratio in the offspring, you know that each parent is heterozygous for both genes. Caution: Don't assume that the reported numbers will exactly equal the predicted ratios. For example, if there are 13 offspring with the dominant trait and 11 with the recessive, assume that the ratio is one dominant to one recessive.

7. For pedigree problems, use the tips in Figure 14.15 and below to determine what kind of trait is involved.
   a. If parents without the trait have offspring with the trait, the trait must be recessive and the parents both carriers.
   b. If the trait is seen in every generation, it is most likely dominant (see the next possibility, though).
   c. If both parents have the trait, then in order for it to be recessive, all offspring must show the trait.
   d. To determine the likely genotype of a certain individual in a pedigree, first label the genotypes of all the family members you can. Even if some of the genotypes are incomplete, label what you do know. For example, if an individual has the dominant phenotype, the genotype must be AA or Aa; you can write this as $A\_$. Try different possibilities to see which fits the results. Use the rules of probability to calculate the probability of each possible genotype being the correct one.

GENETICS PROBLEMS

1. Match each term on the left with a statement on the right.

Term	Statement
__ Gene	a. Has no effect on phenotype in a heterozygote
__ Allele	
__ Character	b. A variant for a character
__ Trait	c. Having two identical alleles for a gene
__ Dominant allele	d. A cross between individuals heterozygous for a single character
__ Recessive allele	
__ Genotype	e. An alternative version of a gene
__ Phenotype	f. Having two different alleles for a gene
__ Homozygous	g. A heritable feature that varies among individuals
__ Heterozygous	
__ Testcross	h. An organism's appearance or observable traits
__ Monohybrid cross	
	i. A cross between an individual with an unknown genotype and a homozygous recessive individual
	j. Determines phenotype in a heterozygote
	k. The genetic makeup of an individual
	l. A heritable unit that determines a character; can exist in different forms

2. **DRAW IT** Two pea plants heterozygous for the characters of pod color and pod shape are crossed. Draw a Punnett square to determine the phenotypic ratios of the offspring.

3. In some plants, a true-breeding, red-flowered strain gives all pink flowers when crossed with a white-flowered strain: $C^R C^R$ (red) $\times C^W C^W$ (white) $\rightarrow C^R C^W$ (pink). If flower position (axial or terminal) is inherited as it is in peas (see Table 14.1), what will be the ratios of genotypes and phenotypes of the F_1 generation resulting from the following cross: axial-red (true-breeding) $\times$ terminal-white? What will be the ratios in the F_2 generation?

4. Flower position, stem length, and seed shape were three characters that Mendel studied. Each is controlled by an independently assorting gene and has dominant and recessive expression as follows:

Character	Dominant	Recessive
Flower position	Axial (A)	Terminal (a)
Stem length	Tall (T)	Dwarf (t)
Seed shape	Round (R)	Wrinkled (r)

If a plant that is heterozygous for all three characters is allowed to self-fertilize, what proportion of the offspring would you expect to be as follows? (*Note:* Use the rules of probability instead of a huge Punnett square.)
a. homozygous for the three dominant traits
b. homozygous for the three recessive traits
c. heterozygous for all three characters
d. homozygous for axial and tall, heterozygous for seed shape

5. A black guinea pig crossed with an albino guinea pig produces 12 black offspring. When the albino is crossed with a second black one, 7 blacks and 5 albinos are obtained. What is the best explanation for this genetic situation? Write genotypes for the parents, gametes, and offspring.

6. In sesame plants, the one-pod condition (P) is dominant to the three-pod condition (p), and normal leaf (L) is dominant to wrinkled leaf (l). Pod type and leaf type are inherited independently. Determine the genotypes for the two parents for all possible matings producing the following offspring:
a. 318 one-pod, normal leaf and 98 one-pod, wrinkled leaf
b. 323 three-pod, normal leaf and 106 three-pod, wrinkled leaf
c. 401 one-pod, normal leaf
d. 150 one-pod, normal leaf, 147 one-pod, wrinkled leaf, 51 three-pod, normal leaf, and 48 three-pod, wrinkled leaf
e. 223 one-pod, normal leaf, 72 one-pod, wrinkled leaf, 76 three-pod, normal leaf, and 27 three-pod, wrinkled leaf

7. A man with type A blood marries a woman with type B blood. Their child has type O blood. What are the genotypes of these individuals? What other genotypes, and in what frequencies, would you expect in offspring from this marriage?

8. Phenylketonuria (PKU) is an inherited disease caused by a recessive allele. If a woman and her husband, who are both carriers, have three children, what is the probability of each of the following?
a. All three children are of normal phenotype.
b. One or more of the three children have the disease.
c. All three children have the disease.
d. At least one child is phenotypically normal.
(*Note:* Remember that the probabilities of all possible outcomes always add up to 1.)

9. The genotype of F_1 individuals in a tetrahybrid cross is *AaBbCcDd*. Assuming independent assortment of these four genes, what are the probabilities that F_2 offspring will have the following genotypes?
a. *aabbccdd*
b. *AaBbCcDd*
c. *AABBCCDD*
d. *AaBBccDd*
e. *AaBBCCdd*

10. What is the probability that each of the following pairs of parents will produce the indicated offspring? (Assume independent assortment of all gene pairs.)
a. *AABBCC* $\times$ *aabbcc* $\rightarrow$ *AaBbCc*
b. *AABbCc* $\times$ *AaBbCc* $\rightarrow$ *AAbbCC*
c. *AaBbCc* $\times$ *AaBbCc* $\rightarrow$ *AaBbCc*
d. *aaBbCC* $\times$ *AABbcc* $\rightarrow$ *AaBbCc*

11. Karen and Steve each have a sibling with sickle-cell disease. Neither Karen nor Steve nor any of their parents have the disease, and none of them have been tested to see if they have the sickle-cell trait. Based on this incomplete information, calculate the probability that if this couple has a child, the child will have sickle-cell disease.

12. In 1981, a stray black cat with unusual rounded, curled-back ears was adopted by a family in California. Hundreds of descendants of the cat have since been born, and cat fanciers hope to develop the curl cat into a show breed. Suppose you owned the first curl cat and wanted to develop a true-breeding variety. How would you determine whether the curl allele is dominant or recessive? How would you obtain true-breeding curl cats? How could you be sure they are true-breeding?

13. Imagine that a newly discovered, recessively inherited disease is expressed only in individuals with type O blood, although the disease and blood group are independently inherited. A normal man with type A blood and a normal woman with type B blood have already had one child with the disease. The woman is now pregnant for a second time. What is the probability that the second child will also have the disease? Assume that both parents are heterozygous for the gene that causes the disease.

14. In tigers, a recessive allele causes an absence of fur pigmentation (a white tiger) and a cross-eyed condition. If two phenotypically normal tigers that are heterozygous at this locus are mated, what percentage of their offspring will be cross-eyed? What percentage of cross-eyed tigers will be white?

15. In maize (corn) plants, a dominant allele *I* inhibits kernel color, while the recessive allele *i* permits color when homozygous. At a different locus, the dominant allele *P* causes purple kernel color, while the homozygous recessive genotype *pp* causes red kernels. If plants heterozygous at both loci are crossed, what will be the phenotypic ratio of the offspring?

16. The pedigree below traces the inheritance of alkaptonuria, a biochemical disorder. Affected individuals, indicated here by the colored circles and squares, are unable to metabolize a substance called alkapton, which colors the urine and stains body tissues. Does alkaptonuria appear to be caused by a dominant allele or by a recessive allele? Fill in the genotypes of the individuals whose genotypes can be deduced. What genotypes are possible for each of the other individuals?

17. A man has six fingers on each hand and six toes on each foot. His wife and their daughter have the normal number of digits. Extra digits is a dominant trait. What fraction of this couple's children would be expected to have extra digits?

18. Imagine that you are a genetic counselor, and a couple planning to start a family comes to you for information. Charles was married once before, and he and his first wife had a child with cystic fibrosis. The brother of his current wife, Elaine, died of cystic fibrosis. What is the probability that Charles and Elaine will have a baby with cystic fibrosis? (Neither Charles nor Elaine has cystic fibrosis.)

19. In mice, black color (*B*) is dominant to white (*b*). At a different locus, a dominant allele (*A*) produces a band of yellow just below the tip of each hair in mice with black fur. This gives a frosted appearance known as agouti. Expression of the recessive allele (*a*) results in a solid coat color. If mice that are heterozygous at both loci are crossed, what is the expected phenotypic ratio of their offspring?

For Genetics Problems answers, see Appendix A.

MEDIA Visit the Study Area at **www.masteringbio.com** for a Practice Test.

EVOLUTION CONNECTION

20. Over the past half century, there has been a trend in the United States and other developed countries for people to marry and start families later in life than did their parents and grandparents. What effects might this trend have on the incidence (frequency) of late-acting dominant lethal alleles in the population?

SCIENTIFIC INQUIRY

21. You are handed a mystery pea plant with tall stems and axial flowers and asked to determine its genotype as quickly as possible. You know that the allele for tall stems (*T*) is dominant to that for dwarf stems (*t*) and that the allele for axial flowers (*A*) is dominant to that for terminal flowers (*a*).
   a. What are *all* the possible genotypes for your mystery plant?
   b. Describe the *one* cross you would do, out in your garden, to determine the exact genotype of your mystery plant.
   c. While waiting for the results of your cross, you predict the results for each possible genotype listed in part a. How do you do this? Why is this not called "performing a cross"?
   d. Explain how the results of your cross and your predictions will help you learn the genotype of your mystery plant.

SCIENCE, TECHNOLOGY, AND SOCIETY

22. Imagine that one of your parents had Huntington's disease. What is the probability that you, too, will someday manifest the disease? There is no cure for Huntington's. Would you want to be tested for the Huntington's allele? Why or why not?

The Chromosomal Basis of Inheritance

15

KEY CONCEPTS

15.1 Mendelian inheritance has its physical basis in the behavior of chromosomes

15.2 Sex-linked genes exhibit unique patterns of inheritance

15.3 Linked genes tend to be inherited together because they are located near each other on the same chromosome

15.4 Alterations of chromosome number or structure cause some genetic disorders

15.5 Some inheritance patterns are exceptions to the standard chromosome theory

OVERVIEW

Locating Genes Along Chromosomes

Gregor Mendel's "hereditary factors" were purely an abstract concept when he proposed their existence in 1860. At that time, no cellular structures were known that could house these imaginary units. Even after chromosomes were first observed, many biologists remained skeptical about Mendel's laws of segregation and independent assortment until there was sufficient evidence that these principles of heredity had a physical basis in chromosomal behavior.

Today, we can show that genes—Mendel's "factors"—are located along chromosomes. We can see the location of a particular gene by tagging chromosomes with a fluorescent dye that highlights that gene. For example, the yellow dots in **Figure 15.1** mark the locus of a specific gene on a homologous pair of human chromosomes. (Because the chromosomes in this light micrograph have already replicated, we see two dots per chromosome, one on each sister chromatid.) In this chapter, which integrates and extends what you learned in the past two chapters, we describe the chromosomal basis for the transmission of genes from parents to offspring, along with some important exceptions to the standard mode of inheritance.

CONCEPT 15.1

Mendelian inheritance has its physical basis in the behavior of chromosomes

Using improved techniques of microscopy, cytologists worked out the process of mitosis in 1875 and meiosis in the 1890s. Cytology and genetics converged when biologists began to see parallels between the behavior of chromosomes and the behavior of Mendel's proposed hereditary factors during sexual life cycles: Chromosomes and genes are both present in pairs in diploid cells; homologous chromosomes separate and alleles segregate during the process of meiosis; and fertilization restores the paired condition for both chromosomes and genes. Around 1902, Walter S. Sutton, Theodor Boveri, and others independently noted these parallels, and the **chromosome theory of inheritance** began to take form. According to this theory, Mendelian genes have specific loci (positions) along chromosomes, and it is the chromosomes that undergo segregation and independent assortment.

Figure 15.2 shows that the behavior of homologous chromosomes during meiosis can account for the segregation of the alleles at each genetic locus to different gametes. The figure also shows that the behavior of nonhomologous chromosomes can account for the independent assortment of the alleles for two or more genes located on different chromosomes. By carefully studying this figure, which traces the same dihybrid pea cross you learned about in Figure 14.8, you can see how the behavior of chromosomes during meiosis in the F_1 generation and subsequent random fertilization give rise to the F_2 phenotypic ratio observed by Mendel.

P Generation

Starting with two true-breeding pea plants, we will follow two genes through the F_1 and F_2 generations. The two genes specify seed color (allele Y for yellow and allele y for green) and seed shape (allele R for round and allele r for wrinkled). These two genes are on different chromosomes. (Peas have seven chromosome pairs, but only two pairs are illustrated here.)

Yellow-round seeds (*YYRR*)

Green-wrinkled seeds (*yyrr*)

×

Meiosis

Fertilization

Gametes

All F_1 plants produce yellow-round seeds (*YyRr*)

F_1 Generation

LAW OF SEGREGATION
The two alleles for each gene separate during gamete formation. As an example, follow the fate of the long chromosomes (carrying *R* and *r*). Read the numbered explanations below.

Meiosis

Two equally probable arrangements of chromosomes at metaphase I

LAW OF INDEPENDENT ASSORTMENT
Alleles of genes on nonhomologous chromosomes assort independently during gamete formation. As an example, follow both the long and short chromosomes along both paths. Read the numbered explanations below.

❶ The *R* and *r* alleles segregate at anaphase I, yielding two types of daughter cells for this locus.

❶ Alleles at both loci segregate in anaphase I, yielding four types of daughter cells, depending on the chromosome arrangement at metaphase I. Compare the arrangement of the *R* and *r* alleles relative to the *Y* and *y* alleles in anaphase I.

Anaphase I

Metaphase II

❷ Each gamete gets one long chromosome with either the *R* or *r* allele.

❷ Each gamete gets a long and a short chromosome in one of four allele combinations.

Gametes

$\frac{1}{4}$ (*YR*) $\frac{1}{4}$ (*yr*) $\frac{1}{4}$ (*Yr*) $\frac{1}{4}$ (*yR*)

F_2 Generation

An $F_1 \times F_1$ cross-fertilization

❸ Fertilization recombines the *R* and *r* alleles at random.

9 ⬤ : 3 ⬤ : 3 ⬤ : 1 ⬤

❸ Fertilization results in the 9:3:3:1 phenotypic ratio in the F_2 generation.

▲ **Figure 15.2 The chromosomal basis of Mendel's laws.** Here we correlate the results of one of Mendel's dihybrid crosses (see Figure 14.8) with the behavior of chromosomes during meiosis (see Figure 13.8). The arrangement of chromosomes at metaphase I of meiosis and their movement during anaphase I account for the segregation and independent assortment of the alleles for seed color and shape. Each cell that undergoes meiosis in an F_1 plant produces two kinds of gametes. If we count the results for all cells, however, each F_1 plant produces equal numbers of all four kinds of gametes because the alternative chromosome arrangements at metaphase I are equally likely.

? *If you crossed an F_1 plant with a plant that was homozygous recessive for both genes (yyrr), how would the phenotypic ratio of the offspring compare with the 9:3:3:1 ratio seen here?*

Morgan's Experimental Evidence: *Scientific Inquiry*

The first solid evidence associating a specific gene with a specific chromosome came early in the 20th century from the work of Thomas Hunt Morgan, an experimental embryologist at Columbia University. Although Morgan was initially skeptical about both Mendelism and the chromosome theory, his early experiments provided convincing evidence that chromosomes are indeed the location of Mendel's heritable factors.

Morgan's Choice of Experimental Organism

Many times in the history of biology, important discoveries have come to those insightful enough or lucky enough to choose an experimental organism suitable for the research problem being tackled. Mendel chose the garden pea because a number of distinct varieties were available. For his work, Morgan selected a species of fruit fly, *Drosophila melanogaster*, a common insect that feeds on the fungi growing on fruit. Fruit flies are prolific breeders; a single mating will produce hundreds of offspring, and a new generation can be bred every two weeks. Morgan's laboratory began using this convenient organism for genetic studies in 1907 and soon became known as "the fly room."

Another advantage of the fruit fly is that it has only four pairs of chromosomes, which are easily distinguishable with a light microscope. There are three pairs of autosomes and one pair of sex chromosomes. Female fruit flies have a homologous pair of X chromosomes, and males have one X chromosome and one Y chromosome.

While Mendel could readily obtain different pea varieties from seed suppliers, Morgan was probably the first person to want different varieties of the fruit fly. He faced the tedious task of carrying out many matings and then microscopically inspecting large numbers of offspring in search of naturally occurring variant individuals. After many months of this, he lamented, "Two years' work wasted. I have been breeding those flies for all that time and I've got nothing out of it." Morgan persisted, however, and was finally rewarded with the discovery of a single male fly with white eyes instead of the usual red. The phenotype for a character most commonly observed in natural populations, such as red eyes in *Drosophila*, is called the **wild type** (Figure 15.3). Traits that are alternatives to the wild type, such as white eyes in *Drosophila*, are called *mutant phenotypes* because they are due to alleles assumed to have originated as changes, or mutations, in the wild-type allele.

Morgan and his students invented a notation for symbolizing alleles in *Drosophila* that is still widely used for fruit flies. For a given character in flies, the gene takes its symbol from the first mutant (non–wild type) discovered. Thus, the allele for white eyes in *Drosophila* is symbolized by *w*. A superscript + identifies the allele for the wild-type trait—w^+ for the allele for red eyes, for example. Over the years, a variety of gene notation systems have been developed for different organisms.

▲ **Figure 15.3 Morgan's first mutant.** Wild-type *Drosophila* flies have red eyes (left). Among his flies, Morgan discovered a mutant male with white eyes (right). This variation made it possible for Morgan to trace a gene for eye color to a specific chromosome (LMs).

For example, human genes are usually written in all capitals, such as *HD* for the allele for Huntington's disease.

Correlating Behavior of a Gene's Alleles with Behavior of a Chromosome Pair

Morgan mated his white-eyed male fly with a red-eyed female. All the F_1 offspring had red eyes, suggesting that the wild-type allele is dominant. When Morgan bred the F_1 flies to each other, he observed the classical 3:1 phenotypic ratio among the F_2 offspring. However, there was a surprising additional result: The white-eye trait showed up only in males. All the F_2 females had red eyes, while half the males had red eyes and half had white eyes. Therefore, Morgan concluded that somehow a fly's eye color was linked to its sex. (If the eye-color gene were unrelated to sex, one would have expected half of the white-eyed flies to be male and half female.)

Recall that a female fly has two X chromosomes (XX), while a male fly has an X and a Y (XY). The correlation between the trait of white eye color and the male sex of the affected F_2 flies suggested to Morgan that the gene involved in his white-eyed mutant was located exclusively on the X chromosome, with no corresponding allele present on the Y chromosome. His reasoning can be followed in **Figure 15.4**. For a male, a single copy of the mutant allele would confer white eyes; since a male has only one X chromosome, there can be no wild-type allele (w^+) present to offset the recessive allele. On the other hand, a female could have white eyes only if both her X chromosomes carried the recessive mutant allele (w). This was impossible for the F_2 females in Morgan's experiment because all the F_1 fathers had red eyes.

Morgan's finding of the correlation between a particular trait and an individual's sex provided support for the chromosome theory of inheritance: namely, that a specific gene is carried on a specific chromosome (in this case, an eye-color gene

In a cross between a wild-type female fruit fly and a mutant white-eyed male, what color eyes will the F₁ and F₂ offspring have?

EXPERIMENT Thomas Hunt Morgan wanted to analyze the behavior of two alleles of a fruit fly eye-color gene. In crosses similar to those done by Mendel with pea plants, Morgan and his colleagues mated a wild-type (red-eyed) female with a mutant white-eyed male.

Morgan then bred an F₁ red-eyed female to an F₁ red-eyed male to produce the F₂ generation.

RESULTS The F₂ generation showed a typical Mendelian ratio of 3 red-eyed flies : 1 white-eyed fly. However, no females displayed the white-eye trait; all white-eyed flies were males.

CONCLUSION All F₁ offspring had red eyes, so the mutant white-eye trait (w) must be recessive to the wild-type red-eye trait (w^+). Since the recessive trait—white eyes—was expressed only in males in the F₂ generation, Morgan deduced that this eye-color gene is located on the X chromosome and that there is no corresponding locus on the Y chromosome.

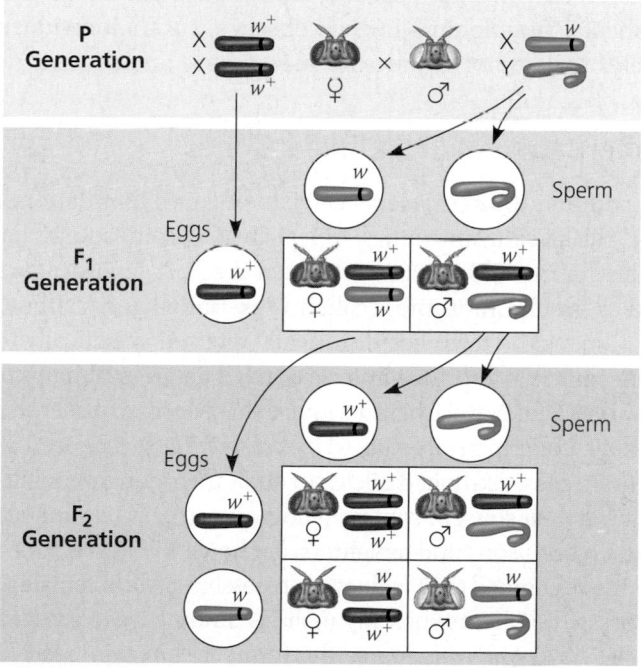

SOURCE T. H. Morgan, Sex-limited inheritance in *Drosophila*, *Science* 32:120–122 (1910).

WHAT IF? Suppose this eye-color gene were located on an autosome. Predict the phenotypes (including gender) of the F₂ flies in this hypothetical cross. (*Hint:* Draw a Punnett square.)

---

on the X chromosome). In addition, Morgan's work indicated that genes located on a sex chromosome exhibit unique inheritance patterns, which we will discuss in the next section. Recognizing the importance of Morgan's early work, many bright students were attracted to his fly room.

CONCEPT CHECK **15.1**

1. Which one of Mendel's laws relates to the inheritance of alleles for a single character? Which law relates to the inheritance of alleles for two characters in a dihybrid cross?
2. What is the physical basis of Mendel's laws?
3. **WHAT IF?** Propose a possible reason that the first naturally occurring mutant fruit fly Morgan saw involved a gene on a sex chromosome.

For suggested answers, see Appendix A.

CONCEPT **15.2**
Sex-linked genes exhibit unique patterns of inheritance

As you just learned, Morgan's discovery of a trait (white eyes) that correlated with the sex of flies was a key episode in the development of the chromosome theory of inheritance. Because the identity of the sex chromosomes in an individual could be inferred by observing the sex of the fly, the behavior of the two members of the pair of sex chromosomes could be correlated with the behavior of the two alleles of the eye-color gene. In this section, we consider the role of sex chromosomes in inheritance in more detail. We begin by reviewing the chromosomal basis of sex determination in humans and some other animals.

The Chromosomal Basis of Sex

Whether we are male or female is one of our more obvious phenotypic characters. Although the anatomical and physiological differences between women and men are numerous, the chromosomal basis for determining sex is rather simple. In humans and other mammals, there are two varieties of sex chromosomes, designated X and Y. The Y chromosome is much smaller than the X chromosome (**Figure 15.5**). A person who inherits two X chromosomes, one from each parent, usually develops as a female. A male develops from a zygote containing one X chromosome and one Y chromosome

▲ Figure 15.5 **Human sex chromosomes.**

(Figure 15.6a). Short segments at either end of the Y chromosome are the only regions that are homologous with corresponding regions of the X. These homologous regions allow the X and Y chromosomes in males to pair and behave like homologous chromosomes during meiosis in the testes.

(a) The X-Y system. In mammals, the sex of an offspring depends on whether the sperm cell contains an X chromosome or a Y.

(b) The X-0 system. In grasshoppers, cockroaches, and some other insects, there is only one type of sex chromosome, the X. Females are XX; males have only one sex chromosome (X0). Sex of the offspring is determined by whether the sperm cell contains an X chromosome or no sex chromosome.

(c) The Z-W system. In birds, some fishes, and some insects, the sex chromosomes present in the egg (not the sperm) determine the sex of offspring. The sex chromosomes are designated Z and W. Females are ZW and males are ZZ.

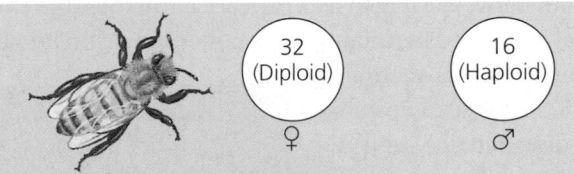

(d) The haplo-diploid system. There are no sex chromosomes in most species of bees and ants. Females develop from fertilized eggs and are thus diploid. Males develop from unfertilized eggs and are haploid; they have no fathers.

▲ **Figure 15.6 Some chromosomal systems of sex determination.** Numerals indicate the number of autosomes in the species pictured. In *Drosophila*, males are XY, but sex depends on the ratio between the number of X chromosomes and the number of autosome sets, not simply on the presence of a Y chromosome.

In both testes and ovaries, the two sex chromosomes segregate during meiosis, and each gamete receives one. Each egg contains one X chromosome. In contrast, sperm fall into two categories: Half the sperm cells a male produces contain an X chromosome, and half contain a Y chromosome. We can trace the sex of each offspring to the moment of conception: If a sperm cell bearing an X chromosome happens to fertilize an egg, the zygote is XX, a female; if a sperm cell containing a Y chromosome fertilizes an egg, the zygote is XY, a male (see Figure 15.6a). Thus, sex determination is a matter of chance—a fifty-fifty chance. Besides the mammalian X-Y system, three other chromosomal systems for determining sex are shown in **Figure 15.6b–d**.

In humans, the anatomical signs of sex begin to emerge when the embryo is about 2 months old. Before then, the rudiments of the gonads are generic—they can develop into either testes or ovaries, depending on whether or not a Y chromosome is present. In 1990, a British research team identified a gene on the Y chromosome required for the development of testes. They named the gene *SRY*, for *s*ex-determining *r*egion of *Y*. In the absence of *SRY*, the gonads develop into ovaries. The biochemical, physiological, and anatomical features that distinguish males and females are complex, and many genes are involved in their development. In fact, *SRY* codes for a protein that regulates other genes.

Researchers have sequenced the human Y chromosome and have identified 78 genes, which code for about 25 proteins (some genes are duplicates). About half of these genes are expressed only in the testis, and some are required for normal testicular functioning. In their absence, an XY individual is male but does not produce normal sperm.

Inheritance of Sex-Linked Genes

In addition to their role as carriers of genes that determine sex, the sex chromosomes, especially X chromosomes, have genes for many characters unrelated to sex. A gene located on either sex chromosome is called a **sex-linked gene**, although in humans the term has historically referred specifically to a gene on the X chromosome. Sex-linked genes in humans follow the same pattern of inheritance that Morgan observed for the eye-color locus he studied in *Drosophila* (see Figure 15.4). Fathers pass sex-linked alleles to all of their daughters but to none of their sons. In contrast, mothers can pass sex-linked alleles to both sons and daughters, as shown in **Figure 15.7**.

If a sex-linked trait is due to a recessive allele, a female will express the phenotype only if she is a homozygote. Because males have only one locus, the terms *homozygous* and *heterozygous* lack meaning for describing their sex-linked genes; the term *hemizygous* is used in such cases. Any male receiving the recessive allele from his mother will express the trait. For this reason, far more males than females have sex-linked recessive disorders. However, even though the chance of a female inheriting a double dose of the mutant allele is much less

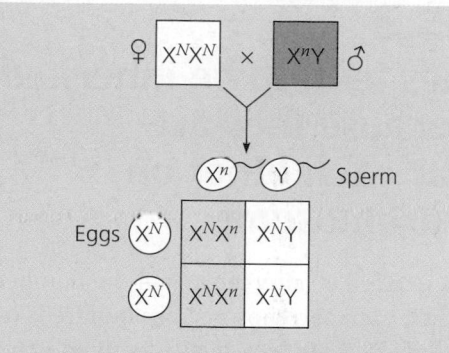

(a) A color-blind father will transmit the mutant allele to all daughters but to no sons. When the mother is a dominant homozygote, the daughters will have the normal phenotype but will be carriers of the mutation.

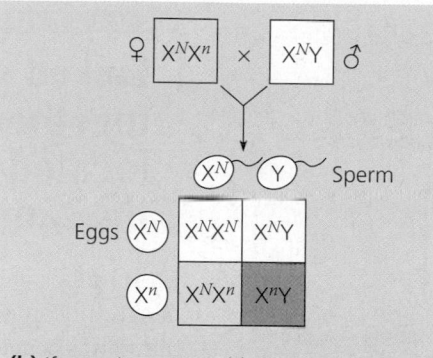

(b) If a carrier mates with a male who has normal color vision, there is a 50% chance that each daughter will be a carrier like her mother and a 50% chance that each son will have the disorder.

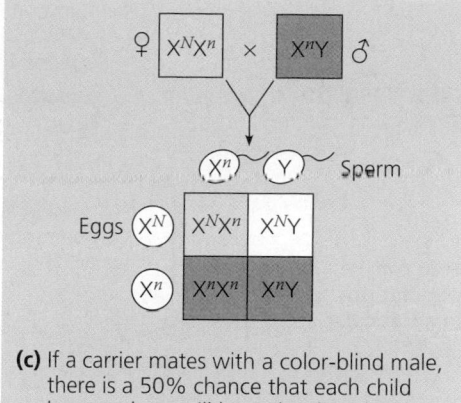

(c) If a carrier mates with a color-blind male, there is a 50% chance that each child born to them will have the disorder, regardless of sex. Daughters who have normal color vision will be carriers, whereas males who have normal color vision will be free of the recessive allele.

▲ **Figure 15.7 The transmission of sex-linked recessive traits.** In this diagram, color blindness is used as an example. The superscript N represents the dominant allele for normal color vision carried on the X chromosome, and the superscript n represents the recessive allele, which has a mutation causing color blindness. White boxes indicate unaffected individuals, light orange boxes indicate carriers, and dark orange boxes indicate color-blind individuals.

? *If a color-blind woman married a man who had normal color vision, what would be the probable phenotypes of their children?*

than the probability of a male inheriting a single dose, there *are* females with sex-linked disorders. For instance, color blindness is a mild disorder inherited as a sex-linked trait. A color-blind daughter may be born to a color-blind father whose mate is a carrier (see Figure 15.7c). Because the sex-linked allele for color blindness is relatively rare, though, the probability that such a man and woman will mate is low.

A number of human sex-linked disorders are much more serious than color blindness. An example is **Duchenne muscular dystrophy**, which affects about one out of every 3,500 males born in the United States. The disease is characterized by a progressive weakening of the muscles and loss of coordination. Affected individuals rarely live past their early 20s. Researchers have traced the disorder to the absence of a key muscle protein called dystrophin and have mapped the gene for this protein to a specific locus on the X chromosome.

Hemophilia is a sex-linked recessive disorder defined by the absence of one or more of the proteins required for blood clotting. When a person with hemophilia is injured, bleeding is prolonged because a firm clot is slow to form. Small cuts in the skin are usually not a problem, but bleeding in the muscles or joints can be painful and can lead to serious damage. Today, people with hemophilia are treated as needed with intravenous injections of the missing protein.

X Inactivation in Female Mammals

Since female mammals, including humans, inherit two X chromosomes, you may wonder whether females make twice as much of the proteins encoded by genes on the X chromosome, compared to the amounts in males. In fact, one X chromosome

in each cell in females becomes almost completely inactivated during embryonic development. As a result, the cells of females and males have the same effective dose (one copy) of these genes. The inactive X in each cell of a female condenses into a compact object called a **Barr body**, which lies along the inside of the nuclear envelope. Most of the genes of the X chromosome that forms the Barr body are not expressed. In the ovaries, Barr-body chromosomes are reactivated in the cells that give rise to eggs, so every female gamete has an active X.

British geneticist Mary Lyon demonstrated that selection of which X chromosome will form the Barr body occurs randomly and independently in each embryonic cell present at the time of X inactivation. As a consequence, females consist of a *mosaic* of two types of cells: those with the active X derived from the father and those with the active X derived from the mother. After an X chromosome is inactivated in a particular cell, all mitotic descendants of that cell have the same inactive X. Thus, if a female is heterozygous for a sex-linked trait, about half her cells will express one allele, while the others will express the alternate allele. **Figure 15.8**, on the next page, shows how this mosaicism results in the mottled coloration of a tortoiseshell cat. In humans, mosaicism can be observed in a recessive X-linked mutation that prevents the development of sweat glands. A woman who is heterozygous for this trait has patches of normal skin and patches of skin lacking sweat glands.

Inactivation of an X chromosome involves modification of the DNA, including attachment of methyl groups ($-CH_3$) to one of the nitrogenous bases of DNA nucleotides. (The regulatory role of DNA methylation is discussed further in Chapter 18.) Researchers also have discovered an X chromosome gene called *XIST* (for <u>X-i</u>nactive <u>s</u>pecific <u>t</u>ranscript) that is active

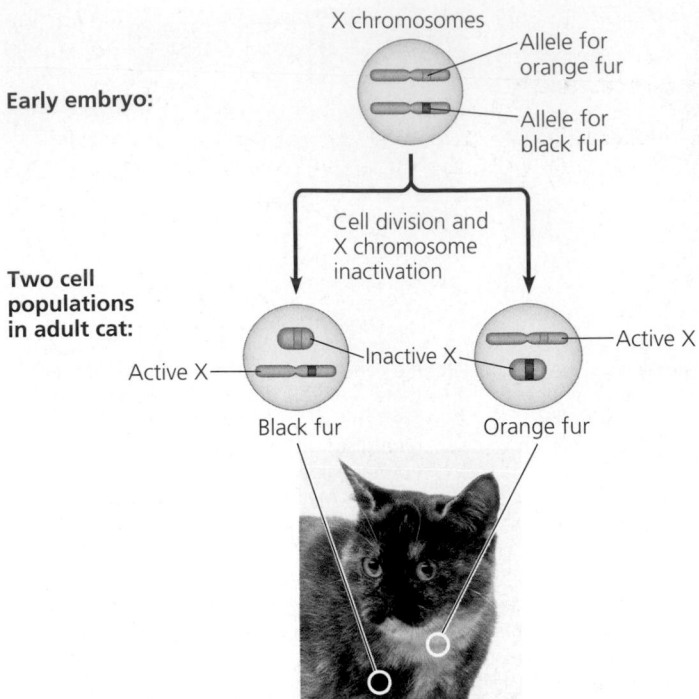

Early embryo:

X chromosomes
— Allele for orange fur
— Allele for black fur

Cell division and X chromosome inactivation

Two cell populations in adult cat:

Active X — — Inactive X
Active X

Black fur   Orange fur

▲ **Figure 15.8 X inactivation and the tortoiseshell cat.** The tortoiseshell gene is on the X chromosome, and the tortoiseshell phenotype requires the presence of two different alleles, one for orange fur and one for black fur. Normally, only females can have both alleles, because only they have two X chromosomes. If a female is heterozygous for the tortoiseshell gene, she is tortoiseshell. Orange patches are formed by populations of cells in which the X chromosome with the orange allele is active; black patches have cells in which the X chromosome with the black allele is active. ("Calico" cats also have white areas, which are determined by yet another gene.)

only on the Barr-body chromosome. Multiple copies of the RNA product of this gene apparently attach to the X chromosome on which they are made, eventually almost covering it. Interaction of this RNA with the chromosome seems to initiate X inactivation, and regulation of this process by other genes is currently an active area of research.

CONCEPT CHECK 15.2

1. A white-eyed female *Drosophila* is mated with a red-eyed (wild-type) male, the reciprocal cross of the one shown in Figure 15.4. What phenotypes and genotypes do you predict for the offspring?

2. Neither Tim nor Rhoda has Duchenne muscular dystrophy, but their firstborn son does have it. What is the probability that a second child of this couple will have the disease? What is the probability if the second child is a boy? A girl?

3. **WHAT IF?** During early embryonic development of female carriers for color blindness, the normal allele is inactivated by chance in about half the cells. Why, then, aren't 50% of female carriers color-blind?

For suggested answers, see Appendix A.

Linked genes tend to be inherited together because they are located near each other on the same chromosome

The number of genes in a cell is far greater than the number of chromosomes; in fact, each chromosome has hundreds or thousands of genes. (Only 78 genes have been identified so far on the Y chromosome, but more may be found as methods for analyzing genetic sequences become more refined.) Genes located on the same chromosome that tend to be inherited together in genetic crosses are said to be **linked genes**. (Note the distinction between the terms *sex-linked gene*, referring to a single gene on a sex chromosome, and *linked genes*, referring to two or more genes on the same chromosome that tend to be inherited together.) When geneticists follow linked genes in breeding experiments, the results deviate from those expected from Mendel's law of independent assortment.

How Linkage Affects Inheritance

To see how linkage between genes affects the inheritance of two different characters, let's examine another of Morgan's *Drosophila* experiments. In this case, the characters are body color and wing size, each with two different phenotypes. Wild-type flies have gray bodies and normal-sized wings. In addition to these flies, Morgan had doubly mutant flies with black bodies and wings much smaller than normal, called vestigial wings. The mutant alleles are recessive to the wild-type alleles, and neither gene is on a sex chromosome. In his investigation of these two genes, Morgan carried out the crosses shown in **Figure 15.9**.

In these crosses, Morgan observed a much higher proportion of parental phenotypes than would be expected if the two genes assorted independently. Based on these results, he concluded that body color and wing size are usually inherited together in specific combinations (the parental combinations) because the genes for these characters are on the same chromosome:

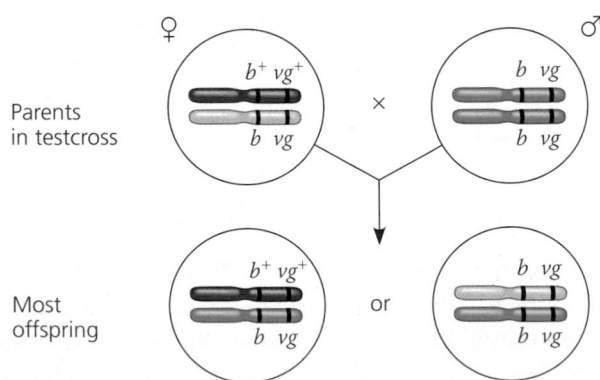

Parents in testcross

♀ $b^+ vg^+$ / $b\ vg$ ×   ♂ $b\ vg$ / $b\ vg$

Most offspring

$b^+ vg^+$ / $b\ vg$ or $b\ vg$ / $b\ vg$

Inquiry

How does linkage between two genes affect inheritance of characters?

EXPERIMENT   Morgan wanted to know whether the genes for body color and wing size were on the same chromosome, and if so, how this affected their inheritance. The alleles for body color are b^+ (gray) and b (black), and those for wing size are vg^+ (normal) and vg (vestigial).

Morgan first mated true-breeding wild-type flies with black, vestigial-winged flies to produce heterozygous F$_1$ dihybrids ($b^+ b$ $vg^+ vg$), all of which are wild-type in appearance.

He then mated wild-type F$_1$ dihybrid females with black, vestigial-winged males.

The male's sperm contributes only recessive alleles, so the phenotype of the offspring reflects the genotype of the female's eggs.

Note: Although only females (with pointed abdomen) are shown, half the offspring in each class would be male (with rounded abdomen).

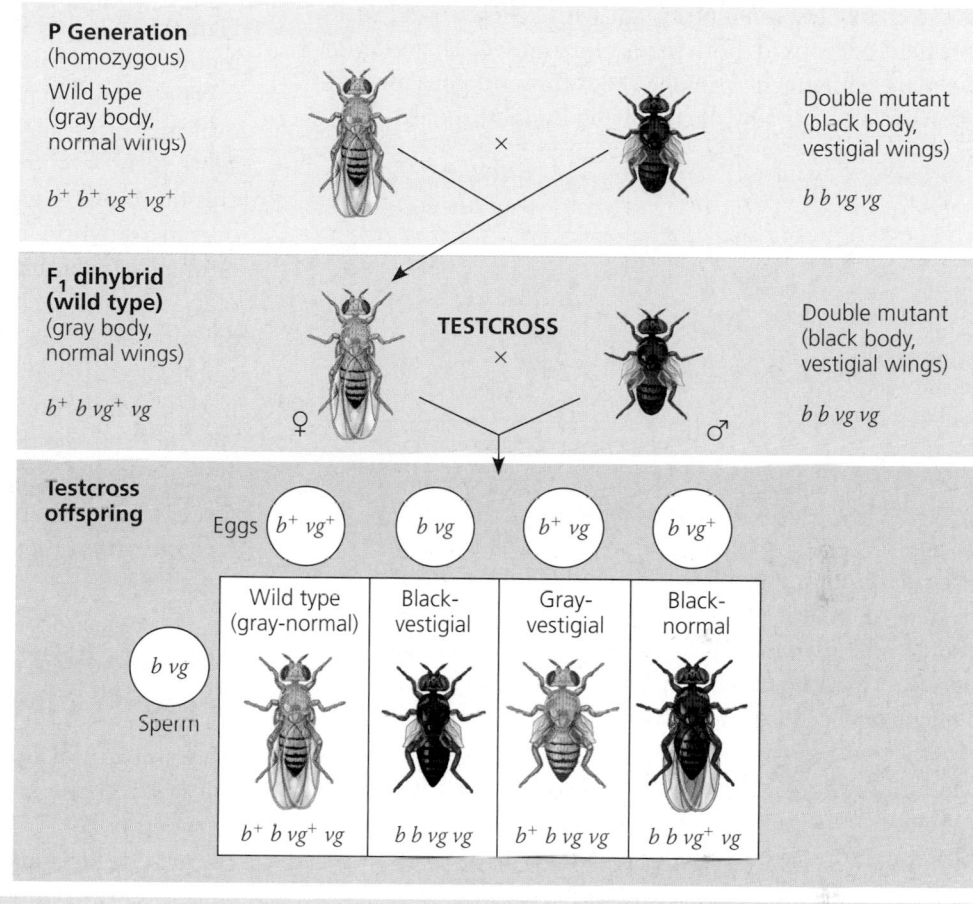

PREDICTED RATIOS

If genes are located on different chromosomes:	1	:	1	:	1	:	1
If genes are located on the same chromosome *and* parental alleles are always inherited together:	1	:	1	:	0	:	0

RESULTS

	965	:	944	:	206	:	185

CONCLUSION   Since most offspring had a parental phenotype, Morgan concluded that the genes for body color and wing size are located on the same chromosome. However, the production of a relatively small number of offspring with nonparental phenotypes indicated that some mechanism occasionally breaks the linkage between specific alleles of genes on the same chromosome.

SOURCE   T. H. Morgan, The explanation of a new sex ratio in *Drosophila, Science* 36:718–720 (1912).

WHAT IF?   If the parental flies had been true-breeding for gray body with vestigial wings and black body with normal wings, which phenotypic class(es) would be largest among the testcross offspring?

However, as Figure 15.9 shows, both of the nonparental phenotypes were also produced in Morgan's experiments, suggesting that the body-color and wing-size genes are only partially linked genetically. To understand this conclusion, we need to further explore **genetic recombination**, the production of offspring with combinations of traits that differ from those found in either parent.

Genetic Recombination and Linkage

In Chapter 13, you learned that meiosis and random fertilization generate genetic variation among offspring of sexually reproducing organisms. Here we will examine the chromosomal basis of recombination in relation to the genetic findings of Mendel and Morgan.

Recombination of Unlinked Genes: Independent Assortment of Chromosomes

Mendel learned from crosses in which he followed two characters that some offspring have combinations of traits that do not match those of either parent. For example, we can represent the cross between a pea plant with yellow-round seeds that is heterozygous for both seed color and seed shape (*YyRr*) and a plant with green-wrinkled seeds (homozygous for both recessive alleles, *yyrr*) by the following Punnett square

Gametes from yellow-round heterozygous parent (*YyRr*)

Gametes from green-wrinkled homozygous recessive parent (*yyrr*)

YR *yr* *Yr* *yR*

yr

YyRr *yyrr* *Yyrr* *yyRr*

Parental-type offspring

Recombinant offspring

Notice in this Punnett square that one-half of the offspring are expected to inherit a phenotype that matches one of the parental phenotypes. These offspring are called **parental types**. But two nonparental phenotypes are also found among the offspring. Because these offspring have new combinations of seed shape and color, they are called **recombinant types**, or **recombinants** for short. When 50% of all offspring are recombinants, as in this example, geneticists say that there is a 50% frequency of recombination. The predicted phenotypic ratios among the offspring are similar to what Mendel actually found in *YyRr* × *yyrr* crosses (a type of testcross).

A 50% frequency of recombination in such testcrosses is observed for any two genes that are located on different chromosomes and are thus unlinked. The physical basis of recombination between unlinked genes is the random orientation of homologous chromosomes at metaphase I of meiosis, which leads to the independent assortment of the two unlinked genes (see Figure 13.11 and the question in the Figure 15.2 legend).

Recombination of Linked Genes: Crossing Over

Now let's return to Morgan's fly room to see how we can explain the results of the *Drosophila* testcross illustrated in Figure 15.9. Recall that most of the offspring from the testcross for body color and wing size had parental phenotypes. That suggested that the two genes were on the same chromosome, since the occurrence of parental types with a frequency greater than 50% indicates that the genes are linked. About 17% of offspring, however, were recombinants.

Faced with these results, Morgan proposed that some process must occasionally break the physical connection between specific alleles of genes on the same chromosome. Sub-

sequent experiments demonstrated that this process, now called **crossing over**, accounts for the recombination of linked genes. In crossing over, which occurs while replicated homologous chromosomes are paired during prophase of meiosis I, a set of proteins orchestrates an exchange of corresponding segments of one maternal and one paternal chromatid (see Figure 13.12). In effect, end portions of two nonsister chromatids trade places each time a crossover occurs.

The recombinant chromosomes resulting from crossing over may bring alleles together in new combinations, and the subsequent events of meiosis distribute the recombinant chromosomes to gametes. **Figure 15.10** shows how crossing over in a dihybrid female fly resulted in recombinant eggs and ultimately recombinant offspring in Morgan's testcross. Most of the eggs had a chromosome with either the $b^+ vg^+$ or $b\ vg$ parental genotype for body color and wing size, but some eggs had a recombinant chromosome ($b^+ vg$ or $b\ vg^+$). Fertilization of these various classes of eggs by homozygous recessive sperm ($b\ vg$) produced an offspring population in which 17% exhibited a nonparental, recombinant phenotype. As we discuss next, the percentage of recombinant offspring, the *recombination frequency*, is related to the distance between linked genes.

Mapping the Distance Between Genes Using Recombination Data: *Scientific Inquiry*

The discovery of linked genes and recombination due to crossing over led one of Morgan's students, Alfred H. Sturtevant, to a method for constructing a **genetic map**, an ordered list of the genetic loci along a particular chromosome.

Sturtevant hypothesized that recombination frequencies calculated from experiments like the one in Figures 15.9 and 15.10 depend on the distances between genes on a chromosome. He assumed that crossing over is a random event, with the chance of crossing over approximately equal at all points along a chromosome. Based on these assumptions, Sturtevant predicted that *the farther apart two genes are, the higher the probability that a crossover will occur between them and therefore the higher the recombination frequency*. His reasoning was simple: The greater the distance between two genes, the more points there are between them where crossing over can occur. Using recombination data from various fruit fly crosses, Sturtevant proceeded to assign relative positions to genes on the same chromosomes—that is, to *map* genes.

A genetic map based on recombination frequencies is called a **linkage map**. **Figure 15.11**, on page 296, shows Sturtevant's linkage map of three genes: the body-color (*b*) and wing-size (*vg*) genes depicted in Figure 15.10 and a third gene, called cinnabar (*cn*). Cinnabar is one of many *Drosophila* genes affecting eye color. Cinnabar eyes, a mutant phenotype, are a brighter red than the wild-type color. The recombination frequency between *cn* and *b* is 9%; that between *cn* and *vg*,

Testcross parents

Gray body, normal wings
(F₁ dihybrid)

Black body, vestigial wings
(double mutant)

b^+ vg^+
b vg

b vg
b vg

♀

♂

Replication of chromosomes

Replication of chromosomes

b^+ vg^+
b^+ vg^+
b vg
b vg

b vg
b vg
b vg
b vg

Meiosis I: Crossing over between b and vg loci produces new allele combinations.

Meiosis I and II: No new allele combinations are produced.

b^+ vg^+
b^+ vg
b vg^+
b vg

Meiosis II: Separation of chromatids produces recombinant gametes with the new allele combinations.

Recombinant chromosomes

Eggs

b^+ vg^+

b vg

b^+ vg

b vg^+

Testcross offspring

965 Wild type (gray-normal)	944 Black-vestigial	206 Gray-vestigial	185 Black-normal
b^+ vg^+	b vg	b^+ vg	b vg^+
b vg	b vg	b vg	b vg

b vg

Sperm

Parental-type offspring   Recombinant offspring

$$\text{Recombination frequency} = \frac{391 \text{ recombinants}}{2{,}300 \text{ total offspring}} \times 100 = 17\%$$

◄ **Figure 15.10 Chromosomal basis for recombination of linked genes.** In these diagrams re-creating the testcross in Figure 15.9, we track chromosomes as well as genes. The maternal chromosomes are color-coded red and pink to distinguish one homolog from the other before any meiotic crossing over has taken place. Because crossing over between the b and vg loci occurs in some, but not all, egg-producing cells, more eggs with parental-type chromosomes than with recombinant ones are produced in the mating females. Fertilization of the eggs by sperm of genotype b vg gives rise to some recombinant offspring. The recombination frequency is the percentage of recombinant flies in the total pool of offspring.

DRAW IT *Suppose, as in the question at the bottom of Figure 15.9, that the parental flies were true-breeding for gray body with vestigial wings and black body with normal wings. Draw the chromosomes in each of the four possible kinds of eggs from an F₁ female, and label each chromosome as "parental" or "recombinant."*

9.5%; and that between b and vg, 17%. In other words, crossovers between cn and b and between cn and vg are about half as frequent as crossovers between b and vg. Only a map that locates cn about midway between b and vg is consistent with these data, as you can prove to yourself by drawing alternative maps. Sturtevant expressed the distances between genes in **map units**, defining one map unit as equivalent to a 1% recombination frequency. Today, map units are often called *centimorgans* in honor of Morgan.

In practice, the interpretation of recombination data is more complicated than this example suggests. For example, some genes on a chromosome are so far from each other that a crossover between them is virtually certain. The observed fre-

quency of recombination in crosses involving two such genes can have a maximum value of 50%, a result indistinguishable from that for genes on different chromosomes. In this case, the physical connection between genes on the same chromosome is not reflected in the results of genetic crosses. Despite being on the same chromosome and thus being *physically linked*, the genes are *genetically unlinked*; alleles of such genes assort independently, as if they were on different chromosomes. In fact, several of the genes for pea characters that Mendel studied are now known to be on the same chromosome, but the distance between them is so great that linkage is not observed in genetic crosses. Consequently, they behaved as if they were on different chromosomes in Mendel's experiments. Genes located far

Research Method

Constructing a Linkage Map

APPLICATION   A linkage map shows the relative locations of genes along a chromosome.

TECHNIQUE   A linkage map is based on the assumption that the probability of a crossover between two genetic loci is proportional to the distance separating the loci. The recombination frequencies used to construct a linkage map for a particular chromosome are obtained from experimental crosses, such as the cross depicted in Figures 15.9 and 15.10. The distances between genes are expressed as map units (centimorgans), with one map unit equivalent to a 1% recombination frequency. Genes are arranged on the chromosome in the order that best fits the data.

RESULTS   In this example, the observed recombination frequencies between three *Drosophila* gene pairs (*b–cn* 9%, *cn–vg* 9.5%, and *b–vg* 17%) best fit a linear order in which *cn* is positioned about halfway between the other two genes:

The *b–vg* recombination frequency (17%) is slightly less than the sum of the *b–cn* and *cn–vg* frequencies (9 + 9.5 = 18.5%) because of the few times that a crossover occurs between *b* and *cn* and an additional crossover occurs between *cn* and *vg*. The second crossover would "cancel out" the first, reducing the observed *b–vg* recombination frequency while contributing to the frequency between each of the closer pairs of genes. The value of 18.5% (18.5 map units) is closer to the actual distance between the genes, so a geneticist would add the smaller distances in constructing a map.

apart on a chromosome are mapped by adding the recombination frequencies from crosses involving a set of closer pairs of genes lying between the two distant genes.

Using recombination data, Sturtevant and his colleagues were able to map numerous *Drosophila* genes in linear arrays. They found that the genes clustered into four groups of linked genes. Because light microscopy had revealed four pairs of chromosomes in *Drosophila* cells, the linkage map thus provided additional evidence that genes are located on chromosomes. Each chromosome has a linear array of specific genes, each with its own locus **(Figure 15.12)**.

Because a linkage map is based only on recombination frequencies, it gives only an approximate picture of a chromosome. The frequency of crossing over is not actually uniform over the length of a chromosome, as Sturtevant assumed, and therefore map units do not correspond to actual physical distances (in nanometers, for instance). A linkage map does portray the order of genes along a chromosome, but it does not accurately portray the precise locations of those genes. Other methods enable geneticists to construct **cytogenetic maps** of chromosomes, which

▲ **Figure 15.12 A partial genetic (linkage) map of a *Drosophila* chromosome.** This simplified map shows just a few of the genes that have been mapped on *Drosophila* chromosome II. The number at each gene locus indicates the number of map units between that locus and the locus for arista length (left). Notice that more than one gene can affect a given phenotypic characteristic, such as eye color. Also, note that in contrast to the homologous autosomes (II–IV), the X and Y sex chromosomes (I) have distinct shapes.

locate genes with respect to chromosomal features, such as stained bands, that can be seen in the microscope. The ultimate maps, which we will discuss in Chapter 21, show the physical distances between gene loci in DNA nucleotides. Comparing a linkage map with such a physical map or with a cytogenetic map of the same chromosome, we find that the linear order of genes is identical in all the maps, but the spacing between genes is not.

CONCEPT CHECK   **15.3**

1. When two genes are located on the same chromosome, what is the physical basis for the production of recombinant offspring in a testcross between a dihybrid parent and a double-mutant (recessive) parent?
2. For each type of offspring of the testcross in Figure 15.9, explain the relationship between its phenotype and the alleles contributed by the female parent.
3. **WHAT IF?**   Genes *A*, *B*, and *C* are located on the same chromosome. Testcrosses show that the recombination frequency between *A* and *B* is 28% and between *A* and *C* is 12%. Can you determine the linear order of these genes? Explain.

For suggested answers, see Appendix A.

Alterations of chromosome number or structure cause some genetic disorders

As you have learned so far in this chapter, the phenotype of an organism can be affected by small-scale changes involving individual genes. Random mutations are the source of all new alleles, which can lead to new phenotypic traits.

Large-scale chromosomal changes can also affect an organism's phenotype. Physical and chemical disturbances, as well as errors during meiosis, can damage chromosomes in major ways or alter their number in a cell. Large-scale chromosomal alterations often lead to spontaneous abortion (miscarriage) of a fetus, and individuals born with these types of genetic defects commonly exhibit various developmental disorders. In plants, such genetic defects may be tolerated to a greater extent than in animals.

Abnormal Chromosome Number

Ideally, the meiotic spindle distributes chromosomes to daughter cells without error. But there is an occasional mishap, called a **nondisjunction**, in which the members of a pair of homologous chromosomes do not move apart properly during meiosis I or sister chromatids fail to separate during meiosis II (**Figure 15.13**). In these cases, one gamete receives two of the same type of chromosome and another gamete receives no copy. The other chromosomes are usually distributed normally.

If either of the aberrant gametes unites with a normal one at fertilization, the zygote will also have an abnormal number of a chromosome, a condition known as **aneuploidy**. (Aneuploidy may involve more than one chromosome.) Fertilization involving a gamete that has no copy of a particular chromosome will lead to a missing chromosome in the zygote (so that the cell has $2n - 1$ chromosomes); the aneuploid zygote is said to be **monosomic** for that chromosome. If a chromosome is present in triplicate in the zygote (so that the cell has $2n + 1$ chromosomes), the aneuploid cell is **trisomic** for that chromosome. Mitosis will subsequently transmit the anomaly to all embryonic cells. If the organism survives, it usually has a set of traits caused by the abnormal dose of the genes associated with the extra or missing chromosome. Down syndrome is an example of trisomy in humans that will be discussed later. Nondisjunction can also occur during mitosis. If such an error takes place early in embryonic development, then the aneuploid condition is passed along by mitosis to a large number of cells and is likely to have a substantial effect on the organism.

Some organisms have more than two complete chromosome sets in all somatic cells. The general term for this chromosomal alteration is **polyploidy**; the specific terms *triploidy* ($3n$) and *tetraploidy* ($4n$) indicate three or four chromosomal sets, respectively. One way a triploid cell may arise is by the fertilization of an abnormal diploid egg produced by nondisjunction of all its chromosomes. Tetraploidy could result from the failure of a $2n$ zygote to divide after replicating its chromosomes. Subsequent normal mitotic divisions would then produce a $4n$ embryo.

Polyploidy is fairly common in the plant kingdom. As we will see in Chapter 24, the spontaneous origin of polyploid individuals plays an important role in the evolution of plants. Many of the plant species we eat are polyploid; for example, bananas are triploid and wheat is hexaploid ($6n$). In the animal kingdom, polyploid species are much less common, although they are known to occur among fishes and amphibians. Researchers in Chile were the first to identify a polyploid mammal, a rodent whose cells are tetraploid (**Figure 15.14**, on the next page); a closely related species also appears to be tetraploid. In general, polyploids are more nearly normal in appearance than aneuploids. One extra (or missing) chromosome apparently disrupts genetic balance more than does an entire extra set of chromosomes.

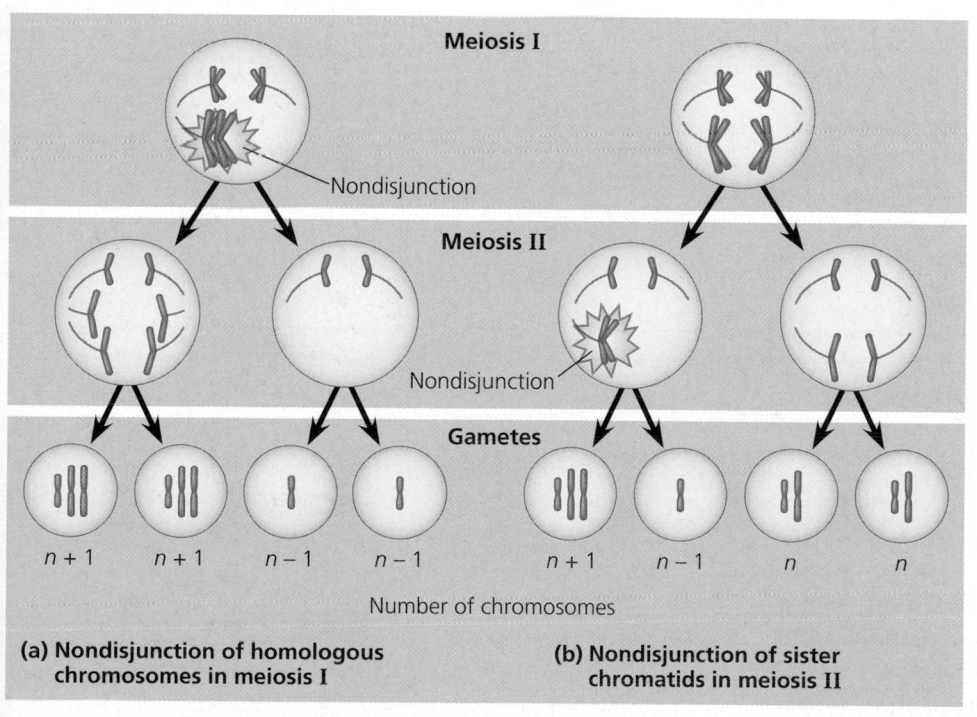

(a) Nondisjunction of homologous chromosomes in meiosis I

(b) Nondisjunction of sister chromatids in meiosis II

▲ **Figure 15.13 Meiotic nondisjunction.** Gametes with an abnormal chromosome number can arise by nondisjunction in either meiosis I or meiosis II.

▲ **Figure 15.14 A tetraploid mammal.** The somatic cells of this burrowing rodent, *Tympanoctomys barrerae*, have about twice as many chromosomes as those of closely related species. Interestingly, its sperm's head is unusually large, presumably a necessity for holding all that genetic material. Scientists think that this tetraploid species may have arisen when an ancestor doubled its chromosome number, presumably by errors in mitosis or meiosis within the animal's reproductive organs.

Alterations of Chromosome Structure

Errors in meiosis or damaging agents such as radiation can cause breakage of a chromosome, which can lead to four types of changes in chromosome structure (**Figure 15.15**). A **deletion** occurs when a chromosomal fragment is lost. The affected chromosome is then missing certain genes. (If the centromere is deleted, the entire chromosome will be lost.) The "deleted" fragment may become attached as an extra segment to a sister chromatid, producing a **duplication**. Alterna-

tively, a detached fragment could attach to a nonsister chromatid of a homologous chromosome. In that case, though, the "duplicated" segments might not be identical because the homologs could carry different alleles of certain genes. A chromosomal fragment may also reattach to the original chromosome but in the reverse orientation, producing an **inversion**. A fourth possible result of chromosomal breakage is for the fragment to join a nonhomologous chromosome, a rearrangement called a **translocation**.

Deletions and duplications are especially likely to occur during meiosis. In crossing over, nonsister chromatids sometimes exchange unequal-sized segments of DNA, so that one partner gives up more genes than it receives. The products of such a *nonreciprocal* crossover are one chromosome with a deletion and one chromosome with a duplication.

A diploid embryo that is homozygous for a large deletion (or has a single X chromosome with a large deletion, in a male) is usually missing a number of essential genes, a condition that is ordinarily lethal. Duplications and translocations also tend to be harmful. In reciprocal translocations, in which segments are exchanged between nonhomologous chromosomes, and in inversions, the balance of genes is not abnormal—all genes are present in their normal doses. Nevertheless, translocations and inversions can alter phenotype because a gene's expression can be influenced by its location among neighboring genes; such events sometimes have devastating effects.

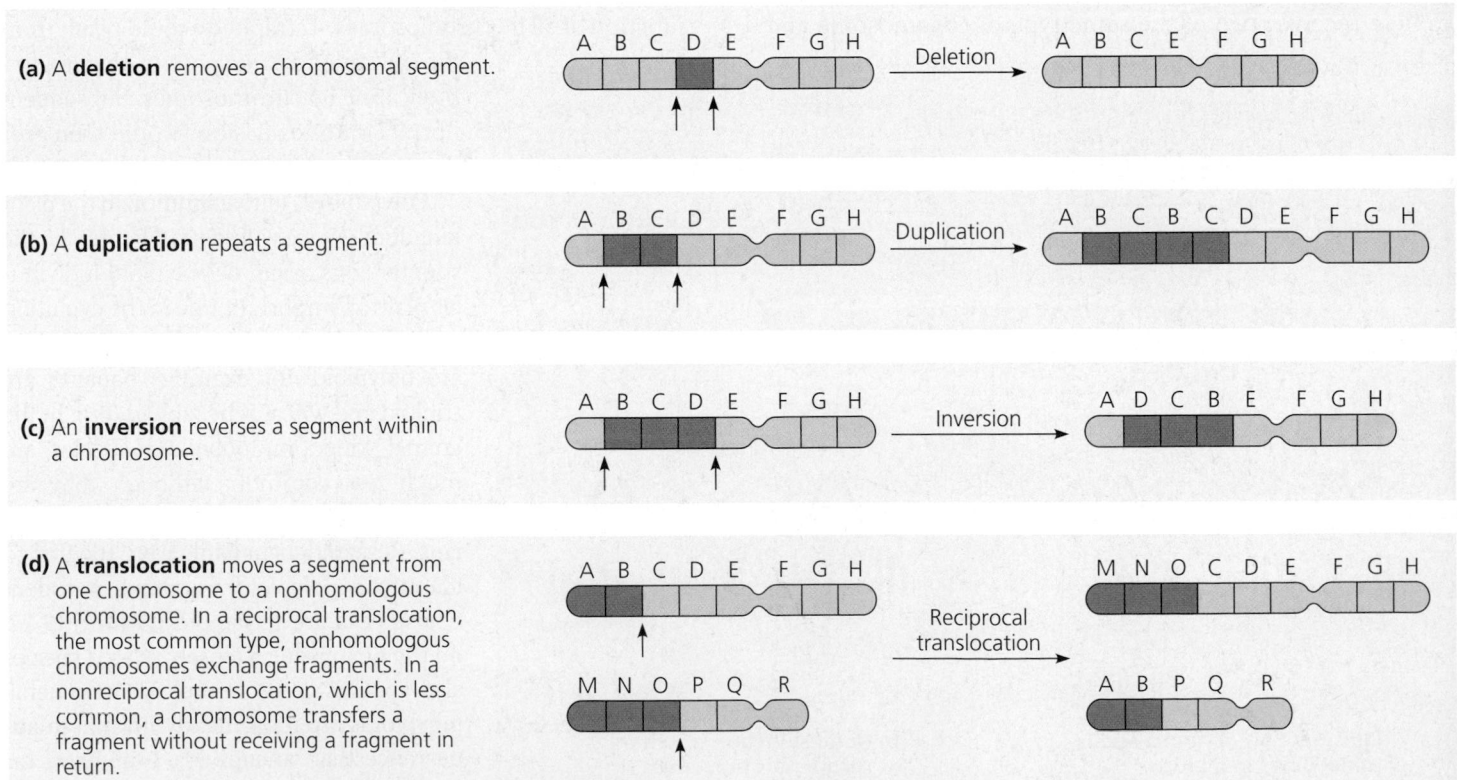

(a) A **deletion** removes a chromosomal segment.

(b) A **duplication** repeats a segment.

(c) An **inversion** reverses a segment within a chromosome.

(d) A **translocation** moves a segment from one chromosome to a nonhomologous chromosome. In a reciprocal translocation, the most common type, nonhomologous chromosomes exchange fragments. In a nonreciprocal translocation, which is less common, a chromosome transfers a fragment without receiving a fragment in return.

▲ **Figure 15.15 Alterations of chromosome structure.** Vertical arrows indicate breakage points. Dark purple highlights the chromosomal parts affected by the rearrangements.

Human Disorders Due to Chromosomal Alterations

Alterations of chromosome number and structure are associated with a number of serious human disorders. As described earlier, nondisjunction in meiosis results in aneuploidy in gametes and any resulting zygotes. Although the frequency of aneuploid zygotes may be quite high in humans, most of these chromosomal alterations are so disastrous to development that the embryos are spontaneously aborted long before birth. However, some types of aneuploidy appear to upset the genetic balance less than others, with the result that individuals with certain aneuploid conditions can survive to birth and beyond. These individuals have a set of traits—a *syndrome*—characteristic of the type of aneuploidy. Genetic disorders caused by aneuploidy can be diagnosed before birth by fetal testing (see Figure 14.18).

Down Syndrome (Trisomy 21)

One aneuploid condition, **Down syndrome**, affects approximately one out of every 700 children born in the United States (Figure 15.16). Down syndrome is usually the result of an extra chromosome 21, so that each body cell has a total of 47 chromosomes. Because the cells are trisomic for chromosome 21, Down syndrome is often called *trisomy 21*. Down syndrome includes characteristic facial features, short stature, heart defects, susceptibility to respiratory infection, and mental retardation. Furthermore, individuals with Down syndrome are prone to developing leukemia and Alzheimer's disease. Although people with Down syndrome, on average,

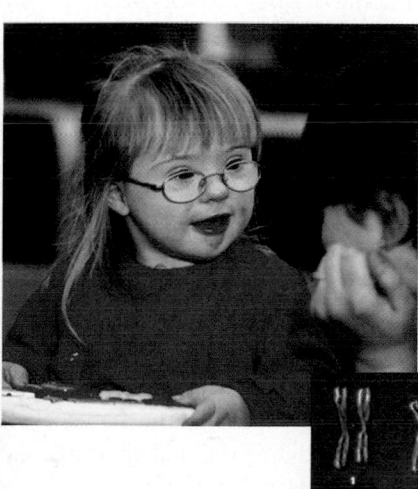

▲ Figure 15.16 **Down syndrome.** The child exhibits the facial features characteristic of Down syndrome. The karyotype shows trisomy 21, the most common cause of this disorder.

have a life span shorter than normal, some live to middle age or beyond. Most are sexually underdeveloped and sterile.

The frequency of Down syndrome increases with the age of the mother. While the disorder occurs in just 0.04% of children born to women under age 30, the risk climbs to 0.92% for mothers at age 40 and is even higher for older mothers. The correlation of Down syndrome with maternal age has not yet been explained. Most cases result from nondisjunction during meiosis I, and some research points to an age-dependent abnormality in a meiosis checkpoint that normally delays anaphase until all the kinetochores are attached to the spindle (like the M phase checkpoint of the mitotic cell cycle; see Chapter 12). Trisomies of some other chromosomes also increase in incidence with maternal age, although infants with other autosomal trisomies rarely survive for long. Prenatal screening for trisomies in the embryo is now offered to all pregnant women since the possible benefits outweigh any risks.

Aneuploidy of Sex Chromosomes

Nondisjunction of sex chromosomes produces a variety of aneuploid conditions. Most of these conditions appear to upset genetic balance less than aneuploid conditions involving autosomes. This may be because the Y chromosome carries relatively few genes and because extra copies of the X chromosome become inactivated as Barr bodies in somatic cells.

An extra X chromosome in a male, producing XXY, occurs approximately once in every 2,000 live births. People with this disorder, called *Klinefelter syndrome*, have male sex organs, but the testes are abnormally small and the man is sterile. Even though the extra X is inactivated, some breast enlargement and other female body characteristics are common. Affected individuals may have subnormal intelligence. Males with an extra Y chromosome (XYY) do not exhibit any well-defined syndrome, but they tend to be somewhat taller than average.

Females with trisomy X (XXX), which occurs once in approximately 1,000 live births, are healthy and cannot be distinguished from XX females except by karyotype. Monosomy X, called *Turner syndrome*, occurs about once in every 5,000 births and is the only known viable monosomy in humans. Although these X0 individuals are phenotypically female, they are sterile because their sex organs do not mature. When provided with estrogen replacement therapy, girls with Turner syndrome do develop secondary sex characteristics. Most have normal intelligence.

Disorders Caused by Structurally Altered Chromosomes

Many deletions in human chromosomes, even in a heterozygous state, cause severe problems. One such syndrome, known as *cri du chat* ("cry of the cat"), results from a specific deletion in chromosome 5. A child born with this deletion is mentally retarded, has a small head with unusual facial features, and has a cry that sounds like the mewing of a distressed cat. Such individuals usually die in infancy or early childhood.

Chromosomal translocations have been implicated in certain cancers, including *chronic myelogenous leukemia* (*CML*). This disease occurs when a reciprocal translocation happens during mitosis of cells that will become white blood cells. In these cells, the exchange of a large portion of chromosome 22 with a small fragment from a tip of chromosome 9 produces a much shortened, easily recognized chromosome 22, called the *Philadelphia chromosome* (**Figure 15.17**). We will discuss how such an exchange can cause cancer in Chapter 18.

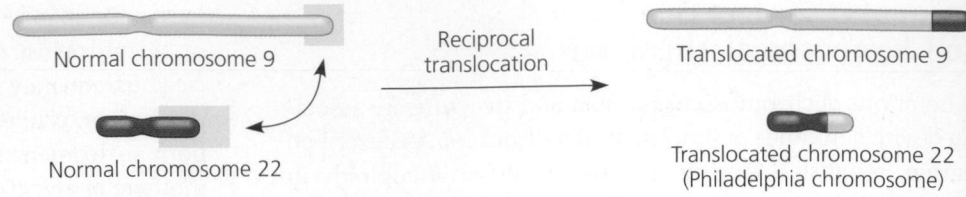

▲ **Figure 15.17 Translocation associated with chronic myelogenous leukemia (CML).** The cancerous cells in nearly all CML patients contain an abnormally short chromosome 22, the so-called Philadelphia chromosome, and an abnormally long chromosome 9. These altered chromosomes result from the translocation shown here, which presumably occurred in a single white blood cell precursor undergoing mitosis and was then passed along to all descendant cells.

CONCEPT CHECK 15.4

1. More common than completely polyploid animals are mosaic polyploids, animals that are diploid except for patches of polyploid cells. How might a mosaic tetraploid—an animal with some cells containing four sets of chromosomes—arise?

2. About 5% of individuals with Down syndrome have a chromosomal translocation in which a third copy of chromosome 21 is attached to chromosome 14. If this translocation occurred in a parent's gonad, how could it lead to Down syndrome in a child?

3. **WHAT IF?** The ABO blood type locus has been mapped on chromosome 9. A father who has type AB blood and a mother who has type O blood have a child with trisomy 9 and type A blood. Using this information, can you tell in which parent the nondisjunction occurred? Explain your answer.

For suggested answers, see Appendix A.

CONCEPT 15.5
Some inheritance patterns are exceptions to the standard chromosome theory

In the previous section, you learned about deviations from the usual patterns of chromosomal inheritance due to abnormal events in meiosis and mitosis. We conclude this chapter by describing two normally occurring exceptions to Mendelian genetics, one involving genes located in the nucleus and the other involving genes located outside the nucleus. In both cases, the sex of the parent contributing an allele is a factor in the pattern of inheritance.

Genomic Imprinting

Throughout our discussions of Mendelian genetics and the chromosomal basis of inheritance, we have assumed that a given allele will have the same effect whether it was inherited from the mother or the father. This is probably a safe assumption most of the time. For example, when Mendel crossed purple-flowered pea plants with white-flowered pea plants, he observed the same results regardless of whether the purple-flowered parent supplied the eggs or the sperm. In recent years, however, geneticists have identified two to three dozen traits in mammals that depend on which parent passed along the alleles for those traits. Such variation in phenotype depending on whether an allele is inherited from the male or female parent is called **genomic imprinting**. (Note that this phenomenon is different from sex linkage; most imprinted genes are on autosomes.)

Genomic imprinting occurs during the formation of gametes and results in the silencing of one allele of certain genes. Because these genes are imprinted differently in sperm and eggs, a zygote expresses only one allele of an imprinted gene, either the allele inherited from the female parent or the allele inherited from the male parent. The imprints are transmitted to all the body cells during development, so either the maternal or paternal allele of a given imprinted gene is expressed in every cell of that organism. In each generation, the old imprints are "erased" in gamete-producing cells, and the chromosomes of the developing gametes are newly imprinted according to the sex of the individual forming the gametes. In a given species, the imprinted genes are always imprinted in the same way. For instance, a gene imprinted for maternal allele expression is always imprinted for maternal allele expression, generation after generation.

Consider, for example, the mouse gene for insulin-like growth factor 2 (*Igf2*), one of the first imprinted genes to be identified. Although this growth factor is required for normal prenatal growth, only the paternal allele is expressed (**Figure 15.18a**). Evidence that the *Igf2* gene is imprinted initially came from crosses between wild-type mice and dwarf mice homozygous for a recessive mutation in the *Igf2* gene. The phenotypes of heterozygous offspring (which had one normal allele and one

(a) Homozygote. A mouse homozygous for the wild-type *Igf2* allele is normal sized. Only the paternal allele of this gene is expressed.

Paternal chromosome — Normal *Igf2* allele is expressed
Maternal chromosome — Normal *Igf2* allele is not expressed
Wild-type mouse (normal size)

Mutant *Igf2* allele inherited from mother
Normal size mouse (wild type)
Normal *Igf2* allele is expressed
Mutant *Igf2* allele is not expressed

Mutant *Igf2* allele inherited from father
Dwarf mouse (mutant)
Mutant *Igf2* allele is expressed
Normal *Igf2* allele is not expressed

(b) Heterozygotes. Matings between wild-type mice and those homozygous for the recessive mutant *Igf2* allele produce heterozygous offspring. The mutant phenotype is seen only when the father contributed the mutant allele because the maternal allele is not expressed.

▲ **Figure 15.18 Genomic imprinting of the mouse *Igf2* gene.**

mutant) differed, depending on whether the mutant allele came from the mother or the father **(Figure 15.18b).**

What exactly is a genomic imprint? In many cases, it seems to consist of methyl (—CH₃) groups that are added to cytosine nucleotides of one of the alleles. Such methylation may directly silence the allele, an effect consistent with evidence that heavily methylated genes are usually inactive (see Chapter 18). However, for a few genes, methylation has been shown to *activate* expression of the allele. This is the case for the *Igf2* gene: Methylation of certain cytosines on the paternal chromosome leads to expression of the paternal *Igf2* allele.

Genomic imprinting is thought to affect only a small fraction of the genes in mammalian genomes, but most of the known imprinted genes are critical for embryonic development. In experiments with mice, for example, embryos engineered to inherit both copies of certain chromosomes from the same parent usually die before birth, whether that parent is male or female. In 2004, however, scientists in Japan combined the genetic material from two eggs in a zygote while allowing

expression of the *Igf2* gene from only one of the egg nuclei. The zygote developed into an apparently healthy mouse, shown in the photograph at the right. Apparently, normal development requires that embryonic cells have exactly one active copy—not zero, not two—of certain genes. The association of aberrant imprinting with abnormal development and certain cancers has stimulated numerous studies of how different genes are imprinted.

Inheritance of Organelle Genes

Although our focus in this chapter has been on the chromosomal basis of inheritance, we end with an important amendment: Not all of a eukaryotic cell's genes are located on nuclear chromosomes, or even in the nucleus. Some genes are located in organelles in the cytoplasm; because they are outside the nucleus, these genes are sometimes called *extranuclear genes* or *cytoplasmic genes.* Mitochondria, as well as chloroplasts and other plant plastids, contain small circular DNA molecules that carry a number of genes. These organelles reproduce themselves and transmit their genes to daughter organelles. Organelle genes are not distributed to offspring according to the same rules that direct the distribution of nuclear chromosomes during meiosis, so they do not display Mendelian inheritance.

The first hint that extranuclear genes exist came from studies by the German scientist Karl Correns on the inheritance of yellow or white patches on the leaves of an otherwise green plant. In 1909, he observed that the coloration of the offspring was determined only by the maternal parent (the source of eggs) and not by the paternal parent (the source of sperm). Subsequent research showed that such coloration patterns, or variegation, are due to mutations in plastid genes that control pigmentation **(Figure 15.19).** In most plants, a zygote receives all its plastids from the cytoplasm of the egg and none from the sperm, which contributes little more than a haploid set of chromosomes. As the zygote develops, plastids containing

▶ **Figure 15.19 Variegated leaves from *Croton dioicus*.** Variegated (striped or spotted) leaves result from mutations in pigment genes located in plastids, which generally are inherited from the maternal parent.

wild-type or mutant pigment genes are distributed randomly to daughter cells. The pattern of leaf coloration exhibited by a plant depends on the ratio of wild-type to mutant plastids in its various tissues.

Similar maternal inheritance is also the rule for mitochondrial genes in most animals and plants, because almost all the mitochondria passed on to a zygote come from the cytoplasm of the egg. The products of most mitochondrial genes help make up the protein complexes of the electron transport chain and ATP synthase (see Chapter 9). Defects in one or more of these proteins, therefore, reduce the amount of ATP the cell can make and have been shown to cause a number of rare human disorders. Because the parts of the body most susceptible to energy deprivation are the nervous system and the muscles, most mitochondrial diseases primarily affect these systems. For example, *mitochondrial myopathy* causes weakness, intolerance of exercise, and muscle deterioration. Another mitochondrial disorder is *Leber's hereditary optic neuropathy*, which can produce sudden blindness in people as young as their 20s or 30s. The four mutations found thus far to cause this disorder affect oxidative phosphorylation during cellular respiration, a crucial function for the cell.

In addition to the rare diseases clearly caused by defects in mitochondrial DNA, mitochondrial mutations inherited from a person's mother may contribute to at least some cases of diabetes and heart disease, as well as to other disorders that commonly debilitate the elderly, such as Alzheimer's disease. In the course of a lifetime, new mutations gradually accumulate in our mitochondrial DNA, and some researchers think that these mutations play a role in the normal aging process.

Wherever genes are located in the cell—in the nucleus or in cytoplasmic organelles—their inheritance depends on the precise replication of DNA, the genetic material. In the next chapter, you will learn how this molecular reproduction occurs.

CONCEPT CHECK 15.5

1. Gene dosage, the number of active copies of a gene, is important to proper development. Identify and describe two processes that establish the proper dosage of certain genes.
2. Reciprocal crosses between two primrose varieties, A and B, produced the following results: A female × B male ⟶ offspring with all green (nonvariegated) leaves. B female × A male ⟶ offspring with spotted (variegated) leaves. Explain these results.
3. **WHAT IF?** Mitochondrial genes are critical to the energy metabolism of cells, but mitochondrial disorders caused by mutations in these genes are generally not lethal. Why not?

For suggested answers, see Appendix A.

Chapter 15 Review

SUMMARY OF KEY CONCEPTS

CONCEPT 15.1

Mendelian inheritance has its physical basis in the behavior of chromosomes (pp. 286–289)

▶ The behavior of chromosomes during meiosis accounts for Mendel's laws of segregation and independent assortment.

▶ **Morgan's Experimental Evidence:** *Scientific Inquiry* Morgan's discovery that transmission of the X chromosome in *Drosophila* correlates with inheritance of an eye-color trait was the first solid evidence indicating that a specific gene is associated with a specific chromosome.

MEDIA

MP3 Tutor Chromosomal Basis of Inheritance

CONCEPT 15.2

Sex-linked genes exhibit unique patterns of inheritance (pp. 289–292)

▶ **The Chromosomal Basis of Sex** Sex is an inherited phenotypic character usually determined by which sex chromosomes are present. Humans and other mammals have an X-Y system in which sex is determined by whether a Y chromosome is present. Other systems are found in birds, fishes, and insects.

▶ **Inheritance of Sex-Linked Genes** The sex chromosomes carry genes for some traits that are unrelated to sex characteristics. For instance, recessive alleles causing color blindness are carried on the X chromosome. Fathers transmit this and other sex-linked alleles to all daughters but to no sons. Any male who inherits such an allele from his mother will express the trait.

▶ **X Inactivation in Female Mammals** In mammalian females, one of the two X chromosomes in each cell is randomly inactivated during early embryonic development. If a female is heterozygous for a particular gene located on the X chromosome, she will be mosaic for that character, with about half her cells expressing the maternal allele and about half expressing the paternal allele.

MEDIA

Activity Sex-Linked Genes
Investigation What Can Fruit Flies Reveal About Inheritance?

CONCEPT 15.3

Linked genes tend to be inherited together because they are located near each other on the same chromosome (pp. 292–296)

▶ **How Linkage Affects Inheritance**

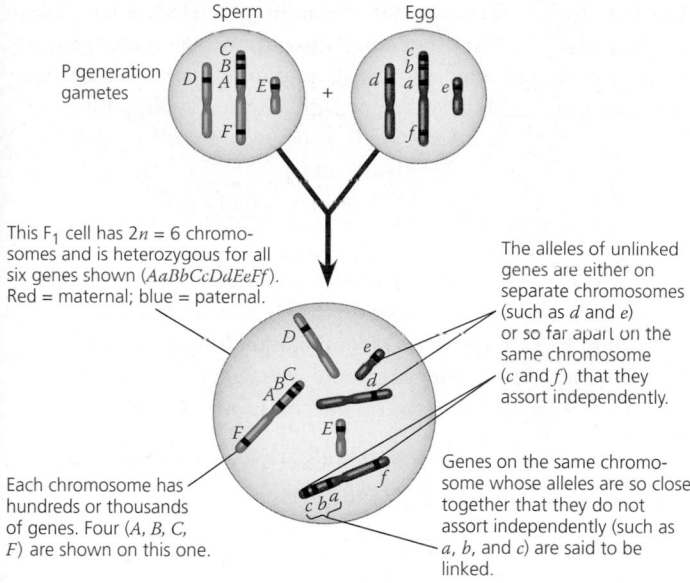

Sperm   Egg

P generation gametes

This F₁ cell has $2n = 6$ chromosomes and is heterozygous for all six genes shown ($AaBbCcDdEeFf$). Red = maternal; blue = paternal.

The alleles of unlinked genes are either on separate chromosomes (such as d and e) or so far apart on the same chromosome (c and f) that they assort independently.

Each chromosome has hundreds or thousands of genes. Four (A, B, C, F) are shown on this one.

Genes on the same chromosome whose alleles are so close together that they do not assort independently (such as a, b, and c) are said to be linked.

▶ **Genetic Recombination and Linkage** Recombinant offspring exhibit new combinations of traits inherited from two parents. Because of the independent assortment of chromosomes, unlinked genes exhibit a 50% frequency of recombination in the gametes. For linked genes, crossing over between nonsister chromatids during meiosis I accounts for the observed recombinants, always less than 50% of the total.

▶ **Mapping the Distance Between Genes Using Recombination Data:** *Scientific Inquiry* The order of genes on a chromosome and the relative distances between them can be deduced from recombination frequencies observed in genetic crosses. The farther apart genes are, the more likely their allele combinations will be recombined during crossing over.

> **MEDIA**
>
> **Activity** Linked Genes and Crossing Over
> **Biology Labs On-Line** FlyLab
> **Biology Labs On-Line** PedigreeLab

CONCEPT **15.4**

Alterations of chromosome number or structure cause some genetic disorders (pp. 297–300)

▶ **Abnormal Chromosome Number** Aneuploidy can result from nondisjunction during meiosis. When a normal gamete unites with one containing two copies or no copies of a particular chromosome, the resulting zygote and its descendant cells either have one extra copy of that chromosome (trisomy, $2n + 1$) or are missing a copy (monosomy, $2n - 1$). Polyploidy (more than two complete sets of chromosomes) can result from complete nondisjunction during gamete formation.

▶ **Alterations of Chromosome Structure** Chromosome breakage can result in deletions, inversions, duplications, and translocations.

▶ **Human Disorders Due to Chromosomal Alterations** Changes in the number of chromosomes per cell or in the structure of individual chromosomes can affect phenotype. Such alterations cause Down syndrome (usually due to trisomy of chromosome 21), certain cancers associated with chromosomal translocations, and various other human disorders.

> **MEDIA**
>
> **Activity** Polyploid Plants

CONCEPT **15.5**

Some inheritance patterns are exceptions to the standard chromosome theory (pp. 300–302)

▶ **Genomic Imprinting** In mammals, the phenotypic effects of certain genes depend on which allele is inherited from each parent. Imprints are formed during gamete production, with the result that one allele (either maternal or paternal) is not expressed in offspring.

▶ **Inheritance of Organelle Genes** The inheritance of traits controlled by the genes present in mitochondria and plastids depends solely on the maternal parent because the zygote's cytoplasm comes from the egg. Some diseases affecting the nervous and muscular systems are caused by defects in mitochondrial genes that prevent cells from making enough ATP.

TESTING YOUR KNOWLEDGE

GENETICS PROBLEMS

1. A man with hemophilia (a recessive, sex-linked condition) has a daughter of normal phenotype. She marries a man who is normal for the trait. What is the probability that a daughter of this mating will be a hemophiliac? That a son will be a hemophiliac? If the couple has four sons, what is the probability that all four will be born with hemophilia?

2. Pseudohypertrophic muscular dystrophy is an inherited disorder that causes gradual deterioration of the muscles. It is seen almost exclusively in boys born to apparently normal parents and usually results in death in the early teens. Is this disorder caused by a dominant or a recessive allele? Is its inheritance sex-linked or autosomal? How do you know? Explain why this disorder is almost never seen in girls.

3. Red-green color blindness is caused by a sex-linked recessive allele. A color-blind man marries a woman with normal vision whose father was color-blind. What is the probability that they will have a color-blind daughter? What is the probability that their first son will be color-blind? (Note the different wording in the two questions.)

4. A wild-type fruit fly (heterozygous for gray body color and normal wings) is mated with a black fly with vestigial wings. The offspring have the following phenotypic distribution: wild type, 778; black-vestigial, 785; black-normal, 158; gray-vestigial, 162. What is the recombination frequency between these genes for body color and wing size?

5. In another cross, a wild-type fruit fly (heterozygous for gray body color and red eyes) is mated with a black fruit fly with purple eyes. The offspring are as follows: wild type, 721; black-purple, 751; gray-purple, 49; black-red, 45. What is the recombination frequency between these genes for body color and eye color? Using information from problem 4, what fruit flies (genotypes and phenotypes) would you mate to determine the sequence of the body-color, wing-size, and eye-color genes on the chromosome?

6. **DRAW IT** A fruit fly that is true-breeding for gray body with vestigial wings ($b^+ b^+ vg vg$) is mated with one that is true-breeding for black body with normal wings ($b b vg^+ vg^+$).
   a. Draw the chromosomes for the P generation flies, using red for the gray fly and pink for the black one. Show the position of each allele.
   b. Draw the chromosomes and label the alleles of an F_1 fly.
   c. Suppose an F_1 female is testcrossed. Draw the chromosomes of the resulting offspring in a Punnett square.
   d. Knowing that the distance between these two genes is 17 map units, predict the phenotypic ratios of these offspring.

7. What pattern of inheritance would lead a geneticist to suspect that an inherited disorder of cell metabolism is due to a defective mitochondrial gene?

8. Women born with an extra X chromosome (XXX) are healthy and phenotypically indistinguishable from normal XX women. What is a likely explanation for this finding? How could you test this explanation?

9. Determine the sequence of genes along a chromosome based on the following recombination frequencies: A–B, 8 map units; A–C, 28 map units; A–D, 25 map units; B–C, 20 map units; B–D, 33 map units.

10. Assume that genes A and B are linked and are 50 map units apart. An animal heterozygous at both loci is crossed with one that is homozygous recessive at both loci. What percentage of the offspring will show phenotypes resulting from crossovers? If you did not know that genes A and B were linked, how would you interpret the results of this cross?

11. A space probe discovers a planet inhabited by creatures that reproduce with the same hereditary patterns seen in humans. Three phenotypic characters are height (T = tall, t = dwarf), head appendages (A = antennae, a = no antennae), and nose morphology (S = upturned snout, s = downturned snout). Since the creatures are not "intelligent," Earth scientists are able to do some controlled breeding experiments using various heterozygotes in testcrosses. For tall heterozygotes with antennae, the offspring are: tall-antennae, 46; dwarf-antennae, 7; dwarf-no antennae, 42; tall-no antennae, 5. For heterozygotes with antennae and an upturned snout, the offspring are: antennae-upturned snout, 47; antennae-downturned snout, 2; no antennae-downturned snout, 48; no antennae-upturned snout, 3. Calculate the recombination frequencies for both experiments.

12. Using the information from problem 11, scientists do a further testcross using a heterozygote for height and nose morphology. The offspring are: tall-upturned snout, 40; dwarf-upturned snout, 9; dwarf-downturned snout, 42; tall-downturned snout, 9. Calculate the recombination frequency from these data; then use your answer from problem 11 to determine the correct sequence of the three linked genes.

13. Two genes of a flower, one controlling blue (B) versus white (b) petals and the other controlling round (R) versus oval (r) stamens, are linked and are 10 map units apart. You cross a homozygous blue-oval plant with a homozygous white-round plant. The resulting F_1 progeny are crossed with homozygous white-oval plants, and 1,000 F_2 progeny are obtained. How many F_2 plants of each of the four phenotypes do you expect?

14. You design *Drosophila* crosses to provide recombination data for gene a, which is located on the chromosome shown in Figure 15.12. Gene a has recombination frequencies of 14% with the vestigial-wing locus and 26% with the brown-eye locus. Where is a located on the chromosome?

15. Banana plants, which are triploid, are seedless and therefore sterile. Propose a possible explanation.

For Genetics Problems answers, see Appendix A.

MEDIA Visit the Study Area at **www.masteringbio.com** for a Practice Test.

EVOLUTION CONNECTION

16. You have seen that crossing over, or recombination, is thought to be evolutionarily advantageous because it continually shuffles genetic alleles into novel combinations, allowing evolutionary processes to occur. Until recently, it was thought that the genes on the Y chromosome might degenerate because they lack homologous genes on the X chromosome with which to recombine. However, when the Y chromosome was sequenced, eight large regions were found to be internally homologous to each other, and quite a few of the 78 genes represent duplicates. (Y chromosome researcher David Page has called it a "hall of mirrors.") What might be a benefit of these regions?

SCIENTIFIC INQUIRY

17. Butterflies have an X-Y sex determination system that is different from that of flies or humans. Female butterflies may be either XY or XO, while butterflies with two or more X chromosomes are males. This photograph shows a tiger swallowtail *gynandromorph*, an individual that is half male (left side) and half female (right side). Given that the first division of the zygote divides the embryo into the future right and left halves of the butterfly, propose a hypothesis that explains how nondisjunction during the first mitosis might have produced this unusual-looking butterfly.

16

The Molecular Basis of Inheritance

KEY CONCEPTS

16.1 DNA is the genetic material

16.2 Many proteins work together in DNA replication and repair

16.3 A chromosome consists of a DNA molecule packed together with proteins

OVERVIEW

Life's Operating Instructions

In April 1953, James Watson and Francis Crick shook the scientific world with an elegant double-helical model for the structure of deoxyribonucleic acid, or DNA. **Figure 16.1** shows Watson (left) and Crick admiring their DNA model, which they built from tin and wire. Over the past 50 years, their model has evolved from a novel proposition to an icon of modern biology. DNA, the substance of inheritance, is the most celebrated molecule of our time. Mendel's heritable factors and Morgan's genes on chromosomes are, in fact, composed of DNA. Chemically speaking, your genetic endowment is the DNA contained in the 46 chromosomes you inherited from your parents and in the mitochondria passed along by your mother.

Of all nature's molecules, nucleic acids are unique in their ability to direct their own replication from monomers. Indeed, the resemblance of offspring to their parents has its basis in the precise replication of DNA and its transmission from one generation to the next. Hereditary information is encoded in the chemical language of DNA and reproduced in all the cells of your body. It is this DNA program that directs the development of your biochemical, anatomical, physiological, and, to some extent, behavioral traits. In this chapter, you will learn how biologists deduced that DNA is the genetic material and how Watson and Crick discovered its structure. You will also see how DNA is replicated—the molecular basis of inheritance—and how cells repair their DNA. Finally, you will explore how a molecule of DNA is packed together with proteins in a chromosome.

DNA is the genetic material

Today, even schoolchildren have heard of DNA, and scientists routinely manipulate DNA in the laboratory, often to change the heritable traits of cells in their experiments. Early in the 20th century, however, the identification of the molecules of inheritance loomed as a major challenge to biologists.

The Search for the Genetic Material: *Scientific Inquiry*

Once T. H. Morgan's group showed that genes are located along chromosomes (described in Chapter 15), the two chemical components of chromosomes—DNA and protein—became the candidates for the genetic material. Until the 1940s, the case for proteins seemed stronger, especially since biochemists had identified them as a class of macromolecules with great heterogeneity and specificity of function, essential requirements for the hereditary material. Moreover, little was known about nucleic acids, whose physical and chemical properties seemed far too uniform to account for the multitude of specific inherited traits exhibited by every organism. This view gradually changed as experiments with microorganisms yielded unexpected results. As with the work of Mendel and Morgan, a key factor in determining the identity of the genetic material was the choice of appropriate experimental organisms. The role of DNA in heredity was first worked out by studying bacteria and the viruses that infect them, which are far simpler than pea plants, fruit flies, or humans. In this section, we will trace the search for the genetic material in some detail as a case study in scientific inquiry.

Evidence That DNA Can Transform Bacteria

We can trace the discovery of the genetic role of DNA back to 1928. While attempting to develop a vaccine against pneumonia, a British medical officer named Frederick Griffith studied *Streptococcus pneumoniae*, a bacterium that causes pneumonia in mammals. Griffith had two strains (varieties) of the bacterium, one pathogenic (disease-causing) and one nonpathogenic (harmless). He was surprised to find that when he killed

the pathogenic bacteria with heat and then mixed the cell remains with living bacteria of the nonpathogenic strain, some of the living cells became pathogenic (**Figure 16.2**). Furthermore, this newly acquired trait of pathogenicity was inherited by all the descendants of the transformed bacteria. Clearly, some chemical component of the dead pathogenic cells caused this heritable change, although the identity of the substance was not known. Griffith called the phenomenon **transformation**, now defined as a change in genotype and phenotype due to the assimilation of external DNA by a cell. (This use of the word *transformation* should not be confused with the conversion of a normal animal cell to a cancerous one, discussed in Chapter 12.)

Griffith's work set the stage for a 14-year search by American bacteriologist Oswald Avery for the identity of the transforming substance. Avery focused on the three main candidates: DNA, RNA (the other nucleic acid), and protein. Avery broke open the heat-killed pathogenic bacteria and extracted the cellular contents. In separate samples, he used specific treatments that inactivated each of the three types of molecules. He then tested each treated sample for its ability to transform live nonpathogenic bacteria. Only when DNA was allowed to remain active did transformation occur. In 1944, Avery and his colleagues Maclyn McCarty and Colin MacLeod announced that the transforming agent was DNA. Their discovery was greeted with interest but considerable skepticism, in part because of the lingering belief that proteins were better candidates to be the genetic material. Moreover, many biologists were not convinced that the genes of bacteria would be similar in composition and function to those of more complex organisms. But the major reason for the continued doubt was that so little was known about DNA.

Evidence That Viral DNA Can Program Cells

Additional evidence for DNA as the genetic material came from studies of viruses that infect bacteria (**Figure 16.3**). These

---

▼ Figure 16.2 Inquiry

Can a genetic trait be transferred between different bacterial strains?

EXPERIMENT   Frederick Griffith studied two strains of the bacterium *Streptococcus pneumoniae*. Bacteria of the S (smooth) strain can cause pneumonia in mice; they are pathogenic because they have a capsule that protects them from an animal's defense system. Bacteria of the R (rough) strain lack a capsule and are nonpathogenic. To test for the trait of pathogenicity, Griffith injected mice with the two strains as shown below:

Living S cells (control)	Living R cells (control)	Heat-killed S cells (control)	Mixture of heat-killed S cells and living R cells

RESULTS

Mouse dies   **Mouse healthy**   **Mouse healthy**   **Mouse dies**

In blood sample, living S cells are found that can reproduce, yielding more S cells.

CONCLUSION   Griffith concluded that the living R bacteria had been transformed into pathogenic S bacteria by an unknown, heritable substance from the dead S cells that allowed the R cells to make capsules.

SOURCE   F. Griffith, The significance of pneumococcal types, *Journal of Hygiene* 27:113–159 (1928).

WHAT IF?   How did this experiment rule out the possibility that the R cells could have simply used the capsules of the dead S cells to become pathogenic?

▲ **Figure 16.3 Viruses infecting a bacterial cell.** T2 and related phages attach to the host cell and inject their genetic material through the plasma membrane, while the head and tail parts remain on the outer bacterial surface (colorized TEM).

viruses are called **bacteriophages** (meaning "bacteria-eaters"), or just **phages**. Viruses are much simpler than cells. A virus is little more than DNA (or sometimes RNA) enclosed by a protective coat, which is often simply protein. To reproduce, a virus must infect a cell and take over the cell's metabolic machinery.

Phages have been widely used as tools by researchers in molecular genetics. In 1952, Alfred Hershey and Martha Chase performed experiments showing that DNA is the genetic material of a phage known as T2. This is one of many phages that infect *Escherichia coli* (*E. coli*), a bacterium that normally lives in the intestines of mammals. At that time, biologists already knew that T2, like many other phages, was composed almost entirely of DNA and protein. They also knew that the T2 phage could quickly turn an *E. coli* cell into a T2-producing factory that released many copies when the cell ruptured. Somehow, T2 could reprogram its host cell to produce viruses. But which viral component—protein or DNA—was responsible?

Hershey and Chase answered this question by devising an experiment showing that only one of the two components of T2 actually enters the *E. coli* cell during infection (**Figure 16.4**). In

▼ Figure 16.4 Inquiry

Is protein or DNA the genetic material of phage T2?

EXPERIMENT Alfred Hershey and Martha Chase used radioactive sulfur and phosphorus to trace the fates of protein and DNA, respectively, of T2 phages that infected bacterial cells. They wanted to see which of these molecules entered and could reprogram the cells to make more phages.

❶ Mixed radioactively labeled phages with bacteria. The phages infected the bacterial cells.

❷ Agitated the mixture in a blender to free phage parts outside the bacteria from the cells.

❸ Centrifuged the mixture so that bacteria formed a pellet at the bottom of the test tube; free phages and phage parts, which are lighter, remained suspended in the liquid.

❹ Measured the radioactivity in the pellet and the liquid.

Phage
Radioactive protein
Bacterial cell
DNA

Batch 1: Phages were grown with radioactive sulfur (^{35}S), which was incorporated into phage protein (pink).

Empty protein shell
Phage DNA
Centrifuge
Radioactivity (phage protein) in liquid
Pellet (bacterial cells and contents)

Radioactive DNA

Batch 2: Phages were grown with radioactive phosphorus (^{32}P), which was incorporated into phage DNA (blue).

Centrifuge
Pellet
Radioactivity (phage DNA) in pellet

RESULTS When proteins were labeled (batch 1), radioactivity remained outside the cells; but when DNA was labeled (batch 2), radioactivity was found inside the cells. Bacterial cells with radioactive phage DNA released new phages with some radioactive phosphorus.

CONCLUSION Phage DNA entered bacterial cells, but phage proteins did not. Hershey and Chase concluded that DNA, not protein, functions as the genetic material of phage T2.

SOURCE A. D. Hershey and M. Chase, Independent functions of viral protein and nucleic acid in growth of bacteriophage, *Journal of General Physiology* 36:39–56 (1952).

WHAT IF? How would the results have differed if proteins carried the genetic information?

their experiment, they used a radioactive isotope of sulfur to tag protein in one batch of T2 and a radioactive isotope of phosphorus to tag DNA in a second batch. Because protein, but not DNA, contains sulfur, radioactive sulfur atoms were incorporated only into the protein of the phage. In a similar way, the atoms of radioactive phosphorus labeled only the DNA, not the protein, because nearly all the phage's phosphorus is in its DNA. In the experiment, separate samples of nonradioactive *E. coli* cells were allowed to be infected by the protein-labeled and DNA-labeled batches of T2. The researchers then tested the two samples shortly after the onset of infection to see which type of molecule—protein or DNA—had entered the bacterial cells and would therefore be capable of reprogramming them.

Hershey and Chase found that the phage DNA entered the host cells but the phage protein did not. Moreover, when these bacteria were returned to a culture medium, the infection ran its course, and the *E. coli* released phages that contained some radioactive phosphorus, further showing that the DNA inside the cell played an ongoing role during the infection process.

Hershey and Chase concluded that the DNA injected by the phage must be the molecule carrying the genetic information that makes the cells produce new viral DNA and proteins. The Hershey-Chase experiment was a landmark study because it provided powerful evidence that nucleic acids, rather than proteins, are the hereditary material, at least for viruses.

Additional Evidence That DNA Is the Genetic Material

Further evidence that DNA is the genetic material came from the laboratory of biochemist Erwin Chargaff. It was already known that DNA is a polymer of nucleotides, each consisting of three components: a nitrogenous (nitrogen-containing) base, a pentose sugar called deoxyribose, and a phosphate group (Figure 16.5). The base can be adenine (A), thymine (T), guanine (G), or cytosine (C). Chargaff analyzed the base composition of DNA from a number of different organisms. In 1950, he reported that the base composition of DNA varies from one species to another. For example, 30.3% of human DNA nucleotides have the base A, whereas DNA from the bacterium *E. coli* has only 26.0% A. This evidence of molecular diversity among species, which had been presumed absent from DNA, made DNA a more credible candidate for the genetic material.

Chargaff also noticed a peculiar regularity in the ratios of nucleotide bases within a single species. In the DNA of each species he studied, the number of adenines approximately equaled the number of thymines, and the number of guanines approximately equaled the number of cytosines. In human DNA, for example, the four bases are present in these percentages: A = 30.3% and T = 30.3%; G = 19.5% and C = 19.9%. The equivalences for any given species between the number of A and T bases and the number of G and C bases became known as *Chargaff's rules*. The basis for these rules remained unexplained until the discovery of the double helix.

▲ **Figure 16.5 The structure of a DNA strand.** Each nucleotide monomer consists of a nitrogenous base (T, A, C, or G), the sugar deoxyribose (blue), and a phosphate group (yellow). The phosphate of one nucleotide is attached to the sugar of the next, resulting in a "backbone" of alternating phosphates and sugars from which the bases project. The polynucleotide strand has directionality, from the 5′ end (with the phosphate group) to the 3′ end (with the —OH group). 5′ and 3′ refer to the numbers assigned to the carbons in the sugar ring.

Building a Structural Model of DNA: *Scientific Inquiry*

Once most biologists were convinced that DNA was the genetic material, the challenge was to determine how the structure of DNA could account for its role in inheritance. By the early 1950s, the arrangement of covalent bonds in a nucleic acid polymer was well established (see Figure 16.5), and researchers focused on discovering the three-dimensional structure of DNA. Among the scientists working on the problem were Linus Pauling, at the California Institute of Technology, and Maurice Wilkins and Rosalind Franklin, at King's College in London. First to come up with the correct answer, however, were two scientists who were relatively unknown at the time—the American James Watson and the Englishman Francis Crick.

The brief but celebrated partnership that solved the puzzle of DNA structure began soon after Watson journeyed to Cambridge University, where Crick was studying protein structure with a technique called X-ray crystallography (see Figure 5.25). While visiting the laboratory of Maurice Wilkins, Watson saw an X-ray diffraction image of DNA produced by Wilkins's accomplished colleague Rosalind Franklin (Figure 16.6a). Images produced by X-ray crystallography are not actually pictures of molecules. The spots and smudges in Figure 16.6b were produced by X-rays that were diffracted (deflected) as they passed through aligned fibers of purified DNA. Crystallographers use mathematical equations to translate such patterns into information about the three-dimensional shapes of molecules, and Watson was familiar with the types of patterns that helical molecules produce. A careful study of Franklin's X-ray diffraction photo of DNA not only told him that DNA was helical in shape, but also enabled him to approximate the width of the helix and the spacing of the nitrogenous bases along it. The width of the helix suggested that it was made up of two strands, contrary to a three-stranded model that Linus Pauling had proposed a short time earlier. The presence of two strands accounts for the now-familiar term **double helix** (Figure 16.7).

Watson and Crick began building models of a double helix that would conform to the X-ray measurements and what was

(a) Rosalind Franklin

(b) Franklin's X-ray diffraction photograph of DNA

▲ **Figure 16.6 Rosalind Franklin and her X-ray diffraction photo of DNA.** Franklin, a very accomplished X-ray crystallographer, conducted critical experiments resulting in the photograph that allowed Watson and Crick to deduce the double-helical structure of DNA. Franklin died of cancer in 1958, when she was only 38. Her colleague Maurice Wilkins received the Nobel Prize in 1962 along with Watson and Crick.

then known about the chemistry of DNA. Having also read an unpublished annual report summarizing Franklin's work, they knew she had concluded that the sugar-phosphate backbones were on the outside of the double helix. This arrangement was appealing because it put the relatively hydrophobic nitrogenous

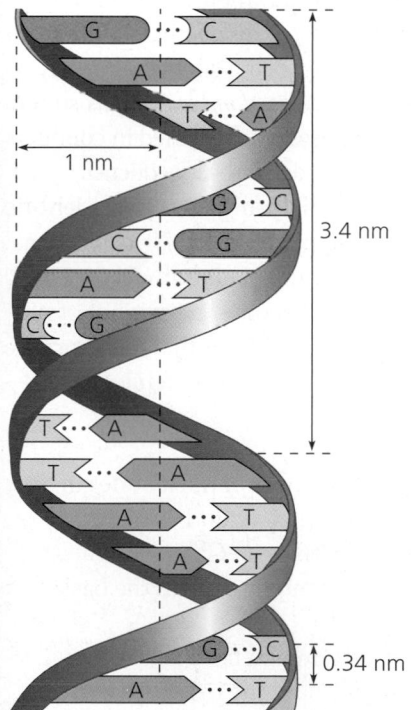

(a) Key features of DNA structure

(b) Partial chemical structure

(c) Space-filling model

▲ **Figure 16.7 The double helix. (a)** The "ribbons" in this diagram represent the sugar-phosphate backbones of the two DNA strands. The helix is "right-handed," curving up to the right. The two strands are held together by hydrogen bonds (dotted lines) between the nitrogenous bases, which are paired in the interior of the double helix. **(b)** For clarity, the two DNA strands are shown untwisted in this partial chemical structure. Strong covalent bonds link the units of each strand, while weaker hydrogen bonds hold one strand to the other. Notice that the strands are antiparallel, meaning that they are oriented in opposite directions. **(c)** The tight stacking of the base pairs is clear in this computer model. Van der Waals attractions between the stacked pairs play a major role in holding the molecule together (see Chapter 2).

bases in the molecule's interior and thus away from the surrounding aqueous solution. Watson constructed a model with the nitrogenous bases facing the interior of the double helix. In this model, the two sugar-phosphate backbones are antiparallel—that is, their subunits run in opposite directions to each other (see Figure 16.7). You can imagine the overall arrangement as a rope ladder with rigid rungs. The side ropes are the equivalent of the sugar-phosphate backbones, and the rungs represent pairs of nitrogenous bases. Now imagine holding one end of the ladder and twisting the other end, forming a spiral. Franklin's X-ray data indicated that the helix makes one full turn every 3.4 nm along its length. With the bases stacked just 0.34 nm apart, there are ten layers of base pairs, or rungs of the ladder, in each full turn of the helix.

The nitrogenous bases of the double helix are paired in specific combinations: adenine (A) with thymine (T), and guanine (G) with cytosine (C). It was mainly by trial and error that Watson and Crick arrived at this key feature of DNA. At first, Watson imagined that the bases paired like with like—for example, A with A and C with C. But this model did not fit the X-ray data, which suggested that the double helix had a uniform diameter. Why is this requirement inconsistent with like-with-like pairing of bases? Adenine and guanine are purines, nitrogenous bases with two organic rings. In contrast, cytosine and thymine belong to the family of nitrogenous bases known as pyrimidines, which have a single ring. Thus, purines (A and G) are about twice as wide as pyrimidines (C and T). A purine-purine pair is too wide and a pyrimidine-pyrimidine pair too narrow to account for the 2-nm diameter of the double helix. Always pairing a purine with a pyrimidine, however, results in a uniform diameter:

Purine + purine: too wide

Pyrimidine + pyrimidine: too narrow

Purine + pyrimidine: width consistent with X-ray data

Watson and Crick reasoned that there must be additional specificity of pairing dictated by the structure of the bases. Each base has chemical side groups that can form hydrogen bonds with its appropriate partner: Adenine can form two hydrogen bonds with thymine and only thymine; guanine forms three hydrogen bonds with cytosine and only cytosine. In shorthand, A pairs with T, and G pairs with C (**Figure 16.8**).

The Watson-Crick model explained the basis for Chargaff's rules. Wherever one strand of a DNA molecule has an A, the partner strand has a T. And a G in one strand is always paired with a C in the complementary strand. Therefore, in the DNA of any organism, the amount of adenine equals the amount of thymine,

Adenine (A)   **Thymine (T)**

Guanine (G)   **Cytosine (C)**

▲ **Figure 16.8 Base pairing in DNA.** The pairs of nitrogenous bases in a DNA double helix are held together by hydrogen bonds, shown here as pink dotted lines.

and the amount of guanine equals the amount of cytosine. Although the base-pairing rules dictate the combinations of nitrogenous bases that form the "rungs" of the double helix, they do not restrict the sequence of nucleotides *along* each DNA strand. The linear sequence of the four bases can be varied in countless ways, and each gene has a unique order, or base sequence.

In April 1953, Watson and Crick surprised the scientific world with a succinct, one-page paper in the British journal *Nature.** The paper reported their molecular model for DNA: the double helix, which has since become the symbol of molecular biology. The beauty of the model was that the structure of DNA suggested the basic mechanism of its replication.

CONCEPT CHECK 16.1

1. A fly has the following percentages of nucleotides in its DNA: 27.3% A, 27.6% T, 22.5% G, and 22.5% C. How do these numbers demonstrate Chargaff's rules?
2. How did Watson and Crick's model explain the basis for Chargaff's rules?
3. **WHAT IF?** If transformation had not occurred in Griffith's experiment, how would the results have differed? Explain.

For suggested answers, see Appendix A.

---

* J. D. Watson and F. H. C. Crick, Molecular structure of nucleic acids: a structure for deoxyribose nucleic acids, *Nature* 171:737–738 (1953).

Many proteins work together in DNA replication and repair

The relationship between structure and function is manifest in the double helix. The idea that there is specific pairing of nitrogenous bases in DNA was the flash of inspiration that led Watson and Crick to the correct double helix. At the same time, they saw the functional significance of the base-pairing rules. They ended their classic paper with this wry statement: "It has not escaped our notice that the specific pairing we have postulated immediately suggests a possible copying mechanism for the genetic material." In this section, you will learn about the basic principle of DNA replication, as well as some important details of the process.

The Basic Principle: Base Pairing to a Template Strand

In a second paper, Watson and Crick stated their hypothesis for how DNA replicates:

> Now our model for deoxyribonucleic acid is, in effect, a pair of templates, each of which is complementary to the other. We imagine that prior to duplication the hydrogen bonds are broken, and the two chains unwind and separate. Each chain then acts as a template for the formation onto itself of a new companion chain, so that eventually we shall have two pairs of chains, where we only had one before. Moreover, the sequence of the pairs of bases will have been duplicated exactly.*

---

* F. H. C. Crick and J. D. Watson, The complementary structure of deoxyribonucleic acid, *Proceedings of the Royal Society of London A* 223:80 (1954).

Figure 16.9 illustrates Watson and Crick's basic idea. To make it easier to follow, we show only a short section of double helix in untwisted form. Notice that if you cover one of the two DNA strands of Figure 16.9a, you can still determine its linear sequence of bases by referring to the uncovered strand and applying the base-pairing rules. The two strands are complementary; each stores the information necessary to reconstruct the other. When a cell copies a DNA molecule, each strand serves as a template for ordering nucleotides into a new, complementary strand. Nucleotides line up along the template strand according to the base-pairing rules and are linked to form the new strands. Where there was one double-stranded DNA molecule at the beginning of the process, there are soon two, each an exact replica of the "parent" molecule. The copying mechanism is analogous to using a photographic negative to make a positive image, which can in turn be used to make another negative, and so on.

This model of DNA replication remained untested for several years following publication of the DNA structure. The requisite experiments were simple in concept but difficult to perform. Watson and Crick's model predicts that when a double helix replicates, each of the two daughter molecules will have one old strand, derived from the parent molecule, and one newly made strand. This **semiconservative model** can be distinguished from a conservative model of replication, in which the two parent strands somehow come back together after the process (that is, the parent molecule is conserved). In yet a third model, called the dispersive model, all four strands of DNA following replication have a mixture of old and new DNA (**Figure 16.10**, on the next page). Although mechanisms for conservative or dispersive DNA replication are not easy to devise, these models remained possibilities until they could be ruled out. After two years of preliminary work in the late

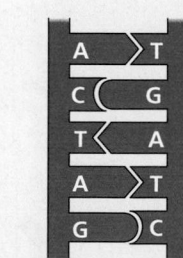

(a) The parent molecule has two complementary strands of DNA. Each base is paired by hydrogen bonding with its specific partner, A with T and G with C.

(b) The first step in replication is separation of the two DNA strands. Each parental strand can now serve as a template that determines the order of nucleotides along a new, complementary strand.

(c) The complementary nucleotides line up and are connected to form the sugar-phosphate backbones of the new strands. Each "daughter" DNA molecule consists of one parental strand (dark blue) and one new strand (light blue).

▲ **Figure 16.9 A model for DNA replication: the basic concept.** In this simplified illustration, a short segment of DNA has been untwisted into a structure that resembles a ladder. The rails of the ladder are the sugar-phosphate backbones of the two DNA strands; the rungs are the pairs of nitrogenous bases. Simple shapes symbolize the four kinds of bases. Dark blue represents DNA strands present in the parent molecule; light blue represents newly synthesized DNA.

Parent cell · **First replication** · **Second replication**

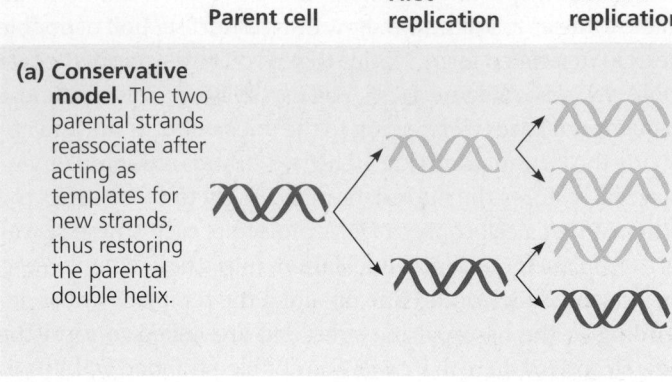

(a) Conservative model. The two parental strands reassociate after acting as templates for new strands, thus restoring the parental double helix.

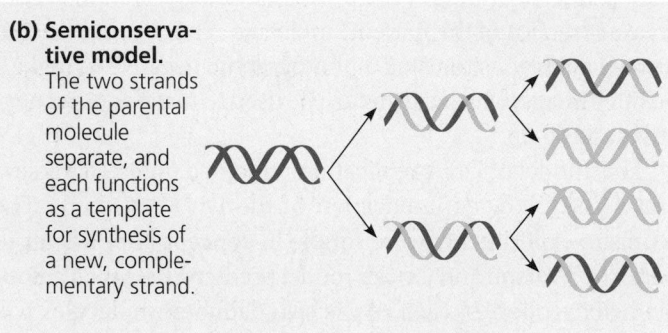

(b) Semiconservative model. The two strands of the parental molecule separate, and each functions as a template for synthesis of a new, complementary strand.

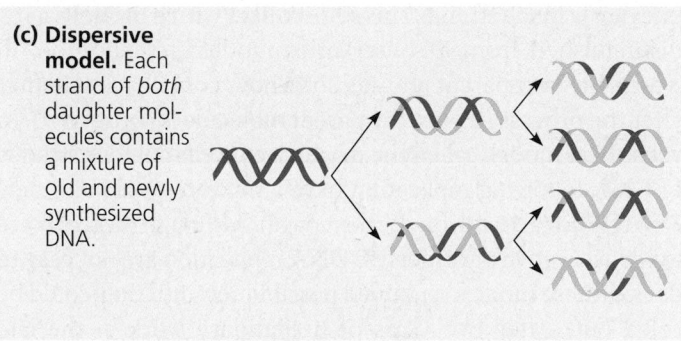

(c) Dispersive model. Each strand of *both* daughter molecules contains a mixture of old and newly synthesized DNA.

▲ **Figure 16.10 Three alternative models of DNA replication.** Each short segment of double helix symbolizes the DNA within a cell. Beginning with a parent cell, we follow the DNA for two generations of cells—two rounds of DNA replication. Newly made DNA is light blue.

1950s, Matthew Meselson and Franklin Stahl devised a clever experiment that distinguished between the three models. Their experiment supported the semiconservative model of DNA replication, as predicted by Watson and Crick, and is widely acknowledged among biologists to be a classic example of elegant experimental design **(Figure 16.11)**.

The basic principle of DNA replication is conceptually simple. However, the actual process involves some complicated biochemical gymnastics, as we will now see.

DNA Replication: *A Closer Look*

The bacterium *E. coli* has a single chromosome of about 4.6 million nucleotide pairs. In a favorable environment, an *E. coli* cell

---

▼ **Figure 16.11** **Inquiry**

Does DNA replication follow the conservative, semiconservative, or dispersive model?

EXPERIMENT At the California Institute of Technology, Matthew Meselson and Franklin Stahl cultured *E. coli* for several generations in a medium containing nucleotide precursors labeled with a heavy isotope of nitrogen, ^{15}N. The scientists then transferred the bacteria to a medium with only ^{14}N, a lighter isotope. Two DNA samples were taken from this flask, one at 20 minutes and one at 40 minutes, after the first and second replications, respectively. Meselson and Stahl could distinguish DNA of different densities by centrifuging DNA extracted from the bacteria.

❶ Bacteria cultured in medium containing ^{15}N

❷ Bacteria transferred to medium containing ^{14}N

RESULTS

❸ DNA sample centrifuged after 20 min (after first replication)

❹ DNA sample centrifuged after 40 min (after second replication)

Less dense ↑ ↓ More dense

CONCLUSION Meselson and Stahl compared their results to those predicted by each of the three models in Figure 16.10, as shown below. The first replication in the ^{14}N medium produced a band of hybrid (^{15}N-^{14}N) DNA. This result eliminated the conservative model. The second replication produced both light and hybrid DNA, a result that refuted the dispersive model and supported the semiconservative model. They therefore concluded that DNA replication is semiconservative.

First replication · **Second replication**

Conservative model

Semiconservative model

Dispersive model

SOURCE M. Meselson and F. W. Stahl, The replication of DNA in *Escherichia coli*, *Proceedings of the National Academy of Sciences USA* 44:671–682 (1958).

Inquiry in Action Read and analyze the original paper in *Inquiry in Action: Interpreting Scientific Papers.*

WHAT IF? If Meselson and Stahl had first grown the cells in ^{14}N-containing medium and then moved them into ^{15}N-containing medium before taking samples, what would have been the result?

can copy all this DNA and divide to form two genetically identical daughter cells in less than an hour. Each of *your* cells has 46 DNA molecules in its nucleus, one long double-helical molecule per chromosome. In all, that represents about 6 billion base pairs, or over a thousand times more DNA than is found in a bacterial cell. If we were to print the one-letter symbols for these bases (A, G, C, and T) the size of the letters you are now reading, the 6 billion base pairs of information in a diploid human cell would fill about 1,200 books as thick as this text. Yet it takes a cell just a few hours to copy all of this DNA. This replication of an enormous amount of genetic information is achieved with very few errors—only about one per 10 billion nucleotides. The copying of DNA is remarkable in its speed and accuracy.

More than a dozen enzymes and other proteins participate in DNA replication. Much more is known about how this "replication machine" works in bacteria (such as *E. coli*) than

in eukaryotes, and we will describe the basic steps of the process for *E. coli*, except where otherwise noted. What scientists have learned about eukaryotic DNA replication suggests, however, that most of the process is fundamentally similar for prokaryotes and eukaryotes.

Getting Started

The replication of a DNA molecule begins at special sites called **origins of replication**, short stretches of DNA having a specific sequence of nucleotides. The *E. coli* chromosome, like many other bacterial chromosomes, is circular and has a single origin. Proteins that initiate DNA replication recognize this sequence and attach to the DNA, separating the two strands and opening up a replication "bubble." Replication of DNA then proceeds in both directions until the entire molecule is copied **(Figure 16.12a)**. In

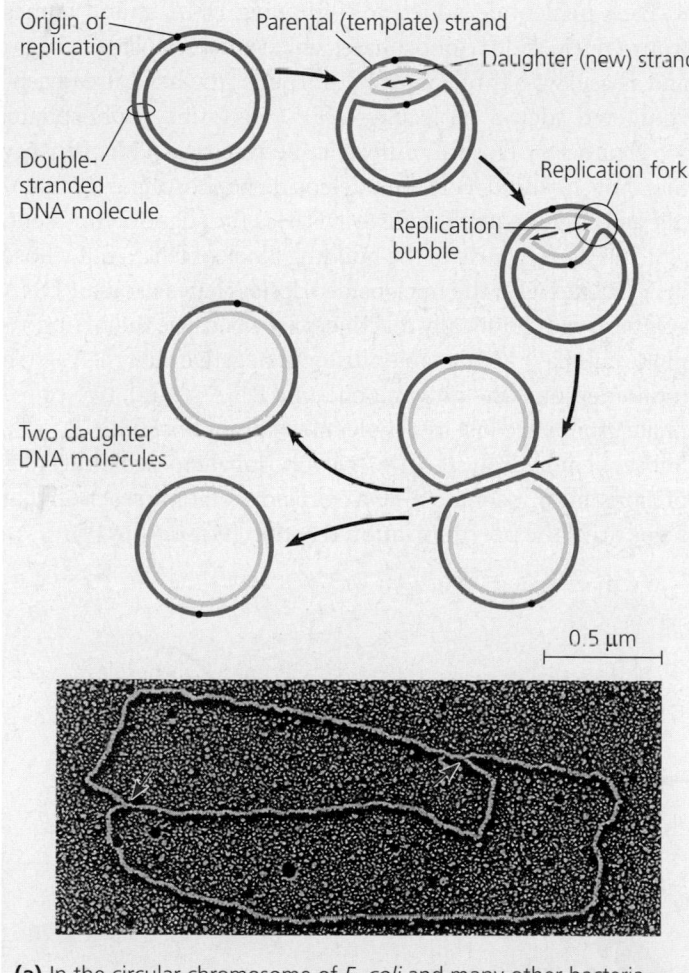

(a) In the circular chromosome of *E. coli* and many other bacteria, only one origin of replication is present. The parental strands separate at the origin, forming a replication bubble with two forks. Replication proceeds in both directions until the forks meet on the other side, resulting in two daughter DNA molecules. The TEM shows a bacterial chromosome with a replication bubble.

(b) In each linear chromosome of eukaryotes, DNA replication begins when replication bubbles form at many sites along the giant DNA molecule. The bubbles expand as replication proceeds in both directions. Eventually, the bubbles fuse and synthesis of the daughter strands is complete. The TEM shows three replication bubbles along the DNA of a cultured Chinese hamster cell.

▲ **Figure 16.12 Origins of replication in *E. coli* and eukaryotes.** The red arrows indicate the movement of the replication forks and thus the overall directions of DNA replication within each bubble.

DRAW IT *In the TEM in (b), add arrows for the third bubble.*

contrast to a bacterial chromosome, a eukaryotic chromosome may have hundreds or even a few thousand replication origins. Multiple replication bubbles form and eventually fuse, thus speeding up the copying of the very long DNA molecules **(Figure 16.12b)**. As in bacteria, eukaryotic DNA replication proceeds in both directions from each origin.

At each end of a replication bubble is a **replication fork**, a Y-shaped region where the parental strands of DNA are being unwound. Several kinds of proteins participate in the unwinding **(Figure 16.13)**. **Helicases** are enzymes that untwist the double helix at the replication forks, separating the two parental strands and making them available as template strands. After parental strand separation, **single-strand binding proteins** bind to the unpaired DNA strands, stabilizing them. The untwisting of the double helix causes tighter twisting and strain ahead of the replication fork. **Topoisomerase** helps relieve this strain by breaking, swiveling, and rejoining DNA strands.

The unwound sections of parental DNA strands are now available to serve as templates for the synthesis of new complementary DNA strands. However, the enzymes that synthesize DNA cannot *initiate* the synthesis of a polynucleotide; they can only add nucleotides to the end of an already existing chain that is base-paired with the template strand. The initial nucleotide chain that is produced during DNA synthesis is actually a short stretch of RNA, not DNA. This RNA chain is called a **primer** and is synthesized by the enzyme **primase** (see Figure 16.13). Primase starts an RNA chain from a single RNA nucleotide, adding RNA nucleotides one at a time, using the parental DNA strand as a template. The completed primer, generally 5 to 10 nucleotides long, is thus base-paired to the template strand. The new DNA strand will start from the 3′ end of the RNA primer.

Synthesizing a New DNA Strand

Enzymes called **DNA polymerases** catalyze the synthesis of new DNA by adding nucleotides to a preexisting chain. In *E. coli*, there are several different DNA polymerases, but two appear to play the major roles in DNA replication: DNA polymerase III and DNA polymerase I. The situation in eukaryotes is more complicated, with at least 11 different DNA polymerases discovered so far; however, the general principles are the same.

Most DNA polymerases require a primer and a DNA template strand, along which complementary DNA nucleotides line up. In *E. coli*, DNA polymerase III (abbreviated DNA pol III) adds a DNA nucleotide to the RNA primer and then continues adding DNA nucleotides, complementary to the parental DNA template strand, to the growing end of the new DNA strand. The rate of elongation is about 500 nucleotides per second in bacteria and 50 per second in human cells.

Each nucleotide added to a growing DNA strand comes from a nucleoside triphosphate, which is a nucleoside (a sugar and a base) with three phosphate groups. You have already encountered such a molecule—ATP (adenosine triphosphate; see Figure 8.8). The only difference between the ATP of energy metabolism and dATP, the nucleoside triphosphate that supplies an adenine nucleotide to DNA, is the sugar component, which is deoxyribose in the building block of DNA, but ribose in ATP. Like ATP, the nucleoside triphosphates used for DNA synthesis are chemically reactive, partly because their triphosphate tails have an unstable cluster of negative charge. As each monomer joins the growing end of a DNA strand, two phosphate groups are lost as a molecule of pyrophosphate $\text{P}—\text{P}_i$. Subsequent hydrolysis of the pyrophosphate to two molecules of inorganic phosphate P_i is a coupled exergonic reaction that helps drive the polymerization reaction **(Figure 16.14)**.

▶ **Figure 16.13 Some of the proteins involved in the initiation of DNA replication.** The same proteins function at both replication forks in a replication bubble. For simplicity, only one fork is shown.

Topoisomerase breaks, swivels, and rejoins the parental DNA ahead of the replication fork, relieving the strain caused by unwinding.

Single-strand binding proteins stabilize the unwound parental strands.

Primase synthesizes RNA primers, using the parental DNA as a template.

Helicase unwinds and separates the parental DNA strands.

3′

5′ RNA primer

3′

5′

5′

3′

Sugar

Phosphate

Base

New strand
5′ end

Template strand
3′ end

3′ end

OH

Nucleoside
triphosphate

5′ end

DNA polymerase

Pyrophosphate

2 ℗ᵢ

5′ end

3′ end

OH

3′ end

5′ end

◀ **Figure 16.14 Incorporation of a nucleotide into a DNA strand.** DNA polymerase catalyzes the addition of a nucleoside triphosphate to the 3′ end of a growing DNA strand, with the release of two phosphates.

? *Use this diagram to explain what we mean when we say that each DNA strand has directionality.*

Antiparallel Elongation

As we have noted previously, the two ends of a DNA strand are different, giving each strand directionality, like a one-way street (see Figure 16.5). In addition, the two strands of DNA in a double helix are antiparallel, meaning that they are oriented in opposite directions to each other, like a divided highway (see Figure 16.14). Clearly, the two new strands formed during DNA replication must also be antiparallel to their template strands.

How does the antiparallel arrangement of the double helix affect replication? Because of their structure, DNA polymerases can add nucleotides only to the free 3′ end of a primer or growing DNA strand, never to the 5′ end (see Figure 16.14). Thus, a new DNA strand can elongate only in the 5′→3′ direction. With this in mind, let's examine a replication fork (**Figure 16.15**). Along one template strand, DNA polymerase III can synthesize a complementary strand continuously by elongating the new DNA in the mandatory 5′→3′ direction. DNA pol III simply nestles in the replication fork on that template strand and continuously adds nucleotides to the new complementary strand as the fork progresses. The DNA strand made by this mechanism is called the **leading strand**. Only one primer is required for DNA pol III to synthesize the leading strand (see Figure 16.15).

To elongate the other new strand of DNA in the mandatory 5′→3′ direction, DNA pol III must work along the other template strand in the direction *away from* the replication fork. The DNA strand elongating in this direction is called the **lagging strand.*** In contrast to the leading strand, which elongates continuously,

---

* Synthesis of the leading strand and synthesis of the lagging strand occur concurrently and at the same rate. The lagging strand is so named because its synthesis is delayed slightly relative to synthesis of the leading strand; each new fragment of the lagging strand cannot be started until enough template has been exposed at the replication fork.

Overview

Origin of replication

Leading strand

Lagging strand

Primer

Lagging strand

Leading strand

Overall directions of replication

❶ After RNA primer is made, DNA pol III starts to synthesize the leading strand.

Origin of replication

3′
5′

RNA primer

"Sliding clamp"

DNA pol III

Parental DNA

5′
3′

3′
5′

5′
3′

5′

❷ The leading strand is elongated continuously in the 5′→ 3′ direction as the fork progresses.

▲ **Figure 16.15 Synthesis of the leading strand during DNA replication.** This diagram focuses on the left replication fork shown in the overview box. DNA polymerase III (DNA pol III), shaped like a cupped hand, is closely associated with a protein called the "sliding clamp" that encircles the newly synthesized double helix like a doughnut. The sliding clamp moves DNA pol III along the DNA template strand.

Overview

Leading strand Origin of replication Lagging strand

Lagging strand

② ①

Leading strand

Overall directions of replication

① Primase joins RNA nucleotides into a primer.

3′   5′
5′   3′
Template strand

② DNA pol III adds DNA nucleotides to the primer, forming Okazaki fragment 1.

3′   5′
RNA primer ①
5′   3′ 5′

③ After reaching the next RNA primer to the right, DNA pol III detaches.

Okazaki fragment

3′   3′
5′
3′
5′   ①

④ After fragment 2 is primed, DNA pol III adds DNA nucleotides until it reaches the fragment 1 primer and detaches.

3′ 5′
②   ①   3′
5′

⑤ DNA pol I replaces the RNA with DNA, adding to the 3′ end of fragment 2.

3′ 5′
②   ①   3′
5′

⑥ DNA ligase forms a bond between the newest DNA and the DNA of fragment 1.

⑦ The lagging strand in this region is now complete.

3′ 5′
②   ① 3′
5′

Overall direction of replication

▲ Figure 16.16 **Synthesis of the lagging strand.**

the lagging strand is synthesized discontinuously, as a series of segments. These segments of the lagging strand are called **Okazaki fragments**, after the Japanese scientist who discovered them. The fragments are about 1,000 to 2,000 nucleotides long in *E. coli* and 100 to 200 nucleotides long in eukaryotes.

Figure 16.16 illustrates the steps in the synthesis of the lagging strand. Whereas only one primer is required on the leading strand, each Okazaki fragment on the lagging strand must be primed separately. Another DNA polymerase, DNA polymerase I (DNA pol I), replaces the RNA nucleotides of the primers with DNA versions, adding them one by one onto the 3′ end of the adjacent Okazaki fragment (fragment 2 in Figure 16.16). But DNA pol I cannot join the final nucleotide of this replacement DNA segment to the first DNA nucleotide of the Okazaki fragment whose primer was just replaced (fragment 1 in Figure 16.16). Another enzyme, **DNA ligase**, accomplishes this task, joining the sugar-phosphate backbones of all the Okazaki fragments into a continuous DNA strand.

Figure 16.17 and **Table 16.1**, on the next page, summarize DNA replication. Study them carefully before proceeding.

The DNA Replication Complex

It is traditional—and convenient—to represent DNA polymerase molecules as locomotives moving along a DNA "railroad track," but such a model is inaccurate in two important ways. First, the various proteins that participate in DNA replication actually form a single large complex, a "DNA replication machine." Many protein-protein interactions facilitate the efficiency of this complex. For example, by interacting with other proteins at the fork, primase apparently acts as a molecular brake, slowing progress of the replication fork and coordinating the rate of replication on the leading and lagging strands. Second, the DNA replication complex does not move along the DNA; rather, the DNA moves through the complex during the replication process. In eukaryotic cells, multiple copies of the complex, perhaps grouped into "factories," may be anchored to the nuclear matrix, a framework of fibers extending through the interior of the nucleus. Recent studies support a model in which two DNA polymerase molecules, one on each template strand, "reel in" the parental DNA and extrude newly made daughter DNA molecules. Additional evidence suggests that the lagging strand is looped back through the complex, so that when a DNA polymerase completes synthesis of an Okazaki fragment and dissociates, it doesn't have far to travel to reach the primer for the next fragment, near the replication fork. This looping of the lagging strand enables more Okazaki fragments to be synthesized in less time.

Proofreading and Repairing DNA

We cannot attribute the accuracy of DNA replication solely to the specificity of base pairing. Although errors in the completed DNA molecule amount to only one in 10 billion nucleotides, initial pairing errors between incoming nucleotides and those in

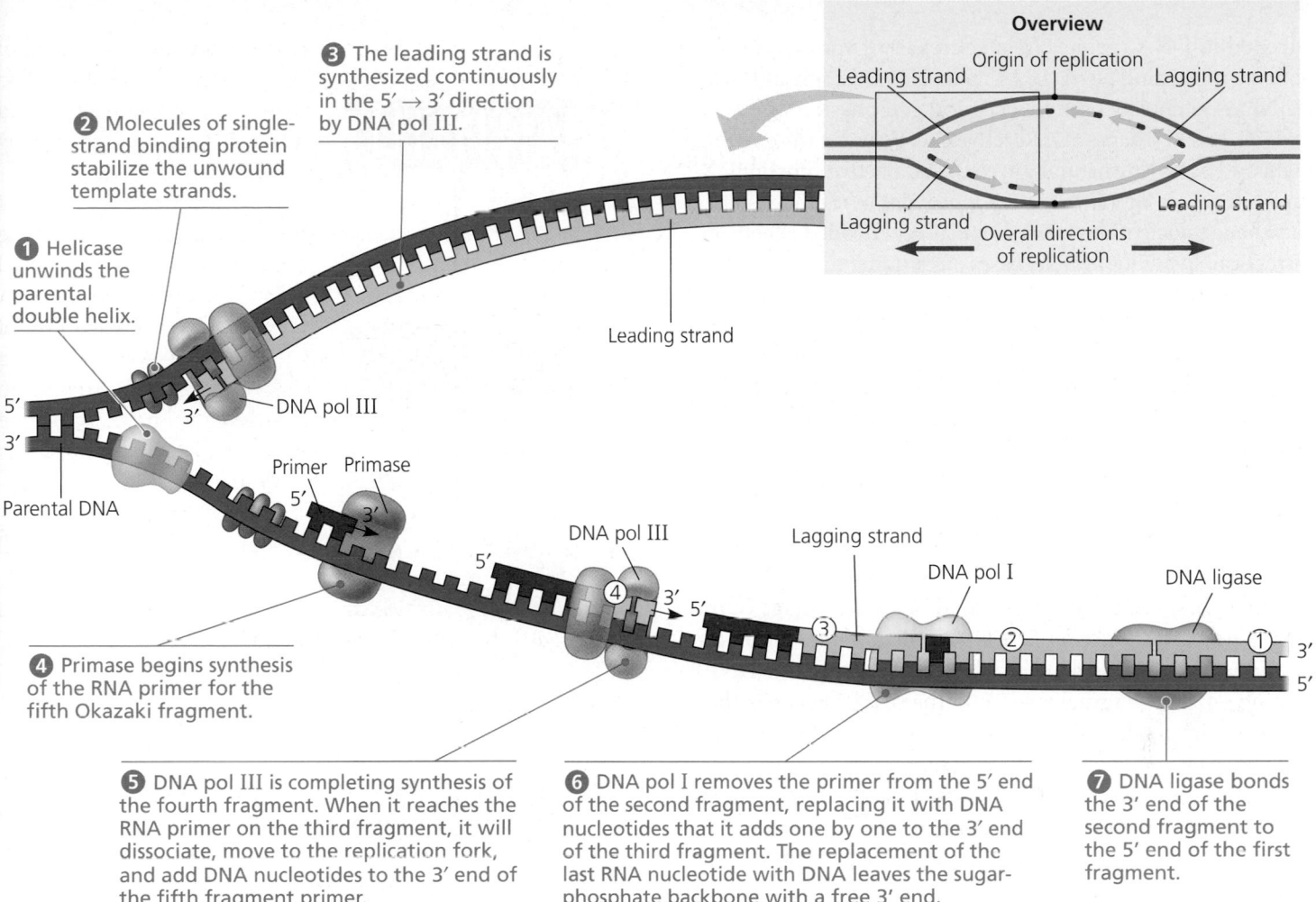

3 The leading strand is synthesized continuously in the 5′ → 3′ direction by DNA pol III.

2 Molecules of single-strand binding protein stabilize the unwound template strands.

1 Helicase unwinds the parental double helix.

Parental DNA

DNA pol III

Primer Primase

Leading strand

Overview

Leading strand Origin of replication Lagging strand

Lagging strand Overall directions of replication Leading strand

DNA pol III

Lagging strand

DNA pol I

DNA ligase

4 Primase begins synthesis of the RNA primer for the fifth Okazaki fragment.

5 DNA pol III is completing synthesis of the fourth fragment. When it reaches the RNA primer on the third fragment, it will dissociate, move to the replication fork, and add DNA nucleotides to the 3′ end of the fifth fragment primer.

6 DNA pol I removes the primer from the 5′ end of the second fragment, replacing it with DNA nucleotides that it adds one by one to the 3′ end of the third fragment. The replacement of the last RNA nucleotide with DNA leaves the sugar-phosphate backbone with a free 3′ end.

7 DNA ligase bonds the 3′ end of the second fragment to the 5′ end of the first fragment.

▲ **Figure 16.17 A summary of bacterial DNA replication.** The detailed diagram shows one replication fork, but as indicated in the overview (upper right), replication usually occurs simultaneously at two forks, one at either end of a replication bubble. Viewing each daughter strand in its entirety in the overview, you can see that half of it is made continuously as the leading strand, while the other half (on the other side of the origin) is synthesized in fragments as the lagging strand.

the template strand are 100,000 times more common—an error rate of one in 100,000 nucleotides. During DNA replication, DNA polymerases proofread each nucleotide against its template as soon as it is added to the growing strand. Upon finding an incorrectly paired nucleotide, the polymerase removes the nucleotide and then resumes synthesis. (This action is similar to fixing a word processing error by using the "delete" key and then entering the correct letter.)

Mismatched nucleotides sometimes evade proofreading by a DNA polymerase. In **mismatch repair**, enzymes remove and replace incorrectly paired nucleotides that have resulted from replication errors. Researchers spotlighted the importance of such enzymes when they found that a hereditary defect in one of them is associated with a form of colon cancer. Apparently, this defect allows cancer-causing errors to accumulate in the DNA at a faster rate than normal.

Incorrectly paired or altered nucleotides can also arise after replication. In fact, maintenance of the genetic information

Table 16.1 Bacterial DNA Replication Proteins and Their Functions

Protein	Function
Helicase	Unwinds parental double helix at replication forks
Single-strand binding protein	Binds to and stabilizes single-stranded DNA until it can be used as a template
Topoisomerase	Relieves "overwinding" strain ahead of replication forks by breaking, swiveling, and rejoining DNA strands
Primase	Synthesizes an RNA primer at 5′ end of leading strand and of each Okazaki fragment of lagging strand
DNA pol III	Using parental DNA as a template, synthesizes new DNA strand by covalently adding nucleotides to the 3′ end of a pre-existing DNA strand or RNA primer
DNA pol I	Removes RNA nucleotides of primer from 5′ end and replaces them with DNA nucleotides
DNA ligase	Joins 3′ end of DNA that replaces primer to rest of leading strand and joins Okazaki fragments of lagging strand

encoded in DNA requires frequent repair of various kinds of damage to existing DNA. DNA molecules are constantly subjected to potentially harmful chemical and physical agents, as we'll discuss in Chapter 17. Reactive chemicals (in the environment and occurring naturally in cells), radioactive emissions, X-rays, ultraviolet light, and certain molecules in cigarette smoke can change nucleotides in ways that affect encoded genetic information. In addition, DNA bases often undergo spontaneous chemical changes under normal cellular conditions. However, these changes in DNA are usually corrected before they become mutations perpetuated through successive replications. Each cell continuously monitors and repairs its genetic material. Because repair of damaged DNA is so important to the survival of an organism, it is no surprise that many different DNA repair enzymes have evolved. Almost 100 are known in *E. coli*, and about 130 have been identified so far in humans.

Most cellular systems for repairing incorrectly paired nucleotides, whether they are due to DNA damage or to replication errors, use a mechanism that takes advantage of the base-paired structure of DNA. Often, a segment of the strand containing the damage is cut out (excised) by a DNA-cutting enzyme—a **nuclease**—and the resulting gap is then filled in with nucleotides, using the undamaged strand as a template. The enzymes involved in filling the gap are a DNA polymerase and DNA ligase. One such DNA repair system is called **nucleotide excision repair** (**Figure 16.18**).

An important function of the DNA repair enzymes in our skin cells is to repair genetic damage caused by the ultraviolet rays of sunlight. One type of damage, shown in Figure 16.18, is the covalent linking of thymine bases that are adjacent on a DNA strand. Such *thymine dimers* cause the DNA to buckle and interfere with DNA replication. The importance of repairing this kind of damage is underscored by the disorder xeroderma pigmentosum, which in most cases is caused by an inherited defect in a nucleotide excision repair enzyme. Individuals with this disorder are hypersensitive to sunlight; mutations in their skin cells caused by ultraviolet light are left uncorrected and cause skin cancer.

Replicating the Ends of DNA Molecules

In spite of the impressive capabilities of DNA polymerases, there is a small portion of the cell's DNA that DNA polymerases can neither replicate nor repair. For linear DNA, such as the DNA of eukaryotic chromosomes, the fact that a DNA polymerase can add nucleotides only to the 3′ end of a preexisting polynucleotide leads to an apparent problem. The usual replication machinery provides no way to complete the 5′ ends of daughter DNA strands. Even if an Okazaki fragment can be started with an RNA primer bound to the very end of the template strand, once that primer is removed, it cannot be replaced with DNA because there is no 3′ end available for nucleotide addition (**Figure 16.19**). As a

1 A thymine dimer distorts the DNA molecule.

2 A nuclease enzyme cuts the damaged DNA strand at two points and the damaged section is removed.

Nuclease

DNA polymerase

3 Repair synthesis by a DNA polymerase fills in the missing nucleotides.

DNA ligase

4 DNA ligase seals the free end of the new DNA to the old DNA, making the strand complete.

▲ **Figure 16.18 Nucleotide excision repair of DNA damage.** A team of enzymes detects and repairs damaged DNA. This figure shows DNA containing a thymine dimer, a type of damage often caused by ultraviolet radiation. A nuclease enzyme cuts out the damaged region of DNA, and a DNA polymerase (in bacteria, DNA pol I) replaces it with nucleotides complementary to the undamaged strand. DNA ligase completes the process by closing the remaining break in the sugar-phosphate backbone.

result, repeated rounds of replication produce shorter and shorter DNA molecules with uneven ("staggered") ends.

The shortening of DNA does not occur in most prokaryotes because their DNA is circular and therefore has no ends. But what protects the genes of eukaryotes from being eroded away during successive rounds of DNA replication? It turns out that eukaryotic chromosomal DNA molecules have special nucleotide sequences called **telomeres** at their ends (**Figure 16.20**). Telomeres do not contain genes; instead, the DNA typically consists of multiple repetitions of one short nucleotide sequence. In each human telomere, for example, the six-nucleotide sequence TTAGGG is repeated between 100 and 1,000 times. Telomeric DNA protects the organism's genes. In addition, specific proteins associated with telomeric DNA prevent the staggered ends of the daughter molecule from activating the cell's systems for monitoring DNA damage. (Staggered ends of a DNA molecule, which often result from double-strand breaks, can trig-

Last fragment   Previous fragment

Lagging strand —
RNA primer
5'
3'
Parental strand —

Primer removed but cannot be replaced with DNA because no 3' end available for DNA polymerase

Removal of primers and replacement with DNA where a 3' end is available

5'
3'

Second round of replication

5'
New leading strand 3'

New lagging strand 5'
3'

Further rounds of replication

Shorter and shorter daughter molecules

▲ **Figure 16.19 Shortening of the ends of linear DNA molecules.** Here we follow the end of one strand of a DNA molecule through two rounds of replication. After the first round, the new lagging strand is shorter than its template. After a second round, both the leading and lagging strands have become shorter than the original parental DNA. Although not shown here, the other ends of these DNA molecules also become shorter.

ger signal transduction pathways leading to cell cycle arrest or cell death.)

Telomeres do not prevent the shortening of DNA molecules due to successive rounds of replication; they just postpone the erosion of genes near the ends of DNA molecules. As shown in Figure 16.19, telomeres become shorter during every round of replication. As we would expect, telomeric DNA does tend to be shorter in dividing somatic cells of older individuals and in cultured cells that have divided many times. It has been proposed that shortening of telomeres is somehow connected to the aging process of certain tissues and even to aging of the organism as a whole.

But what about the cells whose genomes must persist unchanged from an organism to its offspring over many generations? If the chromosomes of germ cells (which give rise to gametes) became shorter in every cell cycle, essential genes

▲ **Figure 16.20 Telomeres.** Eukaryotes have repetitive, noncoding sequences called telomeres at the ends of their DNA. Telomeres are stained orange in these mouse chromosomes (LM).

would eventually be missing from the gametes they produce. However, this does not occur: An enzyme called **telomerase** catalyzes the lengthening of telomeres in eukaryotic germ cells, thus restoring their original length and compensating for the shortening that occurs during DNA replication. Telomerase is not active in most human somatic cells, but its activity in germ cells results in telomeres of maximum length in the zygote.

Normal shortening of telomeres may protect organisms from cancer by limiting the number of divisions that somatic cells can undergo. Cells from large tumors often have unusually short telomeres, as one would expect for cells that have undergone many cell divisions. Further shortening would presumably lead to self-destruction of the tumor cells. Intriguingly, researchers have found telomerase activity in cancerous somatic cells, suggesting that its ability to stabilize telomere length may allow these cancer cells to persist. Many cancer cells do seem capable of unlimited cell division, as do immortal strains of cultured cells (see Chapter 12). If telomerase is indeed an important factor in many cancers, it may provide a useful target for both cancer diagnosis and chemotherapy.

Thus far in this chapter, you have learned about the structure and replication of a DNA molecule. In the next section, we'll examine how DNA is packaged into chromosomes, the structures that carry the genetic information.

CONCEPT CHECK 16.2

1. What role does complementary base pairing play in the replication of DNA?
2. Identify two major functions of DNA pol III in DNA replication.
3. **WHAT IF?** If the DNA pol I in a given cell were nonfunctional, how would that affect the synthesis of a *leading* strand? In the overview box in Figure 16.17, point out where DNA pol I would normally function on the top leading strand.

For suggested answers, see Appendix A.

CONCEPT 16.3

A chromosome consists of a DNA molecule packed together with proteins

The main component of the genome in most bacteria is one double-stranded, circular DNA molecule that is associated with a small amount of protein. Although we refer to this structure as the *bacterial chromosome*, it is very different from a eukaryotic chromosome, which consists of one linear DNA molecule associated with a large amount of protein. In *E. coli*, the chromosomal DNA consists of about 4.6 million nucleotide pairs, representing about 4,400 genes. This is 100 times more DNA than is found in a typical virus, but only about one-thousandth as much DNA as in a human somatic cell. Still, it is a lot of DNA to be packaged in such a small container.

Stretched out, the DNA of an *E. coli* cell would measure about a millimeter in length, 500 times longer than the cell.

▼ **Figure 16.21**

Exploring Chromatin Packing in a Eukaryotic Chromosome

This series of diagrams and transmission electron micrographs depicts a current model for the progressive levels of DNA coiling and folding. The illustration zooms out from a single molecule of DNA to a metaphase chromosome, which is large enough to be seen with a light microscope.

Nucleosome (10 nm in diameter)

DNA double helix (2 nm in diameter)

H1

Histone tail

Histones

1 DNA, the double helix

Shown here is a ribbon model of DNA, with each ribbon representing one of the sugar-phosphate backbones. As you will recall from Figure 16.7, the phosphate groups along the backbone contribute a negative charge along the outside of each strand. The TEM shows a molecule of naked DNA; the double helix alone is 2 nm across.

2 Histones

Proteins called histones are responsible for the first level of DNA packing in chromatin. Although each histone is small—containing about 100 amino acids—the total mass of histone in chromatin approximately equals the mass of DNA. More than a fifth of a histone's amino acids are positively charged (lysine or arginine) and bind tightly to the negatively charged DNA.

Four types of histones are most common in chromatin: H2A, H2B, H3, and H4. The histones are very similar among eukaryotes; for example, all but two of the amino acids in cow H4 are identical to those in pea H4. The apparent conservation of histone genes during evolution probably reflects the pivotal role of histones in organizing DNA within cells.

The four main types of histones are critical to the next level of DNA packing. (A fifth type of histone, called H1, is involved in a further stage of packing.)

3 Nucleosomes, or "beads on a string" (10-nm fiber)

In electron micrographs, unfolded chromatin is 10 nm in diameter (the *10-nm fiber*). Such chromatin resembles beads on a string (see the TEM). Each "bead" is a *nucleosome*, the basic unit of DNA packing; the "string" between beads is called *linker DNA*.

A nucleosome consists of DNA wound twice around a protein core composed of two molecules each of the four main histone types. The amino end (N-terminus) of each histone (the *histone tail*) extends outward from the nucleosome.

In the cell cycle, the histones leave the DNA only briefly during DNA replication. Generally, they do the same during gene expression, another process that requires access to the DNA by the cell's molecular machinery. Chapter 18 will discuss some recent findings about the role of histone tails and nucleosomes in the regulation of gene expression.

Within a bacterium, however, certain proteins cause the chromosome to coil and "supercoil," densely packing it so that it fills only part of the cell. Unlike the nucleus of a eukaryotic cell, this dense region of DNA in a bacterium, called the **nucleoid**, is not bounded by membrane (see Figure 6.6).

Eukaryotic chromosomes each contain a single linear DNA double helix that, in humans, averages about 1.5×10^8 nucleotide pairs. This is an enormous amount of DNA relative to a chromosome's condensed length. If completely stretched out, such a DNA molecule would be about 4 cm long, thousands of times the diameter of a cell nucleus—and that's not even considering the DNA of the other 45 human chromosomes!

In the cell, eukaryotic DNA is precisely combined with a large amount of protein. Together, this complex of DNA and protein, called **chromatin**, fits into the nucleus through an elaborate, multilevel system of DNA packing. Our current view of the successive levels of DNA packing in a chromosome is outlined in **Figure 16.21**. Study this figure carefully before reading further.

30-nm fiber

Chromatid (700 nm)

Loops

Scaffold

300-nm fiber

Replicated chromosome (1,400 nm)

4 30-nm fiber

The next level of packing is due to interactions between the histone tails of one nucleosome and the linker DNA and nucleosomes on either side. A fifth histone, H1, is involved at this level. These interactions cause the extended 10-nm fiber to coil or fold, forming a chromatin fiber roughly 30 nm in thickness, the *30-nm fiber*. Although the 30-nm fiber is quite prevalent in the interphase nucleus, the packing arrangement of nucleosomes in this form of chromatin is still a matter of some debate.

5 Looped domains (300-nm fiber)

The 30-nm fiber, in turn, forms loops called *looped domains* attached to a chromosome scaffold made of proteins, thus making up a *300-nm fiber*. The scaffold is rich in one type of topoisomerase, and H1 molecules also appear to be present.

6 Metaphase chromosome

In a mitotic chromosome, the looped domains themselves coil and fold in a manner not yet fully understood, further compacting all the chromatin to produce the characteristic metaphase chromosome shown in the micrograph above. The width of one chromatid is 700 nm. Particular genes always end up located at the same places in metaphase chromosomes, indicating that the packing steps are highly specific and precise.

Chromatin undergoes striking changes in its degree of packing during the course of the cell cycle (see Figure 12.6). In interphase cells stained for light microscopy, the chromatin usually appears as a diffuse mass within the nucleus, suggesting that the chromatin is highly extended. As a cell prepares for mitosis, its chromatin coils and folds up (condenses), eventually forming a characteristic number of short, thick metaphase chromosomes that are distinguishable from each other with the light microscope.

Though interphase chromatin is generally much less condensed than the chromatin of mitotic chromosomes, it shows several of the same levels of higher-order packing. Some of the chromatin comprising a chromosome seems to be present as a 10-nm fiber, but much is compacted into a 30-nm fiber, which in some regions is further folded into looped domains. Although an interphase chromosome lacks an obvious scaffold, its looped domains appear to be attached to the nuclear lamina, on the inside of the nuclear envelope, and perhaps also to fibers of the nuclear matrix. These attachments may help organize regions of chromatin where genes are active. The chromatin of each chromosome occupies a specific restricted area within the interphase nucleus, and the chromatin fibers of different chromosomes do not become entangled.

Even during interphase, the centromeres and telomeres of chromosomes, as well as other chromosomal regions in some cells, exist in a highly condensed state similar to that seen in a metaphase chromosome. This type of interphase chromatin, visible as irregular clumps with a light microscope, is called **heterochromatin**, to distinguish it from the less compacted, more dispersed **euchromatin** ("true chromatin"). Because of its compaction, heterochromatin DNA is largely inaccessible to the machinery in the cell responsible for expressing (making use of) the genetic information coded in the DNA. In contrast, the looser packing of euchromatin makes its DNA accessible to this machinery, so the genes present in euchromatin can be expressed.

The chromosome is a dynamic structure that is condensed, loosened, modified, and remodeled as necessary for various cell processes, including mitosis, meiosis, and gene activity. The pathways regulating these transformations are currently a focus of intense study by researchers. It has become clear that histones are not simply inert spools around which the DNA is wrapped. Instead, they can undergo chemical modifications that result in changes in chromatin organization. Terry Orr-Weaver, the scientist interviewed at the beginning of this unit (pp. 246–247), has long been interested in the molecular mechanisms of chromosome dynamics during mitosis and meiosis. Using a genetic approach in *Drosophila*, she and her colleagues showed that phosphorylation of a specific amino acid on a histone tail plays a crucial role in chromosome behavior during prophase I of meiosis **(Figure 16.22)**.

▼ **Figure 16.22** **Inquiry**

What role does histone phosphorylation play in chromosome behavior during meiosis?

EXPERIMENT   Terry Orr-Weaver and colleagues at the Massachusetts Institute of Technology mutagenized fruit flies and looked for mutations that caused sterility, reasoning that such mutations might be found in genes coding for proteins that play important roles during meiosis. They found a mutation in the *nhk-1* gene that caused sterility in *Drosophila* females. They knew that the gene product, nucleosomal histone kinase-1, or NHK-1, is an enzyme that phosphorylates a specific amino acid on the tail of histone H2A. They hypothesized that sterility is caused by unsuccessful meiosis due to abnormal chromosome behavior when this enzyme does not function properly.

To test this hypothesis, they observed chromosome behavior closely during meiosis in ovarian cells of normal and mutant flies. In one experiment, they used a red fluorescent dye to mark the location of DNA and a green fluorescent dye to mark the location of the protein *condensin*, which normally coats the chromosomes at the end of prophase I and helps them condense.

RESULTS   At the end of prophase I in ovarian cells of normal flies, condensin and DNA were both localized to a very small region in the nucleus (below left; the yellow color is the result of green and red dyes located together). However, in mutant flies, condensin was spread diffusely throughout the nucleus while the DNA was restricted to the periphery of the nucleus (below right; the red of the DNA is very faint). This result suggested that condensin does not coat the chromosomes in the cells of mutant flies and that, consequently, the chromosomes don't condense.

Condensin and DNA (yellow)   Outline of nucleus   Condensin (green)   DNA (red at periphery)

 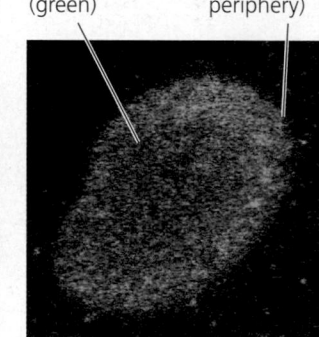

Normal cell nucleus   **Mutant cell nucleus**

CONCLUSION   Because this process and others during meiosis are not completed successfully when the histone kinase NHK-1 does not function properly, the researchers concluded that a specific phosphorylation of histone H2A is necessary for normal chromosome behavior during meiosis.

SOURCE   I. Ivanovska, T. Khandan, T. Ito, and T. L. Orr-Weaver, A histone code in meiosis: the histone kinase, NHK-1, is required for proper chromosomal architecture in *Drosophila* oocytes, *Genes and Development* 19:2571–2582 (2005).

WHAT IF?   Suppose a researcher discovered a mutant fly in which the histone H2A tail was missing the specific amino acid usually phosphorylated by the histone kinase NHK-1. How would this mutation likely affect chromosome behavior during meiosis in ovarian cells?

Phosphorylation and other chemical modifications of histones also have multiple effects on gene activity, as you will see in Chapter 18.

In this chapter, you have learned how DNA molecules are arranged in chromosomes and how DNA replication provides the copies of genes that parents pass to offspring. However, it is not enough that genes be copied and transmitted; the information they carry must be used by the cell. In other words, genes must also be "expressed." In the next chapter, we will examine how the cell translates genetic information encoded in DNA.

CONCEPT CHECK 16.3

1. Describe the structure of a nucleosome, the basic unit of DNA packing in eukaryotic cells.
2. What two properties distinguish heterochromatin from euchromatin?
3. **WHAT IF?** Although the proteins that cause the *E. coli* chromosome to coil are not histones, what property would you expect them to share with histones, given their ability to bind to DNA?

For suggested answers, see Appendix A.

Chapter 16 Review

MEDIA Go to **www.campbellbiology.com** for BioFlix 3-D Animations, MP3 Tutors, Videos, Practice Tests, an eBook, and more.

SUMMARY OF KEY CONCEPTS

CONCEPT 16.1

DNA is the genetic material (pp. 305–310)

▶ **The Search for the Genetic Material:** *Scientific Inquiry* Experiments with bacteria and with phages provided the first strong evidence that the genetic material is DNA.

▶ **Building a Structural Model of DNA:** *Scientific Inquiry* Watson and Crick deduced that DNA is a double helix. Two antiparallel sugar-phosphate chains wind around the outside of the molecule; the nitrogenous bases project into the interior, where they hydrogen-bond in specific pairs, A with T, G with C.

MEDIA

Activity The Hershey-Chase Experiment
Activity DNA and RNA Structure
Activity DNA Double Helix

CONCEPT 16.2

Many proteins work together in DNA replication and repair (pp. 311–319)

▶ **The Basic Principle: Base Pairing to a Template Strand** The Meselson-Stahl experiment showed that DNA replication is semiconservative: The parent molecule unwinds, and each strand then serves as a template for the synthesis of a new strand according to base-pairing rules.

▶ **DNA Replication:** *A Closer Look*

▶ **Proofreading and Repairing DNA** DNA polymerases proofread new DNA, replacing incorrect nucleotides. In mismatch repair, enzymes correct errors that persist. Nucleotide excision repair is a general process by which enzymes cut out and replace damaged stretches of DNA.

▶ **Replicating the Ends of DNA Molecules** The ends of eukaryotic chromosomal DNA get shorter with each round of replication. The presence of telomeres, repetitive sequences at the ends of linear DNA molecules, postpones the erosion of genes. Telomerase catalyzes the lengthening of telomeres in germ cells.

MEDIA

Activity DNA Replication: An Overview
Investigation What Is the Correct Model for DNA Replication?
Activity DNA Replication: A Closer Look
Activity DNA Replication: A Review

CONCEPT 16.3

A chromosome consists of a DNA molecule packed together with proteins (pp. 320–323)

▶ The bacterial chromosome is usually a circular DNA molecule with some associated proteins. Eukaryotic chromatin making up a chromosome is composed mostly of DNA, histones, and other proteins. The histones bind to each other and to the DNA to form nucleosomes, the most basic units of DNA packing. Histone tails extend outward from each bead-like nucleosome core. Additional folding leads ultimately to the highly condensed chromatin of the metaphase chromosome. In interphase cells, most chromatin is less compacted (euchromatin), but some remains highly condensed (heterochromatin). Histone modifications may influence the state of chromatin condensation.

MEDIA

Activity DNA Packing

TESTING YOUR KNOWLEDGE

SELF-QUIZ

1. In his work with pneumonia-causing bacteria and mice, Griffith found that
   a. the protein coat from pathogenic cells was able to transform nonpathogenic cells.
   b. heat-killed pathogenic cells caused pneumonia.
   c. some substance from pathogenic cells was transferred to nonpathogenic cells, making them pathogenic.
   d. the polysaccharide coat of bacteria caused pneumonia.
   e. bacteriophages injected DNA into bacteria.

2. *E. coli* cells grown on ^{15}N medium are transferred to ^{14}N medium and allowed to grow for two more generations (two rounds of DNA replication). DNA extracted from these cells is centrifuged. What density distribution of DNA would you expect in this experiment?
   a. one high-density and one low-density band
   b. one intermediate-density band
   c. one high-density and one intermediate-density band
   d. one low-density and one intermediate-density band
   e. one low-density band

3. A biochemist isolates and purifies molecules needed for DNA replication. When she adds some DNA, replication occurs, but each DNA molecule consists of a normal strand paired with numerous segments of DNA a few hundred nucleotides long. What has she probably left out of the mixture?
   a. DNA polymerase
   b. DNA ligase
   c. nucleotides
   d. Okazaki fragments
   e. primase

4. What is the basis for the difference in how the leading and lagging strands of DNA molecules are synthesized?
   a. The origins of replication occur only at the 5' end.
   b. Helicases and single-strand binding proteins work at the 5' end.
   c. DNA polymerase can join new nucleotides only to the 3' end of a growing strand.
   d. DNA ligase works only in the 3'→5' direction.
   e. Polymerase can work on only one strand at a time.

5. In analyzing the number of different bases in a DNA sample, which result would be consistent with the base-pairing rules?
   a. A = G
   b. A + G = C + T
   c. A + T = G + T
   d. A = C
   e. G = T

6. The elongation of the leading strand during DNA synthesis
   a. progresses away from the replication fork.
   b. occurs in the 3'→5' direction.
   c. produces Okazaki fragments.
   d. depends on the action of DNA polymerase.
   e. does not require a template strand.

7. The spontaneous loss of amino groups from adenine results in hypoxanthine, an uncommon base, opposite thymine in DNA. What combination of molecules could repair such damage?
   a. nuclease, DNA polymerase, DNA ligase
   b. telomerase, primase, DNA polymerase
   c. telomerase, helicase, single-strand binding protein
   d. DNA ligase, replication fork proteins, adenylyl cyclase
   e. nuclease, telomerase, primase

8. In a nucleosome, the DNA is wrapped around
   a. polymerase molecules.
   b. ribosomes.
   c. histones.
   d. a thymine dimer.
   e. satellite DNA.

For Self-Quiz answers, see Appendix A.

MEDIA Visit **www.campbellbiology.com** for a Practice Test.

EVOLUTION CONNECTION

9. Some bacteria may be able to respond to environmental stress by increasing the rate at which mutations occur during cell division. How might this be accomplished? Might there be an evolutionary advantage of this ability? Explain.

SCIENTIFIC INQUIRY

10. **DRAW IT** Model building can be an important part of the scientific process. The illustration above is a computer-generated model of a DNA replication complex. The parental and newly synthesized DNA strands are color-coded differently, as are each of the following three proteins: DNA pol III, the sliding clamp, and single-strand binding protein. Use what you've learned in this chapter to clarify this model by labeling each DNA strand and each protein and showing the overall direction of DNA replication.

17 From Gene to Protein

KEY CONCEPTS

17.1 Genes specify proteins via transcription and translation

17.2 Transcription is the DNA-directed synthesis of RNA: *a closer look*

17.3 Eukaryotic cells modify RNA after transcription

17.4 Translation is the RNA-directed synthesis of a polypeptide: *a closer look*

17.5 Point mutations can affect protein structure and function

17.6 While gene expression differs among the domains of life, the concept of a gene is universal

OVERVIEW

The Flow of Genetic Information

In 2006, a young albino deer seen frolicking with several brown deer in the mountains of eastern Germany elicited a public outcry (**Figure 17.1**). A local hunting organization said the albino deer suffered from a "genetic disorder" and should be shot. Some people felt the deer should merely be prevented from mating with other deer in order to safeguard the gene pool of the population. Others favored relocating the albino deer to a nature reserve because they worried that it might be more noticeable to predators if left in the wild. A German rock star even held a benefit concert to raise funds for the relocation. What led to the striking phenotype of this deer, the cause of this lively debate?

You learned in Chapter 14 that inherited traits are determined by genes and that the trait of albinism is caused by a recessive allele of a pigmentation gene. The information content of genes is in the form of specific sequences of nucleotides along strands of DNA, the genetic material. But how does this information determine an organism's traits? Put another way, what does a gene actually say? And how is its

message translated by cells into a specific trait, such as brown hair, type A blood, or, in the case of an albino deer, a total lack of pigment? The albino deer has a faulty version of a key protein, an enzyme required for pigment synthesis, and this protein is faulty because the gene that codes for it contains incorrect information.

This example illustrates the main point of this chapter: The DNA inherited by an organism leads to specific traits by dictating the synthesis of proteins and of RNA molecules involved in protein synthesis. In other words, proteins are the link between genotype and phenotype. **Gene expression** is the process by which DNA directs the synthesis of proteins (or, in some cases, just RNAs). The expression of genes that code for proteins includes two stages: transcription and translation. This chapter describes the flow of information from gene to protein in detail and explains how genetic mutations affect organisms through their proteins. Gene expression involves similar processes in all three domains of life. Understanding these processes will allow us to revisit the concept of the gene in more detail at the end of the chapter.

CONCEPT 17.1

Genes specify proteins via transcription and translation

Before going into the details of how genes direct protein synthesis, let's step back and examine how the fundamental relationship between genes and proteins was discovered.

Evidence from the Study of Metabolic Defects

In 1909, British physician Archibald Garrod was the first to suggest that genes dictate phenotypes through enzymes that catalyze specific chemical reactions in the cell. Garrod postulated that the symptoms of an inherited disease reflect a person's inability to make a particular enzyme. He referred to such diseases as "inborn errors of metabolism." Garrod gave as one example the hereditary condition called alkaptonuria, in which the urine is black because it contains the chemical alkapton, which darkens upon exposure to air. Garrod reasoned that most people have an enzyme that metabolizes alkapton, whereas people with alkaptonuria have inherited an inability to make that enzyme.

Garrod may have been the first person to recognize that Mendel's principles of heredity apply to humans as well as peas. Garrod's realization was ahead of its time, but research conducted several decades later supported his hypothesis that a gene dictates the production of a specific enzyme. Biochemists accumulated much evidence that cells synthesize and degrade most organic molecules via metabolic pathways, in which each chemical reaction in a sequence is catalyzed by a specific enzyme (see p. 142). Such metabolic pathways lead, for instance, to the synthesis of the pigments that give fruit flies (*Drosophila*) their eye color (see Figure 15.3). In the 1930s, George Beadle and Boris Ephrussi speculated that in *Drosophila*, each of the various mutations affecting eye color blocks pigment synthesis at a specific step by preventing production of the enzyme that catalyzes that step. However, neither the chemical reactions nor the enzymes that catalyze them were known at the time.

Nutritional Mutants in Neurospora: Scientific Inquiry

A breakthrough in demonstrating the relationship between genes and enzymes came a few years later, when Beadle and Edward Tatum began working with a bread mold, *Neurospora crassa*. Using a treatment shown in the 1920s to cause genetic changes, they bombarded *Neurospora* with X-rays and then looked among the survivors for mutants that differed in their nutritional needs from the wild-type mold. Wild-type *Neurospora* has modest food requirements. It can survive in the laboratory on a moist support medium called agar, mixed only with inorganic salts, glucose, and the vitamin biotin. From this *minimal medium*, the mold cells use their metabolic pathways to produce all the other molecules they need. Beadle and Tatum identified mutants that could not survive on minimal medium, apparently because they were unable to synthesize certain essential molecules from the minimal ingredients. To ensure survival of these nutritional mutants, Beadle and Tatum allowed them to grow on a *complete growth medium*, which consisted of minimal medium supplemented with all 20 amino acids and a few other nutrients. The complete growth medium could support any mutant that couldn't synthesize one of the supplements.

To characterize the metabolic defect in each nutritional mutant, Beadle and Tatum took samples from the mutant growing on complete medium and distributed them to a number of different vials. Each vial contained minimal medium plus a single additional nutrient. The particular supplement that allowed growth indicated the metabolic defect. For example, if the only supplemented vial that supported growth of the mutant was the one fortified with the amino acid arginine, the researchers could conclude that the mutant was defective in the biochemical pathway that wild-type cells use to synthesize arginine.

Beadle and Tatum went on to pin down each mutant's defect more specifically. **Figure 17.2** shows how they used additional tests to distinguish among three classes of arginine-requiring mutants. Mutants in each class required a different set of compounds along the arginine-synthesizing pathway, which has three steps. Based on their results, the researchers reasoned that each class must be blocked at a different step in this pathway because mutants in that class lacked the enzyme that catalyzes the blocked step.

Because each mutant was defective in a single gene, Beadle and Tatum's results provided strong support for the *one gene–one enzyme hypothesis*, as they dubbed it, which states that the function of a gene is to dictate the production of a specific enzyme. Further support for this hypothesis came from experiments that identified the specific enzymes lacking in the mutants. Beadle and Tatum shared a Nobel Prize in 1958 for "their discovery that genes act by regulating definite chemical events" (in the words of the Nobel committee).

The Products of Gene Expression: A Developing Story

As researchers learned more about proteins, they made revisions to the one gene–one enzyme hypothesis. First of all, not all proteins are enzymes. Keratin, the structural protein of animal hair, and the hormone insulin are two examples of nonenzyme proteins. Because proteins that are not enzymes are nevertheless gene products, molecular biologists began to think in terms of one gene–one protein. However, many proteins are constructed from two or more different polypeptide chains, and each polypeptide is specified by its own gene. For example, hemoglobin, the oxygen-transporting protein of vertebrate red blood cells, is built from two kinds of polypeptides, and thus two genes code for this protein (see Figure 5.21). Beadle and Tatum's idea was therefore restated as the *one gene–one polypeptide hypothesis*. Even this description is not entirely accurate, though. First, many eukaryotic genes can code for a set of closely related polypeptides in a process called alternative splicing, which you will learn about later in this chapter. Second, quite a few genes code for RNA molecules that have important functions in cells even though they are never translated into protein. For now, we will focus on genes that do code for polypeptides. (Note that it is common to refer to these gene products as proteins, rather than more precisely as polypeptides—a practice you will encounter in this book.)

▼ Figure 17.2 Inquiry

Do individual genes specify the enzymes that function in a biochemical pathway?

EXPERIMENT   Working with the mold *Neurospora crassa*, George Beadle and Edward Tatum, then at Stanford University, isolated mutants that required arginine in their growth medium. The researchers showed that these mutants fell into three classes, each defective in a different gene. From other considerations, they suspected that the metabolic pathway of arginine biosynthesis involved a precursor nutrient and the intermediate molecules ornithine and citrulline. Their most famous experiment, shown here, tested both their one gene–one enzyme hypothesis and their postulated arginine-synthesizing pathway. In this experiment, they grew their three classes of mutants under the four different conditions shown in the Results section below. They included minimal medium (MM) as a control because they knew that wild-type cells could grow on MM but mutant cells could not. (See test tubes on the right.)

Growth:
Wild-type
cells growing
and dividing

No growth:
Mutant cells
cannot grow
and divide

Minimal medium

RESULTS   The wild-type strain was capable of growth under all experimental conditions, requiring only the minimal medium. The three classes of mutants each had a specific set of growth requirements. For example, class II mutants could not grow when ornithine alone was added but could grow when either citrulline or arginine was added.

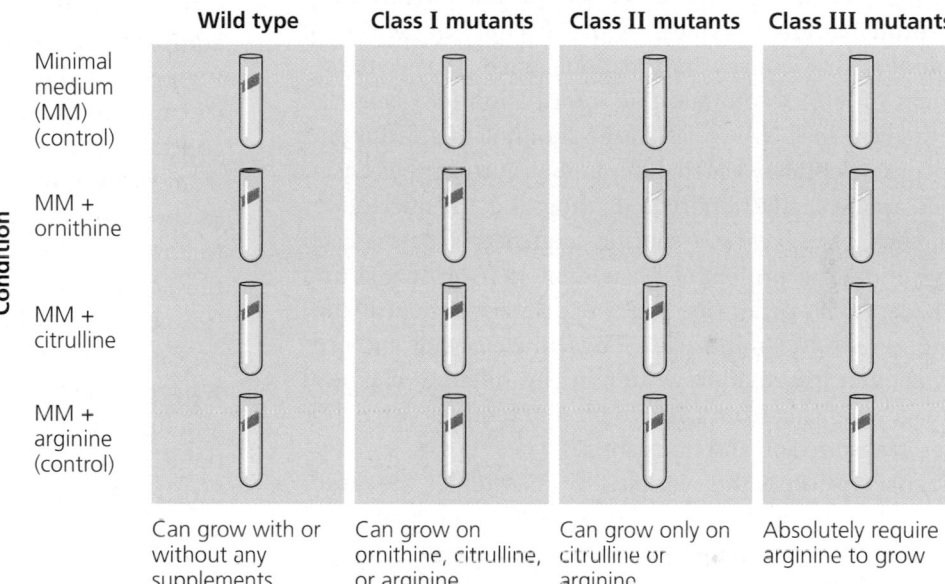

Classes of *Neurospora crassa*

	Wild type	Class I mutants	Class II mutants	Class III mutants
Minimal medium (MM) (control)				
MM + ornithine				
MM + citrulline				
MM + arginine (control)				

Condition

Can grow with or without any supplements

Can grow on ornithine, citrulline, or arginine

Can grow only on citrulline or arginine

Absolutely require arginine to grow

CONCLUSION   From the growth requirements of the mutants, Beadle and Tatum deduced that each class of mutant was unable to carry out one step in the pathway for synthesizing arginine, presumably because it lacked the necessary enzyme. Because each of their mutants was mutated in a single gene, they concluded that each mutated gene must normally dictate the production of one enzyme. Their results supported the one gene–one enzyme hypothesis and also confirmed the arginine pathway. (Notice in the Results that a mutant can grow only if supplied with a compound made *after* the defective step, because this bypasses the defect.)

Wild type	Class I mutants (mutation in gene *A*)	Class II mutants (mutation in gene *B*)	Class III mutants (mutation in gene *C*)

Gene *A* →   Gene *B* →   Gene *C* →

Wild type:
Precursor — Enzyme A → Ornithine — Enzyme B → Citrulline — Enzyme C → Arginine

Class I mutants:
Precursor — Enzyme A ✗ → Ornithine — Enzyme B → Citrulline — Enzyme C → Arginine

Class II mutants:
Precursor — Enzyme A → Ornithine — Enzyme B ✗ → Citrulline — Enzyme C → Arginine

Class III mutants:
Precursor — Enzyme A → Ornithine — Enzyme B → Citrulline — Enzyme C ✗ → Arginine

SOURCE   G. W. Beadle and E. L. Tatum, Genetic control of biochemical reactions in *Neurospora*, *Proceedings of the National Academy of Sciences* 27:499–506 (1941).

WHAT IF?   Suppose the experiment had shown that class I mutants could grow only in MM supplemented by ornithine or arginine and that class II mutants could grow in MM supplemented by citrulline, ornithine, or arginine. What conclusions would Beadle and Tatum have drawn from those results regarding the biochemical pathway and the defect in class I and class II mutants?

Basic Principles of Transcription and Translation

Genes provide the instructions for making specific proteins. But a gene does not build a protein directly. The bridge between DNA and protein synthesis is the nucleic acid RNA. You learned in Chapter 5 that RNA is chemically similar to DNA, except that it contains ribose instead of deoxyribose as its sugar and has the nitrogenous base uracil rather than thymine (see Figure 5.27). Thus, each nucleotide along a DNA strand has A, G, C, or T as its base, and each nucleotide along an RNA strand has A, G, C, or U as its base. An RNA molecule usually consists of a single strand.

It is customary to describe the flow of information from gene to protein in linguistic terms because both nucleic acids and proteins are polymers with specific sequences of monomers that convey information, much as specific sequences of letters communicate information in a language like English. In DNA or RNA, the monomers are the four types of nucleotides, which differ in their nitrogenous bases. Genes are typically hundreds or thousands of nucleotides long, each gene having a specific sequence of bases. Each polypeptide of a protein also has monomers arranged in a particular linear order (the protein's primary structure), but its monomers are amino acids. Thus, nucleic acids and proteins contain information written in two different chemical languages. Getting from DNA to protein requires two major stages: transcription and translation.

Transcription is the synthesis of RNA under the direction of DNA. Both nucleic acids use the same language, and the information is simply transcribed, or copied, from one molecule to the other. Just as a DNA strand provides a template for the synthesis of a new complementary strand during DNA replication, it also can serve as a template for assembling a complementary sequence of RNA nucleotides. For a protein-coding gene, the resulting RNA molecule is a faithful transcript of the gene's protein-building instructions, in the same way that your college transcript is an accurate record of your grades, and like a transcript, it can be sent out in multiple copies. This type of RNA molecule is called **messenger RNA (mRNA)** because it carries a genetic message from the DNA to the protein-synthesizing machinery of the cell. (Transcription is the general term for the synthesis of *any* kind of RNA on a DNA template. Later in this chapter, you will learn about some other types of RNA produced by transcription.)

Translation is the synthesis of a polypeptide, which occurs under the direction of mRNA. During this stage, there is a change in language: The cell must translate the base sequence of an mRNA molecule into the amino acid sequence of a polypeptide. The sites of translation are **ribosomes**, complex particles that facilitate the orderly linking of amino acids into polypeptide chains.

Transcription and translation occur in all organisms. Recall from Chapter 1 that there are three domains of life: Bacteria, Archaea, and Eukarya. Organisms in the first two domains are grouped as prokaryotes because their cells lack a membrane-bounded nucleus—a defining feature of eukaryotic cells. Most studies of transcription and translation have been done on bacteria and eukaryotes, which are therefore our main focus in this chapter. Although our understanding of these processes in archaea lags behind, in the last section we will discuss a few aspects of archaeal gene expression.

The basic mechanics of transcription and translation are similar for bacteria and eukaryotes, but there is an important difference in the flow of genetic information within the cells. Because bacteria do not have nuclei, their DNA is not segregated from ribosomes and the other protein-synthesizing equipment **(Figure 17.3a)**. As you will see later, this lack of segregation allows translation of an mRNA to begin while its transcription is still in progress. In a eukaryotic cell, by contrast, the nuclear envelope separates transcription from translation in space and time **(Figure 17.3b)**. Transcription occurs in the nucleus, and mRNA is transported to the cytoplasm, where translation occurs. But before they can leave the nucleus, eukaryotic RNA transcripts from protein-coding genes are modified in various ways to produce the final, functional mRNA. The transcription of a protein-coding eukaryotic gene results in *pre-mRNA*, and further processing yields the finished mRNA. The initial RNA transcript from any gene, including those coding for RNA that is not translated into protein, is more generally called a **primary transcript**.

Let's summarize: Genes program protein synthesis via genetic messages in the form of messenger RNA. Put another way, cells are governed by a molecular chain of command with a directional flow of genetic information: DNA → RNA → protein. This concept was dubbed the *central dogma* by Francis Crick in 1956. How has the concept held up over time? In the 1970s, scientists were surprised to discover that some RNA molecules can act as templates for DNA, a process you'll read about in Chapter 19. However, this rare exception does not invalidate the idea that, in general, genetic information flows from DNA to RNA to protein. In the next section, we discuss how the instructions for assembling amino acids into a specific order are encoded in nucleic acids.

The Genetic Code

When biologists began to suspect that the instructions for protein synthesis were encoded in DNA, they recognized a problem: There are only four nucleotide bases to specify 20 amino acids. Thus, the genetic code cannot be a language like Chinese, where each written symbol corresponds to a word. How many bases, then, correspond to an amino acid?

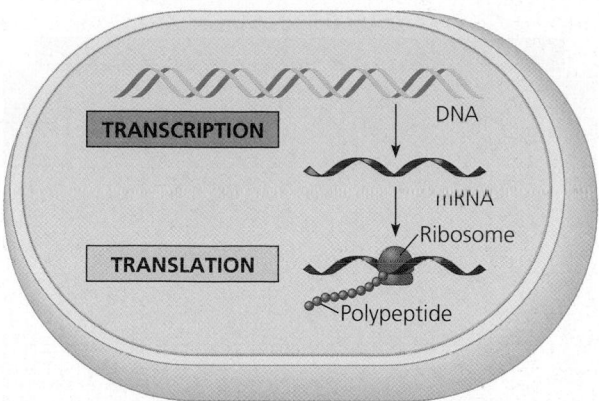

(a) **Bacterial cell.** In a bacterial cell, which lacks a nucleus, mRNA produced by transcription is immediately translated without additional processing.

(b) **Eukaryotic cell.** The nucleus provides a separate compartment for transcription. The original RNA transcript, called pre-mRNA, is processed in various ways before leaving the nucleus as mRNA.

▲ **Figure 17.3 Overview: the roles of transcription and translation in the flow of genetic information.** In a cell, inherited information flows from DNA to RNA to protein. The two main stages of information flow are transcription and translation. A miniature version of part (a) or (b) accompanies several figures later in the chapter as an orientation diagram to help you see where a particular figure fits into the overall scheme.

Codons: Triplets of Bases

If each nucleotide base were translated into an amino acid, only 4 of the 20 amino acids could be specified. Would a language of two-letter code words suffice? The two-base sequence AG, for example, could specify one amino acid, and GT could specify another. Since there are four possible bases

in each position, this would give us 16 (that is, 4^2) possible arrangements—still not enough to code for all 20 amino acids.

Triplets of nucleotide bases are the smallest units of uniform length that can code for all the amino acids. If each arrangement of three consecutive bases specifies an amino acid, there can be 64 (that is, 4^3) possible code words—more than enough to specify all the amino acids. Experiments have verified that the flow of information from gene to protein is based on a **triplet code**: The genetic instructions for a polypeptide chain are written in the DNA as a series of nonoverlapping, three-nucleotide words. For example, the base triplet AGT at a particular position along a DNA strand results in the placement of the amino acid serine at the corresponding position of the polypeptide being produced.

During transcription, the gene determines the sequence of bases along the length of an mRNA molecule (**Figure 17.4**). For each gene, only one of the two DNA strands is transcribed. This strand is called the **template strand** because it provides the pattern, or template, for the sequence of nucleotides in an RNA transcript. A given DNA strand is the template strand for some genes along a DNA molecule, while for other genes the complementary strand functions as the template. Note that

▲ **Figure 17.4 The triplet code.** For each gene, one DNA strand functions as a template for transcription. The base-pairing rules for DNA synthesis also guide transcription, but uracil (U) takes the place of thymine (T) in RNA. During translation, the mRNA is read as a sequence of base triplets, called codons. Each codon specifies an amino acid to be added to the growing polypeptide chain. The mRNA is read in the 5′ → 3′ direction.

for a particular gene, the same strand is used as the template every time it is transcribed.

An mRNA molecule is complementary rather than identical to its DNA template because RNA bases are assembled on the template according to base-pairing rules. The pairs are similar to those that form during DNA replication, except that U, the RNA substitute for T, pairs with A and the mRNA nucleotides contain ribose instead of deoxyribose. Like a new strand of DNA, the RNA molecule is synthesized in an antiparallel direction to the template strand of DNA. (To review what is meant by "antiparallel" and the 5′ and 3′ ends of a nucleic acid chain, see Figure 16.7.) For example, the base triplet ACC along the DNA (written as 3′-ACC-5′) provides a template for 5′-UGG-3′ in the mRNA molecule. The mRNA base triplets are called **codons**, and they are customarily written in the 5′ → 3′ direction. In our example, UGG is the codon for the amino acid tryptophan (abbreviated Trp). The term *codon* is also used for the DNA base triplets along the *nontemplate* strand. These codons are complementary to the template strand and thus identical in sequence to the mRNA except that they have T instead of U. (For this reason, the nontemplate DNA strand is sometimes called the "coding strand.")

During translation, the sequence of codons along an mRNA molecule is decoded, or translated, into a sequence of amino acids making up a polypeptide chain. The codons are read by the translation machinery in the 5′ → 3′ direction along the mRNA. Each codon specifies which one of the 20 amino acids will be incorporated at the corresponding position along a polypeptide. Because codons are base triplets, the number of nucleotides making up a genetic message must be three times the number of amino acids in the protein product. For example, it takes 300 nucleotides along an mRNA strand to code for the amino acids in a polypeptide that is 100 amino acids long.

Cracking the Code

Molecular biologists cracked the code of life in the early 1960s when a series of elegant experiments disclosed the amino acid translations of each of the RNA codons. The first codon was deciphered in 1961 by Marshall Nirenberg, of the National Institutes of Health, and his colleagues. Nirenberg synthesized an artificial mRNA by linking identical RNA nucleotides containing uracil as their base. No matter where this message started or stopped, it could contain only one codon in repetition: UUU. Nirenberg added this "poly-U" to a test-tube mixture containing amino acids, ribosomes, and the other components required for protein synthesis. His artificial system translated the poly-U into a polypeptide containing many units of the amino acid phenylalanine (Phe), strung together as a long polyphenylalanine chain. Thus, Nirenberg determined that the mRNA codon UUU specifies the amino acid phenylalanine. Soon, the amino acids specified by the codons AAA, GGG, and CCC were also determined.

▲ **Figure 17.5 The dictionary of the genetic code.** The three bases of an mRNA codon are designated here as the first, second, and third bases, reading in the 5′ → 3′ direction along the mRNA. (Practice using this dictionary by finding the codons in Figure 17.4.) The codon AUG not only stands for the amino acid methionine (Met) but also functions as a "start" signal for ribosomes to begin translating the mRNA at that point. Three of the 64 codons function as "stop" signals, marking the end of a genetic message. See Figure 5.17 for a list of the three-letter abbreviations for all the amino acids.

Although more elaborate techniques were required to decode mixed triplets such as AUA and CGA, all 64 codons were deciphered by the mid-1960s. As **Figure 17.5** shows, 61 of the 64 triplets code for amino acids. The three codons that do not designate amino acids are "stop" signals, or termination codons, marking the end of translation. Notice that the codon AUG has a dual function: It codes for the amino acid methionine (Met) and also functions as a "start" signal, or initiation codon. Genetic messages begin with the mRNA codon AUG, which signals the protein-synthesizing machinery to begin translating the mRNA at that location. (Because AUG also stands for methionine, polypeptide chains begin with methionine when they are synthesized. However, an enzyme may subsequently remove this starter amino acid from the chain.)

Notice in Figure 17.5 that there is redundancy in the genetic code, but no ambiguity. For example, although codons GAA and GAG both specify glutamic acid (redundancy), neither of them ever specifies any other amino acid (no ambiguity). The redundancy in the code is not altogether random. In many cases, codons that are synonyms for a particular amino acid differ only in the third base of the triplet. We will consider a possible benefit of this redundancy later in the chapter.

Our ability to extract the intended message from a written language depends on reading the symbols in the correct groupings—that is, in the correct **reading frame**. Consider this statement: "The red dog ate the bug." Group the letters incorrectly by starting at the wrong point, and the result will probably be gibberish: for example, "her edd oga tet heb ug." The reading frame is also important in the molecular language of cells. The short stretch of polypeptide shown in Figure 17.4, for instance, will be made correctly only if the mRNA nucleotides are read from left to right (5′ → 3′) in the groups of three shown in the figure: <u>UGG</u> <u>UUU</u> <u>GGC</u> <u>UCA</u>. Although a genetic message is written with no spaces between the codons, the cell's protein-synthesizing machinery reads the message as a series of nonoverlapping three-letter words. The message is *not* read as a series of overlapping words—<u>UGG</u><u>UUU</u>, and so on—which would convey a very different message.

Evolution of the Genetic Code

The genetic code is nearly universal, shared by organisms from the simplest bacteria to the most complex plants and animals. The RNA codon CCG, for instance, is translated as the amino acid proline in all organisms whose genetic code has been examined. In laboratory experiments, genes can be transcribed and translated after being transplanted from one species to another, sometimes with quite striking results, as shown in **Figure 17.6**! Bacteria can be programmed by the insertion of human genes to synthesize certain human proteins for medical use, such as insulin. Such applications have produced many exciting developments in the area of biotechnology (see Chapter 20).

Exceptions to the universality of the genetic code include translation systems in which a few codons differ from the standard ones. Slight variations in the genetic code exist in certain unicellular eukaryotes and in the organelle genes of some species. There are also exceptions in which stop codons can be translated into one of two amino acids not found in most organisms. Although one of these amino acids (pyrrolysine) has been detected thus far only in archaea, the other (selenocysteine) is a component of some bacterial proteins and even some human enzymes. Despite these exceptions, the evolutionary significance of the code's *near* universality is clear. A language shared by all living things must have been operating very early in the history of life—early enough to be present in the common ancestor of all present-day organisms. A shared genetic vocabulary is a reminder of the kinship that bonds all life on Earth.

CONCEPT CHECK 17.1

1. What polypeptide product would you expect from a poly-G mRNA that is 30 nucleotides long?
2. **DRAW IT** The template strand of a gene contains the sequence 3′-TTCAGTCGT-5′. Draw the nontemplate sequence and the mRNA sequence, indicating 5′ and 3′ ends of each. Compare the two sequences.
3. **WHAT IF?** Imagine that the nontemplate sequence in question 2 was transcribed instead of the template sequence. Draw the mRNA sequence and translate it using Figure 17.5. (Be sure to pay attention to the 5′ and 3′ ends.) Predict how well the protein synthesized from the nontemplate strand would function, if at all.

For suggested answers, see Appendix A.

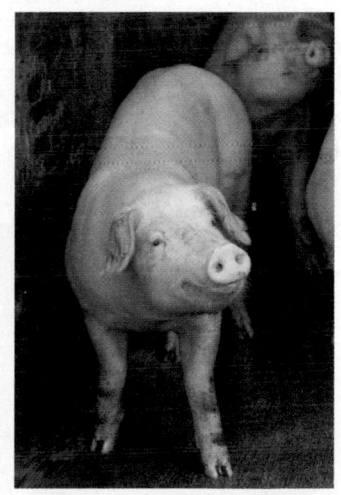

(a) Tobacco plant expressing a firefly gene. The yellow glow is produced by a chemical reaction catalyzed by the protein product of the firefly gene.

(b) Pig expressing a jellyfish gene. Researchers injected the gene for a fluorescent protein into fertilized pig eggs. One of the eggs developed into this fluorescent pig.

▲ **Figure 17.6 Expression of genes from different species.** Because diverse forms of life share a common genetic code, one species can be programmed to produce proteins characteristic of a second species by introducing DNA from the second species into the first.

CONCEPT 17.2

Transcription is the DNA-directed synthesis of RNA: *a closer look*

Now that we have considered the linguistic logic and evolutionary significance of the genetic code, we are ready to re-examine transcription, the first stage of gene expression, in more detail.

Molecular Components of Transcription

Messenger RNA, the carrier of information from DNA to the cell's protein-synthesizing machinery, is transcribed from the template strand of a gene. An enzyme called an **RNA polymerase** pries the two strands of DNA apart and joins the RNA nucleotides as they base-pair along the DNA template **(Figure 17.7)**. Like the DNA polymerases that function in DNA replication, RNA polymerases can assemble a polynucleotide only in its $5' \rightarrow 3'$ direction. Unlike DNA polymerases, however, RNA polymerases are able to start a chain from scratch; they don't need a primer.

Specific sequences of nucleotides along the DNA mark where transcription of a gene begins and ends. The DNA sequence where RNA polymerase attaches and initiates transcription is known as the **promoter**; in bacteria, the sequence that signals the end of transcription is called the **terminator**. (The termination mechanism is different in eukaryotes; we'll describe it later.) Molecular biologists refer to the direction of transcription as "downstream" and the other direction as "upstream." These terms are also used to describe the positions of nucleotide sequences within the DNA or RNA. Thus, the pro-

moter sequence in DNA is said to be upstream from the terminator. The stretch of DNA that is transcribed into an RNA molecule is called a **transcription unit**.

Bacteria have a single type of RNA polymerase that synthesizes not only mRNA but also other types of RNA that function in protein synthesis, such as ribosomal RNA. In contrast, eukaryotes have at least three types of RNA polymerase in their nuclei. The one used for mRNA synthesis is called RNA polymerase II. The other RNA polymerases transcribe RNA molecules that are not translated into protein. In the discussion of transcription that follows, we start with the features of mRNA synthesis common to both bacteria and eukaryotes and then describe some key differences.

Synthesis of an RNA Transcript

The three stages of transcription, as shown in Figure 17.7 and described next, are initiation, elongation, and termination of the RNA chain. Study Figure 17.7 to familiarize yourself with the stages and the terms used to describe them.

RNA Polymerase Binding and Initiation of Transcription

The promoter of a gene includes within it the transcription start point (the nucleotide where RNA synthesis actually begins) and typically extends several dozen nucleotide pairs

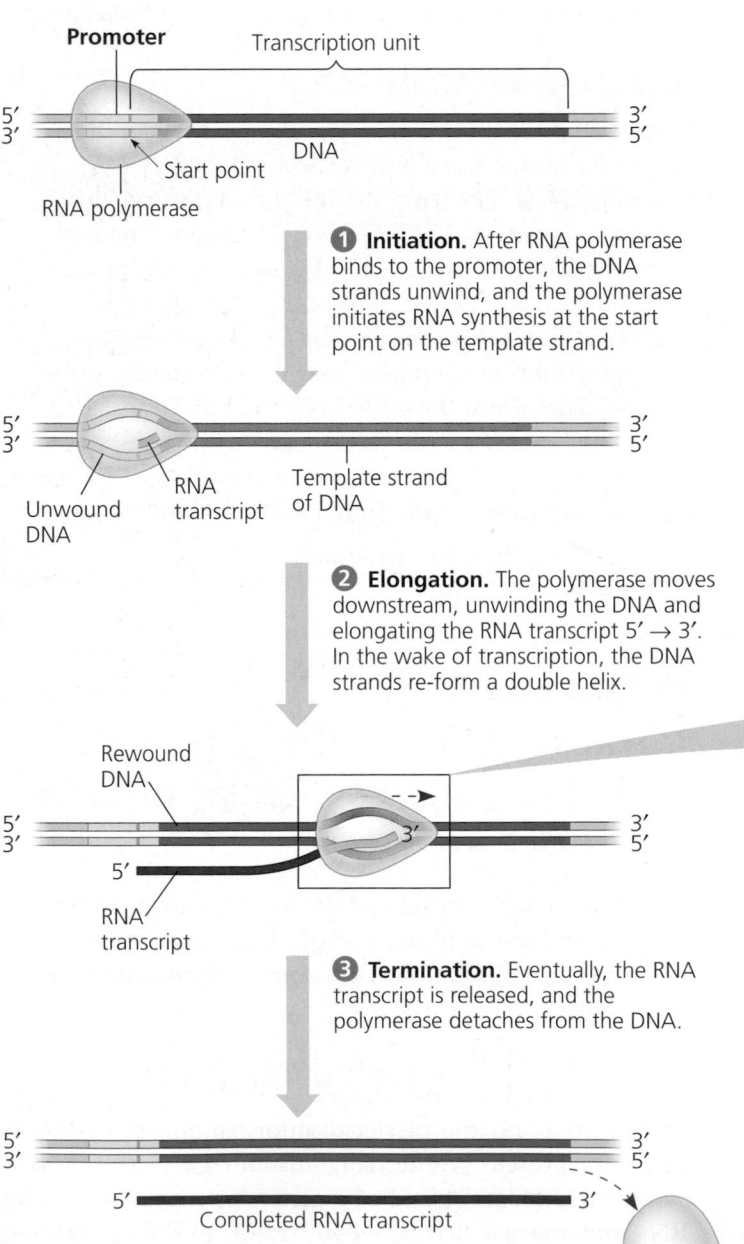

1 Initiation. After RNA polymerase binds to the promoter, the DNA strands unwind, and the polymerase initiates RNA synthesis at the start point on the template strand.

2 Elongation. The polymerase moves downstream, unwinding the DNA and elongating the RNA transcript $5' \rightarrow 3'$. In the wake of transcription, the DNA strands re-form a double helix.

3 Termination. Eventually, the RNA transcript is released, and the polymerase detaches from the DNA.

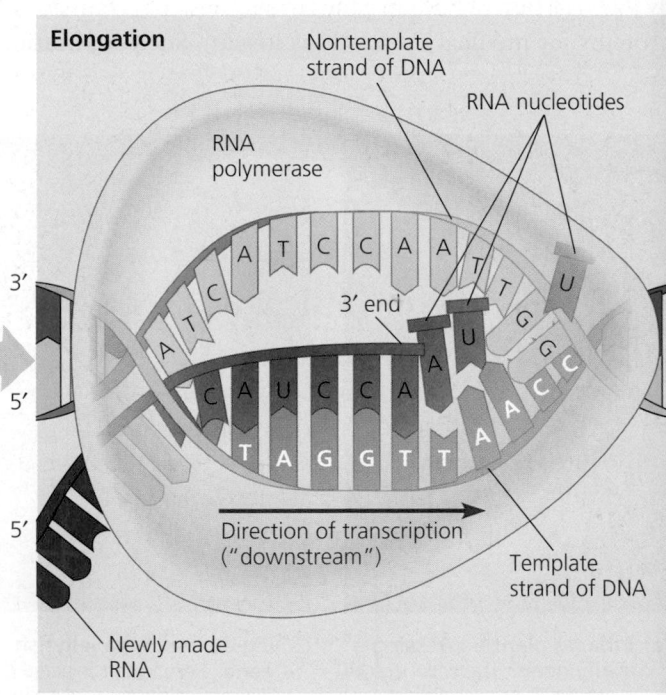

▲ **Figure 17.7 The stages of transcription: initiation, elongation, and termination.** This general depiction of transcription applies to both bacteria and eukaryotes, but the details of termination differ, as described in the text. Also, in a bacterium, the RNA transcript is immediately usable as mRNA; in a eukaryote, the RNA transcript must first undergo processing.

upstream from the start point. In addition to serving as a binding site for RNA polymerase and determining where transcription starts, the promoter determines which of the two strands of the DNA helix is used as the template.

Certain sections of a promoter are especially important for binding RNA polymerase. In bacteria, the RNA polymerase itself specifically recognizes and binds to the promoter. In eukaryotes, a collection of proteins called **transcription factors** mediate the binding of RNA polymerase and the initiation of transcription. Recall from Chapter 16 that the DNA of a eukaryotic chromosome is complexed with histones and other proteins in the form of chromatin. The roles of these proteins in making the DNA accessible to transcription factors will be discussed in Chapter 18. Only after certain transcription factors are attached to the promoter does RNA polymerase II bind to it. The whole complex of transcription factors and RNA polymerase II bound to the promoter is called a **transcription initiation complex**. **Figure 17.8** shows the role of transcription factors and a crucial promoter DNA sequence called a **TATA box** in forming the initiation complex at a eukaryotic promoter.

The interaction between eukaryotic RNA polymerase II and transcription factors is an example of the importance of protein-protein interactions in controlling eukaryotic transcription. Once the polymerase is firmly attached to the promoter DNA, the two DNA strands unwind there, and the enzyme starts transcribing the template strand.

Elongation of the RNA Strand

As RNA polymerase moves along the DNA, it continues to untwist the double helix, exposing about 10 to 20 DNA bases at a time for pairing with RNA nucleotides (see Figure 17.7). The enzyme adds nucleotides to the 3' end of the growing RNA molecule as it continues along the double helix. In the wake of this advancing wave of RNA synthesis, the new RNA molecule peels away from its DNA template and the DNA double helix re-forms. Transcription progresses at a rate of about 40 nucleotides per second in eukaryotes.

A single gene can be transcribed simultaneously by several molecules of RNA polymerase following each other like trucks in a convoy. A growing strand of RNA trails off from each polymerase, with the length of each new strand reflecting how far along the template the enzyme has traveled from the start point (see the mRNA molecules in Figure 17.24). The congregation of many polymerase molecules simultaneously transcribing a single gene increases the amount of mRNA transcribed from it, which helps the cell make the encoded protein in large amounts.

Termination of Transcription

The mechanism of termination differs between bacteria and eukaryotes. In bacteria, transcription proceeds through a terminator sequence in the DNA. The transcribed terminator

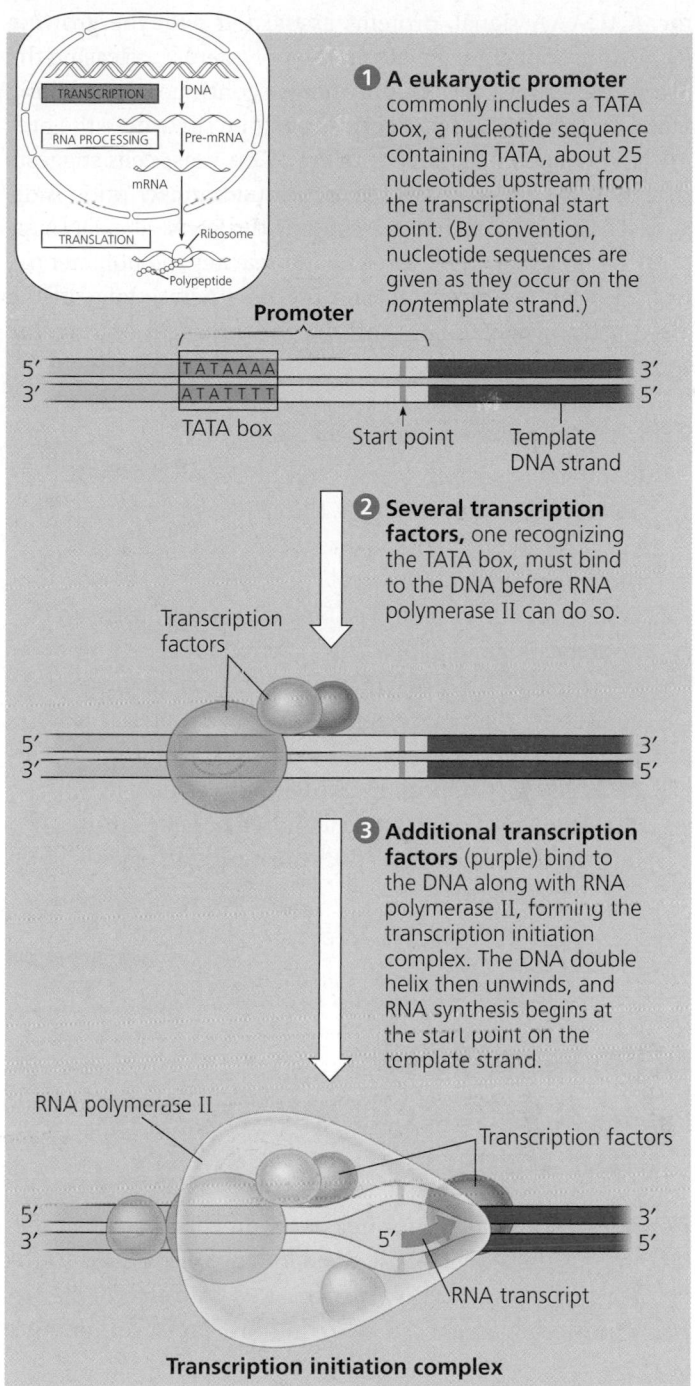

1 **A eukaryotic promoter** commonly includes a TATA box, a nucleotide sequence containing TATA, about 25 nucleotides upstream from the transcriptional start point. (By convention, nucleotide sequences are given as they occur on the *non*template strand.)

Promoter

5'
3'

TATAAAA
ATATTTT

3'
5'

TATA box   Start point   Template DNA strand

2 **Several transcription factors,** one recognizing the TATA box, must bind to the DNA before RNA polymerase II can do so.

Transcription factors

5'
3'

3'
5'

3 **Additional transcription factors** (purple) bind to the DNA along with RNA polymerase II, forming the transcription initiation complex. The DNA double helix then unwinds, and RNA synthesis begins at the start point on the template strand.

RNA polymerase II

Transcription factors

5'
3'

5'

3'
5'

RNA transcript

Transcription initiation complex

▲ **Figure 17.8 The initiation of transcription at a eukaryotic promoter.** In eukaryotic cells, proteins called transcription factors mediate the initiation of transcription by RNA polymerase II.

? *Explain how the interaction of RNA polymerase with the promoter would differ if the figure showed transcription initiation for bacteria.*

(an RNA sequence) functions as the termination signal, causing the polymerase to detach from the DNA and release the transcript, which is available for immediate use as mRNA. In eukaryotes, RNA polymerase II transcribes a sequence on the DNA called the polyadenylation signal sequence, which codes for a polyadenylation signal (AAUAAA) in the pre-mRNA. Then, at a point about 10 to 35 nucleotides downstream from the AAUAAA signal, proteins associated with the growing RNA transcript cut it free from the polymerase, releasing the pre-mRNA. However, the polymerase continues transcribing DNA for hundreds of nucleotides past the site where the pre-mRNA was released. Recent research on yeast cells suggests that the RNA produced by this continued transcription is digested by an enzyme that moves along the RNA. The data support the idea that when the enzyme reaches the polymerase, transcription is terminated and the polymerase falls off the DNA. Meanwhile, the pre-mRNA undergoes processing, the topic of the next section.

CONCEPT CHECK **17.2**

1. Compare DNA polymerase and RNA polymerase in terms of how they function, the requirement for a template and primer, the direction of synthesis, and the type of nucleotides used.
2. What is a promoter, and is it located at the upstream or downstream end of a transcription unit?
3. What makes RNA polymerase start transcribing a gene at the right place on the DNA in a bacterial cell? In a eukaryotic cell?
4. **WHAT IF?** Suppose X-rays caused a sequence change in the TATA box of a particular gene's promoter. How would that affect transcription of the gene? (See Figure 17.8.)

For suggested answers, see Appendix A.

CONCEPT 17.3
Eukaryotic cells modify RNA after transcription

Enzymes in the eukaryotic nucleus modify pre-mRNA in specific ways before the genetic messages are dispatched to the cytoplasm. During this **RNA processing**, both ends of the primary transcript are altered. Also, in most cases, certain interior sections of the RNA molecule are cut out and the remaining parts spliced together. These modifications produce an mRNA molecule ready for translation.

Alteration of mRNA Ends

Each end of a pre-mRNA molecule is modified in a particular way **(Figure 17.9)**. The 5' end is synthesized first; it receives a **5' cap**, a modified form of a guanine (G) nucleotide added onto the 5' end after transcription of the first 20 to 40 nucleotides. The 3' end of the pre-mRNA molecule is also modified before the mRNA exits the nucleus. Recall that the pre-mRNA is released soon after the polyadenylation signal, AAUAAA, is transcribed. At the 3' end, an enzyme adds 50 to 250 more adenine (A) nucleotides, forming a **poly-A tail**. The 5' cap and poly-A tail share several important functions. First, they seem to facilitate the export of the mature mRNA from the nucleus. Second, they help protect the mRNA from degradation by hydrolytic enzymes. And third, they help ribosomes attach to the 5' end of the mRNA once the mRNA reaches the cytoplasm. Figure 17.9 shows a diagram of a eukaryotic mRNA molecule with cap and tail. The figure also shows the untranslated regions (UTRs) at the 5' and 3' ends of the mRNA (referred to as the 5' UTR and 3' UTR). The UTRs are parts of the mRNA that will not be translated into protein, but they have other functions, such as ribosome binding.

Split Genes and RNA Splicing

A remarkable stage of RNA processing in the eukaryotic nucleus is the removal of large portions of the RNA molecule that is initially synthesized—a cut-and-paste job called **RNA splicing**, similar to editing a video **(Figure 17.10)**. The average length of a transcription unit along a human DNA molecule is about 27,000 base pairs, so the primary RNA transcript is also that long. However, it takes only 1,200 nucleotides in RNA to code for the average-sized protein of 400 amino acids. (Remember, each amino acid is encoded by a *triplet* of nucleotides.) This means that most eukaryotic genes and their RNA transcripts have long noncoding stretches of nucleotides, regions that are not

▲ **Figure 17.9 RNA processing: addition of the 5' cap and poly-A tail.** Enzymes modify the two ends of a eukaryotic pre-mRNA molecule. The modified ends may promote the export of mRNA from the nucleus, and they help protect the mRNA from degradation. When the mRNA reaches the cytoplasm, the modified ends, in conjunction with certain cytoplasmic proteins, facilitate ribosome attachment. The 5' cap and poly-A tail are not translated into protein, nor are the regions called the 5' untranslated region (5' UTR) and 3' untranslated region (3' UTR).

▲ **Figure 17.10 RNA processing: RNA splicing.** The RNA molecule shown here codes for β-globin, one of the polypeptides of hemoglobin. The numbers under the RNA refer to codons; β-globin is 146 amino acids long. The β-globin gene and its pre-mRNA transcript have three exons, corresponding to sequences that will leave the nucleus as mRNA. (The 5′ UTR and 3′ UTR are parts of exons because they are included in the mRNA; however, they do not code for protein.) During RNA processing, the introns are cut out and the exons spliced together. In many genes, the introns are much larger relative to the exons than they are in the β-globin gene. (The pre-mRNA is not drawn to scale.)

translated. Even more surprising is that most of these noncoding sequences are interspersed between coding segments of the gene and thus between coding segments of the pre-mRNA. In other words, the sequence of DNA nucleotides that codes for a eukaryotic polypeptide is usually not continuous; it is split into segments. The noncoding segments of nucleic acid that lie between coding regions are called intervening sequences, or **introns**. The other regions are called **exons**, because they are eventually expressed, usually by being translated into amino acid sequences. (Exceptions include the UTRs of the exons at the ends of the RNA, which make up part of the mRNA but are not translated into protein. Because of these exceptions, you may find it helpful to think of exons as sequences of RNA that *exit* the nucleus.) The terms *intron* and *exon* are used for both RNA sequences and the DNA sequences that encode them.

In making a primary transcript from a gene, RNA polymerase II transcribes both introns and exons from the DNA, but the mRNA molecule that enters the cytoplasm is an abridged version. The introns are cut out from the molecule and the exons joined together, forming an mRNA molecule with a continuous coding sequence. This is the process of RNA splicing.

How is pre-mRNA splicing carried out? Researchers have learned that the signal for RNA splicing is a short nucleotide sequence at each end of an intron. Particles called *small nuclear ribonucleoproteins*, abbreviated *snRNPs* (pronounced "snurps"), recognize these splice sites. As the name implies, snRNPs are located in the cell nucleus and are composed of RNA and protein molecules. The RNA in a snRNP particle is called a *small nuclear RNA (snRNA)*; each molecule is about 150 nucleotides long. Several different snRNPs join with additional proteins to form an even larger assembly called a **spliceosome**, which is almost as big as a ribosome. The spliceosome interacts with certain sites along an intron, releasing the intron and joining together the two exons that flanked the intron **(Figure 17.11)**. There is strong evidence that snRNAs catalyze these processes, as well as participating in spliceosome assembly and splice site recognition.

▲ **Figure 17.11 The roles of snRNPs and spliceosomes in pre-mRNA splicing.** The diagram shows only a portion of the pre-mRNA transcript; additional introns and exons lie downstream from the ones pictured here. **①** Small nuclear ribonucleoproteins (snRNPs) and other proteins form a molecular complex called a spliceosome on a pre-mRNA molecule containing exons and introns. **②** Within the spliceosome, snRNA base-pairs with nucleotides at specific sites along the intron. **③** The spliceosome cuts the pre-mRNA, releasing the intron, and at the same time splices the exons together. The spliceosome then comes apart, releasing mRNA, which now contains only exons.

Ribozymes

The idea of a catalytic role for snRNA arose from the discovery of **ribozymes**, RNA molecules that function as enzymes. In some organisms, RNA splicing can occur without proteins or even additional RNA molecules: The intron RNA functions as a ribozyme and catalyzes its own excision! For example, in the ciliate protist *Tetrahymena*, self-splicing occurs in the production of ribosomal RNA (rRNA), a component of the organism's ribosomes. The pre-rRNA actually removes its own introns. The discovery of ribozymes rendered obsolete the idea that all biological catalysts are proteins.

Three properties of RNA enable some RNA molecules to function as enzymes. First, because RNA is single-stranded, a region of an RNA molecule may base-pair with a complementary region elsewhere in the same molecule, which gives the molecule a particular three-dimensional structure. A specific structure is essential to the catalytic function of ribozymes, just as it is for enzymatic proteins. Second, like certain amino acids in an enzymatic protein, some of the bases in RNA contain functional groups that may participate in catalysis. Third, the ability of RNA to hydrogen-bond with other nucleic acid molecules (either RNA or DNA) adds specificity to its catalytic activity. For example, complementary base pairing between the RNA of the spliceosome and the RNA of a primary RNA transcript precisely locates the region where the ribozyme catalyzes splicing. Later in this chapter, you will see how these properties of RNA also allow it to perform important noncatalytic roles in the cell, such as recognition of the three-nucleotide codons on mRNA.

The Functional and Evolutionary Importance of Introns

What could be the biological functions of introns and RNA splicing? While specific functions may not have been identified for most introns, at least some contain sequences that regulate gene activity. And the splicing process itself is necessary for the passage of mRNA from the nucleus to the cytoplasm.

One consequence of the presence of introns in genes is that a single gene can encode more than one kind of polypeptide. Many genes are known to give rise to two or more different polypeptides, depending on which segments are treated as exons during RNA processing; this is called **alternative RNA splicing** (see Figure 18.11). For example, sex differences in fruit flies are largely due to differences in how males and females splice the RNA transcribed from certain genes. Results from the Human Genome Project (discussed in Chapter 21) suggest that alternative RNA splicing is one reason humans can get along with a relatively small number of genes—about one and a half times as many as a fruit fly. Because of alternative splicing, the number of different protein products an organism produces can be much greater than its number of genes.

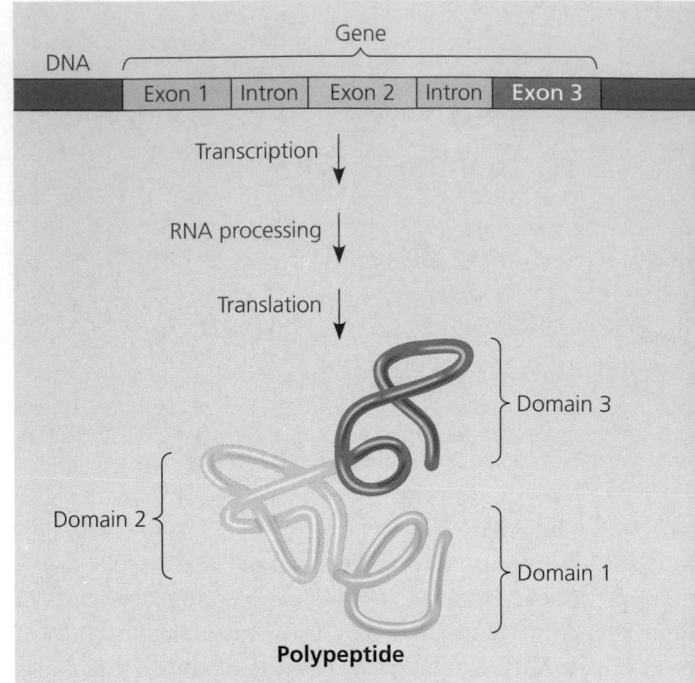

▲ **Figure 17.12 Correspondence between exons and protein domains.**

Proteins often have a modular architecture consisting of discrete structural and functional regions called **domains**. One domain of an enzymatic protein, for instance, might include the active site, while another might attach the protein to a cellular membrane. In quite a few cases, different exons code for the different domains of a protein **(Figure 17.12)**.

The presence of introns in a gene may facilitate the evolution of new and potentially useful proteins as a result of a process known as *exon shuffling*. Introns increase the probability of potentially beneficial crossing over between the exons of alleles—simply by providing more terrain for crossovers without interrupting coding sequences. We can also imagine the occasional mixing and matching of exons between completely different (nonallelic) genes. Exon shuffling of either sort could lead to new proteins with novel combinations of functions. While most of the shuffling would result in nonbeneficial changes, occasionally a beneficial variant might arise.

CONCEPT CHECK 17.3

1. How does alteration of the 5′ and 3′ ends of pre-mRNA affect the mRNA that exits the nucleus?
2. How is RNA splicing similar to editing a video?
3. **WHAT IF?** In nematode worms, a gene that codes for an ATPase has two alternatives for exon 4 and three alternatives for exon 7. How many different forms of the protein could be made from this gene?

For suggested answers, see Appendix A.

Translation is the RNA-directed synthesis of a polypeptide: *a closer look*

We will now examine in greater detail how genetic information flows from mRNA to protein—the process of translation. As we did for transcription, we'll concentrate on the basic steps of translation that occur in both bacteria and eukaryotes, while pointing out key differences.

Molecular Components of Translation

In the process of translation, a cell interprets a genetic message and builds a polypeptide accordingly. The message is a series of codons along an mRNA molecule, and the interpreter is called **transfer RNA (tRNA)**. The function of tRNA is to transfer amino acids from the cytoplasmic pool of amino acids to a ribosome. A cell keeps its cytoplasm stocked with all 20 amino acids, either by synthesizing them from other compounds or by taking them up from the surrounding solution. The ribosome adds each amino acid brought to it by tRNA to the growing end of a polypeptide chain (**Figure 17.13**).

Molecules of tRNA are not all identical. The key to translating a genetic message into a specific amino acid sequence is that each type of tRNA molecule translates a particular mRNA codon into a particular amino acid. As a tRNA molecule arrives at a ribosome, it bears a specific amino acid at one end. At the other end of the tRNA is a nucleotide triplet called an **anticodon**, which base-pairs with a complementary codon on mRNA. For example, consider the mRNA codon UUU, which is translated as the amino acid phenylalanine. The tRNA that base-pairs with this codon by hydrogen bonding has AAA as its anticodon and carries phenylalanine at its other end (see the middle tRNA on the ribosome in Figure 17.13). As an mRNA molecule is moved through a ribosome, phenylalanine will be added to the polypeptide chain whenever the codon UUU is presented for translation. Codon by codon, the genetic message is translated as tRNAs deposit amino acids in the order prescribed, and the ribosome joins the amino acids into a chain. The tRNA molecule is a translator because it can read a nucleic acid word (the mRNA codon) and interpret it as a protein word (the amino acid).

Translation is simple in principle but complex in its biochemistry and mechanics, especially in the eukaryotic cell. In dissecting translation, we'll concentrate on the slightly less complicated version of the process that occurs in bacteria. Let's first look at the major components in this cellular process. Then we will see how they act together to make a polypeptide.

▲ **Figure 17.13 Translation: the basic concept.** As a molecule of mRNA is moved through a ribosome, codons are translated into amino acids, one by one. The interpreters are tRNA molecules, each type with a specific anticodon at one end and a corresponding amino acid at the other end. A tRNA adds its amino acid cargo to a growing polypeptide chain when the anticodon hydrogen-bonds to a complementary codon on the mRNA. The figures that follow show some of the details of translation in a bacterial cell.

MEDIA **BioFlix** Visit **www.campbellbiology.com** for the BioFlix 3-D Animation on Protein Synthesis.

The Structure and Function of Transfer RNA

Like mRNA and other types of cellular RNA, transfer RNA molecules are transcribed from DNA templates. In a eukaryotic cell, tRNA, like mRNA, is made in the nucleus and must travel from the nucleus to the cytoplasm, where translation occurs. In both bacterial and eukaryotic cells, each tRNA molecule is used repeatedly, picking up its designated amino acid in the cytosol, depositing this cargo onto a polypeptide chain at the ribosome, and then leaving the ribosome, ready to pick up another amino acid.

A tRNA molecule consists of a single RNA strand that is only about 80 nucleotides long (compared to hundreds of nucleotides for most mRNA molecules). Because of the presence of complementary stretches of bases that can hydrogen-bond to each other, this single strand can fold back upon itself and form a molecule with a three-dimensional structure. Flattened into one plane to reveal this base pairing, a tRNA molecule

(a) Two-dimensional structure. The four base-paired regions and three loops are characteristic of all tRNAs, as is the base sequence of the amino acid attachment site at the 3' end. The anticodon triplet is unique to each tRNA type, as are some sequences in the other two loops. (The asterisks mark bases that have been chemically modified, a characteristic of tRNA.)

(b) Three-dimensional structure

(c) Symbol used in this book

▲ **Figure 17.14 The structure of transfer RNA (tRNA).** Anticodons are conventionally written 3' → 5' to align properly with codons written 5' → 3' (see Figure 17.13). For base pairing, RNA strands must be antiparallel, like DNA. For example, anticodon 3'-AAG-5' pairs with mRNA codon 5'-UUC-3'.

▲ **Figure 17.15 An aminoacyl-tRNA synthetase joining a specific amino acid to a tRNA.** Linkage of the tRNA and amino acid is an endergonic process that occurs at the expense of ATP. The ATP loses two phosphate groups, becoming AMP (adenosine monophosphate).

looks like a cloverleaf **(Figure 17.14a)**. The tRNA actually twists and folds into a compact three-dimensional structure that is roughly L-shaped **(Figure 17.14b)**. The loop extending from one end of the L includes the anticodon, the particular base triplet that base-pairs to a specific mRNA codon. From the other end of the L-shaped tRNA molecule protrudes its 3'

end, which is the attachment site for an amino acid. Thus, the structure of a tRNA molecule fits its function.

The accurate translation of a genetic message requires two processes that involve molecular recognition. First, a tRNA that binds to an mRNA codon specifying a particular amino acid must carry that amino acid, and no other, to the ribosome. The correct matching up of tRNA and amino acid is carried out by a family of related enzymes called **aminoacyl-tRNA synthetases** **(Figure 17.15)**. The active site of each type of aminoacyl-tRNA synthetase fits only a specific combination of amino acid and tRNA. There are 20 different synthetases, one for each amino acid; each synthetase is able to bind all the different tRNAs that code for its particular amino acid. The synthetase catalyzes the covalent attachment of the amino acid to its tRNA in a process driven by the hydrolysis of ATP. The resulting aminoacyl tRNA, also called a charged tRNA, is released from the enzyme and is then available to deliver its amino acid to a growing polypeptide chain on a ribosome.

The second recognition process involves matching up the tRNA anticodon with the appropriate mRNA codon. If one tRNA variety existed for each mRNA codon that specifies an amino acid, there would be 61 tRNAs (see Figure 17.5). In fact, there are only about 45, signifying that some tRNAs must be able to bind to more than one codon. Such versatility is possible because the rules for base pairing between the third base of a codon and the corresponding base of a tRNA anticodon are relaxed compared to those at other codon positions. For example, the base U at the 5' end of a tRNA anticodon can pair with either A or G in the third position (at the 3' end) of an mRNA codon. The flexible base pairing at this codon position is called **wobble**. Wobble explains why the synonymous codons for a given amino acid can differ in their third base, but usually not in their other bases. For example, a tRNA with the anticodon 3'-UCU-5' can base-pair with either the mRNA codon 5'-AGA-3' or 5'-AGG-3', both of which code for arginine (see Figure 17.5).

Ribosomes

Ribosomes facilitate the specific coupling of tRNA anticodons with mRNA codons during protein synthesis. A ribosome is made up of two subunits, called the large and small subunits **(Figure 17.16)**. The ribosomal subunits are constructed of proteins and RNA molecules named **ribosomal RNAs**, or **rRNAs**. In eukaryotes, the subunits are made in the nucleolus. Ribosomal RNA genes on the chromosomal DNA are transcribed, and the RNA is processed and assembled with proteins imported from the cytoplasm. The resulting ribosomal subunits are then exported via nuclear pores to the cytoplasm. In both bacteria and eukaryotes, large and small subunits join to form a functional ribosome only when they attach to an mRNA molecule. About two-thirds of the mass of a ribosome consists of rRNAs, either three molecules (in bacteria) or four (in eukaryotes). Because most cells contain thousands of ribosomes, rRNA is the most abundant type of cellular RNA.

Although the ribosomes of bacteria and eukaryotes are very similar in structure and function, those of eukaryotes are slightly larger and differ somewhat from bacterial ribosomes in their molecular composition. The differences are medically significant. Certain antibiotic drugs can inactivate bacterial ribosomes without inhibiting the ability of eukaryotic ribosomes to make proteins. These drugs, including tetracycline and streptomycin, are used to combat bacterial infections.

(a) Computer model of functioning ribosome. This is a model of a bacterial ribosome, showing its overall shape. The eukaryotic ribosome is roughly similar. A ribosomal subunit is an aggregate of ribosomal RNA molecules and proteins.

(b) Schematic model showing binding sites. A ribosome has an mRNA binding site and three tRNA binding sites, known as the A, P, and E sites. This schematic ribosome will appear in later diagrams.

(c) Schematic model with mRNA and tRNA. A tRNA fits into a binding site when its anticodon base-pairs with an mRNA codon. The P site holds the tRNA attached to the growing polypeptide. The A site holds the tRNA carrying the next amino acid to be added to the polypeptide chain. Discharged tRNA leaves from the E site.

▲ **Figure 17.16 The anatomy of a functioning ribosome.**

The structure of a ribosome reflects its function of bringing mRNA together with tRNAs carrying amino acids. In addition to a binding site for mRNA, each ribosome has three binding sites for tRNA (see Figure 17.16). The **P site** (peptidyl-tRNA site) holds the tRNA carrying the growing polypeptide chain, while the **A site** (aminoacyl-tRNA site) holds the tRNA carrying the next amino acid to be added to the chain. Discharged tRNAs leave the ribosome from the **E site** (exit site). The ribosome holds the tRNA and mRNA in close proximity and positions the new amino acid for addition to the carboxyl end of the growing polypeptide. It then catalyzes the formation of the peptide bond. As the polypeptide becomes longer, it passes through an *exit tunnel* in the ribosome's large subunit. When the polypeptide is complete, it is released to the cytosol through the exit tunnel.

Recent research strongly supports the hypothesis that rRNA, not protein, is primarily responsible for both the structure and the function of the ribosome. The proteins, which are largely on the exterior, support the shape changes of the rRNA molecules as they carry out catalysis during translation. Ribosomal RNA is the main constituent of the interface between the two subunits and of the A and P sites, and it is the catalyst of peptide bond formation. Thus, a ribosome can be regarded as one colossal ribozyme!

Building a Polypeptide

We can divide translation, the synthesis of a polypeptide chain, into three stages (analogous to those of transcription): initiation, elongation, and termination. All three stages require protein "factors" that aid in the translation process. For certain aspects of chain initiation and elongation, energy is also required. It is provided by the hydrolysis of GTP (guanosine triphosphate), a molecule closely related to ATP.

Ribosome Association and Initiation of Translation

The initiation stage of translation brings together mRNA, a tRNA bearing the first amino acid of the polypeptide, and the two subunits of a ribosome **(Figure 17.17)**. First, a small ribosomal subunit binds to both mRNA and a specific initiator tRNA, which carries the amino acid methionine. In bacteria, the small subunit can bind these two in either order; it binds the mRNA at a specific RNA sequence, just upstream of the start codon, AUG. In eukaryotes, the small subunit, with the initiator tRNA already bound, binds to the 5′ cap of the mRNA and then moves, or *scans*, downstream along the mRNA until it reaches the start codon, and the initiator tRNA hydrogen-bonds to it. In either case, the start codon signals the start of translation; this is important because it establishes the codon reading frame for the mRNA.

The union of mRNA, initiator tRNA, and a small ribosomal subunit is followed by the attachment of a large ribosomal subunit, completing the *translation initiation complex*. Proteins called *initiation factors* are required to bring all these components together. The cell also expends energy in the form of a GTP molecule to form the initiation complex. At the completion of the initiation process, the initiator tRNA sits in the P site of the ribosome, and the vacant A site is ready for the next aminoacyl tRNA. Note that a polypeptide is always synthesized in one direction, from the initial methionine at the amino end, also called the N-terminus, toward the final amino acid at the carboxyl end, also called the C-terminus (see Figure 5.18).

► **Figure 17.17 The initiation of translation.**

❶ A small ribosomal subunit binds to a molecule of mRNA. In a bacterial cell, the mRNA binding site on this subunit recognizes a specific nucleotide sequence on the mRNA just upstream of the start codon. An initiator tRNA, with the anticodon UAC, base-pairs with the start codon, AUG. This tRNA carries the amino acid methionine (Met).

❷ The arrival of a large ribosomal subunit completes the initiation complex. Proteins called initiation factors (not shown) are required to bring all the translation components together. GTP provides the energy for the assembly. The initiator tRNA is in the P site; the A site is available to the tRNA bearing the next amino acid.

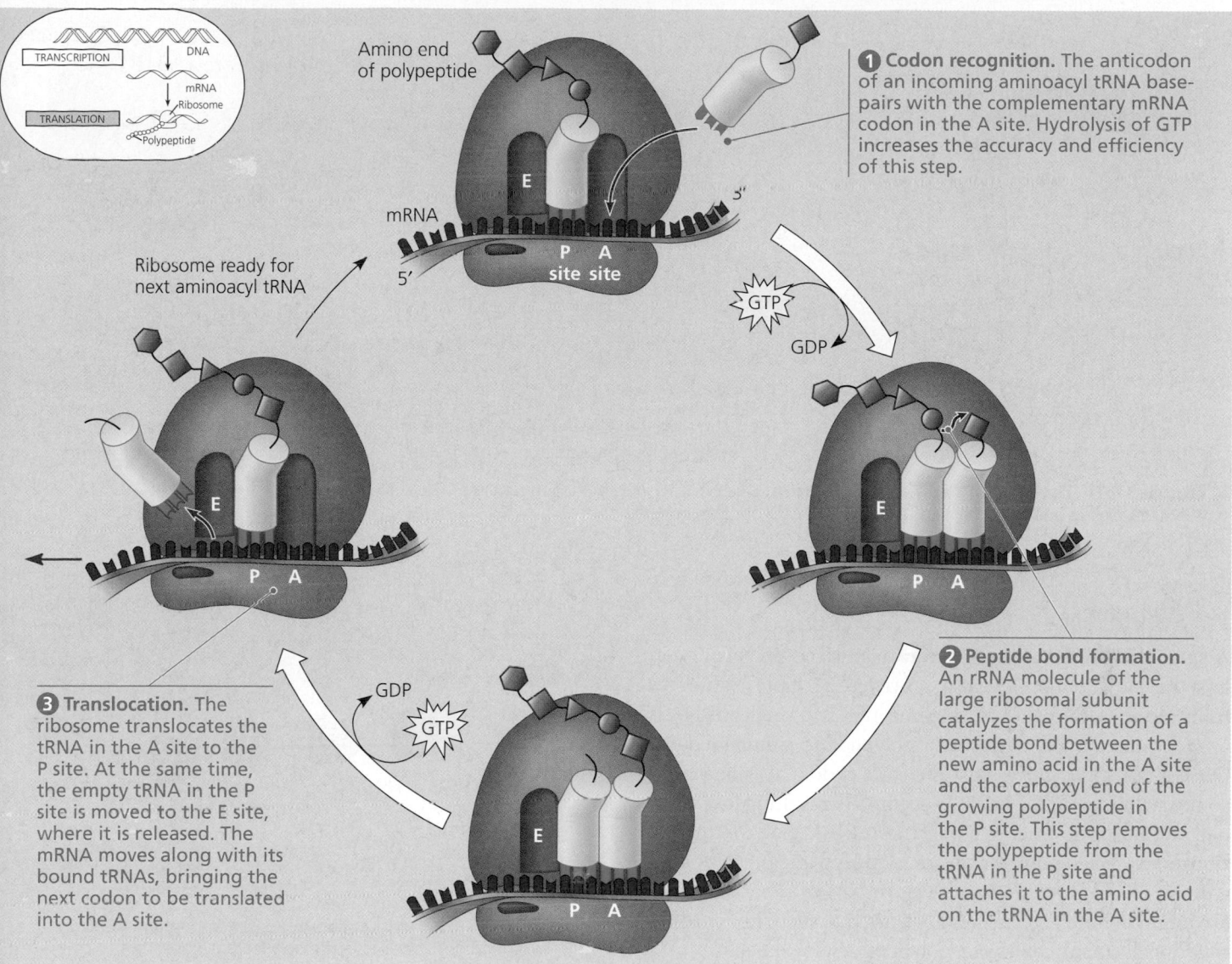

Amino end
of polypeptide

Ribosome ready for
next aminoacyl tRNA

mRNA

5′

3′

① Codon recognition. The anticodon
of an incoming aminoacyl tRNA base-
pairs with the complementary mRNA
codon in the A site. Hydrolysis of GTP
increases the accuracy and efficiency
of this step.

GTP

GDP

E

P   A
site site

E

P   A

E

P   A

GDP

GTP

E

P   A

③ Translocation. The
ribosome translocates the
tRNA in the A site to the
P site. At the same time,
the empty tRNA in the P
site is moved to the E site,
where it is released. The
mRNA moves along with its
bound tRNAs, bringing the
next codon to be translated
into the A site.

② Peptide bond formation.
An rRNA molecule of the
large ribosomal subunit
catalyzes the formation of a
peptide bond between the
new amino acid in the A site
and the carboxyl end of the
growing polypeptide in
the P site. This step removes
the polypeptide from the
tRNA in the P site and
attaches it to the amino acid
on the tRNA in the A site.

▲ **Figure 17.18 The elongation cycle of translation.** The hydrolysis of GTP plays an
important role in the elongation process. Not shown are the proteins called elongation factors.

Elongation of the Polypeptide Chain

In the elongation stage of translation, amino acids are added one
by one to the preceding amino acid. Each addition involves the
participation of several proteins called *elongation factors* and
occurs in a three-step cycle described in **Figure 17.18**. Energy
expenditure occurs in the first and third steps. Codon recognition requires hydrolysis of one molecule of GTP, which increases the accuracy and efficiency of this step. One more GTP
is hydrolyzed to provide energy for the translocation step.

The mRNA is moved through the ribosome in one direction
only, 5′ end first; this is equivalent to the ribosome moving
5′ → 3′ on the mRNA. The important point is that the ribosome and the mRNA move relative to each other, unidirec-
tionally, codon by codon. The elongation cycle takes less than
a tenth of a second in bacteria and is repeated as each amino acid
is added to the chain until the polypeptide is completed.

Termination of Translation

The final stage of translation is termination (**Figure 17.19**, on
the next page). Elongation continues until a stop codon in the
mRNA reaches the A site of the ribosome. The base triplets
UAG, UAA, and UGA do not code for amino acids but instead
act as signals to stop translation. A protein called a *release factor* binds directly to the stop codon in the A site. The release
factor causes the addition of a water molecule instead of an
amino acid to the polypeptide chain. This reaction breaks (hydrolyzes) the bond between the completed polypeptide and
the tRNA in the P site, releasing the polypeptide through the
exit tunnel of the ribosome's large subunit (see Figure 17.16a).
The remainder of the translation assembly then comes apart
in a multistep process, aided by other protein factors. Breakdown of the translation assembly requires the hydrolysis of
two more GTP molecules.

1. When a ribosome reaches a stop codon on mRNA, the A site of the ribosome accepts a "release factor," a protein shaped like a tRNA, instead of an aminoacyl tRNA.

2. The release factor promotes hydrolysis of the bond between the tRNA in the P site and the last amino acid of the polypeptide, thus freeing the polypeptide from the ribosome.

3. The two ribosomal subunits and the other components of the assembly dissociate.

▲ **Figure 17.19 The termination of translation.** Like elongation, termination requires GTP hydrolysis as well as additional protein factors, which are not shown here.

Polyribosomes

A single ribosome can make an average-sized polypeptide in less than a minute. Typically, however, multiple ribosomes translate an mRNA at the same time; that is, a single mRNA is used to make many copies of a polypeptide simultaneously. Once a ribosome moves past the start codon, a second ribosome can attach to the mRNA, eventually resulting in a number of ribosomes trailing along the mRNA. Such strings of ribosomes, called **polyribosomes** (or **polysomes**), can be seen with an electron microscope (**Figure 17.20**). Polyribosomes are found in both bacterial and eukaryotic cells. They enable a cell to make many copies of a polypeptide very quickly.

Completing and Targeting the Functional Protein

The process of translation is often not sufficient to make a functional protein. In this section, you will learn about modifications that polypeptide chains undergo after the translation process as well as some of the mechanisms used to target completed proteins to specific sites in the cell.

Protein Folding and Post-Translational Modifications

During its synthesis, a polypeptide chain begins to coil and fold spontaneously as a consequence of its amino acid sequence (primary structure), forming a protein with a specific shape: a three-dimensional molecule with secondary and tertiary structure (see Figure 5.21). Thus, a gene determines primary structure, and primary structure in turn determines shape. In many cases, a chaperone protein (chaperonin) helps the polypeptide fold correctly (see Figure 5.24).

Additional steps—*post-translational modifications*—may be required before the protein can begin doing its particular job

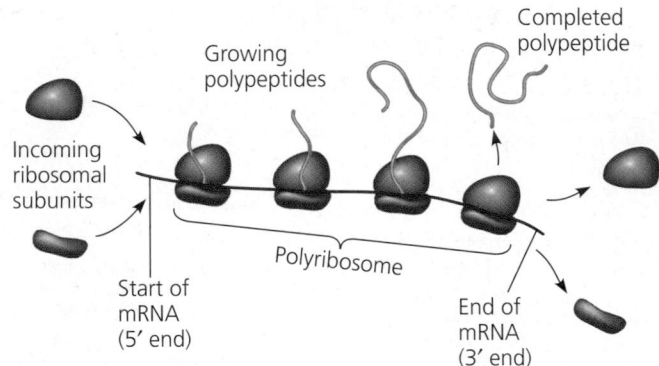

(a) An mRNA molecule is generally translated simultaneously by several ribosomes in clusters called polyribosomes.

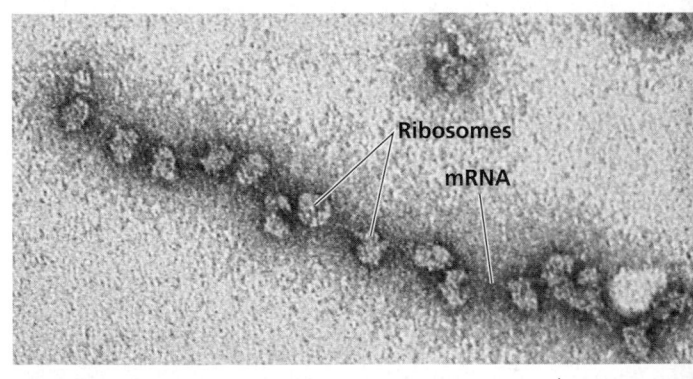

(b) This micrograph shows a large polyribosome in a bacterial cell (TEM).   0.1 μm

▲ **Figure 17.20 Polyribosomes.**

in the cell. Certain amino acids may be chemically modified by the attachment of sugars, lipids, phosphate groups, or other additions. Enzymes may remove one or more amino acids from the leading (amino) end of the polypeptide chain. In some cases, a polypeptide chain may be enzymatically cleaved into two or more pieces. For example, the protein insulin is first synthesized as a single polypeptide chain but becomes active only after an enzyme cuts out a central part of the chain, leaving a protein made up of two polypeptide chains connected by disulfide bridges. In other cases, two or more polypeptides that are synthesized separately may come together, becoming the subunits of a protein that has quaternary structure. A familiar example is hemoglobin (see Figure 5.21).

Targeting Polypeptides to Specific Locations

In electron micrographs of eukaryotic cells active in protein synthesis, two populations of ribosomes (and polyribosomes) are evident: free and bound (see Figure 6.11). Free ribosomes are suspended in the cytosol and mostly synthesize proteins that stay in the cytosol and function there. In contrast, bound ribosomes are attached to the cytosolic side of the endoplasmic reticulum (ER) or to the nuclear envelope. Bound ribosomes make proteins of the endomembrane system (the nuclear envelope, ER, Golgi apparatus, lysosomes, vacuoles, and plasma membrane) as well as proteins secreted from the cell, such as insulin. The ribosomes themselves are identical and can switch their status from free to bound.

What determines whether a ribosome will be free in the cytosol or bound to rough ER at any given time? Polypeptide synthesis always begins in the cytosol, when a free ribosome starts to translate an mRNA molecule. There the process continues to completion—*unless* the growing polypeptide itself cues the ribosome to attach to the ER. The polypeptides of proteins destined for the endomembrane system or for secretion are marked by a **signal peptide**, which targets the protein to the ER **(Figure 17.21)**. The signal peptide, a sequence of about 20 amino acids at or near the leading (amino) end of the polypeptide, is recognized as it emerges from the ribosome by a protein-RNA complex called a **signal-recognition particle (SRP)**. This particle functions as an adapter that brings the ribosome to a receptor protein built into the ER membrane. This receptor is part of a multiprotein translocation complex. Polypeptide synthesis continues there, and the growing polypeptide snakes across the membrane into the ER lumen via a protein pore. The signal peptide is usually removed by an enzyme. The rest of the completed polypeptide, if it is to be secreted from the cell, is released into solution within the ER lumen (as in Figure 17.21). Alternatively, if the polypeptide is to be a membrane protein, it remains partially embedded in the ER membrane.

❶ Polypeptide synthesis begins on a free ribosome in the cytosol.

❷ An SRP binds to the signal peptide, halting synthesis momentarily.

❸ The SRP binds to a receptor protein in the ER membrane. This receptor is part of a protein complex (a translocation complex) that has a membrane pore and a signal-cleaving enzyme.

❹ The SRP leaves, and polypeptide synthesis resumes, with simultaneous translocation across the membrane. (The signal peptide stays attached to the translocation complex.)

❺ The signal-cleaving enzyme cuts off the signal peptide.

❻ The rest of the completed polypeptide leaves the ribosome and folds into its final conformation.

▲ **Figure 17.21 The signal mechanism for targeting proteins to the ER.** A polypeptide destined for the endomembrane system or for secretion from the cell begins with a signal peptide, a series of amino acids that targets it for the ER. This figure shows the synthesis of a secretory protein and its simultaneous import into the ER. In the ER and then in the Golgi, the protein will be processed further. Finally, a transport vesicle will convey it to the plasma membrane for release from the cell (see Figure 7.10).

Other kinds of signal peptides are used to target polypeptides to mitochondria, chloroplasts, the interior of the nucleus, and other organelles that are not part of the endomembrane system. The critical difference in these cases is that translation is completed in the cytosol before the polypeptide is imported into the organelle. The mechanisms of translocation also vary, but in all cases studied to date, the "zip codes" that address proteins for secretion or to cellular locations are signal peptides of some sort. Bacteria also employ signal peptides to target proteins for secretion.

CONCEPT 17.5

Point mutations can affect protein structure and function

Now that you have explored the process of gene expression, you are ready to understand the effects of changes to the genetic information of a cell (or virus). These changes, called **mutations**, are responsible for the huge diversity of genes found among organisms because mutations are the ultimate source of new genes. In Figure 15.15, we considered large-scale mutations, chromosomal rearrangements that affect long segments of DNA. Here we examine **point mutations**, chemical changes in a single base pair of a gene.

If a point mutation occurs in a gamete or in a cell that gives rise to gametes, it may be transmitted to offspring and to a succession of future generations. If the mutation has an adverse effect on the phenotype of an organism, the mutant condition is referred to as a genetic disorder or hereditary disease. For example, we can trace the genetic basis of sickle-cell disease to the mutation of a single base pair in the gene that encodes the β-globin polypeptide of hemoglobin. The change of a single nucleotide in the DNA's template strand leads to the production of an abnormal protein (**Figure 17.22**; also see Figure 5.22). In individuals who are homozygous for the mutant allele, the sickling of red blood cells caused by the altered hemoglobin produces the multiple symptoms associated with sickle-cell disease (see Chapter 14). Another example is a heart condition responsible for some incidents of sudden death in young athletes, called familial cardiomyopathy. Point mutations in several genes have been identified, each of which can lead to this disorder.

Types of Point Mutations

Point mutations within a gene can be divided into two general categories: base-pair substitutions and base-pair insertions or deletions. Let's now consider how these mutations affect proteins.

Substitutions

A **base-pair substitution** is the replacement of one nucleotide and its partner with another pair of nucleotides (**Figure 17.23a**). Some substitutions are called *silent mutations* because, owing to the redundancy of the genetic code, they have no effect on the encoded protein. In other words, a change in a base pair may transform one codon into another that is translated into the same amino acid. For example, if 3'-CCG-5' on the template strand mutated to 3'-CCA-5', the mRNA codon that used to be GGC would become GGU, but a glycine would still be inserted at the proper location in the protein (see Figure 17.5). Substitutions that change one amino acid to another one are called **missense mutations**. Such a mutation may have little effect on the protein: The new amino acid may have properties similar to those of the amino acid it replaces, or it may be in a region of the protein where the exact sequence of amino acids is not essential to the protein's function.

▲ **Figure 17.22 The molecular basis of sickle-cell disease: a point mutation.** The allele that causes sickle-cell disease differs from the wild-type (normal) allele by a single DNA base pair.

(a) Base-pair substitution

(b) Base-pair insertion or deletion

▲ **Figure 17.23 Types of point mutations.** Mutations are changes in DNA that result in changes in the mRNA.

However, the base-pair substitutions of greatest interest are those that cause a major change in a protein. The alteration of a single amino acid in a crucial area of a protein—such as in the part of hemoglobin shown in Figure 17.22 or in the active site of an enzyme—will significantly alter protein activity. Occasionally, such a mutation leads to an improved protein or one with novel capabilities, but much more often such mutations are detrimental, leading to a useless or less active protein that impairs cellular function.

Substitution mutations are usually missense mutations; that is, the altered codon still codes for an amino acid and thus makes sense, although not necessarily the *right* sense.

But a point mutation can also change a codon for an amino acid into a stop codon. This is called a **nonsense mutation**, and it causes translation to be terminated prematurely; the resulting polypeptide will be shorter than the polypeptide encoded by the normal gene. Nearly all nonsense mutations lead to nonfunctional proteins.

Insertions and Deletions

Insertions and **deletions** are additions or losses of nucleotide pairs in a gene **(Figure 17.23b)**. These mutations have a disastrous effect on the resulting protein more often than substitutions do. Insertion or deletion of nucleotides may alter the reading frame of the genetic message, the triplet grouping of bases on the mRNA that is read during translation. Such a mutation, called a **frameshift mutation**, will occur whenever the number of nucleotides inserted or deleted is not a multiple of three. All the nucleotides that are downstream of the deletion or insertion will be improperly grouped into codons, and the result will be extensive missense, usually ending sooner or later in nonsense and premature termination. Unless the frameshift is very near the end of the gene, the protein is almost certain to be nonfunctional.

Mutagens

Mutations can arise in a number of ways. Errors during DNA replication or recombination can lead to base-pair substitutions, insertions, or deletions, as well as to mutations affecting longer stretches of DNA. If an incorrect base is added to a growing chain during replication, for example, that base will then be mismatched with the base on the other strand. In many cases, the error will be corrected by systems you learned about in Chapter 16. Otherwise, the incorrect base will be used as a template in the next round of replication, resulting in a mutation. Such mutations are called *spontaneous mutations*. It is difficult to calculate the rate at which such mutations occur. Rough estimates have been made of the rate of mutation during DNA replication for both *E. coli* and eukaryotes, and the numbers are similar: About one nucleotide in every 10^{10} is altered, and the change is passed on to the next generation of cells.

A number of physical and chemical agents, called **mutagens**, interact with DNA in ways that cause mutations. In the 1920s, Hermann Muller discovered that X-rays caused genetic changes in fruit flies, and he used X-rays to make *Drosophila* mutants for his genetic studies. But he also recognized an alarming implication of his discovery: X-rays and other forms of high-energy radiation pose hazards to the genetic material of people as well as laboratory organisms. Mutagenic radiation, a physical mutagen, includes ultraviolet (UV) light, which can cause disruptive thymine dimers in DNA (see Figure 16.18).

Chemical mutagens fall into several categories. Base analogs are chemicals that are similar to normal DNA bases but that pair incorrectly during DNA replication. Some other chemical mutagens interfere with correct DNA replication by inserting themselves into the DNA and distorting the double helix. Still other mutagens cause chemical changes in bases that change their pairing properties.

Researchers have developed various methods to test the mutagenic activity of chemicals. A major application of these tests is the preliminary screening of chemicals to identify those that may cause cancer. This approach makes sense because most carcinogens (cancer-causing chemicals) are mutagenic, and conversely, most mutagens are carcinogenic.

1. What happens when one nucleotide pair is lost from the middle of the coding sequence of a gene?
2. **WHAT IF?** A gene whose template strand contains the sequence 3'-TACTTGTCCGATATC-5' is mutated to 3'-TACTTGTCCAATATC-5'. For both normal and mutant genes, draw the double-stranded DNA, the resulting mRNA, and the amino acid sequence each encodes. What is the effect of the mutation on the amino acid sequence?

For suggested answers, see Appendix A.

While gene expression differs among the domains of life, the concept of a gene is universal

Although bacteria and eukaryotes carry out transcription and translation in very similar ways, we have noted certain differences in cellular machinery and in details of the processes in these two domains. The division of organisms into three domains was established about 40 years ago, when archaea were recognized as distinct from bacteria. Like bacteria, archaea are prokaryotes. However, archaea share many aspects of the mechanisms of gene expression with eukaryotes, as well as a few with bacteria.

Comparing Gene Expression in Bacteria, Archaea, and Eukarya

Recent advances in molecular biology have enabled researchers to determine the complete nucleotide sequences of hundreds of genomes, including many genomes from each domain. This wealth of data allows us to compare gene and protein sequences across domains. Foremost among genes of interest are those that encode components of such fundamental biological processes as transcription and translation.

Bacterial and eukaryotic RNA polymerases differ significantly from each other. In contrast, the single RNA polymerase of archaea resembles the three eukaryotic RNA polymerases, and archaea and eukaryotes use a complex set of transcription factors, unlike bacteria. Transcription is terminated differently in bacteria and eukaryotes. Here again, the little that is known about archaeal transcription termination suggests it may be more like the eukaryotic process.

As far as translation is concerned, bacterial and eukaryotic ribosomes are slightly different. Archaeal ribosomes are the same size as bacterial ribosomes, but their sensitivity to chemical inhibitors most closely matches that of eukaryotic ribosomes. We mentioned earlier that initiation of translation is slightly different in bacteria and eukaryotes. In this respect, the archaeal process is more like that of bacteria.

▲ **Figure 17.24 Coupled transcription and translation in bacteria.** In bacterial cells, the translation of mRNA can begin as soon as the leading (5′) end of the mRNA molecule peels away from the DNA template. The micrograph (TEM) shows a strand of *E. coli* DNA being transcribed by RNA polymerase molecules. Attached to each RNA polymerase molecule is a growing strand of mRNA, which is already being translated by ribosomes. The newly synthesized polypeptides are not visible in the micrograph but are shown in the diagram.

? *Which one of the mRNA molecules started transcription first? On that mRNA, which ribosome started translating first?*

The most important differences between bacteria and eukaryotes with regard to gene expression arise from the bacterial cell's relative absence of compartmental organization. Like a one-room workshop, a bacterial cell ensures a streamlined operation. In the absence of a nucleus, it can simultaneously transcribe and translate the same gene **(Figure 17.24)**, and the newly made protein can quickly diffuse to its site of function. Little is currently known about whether the processes of transcription and translation are coupled like this in archaeal cells, but most researchers suspect that they are, since archaea lack a nuclear envelope. In contrast, the eukaryotic cell's nuclear envelope segregates transcription from translation and provides a compartment for extensive RNA processing. This processing stage includes additional steps whose regulation can help coordinate the eukaryotic cell's elaborate activities (see Chapter 18). Finally, eukaryotic cells have complicated mechanisms for targeting proteins to the appropriate cellular compartment (organelle).

Learning more about the proteins and RNAs involved in archaeal transcription and translation will tell us much about the evolution of these processes in all three domains. In spite of the differences in gene expression cataloged here, however, the idea of the gene itself is a unifying concept among all forms of life.

What Is a Gene? *Revisiting the Question*

Our definition of a gene has evolved over the past few chapters, as it has through the history of genetics. We began with the Mendelian concept of a gene as a discrete unit of inheritance that affects a phenotypic character (Chapter 14). We saw that Morgan and his colleagues assigned such genes to specific loci on chromosomes (Chapter 15). We went on to view a gene as a region of specific nucleotide sequence along the length of a DNA molecule in a chromosome (Chapter 16). Finally, in this chapter, we have considered a functional definition of a gene as a DNA sequence that codes for a specific polypeptide chain. **(Figure 17.25**, on the next page, summarizes the path from gene to polypeptide in a eukaryotic cell.) All these definitions are useful, depending on the context in which genes are being studied.

Clearly, the statement that a gene codes for a polypeptide is too simple. Most eukaryotic genes contain noncoding segments (introns), so large portions of these genes have no corresponding segments in polypeptides. Molecular biologists also often include promoters and certain other regulatory regions of DNA within the boundaries of a gene. These DNA sequences are not transcribed, but they can be considered part of the functional gene because they must be present for transcription to occur. Our molecular definition of a gene must also be broad enough to include the DNA that is transcribed into rRNA, tRNA, and other RNAs that are not translated. These genes have no polypeptide products but play crucial roles in the cell. Thus, we arrive at the following definition: *A gene is a region of DNA that can be expressed to produce a final functional product that is either a polypeptide or an RNA molecule.*

When considering phenotypes, however, it is often useful to start by focusing on genes that code for polypeptides. In this chapter, you have learned in molecular terms how a typical gene is expressed—by transcription into RNA and then translation into a polypeptide that forms a protein of specific structure and function. Proteins, in turn, bring about an organism's observable phenotype.

A given type of cell expresses only a subset of its genes. This is an essential feature in multicellular organisms: You'd be in trouble if the lens cells in your eyes started expressing the genes for hair proteins, which are normally expressed only in hair follicle cells! Gene expression is precisely regulated. We'll explore gene regulation in the next chapter, beginning with the simpler case of bacteria and continuing with eukaryotes.

CONCEPT CHECK 17.6

1. Would the coupling of processes shown in Figure 17.24 be found in a eukaryotic cell? Explain.

2. **WHAT IF?** In eukaryotic cells, mRNAs have been found to have a circular arrangement in which the poly-A tail is held by proteins near the 5′ end cap. How might this increase translation efficiency?

For suggested answers, see Appendix A.

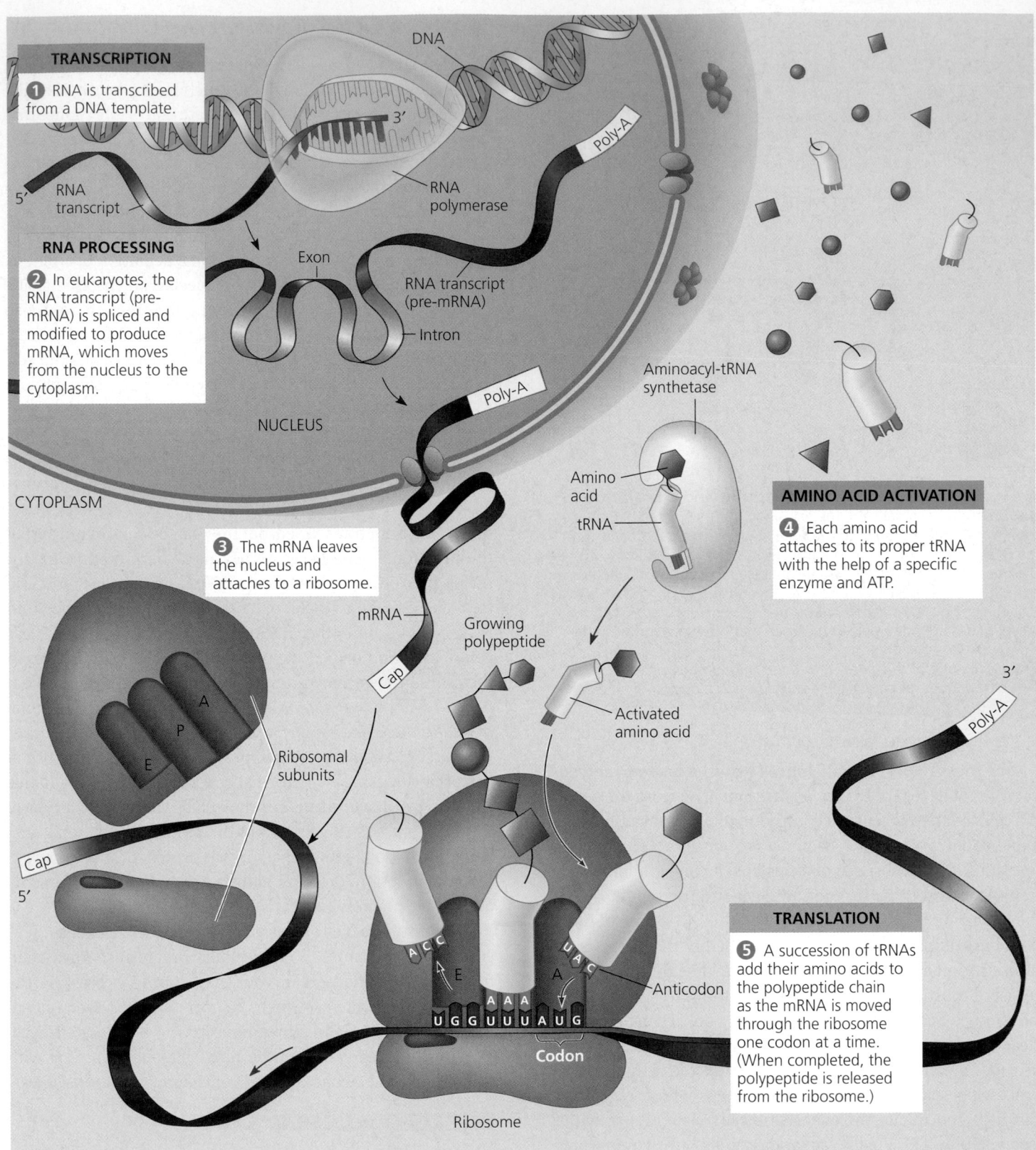

TRANSCRIPTION

1 RNA is transcribed from a DNA template.

DNA

5′ RNA transcript

3′

RNA polymerase

Poly-A

RNA PROCESSING

2 In eukaryotes, the RNA transcript (pre-mRNA) is spliced and modified to produce mRNA, which moves from the nucleus to the cytoplasm.

Exon

RNA transcript (pre-mRNA)

Intron

NUCLEUS

Poly-A

CYTOPLASM

3 The mRNA leaves the nucleus and attaches to a ribosome.

Aminoacyl-tRNA synthetase

Amino acid

tRNA

AMINO ACID ACTIVATION

4 Each amino acid attaches to its proper tRNA with the help of a specific enzyme and ATP.

mRNA

Growing polypeptide

Cap

Activated amino acid

3′

Poly-A

Ribosomal subunits

A

P

E

Cap

5′

A|C|C

E

U|A|C

A

Anticodon

TRANSLATION

5 A succession of tRNAs add their amino acids to the polypeptide chain as the mRNA is moved through the ribosome one codon at a time. (When completed, the polypeptide is released from the ribosome.)

A A A

U G G U U U A U G

Codon

Ribosome

▲ **Figure 17.25 A summary of transcription and translation in a eukaryotic cell.** This diagram shows the path from one gene to one polypeptide. Keep in mind that each gene in the DNA can be transcribed repeatedly into many identical RNA molecules and that each mRNA can be translated repeatedly to yield many identical polypeptide molecules. (Also, remember that the final products of some genes are not polypeptides but RNA molecules, including tRNA and rRNA.) In general, the steps of transcription and translation are similar in bacterial, archaeal, and eukaryotic cells. The major difference is the occurrence of RNA processing in the eukaryotic nucleus. Other significant differences are found in the initiation stages of both transcription and translation and in the termination of transcription.

Chapter 17 Review

SUMMARY OF KEY CONCEPTS

CONCEPT 17.1
Genes specify proteins via transcription and translation (pp. 325–331)

▶ **Evidence from the Study of Metabolic Defects** DNA controls metabolism by directing cells to make specific enzymes and other proteins. Beadle and Tatum's experiments with mutant strains of *Neurospora* supported the one gene–one enzyme hypothesis. Genes code for polypeptide chains or for RNA molecules.

▶ **Basic Principles of Transcription and Translation** Transcription is the nucleotide-to-nucleotide transfer of information from DNA to RNA, while translation is the informational transfer from nucleotide sequence in RNA to amino acid sequence in a polypeptide.

▶ **The Genetic Code** Genetic information is encoded as a sequence of nonoverlapping base triplets, or codons. A codon in messenger RNA (mRNA) either is translated into an amino acid (61 of the 64 codons) or serves as a stop signal (3 codons). Codons must be read in the correct reading frame.

> **MEDIA**
>
> **Investigation** How Is a Metabolic Pathway Analyzed?
> **MP3 Tutor** DNA to RNA to Protein
> **Activity** Overview of Protein Synthesis

CONCEPT 17.2
Transcription is the DNA-directed synthesis of RNA: *a closer look* (pp. 331–334)

▶ **Molecular Components of Transcription** RNA synthesis is catalyzed by RNA polymerase. It follows the same base-pairing rules as DNA replication, except that in RNA, uracil substitutes for thymine.

▶ **Synthesis of an RNA Transcript** The three stages of transcription are initiation, elongation, and termination. Promoters signal the initiation of RNA synthesis. Transcription factors help eukaryotic RNA polymerase recognize promoter sequences. The mechanisms of termination are different in bacteria and eukaryotes.

> **MEDIA**
>
> **Activity** Transcription

CONCEPT 17.3
Eukaryotic cells modify RNA after transcription (pp. 334–336)

▶ **Alteration of mRNA Ends** Eukaryotic mRNA molecules are processed before leaving the nucleus by modification of their ends and by RNA splicing. The 5′ end receives a modified nucleotide cap, and the 3′ end a poly-A tail.

▶ **Split Genes and RNA Splicing** Most eukaryotic genes have introns interspersed among the coding regions, the exons. In RNA splicing, introns are removed and exons joined. RNA splicing is typically carried out by spliceosomes, but in some cases, RNA alone catalyzes its own splicing. The catalytic ability of some RNA molecules, called ribozymes, derives from the inherent properties of RNA. The presence of introns allows for alternative RNA splicing.

> **MEDIA**
>
> **Activity** RNA Processing

CONCEPT 17.4
Translation is the RNA-directed synthesis of a polypeptide: *a closer look* (pp. 337–344)

▶ **Molecular Components of Translation** A cell translates an mRNA message into protein using transfer RNAs (tRNAs). After binding specific amino acids, tRNAs line up via their anticodons at complementary codons on mRNA. Ribosomes help facilitate this coupling with binding sites for mRNA and tRNA.

▶ **Building a Polypeptide** Ribosomes coordinate the three stages of translation: initiation, elongation, and termination. The formation of peptide bonds between amino acids is catalyzed by rRNA. A number of ribosomes can translate a single mRNA molecule simultaneously, forming a polyribosome.

▶ **Completing and Targeting the Functional Protein** After translation, modifications to proteins can affect their three-dimensional shape. Free ribosomes in the cytosol initiate synthesis of all proteins, but proteins destined for the endomembrane system or for secretion are transported into the ER. Such proteins have a signal peptide to which a signal-recognition particle (SRP) binds, enabling the translating ribosome to bind to the ER.

> **MEDIA**
>
> **BioFlix 3-D Animation** Protein Synthesis
> **Activity** Translation
> **Biology Labs On-Line** TranslationLab

CONCEPT 17.5
Point mutations can affect protein structure and function (pp. 344–346)

▶ **Types of Point Mutations** A point mutation is a change in one DNA base pair, which may lead to production of a nonfunctional protein. Base-pair substitutions can cause missense or nonsense mutations. Base-pair insertions or deletions may produce frameshift mutations.

▶ **Mutagens** Spontaneous mutations can occur during DNA replication, recombination, or repair. Chemical and physical mutagens cause DNA damage that can alter genes.

CONCEPT **17.6**

While gene expression differs among the domains of life, the concept of a gene is universal (pp. 346–348)

▶ **Comparing Gene Expression in Bacteria, Archaea, and Eukarya** Because bacterial cells lack a nuclear envelope, translation can begin while transcription is still in progress. Archaeal cells show similarities to both eukaryotic and bacterial cells in their processes of gene expression. In a eukaryotic cell, the nuclear envelope separates transcription from translation, and extensive RNA processing occurs in the nucleus.

▶ **What Is a Gene?** *Revisiting the Question* A gene is a region of DNA whose final functional product is either a polypeptide or an RNA molecule.

TESTING YOUR KNOWLEDGE

SELF-QUIZ

1. In eukaryotic cells, transcription cannot begin until
   a. the two DNA strands have completely separated and exposed the promoter.
   b. several transcription factors have bound to the promoter.
   c. the 5′ caps are removed from the mRNA.
   d. the DNA introns are removed from the template.
   e. DNA nucleases have isolated the transcription unit.

2. Which of the following is *not* true of a codon?
   a. It consists of three nucleotides.
   b. It may code for the same amino acid as another codon.
   c. It never codes for more than one amino acid.
   d. It extends from one end of a tRNA molecule.
   e. It is the basic unit of the genetic code.

3. The anticodon of a particular tRNA molecule is
   a. complementary to the corresponding mRNA codon.
   b. complementary to the corresponding triplet in rRNA.
   c. the part of tRNA that bonds to a specific amino acid.
   d. changeable, depending on the amino acid that attaches to the tRNA.
   e. catalytic, making the tRNA a ribozyme.

4. Which of the following is *not* true of RNA processing?
   a. Exons are cut out before mRNA leaves the nucleus.
   b. Nucleotides may be added at both ends of the RNA.
   c. Ribozymes may function in RNA splicing.
   d. RNA splicing can be catalyzed by spliceosomes.
   e. A primary transcript is often much longer than the final RNA molecule that leaves the nucleus.

5. Using Figure 17.5, identify a 5′ → 3′ sequence of nucleotides in the DNA template strand for an mRNA coding for the polypeptide sequence Phe-Pro-Lys.

   a. 5′-UUUGGGAAA-3′   d. 5′-CTTCGGGAA-3′
   b. 5′-GAACCCCTT-3′   e. 5′-AAACCCUUU-3′
   c. 5′-AAAACCTTT-3′

6. Which of the following mutations would be *most* likely to have a harmful effect on an organism?
   a. a base-pair substitution
   b. a deletion of three nucleotides near the middle of a gene
   c. a single nucleotide deletion in the middle of an intron
   d. a single nucleotide deletion near the end of the coding sequence
   e. a single nucleotide insertion downstream of, and close to, the start of the coding sequence

7. Which component is *not* directly involved in translation?
   a. mRNA   d. ribosomes
   b. DNA   e. GTP
   c. tRNA

8. **DRAW IT** Review the roles of RNA by filling in the following table:

Type of RNA	Functions
Messenger RNA (mRNA)	
Transfer RNA (tRNA)	
	Plays catalytic (ribozyme) roles and structural roles in ribosomes
Primary transcript	
Small nuclear RNA (snRNA)	

For Self-Quiz answers, see Appendix A.

MEDIA Visit www.campbellbiology.com for a Practice Test.

EVOLUTION CONNECTION

9. The genetic code (see Figure 17.5) is rich with evolutionary implications. For instance, notice that the 20 amino acids are not randomly scattered; most amino acids are coded for by a similar set of codons. What evolutionary explanations can be given for this pattern? (*Hint:* There is one explanation relating to historical ancestry, and some less obvious ones of a "form-fits-function" type.)

SCIENTIFIC INQUIRY

10. Knowing that the genetic code is almost universal, a scientist uses molecular biological methods to insert the human β-globin gene (shown in Figure 17.10) into bacterial cells, hoping the cells will express it and synthesize functional β-globin protein. Instead, the protein produced is nonfunctional and is found to contain many fewer amino acids than does β-globin made by a eukaryotic cell. Explain why.

Biological Inquiry: A Workbook of Investigative Cases Explore translation and use of sequence data in testing hypotheses with the case "The Doctor's Dilemma."

Regulation of Gene Expression

18

▲ Figure 18.1 **What regulates the precise pattern of expression of different genes?**

OVERVIEW

Conducting the Genetic Orchestra

An oboe squawks loudly, several violins squeak shrilly, and a tuba adds its rumble to the noisy chaos. Then the conductor's baton rises, pauses, and begins a series of elaborate movements, directing specific instruments to join in and others to raise or lower their volume at exact moments. Properly balanced and timed, discordant sounds are thus transformed into a beautiful symphony that enraptures the audience.

In a similar way, cells intricately and precisely regulate their gene expression. Both prokaryotes and eukaryotes must alter their patterns of gene expression in response to changes in environmental conditions. Multicellular eukaryotes must also develop and maintain multiple cell types. Each cell type contains the same genome but expresses a different subset of genes, a significant challenge in gene regulation.

An adult fruit fly, for example, develops from a single fertilized egg, passing through a wormlike stage called a larva. At every stage, gene expression is carefully regulated, ensuring that the right genes are expressed only at the correct time and place. In

the larva, the adult wing forms in a disk-shaped pocket of several thousand cells, shown in **Figure 18.1**. The tissue in this image has been treated to reveal the mRNA for three genes—labeled red, blue, and green—using techniques covered in Chapter 20. (Red and green together appear yellow.) The intricate pattern of expression for each gene is the same from larva to larva at this stage, and it provides a graphic display of the precision of gene regulation. But what is the molecular basis for this pattern? Why is one particular gene expressed only in the few hundred cells that appear blue in this image and not in the other cells?

In this chapter, we first explore how bacteria regulate expression of their genes in response to different environmental conditions. We then examine how eukaryotes regulate gene expression to maintain different cell types. Gene expression in eukaryotes, as in bacteria, is often regulated at the stage of transcription, but control at other levels of gene expression is also important. In recent years, researchers have been surprised to discover the many roles played by RNA molecules in regulating eukaryotic gene expression, a topic we cover next. Putting together these aspects of gene regulation, we then consider how a carefully orchestrated program of gene regulation can allow a single cell—the fertilized egg—to become a fully functioning organism made up of many different cell types. Finally, we investigate how disruptions in gene regulation can lead to cancer. Orchestrating proper gene expression by all cells is crucial to the functions of life.

CONCEPT 18.1

Bacteria often respond to environmental change by regulating transcription

Bacterial cells that can conserve resources and energy have a selective advantage over cells that are unable to do so. Thus, natural selection has favored bacteria that express only the genes whose products are needed by the cell.

Consider, for instance, an individual *E. coli* cell living in the erratic environment of a human colon, dependent for its nutrients on the whimsical eating habits of its host. If the environment is lacking in the amino acid tryptophan, which the bacterium needs to survive, the cell responds by activating a metabolic pathway that makes tryptophan from another compound. Later, if the human host eats a tryptophan-rich meal, the bacterial cell stops producing tryptophan, thus saving itself from squandering its resources to produce a substance that is available from the surrounding solution in prefabricated form. This is just one example of how bacteria tune their metabolism to changing environments.

Metabolic control occurs on two levels, as shown for the synthesis of tryptophan in **Figure 18.2**. First, cells can adjust the activity of enzymes already present. This is a fairly fast response, which relies on the sensitivity of many enzymes to chemical cues that increase or decrease their catalytic activity (see Chapter 8). The activity of the first enzyme in the tryptophan synthesis pathway is inhibited by the pathway's end product (Figure 18.2a). Thus, if tryptophan accumulates in a cell, it shuts down the synthesis of more tryptophan by in-

hibiting enzyme activity. Such *feedback inhibition*, typical of anabolic (biosynthetic) pathways, allows a cell to adapt to short-term fluctuations in the supply of a substance it needs.

Second, cells can adjust the production level of certain enzymes; that is, they can regulate the expression of the genes encoding the enzymes. If, in our example, the environment provides all the tryptophan the cell needs, the cell stops making the enzymes that catalyze the synthesis of tryptophan (Figure 18.2b). In this case, the control of enzyme production occurs at the level of transcription, the synthesis of messenger RNA coding for these enzymes. More generally, many genes of the bacterial genome are switched on or off by changes in the metabolic status of the cell. The basic mechanism for this control of gene expression in bacteria, described as the *operon model*, was discovered in 1961 by François Jacob and Jacques Monod at the Pasteur Institute in Paris. Let's see what an operon is and how it works, using the control of tryptophan synthesis as our first example.

Operons: The Basic Concept

E. coli synthesizes the amino acid tryptophan from a precursor molecule in the multistep pathway shown in Figure 18.2. Each reaction in the pathway is catalyzed by a specific enzyme, and the five genes that code for the subunits of these enzymes are clustered together on the bacterial chromosome. A single promoter serves all five genes, which together constitute a transcription unit. (Recall from Chapter 17 that a promoter is a site where RNA polymerase can bind to DNA and begin transcription.) Thus, transcription gives rise to one long mRNA molecule that codes for the five polypeptides making up the enzymes in the tryptophan pathway. The cell can translate this one mRNA into five separate polypeptides because the mRNA is punctuated with start and stop codons that signal where the coding sequence for each polypeptide begins and ends.

A key advantage of grouping genes of related function into one transcription unit is that a single on-off "switch" can control the whole cluster of functionally related genes; in other words, these genes are under *coordinate control*. When an *E. coli* cell must make tryptophan for itself because the nutrient medium lacks this amino acid, all the enzymes for the metabolic pathway are synthesized at one time. The switch is a segment of DNA called an **operator**. Both its location and name suit its function: Positioned within the promoter or, in some cases, between the promoter and the enzyme-coding genes, the operator controls the access of RNA polymerase to the genes. All together, the operator, the promoter, and the genes they control—the entire stretch of DNA required for enzyme production for the tryptophan pathway—constitute an **operon**. The *trp* operon (*trp* for tryptophan) is one of many operons in the *E. coli* genome (**Figure 18.3**).

If the operator is the switch for controlling transcription, how does this switch work? By itself, the *trp* operon is turned on; that

▲ **Figure 18.2 Regulation of a metabolic pathway.** In the pathway for tryptophan synthesis, an abundance of tryptophan can both **(a)** inhibit the activity of the first enzyme in the pathway (feedback inhibition), a rapid response, and **(b)** repress expression of the genes encoding all subunits of the enzymes in the pathway, a longer-term response. Genes *trpE* and *trpD* encode the two subunits of enzyme 1, and genes *trpB* and *trpA* encode the two subunits of enzyme 3. (The genes were named before the order in which they functioned in the pathway was determined.) The ⊖ symbol stands for inhibition.

(a) Tryptophan absent, repressor inactive, operon on. RNA polymerase attaches to the DNA at the promoter and transcribes the operon's genes.

(b) Tryptophan present, repressor active, operon off. As tryptophan accumulates, it inhibits its own production by activating the repressor protein, which binds to the operator, blocking transcription.

▲ **Figure 18.3 The *trp* operon in *E. coli*: regulated synthesis of repressible enzymes.** Tryptophan is an amino acid produced by an anabolic pathway catalyzed by repressible enzymes. **(a)** The five genes encoding the polypeptide subunits of the enzymes in this pathway (see Figure 18.2) are grouped, along with a promoter, into the *trp* operon. The *trp* operator (the repressor-binding site) is located within the *trp* promoter (the RNA polymerase-binding site). **(b)** Accumulation of tryptophan, the end product of the pathway, represses transcription of the *trp* operon, thus blocking synthesis of all the enzymes in the pathway.

? *Describe what happens to the* trp *operon as the cell uses up its store of tryptophan.*

is, RNA polymerase can bind to the promoter and transcribe the genes of the operon. The operon can be switched off by a protein called the *trp* **repressor**. The repressor binds to the operator and blocks attachment of RNA polymerase to the promoter, preventing transcription of the genes. A repressor protein is specific for the operator of a particular operon. For example, the repressor that switches off the *trp* operon by binding to the *trp* operator has no effect on other operons in the *E. coli* genome.

The *trp* repressor is the product of a **regulatory gene** called *trpR*, which is located some distance from the operon it controls and has its own promoter. Regulatory genes are expressed continuously, although at a low rate, and a few *trp* repressor molecules are always present in *E. coli* cells. Why, then, is the *trp* operon not switched off permanently? First, the binding of repressors to operators is reversible. An operator vacillates between two states: one without the repressor bound and one with the repressor bound. The relative duration of each state depends on the number of active repressor molecules around. Second, the *trp* repressor, like most regulatory proteins, is an allosteric protein, with two alternative shapes, active and inactive (see Figure 8.20). The *trp* repressor is synthesized in an inactive form with little affinity for the *trp* operator. Only if tryptophan binds to the *trp* repressor at an allosteric site does the repressor protein change to the active form that can attach to the operator, turning the operon off.

Tryptophan functions in this system as a **corepressor**, a small molecule that cooperates with a repressor protein to switch an operon off. As tryptophan accumulates, more tryptophan molecules associate with *trp* repressor molecules, which can then bind to the *trp* operator and shut down production of the tryptophan pathway enzymes. If the cell's tryptophan level drops, transcription of the operon's genes resumes. This is one example of how gene expression can respond to changes in the cell's internal and external environment.

Repressible and Inducible Operons: Two Types of Negative Gene Regulation

The *trp* operon is said to be a *repressible operon* because its transcription is usually on but can be inhibited (repressed) when a specific small molecule (in this case, tryptophan) binds allosterically to a regulatory protein. In contrast, an *inducible operon* is usually off but can be stimulated (induced) when a specific small molecule interacts with a regulatory protein. The classic example of an inducible operon is the *lac* operon (*lac* for lactose), which was the subject of Jacob and Monod's pioneering research.

The disaccharide lactose (milk sugar) is available to *E. coli* in the human colon if the host drinks milk. Lactose metabolism begins with hydrolysis of the disaccharide into its component monosaccharides, glucose and galactose, a reaction catalyzed by the enzyme β-galactosidase. Only a few molecules of this enzyme are present in an *E. coli* cell growing in the absence of lactose. If lactose is added to the bacterium's environment, however, the number of β-galactosidase molecules in the cell increases a thousandfold within about 15 minutes.

The gene for β-galactosidase is part of the *lac* operon, which includes two other genes coding for enzymes that function in lactose utilization. The entire transcription unit is un-

der the command of a single operator and promoter. The regulatory gene, *lacI*, located outside the operon, codes for an allosteric repressor protein that can switch off the *lac* operon by binding to the operator. So far, this sounds just like regulation of the *trp* operon, but there is one important difference. Recall that the *trp* repressor is inactive by itself and requires tryptophan as a corepressor in order to bind to the operator. The *lac* repressor, in contrast, is active by itself, binding to the operator and switching the *lac* operon off. In this case, a specific small molecule, called an **inducer**, *inactivates* the repressor.

For the *lac* operon, the inducer is allolactose, an isomer of lactose formed in small amounts from lactose that enters the cell. In the absence of lactose (and hence allolactose), the *lac* repressor is in its active configuration, and the genes of the *lac* operon are silenced **(Figure 18.4a)**. If lactose is added to the cell's surroundings, allolactose binds to the *lac* repressor and alters its conformation, nullifying the repressor's ability to attach to the operator. Without bound repressor, the *lac*

(a) Lactose absent, repressor active, operon off. The *lac* repressor is innately active, and in the absence of lactose it switches off the operon by binding to the operator.

▼ **Figure 18.4 The *lac* operon in *E.coli*: regulated synthesis of inducible enzymes.** *E. coli* uses three enzymes to take up and metabolize lactose. The genes for these three enzymes are clustered in the *lac* operon. One gene, *lacZ*, codes for ß-galactosidase, which hydrolyzes lactose to glucose and galactose. The second gene, *lacY*, codes for a permease, the membrane protein that transports lactose into the cell. The third gene, *lacA*, codes for an enzyme called transacetylase, whose function in lactose metabolism is still unclear. The gene for the *lac* repressor, *lacI*, happens to be adjacent to the *lac* operon, an unusual situation. The function of the darker green region at the upstream (left) end of the promoter is revealed in Figure 18.5.

(b) Lactose present, repressor inactive, operon on. Allolactose, an isomer of lactose, derepresses the operon by inactivating the repressor. In this way, the enzymes for lactose utilization are induced.

operon is transcribed into mRNA for the lactose-utilizing enzymes (Figure 18.4b).

In the context of gene regulation, the enzymes of the lactose pathway are referred to as *inducible enzymes* because their synthesis is induced by a chemical signal (allolactose, in this case). Analogously, the enzymes for tryptophan synthesis are said to be repressible. *Repressible enzymes* generally function in anabolic pathways, which synthesize essential end products from raw materials (precursors). By suspending production of an end product when it is already present in sufficient quantity, the cell can allocate its organic precursors and energy for other uses. In contrast, inducible enzymes usually function in catabolic pathways, which break down a nutrient to simpler molecules. By producing the appropriate enzymes only when the nutrient is available, the cell avoids wasting energy and precursors making proteins that are not needed.

Regulation of both the *trp* and *lac* operons involves the *negative* control of genes, because the operons are switched off by the active form of the repressor protein. It may be easier to see this for the *trp* operon, but it is also true for the *lac* operon. Allolactose induces enzyme synthesis not by acting directly on the genome, but by freeing the *lac* operon from the negative effect of the repressor. Gene regulation is said to be *positive* only when a regulatory protein interacts directly with the genome to switch transcription on. Let's look at an example of positive control of genes, again involving the *lac* operon.

Positive Gene Regulation

When glucose and lactose are both present in its environment, *E. coli* preferentially uses glucose. The enzymes for glucose breakdown in glycolysis (see Figure 9.9) are continually present. Only when lactose is present *and* glucose is in short supply does *E. coli* use lactose as an energy source, and only then does it synthesize appreciable quantities of the enzymes for lactose breakdown.

How does the *E. coli* cell sense the glucose concentration and relay this information to the genome? Again, the mechanism depends on the interaction of an allosteric regulatory protein with a small organic molecule, in this case **cyclic AMP (cAMP)**, which accumulates when glucose is scarce (see Figure 11.10 for the structure of cAMP). The regulatory protein, called *catabolite activator protein (CAP)*, is an **activator**, a protein that binds to DNA and stimulates transcription of a gene. When cAMP binds to this regulatory protein, CAP assumes its active shape and can attach to a specific site at the upstream end of the *lac* promoter (Figure 18.5a). This attachment increases the affinity of RNA polymerase for the promoter, which is actually rather low even when no repressor is bound to the operator. By facilitating the binding of RNA polymerase to the promoter and thereby increasing the rate of transcription, the attachment of CAP to the promoter directly stimulates gene expression. Therefore, this mechanism qualifies as positive regulation.

If the amount of glucose in the cell increases, the cAMP concentration falls, and without cAMP, CAP detaches from the operon. Because CAP is inactive, RNA polymerase binds less efficiently to the promoter, and transcription of the *lac* operon proceeds at only a low level, even in the presence of lactose (Figure 18.5b). Thus, the *lac* operon is under dual control: negative control by the *lac* repressor and positive control by CAP. The state of the *lac* repressor (with or without bound allolactose) determines whether or not transcription of the *lac* operon's genes occurs at all; the state of CAP (with or without bound cAMP) controls the *rate* of transcription if the operon is repressor-free. It is as though the operon has both an on-off switch and a volume control.

(a) Lactose present, glucose scarce (cAMP level high): abundant *lac* mRNA synthesized. If glucose is scarce, the high level of cAMP activates CAP, and the *lac* operon produces large amounts of mRNA coding for the enzymes in the lactose pathway.

(b) Lactose present, glucose present (cAMP level low): little *lac* mRNA synthesized. When glucose is present, cAMP is scarce, and CAP is unable to stimulate transcription.

▲ **Figure 18.5 Positive control of the *lac* operon by catabolite activator protein (CAP).** RNA polymerase has high affinity for the *lac* promoter only when catabolite activator protein (CAP) is bound to a DNA site at the upstream end of the promoter. CAP attaches to its DNA site only when associated with cyclic AMP (cAMP), whose concentration in the cell rises when the glucose concentration falls. Thus, when glucose is present, even if lactose also is available, the cell preferentially catabolizes glucose and makes very little of the lactose-utilizing enzymes.

In addition to the *lac* operon, CAP helps regulate other operons that encode enzymes used in catabolic pathways. All told, it may affect the expression of more than 100 genes in *E. coli*. When glucose is plentiful and CAP is inactive, the synthesis of enzymes that catabolize compounds other than glucose generally slows down. The ability to catabolize other compounds, such as lactose, enables a cell deprived of glucose to survive. The compounds present in the cell at the moment determine which operons are switched on—the result of simple interactions of activator and repressor proteins with the promoters of the genes in question.

CONCEPT CHECK 18.1

1. How does binding of the *trp* corepressor and the *lac* inducer to their respective repressor proteins alter repressor function and transcription in each case?
2. A certain mutation in *E. coli* changes the *lac* operator so that the active repressor cannot bind. How would this affect the cell's production of β-galactosidase?
3. **WHAT IF?** Describe binding of RNA polymerase, repressors, and activators to the *lac* operon when both lactose and glucose are scarce. What would be the effect on transcription? How might the transcription of other genes outside the *lac* operon be regulated if another sugar were present?

For suggested answers, see Appendix A.

CONCEPT 18.2
Eukaryotic gene expression can be regulated at any stage

All organisms, whether prokaryotes or eukaryotes, must regulate which genes are expressed at any given time. Both unicellular organisms and the cells of multicellular organisms must continually turn genes on and off in response to signals from their external and internal environments. Regulation of gene expression is also essential for cell specialization in multicellular organisms, which are made up of different types of cells, each with a distinct role. To perform its role, each cell type must maintain a specific program of gene expression in which certain genes are expressed and others are not.

Differential Gene Expression

A typical human cell probably expresses about 20% of its genes at any given time. Highly differentiated cells, such as muscle or nerve cells, express an even smaller fraction of their genes. Almost all the cells in an organism contain an identical genome. (Cells of the immune system are one exception. During their differentiation, rearrangement of the immunoglobulin genes results in a change in the genome, as you will see in

Chapter 43.) However, the subset of genes expressed in the cells of each type is unique, allowing these cells to carry out their specific function. The differences between cell types, therefore, are due not to different genes being present, but to **differential gene expression**, the expression of different genes by cells with the same genome.

The genomes of eukaryotes may contain tens of thousands of genes, but for quite a few species, only a small amount of the DNA—about 1.5% in humans—codes for protein. The rest of the DNA either codes for RNA products, such as tRNAs, or isn't transcribed at all. The transcription factors of a cell must locate the right genes at the right time, a task on a par with finding a needle in a haystack. When gene expression goes awry, serious imbalances and diseases, including cancer, can arise.

Figure 18.6 summarizes the entire process of gene expression in a eukaryotic cell, highlighting key stages in the expression of a protein-coding gene. Each stage depicted in Figure 18.6 is a potential control point at which gene expression can be turned on or off, accelerated, or slowed down.

Only 40 years ago, an understanding of the mechanisms that control gene expression in eukaryotes seemed almost hopelessly out of reach. Since then, new research methods, notably advances in DNA technology (see Chapter 20), have enabled molecular biologists to uncover many of the details of eukaryotic gene regulation. In all organisms, a common control point for gene expression is at transcription; regulation at this stage is often in response to signals coming from outside the cell, such as hormones or other signaling molecules. For that reason, the term *gene expression* is often equated with transcription for both bacteria and eukaryotes. While this is most often the case for bacteria, the greater complexity of eukaryotic cell structure and function provides opportunities for regulating gene expression at many additional stages (see Figure 18.6). In the remainder of this section, we'll examine some of the important control points of eukaryotic gene expression more closely.

Regulation of Chromatin Structure

Recall that the DNA of eukaryotic cells is packaged with proteins in an elaborate complex known as chromatin, the basic unit of which is the nucleosome (see Figure 16.21). The structural organization of chromatin not only packs a cell's DNA into a compact form that fits inside the nucleus but also helps regulate gene expression in several ways. The location of a gene's promoter relative to nucleosomes and to the sites where the DNA attaches to the chromosome scaffold or nuclear lamina can affect whether the gene is transcribed. In addition, genes within heterochromatin, which is highly condensed, are usually not expressed. The repressive effect of heterochromatin has been seen in experiments in which a transcriptionally active gene was inserted into a region of heterochromatin in yeast cells; the inserted gene was no longer expressed. Lastly, as revealed in a flurry of recent research, certain chemical modifications to the histones and DNA

▲ **Figure 18.6 Stages in gene expression that can be regulated in eukaryotic cells.** In this diagram, the colored boxes indicate the processes most often regulated; each color indicates the type of molecule that is affected (blue = DNA, orange = RNA, purple = protein). The nuclear envelope separating transcription from translation in eukaryotic cells offers an opportunity for post-transcriptional control in the form of RNA processing that is absent in prokaryotes. In addition, eukaryotes have a greater variety of control mechanisms operating before transcription and after translation. The expression of any given gene, however, does not necessarily involve every stage shown; for example, not every polypeptide is cleaved.

of chromatin can influence both chromatin structure and gene expression. Here we examine the effects of these modifications, which are catalyzed by specific enzymes.

Histone Modifications

There is mounting evidence that chemical modifications to histones, the proteins around which the DNA is wrapped in nucleosomes, play a direct role in the regulation of gene transcription. The N-terminus of each histone molecule in a nucleosome protrudes outward from the nucleosome **(Figure 18.7a)**. These

(a) Histone tails protrude outward from a nucleosome. This is an end view of a nucleosome. The amino acids in the N-terminal tails are accessible for chemical modification.

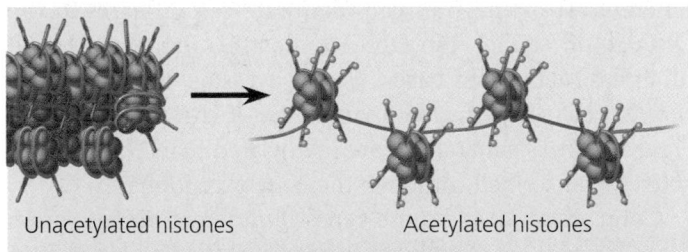

(b) Acetylation of histone tails promotes loose chromatin structure that permits transcription. A region of chromatin in which nucleosomes are unacetylated forms a compact structure (left) in which the DNA is not transcribed. When nucleosomes are highly acetylated (right), the chromatin becomes less compact, and the DNA is accessible for transcription.

▲ **Figure 18.7 A simple model of histone tails and the effect of histone acetylation.** In addition to acetylation, histones can undergo several other types of modifications that also help determine the chromatin configuration in a region.

histone tails are accessible to various modifying enzymes, which catalyze the addition or removal of specific chemical groups.

In **histone acetylation,** acetyl groups ($-COCH_3$) are attached to lysines in histone tails; deacetylation is the removal of acetyl groups. When the lysines are acetylated, their positive charges are neutralized and the histone tails no longer bind to neighboring nucleosomes **(Figure 18.7b)**. Recall that such binding promotes the folding of chromatin into a more compact structure; when this binding does not occur, chromatin has a looser structure. As a result, transcription proteins have easier access to genes in an acetylated region. Researchers have shown that some enzymes that acetylate or deacetylate histones are closely associated with or even components of the transcription factors that bind to promoters (see Figure 17.8). These observations suggest that histone acetylation enzymes may promote the initiation of transcription not only by remodeling chromatin structure, but also by binding to and thus "recruiting" components of the transcription machinery.

Several other chemical groups can be reversibly attached to amino acids in histone tails—for example, methyl groups and phosphate groups. The addition of methyl groups ($-CH_3$) to histone tails (methylation) can promote condensation of the chromatin. The addition of a phosphate group to an amino acid (phosphorylation) next to a methylated amino acid can have the opposite effect. The recent discovery that these and many other modifications to histone tails can affect chromatin structure and gene expression has led to the *histone code hypothesis.* This hypothesis proposes that specific combinations of modifications, rather than the overall level of histone acetylation, help determine the chromatin configuration, which in turn influences transcription.

DNA Methylation

While some enzymes methylate the tails of histone proteins, a different set of enzymes can methylate certain bases in the DNA itself. In fact, the DNA of most plants, animals, and fungi has methylated bases, usually cytosine. Inactive DNA, such as that of inactivated mammalian X chromosomes (see Figure 15.8), is generally more methylated than DNA that is actively transcribed, although there are exceptions.

Comparison of the same genes in different tissues shows that the genes are usually more heavily methylated in cells in which they are not expressed. Removal of the extra methyl groups can turn on some of these genes. Moreover, researchers have discovered proteins that bind to methylated DNA and recruit histone deacetylation enzymes. Thus, a dual mechanism, involving both DNA methylation and histone deacetylation, can repress transcription.

At least in some species, DNA methylation seems to be essential for the long-term inactivation of genes that occurs during normal cell differentiation in the embryo. For instance, experiments have shown that deficient DNA methylation due to lack of a methylating enzyme leads to abnormal embryonic development in organisms as different as mice and *Arabidopsis* (a plant). Once methylated, genes usually stay that way through successive cell divisions in a given individual. At DNA sites where one strand is already methylated, methylation enzymes correctly methylate the daughter strand after each round of DNA replication. Methylation patterns are thus passed on, and cells forming specialized tissues keep a chemical record of what occurred during embryonic development. A methylation pattern maintained in this way also accounts for **genomic imprinting** in mammals, where methylation permanently regulates expression of either the maternal or paternal allele of particular genes at the start of development (see Chapter 15).

Epigenetic Inheritance

The chromatin modifications that we have just discussed do not entail a change in the DNA sequence, yet they may be passed along to future generations of cells. Inheritance of traits transmitted by mechanisms not directly involving the nucleotide sequence is called **epigenetic inheritance**. Whereas mutations in the DNA are permanent changes, modifications to the chromatin can be reversed, by processes that are not yet fully understood. The molecular systems for chromatin modification may well interact with each other in a regulated way. In *Drosophila*, for example, experiments have suggested that a particular histone-modifying enzyme recruits a DNA methylation enzyme to one region and that the two enzymes collaborate to silence a particular set of genes.

Researchers are amassing more and more evidence for the importance of epigenetic information in the regulation of gene expression. Epigenetic variations might help explain why one identical twin acquires a genetically based disease, such as schizophrenia, but the other does not, despite their identical genomes. Alterations in normal patterns of DNA methylation are seen in some cancers, where they are associated with inappropriate gene expression. Evidently, enzymes that modify chromatin structure are integral parts of the eukaryotic cell's machinery for regulating transcription.

Regulation of Transcription Initiation

Chromatin-modifying enzymes provide initial control of gene expression by making a region of DNA either more or less able to bind the transcription machinery. Once the chromatin of a gene is optimally modified for expression, the initiation of transcription is the next major step at which gene expression is regulated. As in bacteria, the regulation of transcription initiation in eukaryotes involves proteins that bind to DNA and either facilitate or inhibit binding of RNA polymerase. The process is more complicated in eukaryotes, however. Before looking at how eukaryotic cells control their transcription,

Organization of a Typical Eukaryotic Gene

A eukaryotic gene and the DNA elements (segments) that control it are typically organized as shown in **Figure 18.8**, which extends what you learned about eukaryotic genes in Chapter 17. Recall that a cluster of proteins called a *transcription initiation complex* assembles on the promoter sequence at the "upstream" end of the gene. One of these proteins, RNA polymerase II, then proceeds to transcribe the gene, synthesizing a primary RNA transcript (pre-mRNA). RNA processing includes enzymatic addition of a 5′ cap and a poly-A tail, as well as splicing out of introns, to yield a mature mRNA. Associated with most eukaryotic genes are multiple **control elements**, segments of noncoding DNA that help regulate transcription by binding certain proteins. These control elements and the proteins they bind are critical to the precise regulation of gene expression seen in different cell types.

The Roles of Transcription Factors

To initiate transcription, eukaryotic RNA polymerase requires the assistance of proteins called transcription factors. Some transcription factors, such as those illustrated in Figure 17.8,

are essential for the transcription of *all* protein-coding genes; therefore, they are often called *general transcription factors*. Only a few general transcription factors independently bind a DNA sequence, such as the TATA box within the promoter; the others primarily bind proteins, including each other and RNA polymerase II. Protein-protein interactions are crucial to the initiation of eukaryotic transcription. Only when the complete initiation complex has assembled can the polymerase begin to move along the DNA template strand, producing a complementary strand of RNA.

The interaction of general transcription factors and RNA polymerase II with a promoter usually leads to only a low rate of initiation and production of few RNA transcripts. In eukaryotes, high levels of transcription of particular genes at the appropriate time and place depend on the interaction of control elements with another set of proteins, which can be thought of as *specific transcription factors*.

Enhancers and Specific Transcription Factors   As you can see in Figure 18.8, some control elements, named *proximal control elements*, are located close to the promoter. (Although some biologists consider proximal control elements part of the promoter, we do not.) The more distant *distal control elements*, groupings of which are called **enhancers**, may be thousands of nucleotides upstream or downstream of a gene

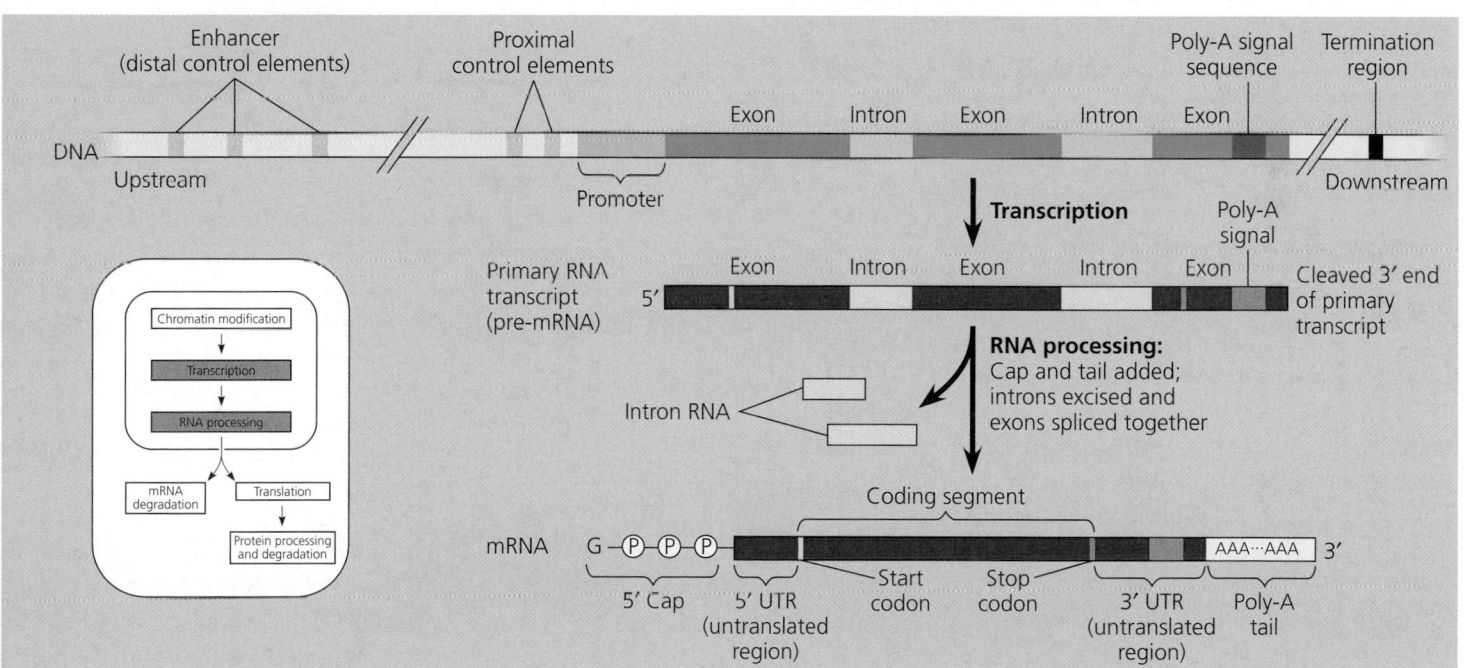

▲ **Figure 18.8 A eukaryotic gene and its transcript.** Each eukaryotic gene has a promoter, a DNA sequence where RNA polymerase binds and starts transcription, proceeding "downstream." A number of control elements (gold) are involved in regulating the initiation of transcription; these are DNA sequences located near (proximal to) or

far from (distal to) the promoter. Distal control elements can be grouped together as enhancers, one of which is shown for this gene. A polyadenylation (poly-A) signal sequence in the last exon of the gene is transcribed into an RNA sequence that signals where the transcript is cleaved and the poly-A tail added. Transcription may continue for hundreds of

nucleotides beyond the poly-A signal before terminating. RNA processing of the primary transcript into a functional mRNA involves three steps: addition of the 5′ cap, addition of the poly-A tail, and splicing. In the cell, the 5′ cap is added soon after transcription is initiated; splicing and poly-A tail addition may also occur while transcription is still under way (see Figure 17.9).

or even within an intron. A given gene may have multiple enhancers, each active at a different time or in a different cell type or location in the organism. Each enhancer, however, is associated with only that gene and no other.

In eukaryotes, the rate of gene expression can be strongly increased or decreased by the binding of proteins, either activators or repressors, to the control elements of enhancers. **Figure 18.9** shows a current model for how binding of activators to an enhancer located far from the promoter can influence transcription. Protein-mediated bending of the DNA is thought to bring the bound activators in contact with a group of so-called *mediator proteins*, which in turn interact with proteins at the promoter. These multiple protein-protein interactions help assemble and position the initiation complex on the promoter. Support for this

model includes a study showing that the proteins regulating a mouse globin gene contact both the gene's promoter and an enhancer located about 50,000 nucleotides upstream. Clearly, these two regions in the DNA must be brought together in a very specific fashion for this interaction to occur.

Hundreds of transcription activators have been discovered in eukaryotes. Researchers have identified two common structural elements in a large number of activator proteins: a DNA-binding domain—a part of the protein's three-dimensional structure that binds to DNA—and one or more activation domains. Activation domains bind other regulatory proteins or components of the transcription machinery, facilitating a sequence of protein-protein interactions that result in transcription of a given gene.

1 Activator proteins bind to distal control elements grouped as an enhancer in the DNA. This enhancer has three binding sites.

2 A DNA-bending protein brings the bound activators closer to the promoter. General transcription factors, mediator proteins, and RNA polymerase are nearby.

3 The activators bind to certain mediator proteins and general transcription factors, helping them form an active transcription initiation complex on the promoter.

▲ **Figure 18.9 A model for the action of enhancers and transcription activators.** Bending of the DNA by a protein enables enhancers to influence a promoter hundreds or even thousands of nucleotides away. Specific transcription factors called activators bind to the enhancer DNA sequences and then to a group of mediator proteins, which in turn bind to general transcription factors, assembling the transcription initiation complex. These protein-protein interactions facilitate the correct positioning of the complex on the promoter and the initiation of RNA synthesis. Only one enhancer (with three orange control elements) is shown here, but a gene may have several enhancers that act at different times or in different cell types.

Specific transcription factors that function as repressors can inhibit gene expression in several different ways. Some repressors bind directly to control element DNA (in enhancers or elsewhere), blocking activator binding or, in some cases, turning off transcription even when activators are bound. Other repressors block the binding of activators to proteins that allow the activators to bind to DNA.

In addition to influencing transcription directly, some activators and repressors act indirectly by affecting chromatin structure. Studies using yeast and mammalian cells show that some activators recruit proteins that acetylate histones near the promoters of specific genes, thus promoting transcription (see Figure 18.7). Similarly, some repressors recruit proteins that deacetylate histones, leading to reduced transcription, a phenomenon referred to as *silencing*. Indeed, recruitment of chromatin-modifying proteins seems to be the most common mechanism of repression in eukaryotes.

Combinatorial Control of Gene Activation

In eukaryotes, the precise control of transcription depends largely on the binding of activators to DNA control elements. Considering the great number of genes that must be regulated in a typical animal or plant cell, the number of completely different nucleotide sequences found in control elements is surprisingly small. A dozen or so short nucleotide sequences appear again and again in the control elements for different genes. On average, each enhancer is composed of about ten control elements, each of which can bind only one or two specific transcription factors. The particular *combination* of control elements in an enhancer associated with a gene turns out to be more important than the presence of a single unique control element in regulating transcription of the gene.

Even with only a dozen control element sequences available, a very large number of combinations are possible. A particular combination of control elements will be able to activate transcription only when the appropriate

activator proteins are present, which may occur at a precise time during development or in a particular cell type. **Figure 18.10** illustrates how the use of different combinations of just a few control elements can allow differential regulation of transcription in two cell types.

(a) Liver cell. The albumin gene is expressed, and the crystallin gene is not.

(b) Lens cell. The crystallin gene is expressed, and the albumin gene is not.

▲ **Figure 18.10 Cell type–specific transcription.** Both liver cells and lens cells have the genes for making the proteins albumin and crystallin, but only liver cells make albumin (a blood protein) and only lens cells make crystallin (the main protein of lenses). The specific transcription factors made in a cell determine which genes are expressed. In this example, the genes for albumin and crystallin are shown at the top, each with an enhancer made up of three different control elements. Although the enhancers for the two genes share one control element (gray), each enhancer has a unique combination of elements. All the activators required for high-level expression of the albumin gene are present only in liver cells (a), whereas the activators needed for expression of the crystallin gene are present only in lens cells (b). For simplicity, we consider only the role of activators here, although the presence or absence of repressors may also influence transcription in certain cell types.

? *Describe the enhancer for the albumin gene in each cell. How would the nucleotide sequence of this enhancer in the liver cell compare with that in the lens cell?*

Coordinately Controlled Genes in Eukaryotes

How does the eukaryotic cell deal with genes of related function that need to be turned on or off at the same time? Earlier in this chapter, you learned that in bacteria, such coordinately controlled genes are often clustered into an operon, which is regulated by a single promoter and transcribed into a single mRNA molecule. Thus, the genes are expressed together, and the encoded proteins are produced concurrently. Operons that work in this way have not been found in eukaryotic cells, with some exceptions.

Analysis of the genomes of several eukaryotic species has revealed some co-expressed genes that are clustered near one another on the same chromosome. Examples include certain genes in the testis of the fruit fly and muscle-related genes in a small worm called a nematode. But in contrast to the genes of bacterial operons, each gene in such a cluster has its own promoter and is individually transcribed. The coordinate regulation of these clustered genes is thought to involve changes in chromatin structure that make the entire group of genes either available or unavailable for transcription. In other cases, including 15% of nematode genes, several related genes do share a promoter and are transcribed into a single pre-mRNA. Unlike in bacteria, however, the RNA transcript is processed into separate mRNAs. The nematode operons do not appear to be evolutionarily related to bacterial operons.

More commonly, co-expressed eukaryotic genes, such as genes coding for the enzymes of a metabolic pathway, are found scattered over different chromosomes. In these cases, coordinate gene expression seems to depend on the association of a specific combination of control elements with every gene of a dispersed group. The presence of these elements can be compared to the raised flags on a few mailboxes out of many, signaling to the mail carrier to check those boxes. Copies of the activators that recognize the control elements bind to them, promoting simultaneous transcription of the genes, no matter where they are in the genome.

Coordinate control of dispersed genes in a eukaryotic cell often occurs in response to chemical signals from outside the cell. A steroid hormone, for example, enters a cell and binds to a specific intracellular receptor protein, forming a hormone-receptor complex that serves as a transcription activator (see Figure 11.8). Every gene whose transcription is stimulated by a particular steroid hormone, regardless of its chromosomal location, has a control element recognized by that hormone-receptor complex. This is how estrogen activates a group of genes that stimulate cell division in uterine cells, preparing the uterus for pregnancy.

Many signal molecules, such as nonsteroid hormones and growth factors, bind to receptors on a cell's surface and never actually enter the cell. Such molecules can control gene expression indirectly by triggering signal transduction pathways that lead to activation of particular transcription activators or repressors (see Figure 11.14). The principle of coordinate regulation is the same as in the case of steroid hormones: Genes with the same control elements are activated by the same chemical signals. Systems for coordinating gene regulation probably arose early in evolutionary history and evolved by the duplication and distribution of control elements within the genome.

Mechanisms of Post-Transcriptional Regulation

Transcription alone does not constitute gene expression. The expression of a protein-coding gene is ultimately measured by the amount of functional protein a cell makes, and much happens between the synthesis of the RNA transcript and the activity of the protein in the cell. Researchers are discovering more and more regulatory mechanisms that operate at various stages after transcription (see Figure 18.6). These mechanisms allow a cell to fine-tune gene expression rapidly in response to environmental changes without altering its transcription patterns. Here we discuss how cells can regulate gene expression once a gene has been transcribed.

RNA Processing

RNA processing in the nucleus and the export of mature RNA to the cytoplasm provide several opportunities for regulating gene expression that are not available in prokaryotes. One example of regulation at the RNA-processing level is **alternative RNA splicing**, in which different mRNA molecules are produced from the same primary transcript, depending on which RNA segments are treated as exons and which as introns. Regulatory proteins specific to a cell type control intron-exon choices by binding to regulatory sequences within the primary transcript.

A simple example of alternative RNA splicing is shown in **Figure 18.11** for the troponin T gene, which encodes two different (though related) proteins. Other genes offer possibilities for greater numbers of products. For instance, researchers have discovered a fruit fly gene that has enough alternatively spliced exons to generate more than 38,000 different proteins, although only a small number have been found to be synthesized. It is clear that alternative RNA splicing can significantly expand the repertoire of a eukaryotic genome.

mRNA Degradation

The life span of mRNA molecules in the cytoplasm is important in determining the pattern of protein synthesis in a cell. Bacterial mRNA molecules typically are degraded by enzymes within a few minutes of their synthesis. This short life span of mRNAs is one reason bacteria can change their patterns of protein synthesis so quickly in response to environmental changes. In contrast, mRNAs in multicellular eukaryotes typically survive for hours, days, or even weeks. For instance, the mRNAs for the hemoglobin polypeptides

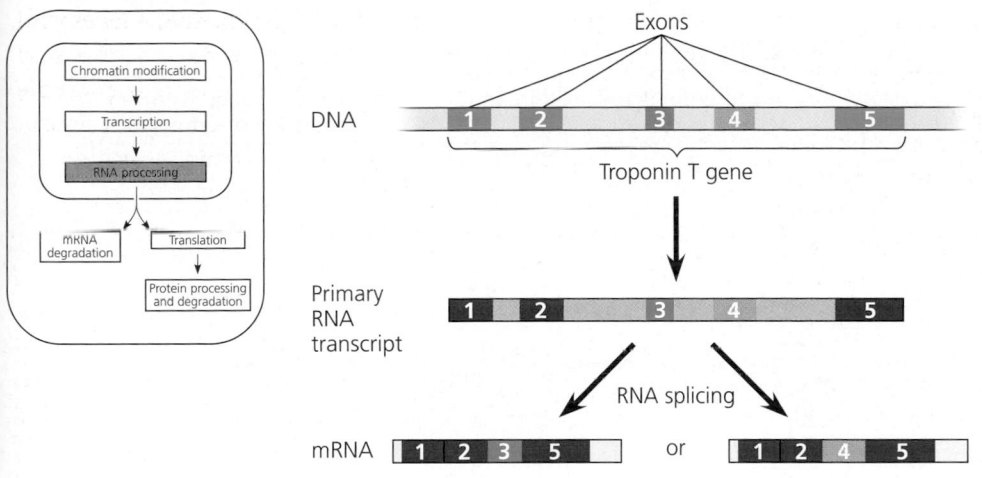

Exons

DNA

Troponin T gene

Primary RNA transcript

RNA splicing

mRNA | 1 | 2 | 3 | 5 | or | 1 | 2 | 4 | 5 |

◀ **Figure 18.11 Alternative RNA splicing of the troponin T gene.** The primary transcript of this gene can be spliced in more than one way, generating different mRNA molecules. Notice that one mRNA molecule has ended up with exon 3 (green) and the other with exon 4 (purple). These two mRNAs are translated into different but related muscle proteins.

(α-globin and β-globin) in developing red blood cells are unusually stable, and these long-lived mRNAs are translated repeatedly in these cells.

Research on yeast species suggests that a common pathway of mRNA breakdown begins with the enzymatic shortening of the poly-A tail (see Figure 18.8). This helps trigger the action of enzymes that remove the 5′ cap (the two ends of the mRNA may be briefly held together by the proteins involved). Removal of the cap, a critical step, is also regulated by particular nucleotide sequences within the mRNA. Once the cap is removed, nuclease enzymes rapidly chew up the mRNA.

Nucleotide sequences that affect how long an mRNA remains intact are often found in the untranslated region (UTR) at the 3′ end of the molecule (see Figure 18.8). In one experiment, researchers transferred such a sequence from the short-lived mRNA for a growth factor to the 3′ end of a normally stable globin mRNA. The globin mRNA was quickly degraded.

During the past few years, other mechanisms that degrade or block expression of mRNA molecules have come to light. These mechanisms involve an important group of newly discovered RNA molecules that regulate gene expression at several levels, and we will discuss them later in this chapter.

Initiation of Translation

Translation presents another opportunity for regulating gene expression; such regulation occurs most commonly at the initiation stage (see Figure 17.17). The initiation of translation of some mRNAs can be blocked by regulatory proteins that bind to specific sequences or structures within the untranslated region at the 5′ end (5′ UTR) of the mRNA, preventing the attachment of ribosomes. (Recall from Chapter 17 that both the 5′ cap and the poly-A tail of an mRNA molecule are important for ribosome binding.) A different mechanism for blocking translation is seen in a variety of mRNAs present in the eggs of many organisms: Initially, these stored mRNAs lack poly-A tails of sufficient length to allow translation initiation. At the

appropriate time during embryonic development, however, a cytoplasmic enzyme adds more adenine (A) nucleotides, prompting translation to begin.

Alternatively, translation of *all* the mRNAs in a cell may be regulated simultaneously. In a eukaryotic cell, such "global" control usually involves the activation or inactivation of one or more of the protein factors required to initiate translation. This mechanism plays a role in starting translation of mRNAs that are stored in eggs. Just after fertilization, translation is triggered by the sudden activation of translation initiation factors. The response is a burst of synthesis of the proteins encoded by the stored mRNAs. Some plants and algae store mRNAs during periods of darkness; light then triggers the reactivation of the translational apparatus.

Protein Processing and Degradation

The final opportunities for controlling gene expression occur after translation. Often, eukaryotic polypeptides must be processed to yield functional protein molecules. For instance, cleavage of the initial insulin polypeptide (pro-insulin) forms the active hormone. In addition, many proteins undergo chemical modifications that make them functional. Regulatory proteins are commonly activated or inactivated by the reversible addition of phosphate groups, and proteins destined for the surface of animal cells acquire sugars. Cell-surface proteins and many others must also be transported to target destinations in the cell in order to function. Regulation might occur at any of the steps involved in modifying or transporting a protein.

Finally, the length of time each protein functions in the cell is strictly regulated by means of selective degradation. Many proteins, such as the cyclins involved in regulating the cell cycle, must be relatively short-lived if the cell is to function appropriately (see Figure 12.17). To mark a particular protein for destruction, the cell commonly attaches molecules of a small protein called ubiquitin to the protein. Giant protein complexes called **proteasomes** then recognize the ubiquitin-tagged

1 Multiple ubiquitin molecules are attached to a protein by enzymes in the cytosol.

2 The ubiquitin-tagged protein is recognized by a proteasome, which unfolds the protein and sequesters it within a central cavity.

3 Enzymatic components of the proteasome cut the protein into small peptides, which can be further degraded by other enzymes in the cytosol.

Ubiquitin

Proteasome

Proteasome and ubiquitin to be recycled

Protein to be degraded

Ubiquitinated protein

Protein entering a proteasome

Protein fragments (peptides)

▲ **Figure 18.12 Degradation of a protein by a proteasome.** A proteasome, an enormous protein complex shaped like a trash can, chops up unneeded proteins in the cell. In most cases, the proteins attacked by a proteasome have been tagged with short chains of ubiquitin, a small protein. Steps 1 and 3 require ATP. Eukaryotic proteasomes are as massive as ribosomal subunits and are distributed throughout the cell. Their shape somewhat resembles that of chaperone proteins, which protect protein structure rather than destroy it (see Figure 5.24).

proteins and degrade them **(Figure 18.12)**. The importance of proteasomes is underscored by the finding that mutations making specific cell cycle proteins impervious to proteasome degradation can lead to cancer.

CONCEPT CHECK 18.2

1. In general, what is the effect of histone acetylation and DNA methylation on gene expression?
2. Compare the roles of general and specific transcription factors in regulating gene expression.
3. Suppose you compared the nucleotide sequences of the distal control elements in the enhancers of three genes that are expressed only in muscle tissue. What would you expect to find? Why?
4. Once mRNA encoding a particular protein reaches the cytoplasm, what are four mechanisms that can regulate the amount of the protein that is active in the cell?
5. **WHAT IF?** Examine Figure 18.10 and suggest a mechanism by which the yellow activator protein comes to be present in the liver cell but not in the lens cell.

For suggested answers, see Appendix A.

CONCEPT **18.3**

Noncoding RNAs play multiple roles in controlling gene expression

Recall that only 1.5% of the human genome—and a similarly small percentage of the genome of many other multicellular eukaryotes—codes for proteins. Of the remainder, a very small fraction consists of genes for small RNAs, such as ribosomal RNA and transfer RNA. Until recently, most of the rest of the DNA was assumed to be untranscribed. The general idea was that since it didn't code for proteins or the few known types of RNA, such DNA didn't contain meaningful genetic information. However, a flood of recent data has contradicted this idea. For example, a study of two human chromosomes showed that ten times as much of the genome was transcribed as was predicted by the number of protein-coding exons present. Introns accounted for some of this transcribed, nontranslated RNA, but only a small fraction of the total. These and other results suggest that a significant amount of the genome may be transcribed into non-protein-coding RNAs (also called *noncoding RNAs*), including a variety of small RNAs. While many questions about the functions of these RNAs remain unanswered, researchers are uncovering more evidence of their biological roles every day.

Biologists are excited about these recent discoveries, which hint at a large, diverse population of RNA molecules in the cell that play crucial roles in regulating gene expression—and have gone largely unnoticed until now. Clearly, we must revise our long-standing view that because they code for proteins, mRNAs are the most important RNAs functioning in the cell. It's as if we've been so focused on the famous ruler of a country that we've completely overlooked the many advisors and cabinet members working behind the scenes.

Regulation by noncoding RNAs is known to occur at two points in the pathway of gene expression: mRNA translation and chromatin configuration. We will focus on several types of small RNAs that have been extensively studied in the past few years; the importance of these RNAs was recognized when they were the focus of the 2006 Nobel Prize in Physiology or Medicine.

Effects on mRNAs by MicroRNAs and Small Interfering RNAs

Since 1993, a number of research studies have uncovered small single-stranded RNA molecules, called **microRNAs (miRNAs)**, that are capable of binding to complementary sequences in mRNA molecules. The miRNAs are formed from longer RNA precursors that fold back on themselves, forming one or more short double-stranded hairpin structures, each held together by hydrogen bonds **(Figure 18.13)**. After each hairpin is cut away from the precursor, it is trimmed by an enzyme (fittingly called Dicer) into a short double-stranded fragment of about 20 nucleotide pairs. One of the two strands is degraded, while the other strand, which is the miRNA, forms a complex with one or more proteins; the miRNA allows the complex to bind to any mRNA molecule with the complementary sequence. The miRNA-protein complex then either degrades the target mRNA or blocks its translation. It has been estimated that expression of up to one-third of all human genes may be regulated by miRNAs, a remarkable figure given that the existence of miRNAs was unknown a mere two decades ago.

A growing understanding of the miRNA pathway provided an explanation for a perplexing observation: Researchers had found that injecting double-stranded RNA molecules into a cell somehow turned off expression of a gene with the same sequence as the RNA. They called this experimental phenomenon **RNA interference (RNAi)**. It was later shown to be due to **small interfering RNAs (siRNAs)**, which are similar in size and function to miRNAs. In fact, subsequent research showed that the same cellular machinery generates miRNAs and siRNAs and that both can associate with the same proteins, producing similar results. The distinction between miRNAs and siRNAs is based on the nature of the precursor molecule for each. While an miRNA is usually formed from a single hairpin in a precursor RNA (see Figure 18.13), siRNAs are formed from much longer double-stranded RNA molecules, each of which gives rise to many siRNAs.

We mentioned that laboratory investigators had injected double-stranded RNAs into cells, and you may wonder whether such molecules are ever found naturally. As you will learn in Chapter 19, some viruses have double-stranded RNA genomes. Because the cellular RNAi pathway can lead to the destruction of

▶ **Figure 18.13 Regulation of gene expression by miRNAs.** RNA transcripts are processed into miRNAs, which prevent expression of mRNAs containing complementary sequences.

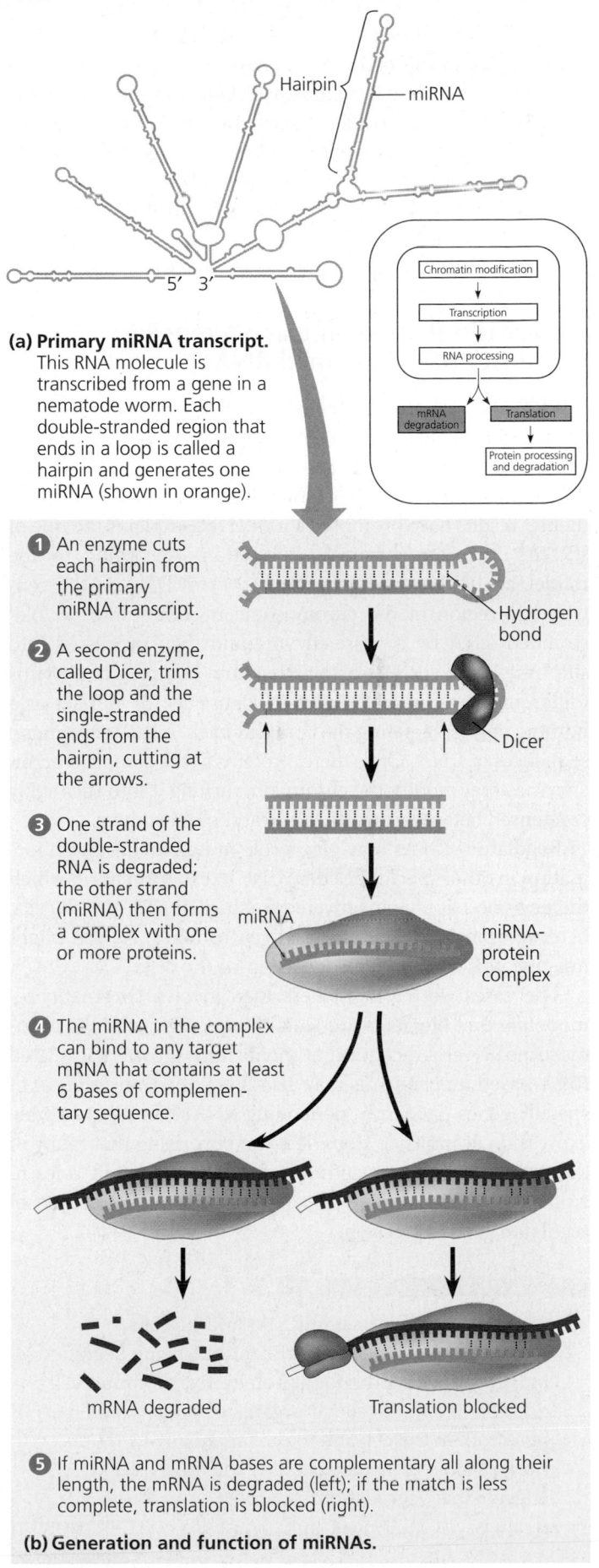

(a) Primary miRNA transcript. This RNA molecule is transcribed from a gene in a nematode worm. Each double-stranded region that ends in a loop is called a hairpin and generates one miRNA (shown in orange).

① An enzyme cuts each hairpin from the primary miRNA transcript.

② A second enzyme, called Dicer, trims the loop and the single-stranded ends from the hairpin, cutting at the arrows.

③ One strand of the double-stranded RNA is degraded; the other strand (miRNA) then forms a complex with one or more proteins.

④ The miRNA in the complex can bind to any target mRNA that contains at least 6 bases of complementary sequence.

mRNA degraded   Translation blocked

⑤ If miRNA and mRNA bases are complementary all along their length, the mRNA is degraded (left); if the match is less complete, translation is blocked (right).

(b) Generation and function of miRNAs.

RNAs with sequences complementary to those found in double-stranded RNAs, this pathway may have evolved as a natural defense against infection by such viruses. However, the fact that the RNAi pathway can also affect the expression of nonviral cellular genes may reflect a different evolutionary origin for the RNAi pathway. Moreover, some species apparently produce their own long double-stranded RNA precursors to small RNAs such as siRNAs. Once produced, these RNAs can interfere with gene expression at stages other than translation, as we'll discuss next.

Chromatin Remodeling and Silencing of Transcription by Small RNAs

In addition to affecting mRNAs, small RNAs can cause remodeling of chromatin structure. In yeast, siRNAs produced by the yeast cells themselves appear to be crucial for the formation of heterochromatin at the centromeres of chromosomes. Experimental results have prompted a model that explains the role of siRNAs in heterochromatin formation. According to the model, an RNA transcript produced from DNA in the centromeric region of the chromosome is copied into double-stranded RNA by a yeast enzyme and then processed into siRNAs. These siRNAs associate with a complex of proteins (different from the one shown in Figure 18.13) and act as a homing device, targeting the complex back to the centromeric sequences of DNA. Once there, proteins in the complex recruit enzymes that modify the chromatin, turning it into the highly condensed heterochromatin found at the centromere.

Regulatory RNAs may play a role in heterochromatin formation in other species besides yeast. In experiments in which the enzyme Dicer is inactivated in chicken and mouse cells, heterochromatin fails to form at centromeres. As you might imagine, this has dire consequences for the cells.

The cases we have just described involve chromatin remodeling that blocks expression of large regions of the chromosome. Several recent experiments have shown that related RNA-based mechanisms may also block the transcription of specific genes. Evidently, noncoding RNAs can regulate gene expression at multiple steps. It is not surprising that many of the miRNAs characterized thus far play important roles in embryonic development—perhaps the ultimate example of regulated gene expression.

CONCEPT CHECK 18.3

1. Compare and contrast miRNAs and siRNAs.
2. **WHAT IF?** Imagine that the mRNA being degraded in Figure 18.13 codes for a protein that promotes cell division in a multicellular organism. What would happen, both in the cell and to the organism, if a mutation disabled the gene encoding the miRNA that triggers this degradation?

For suggested answers, see Appendix A.

A program of differential gene expression leads to the different cell types in a multicellular organism

In the embryonic development of multicellular organisms, a fertilized egg (a zygote) gives rise to cells of many different types, each with a different structure and corresponding function. Typically, cells are organized into tissues, tissues into organs, organs into organ systems, and organ systems into the whole organism. Thus, any developmental program must produce cells of different types that form higher-level structures arranged in a particular way in three dimensions. The processes that occur during development in plants and animals are detailed in Chapters 35 and 47, respectively. In this chapter, we focus instead on the program of regulation of gene expression that orchestrates development, using a few animal species as examples.

A Genetic Program for Embryonic Development

The photos in **Figure 18.14** illustrate the dramatic difference between a zygote and the organism it becomes. This remarkable transformation results from three interrelated processes: cell division, cell differentiation, and morphogenesis. Through a succession of mitotic cell divisions, the zygote gives rise to a large number of cells. Cell division alone, however, would produce only a great ball of identical cells, nothing like a tadpole. During embryonic development, cells not only increase in number, but also undergo **cell differentiation**, the process by which cells become specialized in structure and function. Moreover, the different kinds of cells are not randomly distributed but are organized into tissues and organs in a particular three-dimensional

(a) Fertilized eggs of a frog   (b) Newly hatched tadpole

▲ **Figure 18.14 From fertilized egg to animal: What a difference four days makes.** It takes just four days for cell division, differentiation, and morphogenesis to transform each of the fertilized frog eggs shown in (a) into a tadpole like the one in (b).

arrangement. The physical processes that give an organism its shape constitute **morphogenesis**, meaning "creation of form."

All three processes have their basis in cellular behavior. Even morphogenesis, the shaping of the organism, can be traced back to changes in the shape, motility, and other characteristics of the cells that make up various regions of the embryo. As you have seen, the activities of a cell depend on the genes it expresses and the proteins it produces. Almost all cells in an organism have the same genome; therefore, differential gene expression results from the genes being regulated differently in each cell type.

In Figure 18.10, you saw a simplified view of how differential gene expression occurs in two cell types, a liver cell and a lens cell. Each of these fully differentiated cells has a particular mix of specific activators that turn on the collection of genes whose products are required in the cell. The fact that both cells arose through a series of mitoses from a common fertilized egg inevitably leads to a question: How do different sets of activators come to be present in the two cells?

It turns out that materials placed into the egg by the mother set up a sequential program of gene regulation that is carried out as cells divide, and this program makes the cells become different from each other in a coordinated fashion. To understand how this works, we will consider two basic developmental processes: First, we'll explore how cells that arise from early embryonic mitoses develop the differences that start each cell along its own differentiation pathway. Second, we'll see how cellular differentiation leads to one particular cell type, using muscle development as an example.

Cytoplasmic Determinants and Inductive Signals

What generates the first differences among cells in an early embryo? And what controls the differentiation of all the various cell types as development proceeds? By this point in the chapter, you can probably deduce the answer: The specific genes expressed in any particular cell of a developing organism determine its path. Two sources of information, used to varying extents in different species, "tell" a cell which genes to express at any given time during embryonic development.

One important source of information early in development is the egg's cytoplasm, which contains both RNA and proteins encoded by the mother's DNA. The cytoplasm of an unfertilized egg is not homogeneous. Messenger RNA, proteins, other substances, and organelles are distributed unevenly in the unfertilized egg, and this unevenness has a profound impact on the development of the future embryo in many species. Maternal substances in the egg that influence the course of early development are called **cytoplasmic determinants** (**Figure 18.15a**). After fertilization, early

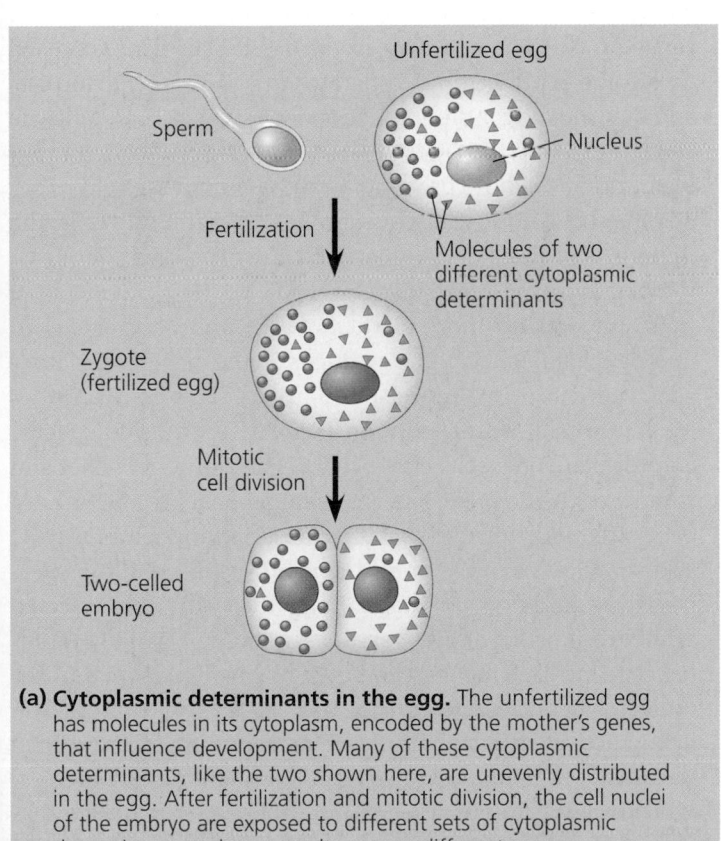

(a) Cytoplasmic determinants in the egg. The unfertilized egg has molecules in its cytoplasm, encoded by the mother's genes, that influence development. Many of these cytoplasmic determinants, like the two shown here, are unevenly distributed in the egg. After fertilization and mitotic division, the cell nuclei of the embryo are exposed to different sets of cytoplasmic determinants and, as a result, express different genes.

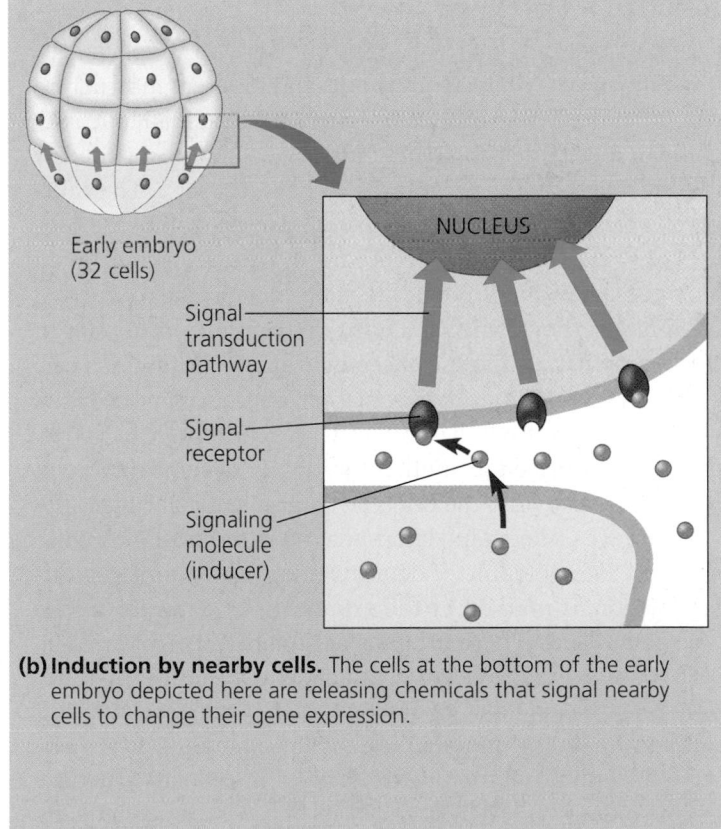

(b) Induction by nearby cells. The cells at the bottom of the early embryo depicted here are releasing chemicals that signal nearby cells to change their gene expression.

▲ Figure 18.15 **Sources of developmental information for the early embryo.**

mitotic divisions distribute the zygote's cytoplasm into separate cells. The nuclei of these cells may thus be exposed to different cytoplasmic determinants, depending on which portions of the zygotic cytoplasm a cell received. The combination of cytoplasmic determinants in a cell helps determine its developmental fate by regulating expression of the cell's genes during the course of cell differentiation.

The other major source of developmental information, which becomes increasingly important as the number of embryonic cells increases, is the environment around a particular cell. Most influential are the signals impinging on an embryonic cell from other embryonic cells in the vicinity, including contact with cell-surface molecules on neighboring cells and the binding of growth factors secreted by neighboring cells. Such signals cause changes in the target cells, a process called **induction** (Figure 18.15b). The molecules conveying these signals within the target cell are cell-surface receptors and other proteins expressed by the embryo's own genes. In general, the signaling molecules send a cell down a specific developmental path by causing changes in its gene expression that eventually result in observable cellular changes. Thus, interactions between embryonic cells help induce differentiation of the many specialized cell types making up a new organism.

Sequential Regulation of Gene Expression During Cellular Differentiation

As the tissues and organs of an embryo develop and their cells differentiate, the cells become noticeably different in structure and function. These observable changes are actually the outcome of a cell's developmental history beginning at the first mitotic division of the zygote, as we have just seen. The earliest changes that set a cell on a path to specialization are subtle ones, showing up only at the molecular level. Before biologists knew much about the molecular changes occurring in embryos, they coined the term **determination** to refer to the events that lead to the observable differentiation of a cell. Once it has undergone determination, an embryonic cell is irreversibly committed to its final fate. If a committed cell is experimentally placed in another location in the embryo, it will still differentiate into the cell type that is its normal fate.

Today we understand determination in terms of molecular changes. The outcome of determination, observable cell differentiation, is marked by the expression of genes for *tissue-specific proteins.* These proteins are found only in a specific cell type and give the cell its characteristic structure and function. The first evidence of differentiation is the appearance of mRNAs for these proteins. Eventually, differentiation is observable with a microscope as changes in cellular structure. On the molecular level, different sets of genes are sequentially expressed in a regulated manner as new cells arise from division of their precursors. A number of the steps in gene expression may be regulated during differentiation, with transcription among the most important. In the fully differentiated cell, transcription remains the principal regulatory point for maintaining appropriate gene expression.

Differentiated cells are specialists at making tissue-specific proteins. For example, as a result of transcriptional regulation, liver cells specialize in making albumin, and lens cells specialize in making crystallin (see Figure 18.10). Skeletal muscle cells in vertebrates are another instructive example. Each of these cells is a long fiber containing many nuclei within a single plasma membrane. Skeletal muscle cells have high concentrations of muscle-specific versions of the contractile proteins myosin and actin, as well as membrane receptor proteins that detect signals from nerve cells.

Muscle cells develop from embryonic precursor cells that have the potential to develop into a number of cell types, including cartilage cells and fat cells, but particular conditions commit them to becoming muscle cells. Although the committed cells appear unchanged under the microscope, determination has occurred, and they are now *myoblasts.* Eventually, myoblasts start to churn out large amounts of muscle-specific proteins and fuse to form mature, elongated, multinucleate skeletal muscle cells (Figure 18.16, left).

Researchers have worked out what happens at the molecular level during muscle cell determination by growing myoblasts in culture and analyzing them using molecular biological techniques you will learn about in Chapter 20. In a series of experiments, they isolated different genes, caused each to be expressed in a separate embryonic precursor cell, and then looked for differentiation into myoblasts and muscle cells. In this way, they identified several so-called "master regulatory genes" whose protein products commit the cells to becoming skeletal muscle. Thus, in the case of muscle cells, the molecular basis of determination is the expression of one or more of these master regulatory genes.

To understand more about how commitment occurs in muscle cell differentiation, let's focus on the master regulatory gene called *myoD* (Figure 18.16, right). This gene encodes MyoD protein, a transcription factor that binds to specific control elements in the enhancers of various target genes and stimulates their expression. Some target genes for MyoD encode still other muscle-specific transcription factors. MyoD also stimulates expression of the *myoD* gene itself, thus perpetuating its effect in maintaining the cell's differentiated state. Presumably, all the genes activated by MyoD have enhancer control elements recognized by MyoD and are thus coordinately controlled. Finally, the secondary transcription factors activate the genes for proteins such as myosin and actin that confer the unique properties of skeletal muscle cells.

The MyoD protein deserves its designation as a master regulatory gene. Researchers have shown that it is even capable of changing some kinds of fully differentiated nonmuscle cells, such as fat cells and liver cells, into muscle cells. Why doesn't

① **Determination.** Signals from other cells lead to activation of a master regulatory gene called *myoD*, and the cell makes MyoD protein, a specific transcription factor that acts as an activator. The cell, now called a myoblast, is irreversibly committed to becoming a skeletal muscle cell.

② **Differentiation.** MyoD protein stimulates the *myoD* gene further and activates genes encoding other muscle-specific transcription factors, which in turn activate genes for muscle proteins. MyoD also turns on genes that block the cell cycle, thus stopping cell division. The nondividing myoblasts fuse to become mature multinucleate muscle cells, also called muscle fibers.

Part of a muscle fiber (fully differentiated cell)

▲ **Figure 18.16 Determination and differentiation of muscle cells.** Skeletal muscle cells arise from embryonic cells as a result of changes in gene expression. (In this depiction, the process of gene activation is greatly simplified.)

WHAT IF? *What would happen if a mutation in the* myoD *gene resulted in a MyoD protein that could not activate the* myoD *gene?*

it work on *all* kinds of cells? One likely explanation is that activation of the muscle-specific genes is not solely dependent on MyoD but requires a particular *combination* of regulatory proteins, some of which are lacking in cells that do not respond to MyoD. The determination and differentiation of other kinds of tissues may play out in a similar fashion.

We have now seen how different programs of gene expression that are activated in the fertilized egg can result in differentiated cells and tissues. But for the tissues to function effectively in the organism as a whole, the organism's *body plan*—its overall three-dimensional arrangement—must be established and superimposed on the differentiation process. Next we'll investigate the molecular basis for the establishment of the body plan, using the well-studied *Drosophila* as an example.

Pattern Formation: Setting Up the Body Plan

Cytoplasmic determinants and inductive signals both contribute to the development of a spatial organization in which the tissues and organs of an organism are all in their characteristic places. This process is called **pattern formation**.

Pattern formation in animals begins in the early embryo, when the major axes of an animal are established. Before construction begins on a new building, the locations of the front, back, and sides are determined. In the same way, before the tissues and organs of a bilaterally symmetrical animal appear, the relative positions of the animal's head and tail, right and left sides, and back and front are set up, thus establishing the three major body axes. The molecular cues that control pattern formation, collectively called **positional information**, are provided by cytoplasmic determinants and inductive signals (see Figure 18.15). These cues tell a cell its location relative to the body axes and to neighboring cells and determine how the cell and its progeny will respond to future molecular signals.

During the first half of the 20th century, classical embryologists made detailed anatomical observations of embryonic development in a number of species and performed experiments in which they manipulated embryonic tissues (see

Chapter 47). Although this research laid the groundwork for understanding the mechanisms of development, it did not reveal the specific molecules that guide development or determine how patterns are established.

Then, in the 1940s, scientists began using the genetic approach—the study of mutants—to investigate *Drosophila* development. That approach has had spectacular success. These studies have established that genes control development and have led to an understanding of the key roles that specific molecules play in defining position and directing differentiation. By combining anatomical, genetic, and biochemical approaches to the study of *Drosophila* development, researchers have discovered developmental principles common to many other species, including humans.

The Life Cycle of Drosophila

Fruit flies and other arthropods have a modular construction, an ordered series of segments. These segments make up the body's three major parts: the head, the thorax (the midbody, from which the wings and legs extend), and the abdomen (Figure 18.17a). Like other bilaterally symmetrical animals, *Drosophila* has an anterior-posterior (head-to-tail) axis, a dorsal-ventral (back-to-belly) axis, and a right-left axis. In *Drosophila*, cytoplasmic determinants that are localized in the unfertilized egg provide positional information for the placement of anterior-posterior and dorsal-ventral axes even before fertilization. We'll focus here on the molecules involved in establishing the anterior-posterior axis.

The *Drosophila* egg develops in the female's ovary, surrounded by ovarian cells called nurse cells and follicle cells (Figure 18.17b, top). These support cells supply the egg with nutrients, mRNAs, and other substances needed for development and make the egg shell. After fertilization and laying of the egg, embryonic development results in the formation of a segmented larva, which goes through three larval stages. Then, in a process much like that by which a caterpillar becomes a butterfly, the fly larva forms a cocoon in which it metamorphoses into the adult fly pictured in Figure 18.17a.

Genetic Analysis of Early Development: Scientific Inquiry

Edward B. Lewis was a visionary American biologist who, in the 1940s, first showed the value of the genetic approach to studying embryonic development in *Drosophila*. Lewis studied bizarre mutant flies with developmental defects that led to extra wings or legs in the wrong places (Figure 18.18). He located the mutations on the fly's genetic map, thus connecting the developmental abnormalities to specific genes. This research supplied the first concrete evidence that genes somehow direct the developmental processes studied by embryologists. The genes Lewis discovered, called **homeotic genes**, control pattern formation in the late embryo, larva, and adult.

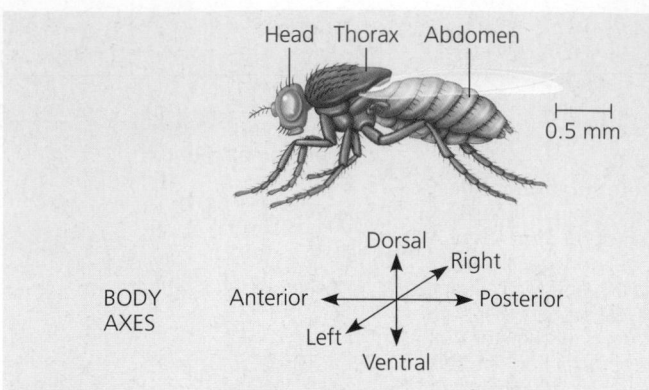

(a) Adult. The adult fly is segmented, and multiple segments make up each of the three main body parts—head, thorax, and abdomen. The body axes are shown by arrows.

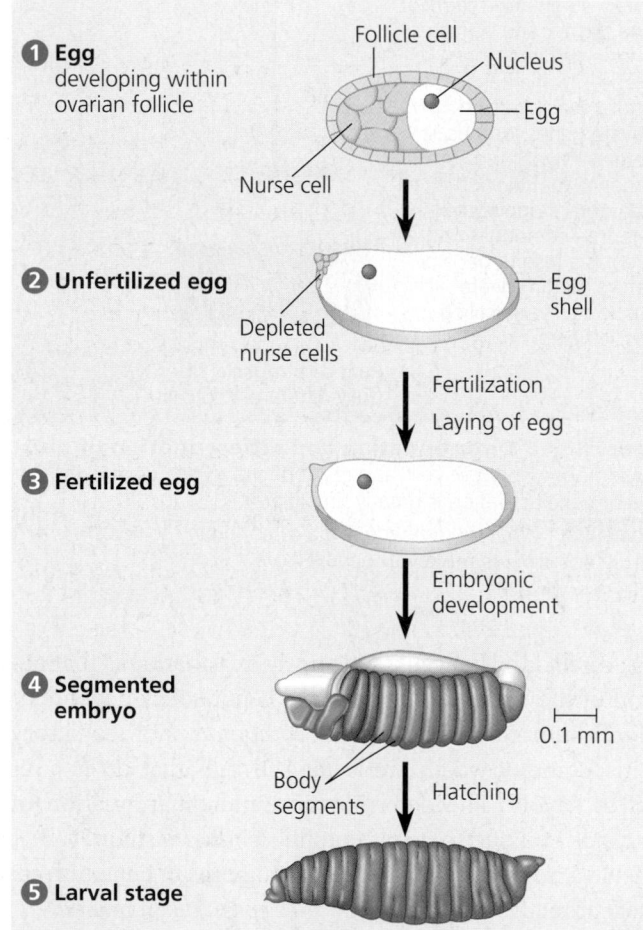

(b) Development from egg to larva. ❶ The yellow egg is surrounded by other cells that form a structure called the follicle within one of the mother's ovaries. ❷ The nurse cells shrink as they supply nutrients and mRNAs to the developing egg, which grows larger. Eventually, the mature egg fills the egg shell that is secreted by the follicle cells. ❸ The egg is fertilized within the mother and then laid. ❹ Embryonic development forms ❺ a larva, which goes through three stages. The third stage forms a cocoon (not shown), within which the larva metamorphoses into the adult shown in (a).

▲ **Figure 18.17 Key developmental events in the life cycle of *Drosophila*.**

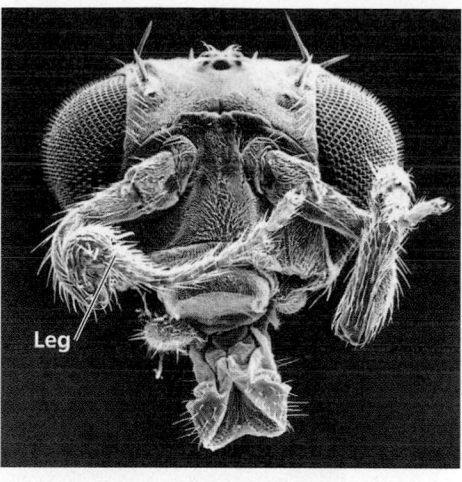

Wild type   Mutant

◀ **Figure 18.18 Abnormal pattern formation in *Drosophila*.** Mutations in certain regulatory genes, called homeotic genes, cause a misplacement of structures in an animal. These micrographs contrast the head of a wild-type fly, bearing a pair of small antennae, with that of a homeotic mutant, bearing a pair of legs in place of antennae (SEMs).

Insight into pattern formation during early embryonic development did not come for another 30 years, when two researchers in Germany, Christiane Nüsslein-Volhard and Eric Wieschaus, set out to identify *all* the genes that affect segment formation in *Drosophila*. The project was daunting for three reasons. The first was the sheer number of *Drosophila* genes, now known to total about 13,700. The genes affecting segmentation might be just a few needles in a haystack or might be so numerous and varied that the scientists would be unable to make sense of them. Second, mutations affecting a process as fundamental as segmentation would surely be **embryonic lethals**, mutations with phenotypes causing death at the embryonic or larval stage. Because organisms with embryonic lethal mutations never reproduce, they cannot be bred for study. The researchers dealt with this problem by looking for recessive mutations, which can be propagated in heterozygous flies. Third, cytoplasmic determinants in the egg were known to play a role in axis formation, and therefore the researchers knew they would have to study the mother's genes as well as those of the embryo. It is the mother's genes that we will discuss further as we focus on how the anterior-posterior body axis is set up in the developing egg.

Nüsslein-Volhard and Wieschaus began their search for segmentation genes by exposing flies to a mutagenic chemical that affected the flies' gametes. They mated the mutagenized flies and then scanned their descendants for dead embryos or larvae with abnormal segmentation or other defects. For example, to find genes that might set up the anterior-posterior axis, they looked for embryos or larvae with abnormal ends, such as two heads or two tails, predicting that such abnormalities would arise from mutations in maternal genes required for correctly setting up the offspring's head or tail end.

Using this approach, Nüsslein-Volhard and Wieschaus eventually identified about 1,200 genes essential for pattern formation during embryonic development. Of these, about 120 were essential for normal segmentation. Over several years, the researchers were able to group these segmentation genes by general function, to map them, and to clone many of them for further study in the lab. The result was a detailed molecular understanding of the early steps in pattern formation in *Drosophila*.

When the results of Nüsslein-Volhard and Wieschaus were combined with Lewis's earlier work, a coherent picture of *Drosophila* development emerged. In recognition of their discoveries, the three researchers were awarded a Nobel Prize in 1995.

Let's consider further the genes that Nüsslein-Volhard, Wieschaus, and co-workers found for cytoplasmic determinants deposited in the egg by the mother. These genes set up the initial pattern of the embryo by regulating gene expression in broad regions of the early embryo.

Axis Establishment

As we mentioned earlier, cytoplasmic determinants in the egg are the substances that initially establish the axes of the *Drosophila* body. These substances are encoded by genes of the mother, fittingly called maternal effect genes. A **maternal effect gene** is a gene that, when mutant in the mother, results in a mutant phenotype in the offspring, regardless of the offspring's own genotype. In fruit fly development, the mRNA or protein products of maternal effect genes are placed in the egg while it is still in the mother's ovary. When the mother has a mutation in such a gene, she makes a defective gene product (or none at all), and her eggs are defective; when these eggs are fertilized, they fail to develop properly.

Because they control the orientation (polarity) of the egg and consequently of the fly, maternal effect genes are also called **egg-polarity genes**. One group of these genes sets up the anterior-posterior axis of the embryo, while a second group establishes the dorsal-ventral axis. Like mutations in segmentation genes, mutations in maternal effect genes are generally embryonic lethals.

Bicoid: A Morphogen Determining Head Structures To see how maternal effect genes determine the body axes of the offspring, we will focus on one such gene, called *bicoid*, a term meaning "two-tailed." An embryo whose mother has a mutant *bicoid* gene lacks the front half of its body and has posterior structures at both ends **(Figure 18.19)**. This phenotype suggested to Nüsslein-Volhard and her colleagues that the product of the mother's *bicoid* gene is essential for setting up the anterior end of the fly and might be concentrated at the future anterior end of the embryo. This hypothesis is a specific example of the *morphogen gradient hypothesis* first proposed by embryologists a century ago; in this hypothesis, gradients of

---

▼ **Figure 18.19** **Inquiry**

Is Bicoid a morphogen that determines the anterior end of a fruit fly?

EXPERIMENT Using a genetic approach to study *Drosophila* development, Christiane Nüsslein-Volhard and colleagues at the European Molecular Biology Laboratory in Heidelberg, Germany, obtained many embryos and larvae with defects in their body patterns, some due to mutations in the mother's genes. One such gene was called *bicoid*, meaning "two-tailed," because its mutation resulted in larvae with two tails and no head. Subsequent studies analyzed expression of the *bicoid* gene.

The researchers hypothesized that *bicoid* normally codes for a morphogen that specifies the head (anterior) end of the embryo. To test this hypothesis, they used molecular techniques to determine where the mRNA and protein encoded by this gene were found in the fertilized egg and early embryo.

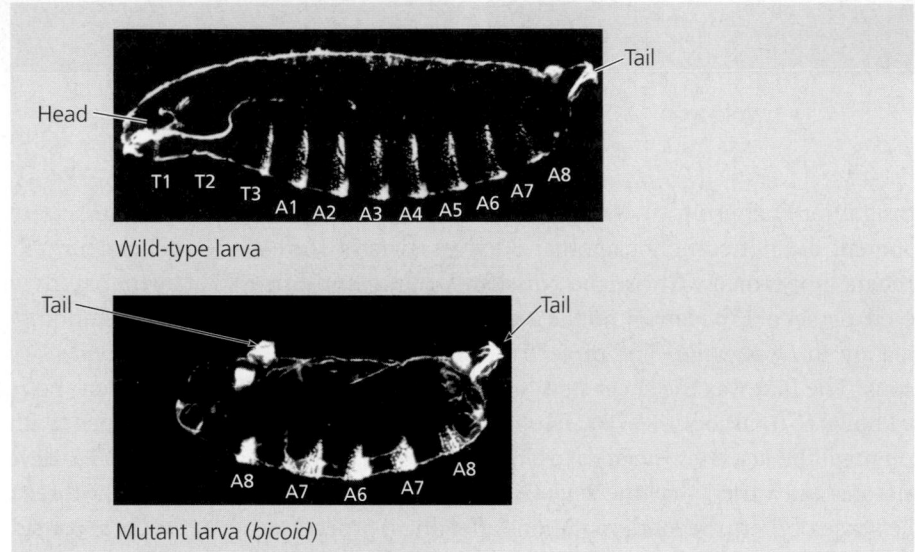

Wild-type larva

Mutant larva (*bicoid*)

RESULTS *Bicoid* mRNA (dark blue) was confined to the anterior end of the unfertilized egg. Later in development, Bicoid protein was seen to be concentrated in cells at the anterior end of the embryo.

Bicoid mRNA in mature unfertilized egg

Fertilization, translation of *bicoid* mRNA

Anterior end

Bicoid protein in early embryo

CONCLUSION The results support the hypothesis that Bicoid protein is a morphogen specifying formation of head-specific structures.

Developing egg

Bicoid mRNA in mature unfertilized egg

Bicoid protein in early embryo

SOURCE C. Nüsslein-Volhard et al., Determination of anteroposterior polarity in *Drosophila*, *Science* 238:1675–1681 (1987). W. Driever and C. Nüsslein-Volhard, A gradient of *bicoid* protein in *Drosophila* embryos, *Cell* 54:83–93 (1988). T. Berleth et al., The role of localization of *bicoid* RNA in organizing the anterior pattern of the *Drosophila* embryo, *EMBO Journal* 7:1749–1756 (1988).

WHAT IF? If the hypothesis is correct, predict what would happen if you injected *bicoid* mRNA into the anterior end of an egg from a female mutant for *bicoid*.

substances called **morphogens** establish an embryo's axes and other features of its form.

DNA technology and other modern biochemical methods enabled the researchers to test whether the *bicoid* product is in fact a morphogen that determines the anterior end of the fly. The first question they asked was whether the mRNA and protein products of these genes are located in the egg in a position consistent with the hypothesis. They found that *bicoid* mRNA is highly concentrated at the extreme anterior end of the mature egg, as predicted by the hypothesis (see Figure 18.19). The mRNA is produced in nurse cells, transferred to the egg via cytoplasmic bridges, and anchored to the cytoskeleton at the anterior end of the egg. After the egg is fertilized, the mRNA is translated into protein. The Bicoid protein then diffuses from the anterior end toward the posterior, resulting in a gradient of protein within the early embryo, with the highest concentration at the anterior end. These results are consistent with the hypothesis that Bicoid protein is responsible for specifying the fly's anterior end. To test the hypothesis more specifically, scientists injected pure *bicoid* mRNA into various regions of early embryos. The protein that resulted from its translation caused anterior structures to form at the injection sites.

The *bicoid* research was groundbreaking for several reasons. First, it led to the identification of a specific protein required for some of the earliest steps in pattern formation. It thus helped us understand how different regions of the egg can give rise to cells that go down different developmental pathways. Second, it increased our understanding of the mother's critical role in the initial phases of embryonic development. (As one developmental biologist has put it, "Mom tells Junior which way is up.") Finally, the principle that a gradient of morphogens can determine polarity and position has proved to be a key developmental concept for a number of species, just as early embryologists had thought.

In *Drosophila*, gradients of specific proteins determine the posterior end as well as the anterior and also are responsible for establishing the dorsal-ventral axis. Later, positional information operating on an ever finer scale establishes a specific number of correctly oriented segments and finally triggers the formation of each segment's characteristic structures. When the genes operating in this final step are abnormal, the pattern of the adult is abnormal, as you saw in Figure 18.18.

In this section, we have seen how a carefully orchestrated program of sequential gene regulation controls the transformation of a fertilized egg into a multicellular organism. The program is carefully balanced between turning on the genes for differentiation in the right place and turning off other genes. Even when an organism is fully developed, gene expression is regulated in a similarly fine-tuned manner. In the final section of the chapter, we'll consider how fine this tuning is, by looking at how specific changes in expression of one or a few genes can lead to the development of cancer.

CONCEPT CHECK 18.4

1. As you learned in Chapter 12, mitosis gives rise to two daughter cells that are genetically identical to the parent cell. Yet you, the product of many mitotic divisions, are not composed of identical cells. Why?
2. The signaling molecules released by an embryonic cell can induce changes in a neighboring cell without entering the cell. How?
3. Why are fruit fly maternal effect genes also called egg-polarity genes?
4. **WHAT IF?** In the blowup box in Figure 18.15b, the lower cell is synthesizing signaling molecules, whereas the upper cell is expressing signal receptors. In terms of gene regulation, explain how these cells came to have different functions.

For suggested answers, see Appendix A.

CONCEPT 18.5

Cancer results from genetic changes that affect cell cycle control

In Chapter 12, we considered cancer as a set of diseases in which cells escape from the control mechanisms that normally limit their growth. Now that we have discussed the molecular basis of gene expression and its regulation, we are ready to look at cancer more closely. The gene regulation systems that go wrong during cancer turn out to be the very same systems that play important roles in embryonic development, the immune response, and many other biological processes. Thus, research into the molecular basis of cancer has both benefited from and informed many other fields of biology.

Types of Genes Associated with Cancer

The genes that normally regulate cell growth and division during the cell cycle include genes for growth factors, their receptors, and the intracellular molecules of signaling pathways. (To review the cell cycle, see Chapter 12.) Mutations that alter any of these genes in somatic cells can lead to cancer. The agent of such change can be random spontaneous mutation. However, it is likely that many cancer-causing mutations result from environmental influences, such as chemical carcinogens, X-rays and other high-energy radiation, and certain viruses.

An early breakthrough in understanding cancer came in 1911, when Peyton Rous, an American pathologist, discovered a virus that causes cancer in chickens. Since then, scientists have recognized a number of *tumor viruses* that cause cancer in various animals, including humans (see Table 19.1). The Epstein-Barr virus, which causes infectious mononucleosis, has been linked to several types of cancer, notably Burkitt's lymphoma. Papillomaviruses are associated with cancer of the cervix, and a virus called HTLV-1 causes a type of adult leukemia. Worldwide, viruses seem to play a role in about 15% of the cases of human cancer.

Oncogenes and Proto-Oncogenes

Research on tumor viruses led to the discovery of cancer-causing genes called **oncogenes** (from the Greek *onco*, tumor) in certain retroviruses (see Chapter 19). Subsequently, close counterparts of these oncogenes were found in the genomes of humans and other animals. The normal versions of the cellular genes, called **proto-oncogenes**, code for proteins that stimulate normal cell growth and division.

How might a proto-oncogene—a gene that has an essential function in normal cells—become an oncogene, a cancer-causing gene? In general, an oncogene arises from a genetic change that leads to an increase either in the amount of the proto-oncogene's protein product or in the intrinsic activity of each protein molecule. The genetic changes that convert proto-oncogenes to oncogenes fall into three main categories: movement of DNA within the genome, amplification of a proto-oncogene, and point mutations in a control element or in the proto-oncogene itself **(Figure 18.20)**.

Cancer cells are frequently found to contain chromosomes that have broken and rejoined incorrectly, translocating fragments from one chromosome to another (see Figure 15.15). Now that you have learned how gene expression is regulated, you can understand the possible consequences of such translocations. If a translocated proto-oncogene ends up near an especially active promoter (or other control element), its transcription may increase, making it an oncogene. The second main type of genetic change, amplification, increases the number of copies of the proto-oncogene in the cell. The third

possibility is a point mutation either (1) in the promoter or an enhancer that controls a proto-oncogene, causing an increase in its expression, or (2) in the coding sequence, changing the gene's product to a protein that is more active or more resistant to degradation than the normal protein. All these mechanisms can lead to abnormal stimulation of the cell cycle and put the cell on the path to malignancy.

Tumor-Suppressor Genes

In addition to genes whose products normally promote cell division, cells contain genes whose normal products *inhibit* cell division. Such genes are called **tumor-suppressor genes** because the proteins they encode help prevent uncontrolled cell growth. Any mutation that decreases the normal activity of a tumor-suppressor protein may contribute to the onset of cancer, in effect stimulating growth through the absence of suppression.

The protein products of tumor-suppressor genes have various functions. Some tumor-suppressor proteins normally repair damaged DNA, a function that prevents the cell from accumulating cancer-causing mutations. Other tumor-suppressor proteins control the adhesion of cells to each other or to the extracellular matrix; proper cell anchorage is crucial in normal tissues—and often absent in cancers. Still other tumor-suppressor proteins are components of cell-signaling pathways that inhibit the cell cycle.

Interference with Normal Cell-Signaling Pathways

The proteins encoded by many proto-oncogenes and tumor-suppressor genes are components of cell-signaling pathways **(Figure 18.21)**. Let's take a closer look at how such proteins function in normal cells and what goes wrong with their function in cancer cells. We will focus on the products of two key

▲ **Figure 18.20 Genetic changes that can turn proto-oncogenes into oncogenes.**

(a) Cell cycle–stimulating pathway.
This pathway is triggered by ❶ a growth factor that binds to ❷ its receptor in the plasma membrane. The signal is relayed to ❸ a G protein called Ras. Like all G proteins, Ras is active when GTP is bound to it. Ras passes the signal to ❹ a series of protein kinases. The last kinase activates ❺ a transcription activator that turns on one or more genes for proteins that stimulate the cell cycle. If a mutation makes Ras or any other pathway component abnormally active, excessive cell division and cancer may result.

(b) Cell cycle–inhibiting pathway. In this pathway, ❶ DNA damage is an intracellular signal that is passed via ❷ protein kinases and leads to activation of ❸ p53. Activated p53 promotes transcription of the gene for a protein that inhibits the cell cycle. The resulting suppression of cell division ensures that the damaged DNA is not replicated. Mutations causing deficiencies in any pathway component can contribute to the development of cancer.

(c) Effects of mutations. Increased cell division, possibly leading to cancer, can result if the cell cycle is overstimulated, as in (a), or not inhibited when it normally would be, as in (b).

▲ **Figure 18.21 Signaling pathways that regulate cell division.** Both stimulatory and inhibitory pathways regulate the cell cycle, commonly by influencing transcription. Cancer can result from aberrations in such pathways, which may be caused by mutations, either spontaneous or environmentally triggered.

? *Looking at the pathway in (b), explain whether a cancer-causing mutation in a tumor-suppressor gene, such as p53, is more likely to be a recessive or a dominant mutation.*

genes, the *ras* proto-oncogene and the *p53* tumor-suppressor gene. Mutations in *ras* occur in about 30% of human cancers, mutations in *p53* in more than 50%.

The Ras protein, encoded by the **ras gene** (named for <u>ra</u>t <u>s</u>arcoma, a connective tissue cancer), is a G protein that relays a signal from a growth factor receptor on the plasma membrane to a cascade of protein kinases (see Chapter 11). The cellular response at the end of the pathway is the synthesis of a protein that stimulates the cell cycle (**Figure 18.21a**). Normally, such a pathway will not operate unless triggered by the appropriate growth factor. But certain mutations in the *ras* gene can lead to production of a hyperactive Ras protein that triggers the kinase cascade even in the absence of growth factor, resulting in increased cell division. In fact, hyperactive versions or excess amounts of any of the pathway's components can have the same outcome: excessive cell division.

Figure 18.21b shows a pathway in which a signal leads to the synthesis of a protein that suppresses the cell cycle. In this case, the signal is damage to the cell's DNA, perhaps as the result of exposure to ultraviolet light. Operation of this signaling pathway blocks the cell cycle until the damage has been repaired. Otherwise, the damage might contribute to tumor formation by causing mutations or chromosomal abnormalities. Thus, the genes for the components of the pathway act as tumor-suppressor genes. The **p53 gene**, named for the 53,000-dalton molecular weight of its protein product, is a tumor-suppressor gene. The protein it encodes is a specific transcription factor that promotes the synthesis of cell cycle–inhibiting proteins. That is why a mutation that knocks out the *p53* gene, like a mutation that leads to a hyperactive Ras protein, can lead to excessive cell growth and cancer (**Figure 18.21c**).

The *p53* gene has been called the "guardian angel of the genome." Once activated, for example by DNA damage, the p53 protein functions as an activator for several genes. Often it activates a gene called *p21*, whose product halts the cell cycle by binding to cyclin-dependent kinases, allowing time for the cell to repair the DNA; the p53 protein can also turn on genes directly involved in DNA repair. When DNA damage is irreparable, p53 activates "suicide" genes, whose protein products cause cell death by apoptosis (see Figure 11.20). Thus, in at least three ways, p53 prevents a cell from passing on mutations due to DNA damage. If mutations do accumulate and the cell survives through many divisions—as is more likely if the *p53* tumor-suppressor gene is defective or missing—cancer may ensue.

The Multistep Model of Cancer Development

More than one somatic mutation is generally needed to produce all the changes characteristic of a full-fledged cancer cell. This may help explain why the incidence of cancer increases greatly with age. If cancer results from an accumulation of mutations and if mutations occur throughout life, then the longer we live, the more likely we are to develop cancer.

The model of a multistep path to cancer is well supported by studies of one of the best-understood types of human cancer, colorectal cancer. About 135,000 new cases of colorectal cancer are diagnosed each year in the United States, and the disease causes 60,000 deaths each year. Like most cancers, colorectal cancer develops gradually (**Figure 18.22**). The first sign is often a polyp, a small, benign growth in the colon lining. The cells of the polyp look normal, although they divide unusually frequently. The tumor grows and may eventually become malignant, invading other tissues. The development of a malignant tumor is paralleled by a gradual accumulation of mutations that convert proto-oncogenes to oncogenes and knock out tumor-suppressor genes. A *ras* oncogene and a mutated *p53* tumor-suppressor gene are often involved.

About a half dozen changes must occur at the DNA level for a cell to become fully cancerous. These usually include the appearance of at least one active oncogene and the mutation or

▼ Figure 18.22 **A multistep model for the development of colorectal cancer.** Affecting the colon and/or rectum, this type of cancer is one of the best understood. Changes in a tumor parallel a series of genetic changes, including mutations affecting several tumor-suppressor genes (such as *p53*) and the *ras* proto-oncogene. Mutations of tumor-suppressor genes often entail loss (deletion) of the gene. *APC* stands for "adenomatous polyposis coli," and *DCC* stands for "deleted in colorectal cancer." Other mutation sequences can also lead to colorectal cancer.

Colon

Colon wall

1 Loss of tumor-suppressor gene *APC* (or other)

2 Activation of *ras* oncogene

3 Loss of tumor-suppressor gene *DCC*

4 Loss of tumor-suppressor gene *p53*

5 Additional mutations

Normal colon epithelial cells

Small benign growth (polyp)

Larger benign growth (adenoma)

Malignant tumor (carcinoma)

loss of several tumor-suppressor genes. Furthermore, since mutant tumor-suppressor alleles are usually recessive, in most cases mutations must knock out *both* alleles in a cell's genome to block tumor suppression. (Most oncogenes, on the other hand, behave as dominant alleles.) In many malignant tumors, the gene for telomerase is activated. This enzyme reverses the shortening of chromosome ends during DNA replication (see Figure 16.19). Production of telomerase in cancer cells removes a natural limit on the number of times the cells can divide.

Inherited Predisposition and Other Factors Contributing to Cancer

The fact that multiple genetic changes are required to produce a cancer cell helps explain the observation that cancers can run in families. An individual inheriting an oncogene or a mutant allele of a tumor-suppressor gene is one step closer to accumulating the necessary mutations for cancer to develop than is an individual without any such mutations.

Geneticists are devoting much effort to identifying inherited cancer alleles so that predisposition to certain cancers can be detected early in life. About 15% of colorectal cancers, for example, involve inherited mutations. Many of these affect the tumor-suppressor gene called *adenomatous polyposis coli*, or *APC* (see Figure 18.22). This gene has multiple functions in the cell, including regulation of cell migration and adhesion. Even in patients with no family history of the disease, the *APC* gene is mutated in 60% of colorectal cancers. In these individuals, new mutations must occur in both *APC* alleles before the gene's function is lost. Since only 15% of colorectal cancers are associated with known inherited mutations, researchers continue in their efforts to identify "markers" that could predict the risk of developing this type of cancer.

There is evidence of a strong inherited predisposition in 5–10% of patients with breast cancer. This is the second most common type of cancer in the United States, striking over 180,000 women (and some men) annually and killing 40,000 each year. Mutations in the *BRCA1* or *BRCA2* gene are found in at least half of inherited breast cancers **(Figure 18.23)**. (*BRCA* stands for *br*east *ca*ncer.) A woman who inherits one mutant *BRCA1* allele has a 60% probability of developing breast cancer before the age of 50, compared with only a 2% probability for an individual homozygous for the normal allele. Both *BRCA1* and *BRCA2* are considered tumor-suppressor genes because their wild-type alleles protect against breast cancer and their mutant alleles are recessive. Apparently, the BRCA1 and BRCA2 proteins both function in the cell's DNA damage repair pathway. More is known about BRCA2, which, in association with another protein, helps to repair breaks that occur in both strands of DNA, crucial for maintaining undamaged DNA in a cell's nucleus.

Because DNA breakage can contribute to cancer, it makes sense that the risk of cancer can be lowered by minimizing exposure to DNA-damaging agents, such as the ultraviolet radia-

▲ **Figure 18.23 Tracking the molecular basis of breast cancer.** In 1990, after 16 years of research, geneticist Mary-Claire King convincingly demonstrated that mutations in one gene— *BRCA1*—are associated with increased susceptibility to breast cancer, a finding that flew in the face of medical opinion at the time. Her lab is currently working to identify the environmental conditions that may affect the timing of cancer development in people who carry mutations in *BRCA1* and another breast cancer gene, *BRCA2*.

tion in sunlight and chemicals found in cigarette smoke. Novel methods for early diagnosis and treatment of specific cancers are being developed that rely on new techniques for analyzing, and perhaps interfering with, gene expression in tumors. Ultimately, such approaches may lower the death rate from cancer.

The study of genes associated with cancer, inherited or not, increases our basic understanding of how disruption of normal gene regulation results in this disease. We've come a long way in our understanding since Peyton Rous's discovery. We now know that viruses can contribute to cancer development in several ways if they integrate their genetic material into the DNA of infected cells. Viral integration may donate an oncogene to the cell, disrupt a tumor-suppressor gene, or convert a protooncogene to an oncogene. In addition, some viruses produce proteins that inactivate p53 and other tumor-suppressor proteins, thus making the cell more prone to becoming cancerous. Although viruses are little more than a nucleic acid surrounded by a protective coat, they are powerful biological agents. You'll learn more about how viruses function in the next chapter.

CONCEPT CHECK 18.5

1. Compare the usual functions of proteins encoded by proto-oncogenes with those encoded by tumor-suppressor genes.
2. Under what circumstances is cancer considered to have a hereditary component?
3. **WHAT IF?** Explain how the types of mutations that lead to cancer are different for a proto-oncogene and a tumor-suppressor gene, in terms of the effect of the mutation on the activity of the gene product.

For suggested answers, see Appendix A.

SUMMARY OF KEY CONCEPTS

CONCEPT 18.1

Bacteria often respond to environmental change by regulating transcription (pp. 351–356)

▶ **Operons: The Basic Concept** Cells control metabolism by regulating enzyme activity or the expression of genes coding for enzymes. In bacteria, genes are often clustered into operons, with one promoter serving several adjacent genes. An operator site on the DNA switches the operon on or off, resulting in coordinate regulation of the genes.

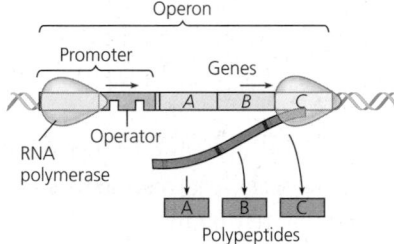

▶ **Repressible and Inducible Operons: Two Types of Negative Gene Regulation** In either type of operon, binding of a specific repressor protein to the operator shuts off transcription. (The repressor is encoded by a separate regulatory gene.) In a repressible operon, the repressor is active when bound to a corepressor, usually the end product of an anabolic pathway.

In an inducible operon, binding of an inducer to an innately active repressor inactivates the repressor and turns on transcription. Inducible enzymes usually function in catabolic pathways.

▶ **Positive Gene Regulation** Some operons are also subject to positive control via a stimulatory activator protein, such as catabolite activator protein (CAP), which promotes transcription when bound to a site within the promoter.

MEDIA

MP3 Tutor Control of Gene Expression
Activity The *lac* Operon in *E. coli*

CONCEPT 18.2

Eukaryotic gene expression can be regulated at any stage (pp. 356–364)

Chromatin modification
- Genes in highly compacted chromatin are generally not transcribed.
- Histone acetylation seems to loosen chromatin structure, enhancing transcription.
- DNA methylation generally reduces transcription.

Transcription
- Regulation of transcription initiation: DNA control elements bind specific transcription factors.

Bending of the DNA enables activators to contact proteins at the promoter, initiating transcription.
- Coordinate regulation:
  Enhancer for liver-specific genes   Enhancer for lens-specific genes

RNA processing
- Alternative RNA splicing:

  Primary RNA transcript

  mRNA   or

mRNA degradation
- Each mRNA has a characteristic life span, determined in part by sequences in the 5' and 3' UTRs.

Translation
- Initiation of translation can be controlled via regulation of initiation factors.

Protein processing and degradation
- Protein processing and degradation by proteasomes are subject to regulation.

CONCEPT 18.3

Noncoding RNAs play multiple roles in controlling gene expression (pp. 364–366)

Chromatin modification
- Small RNAs can promote the formation of heterochromatin in certain regions, blocking transcription.

Translation
- miRNA or siRNA can block the translation of specific mRNAs.

mRNA degradation
- miRNA or siRNA can target specific mRNAs for destruction.

MEDIA

Activity Overview: Control of Gene Expression
Activity Control of Transcription
Activity Post-Transcriptional Control Mechanisms
Activity Review: Control of Gene Expression
Investigation How Do You Design a Gene Expression System?

CONCEPT ▇ 18.4

A program of differential gene expression leads to the different cell types in a multicellular organism (pp. 366–373)

▶ **A Genetic Program for Embryonic Development** Embryonic cells undergo differentiation, becoming specialized in structure and function. Morphogenesis encompasses the processes that give shape to the organism and its various parts. Cells differ in structure and function not because they contain different genes but because they express different portions of a common genome.

▶ **Cytoplasmic Determinants and Inductive Signals** Cytoplasmic determinants in the unfertilized egg regulate the expression of genes in the zygote that affect the developmental fate of embryonic cells. In the process called induction, signaling molecules from embryonic cells cause transcriptional changes in nearby target cells.

▶ **Sequential Regulation of Gene Expression During Cellular Differentiation** Differentiation is heralded by the appearance of tissue-specific proteins, which enable differentiated cells to carry out their specialized roles.

▶ **Pattern Formation: Setting Up the Body Plan** In animals, pattern formation, the development of a spatial organization of tissues and organs, begins in the early embryo. Positional information, the molecular cues that control pattern formation, tell a cell its location relative to the body's axes and to other cells. In *Drosophila*, gradients of morphogens encoded by maternal effect genes determine the body axes. For example, the gradient of Bicoid protein determines the anterior-posterior axis.

MEDIA

Activity Signal Transduction Pathways
Activity Role of *bicoid* Gene in *Drosophila* Development
Investigation How Do *bicoid* Mutations Alter Development?

CONCEPT ▇ 18.5

Cancer results from genetic changes that affect cell cycle control (pp. 373–377)

▶ **Types of Genes Associated with Cancer** The products of proto-oncogenes and tumor-suppressor genes control cell division. A DNA change that makes a proto-oncogene excessively active converts it to an oncogene, which may promote excessive cell division and cancer. A tumor-suppressor gene encodes a protein that inhibits abnormal cell division. A mutation in such a gene that reduces the activity of its protein product may also lead to excessive cell division and possibly to cancer.

▶ **Interference with Normal Cell-Signaling Pathways** Many proto-oncogenes and tumor-suppressor genes encode components of growth-stimulating and growth-inhibiting signaling pathways, respectively. A hyperactive version of a protein in a stimulatory pathway, such as Ras (a G protein), functions as an oncogene protein. A defective version of a protein in an inhibitory pathway, such as p53 (a transcription activator), fails to function as a tumor suppressor.

▶ **The Multistep Model of Cancer Development** Normal cells are converted to cancer cells by the accumulation of mutations affecting proto-oncogenes and tumor-suppressor genes.

▶ **Inherited Predisposition and Other Factors Contributing to Cancer** Individuals who inherit a mutant oncogene or tumor-suppressor allele have an increased risk of developing cancer. Certain viruses promote cancer by integration of viral DNA into a cell's genome.

TESTING YOUR KNOWLEDGE

SELF-QUIZ

1. If a particular operon encodes enzymes for making an essential amino acid and is regulated like the *trp* operon, then
   a. the amino acid inactivates the repressor.
   b. the enzymes produced are called inducible enzymes.
   c. the repressor is active in the absence of the amino acid.
   d. the amino acid acts as a corepressor.
   e. the amino acid turns on transcription of the operon.

2. Muscle cells differ from nerve cells mainly because they
   a. express different genes.
   b. contain different genes.
   c. use different genetic codes.
   d. have unique ribosomes.
   e. have different chromosomes.

3. What would occur if the repressor of an inducible operon were mutated so it could not bind the operator?
   a. irreversible binding of the repressor to the promoter
   b. reduced transcription of the operon's genes
   c. buildup of a substrate for the pathway controlled by the operon
   d. continuous transcription of the operon's genes
   e. overproduction of catabolite activator protein (CAP)

4. The functioning of enhancers is an example of
   a. transcriptional control of gene expression.
   b. a post-transcriptional mechanism for editing mRNA.
   c. the stimulation of translation by initiation factors.
   d. post-translational control that activates certain proteins.
   e. a eukaryotic equivalent of prokaryotic promoter functioning.

5. Absence of *bicoid* mRNA from a *Drosophila* egg leads to the absence of anterior larval body parts and mirror-image duplication of posterior parts. This is evidence that the product of the *bicoid* gene
   a. is transcribed in the early embryo.
   b. normally leads to formation of tail structures.
   c. normally leads to formation of head structures.
   d. is a protein present in all head structures.
   e. leads to programmed cell death.

6. Which of the following statements about the DNA in one of your brain cells is true?
   a. Most of the DNA codes for protein.
   b. The majority of genes are likely to be transcribed.
   c. Each gene lies immediately adjacent to an enhancer.
   d. Many genes are grouped into operon-like clusters.
   e. It is the same as the DNA in one of your heart cells.

7. Cell differentiation always involves
   a. the production of tissue-specific proteins, such as muscle actin.
   b. the movement of cells.
   c. the transcription of the *myoD* gene.
   d. the selective loss of certain genes from the genome.
   e. the cell's sensitivity to environmental cues, such as light or heat.

8. Which of the following is an example of post-transcriptional control of gene expression?
   a. the addition of methyl groups to cytosine bases of DNA
   b. the binding of transcription factors to a promoter
   c. the removal of introns and splicing together of exons
   d. gene amplification contributing to cancer
   e. the folding of DNA to form heterochromatin

9. Within a cell, the amount of protein made using a given mRNA molecule depends partly on
   a. the degree of DNA methylation.
   b. the rate at which the mRNA is degraded.
   c. the presence of certain transcription factors.
   d. the number of introns present in the mRNA.
   e. the types of ribosomes present in the cytoplasm.

10. Proto-oncogenes can change into oncogenes that cause cancer. Which of the following best explains the presence of these potential time bombs in eukaryotic cells?
    a. Proto-oncogenes first arose from viral infections.
    b. Proto-oncogenes normally help regulate cell division.
    c. Proto-oncogenes are genetic "junk."
    d. Proto-oncogenes are mutant versions of normal genes.
    e. Cells produce proto-oncogenes as they age.

11. **DRAW IT** The diagram below shows five genes (with their enhancers) from the genome of a certain species. Imagine that orange, blue, green, black, red, and purple activator proteins exist that can bind to the appropriately color-coded control elements in the enhancers of these genes.

a. Draw an X above enhancer elements (of all the genes) that would have activators bound in a cell in which only gene 5 is transcribed. Which colored activators would be present?
b. Draw a dot above all enhancer elements that would have activators bound in a cell in which the green, blue, and orange activators are present. Which gene(s) would be transcribed?
c. Imagine that genes 1, 2, and 4 code for nerve-specific proteins, and genes 3 and 5 are skin specific. Which activators would have to be present in each cell type to ensure transcription of the appropriate genes?

For Self-Quiz answers, see Appendix A.

MEDIA Visit **www.campbellbiology.com** for a Practice Test.

EVOLUTION CONNECTION

12. DNA sequences can act as "tape measures of evolution" (see Chapter 5). Scientists analyzing the human genome sequence were surprised to find that some of the regions of the human genome that are most highly conserved (similar to comparable regions in other species) don't code for proteins. Propose a possible explanation for this observation.

SCIENTIFIC INQUIRY

13. Prostate cells usually require testosterone and other androgens to survive. But some prostate cancer cells thrive despite treatments that eliminate androgens. One hypothesis is that estrogen, often considered a female hormone, may be activating genes normally controlled by an androgen in these cancer cells. Describe one or more experiments to test this hypothesis. (See Figure 11.8 to review the action of these steroid hormones.)

    Biological Inquiry: A Workbook of Investigative Cases Explore gene regulation by the hedgehog pathway with the case "Shh: Silencing the Hedgehog Pathway."

SCIENCE, TECHNOLOGY, AND SOCIETY

14. Trace amounts of dioxin were present in Agent Orange, a defoliant sprayed on vegetation during the Vietnam War. Animal tests suggest that dioxin can cause birth defects, cancer, liver and thymus damage, and immune system suppression, sometimes leading to death. But the animal tests are equivocal; a hamster is not affected by a dose that can kill a guinea pig. Dioxin acts somewhat like a steroid hormone, entering a cell and binding to a receptor protein that then attaches to the cell's DNA. How might this mechanism help explain the variety of dioxin's effects on different body systems and in different animals? How might you determine whether a type of illness is related to dioxin exposure? How might you determine whether a particular individual became ill as a result of exposure to dioxin? Which would be more difficult to demonstrate? Why?

Viruses

▲ Figure 19.1 **Are the tiny viruses infecting this *E. coli* cell alive?**

OVERVIEW

A Borrowed Life

The photo in **Figure 19.1** shows a remarkable event: the attack of a bacterial cell by numerous structures that resemble miniature lollipops. These structures, a type of virus called T4 bacteriophage, are seen infecting the bacterium *Escherichia coli* in this colorized SEM. By injecting its DNA into the cell, the virus sets in motion a genetic takeover of the bacterium, recruiting cellular machinery to mass-produce many new viruses.

Recall that bacteria and other prokaryotes are cells much smaller and more simply organized than those of eukaryotes, such as plants and animals. Viruses are smaller and simpler still. Lacking the structures and metabolic machinery found in cells, most viruses are little more than genes packaged in protein coats.

Are viruses living or nonliving? Early on, they were considered biological chemicals; in fact, the Latin root for the word *virus* means "poison." Because viruses are capable of causing a wide variety of diseases and can be spread between organisms, researchers in the late 1800s saw a parallel with bacteria and proposed that viruses were the simplest of living forms. However, viruses cannot reproduce or carry out metabolic activities outside of a host cell. Most biologists studying viruses today would probably agree that they are not alive but exist in a shady area between life-forms and chemicals. The simple phrase used recently by two researchers describes them aptly enough: Viruses lead "a kind of borrowed life."

To a large extent, molecular biology was born in the laboratories of biologists studying viruses that infect bacteria. Experiments with viruses provided important evidence that genes are made of nucleic acids, and they were critical in working out the molecular mechanisms of the fundamental processes of DNA replication, transcription, and translation.

Beyond their value as experimental systems, viruses have unique genetic mechanisms that are interesting in their own right and that also help us understand how viruses cause disease. In addition, the study of viruses has led to the development of techniques that enable scientists to manipulate genes and transfer them from one organism to another. These techniques play an important role in basic research, biotechnology, and medical applications. For instance, viruses are used as agents of gene transfer in gene therapy (see Chapter 20).

In this chapter, we will explore the biology of viruses. We will begin with the structure of these simplest of all genetic systems and then describe their reproductive cycles. Next, we will discuss the role of viruses as disease-causing agents, or pathogens, and conclude by considering some even simpler infectious agents, viroids and prions.

CONCEPT 19.1
A virus consists of a nucleic acid surrounded by a protein coat

Scientists were able to detect viruses indirectly long before they were actually able to see them. The story of how viruses were discovered begins near the end of the 19th century.

The Discovery of Viruses: *Scientific Inquiry*

Tobacco mosaic disease stunts the growth of tobacco plants and gives their leaves a mottled, or mosaic, coloration. In 1883, Adolf Mayer, a German scientist, discovered that he could transmit the disease from plant to plant by rubbing sap extracted from diseased leaves onto healthy plants. After an unsuccessful search for an infectious microbe in the sap, Mayer suggested that the disease was caused by unusually small bacteria that were invisible under a microscope. This hypothesis was tested a decade later by Dimitri Ivanowsky, a Russian biologist who passed sap from infected tobacco leaves through a filter designed to remove bacteria. After filtration, the sap still produced mosaic disease.

But Ivanowsky clung to the hypothesis that bacteria caused tobacco mosaic disease. Perhaps, he reasoned, the bacteria were small enough to pass through the filter or made a toxin that could do so. The second possibility was ruled out when the Dutch botanist Martinus Beijerinck carried out a classic series of experiments that showed that the infectious agent in the filtered sap could reproduce (**Figure 19.2**).

In fact, the pathogen reproduced only within the host it infected. In further experiments, Beijerinck showed that unlike bacteria used in the lab at that time, the mysterious agent of mosaic disease could not be cultivated on nutrient media in test tubes or petri dishes. Beijerinck imagined a reproducing particle much smaller and simpler than a bacterium, and he is generally credited with being the first scientist to voice the concept of a virus. His suspicions were confirmed in 1935 when the American scientist Wendell Stanley crystallized the infectious particle, now known as tobacco mosaic virus (TMV). Subsequently, TMV and many other viruses were actually seen with the help of the electron microscope.

Structure of Viruses

The tiniest viruses are only 20 nm in diameter—smaller than a ribosome. Millions could easily fit on a pinhead. Even the largest known virus, which has a diameter of several hundred nanometers, is barely visible in the light microscope. Stanley's discovery that some viruses could be crystallized was exciting and puzzling news. Not even the simplest of cells can aggregate into regular crystals. But if viruses are not cells, then what are they? Examining the structure of viruses more closely reveals that they are infectious particles consisting of nucleic acid enclosed in a protein coat and, in some cases, a membranous envelope.

Viral Genomes

We usually think of genes as being made of double-stranded DNA—the conventional double helix—but many viruses defy this convention. Their genomes may consist of double-stranded DNA, single-stranded DNA, double-stranded RNA, or single-stranded RNA, depending on the kind of virus. A virus is called a DNA virus or an RNA virus, according to the kind of nucleic acid that makes up its genome. In either case, the genome is usually organized as a single linear or circular molecule of nucleic acid, although the genomes of some

▼ Figure 19.2 **Inquiry**

What causes tobacco mosaic disease?

EXPERIMENT In the late 1800s, Martinus Beijerinck, of the Technical School in Delft, the Netherlands, investigated the properties of the agent that causes tobacco mosaic disease (then called spot disease).

RESULTS When the filtered sap was rubbed on healthy plants, they became infected. Their sap, when extracted and filtered, could then act as the source of infection for another group of plants. Each successive group of plants developed the disease to the same extent as earlier groups.

❶ Extracted sap from tobacco plant with tobacco mosaic disease

❷ Passed sap through a porcelain filter known to trap bacteria

❸ Rubbed filtered sap on healthy tobacco plants

❹ Healthy plants became infected

CONCLUSION The infectious agent was apparently not a bacterium because it could pass through a bacterium-trapping filter. The pathogen must have been reproducing in the plants because its ability to cause disease was undiluted after several transfers from plant to plant.

SOURCE M. J. Beijerinck, Concerning a *contagium vivum fluidum* as cause of the spot disease of tobacco leaves, *Verhandelingen der Koninkyke akademie Wettenschappen te Amsterdam* 65:3–21 (1898). Translation published in English as Phytopathological Classics Number 7 (1942), American Phytopathological Society Press, St. Paul, MN.

WHAT IF? If Beijerinck had observed that the infection of each group was weaker than that of the previous group and that ultimately the sap could no longer cause disease, what might he have concluded?

viruses consist of multiple molecules of nucleic acid. The smallest viruses known have only four genes in their genome, while the largest have several hundred to a thousand. For comparison, bacterial genomes contain about 200 to a few thousand genes.

Capsids and Envelopes

The protein shell enclosing the viral genome is called a **capsid**. Depending on the type of virus, the capsid may be rod-shaped, polyhedral, or more complex in shape (like T4). Capsids are built from a large number of protein subunits called *capsomeres*, but the number of different *kinds* of proteins in a capsid is usually small. Tobacco mosaic virus has a rigid, rod-shaped capsid made from over a thousand molecules of a single type of protein arranged in a helix; rod-shaped viruses are commonly called *helical viruses* for this reason (**Figure 19.3a**). Adenoviruses, which infect the respiratory tracts of animals, have 252 identical protein molecules arranged in a polyhedral capsid with 20 triangular facets—an icosahedron; thus, these and other similarly shaped viruses are referred to as *icosahedral viruses* (**Figure 19.3b**).

Some viruses have accessory structures that help them infect their hosts. For instance, a membranous envelope surrounds the capsids of influenza viruses and many other viruses found in animals (**Figure 19.3c**). These **viral envelopes**, which are derived from the membranes of the host cell, contain host cell phospholipids and membrane proteins. They also contain proteins and glycoproteins of viral origin. (Glycoproteins are proteins with carbohydrates covalently attached.) Some viruses carry a few viral enzyme molecules within their capsids.

Many of the most complex capsids are found among the viruses that infect bacteria, called **bacteriophages**, or simply **phages**. The first phages studied included seven that infect *E. coli*. These seven phages were named type 1 (T1), type 2 (T2), and so forth, in the order of their discovery. The three T-even phages (T2, T4, and T6) turned out to be very similar in structure. Their capsids have elongated icosahedral heads enclosing their DNA. Attached to the head is a protein tail piece with fibers by which the phages attach to a bacterium (**Figure 19.3d**). In the next section, we'll examine how these few viral parts function together with cellular components to produce large numbers of viral progeny.

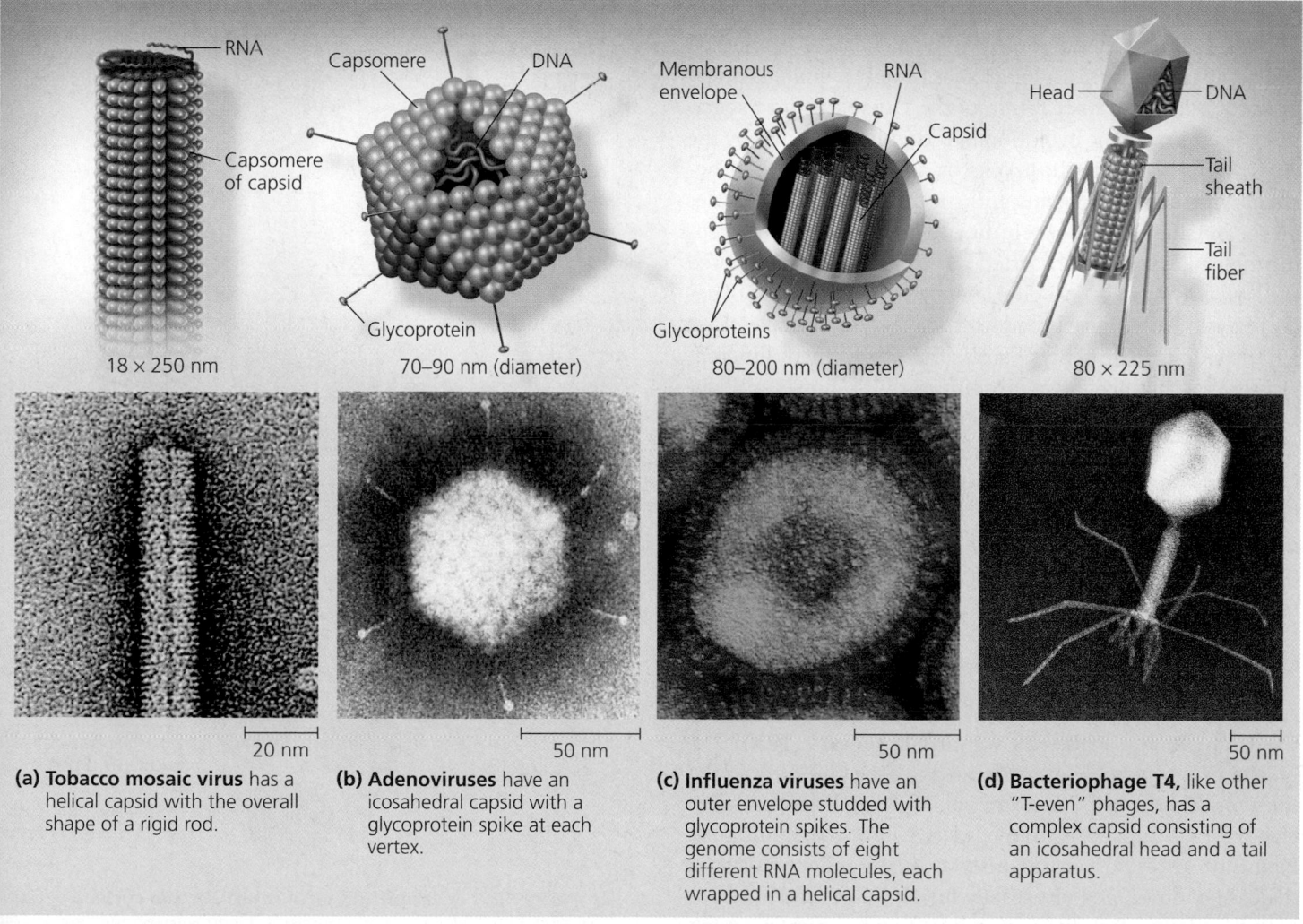

(a) Tobacco mosaic virus has a helical capsid with the overall shape of a rigid rod.

(b) Adenoviruses have an icosahedral capsid with a glycoprotein spike at each vertex.

(c) Influenza viruses have an outer envelope studded with glycoprotein spikes. The genome consists of eight different RNA molecules, each wrapped in a helical capsid.

(d) Bacteriophage T4, like other "T-even" phages, has a complex capsid consisting of an icosahedral head and a tail apparatus.

▲ **Figure 19.3 Viral structure.** Viruses are made up of nucleic acid (DNA or RNA) enclosed in a protein coat (the capsid) and sometimes further wrapped in a membranous envelope. The individual protein subunits making up the capsid are called capsomeres. Although diverse in size and shape, viruses have common structural features, most of which appear in the four examples shown here. (All the micrographs are colorized TEMs.)

CONCEPT CHECK 19.1

1. Compare the structures of tobacco mosaic virus (TMV) and influenza virus (see Figure 19.3).

2. **WHAT IF?** In 2005, scientists discovered a virus that could, under certain conditions, develop pointed projections at each end while outside a host cell. How does this observation fit with the characterization of viruses as nonliving?

For suggested answers, see Appendix A.

CONCEPT 19.2
Viruses reproduce only in host cells

Viruses lack metabolic enzymes and equipment for making proteins, such as ribosomes. They are obligate intracellular parasites; in other words, they can reproduce only within a host cell. It is fair to say that viruses in isolation are merely packaged sets of genes in transit from one host cell to another.

Each type of virus can infect cells of only a limited variety of hosts, called the **host range** of the virus. This host specificity results from the evolution of recognition systems by the virus. Viruses identify host cells by a "lock-and-key" fit between viral surface proteins and specific receptor molecules on the outside of cells. (According to one model, such receptor molecules originally carried out functions that benefited the host cell but were co-opted later by viruses as portals of entry.) Some viruses have broad host ranges. For example, West Nile virus and equine encephalitis virus are distinctly different viruses that can each infect mosquitoes, birds, horses, and humans. Other viruses have host ranges so narrow that they infect only a single species. Measles virus, for instance, can infect only humans. Furthermore, viral infection of multicellular eukaryotes is usually limited to particular tissues. Human cold viruses infect only the cells lining the upper respiratory tract, and the AIDS virus binds to receptors present only on certain types of white blood cells.

General Features of Viral Reproductive Cycles

A viral infection begins when a virus binds to a host cell and the viral genome makes its way inside **(Figure 19.4)**. The mechanism of genome entry depends on the type of virus and the type of host cell. For example, T-even phages use their elaborate tail apparatus to inject DNA into a bacterium (see Figure 19.3d). Other viruses are taken up by endocytosis or, in the case of enveloped viruses, by fusion of the viral envelope with the plasma membrane. Once the viral genome is inside, the proteins it encodes can commandeer the host, reprogramming the cell to copy the viral nucleic acid and manufacture viral proteins. The host provides the nucleotides for

making viral nucleic acids, as well as enzymes, ribosomes, tRNAs, amino acids, ATP, and other components needed for making the viral proteins. Most DNA viruses use the DNA polymerases of the host cell to synthesize new genomes along the templates provided by the viral DNA. In contrast, to replicate their genomes, RNA viruses use virally encoded polymerases that can use RNA as a template. (Uninfected cells generally make no enzymes for carrying out this process.)

After the viral nucleic acid molecules and capsomeres are produced, they spontaneously self-assemble into new viruses. In fact, researchers can separate the RNA and capsomeres of TMV and then reassemble complete viruses simply by mixing the components together under the right conditions. The simplest type of viral reproductive cycle ends with the exit of

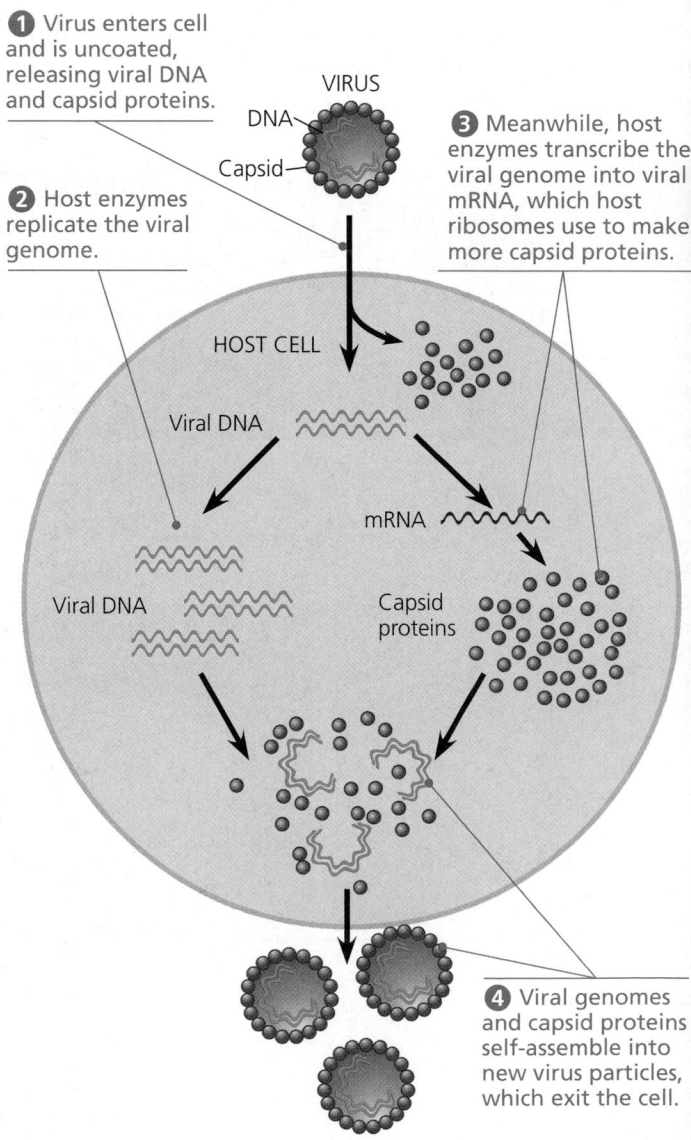

1 Virus enters cell and is uncoated, releasing viral DNA and capsid proteins.

2 Host enzymes replicate the viral genome.

3 Meanwhile, host enzymes transcribe the viral genome into viral mRNA, which host ribosomes use to make more capsid proteins.

4 Viral genomes and capsid proteins self-assemble into new virus particles, which exit the cell.

VIRUS

DNA

Capsid

HOST CELL

Viral DNA

Viral DNA

mRNA

Capsid proteins

▲ **Figure 19.4 A simplified viral reproductive cycle.** A virus is an obligate intracellular parasite that uses the equipment and small molecules of its host cell to reproduce. In this simplest of viral cycles, the parasite is a DNA virus with a capsid consisting of a single type of protein.

? *Label each of the straight black arrows with one word representing the name of the process that is occurring.*

hundreds or thousands of viruses from the infected host cell, a process that often damages or destroys the cell. Such cellular damage and death, as well as the body's responses to this destruction, cause many of the symptoms associated with viral infections. The viral progeny that exit a cell have the potential to infect additional cells, spreading the viral infection.

There are many variations on the simplified viral reproductive cycle we have traced in this general description. We will now take a closer look at some of these variations in bacterial viruses (phages) and animal viruses; later in the chapter, we will consider plant viruses.

Reproductive Cycles of Phages

Phages are the best understood of all viruses, although some of them are also among the most complex. Research on phages led to the discovery that some double-stranded DNA viruses can reproduce by two alternative mechanisms: the lytic cycle and the lysogenic cycle.

The Lytic Cycle

A phage reproductive cycle that culminates in death of the host cell is known as a **lytic cycle**. The term refers to the last stage of infection, during which the bacterium lyses (breaks open) and releases the phages that were produced within the cell. Each of these phages can then infect a healthy cell, and a few successive lytic cycles can destroy an entire bacterial population in just a few hours. A phage that reproduces only by a lytic cycle is a **virulent phage**. Figure 19.5 illustrates the major steps in the lytic cycle of T4, a typical virulent phage. The figure and legend describe the process, which you should study before proceeding.

After reading about the lytic cycle, you may wonder why phages haven't exterminated all bacteria. In fact, phage treatments have been used medically in some countries to help control bacterial infections in patients. Solutions containing bacteriophages have also been sprayed on chicken carcasses, significantly reducing bacterial contamination of poultry on the way to the marketplace. Bacteria are not defenseless, however. First, natural selection favors bacterial mutants with receptors that are no longer recognized by a particular type of phage. Second, when phage DNA successfully enters a bacterium, the DNA often is identified as foreign and cut up by cellular enzymes called **restriction enzymes**, which are so named because their activity *restricts* the ability of the phage to infect the bacterium. The bacterial cell's own DNA is methylated in a

▶ **Figure 19.5 The lytic cycle of phage T4, a virulent phage.** Phage T4 has almost 300 genes, which are transcribed and translated using the host cell's machinery. One of the first phage genes translated after the viral DNA enters the host cell codes for an enzyme that degrades the host cell's DNA (step 2); the phage DNA is protected from breakdown because it contains a modified form of cytosine that is not recognized by the enzyme. The entire lytic cycle, from the phage's first contact with the cell surface to cell lysis, takes only 20–30 minutes at 37°C.

Phage assembly

Head Tail Tail fibers

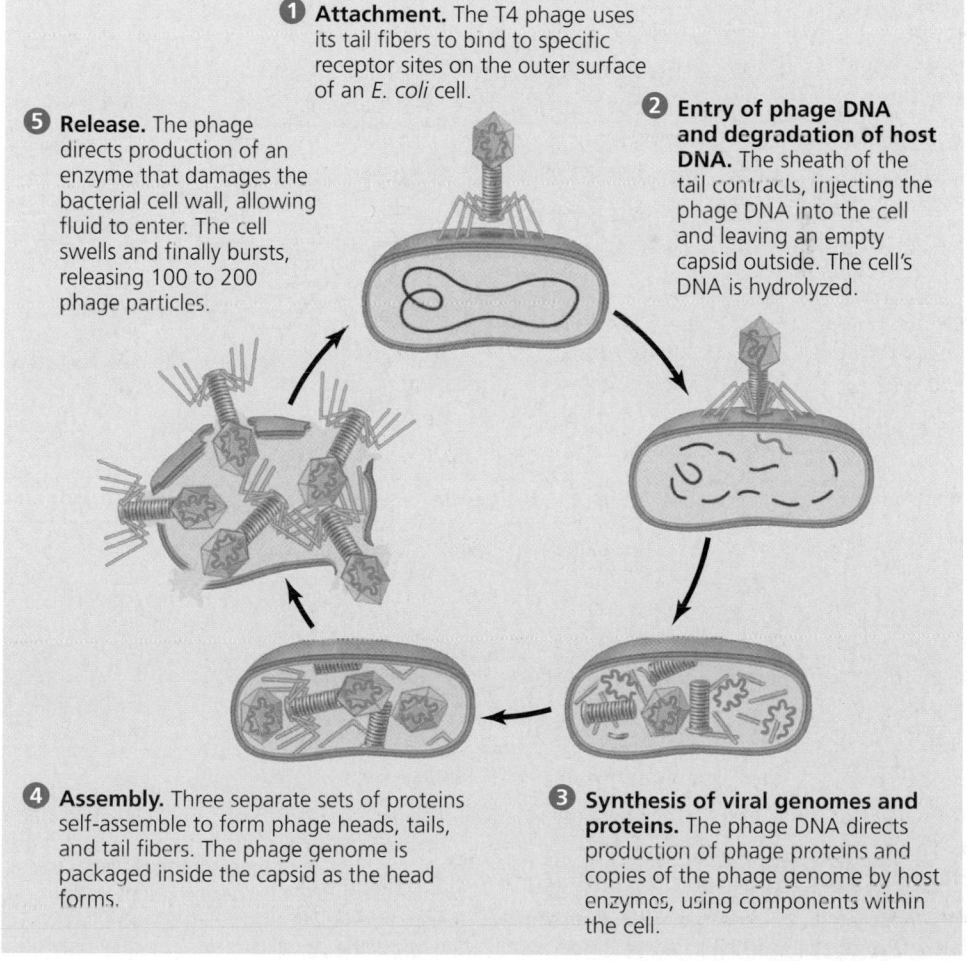

❶ **Attachment.** The T4 phage uses its tail fibers to bind to specific receptor sites on the outer surface of an *E. coli* cell.

❷ **Entry of phage DNA and degradation of host DNA.** The sheath of the tail contracts, injecting the phage DNA into the cell and leaving an empty capsid outside. The cell's DNA is hydrolyzed.

❸ **Synthesis of viral genomes and proteins.** The phage DNA directs production of phage proteins and copies of the phage genome by host enzymes, using components within the cell.

❹ **Assembly.** Three separate sets of proteins self-assemble to form phage heads, tails, and tail fibers. The phage genome is packaged inside the capsid as the head forms.

❺ **Release.** The phage directs production of an enzyme that damages the bacterial cell wall, allowing fluid to enter. The cell swells and finally bursts, releasing 100 to 200 phage particles.

way that prevents attack by its own restriction enzymes. But just as natural selection favors bacteria with mutant receptors or effective restriction enzymes, it also favors phage mutants that can bind the altered receptors or are resistant to particular restriction enzymes. Thus, the parasite-host relationship is in constant evolutionary flux.

There is yet a third important reason bacteria have been spared from extinction as a result of phage activity. Instead of lysing their host cells, many phages coexist with them in a state called lysogeny, which we'll now discuss.

The Lysogenic Cycle

In contrast to the lytic cycle, which kills the host cell, the **lysogenic cycle** allows replication of the phage genome without destroying the host. Phages capable of using both modes of reproducing within a bacterium are called **temperate phages**. A temperate phage called lambda, written with the Greek letter λ, is widely used in biological research. Phage λ resembles T4, but its tail has only one, short tail fiber.

Infection of an *E. coli* cell by phage λ begins when the phage binds to the surface of the cell and injects its linear DNA genome **(Figure 19.6)**. Within the host, the λ DNA molecule forms a circle. What happens next depends on the reproductive mode: lytic cycle or lysogenic cycle. During a lytic cycle, the viral genes im-

mediately turn the host cell into a λ-producing factory, and the cell soon lyses and releases its viral products. During a lysogenic cycle, however, the λ DNA molecule is incorporated into a specific site on the *E. coli* chromosome by viral proteins that break both circular DNA molecules and join them to each other. When integrated into the bacterial chromosome in this way, the viral DNA is known as a **prophage**. One prophage gene codes for a protein that prevents transcription of most of the other prophage genes. Thus, the phage genome is mostly silent within the bacterium. Every time the *E. coli* cell prepares to divide, it replicates the phage DNA along with its own and passes the copies on to daughter cells. A single infected cell can quickly give rise to a large population of bacteria carrying the virus in prophage form. This mechanism enables viruses to propagate without killing the host cells on which they depend.

The term *lysogenic* implies that prophages are capable of generating active phages that lyse their host cells. This occurs when the λ genome is induced to exit the bacterial chromosome and initiate a lytic cycle. An environmental signal, such as a certain chemical or high-energy radiation, usually triggers the switchover from the lysogenic to the lytic mode.

In addition to the gene for the transcription-preventing protein, a few other prophage genes may be expressed during lysogeny. Expression of these genes may alter the host's phenotype, a phenomenon that can have important medical

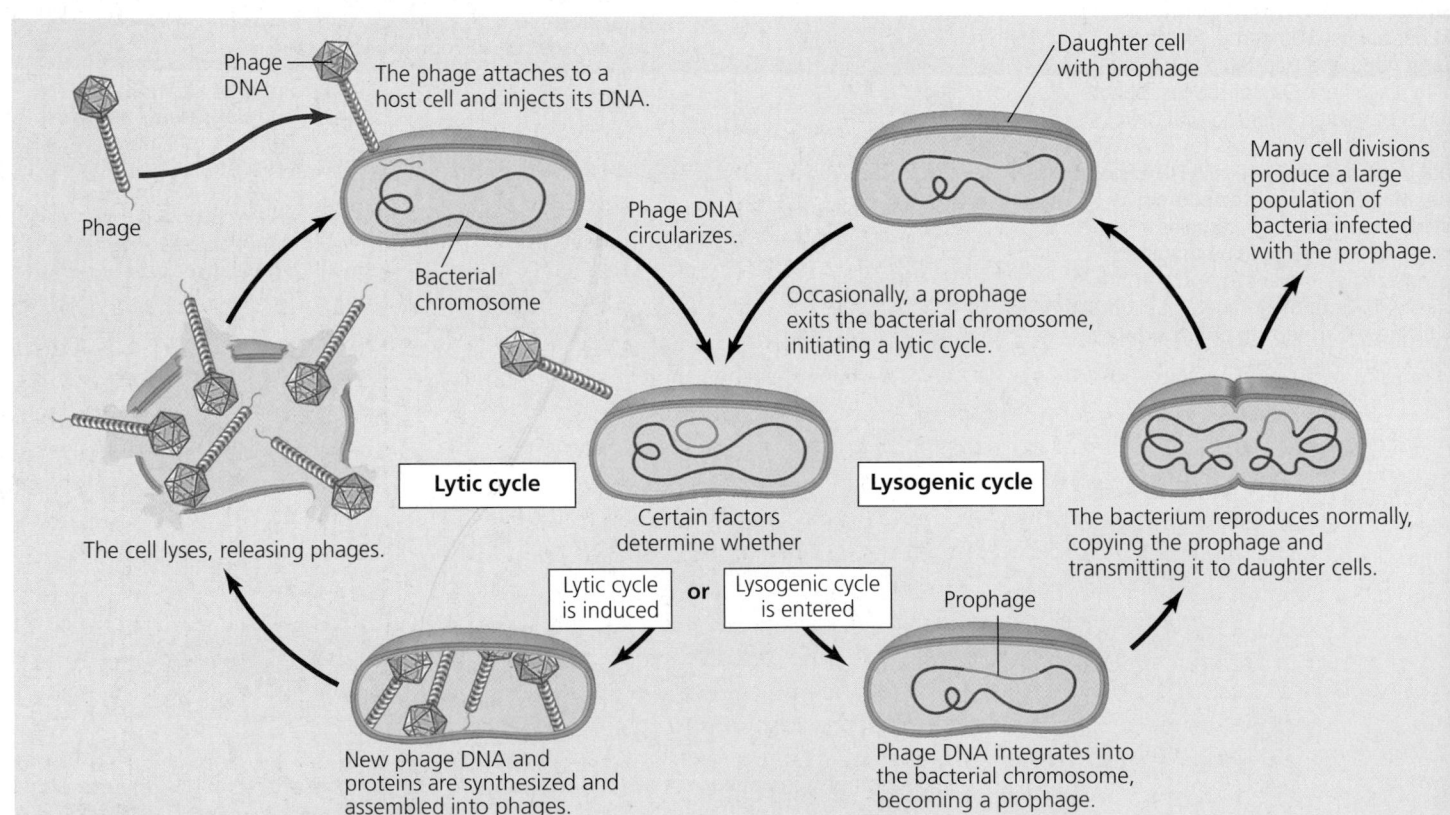

▲ **Figure 19.6 The lytic and lysogenic cycles of phage λ, a temperate phage.** After entering the bacterial cell and circularizing, the λ DNA can immediately initiate the production of a large number of progeny phages (lytic cycle) or integrate into the bacterial chromosome (lysogenic cycle). In most cases, phage λ follows the lytic pathway, which is similar to that detailed in Figure 19.5. However, once a lysogenic cycle begins, the prophage may be carried in the host cell's chromosome for many generations. Phage λ has one main tail fiber, which is short.

Table 19.1 Classes of Animal Viruses

Class/Family	Envelope	Examples/Disease
I. Double-stranded DNA (dsDNA)		
Adenovirus (see Figure 19.3b)	No	Respiratory diseases; tumors
Papovavirus	No	Papillomavirus (warts, cervical cancer); polyomavirus (tumors)
Herpesvirus	Yes	Herpes simplex I and II (cold sores, genital sores); varicella zoster (shingles, chicken pox); Epstein-Barr virus (mononucleosis, Burkitt's lymphoma)
Poxvirus	Yes	Smallpox virus; cowpox virus
II. Single-stranded DNA (ssDNA)		
Parvovirus	No	B19 parvovirus (mild rash)
III. Double-stranded RNA (dsRNA)		
Reovirus	No	Rotavirus (diarrhea); Colorado tick fever virus
IV. Single-stranded RNA (ssRNA); serves as mRNA		
Picornavirus	No	Rhinovirus (common cold); poliovirus, hepatitis A virus, and other enteric (intestinal) viruses
Coronavirus	Yes	Severe acute respiratory syndrome (SARS)
Flavivirus	Yes	Yellow fever virus; West Nile virus; hepatitis C virus
Togavirus	Yes	Rubella virus; equine encephalitis viruses
V. ssRNA; template for mRNA synthesis		
Filovirus	Yes	Ebola virus (hemorrhagic fever)
Orthomyxovirus (see Figures 19.3c and 19.9b)	Yes	Influenza virus
Paramyxovirus	Yes	Measles virus; mumps virus
Rhabdovirus	Yes	Rabies virus
VI. ssRNA; template for DNA synthesis		
Retrovirus (see Figure 19.8)	Yes	HIV, human immunodeficiency virus (AIDS); RNA tumor viruses (leukemia)

significance. For example, the three species of bacteria that cause the human diseases diphtheria, botulism, and scarlet fever would not be so harmful to humans without certain prophage genes that cause the host bacteria to make toxins. And the difference between the *E. coli* strain that resides in our intestines and the O157:H7 strain that has caused several deaths by food poisoning appears to be the presence of prophages in the O157:H7 strain.

Reproductive Cycles of Animal Viruses

Everyone has suffered from viral infections, whether cold sores, influenza, or the common cold. Like all viruses, those that cause illness in humans and other animals can reproduce only inside host cells. Many variations on the basic scheme of viral infection and reproduction are represented among the animal viruses. One key variable is the nature of the viral genome: Is it composed of DNA or RNA? Is it double-stranded or single-stranded? The nature of the genome is the basis for the common classification of viruses shown in **Table 19.1**. Single-stranded RNA viruses are further classified into three classes (IV–VI) according to how the RNA genome functions in a host cell.

Whereas few bacteriophages have an envelope or RNA genome, many animal viruses have both. In fact, nearly all animal viruses with RNA genomes have an envelope, as do some with DNA genomes (see Table 19.1). Rather than consider all the mechanisms of viral infection and reproduction, we will focus on the roles of viral envelopes and on the functioning of RNA as the genetic material of many animal viruses.

Viral Envelopes

An animal virus equipped with an envelope—that is, an outer membrane—uses it to enter the host cell. Protruding from the outer surface of this envelope are viral glycoproteins that bind to specific receptor molecules on the surface of a host cell. **Figure 19.7**, on the next page, outlines the events in the reproductive cycle of an enveloped virus with an RNA genome. The protein parts of envelope glycoproteins are made by ribosomes bound to the endoplasmic reticulum (ER) of the host cell; cellular enzymes in the ER and Golgi apparatus then add the sugars. The resulting viral glycoproteins, embedded in host cell-derived membrane, are transported to the cell surface. In a process much like exocytosis, new viral capsids are wrapped in membrane as they bud from the cell. In other words, the viral envelope is derived from the host cell's plasma membrane, although some of the molecules of this membrane are specified by viral genes. The enveloped viruses are now free to infect other cells. This reproductive cycle does not necessarily kill the host cell, in contrast to the lytic cycles of phages.

Some viruses have envelopes that are not derived from plasma membrane. Herpesviruses, for example, are temporarily cloaked in membrane derived from the nuclear envelope of the host; they then shed this membrane in the cytoplasm and acquire a new envelope made from membrane of the Golgi apparatus. These

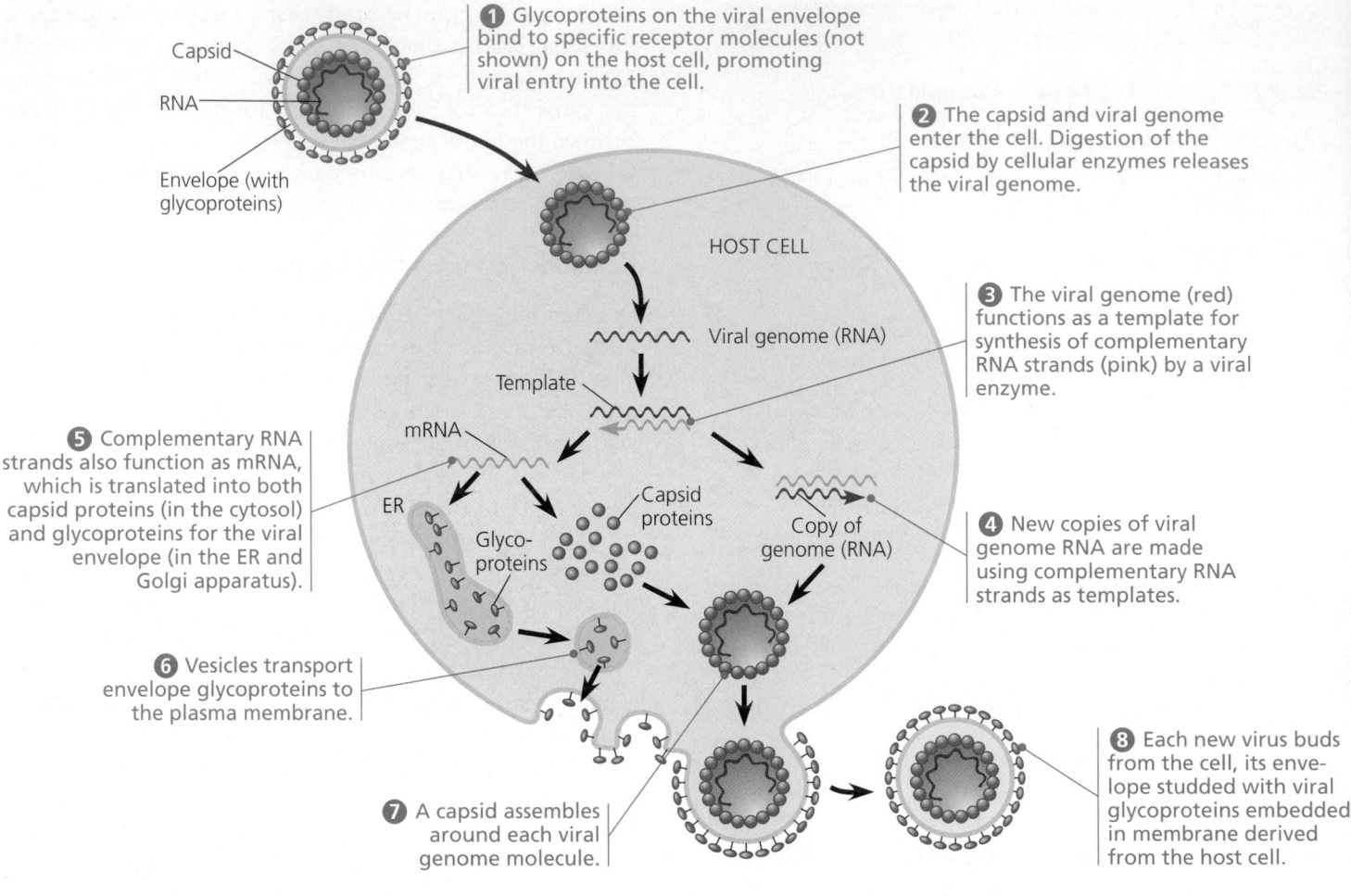

1 Glycoproteins on the viral envelope bind to specific receptor molecules (not shown) on the host cell, promoting viral entry into the cell.

Capsid

RNA

Envelope (with glycoproteins)

2 The capsid and viral genome enter the cell. Digestion of the capsid by cellular enzymes releases the viral genome.

HOST CELL

Viral genome (RNA)

Template

3 The viral genome (red) functions as a template for synthesis of complementary RNA strands (pink) by a viral enzyme.

mRNA

5 Complementary RNA strands also function as mRNA, which is translated into both capsid proteins (in the cytosol) and glycoproteins for the viral envelope (in the ER and Golgi apparatus).

ER

Glyco-proteins

Capsid proteins

Copy of genome (RNA)

4 New copies of viral genome RNA are made using complementary RNA strands as templates.

6 Vesicles transport envelope glycoproteins to the plasma membrane.

8 Each new virus buds from the cell, its envelope studded with viral glycoproteins embedded in membrane derived from the host cell.

7 A capsid assembles around each viral genome molecule.

▲ **Figure 19.7 The reproductive cycle of an enveloped RNA virus.** Shown here is a virus with a single-stranded RNA genome that functions as a template for synthesis of mRNA. Some enveloped viruses enter the host cell by fusion of the envelope with the cell's plasma membrane; others enter by endocytosis. For all enveloped RNA viruses, the formation of new envelopes for progeny viruses occurs by the mechanism depicted in this figure.

? *Name a virus that has infected you and has a reproductive cycle matching this one. (Hint: See Table 19.1.)*

viruses have a double-stranded DNA genome and reproduce within the host cell nucleus, using a combination of viral and cellular enzymes to replicate and transcribe their DNA. In the case of herpesviruses, copies of the viral DNA can remain behind as mini-chromosomes in the nuclei of certain nerve cells. There they remain latent until some sort of physical or emotional stress triggers a new round of active virus production. The infection of other cells by these new viruses causes the blisters characteristic of herpes, such as cold sores or genital sores. Once someone acquires a herpesvirus infection, flare-ups may recur throughout the person's life.

RNA as Viral Genetic Material

Although some phages and most plant viruses are RNA viruses, the broadest variety of RNA genomes is found among the viruses that infect animals. Among the three types of single-stranded RNA genomes found in animal viruses, the genome of class IV viruses can directly serve as mRNA and thus can be translated into viral protein immediately after infection. Figure 19.7 shows a virus of class V, in which the RNA

genome serves as a *template* for mRNA synthesis. The RNA genome is transcribed into complementary RNA strands, which function both as mRNA and as templates for the synthesis of additional copies of genomic RNA. All viruses that require RNA → RNA synthesis to make mRNA use a viral enzyme capable of carrying out this process; there are no such enzymes in most cells. The viral enzyme is packaged with the genome inside the viral capsid.

The RNA animal viruses with the most complicated reproductive cycles are the **retroviruses** (class VI). These viruses are equipped with an enzyme called **reverse transcriptase**, which transcribes an RNA template into DNA, providing an RNA → DNA information flow, the opposite of the usual direction. This unusual phenomenon is the source of the name retroviruses (*retro* means "backward"). Of particular medical importance is **HIV (human immunodeficiency virus)**, the retrovirus that causes **AIDS (acquired immunodeficiency syndrome)**. HIV and other retroviruses are enveloped viruses that contain two identical molecules of single-stranded RNA and two molecules of reverse transcriptase.

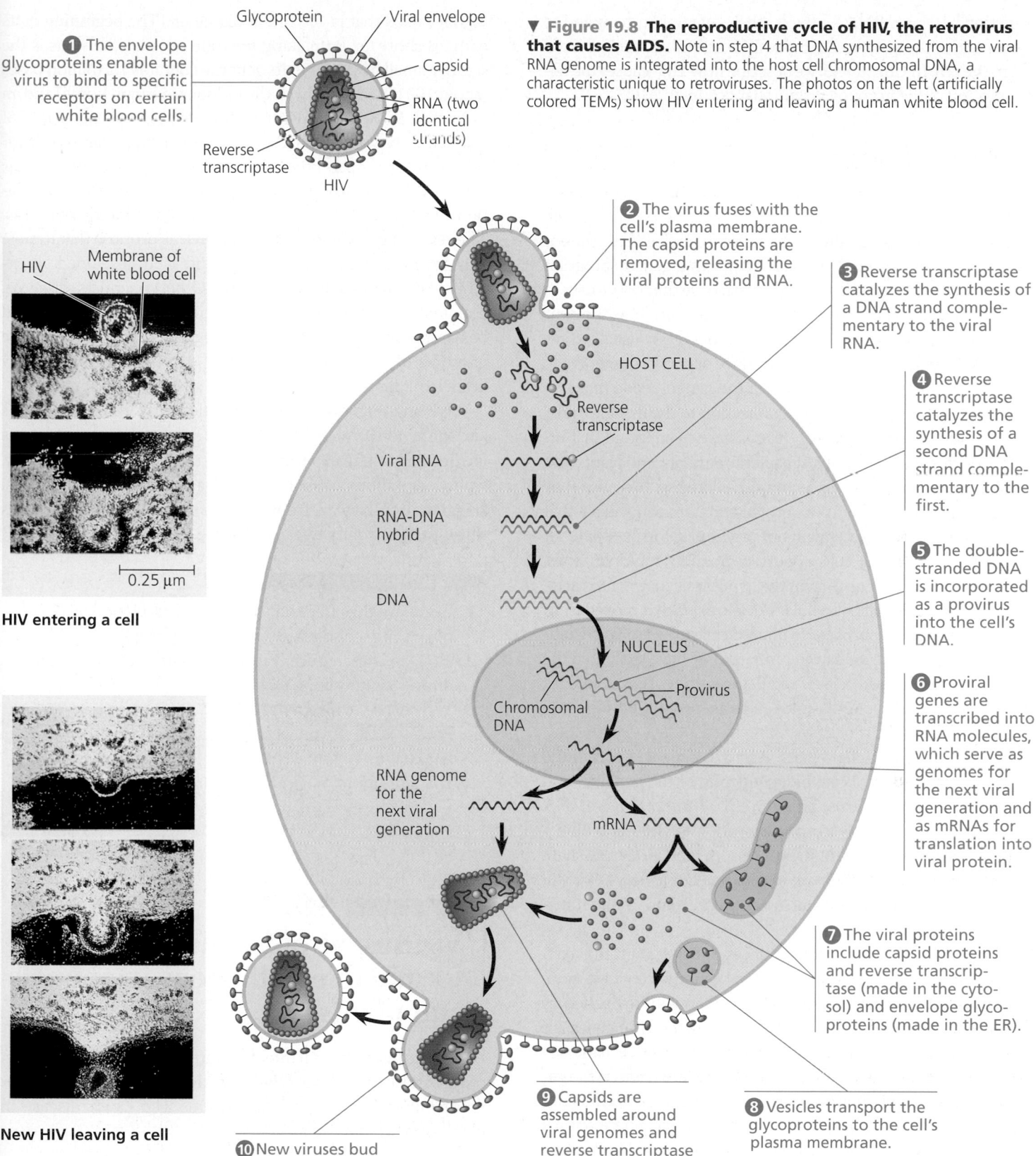

1 The envelope glycoproteins enable the virus to bind to specific receptors on certain white blood cells.

Glycoprotein — Viral envelope — Capsid — RNA (two identical strands) — Reverse transcriptase — HIV

▼ **Figure 19.8 The reproductive cycle of HIV, the retrovirus that causes AIDS.** Note in step 4 that DNA synthesized from the viral RNA genome is integrated into the host cell chromosomal DNA, a characteristic unique to retroviruses. The photos on the left (artificially colored TEMs) show HIV entering and leaving a human white blood cell.

2 The virus fuses with the cell's plasma membrane. The capsid proteins are removed, releasing the viral proteins and RNA.

3 Reverse transcriptase catalyzes the synthesis of a DNA strand complementary to the viral RNA.

4 Reverse transcriptase catalyzes the synthesis of a second DNA strand complementary to the first.

5 The double-stranded DNA is incorporated as a provirus into the cell's DNA.

6 Proviral genes are transcribed into RNA molecules, which serve as genomes for the next viral generation and as mRNAs for translation into viral protein.

7 The viral proteins include capsid proteins and reverse transcriptase (made in the cytosol) and envelope glycoproteins (made in the ER).

8 Vesicles transport the glycoproteins to the cell's plasma membrane.

9 Capsids are assembled around viral genomes and reverse transcriptase molecules.

10 New viruses bud off from the host cell.

HOST CELL

Reverse transcriptase

Viral RNA

RNA-DNA hybrid

DNA

NUCLEUS

Chromosomal DNA — Provirus

RNA genome for the next viral generation

mRNA

HIV — Membrane of white blood cell

0.25 μm

HIV entering a cell

New HIV leaving a cell

Figure 19.8 traces the HIV reproductive cycle, which is typical of a retrovirus. After HIV enters a host cell, its reverse transcriptase molecules are released into the cytoplasm, where they catalyze synthesis of viral DNA. The newly made viral DNA then enters the cell's nucleus and integrates into the DNA of a chromosome. The integrated viral DNA, called a **provirus**, never leaves the host's genome, remaining a permanent resident of the cell. (Recall that a prophage, in contrast, leaves the host's genome at the start of a lytic cycle.) The host's RNA polymerase transcribes the proviral DNA into RNA molecules, which can function both as mRNA for the synthesis of viral proteins and as genomes for the new viruses that will be assembled and released from the cell. In Chapter 43, we describe how HIV causes the deterioration of the immune system that occurs in AIDS.

Evolution of Viruses

We began this chapter by asking whether or not viruses are alive. Viruses do not really fit our definition of living organisms. An isolated virus is biologically inert, unable to replicate its genes or regenerate its own supply of ATP. Yet it has a genetic program written in the universal language of life. Do we think of viruses as nature's most complex associations of molecules or as the simplest forms of life? Either way, we must bend our usual definitions. Although viruses cannot reproduce or carry out metabolic activities independently, their use of the genetic code makes it hard to deny their evolutionary connection to the living world.

How did viruses originate? Viruses have been found that infect every form of life—not just bacteria, animals, and plants, but also archaea, fungi, and algae and other protists. Because they depend on cells for their own propagation, it seems likely that viruses are not the descendants of precellular forms of life but evolved *after* the first cells appeared, possibly multiple times. Most molecular biologists favor the hypothesis that viruses originated from naked bits of cellular nucleic acids that moved from one cell to another, perhaps via injured cell surfaces. The evolution of genes coding for capsid proteins may have facilitated the infection of uninjured cells. Candidates for the original sources of viral genomes include plasmids and transposons. *Plasmids* are small, circular DNA molecules found in bacteria and in the unicellular eukaryotes called yeasts. Plasmids exist apart from the cell's genome, can replicate independently of the genome, and are occasionally transferred between cells. *Transposons* are DNA segments that can move from one location to another within a cell's genome. Thus, plasmids, transposons, and viruses all share an important feature: They are *mobile genetic elements*. We will discuss plasmids in more detail in Chapters 20 and 27 and transposons in Chapter 21.

Consistent with this vision of pieces of DNA shuttling from cell to cell is the observation that a viral genome can have more in common with the genome of its host than with the genomes of viruses that infect other hosts. Indeed, some viral genes are essentially identical to genes of the host. On the other hand, recent sequencing of many viral genomes has shown that the genetic sequences of some viruses are quite similar to those of seemingly distantly related viruses; for example, some animal viruses share similar sequences with plant viruses. This genetic similarity may reflect the persistence of groups of viral genes that were favored by natural selection during the early evolution of viruses and the eukaryotic cells that served as their hosts.

The debate about the origin of viruses has been reinvigorated recently by reports of mimivirus, the largest virus yet discovered. Mimivirus is a double-stranded DNA virus with an icosa-hedral capsid that is 400 nm in diameter. (The beginning of its name is short for *mi*micking *mi*crobe because the virus is the size of a small bacterium.) Its genome contains 1.2 million bases (about 100 times as many as the influenza virus genome) and an estimated 1,000 genes. Perhaps the most surprising aspect of mimivirus, however, is that some of the genes appear to code for products previously thought to be hallmarks of cellular genomes. These products include proteins involved in translation, DNA repair, protein folding, and polysaccharide synthesis. The researchers who described mimivirus propose that it most likely evolved *before* the first cells and then developed an exploitative relationship with them. Other scientists disagree, maintaining that the virus evolved more recently than cells and has simply been efficient at scavenging genes from its hosts. The question of whether some viruses deserve their own early branch on the tree of life may not be answered for some time.

The ongoing evolutionary relationship between viruses and the genomes of their host cells is an association that makes viruses very useful experimental systems in molecular biology. Knowledge about viruses also has many practical applications, since viruses have a tremendous impact on all organisms through their ability to cause disease.

CONCEPT CHECK **19.2**

1. Compare the effect on the host cell of a lytic (virulent) phage and a lysogenic (temperate) phage.
2. How do some viruses reproduce without possessing or ever synthesizing DNA?
3. Why is HIV called a retrovirus?
4. **WHAT IF?** If you were a researcher trying to combat HIV infection, what molecular processes could you attempt to block? (See Figure 19.8.)

For suggested answers, see Appendix A.

CONCEPT **19.3**

Viruses, viroids, and prions are formidable pathogens in animals and plants

Diseases caused by viral infections afflict humans, agricultural crops, and livestock worldwide. Other smaller, less complex entities known as viroids and prions also cause disease in plants and animals, respectively.

Viral Diseases in Animals

A viral infection can produce symptoms by a number of different routes. Viruses may damage or kill cells by causing the release of hydrolytic enzymes from lysosomes. Some viruses cause infected cells to produce toxins that lead to disease symptoms, and some have molecular components that are toxic, such as envelope proteins. How much damage a virus causes depends partly on the ability of the infected tissue to regenerate by cell division. People usually recover completely from colds because the epithelium of the respiratory tract, which the viruses infect, can efficiently repair itself. In contrast, damage inflicted by poliovirus to mature nerve cells is permanent, because these cells do not divide and usually cannot be replaced. Many of the temporary symptoms associated with viral infections, such as fever and aches, actually result from the body's own efforts at defending itself against infection rather than from cell death caused by the virus.

The immune system is a complex and critical part of the body's natural defenses (see Chapter 43). It is also the basis for the major medical tool for preventing viral infections— vaccines. A **vaccine** is a harmless variant or derivative of a pathogen that stimulates the immune system to mount defenses against the harmful pathogen. Smallpox, a viral disease that was at one time a devastating scourge in many parts of the world, was eradicated by a vaccination program carried out by the World Health Organization. The very narrow host range of the smallpox virus—it infects only humans—was a critical factor in the success of this program. Similar worldwide vaccination campaigns are currently under way to eradicate polio and measles. Effective vaccines are also available against rubella, mumps, hepatitis B, and a number of other viral diseases.

Although vaccines can prevent certain viral illnesses, medical technology can do little, at present, to cure most viral infections once they occur. The antibiotics that help us recover from bacterial infections are powerless against viruses. Antibiotics kill bacteria by inhibiting enzymes specific to bacteria but have no effect on eukaryotic or virally encoded enzymes. However, the few enzymes that are encoded by viruses have provided targets for other drugs. Most antiviral drugs resemble nucleosides and as a result interfere with viral nucleic acid synthesis. One such drug is acyclovir, which impedes herpesvirus reproduction by inhibiting the viral polymerase that synthesizes viral DNA. Similarly, azidothymidine (AZT) curbs HIV reproduction by interfering with the synthesis of DNA by reverse transcriptase. In the past two decades, much effort has gone into developing drugs against HIV. Currently, multidrug treatments, sometimes called "cocktails," have been found to be most effective. Such treatments commonly include a combination of two nucleoside mimics and a protease inhibitor, which interferes with an enzyme required for assembly of the viruses.

Emerging Viruses

Viruses that appear suddenly or are new to medical scientists are often referred to as *emerging viruses*. HIV, the AIDS virus, is a classic example: This virus appeared in San Francisco in the early 1980s, seemingly out of nowhere, although later studies uncovered a case in the Belgian Congo that occurred as early as 1959. The deadly Ebola virus, recognized initially in 1976 in central Africa, is one of several emerging viruses that cause *hemorrhagic fever*, an often fatal syndrome (set of symptoms) characterized by fever, vomiting, massive bleeding, and circulatory system collapse. A number of other dangerous emerging viruses cause encephalitis, inflammation of the brain. One example is the West Nile virus, which appeared in North America for the first time in 1999 and has spread to all 48 contiguous states in the United States.

Severe acute respiratory syndrome (*SARS*) first appeared in southern China in November 2002. A global outbreak that occurred during the following eight months infected about 8,000 people and killed more than 700. Researchers quickly identified the infectious agent as a *coronavirus*, a virus with a single-stranded RNA genome (class IV) that had not previously been known to cause disease in humans. Public health workers responded rapidly, isolating patients and quarantining those who had come in contact with them. Because of low infectivity and other characteristics of the SARS virus, this rapid response succeeded in quelling the outbreak before it could infect a much larger population.

How do such viruses burst on the human scene, giving rise to harmful diseases that were previously rare or even unknown? Three processes contribute to the emergence of viral diseases. The first, and perhaps most important, is the mutation of existing viruses. RNA viruses tend to have an unusually high rate of mutation because errors in replicating their RNA genomes are not corrected by proofreading. Some mutations change existing viruses into new genetic varieties (strains) that can cause disease, even in individuals who are immune to the ancestral virus. For instance, general outbreaks of flu, or flu **epidemics**, are caused by new strains of influenza virus genetically different enough from earlier strains that people have little immunity to them.

A second process that can lead to the emergence of viral diseases is the dissemination of a viral disease from a small, isolated human population. For instance, AIDS went unnamed and virtually unnoticed for decades before it began to spread around the world. In this case, technological and social factors, including affordable international travel, blood transfusions, sexual promiscuity, and the abuse of intravenous drugs, allowed a previously rare human disease to become a global scourge.

A third source of new viral diseases in humans is the spread of existing viruses from other animals. Scientists estimate that about three-quarters of new human diseases originate in this way. Animals that harbor and can transmit a particular virus but are generally unaffected by it are said to act as a natural reservoir for that virus. For example, a species of bat has been identified as the likely natural reservoir of the SARS virus. Bats are sold as food in China, and their dried feces are even sold for medicinal uses; either of these practices could provide a route for transmission of the virus to humans.

Flu epidemics provide an instructive example of the effects of viruses moving between species. There are three types of influenza virus: types B and C, which infect only humans and have never caused an epidemic, and type A, which infects a wide range of animals, including birds, pigs, horses, and humans. Influenza A strains have caused three major flu epidemics among humans in the last 100 years. The worst was the "Spanish flu" **pandemic** (a global epidemic) of 1918–1919, which killed about 40 million people, including many World War I soldiers **(Figure 19.9a)**. Evidence points to birds as the source of the 1918 flu pandemic.

A likely scenario for that pandemic and others is that they began when the virus mutated as it passed from one host species to another. When an animal is infected with more than one strain of flu virus, the different strains can undergo genetic recombination if the RNA molecules making up their genomes mix and match during viral assembly. Coupled with mutation, these changes can lead to the emergence of a viral strain that is capable of infecting human cells. Having never

been exposed to that particular strain before, humans will lack immunity, and the recombinant virus has the potential to be highly pathogenic. If such a flu virus recombines with viruses that circulate widely among humans, it may acquire the ability to spread easily from person to person, dramatically increasing the potential for a major human outbreak.

Different strains of influenza A are given standardized names; for example, the strain that caused the 1918 flu is called H1N1. The name identifies which forms of two viral surface proteins are present: hemagglutinin (H) and neuraminidase (N). There are 16 different types of hemagglutinin, a protein that helps the flu virus attach to host cells, and 9 types of neuraminidase, an enzyme that helps release new virus particles from infected cells. Water birds have been found that carry viruses with all possible combinations of H and N.

In 1997, at least 18 people in Hong Kong were infected with an H5N1 virus **(Figure 19.9b)**; six of these people subsequently died. The same strain, previously seen only in wild birds, had killed several thousand chickens earlier that year, presumably passed along from wild birds or other species. A mass culling of all of Hong Kong's 1.5 million domestic birds appeared to stop that outbreak. Beginning in 2002, however, new cases of H5N1 human infection began to crop up around southeast Asia. By 2007, the disease caused by this virus, now called "avian flu," had killed about 160 people. Perhaps even more alarming is the overall mortality rate, which is greater than 50%. More than 100 million birds have either died from the disease or been killed to prevent the spread of infection; efforts are under way to vaccinate birds of several species **(Figure 19.9c)**.

The geographical and host ranges of avian flu virus continue to expand. It has shown up in wild or domestic birds in Africa and Europe, as well as in pigs, tigers, and domestic cats and dogs. The expanding host range provides increasing opportunities for different strains of virus to reassort their genetic material and for new strains to emerge. If the H5N1 avian flu virus evolves so that it can spread easily from person to person, it could bring about a major human outbreak. Human-to-human transmission is strongly suspected in several cases where the disease has clustered in families, but so far the disease has not spread beyond small groups to cause an epidemic. For those studying emerging viruses and their ability to give rise to a human pandemic, avian flu provides a sobering lesson in progress.

As we have seen, emerging viruses are generally not new; rather, they are existing viruses that mutate, disseminate more widely in the current host species, or spread to new host species. Changes in host behavior or environmental changes can increase the viral traffic responsible for emerging diseases. For example, new roads through remote areas can allow viruses to spread between previously isolated human populations. Also, the destruction of forests to expand cropland can bring humans into contact with other animals that may host viruses capable of infecting humans.

(a) The 1918 flu pandemic. Many of those infected were treated in large makeshift hospitals, such as this one.

0.5 μm

(b) Influenza A H5N1 virus. Virus particles are seen budding from an infected cell in this colorized TEM.

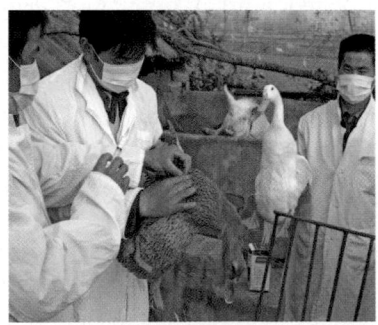

(c) Vaccinating ducks. Veterinarians administer vaccinations in a region of China reporting cases of avian flu, caused by strain H5N1.

▲ **Figure 19.9 Influenza in humans and other animals.**

Viral Diseases in Plants

More than 2,000 types of viral diseases of plants are known, and together they account for an estimated annual loss of $15 billion worldwide due to their destruction of agricultural and horticultural crops. Common signs of viral infection include bleached or brown spots on leaves and fruits, stunted growth, and damaged flowers or roots, all tending to diminish the yield and quality of crops (Figure 19.10).

Plant viruses have the same basic structure and mode of reproduction as animal viruses. Most plant viruses discovered thus far, including tobacco mosaic virus (TMV), have an RNA genome. Many have a helical capsid, like TMV (see Figure 19.3a); others have an icosahedral capsid.

Viral diseases of plants spread by two major routes. In the first route, called *horizontal transmission*, a plant is infected from an external source of the virus. Because the invading virus must get past the plant's outer protective layer of cells (the epidermis), a plant becomes more susceptible to viral infections if it has been damaged by wind, injury, or herbivores. Herbivores, especially insects, pose a double threat because they can also act as carriers of viruses, transmitting disease from plant to plant. Farmers and gardeners may transmit plant viruses inadvertently on pruning shears and other tools. The other route of viral infection is *vertical transmission*, in which a plant inherits a viral infection from a parent. Vertical transmission can occur in asexual propagation (for example, cuttings) or in sexual reproduction via infected seeds.

Once a virus enters a plant cell and begins reproducing, viral genomes and associated proteins can spread throughout the plant by means of plasmodesmata, the cytoplasmic connections that penetrate the walls between adjacent plant cells (see Figure 6.28). The passage of viral macromolecules from cell to cell is facilitated by virally encoded proteins that cause enlargement of plasmodesmata. Scientists have not yet devised cures for most viral plant diseases. Consequently, their efforts are focused largely on reducing the transmission of such diseases and on breeding resistant varieties of crop plants.

Viroids and Prions: The Simplest Infectious Agents

As small and simple as viruses are, they dwarf another class of pathogens: **viroids**. These are circular RNA molecules, only a few hundred nucleotides long, that infect plants. Viroids do not encode proteins but can replicate in host plant cells, apparently using host cell enzymes. These small RNA molecules seem to cause errors in the regulatory systems that control plant growth, and the typical signs of viroid diseases are abnormal development and stunted growth. One viroid disease, called cadang-cadang, has killed more than 10 million coconut palms in the Philippines.

An important lesson from viroids is that a single molecule can be an infectious agent that spreads a disease. But viroids are nucleic acid, whose ability to be replicated is well known. Even more surprising is the evidence for infectious *proteins*, called **prions**, which appear to cause a number of degenerative brain diseases in various animal species. These diseases include scrapie in sheep; mad cow disease, which has plagued the European beef industry in recent years; and Creutzfeldt-Jakob disease in humans, which has caused the death of some 150 people in Great Britain over the past decade. Prions are most likely transmitted in food, as may occur when people eat prion-laden beef from cattle with mad cow disease. Kuru, another human disease caused by prions, was identified in the early 1900s among the South Fore natives of New Guinea. A kuru epidemic peaked there in the 1960s, puzzling scientists, who at first thought the disease had a genetic basis. Eventually, however, anthropological investigations ferreted out how the disease was spread: ritual cannibalism, a widespread practice among South Fore natives at that time.

Two characteristics of prions are especially alarming. First, prions act very slowly, with an incubation period of at least ten years before symptoms develop. The lengthy incubation period prevents sources of infection from being identified until long after the first cases appear, allowing many more infections to occur. Second, prions are virtually indestructible; they are not destroyed or deactivated by heating to normal cooking temperatures. To date, there is no known cure for

▲ **Figure 19.10 Viral infection of plants.** Infection with particular viruses causes irregular brown patches on tomatoes (left), black blotching on squash (center), and streaking in tulips due to redistribution of pigment granules (right).

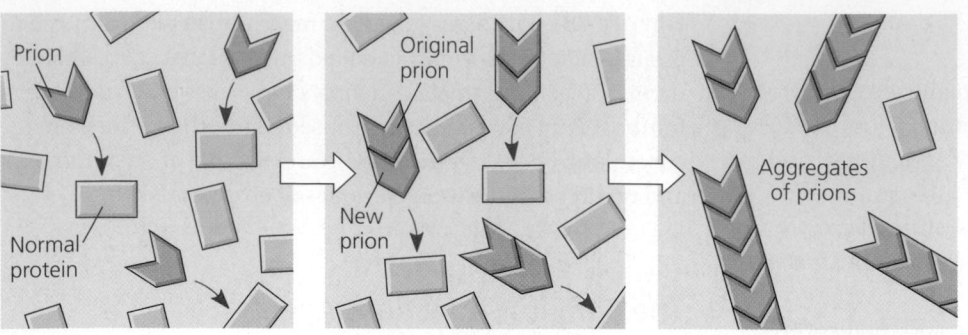

Figure 19.11 Model for how prions propagate. Prions are misfolded versions of normal brain proteins. When a prion contacts a normally folded version of the same protein, it may induce the normal protein to assume the abnormal shape. The resulting chain reaction may continue until high levels of prion aggregation cause cellular malfunction and eventual degeneration of the brain.

prion diseases, and the only hope for developing effective treatments lies in understanding the process of infection.

How can a protein, which cannot replicate itself, be a transmissible pathogen? According to the leading model, a prion is a misfolded form of a protein normally present in brain cells. When the prion gets into a cell containing the normal form of the protein, the prion somehow converts normal protein molecules to the misfolded prion versions. Several prions then aggregate into a complex that can convert other normal proteins to prions, which join the chain (Figure 19.11). Prion aggregation interferes with normal cellular functions and causes disease symptoms. This model was greeted with much skepticism when it was first proposed by Stanley Prusiner in the early 1980s, but it is now widely accepted. Prusiner was awarded the Nobel Prize in 1997 for his work on prions.

CONCEPT CHECK 19.3

1. Describe two ways a preexisting virus can become an emerging virus.
2. Contrast horizontal and vertical transmission of viruses in plants.
3. TMV has been isolated from virtually all commercial tobacco products. Why, then, is TMV infection not an additional hazard for smokers?
4. **WHAT IF?** How might the H5N1 avian flu virus have spread from Asia to Africa and Europe? Is it likely that human air travel could have spread this virus? How could you test your hypothesis?

For suggested answers, see Appendix A.

Chapter 19 Review

MEDIA Go to www.campbellbiology.com for BioFlix 3-D Animations, MP3 Tutors, Videos, Practice Tests, an eBook, and more.

SUMMARY OF KEY CONCEPTS

CONCEPT 19.1

A virus consists of a nucleic acid surrounded by a protein coat (pp. 381–384)

▶ **The Discovery of Viruses: *Scientific Inquiry*** Researchers discovered viruses in the late 1800s by studying a plant disease, tobacco mosaic disease.

▶ **Structure of Viruses** A virus is a small nucleic acid genome enclosed in a protein capsid and sometimes a membranous envelope containing viral proteins that help viruses enter cells. The genome may be single- or double-stranded DNA or RNA.

CONCEPT 19.2

Viruses reproduce only in host cells (pp. 384–390)

▶ **General Features of Viral Reproductive Cycles** Viruses use enzymes, ribosomes, and small molecules of host cells to synthesize progeny viruses. Each type of virus has a characteristic host range.

▶ **Reproductive Cycles of Phages** Phages (viruses that infect bacteria) can reproduce by two alternative mechanisms: the lytic cycle and the lysogenic cycle.

Lytic cycle
• Virulent or temperate phage
• Destruction of host DNA
• Production of new phages
• Lysis of host cell causes release of progeny phages

Lysogenic cycle
• Temperate phage only
• Genome integrates into bacterial chromosome as prophage, which
(1) is replicated and passed on to daughter cells and
(2) can be induced to leave the chromosome and initiate a lytic cycle

► **Reproductive Cycles of Animal Viruses** Many animal viruses have an envelope. Retroviruses (such as HIV) use the enzyme reverse transcriptase to copy their RNA genome into DNA, which can be integrated into the host genome as a provirus.

► **Evolution of Viruses** Since viruses can reproduce only within cells, they probably evolved after the first cells appeared, perhaps as packaged fragments of cellular nucleic acid. The origin of viruses is still being debated.

MEDIA

Activity Simplified Viral Reproductive Cycle
Activity Phage Lytic Cycle
Activity Phage Lysogenic and Lytic Cycles
Activity Retrovirus (HIV) Reproductive Cycle

CONCEPT 19.3

Viruses, viroids, and prions are formidable pathogens in animals and plants (pp. 390–394)

► **Viral Diseases in Animals** Symptoms may be caused by direct viral harm to cells or by the body's immune response. Vaccines stimulate the immune system to defend the host against specific viruses.

► **Emerging Viruses** Outbreaks of "new" viral diseases in humans are usually caused by existing viruses that expand their host territory. The H5N1 avian flu virus is being closely monitored for its potential to cause a serious flu pandemic.

► **Viral Diseases in Plants** Viruses enter plant cells through damaged cell walls (horizontal transmission) or are inherited from a parent (vertical transmission).

► **Viroids and Prions: The Simplest Infectious Agents** Viroids are naked RNA molecules that infect plants and disrupt their growth. Prions are slow-acting, virtually indestructible infectious proteins that cause brain diseases in mammals.

MEDIA

Investigation What Causes Infections in AIDS Patients?
Investigation Why Do AIDS Rates Differ Across the U.S.?

TESTING YOUR KNOWLEDGE

SELF-QUIZ

1. A bacterium is infected with an experimentally constructed bacteriophage composed of the T2 phage protein coat and T4 phage DNA. The new phages produced would have
   a. T2 protein and T4 DNA.
   b. T2 protein and T2 DNA.
   c. a mixture of the DNA and proteins of both phages.
   d. T4 protein and T4 DNA.
   e. T4 protein and T2 DNA.

2. RNA viruses require their own supply of certain enzymes because
   a. host cells rapidly destroy the viruses.
   b. host cells lack enzymes that can replicate the viral genome.
   c. these enzymes translate viral mRNA into proteins.
   d. these enzymes penetrate host cell membranes.
   e. these enzymes cannot be made in host cells.

3. Which of the following characteristics, structures, or processes is common to both bacteria and viruses?
   a. metabolism
   b. ribosomes

c. genetic material composed of nucleic acid
d. cell division
e. independent existence

4. Emerging viruses arise by
   a. mutation of existing viruses.
   b. the spread of existing viruses to new host species.
   c. the spread of existing viruses more widely within their host species.
   d. all of the above
   e. none of the above

5. To cause a human pandemic, the H5N1 avian flu virus would have to
   a. spread to primates such as chimpanzees.
   b. develop into a virus with a different host range.
   c. become capable of human-to-human transmission.
   d. arise independently in chickens in North and South America.
   e. become much more pathogenic.

6. **DRAW IT** Redraw Figure 19.7 to show the reproductive cycle of a virus with a single-stranded genome that can function as mRNA (a class IV virus).

For Self-Quiz answers, see Appendix A.

MEDIA Visit **www.campbellbiology.com** for a Practice Test.

EVOLUTION CONNECTION

7. The success of some viruses lies in their ability to evolve rapidly within the host. Such a virus evades the host's defenses by mutating and producing many altered progeny viruses before the body can mount an attack. Thus, the viruses present late in infection differ from those that initially infected the body. Discuss this as an example of evolution in microcosm. Which viral lineages tend to predominate?

SCIENTIFIC INQUIRY

8. When bacteria infect an animal, the number of bacteria in the body increases in an exponential fashion (graph A). After infection by a virulent animal virus with a lytic reproductive cycle, there is no evidence of infection for a while. Then, the number of viruses rises suddenly and subsequently increases in a series of steps (graph B). Explain the difference in the curves.

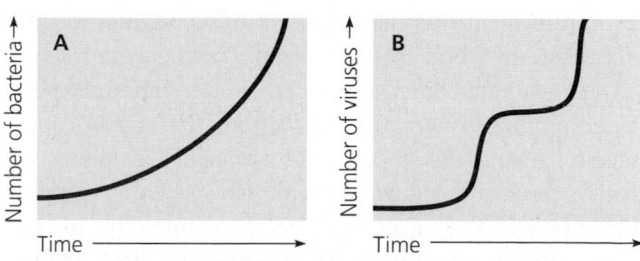

Biological Inquiry: A Workbook of Investigative Cases Explore West Nile virus in the case "The Donor's Dilemma." Explore the immune response to flu pathogens with the case "Pandemic Flu (Past and Possible)."

Biotechnology

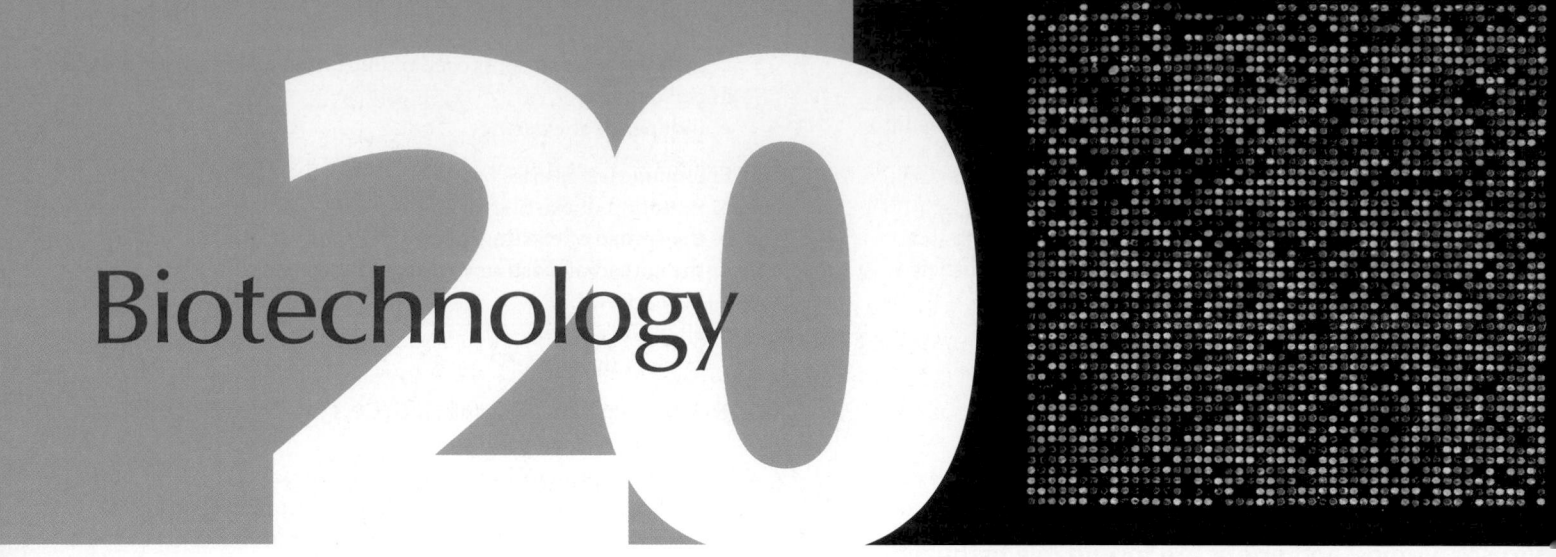

▲ **Figure 20.1 How can this array of spots be used to compare normal and cancerous tissues?**

KEY CONCEPTS

20.1 DNA cloning yields multiple copies of a gene or other DNA segment

20.2 DNA technology allows us to study the sequence, expression, and function of a gene

20.3 Cloning organisms may lead to production of stem cells for research and other applications

20.4 The practical applications of DNA technology affect our lives in many ways

OVERVIEW

The DNA Toolbox

In 1995, a major scientific milestone was announced: For the first time, researchers had sequenced the entire genome of a free-living organism, the bacterium *Haemophilus influenzae*. This news electrified the scientific community. Few among them would have dared to dream that a mere 12 years later, genome sequencing would be under way for more than 2,000 species. By 2007, researchers had completely sequenced hundreds of prokaryotic genomes and dozens of eukaryotic ones, including all 3 billion base pairs of the human genome.

Ultimately, these achievements can be attributed to advances in DNA technology—methods of working with and manipulating DNA—that had their roots in the 1970s. A key accomplishment was the invention of techniques for making **recombinant DNA**, DNA molecules formed when segments of DNA from two different sources—often different species—are combined *in vitro* (in a test tube). This advance set the stage for further development of powerful techniques for analyzing genes and gene expression. How scientists prepare recombinant DNA and use DNA technology to answer fundamental biological questions are one focus of this chapter.

Another focus of the chapter is how our lives are affected by **biotechnology**, the manipulation of organisms or their compo-

nents to make useful products. Biotechnology has a long history that includes such early practices as selective breeding of farm animals and using microorganisms to make wine and cheese. Today, biotechnology also encompasses **genetic engineering**, the direct manipulation of genes for practical purposes. Genetic engineering has launched a revolution in biotechnology, greatly expanding the scope of its potential applications. Tools from the DNA toolbox are now applied in ways that were unthinkable only a decade ago, affecting everything from agriculture to criminal law to medical research. For instance, on the DNA microarray in **Figure 20.1**, the colored spots represent the relative level of expression of 2,400 human genes. Using microarray analysis, researchers can quickly compare gene expression in different samples, such as those obtained from normal and cancerous tissues. The knowledge gained from such gene expression studies is making a significant contribution to the study of cancer and other diseases.

In this chapter, we first describe the main techniques for manipulating DNA and analyzing gene expression and function. Next, we explore parallel advances in cloning organisms and producing stem cells, techniques that have both expanded our basic understanding of biology and enhanced our ability to apply this understanding to global problems. Finally, we survey the practical applications of biotechnology and consider some of the social and ethical issues that arise as modern biotechnology becomes more pervasive in our lives.

CONCEPT 20.1

DNA cloning yields multiple copies of a gene or other DNA segment

The molecular biologist studying a particular gene faces a challenge. Naturally occurring DNA molecules are very long, and a single molecule usually carries many genes. Moreover, in many eukaryotic genomes, genes occupy only a small proportion of the chromosomal DNA, the rest being noncoding nucleotide sequences. A single human gene, for example, might constitute only $\frac{1}{100,000}$ of a chromosomal DNA molecule. As a further complication, the distinctions between a gene and the surrounding DNA are subtle, consisting only of differences in nucleotide sequence. To work directly with specific genes, scientists have developed methods for preparing well-defined segments of DNA in multiple identical copies, a process called *DNA cloning*.

of a cloned gene from bacteria for use in basic research or to endow an organism with a new metabolic capability, such as pest resistance. For example, a resistance gene present in one crop species might be cloned and transferred into plants of another species. Alternatively, a protein with medical uses, such as human growth hormone, can be harvested in large quantities from cultures of bacteria carrying the cloned gene for the protein.

Most protein-coding genes exist in only one copy per haploid genome—roughly one part per million in the case of human DNA—so the ability to prepare large amounts of

DNA Cloning and Its Applications: *A Preview*

Most methods for cloning pieces of DNA in the laboratory share certain general features. One common approach uses bacteria, most often *Escherichia coli*. Recall from Chapter 16 that the *E. coli* chromosome is a large circular molecule of DNA. In addition, *E. coli* and many other bacteria have **plasmids**, small circular DNA molecules that replicate separately from the bacterial chromosome. A plasmid has only a small number of genes; these genes may be useful when the bacterium is in a particular environment but may not be required for survival or reproduction under most conditions.

To clone pieces of DNA in the laboratory, researchers first isolate a plasmid from a bacterial cell and insert DNA from another source ("foreign" DNA) into it **(Figure 20.2)**. The resulting plasmid is now a recombinant DNA molecule, combining DNA from two sources. The plasmid is then returned to a bacterial cell, producing a *recombinant bacterium*. This single cell reproduces through repeated cell divisions to form a clone of cells, a population of genetically identical cells. Because the dividing bacteria replicate the recombinant plasmid and pass it on to their descendants, the foreign DNA and any genes it carries are cloned at the same time. The production of multiple copies of a single gene is called **gene cloning**.

Gene cloning is useful for two basic purposes: to make many copies of a particular gene and to produce a protein product. Researchers can isolate copies

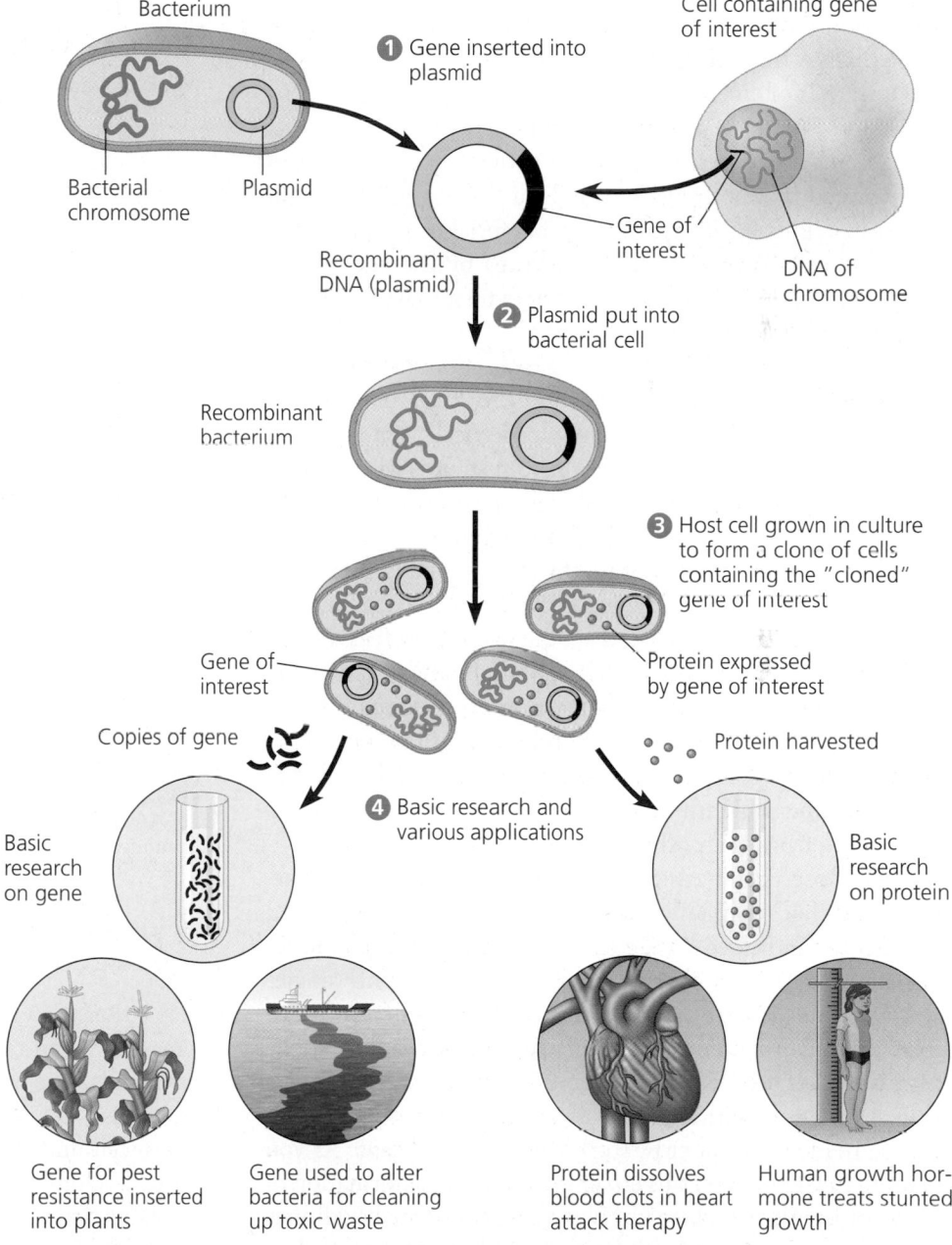

▲ **Figure 20.2 A preview of gene cloning and some uses of cloned genes.** In this simplified diagram of gene cloning, we start with a plasmid isolated from a bacterial cell and a gene of interest from another organism. Only one copy of the plasmid and one copy of the gene of interest are shown at the top of the figure, but the starting materials would include many copies of each.

such rare DNA fragments is crucial for any application involving a single gene. In the rest of this chapter, you will learn more about the techniques outlined in Figure 20.2 and related methods.

Using Restriction Enzymes to Make Recombinant DNA

Gene cloning and genetic engineering rely on the use of enzymes that cut DNA molecules at a limited number of specific locations. These enzymes, called restriction endonucleases, or **restriction enzymes**, were discovered in the late 1960s by researchers studying bacteria. As you learned in Chapter 19, restriction enzymes protect the bacterial cell by cutting up foreign DNA from other organisms or phages.

Hundreds of different restriction enzymes have been identified and isolated. Each restriction enzyme is very specific, recognizing a particular short DNA sequence, or **restriction site**, and cutting both DNA strands at precise points within this restriction site. The DNA of a bacterial cell is protected from the cell's own restriction enzymes by the addition of methyl groups ($-CH_3$) to adenines or cytosines within the sequences recognized by the enzymes.

The top of **Figure 20.3** illustrates a restriction site recognized by a particular restriction enzyme from *E. coli*. As shown in this example, most restriction sites are symmetrical. That is, the sequence of nucleotides is the same on both strands when read in the 5′ → 3′ direction. Most restriction enzymes recognize sequences containing four to eight nucleotides. Because any sequence this short usually occurs (by chance) many times in a long DNA molecule, a restriction enzyme will make many cuts in a DNA molecule, yielding a set of **restriction fragments**. All copies of a particular DNA molecule always yield the same set of restriction fragments when exposed to the same restriction enzyme. In other words, a restriction enzyme cuts a DNA molecule in a reproducible way. (Later you will learn how the different fragments can be separated and distinguished from each other.)

The most useful restriction enzymes cleave the sugar-phosphate backbones in the two DNA strands in a staggered manner, as indicated in Figure 20.3. The resulting double-stranded restriction fragments have at least one single-stranded end, called a **sticky end**. These short extensions can form hydrogen-bonded base pairs with complementary sticky ends on any other DNA molecules cut with the same enzyme. The associations formed in this way are only temporary but can be made permanent by the enzyme **DNA ligase**. As you learned in Chapter 16, this enzyme catalyzes the formation of covalent bonds that close up the sugar-phosphate backbones of DNA strands; for example, it joins Okazaki fragments during replication. You can see at the bottom of Figure 20.3 that the ligase-catalyzed joining of DNA from two different sources produces a stable recombinant DNA molecule.

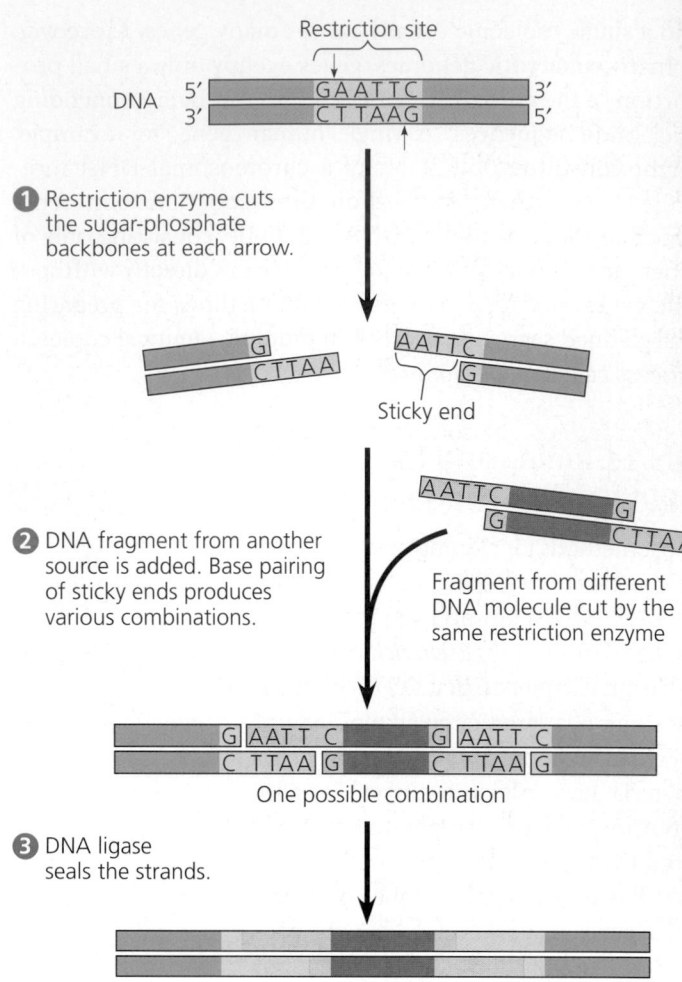

1 Restriction enzyme cuts the sugar-phosphate backbones at each arrow.

Sticky end

2 DNA fragment from another source is added. Base pairing of sticky ends produces various combinations.

Fragment from different DNA molecule cut by the same restriction enzyme

One possible combination

3 DNA ligase seals the strands.

Recombinant DNA molecule

▲ **Figure 20.3 Using a restriction enzyme and DNA ligase to make recombinant DNA.** The restriction enzyme in this example (called *Eco*RI) recognizes a specific six-base-pair sequence, the restriction site, and makes staggered cuts in the sugar-phosphate backbones within this sequence, producing fragments with sticky ends. Any fragments with complementary sticky ends can base-pair, including the two original fragments; if the fragments come from different DNA molecules, the product is recombinant DNA.

DRAW IT *The restriction enzyme* Hind III *recognizes the sequence 5′-AAGCTT-3′, cutting between the two 'A's. Draw the double-stranded sequence before and after the enzyme cuts.*

Cloning a Eukaryotic Gene in a Bacterial Plasmid

Now that you've learned about restriction enzymes and DNA ligase, we can take a closer look at how genes are cloned in plasmids. The original plasmid is called a **cloning vector**, defined as a DNA molecule that can carry foreign DNA into a host cell and replicate there. Bacterial plasmids are widely used as cloning vectors for several reasons. They can be easily isolated from bacteria, manipulated to form recombinant plasmids by insertion of foreign DNA *in vitro*, and then reintroduced into bacterial cells. Moreover, recombinant bacterial plasmids (and the foreign DNA they carry) multiply rapidly owing to the high reproductive rate of their host cells.

Producing Clones of Cells Carrying Recombinant Plasmids

Let's say we are researchers interested in studying the β-globin gene in a particular species of hummingbird to see if this oxygen-carrying protein is different from its counterpart in other, less metabolically active species. **Figure 20.4** details one method for cloning hummingbird genes using a bacterial plasmid as the cloning vector.

❶ We begin by isolating hummingbird genomic DNA from hummingbird cells. We also isolate our chosen vector, a particular bacterial plasmid from *E. coli* cells. The plasmid has been engineered to carry two genes that will later prove useful: *amp^R*, which makes *E. coli* cells resistant to the antibiotic ampicillin, and *lacZ*, which encodes an enzyme called β-galactosidase that hydrolyzes the sugar lactose. This enzyme can also hydrolyze a similar synthetic molecule called X-gal to form a blue product. The plasmid contains only one copy of the restriction site recognized by the restriction enzyme used in the next step; that site is within the *lacZ* gene.

❷ Both the plasmid and the hummingbird DNA are cut with the same restriction enzyme, and then ❸ the fragments are mixed together, allowing base pairing between their complementary sticky ends. We then add DNA ligase, which covalently bonds the sugar-phosphate backbones of the fragments whose sticky ends have base-paired. Some of the resulting recombinant plasmids contain hummingbird DNA fragments like the three shown in Figure 20.4; one of the three carries the β-globin gene. This step will also generate other products, such as plasmids containing several hummingbird DNA fragments, a combination of two plasmids, or a rejoined, nonrecombinant version of the original plasmid.

❹ The DNA mixture is then added to bacteria that have a mutation in the *lacZ* gene on their own chromosome, making them unable to hydrolyze lactose or X-gal. Under suitable experimental conditions, the cells take up foreign DNA by

▼ **Figure 20.4** **Research Method**

Cloning Genes in Bacterial Plasmids

APPLICATION Gene cloning is a process that produces many copies of a gene of interest. These copies can be used in sequencing the gene, in producing its encoded protein, or in basic research or other applications.

TECHNIQUE In this example, hummingbird genes are inserted into plasmids from *E. coli*. Only three plasmids and three hummingbird DNA fragments are shown, but millions of copies of the plasmid and a mixture of millions of different hummingbird DNA fragments would be present in the samples.

❶ Isolate plasmid DNA from bacterial cells and DNA from hummingbird cells. The hummingbird DNA contains the gene of interest.

❷ Cut both DNA samples with the same restriction enzyme, one that makes a single cut within the *lacZ* gene and many cuts within the hummingbird DNA.

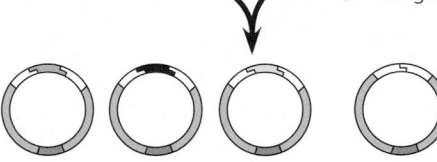

❸ Mix the cut plasmids and DNA fragments. Some join by base pairing; add DNA ligase to seal them together. The products are recombinant plasmids and many nonrecombinant plasmids.

❹ Mix the DNA with bacterial cells that have a mutation in their own *lacZ* gene. Some cells take up a recombinant plasmid or other DNA molecule by transformation.

❺ Plate the bacteria on agar containing ampicillin and X-gal, a molecule resembling lactose. Incubate until colonies grow.

RESULTS Only a cell that took up a plasmid, which has the *amp^R* gene, will reproduce and form a colony. Colonies with nonrecombinant plasmids will be blue, because they can hydrolyze X-gal, forming a blue product. Colonies with recombinant plasmids, in which *lacZ* is disrupted, will be white, because they cannot hydrolyze X-gal.

WHAT IF? *If the medium used in step 5 did not contain ampicillin, what other colonies would grow? What color would they be?*

transformation (see pp. 306 and 561). Some cells acquire a recombinant plasmid carrying a gene, while others may take up a nonrecombinant plasmid, a fragment of noncoding hummingbird DNA, or nothing at all. The *amp^R* and *lacZ* genes on the plasmid can help us sort out these possibilities.

⑤ First, plating out all the bacteria on solid nutrient medium (agar) containing ampicillin allows us to distinguish the cells that have taken up plasmids, whether recombinant or not, from the other cells. Under these conditions, only cells with a plasmid will reproduce because only they have the *amp^R* gene conferring resistance to the ampicillin in the medium. Each reproducing bacterium forms a clone of cells. Once the clone contains between 10^5 and 10^8 cells, it is visible as a mass, or *colony*, on the agar. As cells reproduce, any foreign genes carried by recombinant plasmids are also copied (cloned).

Second, the presence of X-gal in the medium allows us to distinguish colonies with recombinant plasmids from those with nonrecombinant plasmids. Colonies containing nonrecombinant plasmids have the *lacZ* gene intact and will produce functional β-galactosidase. These colonies will be blue because the enzyme hydrolyzes the X-gal in the medium, forming a blue product. In contrast, no functional β-galactosidase is produced in colonies containing recombinant plasmids with foreign DNA inserted into the *lacZ* gene; these colonies will therefore be white.

The procedure to this point will have cloned many different hummingbird DNA fragments, not just the β-globin gene that interests us. In fact, taken together, the white colonies should represent all the DNA sequences from the hummingbird genome, including noncoding regions as well as genes. How do we find the colony (cell clone) carrying the β-globin gene among the many clones carrying other pieces of hummingbird DNA? Before addressing this question, we must consider how the clones are stored.

Storing Cloned Genes in DNA Libraries

The cloning procedure in Figure 20.4, which starts with a mixture of fragments from the entire genome of an organism, is called a "shotgun" approach; no single gene is targeted for cloning. Thousands of different recombinant plasmids are produced in step 3, and a clone of cells carrying each type of plasmid ends up as a white colony in step 5. The complete set of plasmid-containing cell clones, each carrying copies of a particular segment from the initial genome, is referred to as a **genomic library** (Figure 20.5a). Each "plasmid clone" in the library is like a book containing specific information. Today, scientists often obtain such libraries (or even particular cloned genes) from another researcher, a commercial source, or a sequencing center.

Certain bacteriophages have also been used as cloning vectors for making genomic libraries. Fragments of foreign DNA

(a) Plasmid library. Shown are three of the thousands of "books" in a plasmid library. Each "book" is a clone of bacterial cells, which contain copies of a particular foreign genome fragment (pink, yellow, black segments) in their recombinant plasmids.

(b) Phage library. The same three foreign genome segments are shown in three "books" of a phage library.

(c) A library of bacterial artificial chromosome (BAC) clones. Such libraries are usually stored in a "multiwell" plastic plate; a 384-well plate is shown here. Each clone occupies one well. (The library of an entire genome would require many such plates.) Plasmid libraries can also be stored this way.

▲ **Figure 20.5 Genomic libraries.** A genomic library is a collection of many bacterial or phage clones. Each clone carries copies of a particular DNA segment from a foreign genome, integrated into an appropriate DNA vector, such as a plasmid or a trimmed-down phage genome. In a complete genomic library, the foreign DNA segments cover the entire genome of an organism. Note that the bacterial chromosomes in (a) and (c) are not drawn to scale; they are actually about 1,000 times as large as the vectors.

can be spliced into a trimmed-down version of a phage genome, as into a plasmid, by using a restriction enzyme and DNA ligase. The normal infection process allows production of many new phage particles, each carrying the foreign DNA. An advantage of using phages as vectors is that while a standard plasmid can carry a DNA insert no larger than 12,000 base pairs (12 kb), a phage can carry an insert of about 25 kb. A genomic library made using phages is stored as a collection of phage clones (Figure 20.5b). Because restriction enzymes do not recognize gene boundaries, some genes in either type of genomic library will be cut and divided up among two or more clones.

Another type of vector used in library construction is a **bacterial artificial chromosome (BAC)**. In spite of the name, these are simply large plasmids, trimmed down so they contain just the genes necessary to ensure replication and capable of carrying inserts of 100–300 kb. The very large insert size minimizes the number of clones needed to make up the genomic library, but it also makes them more challenging to work with in the lab. BAC clones are usually stored in multiwelled plastic plates, with one clone per well (Figure 20.5c). This orderly storage of clones, identified by their location in the plate, makes screening for the gene of interest very efficient, as we will see.

Researchers can make another kind of DNA library by starting with mRNA extracted from cells (Figure 20.6). The enzyme reverse transcriptase (obtained from retroviruses) is used *in vitro* to make single-stranded DNA transcripts of the mRNA molecules. Recall that the 3′ end of the mRNA has a stretch of adenine (A) ribonucleotides called a poly-A tail. This feature allows use of a short strand of thymine (dT) deoxyribonucleotides as a primer for the reverse transcriptase. Following enzymatic degradation of the mRNA, a second DNA strand, complementary to the first, is synthesized by DNA polymerase. The resulting double-stranded DNA is called **complementary DNA (cDNA)**. For creating a library, the cDNA is modified by the addition of restriction enzyme recognition sequences at each end. Then the cDNA is inserted into vector DNA in a manner similar to the insertion of genomic DNA fragments. The extracted mRNA is a mixture of all the mRNA molecules in the original cells, transcribed from many different genes. Therefore, the cDNAs that are cloned make up a **cDNA library** containing a collection of genes. However, a cDNA library represents only part of the genome—only the subset of genes that were transcribed in the cells from which the mRNA was isolated.

Genomic and cDNA libraries each have advantages, depending on what is being studied. If you want to clone a gene but don't know what cell type expresses it or cannot obtain enough cells of the appropriate type, a genomic library is almost certain to contain the gene. Also, if you are interested in the regulatory sequences or introns associated with a gene, a genomic library is required because these sequences are absent from the fully processed mRNAs used in making a cDNA library. For this very reason, if you are interested only in the coding sequence of a gene, you can obtain a stripped-down

① Reverse transcriptase is added to a test tube containing mRNA isolated from the cell.

DNA in nucleus

mRNAs in cytoplasm

② Reverse transcriptase makes the first DNA strand using the RNA as a template and a stretch of dT's as a DNA primer.

mRNA Reverse transcriptase Poly-A tail
5′ .... A A A A A A 3′
    3′ T T T T T 5′
DNA strand DNA Primer

③ mRNA is degraded by another enzyme.

5′ .... A A A A A A 3′
3′ T T T T T 5′

④ DNA polymerase synthesizes the second strand, using a primer in the reaction mixture. (Several options exist for primers.)

5′
3′ 3′
DNA polymerase 5′

⑤ The result is cDNA, which carries the complete coding sequence of the gene but no introns.

5′ 3′
3′ 5′
cDNA

▲ Figure 20.6 **Making complementary DNA (cDNA) for a eukaryotic gene.** Complementary DNA is DNA made *in vitro* using mRNA as a template for the first strand. Because the mRNA contains only exons, the resulting double-stranded cDNA carries the complete coding sequence of the gene but no introns. Although only one mRNA is shown here, the final collection of cDNAs would reflect all the mRNAs that were present in the cell.

version of the gene from a cDNA library. In our example of the hummingbird β-globin protein, a cDNA library would serve us well. We know which cells express the gene, so we could start making the library by isolating mRNA from hummingbird red blood cells. A cDNA library is also useful for studying the set of genes responsible for the specialized functions of a particular cell type, such as brain or liver cells. Finally, by making cDNA from cells of the same type at different times in the life of an organism, researchers can trace changes in patterns of gene expression during development.

Screening a Library for Clones Carrying a Gene of Interest

Now, returning to the results in Figure 20.4, we're ready to screen all the colonies with recombinant plasmids (the white colonies) for a clone of cells containing the hummingbird β-globin gene. We can detect this gene's DNA by its ability to base-pair with a complementary sequence on another nucleic acid molecule, using **nucleic acid hybridization**. The complementary molecule, a short, single-stranded nucleic acid that can be either RNA or DNA, is called a **nucleic acid probe**. If we know at least part of the nucleotide sequence of the gene of interest (perhaps from knowing the amino acid sequence of the protein it encodes or, as in our case, the gene's nucleotide sequence in a closely related species), we can synthesize a probe complementary to it. For example, if part of the sequence on one strand of the desired gene were

5′ ⸱⸱⸱GGCTAACTTAGC⸱⸱⸱ 3′

then we would synthesize this probe:

3′ CCGATTGAATCG 5′

Each probe molecule, which will hydrogen-bond specifically to a complementary sequence in the desired gene, is labeled with a radioactive isotope or a fluorescent tag so we can track it.

Recall that the clones in our hummingbird genomic library have been stored in a multiwell plate (see Figure 20.5c). If we transfer a few cells from each well to a defined location on a membrane made of nylon or nitrocellulose, we can screen a large number of clones simultaneously for the presence of DNA complementary to our DNA probe **(Figure 20.7)**.

Once we've identified the location of a clone carrying the β-globin gene, we can grow some cells from that colony in liquid

▼ Figure 20.7 **Research Method**

Detecting a Specific DNA Sequence by Hybridization with a Nucleic Acid Probe

APPLICATION   Hybridization with a complementary nucleic acid probe detects a specific DNA sequence within a mixture of DNA molecules. In this example, a collection of bacterial clones from a hummingbird genomic library is screened to identify clones that carry a recombinant plasmid bearing the gene of interest. The library is stored in many multiwell plates, with one clone per well (see Figure 20.5c).

TECHNIQUE   Cells from each clone are applied to a special nylon membrane. Each membrane has room for thousands of clones (many more than are shown here) so only a few membranes are needed to hold samples of all the clones in the library. This set of membranes is an *arrayed library* that can be screened for a specific gene using a labeled probe. Here the label is a radioactive nucleotide, but other commonly used labels include enzymes, covalently linked to the probe nucleotides, that can produce either a colored or luminescent product.

1 Plate by plate, cells from each well, representing one clone, are transferred to a defined spot on a special nylon membrane. The nylon membrane is treated to break open the cells and denature their DNA; the resulting single-stranded DNA molecules stick to the membrane.

2 The membrane is then incubated in a solution of radioactive probe molecules complementary to the gene of interest. Because the DNA immobilized on the membrane is single-stranded, the single-stranded probe can base-pair with any complementary DNA on the membrane. Excess DNA is then rinsed off. (One spot with radioactive probe–DNA hybrids is shown here in orange but would not be visible yet.)

3 The membrane is laid under photographic film, allowing any radioactive areas to expose the film (autoradiography). Black spots on the film correspond to the locations on the membrane of DNA that has hybridized to the probe. This location can be traced back to the original well containing the bacterial clone that holds the gene of interest.

RESULTS   The location of the black spot on the photographic film identifies the clone containing the gene of interest. By using probes with different nucleotide sequences, researchers can screen the collection of bacterial clones for different genes.

culture in a large tank and then easily isolate many copies of the gene for our studies. We can also use the cloned gene as a probe to identify similar or identical genes in DNA from other sources, such as other species of birds.

Expressing Cloned Eukaryotic Genes

Once a particular gene has been cloned in host cells, its protein product can be produced in large amounts for research purposes or valuable practical applications, which we'll explore in Concept 20.4. Cloned genes can be expressed as protein in either bacterial or eukaryotic cells; each option has advantages and disadvantages.

Bacterial Expression Systems

Getting a cloned eukaryotic gene to function in bacterial host cells can be difficult because certain aspects of gene expression are different in eukaryotes and bacteria. To overcome differences in promoters and other DNA control sequences, scientists usually employ an **expression vector**, a cloning vector that contains a highly active bacterial promoter just upstream of a restriction site where the eukaryotic gene can be inserted in the correct reading frame. The bacterial host cell will recognize the promoter and proceed to express the foreign gene now linked to that promoter. Such expression vectors allow the synthesis of many eukaryotic proteins in bacterial cells.

Another problem with expressing cloned eukaryotic genes in bacteria is the presence of noncoding regions (introns) in most eukaryotic genes. Introns can make a eukaryotic gene very long and unwieldy, and they prevent correct expression of the gene by bacterial cells, which do not have RNA-splicing machinery. This problem can be surmounted by using a cDNA form of the gene, which includes only the exons.

Eukaryotic Cloning and Expression Systems

Molecular biologists can avoid eukaryotic-bacterial incompatibility by using eukaryotic cells such as yeasts, rather than bacteria, as hosts for cloning and/or expressing eukaryotic genes of interest. Yeasts, single-celled fungi, offer two advantages: They are as easy to grow as bacteria, and they have plasmids, a rarity among eukaryotes. Scientists have even constructed recombinant plasmids that combine yeast and bacterial DNA and can replicate in either type of cell. Another useful tool for cloning eukaryotic genes are **yeast artificial chromosomes (YACs)**, which combine the essentials of a eukaryotic chromosome—an origin for DNA replication, a centromere, and two telomeres—with foreign DNA. These chromosome-like vectors behave like ordinary chromosomes during mitosis, cloning the foreign DNA as the yeast cell divides. Because a YAC can carry a much longer DNA segment than can a plasmid vector, a cloned fragment is more likely to contain an entire gene rather than just a portion of it.

Another reason to use eukaryotic host cells for expressing a cloned eukaryotic gene is that many eukaryotic proteins will not function unless they are modified after translation, for example by the addition of carbohydrate or lipid groups. Bacterial cells cannot carry out these modifications, and if the gene product requiring such processing is from a mammal, even yeast cells may not be able to modify the protein correctly. The use of host cells from an animal cell culture may therefore be necessary.

Scientists have developed a variety of methods for introducing recombinant DNA into eukaryotic cells. In **electroporation**, a brief electrical pulse applied to a solution containing cells creates temporary holes in their plasma membranes, through which DNA can enter. (This technique is now commonly used for bacteria as well.) Alternatively, scientists can inject DNA directly into single eukaryotic cells using microscopically thin needles. To get DNA into plant cells, the soil bacterium *Agrobacterium* can be used, as well as other methods you will learn about later. If the introduced DNA is incorporated into a cell's genome by genetic recombination, then it may be expressed by the cell.

Amplifying DNA *in Vitro*: The Polymerase Chain Reaction (PCR)

DNA cloning in cells remains the best method for preparing large quantities of a particular gene or other DNA sequence. However, when the source of DNA is scanty or impure, the **polymerase chain reaction**, or **PCR**, is quicker and more selective. In this technique, any specific target segment within one or many DNA molecules can be quickly amplified (copied many times) in a test tube. With automation, PCR can make billions of copies of a target segment of DNA in a few hours, significantly faster than the days it would take to obtain the same number of copies by screening a DNA library for a clone with the desired gene and letting it replicate within host cells. In fact, PCR is being used increasingly to make enough of a specific DNA fragment to insert it directly into a vector, entirely skipping the steps of making and screening a library. To continue our literary analogy, PCR is like photocopying just one page rather than checking out all the books in a library.

In the PCR procedure, a three-step cycle brings about a chain reaction that produces an exponentially growing population of identical DNA molecules. During each cycle, the reaction mixture is heated to denature (separate) the DNA strands and then cooled to allow annealing (hydrogen bonding) of short, single-stranded DNA primers complementary to sequences on opposite strands at each end of the target sequence; finally, a heat-stable DNA polymerase extends the primers in the $5' \rightarrow 3'$ direction. If a standard DNA polymerase were used, the protein would be denatured along with the DNA during the first heating step and would have to be replaced after each cycle. The key to automating PCR was the discovery of an unusual heat-stable DNA polymerase, first isolated from cells of a bacterial species living in hot springs, that could withstand the heat at the start of each cycle. **Figure 20.8** illustrates the steps in PCR.

Just as impressive as the speed of PCR is its specificity. Only minute amounts of DNA need be present in the starting material, and this DNA can be in a partially degraded state, as long as a few molecules contain the complete target sequence. The key to this high specificity is the primers, which hydrogen-bond *only* to sequences at opposite ends of the target segment. (For high specificity, the primers must be at least 15 or so nucleotides long.) By the end of the third cycle, one-fourth of the molecules are identical to the target segment, with both strands the appropriate length. With each successive cycle, the number of target segment molecules of the correct length doubles, soon greatly outnumbering all other DNA molecules in the reaction.

Despite its speed and specificity, PCR amplification cannot substitute for gene cloning in cells when large amounts of a gene are desired. Occasional errors during PCR replication impose limits on the number of good copies that can be made by this method. When PCR is used to provide the specific DNA fragment for cloning, the resulting clones are sequenced to select clones with error-free inserts.

Devised in 1985, PCR has had a major impact on biological research and biotechnology. PCR has been used to amplify DNA from a wide variety of sources: fragments of ancient DNA from a 40,000-year-old frozen woolly mammoth; DNA from fingerprints or from tiny amounts of blood, tissue, or semen found at crime scenes; DNA from single embryonic cells for rapid prenatal diagnosis of genetic disorders; and DNA of viral genes from cells infected with viruses that are difficult to detect, such as HIV. We'll return to applications of PCR later in the chapter.

The Polymerase Chain Reaction (PCR)

APPLICATION   With PCR, any specific segment—the target sequence—within a DNA sample can be copied many times (amplified), completely *in vitro*.

TECHNIQUE   PCR requires double-stranded DNA containing the target sequence, a heat-resistant DNA polymerase, all four nucleotides, and two 15- to 20-nucleotide DNA strands that serve as primers. One primer is complementary to one end of the target sequence on one strand; the second primer is complementary to the other end of the sequence on the other strand.

RESULTS   After 3 cycles, one-fourth of the molecules match the target sequence exactly. After 30 cycles, more than 99.99% of the molecules match the target sequence.

CONCEPT 20.2

DNA technology allows us to study the sequence, expression, and function of a gene

Once DNA cloning has provided us with large quantities of specific DNA segments, we can tackle some interesting questions about a particular gene and its function. For example, does the sequence of the hummingbird β-globin gene suggest a protein structure that can carry oxygen more efficiently than its counterpart in less metabolically active species? Does a particular human gene differ from person to person, and are certain alleles of that gene associated with a hereditary disorder? Where in the body and when is a given gene expressed? And, ultimately, what role does a certain gene play in an organism?

Before we can begin to address such compelling questions, we must consider a few standard laboratory techniques that are used to analyze the DNA of genes.

Gel Electrophoresis and Southern Blotting

Many approaches for studying DNA molecules involve **gel electrophoresis**. This technique uses a gel made of a polymer, such as a polysaccharide. The gel acts as a molecular sieve to separate nucleic acids or proteins on the basis of size, electrical charge, and other physical properties (**Figure 20.9**). Because nucleic acid molecules carry negative charges on their phosphate groups, they all travel toward the positive pole in

▼ Figure 20.9 **Research Method**

Gel Electrophoresis

APPLICATION Gel electrophoresis is used for separating nucleic acids or proteins that differ in size, electrical charge, or other physical properties. DNA molecules are separated by gel electrophoresis in restriction fragment analysis of both cloned genes (see Figure 20.10) and genomic DNA (see Figure 20.11).

TECHNIQUE Gel electrophoresis separates macromolecules on the basis of their rate of movement through a polymeric gel in an electric field: The distance a DNA molecule travels is inversely proportional to its length. A mixture of DNA molecules, usually fragments produced by restriction enzyme digestion (cutting) or PCR amplification, is separated into bands. Each band contains thousands of molecules of the same length.

① Each sample, a mixture of DNA molecules, is placed in a separate well near one end of a thin slab of gel. The gel is set into a small plastic support and immersed in an aqueous solution in a tray with electrodes at each end.

② When the current is turned on, the negatively charged DNA molecules move toward the positive electrode, with shorter molecules moving faster than longer ones. Bands are shown here in blue, but on an actual gel, the bands would not be visible at this time.

RESULTS After the current is turned off, a DNA-binding dye is added. This dye fluoresces pink in ultraviolet light, revealing the separated bands to which it binds. In the gel below, the pink bands correspond to DNA fragments of different lengths separated by electrophoresis. If all the samples were initially cut with the same restriction enzyme, then the different band patterns indicate that they came from different sources.

an electric field. As they move, the thicket of polymer fibers impedes longer molecules more than it does shorter ones, separating them by length. Thus, gel electrophoresis separates a mixture of linear DNA molecules into bands, each consisting of DNA molecules of the same length.

One useful application of this technique is *restriction fragment analysis*, which can rapidly provide useful information about DNA sequences. In this type of analysis, the DNA fragments produced by restriction enzyme digestion (cutting) of a DNA molecule are sorted by gel electrophoresis. When the mixture of restriction fragments undergoes electrophoresis, it yields a band pattern characteristic of the starting molecule and the restriction enzyme used. In fact, the relatively small DNA molecules of viruses and plasmids can be identified simply by their restriction fragment patterns. Because DNA can be recovered undamaged from gels, the procedure also provides a way to prepare pure samples of individual fragments—if the bands can be clearly resolved. (Very large DNA molecules, such as those of eukaryotic chromosomes, yield so many fragments that they appear as a smear instead of distinct bands.)

Restriction fragment analysis is also useful for comparing two different DNA molecules—for example, two alleles of a gene. A restriction enzyme recognizes a specific sequence of nucleotides, and a change in even one base pair of that sequence will prevent it from cutting at a particular site. Therefore, if the nucleotide differences between two alleles occur within a restriction site, digestion with the enzyme that recognizes the site will produce a different mixture of fragments from each allele. Each mixture will give its own band pattern in gel electrophoresis. For example, sickle-cell disease is caused by mutation of a single nucleotide located within a restriction sequence in the human β-globin gene (see Figure 17.22 and p. 278). Consequently, restriction fragment analysis by electrophoresis can distinguish the normal and sickle-cell alleles of the β-globin gene, as shown in **Figure 20.10**.

The starting materials in Figure 20.10 are samples of the cloned and purified β-globin alleles. But what can we do if we don't have purified alleles to start with? Suppose we wanted to determine whether a person is a heterozygous carrier of the mutant allele for sickle-cell disease. In this case, we would directly compare the genomic DNA from that person with DNA from both a person who has sickle-cell disease (and is homozygous for the mutant allele) and a person who is homozygous for the normal allele. As we mentioned already, electrophoresis of genomic DNA digested with a restriction enzyme and stained with a DNA-binding dye yields too many bands to distinguish them individually. However, a method called **Southern blotting** (developed by British biochemist Edwin Southern), which combines gel electrophoresis and nucleic acid hybridization, allows us to detect just those bands that include parts of the β-globin gene. The principle is the same as in nucleic acid hybridization for screening bacterial clones (see Figure 20.7). In Southern blotting, the probe is usu-

(a) *Dde*I restriction sites in normal and sickle-cell alleles of β-globin gene. Shown here are the cloned alleles, separated from the vector DNA but including some DNA next to the coding sequence. The normal allele contains two sites within the coding sequence recognized by the *Dde*I restriction enzyme. The sickle-cell allele lacks one of these sites.

(b) Electrophoresis of restriction fragments from normal and sickle-cell alleles. Samples of each purified allele were cut with the *Dde*I enzyme and then subjected to gel electrophoresis, resulting in three bands for the normal allele and two bands for the sickle-cell allele. (The tiny fragments on the ends of both initial DNA molecules are identical and are not seen here.)

▲ Figure 20.10 **Using restriction fragment analysis to distinguish the normal and sickle-cell alleles of the human β-globin gene. (a)** The sickle-cell mutation destroys one of the *Dde*I restriction sites within the gene. **(b)** As a result, digestion with the *Dde*I enzyme generates different fragments from the normal and sickle-cell alleles.

WHAT IF? *Given recombinant bacterial clones carrying each of these alleles, how would you isolate the DNA of the alleles to provide the pure samples run on the gel in (b)? (Hint: Study Figures 20.4 and 20.9.)*

ally a radioactive single-stranded DNA molecule that is complementary to the gene of interest. **Figure 20.11** outlines the entire procedure and demonstrates how it can differentiate a heterozygote (in this case, for the sickle-cell allele) from an individual homozygous for the normal allele.

The identification of carriers of mutant alleles associated with genetic diseases is only one of the ways Southern blotting has been used. In fact, this technique has been a laboratory workhorse for many years. Recently, however, it has been supplanted by more rapid methods, often involving PCR amplification of the specific parts of genomes that may differ.

Research Method

Southern Blotting of DNA Fragments

APPLICATION   Researchers can detect specific nucleotide sequences within a complex DNA sample with this method. In particular, Southern blotting is useful for comparing the restriction fragments produced from different samples of genomic DNA.

TECHNIQUE   In this example, we compare genomic DNA samples from three individuals: a homozygote for the normal β-globin allele (I), a homozygote for the mutant sickle-cell allele (II), and a heterozygote (III). As in Figure 20.7, we show a radioactively labeled probe, but other methods of probe labeling and detection are also used.

1 Preparation of restriction fragments. Each DNA sample is mixed with the same restriction enzyme, in this case *Dde*I. Digestion of each sample yields a mixture of thousands of restriction fragments.

2 Gel electrophoresis. The restriction fragments in each sample are separated by electrophoresis, forming a characteristic pattern of bands. (In reality, there would be many more bands than shown here, and they would be invisible unless stained.)

3 DNA transfer (blotting). With the gel arranged as shown above, capillary action pulls the alkaline solution upward through the gel, transferring the DNA to a nitrocellulose membrane, producing the blot; the DNA is denatured in the process. (Another version of this method uses an electrical current to hasten the DNA transfer.) The single strands of DNA stuck to the nitrocellulose are positioned in bands corresponding to those on the gel.

4 Hybridization with radioactive probe. The nitrocellulose blot is exposed to a solution containing a radioactively labeled probe. In this example, the probe is single-stranded DNA complementary to the β-globin gene. Probe molecules attach by base-pairing to any restriction fragments containing a part of the β-globin gene. (The bands would not be visible yet.)

5 Probe detection. A sheet of photographic film is laid over the blot. The radioactivity in the bound probe exposes the film to form an image corresponding to those bands containing DNA that base-paired with the probe.

RESULTS   Because the band patterns for the three samples are clearly different, this method can be used to identify heterozygous carriers of the sickle-cell allele (III), as well as those with the disease, who have two mutant alleles (II), and unaffected individuals, who have two normal alleles (I). The band patterns for samples I and II resemble those observed for the purified normal and mutant alleles, respectively, seen in Figure 20.10b. The band pattern for the sample from the heterozygote (III) is a combination of the patterns for the two homozygotes (I and II).

▼ Figure 20.12 Research Method

Dideoxy Chain Termination Method for Sequencing DNA

APPLICATION The sequence of nucleotides in any cloned DNA fragment up to about 800 base pairs in length can be determined rapidly with machines that carry out sequencing reactions and separate the labeled reaction products by length.

TECHNIQUE This method synthesizes a set of DNA strands complementary to the original DNA fragment. Each strand starts with the same primer and ends with a dideoxyribonucleotide (ddNTP), a modified nucleotide. Incorporation of a ddNTP terminates a growing DNA strand because it lacks a 3' —OH group, the site for attachment of the next nucleotide (see Figure 16.14). In the set of strands synthesized, each nucleotide position along the original sequence is represented by strands ending at that point with the complementary ddNTP. Because each type of ddNTP is tagged with a distinct fluorescent label, the identity of the ending nucleotides of the new strands, and ultimately the entire original sequence, can be determined.

1 The fragment of DNA to be sequenced is denatured into single strands and incubated in a test tube with the necessary ingredients for DNA synthesis: a primer designed to base pair with the known 3' end of the template strand, DNA polymerase, the four deoxyribonucleotides, and the four dideoxyribonucleotides, each tagged with a specific fluorescent molecule.

2 Synthesis of each new strand starts at the 3' end of the primer and continues until a dideoxyribonucleotide is inserted, at random, instead of the normal equivalent deoxyribonucleotide. This prevents further elongation of the strand. Eventually, a set of labeled strands of various lengths is generated, with the color of the tag representing the last nucleotide in the sequence.

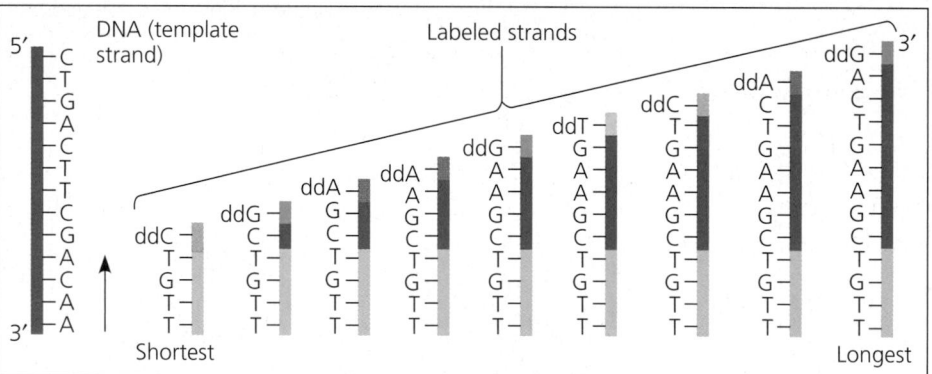

3 The labeled strands in the mixture are separated by passage through a polyacrylamide gel, with shorter strands moving through faster. For DNA sequencing, the gel is formed in a capillary tube rather than a slab like that shown in Figure 20.9. The small size of the tube allows a fluorescence detector to sense the color of each fluorescent tag as the strands come through. Strands differing in length by as little as one nucleotide can be distinguished from each other.

RESULTS The color of the fluorescent tag on each strand indicates the identity of the nucleotide at its end. The results can be printed out as a spectrogram, and the sequence, which is complementary to the template strand, can then be read from bottom (shortest strand) to top (longest strand). (Notice that the sequence here begins after the primer.)

DNA Sequencing

Once a gene is cloned, its complete nucleotide sequence can be determined. Today, sequencing is automated, carried out by sequencing machines. The automated procedure is based on a technique called the *dideoxyribonucleotide* (or *dideoxy*, for short) *chain termination method*, for reasons you can see in **Figure 20.12**. This method was developed by British biochemist Frederick Sanger, who received the Nobel Prize in 1980 for this accomplishment. (One of only four people to win two Nobel Prizes, Sanger also won one in 1975 for determining the amino acid sequence of insulin.)

Knowing the sequence of a gene allows researchers to compare it directly with genes in other species, where the function of the gene product may be known. If two genes from different species are quite similar in sequence, it is reasonable to suppose that their gene products perform similar functions. In this way, sequence comparisons provide clues to a gene's function, a topic we'll return to shortly. Another set of clues is provided by experimental approaches that analyze when and where a gene is expressed.

Analyzing Gene Expression

Having cloned a given gene, researchers can make labeled nucleic acid probes that will hybridize with mRNAs transcribed from the gene. The probes can provide information about when or where in the organism the gene is transcribed. Transcription levels are commonly used as a measure of gene expression.

Studying the Expression of Single Genes

Suppose we want to find out how the expression of the β-globin gene changes during the embryonic development of the hummingbird. There are at least two ways to do this.

The first is called **Northern blotting** (a play on words based on this method's similarity to Southern blotting). In this method, we carry out gel electrophoresis on samples of mRNA from hummingbird embryos at different stages of development, transfer the samples to a nitrocellulose membrane, and then allow the mRNAs on the membrane to hybridize with a labeled probe recognizing β-globin mRNA. If we expose a film to the membrane, the resulting image will look similar to the Southern blot in Figure 20.11, with one band of a given size showing up in each sample. If the mRNA band is seen at a particular stage, we can hypothesize that the protein functions during events taking place at that stage. Like Southern blotting, Northern blotting has been a mainstay over the years, but it is being supplanted in many labs by other techniques.

A method that is quicker and more sensitive (and therefore becoming more widely used) is the **reverse transcriptase–polymerase chain reaction**, or **RT-PCR** (Figure 20.13). Analysis of hummingbird β-globin gene expression with RT-PCR be-

▼ **Figure 20.13** **Research Method**

RT-PCR Analysis of the Expression of Single Genes

APPLICATION RT-PCR uses the enzyme reverse transcriptase (RT) in combination with PCR and gel electrophoresis. RT-PCR can be used to compare gene expression between samples—for instance, in different embryonic stages, in different tissues, or in the same type of cell under different conditions.

TECHNIQUE In this example, samples containing mRNAs from six embryonic stages of hummingbird were processed as shown below. (The mRNA from only one stage is shown.)

1. **cDNA synthesis** is carried out by incubating the mRNAs with reverse transcriptase and other necessary components.

2. **PCR amplification** of the sample is performed using primers specific to the hummingbird β-globin gene.

3. **Gel electrophoresis** will reveal amplified DNA products only in samples that contained mRNA transcribed from the β-globin gene.

RESULTS The mRNA for this gene first is expressed at stage 2 and continues to be expressed through stage 6. The size of the amplified fragment depends on the distance between the primers that were used.

gins similarly to Northern blotting, with the isolation of mRNAs from different developmental stages of hummingbird embryos. Reverse transcriptase is added next to make cDNA, which then serves as a template for PCR amplification using primers from the β-globin gene. When the products are run on a gel, copies of the amplified region will be observed as bands only in samples that originally contained the β-globin mRNA. In the case of hummingbird β-globin, for instance, we might expect to see a band appear at the stage when red blood cells begin forming, with all subsequent stages showing the same band. RT-PCR can also be carried out with mRNAs collected from different tissues at one time to discover which tissue is producing a specific mRNA.

An alternative way to determine which tissues or cells are expressing certain genes is to track down the location of specific mRNAs using labeled probes in place, or *in situ*, in the in-

▲ **Figure 20.14 Determining where genes are expressed by *in situ* hybridization analysis.** This *Drosophila* embryo was incubated in a solution containing probes for five different mRNAs, each probe labeled with a different fluorescently colored tag. The embryo was then viewed using fluorescence microscopy. Each color marks where a specific gene is expressed as mRNA.

tact organism. This technique, called ***in situ* hybridization**, is most often carried out with probes labeled by attachment of fluorescent dyes (see Chapter 6). Different probes can be labeled with different dyes, sometimes with strikingly beautiful results **(Figure 20.14)**.

Studying the Expression of Interacting Groups of Genes

A major goal of biologists is to learn how genes act together to produce and maintain a functioning organism. Now that the entire genomes of a number of organisms have been sequenced, it is possible to study the expression of large groups of genes—a systems approach. Researchers use genome sequences as probes to investigate which genes are transcribed in different situations, such as in different tissues or at different stages of development. They also look for groups of genes that are expressed in a coordinated manner, with the aim of identifying networks of gene expression across an entire genome.

The basic strategy in such global (genome-wide) expression studies is to isolate the mRNAs made in particular cells, use these molecules as templates for making the corresponding cDNAs by reverse transcription, and then employ nucleic acid hybridization to compare this set of cDNAs with a collection of DNA fragments representing all or part of the genome. The results identify the subset of genes in the genome that are being expressed at a given time or under certain conditions. DNA technology makes such studies possible; with automation, they are easily performed on a large scale. Scientists can now measure the expression of thousands of genes at one time.

Genome-wide expression studies are made possible by **DNA microarray assays**. A DNA microarray consists of tiny amounts of a large number of single-stranded DNA fragments representing different genes fixed to a glass slide in a tightly spaced array, or grid (see Figure 20.1). (The microarray is also called a *DNA chip* by analogy to a computer chip.) Ideally, these fragments represent all the genes of an organism. **Figure 20.15** outlines how the DNA fragments on a microarray are tested for

▼ **Figure 20.15** **Research Method**

DNA Microarray Assay of Gene Expression Levels

APPLICATION With this method, researchers can test thousands of genes simultaneously to determine which ones are expressed in a particular tissue, under different environmental conditions, in various disease states, or at different developmental stages. They can also look for coordinated gene expression.

TECHNIQUE

❶ Isolate mRNA.

Tissue sample

mRNA molecules

❷ Make cDNA by reverse transcription, using fluorescently labeled nucleotides.

Labeled cDNA molecules (single strands)

❸ Apply the cDNA mixture to a microarray, a microscope slide on which copies of single-stranded DNA fragments from the organism's genes are fixed, a different gene in each spot. The cDNA hybridizes with any complementary DNA on the microarray.

DNA fragments representing specific genes

DNA microarray

❹ Rinse off excess cDNA; scan microarray for fluorescence. Each fluorescent spot (yellow) represents a gene expressed in the tissue sample.

DNA microarray with 2,400 human genes (actual size)

RESULTS The intensity of fluorescence at each spot is a measure of the expression in the tissue sample of the gene represented by that spot. Most often, as in the actual microarray above, two different samples are tested together by labeling the cDNAs prepared from each sample with labels of different colors, often green and red. The resulting color at a spot reveals the relative levels of expression of a particular gene in the two samples: Green indicates expression in one sample, red in the other, yellow in both, and black in neither. (See Figure 20.1 for a larger view.)

hybridization with cDNA molecules that have been prepared from the mRNAs in particular cells of interest and labeled with fluorescent dyes.

Using this technique, researchers have performed DNA microarray assays on more than 90% of the genes of the nematode *Caenorhabditis elegans*, during every stage of its life cycle. The results show that expression of nearly 60% of the genes changes dramatically during development and that many genes are expressed in a sex-specific pattern. This study supports the model held by most developmental biologists that embryonic development involves a complex and elaborate program of gene expression, rather than simply the expression of a small number of important genes. This example illustrates the ability of DNA microarrays to reveal general profiles of gene expression over the lifetime of an organism.

In addition to uncovering gene interactions and providing clues to gene function, DNA microarray assays may contribute to a better understanding of diseases and suggest new diagnostic techniques or therapies. For instance, comparing patterns of gene expression in breast cancer tumors and noncancerous breast tissue has already resulted in more informed and effective treatment protocols. Ultimately, information from DNA microarray assays should provide a grander view of how ensembles of genes interact to form an organism and maintain its vital systems.

Determining Gene Function

How do scientists determine the function of a gene identified by the techniques described thus far in the chapter? Perhaps the most common approach is to disable the gene and then observe the consequences in the cell or organism. In one application of this approach, called *in vitro* **mutagenesis**, specific mutations are introduced into a cloned gene, and then the mutated gene is returned to a cell in such a way that it disables ("knocks out") the normal cellular copies of the same gene. If the introduced mutations alter or destroy the function of the gene product, the phenotype of the mutant cell may help reveal the function of the missing normal protein. Using molecular and genetic techniques worked out in the 1980s, researchers can even generate mice with any given gene disabled, in order to study the role of that gene in development and in the adult. Mario Capecchi, Martin Evans, and Oliver Smithies received the 2007 Nobel Prize in Medicine for first accomplishing this feat. Several projects currently underway aim to disable every one of the over 20,000 genes in the mouse genome. These ambitious efforts will enhance our understanding of mammalian gene function.

A newer method for silencing expression of selected genes exploits the phenomenon of **RNA interference (RNAi)**, described in Chapter 18. This experimental approach uses synthetic double-stranded RNA molecules matching the sequence of a particular gene to trigger breakdown of the gene's messenger RNA or to block its translation. To date, the RNAi technique has been used successfully to reduce ("knock down") the expression of specific genes in mammalian cells, including human cells in culture, and plans are under way to try RNAi for the treatment of certain human disorders, including macular degeneration of the eye. In other organisms, such as the nematode and the fruit fly, RNAi has already proved valuable for analyzing the functions of genes on a large scale. In one study, RNAi was used to prevent expression of 86% of the genes in early nematode embryos, one gene at a time. Analysis of the phenotypes of the worms that developed from these embryos allowed the researchers to classify most of the genes into a small number of groups by function. This type of genome-wide analysis of gene function is sure to become more common as research focuses on the importance of interactions between genes in the system as a whole—the basis of systems biology (see Chapter 1).

The techniques and experimental approaches you have learned about thus far have already taught us a great deal about genes and the functions of their products. This DNA research is now being augmented by the development of powerful techniques for cloning whole multicellular organisms. An aim of this work is to obtain special types of cells, called stem cells, that give rise to all the different kinds of tissues. On a basic level, stem cells would allow scientists to use the DNA methods previously discussed to study the process of cell differentiation. On a more applied level, recombinant DNA techniques could be used to alter stem cells for the treatment of disease. Methods involving the cloning of organisms and production of stem cells are the subject of the next section.

CONCEPT CHECK 20.2

1. Suppose you carried out electrophoresis on a sample of genomic DNA isolated from an individual and treated with a restriction enzyme. After staining the gel with a DNA-binding dye, what would you see? Explain.

2. Describe the roles played by complementary base pairing between nucleic acid strands in each of the following techniques: Southern blotting, DNA sequencing, Northern blotting, RT-PCR, and microarray analysis.

3. **WHAT IF?** Look at the microarray in Figure 20.1, which is a larger version of the one in Figure 20.15. If one sample, labeled with a green fluorescent dye, was from normal tissue, and the other, labeled red, was from cancerous tissue, what does this mean for a spot that is green? Red? Yellow? Black? Based on their expression patterns, which genes would you be interested in examining further if you were studying cancer? Explain.

For suggested answers, see Appendix A.

CONCEPT 20.3

Cloning organisms may lead to production of stem cells for research and other applications

In parallel with advances in DNA technology, scientists have been developing and refining methods for cloning whole multicellular organisms from single cells. In this context, cloning produces one or more organisms genetically identical to the "parent" that donated the single cell. This is often called *organismal cloning* to differentiate it from gene cloning and, more significantly, from cell cloning—the division of an asexually reproducing cell into a collection of genetically identical cells. (The common theme for all types of cloning is that the product is genetically identical to the parent. In fact, the word *clone* comes from the Greek *klon*, meaning "twig.") The current interest in organismal cloning arises primarily from its potential to generate stem cells, which can in turn generate many different tissues.

The cloning of plants and animals was first attempted over 50 years ago in experiments designed to answer basic biological questions. For example, researchers wondered if all the cells of an organism have the same genes (a concept called *genomic equivalence*) or if cells lose genes during the process of differentiation (see Chapter 18). One way to answer this question is to see whether a differentiated cell can generate a whole organism—in other words, whether cloning an organism is possible. Let's discuss these early experiments before we consider more recent progress in organismal cloning and procedures for producing stem cells.

Cloning Plants: Single-Cell Cultures

The successful cloning of whole plants from single differentiated cells was accomplished during the 1950s by F. C. Steward and his students at Cornell University, who worked with carrot plants (Figure 20.16). They found that differentiated cells taken from the root (the carrot) and incubated in culture medium could grow into normal adult plants, each genetically identical to the parent plant. These results showed that differentiation does not necessarily involve irreversible changes in the DNA. In plants, at least, mature cells can "dedifferentiate" and then give rise to all the specialized cell types of the organism. Any cell with this potential is said to be **totipotent**.

Plant cloning is now used extensively in agriculture. For some plants, such as orchids, cloning is the only commercially practical means of reproducing plants. In other cases, cloning has been used to reproduce a plant with valuable characteristics, such as the ability to resist a plant pathogen. In fact, you yourself may be a plant cloner: If you have ever grown a new plant from a cutting, you have practiced cloning!

▼ Figure 20.16 **Inquiry**

Can a differentiated plant cell develop into a whole plant?

EXPERIMENT In 1958, F. C. Steward and colleagues at Cornell University tested individual cells from a fully formed carrot for their ability to form a plant.

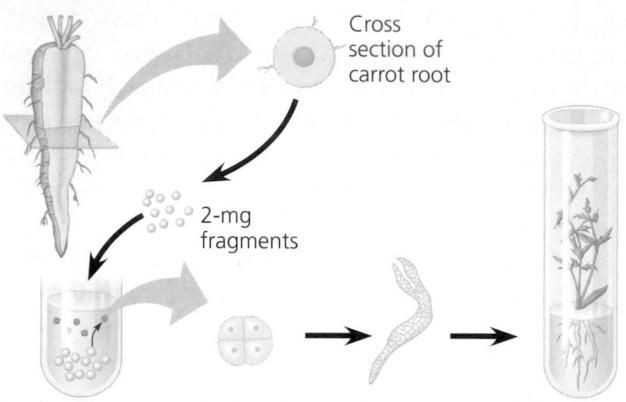

Cross section of carrot root

2-mg fragments

Fragments were cultured in nutrient medium; stirring caused single cells to shear off into the liquid.

Single cells free in suspension began to divide.

Embryonic plant developed from a cultured single cell.

Plantlet was cultured on agar medium. Later it was planted in soil.

RESULTS A single somatic (nonreproductive) carrot cell developed into a mature carrot plant. The new plant was a genetic duplicate (clone) of the parent plant.

Adult plant

CONCLUSION At least some differentiated somatic cells in plants are totipotent, able to reverse their differentiation and then give rise to all the cell types in a mature plant.

SOURCE F. C. Steward et al., Growth and organized development of cultured cells. II. Organization in cultures grown from suspended cells, *American Journal of Botany* 45:705–708 (1958).

WHAT IF? If each individual cell had developed into only one type of tissue instead of a whole plant, what might the researchers have concluded?

Cloning Animals: Nuclear Transplantation

Differentiated cells from animals generally do not divide in culture, much less develop into the multiple cell types of a new organism. Therefore, early researchers had to use a different approach to the question of whether differentiated animal cells can be totipotent. Their approach was to remove the nucleus of an unfertilized or fertilized egg and replace it with the nucleus of a differentiated cell, a procedure called *nuclear transplantation*. If the nucleus from the differentiated donor cell retains its full genetic capability, then it should be able to direct development of the recipient cell into all the tissues and organs of an organism.

Such experiments were conducted on frogs by Robert Briggs and Thomas King in the 1950s and by John Gurdon in the 1970s. These researchers transplanted a nucleus from an embryonic or tadpole cell into an enucleated (nucleus-lacking) egg of the same species. In Gurdon's experiments, the transplanted nucleus was often able to support normal development of the egg into a tadpole (**Figure 20.17**). However, he found that the potential of a transplanted nucleus to direct normal development was inversely related to the age of the donor: the older the donor nucleus, the lower the percentage of normally developing tadpoles.

From these results, Gurdon concluded that something in the nucleus *does* change as animal cells differentiate. In frogs and most other animals, nuclear potential tends to be restricted more and more as embryonic development and cell differentiation progress.

Reproductive Cloning of Mammals

In addition to cloning frogs, researchers have long been able to clone mammals using nuclei or cells from a variety of early embryos. But it was not known whether a nucleus from a fully differentiated cell could be reprogrammed to succeed in acting as a donor nucleus. In 1997, however, Scottish researchers captured newspaper headlines when they announced the birth of Dolly, a lamb cloned from an adult sheep by nuclear transplantation from a differentiated cell (**Figure 20.18**, on the next page). These researchers achieved the necessary dedifferentiation of donor nuclei by culturing mammary cells in nutrient-poor medium. They then fused these cells with enucleated sheep eggs. The resulting diploid cells divided to form early embryos, which were implanted into surrogate mothers. Out of several hundred implanted embryos, one successfully completed normal development, and Dolly was born.

Later analyses showed that Dolly's chromosomal DNA was indeed identical to that of the nucleus donor. (Her mitochondrial DNA came from the egg donor, as expected.) In 2003, at age 6, Dolly suffered complications from a lung disease usually seen only in much older sheep and was euthanized. Dolly's premature death, as well as her arthritic condition, led to speculation that her cells were in some way not quite as healthy as those of a normal sheep, possibly reflecting incomplete reprogramming of the original transplanted nucleus.

Since 1997, researchers have cloned numerous other mammals, including mice, cats, cows, horses, mules, pigs, and dogs. In most cases, their goal has been the production of new indi-

▼ **Figure 20.17** **Inquiry**

Can the nucleus from a differentiated animal cell direct development of an organism?

EXPERIMENT   John Gurdon and colleagues at Oxford University, in England, destroyed the nuclei of frog eggs by exposing the eggs to ultraviolet light. They then transplanted nuclei from cells of frog embryos and tadpoles into the enucleated eggs.

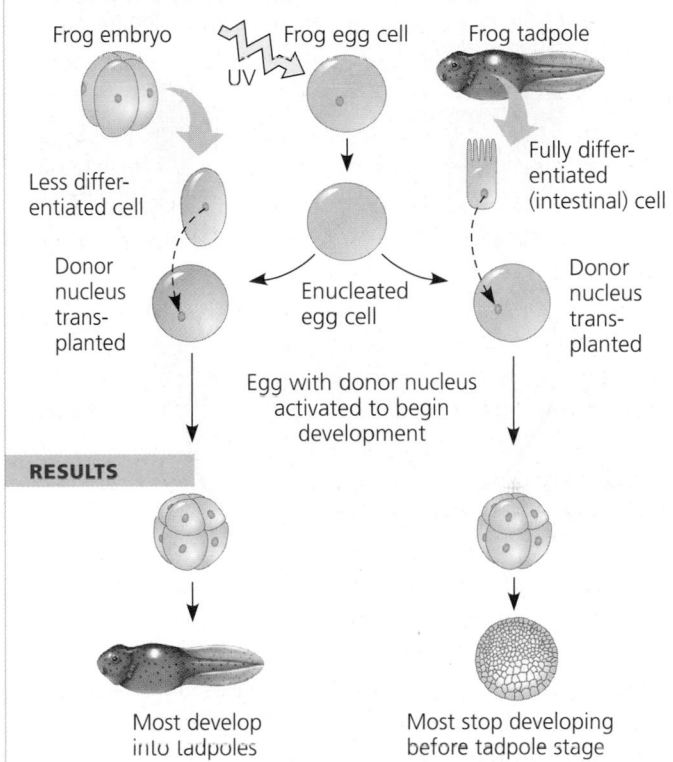

RESULTS

When the transplanted nuclei came from an early embryo, whose cells are relatively undifferentiated, most of the recipient eggs developed into tadpoles. But when the nuclei came from the fully differentiated intestinal cells of a tadpole, fewer than 2% of the eggs developed into normal tadpoles, and most of the embryos stopped developing at a much earlier stage.

CONCLUSION   The nucleus from a differentiated frog cell can direct development of a tadpole. However, its ability to do so decreases as the donor cell becomes more differentiated, presumably because of changes in the nucleus.

SOURCE   J. B. Gurdon et al., The developmental capacity of nuclei transplanted from keratinized cells of adult frogs, *Journal of Embryology and Experimental Morphology* 34:93–112 (1975).

WHAT IF?   If each cell in a four-cell embryo was already so specialized that it was not totipotent, what results would you predict for the experiment on the left side of the figure?

viduals; this is known as *reproductive cloning*. We have already learned a lot from such experiments. For example, cloned animals of the same species do *not* always look or behave identically. In a herd of cows cloned from the same line of cultured cells, certain cows are dominant in behavior and others are

Reproductive Cloning of a Mammal by Nuclear Transplantation

APPLICATION This method is used to produce cloned animals whose nuclear genes are identical to those of the animal supplying the nucleus.

TECHNIQUE Shown here is the procedure used to produce Dolly, the first reported case of a mammal cloned using the nucleus of a differentiated cell.

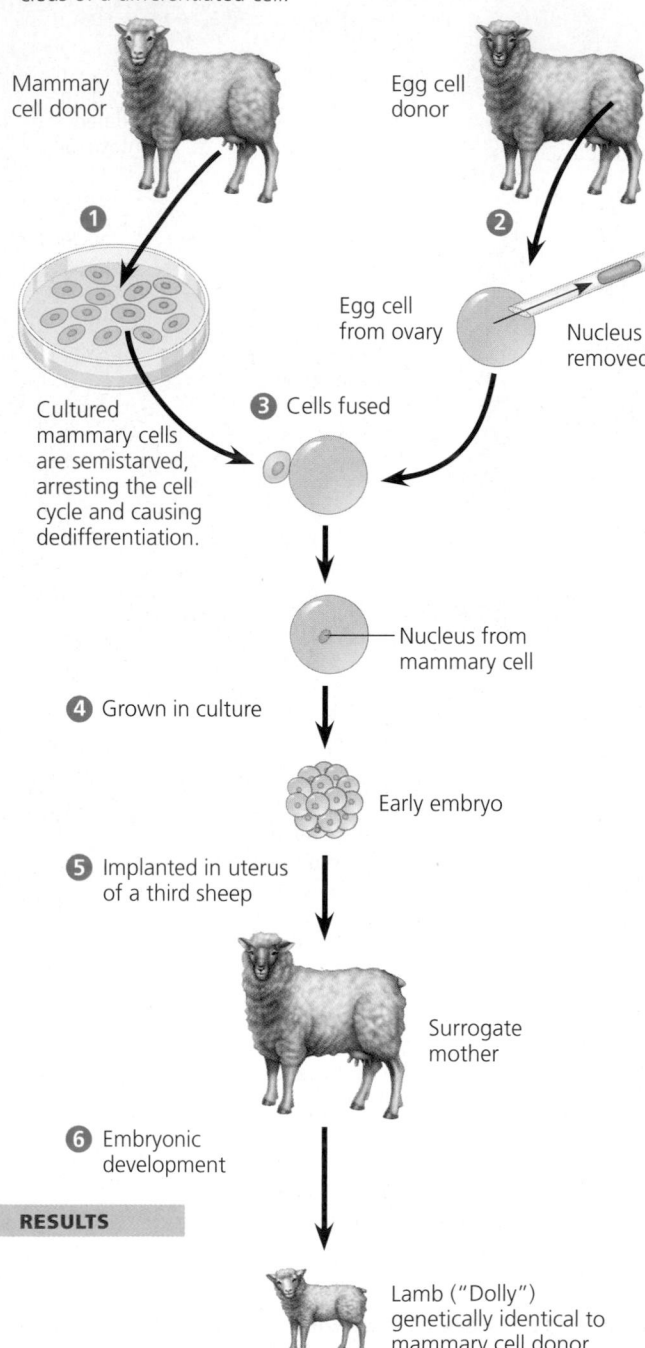

Mammary cell donor

Egg cell donor

① ②

Egg cell from ovary

Nucleus removed

Cultured mammary cells are semistarved, arresting the cell cycle and causing dedifferentiation.

③ Cells fused

Nucleus from mammary cell

④ Grown in culture

Early embryo

⑤ Implanted in uterus of a third sheep

Surrogate mother

⑥ Embryonic development

RESULTS

Lamb ("Dolly") genetically identical to mammary cell donor

The genetic makeup of the cloned animal is identical to that of the animal supplying the nucleus but differs from that of the egg donor and surrogate mother. (The latter two are "Scottish blackface" sheep, with dark faces.)

▲ **Figure 20.19 CC, the first cloned cat, and her single parent.** Rainbow (left) donated the nucleus in a cloning procedure that resulted in CC (right). However, the two cats are not identical: Rainbow is a classic calico cat with orange patches on her fur and has a "reserved personality," while CC has a gray and white coat and is more playful.

more submissive. Another example of nonidentity in clones is the first cloned cat, named CC for Carbon Copy **(Figure 20.19)**. She has a calico coat, like her single female parent, but the color and pattern are different because of random X chromosome inactivation, which is a normal occurrence during embryonic development (see Figure 15.8). And identical human twins, which are naturally occurring "clones," are always slightly different. Clearly, environmental influences and random phenomena can play a significant role during development.

The successful cloning of so many mammals has heightened speculation about the cloning of humans. Scientists in several labs around the world have tackled the first steps of this feat. In the most common approach, nuclei from differentiated human cells are transplanted into unfertilized enucleated eggs, and the eggs are stimulated to divide. In 2001, a research group in Massachusetts observed a few early cell divisions in such an experiment. A few years later, South Korean researchers reported cloning embryos to an early stage called the blastocyst stage. This apparent success of human cloning techniques raised unprecedented ethical issues, igniting a heated debate. The later retraction of the Korean report has bought us a little more time to consider such issues.

Problems Associated with Animal Cloning

In most nuclear transplantation studies thus far, only a small percentage of cloned embryos develop normally to birth. And like Dolly, many cloned animals exhibit defects. Cloned mice, for instance, are prone to obesity, pneumonia, liver failure, and premature death. Scientists assert that even cloned animals that appear normal are likely to have subtle defects.

In recent years, we have begun to uncover some reasons for the low efficiency of cloning and the high incidence of abnormalities. In the nuclei of fully differentiated cells, a small subset of genes is turned on and expression of the rest is repressed. This regulation often is the result of epigenetic changes in chromatin, such as acetylation of histones or methylation of DNA (see Figure 18.7). During the nuclear transfer procedure, many of these changes must be reversed in the later-stage nucleus from a donor animal for genes to be expressed or repressed appropriately in early stages of development. Researchers have found that the DNA in embryonic cells from cloned embryos, like that of differentiated cells, often has more methyl groups than does the DNA in equivalent cells from uncloned embryos of the same species. This finding suggests that the reprogramming of donor nuclei requires chromatin restructuring, which occurs incompletely during cloning procedures. Because DNA methylation helps regulate gene expression, misplaced methyl groups in the DNA of donor nuclei may interfere with the pattern of gene expression necessary for normal embryonic development. In fact, the success of a cloning attempt may depend in large part on whether or not the chromatin structure in the donor nucleus can be restored to that of a newly fertilized egg.

Stem Cells of Animals

The major goal of cloning human embryos is not reproduction, but the production of stem cells for treating human diseases. A **stem cell** is a relatively unspecialized cell that can both reproduce itself indefinitely and, under appropriate conditions, differentiate into specialized cells of one or more types. Thus, stem cells are able both to replenish their own population and to generate cells that travel down specific differentiation pathways.

Many early animal embryos contain stem cells capable of giving rise to differentiated embryonic cells of any type. Stem cells can be isolated from early embryos at a stage called the blastula stage or its human equivalent, the blastocyst stage (Figure 20.20). In culture, these *embryonic stem (ES) cells* reproduce indefinitely; and depending on culture conditions, they can be made to differentiate into a variety of specialized cells, including even eggs and sperm.

The adult body also has stem cells, which serve to replace nonreproducing specialized cells as needed. In contrast to ES cells, *adult stem cells* are not able to give rise to all cell types in the organism, though they can generate multiple types. For example, one of the several types of stem cells in bone marrow can generate all the different kinds of blood cells (see Figure 20.20), and another can differentiate into bone, cartilage, fat, muscle, and the linings of blood vessels. To the surprise of many, the adult brain has been found to contain stem cells that continue to produce certain kinds of nerve cells there. And recently, re-

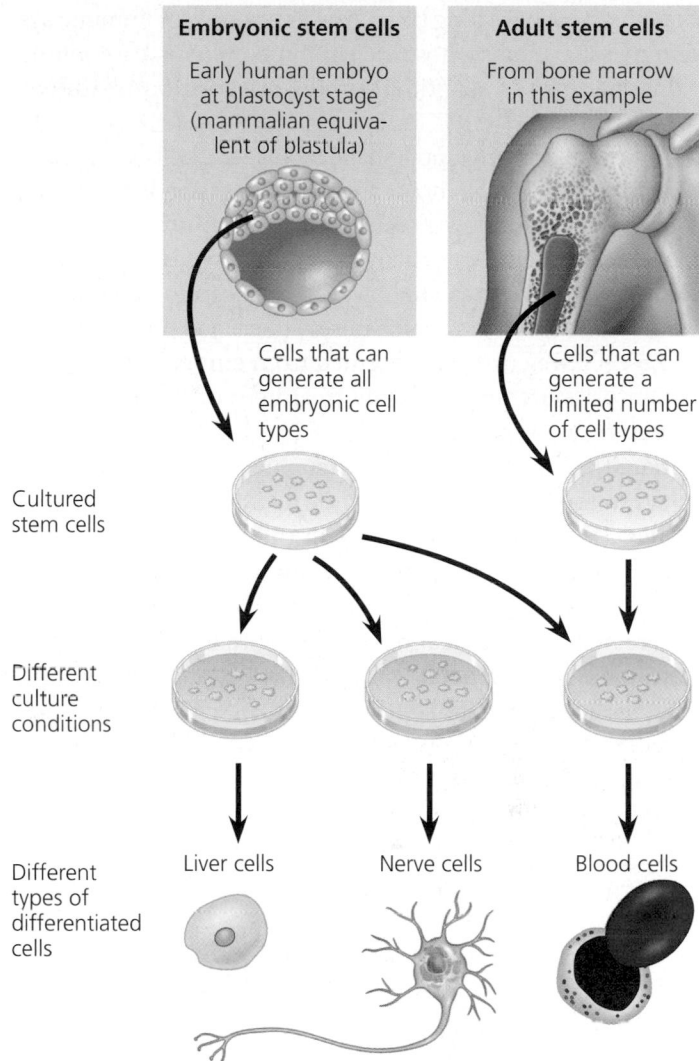

▲ **Figure 20.20 Working with stem cells.** Animal stem cells, which can be isolated from early embryos or adult tissues and grown in culture, are self-perpetuating, relatively undifferentiated cells. Embryonic stem cells are easier to grow than adult stem cells and can theoretically give rise to *all* types of cells in an organism. The range of cell types that can arise from adult stem cells is not yet fully understood.

searchers have reported finding stem cells in skin, hair, eyes, and dental pulp. Although adult animals have only tiny numbers of stem cells, scientists are learning to identify and isolate these cells from various tissues and, in some cases, to grow them in culture. With the right culture conditions (for instance, the addition of specific growth factors), cultured stem cells from adult animals have been made to differentiate into multiple types of specialized cells.

Research with embryonic or adult stem cells is a source of valuable data about differentiation and has enormous potential for medical applications. The ultimate aim is to supply cells for the repair of damaged or diseased organs: for example, insulin-producing pancreatic cells for people with diabetes or certain kinds of brain cells for people with Parkinson's disease or Huntington's disease. Adult stem cells from bone marrow have long been used as a source of immune system cells in patients whose own immune systems are nonfunctional because of genetic disorders or radiation treatments for cancer.

The developmental potential of adult stem cells is limited to certain tissues. ES cells hold more promise than adult stem cells for medical applications because ES cells are **pluripotent**, capable of differentiating into many different cell types. The only way to obtain ES cells thus far, however, has been to harvest them from human embryos, which raises ethical and political issues.

ES cells are currently obtained from embryos donated by patients undergoing infertility treatment or from long-term cell cultures originally established with cells isolated from donated embryos. If scientists are able to clone human embryos to the blastocyst stage, they might be able to use such clones as the source of ES cells in the future. Furthermore, with a donor nucleus from a person with a particular disease, they might be able to produce ES cells for treatment that match the patient and are thus not rejected by his or her immune system. When the main aim of cloning is to produce ES cells to treat disease, the process is called *therapeutic cloning*. Although most people believe that reproductive cloning of humans is unethical, opinions vary about the morality of therapeutic cloning.

Resolving the debate now seems less imperative due to recent reports that ES cells can be acquired by turning back the clock in fully differentiated adult cells. Accomplishing this feat, which posed formidable obstacles, was announced in 2007, first by labs using mouse skin cells and then by others using human skin cells. In all cases, researchers transformed the skin cells into ES cells by using retroviruses to introduce extra cloned copies of four "stem cell" master regulatory genes. All tests carried out so far indicate that the transformed cells, which are known as *induced pluripotent stem (iPS) cells*, can do everything ES cells can do. Fine-tuning of techniques to direct iPS cells to become specific cell types is an area of intense research that has already seen some success. These cell types could eventually provide tailor-made "replacement" cells for patients without using any human eggs or embryos, thus circumventing most ethical objections.

CONCEPT CHECK 20.3

1. If you clone a carrot, will all the progeny plants ("clones") look identical? Why or why not?
2. Based on current knowledge, how would you explain the difference in the percentage of tadpoles that developed from the two kinds of donor nuclei in Figure 20.17?
3. **WHAT IF?** If you were a doctor who wanted to use iPS cells to treat a patient with severe diabetes, what new technique would have to be developed?

For suggested answers, see Appendix A.

CONCEPT 20.4
The practical applications of DNA technology affect our lives in many ways

DNA technology is in the news almost every day. Most often, the topic is a new and promising application in medicine, but this is just one of numerous fields benefiting from DNA technology and genetic engineering.

Medical Applications

One important use of DNA technology is the identification of human genes whose mutation plays a role in genetic diseases. These discoveries may lead to ways of diagnosing, treating, and even preventing such conditions. DNA technology is also contributing to our understanding of "nongenetic" diseases, from arthritis to AIDS, since a person's genes influence susceptibility to these diseases. Furthermore, diseases of all sorts involve changes in gene expression within the affected cells and often within the patient's immune system. By using DNA microarray assays or other techniques to compare gene expression in healthy and diseased tissues, as seen in Figure 20.1, researchers hope to find many of the genes that are turned on or off in particular diseases. These genes and their products are potential targets for prevention or therapy.

Diagnosis of Diseases

A new chapter in the diagnosis of infectious diseases has been opened by DNA technology, in particular the use of PCR and labeled nucleic acid probes to track down pathogens. For example, because the sequence of the RNA genome of HIV is known, RT-PCR can be used to amplify, and thus detect, HIV RNA in blood or tissue samples (see Figure 20.13). RT-PCR is often the best way to detect an otherwise elusive infective agent.

Medical scientists can now diagnose hundreds of human genetic disorders by using PCR with primers that target the genes associated with these disorders. The amplified DNA product is then sequenced to reveal the presence or absence of the disease-causing mutation. Among the genes for human diseases that have been identified are those for sickle-cell disease, hemophilia, cystic fibrosis, Huntington's disease, and Duchenne muscular dystrophy. Individuals afflicted with such diseases can often be identified before the onset of symptoms, even before birth. PCR can also be used to identify symptomless carriers of potentially harmful recessive alleles, essentially replacing Southern blotting for this purpose.

For some genetic disorders, medical scientists can detect an abnormal disease-causing allele by testing for *genetic markers* that are known to be very close (linked) to the allele. A genetic marker is a DNA sequence that varies in a population; in a gene, such sequence variation is the basis of different alleles. Just like coding sequences, noncoding DNA at a specific locus on a chromosome may exhibit small nucleotide differences among individuals. Variations in DNA sequence are called *polymorphisms* (from the Greek for "many forms").

Among the most useful of these genetic markers are single base-pair variations in the genomes of the human population. A single base-pair site where variation is found in at least 1% of the population is called a **single nucleotide polymorphism** (**SNP**, pronounced "snip"). SNPs occur on average about once in 100 to 300 base pairs in the human genome and are found in both coding and noncoding DNA sequences. (About 99% of our genome doesn't code for protein, as you will learn in Chapter 21.)

Some SNPs alter the sequence recognized by a restriction enzyme, as is the case for the single-nucleotide difference between the alleles for normal and sickle-cell β-globin. Such alterations change the lengths of the restriction fragments formed by digestion with that enzyme (see Figure 20.10). This type of sequence change, which can occur in either coding or noncoding regions, is called a **restriction fragment length polymorphism** (**RFLP**, pronounced "Rif-lip"). Scientists figured out how to use Southern blotting to detect RFLPs almost 30 years ago, realizing that RFLPs could serve as useful genetic markers. It is not necessary to actually sequence the DNA of multiple individuals to find SNPs; today they can be detected by very sensitive microarray analysis or by PCR.

But how can RFLPs or other SNPs help us diagnose a genetic disorder? The presence of an abnormal allele can be diagnosed with reasonable accuracy if a closely linked SNP marker has been found **(Figure 20.21)**. Alleles for Huntington's disease and a number of other genetic diseases were first detected by means of RFLPs in this indirect way. If the marker and the gene itself are close enough, crossing over between the marker and the gene is very unlikely during gamete formation. Therefore, the marker and gene will almost always be inherited together, even though the marker is not part of the gene. The same principle applies to all kinds of markers.

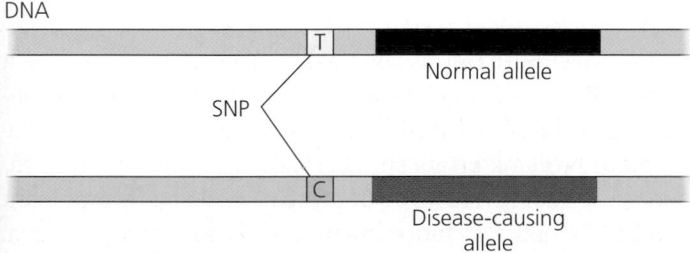

▲ **Figure 20.21 Single nucleotide polymorphisms (SNPs) as genetic markers for disease-causing alleles.** This diagram depicts homologous segments of DNA from a family in which some members have a genetic disease. In this family, unaffected family members have a T at a particular SNP locus. If a family member has a C at that locus, there is a high probability that the individual has also inherited the disease-causing allele. (Here, only a single strand is shown for each DNA molecule.)

Human Gene Therapy

Gene therapy—introducing genes into an afflicted individual for therapeutic purposes—holds great potential for treating disorders traceable to a single defective gene. In theory, a normal allele of the defective gene could be inserted into the somatic cells of the tissue affected by the disorder.

For gene therapy of somatic cells to be permanent, the cells that receive the normal allele must be ones that multiply throughout the patient's life. Bone marrow cells, which include the stem cells that give rise to all the cells of the blood and immune system, are prime candidates. **Figure 20.22** outlines one possible procedure for gene therapy of an individual whose bone marrow cells do not produce a vital enzyme because of a single defective gene. One type of severe combined immunodeficiency (SCID) is caused by just this kind of defect. If the treatment is successful, the patient's bone marrow cells will begin producing the missing protein, and the patient will be cured.

▲ **Figure 20.22 Gene therapy using a retroviral vector.** A retrovirus that has been rendered harmless is used as a vector in this procedure, which exploits the ability of a retrovirus to insert a DNA transcript of its RNA genome into the chromosomal DNA of its host cell (see Figure 19.8). If the foreign gene carried by the retroviral vector is expressed, the cell and its descendants will possess the gene product, and the patient may be cured. Cells that reproduce throughout life, such as bone marrow cells, are ideal candidates for gene therapy.

The procedure shown in Figure 20.22 has been used in gene therapy trials for SCID. In a trial begun in France in 2000, ten young children with SCID were treated by the same procedure. Nine of these patients showed significant, definitive improvement after two years, the first indisputable success of gene therapy. However, three of the patients subsequently developed leukemia, a type of blood cell cancer, and one of them died. Researchers discovered that in two cases, the retroviral vector used to carry the normal allele into bone marrow cells had inserted near a gene involved in the proliferation and development of blood cells, which could have led to the leukemia. In a recent experiment on mice, a replacement of the mouse version of the same gene led to a high incidence of lymphoma, also a blood cancer. These results suggest that an unknown function of the gene itself may be responsible.

Gene therapy also raises several other technical questions. For example, how can the activity of the transferred gene be controlled so that cells make appropriate amounts of the gene product at the right time and in the right place? How can we be sure that the insertion of the therapeutic gene does not harm some other necessary cell function? As more is learned about DNA control elements and gene interactions, researchers may be able to answer such questions.

In addition to technical challenges, gene therapy raises ethical questions. Some critics believe that tampering with human genes in any way is immoral. Other observers see no fundamental difference between the transplantation of genes into somatic cells and the transplantation of organs.

Treatment of human germ-line cells in the hope of correcting a defect in future generations raises further ethical issues. Such genetic engineering is routinely done in laboratory mice, and the technical problems relating to similar genetic engineering in humans will eventually be solved. Under what circumstances, if any, should we alter the genomes of human germ lines? Would this inevitably lead to the practice of eugenics, a deliberate effort to control the genetic makeup of human populations? From a biological perspective, the elimination of unwanted alleles from the gene pool could backfire. Genetic variation is a necessary ingredient for the survival of a species as environmental conditions change with time. Alleles that are damaging under some conditions may be advantageous under other conditions (one example is the sickle-cell allele, discussed in Chapter 14). Are we willing to risk making genetic changes that could be detrimental to the survival of our species in the future? We may have to face this question soon.

Pharmaceutical Products

The pharmaceutical industry derives significant benefit from advances in DNA technology and genetic research, applying them to the development of useful drugs to treat diseases. Pharmaceutical products are synthesized using methods of either organic chemistry or biotechnology, depending on the nature of the product.

Synthesis of Small Molecules for Use as Drugs An exciting recent development has been the synthesis of small molecules that are tailored to combat certain cancers by blocking the function of a protein crucial for the tumor cells' survival. One drug, imatinib (trade name Gleevec), is a small molecule that inhibits a specific receptor tyrosine kinase (see Figure 11.7). The overexpression of this receptor, resulting from a chromosomal translocation, is instrumental in causing chronic myelogenous leukemia (CML; see Figure 15.17). Patients in the early stages of CML who are treated with imatinib have exhibited nearly complete, sustained remission from the cancer. Drugs that work like this have also been used with success to treat a few types of lung and breast cancers. This approach is feasible only for cancers for which the molecular basis is fairly well understood.

Pharmaceutical products that are proteins can be synthesized on a large scale, using cells or whole organisms. Cell cultures are more widely used at present.

Protein Production in Cell Cultures You learned earlier in the chapter about DNA cloning and gene expression systems for producing large quantities of proteins that are present naturally in only minute amounts. The host cells used in such expression systems can even be engineered to secrete a protein as it is made, thereby simplifying the task of purifying it by traditional biochemical methods.

Among the first pharmaceutical products "manufactured" in this way were human insulin and human growth hormone (HGH). Some 2 million people with diabetes in the United States depend on insulin treatment to control their disease. Human growth hormone has been a boon to children born with a form of dwarfism caused by inadequate amounts of HGH. Another important pharmaceutical product produced by genetic engineering is tissue plasminogen activator (TPA). If administered shortly after a heart attack, TPA helps dissolve blood clots and reduces the risk of subsequent heart attacks.

Cells in culture can also be used to produce vaccines, which stimulate the immune system to defend the body against specific pathogens (see Chapter 43). A pathogen typically has one or more proteins on its surface that trigger an immune response against it. This type of protein, made by recombinant DNA techniques, can function as a vaccine against the pathogen. Alternatively, genetic engineering can be used to modify a pathogen's genome, resulting in a weakened pathogen that can then serve as a "live" vaccine.

Protein Production by "Pharm" Animals and Plants In some cases, instead of using cell systems *in vitro* to produce large quantities of protein products, pharmaceutical scientists can use whole animals. Their techniques are those we alluded to when we discussed the possibility of genetically engineering human germ-line cells, but they are performed on animals other than humans. Using these methods, scientists can introduce a gene from an animal of one genotype into the genome of another individual, often of a different species. This individual is then called a **transgenic** animal. To do this, they first remove eggs from a female of the recipient species and fertilize them *in vitro*. Meanwhile, they have cloned the desired gene from the donor organism. They then inject the cloned DNA directly into the nuclei of the fertilized eggs. Some of the cells integrate the foreign DNA, the *transgene*, into their genomes and are able to express the foreign gene. The engineered embryos are then surgically implanted in a surrogate mother. If an embryo develops successfully, the result is a transgenic animal, containing a gene from a third "parent," which may be of a different species.

Assuming that the introduced gene encodes a protein desired in large quantities, these transgenic animals can act as pharmaceutical "factories." For example, a transgene for a human blood protein such as antithrombin can be inserted into the genome of a goat in such a way that the transgene's product is secreted in the animal's milk (**Figure 20.23**). The protein can then be purified from the milk, usually more easily than from a cell culture. Researchers have also engineered transgenic chickens that express large amounts of the transgene's product in eggs. Biotechnology companies consider the characteristics of candidate animals in deciding which to use for engineering. For example, goats reproduce faster than cows, and it is possible to harvest more protein from goat milk than from the milk of other rapidly reproducing mammals, such as rabbits.

Human proteins produced in transgenic farm animals for use in humans may differ in some ways from the naturally produced human proteins, possibly because of subtle differences in protein modification. Therefore, such proteins must be

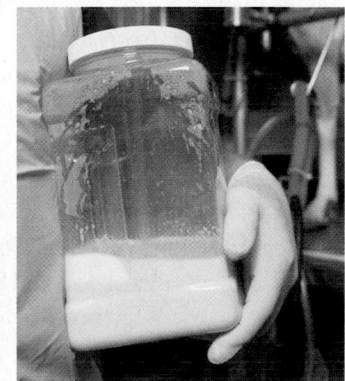

▲ **Figure 20.23 Goats as "pharm" animals.** This transgenic goat carries a gene for a human blood protein, antithrombin, which she secretes in her milk. Patients with a rare hereditary disorder in which this protein is lacking suffer from formation of blood clots in their blood vessels. Easily purified from the goat's milk, the protein is currently under evaluation as an anticlotting agent.

tested very carefully to ensure that they (or contaminants from the farm animals) will not cause allergic reactions or other adverse effects in patients who receive them.

In a novel twist, the pharmaceutical industry is beginning to develop "pharm" plants, analogous to "pharm" animals. Although natural plants have long been sources of drugs, researchers are now creating plants that make human proteins for medical use and viral proteins for use as vaccines. In 2007, the U.S. Food and Drug Administration (FDA) approved a plan to plant over 3,000 acres in Kansas with rice harboring genes for milk proteins. The harvested proteins would be used in rehydration formulas to treat infant diarrhea, a serious problem in developing countries.

Forensic Evidence and Genetic Profiles

In violent crimes, body fluids or small pieces of tissue may be left at the scene or on the clothes or other possessions of the victim or assailant. If enough blood, semen, or tissue is available, forensic laboratories can determine the blood type or tissue type by using antibodies to detect specific cell-surface proteins. However, such tests require fairly fresh samples in relatively large amounts. Also, because many people have the same blood or tissue type, this approach can only exclude a suspect; it cannot provide strong evidence of guilt.

DNA testing, on the other hand, can identify the guilty individual with a high degree of certainty, because the DNA sequence of every person is unique (except for identical twins). Genetic markers that vary in the population can be analyzed for a given person to determine that individual's unique set of genetic markers, or **genetic profile**. (This term is preferred over "DNA fingerprint" by forensic scientists, who want to emphasize the heritable aspect of these markers rather than simply the fact that they produce a pattern on a gel that, like a fingerprint, is visually recognizable.) The FBI started applying DNA technology in forensics in 1988, using RFLP analysis by Southern blotting to detect similarities and differences in DNA samples. This method required much smaller samples of blood or tissue than earlier methods—only about 1,000 cells.

Today, forensic scientists use an even more sensitive method that takes advantage of variations in length of genetic markers called **short tandem repeats (STRs)**. These are tandemly repeated units of 2- to 5-base sequences in specific regions of the genome. The number of repeats present in these regions is highly variable from person to person (polymorphic). For example, one individual may have the sequence ACAT repeated 30 times at one genome locus, whereas another individual may have 18 repeats at this locus. PCR is used to amplify particular STRs, using sets of primers that are labeled with different-colored fluorescent tags; the length of the region, and thus the number of repeats, can then be determined by electrophoresis. Because Southern blotting is not required, this method is quicker than RFLP analysis. And the PCR step allows use of the method even when the DNA is in poor condition or available only in minute quantities. A tissue sample containing as few as 20 cells can be sufficient for PCR amplification.

In a murder case, for example, this method can be used to compare DNA samples from the suspect, the victim, and a small amount of blood found at the crime scene. The forensic scientist tests only a few selected portions of the DNA—usually 13 STR markers. However, even this small set of markers can provide a forensically useful genetic profile because the probability that two people (who are not identical twins) would have exactly the same set of STR markers is vanishingly small. The Innocence Project, a nonprofit organization dedicated to overturning wrongful convictions, uses STR analysis of archived samples from crime scenes to revisit old cases. As of 2006, 18 innocent people had been released from prison as a result of forensic and legal work by this group (**Figure 20.24**).

Genetic profiles can also be useful for other purposes. A comparison of the DNA of a mother, her child, and the purported father can conclusively settle a question of paternity. Sometimes paternity is of historical interest: Genetic profiles provided strong evidence that Thomas Jefferson or one of his close male relatives fathered at least one of the children of his slave Sally Hemings. Genetic profiles can also identify victims of mass casualties. The largest such effort occurred after the attack on the World Trade Center in 2001; more than 10,000 samples of victims' remains were compared with DNA samples from personal items, such as toothbrushes, provided by families. Ultimately, forensic scientists succeeded in identifying almost 3,000 victims using these methods.

Just how reliable is a genetic profile? The greater the number of markers examined in a DNA sample, the more likely it is that the profile is unique to one individual. In forensic cases using STR analysis with 13 markers, the probability of two people having identical DNA profiles is somewhere between one chance in 10 billion and one in several trillion. (For comparison, the world's population in 2007 was about 6.6 billion.) The exact probability depends on the frequency of those markers in the general population. Information on how common various markers are in different ethnic groups is critical because these marker frequencies may vary considerably among ethnic groups and between a particular ethnic group and the population as a whole. With the increasing availability of frequency data, forensic scientists can make extremely accurate statistical calculations. Thus, despite problems that can still arise from insufficient data, human error, or flawed evidence, genetic profiles are now accepted as compelling evidence by legal experts and scientists alike.

(a) In 1984, Earl Washington was convicted and sentenced to death for the 1982 rape and murder of Rebecca Williams. His sentence was commuted to life in prison in 1993 due to new doubts about the evidence. In 2000, STR analysis by forensic scientists associated with The Innocence Project showed conclusively that he was innocent. This photo shows Washington just before his release in 2001, after 17 years in prison.

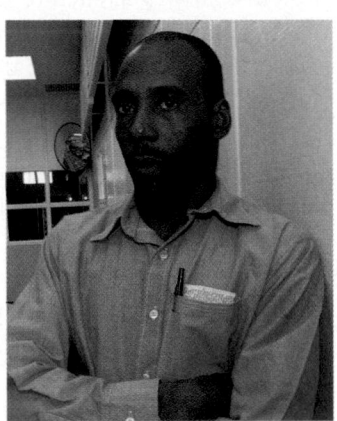

Source of sample	STR marker 1	STR marker 2	STR marker 3
Semen on victim	17, 19	13, 16	12, 12
Earl Washington	16, 18	14, 15	11, 12
Kenneth Tinsley	17, 19	13, 16	12, 12

(b) In STR analysis, selected STR markers in a DNA sample are amplified by PCR, and the PCR products are separated by electrophoresis. The procedure reveals how many repeats are present for each STR locus in the sample. An individual has two alleles per STR locus, each with a certain number of repeats. This table shows the number of repeats for three STR markers in three samples: from semen found on the victim, from Washington, and from another man named Kenneth Tinsley, who was in prison because of an unrelated conviction. These and other STR data (not shown) exonerated Washington and led Tinsley to plead guilty to the murder.

▲ **Figure 20.24 STR analysis used to release an innocent man from prison.**

Environmental Cleanup

Increasingly, the remarkable ability of certain microorganisms to transform chemicals is being exploited for environmental cleanup. If the growth needs of such microbes make them unsuitable for direct use, scientists can now transfer the genes for their valuable metabolic capabilities into other microorganisms, which can then be used to treat environmental problems. For example, many bacteria can extract heavy metals, such as copper, lead, and nickel, from their environments and incorporate the metals into compounds such as copper sulfate or lead sulfate, which are readily recoverable. Genetically engineered microbes may become important in both mining minerals (especially as ore reserves are depleted) and cleaning up highly toxic mining wastes. Biotechnologists are also trying to engineer microbes that can degrade chlorinated hydrocarbons and other harmful compounds. These microbes could be used in wastewater treatment plants or by manufacturers before the compounds are ever released into the environment.

In a more "old-fashioned" application of biotechnology, *biofuels* from crops such as corn, soybeans, and cassava have been proposed as a supplement or even replacement for fossil fuels. In this case, no genetic engineering is involved. To produce "bioethanol," the starch made naturally by the plants is simply converted to sugar and then fermented by microorganisms; a similar process can produce "biodiesel" from plant oils. Either product can be mixed with gasoline or used alone to power vehicles. Proponents say these fuels have less impact on the environment than fossil fuels, but others disagree, asserting that the environmental effects of growing these crops make their total impact greater than that of fossil fuels.

Agricultural Applications

Scientists are working to learn more about the genomes of agriculturally important plants and animals. For a number of years, they have been using DNA technology in an effort to improve agricultural productivity.

Animal Husbandry

The selective breeding of livestock, or animal husbandry, has exploited naturally occurring mutations and genetic recombination for centuries. As we described earlier, DNA technology enables scientists to produce transgenic animals, which speeds up the selective breeding process. The goals of creating a transgenic animal are often the same as the goals of traditional breeding—for instance, to make a sheep with better quality wool, a pig with leaner meat, or a cow that will mature in a shorter time. Scientists might, for example, identify and clone a gene that causes the development of larger muscles (muscles make up most of the meat we eat) in one breed of cattle and transfer it to other cattle or even to sheep.

However, problems such as low fertility or increased susceptibility to disease are not uncommon among farm animals carrying genes from humans and other foreign species. Animal health and welfare are important issues to consider when developing transgenic animals.

Genetic Engineering in Plants

Agricultural scientists have already endowed a number of crop plants with genes for desirable traits, such as delayed ripening and resistance to spoilage and disease. In one striking way, plants are easier to genetically engineer than most animals. For many plant species, a single tissue cell grown in culture can give rise to an adult plant (see Figure 20.16). Thus, genetic manipulations can be performed on an ordinary somatic cell and the cell then used to generate an organism with new traits.

The most commonly used vector for introducing new genes into plant cells is a plasmid, called the **Ti plasmid**, from the soil bacterium *Agrobacterium tumefaciens*. This plasmid integrates a segment of its DNA, known as T DNA, into the chromosomal DNA of its host plant cells. For vector purposes, researchers work with versions of the plasmid that do not cause disease (unlike the wild-type version) and that have been engineered to carry genes of interest within the borders of the T DNA. **Figure 20.25** outlines one method for using the Ti plasmid to produce transgenic plants. Scientists can intro-

---

▼ **Figure 20.25** Research Method

Using the Ti Plasmid to Produce Transgenic Plants

APPLICATION   Genes conferring useful traits, such as pest resistance, herbicide resistance, delayed ripening, and increased nutritional value, can be transferred from one plant variety or species to another using the Ti plasmid as a vector.

TECHNIQUE

❶ The Ti plasmid is isolated from the bacterium *Agrobacterium tumefaciens*. The segment of the plasmid that integrates into the genome of host cells is called T DNA.

Agrobacterium tumefaciens

Ti plasmid

Site where restriction enzyme cuts

T DNA

❷ The foreign gene of interest is inserted into the middle of the T DNA using methods shown in Figure 20.4.

DNA with the gene of interest

Recombinant Ti plasmid

❸ Recombinant plasmids can be introduced into cultured plant cells by electroporation. Or plasmids can be returned to *Agrobacterium*, which is then applied as a liquid suspension to the leaves of susceptible plants, infecting them. Once a plasmid is taken into a plant cell, its T DNA integrates into the cell's chromosomal DNA.

RESULTS   Transformed cells carrying the transgene of interest can regenerate complete plants that exhibit the new trait conferred by the transgene.

Plant with new trait

---

duce recombinant Ti plasmids into plant cells by electroporation. Alternatively, the recombinant plasmid can be put back into *Agrobacterium*; susceptible plants or plant cells growing in culture are then infected with bacteria that contain the recombinant plasmid.

Genetic engineering is rapidly replacing traditional plant-breeding programs, especially for useful traits, such as herbicide or pest resistance, determined by one or a few genes. Crops engineered with a bacterial gene making the plants resistant to herbicides can grow while weeds are destroyed, and genetically engineered crops that can resist destructive insects reduce the need for chemical insecticides. In India, the insertion of a salinity resistance gene from a coastal mangrove plant into the genomes of several rice varieties has resulted in rice plants that can grow in water three times as salty as seawater. The research foundation that carried out this feat of genetic engineering estimates that one-third of all irrigated land has high salinity owing to overirrigation and intensive use of chemical fertilizers, representing a serious threat to the food supply. Thus, salinity-resistant crop plants would be enormously valuable worldwide.

Genetic engineering also has great potential for improving the nutritional value of crop plants. For instance, scientists have developed transgenic rice plants that produce yellow rice grains containing beta-carotene, which our body uses to make vitamin A (see Figure 38.18). This "golden" rice could help prevent vitamin A deficiency in the half of the world's population that depends on rice as a staple food. Currently, large numbers of young children in Southeast Asia suffer from vitamin A deficiency, which leads to vision impairment and increases susceptibility to disease.

Safety and Ethical Questions Raised by DNA Technology

Early concerns about potential dangers associated with recombinant DNA technology focused on the possibility that hazardous new pathogens might be created. What might happen, for instance, if cancer cell genes were transferred into bacteria or viruses? To guard against such rogue microbes, scientists developed a set of guidelines that were adopted as formal government regulations in the United States and some other countries. One safety measure is a set of strict laboratory procedures designed to protect researchers from infection by engineered microbes and to prevent the microbes from accidentally leaving the laboratory. In addition, strains of microorganisms to be used in recombinant DNA experiments are genetically crippled to ensure that they cannot survive outside the laboratory. Finally, certain obviously dangerous experiments have been banned.

Today, most public concern about possible hazards centers not on recombinant microbes but on **genetically modified (GM) organisms** used as food. In common language, a GM organism is one that has acquired by artificial means one or more genes from another species or even from another variety of the same species. Some salmon, for example, have been genetically modified by addition of a more active salmon growth hormone gene. However, the majority of the GM organisms that contribute to our food supply are not animals, but crop plants.

GM crops are widespread in the United States, Argentina, and Brazil; together these countries account for over 80% of the world's acreage devoted to such crops. In the United States, the majority of corn, soybeans, and canola are GM crops, and GM products are not required to be labeled. However, the same foods are an ongoing subject of controversy in Europe, where the GM revolution has met with strong opposition. Many Europeans are concerned about the safety of GM foods and the possible environmental consequences of growing GM plants. Early in 2000, negotiators from 130 countries (including the United States) agreed on a Biosafety Protocol that requires exporters to identify GM organisms present in bulk food shipments and allows importing countries to decide whether the products pose environmental or health risks. Since then, European countries have, on occasion, refused crops from the United States and other countries, leading to trade disputes. Although a small number of GM crops have been grown on European soil, these products have generally failed in local markets, and the future of GM crops in Europe is uncertain.

Advocates of a cautious approach toward GM crops fear that transgenic plants might pass their new genes to close relatives in nearby wild areas. We know that lawn and crop grasses, for example, commonly exchange genes with wild relatives via pollen transfer. If crop plants carrying genes for resistance to herbicides, diseases, or insect pests pollinated wild ones, the offspring might become "super weeds" that are very difficult to control. Another possible hazard, suggested by one laboratory-based study, is that a transgene encoding a pesticide-like protein might cause plants to produce pollen toxic to butterflies. However, scientists with the Agricultural Research Service concluded from a two-year field study that butterflies were unlikely to be exposed to toxic levels of pollen.

As for the risks to human health from GM foods, some people fear that the protein products of transgenes might lead to allergic reactions. Although there is some evidence that this could happen, advocates claim that these proteins could be tested in advance to avoid producing ones that cause allergic reactions.

Today, governments and regulatory agencies throughout the world are grappling with how to facilitate the use of biotechnology in agriculture, industry, and medicine while ensuring that new products and procedures are safe. In the United States, such applications of biotechnology are evaluated for potential risks by various regulatory agencies, including the FDA, the Environmental Protection Agency, the National Institutes of Health, and the Department of Agriculture. Meanwhile, these same agencies and the public must consider the ethical implications of biotechnology.

Advances in biotechnology have allowed us to obtain complete genome sequences for humans and many other species, providing a vast treasure trove of information about genes. We can ask how certain genes differ from species to species, as well as how genes and, ultimately, entire genomes have evolved.

(These are the subjects of Chapter 21.) At the same time, the increasing speed and falling cost of determining the genome sequences of individuals are raising significant ethical questions. Who should have the right to examine someone else's genetic information? How should that information be used? Should a person's genome be a factor in determining eligibility for a job or insurance? Ethical considerations, as well as concerns about potential environmental and health hazards, will likely slow some applications of biotechnology. There is always a danger that too much regulation will stifle basic research and its potential benefits. However, the power of DNA technology and genetic engineering—our ability to profoundly and rapidly alter species that have been evolving for millennia—demands that we proceed with humility and caution.

CONCEPT CHECK **20.4**

1. What is the advantage of using stem cells for gene therapy?
2. List at least three different properties that have been acquired by crop plants via genetic engineering.
3. **WHAT IF?** As a physician, you have a patient with symptoms that suggest a hepatitis A infection. The symptoms come and go, but you have not been able to detect viral proteins in the blood. Knowing that hepatitis A is an RNA virus, what lab tests could you perform to support your diagnosis? Explain what the results would mean.

For suggested answers, see Appendix A.

Chapter 20 Review

MEDIA Go to **www.campbellbiology.com** for BioFlix 3-D Animations, MP3 Tutors, Videos, Practice Tests, an eBook, and more.

SUMMARY OF KEY CONCEPTS

CONCEPT 20.1

DNA cloning yields multiple copies of a gene or other DNA segment (pp. 396–405)

▶ **DNA Cloning and Its Applications: *A Preview*** DNA cloning and other techniques, collectively termed DNA technology, can be used to manipulate and analyze DNA and to produce useful new products and organisms.

▶ **Using Restriction Enzymes to Make Recombinant DNA** Bacterial restriction enzymes cut DNA molecules within short, specific nucleotide sequences to yield a set of double-stranded DNA fragments with single-stranded sticky ends. The sticky ends on fragments from one DNA source can base-pair with complementary sticky ends on fragments from other DNA molecules; sealing of the base-paired fragments with DNA ligase produces recombinant DNA molecules.

▶ **Cloning a Eukaryotic Gene in a Bacterial Plasmid**

Vector — DNA fragments from genomic DNA or cDNA or copy of DNA obtained by PCR

Cut by same restriction enzyme, mixed, and ligated

Recombinant DNA plasmids

Recombinant plasmids are returned to host cells, each of which divides to form a clone of cells. Collections of clones are stored as libraries.

▶ **Expressing Cloned Eukaryotic Genes** Several technical difficulties hinder the expression of cloned eukaryotic genes in bacterial host cells. The use of cultured eukaryotic cells as host cells and yeast artificial chromosomes (YACs) as vectors helps avoid these problems.

▶ **Amplifying DNA *in Vitro*: The Polymerase Chain Reaction (PCR)** PCR can produce many copies of a specific target segment of DNA, using primers that bracket the desired sequence and a heat-resistant DNA polymerase.

MEDIA

Activity Applications of DNA Technology
Activity Restriction Enzymes
Activity Cloning a Gene in Bacteria
Investigation How Can Antibiotic-Resistant Plasmids Transform *E. coli*?

CONCEPT 20.2

DNA technology allows us to study the sequence, expression, and function of a gene (pp. 405–411)

▶ **Gel Electrophoresis and Southern Blotting** DNA restriction fragments of different lengths can be separated by gel electrophoresis. Specific fragments can be identified by Southern blotting, using labeled probes that hybridize to the DNA immobilized on a "blot" of the gel.

▶ **DNA Sequencing** Relatively short DNA fragments can be sequenced by the dideoxy chain termination method, which can be performed in automated sequencing machines.

▶ **Analyzing Gene Expression** Expression of a gene can be investigated using hybridization with labeled probes to look for specific mRNAs, either on a gel (Northern blotting) or in a whole organism (*in situ* hybridization). Also, RNA can be transcribed into cDNA by reverse transcriptase and the cDNA amplified with specific primers (RT-PCR). Microarrays allow researchers to compare the expression of many genes at once in different tissues, at different times, or under different conditions.

▶ **Determining Gene Function** For a gene of unknown function, experimental inactivation of the gene and observation of the resulting phenotypic effects can provide clues to its function.

MEDIA

Activity Gel Electrophoresis of DNA
Activity Analyzing DNA Fragments Using Gel Electrophoresis
Investigation How Can Gel Electrophoresis Be Used to Analyze DNA?

CONCEPT 20.3

Cloning organisms may lead to production of stem cells for research and other applications (pp. 412–416)

▶ Studies showing genomic equivalence (that an organism's cells have the same genome) were the first examples of organismal cloning.

▶ **Cloning Plants: Single-Cell Cultures** Differentiated cells from mature plants are often capable of generating a complete new plant.

▶ **Cloning Animals: Nuclear Transplantation** The nucleus from a differentiated animal cell can sometimes give rise to a new animal if transplanted to an enucleated egg.

▶ **Stem Cells of Animals** Certain stem cells from animal embryos or adult tissues can reproduce and differentiate *in vitro* as well as *in vivo*, offering the potential for medical use.

CONCEPT 20.4

The practical applications of DNA technology affect our lives in many ways (pp. 416–423)

▶ **Medical Applications** DNA technology is increasingly being used in the diagnosis of genetic and other diseases and offers potential for better treatment of genetic disorders or even permanent cures. Single nucleotide polymorphisms (SNPs) and restriction fragment length polymorphisms (RFLPs) are useful as genetic markers linked to disease-causing alleles. Large-scale production of protein hormones and other proteins with therapeutic uses, including safer vaccines, is possible with DNA technology. Some therapeutic proteins are being produced in transgenic "pharm" animals and plants.

▶ **Forensic Evidence and Genetic Profiles** Analysis of genetic markers such as short tandem repeats (STRs) in DNA isolated from tissue or body fluids found at crime scenes can provide definitive evidence that a suspect is guilty or innocent. Such analysis is also useful in parenthood disputes and in identifying the remains of crime victims.

▶ **Environmental Cleanup** Genetically engineered microorganisms can be used to extract minerals from the environment or degrade various types of potentially toxic waste materials.

▶ **Agricultural Applications** The aim of developing transgenic plants and animals is to improve agricultural productivity and food quality.

▶ **Safety and Ethical Questions Raised by DNA Technology** The potential benefits of genetic engineering must be carefully weighed against the potential hazards of creating products or developing procedures that are harmful to humans or the environment.

MEDIA

Activity DNA Fingerprinting
Activity Making Decisions About DNA Technology: Golden Rice

SELF-QUIZ

1. Which of the following tools of recombinant DNA technology is *incorrectly* paired with its use?
   a. restriction enzyme—production of RFLPs
   b. DNA ligase—enzyme that cuts DNA, creating the sticky ends of restriction fragments
   c. DNA polymerase—used in a polymerase chain reaction to amplify sections of DNA
   d. reverse transcriptase—production of cDNA from mRNA
   e. electrophoresis—separation of DNA fragments

2. Which of the following would *not* be true of cDNA produced using human brain tissue as the starting material?
   a. It could be amplified by the polymerase chain reaction.
   b. It could be used to create a complete genomic library.
   c. It is produced from mRNA using reverse transcriptase.
   d. It could be used as a probe to detect genes expressed in the brain.
   e. It lacks the introns of the human genes.

3. Plants are more readily manipulated by genetic engineering than are animals because
   a. plant genes do not contain introns.
   b. more vectors are available for transferring recombinant DNA into plant cells.
   c. a somatic plant cell can often give rise to a complete plant.
   d. genes can be inserted into plant cells by microinjection.
   e. plant cells have larger nuclei.

4. A paleontologist has recovered a bit of tissue from the 400-year-old preserved skin of an extinct dodo (a bird). The researcher would like to compare a specific region of the DNA from the sample with DNA from living birds. Which of the following would be most useful for increasing the amount of dodo DNA available for testing?
   a. RFLP analysis
   b. polymerase chain reaction (PCR)
   c. electroporation
   d. gel electrophoresis
   e. Southern blotting

5. Expression of a cloned eukaryotic gene in a bacterial cell involves many challenges. The use of mRNA and reverse transcriptase is part of a strategy to solve the problem of
   a. post-transcriptional processing.
   b. electroporation.
   c. post-translational processing.
   d. nucleic acid hybridization.
   e. restriction fragment ligation.

6. DNA technology has many medical applications. Which of the following is *not* done routinely at present?
   a. production of hormones for treating diabetes and dwarfism
   b. production of viral proteins for vaccines
   c. introduction of genetically engineered genes into human gametes
   d. prenatal identification of genetic disease genes
   e. genetic testing for carriers of harmful alleles

7. Which of the following sequences in double-stranded DNA is most likely to be recognized as a cutting site for a restriction enzyme?
   a. AAGG b. AGTC c. GGCC d. ACCA e. AAAA
      TTCC   TCAG   CCGG   TGGT   TTTT

8. In recombinant DNA methods, the term *vector* can refer to
   a. the enzyme that cuts DNA into restriction fragments.
   b. the sticky end of a DNA fragment.
   c. a RFLP marker.
   d. a plasmid used to transfer DNA into a living cell.
   e. a DNA probe used to identify a particular gene.

9. **DRAW IT** You are making a genomic library for the aardvark, using a bacterial plasmid as a vector. The green diagram below shows the plasmid, which contains the restriction site for the enzyme used in Figure 20.3. Above the plasmid is a region of linear aardvark DNA. Diagram your cloning procedure, showing what would happen to these two molecules during each step. Use one color for the aardvark DNA and its bases and another color for those of the plasmid. Label each step.

5′ TCCATGAATTCTAAAGCGCTTATGAATTCACGGC 3′
3′ AGGTACTTAAGATTTCGCGAATACTTAAGTGCCG 5′
Aardvark DNA

Plasmid

10. **WHAT IF?** Imagine you want to study human crystallins, proteins present in the lens of the eye. To obtain a sufficient amount of the protein, you decide to clone the crystallin gene. Would you construct a genomic library or a cDNA library? What material would you use as a source of DNA or RNA?

For Self-Quiz answers, see Appendix A.

MEDIA Visit www.campbellbiology.com for a Practice Test.

EVOLUTION CONNECTION

11. If DNA-based technologies become widely used, how might they change the way evolution proceeds, as compared with the natural evolutionary mechanisms of the past 4 billion years?

SCIENTIFIC INQUIRY

12. You hope to study a gene that codes for a neurotransmitter protein in human brain cells. You know the amino acid sequence of the protein. Explain how you might (a) identify the genes expressed in a specific type of brain cell, (b) identify the gene for the neurotransmitter, (c) produce multiple copies of the gene for study, and (d) produce a quantity of the neurotransmitter for evaluation as a potential medication.

SCIENCE, TECHNOLOGY, AND SOCIETY

13. Is there danger of discrimination based on testing for "harmful" genes? What policies can you suggest that would prevent such abuses?

14. Government funding of embryonic stem cell research has been a contentious political issue. Why has this debate been so heated? Summarize the arguments for and against embryonic stem cell research, and explain your own position on the issue.

21 Genomes and Their Evolution

▲ Figure 21.1 **What genomic information makes a human or a chimpanzee?**

OVERVIEW

Reading the Leaves from the Tree of Life

The woman in **Figure 21.1** and her chimpanzee companions are sharing a laugh—or are they? Does each of them perceive a "joke" and react with this joyful facial expression and its accompanying vocalization? With the advent of recent techniques for rapidly sequencing complete genomes, we can now start to address the genetic basis of intriguing questions like this.

The chimpanzee (*Pan troglodytes*) is our closest living relative on the evolutionary tree of life. Its genome was sequenced in 2005, two years after sequencing of the human genome was largely completed. Now that we can compare our genome with that of the chimpanzee base by base, we can tackle the more general issue of what differences in the genetic information account for the distinct characteristics of these two species of primates.

In addition to determining the sequences of the human and chimpanzee genomes, researchers have obtained complete genome sequences for *E. coli* and numerous other prokaryotes, as well as many eukaryotes, including *Saccharomyces cerevisiae* (brewer's yeast), *Caenorhabditis elegans* (a nematode), *Drosophila melanogaster* (fruit fly), *Mus musculus* (house mouse), and *Macaca mulatta* (rhesus macaque). Fragments of DNA have been sequenced even from extinct species, such as the cave bear and the woolly mammoth! These whole and partial genomes are of great interest in their own right and are also providing important insights into evolution and other biological processes. Broadening the human-chimpanzee comparison to the genomes of other primates and more distantly related animals should reveal the sets of genes that control group-defining characteristics. Beyond that, comparisons with the genomes of bacteria, archaea, fungi, protists, and plants should enlighten us about the long evolutionary history of shared ancient genes and their products.

With the genomes of many species fully sequenced, scientists can study whole sets of genes and their interactions, an approach called **genomics**. The sequencing efforts that feed this approach have generated, and continue to generate, enormous volumes of data. The need to deal with this ever-increasing flood of information has spawned the new field of **bioinformatics**, the application of computational methods to the storage and analysis of biological data.

We will begin this chapter by discussing two approaches to genome sequencing and some of the advances in and applications of bioinformatics. We will then summarize what has been learned from the genomes that have been sequenced thus far. Next, we will describe the composition of the human genome as a representative genome of a complex multicellular eukaryote. Finally, we will explore current ideas about how genomes evolve and about how the evolution of developmental mechanisms could have generated the great diversity of life found on Earth today.

New approaches have accelerated the pace of genome sequencing

Sequencing of the human genome, an ambitious undertaking, officially began as the **Human Genome Project** in 1990. Organized by an international, publicly funded consortium of scientists at universities and research institutes, the project involved 20 large sequencing centers in six countries plus a host of other labs working on small projects.

After sequencing of the human genome was largely completed in 2003, the sequence of each chromosome was carefully analyzed and described in a series of papers, the last of which covered chromosome 1 and was published in 2006. With this refinement, researchers termed the sequencing "virtually complete." To reach these milestones, the project proceeded through three stages that provided progressively more detailed views of the human genome: linkage mapping, physical mapping, and DNA sequencing.

Three-Stage Approach to Genome Sequencing

Even before the Human Genome Project began, earlier research had sketched a rough picture of the organization of the genomes of many organisms. For instance, the karyotyping of many species had revealed their chromosome numbers and banding patterns (see Figure 13.3). And some genes had already been located on a particular region of a chromosome by fluorescence *in situ* hybridization (FISH), a method in which fluorescently labeled probes are allowed to hybridize to an immobilized array of whole chromosomes (see Figure 15.1). Cytogenetic maps based on this type of information provided the starting point for more detailed mapping.

With these cytogenetic maps of the chromosomes in hand, the initial stage in sequencing the human genome was to construct a **linkage map** (a type of genetic map; see Chapter 15) of several thousand genetic markers spaced throughout the chromosomes (**Figure 21.2** stage ❶). The order of the markers and the relative distances between them on such a map are based on recombination frequencies (see Figure 15.11). The markers can be genes or any other identifiable sequences in the DNA, such as RFLPs or the short tandem repeats (STRs) discussed in Chapter 20. By 1992, researchers had compiled a human linkage map with some 5,000 markers. Such a map enabled them to locate other markers, including genes, by testing for genetic linkage to the known markers. It was also valuable as a framework for organizing more detailed maps of particular regions.

The next stage was the physical mapping of the human genome. In a **physical map**, the distances between markers are expressed by some physical measure, usually the number

▲ Figure 21.2 **Three-stage approach to sequencing an entire genome.** Starting with a cytogenetic map of each chromosome, researchers with the Human Genome Project proceeded through three stages to reach the ultimate goal, the virtually complete nucleotide sequence of every chromosome.

of base pairs along the DNA. For whole-genome mapping, a physical map is made by cutting the DNA of each chromosome into a number of restriction fragments and then determining the original order of the fragments in the chromosomal DNA. The key is to make fragments that overlap and then use probes or automated nucleotide sequencing of the ends to find the overlaps (Figure 21.2, stage ❷). In this way, fragments can be assigned to a sequential order that corresponds to their order in a chromosome.

Supplies of the DNA fragments used for physical mapping are prepared by DNA cloning. In working with large genomes, researchers carry out several rounds of DNA cutting, cloning, and physical mapping. The first cloning vector is often a yeast artificial chromosome (YAC), which can carry inserted fragments a million base pairs long, or a bacterial artificial chromosome (BAC), which typically carries inserts of 100,000 to 300,000 base pairs. After such long fragments are put in order, each fragment is cut into smaller pieces, which are cloned in plasmids or phages, ordered in turn, and finally sequenced.

The ultimate goal in mapping a genome is to determine the complete nucleotide sequence of each chromosome (Figure 21.2, stage ❸). For the human genome, this was accomplished by sequencing machines, using the dideoxy chain-termination method described in Figure 20.12. Even with automation, the sequencing of all 3.2 billion base pairs in a haploid set of human chromosomes presented a formidable challenge. In fact, a major thrust of the Human Genome Project was the development of technology for faster sequencing. Improvements over the years chipped away at each time-consuming step, enabling the rate of sequencing to accelerate impressively: Whereas a productive lab could typically sequence 1,000 base pairs a day in the 1980s, by the year 2000 each research center working on the Human Genome Project was sequencing 1,000 base pairs *per second*, 24 hours a day, seven days a week. Methods like this that can analyze biological materials very rapidly and produce enormous volumes of data are said to be "high-throughput." Sequencing machines are an example of high-throughput devices.

In practice, the three stages shown in Figure 21.2 overlap in a way that our simplified version does not portray, but they accurately represent the overarching strategy employed in the Human Genome Project. During the project, an alternative strategy for genome sequencing emerged that has been widely adopted due to its extreme efficiency.

Whole-Genome Shotgun Approach to Genome Sequencing

In 1992, emboldened by advances in sequencing and computer technology, molecular biologist J. Craig Venter devised an alternative approach to the sequencing of whole genomes. Called the *whole-genome shotgun approach*, it essentially skips the linkage mapping and physical mapping stages and starts directly with the sequencing of random DNA fragments. Powerful computer programs then assemble the resulting very large number of overlapping short sequences into a single continuous sequence (**Figure 21.3**).

Despite the skepticism of many scientists, the value of Venter's approach became clear in 1995 when he and colleagues reported the first complete genome sequence of an organism, the bacterium *Haemophilus influenzae*. In 1998, he set up a company, Celera Genomics, and declared his intention to sequence the entire human genome. Five years later, Celera Genomics and the public consortium jointly announced that sequencing of the human genome was largely complete, two years before the original target date of the Human Genome Project.

Representatives of the public consortium point out that Celera's accomplishment relied heavily on the consortium's maps and sequence data and that the infrastructure estab-

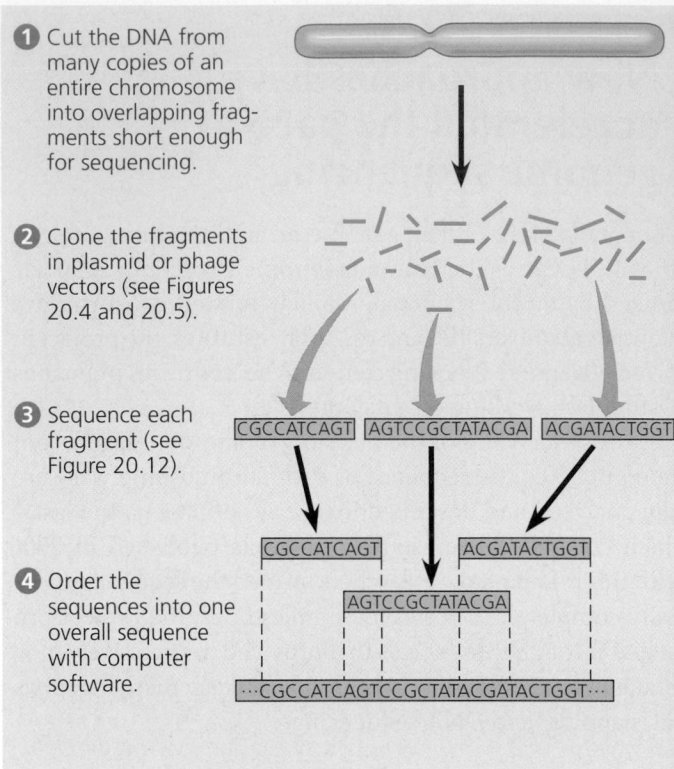

① Cut the DNA from many copies of an entire chromosome into overlapping fragments short enough for sequencing.

② Clone the fragments in plasmid or phage vectors (see Figures 20.4 and 20.5).

③ Sequence each fragment (see Figure 20.12).

④ Order the sequences into one overall sequence with computer software.

▲ **Figure 21.3 Whole-genome shotgun approach to sequencing.** In this approach, developed by Craig Venter and colleagues at the company he founded, Celera Genomics, random DNA fragments are sequenced and then ordered relative to each other. Compare this approach with the hierarchical, three-stage approach shown in Figure 21.2.

? *The fragments in stage 2 of this figure are depicted as scattered, whereas those in stage 2 of Figure 21.2 are drawn in a much more orderly fashion. How do these depictions reflect the two approaches?*

lished by their approach was a tremendous aid to Celera's efforts. Venter, on the other hand, argues for the efficiency and economy of Celera's methods, and indeed, the public consortium has made some use of them as well. Clearly, both approaches are valuable and have contributed to the rapid completion of genome sequencing for quite a few species.

Today, the whole-genome shotgun approach is widely used. Typically, the fragments are cloned into three different vectors, each of which takes a defined size of insert. The known distance between the ends of the inserted DNA is one more piece of information the computer can use to assemble the sequences properly. A recent study comparing the two approaches has shown that whole-genome shotgun sequencing can miss some duplicated sequences, thus underestimating the size of the genome and missing some genes in those regions. The hybrid approach that ended up being used for the human genome, with the more rapid shotgun sequencing being augmented by some mapping of clones, may in fact prove to be most useful in the long run.

As of 2007, there were still some small sections of the human genome that had not been sequenced. Because of the presence of repetitive DNA and for other poorly understood reasons, certain parts of the chromosomes of multicellular organisms resist detailed sequencing by the usual methods.

At first glance, genome sequences of humans and other organisms are simply dry lists of nucleotide bases—millions of A's, T's, C's, and G's in mind-numbing succession. Crucial to making sense of this massive amount of data have been new analytical approaches, which we discuss next.

CONCEPT CHECK 21.1

1. What is the major difference between a linkage map and a physical map of a chromosome?
2. In general, how does the approach to genome mapping used in the Human Genome Project differ from the whole-genome shotgun approach?
3. **WHAT IF?** Imagine you decide to sequence the genome of a field mouse, a species closely related to the lab mouse whose genome has already been sequenced. Why might having the lab mouse sequence available lead you to use the whole-genome shotgun approach instead of the three-stage approach?

For suggested answers, see Appendix A.

CONCEPT 21.2
Scientists use bioinformatics to analyze genomes and their functions

Each of the 20 or so sequencing centers around the world working on the Human Genome Project churned out voluminous amounts of DNA sequence day after day. As the data began to accumulate, the need to coordinate efforts to keep track of all the sequences became clear. Thanks to the foresight of scientists and government officials involved in the Human Genome Project, its goals included the establishment of banks of data, or databases, and the refining of analytical software. These databases and software programs would then be centralized and made readily accessible on the Internet. Accomplishing this aim has accelerated progress in DNA sequence analysis by making bioinformatics resources available to researchers worldwide and by speeding up the dissemination of information.

Centralized Resources for Analyzing Genome Sequences

Government-funded agencies carried out their mandate to establish databases and provide software with which scientists could analyze the sequence data. For example, in the United States, a joint endeavor between the National Library of Medicine and the National Institutes of Health (NIH) created the National Center for Biotechnology Information (NCBI), which maintains a website (www.ncbi.nlm.nih.gov) with extensive bioinformatics resources. On this site are links to databases, software, and a wealth of information about genomics and related topics. Similar websites have also been established by the European Molecular Biology Laboratory and the DNA Data Bank of Japan, two genome centers with which the NCBI collaborates. These large, comprehensive websites are complemented by others maintained by individual or small groups of laboratories. Smaller websites often provide databases and software designed for a narrower purpose, such as studying genetic and genomic changes in one particular type of cancer.

The NCBI database of sequences is called Genbank. As of August 2007, it included the sequences of 76 million fragments of genomic DNA, totaling 80 billion base pairs! Genbank is constantly updated, and the amount of data it contains is estimated to double approximately every 18 months. Any sequence in the database can be retrieved and analyzed using software from the NCBI website or elsewhere.

One software program available on the NCBI website, called BLAST, allows the visitor to compare a DNA sequence with every sequence in Genbank, base by base, to look for similar regions. Another program allows comparison of predicted protein sequences. Yet a third can search any protein sequence for common stretches of amino acids (domains) for which a function is known or suspected, and it can show a three-dimensional model of the domain alongside other relevant information (**Figure 21.4**, on the next page). There is even a software program that can compare a collection of sequences, either nucleic acids or polypeptides, and diagram them in the form of an evolutionary tree based on the sequence relationships. (You'll learn more about such diagrams in Chapter 26.)

The NCBI website also maintains a database that includes all three-dimensional protein structures that have been determined. (To review how protein structures are analyzed, see Figure 5.25.) These structures can be rotated by the viewer to see all sides of the protein. Let's say a researcher has an amino acid sequence for all or part of an unknown protein, and it is similar to an amino acid sequence for which the structure has been worked out. In this event, the possible structure of the unknown protein can be predicted by one software program and compared with all other known protein structures using another program. This information can aid the researcher in determining the function of the unknown protein.

There is a vast array of resources available for researchers anywhere in the world to use. Let us now consider the types of questions scientists can address using these resources.

Identifying Protein-Coding Genes Within DNA Sequences

Using available DNA sequences, geneticists can study genes directly, without having to infer genotype from phenotype, as in classical genetics. But this approach poses a new challenge:

In this window, a partial amino acid sequence from an unknown muskmelon protein ("Query") is aligned with sequences from other proteins that the computer program found to be similar. Each sequence represents a domain called WD40. Four hallmarks of this domain are highlighted in yellow. (Sequence similarity is based on chemical aspects of the amino acids, so the amino acids in each hallmark region are not always identical.)

The Cn3D program displays a three-dimensional ribbon model of cow transducin (the protein highlighted in purple in the Sequence Alignment Viewer). This protein is the only one of those shown for which a structure has been determined. The sequence similarity of the other proteins to cow transducin suggests that their structures are likely to be similar.

Cow transducin contains seven WD40 domains, one of which is highlighted here in gray.

The yellow areas correspond to the WD40 hallmarks highlighted in yellow in the window above.

This window displays information about the WD40 domain from the Conserved Domain Database.

WD40 - Sequence Alignment Viewer

```
                              Query  ~~~ktGGIRL~RHfksVSAVEWHRk~~gDYLSTlvLreSRAVLIHQlsk~
                   Cow [transducin]  ~nvrvSRELA~GHtgyLSCCRFLDd~~nQIVTs~~Sg~DTTCALWDie~
          Mustard weed [transducin]  gtvpvSRMLT~GHrgyVSCCQYVPnedaHLITs~~Sg~DQTCILWDvtt~
                  Corn [GNB protein]  gnmpvSRILT~GHkgyVSSCQYVPdgetRLITS~~Sg~DQTCVLWDvt~
                Human [PAFA protein]  ~~~ecIRTMH~GHdhnVSSVAIMPng~dHIVSA~~Sr~DKTIKMWEvg~
      Nematode [unknown protein #1]  ~~~rcVKTLK~GHtnyVFCCCFNPs~~gTLIAS~~GsfDETIRIWCar~
      Nematode [unknown protein #2]  ~~~rmTKTLK~GHnnyVFCCNFNPq~~sSLVVS~~GsfDESVRIWDvk~
          Fission yeast [FWDR protein] ~~~seCISILhGHtdsVLCLTFDS~~~~TLLVS~~GsaDCTVKLWHfs~
```

WD40 - Cn3D 4.1

CDD Descriptive Items

Name: WD40

WD40 domain, found in a number of eukaryotic proteins that cover a wide variety of functions including adaptor/regulatory modules in signal transduction, pre-mRNA processing and cytoskeleton assembly; typically contains a GH dipeptide 11-24 residues from its N-terminus and the WD dipeptide at its C-terminus and is 40 residues long, hence the name WD40;

▲ **Figure 21.4 Bioinformatics tools available on the Internet.** A website maintained by the National Center for Biotechnology Information allows scientists and the public to access DNA and protein sequences and other stored data. The site includes a link to a protein structure database (Conserved Domain Database, CDD) that can find and describe similar domains in related proteins, as well as software (Cn3D, "see in 3D") that displays three-dimensional models of domains for which the structure has been determined. Some results are shown from a search for regions of proteins similar to an amino acid sequence in a muskmelon protein.

determining the phenotype from the genotype. Given a long DNA sequence from a database such as Genbank, how can we recognize as-yet unknown protein-coding genes and determine their function?

The usual approach is to use software to scan these stored sequences for transcriptional and translational start and stop signals, for RNA-splicing sites, and for other telltale signs of protein-coding genes. The software also looks for certain short sequences that correspond to sequences present in known mRNAs. Thousands of such sequences, called *expressed sequence tags*, or *ESTs*, have been collected from cDNA sequences and are cataloged in computer databases. This type of analysis identifies sequences that may be previously unknown protein-coding genes.

The identities of about half of the human genes were known before the Human Genome Project began. But what about the others, the previously unknown genes revealed by analysis of DNA sequences? Clues about their identities come from comparing the sequences of gene candidates with those of known

genes from other organisms, using the software described previously. Due to redundancy in the genetic code, the DNA sequence itself may vary more than the protein sequence does. Thus, scientists interested in proteins often compare the predicted amino acid sequence of the protein to that of other proteins.

Sometimes a newly identified sequence will match, at least partially, the sequence of a gene or protein whose function is well known. For example, part of a new gene may match a known gene that encodes an important signaling pathway protein such as a protein kinase (see Chapter 11), suggesting that the new gene does, too. Alternatively, the new gene sequence may be similar to a previously encountered sequence whose function is still unknown. Another possibility is that the sequence is entirely unlike anything ever seen before. This was true for about a third of the genes of *E. coli* when its genome was sequenced. In the last case, protein function is usually deduced through a combination of biochemical and functional studies. The biochemical approach aims to determine the three-dimensional structure of the protein as well as other attributes, such as potential binding sites for other molecules. Functional studies usually involve blocking or disabling the gene to see what effect that has on the phenotype. RNAi, described in Chapter 20, is an example of an experimental technique used to block gene function.

Understanding Genes and Their Products at the Systems Level

The impressive computational power provided by the tools of bioinformatics allows the study of whole sets of genes and their interactions, as well as the comparison of genomes from different species. Genomics is a rich source of new insights into fundamental questions about genome organization, regulation of gene expression, growth and development, and evolution.

The success in sequencing genomes and studying entire sets of genes has encouraged scientists to attempt similar systematic study of the full protein sets (*proteomes*) encoded by genomes, an approach called **proteomics**. Proteins, not the genes that encode them, actually carry out most of the activities of the cell. Therefore, we must study when and where proteins are produced in an organism, as well as how they interact in networks, if we are to understand the functioning of cells and organisms.

How Systems Are Studied: An Example

Genomics and proteomics are enabling biologists to approach the study of life from an increasingly global perspective. Using the tools we have described, biologists have begun to compile catalogs of genes and proteins—listings of all the "parts" that contribute to the operation of cells, tissues, and organisms. With such catalogs in hand, researchers have shifted their attention from the individual parts to their functional integration in biological systems. As you may recall, in Chapter 1 we discussed this systems biology approach, which aims to model the dynamic behavior of whole biological systems.

One basic application of the systems biology approach is to define gene circuits and protein interaction networks. To map the protein interaction network in *Drosophila* that was mentioned in Chapter 1, for instance, researchers started with over 10,000 predicted RNA transcripts. They then used molecular techniques to test interactions between the whole or partial protein products of these transcripts. Using statistical tests to select the interactions for which the data were strongest, they ended up with approximately 4,700 proteins that appeared to participate in more than 4,000 interactions. A subset of these interactions is displayed graphically in **Figure 21.5**; the details are more easily seen in the two successive blowups in the figure. To process the vast number of protein-protein interactions generated by this experiment and integrate them into the graphic model required powerful computers, mathematical tools, and newly developed software. Thus, the systems biology approach has really been made possible by advances in bioinformatics.

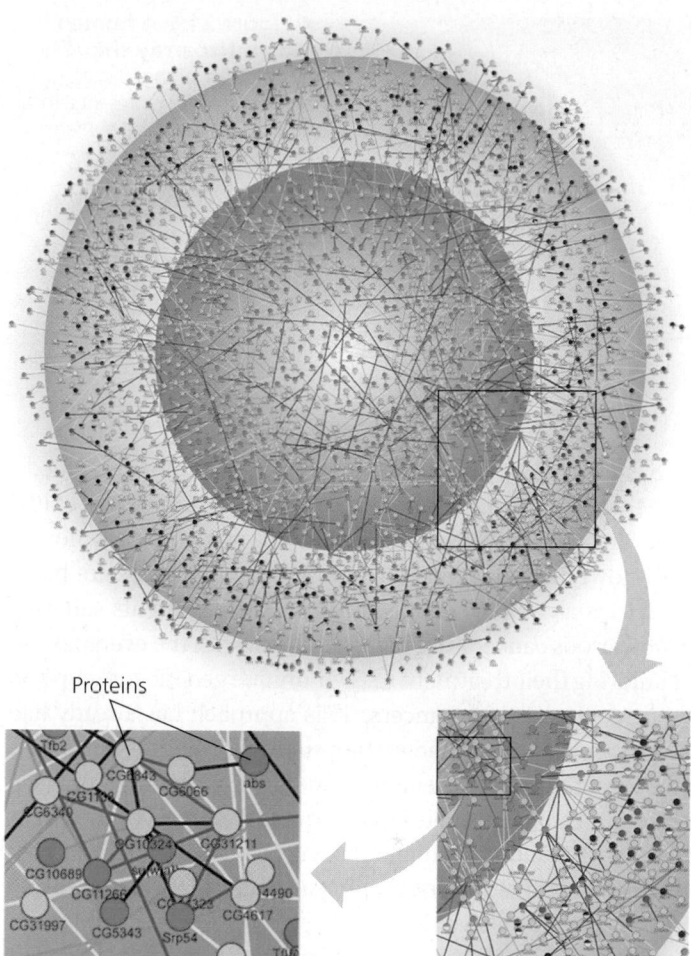

Proteins

▲ **Figure 21.5 The systems biology approach to protein interactions.** This global protein interaction map shows a subset of the most statistically likely interactions (lines) among about 2,300 proteins (small circles) in *Drosophila*. The three background colors in the map correspond to the general location of each protein: Green is the nucleus, blue the cytoplasm, and yellow the plasma membrane. The proteins are also color-coded according to their specific subcellular localization; for example, green circles represent nuclear proteins.

Application of Systems Biology to Medicine

The Cancer Genome Atlas is another example of systems biology in which a large group of interacting genes and gene products are analyzed together. This project, under the joint leadership of the National Cancer Institute and the NIH, aims to understand how changes in biological systems lead to cancer. In a three-year pilot project running from 2007 to 2010, three types of cancer—lung cancer, ovarian cancer, and glioblastoma of the brain—are being analyzed by comparing gene sequences and patterns of gene expression in cancer cells with those of normal cells. A set of approximately 2,000 genes from the cancer cells will be sequenced at several different times during the progression of the disease to monitor changes due to mutations and rearrangements. If this approach proves fruitful, it will be extended to other types of cancer.

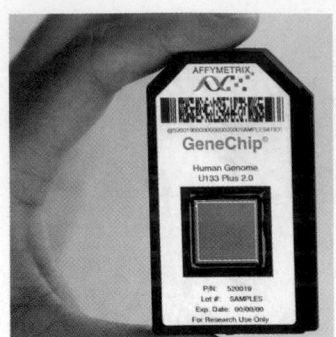

◄ **Figure 21.6 A human gene microarray chip.** Tiny dots of DNA arranged in a grid on this silicon wafer represent almost all of the genes in the human genome. Using this chip, researchers can analyze expression patterns for all human genes at the same time, minimizing the amount of reagents used and ensuring uniform conditions for all the genes.

Systems biology has tremendous potential in human medicine that is just starting to be explored. Silicon and glass "chips" have already been developed that hold a microarray of most of the known human genes (Figure 21.6). Such chips are being used to analyze gene expression patterns in patients suffering from various cancers and other diseases, with the eventual aim of tailoring their treatment to their unique genetic makeup and the specifics of their cancers. This approach has already had modest success in characterizing subsets of several cancers.

Ultimately, every person may carry with their medical records a catalog of their DNA sequence, a sort of genetic bar code, with regions highlighted that predispose them to specific diseases. The potential application for disease prevention and treatment is substantial.

Systems biology is a highly efficient way to study emergent properties at the molecular level. Recall from Chapter 1 that according to the concept of emergent properties, novel properties arise at each successive level of biological complexity as a result of the arrangement of building blocks at the underlying level. The more we are able to learn about the arrangement and interactions of the components of genetic systems, the deeper will be our understanding of organisms. The remaining sections of this chapter will survey what we've learned from genomic studies thus far.

CONCEPT 21.3

Genomes vary in size, number of genes, and gene density

By early 2008, the sequencing of over 700 genomes had been completed and that of more than 2,700 genomes was in progress. In the completely sequenced group, about 600 are genomes of bacteria, and 50 are archaeal genomes. Among the 65 eukaryotic species in the group are vertebrates, invertebrates, protists, fungi, and plants. The accumulated genome sequences contain a wealth of information that we are just beginning to mine. What have we learned so far by comparing the genomes that have now been sequenced? In this section, we will examine the characteristics of genome size, number of genes, and gene density. Because these characteristics are so broad, we will focus on general trends, for which there are often exceptions.

Genome Size

Comparing the three domains (Bacteria, Archaea, and Eukarya), we find a general difference in genome size between prokaryotes and eukaryotes (Table 21.1). While there are some exceptions, most bacterial genomes have between 1 and 6 million base pairs (Mb); the genome of *E. coli*, for instance, has 4.6 Mb. Genomes of archaea are, for the most part, within the size range of bacterial genomes. (Keep in mind, however, that many fewer archaeal genomes have been completely sequenced, so this picture may change.) Eukaryotic genomes tend to be larger: The genome of the single-celled yeast *Saccharomyces cerevisiae* (a fungus) has about 13 Mb, while most animals and plants, which are multicellular, have genomes of at least 100 Mb. There are 180 Mb in the fruit fly genome, while humans have 3,200 Mb, about 500 to 3,000 times as many as a typical bacterium.

Aside from this general difference between prokaryotes and eukaryotes, a comparison of genome sizes among eukaryotes fails to reveal any systematic relationship between genome size and the organism's phenotype. For instance, the genome of *Fritillaria assyriaca*, a flowering plant in the lily family, contains 120 billion base pairs (120,000 Mb), about 40 times the size of the human genome. Even more striking, there is a single-celled amoeba, *Amoeba dubia*, whose genome has 670,000 Mb. (This genome has not yet been sequenced.) On a finer scale, comparing two insect species, the cricket (*Anabrus simplex*) genome turns out to have 11 times as many base pairs as the *Drosophila melanogaster* genome. There is a wide range of genome sizes within the groups of protists, insects, amphibians, and plants and less of a range within mammals and reptiles.

Number of Genes

A similar difference holds true for the number of genes: Bacteria and archaea, in general, have fewer genes than eukaryotes.

Free-living bacteria and archaea have from 1,500 to 7,500 genes, while the number of genes in eukaryotes ranges from about 5,000 for unicellular fungi to at least 40,000 for some multicellular eukaryotes (see Table 21.1).

Within the eukaryotes, the number of genes in a species is often lower than expected from simply considering the size of its genome. Looking at Table 21.1, you can see that the genome of the nematode *C. elegans* is 100 Mb in size and contains roughly 20,000 genes. The *Drosophila* genome, in comparison, is almost twice as big (180 Mb) but has about two-thirds the number of genes—only 13,700 genes.

Considering an example closer to home, we noted that the human genome contains 3,200 Mb, well over ten times the size of either the *Drosophila* or *C. elegans* genome. At the outset of the Human Genome Project, biologists expected somewhere between 50,000 and 100,000 genes to be identified in the completed sequence, based on the number of known human proteins. As the project progressed, the estimate was revised downward several times, and, as of 2007, the most reliable count places the number at 20,488. This relatively low number, similar to the number of genes in the nematode *C. elegans*, has surprised biologists, who had clearly expected many more human genes.

What genetic attributes allow humans (and other vertebrates) to get by with no more genes than nematodes? An important factor is that vertebrate genomes "get more bang for the buck" from their coding sequences because of extensive alternative splicing of RNA transcripts. Recall that this process generates more than one functional protein from a single gene (see Figure 18.11). For instance, nearly all human genes contain multiple exons, and an estimated 75% of these multi-exon genes are spliced in at least two different ways. If we assume that each alternatively spliced human gene on average specifies three different polypeptides, then the total number of different human polypeptides would be about 75,000. Additional polypeptide diversity could result from post-translational modifications such as cleavage or addition of carbohydrate groups in different cell types or at different developmental stages.

Gene Density and Noncoding DNA

In addition to genome size and number of genes, we can compare gene density in different species—in other words, how many genes there are in a given length of DNA. When we compare the genomes of bacteria, archaea, and eukaryotes, we see that eukaryotes generally have larger genomes but fewer genes in a given number of base pairs. Humans have hundreds or thousands of times as many base pairs in their genome as most bacteria, as we already noted, but they have only 5 to 15 times as many genes; thus, gene density is lower in humans (see Table 21.1). Even unicellular eukaryotes, such as yeasts, have fewer genes per million base pairs than bacteria and archaea. Among the genomes that have been sequenced completely thus far, humans and other mammals have the lowest gene density.

In all bacterial genomes studied so far, most of the DNA consists of genes for protein, tRNA, or rRNA; the small amount of other DNA consists mainly of nontranscribed regulatory sequences, such as promoters. The sequence of nucleotides along a bacterial protein-coding gene proceeds from start to finish without interruption by noncoding sequences (introns). In eukaryotic genomes, by contrast, most of the DNA neither encodes protein nor is transcribed into known functional RNA molecules (such as tRNAs), and the DNA includes more complex regulatory sequences. In fact, humans have 10,000 times as much noncoding DNA as bacteria. Some of this DNA in multicellular eukaryotes is present as introns within genes. Indeed, introns account for most of the difference in average length between human genes (27,000 base pairs) and bacterial genes (1,000 base pairs).

Table 21.1 Genome Sizes and Estimated Numbers of Genes*

Organism	Haploid Genome Size (Mb)	Number of Genes	Genes per Mb
Bacteria			
Haemophilus influenzae	1.8	1,700	940
Escherichia coli	4.6	4,400	950
Archaea			
Archaeoglobus fulgidus	2.2	2,500	1,130
Methanosarcina barkeri	4.8	3,600	750
Eukaryotes			
Saccharomyces cerevisiae (yeast, a fungus)	13	6,200	480
Caenorhabditis elegans (nematode)	100	20,000	200
Arabidopsis thaliana (mustard family plant)	118	25,500	215
Drosophila melanogaster (fruit fly)	180	13,700	76
Oryza sativa (rice)	390	40,000	140
Danio rerio (zebrafish)	1,700	23,000	13
Mus musculus (house mouse)	2,600	22,000	11
Homo sapiens (human)	3,200	20,500	7
Fritillaria assyriaca (lily family plant)	120,000	ND	ND

*Some values given here are likely to be revised as genome analysis continues. Mb = million base pairs. ND = not determined.

In addition to introns, multicellular eukaryotes have a vast amount of noncoding DNA between genes. In the next section, we will describe the composition and arrangement of these great stretches of DNA in the human genome.

CONCEPT 21.4
Multicellular eukaryotes have much noncoding DNA and many multigene families

We have spent most of this chapter, and indeed this unit, focusing on genes that code for proteins. Yet the coding regions of these genes and the genes for RNA products such as rRNA, tRNA, and microRNA (miRNA) make up only a small portion of the genomes of most multicellular eukaryotes. The bulk of most eukaryotic genomes consists of DNA sequences that neither code for proteins nor are transcribed to produce known RNAs; this noncoding DNA was often described in the past as "junk DNA." However, much evidence is accumulating that this DNA plays important roles in the cell, an idea supported by its persistence in diverse genomes over many hundreds of generations. For example, comparison of the genomes of humans, rats, and mice has revealed the presence of almost 500 regions of noncoding DNA that are identical in sequence in all three species. This is a higher level of sequence conservation than is seen for protein-coding regions in these species, strongly suggesting that the noncoding regions have important functions. In this section, we examine how genes and noncoding DNA sequences are organized within genomes of multicellular eukaryotes, using the human genome as our main example. Genome organiza-

tion tells us much about how genomes have evolved and continue to evolve, the next subject we'll consider.

Once the sequencing of the human genome was completed, it became clear that only a tiny part—1.5%—codes for proteins or is transcribed into rRNAs or tRNAs. **Figure 21.7** shows what is known about the makeup of the remaining 98.5%. Gene-related regulatory sequences and introns account for 24% of the human genome; the rest, located between functional genes, includes some unique noncoding DNA, such as gene fragments and **pseudogenes**, former genes that have accumulated mutations over a long time and have become nonfunctional. Most intergenic DNA, however, is **repetitive DNA**, which consists of sequences that are present in multiple copies in the genome. Somewhat surprisingly, about three-fourths of this repetitive DNA (44% of the entire human genome) is made up of units called transposable elements and sequences related to them.

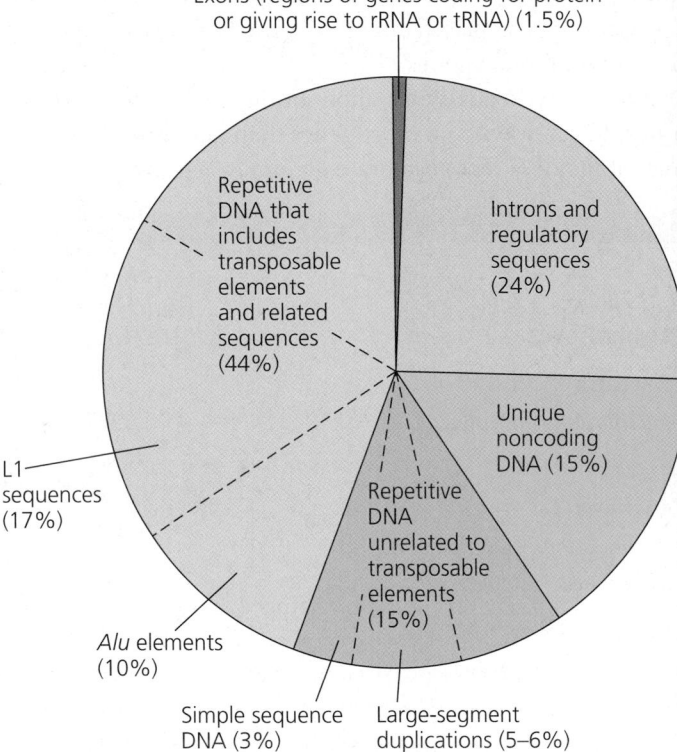

▲ **Figure 21.7 Types of DNA sequences in the human genome.** The gene sequences that code for proteins or are transcribed into rRNA or tRNA molecules make up only about 1.5% of the human genome (dark purple in the pie chart), while introns and regulatory sequences associated with genes (light purple) make up about a quarter. The vast majority of the human genome does not code for proteins or give rise to known RNAs, and much of it is repetitive DNA (dark and light green). Because repetitive DNA is the most difficult to sequence and analyze, classification of some portions is tentative, and the percentages given here may shift slightly as genome analysis proceeds. The genes that are transcribed into miRNAs, which were recently discovered, are found among unique noncoding DNA sequences and within introns; thus, they are included in two segments of this chart.

Transposable Elements and Related Sequences

Both prokaryotes and eukaryotes have stretches of DNA that can move from one location to another within the genome. These stretches are known as *transposable genetic elements*, or simply **transposable elements**. During the process called *transposition*, a transposable element moves from one site in a cell's DNA to a different target site by a type of recombination process. Transposable elements are sometimes called "jumping genes," but the phrase is misleading because they never completely detach from the cell's DNA. (The original and new DNA sites are brought together by DNA bending.)

The first evidence for wandering DNA segments came from American geneticist Barbara McClintock's breeding experiments with Indian corn (maize) in the 1940s and 1950s (**Figure 21.8**). As she tracked corn plants through multiple generations, McClintock identified changes in the color of corn kernels that made sense only if she postulated the existence of genetic elements capable of moving from other locations in the genome into the genes for kernel color, disrupting the genes so that the kernel color was changed. McClintock's discovery was met with great skepticism and virtually discounted at the time. Her careful work and insightful ideas were finally validated many years later when transposable elements were found in bacteria and microbial geneticists learned more about the molecular basis of transposition.

Movement of Transposons and Retrotransposons

Eukaryotic transposable elements are of two types. The first type are **transposons**, which move within a genome by means of a DNA intermediate. Transposons can move by a "cut-and-paste" mechanism, which removes the element from the original site, or by a "copy-and-paste" mechanism, which leaves a copy behind (**Figure 21.9a**).

Most transposable elements in eukaryotic genomes are of the second type, **retrotransposons**, which move by means of an RNA intermediate that is a transcript of the retrotransposon DNA. Retrotransposons always leave a copy at the original site during transposition, since they are initially transcribed into an RNA intermediate (**Figure 21.9b**). To insert at another site, the RNA intermediate is first converted back to DNA by reverse transcriptase, an enzyme encoded in the retrotransposon itself. Thus, reverse transcriptase can be present in cells not infected with retroviruses. (In fact, retroviruses, which were discussed in Chapter 19, may have evolved from retrotransposons.) A cellular enzyme catalyzes insertion of the reverse-transcribed DNA at a new site.

(a) Transposon movement ("copy-and-paste" mechanism)

(b) Retrotransposon movement

▲ Figure 21.9 **Movement of eukaryotic transposable elements.** (a) Movement of transposons by either the cut-and-paste mechanism or the copy-and-paste mechanism (shown here) involves a double-stranded DNA intermediate that is inserted into the genome. **(b)** Movement of retrotransposons begins with formation of a single-stranded RNA intermediate. The remaining steps are essentially identical to part of the retrovirus reproductive cycle (see Figure 19.8). In the movement of transposons by the copy-and-paste mechanism and in the movement of retrotransposons, the DNA sequence remains in the original site as well as appearing in a new site.

? *How would part (a) differ if it showed the cut-and-paste mechanism?*

▲ Figure 21.8 **The effect of transposable elements on corn kernel color.** Barbara McClintock first proposed the idea of mobile genetic elements after observing variegations in corn kernel color. Although her idea was met with skepticism when she proposed it in the 1940s, it was later fully validated. She received the Nobel Prize in 1983, at the age of 81, for her pioneering research.

Sequences Related to Transposable Elements

Multiple copies of transposable elements and sequences related to them are scattered throughout eukaryotic genomes. A single unit is usually hundreds to thousands of base pairs long, and the dispersed "copies" are similar but usually not identical to each other. Some of these are transposable elements that can move; the enzymes required for this movement may be encoded by any transposable element, including the one that is moving. Others are related sequences that have lost the ability to move altogether. Transposable elements and related sequences make up 25–50% of most mammalian genomes (see Figure 21.7) and even higher percentages in amphibians and many plants.

In humans and other primates, a large portion of transposable element–related DNA consists of a family of similar sequences called *Alu elements*. These sequences alone account for approximately 10% of the human genome. *Alu* elements are about 300 nucleotides long, much shorter than most functional transposable elements, and they do not code for any protein. However, many *Alu* elements are transcribed into RNA; its cellular function, if any, is currently unknown.

An even larger percentage (17%) of the human genome is made up of a type of retrotransposon called *LINE-1*, or *L1*. These sequences are much longer than *Alu* elements—about 6,500 base pairs—and have a low rate of transposition. What might account for this low rate? Recent research has uncovered the presence of sequences within L1 that block progress of RNA polymerase, which is necessary for transposition. An accompanying genomic analysis found L1 sequences within the introns of nearly 80% of the human genes that were analyzed, suggesting that L1 may help regulate gene expression. Other researchers have proposed that L1 retrotransposons may have differential effects on gene expression in developing neurons, contributing to the great diversity of neuronal cell types (see Chapter 48).

Although many transposable elements encode proteins, these proteins do not carry out normal cellular functions. Therefore, transposable elements are often included in the "noncoding" DNA category, along with other repetitive sequences.

Other Repetitive DNA, Including Simple Sequence DNA

Repetitive DNA that is not related to transposable elements probably arises due to mistakes during DNA replication or recombination. Such DNA accounts for about 15% of the human genome (see Figure 21.7). About a third of this (5–6% of the human genome) consists of duplications of long stretches of DNA, with each unit ranging from 10,000 to 300,000 base pairs. The large segments seem to have been copied from one chromosomal location to another site on the same or a different chromosome.

In contrast to scattered copies of long sequences, **simple sequence DNA** contains many copies of tandemly repeated short sequences, as in the following example (showing one DNA strand only):

... GTTACGTTACGTTACGTTACGTTACGTTAC ...

In this case, the repeated unit (GTTAC) consists of five nucleotides. Repeated units may contain as many as 500 nucleotides, but often contain fewer than 15 nucleotides, as seen for this example. When the unit contains 2 to 5 nucleotides, the series of repeats is called a **short tandem repeat**, or **STR**; we discussed the use of STR analysis in preparing genetic profiles in Chapter 20. The number of copies of the repeated unit can vary from site to site within a given genome. There could be as many as several hundred thousand repetitions of the GTTAC unit at one site, but only half that number at another. The repeat number can also vary from person to person, producing the variation represented in the genetic profiles that result from STR analysis. Altogether, simple sequence DNA makes up 3% of the human genome.

The nucleotide composition of simple sequence DNA is often different enough from the rest of the cell's DNA to have an intrinsically different density. If genomic DNA is cut into pieces and centrifuged at high speed, segments of different density migrate to different positions in the centrifuge tube. Repetitive DNA isolated in this way was originally called *satellite DNA* because it appeared as a "satellite" band in the centrifuge tube, separate from the rest of the DNA. Now the term is often used interchangeably with simple sequence DNA.

Much of a genome's simple sequence DNA is located at chromosomal telomeres and centromeres, suggesting that this DNA plays a structural role for chromosomes. The DNA at centromeres is essential for the separation of chromatids in cell division (see Chapter 12). Centromeric DNA, along with simple sequence DNA located elsewhere, may also help organize the chromatin within the interphase nucleus. The simple sequence DNA located at telomeres, at the tips of chromosomes, prevents genes from being lost as the DNA shortens with each round of replication (see Chapter 16). Telomeric DNA also binds proteins that protect the ends of a chromosome from degradation and from joining to other chromosomes.

Genes and Multigene Families

We finish our discussion of the various types of DNA sequences in eukaryotic genomes with a closer look at genes. Recall that DNA sequences that code for proteins or give rise to tRNA or rRNA compose a mere 1.5% of the human genome (see Figure 21.7). If we include introns and regulatory sequences associated with genes, the total amount of gene-related DNA—coding and noncoding—constitutes about 25%

of the human genome. Put another way, only about 6% (1.5% out of 25%) of the length of the average gene is represented in the final gene product.

Like the genes of bacteria, many eukaryotic genes are present as unique sequences, with only one copy per haploid set of chromosomes. But in the human genome and the genomes of many other animals and plants, such solitary genes make up less than half of the total transcribed DNA. The rest occurs in **multigene families**, collections of two or more identical or very similar genes.

In multigene families that consist of *identical* DNA sequences, those sequences are usually clustered tandemly and, with the notable exception of the genes for histone proteins, have RNAs as their final products. An example is the family of identical DNA sequences that are the genes for the three largest rRNA molecules **(Figure 21.10a)**. These rRNA molecules are transcribed from a single transcription unit that is repeated tandemly hundreds to thousands of times in one or several clusters in the genome of a multicellular eukaryote.

The many copies of this rRNA transcription unit help cells to quickly make the millions of ribosomes needed for active protein synthesis. The primary transcript is cleaved to yield the three rRNA molecules. These are then combined with proteins and one other kind of rRNA (5S rRNA) to form ribosomal subunits.

The classic examples of multigene families of *nonidentical* genes are two related families of genes that encode globins, a group of proteins that include the α and β polypeptide subunits of hemoglobin. One family, located on chromosome 16 in humans, encodes various forms of α-globin; the other, on chromosome 11, encodes forms of β-globin **(Figure 21.10b)**. The different forms of each globin subunit are expressed at different times in development, allowing hemoglobin to function effectively in the changing environment of the developing animal. In humans, for example, the embryonic and fetal forms of hemoglobin have a higher affinity for oxygen than the adult forms, ensuring the efficient transfer of oxygen from mother to fetus. Also found in the globin gene family clusters are several pseudogenes.

(a) Part of the ribosomal RNA gene family. Three of the hundreds of copies of rRNA transcription units in a salamander genome are shown at the top (TEM). Each "feather" corresponds to a single transcription unit being transcribed by about 100 molecules of RNA polymerase (the dark dots along the DNA), moving left to right. The growing RNA transcripts extend out from the DNA. In the diagram below the TEM, one transcription unit is shown. It includes the genes for three types of rRNA (blue), adjacent to regions that are transcribed but later removed (yellow). A single transcript is made and then processed to yield one molecule of each of the three rRNAs, which are crucial components of the ribosome. A fourth rRNA (5S rRNA) is also found in the ribosome, but the gene encoding it is not part of this transcription unit.

(b) The human α-globin and β-globin gene families. Hemoglobin is composed of two α-globin and two β-globin polypeptide subunits. The genes (dark blue) encoding α- and β-globins are found in two families, organized as shown here. The noncoding DNA separating the functional genes within each family cluster includes pseudogenes (green), nonfunctional versions of the functional genes. Genes and pseudogenes are named with Greek letters.

▲ **Figure 21.10 Gene families.**
? In (a), how could you determine the direction of transcription if it wasn't indicated by the red arrow?

The arrangement of the genes in gene families has given biologists insight into the evolution of genomes. We will consider some of the processes that have shaped the genomes of different species over evolutionary time in the next section.

CONCEPT CHECK 21.4

1. Discuss the characteristics of mammalian genomes that make them larger than prokaryotic genomes.
2. How are introns, transposable elements, and simple sequence DNA distributed differently in the genome?
3. Discuss the differences in the organization of the rRNA gene family and the globin gene families. For each, explain how the existence of a family of genes benefits the organism.
4. **WHAT IF?** Imagine you have found a DNA sequence similar to that of a known gene, but with quite a few nucleotide differences. How would you determine whether the "gene" you found is functional?

For suggested answers, see Appendix A.

CONCEPT 21.5
Duplication, rearrangement, and mutation of DNA contribute to genome evolution

The basis of change at the genomic level is mutation, which underlies much of genome evolution. It seems likely that the earliest forms of life had a minimal number of genes—those necessary for survival and reproduction. If this were indeed the case, one aspect of evolution must have been an increase in the size of the genome, with the extra genetic material providing the raw material for gene diversification. In this section, we will first describe how extra copies of all or part of a genome can arise and then consider subsequent processes that can lead to the evolution of proteins (or RNA products) with slightly different or entirely new functions.

Duplication of Entire Chromosome Sets

An accident in meiosis can result in one or more extra sets of chromosomes, a condition known as polyploidy. Although such accidents would most often be lethal, in rare cases they could facilitate the evolution of genes. In a polyploid organism, one set of genes can provide essential functions for the organism. The genes in the one or more extra sets can diverge by accumulating mutations; these variations may persist if the organism carrying them survives and reproduces. In this way, genes with novel functions can evolve. As long as one copy of an essential gene is expressed, the divergence of another copy can lead to its encoded protein acting in a novel

way, thereby changing the organism's phenotype. The outcome of this accumulation of mutations may be the branching off of a new species, as happens often in plants (see Chapter 24). Polyploid animals also exist, but they are rare.

Alterations of Chromosome Structure

Scientists have long known that sometime in the last 6 million years, when the ancestors of humans and chimpanzees diverged as species, the fusion of two ancestral chromosomes in the human line led to different haploid numbers for humans ($n = 23$) and chimpanzees ($n = 24$). With the recent explosion in genomic sequence information, we can now compare the chromosomal organization of many different species on a much finer scale. This information allows us to make inferences about the evolutionary processes that shape chromosomes and may drive speciation.

In one study, for example, researchers compared the DNA sequence of each human chromosome with the whole genome sequence of the mouse. **Figure 21.11** shows the results of this comparison for human chromosome 16: Large blocks of genes on this chromosome are found on four mouse chromosomes, indicating that the genes in each block stayed together during the evolution of the mouse and human lineages. Performing the same comparative analysis between chromosomes of humans

Human chromosome 16

Blocks of DNA sequence

Blocks of similar sequences in four mouse chromosomes:

7   8   16   17

▲ **Figure 21.11 Similar blocks of sequences on human and mouse chromosomes.** DNA sequences very similar to large blocks of human chromosome 16 are found on mouse chromosomes 7, 8, 16, and 17. This suggests that the DNA sequence in each block has stayed together in the mouse and human lineages since the time they diverged from a common ancestor.

and six other mammalian species allowed the researchers to re-construct the evolutionary history of chromosomal rearrange-ments in these eight species. They found many duplications and inversions of large portions of chromosomes, the result of mis-takes during meiotic recombination in which the DNA broke and was rejoined incorrectly. The rate of these events seems to have accelerated about 100 million years ago, around the time large dinosaurs became extinct and the number of mammalian species increased rapidly. The apparent coincidence is interest-ing because chromosomal rearrangements are thought to con-tribute to the generation of new species. Although two individuals with different arrangements could still mate and produce offspring, the offspring would have two nonequivalent sets of chromosomes, making meiosis inefficient or even im-possible. Thus, chromosomal rearrangements would lead to two populations that could not successfully mate with each other, a step on the way to their becoming two separate species. (You'll learn more about this in Chapter 24.)

Somewhat unexpectedly, the same study also unearthed a pattern with medical relevance. Analysis of the chromosomal breakage points associated with the rearrangements showed that they were not randomly distributed, but that specific sites were used over and over again. A number of these recombina-tion "hot spots" correspond to locations of chromosomal re-arrangements within the human genome that are associated with congenital diseases. Researchers are, of course, looking at the other sites as well for their possible association with as yet unidentified diseases.

Duplication and Divergence of Gene-Sized Regions of DNA

Errors during meiosis can also lead to the duplication of chro-mosomal regions that are smaller than the ones we've just dis-cussed, including segments the length of individual genes. Unequal crossing over during prophase I of meiosis, for in-stance, can result in one chromosome with a deletion and an-other with a duplication of a particular gene. As illustrated in **Figure 21.12**, transposable elements in the genome can pro-vide sites where nonsister chromatids can cross over, even when their homologous sequences are not correctly aligned.

Also, slippage can occur during DNA replication, such that the template shifts with respect to the new complementary strand, and a part of the template strand is either skipped by the replication machinery or used twice as a template. As a re-sult, a segment of DNA is deleted or duplicated. It is easy to imagine how such errors could occur in regions of repeats like the simple sequence DNA described previously. The variable number of repeated units of simple sequence DNA at a given site, used for STR analysis, is probably due to errors like these. Evidence that unequal crossing over and template slippage during DNA replication lead to duplication of genes is found in the existence of multigene families.

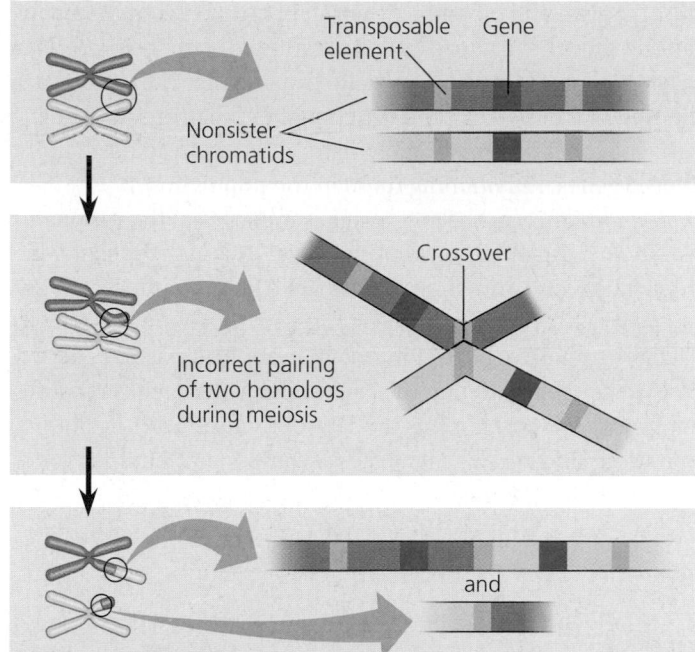

▲ **Figure 21.12 Gene duplication due to unequal crossing over.** One mechanism by which a gene (or other DNA segment) can be duplicated is recombination during meiosis between copies of a transposable element flanking the gene. Such recombination between misaligned nonsister chromatids of homologous chromosomes produces one chromatid with two copies of the gene and one chromatid with no copy.

Evolution of Genes with Related Functions: The Human Globin Genes

Duplication events can lead to the evolution of genes with re-lated functions, such as those of the α-globin and β-globin gene families (see Figure 21.10b). A comparison of gene sequences within a multigene family can suggest the order in which the genes arose. This approach to re-creating the evolutionary his-tory of the globin genes indicates that they all evolved from one common ancestral globin gene that underwent duplication and divergence into the α-globin and β-globin ancestral genes about 450–500 million years ago (**Figure 21.13**, on the next page). Each of these genes was later duplicated several times, and the copies then diverged from each other in sequence, yielding the current family members. In fact, the common ancestral globin gene also gave rise to the oxygen-binding muscle protein myo-globin and to the plant protein leghemoglobin. The latter two proteins function as monomers, and their genes are included in a "globin superfamily."

After the duplication events, the differences between the genes in the globin families undoubtedly arose from mutations that accumulated in the gene copies over many generations. The current model is that the necessary function provided by an α-globin protein, for example, was fulfilled by one gene, while other copies of the α-globin gene accumulated random mutations. Many mutations may have had an adverse effect on the organism and others may have had no effect, but a few mutations must have altered the function of the protein product in a way that was advantageous to the organism at a particular life stage without substantially changing the protein's oxygen-carrying function. Presumably, natural selection acted on these altered genes, maintaining them in the population.

The similarity in the amino acid sequences of the various α-globin and β-globin polypeptides supports this model of gene duplication and mutation **(Table 21.2)**. The amino acid sequences of the β-globins, for instance, are much more similar to each other than to the α-globin sequences. The existence of several pseudogenes among the functional globin genes provides additional evidence for this model (see Figure 21.10b): Random mutations in these "genes" over evolutionary time have destroyed their function.

▲ **Figure 21.13 A model for the evolution of the human α-globin and β-globin gene families from a single ancestral globin gene.**

? *The green elements are pseudogenes. Explain how they could have arisen after gene duplication.*

Table 21.2 Percentage of Similarity in Amino Acid Sequence Between Human Globin Proteins

		α-Globins		β-Globins		
		α	ζ	β	γ	ε
α-Globins	α	—	58	42	39	37
	ζ	58	—	34	38	37
β-Globins	β	42	34	—	73	75
	γ	39	38	73	—	80
	ε	37	37	75	80	—

Evolution of Genes with Novel Functions

In the evolution of the globin gene families, gene duplication and subsequent divergence produced family members whose protein products performed similar functions (oxygen transport). Alternatively, one copy of a duplicated gene can undergo alterations that lead to a completely new function for the protein product. The genes for lysozyme and α-lactalbumin are good examples.

Lysozyme is an enzyme that helps protect animals against bacterial infection by hydrolyzing bacterial cell walls; α-lactalbumin is a nonenzymatic protein that plays a role in milk production in mammals. The two proteins are quite similar in their amino acid sequences and three-dimensional structures. Both genes are found in mammals, whereas only the lysozyme gene is present in birds. These findings suggest that at some time after the lineages leading to mammals and birds had separated, the lysozyme gene underwent a duplication event in the mammalian lineage but not in the avian lineage. Subsequently, one copy of the duplicated lysozyme gene evolved into a gene encoding α-lactalbumin, a protein with a completely different function.

Rearrangements of Parts of Genes: Exon Duplication and Exon Shuffling

Rearrangement of existing DNA sequences within genes has also contributed to genome evolution. The presence of introns in most genes of multicellular eukaryotes may have promoted the evolution of new and potentially useful proteins by facilitating the duplication or repositioning of exons in the genome. Recall from Chapter 17 that an exon often codes for a domain, a distinct structural or functional region of a protein.

We've already seen that unequal crossing over during meiosis can lead to duplication of a gene on one chromosome and its loss from the homologous chromosome (see Figure 21.12). By a similar process, a particular exon within a gene could be duplicated on one chromosome and deleted from the other. The gene with the duplicated exon would code for a protein containing a second copy of the encoded domain. This change in the protein's structure could augment its function by increasing its stability, enhancing

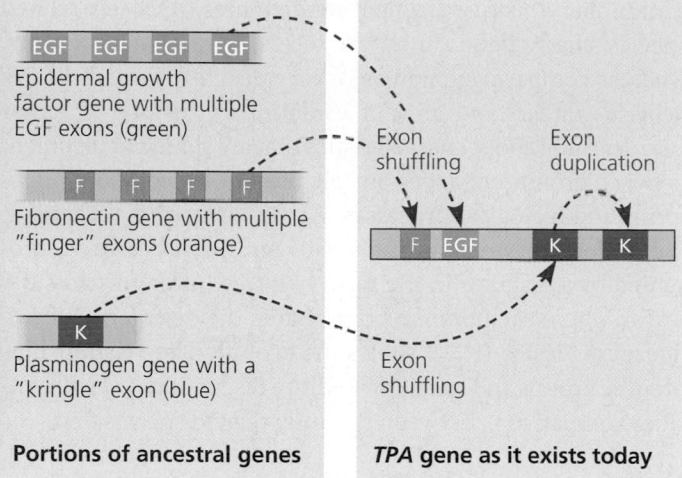

| Portions of ancestral genes | TPA gene as it exists today |

▲ Figure 21.14 Evolution of a new gene by exon shuffling. Exon shuffling could have moved exons from ancestral forms of the genes for epidermal growth factor, fibronectin, and plasminogen (left) into the evolving gene for tissue plasminogen activator, TPA (right). The order in which these events might have occurred is unknown. Duplication of the "kringle" exon from the plasminogen gene after its movement could account for the two copies of this exon in the *TPA* gene. Each type of exon encodes a particular domain in the TPA protein.

? *How could the presence of transposable elements in introns have facilitated the exon shuffling shown here?*

its ability to bind a particular ligand, or altering some other property. Quite a few protein-coding genes have multiple copies of related exons, which presumably arose by duplication and then diverged. The gene encoding the extracellular matrix protein collagen is a good example. Collagen is a structural protein with a highly repetitive amino acid sequence, which is reflected in the repetitive pattern of exons in the collagen gene.

Alternatively, we can imagine the occasional mixing and matching of different exons either within a gene or between two nonallelic genes owing to errors in meiotic recombination. This process, termed *exon shuffling*, could lead to new proteins with novel combinations of functions. As an example, let's consider the gene for tissue plasminogen activator (TPA). The TPA protein is an extracellular protein that helps control blood clotting. It has four domains of three types, each encoded by an exon; one exon is present in two copies. Because each type of exon is also found in other proteins, the gene for TPA is thought to have arisen by several instances of exon shuffling and duplication **(Figure 21.14)**.

How Transposable Elements Contribute to Genome Evolution

The persistence of transposable elements as a large fraction of some eukaryotic genomes is consistent with the idea that they play an important role in shaping a genome over evolutionary time. These elements can contribute to the evolution of the genome in several ways. They can promote recombination,

disrupt cellular genes or control elements, and carry entire genes or individual exons to new locations.

Transposable elements of similar sequence scattered throughout the genome facilitate recombination between different chromosomes by providing homologous regions for crossing over. Most such alterations are probably detrimental, causing chromosomal translocations and other changes in the genome that may be lethal to the organism. But over the course of evolutionary time, an occasional recombination event of this sort may be advantageous to the organism.

The movement of a transposable element can also have direct consequences. For instance, if a transposable element "jumps" into the middle of a protein-coding sequence, it will prevent the production of a normal transcript of the gene. If a transposable element inserts within a regulatory sequence, the transposition may lead to increased or decreased production of one or more proteins. Transposition caused both types of effects on the genes coding for pigment-synthesizing enzymes in McClintock's corn kernels. Again, while such changes may usually be harmful, in the long run some may prove beneficial by providing a survival advantage.

During transposition, a transposable element may carry along a gene or group of genes to a new position in the genome. This mechanism probably accounts for the location of the α-globin and β-globin gene families on different human chromosomes, as well as the dispersion of the genes of certain other gene families. By a similar tag-along process, an exon from one gene may be inserted into another gene in a mechanism similar to that of exon shuffling during recombination. For example, an exon may be inserted by transposition into the intron of a protein-coding gene. If the inserted exon is retained in the RNA transcript during RNA splicing, the protein that is synthesized will have an additional domain, which may confer a new function on the protein.

A recent study reveals yet another way that transposable elements can bring about new coding sequences. This work shows that an *Alu* element may hop into an intron in a way that creates a weak alternative splice site in the RNA transcript. During processing of the transcript, the regular splice sites are used more often, so that the original protein is made. On occasion, however, splicing occurs at the new weak site, with the result that some of the *Alu* element ends up in the mRNA, coding for a new portion of the protein. In this way, alternative genetic combinations may be "tried out" while the function of the original gene product is retained.

Clearly, all the processes discussed in this section most often produce either harmful effects, which may be lethal, or no effect at all. In a few cases, however, small beneficial changes may occur. Over many generations, the resulting genetic diversity provides valuable raw material for natural selection. Diversification of genes and their products is an important factor in the evolution of new species. Thus, the accumulation of changes in the genome of each species provides a record of its evolutionary history. To read this record, we must be able to identify genomic changes. Comparing the genomes of different species allows us to do that and has increased our understanding of how genomes evolve. You will learn more about these topics in the final section.

CONCEPT 21.6
Comparing genome sequences provides clues to evolution and development

One researcher has likened the current state of biology to the Age of Exploration in the 15th century after major improvements in navigation and the building of faster ships. In the last 20 years, we have seen rapid advances in genome sequencing and data collection, new techniques for assessing gene activity across the whole genome, and refined approaches for understanding how genes and their products work together in complex systems. We are truly poised on the brink of a new world.

Comparisons of genome sequences from different species reveal much about the evolutionary history of life, from very ancient to more recent. Similarly, comparative studies of the genetic programs that direct embryonic development in different species are beginning to clarify the mechanisms that generated the great diversity of life-forms present today. In this final section of the chapter, we will discuss what has been learned from these two approaches.

Comparing Genomes

The more similar in sequence the genes and genomes of two species are, the more closely related those species are in their evolutionary history. Comparing genomes of closely related species sheds light on more recent evolutionary events, whereas comparing genomes of very distantly related species helps us understand ancient evolutionary history. In either case, learning about characteristics that are shared or divergent between groups enhances our picture of the evolution of life-forms and biological processes. As you learned in Chapter 1, the evolutionary relationships between species can be represented by a diagram in the form of a tree (often turned sideways), where each branch point marks the divergence of two lineages. **Figure 21.15** shows the evolutionary relationships of some groups and species we will be discussing. We will consider comparisons between distantly related species first.

Comparing Distantly Related Species

Analyzing which genes have remained similar—that is, are *highly conserved*—in distantly related species can help clarify evolutionary relationships among species that diverged from each other long ago. Indeed, comparisons of the complete genome sequences of bacteria, archaea, and eukaryotes indicate that these three groups diverged between 2 and 4 billion years ago and strongly support the theory that they are the fundamental domains of life (see Figure 21.15).

In addition to their value in evolutionary biology, comparative genomic studies confirm the relevance of research on model organisms to our understanding of biology in general and human biology in particular. Genes that evolved a very long time ago can still be surprisingly similar in disparate species. As a case in point, several genes in yeast are so similar to certain human disease genes that researchers have deduced the functions of the disease genes by studying their yeast counterparts. This striking similarity underscores the common origin of these two distantly related species.

Comparing Closely Related Species

The genomes of two closely related species are likely to be organized similarly because of their relatively recent divergence. As we mentioned earlier, this allows the fully sequenced genome of one species to be used as a scaffold for assembling the genomic sequences of a closely related species, accelerating mapping of the second genome. For instance, using the human genome sequence as a guide, researchers were able to quickly sequence the mouse genome.

The recent divergence of two closely related species also underlies the small number of gene differences that are found when their genomes are compared. The particular genetic differences can therefore be more easily correlated with phenotypic differences between the two species. An exciting application of this type of analysis is seen as researchers compare the human genome with the genomes of the chimpanzee, mouse, rat, and other mammals. Identifying the genes shared by all of these species but not by nonmammals should give clues about what it

▲ **Figure 21.15 Evolutionary relationships of the three domains of life.** This tree diagram shows the ancient divergence of bacteria, archaea, and eukaryotes. A portion of the eukaryote lineage is expanded in the inset to show the more recent divergence of three mammalian species discussed in this chapter.

takes to make a mammal, while finding the genes shared by chimpanzees and humans but not by rodents should tell us something about primates. And, of course, comparing the human genome with that of the chimpanzee should help us answer the tantalizing question we asked at the beginning of the chapter: What genomic information makes a human or a chimpanzee?

An analysis of the overall composition of the human and chimpanzee genomes, which are thought to have diverged only about 6 million years ago (see Figure 21.15), reveals some general differences. Considering single base substitutions, the two genomes differ by only 1.2%. When researchers looked at longer stretches of DNA, however, they were surprised to find a further 2.7% difference due to insertions or deletions of larger regions in the genome of one or the other species; many of the insertions were duplications or other repetitive DNA. In fact, a third of the human duplications are not present in the chimpanzee genome, and some of these duplications contain regions associated with human diseases. There are more *Alu* elements in the human genome than in that of the chimpanzee, and the latter contains many copies of a retroviral provirus not present in humans. All of these observations provide clues to the forces that might have swept the two genomes along different paths, but we don't have a complete picture yet. We also don't know how these differences might account for the distinct characteristics of each species.

To discover the basis for the phenotypic differences between the two species, biologists are studying specific genes and types of genes that differ between humans and chimpanzees and comparing them with their counterparts in other mammals. This approach has revealed a number of genes that are apparently changing (evolving) faster in the human than in either the chimpanzee or the mouse. Among them are genes involved in defense against malaria and tuberculosis and at least one gene that regulates brain size. When genes are classified by function, the genes that seem to be evolving the fastest are those that code for transcription factors. This is exciting news because transcription factors regulate gene expression and thus play a key role in orchestrating the overall genetic program.

One transcription factor whose gene shows evidence of rapid change in the human lineage is called FOXP2. Several lines of evidence suggest that the *FOXP2* gene functions in vocalization in vertebrates. For one thing, mutations in this gene can produce severe speech and language impairment in humans. Moreover, the *FOXP2* gene is expressed in the brains of zebra finches and canaries at the time when these songbirds are learning their songs. But perhaps the strongest evidence comes from a "knock-out" experiment in which Joseph Buxbaum and colleagues disrupted the *FOXP2* gene in mice and analyzed the resulting phenotype (**Figure 21.16**, on the next page). The homozygous mutant mice had malformed brains and failed to emit normal ultrasonic vocalizations, and mice with one faulty copy of the gene also showed significant problems with vocalization. These results support the idea that the *FOXP2* gene product turns on genes involved in vocalization.

Expanding on this notion, researchers are exploring the question of whether differences between the human and chimpanzee FOXP2 proteins could account for the ability of humans, but not chimpanzees, to communicate by speech. There are only two amino acid differences between the human and chimpanzee FOXP2 proteins, and the effect of these differences on the function of the human protein is an intriguing question, whose answer is not yet known.

The *FOXP2* story is an excellent example of how different approaches complement each other in uncovering biological phenomena of widespread importance. The experiment described in Figure 21.16 uses mice as a model for humans because it would be unethical (as well as impractical) to carry out such an experiment in humans. Mice and humans diverged about 65.5 million years ago (see Figure 21.15) and share about 85% of their genes. This genetic similarity can be exploited in

▼ Figure 21.16 **Inquiry**

What is the function of a gene (*FOXP2*) that is rapidly evolving in the human lineage?

EXPERIMENT Several lines of evidence support a role for the *FOXP2* gene in the development of speech and language in humans and of vocalization in other vertebrates. In 2005, Joseph Buxbaum and collaborators at the Mount Sinai School of Medicine and several other institutions set out to test the function of *FOXP2*. They used the mouse, a model organism in which genes can be easily knocked out, as a representative vertebrate that vocalizes. Mice produce ultrasonic squeaks, referred to as whistles, to communicate stress. The researchers applied genetic engineering techniques to produce mice in which one or both copies of *FOXP2* were disrupted.

| Wild type: two normal copies of *FOXP2* | Heterozygote: one copy of *FOXP2* disrupted | Homozygote: both copies of *FOXP2* disrupted |

They then compared the phenotypes of these mice. Two of the characters they examined are included here: brain anatomy and vocalization.

Experiment 1: Researchers cut thin sections of brain and stained them with reagents, allowing visualization of brain anatomy in a UV fluorescence microscope.

Experiment 2: Researchers separated each newborn pup from its mother and recorded the number of ultrasonic whistles produced by the pup.

RESULTS

Experiment 1: Disruption of both copies of *FOXP2* led to brain abnormalities in which the cells were disorganized. Phenotypic effects on the brain of heterozygotes, with one disrupted copy, were less severe.

Experiment 2: Disruption of both copies of *FOXP2* led to an absence of ultrasonic vocalization in response to stress. The effect on vocalization in the heterozygote was also extreme.

Wild type

Heterozygote

Homozygote

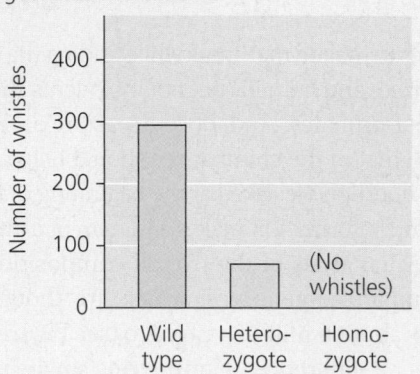

CONCLUSION *FOXP2* plays a significant role in the development of functional communication systems in mice. The results augment evidence from studies of birds and humans, supporting the hypothesis that *FOXP2* may act similarly in diverse organisms.

SOURCE W. Shu et al., Altered ultrasonic vocalization in mice with a disruption in the *Foxp2* gene, *Proceedings of the National Academy of Sciences* 102:9643–9648 (2005).

WHAT IF? Since the results support a role for mouse *FOXP2* in vocalization, you might wonder whether the human FOXP2 protein is a key regulator of speech. If you were given the amino acid sequences of wild-type and mutant human FOXP2 proteins and the wild-type chimpanzee FOXP2 protein, how would you investigate this question? What further clues could you obtain by comparing these sequences to that of the mouse FOXP2 protein?

studying other human genetic disorders. If researchers know the organ or tissue that is affected by a particular genetic disorder, they can look for genes that are expressed in these locations in experiments using mice. This approach has revealed several human genes of interest, including one that may contribute to Down syndrome.

Further research efforts are under way to extend genomic studies to many more microbial species, additional primates, and neglected species from diverse branches of the tree of life. These studies will advance our understanding of all aspects of biology, including health and ecology as well as evolution.

Comparing Genomes Within a Species

Another exciting prospect that stems from our ability to analyze genomes is increasing our understanding of the spectrum of genetic variation in humans. Because the history of the human species is so short—probably about 200,000 years—the amount of DNA variation among humans is small compared to that of many other species. Much of our diversity seems to be in the form of single nucleotide polymorphisms (SNPs, described in Chapter 20), usually detected by DNA sequencing. In the human genome, SNPs occur on average about once in 100 to 300 base pairs.

Scientists have already identified the location of several million SNP sites in the human genome and continue to find more. In the course of this search, they have also found other variations—including inversions, deletions, and duplications—that occur without apparent ill effect on the individual carrying them. These variations, as well as SNPs, will be useful genetic markers for studying human evolution, the differences between human populations, and the migratory routes of human populations throughout history. Such polymorphisms in human DNA will also be valuable markers for identifying genes that cause diseases or affect our health in more subtle ways. As well as informing us about evolution, analysis of the differences in individual genomes is likely to change the practice of medicine later in the 21st century.

Comparing Developmental Processes

Biologists in the field of evolutionary developmental biology, or **evo-devo** as it is often called, compare developmental processes of different multicellular organisms. Their aim is to understand how these processes have evolved and how changes in them can modify existing organismal features or lead to new ones. With the advent of molecular techniques and the recent flood of genomic information, we are beginning to realize that the genomes of related species with strikingly different forms may have only minor differences in gene sequence or regulation. Discovering the molecular basis underlying these differences in turn helps us understand the origin of the myriad diverse forms that cohabit this planet, thus informing our study of evolution.

Widespread Conservation of Developmental Genes Among Animals

In Chapter 18, you learned about the homeotic genes in *Drosophila*, which specify the identity of body segments in the fruit fly (see Figure 18.18). Molecular analysis of the homeotic genes in *Drosophila* has shown that they all include a 180-nucleotide sequence called a **homeobox**, which specifies a 60-amino-acid *homeodomain* in the encoded proteins. An identical or very similar nucleotide sequence has been discovered in the homeotic genes of many invertebrates and ver-

tebrates. The sequences are so similar between humans and fruit flies, in fact, that one researcher has whimsically referred to flies as "little people with wings." The resemblance even extends to the organization of these genes: The vertebrate genes homologous to the homeotic genes of fruit flies have kept the same chromosomal arrangement **(Figure 21.17)**. Homeobox-containing sequences have also been found in regulatory genes of much more distantly related eukaryotes, including plants and yeasts. From these similarities, we can deduce that the homeobox DNA sequence evolved very early in the history of

▲ **Figure 21.17 Conservation of homeotic genes in a fruit fly and a mouse.** Homeotic genes that control the form of anterior and posterior structures of the body occur in the same linear sequence on chromosomes in *Drosophila* and mice. Each colored band on the chromosomes shown here represents a homeotic gene. In fruit flies, all homeotic genes are found on one chromosome. The mouse and other mammals have the same or similar sets of genes on four chromosomes. The color code indicates the parts of the embryos in which these genes are expressed and the adult body regions that result. All of these genes are essentially identical in flies and mice, except for those represented by black bands, which are less similar in the two animals.

life and was sufficiently valuable to organisms to have been conserved in animals and plants virtually unchanged for hundreds of millions of years.

Homeotic genes in animals were named *Hox* genes, short for *homeobox*-containing genes, because homeotic genes were the first genes found to have this sequence. Other homeobox-containing genes were later found that do not act as homeotic genes; that is, they do not directly control the identity of body parts. However, most of these genes, in animals at least, are associated with development, suggesting their ancient and fundamental importance in that process. In *Drosophila*, for example, homeoboxes are present not only in the homeotic genes but also in the egg-polarity gene *bicoid* (see Chapter 18), in several of the segmentation genes, and in a master regulatory gene for eye development.

Researchers have discovered that the homeobox-encoded homeodomain is the part of a protein that binds to DNA when the protein functions as a transcriptional regulator. However, the shape of the homeodomain allows it to bind to any DNA segment; by itself it cannot select a specific sequence. Rather, other domains in a homeodomain-containing protein, ones that are more variable, determine which genes the protein regulates. Interaction of these latter domains with still other transcription factors helps a homeodomain-containing protein recognize specific enhancers in the DNA. Proteins with homeodomains probably regulate development by coordinating the transcription of batteries of developmental genes, switching them on or off. In embryos of *Drosophila* and other animal species, different combinations of homeobox genes are active in different parts of the embryo. This selective expression of regulatory genes, varying over time and space, is central to pattern formation.

Developmental biologists have found that in addition to homeotic genes, many other genes involved in development are highly conserved from species to species. These include numerous genes encoding components of signaling pathways. The extraordinary similarity among particular developmental genes in different animal species raises a question: How can the same genes be involved in the development of animals whose forms are so very different from each other?

Current studies are suggesting answers to this question. In some cases, small changes in regulatory sequences of particular genes cause changes in gene expression patterns that can lead to major changes in body form. For example, the differing patterns of expression of the *Hox* genes along the body axis in insects and crustaceans can explain the variation in number of leg-bearing segments among these segmented animals (**Figure 21.18**). Also, recent research suggests that the same *Hox* gene product may have subtly dissimilar effects in different species, turning on new genes or turning on the same genes at higher or lower levels. In other cases, similar genes direct distinct developmental processes in different organisms, resulting in diverse body shapes. Several *Hox* genes, for instance, are expressed in the embryonic and larval stages of the sea urchin, a nonsegmented animal that has a body plan quite different from those of insects and mice. Sea urchin adults make the pincushion-shaped shells you may have seen on the beach. They are among the organisms long used in classical embryological studies (see Chapter 47).

▲ **Figure 21.18 Effect of differences in *Hox* gene expression during development in crustaceans and insects.** Changes in the expression patterns of four *Hox* genes have occurred over evolutionary time. These changes account in part for the different body plans of the brine shrimp *Artemia*, a crustacean (top), and the grasshopper, an insect. Shown here are regions of the adult body color-coded for expression of the *Hox* genes that determine formation of particular body parts during embryonic development. Each color represents a specific *Hox* gene.

Comparison of Animal and Plant Development

The last common ancestor of animals and plants was probably a single-celled eukaryote that lived hundreds of millions of years ago, so the processes of development must have evolved independently in the two multicellular lineages of organisms. Plants evolved with rigid cell walls, which rule out the morphogenetic movements of cells and tissues that are so important in animals. Instead, morphogenesis in plants relies primarily on differing planes of cell division and on selective cell enlargement. (You will learn about these processes in

Chapter 35.) But despite the differences between animals and plants, there are similarities in the molecular mechanisms of development, which are legacies of their shared unicellular origin.

In both animals and plants, development relies on a cascade of transcriptional regulators turning on or turning off genes in a finely tuned series. For example, work on a small flowering plant in the mustard family, *Arabidopsis thaliana*, has shown that establishing the radial pattern of flower parts, like setting up the head-to-tail axis in *Drosophila*, involves a cascade of transcription factors. The genes that direct these processes, however, differ considerably in animals and plants. While quite a few of the master regulatory switches in *Drosophila* are homeobox-containing *Hox* genes, those in *Arabidopsis* belong to a completely different family of genes, called the *Mads-box* genes. And although homeobox-containing genes can be found in plants and *Mads-box* genes in animals, in neither case do they perform the same major roles in development that they do in the other group. Thus, molecular evidence supports the supposition that developmental programs evolved separately in animals and plants.

In this final chapter of the genetics unit, you have learned how studying genomic composition and comparing the genomes of different species can disclose much about how genomes evolve. Further, comparing developmental programs, we can see that the unity of life is reflected in the similarity of molecular and cellular mechanisms used to establish body pattern, although the genes directing development may differ among organisms. The similarities between genomes reflect the common ancestry of life on Earth. But the differences are also crucial, for they have created the huge diversity of organisms that have evolved. In the remainder of the book, we expand our perspective beyond the level of molecules, cells, and genes to explore this diversity on the organismal level.

CONCEPT CHECK 21.6

1. Would you expect the genome of the macaque (a monkey) to be more similar to the mouse genome or the human genome? Why?
2. The DNA sequences called homeoboxes, which help homeotic genes in animals direct development, are common to flies and mice. Given this similarity, explain why these animals are so different.
3. **WHAT IF?** There are three times as many *Alu* elements in the human genome as in the chimpanzee genome. How do you think these extra *Alu* elements arose in the human genome? Propose a role they might have played in the divergence of these two species.

For suggested answers, see Appendix A.

Chapter 21 Review

SUMMARY OF KEY CONCEPTS

CONCEPT 21.1

New approaches have accelerated the pace of genome sequencing (pp. 427–429)

► **Three-Stage Approach to Genome Sequencing** In linkage mapping, the order of genes and other inherited markers in the genome and the relative distances between them can be determined from recombination frequencies. Next, physical mapping uses overlaps between DNA fragments to order the fragments and determine the distance in base pairs between markers. Finally, the ordered fragments are sequenced, providing the finished genome sequence.

► **Whole-Genome Shotgun Approach to Genome Sequencing** The whole genome is cut into many small, overlapping fragments that are sequenced; computer software then assembles the complete sequence. Correct assembly is made easier when mapping information is also available.

CONCEPT 21.2

Scientists use bioinformatics to analyze genomes and their functions (pp. 429–432)

► **Centralized Resources for Analyzing Genome Sequences** Websites on the Internet provide centralized access to genome sequence databases, analytical tools, and genome-related information.

► **Identifying Protein-Coding Genes Within DNA Sequences** Computer analysis of genome sequences helps researchers identify sequences likely to encode proteins. Comparison of the sequences of "new" genes with those of known genes in other species may help identify functions of new genes. For a gene of unknown function, experimental inactivation of the gene and observation of the resulting phenotypic effects can provide clues to its function.

► **Understanding Genes and Their Products at the Systems Level** Using the computer-based tools of bioinformatics, scientists can compare genomes and study sets of genes and proteins as whole systems (genomics and proteomics). Studies include large-scale analyses of protein interactions.

Genomes vary in size, number of genes, and gene density (pp. 432–434)

	Bacteria	Archaea	Eukarya
Genome size	Most are 1–6 Mb		Most are 10–4,000 Mb, but a few are much larger
Number of genes	1,500–7,500		5,000–40,000
Gene density	Higher than in eukaryotes		Lower than in prokaryotes (Within eukaryotes, lower density is correlated with larger genomes.)
Introns	None in protein-coding genes	Present in some genes	Unicellular eukaryotes: present, but prevalent only in some species Multicellular eukaryotes: present in most genes
Other noncoding DNA	Very little		Can be large amounts; generally more repetitive noncoding DNA in multicellular eukaryotes

CONCEPT 21.4

Multicellular eukaryotes have much noncoding DNA and many multigene families (pp. 434–438)

▶ Only 1.5% of the human genome codes for proteins or gives rise to rRNAs or tRNAs; the rest is noncoding DNA, including repetitive DNA.

▶ **Transposable Elements and Related Sequences** The most abundant type of repetitive DNA in multicellular eukaryotes consists of transposable elements and related sequences. Two types of transposable elements occur in eukaryotes: transposons, which move via a DNA intermediate, and retrotransposons, which are more prevalent and move via an RNA intermediate. Each element may be hundreds or thousands of base pairs long, and similar but usually not identical copies are dispersed throughout the genome.

▶ **Other Repetitive DNA, Including Simple Sequence DNA** Short noncoding sequences that are tandemly repeated thousands of times (simple sequence DNA, which includes STRs) are especially prominent in centromeres and telomeres, where they probably play structural roles in the chromosome.

▶ **Genes and Multigene Families** Though many eukaryotic genes are present in one copy per haploid chromosome set, others (most, in some species) are members of a family of related genes. The transcription unit corresponding to the three largest rRNAs is tandemly repeated hundreds to thousands of times at one or several chromosomal sites, enabling the cell to quickly make the rRNA for millions of ribosomes. The multiple, slightly different genes in the two globin gene families encode polypeptides used at different developmental stages of an animal.

CONCEPT 21.5

Duplication, rearrangement, and mutation of DNA contribute to genome evolution (pp. 438–442)

▶ **Duplication of Entire Chromosome Sets** Accidents in cell division can lead to extra copies of all or part of a genome, which may then diverge if one set accumulates sequence changes.

▶ **Alterations of Chromosome Structure** The chromosomal organization of genomes can be compared among species, providing information about evolutionary relationships. Within a given species, rearrangements of chromosomes are thought to contribute to the emergence of new species.

▶ **Duplication and Divergence of Gene-Sized Regions of DNA** The genes encoding the various globin proteins evolved from one common ancestral globin gene, which duplicated and diverged into α-globin and β-globin ancestral genes. Subsequent duplication and random mutation gave rise to the present globin genes, all of which code for oxygen-binding proteins. The copies of some duplicated genes have diverged so much that the functions of their encoded proteins are now substantially different.

▶ **Rearrangements of Parts of Genes: Exon Duplication and Exon Shuffling** Rearrangement of exons within and between genes during evolution has led to genes containing multiple copies of similar exons and/or several different exons derived from other genes.

▶ **How Transposable Elements Contribute to Genome Evolution** Movement of transposable elements or recombination between copies of the same element occasionally generates new sequence combinations that are beneficial to the organism. Such mechanisms can alter the functions of genes or their patterns of expression and regulation.

MEDIA

Biology Labs On-Line HemoglobinLab

CONCEPT 21.6

Comparing genome sequences provides clues to evolution and development (pp. 442–447)

▶ **Comparing Genomes** Comparative studies of genomes from widely divergent and closely related species provides valuable information about ancient and more recent evolutionary history, respectively. Human and chimpanzee sequences show about 4% difference, mostly due to insertions, deletions, and duplications in one lineage. Along with nucleotide variations in specific genes (such as *FOXP2*, a gene affecting speech), these differences may account for the distinct characteristics of the two species. Single nucleotide polymorphisms among individuals in a species can also yield information about the history of that species.

▶ **Comparing Developmental Processes** Homeotic genes and some other genes associated with animal development contain a homeobox region, whose sequence is identical or similar in diverse species. Related sequences are present in the genes of plants and yeasts. Other developmental genes also are highly conserved among animal species, but they may play different roles in the development of different species. During embryonic development in both plants and animals, a cascade of transcription regulators turns genes on or off in a carefully regulated sequence. However, the genes that direct analogous developmental processes differ considerably in sequence in plants and animals as a result of their remote ancestry.

SELF-QUIZ

1. Bioinformatics includes all of the following *except*
   a. using computer programs to align DNA sequences.
   b. analyzing protein interactions in a species.
   c. using molecular biology to combine DNA from two different sources in a test tube.
   d. development of computer-based tools for genome analysis.
   e. use of mathematical tools to make sense of biological systems.

2. Which of the following has the largest genome and the fewest genes per million base pairs?
   a. *Haemophilus influenzae* (bacterium)
   b. *Saccharomyces cerevisiae* (yeast)
   c. *Arabidopsis thaliana* (plant)
   d. *Drosophila melanogaster* (fruit fly)
   e. *Homo sapiens* (human)

3. One of the characteristics of retrotransposons is that
   a. they code for an enzyme that synthesizes DNA using an RNA template.
   b. they are found only in animal cells.
   c. they generally move by a cut-and-paste mechanism.
   d. they contribute a significant portion of the genetic variability seen within a population of gametes.
   e. their amplification is dependent on a retrovirus.

4. Multigene families are
   a. groups of enhancers that control transcription.
   b. usually clustered at the telomeres.
   c. equivalent to the operons of prokaryotes.
   d. sets of genes that are coordinately controlled.
   e. sets of identical or similar genes that have evolved by gene duplication.

5. Two eukaryotic proteins have one domain in common but are otherwise very different. Which of the following processes is most likely to have contributed to this similarity?
   a. gene duplication
   b. RNA splicing
   c. exon shuffling
   d. histone modification
   e. random point mutations

6. Homeotic genes
   a. encode transcription factors that control the expression of genes responsible for specific anatomical structures.
   b. are found only in *Drosophila* and other arthropods.
   c. are the only genes that contain the homeobox domain.
   d. encode proteins that form anatomical structures in the fly.
   e. are responsible for patterning during plant development.

7. **DRAW IT** At the top of the next column are the amino acid sequences (using the single-letter code; see Figure 5.17) of four short segments of the FOXP2 protein from six species: chimpanzee, orangutan, gorilla, rhesus macaque, mouse, and human. These segments contain all of the amino acid differences between the FOXP2 proteins of these species.

   1. ATETI...PKSSD...TSSTT...NARRD
   2. ATETI...PKSSF...TSSTT...NARRD
   3. ATETI...PKSSD...TSSTT...NARRD
   4. ATETI...PKSSD...TSSNT...SARRD
   5. ATETI...PKSSD...TSSTT...NARRD
   6. VTETI...PKSSD...TSSTT...NARRD

   Use a highlighter to color any amino acid that varies among the species. (Color that amino acid in all sequences.) Then answer the following questions.
   a. The chimpanzee, gorilla, and rhesus macaque (C, G, R) sequences are identical. Which lines correspond to those sequences?
   b. The human sequence differs from that of the C, G, R species at two amino acids. Which line corresponds to the human sequence? Underline the two differences.
   c. The orangutan sequence differs from the C, G, R sequence at one amino acid (having valine instead of alanine) and from the human sequence at three amino acids. Which line corresponds to the orangutan sequence?
   d. How many amino acid differences are there between the mouse and the C, G, R species? Circle the amino acid(s) that differ(s) in the mouse. How many amino acid differences are there between the mouse and the human? Draw a square around the amino acid(s) that differ(s) in the mouse.
   e. Primates and rodents diverged between 60 and 100 million years ago, and chimpanzees and humans diverged about 6 million years ago. Knowing that, what can you conclude by comparing the amino acid differences between the mouse and the C, G, R species with the differences between the human and the C, G, R species?

For Self-Quiz answers, see Appendix A.

MEDIA Visit **www.campbellbiology.com** for a Practice Test.

EVOLUTION CONNECTION

8. Genes important in the embryonic development of animals, such as homeobox-containing genes, have been relatively well conserved during evolution; that is, they are more similar among different species than are many other genes. Why is this?

SCIENTIFIC INQUIRY

9. The scientists mapping the SNPs in the human genome noticed that groups of SNPs tended to be inherited together, in blocks known as haplotypes, ranging in length from 5,000 to 200,000 base pairs. There are as few as four or five commonly occurring combinations of SNPs per haplotype. Propose an explanation for this observation, integrating what you've learned throughout this chapter and this unit.

Mechanisms of Evolution

AN INTERVIEW WITH
Scott V. Edwards

Birds—and the birds of Australia in particular—might seem a surprising focus for a scientist who grew up in New York City, but they are the main subjects of Scott Edwards's research on evolution. A graduate of Harvard College, with a Ph.D. from the University of California, Berkeley, and postdoctoral work at the University of Florida, Dr. Edwards was at the University of Washington until he returned to Harvard in 2003 as Professor of Organismic and Evolutionary Biology. Jane Reece and Michael Cain interviewed Dr. Edwards at Harvard's Museum of Comparative Zoology, where he is Curator of Ornithology and the head of an active research group.

How big is the bird collection here?

Since the Museum of Comparative Zoology was founded in 1859, its collection of bird specimens has grown to 350,000 specimens, the largest university collection in the world. Each specimen is tagged with data about the location where it was obtained, the date, often the bird's sex and weight, and other pertinent information. The collection provides a remarkable record of how bird species have changed over the years, as environments have changed. Using the oldest specimens here, we can now compare the sizes, shapes, and genes of birds from populations separated by more than a century. What's exciting now is that all the information is being digitized, so that we can easily look at large amounts of data from multiple museums.

Were you interested in birds as a child?

When I was about six years old, we moved from an urban neighborhood to Riverdale, in the northwest corner of the Bronx. There were actually trees there, and we were close to the Hudson River. A few years later, a neighbor took me bird watching—and the rest is history. I'll never forget how impressed I was with my first Northern flicker; it was just remarkable to me that this bizarrely colored woodpecker lived right in my backyard.

Later, as an undergraduate biology major, I really needed a break after taking organic chemistry, and I was able to take a year off. I volunteered at the Smithsonian for several months and then at national parks in Hawaii and California. It was that first exposure to fieldwork that showed me what biologists do. And when I came back to college, I was much more focused and motivated. I think it should be mandatory for biology majors to work in the field or in a lab for a few months, because that's how you find out what science is all about.

How did you get interested in evolution?

I was impressed with the precision that molecular tools seemed to bring to the study of evolution. I realize now that things are not as precise as I thought, but the DNA code is still a remarkable yardstick for comparing different species on the same scale. I actually didn't like biochemistry or molecular biology until I could connect them with evolution. But coming back from my year off, I worked in a lab that helped me make the connection. The world is very diverse biologically—there are millions of species—and the fact that these species can be compared at the DNA level was a revelation to me.

What led you to study Australian birds?

After entering grad school, I volunteered for a research project on birds of paradise in New Guinea; these are flamboyant songbirds that live in the rain forest. I was hunting around for a project of my own. Several ornithologists directed me to a group of songbirds called babblers, which mostly live in Australia. These birds are fascinating: They live in family groups, using large, domed nests with a hole on the side. Eight or nine of them will clamber into one of these nests. It was very interesting to see the organization of their family groups in the wild and also to study the birds on the DNA level. Were they all related to each other, or not? How different were different families in a single locality? So I ended up doing my dissertation on babblers, comparing individuals within a family, families within a region, and populations in different parts of the continent.

As a postdoc in Florida, you studied the evolution of genes involved in disease resistance in birds. What were these genes?

They're called MHC genes, for Major Histocompatibility Complex. These genes are important components of the immune systems of all vertebrates. In humans, they are the genes you try to match when looking for a compatible donor for an organ transplant. The MHC genes encode proteins that bind to fragments of pathogens and other foreign cells that have been phagocytized. The MHC proteins then move to the cell surface and present the fragments to the rest of the immune system, saying, "Hey, I found something foreign." The MHC is fascinating from an evolutionary standpoint, because pathogens and parasites seem to be major drivers of evolutionary change. They're constantly playing cat and mouse with the host. In the pathogens, more efficient ways of infecting the host keep evolving, while evolving defenses keep pace in their hosts. So MHC genes are under strong selection by pathogens, and we can see signs of that selection when we look at the DNA sequences. In mammals, these genes are wildly diverse compared to typical "housekeeping" genes. I was curious to see if they were as diverse in birds as they are in mammals.

How did so much variation evolve in MHC genes?

There are a couple of different hypotheses. One comes from the idea that the primary drivers of MHC diversity are pathogens. It says that if you are heterozygous—if you have two different alleles for each of these MHC genes—you have a better surveillance system for dealing with the pathogenic world. You're going to be able to recognize at least twice as many pathogens compared to a homozygous individual. When you have a situation where heterozygotes are more fit because they can combat disease, it results in a lot of diversity. The other hypothesis focuses on mating preferences, though it's not inconsistent with the pathogen hypothesis. If it's true that being heterozygous is advantageous, then it would make sense for females to choose mates whose MHC alleles are different from theirs. Scientists in the lab where I was a postdoc documented this in lab mice. We're interested in documenting it in birds, as well. Birds are good organisms for this kind of study because many bird populations are being monitored in great detail. For these populations, researchers know who has mated with whom, and they have blood samples from offspring. So we can look at many different pairings and see if the members of each pair are significantly more different in MHC genes than, say, random pairs in the human population. We have an ongoing project on MHC genes and parasitism in red-winged blackbirds.

Does this research have relevance to avian flu and other bird diseases that threaten humans?

It certainly relates to the important question of whether all individuals of a species are equally susceptible to such a disease. For avian flu and West Nile virus, this is being studied now in chicken and songbird populations. We know that many different species of birds are carrying the highly pathogenic type of flu virus, so a logical next step is to compare different individual birds, both susceptible and resistant, to see if they differ in their MHC genes. One of my postdocs is addressing this kind of question for a bacterial pathogen of the house finch.

What is some other research you're doing?

We want to understand how the MHC evolved in the transition from early reptiles to birds, which are in the reptilian family tree. We've made genomic libraries of DNA from five different species: an emu (an Australian bird that resembles an ostrich), an alligator, a turtle, a tuatara (an ancient reptile that lives in New Zealand), and a garter snake. They make a great system for doing comparative genomics. In addition to looking at MHC genes, which seem to be under strong selection, we also look at neutral markers, which aren't under selection, to track species through space and time.

I go to Australia pretty regularly. Australia is a good natural laboratory for my work because the geography and the geographic ranges of birds are very consistent across different species. We're interested in using genetic tools to understand the times of speciation in different groups of birds. When did an eastern species diverge from the western species? And are those times the same across different species? We're comparing the evolution and geography of different species.

What is a species?

You'd think that a concept like species would be very well hammered out and agreed upon by scientists, but it's actually one of the more contentious areas of biology! I tend to be a traditionalist in this matter; I regard species as reproductively isolated groups of related individuals, as Ernst Mayr defined them in 1942. That is, individuals of one species don't breed with those of other species. The isolation can come about by many different mechanisms. For example, it can result from divergence after a population has colonized a new area. New species arise when gene flow (transfer) between different populations mostly ceases.

Can evolutionary trees give insights into mechanisms of evolution?

One way to use evolutionary trees to look at mechanisms is to focus on the tempo of evolution and the shape of the tree. Do we see a rapid burst of speciation, of many rapid branchings toward the tips, for example? Or do we see very long branches that are unbroken by speciation events? We try to link the branching patterns in these trees to environmental events in the past. In Australia, we're looking at related species in the east and west of the continent, and if we know how long ago these species separated, we may be able to link their separation to specific events, such as intrusions of the sea near a coast or desert formation in inland areas. There are records of such environmental changes going back several hundred thousand years in Australia.

Do you have evidence that speciation can be driven by sexual selection?

In sexual selection, individuals with certain inherited traits—bright plumage, for instance—are more likely than others to obtain mates. We have a lot of indirect evidence that sexual selection can play a role in the formation of new species. When DNA evidence shows that two species that look very different are actually extremely closely related, we can reasonably conclude that the species evolved recently and that some sort of selection was involved. We find this situation in Australian birds of paradise, where different species may have different plumage, different calls, and different behaviors, while being very similar in the neutral components of their genomes. So clearly some sort of selection, probably sexual selection, has driven the phenotypes apart. Birds of paradise, which are fantastically diverse in phenotype, have diverged into different species in the blink of an eye.

Is it true that all the world's songbirds got their start in Australia?

Many lines of evidence suggest that Australia and nearby New Guinea may have been the cradle of songbird evolution. And more broadly, Gondwana may have been the origin of many groups of birds. Gondwana was an ancient supercontinent that included most of the landmasses that are now in the Southern Hemisphere. Some of the oldest fossil songbirds have been found in Australia. The evidence suggests that many new groups of songbirds arose in Australia around 55–65 million years ago. They then spread around the globe. Also, our North American crows and jays trace their roots back to Australia. It's interesting that taxonomists in the early 20th century thought that Australian bird species were all just twigs of evolutionary trees rooted in the Northern Hemisphere. But really, it's the opposite.

. . . we can now compare the sizes, shapes, and genes of birds from populations separated by more than a century.

Inquiry in Action

Learn about an experiment by Scott Edwards in Inquiry Figure 24.3 on page 489.

Left to right: Scott Edwards, Jane Reece, Michael Cain

Descent with Modification
A Darwinian View of Life

22.1 The Darwinian revolution challenged traditional views of a young Earth inhabited by unchanging species

22.2 Descent with modification by natural selection explains the adaptations of organisms and the unity and diversity of life

22.3 Evolution is supported by an overwhelming amount of scientific evidence

OVERVIEW
Endless Forms Most Beautiful

The *Onymacris unguicularis* beetle lives in the coastal Namib desert of southwestern Africa, a land where fog is common, but virtually no rain falls. To obtain the water it needs to survive, the beetle relies on a peculiar "headstanding" behavior **(Figure 22.1)**. Tilting head-downward, the beetle faces into the winds that blow fog across the dunes. Droplets of moisture from the fog collect on the beetle's body and run down into its mouth.

This headstander beetle shares many features with the more than 350,000 other beetle species on Earth, including six pairs of legs, a hard outer surface, and two pairs of wings. But how did there come to be so many variations on the basic beetle theme? The headstander beetle and its many close relatives illustrate three key observations about life: the striking ways in which organisms are suited for life in their environments; the many shared characteristics (unity) of life; and the rich diversity of life. A century and a half ago, Charles Darwin was inspired to develop a scientific explanation for these three broad observations. When he published his hypothesis in *The Origin of Species*, Darwin ushered in a scientific revolution—the era of evolutionary biology.

For now, we will define **evolution** as *descent with modification*, a phrase Darwin used in proposing that Earth's many

▲ Figure 22.1 **How can this beetle survive in the desert, and what is it doing?**

species are descendants of ancestral species that were different from the present-day species. Evolution can also be defined more narrowly as a change in the genetic composition of a population from generation to generation, as we'll explore in Chapter 23. Whether it is defined broadly or narrowly, we can view evolution in two related but different ways: as a pattern and as a process. The *pattern* of evolutionary change is revealed by data from a range of scientific disciplines, including biology, geology, physics, and chemistry. These data are facts—they are observations about the natural world. The *process* of evolution consists of the mechanisms that produce the observed pattern of change. These mechanisms represent natural causes of the natural phenomena we observe. Indeed, the power of evolution as a unifying theory is its ability to explain and connect a vast array of observations about the living world.

As with all general theories in science, we continue to test our theory of evolution by examining whether it can account for new observations and experimental results. In this and the following chapters, we'll examine how ongoing discoveries shape our current understanding of the pattern and process of evolution. To set the stage, we'll first retrace Darwin's quest to explain the adaptations, unity, and diversity of life's "endless forms most beautiful."

CONCEPT 22.1
The Darwinian revolution challenged traditional views of a young Earth inhabited by unchanging species

What impelled Darwin to challenge the prevailing views of his time about Earth and its life? His revolutionary proposal actually had its roots in the work of many other individuals **(Figure 22.2)**.

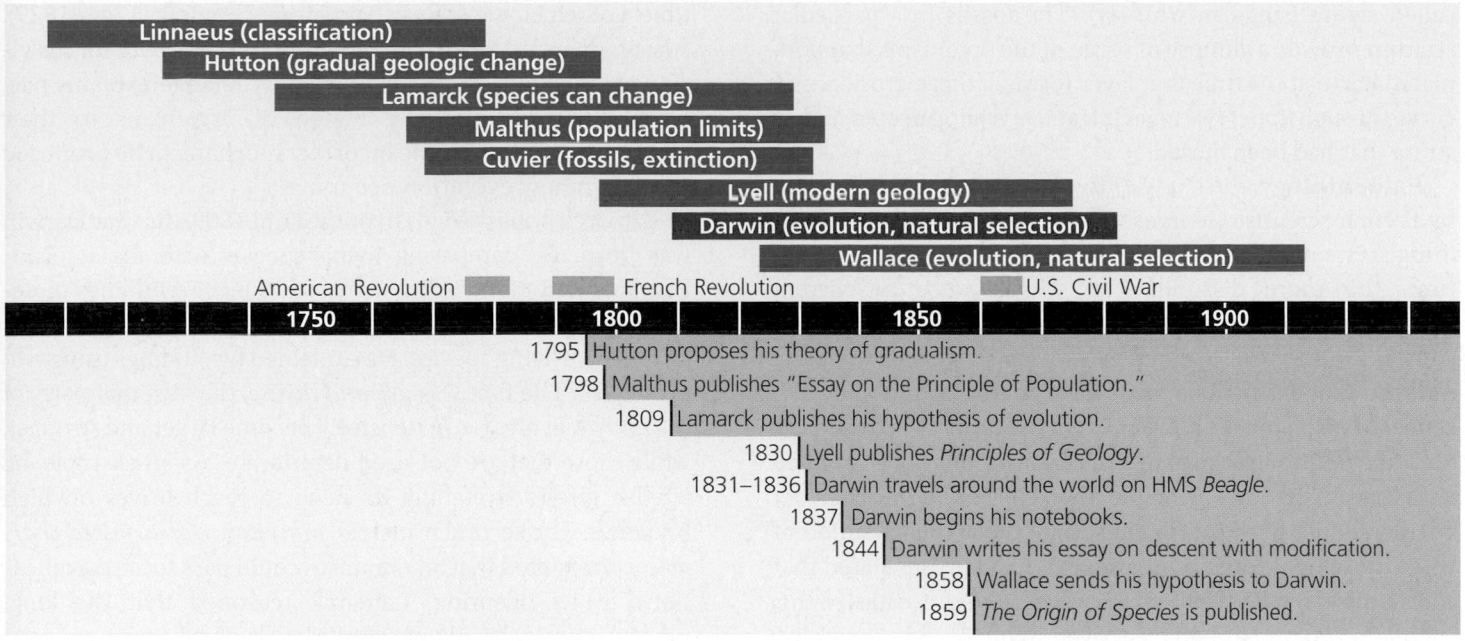

1795 | Hutton proposes his theory of gradualism.
1798 | Malthus publishes "Essay on the Principle of Population."
1809 | Lamarck publishes his hypothesis of evolution.
1830 | Lyell publishes *Principles of Geology.*
1831–1836 | Darwin travels around the world on HMS *Beagle.*
1837 | Darwin begins his notebooks.
1844 | Darwin writes his essay on descent with modification.
1858 | Wallace sends his hypothesis to Darwin.
1859 | *The Origin of Species* is published.

▲ **Figure 22.2 The historical context of Darwin's life and ideas.** The dark blue bars represent the lives of some individuals whose ideas contributed to Darwin's thinking about evolution.

Scala Naturae and Classification of Species

Long before Darwin was born, several Greek philosophers suggested that life might have changed gradually over time. But one philosopher who greatly influenced early Western science, Aristotle (384–322 B.C.), viewed species as fixed (unchanging). Through his observations of nature, Aristotle recognized certain "affinities" among organisms. He concluded that life-forms could be arranged on a ladder, or scale, of increasing complexity, later called the *scala naturae* ("scale of nature"). Each form of life, perfect and permanent, had its allotted rung on this ladder.

These ideas coincided with the Old Testament account of creation, which holds that species were individually designed by God and therefore perfect. In the 1700s, many scientists interpreted the often remarkable match of organisms to their environment as evidence that the Creator had designed each species for a particular purpose.

One such scientist was Carolus Linnaeus (1707–1778), a Swedish physician and botanist who sought to classify life's diversity, in his words, "for the greater glory of God." Linnaeus developed the two-part, or binomial, system of naming species (such as *Homo sapiens* for humans) that is still used today. In contrast to the linear hierarchy of the *scala naturae*, Linnaeus adopted a nested classification system, grouping similar species into increasingly general categories. For example, similar species are grouped in the same genus, similar genera (plural of genus) are grouped in the same family, and so on (see Figure 1.14).

Linnaeus did not ascribe the resemblances among species to evolutionary kinship, but rather to the pattern of their cre-

ation. However, a century later his classification system would play a role in Darwin's argument for evolution.

Ideas About Change over Time

Darwin drew many of his ideas from the work of scientists studying **fossils**, the remains or traces of organisms from the past. Most fossils are found in sedimentary rocks formed from the sand and mud that settle to the bottom of seas, lakes, and swamps **(Figure 22.3)**. New layers of sediment cover older ones and compress them into superimposed layers of rock

❶ Rivers carry sediment into seas and swamps. Over time, sedimentary rock layers (strata) form under water. Some strata contain fossils.

❷ As water levels change and the seafloor is pushed upward, the strata and their fossils are exposed.

Younger stratum with more recent fossils

Older stratum with older fossils

▲ **Figure 22.3 Formation of sedimentary strata with fossils.**

called **strata** (singular, *stratum*). The fossils in a particular stratum provide a glimpse of some of the organisms that populated Earth at the time that layer formed. Later, erosion may carve through upper (younger) strata, revealing deeper (older) strata that had been buried.

Paleontology, the study of fossils, was largely developed by French scientist Georges Cuvier (1769–1832). In examining strata near Paris, Cuvier noted that the older the stratum, the more dissimilar its fossils were to current life-forms. He also observed that from one layer to the next, some new species appeared while others disappeared. He inferred that extinctions must have been a common occurrence in the history of life. Yet Cuvier staunchly opposed the idea of evolution. To explain his observations, he advocated **catastrophism**, the principle that events in the past occurred suddenly and were caused by mechanisms different from those operating in the present. Cuvier speculated that each boundary between strata represented a catastrophe, such as a flood, that had destroyed many of the species living at that time. He proposed that these periodic catastrophes were usually confined to local regions, which were later repopulated by species immigrating from other areas.

In contrast, other scientists suggested that profound change could take place through the cumulative effect of slow but continuous processes. In 1795, Scottish geologist James Hutton (1726–1797) proposed that Earth's geologic features could be explained by gradual mechanisms still operating. For example, he suggested that valleys were often formed by rivers wearing through rocks and that rocks containing marine fossils were formed when sediments that had eroded from the land were carried by rivers to the sea, where they buried dead marine organisms. The leading geologist of Darwin's time, Charles Lyell (1797–1875), incorporated Hutton's thinking into his principle of **uniformitarianism**, which stated that mechanisms of change are constant over time. Lyell proposed that the same geologic processes are operating today as in the past, and at the same rate.

Hutton and Lyell's ideas strongly influenced Darwin's thinking. Darwin agreed that if geologic change results from slow, continuous actions rather than from sudden events, then Earth must be much older than the widely accepted age of a few thousand years. It would, for example, take a very long time for a river to carve a canyon by erosion. He later reasoned that perhaps similarly slow and subtle processes could produce substantial biological change. Darwin was not the first to apply the idea of gradual change to biological evolution, however.

Lamarck's Hypothesis of Evolution

During the 18th century, several naturalists (including Darwin's grandfather, Erasmus Darwin) suggested that life evolves as environments change. But only one of Charles Darwin's predecessors proposed a mechanism for *how* life changes over time: French biologist Jean-Baptiste de Lamarck (1744–1829). Alas, Lamarck is primarily remembered today *not* for his visionary recognition that evolutionary change explains patterns in fossils and the match of organisms to their environments, but for the incorrect mechanism he proposed to explain how evolution occurs.

Lamarck published his hypothesis in 1809, the year Darwin was born. By comparing living species with fossil forms, Lamarck had found what appeared to be several lines of descent, each a chronological series of older to younger fossils leading to a living species. He explained his findings using two principles. The first was *use and disuse*, the idea that parts of the body that are used extensively become larger and stronger, while those that are not used deteriorate. As an example, he cited a giraffe stretching its neck to reach leaves on high branches. The second principle, *inheritance of acquired characteristics*, stated that an organism could pass these modifications to its offspring. Lamarck reasoned that the long, muscular neck of the living giraffe had evolved over many generations as giraffes stretched their necks ever higher.

Lamarck also thought that evolution happens because organisms have an innate drive to become more complex. Darwin rejected this idea, but he, too, thought that variation was introduced into the evolutionary process in part through inheritance of acquired characteristics. Today, however, our understanding of genetics refutes this mechanism: There is no evidence that acquired characteristics can be inherited in the way proposed by Lamarck **(Figure 22.4)**.

Lamarck was vilified in his own time, especially by Cuvier, who denied that species ever evolve. In retrospect, however, Lamarck deserves credit for recognizing that the match of organisms to their environments can be explained by gradual evolutionary change and for proposing a testable mechanism for this change.

▲ **Figure 22.4 Acquired traits cannot be inherited.** This bonsai tree was "trained" to grow as a dwarf by pruning and shaping. However, seeds from this tree would produce offspring of normal size.

CONCEPT **22.2**

Descent with modification by natural selection explains the adaptations of organisms and the unity and diversity of life

As the 19th century dawned, it was generally believed that species had remained unchanged since their creation. A few clouds of doubt about the permanence of species were beginning to gather, but no one could have forecast the thundering storm just beyond the horizon. How did Charles Darwin become the lightning rod for a revolutionary view of life?

Darwin's Research

Charles Darwin (1809–1882) was born in Shrewsbury in western England. Even as a boy, he had a consuming interest in nature. When he was not reading nature books, he was fishing, hunting, and collecting insects. Darwin's father, a physician, could see no future for his son as a naturalist and sent him to medical school in Edinburgh. But Charles found medicine boring and surgery before the days of anesthesia horrifying. He quit medical school and enrolled at Cambridge University, intending to become a clergyman. (At that time in England, many scholars of science belonged to the clergy.)

At Cambridge, Darwin became the protégé of the Reverend John Henslow, a botany professor. Soon after Darwin graduated, Henslow recommended him to Captain Robert FitzRoy, who was preparing the survey ship HMS *Beagle* for a long voyage around the world. Darwin would pay his own way and serve as a conversation partner to the young captain. FitzRoy accepted Darwin because of his education and because they were of the same social class and about the same age.

The Voyage of the Beagle

Darwin embarked from England on the *Beagle* in December 1831. The primary mission of the voyage was to chart poorly known stretches of the South American coastline (**Figure 22.5**). While the ship's crew surveyed the coast, Darwin spent most of his time on shore, observing and collecting thousands of South American plants and animals. He noted the characteristics of plants and animals that made them well suited to such diverse environments as the humid jungles of Brazil, the expansive grasslands of Argentina, and the towering peaks of the Andes.

Darwin observed that the plants and animals in temperate regions of South America more closely resembled species living in the South American tropics than species living in

▲ **Figure 22.5 The voyage of HMS *Beagle*.**

temperate regions of Europe. Furthermore, the fossils he found, though clearly different from living species, were distinctly South American in their resemblance to the living organisms of that continent.

Darwin also spent much time thinking about geology during the voyage. Despite bouts of seasickness, he read Lyell's *Principles of Geology* while aboard the *Beagle.* He experienced geologic change firsthand when a violent earthquake rocked the coast of Chile, and he observed afterward that rocks along the coast had been thrust upward by several feet. Finding fossils of ocean organisms high in the Andes, Darwin inferred that the rocks containing the fossils must have been raised there by a series of many similar earthquakes. These observations reinforced what he had learned from Lyell: The physical evidence did not support the traditional view of a static Earth only a few thousand years old.

Darwin's interest in the geographic distribution of species was further stimulated by the *Beagle*'s stop at the Galápagos, a group of volcanic islands located near the equator about 900 km (540 miles) west of South America. Darwin was fascinated by the unusual organisms he found there. The birds he collected on the Galápagos included several kinds of mockingbirds that, although similar, seemed to be different species. Some were unique to individual islands, while others lived on two or more adjacent islands. Furthermore, although the animals on the Galápagos resembled species living on the South American mainland, most of the Galápagos species were not known from anywhere else in the world. Darwin hypothesized that the Galápagos had been colonized by organisms that had strayed from South America and then diversified, giving rise to new species on the various islands.

Darwin's Focus on Adaptation

During the voyage of the *Beagle*, Darwin observed many examples of **adaptations**, characteristics of organisms that enhance their survival and reproduction in specific environments. Later, as he reassessed his observations, he began to perceive adaptation to the environment and the origin of new species as closely related processes. Could a new species arise from an ancestral form by the gradual accumulation of adaptations to a different environment? From studies made years after Darwin's voyage, biologists have concluded that this is indeed what happened to the diverse group of Galápagos finches we discussed in Chapter 1 (see Figure 1.22). The finches' various beaks and behaviors are adapted to the specific foods available on their home islands **(Figure 22.6)**. Darwin realized that explaining such adaptations was

essential to understanding evolution. As we'll explore further, his explanation of how adaptations arise centered on **natural selection**, a process in which individuals with certain inherited traits leave more offspring than individuals with other traits.

By the early 1840s, Darwin had worked out the major features of his hypothesis. He set these ideas on paper in 1844, when he wrote a long essay on descent with modification and its underlying mechanism, natural selection. Yet he was still reluctant to publish his ideas, apparently because he anticipated the uproar they would cause. Even as he procrastinated, Darwin continued to compile evidence in support of his hypothesis. By the mid-1850s, he had described his ideas to Lyell and a few others. Lyell, who was not yet convinced of evolution, nevertheless urged Darwin to publish on the subject before someone else came to the same conclusions and published first.

In June 1858, Lyell's prediction came true. Darwin received a manuscript from Alfred Russel Wallace (1823–1913), a British naturalist working in the East Indies who had developed a hypothesis of natural selection similar to Darwin's. Wallace asked Darwin to evaluate his paper and forward it to Lyell if it merited publication. Darwin complied, writing to Lyell: "Your words have come true with a vengeance. . . . I never saw a more striking coincidence . . . so all my originality, whatever it may amount to, will be smashed." Lyell and a colleague then presented Wallace's paper, along with extracts from Darwin's unpublished 1844 essay, to the Linnean Society of London on July 1, 1858. Darwin quickly finished his book, titled *On the Origin of Species by Means of Natural Selection* (commonly referred to as *The Origin of Species*), and published it the next year. Although Wallace had

(a) Cactus-eater. The long, sharp beak of the cactus ground finch (*Geospiza scandens*) helps it tear and eat cactus flowers and pulp.

(b) Insect-eater. The green warbler finch (*Certhidea olivacea*) uses its narrow, pointed beak to grasp insects.

(c) Seed-eater. The large ground finch (*Geospiza magnirostris*) has a large beak adapted for cracking seeds that fall from plants to the ground.

▲ **Figure 22.6 Beak variation in Galápagos finches.** The Galápagos Islands are home to more than a dozen species of closely related finches, some found only on a single island. The most striking differences among them are their beaks, which are adapted for specific diets.

submitted his ideas for publication first, he admired Darwin and thought that Darwin had developed the idea of natural selection so extensively that he should be known as its main architect.

Within a decade, Darwin's book and its proponents had convinced most biologists that life's diversity is the product of evolution. Darwin succeeded where previous evolutionists had failed, mainly because he had presented a plausible scientific mechanism with immaculate logic and an avalanche of evidence.

The Origin of Species

In his book, Darwin developed two main ideas: that descent with modification explains life's unity and diversity and that natural selection brings about the match between organisms and their environment.

Descent with Modification

In the first edition of *The Origin of Species*, Darwin never used the word *evolution* (although the final word of the book is "evolved"). Rather, he discussed *descent with modification*, a phrase that summarized his view of life. Darwin perceived unity in life, which he attributed to the descent of all organisms from an ancestor that lived in the remote past. He also thought that as the descendants of that ancestral organism lived in various habitats over millions of years, they had accumulated diverse modifications, or adaptations, that fit them to specific ways of life. Darwin reasoned that over long periods of time, descent with modification eventually led to the rich diversity of life we see today.

Darwin viewed the history of life as a tree, with multiple branchings from a common trunk out to the tips of the youngest twigs **(Figure 22.7)**. The tips of the twigs represent the diversity of organisms living in the present. Each fork of the tree represents an ancestor of all the lines of evolution that subsequently branch from that point. As shown in the tree diagram in **Figure 22.8**, closely related species, such as the Asian elephant and African elephants, are very similar because they shared the same line of descent until a relatively recent split from

▶ **Figure 22.7 "I think..."** In this 1837 sketch, Darwin envisioned the branching pattern of evolution.

Hyracoidea (Hyraxes)

Sirenia (Manatees and relatives)

Moeritherium

Barytherium

Deinotherium

Mammut

Platybelodon

Stegodon

Mammuthus

Elephas maximus (Asia)

Loxodonta africana (Africa)

Loxodonta cyclotis (Africa)

34   24   5.5 2 10⁴ 0

Millions of years ago   Years ago

▲ **Figure 22.8 Descent with modification.** This evolutionary tree of elephants and their relatives is based mainly on fossils—their anatomy, order of appearance in strata, and geographic distribution. Note that most branches of descent ended in extinction. (Time line not to scale.)

? *Based on the tree shown here, approximately when did the most recent ancestor shared by* Mammuthus *(woolly mammoths), Asian elephants, and African elephants live?*

their common ancestor. Note that seven lineages related to elephants have become extinct over the past 30 million years. As a result, there are no living species that fill the gap between the elephants and their nearest relatives today, the manatees and hyraxes. In fact, many branches of evolution, even some major ones, are dead ends: Scientists estimate that over 99% of all species that have ever lived are now extinct.

In his efforts at classification, Linnaeus had realized that some organisms resemble each other more closely than others, but he had not linked these resemblances to evolution. Nonetheless, because he had recognized that the great diversity of organisms could be organized into "groups subordinate to groups" (Darwin's phrase), Linnaeus's system meshed well with Darwin's hypothesis. To Darwin, the Linnaean hierarchy reflected the branching history of the tree of life, with organisms at the various levels related through descent from common ancestors.

Artificial Selection, Natural Selection, and Adaptation

Darwin proposed a mechanism, natural selection, to explain the observable patterns of evolution. He crafted his argument carefully, to persuade even the most skeptical readers. First he discussed familiar examples of selective breeding of domesticated plants and animals. Humans have modified other species over many generations by selecting and breeding individuals that possess desired traits—a process called **artificial selection (Figure 22.9)**.

▲ **Figure 22.9 Artificial selection.** These different vegetables have all been selected from one species of wild mustard. By selecting variations in different parts of the plant, breeders have obtained these divergent results.

▲ **Figure 22.10 Variation in a population.** To the extent that the variation in color and banding patterns in this snail population is heritable, it can be acted on by natural selection.

As a result of artificial selection, crop plants and animals bred as livestock or pets often bear little resemblance to their wild ancestors.

Darwin then described four observations of nature from which he drew two inferences:

Observation #1: Members of a population often vary greatly in their traits **(Figure 22.10)**.

Observation #2: Traits are inherited from parents to offspring.

Observation #3: All species are capable of producing more offspring than their environment can support **(Figure 22.11)**.

Observation #4: Owing to lack of food or other resources, many of these offspring do not survive.

Inference #1: Individuals whose inherited traits give them a higher probability of surviving and reproducing in a given environment tend to leave more offspring than other individuals.

Inference #2: This unequal ability of individuals to survive and reproduce will lead to the accumulation of favorable traits in the population over generations.

Darwin perceived an important connection between natural selection and the capacity of organisms to "overreproduce." He began to make this connection after reading an essay by economist Thomas Malthus, who contended that much of human suffering—disease, famine, and war—was the inescapable consequence of the human population's potential to increase faster than food supplies and other resources. Darwin realized that the capacity to overreproduce was characteristic of all species. Of the many eggs laid, young born, and seeds spread, only a tiny fraction complete their development and leave offspring of their own. The rest are eaten, starved, diseased, un-

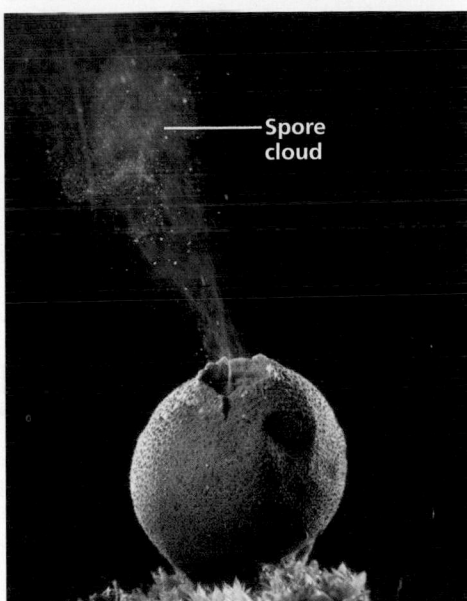

▲ **Figure 22.11 Overproduction of offspring.** A single puffball fungus can produce billions of offspring. If all of these offspring and their descendants survived to maturity, they would carpet the surrounding land surface.

(a) A flower mantid in Malaysia

(b) A stick mantid in Africa

▲ **Figure 22.12 Camouflage as an example of evolutionary adaptation.** Related species of the insects called mantids have diverse shapes and colors that evolved in different environments.

mated, or unable to tolerate physical conditions of the environment such as salinity or temperature.

An organism's traits can influence not only its own performance, but also how well its offspring cope with environmental challenges. For example, an organism might have a heritable trait that gives its offspring an advantage in escaping predators, obtaining food, or tolerating physical conditions. When such advantages increase the number of offspring that survive and reproduce, the traits that are favored will likely appear at a greater frequency in the next generation. Thus, over time, natural selection imposed by factors such as predators, lack of food, or adverse physical conditions can increase the proportion of favorable traits in a population.

How rapidly do such changes occur? Darwin reasoned that if artificial selection can bring about dramatic change in a relatively short period of time, then natural selection should be capable of substantial modification of species over many hundreds of generations. Even if the advantages of some heritable traits over others are slight, the advantageous variations will gradually accumulate in the population, and less favorable variations will diminish. Over time, this process will increase the frequency of individuals with favorable adaptations and hence refine the match between organisms and their environment.

Natural Selection: A Summary

Let's now recap the main ideas of natural selection:

▶ Natural selection is a process in which individuals that have certain heritable characteristics survive and reproduce at a higher rate than other individuals.

▶ Over time, natural selection can increase the match between organisms and their environment (Figure 22.12).

▶ If an environment changes, or if individuals move to a new environment, natural selection may result in adaptation to these new conditions, sometimes giving rise to new species in the process.

One subtle but important point is that although natural selection occurs through interactions between individual organisms and their environment, *individuals do not evolve*. Rather, it is the population that evolves over time.

A second key point is that natural selection can amplify or diminish *only heritable traits*—traits that are passed from organisms to their offspring. Though an organism may become modified during its lifetime, and these acquired characteristics may even help the organism in its environment, there is little evidence that such acquired characteristics can be inherited by offspring.

Third, remember that environmental factors vary from place to place and over time. A trait that is favorable in one place or time may be useless—or even detrimental—in other places or times. Natural selection is always operating, but which traits are favored depends on the environmental context.

Next, we'll survey the wide range of observations that support a Darwinian view of evolution by natural selection.

1. How does the concept of descent with modification explain both the unity and diversity of life?
2. Describe how overreproduction and heritable variation relate to evolution by natural selection.
3. **WHAT IF?** If you discovered a fossil of an extinct mammal that lived high in the Andes, would you predict that it would more closely resemble present-day mammals from South American jungles or present-day mammals that live high in African mountains? Explain.

For suggested answers, see Appendix A.

CONCEPT **22.3**

Evolution is supported by an overwhelming amount of scientific evidence

In *The Origin of Species*, Darwin marshaled a broad range of evidence to support the concept of descent with modification. Still—as he readily acknowledged—there were instances in which key evidence was lacking. For example, Darwin referred to the origin of flowering plants as an "abominable mystery," and he lamented the lack of fossils showing how earlier groups of organisms gave rise to new groups.

In the 150 years since, new discoveries have filled many of the gaps that Darwin identified. The origin of flowering plants, for example, is better understood (see Chapter 30), and many fossils have been discovered that signify the origin of new groups of organisms (see Chapter 25). In this section, we'll consider four types of data that document the pattern of evolution and illuminate the processes by which it occurs: direct observations of evolution, the fossil record, homology, and biogeography.

Direct Observations of Evolutionary Change

Biologists have documented evolutionary change in thousands of scientific studies. We'll examine many such studies throughout this unit, but let's look here at two examples.

Predation and Coloration in Guppies: Scientific Inquiry

Predators (organisms that feed on other species, called prey) are a potent force in shaping the adaptations of their food source. The predator is most likely to feed on prey individuals that are least able to avoid detection, escape, or defend themselves. As a result, such prey individuals are less likely to reproduce and pass their traits to their offspring than are individuals whose traits help them evade predators.

For many years, John Endler, of the University of California, Santa Barbara, has studied the impact of predators on guppies (*Poecilia reticulata*), small freshwater fish that you may know as aquarium pets. He observed that among wild

▼ Figure 22.13

Can predation result in natural selection for color patterns in guppies?

EXPERIMENT John Endler, of the University of California, Santa Barbara, studied wild guppies in the Aripo River system on the Caribbean island of Trinidad. He transplanted 200 guppies from pools containing pike-cichlids, intense guppy predators, to pools containing killifish, less active predators of guppies. He tracked the number of bright-colored spots and the total area of those spots on male guppies in each generation.

Predator: Killifish; preys mainly on juvenile guppies (which do not express the color genes)

Guppies: Adult males have brighter colors than those in "pike-cichlid pools"

Pools with killifish, but no guppies prior to transplant

Experimental transplant of guppies

Predator: Pike-cichlid; preys mainly on adult guppies

Guppies: Adult males are more drab in color than those in "killifish pools"

RESULTS After 22 months (15 generations), the number and total area of colored spots on male guppies in the transplanted population had increased compared to those of males in the source population.

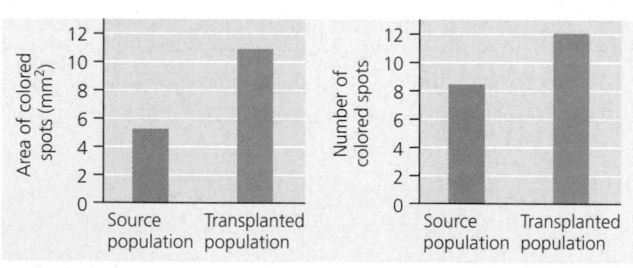

CONCLUSION Endler concluded that the change in predator resulted in different variations (brighter color patterns) being favored in the transplanted population. Over a relatively short time, an observable evolutionary change occurred in this population.

SOURCE J. A. Endler, Natural selection on color patterns in *Poecilia reticulata*, *Evolution* 34:76–91 (1980).

WHAT IF? What would happen if, after 22 months, guppies from the transplanted population were returned to the source pool?

guppy populations in Trinidad, the male guppies' color patterns are so variable that no two males look alike. These highly variable colors are controlled by a number of genes that, in the wild, are only expressed in adult males. Female guppies are attracted to males with bright colors, choosing them as mates more often than they choose males with drab coloring. But the bright colors that attract females might also make the males more conspicuous to predators. Thus, if a guppy population contained both brightly colored and drab males, we might predict that predators would tend to eat more of the brightly colored fish.

Endler wondered how the trade-off between attracting mates and attracting predators affects coloration in male guppies. In the field, he observed that the color patterns of male guppies appeared to correspond to the intensity of predation. In pools that had few predator species, male guppies tended to be brightly colored, whereas in pools that had many predators, males were less brightly colored. Based on these observations, Endler hypothesized that intense predation caused natural selection in male guppies, favoring the trait of drab coloration. He tested this hypothesis by transferring brightly colored guppies to a pool with many predators. As he predicted, over time the transplanted guppy population became less brightly colored.

One guppy predator, the killifish, preys on juvenile guppies that have not yet displayed their adult coloration. Endler predicted that if guppies with drab colors were transferred to a pool with only killifish, eventually the descendants of these guppies would be more brightly colored (because females prefer males with bright colors). **Figure 22.13**, on the facing page, describes this experiment. Indeed, in their new environment, the guppy population rapidly came to feature brighter colors, demonstrating that selection can cause rapid evolution in wild populations.

The Evolution of Drug-Resistant HIV

An example of ongoing natural selection that affects our own lives dramatically is the evolution of drug-resistant pathogens (disease-causing organisms and viruses). This is a particular problem with bacteria and viruses that reproduce rapidly, because individuals that are resistant to a particular drug can increase in number very quickly.

Consider the example of HIV (human immunodeficiency virus), the virus that causes AIDS (see Chapters 19 and 43). Researchers have developed numerous drugs to combat this pathogen, but using these medications selects for viruses resistant to the drugs. A few drug-resistant viruses may be present by chance at the beginning of treatment. Those that survive the early doses reproduce, passing on the alleles that enable them to resist the drug. In this way, the frequency of resistant viruses increases rapidly in the population.

Figure 22.14 illustrates the evolution of HIV resistance to the drug 3TC. Scientists designed 3TC to interfere with reverse transcriptase. HIV uses this enzyme to make a DNA version of

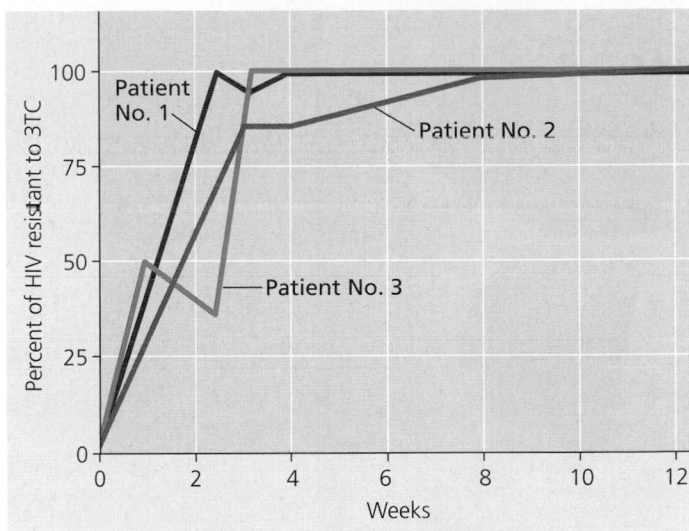

▲ **Figure 22.14 Evolution of drug resistance in HIV.** Rare resistant viruses multiplied quickly when each of these patients was treated with the anti-HIV drug 3TC. Within just a few weeks, 3TC-resistant organisms made up 100% of the virus population in each case.

its RNA genome, which is then inserted into the DNA of the human host cell (see Figure 19.8). Because the 3TC molecule is similar in shape to the cytosine-bearing (C-bearing) nucleotide of DNA, HIV's reverse transcriptase picks up a 3TC molecule instead of a C-bearing nucleotide and inserts the 3TC into a growing DNA chain. This error terminates further elongation of the DNA and thus blocks reproduction of HIV.

The 3TC-resistant varieties of HIV have versions of reverse transcriptase that are able to discriminate between the drug and the normal C-bearing nucleotide. These viruses have no advantage in the absence of 3TC; in fact, they replicate more slowly than viruses that carry the typical version of reverse transcriptase. But once 3TC is added to their environment, it becomes a powerful selecting force, favoring the survival of resistant viruses (see Figure 22.14).

Both the guppy example and the HIV example highlight two key points about natural selection. First, natural selection is a process of editing rather than a creative mechanism. A drug does not *create* resistant pathogens; it *selects for* resistant individuals that were already present in the population. Second, natural selection depends on time and place. It favors those characteristics in a genetically variable population that provide advantage in the current, local environment. What is beneficial in one situation may be useless or even harmful in another. In the guppy example, individuals that have drab colors are at an advantage in pools with fierce predators but at a disadvantage in pools without them.

The Fossil Record

A second type of evidence for evolution comes from fossils. The fossil record shows that past organisms differed from present-day organisms and that many species have become

Latham Shale dig site, San Bernardino County, California

▲ **Figure 22.15 Fossil evidence of evolution in a group of trilobites.** These fossils are just a few in a series discovered in the Latham Shale bed, which was deposited between 513 and 512 million years ago. The sequence shows change over time in the location and angle of the spines of the head shield (the area marked by red dots).

(a) *Pakicetus* (terrestrial)

(b) *Rodhocetus* (predominantly aquatic)

Pelvis and hind limb
(c) *Dorudon* (fully aquatic)

Pelvis and hind limb
(d) *Balaena* (recent whale ancestor)

▲ **Figure 22.16 The transition to life in the sea.** The hypothesis that whales and other cetaceans evolved from terrestrial organisms predicts that cetacean ancestors were four-legged. Indeed, paleontologists have unearthed fossils of extinct cetaceans that had hind limbs, including the four species whose skeletons are depicted here (not drawn to scale). Additional fossils show that *Pakicetus* and *Rodhocetus* had a type of ankle bone that is otherwise unique to a group of land mammals that includes pigs, hippos, cows, camels, and deer. This similarity strongly suggests that cetaceans are most closely related to this group of land mammals.

extinct. Fossils also show the evolutionary changes that have occurred over time in various groups of organisms (**Figure 22.15**).

Over longer time scales, fossils document the origins of major new groups of organisms. An example is the fossil record of early cetaceans, the mammalian order that includes whales, dolphins, and porpoises. The earliest cetaceans lived 50–60 million years ago. The fossil record indicates that prior to that time, most mammals were terrestrial. Although scientists had long realized that whales and other cetaceans must have originated from land mammals, few fossils had been found that revealed how cetacean limb structure had changed over time, leading eventually to the loss of hind limbs and the development of flippers. In the past few decades, however, a series of remarkable fossils have been discovered in Pakistan, Egypt, and North America that document the transition from life on land to life in the sea. Each organism shown in **Figure 22.16** differs from present-day mammals, including present-day whales, and is now extinct. Collectively, these and other early fossils document the formation of new species and the origin of a major new group of mammals, the cetaceans.

In addition to providing evidence of how life on Earth has changed over time—the pattern of evolution—the fossil record also can be used to test evolutionary hypotheses arising from other kinds of evidence. For example, based on anatomical data, scientists think that early land vertebrates evolved from a group of fishes and that early amphibians evolved from descendants of early land vertebrates. If these relationships are correct, we would predict that the earliest fossils of fishes should be older than the earliest fossils of land vertebrates. Similarly, we would predict that the earliest fossil land vertebrates should be older than the earliest fossil amphibians. These predictions can be tested using radioactive dating techniques (see Chapter 25) to determine the age of fossils. To date, all of these predictions have been upheld, which suggests that our understanding of the evolutionary relationships on which the predictions were based is correct.

Homology

A third type of evidence for evolution comes from analyzing similarities among different organisms. As we've discussed, evolution is a process of descent with modification: Characteristics present in an ancestral organism are altered (by natural selection) in its descendants over time as they face different environmental conditions. As a result, related species can have characteristics with an underlying similarity even though they may have very different functions. Such similarity resulting from common ancestry is known as **homology**.

Anatomical and Molecular Homologies

The view of evolution as a remodeling process leads to the prediction that closely related species should share similar features—and they do. Of course, closely related species share the features used to determine their relationship, but they also share many other features. Some of these shared features make little sense except in the context of evolution. For example, the forelimbs of all mammals, including humans, cats, whales, and bats, show the same arrangement of bones from the shoulder to the tips of the digits, even though these appendages have very different functions: lifting, walking, swimming, and flying **(Figure 22.17)**. Such striking anatomical resemblances would be highly unlikely if these structures had arisen anew in each species. Rather, the underlying skeletons of the arms, forelegs, flippers, and wings of different mammals are **homologous structures** that represent variations on a structural theme that was present in their common ancestor.

Comparing early stages of development in different animal species reveals additional anatomical homologies not visible in adult organisms. For example, at some point in their devel-

Chick embryo (LM) Human embryo

▲ **Figure 22.18 Anatomical similarities in vertebrate embryos.** At some stage in their embryonic development, all vertebrates have a tail located posterior to the anus (referred to as a post-anal tail), as well as pharyngeal (throat) pouches. Descent from a common ancestor can explain such similarities.

opment, all vertebrate embryos have a tail located posterior to (behind) the anus, as well as structures called pharyngeal (throat) pouches **(Figure 22.18)**. These homologous throat pouches ultimately develop into structures with very different functions, such as gills in fishes and parts of the ears and throat in humans and other mammals.

Some of the most intriguing homologies concern "leftover" structures of marginal, if any, importance to the organism. These **vestigial structures** are remnants of features that served important functions in the organism's ancestors. For instance, the skeletons of some snakes retain vestiges of the pelvis and leg bones of walking ancestors. Another example is the decreased size and loss of function in cetaceans' hind limbs as these organisms faced the challenges of life in water (see Figure 22.16). We would not expect to see these vestigial structures if snakes and whales had origins separate from other vertebrate animals.

Biologists also observe similarities among organisms at the molecular level. All forms of life use the same genetic language of DNA and RNA, and the genetic code is essentially universal (see Chapter 17). Thus, it is likely that all species descended from common ancestors that used this code. But molecular homologies go beyond a shared code. For example, organisms as dissimilar as humans and bacteria share genes inherited from a very distant common ancestor. Like the forelimbs of humans and whales, these genes have often acquired different functions.

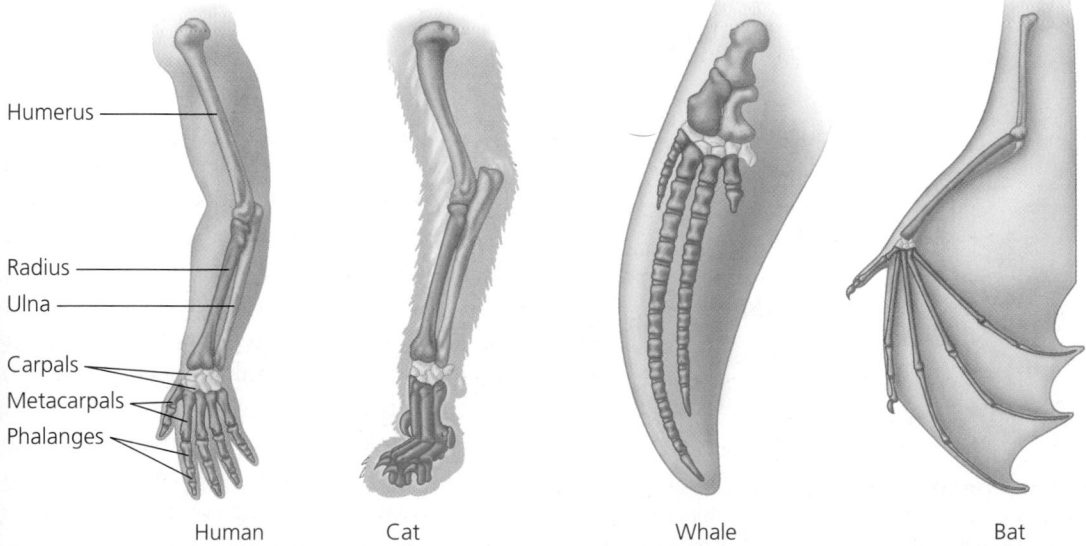

Humerus

Radius
Ulna

Carpals
Metacarpals
Phalanges

Human Cat Whale Bat

▲ **Figure 22.17 Mammalian forelimbs: homologous structures.** Even though they have become adapted for different functions, the forelimbs of all mammals are constructed from the same basic skeletal elements: one large bone (purple), attached to two smaller bones (orange and tan), attached to several small bones (gold), attached to several metacarpals (green), attached to approximately five digits, or phalanges (blue).

Homologies and "Tree Thinking"

Some homologous characteristics, such as the genetic code, are shared by all species because they date to the deep ancestral past. In contrast, homologous characteristics that evolved more recently are shared only within smaller groups of organisms. Consider an example in the tetrapods (from the Greek *tetra*, four, and *pod*, foot), the vertebrate group that consists of amphibians, mammals, and reptiles (including birds—see Figure 22.19). All tetrapods possess the same basic limb bone structure illustrated in Figure 22.17, but the ancestors of tetrapods do not. Thus, homologous characteristics form a nested pattern: All life shares the deepest layer, and each successive smaller group adds their own homologies to those they share with larger groups. This nested pattern is exactly what we would expect to result from descent with modification from a common ancestor.

Biologists often represent the pattern of descent from common ancestors and the resulting homologies with an **evolutionary tree**, a diagram that reflects evolutionary relationships among groups of organisms. We will explore in detail how evolutionary trees are constructed in Chapter 26, but for now, let's consider how we can interpret and use such trees.

Figure 22.19 is an evolutionary tree of tetrapods and their closest living relatives, the lungfishes. In this diagram, each branch point represents the common ancestor of all species that descended from it. For example, lungfishes and all tetrapods descended from ancestor ❶, whereas mammals, lizards and snakes, crocodiles, and birds all descended from ancestor ❸. As expected, the three homologies shown on the tree—tetrapod limbs, the amnion (a protective embryonic membrane), and feathers—form a nested pattern. Tetrapod limbs were present in common ancestor ❷ and hence are found in all of the descendants of that ancestor (the tetrapods). The amnion was present only in ancestor ❸ and hence is shared only by some tetrapods (mammals and reptiles). Feathers were present only in common ancestor ❻ and hence are found only in birds.

To explore "tree thinking" further, note that in Figure 22.19, mammals are positioned closer to amphibians than to birds. As a result, you might conclude that mammals are more closely related to amphibians than they are to birds. However, mammals are actually more closely related to birds than to amphibians because mammals and birds share a more recent common ancestor (ancestor ❸) than do mammals and amphibians (ancestor ❷).

Evolutionary trees are hypotheses that summarize our current understanding of patterns of descent. Our confidence in these relationships, as with any hypothesis, depends on the strength of the supporting data. In the case of Figure 22.19, the tree is supported by a variety of independent data sets, including both anatomical and DNA sequence data. As a result, biologists feel confident that it accurately reflects actual evolutionary history. As you will read in Chapter 26, scientists can use such well-supported evolutionary trees to make specific and sometimes surprising predictions about the biology of organisms.

Convergent Evolution

Although organisms that are closely related share characteristics because of common descent, distantly related organisms can resemble one another for a different reason: **convergent evolution**, the independent evolution of similar features in different lineages. Consider marsupial mammals, many of which live in Australia. Marsupials are distinct from another group of mammals—the eutherians—that live elsewhere on Earth. (Eutherians complete their embryonic development in the uterus, whereas marsupials are born as embryos and complete their development in an external pouch.) Some Australian

Each branch point represents the common ancestor of the lineages beginning there or to the right of it.

Tetrapod limbs

A hatch mark represents a homologous characteristic shared by all the groups to the right of the mark.

Amnion

Feathers

Lungfishes
Amphibians
Mammals
Lizards and snakes
Crocodiles
Ostriches
Hawks and other birds

Tetrapods
Amniotes
Birds

▲ **Figure 22.19 Tree thinking: information provided in an evolutionary tree.** This evolutionary tree for tetrapods and their closest living relatives, the lungfishes, is based on anatomical and DNA sequence data. The purple bars indicate the origin of three important homologies, each of which evolved only once. Birds are nested within and evolved from reptiles; hence, the group of organisms called "reptiles" technically includes birds.

? *Are crocodiles more closely related to lizards or birds? Explain your answer.*

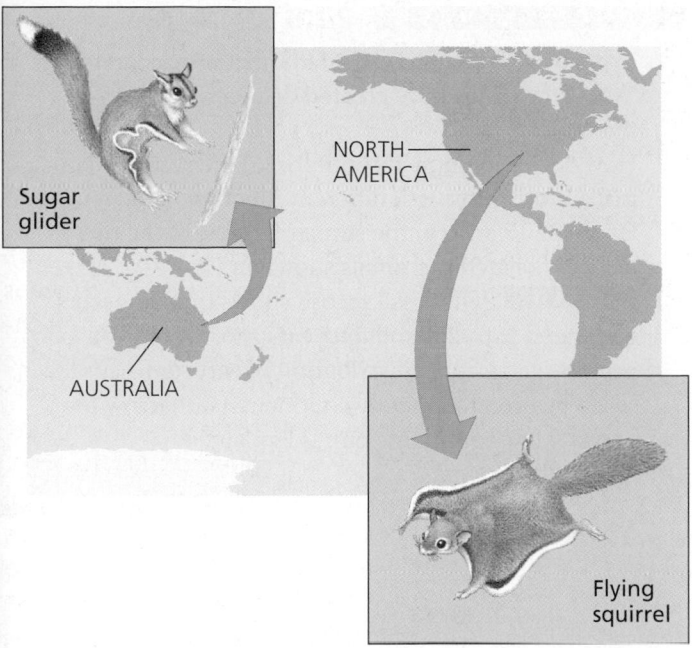

▲ **Figure 22.20 Convergent evolution.** The sugar glider is a marsupial mammal that evolved in isolation on the island continent of Australia. Although sugar gliders superficially resemble the eutherian flying squirrels of North America, the ability to glide through the air evolved independently in these two distantly related groups of mammals.

marsupials have eutherian look-alikes with similar adaptations. For instance, a forest-dwelling Australian marsupial called the sugar glider is superficially very similar to flying squirrels, gliding eutherians that live in North American forests (**Figure 22.20**). But the sugar glider has many other characteristics that make it a marsupial, much more closely related to kangaroos and other Australian marsupials than to flying squirrels or other eutherians. Once again, our understanding of evolution can explain these observations. Although they evolved independently from different ancestors, these two mammals have adapted to similar environments in similar ways. In such examples in which species share features because of convergent evolution, the resemblance is said to be **analogous**, not homologous.

Biogeography

A fourth type of evidence for evolution comes from **biogeography**, the geographic distribution of species. The geographic distribution of organisms is influenced by many factors, including **continental drift**, the slow movement of Earth's continents over time. About 250 million years ago, these movements united all of Earth's landmasses into a single large continent, called **Pangaea** (see Figure 25.13). Roughly 200 million years ago, Pangaea began to break apart; by 20 million years ago, the continents we know today were within a few hundred kilometers of their present locations.

We can use our understanding of evolution and continental drift to predict where fossils of different groups of organisms

might be found. For example, as you will read in Chapter 25, evolutionary biologists have constructed evolutionary trees for horses based on anatomical data. Based on these trees and on the ages of fossils of horse ancestors, researchers estimate that present-day horse species originated 5 million years ago in North America. At that time, North and South America were close to their present locations, but they were not yet connected to one another, making it difficult for horses to travel between them. Thus, we would predict that the oldest horse fossils should be found only on the continent on which horses originated—North America. This prediction and others like it for different groups of organisms have been upheld, providing more evidence for evolution.

We can also use our understanding of evolution to explain biogeographic data. For example, islands generally have many species of plants and animals that are **endemic**, which means they are found nowhere else in the world. Yet, as Darwin described in *The Origin of Species*, most island species are closely related to species from the nearest mainland or a neighboring island. He explained this observation by suggesting that islands are colonized by species from the nearest mainland. These colonists eventually give rise to new species as they adapt to their new environments. Such a process also explains why two islands with similar environments in different parts of the world are populated not by closely related species but rather by species that resemble those of the nearest mainland, where the environment is often quite different.

What Is Theoretical About Darwin's View of Life?

Some people dismiss Darwin's ideas as "just a theory." However, as we have seen, the pattern of evolution—the observation that life has evolved over time—has been documented directly and is supported by a great deal of evidence. In addition, Darwin's explanation of the process of evolution—that natural selection is the primary cause of the observed pattern of evolutionary change—makes sense of massive amounts of data. The effects of natural selection also can be observed and tested in nature.

What, then, is theoretical about evolution? Keep in mind that the scientific meaning of the term *theory* is very different from its meaning in everyday use. The colloquial use of the word *theory* comes close to what scientists mean by a hypothesis. In science, a theory is more comprehensive than a hypothesis. A theory, such as Darwin's theory of evolution by natural selection, accounts for many observations and explains and integrates a great variety of phenomena. Such a unifying theory does not become widely accepted unless its predictions stand up to thorough and continual testing by experiment and additional observation (see Chapter 1). As the next three chapters demonstrate, this has certainly been the case with the theory of evolution by natural selection.

The skepticism of scientists as they continue to test theories prevents these ideas from becoming dogma. For example, although Darwin thought that evolution was a very slow process, we now know that this isn't always true. New species can form in relatively short periods of time (a few thousand years or less; see Chapter 24). Furthermore, as we'll explore throughout this unit, evolutionary biologists now recognize that natural selection is not the only mechanism responsible for evolution. Indeed, the study of evolution today is livelier than ever as scientists find more ways to test the predictions of Darwin's theory.

Although Darwin's theory attributes the diversity of life to natural processes, the diverse products of evolution nevertheless remain elegant and inspiring. As Darwin wrote in the final sentence of *The Origin of Species*, "There is grandeur in this view of life . . . [in which] endless forms most beautiful and most wonderful have been, and are being, evolved."

Chapter 22 Review

SUMMARY OF KEY CONCEPTS

CONCEPT 22.1

The Darwinian revolution challenged traditional views of a young Earth inhabited by unchanging species (pp. 452–455)

▶ *Scala Naturae* and Classification of Species Darwin's proposal that life's diversity has arisen from ancestral species through natural selection was a radical departure from the prevailing views of Western culture.

▶ Ideas About Change over Time In contrast to the principle that events in the past occurred suddenly by mechanisms not operating today, geologists Hutton and Lyell perceived that changes in Earth's surface can result from slow, continuous actions still operating at the present time.

▶ Lamarck's Hypothesis of Evolution Lamarck hypothesized that species evolve, but the mechanisms he proposed are not supported by evidence.

CONCEPT 22.2

Descent with modification by natural selection explains the adaptations of organisms and the unity and diversity of life (pp. 455–460)

▶ Darwin's Research Darwin's experiences during the voyage of the *Beagle* gave rise to his idea that new species originate from ancestral forms through the accumulation of adaptations. He refined his theory for more than 20 years and finally published it in 1859 after learning that Wallace had come to the same idea.

▶ *The Origin of Species* Darwin's book proposed that evolution occurs by natural selection:

Observations

Individuals in a population vary in their heritable characteristics.	Organisms produce more offspring than the environment can support.

Inferences

Individuals that are well suited to their environment tend to leave more offspring than other individuals.

and

Over time, favorable traits accumulate in the population.

CONCEPT 22.3

Evolution is supported by an overwhelming amount of scientific evidence (pp. 460–466)

▶ Direct Observations of Evolutionary Change Researchers have directly observed natural selection leading to adaptive evolution in many studies, including research on wild guppy populations and on pathogens such as HIV.

▶ The Fossil Record Fossils show that past organisms differed from living organisms, that many species have become extinct, and that species have evolved over long periods of time.

- ▶ **Homology** Organisms share characteristics because of common descent (homology) or because natural selection affects independently evolving species in similar environments in similar ways (convergent evolution).
- ▶ **Biogeography** The geographic distribution of organisms is consistent with evolutionary theory.
- ▶ **What Is Theoretical About Darwin's View of Life?** The theory of evolution by natural selection integrates diverse areas of study and stimulates many new questions.

MEDIA

Activity Reconstructing Forelimbs
Investigation How Do Environmental Changes Affect a Population?
Investigation What Are the Patterns of Antibiotic Resistance?

TESTING YOUR KNOWLEDGE

SELF-QUIZ

1. Which of the following is *not* an observation or inference on which natural selection is based?
   a. There is heritable variation among individuals.
   b. Poorly adapted individuals never produce offspring.
   c. Species produce more offspring than the environment can support.
   d. Individuals whose characteristics are best suited to the environment generally leave more offspring than those whose characteristics are less suited.
   e. Only a fraction of the offspring produced by an individual may survive.

2. The upper forelimbs of humans and bats have fairly similar skeletal structures, whereas the corresponding bones in whales have very different shapes and proportions. However, genetic data suggest that all three kinds of organisms diverged from a common ancestor at about the same time. Which of the following is the most likely explanation for these data?
   a. Humans and bats evolved by natural selection, and whales evolved by Lamarckian mechanisms.
   b. Forelimb evolution was adaptive in people and bats, but not in whales.
   c. Natural selection in an aquatic environment resulted in significant changes to whale forelimb anatomy.
   d. Genes mutate faster in whales than in humans or bats.
   e. Whales are not properly classified as mammals.

3. Which of the following observations helped Darwin shape his concept of descent with modification?
   a. Species diversity declines farther from the equator.
   b. Fewer species live on islands than on the nearest continents.
   c. Birds can be found on islands located farther from the mainland than the birds' maximum nonstop flight distance.
   d. South American temperate plants are more similar to the tropical plants of South America than to the temperate plants of Europe.
   e. Earthquakes reshape life by causing mass extinctions.

4. Within a few weeks of treatment with the drug 3TC, a patient's HIV population consists entirely of 3TC-resistant viruses. How can this result best be explained?
   a. HIV can change its surface proteins and resist vaccines.
   b. The patient must have become reinfected with 3TC-resistant viruses.
   c. HIV began making drug-resistant versions of reverse transcriptase in response to the drug.
   d. A few drug-resistant viruses were present at the start of treatment, and natural selection increased their frequency.
   e. The drug caused the HIV RNA to change.

5. DNA sequences in many human genes are very similar to the sequences of corresponding genes in chimpanzees. The most likely explanation for this result is that
   a. humans and chimpanzees share a relatively recent common ancestor.
   b. humans evolved from chimpanzees.
   c. chimpanzees evolved from humans.
   d. convergent evolution led to the DNA similarities.
   e. humans and chimpanzees are not closely related.

6. Which of the following pairs of structures is *least* likely to represent homology?
   a. the wings of a bat and the arms of a human
   b. the hemoglobin of a baboon and that of a gorilla
   c. the mitochondria of a plant and those of an animal
   d. the wings of a bird and those of an insect
   e. the brain of a cat and that of a dog

For Self-Quiz answers, see Appendix A.

MEDIA Visit **www.campbellbiology.com** for a Practice Test.

EVOLUTION CONNECTION

7. Explain why anatomical and molecular homologies generally fit a similar nested pattern.

SCIENTIFIC INQUIRY

8. **DRAW IT** Mosquitoes resistant to the pesticide DDT first appeared in India in 1959, but now are found throughout the world. (a) Graph the data in the table below. (b) Examining the graph, hypothesize why the percentage of mosquitoes resistant to DDT rose rapidly. (c) Suggest an explanation for the global spread of DDT resistance.

Month	Percentage of Mosquitoes Resistant* to DDT
0	4%
8	45%
12	77%

*Mosquitoes were considered resistant if they were not killed within 1 hour of receiving a dose of 4% DDT.

Source: C. F. Curtis et al., Selection for and against insecticide resistance and possible methods of inhibiting the evolution of resistance in mosquitoes, *Ecological Entomology* 3:273–287 (1978).

The Evolution of Populations

23

OVERVIEW

The Smallest Unit of Evolution

One common misconception about evolution is that individual organisms evolve. It is true that natural selection *acts* on individuals: Each organism's combination of traits affects its survival and reproductive success compared to other individuals. But the evolutionary impact of natural selection is only apparent in the changes in a *population* of organisms over time.

Consider the medium ground finch (*Geospiza fortis*), a seed-eating bird that inhabits the Galápagos Islands **(Figure 23.1)**. In 1977, the *G. fortis* population on the island of Daphne Major was decimated by a long period of drought: Of some 1,200 birds, only 180 survived. Researchers Peter and Rosemary Grant observed that the surviving finches tended to have larger, deeper beaks than others in the population. The Grants also observed that during the drought, small, soft seeds were in short supply. The finches mostly fed on large, hard seeds that were more plentiful. The birds with larger, deeper beaks were able to crack these larger seeds, increasing their rate of survival compared to finches with smaller beaks. As a result, the average beak size in the next generation of *G. fortis* was greater than it had been in the pre-drought population. The finch population had evolved by natural selection. However, the *individual*

finches did not evolve. Each bird had a beak of a particular size, which did not grow larger during the drought. Rather, the proportion of large beaks in the population increased over generations: The population evolved, not its individual members.

Focusing on evolutionary change in populations, we can define evolution on its smallest scale, called **microevolution**, as change in allele frequencies in a population over generations. As we will see in this chapter, natural selection is not the only cause of microevolution. In fact, there are three main mechanisms that can cause allele frequency change: natural selection, genetic drift (chance events that alter allele frequencies), and gene flow (the transfer of alleles between populations). Each of these mechanisms has distinctive effects on the genetic composition of populations. However, only natural selection consistently improves the match between organisms and their environment, thus bringing about the type of change we refer to as adaptive evolution. Before we examine natural selection and adaptation more closely, let's revisit how the variations that are the raw material for evolutionary change arise.

CONCEPT 23.1

Mutation and sexual reproduction produce the genetic variation that makes evolution possible

In *The Origin of Species*, Darwin provided abundant evidence that life on Earth has evolved over time, and he proposed natural selection as the primary mechanism for that change. Darwin also emphasized the importance of heritable differences among individuals. He knew that natural selection could not cause evolutionary change unless individuals differed in their inherited characteristics. But Darwin could not explain precisely how organisms pass heritable traits to their offspring.

Just a few years after Darwin published *The Origin of Species*, Gregor Mendel wrote a groundbreaking paper on inheritance in pea plants (see Chapter 14). In that paper, Mendel proposed a particulate model of inheritance, which stated that organisms transmit discrete heritable units (now called genes) to their offspring. Although Darwin never learned about genes, Mendel's paper set the stage for understanding the genetic differences on which evolution is based. Here we'll examine such genetic differences along with two processes that produce them, mutation and sexual reproduction.

Genetic Variation

You probably have no trouble recognizing your friends in a crowd. Each person has a unique genotype, reflected in individual phenotypic variations such as facial features, height, and voice. Indeed, individual variation occurs in all species. In addition to the differences that we can see or hear, species have extensive genetic variation that can only be observed at the molecular level. For example, you cannot identify a person's blood group (A, B, AB, or O) from his or her appearance, but this and many other such inherited characters vary among individuals.

As you read in earlier chapters, however, some phenotypic variation is not heritable (**Figure 23.2** shows a striking example in a caterpillar of the southwestern United States). Phenotype is the product of an inherited genotype and many environmental influences. In a human example, bodybuilders alter their phenotypes dramatically but do not pass their huge muscles on to the next generation. Only the genetic part of variation can have evolutionary consequences.

Variation Within a Population

Characters that vary within a population may be discrete or quantitative. *Discrete characters*, such as the purple or white flower colors of Mendel's pea plants (see Figure 14.3), can be classified on an either-or basis (each plant has flowers that are either purple or white). Many discrete characters are determined by a single gene locus with different alleles that produce distinct phenotypes. However, most heritable variation involves *quantitative characters*, which vary along a continuum within a population. Heritable quantitative variation usually results from the influence of two or more genes on a single phenotypic character.

Whether considering discrete or quantitative characters, biologists can measure genetic variation in a population at both the whole-gene level (gene variability) and the molecular level of DNA (nucleotide variability). Gene variability can be quantified as the **average heterozygosity**, the average percent of loci that are heterozygous. (Recall that a heterozygous individual has two different alleles for a given locus, whereas a homozygous individual has two identical alleles for that locus.) As an example, consider the fruit fly *Drosophila melanogaster*, which has about 13,700 genes in its genome. On average, a fruit fly is heterozygous for about 1,920 of its loci (14%) and homozygous for all the rest. We can therefore say that a *D. melanogaster* population has an average heterozygosity of 14%.

Average heterozygosity is often estimated by surveying the protein products of genes using gel electrophoresis (see Figure 20.9). While useful, this approach cannot detect silent mutations that alter the DNA sequence of a gene but not the amino acid sequence of the protein (see Figure 17.23). To include silent mutations in their estimates of average heterozygosity, researchers must use other approaches, such as PCR-based methods and restriction fragment analyses (see Figures 20.8 and 20.10).

Nucleotide variability is measured by comparing the DNA sequences of two individuals in a population and then

▲ **Figure 23.2 Nonheritable variation.** These caterpillars of the moth *Nemoria arizonaria* owe their different appearances to chemicals in their diets, not to their genotypes. Caterpillars raised on a diet of oak flowers resembled the flowers **(a)**, whereas their siblings raised on oak leaves resembled oak twigs **(b)**.

averaging the data from many such comparisons. The genome of *D. melanogaster* has about 180 million nucleotides, and the sequences of any two fruit flies differ on average by approximately 1.8 million (1%) of their nucleotides. Thus, the nucleotide variability of *D. melanogaster* populations is about 1%.

As in this fruit fly example, gene variability (that is, average heterozygosity) tends to be greater than nucleotide variability. Why is this true? Remember that a gene can consist of thousands of nucleotides. A difference at only one of these nucleotides can be sufficient to make two alleles of that gene different and thereby increase gene variability.

Variation Between Populations

In addition to variation observed within a population, species also exhibit **geographic variation**, differences in the genetic composition of separate populations. **Figure 23.3** illustrates geographic variation in populations of house mice (*Mus musculus*) separated by mountains on the Atlantic island of Madeira. Inadvertently introduced by Portuguese settlers in the 15th century, several populations of mice have evolved in isolation from one another. Researchers have observed differences in the karyotypes (chromosome sets) of these isolated populations. In some of the populations, a

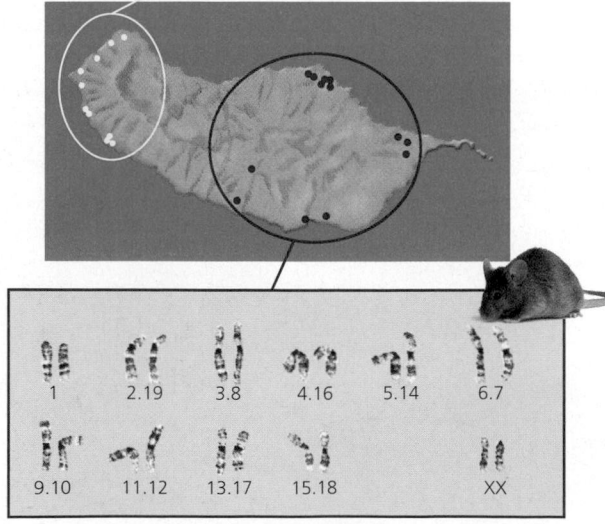

▲ **Figure 23.3 Geographic variation in isolated mouse populations on Madeira.** The number pairs represent fused chromosomes. For example, "2.4" indicates fusion of chromosome 2 and chromosome 4. Mice in the areas indicated by the yellow dots have the set of fused chromosomes in the yellow box; mice in the red-dot locales have the set of fusions in the red box.

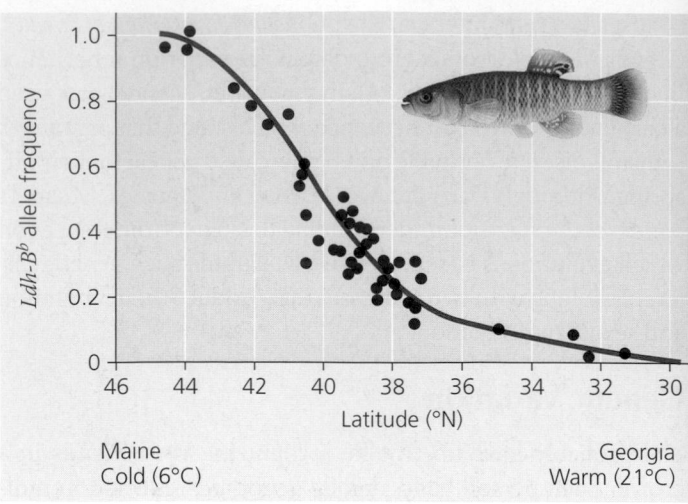

▲ **Figure 23.4 A cline determined by temperature.** In mummichog fish, the frequency of the *Ldh-B^b* allele for the enzyme lactate dehydrogenase-B (which functions in metabolism) decreases in fish sampled from Maine to Georgia. The *Ldh-B^b* allele codes for a form of the enzyme that is a better catalyst in cold water than are other versions of the enzyme. Individuals with the *Ldh-B^b* allele can swim faster in cold water than can individuals with other alleles.

number of the original chromosomes have become fused. However, the patterns of fused chromosomes differ from one population to another. Because these chromosome-level changes leave genes intact, their phenotypic effects on the mice seem to be neutral. Thus, the variation between these populations appears to have resulted from chance events (drift) rather than natural selection.

Other examples of geographic variation occur as a **cline**, a graded change in a character along a geographic axis. Some clines are produced by a gradation in an environmental variable, as illustrated by the impact of temperature on the frequency of a cold-adaptive allele in mummichog fish (*Fundulus heteroclitus*). Clines such as the one depicted in **Figure 23.4** probably result from natural selection—otherwise there would be no reason to expect a close association between the environmental variable and the frequency of the allele. But selection can only operate if multiple alleles exist for a given locus. Such variation in alleles is the product of mutation, as we will discuss next.

Mutation

The ultimate source of new alleles is **mutation**, a change in the nucleotide sequence of an organism's DNA. A mutation is like a shot in the dark—we cannot predict accurately which segments of DNA will be altered or in what way. In multicellular organisms, only mutations in cell lines that produce gametes can be passed to offspring. In plants and fungi, this is not as limiting as it may sound, since many different cell lines can produce gametes (see Figures 29.13, 30.6, and 31.17). But in animals, most mutations occur in somatic cells and are lost when the individual dies.

Point Mutations

A change of as little as one base in a gene—a "point mutation"—can have a significant impact on phenotype, as in sickle-cell disease (see Figure 17.22). Organisms reflect thousands of generations of past selection, and hence their phenotypes generally provide a close match to their environment. As a result, it's unlikely that a new mutation that alters a phenotype will improve it. In fact, most such mutations are at least slightly harmful. But much of the DNA in eukaryotic genomes does not code for protein products, and point mutations in these noncoding regions are often harmless. Also, because of the redundancy in the genetic code, even a point mutation in a gene that encodes a protein will have no effect on the protein's function if the amino acid composition is not changed. Moreover, even if there is a change in an amino acid, this may not affect the protein's shape and function. However—as we will see—on rare occasions, a mutant allele may actually make its bearer better suited to the environment, enhancing reproductive success.

Mutations That Alter Gene Number or Sequence

Chromosomal changes that delete, disrupt, or rearrange many loci at once are almost certain to be harmful. However, when such large-scale mutations leave genes intact, their effects on organisms may be neutral (see Figure 23.3). In rare cases, chromosomal rearrangements may even be beneficial. For example, the translocation of part of one chromosome to a different chromosome could link DNA segments in a way that results in a positive effect.

An important source of variation begins when genes are duplicated due to errors in meiosis (such as unequal crossing over), slippage during DNA replication, or the activities of transposable elements (see Chapters 15 and 21). Duplications of large chromosome segments, like other chromosomal aberrations, are often harmful, but the duplication of smaller pieces of DNA may not be. Gene duplications that do not have severe effects can persist over generations, allowing mutations to accumulate. The result is an expanded genome with new loci that may take on new functions.

Such beneficial increases in gene number appear to have played a major role in evolution. For example, the remote ancestors of mammals carried a single gene for detecting odors that has been duplicated many times. As a result, humans today have about 1,000 olfactory receptor genes, and mice have 1,300. It is likely that such dramatic increases in the number of olfactory genes helped early mammals by enabling them to detect faint odors and to distinguish among many different smells. More recently, about 60% of human olfactory receptor genes have been inactivated by mutations, whereas mice have lost only 20% of theirs. This dramatic difference demonstrates that a versatile sense of smell is more important to mice than it is to us!

Mutation Rates

Mutation rates tend to be low in plants and animals, averaging about one mutation in every 100,000 genes per generation, and they are often even lower in prokaryotes. But prokaryotes typically have short generation spans, so mutations can quickly generate genetic variation in populations of these organisms. The same is true of viruses. For instance, HIV has a generation span of about two days. It also has an RNA genome, which has a much higher mutation rate than a typical DNA genome because of the lack of RNA repair mechanisms in host cells (see Chapter 19). For this reason, it is unlikely that a single-drug treatment would ever be effective against HIV; mutant forms of the virus that are resistant to a particular drug would no doubt proliferate in relatively short order. The most effective AIDS treatments to date have been drug "cocktails" that combine several medications. It is less likely that multiple mutations conferring resistance to *all* the drugs will occur in a short time period.

Sexual Reproduction

In organisms that reproduce sexually, most of the genetic variation in a population results from the unique combination of alleles that each individual receives. Of course, at the nucleotide level, all the differences among these alleles have originated from past mutations. But it is the mechanism of sexual reproduction that shuffles existing alleles and deals them at random to determine individual genotypes.

As described in Chapter 13, three mechanisms contribute to this shuffling: crossing over, independent assortment of chromosomes, and fertilization. During meiosis, homologous chromosomes, one inherited from each parent, trade some of their alleles by crossing over. These homologous chromosomes and the alleles they carry are then distributed at random into gametes. Then, because myriad possible mating combinations exist in a population, fertilization brings together gametes of individuals that are likely to have different genetic backgrounds. The combined effects of these three mechanisms ensure that sexual reproduction rearranges existing alleles into fresh combinations each generation, providing much of the genetic variation that makes evolution possible.

CONCEPT CHECK 23.1

1. (a) Explain why genetic variation within a population is a prerequisite for evolution. (b) What factors can produce genetic variation among populations?
2. Of all the mutations that occur in a population, why do only a small fraction become widespread among the population's members?
3. **WHAT IF?** If a population stopped reproducing sexually (but still reproduced asexually), how would its genetic variation be affected over time? Explain.

For suggested answers, see Appendix A.

CONCEPT 23.2

The Hardy-Weinberg equation can be used to test whether a population is evolving

As we've seen, the individuals in a population must differ genetically for evolution to occur. But the presence of genetic variation does not guarantee that a population will evolve. For that to happen, one of the factors that cause evolution must be at work. In this section, we'll explore how to test whether evolution is occurring in a population. The first step in this process is to clarify what we mean by a population.

Gene Pools and Allele Frequencies

A **population** is a group of individuals of the same species that live in the same area and interbreed, producing fertile offspring. Different populations of a single species may be isolated geographically from one another, thus exchanging genetic material only rarely. Such isolation is common for species that live on widely separated islands or in different lakes. But not all populations are isolated, nor must populations have sharp boundaries (**Figure 23.5**). Still, members of a population typically breed with one another and thus on average are more closely related to each other than to members of other populations.

▲ **Figure 23.5 One species, two populations.** These two caribou populations in the Yukon are not totally isolated; they sometimes share the same area. Nonetheless, members of either population are more likely to breed with members of their own population than with members of the other population.

We can characterize a population's genetic makeup by describing its **gene pool**, which consists of all the alleles for all the loci in all individuals of the population. If only one allele exists for a particular locus in a population, that allele is said to be *fixed* in the gene pool, and all individuals are homozygous for that allele. But if there are two or more alleles for a particular locus in a population, individuals may be either homozygous or heterozygous.

Each allele has a frequency (proportion) in the population. For example, imagine a population of 500 wildflower plants with two alleles, C^R and C^W, for a certain locus that codes for flower pigment. These alleles show incomplete dominance (see Chapter 14); thus, each genotype has a distinct phenotype. Plants homozygous for the C^R allele ($C^R C^R$) produce red pigment and have red flowers; plants homozygous for the C^W allele ($C^W C^W$) produce no red pigment and have white flowers; and heterozygotes ($C^R C^W$) produce some red pigment and have pink flowers. In our population, suppose there are 320 plants with red flowers, 160 with pink flowers, and 20 with white flowers. Because these are diploid organisms, there are a total of 1,000 copies of genes for flower color in the population of 500 individuals. The C^R allele accounts for 800 of these genes ($320 \times 2 = 640$ for $C^R C^R$ plants, plus $160 \times 1 = 160$ for $C^R C^W$ plants).

When studying a locus with two alleles, the convention is to use p to represent the frequency of one allele and q to represent the frequency of the other allele. Thus, p, the frequency of the C^R allele in the gene pool of this population, is $800/1,000 = 0.8 = 80\%$. And because there are only two alleles for this gene, the frequency of the C^W allele, represented by q, must be $200/1,000 = 0.2 = 20\%$. For loci that have more than two alleles, the sum of all allele frequencies must still equal 1 (100%).

Next we'll see how allele and genotype frequencies can be used to test whether evolution is occurring in a population.

The Hardy-Weinberg Principle

One way to assess whether natural selection or other factors are causing evolution at a particular locus is to determine what the genetic makeup of a population would be if it were *not* evolving at that locus. We can then compare that scenario with data from a real population. If there are no differences, we can conclude that the real population is not evolving. If there are differences, we can conclude that the real population is evolving—and then we can try to figure out why.

Hardy-Weinberg Equilibrium

The gene pool of a population that is not evolving can be described by the **Hardy-Weinberg principle**, named for the British mathematician and German physician, respectively, who independently derived it in 1908. This principle states that the frequencies of alleles and genotypes in a population will remain constant from generation to generation, provided that only Mendelian segregation and recombination of alleles are at work. Such a gene pool is said to be in **Hardy-Weinberg equilibrium**.

To understand and use the Hardy-Weinberg principle, it is helpful to think about alleles and genetic crosses in a new way. Previously, we used Punnett squares to determine the genotypes of offspring in a genetic cross (see Figure 14.5). We can take a similar approach here, but instead of considering the possible allele combinations from one genetic cross, our focus now is on the combination of alleles in *all* of the genetic crosses in a population.

Imagine that alleles for a given locus from all of the individuals in a population could be mixed together in a large bin **(Figure 23.6)**. We can think of this bin as holding the population's gene pool for that locus. "Reproduction" occurs by selecting alleles at random from the bin; somewhat similar events occur in nature when fish release sperm and eggs into the water or when pollen (containing plant sperm) is blown about by the wind. By viewing reproduction as a random selection of alleles from the bin (the gene pool), we are in effect assuming that mating occurs at random—that is, that all male-female matings are equally likely.

Let's apply our bin analogy to the hypothetical wildflower population discussed earlier. In that population, the frequency of the allele for red flowers (C^R) is $p = 0.8$, and the frequency of the allele for white flowers (C^W) is $q = 0.2$. Thus, a bin holding all 1,000 flower-color alleles of the 500 wildflowers contains 800 C^R alleles and 200 C^W alleles. Assuming that gametes are formed by selecting alleles at random from the bin, the probability that an egg or sperm contains a C^R or C^W allele is equal to the frequency of these alleles in the bin. Thus, as shown in Figure 23.6, each egg has an 80% chance of containing a C^R allele and a 20% chance of containing a C^W allele; the same is true for each sperm.

Using the rule of multiplication (see Chapter 14), we can now calculate the frequencies of the three possible genotypes, assuming random unions of sperm and eggs. The probability that two C^R alleles will come together is $p \times p = p^2 = 0.8 \times 0.8 = 0.64$. Thus, about 64% of the plants in the next generation will have the genotype $C^R C^R$. The frequency of $C^W C^W$ individuals is expected to be about $q \times q = q^2 = 0.2 \times 0.2 = 0.04$, or 4%. $C^R C^W$ heterozygotes can arise in two different ways. If the sperm provides the C^R allele and the egg provides the C^W allele, the resulting heterozygotes will be $p \times q = 0.8 \times 0.2 = 16\%$ of the total. If the sperm provides the C^W allele and the egg the C^R allele, the heterozygous offspring will make up $q \times p = 0.2 \times 0.8 = 16\%$. The frequency of heterozygotes is thus the sum of these possibilities: $pq + qp = 0.16 + 0.16 = 0.32$, or 32%.

As shown in **Figure 23.7** on the next page, the genotype frequencies in the next generation must add up to 1 (100%). Thus, the equation for Hardy-Weinberg equilibrium states that at a locus with two alleles, the three genotypes will appear in the following proportions:

$$\underset{\substack{\text{Expected} \\ \text{frequency} \\ \text{of genotype} \\ C^R C^R}}{p^2} + \underset{\substack{\text{Expected} \\ \text{frequency} \\ \text{of genotype} \\ C^R C^W}}{2pq} + \underset{\substack{\text{Expected} \\ \text{frequency} \\ \text{of genotype} \\ C^W C^W}}{q^2 = 1}$$

Note that for a locus with two alleles, only three genotypes are possible (in this case, $C^R C^R$, $C^R C^W$, and $C^W C^W$). As a result, the sum of the frequencies of the three genotypes must equal 1 (100%) in *any* population—regardless of whether the population is in Hardy-Weinberg equilibrium. A population is in Hardy-Weinberg equilibrium only if the genotype frequencies are such that the actual frequency of one homozygote is p^2, the actual frequency of the other homozygote is q^2, and the actual frequency of heterozygotes is $2pq$. Finally, as suggested by Figure 23.7, if a population such as our wildflowers is in Hardy-Weinberg equilibrium and its members continue to mate randomly generation after generation, allele and genotype frequencies will remain constant. The system operates somewhat like a deck of cards: No matter how many times the deck is reshuffled to deal out new hands, the deck

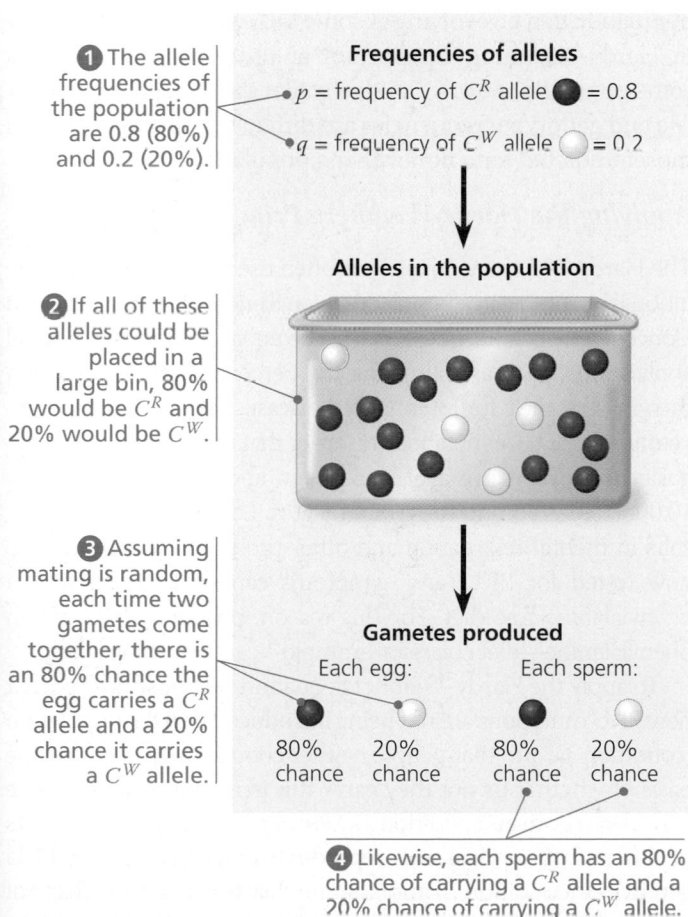

❶ The allele frequencies of the population are 0.8 (80%) and 0.2 (20%).

Frequencies of alleles

- p = frequency of C^R allele ● = 0.8
- q = frequency of C^W allele ○ = 0.2

Alleles in the population

❷ If all of these alleles could be placed in a large bin, 80% would be C^R and 20% would be C^W.

❸ Assuming mating is random, each time two gametes come together, there is an 80% chance the egg carries a C^R allele and a 20% chance it carries a C^W allele.

Gametes produced

Each egg: 80% chance 20% chance

Each sperm: 80% chance 20% chance

❹ Likewise, each sperm has an 80% chance of carrying a C^R allele and a 20% chance of carrying a C^W allele.

▲ **Figure 23.6 Selecting alleles at random from a gene pool.**

Gametes for each generation are drawn at random from the gene pool of the previous generation, as in Figure 23.6:

80% C^R (p = 0.8)   20% C^W (q = 0.2)

Sperm

	C^R (80%)	C^W (20%)
C^R (80%)	64% (p^2) $C^R C^R$	16% (pq) $C^R C^W$
C^W (20%)	16% (qp) $C^R C^W$	4% (q^2) $C^W C^W$

Eggs

If the gametes come together at random, the genotype frequencies of this generation are in Hardy-Weinberg equilibrium:

64% $C^R C^R$, 32% $C^R C^W$, and 4% $C^W C^W$

Gametes of this generation:

64% C^R (from $C^R C^R$ plants) + 16% C^R (from $C^R C^W$ plants) = 80% C^R = 0.8 = p

4% C^W (from $C^W C^W$ plants) + 16% C^W (from $C^R C^W$ plants) = 20% C^W = 0.2 = q

With random mating, these gametes will result in the same mix of genotypes in the next generation:

64% $C^R C^R$, 32% $C^R C^W$, and 4% $C^W C^W$ plants

▲ **Figure 23.7 The Hardy-Weinberg principle.** In our wildflower population, the gene pool remains constant from one generation to the next. Mendelian processes alone do not alter frequencies of alleles or genotypes.

? *If the frequency of the C^R allele is 60%, predict the frequencies of the $C^R C^R$, $C^R C^W$, and $C^W C^W$ genotypes.*

itself remains the same. Aces do not grow more numerous than jacks. And the repeated shuffling of a population's gene pool over the generations cannot, in itself, change the frequency of one allele relative to another.

Conditions for Hardy-Weinberg Equilibrium

The Hardy-Weinberg principle describes a hypothetical population that is not evolving. But in real populations, the allele and genotype frequencies often *do* change over time. Such changes can occur when at least one of the following five conditions of Hardy-Weinberg equilibrium is not met:

1. **No mutations.** By altering alleles or (in large-scale changes) deleting or duplicating entire genes, mutations modify the gene pool.
2. **Random mating.** If individuals mate preferentially within a subset of the population, such as their close relatives (inbreeding), random mixing of gametes does not occur, and genotype frequencies change.
3. **No natural selection.** Differences in the survival and reproductive success of individuals carrying different genotypes can alter allele frequencies.
4. **Extremely large population size.** The smaller the population, the more likely it is that allele frequencies will fluctuate by chance from one generation to the next (genetic drift).
5. **No gene flow.** By moving alleles into or out of populations, gene flow can alter allele frequencies.

Departure from any of these conditions usually results in evolutionary change, which, as we've already described, is common in natural populations. But it is also common for natural populations to be in Hardy-Weinberg equilibrium for specific genes. This apparent contradiction occurs because a population can be evolving at some loci, yet simultaneously be in Hardy-Weinberg equilibrium at other loci. In addition, some populations evolve so slowly that the changes in their allele and genotype frequencies are difficult to distinguish from those predicted for a nonevolving population.

Applying the Hardy-Weinberg Principle

The Hardy-Weinberg equation is often used to test whether evolution is occurring in a population (you'll encounter an example in Concept Check 23.2, question 3). The equation also has medical applications, such as estimating the percentage of a population carrying the allele for an inherited disease. For example, phenylketonuria (PKU), a metabolic disorder that results from homozygosity for a recessive allele, occurs in about one out of every 10,000 babies born in the United States. Left untreated, PKU results in mental retardation and other problems. (Newborns are now tested for PKU, and symptoms can be lessened with a phenylalanine-free diet. For this reason, products that contain phenylalanine—diet colas, for example—carry warning labels.)

To apply the Hardy-Weinberg equation, we must assume that new PKU mutations are not being introduced into the population (condition 1), and that people neither choose their mates on the basis of whether or not they carry this gene nor generally mate with close relatives (condition 2). We must also neglect any effects of differential survival and reproductive success among PKU genotypes (condition 3) and assume that there are no effects of genetic drift (condition 4) or of gene flow from other populations into the United States (condition 5). These assumptions are reasonable: The mutation rate for the PKU gene is low, inbreeding is not common in the United States, selection occurs only against the rare homozygotes (and then only if dietary restrictions are not followed), the United States' population is very large, and populations outside the country have PKU allele frequencies similar to those seen in the United States. If all these assumptions hold, then the frequency of individuals in the population born with PKU will correspond to q^2 in the Hardy-Weinberg equation (q^2 = frequency of homozygotes). Because the allele is recessive, we must estimate the number of heterozygotes rather than counting them directly as we did with the pink flowers. Since we know there is one PKU occurrence per 10,000 births (q^2 = 0.0001), the frequency of the recessive allele for PKU is

$$q = \sqrt{0.0001} = 0.01$$

and the frequency of the dominant allele is

$$p = 1 - q = 1 - 0.01 = 0.99$$

The frequency of carriers, heterozygous people who do not have PKU but may pass the PKU allele to offspring, is

$$2pq = 2 \times 0.99 \times 0.01 = 0.0198$$
(approximately 2% of the U.S. population)

Remember, the assumption of Hardy-Weinberg equilibrium yields an approximation; the real number of carriers may differ. Still, our calculations suggest that harmful recessive alleles at this and other loci can be concealed in a population because they are carried by healthy heterozygotes.

CONCEPT CHECK 23.2

1. Suppose a population of organisms with 500 loci is fixed at half of these loci and has two alleles at each of the other loci. How many different alleles are found in its entire gene pool? Explain.
2. If p is the frequency of allele A, which parts of the Hardy-Weinberg equation correspond to the frequency of individuals that have at least one A allele?
3. **WHAT IF?** For a locus with two alleles (A and a) in a population at risk from an infectious neurodegenerative disease, 16 people had genotype AA, 92 had genotype Aa, and 12 had genotype aa. Use the Hardy-Weinberg equation to determine whether this population appears to be evolving.

For suggested answers, see Appendix A.

CONCEPT 23.3
Natural selection, genetic drift, and gene flow can alter allele frequencies in a population

Note again the five conditions required for a population to be in Hardy-Weinberg equilibrium. A deviation from any of these conditions is a potential cause of evolution. New mutations (violation of condition 1) can alter allele frequencies, but because mutations are rare, the change from one generation to the next is likely to be very small. Nevertheless, as we'll see, mutation ultimately can have a large effect on allele frequencies when it produces new alleles that strongly influence fitness in a positive or negative way. Nonrandom mating (violation of condition 2) can affect the frequencies of homozygous and heterozygous genotypes but by itself usually has no effect on allele frequencies in the gene pool. The three mechanisms that alter allele frequencies directly and cause most evolutionary change are natural selection, genetic drift, and gene flow (violations of conditions 3–5).

Natural Selection

As you read in Chapter 22, Darwin's concept of natural selection is based on differential success in survival and reproduction: Individuals in a population exhibit variations in their heritable traits, and those with traits that are better suited to their environment tend to produce more offspring than those with traits that are less well suited.

We now know that selection results in alleles being passed to the next generation in proportions different from their proportions in the present generation. For example, the fruit fly *Drosophila melanogaster* has an allele that confers resistance to several insecticides, including DDT. This allele has a frequency of 0% in laboratory strains of *D. melanogaster* established from flies collected in the wild in the early 1930s, prior to DDT usage. However, in strains established from flies collected after 1960 (following 20 or more years of DDT usage), the allele frequency is 37%. We can infer that this allele either arose by mutation between 1930 and 1960 or that this allele was present in the population in 1930, but was very rare. In any case, the observed increase in the frequency of this allele most likely occurred because DDT is a powerful poison that is a strong selective force in exposed fly populations.

As the *D. melanogaster* example shows, an allele that confers insecticide resistance will increase in frequency in a population exposed to that insecticide. Such changes are not coincidental. Instead, by consistently favoring some alleles over others, natural selection can cause *adaptive evolution* (evolution that results in a better match between organisms and their environment). We'll explore this process in more detail a little later in this chapter.

Genetic Drift

If you flip a coin 1,000 times, a result of 700 heads and 300 tails might make you suspicious about that coin. But if you flip a coin 10 times, an outcome of 7 heads and 3 tails would not be surprising. The smaller the number of coin flips, the more likely it is that chance alone will cause a deviation from the predicted result—in this case, the prediction is an equal number of heads and tails. Chance events can also cause allele frequencies

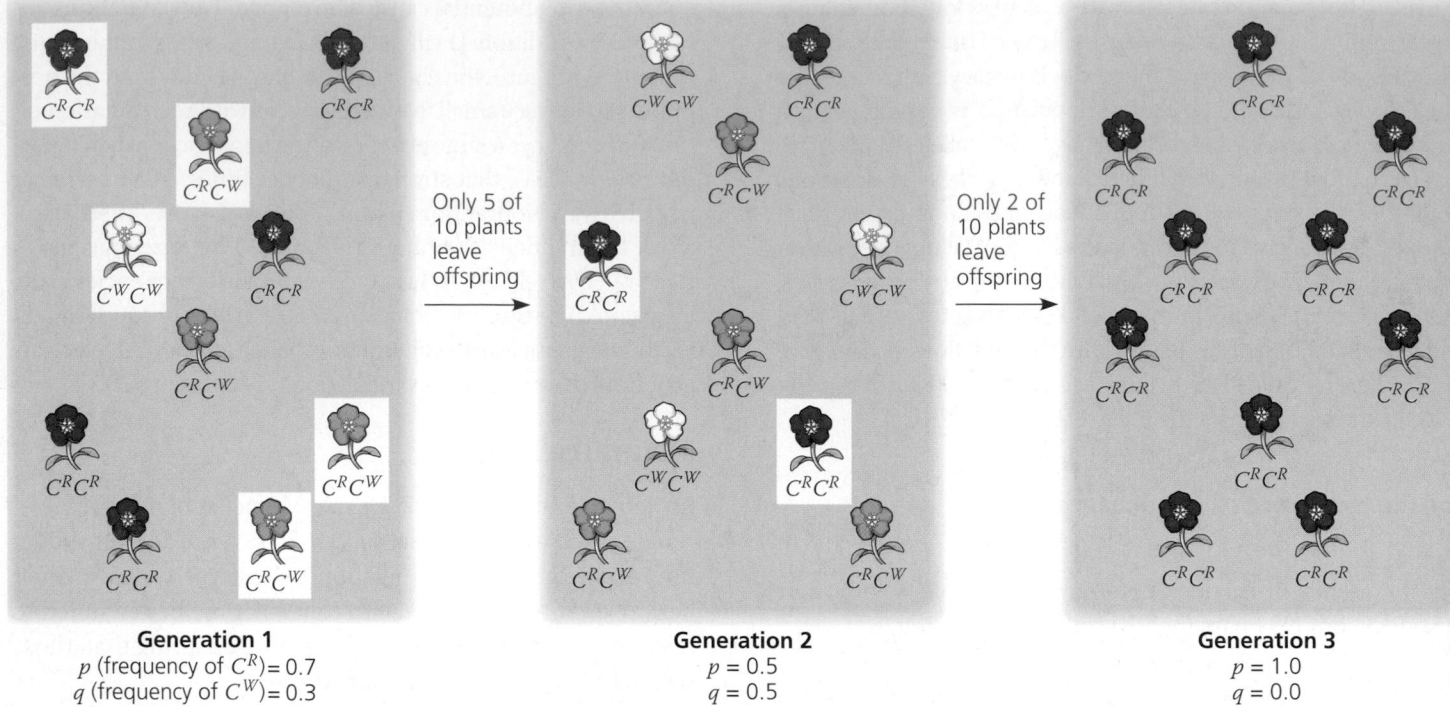

Generation 1
p (frequency of C^R) = 0.7
q (frequency of C^W) = 0.3

Generation 2
$p = 0.5$
$q = 0.5$

Generation 3
$p = 1.0$
$q = 0.0$

▲ **Figure 23.8 Genetic drift.** This small wildflower population has a stable size of ten plants. Suppose that by chance only five plants (those in white boxes) of generation 1 produce fertile offspring. This could occur, for example, if only those plants happened to grow in a location that provided enough nutrients to support the production of offspring. Again by chance, only two plants of generation 2 leave fertile offspring. As a result, by chance alone, the frequency of the C^W allele first increases in generation 2, then falls to zero in generation 3.

to fluctuate unpredictably from one generation to the next, especially in small populations—a process called **genetic drift**.

Figure 23.8 models how genetic drift might affect a small population of our wildflowers. In this example, an allele is lost from the gene pool, but it is purely a matter of chance that the C^W allele is lost, not the C^R allele. Such unpredictable changes in allele frequencies can be caused by chance events associated with survival and reproduction. Perhaps a large animal such as a moose stepped on the three $C^W C^W$ individuals in generation 2, killing them and increasing the chance that only the C^R allele would be passed to the next generation. Allele frequencies can also be affected by chance events that occur during fertilization. For example, suppose two individuals of genotype $C^R C^W$ had a small number of offspring. By chance alone, every egg and sperm pair that generated offspring could happen to have carried the C^R allele, not the C^W allele.

Certain circumstances can result in genetic drift having a significant impact on a population. Two examples are the founder effect and the bottleneck effect.

The Founder Effect

When a few individuals become isolated from a larger population, this smaller group may establish a new population whose gene pool differs from the source population; this is called the **founder effect**. The founder effect might occur, for example, when a few members of a population are blown by a storm to a new island. Genetic drift—in which chance events alter allele frequencies—occurs in such a case because the storm indiscriminately transports some individuals (and their alleles), but not others, from the source population.

The founder effect probably accounts for the relatively high frequency of certain inherited disorders among isolated human populations. For example, in 1814, 15 British colonists founded a settlement on Tristan da Cunha, a group of small islands in the Atlantic Ocean midway between Africa and South America. Apparently, one of the colonists carried a recessive allele for retinitis pigmentosa, a progressive form of blindness that afflicts homozygous individuals. Of the founding colonists' 240 descendants on the island in the late 1960s, 4 had retinitis pigmentosa. The frequency of the allele that causes this disease is ten times higher on Tristan da Cunha than in the populations from which the founders came.

The Bottleneck Effect

A sudden change in the environment, such as a fire or flood, may drastically reduce the size of a population. A severe drop in population size can cause the **bottleneck effect**, so named because the population has passed through a restrictive "bottleneck" in size **(Figure 23.9)**. By chance alone, certain alleles may be overrepresented among the survivors, others may be underrepresented, and some may be absent altogether. Ongoing genetic drift is likely to have substantial effects on the gene pool

▲ **Figure 23.9 The bottleneck effect.** Shaking just a few marbles through the narrow neck of a bottle is analogous to a drastic reduction in the size of a population. By chance, blue marbles are overrepresented in the surviving population and gold marbles are absent.

until the population becomes large enough that chance events have less effect. But even if a population that has passed through a bottleneck ultimately recovers in size, it may have low levels of genetic variation for a long period of time—a legacy of the genetic drift that occurred when the population was small.

One reason it is important to understand the bottleneck effect is that human actions sometimes create severe bottlenecks for other species. The following example illustrates the impact of genetic drift on an endangered population.

Case Study: *Impact of Genetic Drift on the Greater Prairie Chicken*

Millions of greater prairie chickens (*Tympanuchus cupido*) once lived on the prairies of Illinois. As these prairies were converted to farmland and other uses during the 19th and 20th centuries, the number of greater prairie chickens plummeted **(Figure 23.10a)**. By 1993, only two Illinois populations remained, which together harbored fewer than 50 birds. The few surviving birds had low levels of genetic variation, and less than 50% of their eggs hatched, compared to much higher hatching rates of the larger populations in Kansas, Nebraska, and Minnesota **(Figure 23.10b)**.

These data suggest that genetic drift during the bottleneck may have led to a loss of genetic variation and an increase in the frequency of harmful alleles. To investigate this hypothesis, Juan Bouzat, of Bowling Green State University, Ohio, and his colleagues extracted DNA from 15 museum specimens of Illinois greater prairie chickens. Of the 15 birds, 10 had been collected in the 1930s, when there were 25,000 greater prairie chickens in Illinois, and 5 had been collected in the 1960s, when there were 1,000 greater prairie chickens in Illinois. By studying the DNA of these specimens, the researchers were able to obtain a minimum, baseline estimate of how much genetic variation was present in the Illinois population *before* the population shrank to extremely low numbers.

(a) The Illinois population of greater prairie chickens dropped from millions of birds in the 1800s to fewer than 50 birds in 1993.

Location	Population size	Number of alleles per locus	Percentage of eggs hatched
Illinois			
1930–1960s	1,000–25,000	5.2	93
1993	<50	3.7	<50
Kansas, 1998 (no bottleneck)	750,000	5.8	99
Nebraska, 1998 (no bottleneck)	75,000–200,000	5.8	96
Minnesota, 1998 (no bottleneck)	4,000	5.3	85

(b) As a consequence of the drastic reduction in the size of the Illinois population, genetic drift resulted in a drop in the number of alleles per locus (averaged across six loci studied) and a decrease in the percentage of eggs that hatched.

▲ **Figure 23.10 Bottleneck effect and reduction of genetic variation.**

The researchers surveyed six loci and found that the 1993 Illinois greater prairie chicken population had lost nine alleles present in the museum specimens. The 1993 population also had fewer alleles per locus than the pre-bottleneck Illinois or the current Kansas, Nebraska, and Minnesota populations (see Figure 23.10b). Thus, as predicted, drift had reduced the genetic variation of the small 1993 population. Drift may also have increased the frequency of harmful alleles, leading to the low egg-hatching rate. To counteract possible negative effects of genetic drift, the researchers added a total of 271 birds from neighboring states to the Illinois population over four years.

This strategy succeeded. New alleles entered the population, and the egg-hatching rate improved to over 90%. Overall, studies on the Illinois greater prairie chicken illustrate the powerful effects of genetic drift in small populations and provide hope that in at least some populations, these effects can be reversed.

Effects of Genetic Drift: A Summary

The examples we've described highlight four key points:

1. **Genetic drift is significant in small populations.** Chance events can cause an allele to be disproportionately over- or underrepresented in the next generation. Although chance events occur in populations of all sizes, they alter allele frequencies substantially only in small populations.

2. **Genetic drift can cause allele frequencies to change at random.** Because of genetic drift, an allele may increase in frequency one year, then decrease the next; the change from one year to the next is not predictable. Thus, unlike natural selection, which in a given environment consistently favors some alleles over others, genetic drift causes allele frequencies to change at random over time.

3. **Genetic drift can lead to a loss of genetic variation within populations.** By causing allele frequencies to fluctuate randomly over time, genetic drift can eliminate alleles from a population (see Figures 23.8 and 23.10). Because evolution depends on genetic variation, such losses can influence how effectively a population can adapt to a change in the environment.

4. **Genetic drift can cause harmful alleles to become fixed.** Alleles that are neither harmful nor beneficial can be lost or become fixed entirely by chance through genetic drift. In very small populations, genetic drift can also cause alleles that are slightly harmful to become fixed. When this occurs, the population's survival can be threatened (as for the Illinois greater prairie chicken).

Gene Flow

Natural selection and genetic drift are not the only phenomena affecting allele frequencies. Allele frequencies can also change by **gene flow**, the transfer of alleles into or out of a population due to the movement of fertile individuals or their gametes. For example, suppose that near our original hypothetical wildflower population there is another population consisting primarily of white-flowered individuals ($C^W C^W$). Insects carrying pollen from these plants may fly to and pollinate plants in our original population. The introduced C^W alleles would modify our original population's allele frequencies in the next generation.

Because alleles are exchanged among populations, gene flow tends to reduce the genetic differences between populations. If it is extensive enough, gene flow can result in neighboring populations combining into a single population with a common gene pool. For example, humans today move much

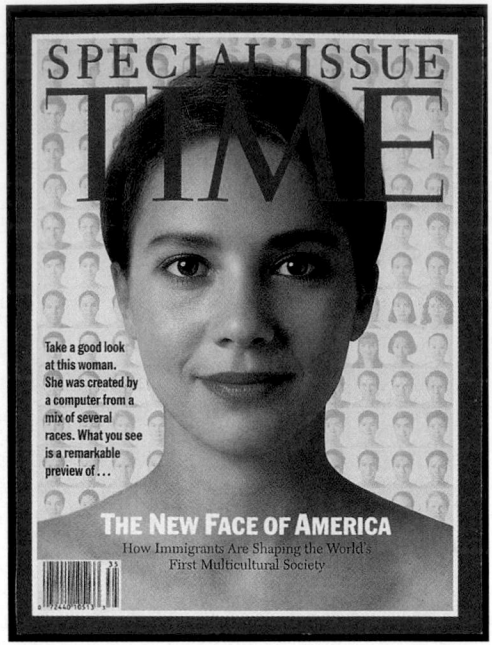

▲ **Figure 23.11 Gene flow and human evolution.** The migration of people throughout the world has increased gene flow between populations that once were isolated from one another. The computer-generated image on this magazine cover illustrates how gene flow can homogenize the gene pools of such populations, thereby reducing geographic variation in appearance.

more freely about the world than in the past. As a result, mating is more common between members of populations that previously were quite isolated (**Figure 23.11**). The result is that gene flow has become an increasingly important agent of evolutionary change in human populations.

When neighboring populations live in different environments, alleles transferred by gene flow may prevent a population from fully adapting to its environment. Consider the example of bent grass (*Agrostis tenuis*) populations growing next to copper mines. These mine soils have high concentrations of copper, causing toxic effects in nontolerant plants. If alleles for copper tolerance are present in the bent grass population, these favorable alleles rapidly spread in the population. However, on nearby soils not contaminated with copper, copper-tolerant plants reproduce poorly compared to nontolerant ones. Thus we might expect that the percentage of plants that are copper tolerant would be close to 100% on mine soils and close to 0% on nearby (uncontaminated) soils. But bent grass is wind pollinated, and the wind can blow pollen from one population to another, moving alleles in the process. Thus, copper-tolerance alleles are transferred to non-mine soils; likewise, alleles associated with copper non-tolerance are transferred to mine soils (**Figure 23.12**).

Sometimes beneficial alleles are transferred very widely. For example, gene flow has resulted in the worldwide spread of several insecticide-resistance alleles in the mosquito *Culex pipiens*, a vector of West Nile virus and malaria. Each of these alleles has a unique genetic signature that allowed researchers

▼ **Figure 23.12 Gene flow and selection.** The bent grass in the foreground of the photo is growing on the tailings of an abandoned mine and is more copper tolerant than the bent grass in the pasture beyond the fence. The graph shows the degree of copper tolerance at various locations. These data suggest that ongoing gene flow prevents each population from adapting fully to its local conditions.

WHAT IF? *If prevailing winds blew the opposite way, how would copper tolerance change at the location marked by the red arrow?*

to document that it arose by mutation in one or a few geographic locations. In their population of origin, these alleles increased because they provided insecticide resistance. These alleles were then transferred to new populations, where again, their frequencies increased as a result of natural selection.

To sum up, gene flow, like mutation, can introduce new alleles into a population. But because it can occur at a higher rate than mutation, gene flow is more likely than mutation to alter allele frequencies directly. And once gene flow or mutation introduces a new allele to a population, natural selection may then cause the new allele to increase in frequency (as in the insecticide-resistance alleles in mosquitoes) or decrease in frequency (as in the copper-tolerance alleles in bent grass in non-mine soil).

CONCEPT 23.4

Natural selection is the only mechanism that consistently causes adaptive evolution

Evolution by natural selection is a blend of chance and "sorting"—chance in the creation of new genetic variations (originally by mutation) and sorting as natural selection favors some alleles over others. Because of this sorting effect, only natural selection consistently increases the frequencies of alleles that provide reproductive advantage and thus leads to adaptive evolution.

A Closer Look at Natural Selection

In examining how natural selection brings about adaptive evolution, we'll begin with the concept of relative fitness and the different ways that an organism's phenotype is subject to natural selection.

Relative Fitness

The phrases "struggle for existence" and "survival of the fittest" are commonly used to describe natural selection, yet these expressions are misleading if taken to mean direct competitive contests among individuals. There *are* animal species in which individuals, usually the males, lock horns or otherwise do combat to determine mating privilege. But reproductive success is generally more subtle and depends on many factors besides outright battle. For example, a barnacle that is more efficient at collecting food than its neighbors may have greater stores of energy and hence be able to produce a larger number of eggs. A moth may have more offspring than other moths in the same population because its body colors more effectively conceal it from predators, improving its chance of surviving long enough to produce more offspring. These examples illustrate how adaptive advantage can lead to greater **relative fitness**: the contribution an individual makes to the gene pool of the next generation, *relative to* the contributions of other individuals.

Although we often refer to the relative fitness of a genotype, remember that the entity that is subjected to natural selection is the whole organism, not the underlying genotype. Thus, selection acts more directly on the phenotype than on the genotype; it acts on the genotype indirectly, via how the genotype affects the phenotype. Furthermore, the relative fitness conferred by a particular allele depends on the entire genetic and environmental context in which it is expressed. For example, an allele that is slightly disadvantageous might increase in frequency by "hitchhiking," that is, as a result of being located close to an allele at another locus that is strongly favored by natural selection (see Chapter 15 to review how distance between genes affects their inheritance).

Directional, Disruptive, and Stabilizing Selection

Natural selection can alter the frequency distribution of heritable traits in three ways, depending on which phenotypes in a population are favored. These three modes of selection are called directional selection, disruptive selection, and stabilizing selection.

Directional selection occurs when conditions favor individuals exhibiting one extreme of a phenotypic range, thereby shifting the frequency curve for the phenotypic character in one direction or the other **(Figure 23.13a)**. Directional selection is common when a population's environment changes or when members of a population migrate to a new (and different) habitat. For instance, fossil evidence indicates that the average size of black bears in Europe increased during each frigid glacial period, only to decrease again during warmer interglacial periods. Larger bears, with a smaller surface-to-

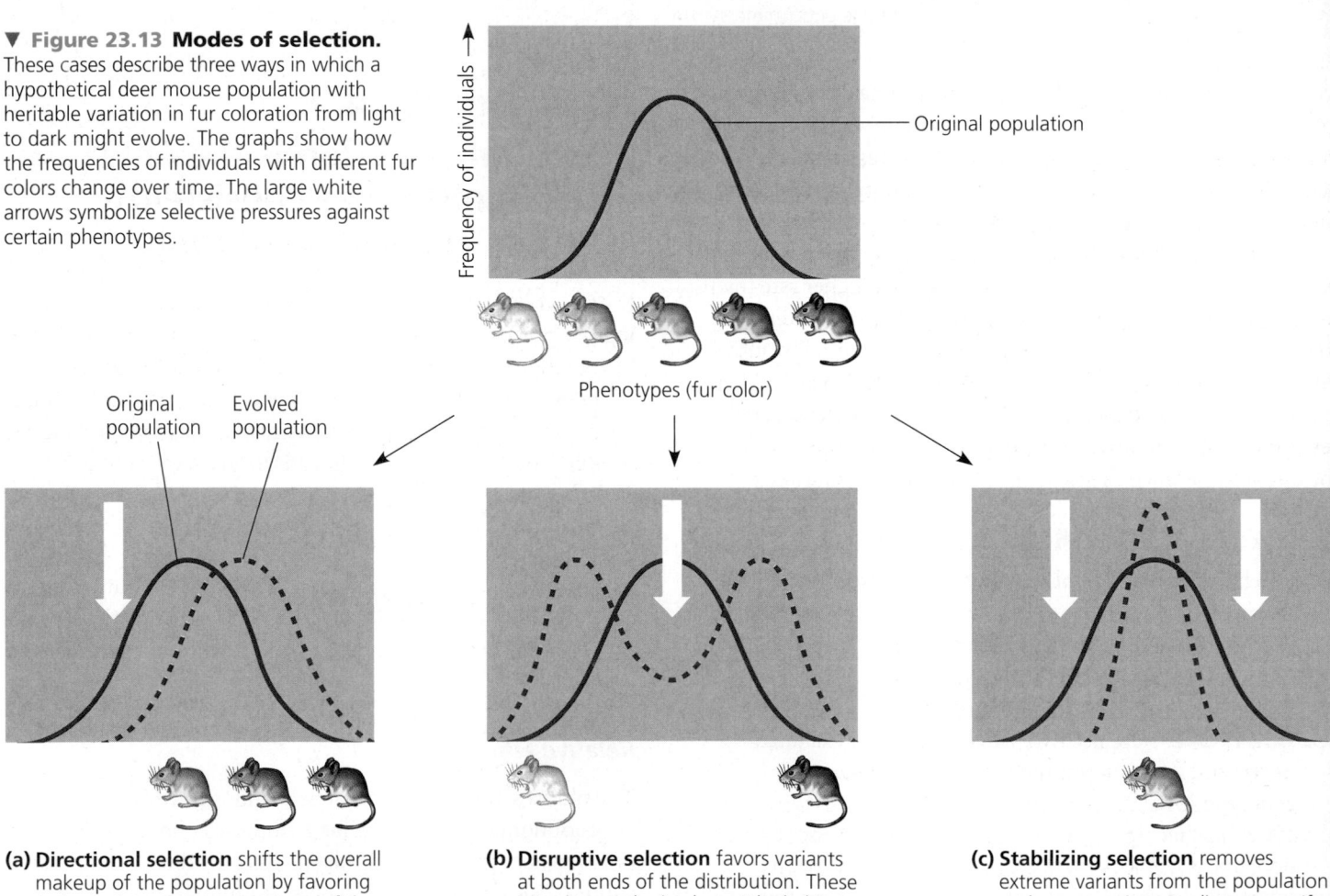

▼ **Figure 23.13 Modes of selection.** These cases describe three ways in which a hypothetical deer mouse population with heritable variation in fur coloration from light to dark might evolve. The graphs show how the frequencies of individuals with different fur colors change over time. The large white arrows symbolize selective pressures against certain phenotypes.

Frequency of individuals →

Original population

Phenotypes (fur color)

Original population   Evolved population

(a) Directional selection shifts the overall makeup of the population by favoring variants that are at one extreme of the distribution. In this case, darker mice are favored because they live among dark rocks, and a darker fur color conceals them from predators.

(b) Disruptive selection favors variants at both ends of the distribution. These mice have colonized a patchy habitat made up of light and dark rocks, with the result that mice of an intermediate color are at a disadvantage.

(c) Stabilizing selection removes extreme variants from the population and preserves intermediate types. If the environment consists of rocks of an intermediate color, both light and dark mice will be selected against.

volume ratio, are better at conserving body heat and surviving periods of extreme cold.

Disruptive selection (Figure 23.13b) occurs when conditions favor individuals at both extremes of a phenotypic range over individuals with intermediate phenotypes. One example is a population of black-bellied seedcracker finches in Cameroon whose members display two distinctly different beak sizes. Small-billed birds feed mainly on soft seeds, whereas large-billed birds specialize in cracking hard seeds. It appears that birds with intermediate-sized bills are relatively inefficient at cracking both types of seeds and thus have lower relative fitness.

Stabilizing selection (Figure 23.13c) acts against both extreme phenotypes and favors intermediate variants. This mode of selection reduces variation and tends to maintain the status quo for a particular phenotypic character. For example, the birth weights of most human babies lie in the range of 3–4 kg (6.6–8.8 pounds); babies who are either much smaller or much larger suffer higher rates of mortality.

Regardless of the mode of selection, however, the basic mechanism remains the same. Selection favors individuals whose heritable phenotypic traits provide higher reproductive success than do the traits of other individuals.

The Key Role of Natural Selection in Adaptive Evolution

The adaptations of organisms include many striking examples. Consider the ability of cuttlefish to rapidly change color, enabling them to blend into different backgrounds **(Figure 23.14a)**. Another example is the remarkable jaws of snakes **(Figure 23.14b)**, which enable them to swallow prey much larger than their own head (a feat analogous to a person swallowing a whole watermelon). Other adaptations, such as a version of an enzyme that shows improved function in cold environments (see Figure 23.4), may be less visually dramatic but just as important for survival and reproduction.

Such adaptations can arise gradually over time as natural selection increases the frequencies of alleles that enhance survival and reproduction. As the proportion of individuals that have favorable traits increases, the match between a species and its environment improves; that is, adaptive evolution occurs. However, as we saw in Chapter 22, the physical and biological components of an organism's environment may change over time. As a result, what constitutes a "good match" between an organism and its environment can be a moving target, making adaptive evolution a continuous, dynamic process.

And what about the two other important mechanisms of evolutionary change in populations, genetic drift and gene flow? Both can, in fact, increase the frequencies of alleles that improve the match between organisms and their environment—but neither does so consistently. Genetic drift can cause the frequency of a slightly beneficial allele to increase, but it also can cause the frequency of such an allele to decrease. Similarly, gene flow may

(a) Color-changing ability in cuttlefish. In a split second, this cuttlefish can blend against its background, enabling it to hide from predators and surprise its prey.

The bones of the upper jaw that are shown in purple are movable.

(b) Movable jaw bones in snakes. The skull bones of most terrestrial vertebrates are relatively rigidly attached to one another, limiting jaw movement. In contrast, most snakes have movable bones in their upper jaw, allowing them to swallow food much larger than their head.

▲ Figure 23.14 **Examples of adaptations.**

introduce alleles that are advantageous or ones that are disadvantageous. Natural selection is the only evolutionary mechanism that consistently leads to adaptive evolution.

Sexual Selection

Charles Darwin was the first to explore the implications of **sexual selection**, a form of natural selection in which individuals with certain inherited characteristics are more likely than other individuals to obtain mates. Sexual selection can result in **sexual dimorphism**, marked differences between the two sexes in secondary sexual characteristics,

▲ **Figure 23.15 Sexual dimorphism and sexual selection.**
Peacocks and peahens show extreme sexual dimorphism. There is
intrasexual selection between competing males, followed by intersexual
selection when the females choose among the showiest males.

which are not directly associated with reproduction or survival **(Figure 23.15)**. These distinctions include differences in size, color, ornamentation, and behavior.

How does sexual selection operate? There are several ways. In **intrasexual selection**, meaning selection within the same sex, individuals of one sex compete directly for mates of the opposite sex. In many species, intrasexual selection occurs among males. For example, a single male may patrol a group of females and prevent other males from mating with them. The patrolling male may defend his status by defeating smaller, weaker, or less fierce males in combat. More often, this male is the psychological victor in ritualized displays that discourage would-be competitors but do not risk injury that would reduce his own fitness (see Figure 51.22). But intrasexual selection has also been observed among females in some species, including ring-tailed lemurs.

In **intersexual selection**, also called *mate choice*, individuals of one sex (usually the females) are choosy in selecting their mates from the other sex. In many cases, the female's choice depends on the showiness of the male's appearance or behavior (see Figure 23.15). What intrigued Darwin about mate choice is that male showiness may not seem adaptive in any other way and may in fact pose some risk. For example, bright plumage may make male birds more visible to predators. But if such characteristics help a male gain a mate, and if this benefit outweighs the risk from predation, then both the bright plumage and the female preference for it will be reinforced because they enhance overall reproductive success.

How do female preferences for certain male characteristics evolve in the first place? One hypothesis is that females prefer male traits that are correlated with "good genes." If the trait preferred by females is indicative of a male's overall genetic quality, both the male trait and female preference for it should increase in frequency. **Figure 23.16** describes one experiment testing this hypothesis in gray tree frogs (*Hyla versicolor*).

▼ **Figure 23.16** **Inquiry**

Do females select mates based on traits indicative of "good genes"?

EXPERIMENT Female gray tree frogs prefer to mate with males that give long mating calls. Allison Welch and colleagues, at the University of Missouri, tested whether the genetic makeup of long-calling (LC) males is superior to that of short-calling (SC) males. The researchers fertilized half the eggs of each female with sperm from an LC male and fertilized the remaining eggs with sperm from an SC male. The resulting half-sibling offspring were raised in a common environment and tracked for two years.

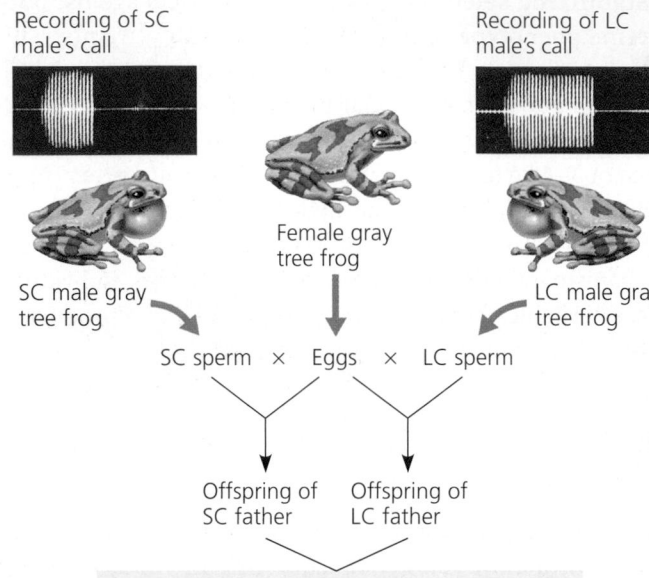

RESULTS

Fitness Measure	1995	1996
Larval growth	NSD	LC better
Larval survival	LC better	NSD
Time to metamorphosis	LC better (shorter)	LC better (shorter)

NSD = no significant difference; LC better = offspring of LC males superior to offspring of SC males.

CONCLUSION Because offspring fathered by an LC male had higher fitness than their half-siblings fathered by an SC male, the team concluded that the duration of a male's mating call is indicative of the male's overall genetic quality. This result supports the hypothesis that female mate choice can be based on a trait that indicates whether the male has "good genes."

SOURCE A.M. Welch et al., Call duration as an indicator of genetic quality in male gray tree frogs, *Science* 280:1928–1930 (1998).

Inquiry in Action Read and analyze the original paper in *Inquiry in Action: Interpreting Scientific Papers.*

WHAT IF? Why did the researchers split each female frog's eggs into two batches for fertilization by different males? Why didn't they mate each female with a single male frog?

Other researchers have shown that in several bird species, the traits preferred by females are related to overall male health. Here, too, female preference appears to be based on traits that reflect "good genes," in this case alleles indicative of a robust immune system.

The Preservation of Genetic Variation

What prevents natural selection from reducing genetic variation by culling all unfavorable genotypes? The tendency for directional and stabilizing selection to reduce variation is countered by mechanisms that preserve or restore it.

Diploidy

Because most eukaryotes are diploid, a considerable amount of genetic variation is hidden from selection in the form of recessive alleles. Recessive alleles that are less favorable than their dominant counterparts, or even harmful in the current environment, can persist by propagation in heterozygous individuals. This latent variation is exposed to natural selection only when both parents carry the same recessive allele and two copies end up in the same zygote. This happens only rarely if the frequency of the recessive allele is very low. Heterozygote protection maintains a huge pool of alleles that might not be favored under present conditions, but which could bring new benefits if the environment changes.

Balancing Selection

Selection itself may preserve variation at some loci. **Balancing selection** occurs when natural selection maintains two or more forms in a population. This type of selection includes heterozygote advantage and frequency-dependent selection.

Heterozygote Advantage   If individuals who are heterozygous at a particular locus have greater fitness than do both kinds of homozygotes, they exhibit **heterozygote advantage**. In such a case, natural selection tends to maintain two or more alleles at that locus. Note that heterozygote advantage is defined in terms of *genotype*, not phenotype. Thus, whether heterozygote advantage represents stabilizing or directional selection depends on the relationship between the genotype and the phenotype. For example, if the phenotype of a heterozygote is intermediate to the phenotypes of both homozygotes, heterozygote advantage is a form of stabilizing selection.

There are relatively few well-documented examples of heterozygote advantage. One such example occurs at the locus in humans that codes for the β polypeptide subunit of hemoglobin, the oxygen-carrying protein of red blood cells. In homozygous individuals, a certain recessive allele at that locus causes sickle-cell disease. The red blood cells of people with sickle-cell disease become distorted in shape (see Figure 5.22), which can lead to serious complications, including damage to the kidney, heart, and brain. However, heterozygotes are pro-

▲ **Figure 23.17 Mapping malaria and the sickle-cell allele.** The sickle-cell allele is most common in Africa, but it is not the only case of heterozygote advantage providing protection against malaria. Alleles at other loci are favored by heterozygote advantage in populations near the Mediterranean Sea and in southeast Asia, where malaria is also widespread.

Distribution of malaria caused by *Plasmodium falciparum* (a parasitic unicellular eukaryote)

Frequencies of the sickle-cell allele

- 0–2.5%
- 2.5–5.0%
- 5.0–7.5%
- 7.5–10.0%
- 10.0–12.5%
- >12.5%

tected against the most severe effects of malaria (although they are not resistant to malarial infection). This protection is important in tropical regions where malaria is a major killer. In such regions, selection favors heterozygotes over homozygous dominant individuals, who are more susceptible to malaria, and also over homozygous recessive individuals, who develop sickle-cell disease. The frequency of the sickle-cell allele in Africa is generally highest in areas where the malaria parasite is most common **(Figure 23.17)**. In some populations, it accounts for 20% of the hemoglobin alleles in the gene pool, a very high frequency for such a harmful allele.

Frequency-Dependent Selection   In **frequency-dependent selection**, the fitness of a phenotype declines if it becomes too common in the population. Consider the scale-eating fish (*Perissodus microlepis*) of Lake Tanganyika in Africa. These fish attack other fish from behind, darting in to remove a few scales from the flank of their prey. Of interest here is a peculiar feature of the scale-eating fish: Some are "left-mouthed" and some are "right-mouthed." Simple Mendelian inheritance determines these phenotypes, with the right-mouthed allele being dominant to the left-mouthed allele. Because their mouth twists to the left, left-mouthed fish always attack their prey's right flank. (To see why, twist your lower jaw and lips to the left and imagine trying to take a bite from the left side of a fish, approaching it from behind.) Similarly, right-mouthed fish always attack from the left. Prey species guard against attack from whatever phenotype of scale-eating fish is most common in the lake. Thus, from year to

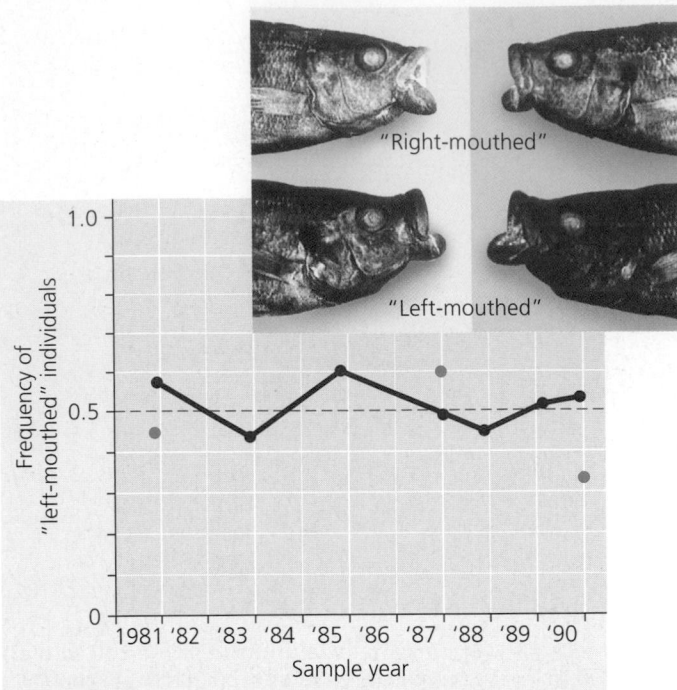

"Right-mouthed"

"Left-mouthed"

▲ **Figure 23.18 Frequency-dependent selection in scale-eating fish (*Perissodus microlepis*).** Michio Hori, of Kyoto University, Japan, noted that the frequency of left-mouthed individuals rises and falls in a regular manner. At each of three time periods when the phenotypes of breeding adults were assessed, adults that reproduced (represented by green dots) had the opposite phenotype of that which was most common in the population. Thus, it appeared that right-mouthed individuals were favored by selection when left-mouthed individuals were more common, and vice versa.

? *What did the researchers measure to determine which phenotype was favored by selection? Are any assumptions implied by this choice? Explain.*

year, selection favors whichever mouth phenotype is least common. As a result, the frequency of left- and right-mouthed fish oscillates over time, and balancing selection (due to frequency dependence) keeps the frequency of each phenotype close to 50% **(Figure 23.18)**.

Neutral Variation

Much of the DNA variation in populations probably has little or no impact on reproductive success, and thus natural selection does not affect this DNA. In humans, many of the nucleotide differences in noncoding sequences appear to confer no selective advantage or disadvantage and therefore are considered **neutral variation**. Mutations that cause changes in proteins also can be neutral. Data from *Drosophila* suggest that roughly half of the amino-acid-changing mutations that arise and subsequently become fixed have little or no selective effect because they have little effect on protein function and reproductive fitness (see Figure 17.23). Over time, the frequencies of alleles that are not affected by natural selection may increase or decrease as a result of genetic drift.

Why Natural Selection Cannot Fashion Perfect Organisms

Though natural selection leads to adaptation, there are several reasons why nature abounds with examples of organisms that are less than ideally "engineered" for their lifestyles.

1. **Selection can act only on existing variations.** Natural selection favors only the fittest phenotypes among those currently in the population, which may not be the ideal traits. New advantageous alleles do not arise on demand.

2. **Evolution is limited by historical constraints.** Each species has a legacy of descent with modification from ancestral forms. Evolution does not scrap the ancestral anatomy and build each new complex structure from scratch; rather, evolution co-opts existing structures and adapts them to new situations. We could imagine that if a terrestrial animal were to adapt to an environment in which flight would be advantageous, it might be best just to grow an extra pair of limbs that would serve as wings. However, evolution does not work in this way—it operates on the traits an organism already has. Thus, in birds and bats, an existing pair of limbs took on new functions for flight as these organisms evolved from walking ancestors.

3. **Adaptations are often compromises.** Each organism must do many different things. A seal spends part of its time on rocks; it could probably walk better if it had legs instead of flippers, but then it would not swim nearly as well. We humans owe much of our versatility and athleticism to our prehensile hands and flexible limbs, but these also make us prone to sprains, torn ligaments, and dislocations: Structural reinforcement has been compromised for agility. **Figure 23.19** depicts another example of evolutionary compromise.

4. **Chance, natural selection, and the environment interact.** Chance events can affect the subsequent evolutionary history of populations. For instance, when a storm blows insects or birds hundreds of kilometers over an ocean to an island, the wind does not necessarily transport those individuals that are best suited to the new environment. Thus, not all alleles present in the founding population's gene pool are better suited to the new environment than the alleles that are "left behind." In addition, the environment at a particular location may change unpredictably from year to year, again limiting the extent to which adaptive evolution results in a close match between the organism and current environmental conditions.

With these four constraints, evolution cannot craft perfect organisms. Natural selection operates on a "better than" basis. We can, in fact, see evidence for evolution in the many imperfections of the organisms it produces.

▲ **Figure 23.19 Evolutionary compromise.** The loud call that enables a Túngara frog to attract mates also attracts more unsavory characters in the neighborhood—in this case, a bat about to seize a meal.

CONCEPT CHECK 23.4

1. What is the relative fitness of a sterile mule? Explain your answer.
2. Explain why natural selection is the only evolutionary mechanism that consistently leads to adaptive evolution.
3. **WHAT IF?** Consider a population in which heterozygotes at a certain locus have an extreme phenotype (such as being much larger than homozygotes) that also confers a selective advantage. Does such a situation represent directional, disruptive, or stabilizing selection? Explain.

For suggested answers, see Appendix A.

Chapter 23 Review

MEDIA Go to **www.campbellbiology.com** for BioFlix 3-D Animations, MP3 Tutors, Videos, Practice Tests, an eBook, and more.

SUMMARY OF KEY CONCEPTS

CONCEPT 23.1

Mutation and sexual reproduction produce the genetic variation that makes evolution possible (pp. 468–471)

▶ **Genetic Variation** Genetic variation includes variation among individuals within a population in discrete and quantitative characters, as well as geographic variation between populations.

▶ **Mutation** New alleles ultimately originate by mutation. Most mutations are harmful or have no effect, but a few may be beneficial.

▶ **Sexual Reproduction** In sexually reproducing organisms, most of the genetic differences among individuals result from crossing over, the independent assortment of chromosomes, and fertilization.

MEDIA

Activity Genetic Variation from Sexual Reproduction

CONCEPT 23.2

The Hardy-Weinberg equation can be used to test whether a population is evolving (pp. 472–475)

▶ **Gene Pools and Allele Frequencies** A population, a localized group of organisms belonging to one species, is united by its gene pool, the aggregate of all the alleles in the population.

▶ **The Hardy-Weinberg Principle** The Hardy-Weinberg principle states that the allele and genotype frequencies of a population will remain constant if the population is large, mating is random, mutation is negligible, there is no gene flow, and there is no natural selection. For such a population, if p and q represent the frequencies of the only two possible alleles at a particular locus, then p^2 is the frequency of one kind of homozygote, q^2 is the frequency of the other kind of homozygote, and $2pq$ is the frequency of the heterozygous genotype.

MEDIA

Investigation How Can the Frequencies of Alleles Be Calculated?

CONCEPT 23.3

Natural selection, genetic drift, and gene flow can alter allele frequencies in a population (pp. 475–479)

▶ **Natural Selection** Differential success in reproduction results in certain alleles being passed to the next generation in greater proportions than others.

▶ **Genetic Drift** Chance fluctuations in allele frequencies from generation to generation tend to reduce genetic variation.

▶ **Gene Flow** Genetic exchange between populations tends to reduce differences between populations over time.

MEDIA

Activity Causes of Evolutionary Change
Biology Labs On-Line PopulationGeneticsLab

CONCEPT 23.4

Natural selection is the only mechanism that consistently causes adaptive evolution (pp. 479–485)

▶ **A Closer Look at Natural Selection** One organism has greater fitness than another if it leaves more fertile descendants. The modes of natural selection differ in how selection acts on phenotype (arrows indicate selective pressure).

Original population   Evolved population

Directional selection   Disruptive selection   Stabilizing selection

► **The Key Role of Natural Selection in Adaptive Evolution**
Natural selection increases the frequencies of alleles that enhance survival and reproduction, thus improving the match between organisms and their environment.

► **Sexual Selection** Sexual selection leads to the evolution of secondary sex characteristics, which can give individuals advantages in mating.

► **The Preservation of Genetic Variation** Diploidy maintains a reservoir of concealed recessive variation in heterozygotes. Genetic variation also can be maintained by balancing selection.

► **Why Natural Selection Cannot Fashion Perfect Organisms** Natural selection can act only on available variation; structures result from modified ancestral anatomy; adaptations are often compromises; and chance, natural selection, and the environment interact.

MEDIA

Biology Labs On-Line EvolutionLab

TESTING YOUR KNOWLEDGE

SELF-QUIZ

1. A fruit fly population has a gene with two alleles, *A1* and *A2*. Tests show that 70% of the gametes produced in the population contain the *A1* allele. If the population is in Hardy-Weinberg equilibrium, what proportion of the flies carry both *A1* and *A2*?
   a. 0.7   b. 0.49   c. 0.21   d. 0.42   e. 0.09

2. There are 40 individuals in population 1, all of which have genotype *A1A1*, and there are 25 individuals in population 2, all of genotype *A2A2*. Assume that these populations are located far from one another and that their environmental conditions are very similar. Based on the information given here, the observed genetic variation is mostly likely an example of
   a. genetic drift.   d. discrete variation.
   b. gene flow.   e. directional selection.
   c. disruptive selection.

3. Natural selection changes allele frequencies because some _____ survive and reproduce more successfully than others.
   a. alleles   c. gene pools   e. individuals
   b. loci   d. species

4. No two people are genetically identical, except for identical twins. The chief cause of genetic variation among human individuals is
   a. new mutations that occurred in the preceding generation.
   b. the reshuffling of alleles in sexual reproduction.
   c. genetic drift due to the small size of the population.
   d. geographic variation within the population.
   e. environmental effects.

5. Sparrows with average-sized wings survive severe storms better than those with longer or shorter wings, illustrating
   a. the bottleneck effect.   d. neutral variation.
   b. stabilizing selection.   e. disruptive selection.
   c. frequency-dependent selection.

For Self-Quiz answers, see Appendix A.

MEDIA Visit **www.campbellbiology.com** for a Practice Test.

EVOLUTION CONNECTION

6. How is the process of evolution revealed by the imperfections of living organisms?

SCIENTIFIC INQUIRY

7. **DRAW IT** Richard Koehn, of the State University of New York, Stony Brook, and Thomas Hilbish, of the University of South Carolina, studied genetic variation in the marine mussel *Mytilus edulis* around Long Island, New York. They measured the frequency of a particular allele (*lap*^{94}) for an enzyme involved in regulating the mussel's internal salt-water balance. The researchers presented their data as a series of pie charts linked to sampling sites within Long Island Sound, where the salinity is highly variable, and along the coast of the open ocean, where salinity is constant:

Data from R.K. Koehn and T.J. Hilbish, The adaptive importance of genetic variation, *American Scientist* 75:134–141 (1987).

Create a data table for the 11 sampling sites by estimating the frequency of *lap*^{94} from the pie charts. (*Hint*: Think of each pie chart as a clock face to help you estimate the proportion of the shaded area.) Then graph the frequencies for sites 1–8 to show how the frequency of this allele changes with increasing salinity in Long Island Sound (from southwest to northeast). How do the data from sites 9–11 compare with the data from the sites within the Sound?

Construct a hypothesis that explains the patterns you observe in the data and that accounts for the following observations: (1) the *lap*^{94} allele helps mussels maintain osmotic balance in water with a high salt concentration but is costly to use in less salty water; and (2) mussels produce larvae that can disperse long distances before they settle on rocks and grow into adults.

SCIENCE, TECHNOLOGY, AND SOCIETY

8. To what extent are humans who live in a technological society exempt from natural selection? Justify your answer.

The Origin of Species

24

▲ **Figure 24.1 How did this flightless bird come to live on the isolated Galápagos Islands?**

OVERVIEW

That "Mystery of Mysteries"

Darwin came to the Galápagos Islands eager to explore landforms newly emerged from the sea. He noted that these volcanic islands, despite their geologic youth, were teeming with plants and animals found nowhere else in the world **(Figure 24.1)**. Later he realized that these species, like the islands, were relatively new. He wrote in his diary: "Both in space and time, we seem to be brought somewhat near to that great fact—that mystery of mysteries—the first appearance of new beings on this Earth."

The "mystery of mysteries" that captivated Darwin is **speciation**, the process by which one species splits into two or more species. Speciation fascinated Darwin (and many biologists since) because it is responsible for the tremendous diversity of life, repeatedly yielding new species that differ from existing ones. Speciation explains not only differences between species, but also similarities between them (the unity of life). When one species splits, the species that result share many characteristics because they are descended from this common ancestral species. For example, DNA similarities indicate that the flightless cormorant (*Phalacrocorax harrisi*) in Figure 24.1 is closely related to flying cormorant species found on the west coast of the Americas. This suggests that the flightless cor-

morant may have originated from an ancestral cormorant species that migrated from the mainland to the Galápagos.

Speciation also forms a conceptual bridge between **microevolution**, changes over time in allele frequencies in a population, and **macroevolution**, the broad pattern of evolution over long time spans. An example of macroevolutionary change is the origin of new groups of organisms, such as mammals or flowering plants, through a series of speciation events. We examined microevolutionary mechanisms (mutation, natural selection, genetic drift, and gene flow) in Chapter 23, and we'll turn to macroevolution in Chapter 25. In this chapter, we will explore the "bridge"—the mechanisms by which new species originate from existing ones. First, however, we need to establish what we actually mean when we talk about "species."

CONCEPT 24.1
The biological species concept emphasizes reproductive isolation

The word *species* is Latin for "kind" or "appearance." In daily life, we commonly distinguish between various "kinds" of organisms—dogs and cats, for instance—from differences in their appearance. But are organisms truly divided into the discrete units we call species, or is this classification an arbitrary attempt to impose order on the natural world? To answer this question, biologists compare not only the morphology (body form) of different groups of organisms but also less obvious differences in physiology, biochemistry, and DNA sequences. The results generally confirm that morphologically distinct species are indeed discrete groups, with many differences in addition to morphological ones.

The Biological Species Concept

The primary definition of species used in this textbook is referred to as the **biological species concept**. According to this concept, as described in 1942 by biologist Ernst Mayr, a **species** is a group of populations whose members have the potential to interbreed in nature and produce viable, fertile offspring—but do not produce viable, fertile offspring with members of other such groups **(Figure 24.2)**. Thus, the members of a biological species are united by being reproductively compatible, at least potentially. All human beings, for example, belong to the same

(a) Similarity between different species. The eastern meadowlark (*Sturnella magna*, left) and the western meadowlark (*Sturnella neglecta*, right) have similar body shapes and colorations. Nevertheless, they are distinct biological species because their songs and other behaviors are different enough to prevent interbreeding should they meet in the wild.

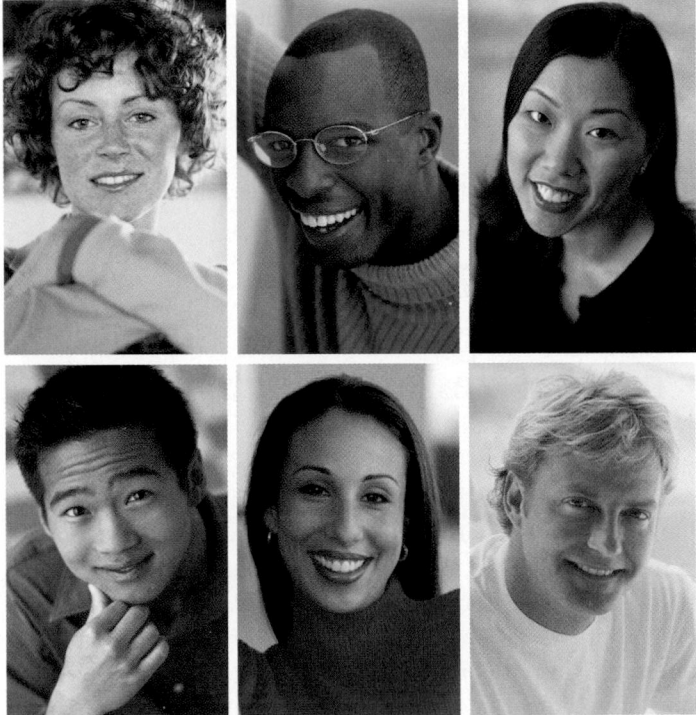

(b) Diversity within a species. As diverse as we may be in appearance, all humans belong to a single biological species (*Homo sapiens*), defined by our capacity to interbreed.

▲ **Figure 24.2 The biological species concept is based on the potential to interbreed rather than on physical similarity.**

species. A businesswoman in Manhattan may be unlikely to meet a dairy farmer in Mongolia, but if the two should happen to meet and mate, they could have viable babies that develop into fertile adults. In contrast, humans and chimpanzees remain distinct biological species even where they share territory, because many factors keep them from interbreeding and producing fertile offspring.

What holds the gene pool of a species together, causing its members to resemble each other more than they resemble other species? To answer this question, we need to reconsider an evolutionary mechanism discussed in Chapter 23: *gene flow*, the transfer of alleles between populations. Members of a species often resemble each other because their populations are connected by gene flow. As you might expect, populations located near one another exchange alleles relatively often. But what about populations separated by long distances? Evolutionary biologist Scott Edwards, interviewed on pages 450–451, examined this question for the grey-crowned babbler, *Pomatostomus temporalis* **(Figure 24.3)**. His results showed that a low level of gene flow occurred between even widely separated populations. Similar results have been found for other animal species, as well as for various fungi and plants. Such results illustrate that gene flow has the potential to hold the gene pool of a species together, so long as it is not outweighed by effects of selection or drift (either of which can result in populations diverging). As we'll explore in the next section, gene flow also plays a key role in the formation of new species.

Reproductive Isolation

Because biological species are defined in terms of reproductive compatibility, the formation of a new species hinges on **reproductive isolation**—the existence of biological factors (barriers) that impede members of two species from producing viable, fertile offspring. Such barriers block gene flow between the species and limit the formation of **hybrids**, offspring that result from an interspecific mating. Although a single barrier may not prevent all gene flow, a combination of several barriers can effectively isolate a species' gene pool.

Clearly, a fly cannot mate with a frog or a fern, but the reproductive barriers between more closely related species are not so obvious. These barriers can be classified according to whether they contribute to reproductive isolation before or after fertilization. **Prezygotic barriers** ("before the zygote") block fertilization from occurring. Such barriers typically act in one of three ways: by impeding members of different species from attempting to mate, by preventing an attempted mating from being completed successfully, or by hindering fertilization if mating is completed successfully. If a sperm cell from one species overcomes prezygotic barriers and fertilizes an ovum from another species, a variety of **postzygotic barriers** ("after the zygote") may contribute to reproductive isolation

▼ Figure 24.3 Inquiry

Does gene flow occur between widely separated populations?

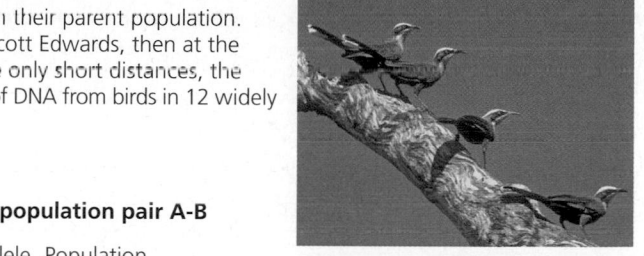

EXPERIMENT In many species, individuals disperse only short distances from their parent population. Can gene flow unify the gene pool of a species with widespread populations? Scott Edwards, then at the University of California, Berkeley, studied gene flow in a bird thought to disperse only short distances, the grey-crowned babbler (*Pomatostomus temporalis*). Edwards sequenced a segment of DNA from birds in 12 widely separated populations (named populations A–L) located throughout Australia and Papua New Guinea. He used these data to construct *gene trees*, evolutionary trees showing patterns of relatedness among the alleles at the locus he studied. If a gene tree showed that some birds in one population had an allele that shared a recent common ancestor with alleles found in a different population, Edwards reasoned that gene flow must have occurred between those populations (see the example tree at right). In this way, Edwards analyzed allele relatedness for various combinations of the 12 study populations.

▼ **Example of a gene tree for population pair A-B**

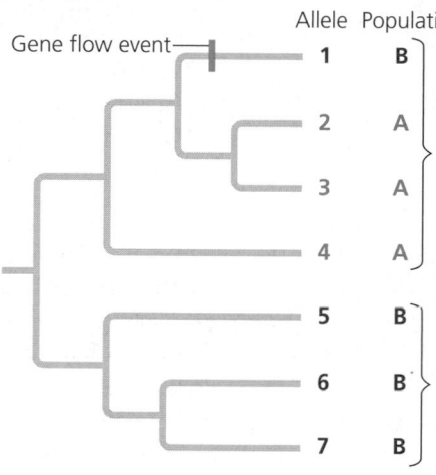

Allele 1 (found in population B) is more closely related to alleles 2, 3, and 4 (found in population A) than it is to alleles 5, 6, and 7 (found in population B).
Inference: Gene flow (at least one event) occurred.

Alleles 5, 6, and 7 (found in population B) are more closely related to one another than to alleles found in population A.
Inference: No gene flow occurred.

RESULTS Among the 12 study populations, Edwards inferred that gene flow occurred in 7 population pairs.

Pair of populations with detected gene flow	Estimated minimum number of gene flow events to account for genetic patterns	Distance between populations (km)
A-B	5	340
K-L	3	720
A-C	2–3	1,390
B-C	2	1,190
F-G	2	760
G-I	2	1,110
C-E	1–2	1,310

CONCLUSION Because gene flow was detected between populations separated by over 1,000 km, Edwards concluded that gene flow can potentially hold the grey-crowned babbler gene pool together even though individuals were thought to disperse only short distances. The long-distance movement of alleles could result from a series of shorter movements by individual birds, or from chance events such as a storm that transports birds to a distant location.

SOURCE S. V. Edwards, Long-distance gene flow in a cooperative breeder detected in genealogies of mitochondrial DNA sequences, *Proceedings of the Royal Society of London, Series B, Biological Sciences* 252:177–185 (1993).

WHAT IF? Do the data indicate that the gene flow event shown on the tree occurred as the transfer of an allele from population A to population B, or the reverse? Explain.

after the hybrid zygote is formed. For example, developmental errors may reduce survival among hybrid embryos. Or problems after birth may cause hybrids to be infertile or may de-

crease their chance of surviving long enough to reproduce. **Figure 24.4**, on the next two pages, describes prezygotic and postzygotic barriers in more detail.

▼ Figure 24.4

Exploring Reproductive Barriers

◄······· **Prezygotic barriers impede mating or hinder fertilization if mating does occur** ·······

Habitat Isolation	Temporal Isolation	Behavioral Isolation	Mechanical Isolation

Individuals of different species

🚫   🚫   🚫   Mating attempt   🚫

Two species that occupy different habitats within the same area may encounter each other rarely, if at all, even though they are not isolated by obvious physical barriers, such as mountain ranges.

Example: Two species of garter snakes in the genus *Thamnophis* occur in the same geographic areas, but one lives mainly in water (a) while the other is primarily terrestrial (b).

Species that breed during different times of the day, different seasons, or different years cannot mix their gametes.

Example: In North America, the geographic ranges of the eastern spotted skunk (*Spilogale putorius*) (c) and the western spotted skunk (*Spilogale gracilis*) (d) overlap, but *S. putorius* mates in late winter and *S. gracilis* mates in late summer.

Courtship rituals that attract mates and other behaviors unique to a species are effective reproductive barriers, even between closely related species. Such behavioral rituals enable *mate recognition*—a way to identify potential mates of the same species.

Example: Blue-footed boobies, inhabitants of the Galápagos, mate only after a courtship display unique to their species. Part of the "script" calls for the male to high-step (e), a behavior that calls the female's attention to his bright blue feet.

Mating is attempted, but morphological differences prevent its successful completion.

Example: The shells of two species of snails in the genus *Bradybaena* spiral in different directions: Moving inward to the center, one spirals in a counter-clockwise direction (f, left), the other in a clockwise direction (f, right). As a result, the snails' genital openings (indicated by arrows) are not aligned, and mating cannot be completed.

(a)

(b)

(c)

(d)

(e)

(f)

Postzygotic barriers prevent a hybrid zygote from developing into a viable, fertile adult

Gametic Isolation	Reduced Hybrid Viability	Reduced Hybrid Fertility	Hybrid Breakdown

Fertilization

Viable, fertile offspring

Sperm of one species may not be able to fertilize the eggs of another species. For instance, sperm may not be able to survive in the reproductive tract of females of the other species, or biochemical mechanisms may prevent the sperm from penetrating the membrane surrounding the other species' eggs.

Example: Gametic isolation separates certain closely related species of aquatic animals, such as sea urchins (g). Sea urchins release their sperm and eggs into the surrounding water, where they fuse and form zygotes. Gametes of different species, such as the red and purple urchins shown here, are unable to fuse because proteins on the surfaces of the eggs and sperm cannot bind to each other.

The genes of different parent species may interact in ways that impair the hybrid's development or survival in its environment.

Example: Some salamander subspecies of the genus *Ensatina* live in the same regions and habitats, where they may occasionally hybridize. But most of the hybrids do not complete development, and those that do are frail (h).

Even if hybrids are vigorous, they may be sterile. If the chromosomes of the two parent species differ in number or structure, meiosis in the hybrids may fail to produce normal gametes. Since the infertile hybrids cannot produce offspring when they mate with either parent species, genes cannot flow freely between the species.

Example: The hybrid offspring of a donkey (i) and a horse (j) is a mule (k), which is robust but sterile.

Some first-generation hybrids are viable and fertile, but when they mate with one another or with either parent species, offspring of the next generation are feeble or sterile.

Example: Strains of cultivated rice have accumulated different mutant recessive alleles at two loci in the course of their divergence from a common ancestor. Hybrids between them are vigorous and fertile (l, left and right), but plants in the next generation that carry too many of these recessive alleles are small and sterile (l, center). Although these rice strains are not yet considered different species, they have begun to be separated by postzygotic barriers.

(h)

(i)

(g)

(j)

(l)

(k)

Limitations of the Biological Species Concept

One strength of the biological species concept is that it directs our attention to how speciation occurs: by the evolution of reproductive isolation. However, the number of species to which this concept can be usefully applied is limited. There is, for example, no way to evaluate the reproductive isolation of fossils. The biological species concept also does not apply to organisms that reproduce asexually all or most of the time, such as prokaryotes. (Many prokaryotes do transfer genes among themselves, as we will discuss in Chapter 27, but this is not part of their reproductive process.) Furthermore, in the biological species concept, species are designated by the *absence* of gene flow. There are, however, many pairs of species that are morphologically and ecologically distinct, and yet gene flow occurs between them. As we'll see, natural selection can cause such species to remain distinct despite gene flow. This observation has led some researchers to argue that the biological species concept overemphasizes gene flow and downplays the role of natural selection. Because of the limitations to the biological species concept, alternative species concepts are useful in certain situations.

Other Definitions of Species

While the biological species concept emphasizes the *separateness* of species from one another due to reproductive barriers, several other definitions emphasize the *unity within* a species. For example, the **morphological species concept** characterizes a species by body shape and other structural features. The morphological species concept has several advantages. It can be applied to asexual and sexual organisms, and it can be useful even without information on the extent of gene flow. In practice, this is how scientists distinguish most species. One disadvantage, however, is that this definition relies on subjective criteria; researchers may disagree on which structural features distinguish a species.

The **ecological species concept** views a species in terms of its ecological niche, the sum of how members of the species interact with the nonliving and living parts of their environment (see Chapter 54). For example, two species of amphibians might be similar in appearance but differ in the foods they eat or in their ability to tolerate dry conditions. Unlike the biological species concept, the ecological species concept can accommodate asexual as well as sexual species; it also emphasizes the role of disruptive natural selection as organisms adapt to different environmental conditions.

The **phylogenetic species concept** defines a species as the smallest group of individuals that share a common ancestor, forming one branch on the tree of life. Biologists trace the phylogenetic history of a species by comparing its characteristics, such as morphology or molecular sequences, with those of other organisms. Such analyses can distinguish groups of individuals

that are sufficiently different to be considered separate species. Of course, the difficulty with this species concept is determining the degree of difference required to indicate separate species.

In addition to those discussed here, more than 20 other species definitions have been proposed. The usefulness of each definition depends on the situation and the research questions being asked. For our purposes of studying how species originate, the biological species concept, with its focus on reproductive barriers, is particularly helpful.

CONCEPT CHECK 24.1

1. (a) Which species concept(s) could you apply to both asexual and sexual species? (b) Which would be most useful for identifying species in the field? Explain.
2. **WHAT IF?** Suppose you are studying two bird species that live in a forest and are not known to interbreed. One species feeds and mates in the treetops and the other on the ground. But in captivity, the birds can interbreed and produce viable, fertile offspring. What type of reproductive barrier most likely keeps these species separate in nature? Explain.

For suggested answers, see Appendix A.

CONCEPT 24.2
Speciation can take place with or without geographic separation

Now that we have a clearer sense of what constitutes a unique species, let's return to our discussion of the process by which such species arise from existing species. Speciation can occur in two main ways, depending on how gene flow is interrupted between populations of the existing species (**Figure 24.5**).

Allopatric ("Other Country") Speciation

In **allopatric speciation** (from the Greek *allos*, other, and *patra*, homeland), gene flow is interrupted when a population is divided into geographically isolated subpopulations. For example, the water level in a lake may subside, resulting in two or more smaller lakes that are now home to separated populations (see Figure 24.5a). Or a river may change course and divide a population of animals that cannot cross it. Allopatric speciation can also occur without geologic remodeling, such as when individuals colonize a remote area and their descendants become geographically isolated from the parent population. The flightless cormorant shown in Figure 24.1 likely originated in this way from an ancestral flying species that migrated to the Galápagos Islands.

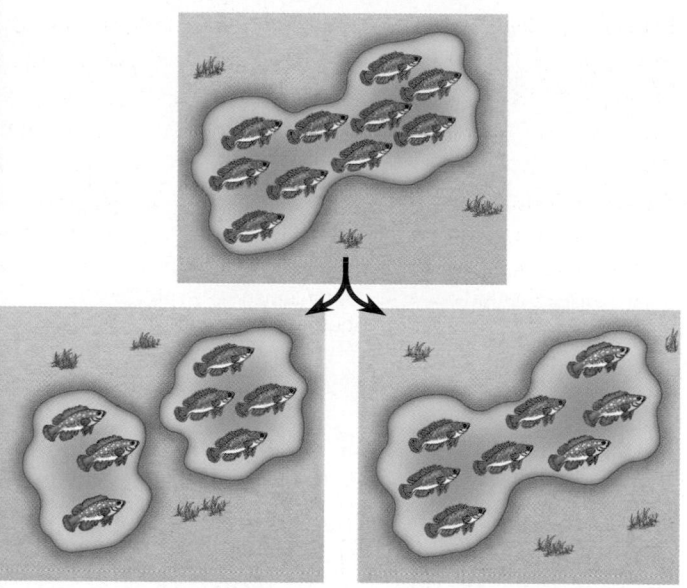

(a) Allopatric speciation. A population forms a new species while geographically isolated from its parent population.

(b) Sympatric speciation. A small population becomes a new species without geographic separation.

▲ Figure 24.5 **Two main modes of speciation.**

The Process of Allopatric Speciation

How formidable must a geographic barrier be to promote allopatric speciation? The answer depends on the ability of the organisms to move about. Birds, mountain lions, and coyotes can cross rivers and canyons. Nor do such barriers hinder the windblown pollen of pine trees or the seeds of many flowering plants. In contrast, small rodents may find a wide river or a deep canyon a formidable barrier **(Figure 24.6)**.

Once geographic separation has occurred, the separated gene pools may diverge through the mechanisms described in Chapter 23. Different mutations arise, natural selection acts on the separated organisms, and genetic drift alters allele frequencies. Reproductive isolation may then arise as a by-product of selection or drift having caused the populations to diverge genetically. For example, in the monkey flower *Mimulus guttatus*, selection has favored the evolution of copper tolerance in populations living near copper mines. Soil copper concentrations in these areas can reach levels that are lethal to nontolerant individuals. When members of copper-tolerant *M. guttatus* populations interbreed with individuals from other populations, the offspring survive poorly. Genetic analyses have shown that the gene for copper tolerance or an allele genetically linked to the copper-tolerance gene is responsible for the poor survival of the hybrid offspring. Thus, selection for copper tolerance appears to have had an important but coincidental side effect: partial reproductive isolation between *M. guttatus* populations.

The gene pools of highly isolated populations (such as those on remote islands) experience very little gene flow and hence are particularly likely to undergo allopatric speciation. For example, in less than 2 million years, the few animals and plants from the South and North American mainlands that colonized the Galápagos Islands gave rise to all the new species now found there.

Evidence of Allopatric Speciation

Many studies provide evidence that speciation can occur in allopatric populations. For example, biogeographic and genetic data together suggest that two present-day groups of frog species, the subfamilies Mantellinae and Rhacophorinae, began to diverge about 88 million years ago, when what is now the island of Madagascar started to separate from the Indian landmass. It appears that these two frog groups shared a common ancestor that lived on the Madagascar-India landmass

A. harrisi

A. leucurus

▲ Figure 24.6 **Allopatric speciation of antelope squirrels on opposite rims of the Grand Canyon.** Harris's antelope squirrel (*Ammospermophilus harrisi*) inhabits the canyon's south rim (left). Just a few kilometers away on the north rim (right) lives the closely related white-tailed antelope squirrel (*Ammospermophilus leucurus*). In contrast, birds and other organisms that can disperse easily across the canyon have not diverged into different species on the two rims.

▶ **Figure 24.7 Allopatric speciation in frogs.** The frog subfamilies Mantellinae and Rhacophorinae diverged when present-day Madagascar separated from India. The maps show the movement of Madagascar (red) and India (blue) over time.

Mantellinae (Madagascar only): 100 species

Rhacophorinae (India/southeast Asia): 310 species

Other Indian/ southeast Asian frogs

Millions of years ago (mya)

88 mya → 65 mya → 56 mya

India

Madagascar

before it began to break apart **(Figure 24.7)**. Following the breakup, allopatric speciation occurred within the separated populations of this common ancestor. The result was the formation of many new species in each location.

The importance of allopatric speciation is also suggested by the fact that regions that are highly subdivided by geographic barriers typically have more species than do regions with fewer barriers. For example, an unusually large number of bird species are found in the mountainous regions of New Guinea, and many unique plants and animals are found on the geographically isolated Hawaiian Islands (we'll return to the origin of Hawaiian species in Chapter 25).

Laboratory and field tests also provide evidence that reproductive isolation between two populations generally increases as the distance between them increases. In one such study of dusky salamanders (*Desmognathus ochrophaeus*), biologists brought individuals from different populations into the laboratory and tested their ability to produce viable, fertile offspring **(Figure 24.8)**. The researchers observed little reproductive isolation in salamanders from neighboring populations. In contrast, salamanders from widely separated populations often failed to reproduce. One possible explanation for these results is that long-distance gene flow is not occurring between the dusky salamander populations (unlike the grey-crowned babblers studied by Scott Edwards). Alternatively, long-distance gene flow between the salamander populations may be outweighed by the effects of natural selection or genetic drift, either of which can cause the populations to diverge. In other studies, researchers have tested whether intrinsic reproductive

barriers develop when populations are isolated experimentally and subjected to different environmental conditions. In such cases, too, the results provide strong support for allopatric speciation **(Figure 24.9**, on the facing page).

We need to emphasize here that although geographic isolation prevents interbreeding between allopatric populations, separation itself is not a biological barrier to reproduction. Biological reproductive barriers such as those described in Figure 24.4 are intrinsic to the organisms themselves. Hence, these barriers can prevent interbreeding when members of different populations come into contact with one another.

▲ **Figure 24.8 Variation in reproductive isolation with distance between populations of dusky salamanders.** The degree of reproductive isolation is represented here by an index ranging from 0 (no isolation) to 2 (complete isolation).

Inquiry

Can divergence of allopatric populations lead to reproductive isolation?

EXPERIMENT   Diane Dodd, then at Yale University, divided a fruit fly population, raising some flies on a starch medium and others on a maltose medium. After one year (about 40 generations), natural selection resulted in divergent evolution: Populations raised on starch digested starch more efficiently, while those raised on maltose digested maltose more efficiently. Dodd then put flies from the same or different populations in mating cages and measured mating frequencies.

Initial population of fruit flies (*Drosophila pseudoobscura*)

Some flies raised on starch medium

Mating experiments after 40 generations

Some flies raised on maltose medium

RESULTS   When flies from "starch populations" were mixed with flies from "maltose populations," the flies tended to mate with like partners. But in the control group shown here, flies from different populations adapted to starch were about as likely to mate with each other as with flies from their own population; similar results were obtained for control groups adapted to maltose.

	Female	
Male	Starch	Maltose
Starch	22	9
Maltose	8	20

Mating frequencies in experimental group

	Female	
Male	Starch population 1	Starch population 2
Starch population 1	18	15
Starch population 2	12	15

Mating frequencies in control group

CONCLUSION   In the experimental group, the strong preference of "starch flies" and "maltose flies" to mate with like-adapted flies indicates that a reproductive barrier was forming between the divergent populations of flies. Although the barrier was not absolute (some mating between starch flies and maltose flies did occur), after 40 generations it appeared to be under way, the result of differing selective pressures as these allopatric populations adapted to different environments.

SOURCE   D. M. B. Dodd, Reproductive isolation as a consequence of adaptive divergence in *Drosophila pseudoobscura*, *Evolution* 43:1308–1311 (1989).

WHAT IF?   How would the results have changed if in each generation a few flies from the starch population had been placed in the maltose population and vice versa? Explain your prediction.

Sympatric ("Same Country") Speciation

In **sympatric speciation** (from the Greek *syn*, together), speciation occurs in populations that live in the same geographic area. How can reproductive barriers form between sympatric populations while their members remain in contact with each other? Although such contact (and the ongoing gene flow that results) makes sympatric speciation less common than allopatric speciation, sympatric speciation can occur if gene flow is reduced by such factors as polyploidy, habitat differentiation, and sexual selection. (Note that these factors can also promote allopatric speciation.)

Polyploidy

A species may originate from an accident during cell division that results in extra sets of chromosomes, a condition called **polyploidy**. There are two distinct forms of polyploidy. An **autopolyploid** (from the Greek *autos*, self) is an individual that has more than two chromosome sets that are all derived from a single species. For example, a failure of cell division could double a cell's chromosome number from the diploid number ($2n$) to a tetraploid number ($4n$) **(Figure 24.10)**. This mutation

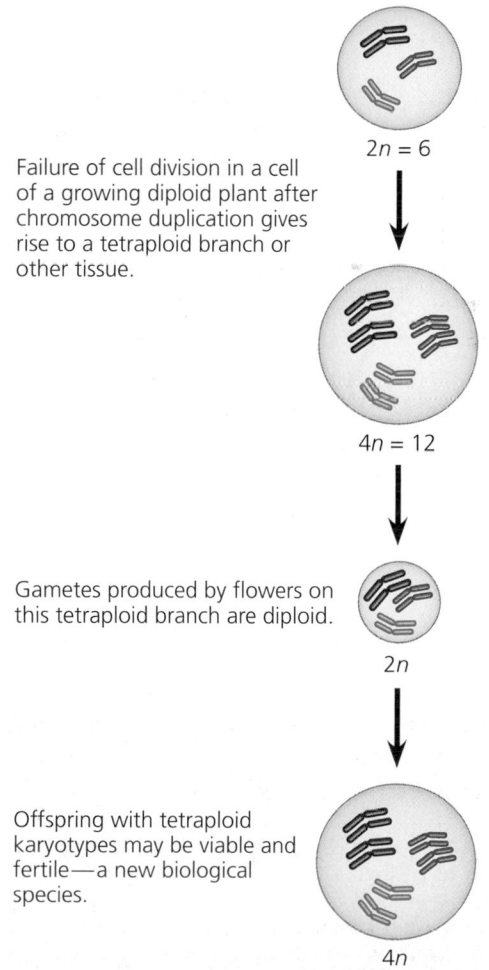

$2n = 6$

Failure of cell division in a cell of a growing diploid plant after chromosome duplication gives rise to a tetraploid branch or other tissue.

$4n = 12$

Gametes produced by flowers on this tetraploid branch are diploid.

$2n$

Offspring with tetraploid karyotypes may be viable and fertile—a new biological species.

$4n$

▲ Figure 24.10 **Sympatric speciation by autopolyploidy in plants.**

causes the tetraploid to be reproductively isolated from diploid plants of the original population, because the triploid ($3n$) offspring of such unions have reduced fertility. However, the tetraploid plants can produce fertile tetraploid offspring by self-pollinating or by mating with other tetraploids. Thus, in just one generation, autopolyploidy can generate reproductive isolation without any geographic separation.

A second form of polyploidy can occur when two different species interbreed and produce hybrid offspring. Most hybrids are sterile because the set of chromosomes from one species cannot pair during meiosis with the set of chromosomes from the other species. However, an infertile hybrid may be able to propagate itself asexually (as many plants can do). In subsequent generations, various mechanisms can change a sterile hybrid into a fertile polyploid called an **allopolyploid (Figure 24.11)**. The allopolyploids are fertile when mating with each other but cannot interbreed with either parent species; thus, they represent a new biological species.

Polyploid speciation occasionally occurs in animals; for example, the gray tree frog *Hyla versicolor* (see Figure 23.16) is thought to have originated in this way. However, polyploidy is far more common in plants. Botanists estimate that more than 80% of the plant species alive today are descended from ancestors that formed by polyploid speciation. One documented example involves two new species of goatsbeard plants (genus *Tragopogon*) that originated in the Pacific Northwest in the mid-1900s. *Tragopogon* first arrived in the region when humans introduced three European species in the early 1900s. These species, *T. dubius, T. pratensis,* and *T. porrifolius,* are now common weeds in abandoned parking lots and other urban sites. In the 1950s, botanists identified two new *Tragopogon* species in regions of Idaho and Washington, where all three European species are also found. One new species, *T. miscellus,* is a tetraploid hybrid of *T. dubius* and *T. pratensis*; the other new species, *T. mirus,* is also an allopolyploid, but its ancestors are *T. dubius* and *T. porrifolius.* Although the *T. mirus* population grows mainly by reproduction of its own members, additional episodes of hybridization between the parent species continue to add new members to the *T. mirus* population—just one example of an ongoing speciation process that can be observed.

Many important agricultural crops—such as oats, cotton, potatoes, tobacco, and wheat—are polyploids. The wheat used for bread, *Triticum aestivum,* is an allohexaploid (six sets of chromosomes, two sets from each of three different species). The first of the polyploidy events that eventually led to modern wheat probably occurred about 8,000 years ago in the Middle East as a spontaneous hybrid of an early cultivated wheat species and a wild grass. Today, plant geneticists generate new polyploids in the laboratory by using chemicals that induce meiotic and mitotic errors. By harnessing the evolutionary process, researchers can produce new hybrid species with desired qualities, such as a hybrid that combines the high yield of wheat with the hardiness of rye.

▲ **Figure 24.11 One mechanism for allopolyploid speciation in plants.** Most hybrids are sterile because their chromosomes are not homologous and cannot pair during meiosis. However, such a hybrid may be able to reproduce asexually. This diagram traces one mechanism that can produce fertile hybrids (allopolyploids) as new species. The new species has a diploid chromosome number equal to the sum of the diploid chromosome numbers of the two parent species.

Habitat Differentiation

Sympatric speciation can also occur when genetic factors enable a subpopulation to exploit a habitat or resource not used by the parent population. Such is the case with the North American apple maggot fly (*Rhagoletis pomonella*). The fly's original habitat was the native hawthorn tree, but about 200 years ago, some populations colonized apple trees that had been introduced by European settlers. As apples mature more quickly than hawthorn fruit, natural selection has favored apple-feeding flies with rapid development. These apple-feeding populations now show temporal isolation from the hawthorn-feeding *R. pomonella*, providing a prezygotic restriction to gene flow between the two populations. Researchers also have identified alleles that benefit the flies that use one host plant but harm the flies that use the other host plant. As a result, natural selection operating on these alleles provides a postzygotic barrier to reproduction, further limiting gene flow. Altogether, although the two populations are still classified as subspecies rather than separate species, sympatric speciation appears to be well under way.

Sexual Selection

There is evidence that sympatric speciation can also be driven by sexual selection. Clues to how this can occur have been found in cichlid fish from one of Earth's hot spots of animal speciation, East Africa's Lake Victoria. This lake was once home to as many as 600 species of cichlids. Genetic data indicate that these species originated within the last 100,000 years from a small number of colonist species that arrived from rivers and lakes located elsewhere. How did so many species—more than double the number of freshwater fish species known in all of Europe—originate within a single lake?

One hypothesis is that subgroups of the original cichlid populations adapted to different food sources and that the resulting genetic divergence contributed to speciation in Lake Victoria. But sexual selection, in which (typically) females select males based on their appearance (see Chapter 23), may also have been a factor. Researchers have studied two closely related sympatric species of cichlids that differ mainly in the coloration of breeding males: Breeding *Pundamilia pundamilia* males have a blue-tinged back, whereas breeding *Pundamilia nyererei* males have a red-tinged back (**Figure 24.12**). Their results suggest that mate choice based on male breeding coloration is the main reproductive barrier that normally keeps the gene pools of these two species separate.

Allopatric and Sympatric Speciation: A Review

Now let's recap the two main modes by which new species form. In allopatric speciation, a new species forms in geographic isolation from its parent population. Geographic isolation severely restricts gene flow. As a result, other reproductive barriers from the ancestral species may arise as a by-product of genetic changes that occur within the isolated population. Many different processes can produce such genetic changes, including natural selection under different environ-

---

▼ Figure 24.12 **Inquiry**

Does sexual selection in cichlids result in reproductive isolation?

EXPERIMENT Ole Seehausen and Jacques van Alphen, then at the University of Leiden, placed males and females of *Pundamilia pundamilia* and *P. nyererei* together in two aquarium tanks, one with natural light and one with a monochromatic orange lamp. Under normal light, the two species are noticeably different in male breeding coloration; under monochromatic orange light, the two species are very similar in color. The researchers then observed the mate choices of the females in each tank.

RESULTS Under normal light, females of each species strongly preferred males of their own species. But under orange light, females of each species responded indiscriminately to males of both species. The resulting hybrids were viable and fertile.

CONCLUSION Seehausen and van Alphen concluded that mate choice by females based on male breeding coloration is the main reproductive barrier that normally keeps the gene pools of these two species separate. Since the species can still interbreed when this prezygotic behavioral barrier is breached in the laboratory, the genetic divergence between the species is likely to be small. This suggests that speciation in nature has occurred relatively recently.

SOURCE O. Seehausen and J. J. M. van Alphen, The effect of male coloration on female mate choice in closely related Lake Victoria cichlids (*Haplochromis nyererei* complex), *Behavioral Ecology and Sociobiology* 42:1–8 (1998).

WHAT IF? If changing the light to orange had not affected the mating behavior of the cichlids, how would the researchers' conclusion in this study have changed?

---

mental conditions, genetic drift, and sexual selection. Once formed, intrinsic reproductive barriers that arise in allopatric populations can prevent interbreeding with the parent population even if the populations come back into contact.

Sympatric speciation, in contrast, requires the emergence of a reproductive barrier that isolates a subset of a population from the remainder of the population in the same area. Though rarer than allopatric speciation, sympatric speciation can occur when gene flow to and from the isolated subpopulation is blocked. This can occur as a result of polyploidy, a condition in which an organism has extra sets of chromosomes. Sympatric speciation also can occur when a subset of a population becomes reproductively isolated because of natural selection that results from a switch to a habitat or food source not used by the parent population. Finally, sympatric speciation can result from sexual selection. Having reviewed the geographic context in which new species form, we'll next explore in more detail what can happen when allopatric populations come back into contact.

CONCEPT CHECK 24.2

1. Summarize key differences between allopatric and sympatric speciation. Which type of speciation is more common, and why?
2. Describe two mechanisms that can decrease gene flow in sympatric populations, thereby making sympatric speciation more likely to occur.
3. **WHAT IF?** Is allopatric speciation more likely to occur on an island close to a mainland or on a more isolated island of the same size? Explain your prediction.

For suggested answers, see Appendix A.

CONCEPT 24.3

Hybrid zones provide opportunities to study factors that cause reproductive isolation

What happens if allopatric populations come back into contact with one another? One possible outcome is the formation of a **hybrid zone**, a region in which members of different species meet and mate, producing at least some offspring of mixed ancestry. In this section, we'll explore hybrid zones and what they reveal about factors that cause the evolution of reproductive isolation.

Patterns Within Hybrid Zones

Hybrid zones exhibit a variety of structures. Some hybrid zones form as narrow bands, such as the one depicted in **Figure 24.13** for two species of toads in the genus *Bombina*, the yellow-bellied toad (*B. variegata*) and the fire-bellied toad (*B. bombina*). This

Yellow-bellied toad, *Bombina variegata*

Fire-bellied toad, *Bombina bombina*

▲ Figure 24.13 **A narrow hybrid zone for *B. variegata* and *B. bombina* in Europe.** The graph shows the pattern of allele frequency changes across the width of the zone near Krakow, Poland.

hybrid zone, represented by the thick red line on the map, extends for 4,000 km but is less than 10 km wide in most places. Across a given "slice" of the hybrid zone, the frequency of alleles specific to yellow-bellied toads typically decreases from close to 100% at the edge where only yellow-bellied toads are found, to 50% in the central portion of the zone, to 0% at the edge where only fire-bellied toads are found.

What causes such a pattern of allele frequencies across a hybrid zone? We can infer that there is an obstacle to gene flow—otherwise alleles from one parent species would also be found in the gene pool of the other parent species. Are geographic barriers reducing gene flow? Not in this case, since the toads move freely throughout the zone. A more important factor is that hybrid toads have increased rates of embryonic mortality and a variety of morphological abnormalities, including ribs that are fused to the spine and malformed tadpole mouthparts. Because the hybrids have poor survival and reproduction, they produce few viable offspring with members of the parent species. As a result, hybrids rarely serve as a stepping-stone from which alleles are passed from one species to the other.

Other hybrid zones have more complicated spatial patterns. Consider the hybrid zone between the ground crickets *Allonemobius fasciatus* and *Allonemobius socius*, both found in the Appalachian Mountains in the eastern United States. The environment has a powerful impact on the fitness of the parent species. *A. fasciatus* is more successful than *A. socius* in colder portions of the zone, and the reverse is true in warm lo-

cations. Thus *A. fasciatus* predominates in cooler sites (high elevation or north-facing locations), and *A. socius* predominates in warmer sites (low elevation or south-facing locations). The topography of this region is complex, with many hills and valleys, so there are many areas where patches of the two species are closely interspersed. As a result, populations of the two parent species come into contact, and hybrids are formed. Unlike the situation in the *Bombina* hybrid zone, where hybrid individuals are consistently less fit than individuals of either parent species, the fitness of *Allonemobius* hybrids varies from year to year and sometimes exceeds that of both parent species. As we'll see, the differences in the fitness of the *Bombina* and *Allonemobius* hybrids lead to different predictions regarding how reproductive barriers for these species change over time.

Hybrid Zones over Time

Studying a hybrid zone is like observing a natural experiment on speciation. Will the result be the rapid formation of a new species, as occurred by polyploidy in the goatsbeard plants of the Pacific Northwest? If not, there are three possible outcomes for the hybrid zone over time **(Figure 24.14)**. Reproductive barriers between species may be strengthened over time (limiting the formation of hybrids) or weakened over time (causing the two species to fuse into a single species). Or hybrids may continue to be produced, creating a long-term, stable hybrid zone. Let's examine what the field evidence suggests about these three possibilities.

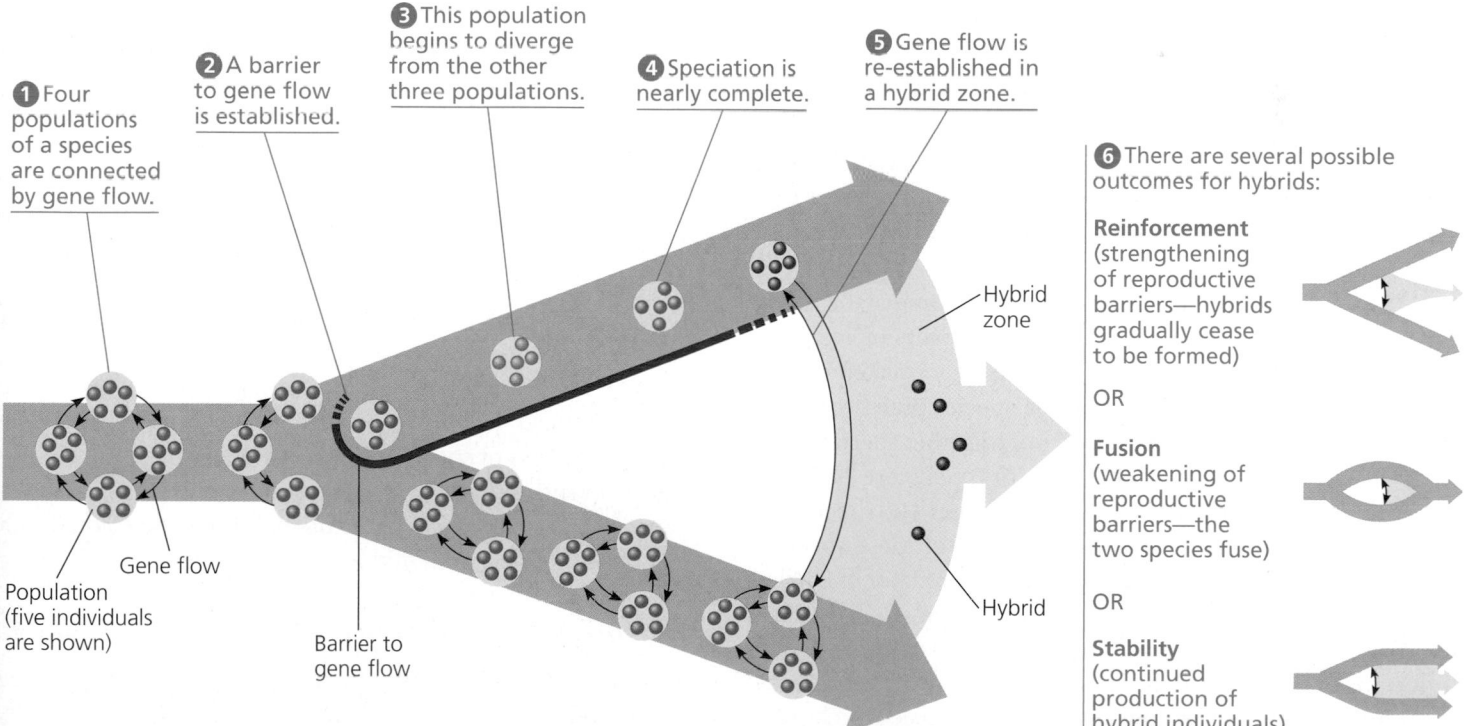

▲ **Figure 24.14 Formation of a hybrid zone and possible outcomes for hybrids over time.** The thick colored arrows represent the passage of time.

WHAT IF? *What might happen if gene flow were re-established at step 3 in this process?*

Reinforcement: Strengthening Reproductive Barriers

When hybrids are less fit than members of their parent species, as in the *Bombina* example, we might expect natural selection to strengthen prezygotic barriers to reproduction, thus reducing the formation of unfit hybrids. Because this process involves *reinforcing* reproductive barriers, it is called **reinforcement**. If reinforcement is occurring, we would predict that barriers to reproduction between species should be stronger for sympatric species than for allopatric species.

As an example, let's consider the evidence for reinforcement in two closely related species of European flycatcher, the pied flycatcher and the collared flycatcher. In allopatric populations of these birds, males of the two species closely resemble one another. But in sympatric populations, the males of the two species look very different: Male pied flycatchers are a dull brown, whereas male collared flycatchers have enlarged patches of white. Female pied and collared flycatchers do not select males of the other species when given a choice between males from sympatric populations, but they frequently do make mistakes when selecting between males from allopatric populations **(Figure 24.15)**. Thus, barriers to reproduction appear to be stronger in birds from sympatric populations than in birds from allopatric populations, as predicted by the reinforcement hypothesis. Similar results have been observed in a number of organisms, including fishes, insects, plants, and other birds. But interestingly, reinforcement does *not* appear to be at work in the case of the *Bombina* toads, as we'll discuss shortly.

Fusion: Weakening Reproductive Barriers

Next let's consider the case in which two species contact one another in a hybrid zone, but the barriers to reproduction are not strong. So much gene flow may occur that reproductive barriers weaken further and the gene pools of the two species become increasingly alike. In effect, the speciation process reverses, eventually causing the two hybridizing species to fuse into a single species.

Such a situation may be occurring among some of the Lake Victoria cichlids we discussed earlier. Many pairs of ecologically similar cichlid species are reproductively isolated by female mate choice—the females of one species prefer to mate with males of one color, while females of the other species prefer to mate with males of a different color (see Figure 24.12).

In the past 30 years, about 200 of the former 600 species of Lake Victoria cichlids have vanished. Some of these species were driven to extinction by an introduced predator, the Nile perch. But many species not eaten by Nile perch also have disappeared. Researchers think that murky waters caused by pollution may have reduced the ability of females to use color to distinguish males of their own species from males of closely related species. If further evidence supports this hypothesis, it would seem that pollution in Lake Victoria has produced a cascade of related effects. First, by decreasing the ability of fe-

Sympatric male pied flycatcher

Allopatric male pied flycatcher

▲ **Figure 24.15 Reinforcement of barriers to reproduction in closely related species of European flycatchers.**

males to distinguish males of their own species, pollution has increased the frequency of mating between members of species that had been isolated reproductively from one another. Second, as a result of these matings, many hybrids have been produced, leading to fusion of the parent species' gene pools and a loss of species **(Figure 24.16)**. Third, future speciation events in Lake Victoria cichlids are now less likely because female mate choice based on male breeding color, which can promote speciation in these fish, is hindered.

Stability: Continued Formation of Hybrid Individuals

Many hybrid zones are stable in the sense that hybrids continue to be produced—a result you might not expect. For example, recall that hybrids are at a strong disadvantage in the *Bombina* hybrid zone. As a result, the offspring of individuals that prefer to mate with members of their own species should survive or

Pundamilia nyererei

Pundamilia pundamilia

Pundamilia "turbid water,"
hybrid offspring from a location
with turbid water

▲ **Figure 24.16 The breakdown of reproductive barriers.**
Increasingly cloudy water in Lake Victoria over the past 30 years may
have weakened reproductive barriers between *P. nyererei* and
P. pundamilia. In areas of cloudy water, the two species have
hybridized extensively, causing their gene pools to fuse.

reproduce better than the unfit hybrid offspring of individuals
that mate indiscriminately with members of the other species.
This suggests that reinforcement should occur, strengthening
reproductive barriers and thereby limiting the production of
hybrid toads. But in more than 20 years of study, no evidence
for reinforcement has been found, and hybrids continue to be
produced. What could explain this surprising finding? One
possibility relates to the narrowness of the *Bombina* hybrid
zone. Perhaps extensive gene flow from outside the zone leads
to the continued production of hybrids and overwhelms selection for increased reproductive isolation inside the hybrid
zone. If the hybrid zone were wider, this would be less likely to
occur, since the center of the zone would receive little gene flow
from distant populations outside the hybrid zone.

In the *Allonemobius* hybrid zone, hybrids sometimes have
higher fitness than the parent species. Thus, we might predict
that many hybrids would be formed, at least in some years. As
these hybrids mated with each other and with members of
both parent species, the gene pools of the parent species could
fuse, reversing the speciation process. However, although hybrids do continue to be formed, more than 20 years of data indicate that they are uncommon and that gene flow between
the parent species is not extensive. Why aren't hybrids more

common? Throughout much of the hybrid zone, the two parent species meet at locations where one or both of them are
near the limit of the environmental conditions that they can
tolerate. As a result, even a slight change in the local environment can cause one or the other of the parent species to disappear from that location. In a 14-year study, researchers
observed several such local extinctions. Thus, because locations where hybrids are formed may appear and disappear rapidly, hybrids remain uncommon, and fusion of the *A. fasciatus*
and *A. socius* gene pools may be prevented by insufficient time
for the reproductive barriers to break down.

In short, sometimes the outcomes in hybrid zones match
our predictions (European flycatchers and cichlid fishes),
and sometimes they don't (*Bombina* and *Allonemobius*). But
whether our predictions are upheld or not, events in hybrid
zones can shed light on how barriers to reproduction between
closely related species change over time. In the next section,
we'll examine how interactions between hybridizing species
can also provide a glimpse into the speed and genetic control
of speciation.

CONCEPT CHECK 24.3

1. What are hybrid zones, and why can they be viewed
   as "natural laboratories" in which to study speciation?
2. **WHAT IF?** Consider two species that diverged
   while geographically separated but resumed contact
   before reproductive isolation was complete. Predict
   what would happen over time if the two species
   mated indiscriminately and (a) hybrid offspring survived and reproduced more poorly than offspring
   from intraspecific matings or (b) hybrid offspring
   survived and reproduced as well as offspring from
   intraspecific matings.

For suggested answers, see Appendix A.

CONCEPT 24.4

Speciation can occur rapidly
or slowly and can result from
changes in few or many genes

Darwin faced many unanswered questions when he began to
ponder that "mystery of mysteries," speciation. As you read in
Chapter 22, he found answers to some of those questions
when he realized that evolution by natural selection helped to
explain both the diversity of life and the adaptations of organisms. But biologists since Darwin have continued to ask fundamental questions about speciation, such as, How long does
it take new species to form? and, How many genes change
when one species splits into two? Answers to these questions
are also beginning to emerge.

The Time Course of Speciation

We can gather information about how long it takes new species to form from broad patterns in the fossil record and from studies that use morphological data (including fossils) or molecular data to assess the time interval between speciation events in particular groups of organisms.

Patterns in the Fossil Record

The fossil record includes many episodes in which new species appear suddenly in a geologic stratum, persist essentially unchanged through several strata, and then disappear. Paleontologists Niles Eldredge, of the American Museum of Natural History, and Stephen Jay Gould (1941–2002), of Harvard University, coined the term **punctuated equilibria** to describe these periods of apparent stasis punctuated by sudden change (Figure 24.17a). Other species do not show a punctuated pattern; instead, they change more gradually over long periods of time (Figure 24.17b).

What do punctuated and gradual patterns tell us about how long it takes new species to form? Suppose that a species survived for 5 million years, but most of the morphological changes that caused it to be designated a new species occurred during the first 50,000 years of its existence—just 1% of its total lifetime. Time periods this short (in geologic terms) often cannot be distinguished in fossil strata, in part because the rate of sediment accumulation is too slow to separate layers this close in time. Thus, based on its fossils, the species would seem to have appeared suddenly and then lingered with little or no change before becoming extinct. Even though such a species may have originated more slowly than its fossils suggest (in this case taking 50,000 years), a punctuated pattern indicates that speciation occurred relatively rapidly. For species whose fossils change much more gradually, we also cannot tell exactly when a new biological species forms, since information about reproductive isolation does not fossilize. However, it is likely that speciation in such groups occurred relatively slowly, perhaps taking millions of years.

Speciation Rates

The punctuated pattern suggests that once the process begins, speciation can be completed relatively rapidly—a suggestion confirmed by a growing number of studies.

For example, research conducted by Loren Rieseberg, then at Indiana University, and colleagues suggests that rapid speciation produced the wild sunflower *Helianthus anomalus*. This species is thought to have originated by the hybridization of two other sunflower species, *H. annuus* and *H. petiolaris*. The hybrid species *H. anomalus* is ecologically distinct and reproductively isolated from both parent species (Figure 24.18). Unlike allopolyploid speciation, in which there is a change in chromosome number after hybridization, in these sunflowers the two parent species and the hybrid all have the same number of chromosomes ($2n = 34$). How then did speciation occur? In laboratory experiments designed to answer this question, only 5% of the F_1 hybrids were fertile. However, after just four more generations in which hybrids mated among themselves and also mated with the parent species, the fertility rose to more than 90%. To explain this finding, Rieseberg and colleagues hypothesized that experimental hybrids whose chromosomes contained blocks of DNA from the parent species that were not compatible with one another failed to reproduce and thus were eliminated by selection. As a result, the chromosomes of the experimental hybrids rapidly became similar in composition to the chromosomes of *H. anomalus* individuals from natural populations (see Figure 24.18).

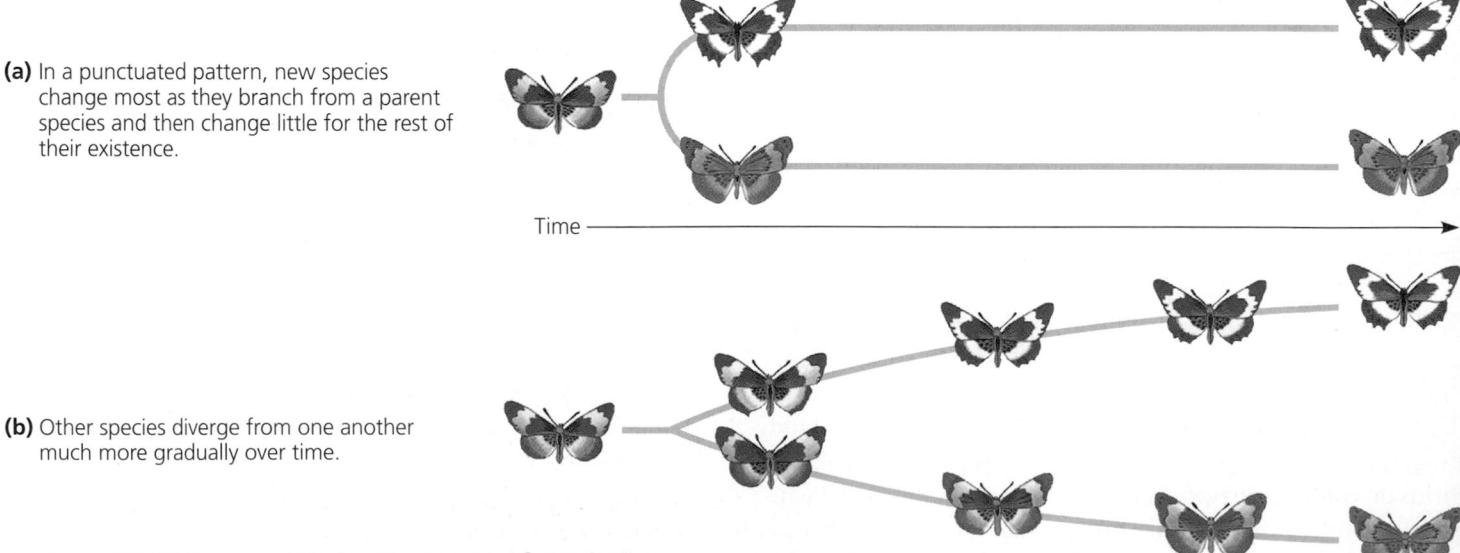

(a) In a punctuated pattern, new species change most as they branch from a parent species and then change little for the rest of their existence.

Time

(b) Other species diverge from one another much more gradually over time.

▲ **Figure 24.17 Two models for the tempo of speciation.**

The sunflower example, along with the apple maggot fly, Lake Victoria cichlid, and fruit fly examples discussed earlier, suggests that new species can form rapidly once divergence begins. But what is the total length of time between speciation events? This interval consists of the time that elapses before populations of a newly formed species start to diverge from one another plus the time it takes for speciation to be complete once divergence begins. It turns out that the total time between speciation events varies considerably. For example, in a survey of data from 84 groups of plants and animals, the interval be-tween speciation events ranged from 4,000 years (in cichlids of Lake Nabugabo, Uganda) to 40 million years (in some beetles). Overall, the time between speciation events averaged 6.5 million years and rarely took less than 500,000 years.

What can we learn from such data? First, the data suggest that on average, millions of years may pass before a newly formed species will itself give rise to another new species. As we'll see in Chapter 25, this result has implications for how long it takes Earth's life to recover from mass extinction events. Second, the extreme variability in the time it takes new species to form indicates that organisms do not have a "speci-ation clock" ticking inside them, causing them to produce new species at regular time intervals. Instead, speciation begins only after gene flow between populations is interrupted, per-haps by an unpredictable event such as a storm that transports a few individuals to an isolated area. Furthermore, once gene flow has been interrupted, the populations must diverge ge-netically to such an extent that they become reproductively isolated—all before another event causes gene flow to resume, reversing the speciation process (see Figure 24.16).

Studying the Genetics of Speciation

Studies of ongoing speciation (as in hybrid zones) can reveal traits that cause reproductive isolation. By identifying the genes that control those traits, scientists can explore a funda-mental question of evolutionary biology: How many genes change when a new species forms?

In a few cases, the evolution of reproductive isolation is due to a change in a single gene. For example, in Japanese snails of the genus *Euhadra*, alleles of a single gene can induce a mechanical barrier to reproduction. This gene controls the direction in which the shells spiral **(Figure 24.19)**. When their shells spiral in different directions, the snails' genitals are oriented in a manner that prevents mating (Figure 24.4f shows a similar example).

A major barrier to reproduction between two closely related species of monkey flower, *Mimulus lewisii* and *M. cardinalis*,

(a) The wild sunflower *Helianthus anomalus* lives in dry sand dune environments. *H. anomalus* originated via the hybridization of two other sunflowers, *H. annuus* and *H. petiolaris*, which live in nearby but moister environments.

Chromosome 1 { H. anomalus / Experimental hybrid }

Chromosome 2 { H. anomalus / Experimental hybrid }

Chromosome 3 { H. anomalus / Experimental hybrid }

Key

■ Region diagnostic for parent species *H. petiolaris*

■ Region diagnostic for parent species *H. annuus*

▨ Region lacking information on parental origin

(b) The genetic composition of three chromosomes in *H. anomalus* and in experimental hybrids. After a five-generation experiment, the chromosomes in the experimental hybrids were similar to the chromosomes of naturally occurring *H. anomalus*.

▲ **Figure 24.18 Rapid speciation in a sunflower hybrid zone.**

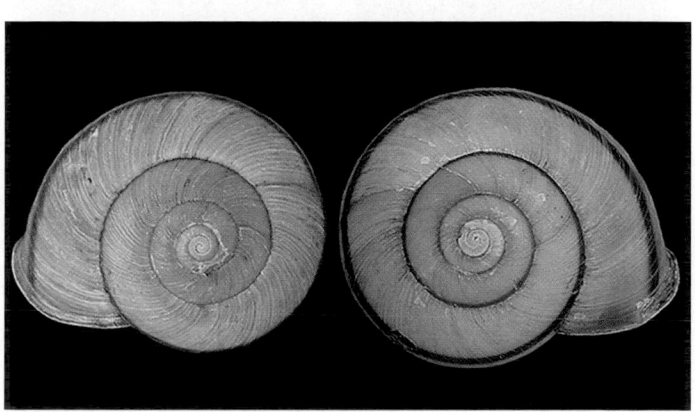

▲ **Figure 24.19 Single-gene speciation.** A mutation in one gene causes the shell of the Japanese land snail (*Euhadra*) to spiral in the opposite direction from others. Snails with opposite spirals cannot mate, resulting in reproductive isolation.

also appears to be influenced by a relatively small number of genes. These two species are isolated both by prezygotic barriers (pollinator choice and partial gametic isolation) and by postzygotic barriers (interspecific crosses produce fewer offspring than intraspecific crosses, and F_1 hybrids have reduced fertility and survival). Of these barriers, pollinator choice accounts for most of the isolation: In a hybrid zone between *M. lewisii* and *M. cardinalis*, nearly 98% of pollinator visits were restricted to one species or the other.

The two monkey flower species are visited by different pollinators: Bumblebees prefer the pink-flowered *M. lewisii* and hummingbirds prefer the red-flowered *M. cardinalis*. Douglas Schemske, of Michigan State University, and colleagues have shown that pollinator choice is affected by at least two loci in the monkey flowers, one of which, the "yellow upper," or *yup*, locus, influences flower color **(Figure 24.20)**. By producing F_1

(a) Typical *Mimulus lewisii*

(b) *M. lewisii* with an *M. cardinalis* flower-color allele

(c) Typical *Mimulus cardinalis*

(d) *M. cardinalis* with an *M. lewisii* flower-color allele

▲ **Figure 24.20 A locus that influences pollinator choice.** Pollinator preferences provide a strong barrier to reproduction between *Mimulus lewisii* and *M. cardinalis*. After transferring the *M. lewisii* allele for a flower-color locus into *M. cardinalis* and vice versa, researchers observed a shift in some pollinators' preferences.

WHAT IF? *If* M. cardinalis *individuals that had the* M. lewisii *yup allele were planted in an area that housed both monkey flower species, how might the production of hybrid offspring be affected?*

hybrids and then performing repeated backcrosses to each parent species, Schemske and colleagues succeeded in transferring the *M. lewisii* allele at this locus into *M. cardinalis*, and vice versa. In a field experiment, *M. lewisii* plants with the *M. cardinalis yup* allele received 68-fold more visits from hummingbirds than did wild-type *M. lewisii*. Similarly, *M. cardinalis* plants with the *M. lewisii yup* allele received 74-fold more visits from bumblebees than did wild-type *M. cardinalis*. Thus, a mutation at a single locus can influence pollinator preference and hence contribute to reproductive isolation in monkey flowers.

In other organisms, the speciation process is influenced by larger numbers of genes and gene interactions. For example, hybrid sterility between two subspecies of *Drosophila pseudoobscura* results from gene interactions among at least four loci, and postzygotic isolation in the sunflower hybrid zone discussed earlier is influenced by at least 26 chromosomal segments (and an unknown number of genes). Overall, studies conducted to date suggest that few or many genes can influence the evolution of reproductive isolation and hence the emergence of a new species—a new addition to the great diversity of life.

From Speciation to Macroevolution

As you've seen in this chapter's examples, speciation may begin with differences as seemingly small as the color on a cichlid's back. However, as speciation occurs again and again, such differences can accumulate and become more pronounced, eventually leading to the formation of new groups of organisms that differ greatly from their ancestors (as in the origin of whales from land-dwelling mammals; see Figure 22.16). Furthermore, as one group of organisms increases in size by producing many new species, another group of organisms may shrink, losing species to extinction. The cumulative effects of many such speciation and extinction events have helped to shape the sweeping evolutionary changes that are documented in the fossil record. In the next chapter, we turn to such large-scale evolutionary changes as we begin our study of macroevolution.

CONCEPT CHECK 24.4

1. Speciation can occur rapidly between diverging populations, yet the length of time between speciation events is often more than a million years. Explain this apparent contradiction.

2. **WHAT IF?** Summarize experimental evidence that the *yup* locus acts as a prezygotic barrier to reproduction in two species of monkey flowers. Do these results demonstrate that the *yup* locus alone controls barriers to reproduction between these closely related monkey flower species? Explain your answer.

For suggested answers, see Appendix A.

MEDIA Go to www.campbellbiology.com for BioFlix 3-D Animations, MP3 Tutors, Videos, Practice Tests, an eBook, and more.

SUMMARY OF KEY CONCEPTS

CONCEPT 24.1

The biological species concept emphasizes reproductive isolation (pp. 487–492)

▶ **The Biological Species Concept** A biological species is a group of populations whose individuals have the potential to interbreed and produce viable, fertile offspring with each other but not with members of other species. The biological species concept emphasizes reproductive isolation through prezygotic and postzygotic barriers that separate gene pools.

▶ **Other Definitions of Species** Although helpful in thinking about how speciation occurs, the biological species concept has limitations. For instance, it cannot be applied to organisms known only as fossils or to organisms that reproduce only asexually. Thus, scientists use other species concepts, such as the morphological species concept, in certain circumstances.

MEDIA

Activity Overview of Macroevolution

CONCEPT 24.2

Speciation can take place with or without geographic separation (pp. 492–498)

▶ **Allopatric ("Other Country") Speciation** Evidence indicates that allopatric speciation can occur when two populations of one species become geographically separated from each other. One or both populations may undergo evolutionary change during the period of separation, resulting in the establishment of prezygotic or postzygotic barriers to reproduction.

▶ **Sympatric ("Same Country") Speciation** A new species can originate while remaining in a geographically overlapping area with the parent species. Plant species (and, more rarely, animals) have evolved sympatrically through polyploidy. Sympatric speciation can also result from habitat shifts and sexual selection.

▶ **Allopatric and Sympatric Speciation:** *A Review*

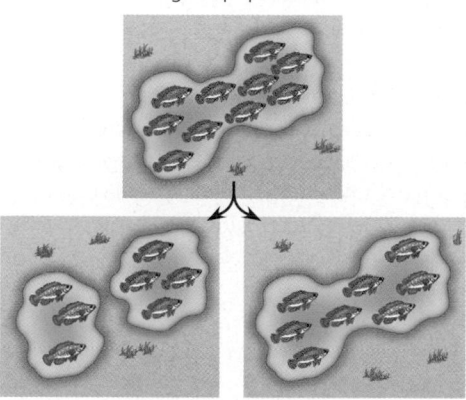

Original population

Allopatric speciation   Sympatric speciation

MEDIA

MP3 Tutor Speciation

CONCEPT 24.3

Hybrid zones provide opportunities to study factors that cause reproductive isolation (pp. 498–501)

▶ **Patterns Within Hybrid Zones** Many groups of organisms form hybrid zones in which members of different species meet and mate, producing at least some offspring of mixed ancestry.

▶ **Hybrid Zones over Time** In many hybrid zones, a limited number of hybrid offspring continue to be produced over time. In others, reinforcement strengthens prezygotic barriers to reproduction, thus decreasing the formation of unfit hybrids. In still other hybrid zones, barriers to reproduction may weaken over time, resulting in the fusion of the species' gene pools (reversing the speciation process).

CONCEPT 24.4

Speciation can occur rapidly or slowly and can result from changes in few or many genes (pp. 501–504)

▶ **The Time Course of Speciation** New species can form rapidly once divergence begins—but it can take millions of years for that to happen. The time interval between speciation events varies considerably, from a few thousand years to tens of millions of years.

▶ **Studying the Genetics of Speciation** New developments in genetics have enabled researchers to identify specific genes involved in some cases of speciation. Results show that speciation can be driven by few or many genes.

▶ **From Speciation to Macroevolution** Due to repeated events, small differences between organisms can accumulate, leading to the formation of new groups of organisms.

MEDIA

Investigation How Do New Species Arise by Genetic Isolation?
Biology Labs On-Line EvolutionLab

TESTING YOUR KNOWLEDGE

SELF-QUIZ

1. The *largest* unit within which gene flow can readily occur is a
   a. population.
   b. species.
   c. genus.
   d. hybrid.
   e. phylum.

2. Bird guides once listed the myrtle warbler and Audubon's warbler as distinct species. Recently, these birds have been classified as eastern and western forms of a single species, the yellow-rumped warbler. Which of the following pieces of evidence, if true, would be cause for this reclassification?
   a. The two forms interbreed often in nature, and their offspring have good survival and reproduction.
   b. The two forms live in similar habitats.
   c. The two forms have many genes in common.
   d. The two forms have similar food requirements.
   e. The two forms are very similar in coloration.

3. Males of different species of the fruit fly *Drosophila* that live in the same parts of the Hawaiian Islands have different elaborate courtship rituals that involve fighting other males and stylized movements that attract females. What type of reproductive isolation does this represent?
   a. habitat isolation
   b. temporal isolation
   c. behavioral isolation
   d. gametic isolation
   e. postzygotic barriers

4. Which of the following factors would *not* contribute to allopatric speciation?
   a. A population becomes geographically isolated from the parent population.
   b. The separated population is small, and genetic drift occurs.
   c. The isolated population is exposed to different selection pressures than the ancestral population.
   d. Different mutations begin to distinguish the gene pools of the separated populations.
   e. Gene flow between the two populations is extensive.

5. Plant species A has a diploid number of 12. Plant species B has a diploid number of 16. A new species, C, arises as an allopolyploid from A and B. The diploid number for species C would probably be
   a. 12.   b. 14.   c. 16.
   d. 28.   e. 56.

6. According to the punctuated equilibria model,
   a. natural selection is unimportant as a mechanism of evolution.
   b. given enough time, most existing species will branch gradually into new species.
   c. most new species accumulate their unique features relatively rapidly as they come into existence, then change little for the rest of their duration as a species.
   d. most evolution occurs in sympatric populations.
   e. speciation is usually due to a single mutation.

For Self-Quiz answers, see Appendix A.

MEDIA   Visit **www.campbellbiology.com** for a Practice Test.

EVOLUTION CONNECTION

7. What is the biological basis for assigning all human populations to a single species? Can you think of a scenario by which a second human species could originate in the future?

SCIENTIFIC INQUIRY

8. **DRAW IT**   In this chapter, you read that bread wheat (*Triticum aestivum*) is an allohexaploid, containing two sets of chromosomes from each of three different parent species. Genetic analysis suggests that the three species pictured below each contributed chromosome sets to *T. aestivum*. (The capital letters here represent sets of chromosomes rather than individual genes.) Evidence also indicates that the first polyploidy event was a spontaneous hybridization of the early cultivated wheat species *T. monococcum* and a wild grass species. Based on this information, draw a diagram of one possible chain of events that could have produced the allohexaploid *T. aestivum*.

Ancestral species:

Triticum monococcum (2*n* = 14)   AA

Wild *Triticum* (2*n* = 14)   BB

Wild *T. tauschii* (2*n* = 14)   DD

Product:

AA BB DD

T. aestivum (bread wheat) (2*n* = 42)

SCIENCE, TECHNOLOGY, AND SOCIETY

9. In the United States, the rare red wolf (*Canis lupus*) has been known to hybridize with coyotes (*Canis latrans*), which are much more numerous. Although red wolves and coyotes differ in terms of morphology, DNA, and behavior, genetic evidence suggests that living red wolf individuals are actually hybrids. Red wolves are designated as an endangered species and hence receive legal protection under the Endangered Species Act. Some people think that their endangered status should be withdrawn because the remaining red wolves are hybrids, not members of a "pure" species. Do you agree? Why or why not?

The History of Life on Earth

25

OVERVIEW

Lost Worlds

Visitors to Antarctica today encounter one of Earth's harshest, most barren environments. In this land of extreme cold where there is almost no liquid water, life is sparse and small—the largest fully terrestrial animal is a fly 5 mm long. But even as early antarctic explorers struggled to survive, some of them made an astonishing discovery: fossil evidence that life once thrived where it now barely exists. Fossils reveal that 500 million years ago, the ocean waters surrounding Antarctica were warm and teeming with tropical invertebrates. Later, the continent was covered in forests for hundreds of millions of years. At various times, a wide range of animals stalked through these forests, including 3-meter-tall predatory "terror birds" and giant dinosaurs such as the voracious *Cryolophosaurus* **(Figure 25.1)**, a 7-meter-long relative of *Tyrannosaurus rex.*

Fossils discovered in other parts of the world tell a similar, if not quite as surprising, story: Past organisms were very different from

▲ **Figure 25.1 What does fossil evidence say about where these dinosaurs lived?**

▲ *Cryolophosaurus* **skull**

those now alive. The sweeping changes in life on Earth revealed by fossils illustrate **macroevolution**, the pattern of evolution over large time scales. Specific examples of macroevolutionary change include the origin of key biochemical processes such as photosynthesis, the emergence of the first terrestrial vertebrates, and the long-term impact of a mass extinction on the diversity of life.

Taken together, such changes provide a grand view of the evolutionary history of life on Earth. We'll examine that history in this chapter, beginning with hypotheses regarding the origin of life. The origin of life is the most speculative topic of the entire unit, for no fossil evidence of that seminal episode exists. We will then turn to the fossil record and what it tells us about major events in the history of life, paying particular attention to factors that have helped to shape the rise and fall of different groups of organisms over time.

CONCEPT 25.1

Conditions on early Earth made the origin of life possible

The earliest evidence of life on Earth comes from fossils of microorganisms that are about 3.5 billion years old. But when and how did the first living cells appear? Observations and experiments in chemistry, geology, and physics have led scientists to propose one scenario that we'll examine here. They hypothesize that chemical and physical processes on early Earth, aided by the emerging force of natural selection, could have produced very simple cells through a sequence of four main stages:

1. The abiotic (nonliving) synthesis of small organic molecules, such as amino acids and nucleotides
2. The joining of these small molecules into macromolecules, including proteins and nucleic acids
3. The packaging of these molecules into "protobionts," droplets with membranes that maintained an internal chemistry different from that of their surroundings
4. The origin of self-replicating molecules that eventually made inheritance possible

Though speculative, this scenario leads to predictions that can be tested in the laboratory. In this section, we will examine some of the evidence for each stage.

Synthesis of Organic Compounds on Early Earth

There is scientific evidence that Earth and the other planets of the solar system formed about 4.6 billion years ago, condensing from a vast cloud of dust and rocks that surrounded the young sun. For the first few hundred million years, life probably could not have originated or survived on Earth because the planet was still being bombarded by huge chunks of rock and ice left over from the formation of the solar system. The collisions generated enough heat to vaporize the available water and prevent seas from forming. This phase likely ended about 3.9 billion years ago.

As the bombardment of early Earth slowed, conditions on the planet were extremely different from those of today. The first atmosphere was probably thick with water vapor, along with various compounds released by volcanic eruptions, including nitrogen and its oxides, carbon dioxide, methane, ammonia, hydrogen, and hydrogen sulfide. As Earth cooled, the water vapor condensed into oceans, and much of the hydrogen quickly escaped into space.

In the 1920s, Russian chemist A. I. Oparin and British scientist J. B. S. Haldane independently hypothesized that Earth's early atmosphere was a reducing (electron-adding) environment, in which organic compounds could have formed from simple molecules. The energy for this organic synthesis could have come from lightning and intense UV radiation. Haldane suggested that the early oceans were a solution of organic molecules, a "primitive soup" from which life arose.

In 1953, Stanley Miller and Harold Urey, of the University of Chicago, tested the Oparin-Haldane hypothesis by creating laboratory conditions comparable to those that scientists at the time thought existed on early Earth (see Figure 4.2). Their apparatus yielded a variety of amino acids found in organisms today, along with other organic compounds. Many laboratories have since repeated the experiment using different recipes for the atmosphere. Some of these variations also produced organic compounds.

However, it is unclear whether the atmosphere of young Earth contained enough methane and ammonia to be reducing. Growing evidence suggests that the early atmosphere was made up primarily of nitrogen and carbon dioxide and was neither reducing nor oxidizing (electron removing). Some recent Miller-Urey-type experiments using such atmospheres have produced organic molecules. In any case, it is likely that small "pockets" of the early atmosphere—perhaps near volcanic openings—were reducing. Perhaps instead of forming in the atmosphere, the first organic compounds formed near submerged volcanoes and deep-sea vents, where hot water and minerals gush into the ocean from Earth's interior (**Figure 25.2**). These regions are also rich in inorganic sulfur and iron compounds, which are important in ATP synthesis by present-day organisms.

Miller-Urey-type experiments demonstrate that the abiotic synthesis of organic molecules is possible. Support for this idea also comes from analyses of the chemical composition of meteorites. Among the meteorites that land on Earth are carbonaceous chondrites, rocks that are 1–2% carbon compounds by mass. Fragments of a fallen 4.5-billion-year-old chondrite found in Australia in 1969 contain more than 80 amino acids, some in large amounts. Remarkably, the proportions of these amino acids are similar to those produced in the Miller-Urey experiment. The chondrite amino acids cannot

▲ **Figure 25.2 A window to early life?** An instrument on the research submarine *Alvin* samples the water around a hydrothermal vent in the Sea of Cortés. More than 1.5 km below the surface, the vent releases hydrogen sulfide and iron sulfide, which react and produce pyrite (fool's gold) and hydrogen gas. Prokaryotes that live near the vent use the hydrogen as an energy source. Such environments are among the most extreme in which life exists today, and some researchers favor the hypothesis that life may have begun in similar regions of early Earth.

be contaminants from Earth because they consist of an equal mix of D and L isomers (see Chapter 4). Organisms make and use only L isomers, with a few rare exceptions.

Abiotic Synthesis of Macromolecules

The presence of small organic molecules, such as amino acids, is not sufficient for the emergence of life as we know it. Every cell has a vast assortment of macromolecules, including enzymes and other proteins and the nucleic acids that are essential for self-replication. Could such macromolecules have formed on early Earth? By dripping solutions of amino acids onto hot sand, clay, or rock, researchers have been able to produce amino acid polymers. The polymers formed spontaneously, without the help of enzymes or ribosomes. But unlike proteins, these polymers are a complex mix of linked and cross-linked amino acids. Nevertheless, it is possible that such polymers may have acted as weak catalysts for a variety of reactions on early Earth.

Protobionts

Two key properties of life are accurate replication and metabolism. Neither property can exist without the other. DNA molecules carry genetic information, including the instructions needed to replicate themselves accurately. But the replication of DNA requires elaborate enzymatic machinery, along with a copious supply of nucleotide building blocks that must be provided by the cell's metabolism (see Chapter 16). While Miller-Urey-type experiments have yielded some of the nitrogenous bases of DNA and RNA, they have not produced anything like nucleotides. If building blocks of nucleic acids were not part of the early organic soup, self-replicating molecules and a metabolism-like source of the building blocks must have appeared together. How did that happen?

The necessary conditions may have been met by **protobionts**, collections of abiotically produced molecules surrounded by a membrane-like structure. Protobionts may exhibit some properties of life, including simple reproduction and metabolism, as well as the maintenance of an internal chemical environment different from that of their surroundings.

Laboratory experiments demonstrate that protobionts could have formed spontaneously from abiotically produced organic compounds. For example, certain small membrane-bounded droplets called liposomes can form when lipids or other organic molecules are added to water. The hydrophobic molecules in the mixture organize into a bilayer at the surface of the droplet, much like the lipid bilayer of a plasma membrane. Liposomes can "reproduce" (**Figure 25.3a**), and because their bilayer is selectively permeable, liposomes undergo osmotic swelling or shrinking when placed in solutions of different solute concentrations. Some of these liposomes can perform simple metabolic reactions, another important step toward the origin of life (**Figure 25.3b**).

Self-Replicating RNA and the Dawn of Natural Selection

The first genetic material was most likely RNA, not DNA. Thomas Cech, of the University of Colorado, and Sidney Altman, of Yale University, found that RNA, which plays a central role in protein synthesis, can also carry out a number of enzyme-like catalytic functions. Cech called these RNA catalysts **ribozymes**. Some ribozymes can make complementary copies of short pieces of RNA, provided that they are supplied with nucleotide building blocks.

Natural selection on the molecular level has produced ribozymes capable of self-replication in the laboratory. How does this occur? Unlike double-stranded DNA, which takes the form of a uniform helix, single-stranded RNA molecules assume a variety of specific three-dimensional shapes mandated by their nucleotide sequences. In a particular environment, RNA molecules with certain base sequences are more stable and replicate faster and with fewer errors than other sequences. The RNA molecule whose sequence is best suited to the surrounding environment and has the greatest ability to replicate itself will leave the most descendant molecules. Its descendants will not be a single RNA "species" but instead will be a family of sequences that differ slightly because of copying

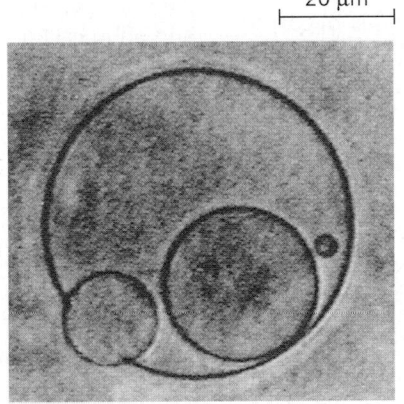

|← 20 μm →|

(a) **Simple reproduction.** This liposome is "giving birth" to smaller liposomes (LM).

(b) **Simple metabolism.** If enzymes—in this case, phosphatase and amylase—are included in the solution from which the droplets self-assemble, some liposomes can carry out simple metabolic reactions and export the products.

▲ Figure 25.3 **Laboratory versions of liposome protobionts.**

errors. Occasionally, a copying error will result in a molecule that folds into a shape that is even more stable or more adept at self-replication than the ancestral sequence. Similar selection events may have occurred on early Earth. Thus, the molecular biology of today may have been preceded by an "RNA world," in which small RNA molecules that carried genetic information were able to replicate and to store information about the protobionts that carried them.

A protobiont with self-replicating, catalytic RNA would differ from its many neighbors that did not carry RNA or that carried RNA without such capabilities. If that protobiont could grow, split, and pass its RNA molecules to its daughters, the daughters would have some of the properties of their parent. Although the first such protobionts must have carried only limited amounts of genetic information, specifying only a few properties, their inherited characteristics could have been acted on by natural selection. The most successful of the early protobionts would have increased in number because they could exploit their resources effectively and pass their abilities on to subsequent generations. The emergence of such protobionts may seem unlikely, but remember that there could have been trillions of protobionts in bodies of water on early Earth. Even those with only a limited capacity for inheritance would have had a huge advantage over the rest.

Once RNA sequences that carried genetic information appeared in protobionts, many further changes would have been possible. For example, RNA could have provided the template on which DNA nucleotides were assembled. Double-stranded DNA is a much more stable repository for genetic information than the more fragile single-stranded RNA. DNA also can be replicated more accurately. Accurate replication was a necessity as genomes grew larger through gene duplication and other processes and as more properties of the protobionts became coded in genetic information. After DNA appeared, perhaps RNA molecules began to take on their present-day roles as intermediates in the translation of genetic programs, and the RNA world gave way to a "DNA world." The stage was now set for a blossoming of diverse life-forms—a change we see documented in the fossil record.

CONCEPT 25.2
The fossil record documents the history of life

Starting with the earliest traces of life, the fossil record opens a window into the world of long ago and provides glimpses of the evolution of life over billions of years. In this section, we'll explore what the fossil record reveals about the major changes in the history of life—what those changes have been and how they may have occurred.

The Fossil Record

Recall from Chapter 22 that sedimentary rocks are the richest source of fossils. As a result, the fossil record is based primarily on the sequence in which fossils have accumulated in sedimentary rock layers called *strata* (see Figure 22.3). Useful information is also provided by other types of fossils, such as insects preserved in amber (fossilized tree sap) and mammals frozen in ice.

The fossil record shows that there have been great changes in the kinds of organisms that dominated life on Earth at different points in time (**Figure 25.4**). Many past organisms were unlike today's organisms, and many organisms that once were common are now extinct. As we'll see later, fossils also document how new groups of organisms arose from previously existing ones.

As substantial and significant as the fossil record is, keep in mind that it is an incomplete chronicle of evolutionary change. Many of Earth's organisms probably did not die in the right place at the right time to be preserved as fossils. Of those fossils that were formed, many were destroyed by later geologic processes, and only a fraction of the others have been discovered. As a result, the known fossil record is biased in favor of species that existed for a long time, were abundant and widespread in certain kinds of environments, and had hard shells, skeletons, or other parts that facilitated their fossilization. Even with its limitations, however, the fossil record is a remarkably detailed account of biological change over the vast scale of geologic time. Furthermore, as shown by the recently unearthed fossils of whale ancestors with hind limbs (see Figure 22.16), gaps in the fossil record continue to be filled by new discoveries.

How Rocks and Fossils Are Dated

Fossils are valuable data for reconstructing the history of life, but only if we can determine where they fit in that unfolding story. While the order of fossils in rock strata tells us the sequence in which the fossils were laid down—their relative ages—it does not tell us their actual (absolute) ages. Examining the relative positions of fossils in strata is like peeling off layers of wallpaper in an old house. You can determine the

▼ **Figure 25.4 Documenting the history of life.** These fossils illustrate representative organisms from different points in time.

Present

100 million years ago

▼ *Rhomaleosaurus victor*, a plesiosaur. These large marine reptiles were important predators from 200 million to 65.5 million years ago.

▼ *Dimetrodon*, the largest known carnivore of its day, was more closely related to mammals than to reptiles. The spectacular "sail" on its back probably functioned in temperature regulation.

▼ Casts of ammonites, a group of molluscs that lived from 400 million to 65 million years ago and ranged in size from a few cm to 2 m.

175

200

270

300

4.5 cm

▲ *Coccosteus cuspidatus*, a placoderm (fishlike vertebrate) that had a bony shield covering its head and front end.

375

▶ *Hallucigenia*, a member of a morphologically diverse group of animals found in the Burgess Shale fossil bed in the Canadian Rockies.

400

1 cm

500

◀ *Dickinsonia costata*, a member of the Ediacaran biota, an extinct group of soft-bodied organisms.

525

2.5 cm

▲ Some prokaryotes bind thin films of sediments together, producing layered rocks called stromatolites, such as these in Shark Bay, Australia.

565

600

▶ A unicellular eukaryote, the alga *Tappania*, from northern Australia.

▲ A section through a fossilized stromatolite.

1,500

3,500

sequence in which the layers were applied, but not the year each layer was added.

How can we determine the absolute age of a fossil? (Note that "absolute" dating does not mean errorless dating, but only that an age is given in years rather than relative terms such as *before* and *after*.) One of the most common techniques is **radiometric dating**, which is based on the decay of radioactive isotopes (see Chapter 2). A radioactive "parent" isotope decays to a "daughter" isotope at a constant rate. The rate of decay is expressed by the **half-life**, the time required for 50% of the parent isotope to decay **(Figure 25.5)**. Each variety of radioactive isotope has a characteristic half-life, which is not affected by temperature, pressure, or other such environmental variables. For example, carbon-14 decays relatively quickly; it has a half-life of 5,730 years. Uranium-238 decays slowly; its half-life is 4.5 billion years.

Fossils contain isotopes of elements that accumulated in the organisms when they were alive. For example, the carbon in a living organism includes the most common carbon isotope, carbon-12, as well as a radioactive isotope, carbon-14. When the organism dies, it stops accumulating carbon, and the amount of carbon-12 in its tissues does not change over time. However, the carbon-14 that it contains at the time of death slowly decays and becomes another element, nitrogen-14. Thus, by measuring the ratio of carbon-14 to carbon-12 in a fossil, we can determine the fossil's age. This method works for fossils up to about 75,000 years old; fossils older than that contain too little carbon-14 to be detected with current techniques. Radioactive isotopes with longer half-lives are used to date older fossils.

Determining the age of old fossils in sedimentary rocks can be challenging. One reason is that organisms do not use ra-dioisotopes that have long half-lives, such as uranium-238, to build their bones or shells. Moreover, the sedimentary rocks themselves tend to be composed of sediments of differing ages. Hence, we usually cannot date old fossils directly. However, geologists can apply an indirect method to infer the absolute age of fossils that are sandwiched between two layers of volcanic rocks. For example, researchers might measure the amount in each rock layer of the radioactive isotope potassium-40, which has a half-life of 1.3 billion years. If the two surrounding rock layers were determined to be 525 million and 535 million years old, the fossils likely represent organisms that lived about 530 million years ago.

The magnetism of rocks can also provide dating information. During the formation of volcanic and sedimentary rocks, iron particles in the rock align themselves with Earth's magnetic field. When the rock hardens, the particles' orientation is frozen in time. Measurements of the magnetism of various rock layers indicate that Earth's north and south magnetic poles have reversed repeatedly in the past. Because these magnetic reversals affect the entire planet at once, reversals in one location can be matched with corresponding patterns elsewhere. This approach allows rocks to be dated when other methods are not available. It also can be used to corroborate ages estimated in other ways.

Now that we've seen how fossils can be dated, let's turn to an example of what we can learn from them.

The Origin of New Groups of Organisms

Some fossils provide a detailed look at the origin of new groups of organisms. Such fossils are central to our understanding of evolution; they illustrate how new features of organisms arise and how long it takes for such changes to occur. We'll examine one such case here, the origin of mammals.

Along with amphibians and reptiles, mammals belong to the group of animals called *tetrapods* (from the Greek *tetra*, four, and *pod*, foot), named for having four limbs. Mammals have a number of unique anatomical features that fossilize readily, allowing scientists to trace their origin. For example, the lower jaw is composed of one bone (the dentary) in mammals but several bones in other tetrapods. In addition, the lower and upper jaws hinge between a different set of bones in mammals than in other tetrapods. As we'll explore in Chapter 34, mammals also have a unique set of three bones that transmit sound in the middle ear (the hammer, anvil, and stirrup), whereas other tetrapods have only one such bone (the stirrup). Finally, the teeth of mammals are differentiated into incisors (for tearing), canines (for piercing), and the multi-pointed premolars and molars (for grinding). In contrast, the teeth of other tetrapods usually consist of a row of undifferentiated, single-pointed teeth.

As detailed in **Figure 25.6**, the fossil record shows that the unique features of mammalian jaws and teeth evolved as a series of gradual modifications. As you study Figure 25.6, bear in

▲ **Figure 25.5 Radiometric dating.** In this diagram, each division of the clock face represents a half-life.

DRAW IT *Relabel the x-axis (time) of this graph to illustrate the radioactive decay of uranium-238 (half-life = 4.5 billion years).*

Exploring The Origin of Mammals

Over the course of 120 million years, mammals originated gradually from a group of tetrapods called synapsids. Shown here are a few of the many fossil organisms whose morphological features represent intermediate steps between living mammals and their synapsid ancestors. The evolutionary context of the origin of mammals is shown in the tree diagram at right.

Key

- ▇ Articular
- ▇ Quadrate
- ▇ Dentary
- ▇ Squamosal

Synapsid (300 mya)

Temporal fenestra

Synapsids had multiple bones in the lower jaw and single-pointed teeth. The jaw hinge was formed by the articular and quadrate bones. Synapsids also had an opening called the temporal fenestra behind the eye socket. Powerful cheek muscles for closing the jaws probably passed through the temporal fenestra. Over time, this opening enlarged and moved in front of the hinge between the lower and upper jaws, thereby increasing the power and precision with which the jaws could be closed (much as moving a doorknob away from the hinge makes a door easier to close).

Therapsid (280 mya)

Temporal fenestra

Later, a group of synapsids called therapsids appeared. Therapsids had large dentary bones, long faces, and the first signs of specialized teeth, large canines.

Early cynodont (260 mya)

Temporal fenestra

In early cynodont therapsids, the dentary was the largest bone in the lower jaw, the temporal fenestra was large and positioned forward of the jaw hinge, and teeth with several cusps first appeared (not visible in the diagram). As in earlier synapsids, the jaw had an articular-quadrate hinge.

Later cynodont (220 mya)

Later cynodonts had teeth with complex cusp patterns and their lower and upper jaws hinged in two locations: They retained the original articular-quadrate hinge and formed a new, second hinge between the dentary and squamosal bones.

Very late cynodont (195 mya)

In the common ancestor of this very late cynodont and mammals, the original articular-quadrate hinge was lost, leaving the dentary-squamosal hinge as the only hinge between the lower and upper jaws (as in living mammals). The articular and quadrate bones migrated into the ear region (not shown), where they functioned in transmitting sound. In the mammal lineage, these two bones later evolved into the familiar hammer and anvil (see Figure 34.31).

mind that it includes just a few examples of the fossil skulls that document the origin of mammals. If all the known fossils in the sequence were arranged by shape and placed side by side, their features would blend smoothly from one group to the next, reflecting how the features of a new group, the mammals, gradually arose in a previously existing group, the cynodonts.

CONCEPT CHECK 25.2

1. Your measurements indicate that a fossilized skull you unearthed has a carbon-14/carbon-12 ratio about $\frac{1}{16}$ that of the skulls of present-day animals. What is the approximate age of the fossilized skull?
2. Describe an example from the fossil record that shows how life has changed over time.
3. **WHAT IF?** Suppose researchers discover a fossil of an organism that lived 300 million years ago, but had mammalian teeth and a mammalian jaw hinge. What inferences might you draw from this fossil about the origin of mammals and the evolution of novel skeletal structures? Explain.

For suggested answers, see Appendix A.

CONCEPT 25.3
Key events in life's history include the origins of single-celled and multicelled organisms and the colonization of land

The study of fossils has helped geologists to establish a **geologic record** of Earth's history, which is divided into three eons (**Table 25.1**, on the facing page). The first two eons—the Archaean and the Proterozoic—together lasted approximately 4 billion years. The Phanerozoic eon, roughly the last half billion years, encompasses most of the time that animals have existed on Earth. It is divided into three eras: the Paleozoic, Mesozoic, and Cenozoic. Each era represents a distinct age in the history of Earth and its life. For example, the Mesozoic era is sometimes called the "age of reptiles" because of its abundance of reptilian fossils, including those of dinosaurs. The boundaries between the eras correspond to major extinction events seen in the fossil record, when many forms of life disappeared and were replaced by forms that evolved from the survivors.

As we've seen, the fossil record provides a sweeping overview of the history of life over geologic time. Here we will focus on a few major events in that history, returning to study the details in Unit Five. **Figure 25.7** uses the analogy of a clock to place these events in the context of the geologic record. This clock will reap-

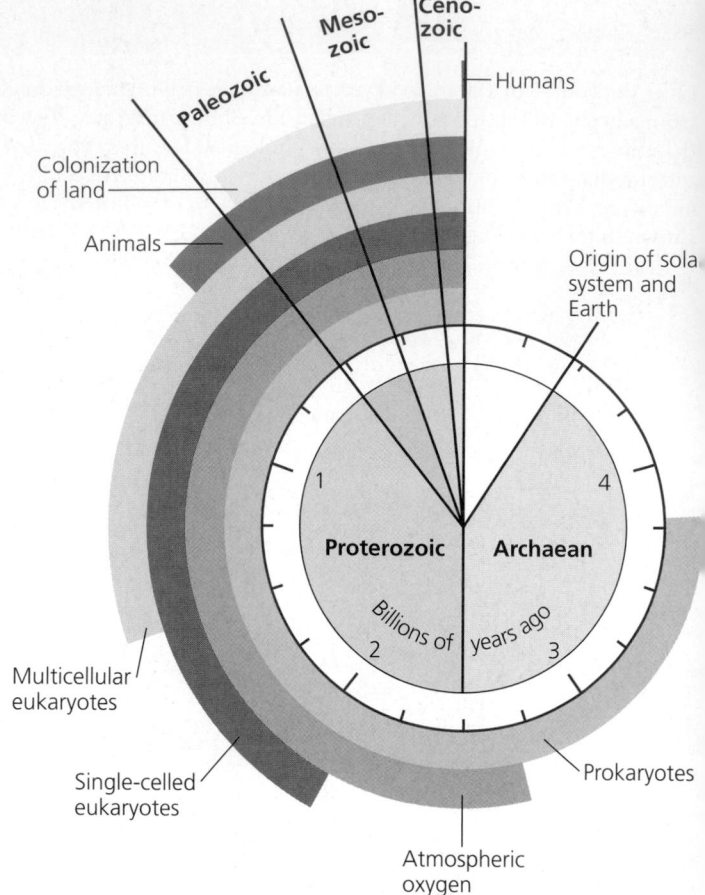

▲ Figure 25.7 **Clock analogy for some key events in Earth's history.** The clock ticks down from the origin of Earth 4.6 billion years ago to the present.

pear at various points in this section as a quick visual reminder of when the events we are discussing took place.

The First Single-Celled Organisms

The earliest evidence of life, dating from 3.5 billion years ago, comes from fossilized stromatolites (see Figure 25.4). **Stromatolites** are layered rocks that form when certain prokaryotes bind thin films of sediment together. Present-day stromatolites are found in a few warm, shallow, salty bays. If microbial communities complex enough to form stromatolites existed 3.5 billion years ago, it is a reasonable hypothesis that single-celled organisms originated much earlier, perhaps as early as 3.9 billion years ago.

Early prokaryotes were Earth's sole inhabitants from at least 3.5 billion years ago to about 2.1 billion years ago. As we will see, these prokaryotes transformed life on our planet.

Table 25.1 The Geologic Record

Relative Duration of Eons	Era	Period	Epoch	Age (Millions of Years Ago)	Some Important Events in the History of Life
Phanerozoic	Cenozoic	Neogene	Holocene	0.01	Historical time
			Pleistocene	1.8	Ice ages; humans appear
			Pliocene	5.3	Origin of genus *Homo*
			Miocene	23	Continued radiation of mammals and angiosperms; apelike ancestors of humans appear
		Paleogene	Oligocene	33.9	Origins of many primate groups, including apes
			Eocene	55.8	Angiosperm dominance increases; continued radiation of most present-day mammalian orders
			Paleocene	65.5	Major radiation of mammals, birds, and pollinating insects
	Mesozoic	Cretaceous		145.5	Flowering plants (angiosperms) appear and diversify; many groups of organisms, including most dinosaurs, become extinct at end of period
		Jurassic		199.6	Gymnosperms continue as dominant plants; dinosaurs abundant and diverse
		Triassic		251	Cone-bearing plants (gymnosperms) dominate landscape; dinosaurs evolve and radiate; origin of mammals
	Paleozoic	Permian		299	Radiation of reptiles; origin of most present-day groups of insects; extinction of many marine and terrestrial organisms at end of period
		Carboniferous		359.2	Extensive forests of vascular plants form; first seed plants appear; origin of reptiles; amphibians dominant
		Devonian		416	Diversification of bony fishes; first tetrapods and insects appear
		Silurian		443.7	Diversification of early vascular plants
		Ordovician		488.3	Marine algae abundant; colonization of land by diverse fungi, plants, and animals
		Cambrian		542	Sudden increase in diversity of many animal phyla (Cambrian explosion)
Proterozoic		Ediacaran		635	Diverse algae and soft-bodied invertebrate animals appear
				2,100	Oldest fossils of eukaryotic cells appear
				2,500	
				2,700	Concentration of atmospheric oxygen begins to increase
Archaean				3,500	Oldest fossils of cells (prokaryotes) appear
				3,800	Oldest known rocks on Earth's surface
				Approx. 4,600	Origin of Earth

Photosynthesis and the Oxygen Revolution

Atmospheric oxygen

Most atmospheric oxygen gas (O_2) is of biological origin, produced during the water-splitting step of photosynthesis. When oxygenic photosynthesis first evolved, the free O_2 it produced probably dissolved in the surrounding water until it reached a high enough concentration to react with dissolved iron. This would have caused the iron to precipitate as iron oxide, which accumulated as sediments. These sediments were compressed into banded iron formations, red layers of rock containing iron oxide that are a source of iron ore today (Figure 25.8). Once all of the dissolved iron had precipitated, additional O_2 dissolved in the water until the seas and lakes became saturated with O_2. After this occurred, the O_2 finally began to "gas out" of the water and enter the atmosphere. This change left its mark in the rusting of iron-rich terrestrial rocks, a process that began about 2.7 billion years ago. This chronology implies that bacteria similar to today's cyanobacteria (oxygen-releasing, photosynthetic bacteria) originated well before 2.7 billion years ago.

The amount of atmospheric O_2 increased gradually from about 2.7 to 2.2 billion years ago, but then shot up relatively rapidly to more than 10% of its present level. This "oxygen revolution" had an enormous impact on life. In certain of its chemical forms, oxygen attacks chemical bonds and can inhibit enzymes and damage cells. As a result the rising concentration of atmospheric O_2 probably doomed many prokaryotic groups. Some species survived in habitats that remained anaerobic, where we find their descendants living today (see Chapter 27). Among other survivors, diverse adaptations to the changing atmosphere evolved, including cellular respiration, which uses O_2 in the process of harvesting the energy stored in organic molecules.

▲ Figure 25.8 **Banded iron formations: evidence of oxygenic photosynthesis.** The reddish streaks in this sedimentary rock are bands of iron oxide.

As mentioned previously, the early, gradual rise in atmospheric O_2 levels was probably brought about by ancient cyanobacteria. A few hundred million years later, the rise in O_2 accelerated. What caused this acceleration? One hypothesis is that this rise followed the evolution of eukaryotic cells containing chloroplasts, as we will discuss in the next section.

The First Eukaryotes

Single-celled eukaryotes

The oldest widely accepted fossils of eukaryotic organisms are about 2.1 billion years old. Recall that eukaryotic cells have more complex organization than prokaryotic cells: Eukaryotic cells have a nuclear envelope, mitochondria, endoplasmic reticulum, and other internal structures that prokaryotes lack. Also, unlike prokaryotic cells, eukaryotic cells have a cytoskeleton, a feature that enables eukaryotic cells to change their shape and thereby surround and engulf other cells.

How did these eukaryotic features evolve from prokaryotic cells? A range of evidence supports a model called **endosymbiosis**, which posits that mitochondria and plastids (a general term for chloroplasts and related organelles) were formerly small prokaryotes that began living within larger cells. The term *endosymbiont* refers to a cell that lives within another cell, called the *host cell*. The prokaryotic ancestors of mitochondria and plastids probably gained entry to the host cell as undigested prey or internal parasites. Though such a process may seem unlikely, scientists have directly observed cases in which endosymbionts that began as prey or parasites came to have a mutually beneficial relationship with the host in as little as five years.

By whatever means the relationships began, we can hypothesize how the symbiosis could have become mutually beneficial. A heterotrophic host could use nutrients released from photosynthetic endosymbionts. And in a world that was becoming increasingly aerobic, a host that was itself an anaerobe would have benefited from endosymbionts that turned the oxygen to advantage. Over time, the host and endosymbionts would have become a single organism, its parts inseparable. Although all eukaryotes have mitochondria or remnants of these organelles, they do not all have plastids. Thus, the model of **serial endosymbiosis** supposes that mitochondria evolved before plastids through a sequence of endosymbiotic events (Figure 25.9).

A great deal of evidence supports the endosymbiotic origin of mitochondria and plastids. The inner membranes of both organelles have enzymes and transport systems that are homologous to those found in the plasma membranes of living prokaryotes. Mitochondria and plastids replicate by a splitting process that is similar to that of certain prokaryotes. In addition, each of these organelles contains a single, circular DNA

Cytoplasm
DNA
Plasma membrane

Ancestral prokaryote

Infolding of plasma membrane

Endoplasmic reticulum
Nucleus
Nuclear envelope

Engulfing of aerobic heterotrophic prokaryote

Cell with nucleus and endomembrane system

Mitochondrion

Ancestral heterotrophic eukaryote

Mitochondrion

Engulfing of photosynthetic prokaryote by some cells

Plastid

Ancestral photosynthetic eukaryote

▲ **Figure 25.9 A model of the origin of eukaryotes through serial endosymbiosis.** The proposed ancestors of mitochondria were aerobic, heterotrophic prokaryotes (meaning they used oxygen to metabolize organic molecules obtained from other organisms). The proposed ancestors of plastids were photosynthetic prokaryotes. Note that the arrows represent change over evolutionary time.

molecule that, like the chromosomes of bacteria, is not associated with histones or large amounts of other proteins. As might be expected of organelles descended from free-living organisms, mitochondria and plastids also have the cellular machinery (including ribosomes) needed to transcribe and translate their DNA into proteins. Finally, in terms of size, nucleotide sequence, and sensitivity to certain antibiotics, the ribosomes of mitochondria and plastids are more similar to prokaryotic ribosomes than they are to the cytoplasmic ribosomes of eukaryotic cells.

The Origin of Multicellularity

An orchestra can play a greater variety of musical compositions than a violin soloist can; the increased complexity of the orchestra makes more variations possible. Likewise, the appearance of structurally complex eukaryotic cells sparked the evolution of greater morphological diversity than was possible for the simpler prokaryotic cells. After the first eukaryotes appeared, a great range of unicellular forms evolved, giving rise to the diversity of single-celled eukaryotes that continue to flourish today. Another wave of diversification also occurred: Some single-celled eukaryotes gave rise to multicellular forms, whose descendants include a variety of algae, plants, fungi, and animals.

The Earliest Multicellular Eukaryotes

Multicellular eukaryotes

Based on comparisons of DNA sequences, researchers have suggested that the common ancestor of multicellular eukaryotes lived 1.5 billion years ago. This result is in rough agreement with the fossil record; the oldest known fossils of multicellular eukaryotes are of relatively small algae that lived about 1.2 billion years ago. Larger and more diverse multicellular eukaryotes do not appear in the fossil record until about 565 million years ago (see Figure 25.4). These fossils, referred to as the Ediacaran biota, were of soft-bodied organisms—some over 1 m long—that lived from 565 to 535 million years ago.

Why were multicellular eukaryotes limited in size and diversity until the late Proterozoic? Geologic evidence indicates that a series of severe ice ages occurred from 750 to 580 million years ago. At various times during this period, glaciers covered all of the planet's landmasses, and the seas were largely iced over. The "snowball Earth" hypothesis suggests that most life would have been confined to areas near deep-sea vents and hot springs or to equatorial regions of the ocean that lacked ice cover. The fossil record of the first major diversification of multicellular eukaryotes (beginning about 565 million years ago) corresponds roughly to the time when snowball Earth thawed. As that diversification came to a close about 30 million years later, the stage was set for another, even more spectacular burst of evolutionary change.

The Cambrian Explosion

Animals

Many phyla of living animals appear suddenly in fossils formed early in the Cambrian period (535–525 million years ago), a phenomenon referred to as the **Cambrian explosion**. Fossils of at least three living animal phyla—Cnidaria (sea anemones and their relatives), Porifera (sponges), and Mollusca (molluscs)—appear in even older rocks dating from the late Proterozoic **(Figure 25.10)**.

Prior to the Cambrian explosion, all large animals were soft-bodied. The fossils of large pre-Cambrian animals reveal little evidence of predation. Instead, these animals appear to have been herbivores (feeding on algae), filter feeders, or scavengers, not hunters. The Cambrian explosion changed all of that. In a relatively short period of time (10 million years), predators over 1 m in length emerged that had claws and other features for capturing prey; simultaneously, new defensive adaptations, such as sharp spines and heavy body armor, appeared in their prey (see Figure 25.4). The safe, slow-moving

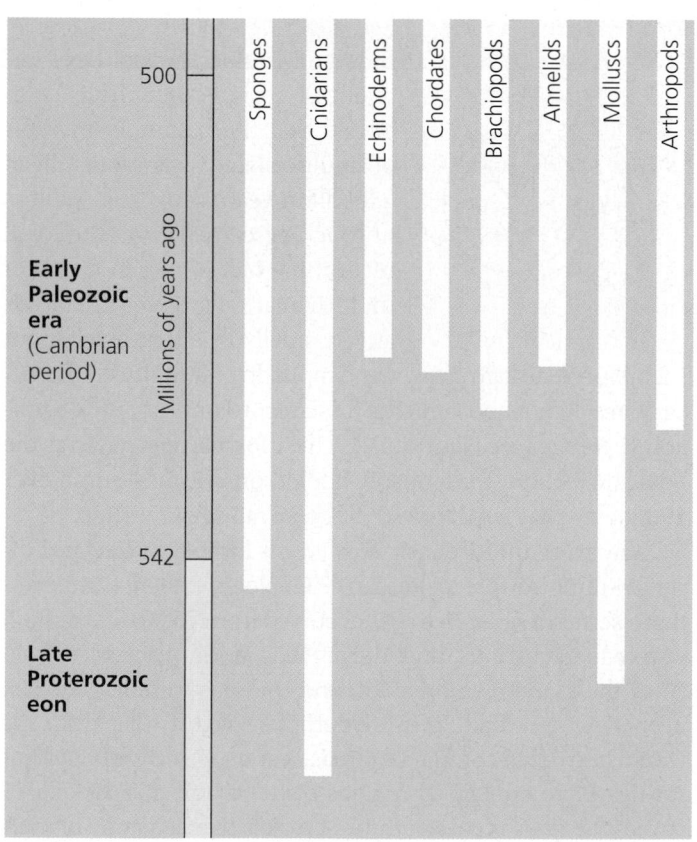

▲ **Figure 25.10 Appearance of selected animal phyla.** The yellow bars indicate earliest appearances of these phyla in the fossil record, although they could have originated earlier.

 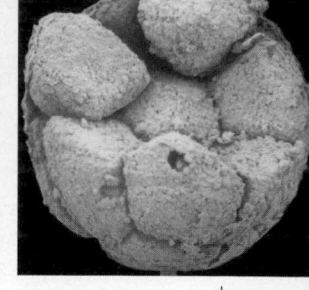

(a) Two-cell stage 150 μm **(b) Later stage** 200 μm

▲ **Figure 25.11 Proterozoic fossils that may be animal embryos (SEM).**

world that characterized larger forms of life before the Cambrian explosion was gone forever.

Although the Cambrian explosion had an enormous impact on life on Earth, it is possible that many animal phyla originated long before that time. Some DNA analyses suggest that most animal phyla originated and began to diverge from one another as early as 700 million to 1 billion years ago. Even if these estimates are not correct, recent fossil discoveries in China suggest that animals similar to members of living animal phyla were present tens of millions of years before the Cambrian explosion. The discoveries include 575-million-year-old fossils of beautifully preserved specimens interpreted by some scientists as animal embryos and by others as members of extinct groups closely related to animals **(Figure 25.11)**. Overall, as noted by Cambridge University paleontologist Simon Conway Morris, "the Cambrian explosion had a long fuse"—at least 40 million years long, based on the Chinese fossils. The fuse may have been hundreds of millions of years long if some animal phyla originated as far back as some DNA-based estimates suggest.

The Colonization of Land

Colonization of land

The colonization of land was another milestone in the history of life. There is fossil evidence that cyanobacteria and other photosynthetic prokaryotes coated damp terrestrial surfaces well over a billion years ago. However, larger forms of life, such as fungi, plants, and animals, did not begin to colonize land until about 500 million years ago. This gradual evolutionary venture out of aquatic environments was associated with adaptations that made it possible to reproduce on land and that helped prevent dehydration. For example, many land plants today have a vascular system for transporting materials internally and a waterproof coating of wax on their leaves that slows the loss of water to the air. Early signs of these adaptations were present 420 million years ago, at which time there were small plants (about 10 cm high) that had a vascular system but lacked true roots or leaves. About 50 million years later, plants had diversified greatly and included reeds and treelike plants with true roots and leaves.

Plants colonized land in the company of fungi. Even today, the roots of most plants are associated with fungi that aid in the absorption of water and minerals from the soil (see Chapter 31). These root fungi, in turn, obtain their organic nutrients from the plants. Such mutually beneficial associations of plants and fungi are evident in some of the oldest fossilized roots, dating this relationship back to the early spread of life onto land.

Although many animal groups are now represented in terrestrial environments, the most widespread and diverse land animals are arthropods (particularly insects and spiders) and tetrapods. The earliest tetrapods found in the fossil record lived about 365 million years ago and appear to have evolved from a group of lobe-finned fishes (see Chapter 34). Tetrapods include humans, although we are late arrivals on the scene. The human lineage diverged from other primates around 6–7 million years ago, and our species originated only about 195,000 years ago. If the clock of Earth's history were rescaled to represent an hour, humans appeared less than 0.2 second ago.

CONCEPT 25.4

The rise and fall of dominant groups reflect continental drift, mass extinctions, and adaptive radiations

From its beginnings, life on Earth has seen the rise and fall of groups of organisms. Anaerobic prokaryotes originated, flourished, and then declined as the oxygen content of the atmosphere rose. Billions of years later, the first tetrapods emerged from the sea, giving rise to amphibians that went on to dominate life on land for 100 million years—until other tetrapods (including dinosaurs and later, mammals) replaced them as the dominant terrestrial vertebrates. These and other major changes in life on Earth have been influenced by large-scale processes such as continental drift, mass extinctions, and adaptive radiations.

Continental Drift

If photographs of Earth were taken from space every 10,000 years and spliced together to make a movie, it would show something many of us find hard to imagine: The seemingly "rock solid" continents we live on move over time. Since the origin of multicellular eukaryotes roughly 1.5 billion years ago, there have been three occasions (1.1 billion, 600 million, and 250 million years ago) in which all of the landmasses of Earth came together to form a supercontinent, then later broke apart. Each time they yielded a different configuration of continents. Looking into the future, geologists estimate that the continents will come together again and form a new supercontinent roughly 250 million years from now.

The continents are part of great plates of Earth's crust that essentially float on the hot, underlying portion of the mantle (Figure 25.12a). These plates move over time in a process

▼ Figure 25.12 **Earth and its continental plates.**

(a) Cutaway view of Earth. The thickness of the crust is exaggerated here.

(b) Major continental plates. The arrows indicate direction of movement. The reddish-orange dots represent zones of violent tectonic activity.

called **continental drift**. Geologists can measure the rate at which the continental plates are moving today—usually only a few centimeters per year. They can also infer the past locations of the continents using the magnetic signal recorded in rocks at the time of their formation. This method works because as a continent shifts its position over time, the direction of magnetic north recorded in its newly formed rocks also changes.

Earth's major continental plates are shown in **Figure 25.12b**. Many important geologic processes, including the formation of mountains and islands, occur at plate boundaries. In some cases, two plates are moving away from one another, as are the North American and Eurasian plates, which are currently drifting apart at a rate of about 2 cm per year. In other cases, two plates are sliding past one another, forming regions where earthquakes are common. California's infamous San Andreas Fault is part of a border where two plates slide past each other. In still other cases, two plates are colliding. Typically, oceanic plates (those found on the bottom of the ocean) are more dense than terrestrial plates. As a result, when an oceanic plate collides with a terrestrial plate, the oceanic plate usually sinks below the terrestrial plate. When two oceanic plates or two terrestrial plates collide with one another, violent upheavals occur and mountains form along the plate boundaries. One spectacular example of this occurred 55 million years ago, when the Indian plate crashed into the Eurasian plate, starting the formation of the Himalayan mountains.

Consequences of Continental Drift

Plate movements rearrange geography slowly, but their cumulative effects are dramatic. In addition to reshaping the physical features of our planet, continental drift also has a major impact on life on Earth.

One reason for its great impact on life is that continental drift alters the habitats in which organisms live. Consider the changes shown in **Figure 25.13**. About 250 million years ago, plate movements brought all the previously separated landmasses together into a supercontinent named **Pangaea**, meaning "all land." Ocean basins became deeper, which lowered sea level and drained shallow coastal seas. At that time, as now, most marine species inhabited shallow waters, and the formation of Pangaea destroyed a considerable amount of that habitat. The interior of the vast continent was cold and dry, probably an even more severe environment than that of central Asia today. Overall, the formation of Pangaea had a tremendous impact on the physical environment and climate, which drove some species to extinction and provided new opportunities for groups of organisms that survived the crisis.

Another effect of continental drift is the climate change that results when a continent shifts northward or southward. The southern tip of Labrador, Canada, for example, once was located near the equator but has moved 40° to the north over the last 200 million years. To appreciate the impact of such a

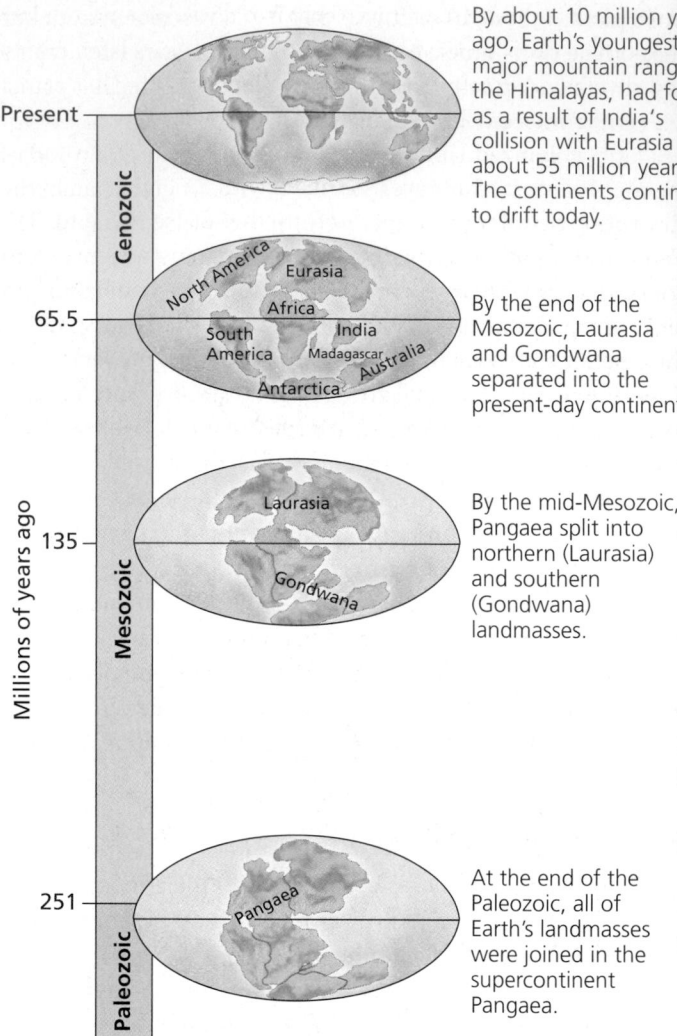

By about 10 million years ago, Earth's youngest major mountain range the Himalayas, had for as a result of India's collision with Eurasia about 55 million years The continents continu to drift today.

By the end of the Mesozoic, Laurasia and Gondwana separated into the present-day continents

By the mid-Mesozoic, Pangaea split into northern (Laurasia) and southern (Gondwana) landmasses.

At the end of the Paleozoic, all of Earth's landmasses were joined in the supercontinent Pangaea.

▲ Figure 25.13 **The history of continental drift during the Phanerozoic eon.**

shift, compare the climate of Wilmington, Delaware (about 40° north latitude), to that of Belem, Brazil (located near the equator). In the winter, temperatures in Wilmington have fallen as low as $-26°C$ ($-15°F$), while temperatures in Belem have never dropped below $18°C$ ($64°F$). When faced with such changes in climate, organisms adapt, move to a new location, or become extinct (this last outcome occurred for most organisms stranded on Antarctica, such as *Cryolophosaurus*, depicted in Figure 25.1). The shifting positions of the continents are also thought to have rerouted the world's ocean currents, causing the global climate to become colder and contributing to the formation of polar ice caps over the past 15 million years.

Continental drift also promotes allopatric speciation on a grand scale. When supercontinents break apart, regions that once were connected become geographically isolated. As the continents drifted apart over the last 200 million years, each became a separate evolutionary arena, with lineages of plants and animals that diverged from those on other continents (see Figure 24.6 for one example).

Finally, continental drift can help explain puzzles about the geographic distribution of extinct organisms, such as why fossils of the same species of Permian freshwater reptiles have been discovered in both Brazil and the West African nation of Ghana. These two parts of the world, now separated by 3,000 km of ocean, were joined together when these reptiles were living. Continental drift also explains much about the current distributions of organisms, such as why Australian fauna and flora contrast so sharply with those of the rest of the world. Marsupial mammals fill ecological roles in Australia analogous to those filled by eutherians (placental mammals) on other continents (see Figure 22.20). Marsupials probably originated in what is now Asia and North America and reached Australia via South America and Antarctica while the continents were still joined. The subsequent breakup of the southern continents set Australia "afloat" like a great ark of marsupials. In Australia, marsupials diversified, and the few early eutherians that lived there became extinct; on other continents, most marsupials became extinct, and the eutherians diversified.

Mass Extinctions

The fossil record shows that the overwhelming majority of species that ever lived are now extinct. A species may become extinct for many reasons. Its habitat may have been destroyed, or its environment may have changed in a manner unfavorable to the species. For example, if ocean temperatures fall by even a few degrees, species that are otherwise well adapted may perish. Even if physical factors in the environment remain stable, biological factors may change—the origin of one species can spell doom for another.

Although extinction occurs on a regular basis, at certain times disruptive global environmental changes have caused the rate of extinction to increase dramatically. When this occurs, a **mass extinction** results, in which large numbers of species become extinct throughout Earth.

The "Big Five" Mass Extinction Events

Five mass extinctions are documented in the fossil record over the past 500 million years **(Figure 25.14)**. These events are particularly well documented for the decimation of hard-bodied animals that lived in shallow seas, the organisms for which the fossil record is most complete. In each mass extinction, 50% or more of Earth's marine species became extinct.

Two mass extinctions—the Permian and the Cretaceous—have received the most attention. The Permian mass extinction, which defines the boundary between the Paleozoic and Mesozoic eras (251 million years ago), claimed about 96% of marine animal species and drastically altered life in the ocean. Terrestrial life was also affected. For example, 8 out of 27 known orders of insects were wiped out. This mass extinction occurred in less than 5 million years, possibly in a few thousands of years—an instant in the context of geologic time.

The Permian mass extinction occurred at the time of enormous volcanic eruptions in what is now Siberia. This period was the most extreme episode of volcanism to have occurred during the past half billion years. Geologic data indicate that an area of 1.6 million km^2 (roughly half the size of western Europe) was covered with a layer of lava hundreds to thousands of meters thick. Besides spewing enormous amounts of lava and ash, the eruptions may have produced enough carbon

◄ **Figure 25.14 Mass extinction and the diversity of life.** The five generally recognized mass extinction events, indicated by red arrows, represent peaks in the extinction rate of marine animal families (red line and left vertical axis). These mass extinctions interrupted the overall increase in the number of marine animal families over time (blue line and right vertical axis).

dioxide to warm the global climate by an estimated 6°C. Reduced temperature differences between the equator and the poles would have slowed the mixing of ocean water, which in turn would have reduced the amount of oxygen available to marine organisms. This oxygen deficit may have been a major cause of the Permian extinction of marine life.

The Cretaceous mass extinction occurred about 65.5 million years ago and marks the boundary between the Mesozoic and Cenozoic eras. This event extinguished more than half of all marine species and eliminated many families of terrestrial plants and animals, including most of the dinosaurs. One clue to a possible cause of the Cretaceous mass extinction is a thin layer of clay enriched in iridium that separates sediments from the Mesozoic and Cenozoic eras. Iridium is an element that is very rare on Earth but common in many of the meteorites and other extraterrestrial objects that occasionally fall to Earth. Walter Alvarez and the late Luis Alvarez, of the University of California, Berkeley, and their colleagues proposed that this clay is fallout from a huge cloud of debris that billowed into the atmosphere when an asteroid or large comet collided with Earth. This cloud would have blocked sunlight and severely disturbed the global climate for several months.

Is there evidence of such an asteroid or comet? Research has focused on the Chicxulub crater, a 65-million-year-old scar beneath sediments off the Yucatán coast of Mexico (Figure 25.15). About 180 km in diameter, the crater is the right size to have been caused by an object with a diameter of 10 km. Critical evaluation of this and other hypotheses for mass extinctions continues.

Is a Sixth Mass Extinction Under Way?

As we will explore in Chapter 56, human actions, such as habitat destruction, are modifying the global environment to such an extent that many species are threatened with extinction. More than a thousand species have become extinct in the last 400 years. Scientists estimate that this rate is 100 to 1,000 times the typical background rate seen in the fossil record. Is a sixth mass extinction now in progress?

This question is difficult to answer, in part because it is hard to document the total number of extinctions occurring today. Tropical rain forests, for example, harbor many undiscovered species. As a result, destroying tropical forest may drive species to extinction before we even learn of their existence. Such uncertainties make it hard to assess the full extent of the current extinction crisis. Even so, it is clear that losses to date have not reached those of the "big five" mass extinctions, in which large percentages of Earth's species became extinct. This does not in any way discount the seriousness of today's situation. Monitoring programs show that many species are declining at an alarming rate. Such data suggest that unless dramatic actions are taken, a sixth (human-caused) mass extinction is likely to occur within the next few centuries or millennia.

Consequences of Mass Extinctions

By removing large numbers of species, a mass extinction can reduce a thriving and complex ecological community to a pale shadow of its former self. In addition, when an evolutionary lineage disappears, it cannot reappear. This changes the course of evolution forever. Consider what would have happened if the early primates living 66 million years ago had died out in the

▲ Figure 25.15 **Trauma for Earth and its Cretaceous life.** The 65-million-year-old Chicxulub impact crater is located in the Caribbean Sea near the Yucatán Peninsula of Mexico. The horseshoe shape of the crater and the pattern of debris in sedimentary rocks indicate that an asteroid or comet struck at a low angle from the southeast. This artist's interpretation represents the impact and its immediate effect—a cloud of hot vapor and debris that could have killed many of the plants and animals in North America within hours.

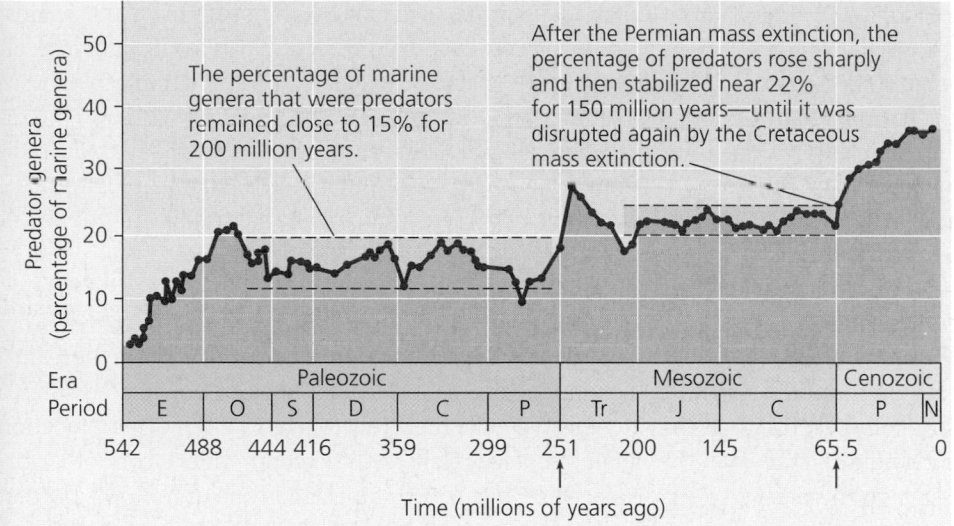

The percentage of marine genera that were predators remained close to 15% for 200 million years.

After the Permian mass extinction, the percentage of predators rose sharply and then stabilized near 22% for 150 million years—until it was disrupted again by the Cretaceous mass extinction.

▲ **Figure 25.16 Mass extinctions and ecology.** The Permian and Cretaceous mass extinctions (indicated by red arrows) altered the ecology of the oceans by increasing the percentage of marine genera that were predators.

Cretaceous mass extinction. Humans would not exist, and life on Earth would differ greatly from how we know it.

The fossil record shows that it typically takes 5–10 million years for the diversity of life to recover to previous levels after a mass extinction. In some cases, it has taken much longer than that: It took about 100 million years for the number of marine families to recover after the Permian mass extinction (see Figure 25.14). These data have sobering implications. If current trends continue and a sixth mass extinction occurs, it will take millions of years for life on Earth to recover.

Mass extinctions can also alter ecological communities by changing the types of organisms found in them. For example, after the Permian and Cretaceous mass extinctions, the percentage of marine organisms that were predators increased substantially **(Figure 25.16)**. A rise in the number of predator species can increase both the pressures faced by prey and the competition among predators for food. In addition, mass extinctions can remove lineages with highly advantageous features. For example, in the late Triassic a group of gastropods (snails and their relatives) arose that could drill through the shells of bivalves (such as clams) and feed on the animals inside. Although shell drilling provided access to a new and abundant source of food, this newly formed group was wiped out during the mass extinction at the end of the Triassic (about 200 million years ago). Another 120 million years passed before another group of gastropods (the oyster drills) exhibited the ability to drill through shells. As their predecessors might have done if they had not origi-

nated shortly before the Triassic mass extinction, oyster drills have since diversified into many new species. Finally, by eliminating so many of Earth's species, mass extinctions can pave the way for adaptive radiations, in which new groups of organisms rise to prominence.

Adaptive Radiations

The fossil record indicates that the diversity of life has increased over the past 250 million years (see Figure 25.14). This increase has been fueled by **adaptive radiations**, periods of evolutionary change in which groups of organisms form many new species whose adaptations allow them to fill different ecological roles, or niches, in their communities. Large-scale adaptive radiations occurred after each of the big five mass extinctions, when survivors became adapted to the many vacant ecological niches. Adaptive radiations have also occurred in groups of organisms that possessed major evolutionary innovations, such as seeds or armored body coverings, or that colonized regions in which they faced little competition from other species.

Worldwide Adaptive Radiations

Fossil evidence indicates that mammals underwent a dramatic adaptive radiation after the extinction of terrestrial dinosaurs 65.5 million years ago **(Figure 25.17)**. Although mammals originated about 180 million years ago, the mammal fossils older than 65.5 million years are mostly small and not morphologically diverse. Many species appear to have been nocturnal based on their large eye sockets, similar to those in living nocturnal mammals. A few early mammals were intermediate in

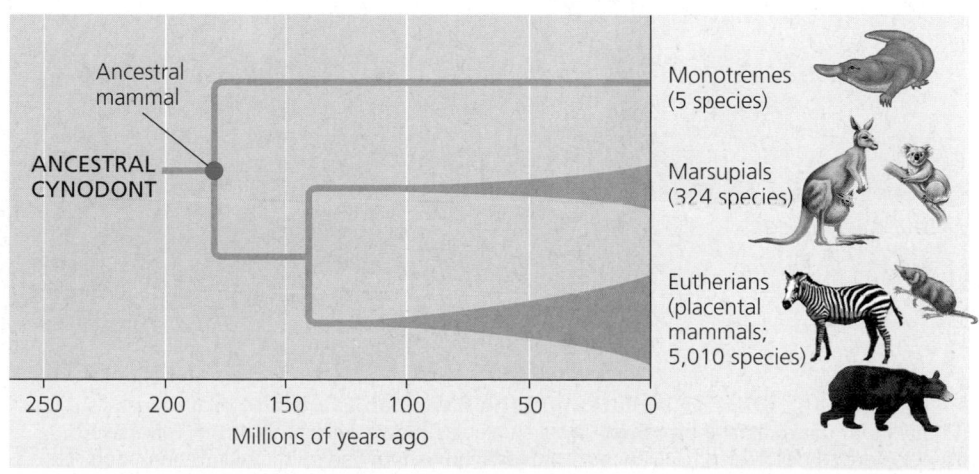

▲ **Figure 25.17 Adaptive radiation of mammals.**

size, such as *Repenomamus giganticus*, a 1-meter-long predator that lived 130 million years ago—but none approached the size of many dinosaurs. Early mammals may have been restricted in size and diversity because they were eaten or outcompeted by the larger and more diverse dinosaurs. With the disappearance of the dinosaurs (except for birds, which are considered members of the same group; see Chapter 34), mammals expanded greatly in both diversity and size, filling the ecological roles once occupied by terrestrial dinosaurs.

The history of life has also been greatly altered by radiations in which groups of organisms increased in diversity as they came to play entirely new ecological roles in their communities. Examples include the rise of photosynthetic prokaryotes, the evolution of large predators in the Cambrian explosion, and the radiations following the colonization of land by plants, insects, and tetrapods. Each of these last three radiations was associated with major evolutionary innovations that facilitated life on land. The radiation of land plants, for example, was associated

with key adaptations, such as stems that support plants against gravity and a waxy coat that protects leaves from water loss. Finally, organisms that arise in an adaptive radiation can serve as a new source of food for still other organisms. In fact, the diversification of land plants stimulated a series of adaptive radiations in insects that ate or pollinated plants, helping to make insects the most diverse group of animals on Earth today.

Regional Adaptive Radiations

Striking adaptive radiations have also occurred over more limited geographic areas. Such radiations can be initiated when a few organisms make their way to a new, often distant location in which they face relatively little competition from other organisms. The Hawaiian archipelago is one of the world's great showcases of this type of adaptive radiation (**Figure 25.18**). Located about 3,500 km from the nearest continent, the volcanic islands are progressively older as one follows the chain toward

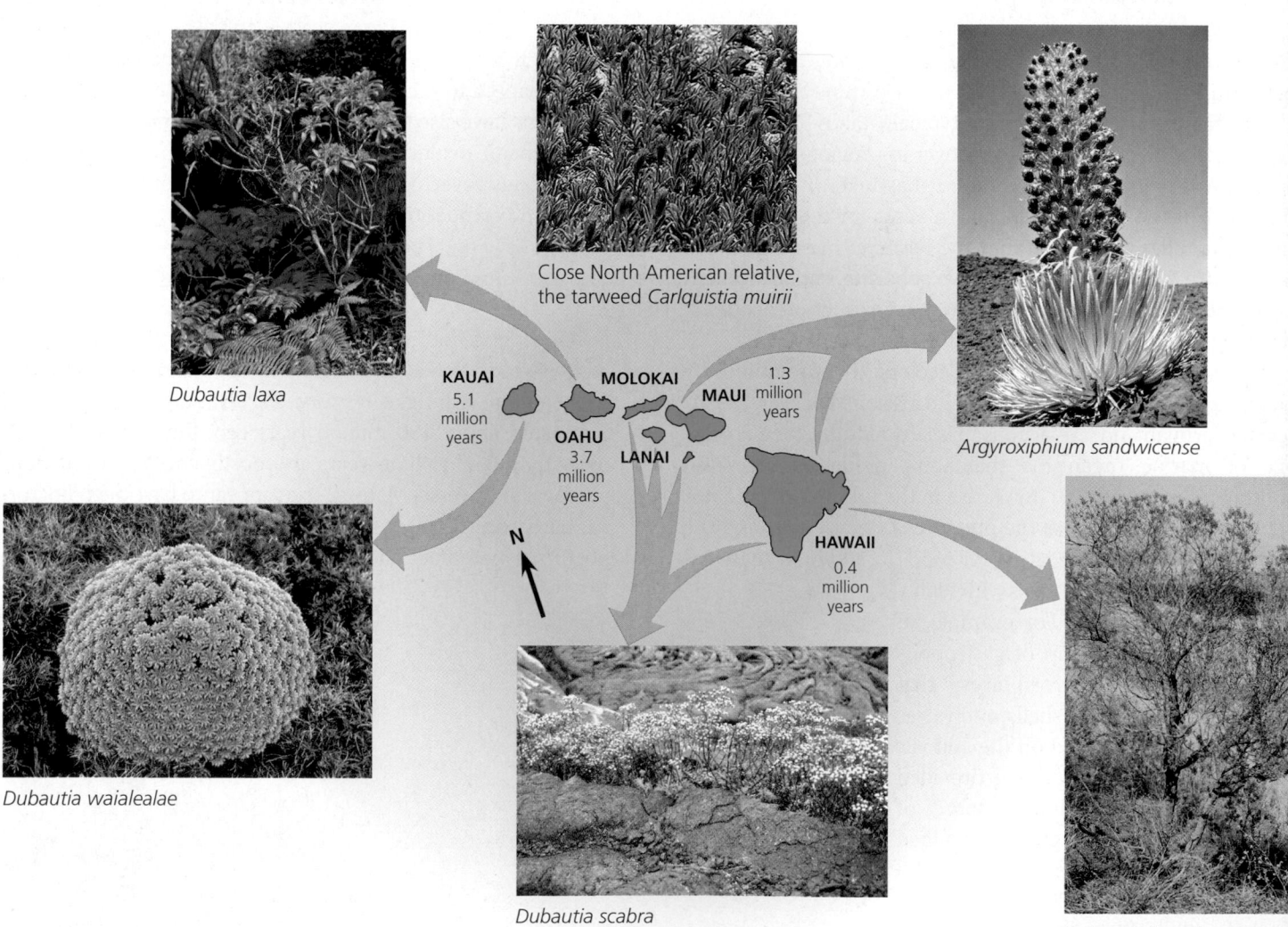

▲ Figure 25.18 Adaptive radiation on the Hawaiian Islands. Molecular analysis indicates that these remarkably varied Hawaiian plants, known collectively as the "silversword alliance," are all descended from an ancestral tarweed that arrived on the islands about 5 million years ago from North America. Members of the silversword alliance have since spread into different habitats and formed new species with strikingly different adaptations.

the northwest; the youngest island, Hawaii, is less than a million years old and still has active volcanoes. Each island was born "naked" and was gradually populated by stray organisms that rode the ocean currents and winds either from far-distant land areas or from older islands of the archipelago itself. The physical diversity of each island, including immense variation in elevation and rainfall, provides many opportunities for evolutionary divergence by natural selection. Multiple invasions followed by speciation events have ignited an explosion of adaptive radiation in Hawaii. Most of the thousands of species that inhabit the islands are found nowhere else on Earth.

CONCEPT CHECK 25.4

1. Explain consequences of continental drift for life on Earth.
2. What factors promote adaptive radiations?
3. **WHAT IF?** If a mass extinction were caused by a single, catastrophic event (such as an asteroid impact), what pattern would you expect regarding the dates when formerly common species lost in the extinction are last observed in the fossil record?

For suggested answers, see Appendix A.

CONCEPT 25.5

Major changes in body form can result from changes in the sequences and regulation of developmental genes

The fossil record tells us what the great changes in the history of life have been and when they occurred. Moreover, an understanding of continental drift, mass extinction, and adaptive radiation provides a picture of how those changes came about. But we can also seek to understand the intrinsic biological mechanisms that underlie changes seen in the fossil record. For this, we turn to genetic mechanisms of change, paying particular attention to genes that influence development.

Evolutionary Effects of Developmental Genes

As you read in Chapter 21, "evo-devo"—research at the interface between evolutionary biology and developmental biology—is illuminating how slight genetic divergences can produce major morphological differences between species. Genes that control development influence the rate, timing, and spatial pattern of change in an organism's form as it develops from a zygote into an adult.

Changes in Rate and Timing

Many striking evolutionary transformations are the result of **heterochrony** (from the Greek *hetero*, different, and *chronos*,

time), an evolutionary change in the rate or timing of developmental events. For example, an organism's shape depends in part on the relative growth rates of different body parts during development. **Figure 25.19a** tracks how changes in such growth rates alter human body proportions during development. Even slight changes in relative rates of growth can change the adult form substantially, as seen in the contrasting shapes of human and chimpanzee skulls **(Figure 25.19b)**.

Heterochrony can also alter the timing of reproductive development relative to the development of nonreproductive organs. If reproductive-organ development accelerates compared to other organs, the sexually mature stage of a species may retain

Newborn   2   5   15   Adult
Age (years)

(a) Differential growth rates in a human. The arms and legs lengthen more during growth than the head and trunk, as can be seen in this conceptualization of an individual at different ages all rescaled to the same height.

Chimpanzee fetus   Chimpanzee adult

Human fetus   Human adult

(b) Comparison of chimpanzee and human skull growth. The fetal skulls of chimpanzees and humans are similar in shape. However, growth in the jaw is accelerated in chimpanzees relative to humans, producing the characteristic elongated skull and sloping forehead of an adult chimpanzee.

▲ Figure 25.19 **Relative growth rates of body parts.**

body features that were juvenile structures in an ancestral species—a condition called **paedomorphosis** (from the Greek *paedos*, of a child, and *morphosis*, formation). For example, most salamander species have aquatic larvae that undergo metamorphosis in becoming adults. But some species grow to adult size and become sexually mature while retaining gills and other larval features (**Figure 25.20**). Such an evolutionary alteration of developmental timing can produce animals that appear very different from their ancestors, even though the overall genetic change may be small. Indeed, recent evidence indicates that a change at a single locus was probably sufficient to bring about paedomorphosis in the axolotl salamander, although other genes may have contributed as well.

Changes in Spatial Pattern

Substantial evolutionary changes can also result from alterations in genes that control the placement and spatial organization of body parts. For example, master regulatory genes called **homeotic genes** (described in Chapters 18 and 21) determine such basic features as where a pair of wings and a pair of legs will develop on a bird or how a plant's flower parts are arranged.

The products of one class of homeotic genes, the *Hox* genes, provide positional information in an animal embryo. This information prompts cells to develop into structures appropriate for a particular location. Changes in *Hox* genes or in how they are expressed can have a profound impact on morphology. For example, among crustaceans, a change in the location where two *Hox* genes (*Ubx* and *Scr*) are expressed correlates with the conversion of a swimming appendage to a feeding appendage.

The evolution of vertebrates from invertebrate animals was an even larger evolutionary change, and it, too, may have been influenced by alterations in *Hox* genes and the genes that regulate them. Two duplications of *Hox* genes have occurred in the vertebrate lineage, and all vertebrate genomes tested to date have both of these duplications. As outlined in **Figure 25.21**,

▲ Figure 25.20 Paedomorphosis. The adults of some species retain features that were juvenile in ancestors. This salamander is an axolotl, an aquatic species that grows to full size, becomes sexually mature, and reproduces while retaining certain larval (tadpole) characteristics, including gills.

Hypothetical vertebrate ancestor (invertebrate) with a single *Hox* cluster

First *Hox* duplication

Hypothetical early vertebrates (jawless) with two *Hox* clusters

Second *Hox* duplication

Vertebrates (with jaws) with four *Hox* clusters

❶ Most invertebrates have one cluster of homeotic genes (the *Hox* complex), shown here as bands on a chromosome. *Hox* genes direct development of major body parts.

❷ A mutation (duplication) of the single *Hox* complex occurred about 520 million years ago and may have provided genetic material associated with the origin of the first vertebrates.

❸ In an early vertebrate, the duplicate set of genes took on entirely new roles, such as directing the development of a backbone.

❹ A second duplication of the *Hox* complex, yielding the four clusters found in most present-day vertebrates, occurred later, about 425 million years ago. This duplication, probably the result of a polyploidy event, may have allowed the development of even greater structural complexity, such as jaws and limbs.

❺ The vertebrate *Hox* complex contains duplicates of many of the same genes as the single invertebrate cluster, in virtually the same linear order on chromosomes, and they direct the sequential development of the same body regions. Scientists infer that the four clusters of the vertebrate *Hox* complex are homologous to the single cluster in invertebrates.

▲ Figure 25.21 *Hox* mutations and the origin of vertebrates.

these duplications may have been instrumental in the origin of novel characteristics in the vertebrates. This hypothesis remains controversial, however, in part because in addition to the *Hox* genes, many other genes (perhaps the entire genome) were duplicated in the vertebrate ancestor. Thus, the origin of novel characteristics cannot be ascribed solely to new *Hox* genes.

The Evolution of Development

The 565-million-year-old fossils of Ediacaran animals suggest that a set of genes sufficient to produce complex animals existed at least 30 million years *before* the Cambrian explosion. If developmental genes have existed for so long, how can we explain the astonishing increases in diversity seen during and since the Cambrian explosion?

Adaptive evolution by natural selection provides one answer to this question. As we've seen throughout this unit, by sorting among differences in the sequence of protein-encoding genes, selection can improve adaptations rapidly. In addition, new genes (created by gene duplication events) may have taken on a wide range of new metabolic and structural functions. Thus, adaptive evolution of new and existing genes may have played a key role in shaping the great diversity of life.

Examples in the previous section suggest that developmental genes may play a critical role. For the remainder of this section, we'll focus on how new morphological forms arise by changing the nucleotide sequences or regulation of developmental genes.

Changes in Genes

New developmental genes arising after gene duplication events very likely facilitated the origin of new morphological forms. But as we discussed regarding the possible role of new *Hox* genes in the origin of vertebrates, it can be difficult to establish causal links between genetic and morphological changes that occurred in the past.

This difficulty was sidestepped in a recent study of developmental changes associated with the divergence of six-legged insects from crustacean-like ancestors that had more than six legs. In insects, such as *Drosophila*, the *Ubx* gene is expressed in the abdomen, while in crustaceans, such as *Artemia*, it is expressed in the main trunk of the body (Figure 25.22). When expressed, the *Ubx* gene suppresses leg formation in insects but not in crustaceans. To examine the workings of this gene, researchers cloned the *Ubx* gene from *Drosophila* and *Artemia*. Next, they genetically engineered fruit fly embryos to express either the *Drosophila Ubx* gene or the *Artemia Ubx* gene throughout their bodies. The *Drosophila* gene suppressed 100% of the limbs in the embryos, as expected, whereas the *Artemia* gene suppressed only 15%.

The researchers then sought to uncover key steps involved in the evolutionary transition from a crustacean *Ubx* gene to an insect *Ubx* gene. Their approach was to identify mutations that would cause the *Artemia Ubx* gene to suppress leg for-

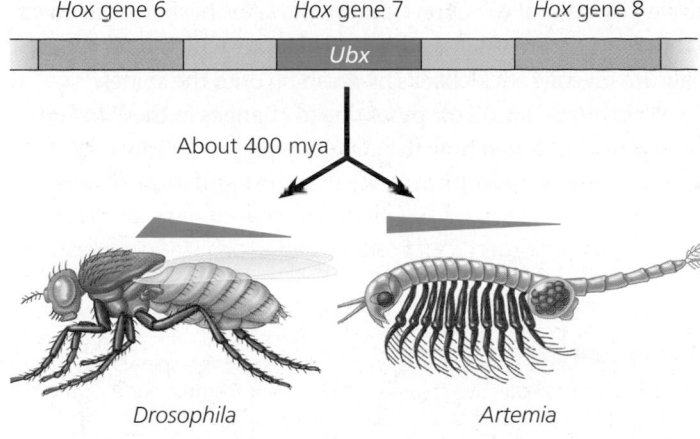

▲ **Figure 25.22 Origin of the insect body plan.** Expression of the *Hox* gene *Ubx* suppresses the formation of legs in fruit flies (*Drosophila*) but not in brine shrimp (*Artemia*), thus helping to build the insect body plan. Fruit fly and brine shrimp *Hox* genes have evolved independently for 400 million years.

mation, thus making the crustacean gene act more like an insect *Ubx* gene. To do this, they constructed a series of "hybrid" *Ubx* genes, each of which contained known segments of the *Drosophila Ubx* gene and known segments of the *Artemia Ubx* gene. By inserting these hybrid genes into fruit fly embryos (one hybrid gene per embryo) and observing their effects on leg development, the researchers were able to pinpoint the exact amino acid changes responsible for the suppression of additional limbs in insects. In so doing, this study provided experimental evidence linking a particular change in the sequence of a developmental gene to a major evolutionary change—the origin of the six-legged insect body plan.

Changes in Gene Regulation

A change in the nucleotide sequence of a gene may affect its function wherever the gene is expressed. In contrast, changes in the regulation of gene expression can be limited to a single cell type (see Chapter 18). Thus, a change in the regulation of a developmental gene may have fewer harmful side effects than a change to the sequence of the gene. This line of reasoning has prompted researchers to suggest that changes in the form of organisms often may be caused by mutations that affect the regulation of developmental genes—not their sequence.

This idea is supported by studies in a variety of species, including three-spine stickleback fish. These fish live in the open ocean and in shallow, coastal waters. In western Canada, they also live in lakes formed when the coastline receded in the past 12,000 years. David Kingsley, of Stanford University, and colleagues have identified a key developmental gene, *Pitx1*, that influences whether the fish have a set of large spines on their ventral (lower) surface, in addition to the three dorsal spines that give them their name. Marine populations have the ventral spines, which help to deter some predators. However, the spines are reduced or absent in lake populations. The loss of ventral spines may have been driven by natural selection because the lakes harbor large invertebrate predators, such as dragonfly larvae, which may at times capture juvenile sticklebacks by grasping onto the spines.

Was the reduction of spines due to changes in the *Pitx1* gene or due to changes in how the gene is expressed (Figure 25.23)? The researchers' results indicate that the regulation of gene expression has changed, not the DNA sequence of the gene. Furthermore, lake sticklebacks do express the *Pitx1* gene in tissues not related to the production of spines (for example, the mouth), illustrating how morphological change can be caused by altering the expression of a developmental gene in some parts of the body but not others.

▼ **Figure 25.23** **Inquiry**

What causes the loss of spines in lake stickleback fish?

EXPERIMENT   Marine populations of the three-spine stickleback fish (*Gasterosteus aculeatus*) have a set of protective spines on their lower (ventral) surface; these spines are lost or reduced in lake populations of this fish. Working at Stanford University, Michael Shapiro, David Kingsley, and colleagues tested two hypotheses about the cause of this morphological change.

Hypothesis A: A change in the DNA sequence of a key developmental gene, *Pitx1*, caused the loss of spines in lake populations. To test this idea, the team used DNA sequencing to compare the coding sequence of the *Pitx1* gene between marine and lake stickleback populations.

Hypothesis B: A change in the regulation of the expression of *Pitx1* caused the loss of spines. To test this idea, the researchers monitored where in the developing embryo the *Pitx1* gene is expressed. They conducted whole-body *in situ* hybridization experiments (see Chapter 20) using *Pitx1* DNA as a probe to detect *Pitx1* mRNA in the fish.

RESULTS

Test of Hypothesis A: Are there differences in the coding sequence of the *Pitx1* gene in marine and lake sticklebacks?

 Result: No →   The 283 amino acids of the *Pitx1* protein are identical in marine and lake stickleback populations.

Test of Hypothesis B: Are there any differences in the regulation of expression of *Pitx1*?

 Result: Yes →   Red arrows indicate regions of *Pitx1* gene expression in the photographs below. *Pitx1* is expressed in the ventral spine and mouth regions of developing marine sticklebacks but only in the mouth region of developing lake sticklebacks.

Marine stickleback embryo   **Lake stickleback embryo**

Close-up of mouth

Close-up of ventral surface

CONCLUSION   The loss or reduction of ventral spines in lake populations of three-spine stickleback fish results from a change in the regulation of *Pitx1* gene expression, not from a change in the gene's sequence.

SOURCE   M. D. Shapiro et al., Genetic and developmental basis of evolutionary pelvic reduction in three-spine sticklebacks, *Nature* 428:717–723 (2004).

WHAT IF?   Describe the set of results that would have led researchers to the conclusion that a change in the coding sequence of the *Pitx1* gene was more important than a change in regulation of gene expression.

1. How can heterochrony cause the evolution of different body forms?
2. Why is it likely that *Hox* genes have played a major role in the evolution of novel morphological forms?
3. **WHAT IF?** Given that changes in morphology are often caused by changes in gene regulation, predict whether noncoding DNA is likely to be affected by natural selection. (Noncoding DNA includes the sequences called control elements that regulate gene expression by binding to transcription factors.)

For suggested answers, see Appendix A.

CONCEPT 25.6
Evolution is not goal oriented

What does our study of macroevolution tell us about how evolution works? To paraphrase the Nobel Prize-winning geneticist François Jacob, evolution is like tinkering—a process in which new forms arise by the slight modification of existing forms. Even large changes, like the ones that produced the first mammals or the six-legged body plan of insects, can result from the gradual modification of existing structures or the slight modification of existing developmental genes.

Evolutionary Novelties

François Jacob's view of evolution harkens back to Darwin's concept of descent with modification. As new species form, novel and complex structures can arise as gradual modifications of ancestral structures. In many cases, complex structures have evolved in increments from simpler versions that performed the same basic function. For example, consider the human eye, an intricate organ constructed from numerous parts that work together in forming an image and transmitting it to the brain. How could the human eye have evolved in gradual increments? Some argue that if the eye needs all of its components to function, a partial eye could not have been of use to our ancestors.

The flaw in this argument, as Darwin himself noted, lies in the assumption that only complicated eyes are useful. In fact, many animals depend on eyes that are far less complex than our own **(Figure 25.24)**. The simplest eyes that we know of are patches of light-sensitive photoreceptor cells. These simple eyes appear to have had a single evolutionary origin and are now found in a variety of animals, including small molluscs called limpets. Such eyes have no equipment for focusing images, but they do enable the animal to distinguish light from dark. Limpets cling more tightly to their rock when a shadow falls on them—a behavioral adaptation that reduces the risk of being eaten. Because limpets have had a long evolutionary history, we can conclude that their "simple" eyes are quite adequate to support their survival and reproduction.

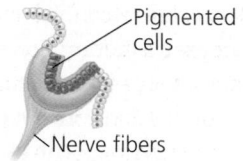

(a) Patch of pigmented cells. The limpet *Patella* has a simple patch of photoreceptors.

(b) Eyecup. The slit shell mollusc *Pleurotomaria* has an eyecup.

(c) Pinhole camera-type eye. The *Nautilus* eye functions like a pinhole camera (an early type of camera lacking a lens).

(d) Eye with primitive lens. The marine snail *Murex* has a primitive lens consisting of a mass of crystal-like cells. The cornea is a transparent region of tissue that protects the eye and helps focus light.

(e) Complex camera-type eye. The squid *Loligo* has a complex eye whose features (cornea, lens, and retina), though similar to those of vertebrate eyes, evolved independently.

▲ **Figure 25.24 A range of eye complexity among molluscs.**

In the animal kingdom, complex eyes have evolved independently from such basic structures many times. Some molluscs, such as squids and octopuses, have eyes as complex as those of humans and other vertebrates (see Figure 25.24). Although complex mollusc eyes evolved independently of vertebrate eyes, both evolved from a simple cluster of photoreceptor cells present in a common ancestor. In each case, the evolution of the complex eye took place through a series of incremental modifications that benefited the eyes' owners at every stage. Evidence for these evolutionary paths comes from phylogenetic analysis of the genes that act as "master regulators" of eye development and are shared by all animals with eyes.

Throughout their evolutionary history, eyes retained their basic function of vision. But evolutionary novelties can also arise when structures that originally played one role gradually acquire a different one. For example, as cynodonts gave rise to early mammals, bones that formerly comprised the jaw hinge (the articular and quadrate; see Figure 25.6) were incorporated into the ear region of mammals, where they eventually took on a new function: the transmission of sound (see Chapter 34).

Structures that evolve in one context but become co-opted for another function are sometimes called *exaptations* to distinguish them from the adaptive origin of the original structure. Note that the concept of exaptation does not imply that a structure somehow evolves in anticipation of future use. Natural selection cannot predict the future; it can only improve a structure in the context of its *current* utility. Novel features, such as the new jaw hinge and ear bones of early mammals, can arise gradually via a series of intermediate stages, each of which has some function in the organism's current context.

Evolutionary Trends

What else can we learn from patterns of macroevolution? Consider evolutionary "trends" observed in the fossil record. For instance, some evolutionary lineages exhibit a trend toward larger or smaller body size. An example is the evolution of the present-day horse (genus *Equus*), a descendant of the 55-million-year-old *Hyracotherium* (**Figure 25.25**). About the size of a large dog, *Hyracotherium* had four toes on its front feet, three toes on its hind feet, and teeth adapted for browsing on bushes and trees. In

▲ **Figure 25.25 The branched evolution of horses.** Using yellow to trace the sequence of fossil horses that are intermediate in form between the present-day horse (*Equus*) and its Eocene ancestor *Hyracotherium* creates the illusion of a progressive trend toward larger size, reduced number of toes, and teeth modified for grazing. In fact, *Equus* is the only surviving twig of an evolutionary bush with many divergent trends.

comparison, present-day horses are larger, have only one toe on each foot, and possess teeth modified for grazing on grasses.

Extracting a single evolutionary progression from the fossil record can be misleading, however; it is like describing a bush as growing toward a single point by tracing only the branches that lead to that twig. For example, by selecting certain species from the available fossils, it is possible to arrange a succession of animals intermediate between *Hyracotherium* and living horses that shows a trend toward large, single-toed species (follow the lineage highlighted in yellow in Figure 25.25). However, if we consider *all* fossil horses known today, this apparent trend vanishes. The genus *Equus* did not evolve in a straight line; it is the only surviving twig of an evolutionary tree that is so branched that it is more like a bush. *Equus* actually descended through a series of speciation episodes that included several adaptive radiations, not all of which led to large, one-toed, grazing horses. For instance, notice in Figure 25.25 that only those lineages derived from *Parahippus* include grazers; other lineages derived from *Miohippus,* all of which are now extinct, remained multi-toed browsers for 35 million years.

Branching evolution *can* result in a real evolutionary trend even if some species counter the trend. One model of long-term trends proposed by Steven Stanley, of Johns Hopkins University, views species as analogous to individuals: Speciation is their birth, extinction is their death, and new species that diverge from them are their offspring. In this model, Stanley suggests that just as individual organisms undergo natural selection, species undergo *species selection.* The species that endure the longest and generate the most new offspring species determine the direction of major evolutionary trends. The species selection model suggests that "differential speciation success" plays a

role in macroevolution similar to the role of differential reproductive success in microevolution. Evolutionary trends can also result directly from natural selection. For example, when horse ancestors invaded the grasslands that spread during the mid-Cenozoic, there was strong selection for grazers that could escape predators by running faster. This trend would not have occurred without open grasslands.

Whatever its cause, an evolutionary trend does not imply that there is some intrinsic drive toward a particular phenotype. Evolution is the result of the interactions between organisms and their current environments; if environmental conditions change, an evolutionary trend may cease or even reverse itself. The cumulative effect of these ongoing interactions between organisms and their environments is enormous: It is through them that the staggering diversity of life—Darwin's "endless forms most beautiful"—has arisen.

CONCEPT CHECK 25.6

1. How can the Darwinian concept of descent with modification explain the evolution of such complex structures as the vertebrate eye?

2. **WHAT IF?** The myxoma virus is highly lethal to European rabbits (*Oryctolagus cuniculus*). In a naive rabbit population (one with no previous exposure to the virus), the virus kills up to 99.8% of infected rabbits. The virus is transmitted between living rabbits by mosquitoes. Describe an evolutionary trend (in either the rabbits or the virus) that might occur after a naive rabbit population first encounters the virus.

For suggested answers, see Appendix A.

Chapter 25 Review

MEDIA Go to www.campbellbiology.com for BioFlix 3-D Animations, MP3 Tutors, Videos, Practice Tests, an eBook, and more.

SUMMARY OF KEY CONCEPTS

CONCEPT 25.1

Conditions on early Earth made the origin of life possible (pp. 507–510)

▶ **Synthesis of Organic Compounds on Early Earth** Earth formed about 4.6 billion years ago. Laboratory experiments simulating a reducing atmosphere have produced organic molecules from inorganic precursors. Amino acids have also been found in meteorites.

▶ **Abiotic Synthesis of Macromolecules** Amino acids polymerize when added to hot sand, clay, or rock.

▶ **Protobionts** Organic compounds can spontaneously assemble in the laboratory into protobionts, membrane-bounded droplets that have some of the properties of cells.

▶ **Self-Replicating RNA and the Dawn of Natural Selection** The first genetic material may have been short pieces of RNA capable of guiding polypeptide synthesis and self-replication. Early protobionts containing such RNA would have been more effective at using resources and would have increased in number through natural selection.

MEDIA

Investigation How Did Life Begin on Early Earth?

CONCEPT 25.2

The fossil record documents the history of life (pp. 510–514)

▶ **The Fossil Record** The fossil record, based largely on fossils found in sedimentary rocks, documents the rise and fall of different groups of organisms over time.

▶ **How Rocks and Fossils Are Dated** Sedimentary strata reveal the relative ages of fossils. The absolute ages of fossils can be estimated by radiometric dating and other methods.

▶ **The Origin of New Groups of Organisms** The fossil record shows how new groups of organisms can arise via the gradual modification of preexisting organisms.

CONCEPT 25.3

Key events in life's history include the origins of single-celled and multicelled organisms and the colonization of land (pp. 514–519)

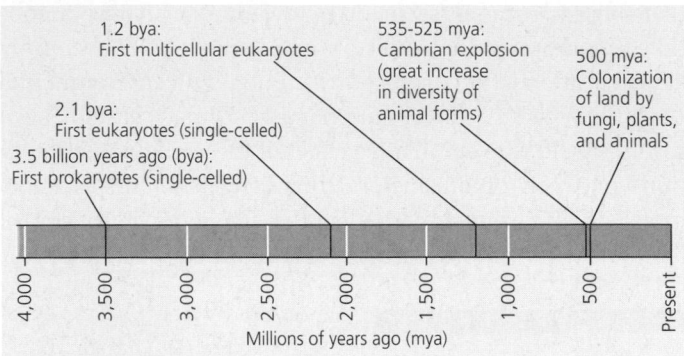

1.2 bya:
First multicellular eukaryotes

535-525 mya:
Cambrian explosion (great increase in diversity of animal forms)

500 mya:
Colonization of land by fungi, plants, and animals

2.1 bya:
First eukaryotes (single-celled)

3.5 billion years ago (bya):
First prokaryotes (single-celled)

Millions of years ago (mya)

MEDIA

Activity A Scrolling Geologic Record
Activity The History of Life

CONCEPT 25.4

The rise and fall of dominant groups reflect continental drift, mass extinctions, and adaptive radiations (pp. 519–525)

▶ **Continental Drift** Continental plates move gradually over time, altering the physical geography and climate of Earth; these changes lead to extinctions in some groups of organisms and bursts of speciation in others.

▶ **Mass Extinctions** Evolutionary history has been punctuated by five mass extinctions that radically altered the history of life. Some of these extinctions may have been caused by changes in continent positions, volcanic activity, or impacts from meteorites or comets.

▶ **Adaptive Radiations** Large increases in the diversity of life have resulted from adaptive radiations that followed mass extinctions. Adaptive radiations have also occurred in groups of organisms that possessed major evolutionary innovations or that colonized new regions in which there was little competition from other organisms.

CONCEPT 25.5

Major changes in body form can result from changes in the sequences and regulation of developmental genes (pp. 525–529)

▶ **Evolutionary Effects of Developmental Genes** Developmental genes affect morphological differences between species by influencing the rate, timing, and spatial patterns of change in an organism's form as it develops into an adult.

▶ **The Evolution of Development** The evolution of new morphological forms can be caused by changes in the nucleotide sequences or regulation of developmental genes.

MEDIA

Activity Allometric Growth

CONCEPT 25.6

Evolution is not goal oriented (pp. 529–531)

▶ **Evolutionary Novelties** Novel and complex biological structures can evolve through a series of incremental modifications, each of which benefits the organism that possesses it.

▶ **Evolutionary Trends** Evolutionary trends can be caused by factors such as natural selection in a changing environment or species selection. Like all aspects of evolution, evolutionary trends result from interactions between organisms and their current environments.

TESTING YOUR KNOWLEDGE

SELF-QUIZ

1. Fossilized stromatolites
   a. all date from 2.7 billion years ago.
   b. formed around deep-sea vents.
   c. resemble structures formed by bacterial communities that are found today in some warm, shallow, salty bays.
   d. provide evidence that plants moved onto land in the company of fungi around 500 million years ago.
   e. contain the first undisputed fossils of eukaryotes and date from 2.1 billion years ago.

2. The oxygen revolution changed Earth's environment dramatically. Which of the following adaptations took advantage of the presence of free oxygen in the oceans and atmosphere?
   a. the evolution of cellular respiration, which used oxygen to help harvest energy from organic molecules
   b. the persistence of some animal groups in anaerobic habitats
   c. the evolution of photosynthetic pigments that protected early algae from the corrosive effects of oxygen
   d. the evolution of chloroplasts after early protists incorporated photosynthetic cyanobacteria
   e. the evolution of multicellular eukaryotic colonies from communities of prokaryotes

3. Select the factor most likely to have caused the animals and plants of India to differ greatly from species in nearby Southeast Asia.
   a. The species have become separated by convergent evolution.
   b. The climates of the two regions are similar.
   c. India is in the process of separating from the rest of Asia.
   d. Life in India was wiped out by ancient volcanic eruptions.
   e. India was a separate continent until 55 million years ago.

4. Adaptive radiations can be a direct consequence of four of the following five factors. Select the exception.
   a. vacant ecological niches
   b. genetic drift
   c. colonization of an isolated region that contains suitable habitat and few competitor species
   d. evolutionary innovation
   e. an adaptive radiation in a group of organisms (such as plants) that another group uses as food

5. A genetic change that caused a certain *Hox* gene to be expressed along the tip of a vertebrate limb bud instead of farther back helped make possible the evolution of the tetrapod limb. This type of change is illustrative of
a. the influence of environment on development.
b. paedomorphosis.
c. a change in a developmental gene or in its regulation that altered the spatial organization of body parts.
d. heterochrony.
e. gene duplication.

6. Which of the following steps has *not* yet been accomplished by scientists studying the origin of life?
a. synthesis of small RNA polymers by ribozymes
b. abiotic synthesis of polypeptides
c. formation of molecular aggregates with selectively permeable membranes
d. formation of protobionts that use DNA to direct the polymerization of amino acids
e. abiotic synthesis of organic molecules

7. A swim bladder is a gas-filled sac that helps fish maintain buoyancy. The evolution of the swim bladder from lungs of an ancestral fish is an example of
a. an evolutionary trend.   d. paedomorphosis.
b. exaptation.   e. adaptive radiation.
c. changes in *Hox* gene expression.

8. **DRAW IT** Use the unlabeled clock diagram below to test your memory of the sequence of key events in the history of life described in this chapter by labeling the colored bars. As a visual aid to help you study, add labels that represent other significant events, including the Cambrian explosion, origin of mammals, and Permian and Cretaceous mass extinctions.

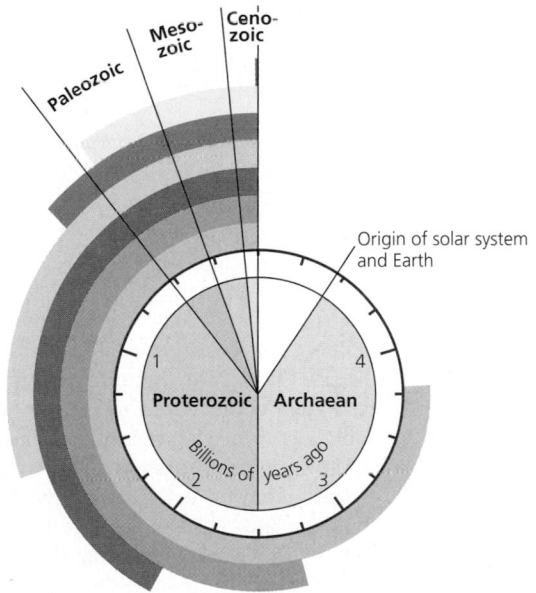

For Self-Quiz answers, see Appendix A.

MEDIA Visit **www.campbellbiology.com** for a Practice Test.

EVOLUTION CONNECTION

9. Describe how gene flow, genetic drift, and natural selection all can influence macroevolution.

SCIENTIFIC INQUIRY

10. Herbivory (plant-eating) has evolved repeatedly in insects, typically from meat-eating or detritus-feeding ancestors (detritus is dead organic matter). Moths and butterflies, for example, eat plants, whereas their "sister group" (the insect group to which they are most closely related), the caddisflies, feed on animals, fungi, or detritus. As illustrated in the phylogenetic tree below, the combined moth/butterfly and caddisfly group shares a common ancestor with flies and fleas. Like caddisflies, flies and fleas are thought to have evolved from ancestors that did not eat plants.
There are 140,000 species of moths and butterflies and 7,000 species of caddisflies. State a hypothesis about the impact of herbivory on adaptive radiations in insects. How could this hypothesis be tested?

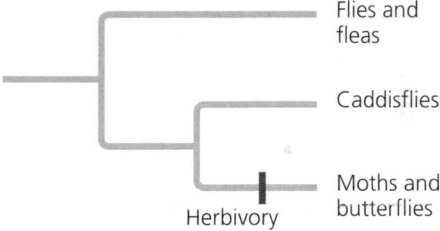

SCIENCE, TECHNOLOGY, AND SOCIETY

11. Experts estimate that human activities cause the extinction of hundreds of species every year. In contrast, the natural rate of extinction is thought to average only a few species per year. If we continue to alter the global environment, especially by destroying tropical rain forests and altering Earth's climate, the likely result will be a wave of extinctions that could rival those at the end of the Cretaceous period. Considering that life has endured five mass extinctions, should we be concerned that we may cause a sixth mass extinction? How would such an extinction differ from previous extinctions? What might be some of the consequences for the surviving species, including ourselves?

Biology Inquiry: A Workbook of Investigative Cases Life on Earth has gone through repeated cycles of mass extinction and diversification. Explore the latter with the case "Unveiling the Carboniferous."

UNIT 5

The Evolutionary History of Biological Diversity

AN INTERVIEW WITH
Sean B. Carroll

Passionately committed to sharing the revelations of evo-devo with students and the public, Sean Carroll is a popular speaker and the author of several acclaimed trade books—as well as a leading researcher on the genetics and evolution of animal development. He completed his formal education in record time, earning a B.A. in Biology at Washington University and a Ph.D. in Immunology at Tufts University School of Medicine in less than six years. Dr. Carroll is now an investigator at the Howard Hughes Medical Institute and a professor of molecular biology and genetics at the University of Wisconsin, Madison. He is a member of the National Academy of Sciences.

How did you get interested in evolutionary biology?

As a kid, I really enjoyed flipping over logs and seeing what was underneath. I was fascinated by reptiles, snakes in particular, and also liked to catch frogs and salamanders. That attraction to wildlife has always nurtured my interest in biology. At Washington University, students like myself could get exposed to almost anything in biology. I would go to seminars on subjects ranging from wolf ecology to the molecular biology of viruses. There I started to learn something about the big questions that were being asked in various disciplines at the time. I was smitten with immunology because of the big questions still open in that field and because of its practical side—vaccines and the treatment of infectious diseases.

But while working on my Ph.D. in immunology, I started reading a lot on my own—Stephen Jay Gould, for example—and going to science talks all over the Boston area. I would just hop on the subway and go to talks at any of three or four different universities. The unanswered questions in evolutionary biology drew me in that direction. At the time, the debate over punctuated equilibrium was fresh,

and this new idea was changing interpretations of the fossil record and raising questions about the rate of morphological change. All this prompted a simple question in my mind: How can we have this debate when we don't know anything about how form is made? And how can we start to get a grip on that?

At around that time, I came across some of the early papers on the developmental genetics of fruit flies, which described fascinating body-pattern mutants—homeotic mutants [see Figure 18.18]. I got it in my head that homeotic genes were the ones that people would have to study to understand the evolution of form. Despite advice to the contrary, I committed myself to studying these kinds of genes in fruit flies.

Let's talk about your book *Endless Forms Most Beautiful: The New Science of Evo Devo and the Making of the Animal Kingdom.* What does the title mean?

The first part of the title is borrowed from the last sentence of Charles Darwin's *Origin of Species:* "from so simple a beginning endless forms most beautiful . . . have been and are being evolved." The "most beautiful" part is important to me because I think that part of our attraction to nature is aesthetic. The book tries to explain what the new science of the last 20 years—advances in developmental genetics and the evolutionary study of development—has revealed about the generation of the physical diversity of the animal kingdom.

There is an intimate connection between development and evolution. Development is the process that gives rise to form, and so the evolution of form comes about through the evolution of development. Understanding how development happens in the first place is the starting point. Then we want to understand how changes in development can evolve. Only a small percentage of our genes are devoted to building body form, maybe a couple of thousand in us and six or seven hundred in a fruit fly. But when those genes are disrupted by mutation, the effects can be pretty catastrophic.

The book looks at the central ideas in evolutionary developmental biology—*evo-devo*, for short. A few of the key discoveries in this area were stunning, completely unanticipated. So the book traces those discoveries and discusses how they force us to look at the evolution of diversity very differently from how previous generations of evolutionary biologists did. The biggest discovery of evo-devo has been that the genes that build the bodies and body parts of fruit flies are shared with us and with virtually every other creature in the animal kingdom. That shows us a deep connection shared by all animals, no matter how different the bodies are. Gene for gene, we are essentially the same as a mouse, a rat, or a dog, and especially a chimpanzee. And the genes involved in building our eyes and our hearts and our bones have been around for 500 million years. So much like astronomy did four centuries ago, evo-devo is contributing to the realization that humans are not the center of everything. The human species is a member of the animal kingdom and not really above or very distinct from the other members.

What are you doing research on now?

We're working on the question of *how* the differences between animal species arise. There has been an idea around biology for a long time that to get new things you need new genes—for new structures, for new capabilities, or for whole new types of animals. But it doesn't look like that at all. Instead, it looks like new things arise because very old genes learn new tricks. We are focusing on understanding the mechanisms of these changes. This involves the question of how a gene involved in setting up the basic body plan and building body parts can change its roles without the whole machine falling apart. How do you change the car while the engine is running? It turns out that body-building genes have very sophisticated and extensive sets of regulatory instructions—control elements in the DNA nearby or embedded within the genes. An individual gene might act in a dozen places in the body in the course of development, but its action in a particular body part at a particular moment in development is controlled independently from its action in other places. We are trying to understand how these regulatory instructions are used, because we think that these are the hot spots of evolution. It is becoming more clear how and why these regulatory elements are the keys to understanding how so much diversity can be generated with a limited set of body-building genes.

The rules for the evolution of body form and physiology are different: In the evolution of physiological processes—for example, respiration, olfaction, or immunity—the evolution of new protein-coding genes has been more important. For example, the multiple types of globins that act at different stages of our life arose as genes were duplicated and the copies then diverged.

Are you using fruit flies currently?
Yes. To get at some of the *general* rules about the evolution of form, we often studied animals that are distant relatives; we might compare a snake with a bird. But if you really want to trace the specific genetic steps involved in the evolution of form, you need to have greater resolving power. The strategy we have taken is to study closely related species, which share a very recent common ancestor. If you take two such "sister" species, you can actually identify the genetic changes that cause the differences in the appearance and behavior of these animals. Fruit flies provide a great opportunity to do that, because *Drosophila melanogaster*, the familiar lab fruit fly, has hundreds of relatives out there in the wild, different species with all sorts of differences in body appearance. For instance, there are *Drosophila* species where the male has large black spots on the tips of the wings that are used in a courtship display. Now, genes that influence mating are among the most important targets of natural selection, because whether the male passes his genes on depends on whether the female is induced to mate. We can compare these flies with flies of sister species that do not have these spots and do not use the same mating ritual. Because the relationship is close, we can pinpoint very specifically the bits of regulatory DNA that have changed. So we are looking at the smoking guns of evolution.

What can one learn about animal phylogeny from DNA sequences versus fossils and morphology?
It's useful to have both—independent but intersecting lines of evidence. There are things you cannot see in fossils that you can learn about by studying DNA, and there is a lot that the molecules cannot tell you about the history of life. You can't look at DNA and know that the dinosaurs existed. Fossils tell you what animals roamed the earth, what structures existed, and even how the structures evolved, if the fossil record is rich enough. When you have extant species, the molecular record is good for figuring out other things. For example, if you want to know whether annelids are more closely related to molluscs or to arthropods— an issue that for a hundred-plus years was argued on the basis of appearance—the molecules now weigh in on the problem. Sometimes the results from molecules are consistent with long-held notions, and sometimes they throw the old notions for a loop.

What does evo-devo tell us about the Cambrian explosion?
Evo-devo tells us that the body-building genes we've been talking about must have been in place in the very early ancestors of most animals, in the ancestors of the animals seen in fossils from the geologic period we call the Cambrian. We can infer that the earliest bilateral animals—"bilaterians," which have left and right sides—had a pretty sophisticated genetic toolkit, and that those animals must have lived prior to the Cambrian. The Cambrian coming-out party may not have been so much a matter of new genes as an ecologically driven explosion of diversity. My personal view is that all the key genes and circuits were probably in place cryptically in small creatures before the Cambrian. So evo-devo is a great window to understanding the mechanism of diversification, but there's a huge ecological story, too.

Going back before the Cambrian, when did the first animals arise, and what did they look like?
The first animals probably appeared about 600 million years ago, give or take a week. I tend to believe that a lot of the early evolution of animals is cryptic because the earliest animals were tiny, soft-bodied organisms and didn't leave a good fossil record. These first animals would have been, by today's standards, dull-looking spongelike things. The first bilaterians probably looked like worms. Also, because there are significant differences between sponges and cnidarians and cnidarians and bilaterians, I think there were all sorts of intermediate phyla that we don't know anything about. Maybe some tremendous breakthrough in finding and analyzing microfossils will lead to discovery of some of the missing phyla.

Why should people who are not going to be evolutionary biologists learn about the evolution of biological diversity?
I think the study of evolution and diversity is as fundamental as studying the history of human civilizations. That's just the last 10,000 years! But our history as animals goes back some 600 million years and as organisms several billion years. In addition, there are important practical reasons. We humans are managing the natural resources on the planet. If we don't understand the basic principles of evolutionary biology, we cannot conduct those activities intelligently for the long term. To take one example, what's the effect of trawling for ocean fish with a 7-cm mesh net? Organisms that are smaller than 7 cm escape and flourish, and ones that are larger than 7 cm are removed. How does that influence the harvest ten years later? We have to understand the fundamental role that selection plays in the real world and that we are a major agent of selection. We can foresee some of the consequences of our activities from the first principles of evolutionary biology.

Evo-devo tells us that the body-building genes . . . must have been in place in the very early ancestors of most animals . . .

Inquiry in Action

Learn about an experiment by Sean Carroll and colleagues in Inquiry Figure 33.28 on page 684.

Jane Reece and Sean Carroll

Phylogeny and the Tree of Life

KEY CONCEPTS

26.1 **Phylogenies show evolutionary relationships**

26.2 **Phylogenies are inferred from morphological and molecular data**

26.3 **Shared characters are used to construct phylogenetic trees**

26.4 **An organism's evolutionary history is documented in its genome**

26.5 **Molecular clocks help track evolutionary time**

26.6 **New information continues to revise our understanding of the tree of life**

OVERVIEW

Investigating the Tree of Life

Look closely at the organism in **Figure 26.1**. Although it resembles a snake, this animal is actually an Australian legless lizard known as the common scaly-foot (*Pygopus lepidopodus*). Why isn't the scaly-foot considered a snake? More generally, how do biologists distinguish and categorize the millions of species on Earth?

An understanding of evolutionary relationships suggests one way to address these questions: We can decide in which "container" to place a species by comparing its traits to those of potential close relatives. For example, the scaly-foot does not have a fused eyelid, a highly mobile jaw, or a short tail posterior to the anus, three traits of snakes. These and other characteristics suggest that despite a superficial resemblance, the scaly-foot is not a snake. Furthermore, a survey of the lizards reveals that the scaly-foot is not alone; the legless condition has evolved repeatedly in lizards. Most legless lizards are burrowers or live in grasslands, and like snakes, these species lost their legs over generations as they adapted to their environments.

Snakes and lizards are part of the continuum of life extending from the earliest organisms to the great variety of species alive today. In this unit, we will survey this diversity and de-

scribe hypotheses regarding how it evolved. As we do so, our emphasis will shift from the *process* of evolution (the evolutionary mechanisms described in Unit Four) to its *pattern* (observations of evolution's products over time).

To set the stage for our survey of life's diversity, in this chapter we consider how biologists trace **phylogeny**, the evolutionary history of a species or group of species. A phylogeny of lizards and snakes, for example, indicates that both the scaly-foot and snakes evolved from lizards with legs—but they evolved from different lineages of legged lizards. Thus, it appears that their legless conditions evolved independently.

To construct a phylogeny such as that of lizards and snakes, biologists utilize **systematics**, a discipline focused on classifying organisms and determining their evolutionary relationships. Systematists use data ranging from fossils to molecules and genes to infer evolutionary relationships **(Figure 26.2)**. This information is enabling biologists to construct a comprehensive tree of life, which will continue to be refined as additional data are collected.

▲ Figure 26.2 **An unexpected family tree.** What are the evolutionary relationships between a human, a mushroom, and a tulip? A phylogeny based on DNA data reveals that—despite appearances—animals (including humans) and fungi (including mushrooms) are more closely related to each other than either is to plants.

CONCEPT 26.1

Phylogenies show evolutionary relationships

As we discussed in Chapter 22, organisms share homologous characteristics because of common ancestry. As a result, we can learn a great deal about a species if we know its evolutionary history. For example, an organism is likely to share many of its genes, metabolic pathways, and structural proteins with its close relatives. We'll consider practical applications of such information at the close of this section, but first we'll examine how organisms are named and classified, the scientific discipline of **taxonomy**. We'll also look at how we can interpret and use diagrams that represent evolutionary history.

Binomial Nomenclature

Common names for organisms—such as monkey, finch, and lilac—convey meaning in casual usage, but they can also cause confusion. Each of these names, for example, refers to more than one species. Moreover, some common names do not accurately reflect the kind of organism they signify. Consider these three "fishes": jellyfish (a cnidarian), crayfish (a small lobsterlike crustacean), and silverfish (an insect). And of course, different languages have different words for various organisms.

To avoid ambiguity when communicating about their research, biologists refer to organisms by Latin scientific names. The two-part format of the scientific name, commonly called a **binomial**, was instituted in the 18th century by Carolus Linnaeus (see Chapter 22). The first part of a binomial is the name of the **genus** (plural, *genera*) to which the species belongs. The second part, called the specific epithet, is unique for each species within the genus. An example of a binomial is *Panthera pardus*, the scientific name for the large cat commonly called the leopard. Notice that the first letter of the genus is capitalized and the entire binomial is italicized. (Newly created scientific names are also "latinized": You can name an insect you discover after a friend, but you must add a Latin ending.) Many of the more than 11,000 binomials assigned by Linnaeus are still used today, including the optimistic name he gave our own species—*Homo sapiens*, meaning "wise man."

Hierarchical Classification

In addition to naming species, Linnaeus also grouped them into a hierarchy of increasingly inclusive categories. The first grouping is built into the binomial: Species that appear to be closely related are grouped into the same genus. For example, the leopard (*Panthera pardus*) belongs to a genus that also includes the African lion (*Panthera leo*), the tiger (*Panthera tigris*), and the jaguar (*Panthera onca*). Beyond genera, taxonomists employ progressively more comprehensive categories of classification. The taxonomic system named after Linnaeus,

the Linnaean system, places related genera in the same **family**, families into **orders**, orders into **classes**, classes into **phyla** (singular, *phylum*), phyla into **kingdoms**, and, more recently, kingdoms into **domains** (Figure 26.3). The resulting biological classification of a particular organism is somewhat like a postal address identifying a person in a particular apartment, in a building with many apartments, on a street with many apartment buildings, in a city with many streets, and so on.

The named taxonomic unit at any level of the hierarchy is called a **taxon** (plural, *taxa*). In the leopard example, *Panthera* is a taxon at the genus level, and Mammalia is a taxon at the class level that includes all the many orders of mammals. Note that in the Linnaean system, taxa broader than the genus are not italicized, though they are capitalized.

Classifying species seems to come naturally to humans—it is a way to structure our view of the world. We lump together various species of trees to which we give the common name of pines and distinguish them from other trees that we call firs. Taxonomists have decided that pines and firs are different enough to be placed in separate genera, yet similar enough to be grouped into the same family, the Pineaceae. As with pines and firs,

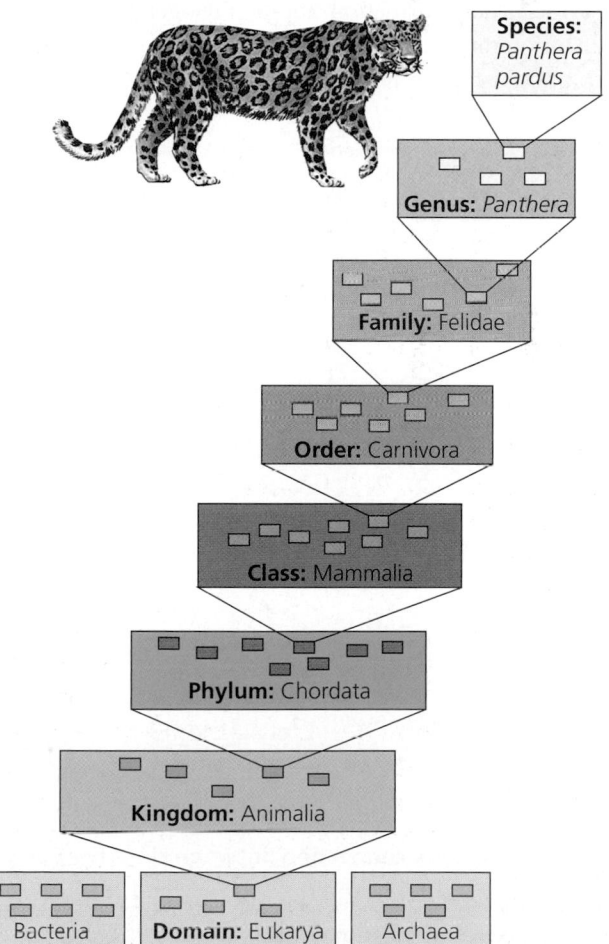

▲ **Figure 26.3 Hierarchical classification.** At each level of the Linnaean classification system, species are placed into groups belonging to more comprehensive groups.

higher levels of classification are usually defined by particular morphological characters chosen by taxonomists, rather than by measurements applicable to all organisms. For this reason, the larger categories often are not comparable between lineages; that is, an order of snails does not exhibit the same degree of morphological or genetic diversity as an order of mammals. Furthermore, as we'll see, the placement of species into orders, classes, and so on, does not necessarily reflect evolutionary history.

Linking Classification and Phylogeny

The evolutionary history of a group of organisms can be represented in a branching diagram called a **phylogenetic tree**. The branching pattern in some cases matches the hierarchical classification of groups nested within more inclusive groups **(Figure 26.4)**. In other situations, however, certain similarities among organisms may lead taxonomists to place a species within a group of organisms (for example, a genus or family) other than the group to which it is most closely related. If systematists conclude that such a mistake has occurred, the organism may be reclassified (that is, placed in a different genus or family) to accurately reflect its evolutionary history. In addition, the categories in the Linnaean classification system may provide little information about phylogeny: We may distinguish 17 families of lizards, but that tells us nothing about their evolutionary relationships to one another.

In fact, such difficulties in aligning Linnaean classification with phylogeny have led some systematists to propose that classification be based entirely on evolutionary relationships. A recent example of this approach is the **PhyloCode**, which only names groups that include a common ancestor and all of its descendants. While PhyloCode would change the way taxa are defined and recognized, the taxonomic names of most species would remain the same. But species would no longer necessarily have "ranks" attached to them, such as family, order, or class. Also, some commonly recognized groups would become part of other groups previously of the same rank. For example, because birds evolved from a group of reptiles, Aves (the Linnaean class to which birds are assigned) would be considered a subgroup of Reptilia (also a class in the Linnaean system). Although PhyloCode is controversial and still being developed, many systematists are adopting the phylogenetic approach on which it is based.

Whether groups are named according to PhyloCode or to Linnaean classification, a phylogenetic tree represents a hypothesis about evolutionary relationships. These relationships often are depicted as a series of dichotomies, or two-way **branch points (Figure 26.5)**. Each branch point represents the divergence of two evolutionary lineages from a common ancestor. For example, in Figure 26.5, branch point ❶ represents the common ancestor of taxa A, B, and C. The position of branch point ❹ to the right of branch point ❶ indicates that taxa B and C diverged after their shared lineage split from that of taxon A. Note that tree branches can be rotated around a branch point without changing their evolutionary relationships.

In Figure 26.5, taxa B and C are **sister taxa**, groups of organisms that share an immediate common ancestor (branch point ❹) and hence are each other's closest relatives. Note also that this tree, like most of the phylogenetic trees in this book, is **rooted**, which means that a branch point within the

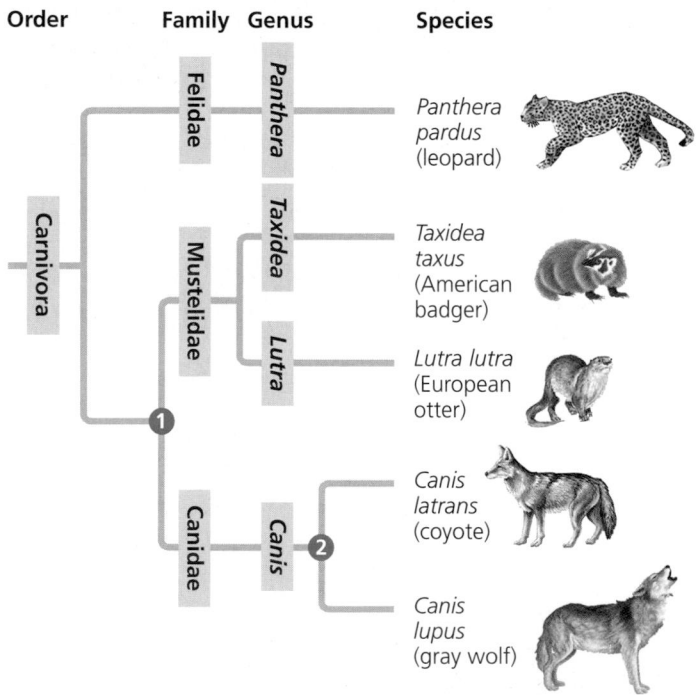

▲ **Figure 26.4 The connection between classification and phylogeny.** Hierarchical classification is reflected in the progressively finer branching of phylogenetic trees. This tree traces possible evolutionary relationships between some of the taxa within order Carnivora, itself a branch of class Mammalia. The branch point ❶ represents the most recent common ancestor of all members of the weasel (Mustelidae) and dog (Canidae) families. The branch point ❷ represents the most recent common ancestor of coyotes and gray wolves.

▲ **Figure 26.5 How to read a phylogenetic tree.**
DRAW IT *Redraw this tree, rotating the branches around branch points* ❷ *and* ❹ *. Does your new version tell a different story about the evolutionary relationships between the taxa? Explain.*

tree (typically, the one farthest to the left) represents the last common ancestor of all taxa in the tree. Finally, the lineage leading to taxa D–F includes a **polytomy**, a branch point from which more than two descendant groups emerge. A polytomy indicates that evolutionary relationships among the descendant taxa are not yet clear.

What We Can and Cannot Learn from Phylogenetic Trees

Let's pause to summarize two key points about phylogenetic trees and what they signify. First, the sequence of branching in a tree does not necessarily indicate the actual (absolute) ages of the particular species. For example, the tree in Figure 26.4 does *not* indicate that the wolf evolved more recently than the European otter; rather, the tree shows only that the most recent common ancestor of the wolf and European otter (branch point ❶) lived before the most recent common ancestor of the wolf and coyote (branch point ❷). To indicate when wolves and European otters evolved, the tree would need to include additional divergences in each evolutionary lineage, as well as the dates when those splits occurred. More generally, unless given specific information about what the branch lengths in a phylogenetic tree mean—for example, that they are proportional to time or genetic change—we should interpret the diagram solely in terms of patterns of descent. No assumptions should be made about when particular species evolved or how much genetic change occurred in each evolutionary lineage.

Second, we cannot assume that a taxon on a phylogenetic tree evolved from the taxon next to it. Figure 26.4 does not indicate that wolves evolved from coyotes or vice versa. We can infer only that the lineage leading to wolves and the lineage leading to coyotes both evolved from the common ancestor ❷.

Applying Phylogenies

Why do biologists care about studying phylogenies? One reason is that a species' phylogeny provides an enormous amount of information. Consider maize (corn), the second most important source of food worldwide (after wheat). From a phylogeny of maize based on DNA data, researchers identified two species of wild grasses that may be the closest living relatives to maize. These two close relatives may prove useful as "reservoirs" of beneficial genes that can be transferred to cultivated maize by plant breeding or genetic engineering. The phylogenetic analysis of maize also led to the identification of the gene responsible for maize's unique fruiting body, the cob.

Phylogenetic trees have played a key role in a wide range of other applications. One example is an investigation into whether food sold as "whale meat" in Japan was illegally harvested from whale species protected under international law **(Figure 26.6)**. Although it is legal to harvest some whales for food, such as Minke whales that are caught in the Southern Hemisphere, this phylogeny indicated that meat from

▼ **Figure 26.6** **Inquiry**

What is the species identity of food being sold as whale meat?

EXPERIMENT C. S. Baker, at the University of Auckland, New Zealand, and S. R. Palumbi, then at the University of Hawaii, purchased 13 samples of "whale meat" from several Japanese fish markets. They sequenced a region with the mitochondrial DNA from each sample and compared their results with the comparable DNA sequence from known whale species. To infer the species identity of their samples, Baker and Palumbi constructed a *gene tree*, a phylogenetic tree that shows patterns of relatedness among DNA sequences rather than among taxa.

RESULTS Baker and Palumbi's analysis yielded the following gene tree:

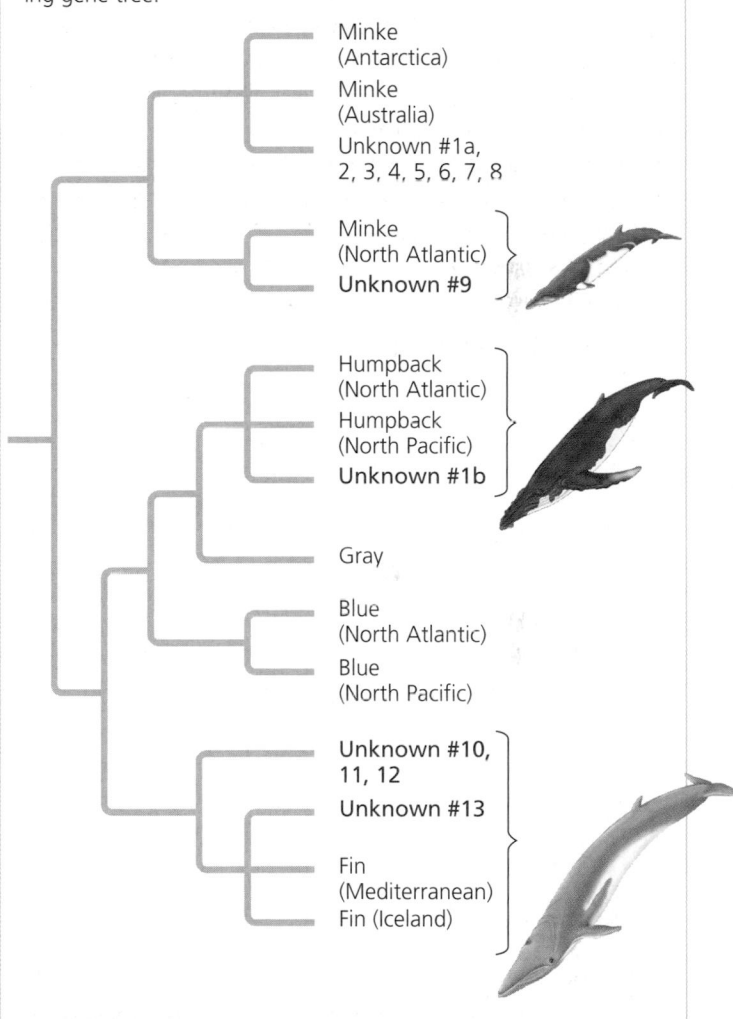

CONCLUSION This analysis indicated that DNA sequences of six of the unknown samples (in red) were most closely related to DNA sequences of whales that are not legal to harvest.

SOURCE C. S. Baker and S. R. Palumbi, Which whales are hunted? A molecular genetic approach to monitoring whaling, *Science* 265:1538–1539 (1994).

WHAT IF? What are some potential sources of error in this study? How might the chances of reaching an erroneous conclusion be reduced?

humpback, fin, and Minke whales caught in the Northern Hemisphere was being sold illegally in fish markets.

Another newsworthy application of phylogeny relates to bioterrorism. In fall 2001, several politicians and journalists were sent envelopes containing anthrax bacteria. Researchers used phylogenetic trees based on DNA data to identify the strain of the bacterium used in the 2001 attacks—information that may eventually help trace the source of the attacks.

How do researchers construct trees like those we've considered here? In the next section, we'll begin to answer that question by examining the data used to estimate phylogenies.

CONCEPT 26.2

Phylogenies are inferred from morphological and molecular data

To infer phylogeny, systematists must gather as much information as possible about the morphology, genes, and biochemistry of the relevant organisms. It is important to focus on features that result from common ancestry, because only these features reflect evolutionary relationships.

Morphological and Molecular Homologies

Recall that similarities due to shared ancestry are called homologies. For example, the similarity in the number and arrangement of bones in the forelimbs of mammals is due to their descent from a common ancestor with the same bone

structure; this is an example of a morphological homology (see Figure 22.17). In the same way, genes or other DNA sequences are homologous if they are descended from sequences carried by a common ancestor.

In general, organisms that share very similar morphologies or similar DNA sequences are likely to be more closely related than organisms with vastly different structures or sequences. In some cases, however, the morphological divergence between related species can be great and their genetic divergence small (or vice versa). Consider the Hawaiian silversword plants discussed in Chapter 25. These species vary dramatically in appearance throughout the islands. Some are tall, twiggy trees, and others are dense, ground-hugging shrubs (see Figure 25.18). But despite these striking phenotypic differences, the silverswords' genes are very similar. Based on these small molecular divergences, scientists estimate that the silversword group began to diverge 5 million years ago, which is also about the time when the oldest of the current islands formed. We'll discuss how scientists use molecular data to make such estimates later in this chapter.

Sorting Homology from Analogy

A potential red herring in constructing a phylogeny is similarity due to convergent evolution—called **analogy**—rather than to shared ancestry (homology). As you read in Chapter 22, convergent evolution occurs when similar environmental pressures and natural selection produce similar (analogous) adaptations in organisms from different evolutionary lineages. For example, the two mole-like animals illustrated in **Figure 26.7** are very similar in their external appearance. However, their internal anatomy, physiology, and reproductive systems are very dissimilar. Australian "moles" are marsupials; their young complete

▲ **Figure 26.7 Convergent evolution of analogous burrowing characteristics.** An elongated body, enlarged front paws, small eyes, and a pad of thickened skin that protects a tapered nose all evolved independently in the marsupial Australian "mole" (top) and a eutherian North American mole (bottom).

their embryonic development in a pouch on the outside of the mother's body. North American moles, in contrast, are eutherians; their young complete their embryonic development in the uterus within the mother's body. Indeed, genetic comparisons and the fossil record provide evidence that the common ancestor of these moles lived 140 million years ago, about the time the marsupial and eutherian mammals diverged. This ancestor and most of its descendants were not mole-like, but analogous characteristics evolved independently in these two mole lineages as they became adapted to similar lifestyles.

Distinguishing between homology and analogy is critical in reconstructing phylogenies. To see why, consider bats and birds, both of which have adaptations that enable flight. This superficial resemblance might imply that bats are more closely related to birds than they are to cats, which cannot fly. But a closer examination reveals that a bat's wing is far more similar to the forelimbs of cats and other mammals than to a bird's wing. Bats and birds descended from a common tetrapod ancestor that lived about 320 million years ago. This common ancestor could not fly. Thus, although the underlying skeletal systems of bats and birds are homologous, their *wings* are not. Flight is enabled in different ways—stretched membranes in the bat wing versus feathers in the bird wing. Fossil evidence also documents that bat wings and bird wings arose independently from the forelimbs of different tetrapod ancestors. Thus, with respect to flight, a bat's wing is *analogous*, not homologous, to a bird's wing. Analogous structures that arose independently are also called **homoplasies** (from the Greek for "to mold in the same way").

Besides corroborative similarities and fossil evidence, another clue to distinguishing between homology and analogy is the complexity of the characters being compared. The more points of resemblance that two complex structures have, the more likely it is that they evolved from a common ancestor. For instance, the skulls of an adult human and an adult chimpanzee both consist of many bones fused together. The compositions of the skulls match almost perfectly, bone for bone. It is highly improbable that such complex structures, matching in so many details, have separate origins. More likely, the genes involved in the development of both skulls were inherited from a common ancestor. The same argument applies to comparisons at the gene level. Genes are sequences of thousands of nucleotides, each of which represents an inherited character in the form of one of the four DNA bases: A (adenine), G (guanine), C (cytosine), or T (thymine). If genes in two organisms share many portions of their nucleotide sequences, it is highly likely that the genes are homologous.

Evaluating Molecular Homologies

Molecular comparisons of nucleic acids often pose technical challenges for researchers. The first step after sequencing the molecules is to align comparable sequences from the species being studied. If the species are very closely related, the se-

quences probably differ at only one or a few sites. In contrast, comparable nucleic acid sequences in distantly related species usually have different bases at many sites and may have different lengths. This is because insertions and deletions accumulate over long periods of time (see Chapter 23).

Suppose, for example, that particular noncoding DNA sequences in a particular gene in two species are very similar, except that the first base of the sequence has been deleted in one of the species. The effect is that the remaining sequence shifts back one notch. A comparison of the two sequences that does not take this deletion into account would overlook what in fact is a very good match. To address such problems, systematists have developed computer programs that estimate the best way to align comparable DNA segments of differing lengths **(Figure 26.8)**.

Such molecular comparisons reveal that a large number of base substitutions and other differences have accumulated between the comparable genes of the Australian mole and a North American mole. The many differences indicate that their lineages have diverged greatly since their common ancestor; thus, we say that the living species are not closely related. In contrast, the high degree of gene sequence similarity among the silverswords supports the hypothesis that they are all very closely related, in spite of their considerable morphological differences.

Just as with morphological characters, it is necessary to distinguish homology from analogy in evaluating molecular

❶ Ancestral homologous DNA segments are identical as species 1 and species 2 begin to diverge from their common ancestor.

1 C C A T C A G A G T C C
2 C C A T C A G A G T C C

❷ Deletion and insertion mutations shift what had been matching sequences in the two species.

Deletion
1 C C A T C A G A G T C C
2 C C A T C A G A G T C C
G T A Insertion

❸ Of the three homologous regions, two (shaded orange) do not align because of these mutations.

1 C C A T C A A G T C C
2 C C A T G T A C A G A G T C C

❹ Homologous regions realign after a computer program adds gaps in sequence 1.

1 C C A T _ _ _ C A _ A G T C C
2 C C A T G T A C A G A G T C C

▲ **Figure 26.8 Aligning segments of DNA.** Systematists use computer software to find and align similar sequences along DNA segments from two species. (In this example, no bases have changed in these sequences since divergence, and so the comparable sequences are still identical once the length is adjusted.)

```
ACGGATAGTCCACTAGGCACTA
TCACCGACAGGTCTTTGACTAG
```

▲ **Figure 26.9 A molecular homoplasy.** These two DNA sequences from organisms that are not closely related coincidentally share 25% of their bases. Statistical tools have been developed to determine whether DNA sequences that share more than 25% of their bases do so because they are homologous.

? *Why might you expect organisms that are not closely related to nevertheless share roughly 25% of their bases?*

similarities for evolutionary studies. Two sequences that resemble each other at many points along their length most likely are homologous (see Figure 26.8). But in organisms that do not appear to be closely related, the bases that their otherwise very different sequences happen to share may simply be coincidental matches, called molecular homoplasies **(Figure 26.9)**. Scientists have developed statistical tools that can help distinguish "distant" homologies from such coincidental matches in extremely divergent sequences.

Scientists have so far sequenced more than 100 billion bases' worth of nucleic acid data from thousands of species. This enormous collection of data has fed a boom in the study of phylogeny. The new data have supported earlier hypotheses regarding many evolutionary relationships, such as that between the Australian and North American moles, and have clarified other relationships, such as those between the various silverswords. In the rest of this chapter and unit, you will see many examples of the tremendous impact of **molecular systematics**, the discipline that uses DNA and other molecular data to determine evolutionary relationships.

CONCEPT 26.3

Shared characters are used to construct phylogenetic trees

In reconstructing phylogenies, the first step is to distinguish homologous features from analogous features (since only the former reflect evolutionary history). Once that task is accomplished, biologists must choose a method of inferring phylogeny from these homologous characters. In this section, we'll examine a widely used set of methods known as cladistics.

Cladistics

In the approach to systematics called **cladistics**, common ancestry is the primary criterion used to classify organisms. Using this methodology, biologists place species into groups called **clades**, each of which includes an ancestral species and all of its descendants **(Figure 26.10a)**. Clades, like taxonomic

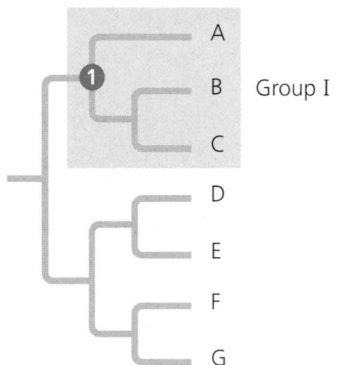

(a) Monophyletic group (clade). Group I, consisting of three species (A, B, C) and their common ancestor ❶, is a clade, also called a monophyletic group. A monophyletic group consists of an ancestral species and *all* of its descendants.

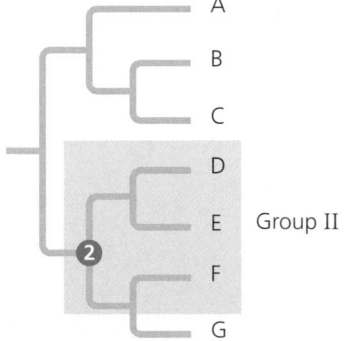

(b) Paraphyletic group. Group II is paraphyletic, meaning that it consists of an ancestral species ❷ and some of its descendants (species D, E, F) but not all of them (missing species G).

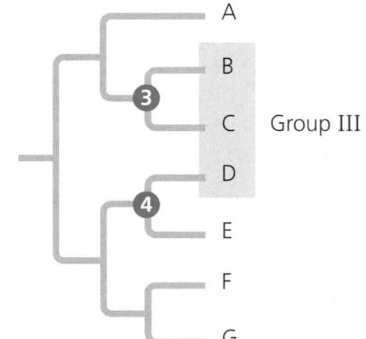

(c) Polyphyletic group. Group III is polyphyletic, meaning that some of its members have different ancestors. In this case, species B and C share common ancestor ❸, but species D has a different ancestor: ❹.

▲ **Figure 26.10 Monophyletic, paraphyletic, and polyphyletic groups.**

ranks, are nested within larger clades. For example, the cat group represents a clade within a larger clade that also includes the dog group. However, a taxon is equivalent to a clade only if it is **monophyletic** (from the Greek meaning "single tribe"), signifying that it consists of an ancestral species and all its descendants (see Figure 26.10a). Contrast this with a **paraphyletic** ("beside the tribe") group, which consists of an ancestral species and some, but not all, of its descendants **(Figure 26.10b)**, or a **polyphyletic** ("many tribes") group, which includes taxa with different ancestors **(Figure 26.10c)**. Next we'll discuss how clades are identified: using shared derived characters.

Shared Ancestral and Shared Derived Characters

As a result of descent with modification, organisms both share characteristics with their ancestors and differ from them (see Chapter 22). For example, all mammals have backbones, but the presence of a backbone does not distinguish mammals from other vertebrates because *all* vertebrates have backbones. The backbone predates the branching of the mammalian clade from other vertebrates. Thus, we say that for mammals, the backbone is a **shared ancestral character**, a character that originated in an ancestor of the taxon. In contrast, hair is a character shared by all mammals but *not* found in their ancestors. Thus, in mammals, hair is considered a **shared derived character**, an evolutionary novelty unique to a particular clade.

Note that a backbone can also qualify as a shared derived character, but only at a deeper branch point that distinguishes all vertebrates from other animals. Among vertebrates, a backbone is considered a shared ancestral character because it was present in the ancestor common to all vertebrates.

Inferring Phylogenies Using Derived Characters

Shared derived characters are unique to particular clades. Because all features of organisms arose at some point in the history of life, it should be possible to determine the clade in which each shared derived character first appeared and to use that information to infer evolutionary relationships.

To see how this analysis is done, consider the set of characters shown in **Figure 26.11a** for each of five vertebrates—a leopard, turtle, salamander, tuna, and lamprey (a jawless aquatic vertebrate). As a basis of comparison, we need to select an outgroup. An **outgroup** is a species or group of species from an evolutionary lineage that is known to have diverged before the lineage that includes the species we are studying (the **ingroup**). A suitable outgroup can be determined based on evidence from morphology, paleontology, embryonic development, and gene sequences. An appropriate outgroup for our example is the lancelet, a small animal that lives in mudflats and (like vertebrates) is a member of the Chordata. Unlike the vertebrates, however, the lancelet does not have a backbone.

By comparing members of the ingroup to each other and to the outgroup, we can determine which characters were derived at the various branch points of vertebrate evolution. For example, *all* of the vertebrates in the ingroup have backbones: This character was present in the ancestral vertebrate, but not in the outgroup. Now note that hinged jaws are a character absent in lampreys but present in other members of the ingroup; this character helps us to identify an early branch point in the vertebrate clade. Proceeding in this way, we can translate the data in our table of characters into a phylogenetic tree **(Figure 26.11b)**.

	TAXA					
CHARACTERS	Lancelet (outgroup)	Lamprey	Tuna	Salamander	Turtle	Leopard
Vertebral column (backbone)	0	1	1	1	1	1
Hinged jaws	0	0	1	1	1	1
Four walking legs	0	0	0	1	1	1
Amniotic (shelled) egg	0	0	0	0	1	1
Hair	0	0	0	0	0	1

(a) Character table. A 0 indicates that a character is absent; a 1 indicates that a character is present.

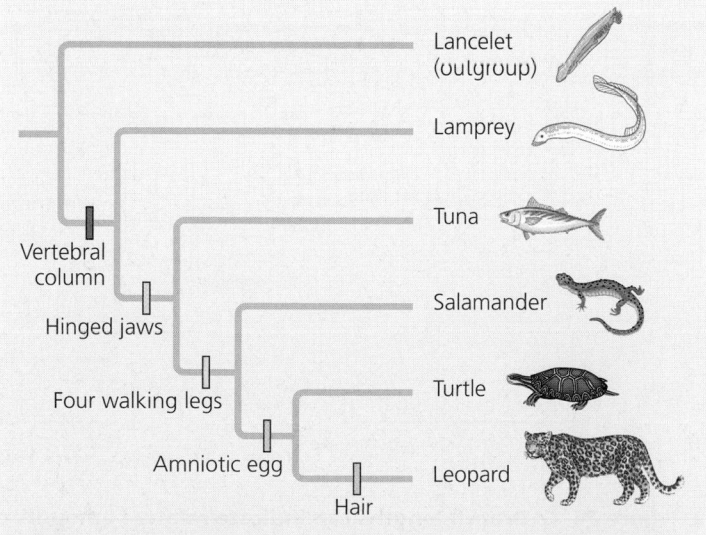

(b) Phylogenetic tree. Analyzing the distribution of these derived characters can provide insight into vertebrate phylogeny.

▲ **Figure 26.11 Constructing a phylogenetic tree.**

Phylogenetic Trees with Proportional Branch Lengths

In the phylogenetic trees we have presented so far, the lengths of the tree's branches do not indicate the degree of evolutionary change in each lineage. Furthermore, the chronology represented by the branching pattern of the tree is relative (earlier versus later) rather than absolute (how many millions of years ago). But in some tree diagrams, branch lengths are proportional to amount of evolutionary change or to the times at which particular events occurred.

For example, the branch length of a phylogenetic tree can reflect the number of changes that have taken place in a particular DNA sequence in that lineage (**Figure 26.12**). Note that in Figure 26.12, the *total length* of the horizontal lines from the base of the tree to the mouse is less than that of the line leading to the outgroup species, the fruit fly *Drosophila*. This implies that in the time since the mouse and fly diverged from a common ancestor, more genetic changes have occurred in the *Drosophila* lineage than in the mouse lineage.

Even though the branches of a phylogenetic tree may have different lengths, among organisms alive today, all the different lineages that descend from a common ancestor have survived for the same number of years. To take an extreme example, humans and bacteria had a common ancestor that lived over 3 billion years ago. Fossils and genetic evidence indicate that this ancestor was a single-celled prokaryote. Even though bacteria have apparently changed little in their structure since that common ancestor, there have nonetheless been 3 billion years of evolution in the bacterial lineage, just as there have been 3 billion years of evolution in the eukaryotic lineage that includes humans.

These equal spans of chronological time can be represented in a phylogenetic tree whose branch lengths are proportional to time (**Figure 26.13**). Such a tree draws on fossil data to place branch points in the context of geologic time. Additionally, it is possible to combine these two types of trees by labeling branch points with information about rates of genetic change or dates of divergence.

Maximum Parsimony and Maximum Likelihood

As the growing database of DNA sequences enables us to study more species, the difficulty of building the phylogenetic tree that best describes their evolutionary history also grows. What if you are analyzing data for 50 species? There are 3×10^{76} different ways to arrange 50 species into a tree! And which tree in this huge forest reflects the true phylogeny? Systematists can never be sure of finding the most accurate tree in such a large data set, but they can narrow the possibilities by applying the principles of maximum parsimony and maximum likelihood.

According to the principle of **maximum parsimony**, we should first investigate the simplest explanation that is consistent with the facts. (The parsimony principle is also called "Occam's razor" after William of Occam, a 14th-century English philosopher who advocated this minimalist problem-solving approach of "shaving away" unnecessary complications.) In the case of trees based on morphology, the most parsimonious tree requires the fewest evolutionary events, as measured by the origin of shared derived morphological characters. For phylogenies based on DNA, the most parsimonious tree requires the fewest base changes.

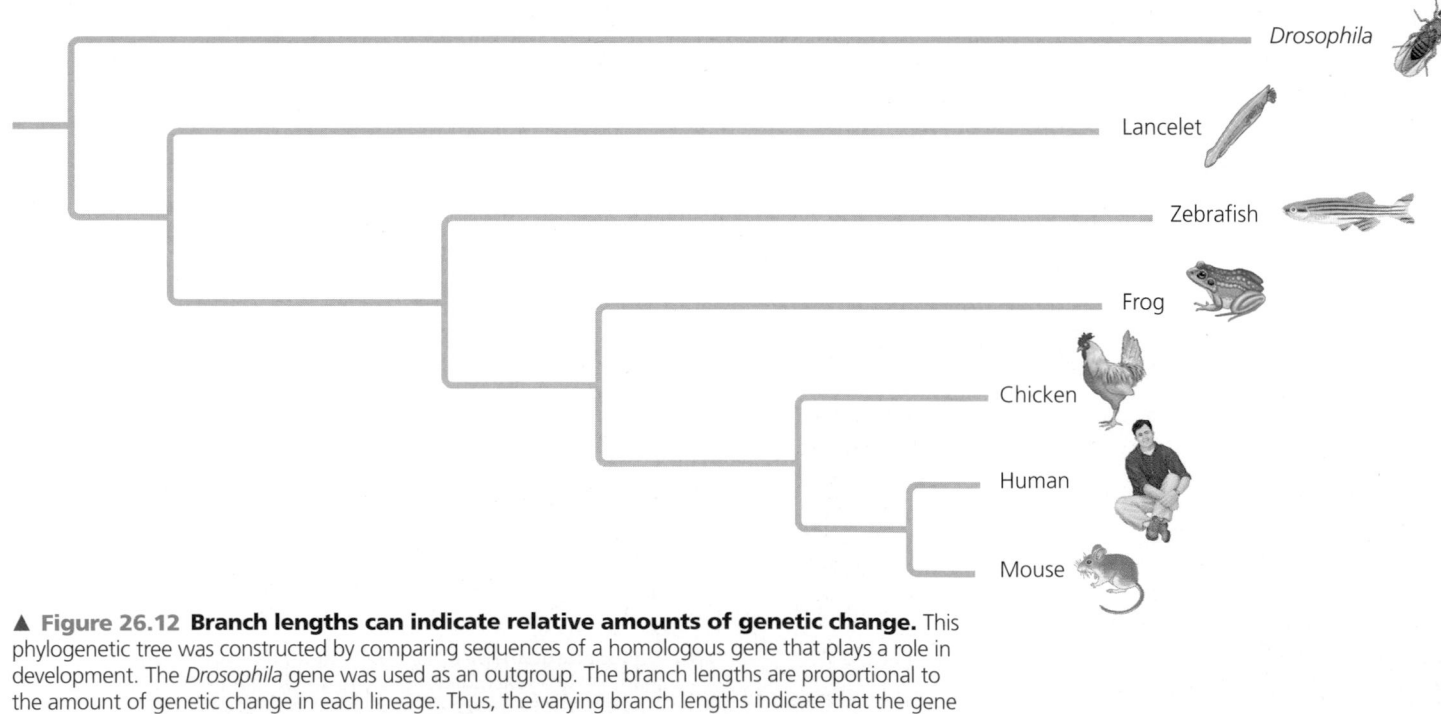

▲ Figure 26.12 **Branch lengths can indicate relative amounts of genetic change.** This phylogenetic tree was constructed by comparing sequences of a homologous gene that plays a role in development. The *Drosophila* gene was used as an outgroup. The branch lengths are proportional to the amount of genetic change in each lineage. Thus, the varying branch lengths indicate that the gene has evolved at slightly different rates in the different lineages.

? *In which vertebrate lineage has the studied gene evolved most rapidly? Explain.*

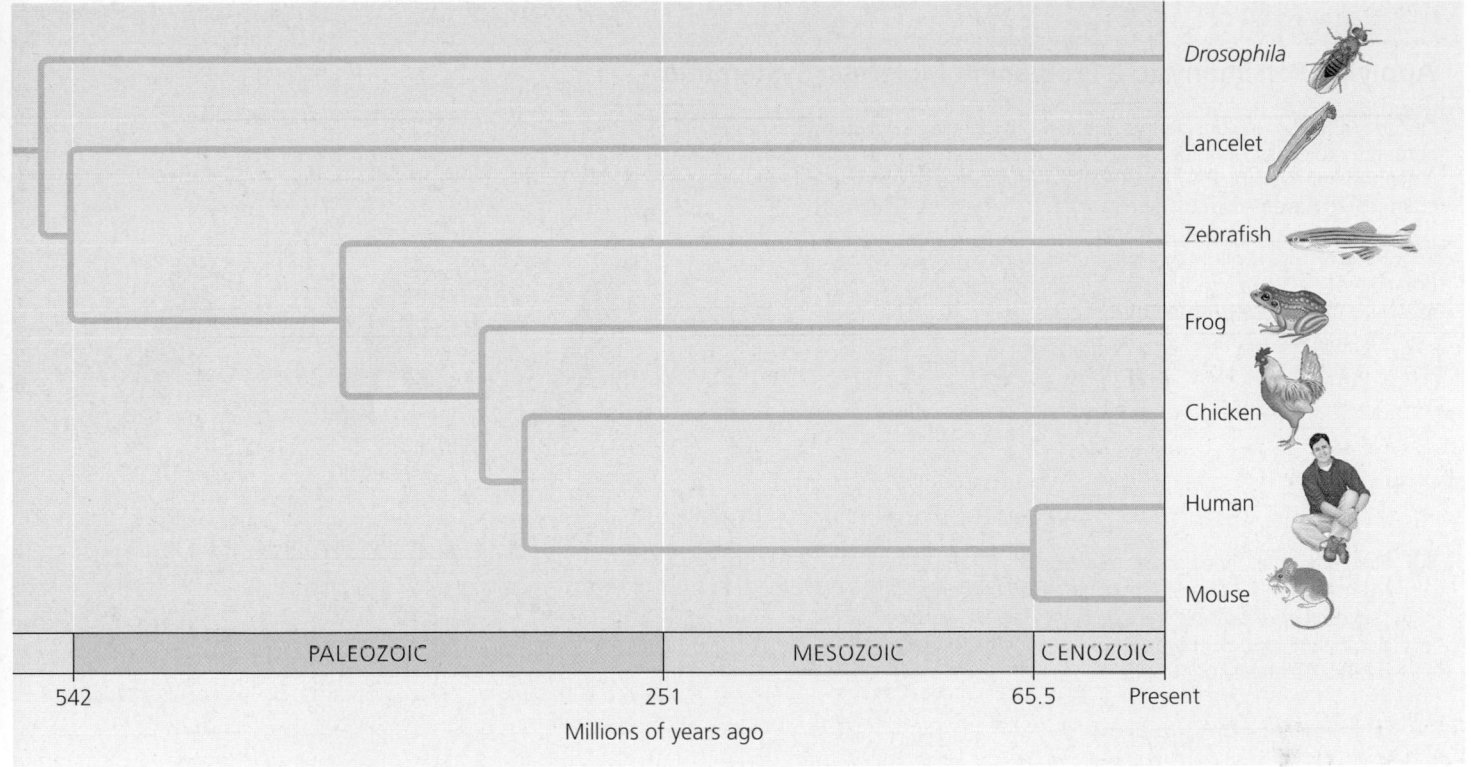

▲ **Figure 26.13 Branch lengths can indicate time.** The relationships shown in this tree are based on the same molecular data as the tree in Figure 26.12. Branch lengths were then drawn to fit the dates of the different branch points based on fossil evidence. As a result, branch lengths are proportional to time. Each evolutionary lineage has the same total length from the base of the tree to the branch tip, indicating that all the lineages have diverged from the common ancestor for equal amounts of time.

The principle of **maximum likelihood** states that given certain rules about how DNA changes over time, a tree can be found that reflects the most likely sequence of evolutionary events. Maximum-likelihood methods are complex, but as a simple example, let us return to the phylogenetic relationships between a human, a mushroom, and a tulip. **Figure 26.14** shows two possible, equally parsimonious trees for this trio. Tree 1 is more likely if we assume that DNA changes have occurred at equal rates along all the branches of the tree from the common ancestor. Tree 2 requires assuming that the rates of evolution slowed greatly in the mushroom lineage and sped up greatly in the tulip lineage. Thus, assuming that equal rates are more common than unequal rates, tree 1 is more likely. We will soon see that many genes do evolve at approximately equal rates in different lineages. But note that if we find new evidence

	Human	Mushroom	Tulip
Human	0	30%	40%
Mushroom		0	40%
Tulip			0

(a) Percentage differences between sequences

▶ **Figure 26.14 Trees with different likelihoods.** Based on percentage differences between genes carried by a human, a mushroom, and a tulip (a), we can construct two possible phylogenetic trees with the same total branch length (b). The sum of the percentages from a point of divergence in a tree equals the percentage differences as listed in (a). For example, in tree 1, the human–tulip divergence is 15% + 5% + 20% − 40%. In tree 2, this divergence also equals 40% (15% + 25%). Assuming that the genes have evolved at the same rate in the different branches, tree 1 is more likely than tree 2.

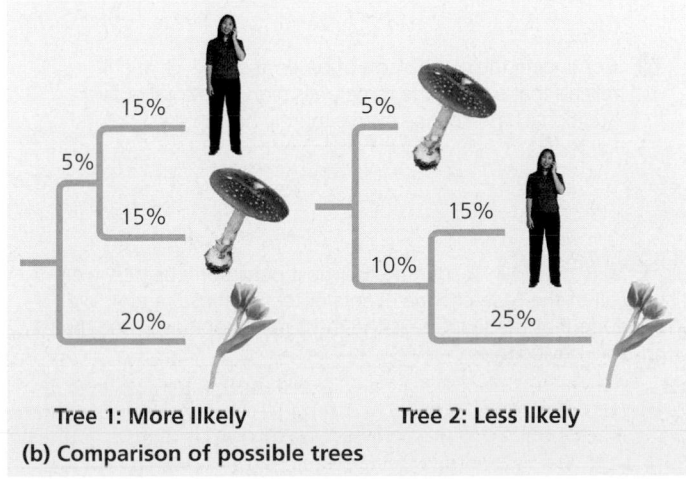

Tree 1: More likely **Tree 2: Less likely**

(b) Comparison of possible trees

Research Method

Applying Parsimony to a Problem in Molecular Systematics

APPLICATION   In considering possible phylogenies for a group of species, systematists compare molecular data for the species. An efficient way to begin is by identifying the most parsimonious hypothesis—the one that requires the fewest evolutionary events (molecular changes) to have occurred.

TECHNIQUE   Follow the numbered steps as we apply the principle of parsimony to a hypothetical phylogenetic problem involving three closely related bird species.

Species I   Species II   Species III

❶ First, draw the three possible phylogenies for the species. (Although only 3 trees are possible when ordering 3 species, the number of possible trees increases rapidly with the number of species: There are 15 trees for 4 species and 34,459,425 trees for 10 species.)

❷ Tabulate the molecular data for the species. In this simplified example, the data represent a DNA sequence consisting of just four nucleotide bases. Data from several outgroup species (not shown) were used to infer the ancestral DNA sequence.

	Site 1	2	3	4
Species I	C	T	A	T
Species II	C	T	T	C
Species III	A	G	A	C
Ancestral sequence	A	G	T	T

❸ Now focus on site 1 in the DNA sequence. In the tree on the left, a single base-change event, represented by the purple hatchmark on the branch leading to species I and II (and labeled 1/C, indicating a change at site 1 to nucleotide C), is sufficient to account for the site 1 data. In the other two trees, two base-change events are necessary.

❹ Continuing the comparison of bases at sites 2, 3, and 4 reveals that each of the three trees requires a total of five additional base-change events (purple hatchmarks).

RESULTS   To identify the most parsimonious tree, we total all of the base-change events noted in steps 3 and 4. We conclude that the first tree is the most parsimonious of the three possible phylogenies.

6 events   7 events   7 events

of unequal rates, tree 2 might be more likely! The likelihood of a tree depends on the assumptions on which it is based.

Many computer programs have been developed to search for trees that are parsimonious and likely. When a large amount of accurate data is available, the methods used in these programs usually yield similar trees. As an example of one method, **Figure 26.15**, on the facing page, walks you through the process of identifying the most parsimonious molecular tree for a three-species problem. Computer programs based on parsimony estimate phylogenies in a similar way: They exhaustively examine all possible trees and select the tree or trees that require fewest evolutionary changes.

Phylogenetic Trees as Hypotheses

This is a good place to reiterate that any phylogenetic tree represents a hypothesis about how the various organisms in the tree are related to one another. The best hypothesis is the one that best fits all the available data. A phylogenetic hypothesis may be modified when new evidence compels systematists to revise their trees. Indeed, while many older phylogenetic hypotheses have been supported, others have been changed or rejected based on new morphological and molecular data.

Thinking of phylogenies as hypotheses also allows us to use them in a powerful way: We can make and test predictions based on the assumption that a phylogeny—our hypothesis—is correct. For example, in an approach known as **phylogenetic bracketing**, we can predict (by parsimony) that features shared by two groups of closely related organisms are present in their common ancestor and all of its descendants, unless independent data indicate otherwise. (Note that here the term *prediction* includes past events, not only future evolutionary change.)

This approach has been used to make novel predictions about dinosaurs. For example, there is evidence that birds descended from the theropods, a group of bipedal dinosaurs within the Saurischian clade. As seen in **Figure 26.16**, the closest living relatives of birds are crocodiles. Birds and crocodiles share numer-

ous features: They have four-chambered hearts, they "sing" to defend territories and attract mates (although a crocodile "song" is more like a bellow), and they build nests. Both birds and crocodiles also care for their eggs by *brooding*, a behavior in which a parent warms the eggs with its body. Birds brood by sitting on their eggs, whereas crocodiles cover their eggs with their neck. Reasoning that any feature shared by birds and crocodiles is likely to have been present in their common ancestor (denoted by the blue dot in Figure 26.16) and *all* of its descendants, biologists predicted that dinosaurs had four-chambered hearts, sang, built nests, and exhibited brooding.

Internal organs, such as the heart, rarely fossilize, and it is, of course, difficult to test whether dinosaurs sang to defend territories and attract mates. However, fossilized dinosaur eggs and nests have provided evidence supporting the prediction of brooding in dinosaurs. First, a fossil embryo of an *Oviraptor* dinosaur was found, still inside its egg. This egg was identical to those found in another fossil, one that showed an *Oviraptor* adult crouching over a group of eggs in a posture similar to that in brooding birds today **(Figure 26.17)**. Researchers suggested

Front limb

Hind limb

Eggs

(a) Fossil remains of *Oviraptor* and eggs. The orientation of the bones, which surround and cover the eggs, suggests that the dinosaur died while incubating or protecting its eggs.

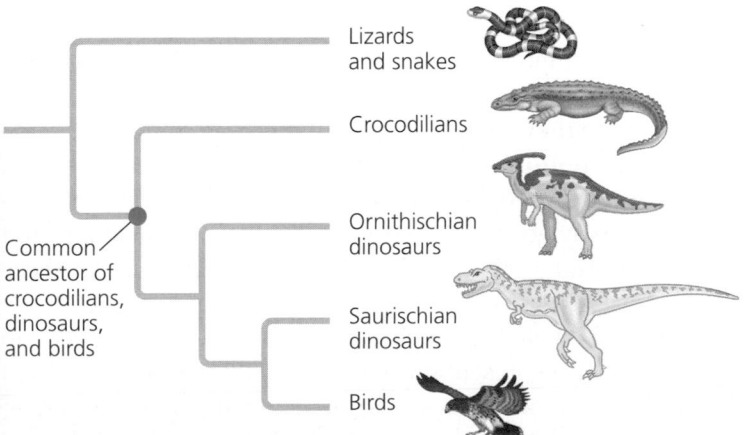

Lizards and snakes

Crocodilians

Ornithischian dinosaurs

Saurischian dinosaurs

Birds

Common ancestor of crocodilians, dinosaurs, and birds

▲ **Figure 26.16 A phylogenetic tree of birds and their close relatives.**

(b) Artist's reconstruction of the dinosaur's posture based on the fossil findings.

▲ Figure 26.17 **Fossils support a phylogenetic prediction: Dinosaurs built nests and brooded their eggs.**

that the *Oviraptor* dinosaur preserved in this second fossil died while incubating or protecting its eggs. The broader conclusion that emerged from this work—that dinosaurs built nests and exhibited brooding—has since been supported by additional fossil discoveries that show that other species of dinosaurs built nests and sat on their eggs. Finally, by supporting predictions based on the phylogenetic hypothesis shown in Figure 26.16, fossil discoveries of nests and brooding in dinosaurs provide independent data that suggest the hypothesis is correct.

CONCEPT CHECK 26.3

1. To distinguish a particular clade of mammals within the larger clade that corresponds to class Mammalia, would hair be a useful character? Why or why not?
2. Why might the most parsimonious tree not necessarily be the most accurate in representing evolutionary relationships for a particular group of species?
3. **WHAT IF?** Draw a phylogenetic tree that includes the relationships from both Figure 25.6 and Figure 26.16. Traditionally, all the taxa shown besides birds and mammals were classified as reptiles. Using a cladistic approach, critique that classification.

For suggested answers, see Appendix A.

CONCEPT 26.4
An organism's evolutionary history is documented in its genome

You have seen throughout this chapter that molecular systematics—using comparisons of nucleic acids or other molecules to deduce relatedness—is a valuable tool for tracing evolutionary history. The molecular approach helps us to understand phylogenetic relationships that cannot be determined by nonmolecular methods such as comparative anatomy. For example, molecular systematics helps us uncover evolutionary relationships between groups that have little common ground for morphological comparison, such as animals and fungi. And molecular methods allow us to reconstruct phylogenies among groups of present-day prokaryotes and other microorganisms for which we have no fossil record at all. Molecular biology has helped to extend systematics to evolutionary relationships far above and below the species level, ranging from the major branches of the tree of life to its finest twigs. Still, the findings are often inconclusive, as in cases where several taxa diverged at nearly the same time in the distant past. The differences may be apparent, but not the order of their appearance.

Different genes evolve at different rates, even in the same evolutionary lineage. As a result, molecular trees can represent short or long periods of time, depending on what genes are used. For example, the DNA that codes for ribosomal RNA (rRNA) changes relatively slowly, and so comparisons of DNA sequences in these genes are useful for investigating relationships between taxa that diverged hundreds of millions of years ago. Studies of rRNA sequences indicate, for example, that fungi are more closely related to animals than to green plants (see Figure 26.2). In contrast, mitochondrial DNA (mtDNA) evolves relatively rapidly and can be used to explore recent evolutionary events. One research team has traced the relationships among Native American groups through their mtDNA sequences. The molecular findings corroborate other evidence that the Pima of Arizona, the Maya of Mexico, and the Yanomami of Venezuela are closely related, probably descending from the first of three waves of immigrants that crossed the Bering land bridge from Asia to the Americas about 13,000 years ago.

Gene Duplications and Gene Families

What does molecular systematics reveal about the evolutionary history of genome change? Consider gene duplication, which plays a particularly important role in evolution because it increases the number of genes in the genome, providing more opportunities for further evolutionary changes. Molecular techniques now allow us to trace the phylogenies of gene duplications and the influence of these duplications on genome evolution. These molecular phylogenies must account for repeated duplications that have resulted in *gene families,* groups of related genes within an organism's genome (see Figure 21.10). Like homologous genes in different species, these duplicated genes have a common ancestor. We distinguish these types of homologous genes by different names: orthologous genes and paralogous genes.

The term **orthologous genes** (from the Greek *orthos,* straight) refers to homologous genes that are found in different species because of speciation **(Figure 26.18a)**. The cytochrome *c* genes (which code for an electron transport chain protein) in humans and dogs are orthologous. **Paralogous genes** (from the Greek *para,* beside) result from gene duplication, so they are found in more than one copy in the same genome **(Figure 26.18b)**. In Chapter 23, you encountered the example of olfactory receptor genes, which have undergone many gene duplications in vertebrates. Humans and mice both have huge families of more than 1,000 of these paralogous genes.

It is possible to describe most of the genes that make up genomes as representing one of these two types of homology. Note that orthologous genes can only diverge after speciation has taken place, with the result that the genes are found in separate gene pools. For example, although the cytochrome *c* genes in humans and dogs serve a similar function, the

▲ Figure 26.18 How two types of homologous genes originate. The colored bands mark regions of the genes where differences in base sequences have accumulated.

(a) Orthologous genes

Ancestral gene

Ancestral species

Speciation with divergence of gene

Species A

Orthologous genes

Species B

(b) Paralogous genes

Species A

Gene duplication and divergence

Paralogous genes

Species A after many generations

gene's sequence in humans has diverged from that in dogs in the time since these species last shared a common ancestor. Paralogous genes, on the other hand, can diverge within a species because they are present in more than one copy in the genome. The paralogous genes that make up the olfactory receptor gene family in humans have diverged from each other during our long evolutionary history. They now specify proteins that confer sensitivity to a wide variety of odors, ranging from various foods to sex pheromones.

Genome Evolution

Now that we can compare the entire genomes of different organisms, including our own, two remarkable facts have emerged. First, orthologous genes are widespread and can extend over huge evolutionary distances. Ninety-nine percent of the genes of humans and mice are detectably orthologous, and 50% of our genes are orthologous with those of yeast. This remarkable commonality demonstrates that all living organisms share many biochemical and developmental pathways.

Second, the number of genes seems not to have increased through duplication at the same rate as perceived phenotypic complexity. Humans have only about four times as many genes as yeast, a single-celled eukaryote, even though—unlike

yeast cells—we have a large, complex brain and a body that contains more than 200 different types of tissues. Evidence is emerging that many human genes are more versatile than those of yeast in that the proteins they encode carry out a wider variety of tasks in various body tissues. Before us lies a huge and exciting scientific challenge: unraveling the mechanisms that enable this genomic versatility.

CONCEPT CHECK 26.4

1. Explain how comparisons between the proteins of two species can yield data about their evolutionary relationship.
2. **WHAT IF?** Suppose gene A is orthologous in species 1 and species 2, and gene B is paralogous to gene A in species 1. Suggest a sequence of two evolutionary events that could result in the following: Gene A differs considerably between species, yet gene A and gene B show little sequence divergence from each other.

For suggested answers, see Appendix A.

CONCEPT 26.5
Molecular clocks help track evolutionary time

One of the long-term goals of evolutionary biology is to understand the relationships among all organisms, including those for which there is no fossil record. When we extend molecular phylogenies beyond the fossil record, however, we must rely on an important assumption about how change occurs at the molecular level.

Molecular Clocks

We stated earlier that researchers have estimated that the common ancestor of Hawaiian silverswords lived about 5 million years ago. How did they make this estimate? They relied on the concept of a **molecular clock**, a yardstick for measuring the absolute time of evolutionary change based on the observation that some genes and other regions of genomes appear to evolve at constant rates. The assumption underlying the molecular clock is that the number of nucleotide substitutions in orthologous genes is proportional to the time that has elapsed since the species branched from their common ancestor (divergence time). In the case of paralogous genes, the number of substitutions is proportional to the time since the genes became duplicated.

We can calibrate the molecular clock of a gene that has a reliable average rate of evolution by graphing the number of genetic differences—for example, nucleotide, codon, or amino acid differences—against the dates of evolutionary branch

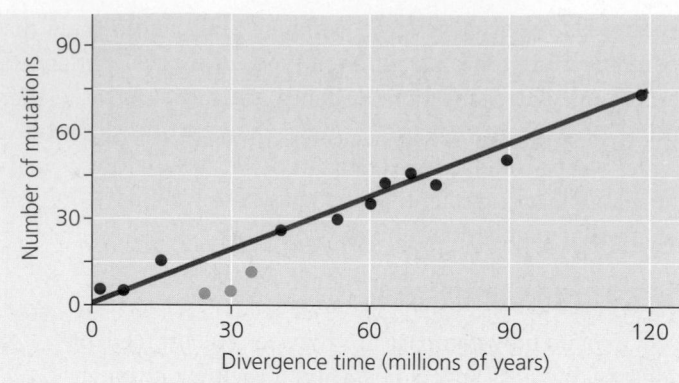

▲ **Figure 26.19 A molecular clock for mammals.** The number of accumulated mutations in seven proteins increased over time in a consistent manner for most mammal species. The three green data points represent primate species, whose proteins appear to have evolved more slowly than those of other mammals. The divergence time for each data point was based on fossil evidence.

❓ *Use the clock to estimate the divergence time for a mammal with a total of 30 mutations in the seven proteins.*

points that are known from the fossil record **(Figure 26.19)**. Such graphs can then be used to estimate the dates of evolutionary episodes that cannot be discerned from the fossil record, such as the origin of the silverswords discussed earlier.

Of course, no gene marks time with complete precision. In fact, some portions of the genome appear to have evolved in irregular fits and starts that are not at all clocklike. And even those genes that seem to have reliable molecular clocks are accurate only in the statistical sense of showing a fairly smooth *average* rate of change. Over time, there may still be chance deviations above and below that average rate. Furthermore, the same gene may evolve at different rates in different groups of organisms, making it necessary to calibrate and use molecular clocks with care. Finally, even among genes that are clocklike, the rate of the clock may vary greatly from one gene to another; some genes evolve a million times faster than others.

Neutral Theory

The regularity of change that enables us to use some genes as molecular clocks raises the possibility that many of the changes in these sequences result from genetic drift (see Chapter 23) and that the changes are mostly neutral—neither adaptive nor detrimental. In the 1960s, Jack King and Thomas Jukes, at the University of California, Berkeley, and Motoo Kimura, at the Japanese National Institute of Genetics, published papers supporting this **neutral theory**—that much evolutionary change in genes and proteins has no effect on fitness and therefore is not influenced by Darwinian selection. Kimura pointed out that many new mutations are harmful and are removed quickly. But if most of the rest are neutral and have little or no effect on fitness, then the rate of molecular change should indeed be regular like a clock. Differences in the clock rate for different genes are a function of how important a gene is. If the

exact sequence of amino acids that a gene specifies is essential to survival, most of the mutational changes will be harmful and only a few will be neutral. As a result, such genes change only slowly. But if the exact sequence of amino acids is less critical, fewer of the new mutations will be harmful and more will be neutral. Such genes change more quickly.

Difficulties with Molecular Clocks

In fact, molecular clocks do not run as smoothly as neutral theory predicts. Many irregularities are likely to be the result of natural selection in which certain DNA changes are favored over others. Consequently, some scientists question the utility of molecular clocks for timing evolution. Their skepticism is part of a broader debate about the extent to which neutral genetic variation can account for some kinds of DNA diversity. Indeed, evidence suggests that almost half the amino acid differences in proteins of two *Drosophila* species, *D. simulans* and *D. yakuba*, are not neutral but have resulted from directional natural selection. But because the direction of natural selection may change repeatedly over long periods of time (and hence may average out), some genes experiencing selection can nevertheless serve as approximate markers of elapsed time.

Another question arises when researchers attempt to extend molecular clocks beyond the time span documented by the fossil record. Although some fossils are more than 3 billion years old, these are very rare. An abundant fossil record extends back only about 550 million years, but molecular clocks have been used to date evolutionary divergences that occurred a billion or more years ago. These estimates assume that the clocks have been constant for all that time. Such estimates are highly uncertain.

In some cases, problems may be avoided by calibrating molecular clocks with many genes rather than just one or a few genes (as is often done). By using many genes, fluctuations in evolutionary rate due to natural selection or other factors that vary over time may average out. For example, one group of researchers constructed molecular clocks of vertebrate evolution from published sequence data for 658 nuclear genes. Despite the broad period of time covered (nearly 600 million years) and the fact that natural selection probably affected some of these genes, their estimates of divergence times agreed closely with fossil-based estimates.

Applying a Molecular Clock: The Origin of HIV

Researchers at Los Alamos National Laboratory in New Mexico used a molecular clock to date the origin of HIV infection in humans. Phylogenetic analysis shows that HIV, the virus that causes AIDS, is descended from viruses that infect chimpanzees and other primates. (The viruses do not cause any AIDS-like diseases in nonhuman hosts.) When did HIV jump to humans? There is no simple answer, because the virus has

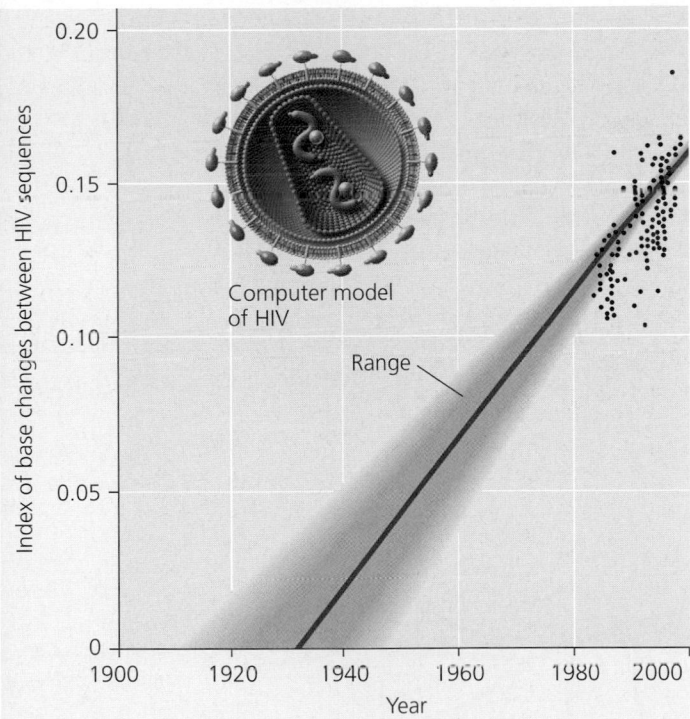

▲ Figure 26.20 Dating the origin of HIV-1 M with a molecular clock. The numerous data points in the upper right-hand corner of this graph are based on DNA sequences for a specific HIV gene in blood samples collected from patients at different known times. If we project the relatively constant rate at which changes occurred in this gene in the 1980s and 1990s back in time, we intersect the x-axis of the graph in the 1930s.

spread to humans more than once. The multiple origins of HIV are reflected in the variety of strains (genetic types) of the virus. HIV's genetic material is made of RNA, and like other RNA viruses, it evolves quickly.

The most widespread strain in humans is HIV-1 M. To pinpoint the earliest HIV-1 M infection, the researchers compared samples of the virus from various times during the epidemic, including one sample from 1959. A comparison of gene sequences showed that the virus has evolved in a clock-like fashion since 1959 **(Figure 26.20)**. By extrapolating from their molecular clock, the researchers concluded that the HIV-1 M strain first spread to humans during the 1930s.

New information continues to revise our understanding of the tree of life

The discovery that the scaly-foot in Figure 26.1 evolved from a different lineage of legless lizards than did snakes is one example of how systematics is used to reconstruct the evolutionary relationships of life's diverse forms. In recent decades, we have gained insight into even the very deepest branches of the tree of life through molecular systematics.

From Two Kingdoms to Three Domains

Early taxonomists classified all known species into two kingdoms: plants and animals. Even with the discovery of the diverse microbial world, the two-kingdom system persisted: Noting that bacteria had a rigid cell wall, taxonomists placed them in the plant kingdom. Eukaryotic unicellular organisms with chloroplasts were also considered plants. Fungi, too, were classified as plants, partly because most fungi, like most plants, are unable to move about, and despite the fact that fungi are not photosynthetic and have little in common structurally with plants. In the two-kingdom system, unicellular organisms that move and ingest food—protozoans—were classified as animals. Microorganisms such as *Euglena* that move and are photosynthetic were claimed by both botanists and zoologists and showed up in both kingdoms.

Taxonomic schemes with more than two kingdoms did not gain broad acceptance until the late 1960s, when many biologists recognized five kingdoms: Monera (prokaryotes), Protista (a diverse kingdom consisting mostly of unicellular organisms), Plantae, Fungi, and Animalia. This system highlighted the two fundamentally different types of cells, prokaryotic and eukaryotic, and set the prokaryotes apart from all eukaryotes by placing them in their own kingdom, Monera.

However, shortly after the widespread adoption of the five-kingdom approach, phylogenies based on genetic data began to reveal a fundamental problem with this system: Some prokaryotes differed as much from each other as they did from eukaryotes. Such difficulties have led biologists to adopt a three-domain system. The three domains—Bacteria, Archaea, and Eukarya—are a taxonomic level higher than the kingdom level. The validity of these domains has now been confirmed by many studies, including an analysis of nearly 100 of the many hundreds of completely sequenced genomes.

The domain Bacteria contains most of the currently known prokaryotes, including the bacteria closely related to chloroplasts and mitochondria. The second domain, Archaea, consists of a diverse group of prokaryotic organisms that inhabit a wide variety of environments. Some archaea can use hydrogen as an energy source, and others were the chief source of the

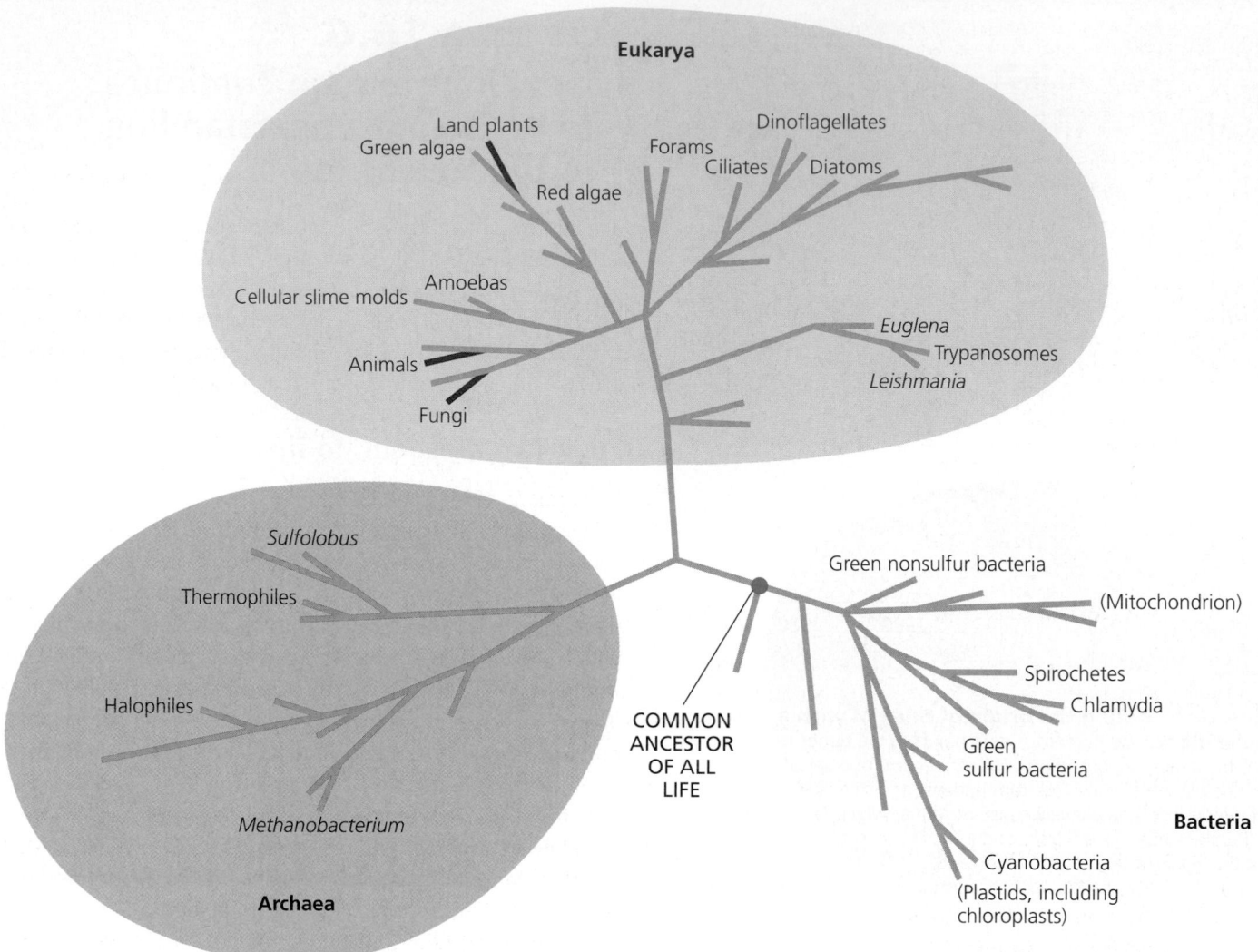

▲ **Figure 26.21 The three domains of life.** Based on rRNA gene sequences, all of life can be grouped into three domains. Branch lengths are proportional to the amount of genetic change in each lineage. (To simplify the figure, only some branches are labeled.) In this diagram, the lineages within Eukarya that are dominated by multicellular organisms (plants, fungi, and animals) are shown in red. All other lineages consist solely or primarily of single-celled organisms.

? *Based on this diagram, which domain was the first to diverge? Which is the sister domain to Eukarya?*

natural gas deposits that are found throughout Earth's crust. As you will read in Chapter 27, bacteria differ from archaea in many structural, biochemical, and physiological characteristics. The third domain, Eukarya, consists of all the organisms that have cells containing true nuclei. This domain includes many groups of single-celled organisms (see Chapter 28) as well as multicellular plants (Chapters 29 and 30), fungi (Chapter 31), and animals (Chapters 32–34). **Figure 26.21** represents one possible phylogenetic tree for the three domains and the many lineages they encompass.

The three-domain system highlights the fact that much of the history of life has been about single-celled organisms. The two prokaryotic domains consist entirely of single-celled organisms, and even in Eukarya, only the branches shown in red (plants, fungi, and animals) are dominated by multicellular organisms. Of the five kingdoms previously recognized by

taxonomists, most biologists continue to recognize Plantae, Fungi, and Animalia, but not Monera and Protista. The kingdom Monera is obsolete because it would have members in two different domains. As you'll read in Chapter 28, the kingdom Protista has also crumbled because it is polyphyletic—it includes members that are more closely related to plants, fungi, or animals than to other protists.

A Simple Tree of All Life

The evolutionary relationships shown in Figure 26.21 can be summarized in a simpler tree **(Figure 26.22)**. In this tree, the first major split in the history of life occurred when the bacteria diverged from other organisms. If this tree is correct, eukaryotes and archaea are more closely related to each other than either is to bacteria.

1 Most recent common ancestor of all living things

2 Gene transfer between mitochondrial ancestor and ancestor of eukaryotes

3 Gene transfer between chloroplast ancestor and ancestor of green plants

Bacteria

Eukarya

Archaea

4   3   2   1   0

Billions of years ago

▲ Figure 26.22 **The role of horizontal gene transfer in the history of life.** This tree shows two major episodes of horizontal gene transfer, the dates of which are uncertain. It is known that many more such events occurred.

This reconstruction of the tree of life is based largely on sequence comparisons of rRNA genes, which code for the RNA parts of ribosomes. Because ribosomes are fundamental to the workings of the cell, rRNA genes have evolved so slowly that homologies between distantly related organisms can still be detected—making these genes very useful for determining evolutionary relationships among deep branches in the history of life. However, other genes reveal a different set of relationships. For example, researchers have found that many of the genes that influence metabolism in yeast (a single-celled eukaryote) are more similar to genes in the domain Bacteria than they are to genes in the domain Archaea—a finding that suggests that the eukaryotes may share a more recent common ancestor with bacteria than with archaea.

Comparisons of complete genomes from the three domains show that there have been substantial movements of genes between organisms in the different domains (see Figure 26.22). These took place through **horizontal gene transfer**, a process in which genes are transferred from one genome to another through mechanisms such as exchange of transposable elements and plasmids, viral infection (see Chapter 19), and perhaps fusions of organisms. Some biologists hypothesize that the first eukaryote may have arisen through a fusion between an ancestral bacterium and an ancestral archaean. Because phylogenetic trees are based on the assumption that genes are passed vertically from one generation to the next, the occurrence of such horizontal transfer events helps to explain why universal trees built using different genes can give inconsistent results.

Eukarya

Bacteria

Archaea

▲ Figure 26.23 **A ring of life.** In this hypothesis, the earliest organisms form a "ring of life" through horizontal gene transfer. Three great domains (Bacteria, Eukarya, and Archaea) eventually emerged from the ring and gave rise to the tremendous diversity of life we observe today.

Is the Tree of Life Really a Ring?

Some scientists have argued that horizontal gene transfers were so common that the early history of life should be represented as a tangled network of connected branches—not a simple, dichotomously branching tree like that in Figure 26.22. Others have suggested that relationships among early organisms are best represented by a ring, not a tree (**Figure 26.23**). In an analysis based on hundreds of genes, these researchers hypothesized that eukaryotes arose as an endosymbiosis between an early bacterium and an early archaean. If correct, eukaryotes are simultaneously most closely related to bacteria *and* archaea—an evolutionary relationship that cannot be depicted in a tree of life, but can be depicted in a *ring* of life.

Although scientists continue to debate whether early steps in the history of life are best represented as a tree, a ring, or a tangled web, in recent decades there have been many exciting discoveries about evolutionary events that occurred later in time. We'll explore such discoveries in the rest of this unit's chapters, beginning with Earth's earliest inhabitants, the prokaryotes.

CONCEPT CHECK   26.6

1. Why is the kingdom Monera no longer considered a valid taxon?
2. Explain why phylogenies based on different genes can yield different branching patterns for the universal tree of life.
3. **WHAT IF?** Draw the three possible dichotomously branching trees showing evolutionary relationships for the domains Bacteria, Archaea, and Eukarya. Two of these trees have been supported by genetic data. Is it likely that the third tree might also receive such support? Explain your answer.

For suggested answers, see Appendix A.

Chapter 26 Review

MEDIA Go to **www.campbellbiology.com** for BioFlix 3-D Animations, MP3 Tutors, Videos, Practice Tests, an eBook, and more.

SUMMARY OF KEY CONCEPTS

CONCEPT 26.1

Phylogenies show evolutionary relationships (pp. 537–540)

▶ **Binomial Nomenclature** Linnaeus's system gives organisms two-part names: a genus plus a specific epithet.

▶ **Hierarchical Classification** Linnaeus introduced a formal system for grouping species in increasingly broad categories: related genera are placed in the same family, families into orders, orders into classes, classes into phyla, phyla into kingdoms, and (more recently) kingdoms into domains.

▶ **Linking Classification and Phylogeny** Systematists depict evolutionary relationships as branching phylogenetic trees. Some systematists propose that classification be based entirely on evolutionary relationships.

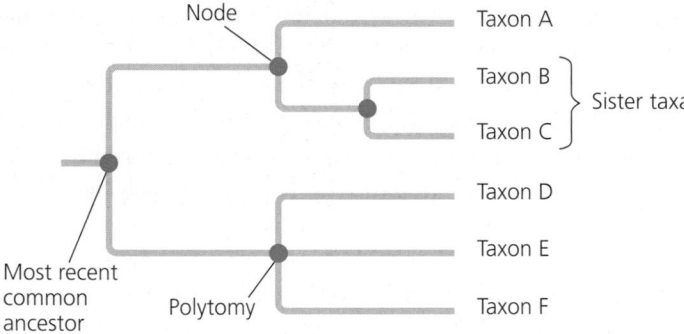

▶ **What We Can and Cannot Learn from Phylogenetic Trees** Unless branch lengths are proportional to time or genetic change, a phylogenetic tree indicates only patterns of descent.

▶ **Applying Phylogenies** Much information can be learned about a species from its evolutionary history; hence, phylogenies are useful in a wide range of applications.

MEDIA

Activity Classification Schemes

CONCEPT 26.2

Phylogenies are inferred from morphological and molecular data (pp. 540–542)

▶ **Morphological and Molecular Homologies** Organisms that share very similar morphologies or DNA sequences are likely to be more closely related than organisms with very different structures and genetic sequences.

▶ **Sorting Homology from Analogy** Homology (similarity due to shared ancestry) must be sorted from analogy (similarity due to convergent evolution).

▶ **Evaluating Molecular Homologies** Computer programs are used to align comparable nucleic acid sequences and to distinguish molecular homologies from coincidental matches between taxa that diverged long ago.

CONCEPT 26.3

Shared characters are used to construct phylogenetic trees (pp. 542–548)

▶ **Cladistics** A clade is a monophyletic grouping that includes an ancestral species and all of its descendants. Clades can be distinguished by their shared derived characters.

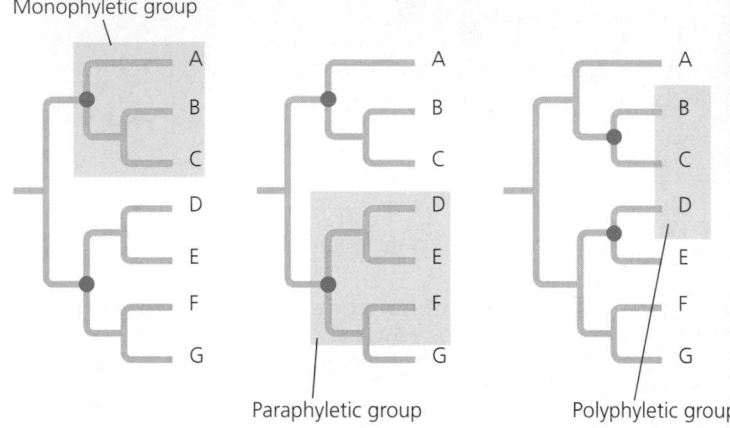

▶ **Phylogenetic Trees with Proportional Branch Lengths** Branch lengths can be drawn proportional to the amount of evolutionary change or time.

▶ **Maximum Parsimony and Maximum Likelihood** Among phylogenies, the most parsimonious tree is the one that requires the fewest evolutionary changes. The most likely tree is the one based on the most likely pattern of changes.

▶ **Phylogenetic Trees as Hypotheses** Well-supported phylogenetic hypotheses are consistent with a wide range of data.

MEDIA

Investigation How Is Phylogeny Determined by Comparing Proteins?

CONCEPT 26.4

An organism's evolutionary history is documented in its genome (pp. 548–549)

▶ **Gene Duplications and Gene Families** Orthologous genes are homologous genes found in different species because of speciation. Paralogous genes arise through duplication within a genome and can diverge within a clade, often adding new functions.

▶ **Genome Evolution** Distantly related species often have orthologous genes. The small variation in gene number in organisms of varying complexity suggests that genes are versatile and may have multiple functions.

CONCEPT 26.5

Molecular clocks help track evolutionary time (pp. 549–551)

▶ **Molecular Clocks** The base sequences of some regions of DNA change at a rate consistent enough to allow dating of episodes in past evolution. Other genes change in a less predictable way.

▶ **Applying a Molecular Clock: The Origin of HIV** A molecular clock analysis suggests that the most common strain of HIV jumped from primates to humans in the 1930s.

CONCEPT 26.6

New information continues to revise our understanding of the tree of life (pp. 551–553)

▶ **From Two Kingdoms to Three Domains** Past classification systems have given way to the current view of the tree of life, which consists of three great domains: Bacteria, Archaea, and Eukarya.

▶ **A Simple Tree of All Life** Phylogenies based on rRNA genes suggest that eukaryotes are most closely related to archaea, while data from other genes suggest a closer relationship to bacteria.

▶ **Is the Tree of Life Really a Ring?** Genetic analyses suggest that the earliest organisms may have formed a "ring of life" in which eukaryotes are equally closely related to bacteria and to archaea.

TESTING YOUR KNOWLEDGE

SELF-QUIZ

1. In Figure 26.4, which similarly inclusive taxon descended from the same common ancestor as Canidae?
   - a. Felidae
   - b. Mustelidae
   - c. Carnivora
   - d. *Canis*
   - e. *Lutra*

2. Three living species X, Y, and Z share a common ancestor T, as do extinct species U and V. A grouping that includes species T, X, Y, and Z makes up
   - a. a valid taxon.
   - b. a monophyletic clade.
   - c. an ingroup, with species U as the outgroup.
   - d. a paraphyletic group.
   - e. a polyphyletic group.

3. In a comparison of birds and mammals, having four appendages is
   - a. a shared ancestral character.
   - b. a shared derived character.
   - c. a character useful for distinguishing birds from mammals.
   - d. an example of analogy rather than homology.
   - e. a character useful for sorting bird species.

4. Based on this tree, which statement is *not* correct?

   - a. The lineage leading to salamanders was the first to diverge from the other lineages.
   - b. Salamanders are a sister group to the group containing lizards, goats, and humans.
   - c. Salamanders are as closely related to goats as to humans.
   - d. Lizards are more closely related to salamanders than to humans.
   - e. The group highlighted by shading is paraphyletic.

5. If you were using cladistics to build a phylogenetic tree of cats, which of the following would be the best outgroup?
   - a. lion
   - b. domestic cat
   - c. wolf
   - d. leopard
   - e. tiger

6. The relative lengths of the amphibian and mouse branches in the phylogeny in Figure 26.12 indicate that
   - a. amphibians evolved before mice.
   - b. mice evolved before amphibians.
   - c. the genes of amphibians and mice have only coincidental homoplasies.
   - d. the homologous gene has evolved more slowly in mice.
   - e. the homologous gene has evolved more rapidly in mice.

7. To apply parsimony to constructing a phylogenetic tree,
   - a. choose the tree that assumes all evolutionary changes are equally probable.
   - b. choose the tree in which the branch points are based on as many shared derived characters as possible.
   - c. base phylogenetic trees only on the fossil record, as this provides the simplest explanation for evolution.
   - d. choose the tree that represents the fewest evolutionary changes, either in DNA sequences or morphology.
   - e. choose the tree with the fewest branch points.

For Self-Quiz answers, see Appendix A.

MEDIA Visit **www.campbellbiology.com** for a Practice Test.

EVOLUTION CONNECTION

8. Darwin suggested looking at a species' close relatives to learn what its ancestors may have been like. How does his suggestion anticipate recent methods, such as phylogenetic bracketing and the use of outgroups in cladistic analysis?

   Biological Inquiry: A Workbook of Investigative Cases Explore the use of outgroups and other aspects of cladistic analysis in "Tree Thinking."

SCIENTIFIC INQUIRY

9. **DRAW IT** (a) Draw a phylogenetic tree based on the first five characters in the table below. Place hatch marks on the tree to indicate the origin(s) of each of the six characters. (b) Assume that tuna and dolphins are sister species and redraw the phylogenetic tree accordingly, keeping other evolutionary relationships the same as in the first tree. Place hatch marks on the tree to indicate the origin(s) of each of the six characters. (c) How many evolutionary changes are required in each tree? Which tree is most parsimonious?

Character	Lancelet (outgroup)	Lamprey	Tuna	Salamander	Turtle	Leopard	Dolphin
Backbone	0	1	1	1	1	1	1
Hinged jaw	0	0	1	1	1	1	1
Four limbs	0	0	0	1	1	1	1*
Amniotic egg	0	0	0	0	1	1	1
Milk	0	0	0	0	0	1	1
Dorsal fin	0	0	1	0	0	0	1

SPECIES

*Although adult dolphins have only two obvious limbs (their flippers), as embryos they have two hind-limb buds, for a total of four limbs.

Bacteria and Archaea 27

OVERVIEW

Masters of Adaptation

After a heavy summer rain, California's Owens Lake can contain waters so hot and salty that they would burn and dehydrate your skin on contact. The salt concentration can reach 32%, more than nine times that of seawater. Yet despite these harsh conditions, the briny lakebed's reddish color, shown in **Figure 27.1**, is caused by organisms, not by minerals or other nonliving sources. What organisms can live in such an inhospitable environment, and how do they do it?

The pink color of Owens Lake comes from trillions of cells of *Halobacterium*, a single-celled prokaryote in domain Archaea that is one of the few kinds of organisms living in the lake. This archaean has a red membrane pigment, bacteriorhodopsin, that uses light energy to drive ATP synthesis. *Halobacterium* is among the most salt-tolerant organisms on Earth—it thrives in salinities that dehydrate and kill other cells. This archaean compensates for osmotic water loss by pumping potassium ions (K^+) or other ions into the cell until the ionic concentration inside the cell matches the concentration outside.

▲ Figure 27.1 **Why is this lakebed red?**

Like *Halobacterium*, many other prokaryotes are master adapters. Examples include *Deinococcus radiodurans*, which can survive 3 million rads of radiation (3,000 times the dose fatal to humans), and *Picrophilus oshimae*, which can grow at a pH of 0.03 (acidic enough to dissolve metal). Other prokaryotes live in environments that are too cold or too hot for most other organisms, and some have even been found living in rocks 3.2 km (2 miles) below Earth's surface.

Prokaryotic species are also very well adapted to more "normal" habitats—the lands and waters in which most other species are found. Their ability to adapt to a broad range of habitats helps to explain why prokaryotes are the most abundant organisms on Earth: Their collective biological mass (biomass) is at least ten times that of all eukaryotes, and the number of prokaryotes in a handful of fertile soil is greater than the number of people who have ever lived. In this chapter, we'll examine the adaptations, diversity, ecological impact, and importance to humans of these small but amazing organisms that comprise two of the three domains of life.

CONCEPT 27.1
Structural and functional adaptations contribute to prokaryotic success

As we discussed in Chapter 25, the first organisms to inhabit Earth are thought to have been prokaryotes. Throughout their long evolutionary history, prokaryotic populations have been (and continue to be) subjected to natural selection under many different environmental conditions. This process ultimately has resulted in the great diversity of adaptations found among prokaryotes today.

In this and the following sections, we'll survey the biology of prokaryotes. Most prokaryotes are unicellular, although some species aggregate temporarily or permanently in colonies.

Prokaryotic cells typically have diameters in the range of 0.5–5 μm, much smaller than the 10–100 μm diameter of many eukaryotic cells. (One notable exception is the giant prokaryote *Thiomargarita namibiensis*, which is about 750 μm in diameter—just visible to the unaided eye.) Prokaryotic cells have a variety of shapes, the three most common of which are spheres (cocci), rods (bacilli), and spirals **(Figure 27.2)**. Finally, although they are unicellular and small, prokaryotes are well organized, achieving all of an organism's life functions within a single cell.

Cell-Surface Structures

A key feature of nearly all prokaryotic cells is the cell wall, which maintains cell shape, provides physical protection, and prevents the cell from bursting in a hypotonic environment (see Chapter 7). In a hypertonic environment, most prokaryotes lose water and shrink away from their wall (plasmolyze), like other walled cells. Severe water loss inhibits cell reproduction. Salt thus can be used to preserve foods because it causes prokaryotes to lose water.

The cell walls of prokaryotes differ in molecular composition and construction from those of eukaryotes. As you read in Chapter 5, eukaryotic cell walls are usually made of cellulose or chitin. In contrast, most bacterial cell walls contain **peptidoglycan**, a network of modified-sugar polymers cross-linked by short polypeptides. This molecular fabric encloses the entire bacterium and anchors other molecules that extend from its surface. Archaeal cell walls contain a variety of polysaccharides and proteins but lack peptidoglycan.

Using a technique called the **Gram stain**, developed by the nineteenth-century Danish physician Hans Christian Gram, scientists can classify many bacterial species into two groups based on differences in cell wall composition. **Gram-positive** bacteria have simpler walls with a relatively large amount of peptidoglycan **(Figure 27.3a)**. **Gram-negative** bacteria have less peptidoglycan and are structurally more complex, with an outer membrane that contains lipopolysaccharides (carbohydrates bonded to lipids) **(Figure 27.3b)**.

◀ Figure 27.2 The most common shapes of prokaryotes.
(a) Cocci (singular, *coccus*) are spherical prokaryotes. They occur singly, in pairs (diplococci), in chains of many cells (streptococci, shown here), and in clusters resembling bunches of grapes (staphylococci). **(b)** Bacilli (singular, *bacillus*) are rod-shaped prokaryotes. They are usually solitary, but in some forms the rods are arranged in chains (streptobacilli). **(c)** Spiral prokaryotes include spirilla, which range from comma-like shapes to long coils, and spirochetes (shown here), which are corkscrew-shaped (colorized SEMs).

1 μm	2 μm	5 μm
(a) Spherical (cocci)	**(b) Rod-shaped (bacilli)**	**(c) Spiral**

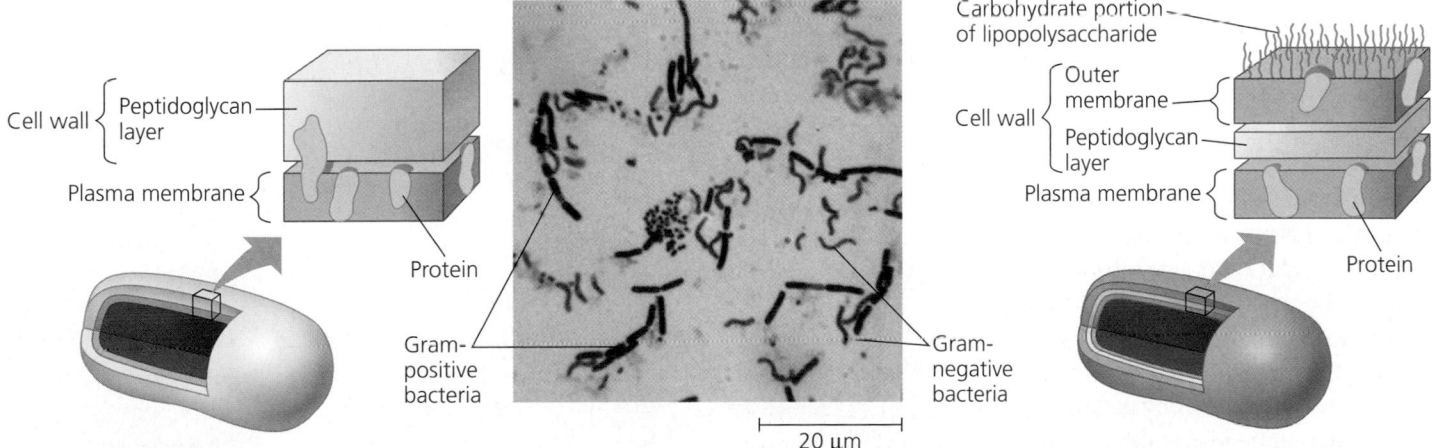

(a) Gram-positive. Gram-positive bacteria have a thick cell wall made of peptidoglycan that traps the crystal violet in the cytoplasm. The alcohol rinse does not remove the crystal violet, which masks the added red safranin dye.

(b) Gram-negative. Gram-negative bacteria have a thinner layer of peptidoglycan, and it is located in a layer between the plasma membrane and an outer membrane. The crystal violet is easily rinsed from the cytoplasm, and the cell appears pink or red.

▲ Figure 27.3 Gram staining. Samples are first stained with crystal violet dye and iodine, then rinsed in alcohol, and finally stained with a red dye such as safranin. The structure of a bacterium's cell wall determines the staining response (LM).

▲ **Figure 27.4 Capsule.** The polysaccharide capsule around this *Streptococcus* bacterium enables the prokaryote to attach to cells in the respiratory tract—in this colorized TEM, a tonsil cell.

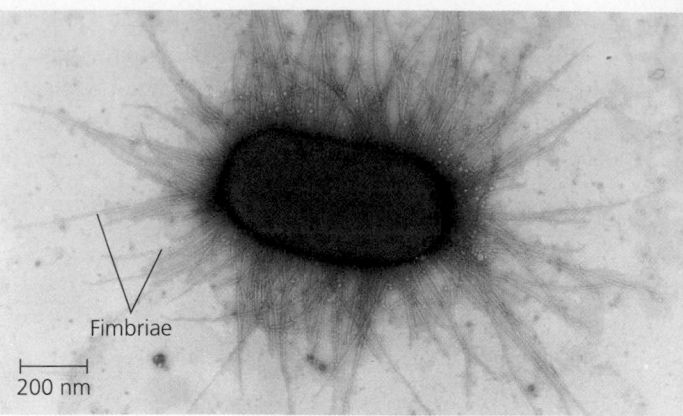

▲ **Figure 27.5 Fimbriae.** These numerous appendages enable some prokaryotes to attach to surfaces or to other prokaryotes (colorized TEM).

Gram staining is a valuable tool in medicine for quickly determining if a patient's infection is due to gram-negative or to gram-positive bacteria. This information has treatment implications. The lipid portions of the lipopolysaccharides in the walls of many gram-negative bacteria are toxic, causing fever or shock. Furthermore, the outer membrane of a gram-negative bacterium helps protect it from the body's defenses. Gram-negative bacteria also tend to be more resistant than gram-positive species to antibiotics because the outer membrane impedes entry of the drugs. However, certain gram-positive species (for example, *Mycobacterium tuberculosis*, which causes tuberculosis) have virulent strains that are resistant to one or more antibiotics.

The effectiveness of certain antibiotics, such as penicillin, derives from their inhibition of the peptidoglycan cross-linking. The resulting cell wall may not be functional, particularly in gram-positive bacteria. Such drugs destroy many species of pathogenic bacteria without adversely affecting human cells, which do not contain peptidoglycan.

The cell wall of many prokaryotes is covered by a **capsule**, a sticky layer of polysaccharide or protein **(Figure 27.4)**. The capsule enables prokaryotes to adhere to their substrate or to other individuals in a colony. Some capsules protect against dehydration, and some shield pathogenic prokaryotes from attacks by their host's immune system.

Some prokaryotes stick to their substrate or to one another by means of hairlike protein appendages called **fimbriae** (singular, *fimbria*) **(Figure 27.5)**; thus, fimbriae are also known as *attachment pili*. The bacterium that causes gonorrhea, *Neisseria gonorrhoeae*, uses fimbriae to fasten itself to the mucous membranes of its host. Fimbriae are usually shorter

and more numerous than **sex pili** (singular, *sex pilus*), appendages that pull two cells together prior to DNA transfer from one cell to the other.

Motility

About half of all prokaryotes are capable of directional movement. Some species can move at velocities exceeding 50 μm/sec—up to 50 times their body length per second. For perspective, consider that a person 1.7 m tall moving that fast would be running 306 km (190 miles) per hour!

Of the various structures that enable prokaryotes to move, the most common are flagella **(Figure 27.6)**. Flagella (singular, *flagellum*) may be scattered over the entire surface of the cell or concentrated at one or both ends. Prokaryotic flagella are one-tenth the width of eukaryotic flagella and are not covered by an

▲ **Figure 27.6 Prokaryotic flagellum.** The motor of the prokaryotic flagellum is the basal apparatus, a system of rings embedded in the cell wall and plasma membrane (TEM). ATP-driven pumps transport protons out of the cell, and the diffusion of protons back into the cell directly powers the basal apparatus, which turns a curved hook. The hook is attached to a filament composed of chains of flagellin, a globular protein. (This diagram shows flagellar structures characteristic of gram-negative bacteria.)

extension of the plasma membrane (see Figures 6.24 and 6.25 to review eukaryotic flagella). The flagella of prokaryotes are also very different from those of eukaryotes in their molecular composition and their mechanism of propulsion.

In a relatively uniform environment, flagellated prokaryotes may move randomly. In a heterogeneous environment, however, many prokaryotes exhibit **taxis**, movement toward or away from a stimulus (from the Greek *taxis*, to arrange). For example, prokaryotes that exhibit *chemotaxis* change their movement pattern in response to chemicals. They may move *toward* nutrients or oxygen (positive chemotaxis) or *away from* a toxic substance (negative chemotaxis). Consider movement patterns in *Escherichia coli*, the well-studied bacterial species that has been called the "lab rat of molecular biology." In 2003, scientists at Princeton University and the Institut Curie in Paris demonstrated that solitary *E. coli* cells exhibit positive chemotaxis toward other members of their species, enabling the formation of colonies.

Internal and Genomic Organization

The cells of prokaryotes are simpler than those of eukaryotes, in both their internal structure and their genomic organization (see Figure 6.6). Prokaryotic cells lack the complex compartmentalization found in eukaryotic cells. However, some prokaryotic cells do have specialized membranes that perform metabolic functions **(Figure 27.7)**. These membranes are usually infoldings of the plasma membrane.

The genome of a prokaryote is structurally different from a eukaryotic genome and in most cases has considerably less DNA. In the majority of prokaryotes, the genome consists of a circular chromosome whose structure includes fewer proteins than found in the linear chromosomes of eukaryotes **(Figure 27.8)**. Also unlike eukaryotes, prokaryotes lack a membrane-bounded nucleus; their chromosome is located in the **nucleoid**, a region of cytoplasm that appears lighter than the surrounding cytoplasm

Chromosome   Plasmids

▲ **Figure 27.8 A prokaryotic chromosome and plasmids.** The thin, tangled loops surrounding this ruptured *E. coli* cell are parts of the cell's large, circular chromosome (colorized TEM). Three of the cell's plasmids, the much smaller rings of DNA, are also shown.

in electron micrographs. In addition to its single chromosome, a typical prokaryotic cell may also have much smaller rings of separately replicating DNA called **plasmids** (see Figure 27.8), most carrying only a few genes.

As explained in Chapters 16 and 17, DNA replication, transcription, and translation are fundamentally similar processes in prokaryotes and eukaryotes, although there are some differences. For example, prokaryotic ribosomes are slightly smaller than eukaryotic ribosomes and differ in their protein and RNA content. These differences allow certain antibiotics, such as erythromycin and tetracycline, to bind to ribosomes and block protein synthesis in prokaryotes but not in eukaryotes. As a result, we can use these antibiotics to kill bacteria without harming ourselves.

Reproduction and Adaptation

Prokaryotes are highly successful in part because of their potential to reproduce quickly in a favorable environment. By binary fission (see Figure 12.11), a single prokaryotic cell divides into 2 cells, which then divide into 4, 8, 16, and so on. Under optimal conditions, many prokaryotes can divide every 1–3 hours; some species can produce a new generation in only 20 minutes. If reproduction continued unchecked at this rate, a single prokaryotic cell could give rise to a colony outweighing Earth in only three days!

In reality, of course, prokaryotic reproduction is limited. The cells eventually exhaust their nutrient supply, poison themselves with metabolic wastes, face competition from other microorganisms, or are consumed by other organisms. Thus, *E. coli*, which can divide as often as every 20 minutes under ideal conditions, more typically divides once every 12 to 24 hours in a

(a) Aerobic prokaryote   **(b) Photosynthetic prokaryote**

▲ **Figure 27.7 Specialized membranes of prokaryotes. (a)** Infoldings of the plasma membrane, reminiscent of the cristae of mitochondria, function in cellular respiration in some aerobic prokaryotes (TEM). **(b)** Photosynthetic prokaryotes called cyanobacteria have thylakoid membranes, much like those in chloroplasts (TEM).

Endospore

0.3 μm

▲ **Figure 27.9 An endospore.** *Bacillus anthracis*, the bacterium that causes the disease anthrax, produces endospores (TEM). An endospore's thick, protective coat helps it survive in the soil for years.

human intestine. But whether cell division occurs every 20 minutes or every few days, reproduction in prokaryotes draws attention to three key features of their biology: *They are small, they reproduce by binary fission, and they have short generation times.* As a result, prokaryotic populations can consist of many trillions of individuals—far more than populations of multicellular eukaryotes, such as plants and animals.

The ability of some prokaryotes to withstand harsh conditions also contributes to their success. Some, like *Halobacterium*, have biochemical adaptations; others have structural adaptations. Certain bacteria, for example, develop resistant cells called **endospores** when an essential nutrient is lacking **(Figure 27.9)**. The original cell produces a copy of its chromosome and surrounds it with a tough wall, forming the endospore. Water is removed from the endospore, and its metabolism halts. The rest of the original cell then disintegrates, leaving the endospore behind. Most endospores are so durable that they can survive in boiling water; killing them requires heating lab equipment to 121°C under high pressure. In less hostile environments, endospores can remain dormant but viable for centuries, able to rehydrate and resume metabolism when their environment improves.

Finally, in part because of their short generation times, prokaryotic populations can evolve substantially in short periods of time. For example, in a remarkable study that spanned 20,000 generations (roughly eight years) of evolution, Vaughn Cooper and Richard Lenski, of Michigan State University, documented adaptive evolution in bacterial populations **(Figure 27.10)**. The ability of prokaryotes to adapt rapidly to new conditions highlights the fact that although the structure of their cells is simpler than that of eukaryotic cells, prokaryotes are not "primitive" or "inferior" in an evolutionary sense. They are, in fact, highly evolved: For over 3.5 billion years, prokaryotic populations have responded successfully to many different types of environmental challenges. As we will see, one reason for this is that their populations harbor high levels of genetic diversity on which selection can act.

▼ **Figure 27.10 Inquiry**

Can prokaryotes evolve rapidly in response to environmental change?

EXPERIMENT   Vaughn Cooper and Richard Lenski, of Michigan State University, tested the ability of *E. coli* populations to adapt to a new environment. They established 12 populations, each founded by a single cell from an asexual strain of *E. coli*, and followed these populations for 20,000 generations (3,000 days). To maintain a continual supply of resources, each day the researchers performed a *serial transfer*: They transferred 0.1 mL of each population to a new tube containing 9.9 mL of fresh growth medium. The growth medium used throughout the experiment represented a challenging environment that contained only low levels of glucose and other resources needed for growth.

Daily serial transfer

0.1 mL
(population sample)

Old tube
(discarded
after
transfer)

New tube
(9.9 mL
growth
medium)

Samples were periodically removed from the 12 populations and grown in competition with the common ancestor in the experimental (low-glucose) environment.

RESULTS   The fitness of the experimental populations, as measured by the rate at which each population grew, increased rapidly for the first 5,000 generations (two years) and more slowly for the next 15,000 generations. The graph below shows the averages for the 12 populations.

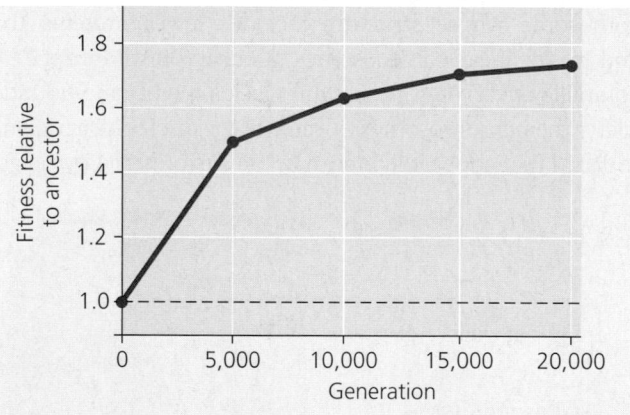

CONCLUSION   Asexual populations of *E. coli* continued to accumulate beneficial mutations for 20,000 generations, allowing rapid evolution of improved performance in their new environment.

SOURCE   V. S. Cooper and R. E. Lenski, The population genetics of ecological specialization in evolving *Escherichia coli* populations, *Nature* 407:736–739 (2000).

WHAT IF?   Suggest possible functions of the genes whose sequence or expression was altered as the experimental populations evolved in the low-glucose environment.

CONCEPT 27.2

Rapid reproduction, mutation, and genetic recombination promote genetic diversity in prokaryotes

As we discussed in Unit Four, genetic variation is a prerequisite for natural selection to occur in a population. The fact that prokaryotes exhibit such a range of adaptations suggests that their populations must have considerable genetic variation—and they do. For example, a ribosomal RNA gene differs more between two strains of *E. coli* than it does between a human and a platypus. In this section, we'll examine three factors that give rise to high levels of genetic diversity in prokaryotes: rapid reproduction, mutation, and genetic recombination.

Rapid Reproduction and Mutation

In sexually reproducing species, the generation of a novel allele by a new mutation is rare at any particular gene. Instead, most of the genetic variation in sexual populations results from the way existing alleles are arranged in new combinations during meiosis and fertilization (see Chapter 13). Prokaryotes do not reproduce sexually, so at first glance their extensive genetic variation may seem puzzling. A closer look, however, reveals that prokaryotic populations may have large amounts of genetic variation as a result of rapid reproduction and mutation.

Consider a prokaryote reproducing by binary fission. After repeated rounds of division, most of the offspring cells are genetically identical to the original parent cell. However, owing to insertions, deletions, and base-pair substitutions in their DNA, some of the offspring cells may differ genetically. The probability of a spontaneous mutation occurring in a

given *E. coli* gene averages only about one in 10 million (1×10^{-7}) per cell division. But among the 2×10^{10} new *E. coli* cells that arise each day in a person's intestine, there will be approximately $(2 \times 10^{10}) \times (1 \times 10^{-7}) = 2,000$ bacteria that have a mutation in that gene. The total number of mutations when all 4,300 *E. coli* genes are considered is about $4,300 \times 2,000 = 9$ million per day per human host.

The important point is that new mutations, though individually rare, can greatly increase genetic diversity in species like *E. coli* that have short generation times and large population sizes. This diversity, in turn, can lead to rapid evolution: Individuals that are genetically better equipped for their local environment tend to survive and reproduce more prolifically than less fit individuals.

Genetic Recombination

Although new mutations are a major source of variation in prokaryotic populations, additional diversity arises from genetic recombination, the combining of DNA from two sources. In eukaryotes, the sexual processes of meiosis and fertilization combine DNA from two individuals in a single zygote. But meiosis and fertilization do not occur in prokaryotes. Instead, three other processes—transformation, transduction, and conjugation—can bring together prokaryotic DNA from different individuals.

Transformation and Transduction

In **transformation**, the genotype and possibly phenotype of a prokaryotic cell are altered by the uptake of foreign DNA from its surroundings. For example, bacteria from a harmless strain of *Streptococcus pneumoniae* can be transformed to pneumonia-causing cells if they are placed into a medium containing dead, broken-open cells of the pathogenic strain (see Figure 16.2). This transformation occurs when a live nonpathogenic cell takes up a piece of DNA carrying the allele for pathogenicity. The foreign allele is then incorporated into the cell's chromosome, replacing the existing nonpathogenic allele—an exchange of homologous DNA segments. The cell is now a recombinant: Its chromosome contains DNA derived from two different cells.

For many years after transformation was discovered in laboratory cultures, most biologists thought the process to be too rare and haphazard to play an important role in natural bacterial populations. But researchers have since learned that many bacteria have cell-surface proteins that recognize DNA from closely related species and transport it into the cell. Once inside the cell, the foreign DNA can be incorporated into the genome by homologous DNA exchange.

In **transduction**, bacteriophages (also called phages, the viruses that infect bacteria) carry bacterial genes from one host cell to another; transduction is a type of horizontal gene transfer (see Chapter 26). For most phages, transduction results from accidents that occur during the phage reproductive

❶ Phage infects a bacterial cell that has alleles A^+ and B^+.

❷ Host DNA (brown) is fragmented, and phage DNA and proteins are made. This is the donor cell.

❸ A bacterial DNA fragment (in this case a fragment with the A^+ allele) may be packaged in a phage capsid.

❹ Phage with the A^+ allele from the donor cell infects a recipient A^-B^- cell, and recombination between donor DNA (brown) and recipient DNA (green) occurs at two places (dotted lines).

❺ The genotype of the resulting recombinant cell (A^+B^-) differs from the genotypes of both the donor (A^+B^+) and the recipient (A^-B^-).

Phage DNA

A^+ B^+

A^+ B^+

Donor cell

A^+

Recombination

A^+

A^- B^-

Recipient cell

A^+ B^-

Recombinant cell

▲ **Figure 27.11 Transduction.** Phages occasionally carry random pieces of the host chromosome containing bacterial genes from one cell (the donor) to another (the recipient). Recombination may cause the transferred DNA to be incorporated into the genome of the recipient.

cycle **(Figure 27.11)**. A virus that carries bacterial DNA may not be able to reproduce because it lacks its own genetic material. However, the virus may be able to attach to another bacterium (a recipient) and inject the piece of bacterial DNA acquired from the first cell (the donor). Some of this DNA may subsequently replace the homologous region of the recipient cell's chromosome by DNA recombination. In such a case, the recipient cell's chromosome becomes a combination of DNA derived from two cells; genetic recombination has occurred.

Conjugation and Plasmids

In a process called **conjugation**, genetic material is transferred between two bacterial cells (of the same or different

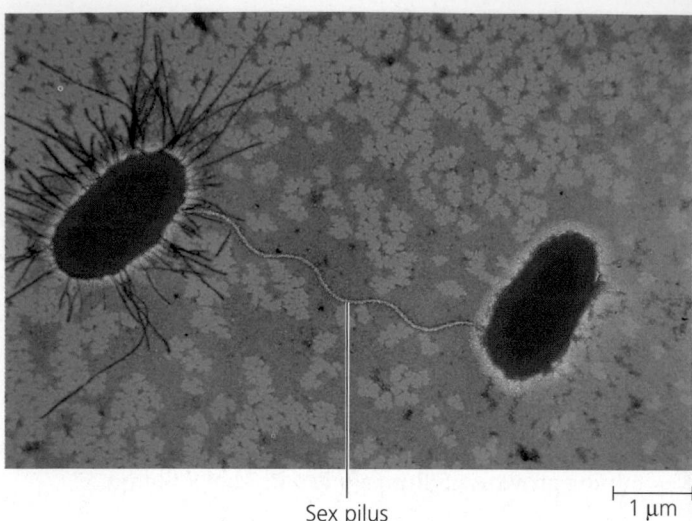

Sex pilus   ⊢1 μm⊣

▲ **Figure 27.12 Bacterial conjugation.** The *E. coli* donor cell (left) extends a sex pilus that attaches to a recipient cell. The two cells will be drawn close together, allowing a mating bridge to form between them (not shown). Through this bridge, the donor will transfer DNA to the recipient (colorized TEM).

WHAT IF? *In a rapidly changing environment, which population would likely be more successful, one that included individuals capable of conjugation or one that did not? Explain.*

species) that are temporarily joined. The DNA transfer is one-way: One cell donates the DNA, and the other receives it. The donor uses sex pili to attach to the recipient **(Figure 27.12)**. After contacting a recipient cell, each sex pilus retracts, pulling the two cells together, much like a grappling hook. A temporary "mating bridge" then forms between the two cells, providing an avenue for DNA transfer.

In most cases, the ability to form sex pili and donate DNA during conjugation results from the presence of a particular piece of DNA called the **F factor** (F for *fertility*). The F factor consists of about 25 genes, most required for the production of sex pili. The F factor can exist either as a plasmid or as a segment of DNA within the bacterial chromosome.

The F Factor as a Plasmid   The F factor in its plasmid form is called the **F plasmid**. Cells containing the F plasmid, designated F^+ cells, function as DNA donors during conjugation. Cells lacking the F factor, designated F^-, function as DNA recipients during conjugation. The F^+ condition is transferable in the sense that an F^+ cell converts an F^- cell to F^+ if a copy of the entire F^+ plasmid is transferred **(Figure 27.13a)**.

The F Factor in the Chromosome   Chromosomal genes can be transferred during conjugation when the donor cell's F factor is integrated into the chromosome. A cell with the F factor built into its chromosome is called an *Hfr cell* (for *high frequency of recombination*). Like an F^+ cell, an Hfr cell functions as a donor during conjugation with an F^- cell **(Figure 27.13b)**. When chromosomal DNA from an Hfr cell enters an F^- cell, homologous regions of the Hfr and F^- chromosomes may align, allowing

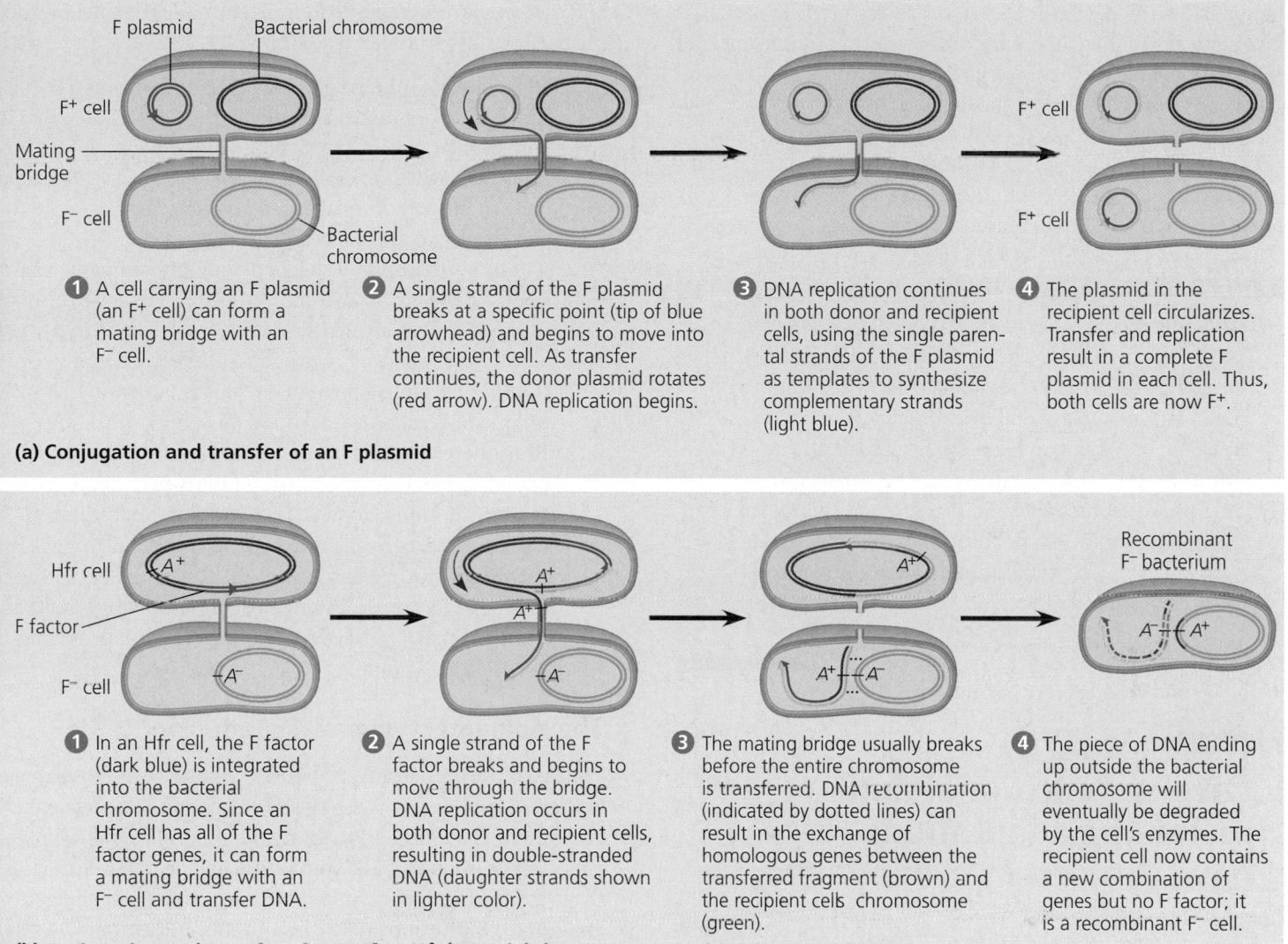

(a) Conjugation and transfer of an F plasmid

① A cell carrying an F plasmid (an F⁺ cell) can form a mating bridge with an F⁻ cell.

② A single strand of the F plasmid breaks at a specific point (tip of blue arrowhead) and begins to move into the recipient cell. As transfer continues, the donor plasmid rotates (red arrow). DNA replication begins.

③ DNA replication continues in both donor and recipient cells, using the single parental strands of the F plasmid as templates to synthesize complementary strands (light blue).

④ The plasmid in the recipient cell circularizes. Transfer and replication result in a complete F plasmid in each cell. Thus, both cells are now F⁺.

(b) Conjugation and transfer of part of an Hfr bacterial chromosome, resulting in recombination

① In an Hfr cell, the F factor (dark blue) is integrated into the bacterial chromosome. Since an Hfr cell has all of the F factor genes, it can form a mating bridge with an F⁻ cell and transfer DNA.

② A single strand of the F factor breaks and begins to move through the bridge. DNA replication occurs in both donor and recipient cells, resulting in double-stranded DNA (daughter strands shown in lighter color).

③ The mating bridge usually breaks before the entire chromosome is transferred. DNA recombination (indicated by dotted lines) can result in the exchange of homologous genes between the transferred fragment (brown) and the recipient cell's chromosome (green).

④ The piece of DNA ending up outside the bacterial chromosome will eventually be degraded by the cell's enzymes. The recipient cell now contains a new combination of genes but no F factor; it is a recombinant F⁻ cell.

▲ **Figure 27.13 Conjugation and recombination in *E. coli*.** The DNA replication that accompanies transfer of an F plasmid or part of an Hfr bacterial chromosome is called *rolling circle replication*. This is sometimes referred to as the "toilet paper model" because of the way the single strand rolls off the donor cell DNA and moves into the recipient cell.

segments of their DNA to be exchanged. This results in the production of a recombinant bacterium that has genes derived from two different cells—a new genetic variant on which evolution can act. Though these processes of horizontal gene transfer have so far been studied almost exclusively in bacteria, it is assumed that they are similarly important in archaea.

R Plasmids and Antibiotic Resistance During the 1950s in Japan, physicians started noticing that some hospital patients with bacterial dysentery, which produces severe diarrhea, did not respond to antibiotics that had generally been effective in the past. Apparently, resistance to these antibiotics had evolved in certain strains of *Shigella*, the bacterium that causes the disease.

Eventually, researchers began to identify the specific genes that confer antibiotic resistance in *Shigella* and other pathogenic bacteria. Sometimes, mutation in a chromosomal gene of the pathogen can confer resistance. For example, a mutation in one gene may make it less likely that the pathogen will transport a particular antibiotic into the cell. Mutation in a different gene may alter the intracellular target protein for an antibiotic molecule, reducing its inhibitory effect. In other cases, bacteria have "resistance genes," which code for enzymes that specifically destroy or otherwise hinder the effectiveness of certain antibiotics, such as tetracycline or ampicillin. Such resistance genes are carried by plasmids known as **R plasmids** (R for *resistance*).

Exposing a bacterial population to a specific antibiotic, whether in a laboratory culture or within a host organism, will kill antibiotic-sensitive bacteria but not those that happen to have R plasmids with genes that counter the antibiotic. The theory of natural selection predicts that under these circumstances, the fraction of the bacterial population carrying genes for antibiotic resistance will increase, and that is exactly what happens. The medical consequences are also predictable: Resistant strains of pathogens are becoming more common, making the treatment of certain bacterial infections more difficult. The problem is compounded by the fact that many R plasmids, like F plasmids, have genes that encode sex pili and enable plasmid transfer from one bacterial cell to another by conjugation. Making the problem still worse, some R plasmids carry as many as ten genes for resistance to that many antibiotics.

CONCEPT CHECK 27.2

1. What features of prokaryotes make it likely that considerable genetic variation will be added to their populations in each generation?
2. Distinguish between the three mechanisms of transferring DNA from one bacterial cell to another.
3. **WHAT IF?** If a nonpathogenic bacterium were to acquire resistance to antibiotics, could this strain pose a health risk to people? Explain. In general, how does genetic recombination among bacteria affect the spread of resistance genes?

For suggested answers, see Appendix A.

CONCEPT 27.3

Diverse nutritional and metabolic adaptations have evolved in prokaryotes

The mechanisms discussed in the previous section—rapid reproduction, mutation, and genetic recombination—underlie the extensive genetic variation found in prokaryotic populations. This variation is reflected in the nutritional adaptations found in prokaryotes. Like all organisms, prokaryotes can be categorized by their nutrition—how they obtain energy and the carbon used in building the organic molecules that make up cells. Nutritional diversity is greater among prokaryotes than among eukaryotes: Every type of nutrition observed in eukaryotes is represented among prokaryotes, along with some nutritional modes unique to prokaryotes.

Organisms that obtain energy from light are called *phototrophs*, and those that obtain energy from chemicals are called *chemotrophs*. Organisms that need only an inorganic compound such as CO_2 as a carbon source are called *autotrophs*. In contrast, *heterotrophs* require at least one organic nutrient—such as glucose—to make other organic compounds. Combining these possibilities for energy sources

and carbon sources results in four major modes of nutrition, described here and summarized in **Table 27.1**.

1. **Photoautotrophs** are photosynthetic organisms that capture light energy and use it to drive the synthesis of organic compounds from CO_2 or other inorganic carbon compounds, such as bicarbonate (HCO_3^-). Cyanobacteria and many other groups of prokaryotes are photoautotrophs, as are plants and algae.
2. **Chemoautotrophs** also need only an inorganic compound such as CO_2 as a carbon source. However, instead of using light as an energy source, they oxidize inorganic substances, such as hydrogen sulfide (H_2S), ammonia (NH_3), or ferrous ions (Fe^{2+}). This mode of nutrition is unique to certain prokaryotes.
3. **Photoheterotrophs** harness energy from light but must obtain carbon in organic form. This mode is unique to certain marine and halophilic (salt-loving) prokaryotes.
4. **Chemoheterotrophs** must consume organic molecules to obtain both energy and carbon. This nutritional mode is widespread among prokaryotes. Fungi, animals, most protists, and even some parasitic plants are also chemoheterotrophs.

The Role of Oxygen in Metabolism

Prokaryotic metabolism also varies with respect to oxygen. **Obligate aerobes** use O_2 for cellular respiration (see Chapter 9) and cannot grow without it. **Obligate anaerobes**, on the other hand, are poisoned by O_2. Some obligate anaerobes live exclusively by fermentation; others extract chemical energy by **anaerobic respiration**, in which substances other than O_2, such as nitrate ions (NO_3^-) or sulfate ions (SO_4^{2-}), accept electrons at the "downhill" end of electron transport chains. **Facultative anaerobes** use O_2 if it is present but can also carry out anaerobic respiration or fermentation in an anaerobic environment.

Table 27.1 Major Nutritional Modes

Mode of Nutrition	Energy Source	Carbon Source	Types of Organisms
Autotroph			
Photoautotroph	Light	CO_2	Photosynthetic prokaryotes (for example, cyanobacteria); plants; certain protists (for example, algae)
Chemoautotroph	Inorganic chemicals	CO_2	Certain prokaryotes (for example, *Sulfolobus*)
Heterotroph			
Photoheterotroph	Light	Organic compounds	Certain prokaryotes (for example, *Rhodobacter*, *Chloroflexus*)
Chemoheterotroph	Organic compounds	Organic compounds	Many prokaryotes (for example, *Clostridium*) and protists; fungi; animals; some plants

Nitrogen Metabolism

Nitrogen is essential for the production of amino acids and nucleic acids in all organisms. Whereas eukaryotes can obtain nitrogen from only a limited group of nitrogen compounds, prokaryotes can metabolize nitrogen in a wide variety of forms. For example, some cyanobacteria and some methanogens (a group of archaea) convert atmospheric nitrogen (N_2) to ammonia (NH_3), a process called **nitrogen fixation**. The cells can then incorporate this "fixed" nitrogen into amino acids and other organic molecules. In terms of their nutrition, nitrogen-fixing cyanobacteria are some of the most self-sufficient organisms, since they need only light, CO_2, N_2, water, and some minerals to grow.

Nitrogen fixation by prokaryotes has a large impact on other organisms. For example, nitrogen-fixing prokaryotes can increase the nitrogen available to plants, which cannot use atmospheric nitrogen but can use the nitrogen compounds that the prokaryotes produce from ammonia. Chapter 55 discusses this and other essential roles that prokaryotes play in the nitrogen cycles of ecosystems.

Metabolic Cooperation

Cooperation between prokaryotes allows them to use environmental resources they could not use as individual cells. In some cases, this cooperation takes place between specialized cells of a colony. For instance, the cyanobacterium *Anabaena* has genes that encode proteins for photosynthesis and for nitrogen fixation, but a single cell cannot carry out both processes at the same time. The reason is that photosynthesis produces O_2, which inactivates the enzymes involved in nitrogen fixation. Instead of living as isolated cells, *Anabaena* forms filamentous colonies (Figure 27.14). Most cells in a filament carry out only photosynthesis, while a few specialized cells called **heterocytes** (formerly called *heterocysts*) carry out only nitrogen fixation. Each heterocyte is surrounded by a thickened cell wall that restricts entry of O_2 produced by neighboring photosynthetic cells. Intercellular connections allow heterocytes to transport fixed nitrogen to neighboring cells and to receive carbohydrates.

Metabolic cooperation between different prokaryotic species often occurs in surface-coating colonies known as **biofilms** (Figure 27.15). Cells in a biofilm secrete signaling molecules that recruit nearby cells, causing the colonies to grow. The cells also produce proteins that stick the cells to the substrate and to one another. Channels in the biofilm allow nutrients to reach cells in the interior and wastes to be expelled. Biofilms damage industrial and medical equipment, contaminate products, and contribute to tooth decay and more serious health problems, altogether costing billions of dollars annually.

In another example of cooperation between prokaryotes, sulfate-consuming bacteria coexist with methane-consuming archaea in ball-shaped aggregates on the ocean floor. The bacteria appear to use the archaea's waste products, such as organic

▲ **Figure 27.14 Metabolic cooperation in a colonial prokaryote.** In the filamentous cyanobacterium *Anabaena*, cells called heterocytes fix nitrogen, while the other cells carry out photosynthesis (LM). *Anabaena* is found in many freshwater lakes.

▲ **Figure 27.15 A biofilm.** The yellow mass in this colorized SEM is dental plaque, a biofilm consisting of numerous bacterial species that forms on tooth surfaces.

compounds and hydrogen. In turn, the bacteria produce compounds that facilitate methane consumption by the archaea. This partnership has global ramifications: Each year, these archaea consume an estimated 300 billion kilograms of methane, a major contributor to the greenhouse effect (see Chapter 55).

CONCEPT CHECK 27.3

1. Distinguish between the four major modes of nutrition, noting which are unique to prokaryotes.
2. A bacterium requires only the amino acid methionine as an organic nutrient and lives in lightless caves. What mode of nutrition does it employ? Explain.
3. **WHAT IF?** Describe what you might eat for a typical meal if humans, like cyanobacteria, could fix nitrogen.

For suggested answers, see Appendix A.

CONCEPT 27.4

Molecular systematics is illuminating prokaryotic phylogeny

Until the late 20th century, systematists based prokaryotic taxonomy on phenotypic criteria such as shape, motility, nutritional mode, and response to Gram staining. These criteria are still valuable in certain contexts, such as the rapid identification of pathogenic bacteria cultured from a patient's blood. But when it comes to prokaryotic phylogeny, comparing these characteristics does not reveal a clear evolutionary history. Applying molecular systematics to the investigation of prokaryotic phylogeny, however, has led to some dramatic conclusions.

Lessons from Molecular Systematics

As discussed in Chapter 26, microbiologists began comparing the sequences of prokaryotic genes in the 1970s. Using small-subunit ribosomal RNA as a marker for evolutionary relationships, Carl Woese and his colleagues concluded that many prokaryotes once classified as bacteria are actually more closely related to eukaryotes and belong in a domain of their own: Archaea. Microbiologists have since analyzed larger amounts of genetic data—in some cases, entire genomes—and have concluded that a few traditional taxonomic groups, such as cyanobacteria, do appear to be monophyletic. However, other groups, such as gram-negative bacteria, are scattered throughout several lineages. **Figure 27.16** shows one phylogenetic hypothesis for some of the major taxa of prokaryotes based on molecular systematics.

One lesson from studying prokaryotic phylogeny is that the genetic diversity of prokaryotes is immense. When researchers began to sequence the genes of prokaryotes, they could investigate only those species that could be cultured in the laboratory—a small fraction of all prokaryotic species. In the 1980s, Norman Pace, of the University of Colorado, pioneered the use of the polymerase chain reaction (PCR; see Chapter 20) to analyze the genes of prokaryotes collected directly from their environment (such as from soil or water samples). Such "genetic prospecting" is now widely used, and each year it adds new branches to the tree of life. (Some researchers suggest that certain branches represent entire new kingdoms.) While only about 6,300 prokaryotic species have been assigned scientific names, a single handful of soil could contain 10,000 prokaryotic species, according to some estimates. You can see why taking full stock of this diversity will require many years of research.

Another important lesson from molecular systematics is the apparent significance of horizontal gene transfer in the evolution of prokaryotes. Over hundreds of millions of years, prokaryotes have acquired genes from even distantly related species, and they continue to do so today. As a result, significant portions of the genomes of many prokaryotes are actually mosaics of genes imported from other species. As we saw in Chapter 26, horizontal gene transfer obscures the location of the root of the tree of life. Still, it is clear that very early in the history of life, the prokaryotes diverged into two main lineages, the archaea and the bacteria (see Figure 27.16).

Archaea

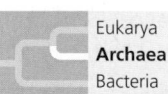

Archaea share certain traits with bacteria and others with eukaryotes **(Table 27.2)**. However, archaea also have many unique characteristics, as we would expect in a taxon that has followed a separate evolutionary path for so long.

The first prokaryotes assigned to domain Archaea live in environments so extreme that few other organisms can survive there. Such organisms are called **extremophiles**, meaning "lovers" of extreme conditions (from the Greek *philos*, lover), and include extreme halophiles and extreme thermophiles.

Extreme halophiles (from the Greek *halo*, salt) live in highly saline environments, such as the Great Salt Lake, the Dead Sea, and Owens Lake (see Figure 27.1). Some species merely tolerate salinity, while others require an environment that is several times saltier than seawater (which has a salinity of 3.5%). For example, the proteins and cell wall of *Halobacterium* have unusual features that improve function in extremely salty environments but render these organisms incapable of survival if the salinity drops below 9%.

Extreme thermophiles (from the Greek *thermos*, hot) thrive in very hot environments **(Figure 27.17)**. For example, archaea in the genus *Sulfolobus* live in sulfur-rich volcanic springs as hot as 90°C. At temperatures this high, the cells of most organisms die because their DNA does not stay together in a double helix, and many of their proteins denature. *Sulfolobus* and other extreme thermophiles avoid this fate because their DNA and proteins have adaptations that make them stable at high temperatures. One extreme thermophile that lives near deep-sea hydrothermal vents in the Pacific Ocean, *Geogemma barossii*, is informally

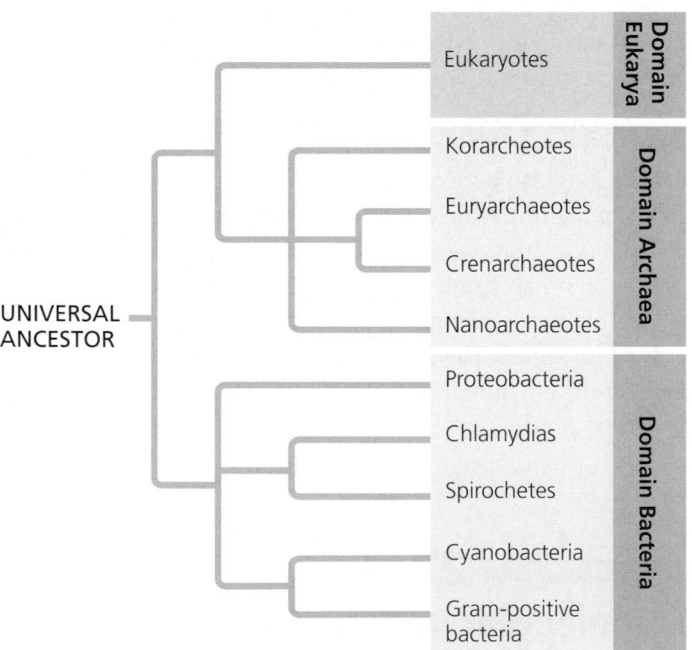

▲ **Figure 27.16 A simplified phylogeny of prokaryotes.** This phylogenetic tree based on molecular data highlights the relationships between the major prokaryotic groups discussed in this chapter. Within Archaea, the placement of the korarcheotes and nanoarcheotes remains unclear.

In the figure:

UNIVERSAL ANCESTOR

Eukaryotes — **Domain Eukarya**

Korarcheotes
Euryarchaeotes
Crenarchaeotes
Nanoarchaeotes — **Domain Archaea**

Proteobacteria
Chlamydias
Spirochetes
Cyanobacteria
Gram-positive bacteria — **Domain Bacteria**

Table 27.2 A Comparison of the Three Domains of Life

CHARACTER	DOMAIN		
	Bacteria	Archaea	Eukarya
Nuclear envelope	Absent	Absent	Present
Membrane-enclosed organelles	Absent	Absent	Present
Peptidoglycan in cell wall	Present	Absent	Absent
Membrane lipids	Unbranched hydrocarbons	Some branched hydrocarbons	Unbranched hydrocarbons
RNA polymerase	One kind	Several kinds	Several kinds
Initiator amino acid for protein synthesis	Formyl-methionine	Methionine	Methionine
Introns in genes	Very rare	Present in some genes	Present
Response to the antibiotics streptomycin and chloramphenicol	Growth inhibited	Growth not inhibited	Growth not inhibited
Histones associated with DNA	Absent	Present in some species	Present
Circular chromosome	Present	Present	Absent
Growth at temperatures > 100°C	No	Some species	No

known as "strain 121," since it can double its cell numbers even at 121°C. Another extreme thermophile, *Pyrococcus furiosus*, is used in biotechnology as a source of DNA polymerase for the PCR technique (see Chapter 20).

Other archaea live in more moderate environments. Some of these are included among the **methanogens**, a group of archaea named for the unique way they obtain energy: They use CO_2 to oxidize H_2, releasing methane as a waste product. Among the strictest of anaerobes, methanogens are poisoned by O_2. Although some methanogens live in extreme environments, such as under kilometers of ice in Greenland, others live in swamps and marshes where other microorganisms have consumed all the O_2. The "marsh gas" found in such environments is the methane produced by these archaea. Other species of methanogens inhabit the anaerobic environment within the guts of cattle, termites, and other herbivores, playing an essential role in the nutrition of these animals. Methanogens also have an important application as decomposers in sewage treatment facilities.

Many extreme halophiles and all known methanogens are archaea in the clade Euryarchaeota (from the Greek *eurys*, broad, a reference to the habitat range of these prokaryotes).

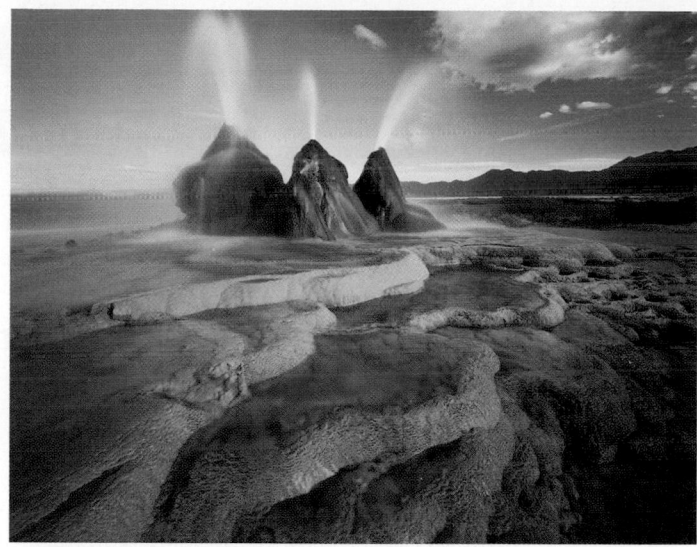

▲ **Figure 27.17 Extreme thermophiles.** Orange and yellow colonies of thermophilic prokaryotes grow in the hot water of a Nevada geyser.

? *How might the enzymes of thermophiles differ from those in other organisms?*

The euryarchaeotes also include some extreme thermophiles, though most thermophilic species belong to a second clade, Crenarchaeota (*cren* means "spring," such as a hydrothermal spring). Recently, genetic prospecting has revealed many species of euryarchaeotes and crenarchaeotes that are not extremophiles. These archaea exist in habitats ranging from farm soils to lake sediments to the surface waters of the open ocean.

New findings continue to update the picture of archaeal phylogeny. In 1996, researchers sampling a hot spring in Yellowstone National Park discovered archaea that do not appear to belong to either Euryarchaeota or Crenarchaeota. They placed these archaea in a new clade, Korarchaeota (from the Greek *koron*, young man). In 2002, researchers exploring hydrothermal vents off the coast of Iceland discovered archaeal cells only 0.4 µm in diameter attached to a much larger crenarchaeote. The genome of the smaller archaean is one of the smallest known of any organism, containing only 500,000 base pairs. Genetic analysis indicates that this prokaryote belongs to a fourth archaeal clade, called Nanoarchaeota (from the Greek *nanos*, dwarf). Within a year after this clade was named, three other DNA sequences from nanoarchaeote species were isolated: one from Yellowstone's hot springs, one from hot springs in Siberia, and one from a hydrothermal vent in the Pacific. As prospecting continues, it seems likely that the tree in Figure 27.16 will undergo further changes.

Bacteria

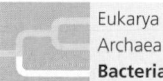

Eukarya
Archaea
Bacteria

Examine **Figure 27.18**, on the following two pages, for a closer look at several major groups of bacteria. Bacteria include the vast majority of prokaryotes that most people are aware of, from the pathogenic species that cause strep throat and tuberculosis to

Exploring Major Groups of Bacteria

PROTEOBACTERIA

This large and diverse clade of gram-negative bacteria includes photoautotrophs, chemoautotrophs, and heterotrophs. Some proteobacteria are anaerobic, while others are aerobic. Molecular systematists currently recognize five subgroups of proteobacteria; the phylogenetic tree at right shows their relationships based on molecular data.

Alpha
Beta
Gamma } Proteobacteria
Delta
Epsilon

Subgroup: Alpha Proteobacteria

Many of the species in this subgroup are closely associated with eukaryotic hosts. For example, *Rhizobium* species live in nodules within the roots of legumes (plants of the pea/bean family), where the bacteria convert atmospheric N_2 to compounds the host plant can use to make proteins. Species in the genus *Agrobacterium* produce tumors in plants; genetic engineers use these bacteria to carry foreign DNA into the genomes of crop plants (see Figure 20.25). As explained in Chapter 25, scientists hypothesize that mitochondria evolved from aerobic alpha proteobacteria through endosymbiosis.

2.5 μm

Rhizobium (arrows) inside a root cell of a legume (TEM)

Subgroup: Beta Proteobacteria

This nutritionally diverse subgroup includes *Nitrosomonas*, a genus of soil bacteria that play an important role in nitrogen recycling by oxidizing ammonium (NH_4^+), producing nitrite (NO_2^-) as a waste product.

1 μm

Nitrosomonas (colorized TEM)

Subgroup: Gamma Proteobacteria

This subgroup's autotrophic members include sulfur bacteria such as *Thiomargarita namibiensis*, which obtain energy by oxidizing H_2S, producing sulfur as a waste product (the small globules in the photograph at right). Some heterotrophic gamma proteobacteria are pathogens; for example, *Legionella* causes Legionnaires' disease, *Salmonella* is responsible for some cases of food poisoning, and *Vibrio cholerae* causes cholera. *Escherichia coli*, a common resident of the intestines of humans and other mammals, normally is not pathogenic.

0.5 μm

Thiomargarita namibiensis containing sulfur wastes (LM)

Subgroup: Delta Proteobacteria

This subgroup includes the slime-secreting myxobacteria (left). When the soil dries out or food is scarce, the cells congregate into a fruiting body that releases resistant "myxospores." These cells found new colonies in favorable environments. Bdellovibrios (right) are delta proteobacteria that attack other bacteria, charging at up to 100 μm/sec (comparable to a human running 600 km/hr) and boring into their prey by spinning at 100 revolutions/sec.

10 μm

Fruiting bodies of *Chondromyces crocatus,* a myxobacterium (SEM)

B. bacteriophorus

5 μm

Bdellovibrio bacteriophorus attacking a larger bacterium (colorized TEM)

Subgroup: Epsilon Proteobacteria

Most species in this subgroup are pathogenic to humans or other animals. Epsilon proteobacteria include *Campylobacter*, which causes blood poisoning and intestinal inflammation, and *Helicobacter pylori*, which causes stomach ulcers.

2 μm

Helicobacter pylori (colorized TEM)

CHLAMYDIAS

These parasites can survive only within animal cells, depending on their hosts for resources as basic as ATP. The gram-negative walls of chlamydias are unusual in that they lack peptidoglycan. One species, *Chlamydia trachomatis*, is the most common cause of blindness in the world and also causes nongonococcal urethritis, the most common sexually transmitted disease in the United States.

Chlamydia (arrows) inside an animal cell (colorized TEM)

SPIROCHETES

These helical heterotrophs spiral through their environment by means of rotating, internal, flagellum-like filaments. Many spirochetes are free-living, but others are notorious pathogenic parasites: *Treponema pallidum* causes syphilis, and *Borrelia burgdorferi* causes Lyme disease (see Figure 27.21).

Leptospira, a spirochete (colorized TEM)

CYANOBACTERIA

These photoautotrophs are the only prokaryotes with plantlike, oxygen-generating photosynthesis. (In fact, chloroplasts likely evolved from an endosymbiotic cyanobacterium; see Chapter 25.) Both solitary and colonial cyanobacteria are abundant wherever there is water, providing an enormous amount of food for freshwater and marine ecosystems. Some filamentous colonies have cells specialized for nitrogen fixation, the process that incorporates atmospheric N_2 into inorganic compounds that can be used in the synthesis of amino acids and other organic molecules (see Figure 27.14).

Two species of *Oscillatoria*, filamentous cyanobacteria (LM)

GRAM-POSITIVE BACTERIA

Gram-positive bacteria rival the proteobacteria in diversity. Species in one subgroup, the actinomycetes (from the Greek *mykes*, fungus, for which these bacteria were once mistaken), form colonies containing branched chains of cells. Two species of actinomycetes cause tuberculosis and leprosy. However, most actinomycetes are free-living species that help decompose the organic matter in soil; their secretions are partly responsible for the "earthy" odor of rich soil. Soil-dwelling species in the genus *Streptomyces* (top) are cultured by pharmaceutical companies as a source of many antibiotics, including streptomycin.

In addition to the colonial actinomycetes, gram-positive bacteria include many solitary species, such as *Bacillus anthracis* (see Figure 27.9), which causes anthrax, and *Clostridium botulinum*, which causes botulism. The various species of *Staphylococcus* and *Streptococcus* are also gram-positive bacteria.

Mycoplasmas (bottom) are the only bacteria known to lack cell walls. They are also the tiniest of all known cells, with diameters as small as 0.1 μm, only about five times as large as a ribosome. Mycoplasmas have remarkably small genomes—*Mycoplasma genitalium* has only 517 genes, for example. Many mycoplasmas are free-living soil bacteria, but others are pathogens.

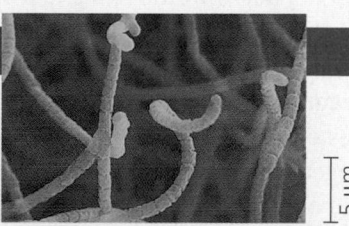

Streptomyces, the source of many antibiotics (colorized SEM)

Hundreds of mycoplasmas covering a human fibroblast cell (colorized SEM)

the beneficial species used to make Swiss cheese and yogurt. Every major mode of nutrition and metabolism is represented among bacteria, and even a small taxonomic group of bacteria may contain species exhibiting many different nutritional modes. As we'll see, the diverse nutritional and metabolic capabilities of bacteria—and archaea—are behind the great impact of these tiny organisms on Earth and its life.

CONCEPT 27.5
Prokaryotes play crucial roles in the biosphere

If humans were to disappear from the planet tomorrow, life on Earth would change for many species, but few would be driven to extinction. In contrast, prokaryotes are so important to the biosphere that if they were to disappear, the prospects of survival for many other species would be dim.

Chemical Recycling

The atoms that make up the organic molecules in all living things were at one time part of inorganic substances in the soil, air, and water. Sooner or later, those atoms will return there. Ecosystems depend on the continual recycling of chemical elements between the living and nonliving components of the environment, and prokaryotes play a major role in this process. For example, chemoheterotrophic prokaryotes function as **decomposers**, breaking down corpses, dead vegetation, and waste products, and thereby unlocking supplies of carbon, nitrogen, and other elements. Without the actions of prokaryotes and other decomposers such as fungi, all life would cease. (See Chapter 55 for a detailed discussion of chemical cycles.)

Prokaryotes also convert inorganic compounds to forms that can be taken up by other organisms. Autotrophic prokaryotes, for example, use CO_2 to make organic compounds, which are then passed up through food chains. Cyanobacteria produce atmospheric O_2, and a variety of prokaryotes fix atmospheric nitrogen (N_2) into forms that other organisms can use to make the building blocks of proteins and nucleic acids. Under some conditions, prokaryotes can increase the availability of nutrients that plants require for growth, such as nitrogen, phosphorus, and potassium **(Figure 27.19)**. Prokaryotes can also *decrease* the availability of

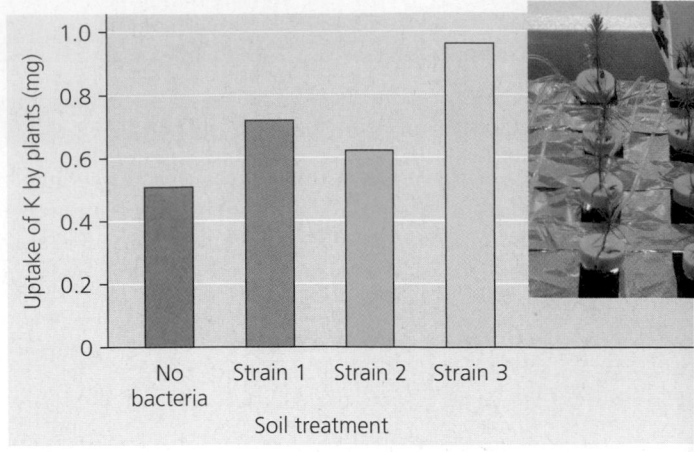

▲ **Figure 27.19 Impact of bacteria on soil nutrient availability.** Pine seedlings grown in soils to which one of three strains of the bacterium *Burkholderia glathei* had been added absorbed more potassium (K) than did seedlings grown in soil without any bacteria. Other results (not shown) demonstrated that strain 3 increased the amount of K released from mineral crystals to the soil.

WHAT IF? *Estimate the average uptake of K for seedlings in soils with bacteria. What would you expect this average to be if bacteria had no effect on nutrient availability?*

key plant nutrients; this occurs when prokaryotes "immobilize" nutrients by using them to synthesize molecules that remain within their cells. Thus, prokaryotes can have complex effects on soil nutrient concentrations. In marine environments, a 2005 study found that an archaean from the clade Crenarchaeota can perform nitrification, a key step in the nitrogen cycle (see Figure 55.14). Crenarchaeotes dominate the oceans by numbers, comprising an estimated 10^{28} cells. The sheer abundance of these organisms suggests that they may have a large impact on the global nitrogen cycle; scientists are investigating this question.

Ecological Interactions

Prokaryotes play a central role in many ecological interactions. Consider **symbiosis** (from a Greek word meaning "living together"), an ecological relationship in which two species live in close contact with one another. Prokaryotes are small, and they often form symbiotic associations with much larger organisms. In general, the larger organism in a symbiotic relationship is known as the **host**, and the smaller is known as the **symbiont**. There are many cases in which a prokaryote and its host participate in **mutualism**, an ecological interaction between two species in which both benefit **(Figure 27.20)**. In other cases, the interaction takes the form of **commensalism**, an ecological relationship in which one species benefits while the other is not harmed or helped in any significant way. For example, more than 150 bacterial species live on the surface of your body, covering portions of your skin with up to 10 million cells per square centimeter. Some of these species are commensalists: You provide them with food, such as the oils that exude from your pores, and a place to live, while they do not harm or benefit you. Finally, some prokaryotes engage in **parasitism**, an ecological relationship in which a **parasite** eats the cell contents, tissues, or body

▲ **Figure 27.20 Mutualism: bacterial "headlights."** The glowing oval below the eye of the flashlight fish (*Photoblepharon palpebratus*) is an organ harboring bioluminescent bacteria. The fish uses the light to attract prey and to signal potential mates. The bacteria receive nutrients from the fish.

fluids of its host; as a group, parasites harm but usually do not kill their host, at least not immediately (unlike a predator). Parasites that cause disease are known as **pathogens**, many of which are prokaryotic. (We'll discuss mutualism, commensalism, and parasitism in greater detail in Chapter 54.)

The well-being of many eukaryotes—yourself included—depends on mutualistic prokaryotes. Human intestines are home to an estimated 500 to 1,000 species of bacteria; their cells outnumber all human cells in the body by as much as ten times. Different species live in different portions of the intestines, and they vary in their ability to process different foods. Many of these species are mutualists, digesting food that our own intestines cannot break down. In 2003, scientists at Washington University in St. Louis published the first complete genome of one of these gut mutualists, *Bacteroides thetaiotaomicron*. The genome includes a large array of genes involved in synthesizing carbohydrates, vitamins, and other nutrients needed by humans. Signals from the bacterium activate human genes that build the network of intestinal blood vessels necessary to absorb nutrient molecules. Other signals induce human cells to produce antimicrobial compounds to which *B. thetaiotaomicron* is not susceptible. This action may reduce the population sizes of other, competing species, thus potentially benefiting both *B. thetaiotaomicron* and its human host.

CONCEPT 27.6

Prokaryotes have both harmful and beneficial impacts on humans

Though the best-known prokaryotes tend to be the bacteria that cause illness in humans, these pathogens represent only a small fraction of prokaryotic species. Many other prokaryotes have positive interactions with humans, and some play essential roles in agriculture and industry.

Pathogenic Bacteria

All the pathogenic prokaryotes known to date are bacteria, and they deserve their negative reputation. Bacteria cause about half of all human diseases. Roughly 2 million people a year die of the lung disease tuberculosis, caused by *Mycobacterium tuberculosis*. And another 2 million people die each year from diarrheal diseases caused by various bacteria.

Some bacterial diseases are transmitted by other species, such as fleas or ticks. In the United States, the most widespread pest-carried disease is Lyme disease, which infects 15,000 to 20,000 people each year (**Figure 27.21**). Caused by a bacterium carried by ticks that live on deer and field mice, Lyme disease can produce debilitating arthritis, heart disease, and nervous disorders if untreated.

Pathogenic prokaryotes usually cause illness by producing poisons, which are classified as exotoxins or endotoxins. **Exotoxins** are proteins secreted by certain bacteria and other organisms. Cholera, a dangerous diarrheal disease, is caused by an exotoxin secreted by the proteobacterium *Vibrio cholerae*. The exotoxin stimulates intestinal cells to release chloride ions into the gut, and water follows by osmosis. In another example, the potentially fatal disease botulism is caused by botulinum toxin, an exotoxin secreted by the gram-positive bacterium *Clostridium botulinum* as it ferments various foods, including improperly canned meat, seafood, and vegetables. Like other exotoxins, the botulinum toxin can produce disease

5 μm

▲ **Figure 27.21 Lyme disease.** Ticks in the genus *Ixodes* spread the disease by transmitting the spirochete *Borrelia burgdorferi* (colorized SEM). A rash may develop at the site of the tick's bite; the rash may be large and ring-shaped (as shown) or much less distinctive.

even if the bacteria that manufacture it are not present. In one such case, eight people contracted botulism after eating salted fish that did not contain any *C. botulinum* bacteria, but did contain the botulinum toxin. Even though the bacterium was no longer present, at some point in the fish preparation process, the bacterium had been able to grow and secrete the toxin.

Endotoxins are lipopolysaccharide components of the outer membrane of gram-negative bacteria. In contrast to exotoxins, endotoxins are released only when the bacteria die and their cell walls break down. Examples of endotoxin-producing bacteria include species in the genus *Salmonella*, which are not normally present in healthy animals. *Salmonella typhi* causes typhoid fever, and several other *Salmonella* species, some of which are frequently found in poultry, cause food poisoning.

Since the 19th century, improved sanitation systems in the industrialized world have greatly reduced the threat of pathogenic bacteria. Antibiotics have saved a great many lives and reduced the incidence of disease. However, resistance to antibiotics is currently evolving in many bacterial strains. As you read earlier, the rapid reproduction of bacteria enables genes conferring resistance to multiply quickly throughout bacterial populations as a result of natural selection, and these genes can spread to other species by horizontal gene transfer.

Horizontal gene transfer can also spread genes associated with virulence, turning normally harmless bacteria into lethal pathogens. *E. coli*, for instance, is ordinarily a harmless symbiont in the human intestines, but pathogenic strains that cause bloody diarrhea have emerged. One of the most dangerous strains, called O157:H7, is a global threat; in the United States alone, there are 75,000 cases of O157:H7 infection per year, often from contaminated beef or produce. In 2001, scientists sequenced the genome of O157:H7 and compared it with the genome of a harmless strain of *E. coli* called K-12. They discovered that 1,387 out of the 5,416 genes in O157:H7 have no counterpart in K-12. Many of these 1,387 genes are found in chromosomal regions that include DNA sequences related to bacteriophage DNA. This result suggests that at least some of the 1,387 genes were incorporated into the genome of O157:H7 through bacteriophage-mediated horizontal gene transfer (see Figure 27.11). Some of the genes found only in O157:H7 are associated with virulence, including genes that code for adhesive fimbriae that enable O157:H7 to attach itself to the intestinal wall and extract nutrients.

Pathogenic bacteria pose a potential threat as weapons of bioterrorism. For example, endospores of *Bacillus anthracis* sent through the mail caused 18 people—5 of whom died—to develop inhalation anthrax (see also Chapter 26). Such scenarios have stimulated intense research on pathogenic prokaryotic species in the hope of developing new vaccines and antibiotics.

Prokaryotes in Research and Technology

On a positive note, we reap many benefits from the metabolic capabilities of both bacteria and archaea. For example, humans have long used bacteria to convert milk into cheese and yogurt. In recent years, our greater understanding of prokaryotes has led to an explosion of new applications in biotechnology; two examples are the use of *E. coli* in gene cloning and of *Agrobacterium tumefaciens* in producing transgenic plants such as Golden Rice (see Chapter 20).

Prokaryotes are the principal agents in **bioremediation**, the use of organisms to remove pollutants from soil, air, or water. For example, anaerobic bacteria and archaea decompose the organic matter in sewage, converting it to material that can be used as landfill or fertilizer after chemical sterilization. Other bioremediation applications include cleaning up oil spills **(Figure 27.22a)** and precipitating radioactive material (such as uranium) out of groundwater.

Bacteria may soon figure prominently in a major industry: plastics. Globally, each year about 350 billion pounds of plastic are produced from petroleum and used to make toys, storage containers, soft drink bottles, and many other items. These products degrade slowly, creating environmental problems. Bacteria can now be used to make natural plastics **(Figure 27.22b)**. For example, some bacteria synthesize a type of polyester known as PHA (polyhydroxyalkanoate), which they use to store chemical energy. When these bacteria are fed sugars derived from corn, the PHA they produce can be extracted, formed into pellets, and used to make durable, biodegradable plastics.

Through genetic engineering, humans can now modify bacteria to produce vitamins, antibiotics, hormones, and other products (see Chapter 20). Researchers are seeking to reduce fossil fuel use by engineering bacteria that can produce ethanol from various forms of biomass, including agricultural waste, switchgrass, fast-growing woody plants such as willows, and corn **(Figure 27.22c)**. One radical idea for modifying bacteria

▲ Figure 27.22 **Some applications of prokaryotes. (a)** Spraying fertilizers on an oil-soaked area stimulates growth of native bacteria that metabolize the oil, speeding the natural breakdown process up to fivefold. **(b)** These bacteria synthesize and store the polyester PHA. The PHA can be extracted and used to make biodegradable plastic products. **(c)** Current research seeks to develop bacteria that produce ethanol (E-85) fuel efficiently from renewable plant products.

comes from Craig Venter, head of The Institute for Genomic Research (TIGR). Venter and his colleagues are attempting to build "synthetic chromosomes" for bacteria—in effect, producing new species from scratch. They hope to "design" bacteria that can perform specific tasks, such as producing large amounts of hydrogen to reduce dependence on fossil fuels. Some scientists, however, question whether this approach may have unanticipated harmful effects.

The usefulness of prokaryotes largely derives from their diverse forms of nutrition and metabolism. All this metabolic versatility evolved prior to the appearance of the structural novelties that heralded the evolution of eukaryotic organisms, to which we devote the remainder of this unit.

CONCEPT CHECK **27.6**

1. Identify at least two ways that prokaryotes have affected you positively today.
2. A pathogenic bacterium's toxin causes symptoms that increase the bacterium's chance of spreading from host to host. Does this information indicate whether the poison is an exotoxin or endotoxin? Explain.
3. **WHAT IF?** In addition to horizontal gene transfer, propose another hypothesis that could account for *E. coli* strain O157:H7 having genes not found in strain K-12. How could your hypothesis be tested?

For suggested answers, see Appendix A.

Chapter 27 Review

MEDIA Go to www.campbellbiology.com for BioFlix 3-D Animations, MP3 Tutors, Videos, Practice Tests, an eBook, and more.

SUMMARY OF KEY CONCEPTS

CONCEPT 27.1

Structural and functional adaptations contribute to prokaryotic success (pp. 556–561)

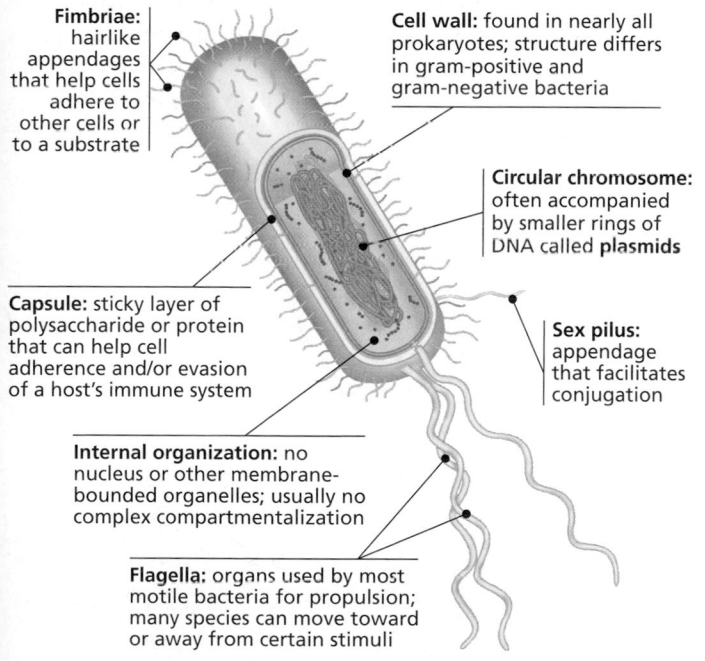

Fimbriae: hairlike appendages that help cells adhere to other cells or to a substrate

Cell wall: found in nearly all prokaryotes; structure differs in gram-positive and gram-negative bacteria

Circular chromosome: often accompanied by smaller rings of DNA called **plasmids**

Capsule: sticky layer of polysaccharide or protein that can help cell adherence and/or evasion of a host's immune system

Sex pilus: appendage that facilitates conjugation

Internal organization: no nucleus or other membrane-bounded organelles; usually no complex compartmentalization

Flagella: organs used by most motile bacteria for propulsion; many species can move toward or away from certain stimuli

▶ **Reproduction and Adaptation** Prokaryotes can reproduce quickly by binary fission. Some form endospores, which can remain viable in harsh conditions for centuries. Prokaryotic populations can evolve in short periods of time in response to changing environmental conditions.

MEDIA
Activity Prokaryotic Cell Structure and Function

CONCEPT 27.2

Rapid reproduction, mutation, and genetic recombination promote genetic diversity in prokaryotes (pp. 561–564)

▶ **Rapid Reproduction and Mutation** Because prokaryotes can often proliferate rapidly, mutations can quickly increase a population's genetic variation, enabling adaptive evolution.

▶ **Genetic Recombination** Genetic diversity in prokaryotes also can arise by recombination of the DNA from two different cells (in bacteria, via transformation, transduction, or conjugation). By transferring advantageous alleles, such as those for antibiotic resistance, genetic recombination can promote adaptive evolution in prokaryotic populations.

MEDIA
Investigation What Are the Patterns of Antibiotic Resistance?

CONCEPT 27.3

Diverse nutritional and metabolic adaptations have evolved in prokaryotes (pp. 564–565)

▶ Examples of all four modes of nutrition—photoautotrophy, chemoautotrophy, photoheterotrophy, and chemoheterotrophy—are found among prokaryotes.

▶ **The Role of Oxygen in Metabolism** Obligate aerobes require O_2, obligate anaerobes are poisoned by O_2, and facultative anaerobes can survive with or without O_2.

▶ **Nitrogen Metabolism** Prokaryotes can metabolize a wide variety of nitrogenous compounds. Some can convert atmospheric nitrogen to ammonia in a process called nitrogen fixation.

▶ **Metabolic Cooperation** Many prokaryotes depend on the metabolic activities of other prokaryotes. In *Anabaena*, photosynthetic cells and nitrogen-fixing cells exchange metabolic products. Some prokaryotes form surface-coating biofilms, typically including different species.

MEDIA
Investigation What Are the Modes of Nutrition in Prokaryotes?

Molecular systematics is illuminating prokaryotic phylogeny (pp. 565–570)

▶ **Lessons from Molecular Systematics** Molecular systematics is leading to a phylogenetic classification of prokaryotes, allowing systematists to identify major new clades.

▶ **Archaea** Archaea share certain traits with bacteria and other traits with eukaryotes. Some archaea, such as extreme thermophiles and extreme halophiles, live in extreme environments. Other archaea, including most methanogens and species in soils, lakes, and oceans, live in moderate environments.

▶ **Bacteria** Diverse nutritional types are scattered among the major groups of bacteria. The two largest groups are the proteobacteria and the gram-positive bacteria.

MEDIA

Activity Classification of Prokaryotes

CONCEPT 27.5

Prokaryotes play crucial roles in the biosphere (pp. 570–571)

▶ **Chemical Recycling** Decomposition by heterotrophic prokaryotes and the synthetic activities of autotrophic and nitrogen-fixing prokaryotes contribute to the recycling of elements in ecosystems.

▶ **Ecological Interactions** Many prokaryotes have a symbiotic relationship with a host; the relationships between prokaryotes and their hosts range from mutualism to commensalism to parasitism.

CONCEPT 27.6

Prokaryotes have both harmful and beneficial impacts on humans (pp. 571–573)

▶ **Pathogenic Bacteria** Pathogenic bacteria typically cause disease by releasing exotoxins or endotoxins and are potential weapons of bioterrorism. Horizontal gene transfer can spread genes associated with virulence to harmless strains.

▶ **Prokaryotes in Research and Technology** Experiments involving bacteria such as *E. coli* and *A. tumefaciens* have led to important advances in DNA technology. Prokaryotes can be used in bioremediation, production of biodegradable plastics, and the synthesis of vitamins, antibiotics, and other products.

TESTING YOUR KNOWLEDGE

SELF-QUIZ

1. Genetic variation in bacterial populations cannot result from
   a. transduction.
   b. transformation.
   c. conjugation.
   d. mutation.
   e. meiosis.

2. Photoautotrophs use
   a. light as an energy source and CO_2 as a carbon source.
   b. light as an energy source and methane as a carbon source.
   c. N_2 as an energy source and CO_2 as a carbon source.
   d. CO_2 as both an energy source and a carbon source.
   e. H_2S as an energy source and CO_2 as a carbon source.

3. Which of the following statements is *not* true?
   a. Archaea and bacteria have different membrane lipids.
   b. Both archaea and bacteria generally lack membrane-enclosed organelles.

c. The cell walls of archaea lack peptidoglycan.
d. Only bacteria have histones associated with DNA.
e. Only some archaea use CO_2 to oxidize H_2, releasing methane.

4. Which of the following features of prokaryotic biology involves metabolic cooperation among cells?
   a. binary fission
   b. endospore formation
   c. endotoxin release
   d. biofilms
   e. photoautotrophy

5. Which prokaryotic group is mismatched with its members?
   a. Proteobacteria—diverse gram-negative bacteria
   b. Gram-positive bacteria—symbionts in legume root nodules
   c. Spirochetes—helical heterotrophs
   d. Chlamydias—intracellular parasites
   e. Cyanobacteria—solitary and colonial photoautotrophs

6. Plantlike photosynthesis that releases O_2 occurs in
   a. cyanobacteria.
   b. chlamydias.
   c. archaea.
   d. actinomycetes.
   e. chemoautotrophic bacteria.

For Self-Quiz answers, see Appendix A.

MEDIA Visit www.campbellbiology.com for a Practice Test.

EVOLUTION CONNECTION

7. Health officials worldwide are concerned about antibiotic resistance in bacteria that cause disease. In patients infected with nonresistant strains of the bacterium that causes tuberculosis, antibiotics can relieve symptoms in a few weeks. However, it takes much longer to halt the infection, and patients may discontinue treatment while bacteria are still present. How can bacteria quickly cause symptoms again if they are not wiped out? How might this result in the evolution of drug-resistant pathogens?

SCIENTIFIC INQUIRY

8. **DRAW IT** The nitrogen-fixing bacterium *Rhizobium* infects the roots of some plant species, forming a mutualism in which the bacterium provides the plant with nitrogen, and the plant provides the bacterium with carbohydrates. Scientists measured how well one such plant species (*Acacia irrorata*) grew when its roots were infected by six different *Rhizobium* strains.

(a) Graph the data. (b) Interpret your graph.

Rhizobium strain	Plant mass (g) after 12 weeks of growth
1	0.91
2	0.06
3	1.56
4	1.72
5	0.14
6	1.03

Source: J. J. Burdon, et al., Variation in the effectiveness of symbiotic associations between native rhizobia and temperate Australian *Acacia*: within species interactions, *Journal of Applied Ecology*, 36:398-408 (1999).

Note: In the absence of *Rhizobium*, after 12 weeks of growth, *Acacia* plants have a mass of about 0.1 g.

Protists

28

KEY CONCEPTS

28.1 Most eukaryotes are single-celled organisms

28.2 Excavates include protists with modified mitochondria and protists with unique flagella

28.3 Chromalveolates may have originated by secondary endosymbiosis

28.4 Rhizarians are a diverse group of protists defined by DNA similarities

28.5 Red algae and green algae are the closest relatives of land plants

28.6 Unikonts include protists that are closely related to fungi and animals

28.7 Protists play key roles in ecological relationships

OVERVIEW

Living Small

Knowing that most prokaryotes are extremely small organisms, you might assume that **Figure 28.1** depicts six prokaryotes and one much larger eukaryote. But in fact, only the organism immediately above the scale bar is a prokaryote. The others are recently discovered members of diverse, mostly unicellular groups of eukaryotes informally known as **protists**. Very small eukaryotes have intrigued scientists for more than 300 years, ever since the Dutch microscopist Antoni van Leeuwenhoek first laid eyes on them. As he discovered, viewing a drop of pond water under a light microscope can reveal a fascinating world of unicellular protists and prokaryotes. Some protists propel themselves with whipping flagella, while others creep along by means of blob-like appendages. Some are shaped like tiny trumpets; others resemble miniature jewelry. Recalling his observations, van Leeuwenhoek wrote, "No more pleasant sight has met my eye than this, of so many thousands of living creatures in one small drop of water."

Until recently, biologists thought that 300 years of observation had uncovered a representative sample of living protist species. But in the last decade, genetic prospecting has turned up a treasure trove of previously unknown protists within the world of microscopic life. As shown in Figure 28.1, many of these newly discovered species have cells just 0.5–2 µm in diameter—as small as many prokaryotes.

The surprising discovery of many species of minuscule protists followed close on the heels of recent findings regarding protist phylogeny. All protists were once classified in a single kingdom, Protista, but advances in eukaryotic systematics have caused the kingdom to crumble. It has become clear that Protista is in fact polyphyletic (see Figure 26.10): Some protists are more closely related to plants, fungi, or animals than they are to other protists. As a result, the kingdom Protista has been abandoned, and various lineages of protists are now recognized as kingdoms in their own right. Most biologists still use the term *protist*, but only as a convenient way to refer to eukaryotes that are neither plants, animals, nor fungi.

In this chapter, you will become acquainted with some of the most significant groups of protists. You will learn about their structural and biochemical adaptations as well as their enormous impact on ecosystems, agriculture, industry, and human health.

CONCEPT 28.1

Most eukaryotes are single-celled organisms

Protists, along with plants, animals, and fungi, are classified as eukaryotes; they are in domain Eukarya, one of the three domains of life. Unlike the cells of prokaryotes, eukaryotic cells have a nucleus and other membrane-bounded organelles, such as mitochondria and the Golgi apparatus. Such organelles provide specific locations in which particular functions are accomplished, making the structure and organization of eukaryotic cells more complex than that of prokaryotic cells.

We'll survey the diversity of eukaryotes throughout the rest of this unit, beginning in this chapter with the protists. As you explore this material, bear in mind that the organisms in most eukaryotic lineages are protists, and most protists are unicellular. Thus, life differs greatly from what we commonly think it is like. The large, multicellular organisms that we know best (plants, animals, and fungi) are the tips of just a few branches on the great tree of life (see Figure 26.21).

Structural and Functional Diversity in Protists

Given the polyphyletic nature of the group once called Protista, it isn't surprising that few general characteristics of protists can be cited without exceptions. In fact, protists exhibit more structural and functional diversity than any other group of eukaryotes.

Most protists are unicellular, although there are some colonial and multicellular species. Single-celled protists are justifiably considered the simplest eukaryotes, but at the cellular level, many protists are very complex—the most elaborate of all cells. In multicellular organisms, essential biological functions are carried out by organs. Unicellular protists carry out the same essential functions, but they do so using subcellular organelles, not multicellular organs. The organelles that protists use are mostly those discussed in Chapter 6, including the nucleus, endoplasmic reticulum, Golgi apparatus, and lysosomes. Certain protists also rely on organelles not found in most other eukaryotic cells, such as contractile vacuoles that pump excess water from the protistan cell (see Figure 7.14).

Protists are more nutritionally diverse than other eukaryote groups. Some protists are photoautotrophs and contain chloroplasts. Some are heterotrophs, absorbing organic molecules or ingesting larger food particles. Still others, called **mixotrophs**, combine photosynthesis *and* heterotrophic nutrition. Photoautotrophy, heterotrophy, and mixotrophy have all arisen independently in many protist lineages.

Reproduction and life cycles also are highly varied among protists. Some protists are exclusively asexual; others can also reproduce sexually or at least employ the sexual processes of meiosis and fertilization. All three basic types of sexual life cycles (see Figure 13.6) are represented among protists, along with some variations that do not quite fit any of these types. We will examine the life cycles of several protist groups later in this chapter.

Endosymbiosis in Eukaryotic Evolution

What gave rise to the enormous diversity of protists that exist today? There is abundant evidence that much of protist diversity has its origins in endosymbiosis, the process in which certain unicellular organisms engulf other cells, which become endosym-

bionts and ultimately organelles in the host cell. For example, as we discussed in Chapter 25, structural, biochemical, and DNA sequence data indicate that the first eukaryotes acquired mitochondria by engulfing an aerobic prokaryote (specifically, an alpha proteobacterium). The early origin of mitochondria is supported by the fact that all eukaryotes studied so far either have mitochondria or show signs that their ancestors had them.

Much evidence also indicates that later in eukaryotic history, one lineage of heterotrophic eukaryotes acquired an additional endosymbiont—a photosynthetic cyanobacterium—that then evolved into plastids. In the model illustrated in **Figure 28.2**, this plastid-bearing lineage eventually gave rise to red algae and green algae. These hypotheses are supported by the observation that the DNA of plastid genes in red algae and green algae closely resembles the DNA of cyanobacteria. In addition, plastids in red algae and green algae are surrounded by two membranes, which correspond to the inner and outer membranes of the gram-negative cyanobacterial endosymbionts.

On several occasions during eukaryotic evolution, red algae and green algae underwent **secondary endosymbiosis**: They were ingested in the food vacuole of heterotrophic eukaryotes and became endosymbionts themselves. For example, protists known as chlorarachniophytes likely evolved when a heterotrophic eukaryote engulfed a green alga. Biologists infer that this process occurred relatively recently in evolutionary time because the engulfed green alga still carries out photosynthesis with its plastids and contains a tiny vestigial nucleus of its own, called a *nucleomorph*. Consistent with the hypothesis that chlorarachniophytes evolved from a eukaryote that engulfed another eukaryote, their plastids are surrounded by *four* membranes. The two inner membranes originated as the inner and outer membranes of the ancient cyanobacterium. The third membrane is derived from the engulfed alga's plasma membrane, and the outermost membrane is derived from the heterotrophic eukaryote's food vacuole. In other protists, plastids acquired by secondary endosymbiosis are surrounded by three membranes, indicating that one of the original four membranes was lost during the course of evolution.

Five Supergroups of Eukaryotes

Our understanding of the evolutionary history of protists has been in a state of flux in recent years. Not only has kingdom Protista been abandoned, but a variety of other hypotheses have been discarded as well. For example, in the early 1990s, many biologists thought that the oldest lineage of living eukaryotes were the *amitochondriate protists*, a group lacking conventional mitochondria and having fewer membrane-bounded organelles than other protist groups. But recent structural and DNA data have undermined this hypothesis. Many of the so-called amitochondriate protists have been shown to have mitochondria—though reduced ones—and some of these organisms are now classified in entirely differ-

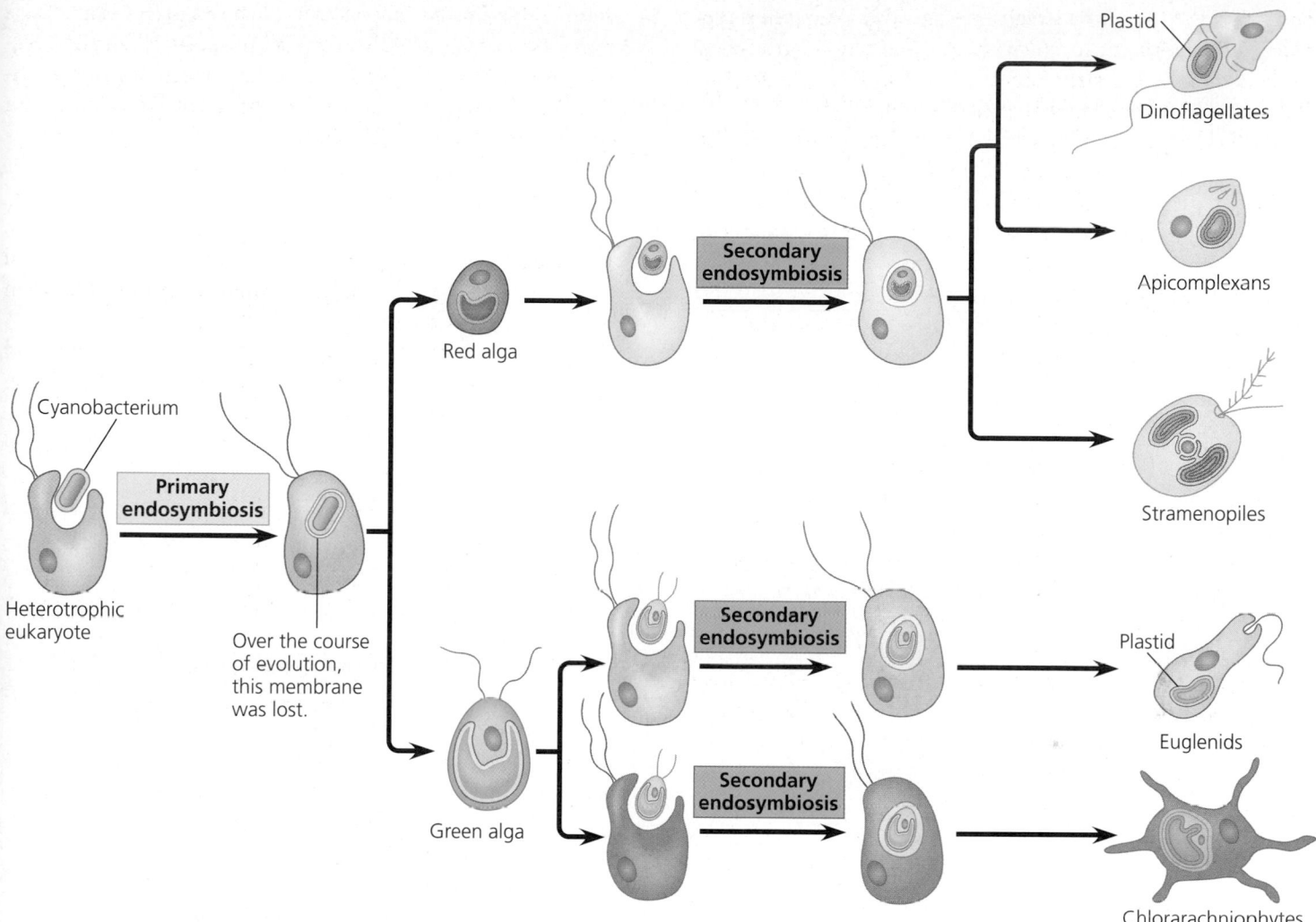

Labels within figure:
- Plastid
- Dinoflagellates
- Cyanobacterium
- Secondary endosymbiosis
- Apicomplexans
- Red alga
- Primary endosymbiosis
- Stramenopiles
- Heterotrophic eukaryote
- Over the course of evolution, this membrane was lost.
- Secondary endosymbiosis
- Plastid
- Euglenids
- Secondary endosymbiosis
- Green alga
- Chlorarachniophytes

▲ **Figure 28.2 Diversity of plastids produced by secondary endosymbiosis.** Studies of plastid-bearing eukaryotes suggest that all plastids evolved from a gram-negative cyanobacterium that was engulfed by an ancestral heterotrophic eukaryote (primary endosymbiosis). That ancestor then diversified into red algae and green algae, some of which were subsequently engulfed by other eukaryotes (secondary endosymbiosis).

ent groups. For example, microsporidians, once considered amitochondriate protists, are now classified as fungi.

The ongoing changes in our understanding of the phylogeny of protists pose challenges to students and instructors alike. Hypotheses about these relationships are a hotbed of scientific activity, changing rapidly as new data cause previous ideas to be modified or discarded. In this chapter, our discussion is organized around one current hypothesis: the five supergroups of eukaryotes shown in **Figure 28.3**, on the next two pages. Because the root of the eukaryotic tree is not known, all five supergroups are shown as diverging simultaneously from a common ancestor—something that we know is not correct, but we do not know which organisms were the first to diverge from the others. In addition, bear in mind that while some of the groups in Figure 28.3 are well supported by morphological and DNA data, others are more controversial. As you read this chapter, it may be helpful to focus less on the

specific names of groups of organisms and more on why the organisms are important and how ongoing research is designed to elucidate their evolutionary relationships.

CONCEPT CHECK **28.1**

1. Cite at least four examples of structural and functional diversity among protists.
2. Summarize the role of endosymbiosis in eukaryotic evolution.
3. **WHAT IF?** After studying Figure 28.3, on the next two pages, draw a simplified version of the phylogenetic tree that shows only the five supergroups of eukaryotes. Now sketch how the tree would look if the unikonts were the first group of eukaryotes to diverge from other eukaryotes.

For suggested answers, see Appendix A.

Exploring Protistan Diversity

In the phylogenetic hypothesis represented in the tree below, the eukaryote groups at the branch tips are related in larger "supergroups," labeled vertically at the far right of the tree. The kingdoms Plantae (land plants), Fungi, and Animalia (animals) have survived from the five-kingdom system of classification. Groups that were formerly classified in the kingdom Protista are highlighted in yellow. Dotted lines indicate evolutionary relationships that are uncertain or under active debate.

Excavata

Diplomonads	Excavata
Parabasalids	
Euglenozoans	

Dinoflagellates	Chromalveolata
Apicomplexans	
Ciliates	
Diatoms	
Golden algae	
Brown algae	
Oomycetes	

Alveolates / Stramenopiles

Chlorarachniophytes	Rhizaria
Forams	
Radiolarians	

Red algae	Archaeplastida
Chlorophytes	
Charophytes	
Land plants	

Green algae

Slime molds	Unikonta
Gymnamoebas	
Entamoebas	
Nucleariids	
Fungi	
Choanoflagellates	
Animals	

Amoebozoans / Opisthokonts

Excavata

Some members of this supergroup have an "excavated" groove on one side of the cell body. Two major clades (the parabasalids and diplomonads) have modified mitochondria; others (the euglenozoans) have flagella that differ in structure from those of other organisms. Excavates include parasites such as *Giardia*, as well as many predatory and photosynthetic species.

5 µm

▲ *Giardia intestinalis*, **a diplomonad parasite.** This diplomonad (colorized SEM) can infect people when they drink water contaminated with feces containing the cysts of the parasite. Drinking such water—even from a seemingly pristine stream—can cause severe diarrhea. Boiling the water kills the parasite.

Chromalveolata

This group may have originated by an ancient secondary endosymbiosis event. Chromalveolates include some of the most important photosynthetic organisms on Earth, such as the diatoms shown here. The group also includes the brown algae that form underwater kelp "forests," as well as important pathogens, such as *Plasmodium*, which causes malaria, and *Phytophthora*, which caused the devastating potato famine in 19th-century Ireland.

▶ **Diatom diversity.** These beautiful single-celled protists are important photosynthetic organisms in aquatic communities (LM).

50 µm

Rhizaria

This group consists of species of amoebas, most of which have pseudopodia that are threadlike in shape. Pseudopodia are extensions that can bulge from any portion of the cell; they are used in movement and in the capture of prey.

20 µm

▲ *Globigerina*, a foram in the supergroup **Rhizaria.** Threadlike pseudopodia extend through pores in the shell, or test (LM). The inset SEM shows a foram test, which contains calcium carbonate that makes it hard.

Archaeplastida

This group of eukaryotes includes red algae and green algae, along with land plants (kingdom Plantae, discussed in Chapters 29 and 30). Red algae and green algae include unicellular species, colonial species (such as the green alga *Volvox*), and multicellular species. Many of the large algae known informally as "seaweeds" are multicellular red or green algae. Protists in Archaeplastida include key photosynthetic species that form the base of the food web in some aquatic communities.

▼ *Volvox*, a colonial freshwater green alga. The colony is a hollow ball whose wall is composed of hundreds of biflagellated cells (see inset LM) embedded in a gelatinous matrix. The cells are usually connected by cytoplasmic strands; if isolated, these cells cannot reproduce. The large colonies seen here will eventually release the small "daughter" colonies within them (LM).

20 µm

50 µm

Unikonta

This group of eukaryotes includes amoebas that have lobe- or tube-shaped pseudopodia, as well as animals, fungi, and protists that are closely related to animals or fungi. According to one current hypothesis, the unikonts may have been the first group of eukaryotes to diverge from other eukaryotes (see Figure 28.23); however, this hypothesis has yet to be widely accepted.

◀ **A unikont amoeba.** This amoeba (*Amoeba proteus*) is using its pseudopodia to engulf a small green alga.

100 µm

Excavates include protists with modified mitochondria and protists with unique flagella

Now that we have examined some of the broad patterns in eukaryotic evolution, we will look more closely at the five main groups of protists shown in Figure 28.3.

We begin this tour with **Excavata** (the excavates), a recently proposed clade that has emerged from morphological studies of the cytoskeleton. Some members of this diverse group also have an "excavated" feeding groove on one side of the cell body.

The excavates include the diplomonads, the parabasalids, and the euglenozoans. Molecular data indicate that each of these three groups is monophyletic, but the data have neither confirmed nor strongly refuted the monophyly of the excavate supergroup. Although unique cytoskeletal features are shared by many excavates, we cannot yet tell whether that is because the excavates are monophyletic or because the common ancestor of eukaryotes had those features. Overall, support for the excavate clade is relatively weak, making it one of the more controversial of the five supergroups.

Diplomonads and Parabasalids

The protists in these two groups lack plastids and have modified mitochondria (until recently, they were thought to lack mitochondria altogether). Most diplomonads and parabasalids are found in anaerobic environments.

Diplomonads have modified mitochondria called *mitosomes*. These organelles lack functional electron transport chains and hence cannot use oxygen to help extract energy from carbohydrates and other organic molecules. Instead, diplomonads get the energy they need from anaerobic biochemical pathways, such as glycolysis (see Chapter 9).

Structurally, diplomonads have two equal-sized nuclei and multiple flagella. Recall that eukaryotic flagella are extensions of the cytoplasm, consisting of bundles of microtubules covered by the cell's plasma membrane (see Figure 6.24). They are quite different from prokaryotic flagella, which are filaments composed of the globular protein flagellin attached to the cell surface (see Figure 27.6).

Many diplomonads are parasites. An infamous example is *Giardia intestinalis* (also known as *Giardia lamblia*; see Figure 28.3), which inhabits the intestines of mammals.

Flagella

Undulating membrane

5 µm

▲ **Figure 28.4 The parabasalid *Trichomonas vaginalis*** (colorized SEM).

Parabasalids also have reduced mitochondria; called *hydrogenosomes,* these organelles generate some energy anaerobically, releasing hydrogen gas as a by-product. The best-known parabasalid is *Trichomonas vaginalis*, a sexually transmitted parasite that infects some 5 million people each year. *T. vaginalis* travels along the mucus-coated lining of the human reproductive and urinary tracts by moving its flagella and by undulating part of its plasma membrane (**Figure 28.4**). In females, if the vagina's normal acidity is disturbed, *T. vaginalis* can outcompete beneficial microorganisms there and infect the vagina. *Trichomonas* infections also can occur in the urethra of males, though often without symptoms. Studies suggest that *T. vaginalis* acquired a particular gene by horizontal gene transfer from bacterial parasites in the vagina. The gene allows *T. vaginalis* to feed on the vaginal lining, aiding the infection process.

Euglenozoans

Protists called **euglenozoans** belong to a diverse clade that includes predatory heterotrophs, photosynthetic autotrophs, and parasites. The main morphological feature that distinguishes protists in this clade is the presence of a spiral or crystalline rod of unknown function inside their flagella (**Figure 28.5**). The two best-studied groups of euglenozoans are the kinetoplastids and the euglenids.

Kinetoplastids

Protists called **kinetoplastids** have a single, large mitochondrion that contains an organized mass of DNA called a *kinetoplast*. These protists include species that feed on prokaryotes in freshwater, marine, and moist terrestrial ecosystems, as well as species that parasitize animals, plants, and other protists. For example, kinetoplastids in the genus *Trypanosoma* cause sleeping sickness in humans, a neurological disease that is invariably fatal if it is not treated. The trypanosomes infect

▲ Figure 28.5 Euglenozoan flagellum. Most euglenozoans have a crystalline rod inside one of their flagella (the TEM is a flagellum shown in cross section). The rod lies alongside the 9 + 2 ring of microtubules found in all eukaryotic flagella (compare with Figure 6.24).

▲ Figure 28.6 *Trypanosoma*, the kinetoplastid that causes sleeping sickness. The purple, ribbon-shaped cells among these red blood cells are the trypanosomes (colorized SEM).

humans via the bite of a vector (carrier) organism, the African tsetse fly **(Figure 28.6)**. Trypanosomes also cause Chagas' disease, which is transmitted by bloodsucking insects and can lead to congestive heart failure.

Trypanosomes evade immune responses with an effective "bait-and-switch" defense. The surface of a trypanosome is coated with millions of copies of a single protein. However, before the host's immune system can recognize the protein and mount an attack, new generations of the parasite switch to another surface protein with a different molecular structure. Frequent changes in the surface protein prevent the host from developing immunity (see Figure 43.25). About a third of *Trypanosoma*'s genome is dedicated to producing these surface proteins.

Euglenids

A **euglenid** has a pocket at one end of the cell from which one or two flagella emerge **(Figure 28.7)**. Many species of the euglenid *Euglena* are mixotrophs: In sunlight they are autotrophic, but when sunlight is unavailable, they can become heterotrophic, absorbing organic nutrients from their environment. Many other euglenids engulf prey by phagocytosis.

CONCEPT CHECK 28.2

1. Why do some biologists describe the mitochondria of diplomonads and parabasalids as "highly reduced"?
2. **WHAT IF?** DNA sequence data for a diplomonad, a euglenid, a plant, and an unidentified protist suggest that the unidentified species is most closely related to the diplomonad. Further studies reveal that the unknown species has fully functional mitochondria. Based on these data, at what point on the phylogenetic tree in Figure 28.3 did the mystery protist's lineage probably diverge from other eukaryote lineages? Explain.

For suggested answers, see Appendix A.

▼ Figure 28.7 *Euglena*, a euglenid commonly found in pond water.

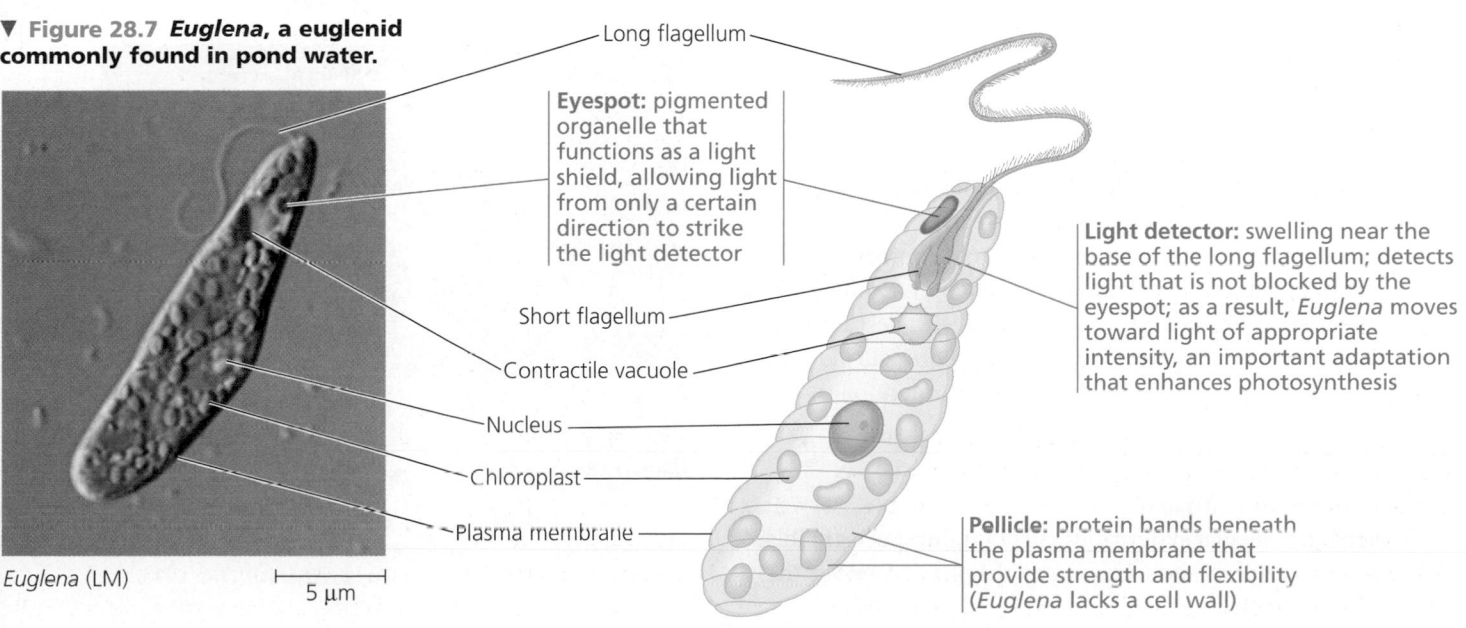

Long flagellum

Eyespot: pigmented organelle that functions as a light shield, allowing light from only a certain direction to strike the light detector

Light detector: swelling near the base of the long flagellum; detects light that is not blocked by the eyespot; as a result, *Euglena* moves toward light of appropriate intensity, an important adaptation that enhances photosynthesis

Short flagellum

Contractile vacuole

Nucleus

Chloroplast

Plasma membrane

Pellicle: protein bands beneath the plasma membrane that provide strength and flexibility (*Euglena* lacks a cell wall)

Euglena (LM)

5 μm

CONCEPT 28.3
Chromalveolates may have originated by secondary endosymbiosis

The supergroup **Chromalveolata** (the chromalveolates), a large, extremely diverse clade of protists, has recently been proposed based on two lines of evidence. First, some (though not all) DNA sequence data suggest that the chromalveolates form a monophyletic group. Second, some data support the hypothesis that the chromalveolates originated more than a billion years ago, when a common ancestor of the group engulfed a single-celled, photosynthetic red alga. Because red algae are thought to have originated by primary endosymbiosis (see Figure 28.2), such an origin for the chromalveolates is referred to as secondary endosymbiosis.

How strong is the evidence that the chromalveolates originated by secondary endosymbiosis? Many species in the clade have plastids whose structure and DNA indicate that they are of red algal origin. Others have reduced plastids that seem to be derived from a red algal endosymbiont. Still other species lack plastids altogether—yet some of these species have plastid genes in their nuclear DNA. Such data have led researchers to suggest that the common ancestor of the chromalveolates had plastids of red algal origin, but that later, some evolutionary lineages within the group lost the plastids. Others question this idea, noting that the entire genome has been sequenced for several chromalveolates that lack plastids, yet no evidence of plastid genes has been found. Overall, the endosymbiotic origin of the chromalveolates is an interesting current hypothesis—but, like any scientific hypothesis, new data may show it to be incorrect.

The chromalveolates are perhaps the most controversial of the five supergroups we describe in this chapter. Even so, for many scientists, this supergroup represents the best current hypothesis for the phylogeny of the two large protist clades to which we now turn: the alveolates and the stramenopiles.

Alveolates

The **alveolates** are a group of protists whose monophyly is well supported by molecular systematics. Structurally, species in this group have membrane-bounded sacs (alveoli) just under the plasma membrane (Figure 28.8). The function of the alveoli is unknown; researchers hypothesize that they may help stabilize the cell surface or regulate the cell's water and ion content.

The alveolates include three subgroups: a group of flagellates (the dinoflagellates), a group of parasites (the apicomplexans), and a group of protists that move using cilia (the ciliates).

Dinoflagellates

The **dinoflagellates** are characterized by cells that are reinforced by cellulose plates. Two flagella located in perpendicular grooves in this "armor" make dinoflagellates (from the Greek *dinos*, whirling) spin as they move through the water (Figure 28.9). Dinoflagellates are abundant components of both marine and freshwater plankton, communities of microorganisms that live near the water's surface. These dinoflagellates include some of the most important photosynthetic species. However, many photosynthetic dinoflagellates are mixotrophic, and roughly half of all dinoflagellates are purely heterotrophic.

Dinoflagellate blooms—episodes of explosive population growth—sometimes cause a phenomenon called "red tide" in

▲ **Figure 28.8 Alveoli.** These sacs under the plasma membrane are a characteristic that distinguishes alveolates from other eukaryotes (TEM).

▲ **Figure 28.9 *Pfiesteria shumwayae*, a dinoflagellate.** Beating of the spiral flagellum, which lies in a groove that encircles the cell, makes this alveolate spin (colorized SEM).

coastal waters. The blooms appear brownish red or pink because of the presence of carotenoids, the most common pigments in dinoflagellate plastids. Toxins produced by certain dinoflagellates (such as *Karenia brevis*, which inhabits the Gulf of Mexico) have caused massive kills of invertebrates and fishes. Humans who eat molluscs that have accumulated the toxins are affected as well, sometimes fatally.

Apicomplexans

Nearly all **apicomplexans** are parasites of animals, and some cause serious human diseases. The parasites spread through their host as tiny infectious cells called *sporozoites*. Apicomplexans are so named because one end (the *apex*) of the sporozoite cell contains a *complex* of organelles specialized for penetrating host cells and tissues. Although apicomplexans are not photosynthetic, recent data show that they retain a modified plastid (apicoplast), most likely of red algal origin.

Most apicomplexans have intricate life cycles with both sexual and asexual stages. Those life cycles often require two or more host species for completion. For example, *Plasmodium*, the parasite that causes malaria, lives in both mosquitoes and humans **(Figure 28.10)**.

Historically, malaria has rivaled tuberculosis as the leading cause of human death by infectious disease. The incidence of malaria was greatly diminished in the 1960s by insecticides that reduced carrier populations of *Anopheles* mosquitoes and by drugs that killed *Plasmodium* in humans. But the emergence of resistant varieties of both *Anopheles* and *Plasmodium* has led to a resurgence of malaria. About 300 million people in the tropics are now infected, and 2 million die each year.

▼ **Figure 28.10 The two-host life cycle of *Plasmodium*, the apicomplexan that causes malaria.**

? *Are morphological differences between sporozoites, merozoites, and gametocytes caused by different genomes or by differences in gene expression? Explain.*

❶ An infected *Anopheles* mosquito bites a person, injecting *Plasmodium* sporozoites in its saliva.

❷ The sporozoites enter the person's liver cells. After several days, the sporozoites undergo multiple divisions and become merozoites, which use their apical complex to penetrate red blood cells (see TEM below).

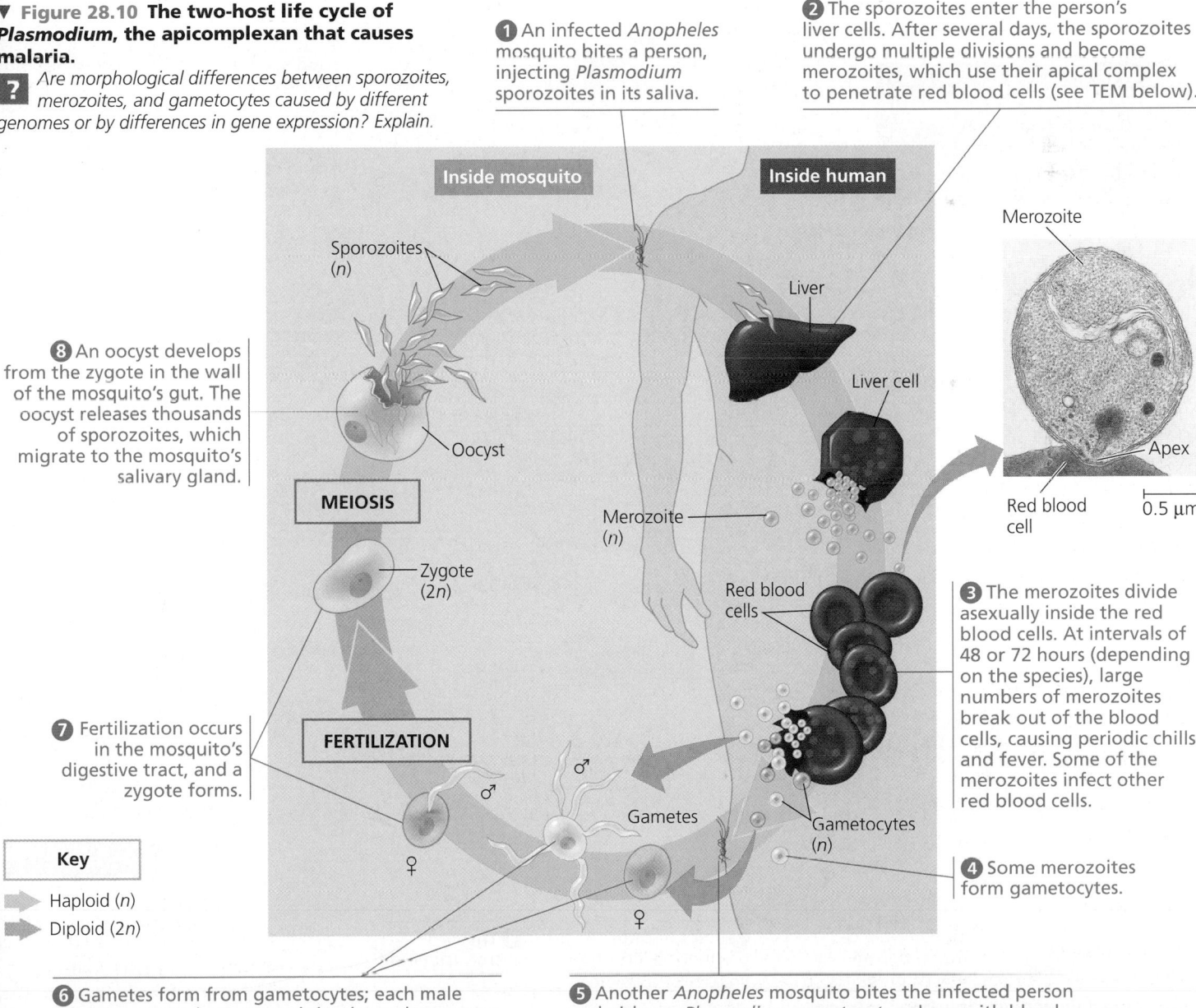

Inside mosquito

Inside human

Sporozoites (*n*)

❽ An oocyst develops from the zygote in the wall of the mosquito's gut. The oocyst releases thousands of sporozoites, which migrate to the mosquito's salivary gland.

Oocyst

MEIOSIS

Zygote (*2n*)

❼ Fertilization occurs in the mosquito's digestive tract, and a zygote forms.

FERTILIZATION

Liver

Liver cell

Merozoite (*n*)

Red blood cells

Gametes

♂

♀

Gametocytes (*n*)

Key

Haploid (*n*)

Diploid (*2n*)

Merozoite

Apex

Red blood cell

0.5 μm

❸ The merozoites divide asexually inside the red blood cells. At intervals of 48 or 72 hours (depending on the species), large numbers of merozoites break out of the blood cells, causing periodic chills and fever. Some of the merozoites infect other red blood cells.

❹ Some merozoites form gametocytes.

❻ Gametes form from gametocytes; each male gametocyte produces several slender male gametes.

❺ Another *Anopheles* mosquito bites the infected person and picks up *Plasmodium* gametocytes along with blood.

The search for malarial vaccines has been hampered by the fact that *Plasmodium* lives mainly inside cells, hidden from the host's immune system. And, like trypanosomes, *Plasmodium* continually changes its surface proteins. The urgent need for treatments inspired an ambitious effort to sequence *Plasmodium*'s genome. Researchers have now tracked the expression of most of the parasite's genes at numerous points in its life cycle. This research could help identify vaccine targets.

Antibiotics that target the apicoplast are also in development. This approach may be effective because the apicoplast, being derived by secondary endosymbiosis from a prokaryote, has metabolic pathways different from those in people.

Ciliates

Ciliates are a large, varied group of protists named for their use of cilia to move and feed **(Figure 28.11a)**. The cilia may

▼ **Figure 28.11 Structure and function in the ciliate *Paramecium caudatum*.**

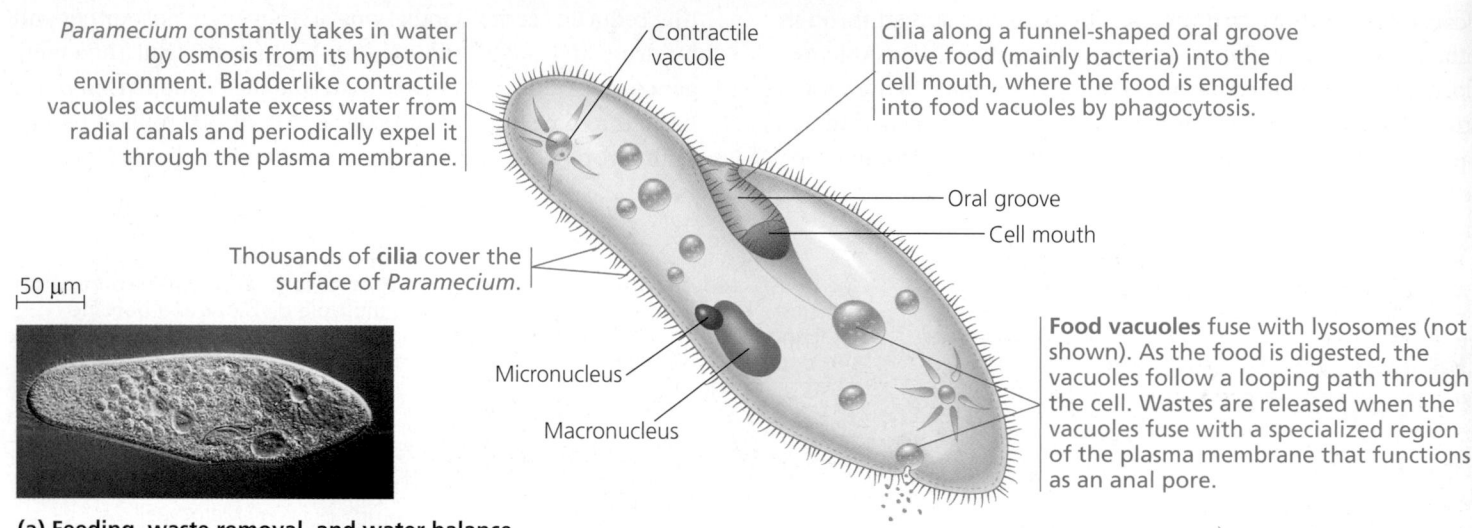

Paramecium constantly takes in water by osmosis from its hypotonic environment. Bladderlike contractile vacuoles accumulate excess water from radial canals and periodically expel it through the plasma membrane.

Contractile vacuole

Cilia along a funnel-shaped oral groove move food (mainly bacteria) into the cell mouth, where the food is engulfed into food vacuoles by phagocytosis.

Oral groove
Cell mouth

50 µm

Thousands of **cilia** cover the surface of *Paramecium*.

Micronucleus

Macronucleus

Food vacuoles fuse with lysosomes (not shown). As the food is digested, the vacuoles follow a looping path through the cell. Wastes are released when the vacuoles fuse with a specialized region of the plasma membrane that functions as an anal pore.

(a) Feeding, waste removal, and water balance.

❶ Two cells of compatible mating strains align side by side and partially fuse.

❷ Meiosis of micronuclei produces four haploid micronuclei in each cell.

❸ Three micronuclei in each cell disintegrate. The remaining micronucleus in each cell divides by mitosis.

MEIOSIS

❹ The cells swap one micronucleus.

Diploid micronucleus

Haploid micronucleus

Compatible mates

The original macronucleus disintegrates.

Diploid micronucleus

Diploid micronucleus

MICRONUCLEAR FUSION

❺ The cells separate.

❾ Two rounds of cytokinesis yield four daughter cells.

❽ Four micronuclei become macronuclei.

❼ Three rounds of mitosis produce eight micronuclei.

❻ The two micronuclei fuse.

Key

Conjugation
Reproduction

(b) Conjugation and reproduction.

completely cover the cell surface or may be clustered in a few rows or tufts. In certain species, rows of tightly packed cilia function collectively in locomotion. Other ciliates scurry about on leg-like structures constructed from many cilia bonded together.

A distinctive feature of ciliates is the presence of two types of nuclei: tiny micronuclei and large macronuclei. A cell has one or more nuclei of each type. Genetic variation results from conjugation, a sexual process in which two individuals exchange haploid micronuclei (Figure 28.11b). Ciliates generally reproduce asexually by binary fission, during which the existing macronucleus disintegrates and a new one is formed from the cell's micronuclei. Each macronucleus typically contains multiple copies of the ciliate's genome. Genes in the macronucleus control the everyday functions of the cell, such as feeding, waste removal, and maintaining water balance (see Figure 28.11a).

Stramenopiles

The **stramenopiles** are a group of marine algae that include some of the most important photosynthetic organisms on the planet, as well as several clades of heterotrophs. Their name (from the Latin *stramen*, straw, and *pilos*, hair) refers to their characteristic flagellum, which has numerous fine, hairlike projections. In most stramenopiles, this "hairy" flagellum is paired with a shorter "smooth" (nonhairy) flagellum (Figure 28.12).

Diatoms

Diatoms are unicellular algae that have a unique glass-like wall made of hydrated silica (silicon dioxide) embedded in an organic matrix. The wall consists of two parts that overlap like a shoe box and its lid (Figure 28.13). These walls provide effective protection from the crushing jaws of predators: In 2003, researchers in Germany found that live diatoms can withstand pressures as great as 1.4 million kg/m², equal to the pressure under each leg of a table supporting an elephant! Much of the diatoms' strength comes from the delicate lacework of holes and grooves in their walls; if the walls were smooth, it would take 60% less force to crush them.

Most of the year, diatoms reproduce asexually by mitosis; each daughter cell receives half of the parental cell wall and generates a new half that fits inside it. Some species form cysts as resistant stages. Sexual reproduction occurs but is not common in diatoms.

With an estimated 100,000 living species, diatoms are a highly diverse group of protists (see Figure 28.3). They are a major component of plankton both in the ocean and in lakes: One bucket of water scooped from the surface of the sea may contain millions of these microscopic algae.

Like golden algae and brown algae, diatoms store energy in the form of a glucose polymer called laminarin. Some diatoms also store energy in oil molecules.

▲ **Figure 28.12 Stramenopile flagella.** Most stramenopiles, such as *Synura petersenii*, have two flagella: one covered with fine, stiff hairs and a shorter one that is smooth.

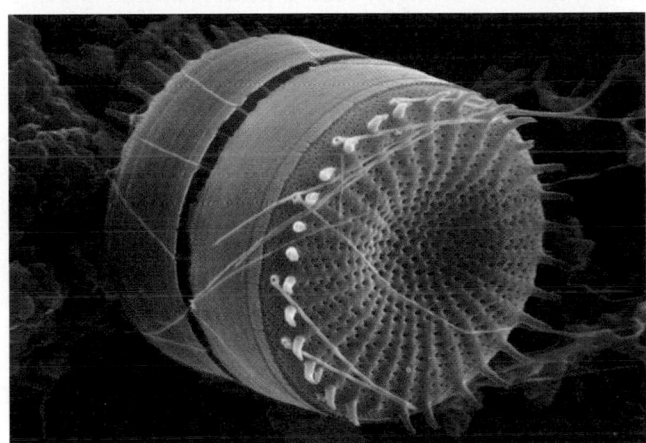

▲ **Figure 28.13 A freshwater diatom** (colorized SEM).

Massive accumulations of fossilized diatom walls are major constituents of the sediments known as diatomaceous earth, which is mined for its quality as a filtering medium and for many other uses. Diatoms also have an interesting application in the field of nanotechnology—the fashioning of microscopic devices. In building their shells, diatoms perform an intricate, three-dimensional self-assembly of microscopic components. Nano-engineers are studying this process as a model for the manufacture of miniature motors and medicine delivery systems.

Diatom populations may increase rapidly (bloom) when ample nutrients are available. Although typically eaten by a variety of protists and invertebrates, during a bloom many diatoms escape this fate. When diatoms that are not eaten die, their bodies sink to the ocean floor. This sinking process is part of a *biological carbon pump* that begins during photosynthesis when diatoms incorporate carbon into their bodies from carbon dioxide in the air. Diatoms that sink to the ocean floor are not very likely to be broken down by bacteria and other decomposers. Hence, the carbon in their bodies is not returned to the air in the form of carbon dioxide respired by decomposers; instead it is "pumped" to the ocean bottom. With an eye toward reducing global warming by lowering atmospheric carbon dioxide levels, some scientists advocate promoting diatom blooms by fertilizing the ocean with nutrients such as iron. Other scientists question the wisdom of this strategy, noting that it is difficult to predict the effects of such large-scale manipulations of ecological communities.

Golden Algae

The characteristic color of **golden algae** results from their yellow and brown carotenoids. The cells of golden algae are typically biflagellated, with both flagella attached near one end of the cell.

Many golden algae are components of freshwater and marine plankton. While all golden algae are photosynthetic, some species are mixotrophic. These mixotrophs can absorb dissolved organic compounds or ingest food particles, including living cells (eukaryotes and prokaryotes), by phagocytosis. Most species are unicellular, but some, such as those in the freshwater genus *Dinobryon*, are colonial **(Figure 28.14)**. If environmental conditions deteriorate, many species form protective cysts that can survive for decades.

Brown Algae

The largest and most complex algae are **brown algae**. All are multicellular, and most are marine. Brown algae are especially common along temperate coasts, where the water is cool. They owe their characteristic brown or olive color to the carotenoids in their plastids.

Many of the species commonly called "seaweeds" are brown algae. (Some large, multicellular species of red and green algae are also referred to as seaweeds. We will examine them later in this chapter.) Brown algae include species that have the most complex multicellular anatomy of all algae; some even have specialized tissues and organs that resemble those in plants. But morphological and DNA evidence indicates that the similarities evolved independently in the algal and plant lineages and are thus analogous, not homologous.

The term **thallus** (plural, *thalli*; from the Greek *thallos*, sprout) refers to an algal body that is plantlike. Unlike the body of a plant, however, a thallus lacks true roots, stems, and leaves. A typical thallus consists of a rootlike **holdfast**, which anchors the alga, and a stemlike **stipe**, which supports leaflike **blades (Figure 28.15)**. The blades provide most of the alga's photosynthetic surface. Some brown algae are equipped with gas-filled, bubble-shaped floats, which help keep the blades up near the water surface. Beyond the intertidal zone in deeper waters live giant seaweeds known as kelps. The stipes of these brown algae may be as long as 60 m—more than half the length of a football field.

Brown algae that inhabit the intertidal zone must cope with water churned by waves and wind, along with low tides that expose the algae to the drying atmosphere and intense rays of the sun. Unique adaptations enable these seaweeds to survive. For example, their cell walls are composed of cellulose and gel-forming polysaccharides that help cushion the thalli from waves and reduce drying when the algae are exposed.

Brown algae are important commodities for humans. Some species are eaten, including *Laminaria* (Japanese "kombu"), which is used in soups. In addition, the gel-forming substance in the cell walls of brown algae, called algin, is used to thicken many processed foods, including pudding, ice cream, and salad dressing.

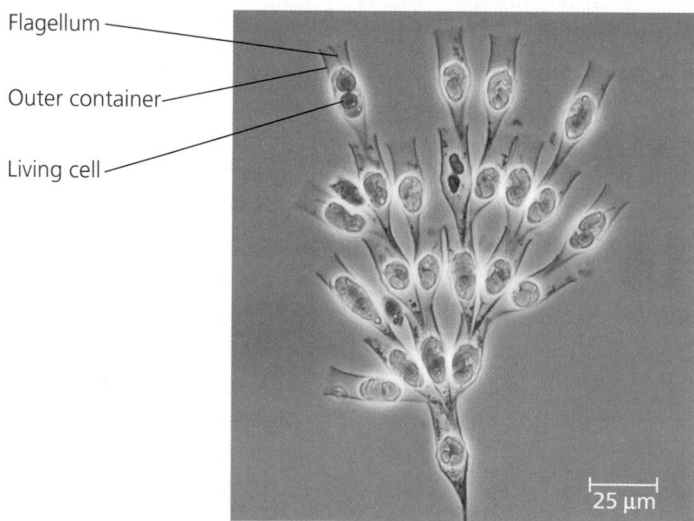

Flagellum

Outer container

Living cell

25 µm

▲ **Figure 28.14** *Dinobryon,* **a colonial golden alga found in fresh water** (LM).

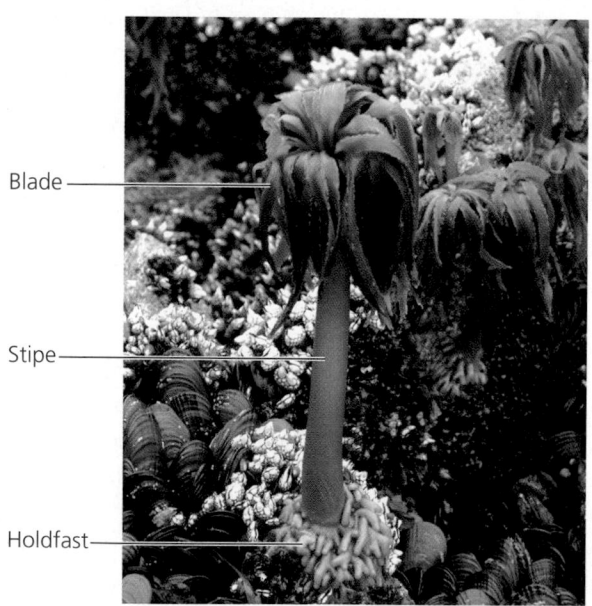

Blade

Stipe

Holdfast

▲ **Figure 28.15 Seaweeds: adapted to life at the ocean's margins.** The sea palm (*Postelsia*) lives on rocks along the coast of the northwestern United States and western Canada. The thallus of this brown alga is well adapted to maintaining a firm foothold despite the crashing surf.

Alternation of Generations

A variety of life cycles have evolved among the multicellular algae. The most complex life cycles include an **alternation of generations**, the alternation of multicellular haploid and diploid forms. Although haploid and diploid conditions alternate in *all* sexual life cycles—human gametes, for example, are haploid—the term *alternation of generations* applies only to life cycles in which both haploid and diploid stages are multicellular. As you will read in Chapter 29, alternation of generations also evolved in plants.

The complex life cycle of the brown alga *Laminaria* provides an example of alternation of generations **(Figure 28.16)**. The diploid individual is called the sporophyte because it produces spores. The spores are haploid and move by means of flagella; the flagellated spores are called *zoospores*. The zoospores develop into haploid male and female gametophytes, which produce gametes. The union of two gametes (fertilization, or syngamy) results in a diploid zygote, which matures and gives rise to a new sporophyte.

In *Laminaria*, the two generations are **heteromorphic**, meaning that the sporophytes and gametophytes are structurally different. Other algal life cycles have an alternation of **isomorphic** generations, in which the sporophytes and gametophytes look similar to each other, although they differ in chromosome number.

1 The sporophytes are usually found in water just below the line of the lowest tides, attached to rocks by branching holdfasts.

Sporangia

2 Cells on the surface of the blade develop into sporangia.

MEIOSIS

3 Sporangia produce zoospores by meiosis.

Sporophyte (2*n*)

Zoospore

4 The zoospores are all structurally alike, but about half of them develop into male gametophytes and half into female gametophytes. The gametophytes are short, branched filaments that grow on subtidal rocks.

Female

7 The zygotes grow into new sporophytes while attached to the remains of the female gametophyte.

Developing sporophyte

Gametophytes (*n*)

Zygote (2*n*)

Male

Mature female gametophyte (*n*)

FERTILIZATION

Egg

Sperm

5 Male gametophytes release sperm, and female gametophytes produce eggs, which remain attached to the female gametophyte. Eggs secrete a chemical signal that attracts sperm of the same species, thereby increasing the probability of fertilization in the ocean.

6 Sperm fertilize the eggs.

Key

→ Haploid (*n*)
→ Diploid (2*n*)

10 cm

▲ Figure 28.16 **The life cycle of the brown alga *Laminaria*: an example of alternation of generations.**

Oomycetes (Water Molds and Their Relatives)

Oomycetes include the water molds, the white rusts, and the downy mildews. Based on their morphology, these organisms were previously classified as fungi (in fact, *oomycete* means "egg fungus"). For example, many oomycetes have multinucleate filaments (hyphae) that resemble fungal hyphae **(Figure 28.17)**. However, there are many differences between oomycetes and fungi. Among the differences, oomycetes typically have cell walls made of cellulose, whereas the walls of fungi consist mainly of another polysaccharide, chitin. Data from molecular systematics have confirmed that oomycetes are not closely related to fungi. Their superficial similarity is a case of convergent evolution. In both oomycetes and fungi, the high surface-to-volume ratio of filamentous structures enhances the uptake of nutrients from the environment.

Although oomycetes descended from plastid-bearing ancestors, they no longer have plastids and do not perform photosynthesis. Instead, they typically acquire nutrients as decomposers or parasites. Most water molds are decomposers that grow as cottony masses on dead algae and animals, mainly in freshwater habitats (see Figure 28.17). White rusts and downy mildews generally live on land as plant parasites.

The ecological impact of oomycetes can be significant. For example, the oomycete *Phytophthora infestans* causes potato late blight, which turns the stalk and stem of potato plants to black slime. Late blight contributed to the devastating Irish famine of the 19th century, in which a million people died and at least that many were forced to leave Ireland. The disease remains a major problem today, causing crop losses of typically 15% in North America and as high as 70% in some parts of Russia where farmers cannot afford pesticides.

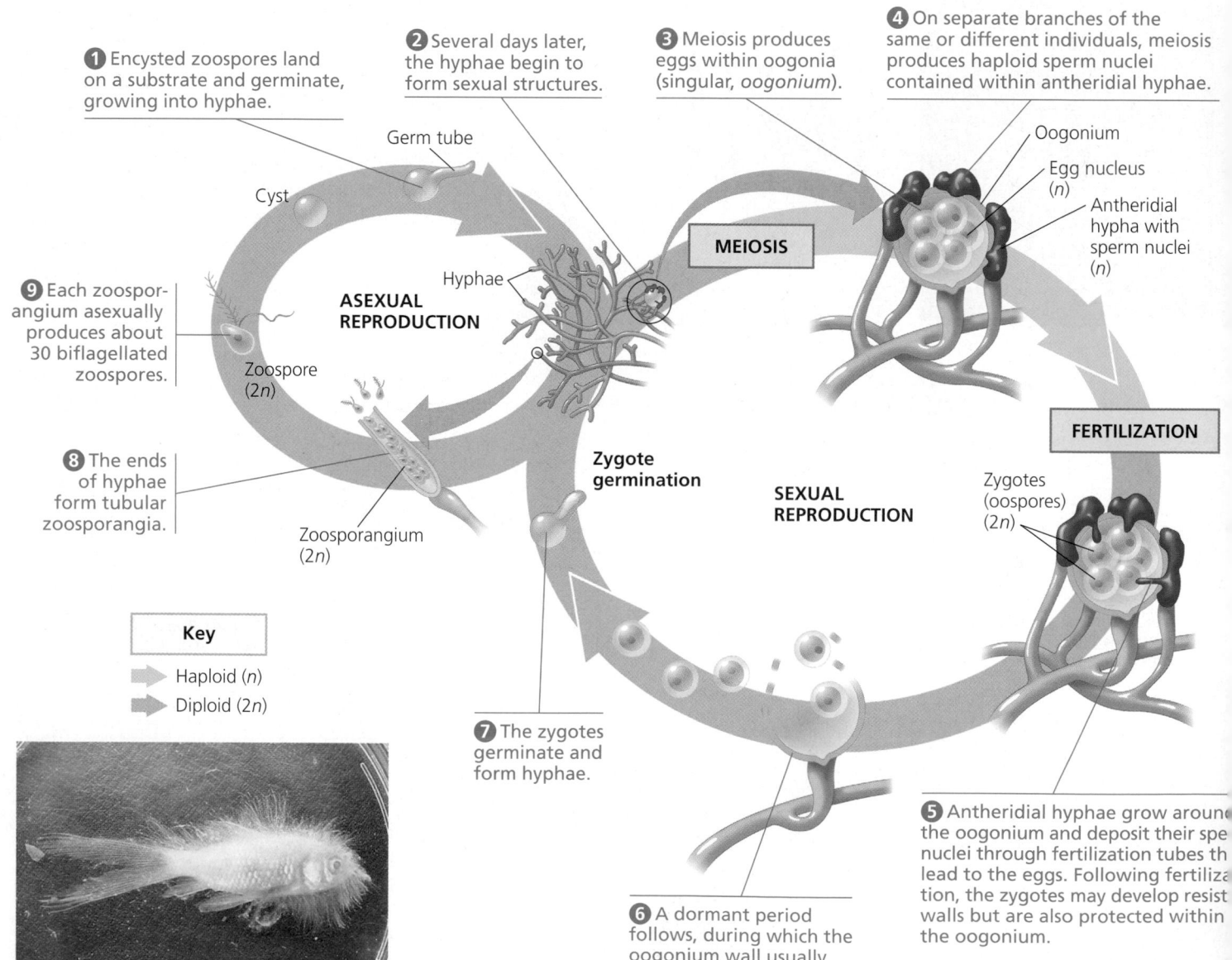

❶ Encysted zoospores land on a substrate and germinate, growing into hyphae.

❷ Several days later, the hyphae begin to form sexual structures.

❸ Meiosis produces eggs within oogonia (singular, *oogonium*).

❹ On separate branches of the same or different individuals, meiosis produces haploid sperm nuclei contained within antheridial hyphae.

Germ tube

Cyst

Oogonium

Egg nucleus (*n*)

Antheridial hypha with sperm nuclei (*n*)

Hyphae

MEIOSIS

ASEXUAL REPRODUCTION

❾ Each zoosporangium asexually produces about 30 biflagellated zoospores.

Zoospore (2*n*)

FERTILIZATION

❽ The ends of hyphae form tubular zoosporangia.

Zoosporangium (2*n*)

Zygote germination

SEXUAL REPRODUCTION

Zygotes (oospores) (2*n*)

Key

→ Haploid (*n*)
→ Diploid (2*n*)

❼ The zygotes germinate and form hyphae.

❺ Antheridial hyphae grow around the oogonium and deposit their sperm nuclei through fertilization tubes that lead to the eggs. Following fertilization, the zygotes may develop resistant walls but are also protected within the oogonium.

❻ A dormant period follows, during which the oogonium wall usually disintegrates.

▲ **Figure 28.17 The life cycle of a water mold.** Water molds help decompose dead insects, fishes, and other animals in fresh water. (Note the hyphal mass growing on the goldfish in the inset.)

To understand this pathogen better, molecular biologists have isolated DNA from a specimen of *P. infestans* preserved from the Irish potato blight of the 1840s. Genetic studies show that in recent decades, the oomycete has acquired genes that make it more aggressive and more resistant to pesticides. Scientists are looking within the genomes of both *Phytophthora* and potatoes to identify new weapons against the disease. In 2003, for example, a team of researchers engineered domestic potatoes that were resistant to late blight by transferring genes from a blight-resistant strain of wild potato.

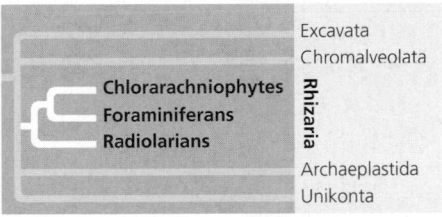

CONCEPT CHECK 28.3

1. Summarize the evidence for and against the hypothesis that the species currently classified as chromalveolates are members of a single clade.
2. Looking back to Chapter 13, which of the three life cycles in Figure 13.6 exhibits alternation of generations? How does it differ from the other two?
3. **WHAT IF?** Would you expect the plastid DNA of photosynthetic dinoflagellates, diatoms, and golden algae to be more similar to the nuclear DNA of plants (domain Eukarya) or to the chromosomal DNA of cyanobacteria (domain Bacteria)? Explain.

For suggested answers, see Appendix A.

CONCEPT 28.4

Rhizarians are a diverse group of protists defined by DNA similarities

Excavata
Chromalveolata

Chlorarachniophytes
Foraminiferans — Rhizaria
Radiolarians

Archaeplastida
Unikonta

The clade **Rhizaria** has recently been proposed based on results from molecular systematics. Although its members vary greatly in morphology, DNA evidence suggests that rhizarians are a monophyletic group.

Many species in Rhizaria are among the organisms referred to as amoebas. **Amoebas** were formerly defined as protists that move and feed by means of **pseudopodia**, extensions that may bulge from almost anywhere on the cell surface. An amoeba moves by extending a pseudopodium and anchoring the tip; more cytoplasm then streams into the pseudopodium. However, based on molecular systematics, it is now clear that amoebas do not constitute a monophyletic group but are dispersed across many distantly related eukaryotic taxa. Most of those that belong to the clade Rhizaria are distinguished morphologically from other amoebas by having threadlike pseudopodia.

Rhizarians include chlorarachniophytes (mentioned earlier in the discussion of secondary endosymbiosis), and two larger groups we'll examine here: forams and radiolarians.

Forams

The protists called **foraminiferans** (from the Latin *foramen*, little hole, and *ferre*, to bear), or **forams**, are named for their porous shells, called **tests** (see Figure 28.3). Foram tests consist of a single piece of organic material hardened with calcium carbonate. The pseudopodia that extend through the pores function in swimming, test formation, and feeding. Many forams also derive nourishment from the photosynthesis of symbiotic algae that live within the tests.

Forams are found in both the ocean and fresh water. Most species live in sand or attach themselves to rocks or algae, but some are abundant in plankton. The largest forams, though single-celled, grow to a diameter of several centimeters.

Ninety percent of all identified species of forams are known from fossils. Along with the calcium-containing remains of other protists, the fossilized tests of forams are part of marine sediments, including sedimentary rocks that are now land formations. Foram fossils are excellent markers for correlating the ages of sedimentary rocks in different parts of the world.

Radiolarians

The protists called **radiolarians** have delicate, intricately symmetrical internal skeletons that are generally made of silica. The pseudopodia of these mostly marine protists radiate from the central body (**Figure 28.18**) and are reinforced by bundles of microtubules. The microtubules are covered by a

Pseudopodia

200 μm

▲ **Figure 28.18 A radiolarian.** Numerous threadlike pseudopodia radiate from the central body of this radiolarian, which is found in the Red Sea (LM).

thin layer of cytoplasm, which engulfs smaller microorganisms that become attached to the pseudopodia. Cytoplasmic streaming then carries the captured prey into the main part of the cell. After radiolarians die, their skeletons settle to the seafloor, where they have accumulated as an ooze that is hundreds of meters thick in some locations.

CONCEPT CHECK 28.4

1. Explain why forams have such a well-preserved fossil record.
2. **WHAT IF?** DNA evidence suggests that a newly discovered amoeba is in the clade Rhizaria—yet its morphology is more similar to amoebas in other eukaryotic groups. Suggest an explanation that could account for these conflicting observations.

For suggested answers, see Appendix A.

CONCEPT 28.5

Red algae and green algae are the closest relatives of land plants

As we described in Chapter 25, molecular systematics and studies of cell structure support the following scenario: More than a billion years ago, a heterotrophic protist acquired a cyanobacterial endosymbiont, and the photosynthetic descendants of this ancient protist evolved into red algae and green algae. At least 475 million years ago, the lineage that produced green algae gave rise to land plants. Together, red algae, green algae, and land plants make up the fourth eukaryotic supergroup, which is called **Archaeplastida**. Archaeplastida is a monophyletic group that descended from the ancient protist that engulfed a cyanobacterium. We will examine land plants in Chapters 29 and 30; here we will look at the diversity of their closest algal relatives, red algae and green algae.

Red Algae

Many of the 6,000 known species of **red algae** (rhodophytes, from the Greek *rhodos*, red) are reddish, owing to a photosynthetic accessory pigment called phycoerythrin, which masks the green of chlorophyll (**Figure 28.19**). However,

species adapted to more shallow water have less phycoerythrin. As a result, red algal species may be greenish red in very shallow water, bright red at moderate depths, and almost black in deep water. Some species lack pigmentation altogether and function heterotrophically as parasites on other red algae.

Red algae are the most abundant large algae in the warm coastal waters of tropical oceans. Their accessory pigments allow them to absorb blue and green light, which penetrate relatively far into the water. A species of red alga has been discovered living

▶ **Bonnemaisonia hamifera.** This red alga has a filamentous form.

20 cm

8 mm

◀ **Dulse (*Palmaria palmata*).** This edible species has a "leafy" form.

▼ **Nori.** The red alga *Porphyra* is the source of a traditional Japanese food.

The seaweed is grown on nets in shallow coastal waters.

The harvested seaweed is spread on bamboo screens to dry.

Paper-thin, glossy sheets of nori make a mineral-rich wrap for rice, seafood, and vegetables in sushi.

▲ **Figure 28.19 Red algae.**

near the Bahamas at a depth of more than 260 m. There are also a small number of freshwater and terrestrial species.

Most red algae are multicellular. Although none are as big as the giant brown kelps, the largest multicellular red algae are included in the informal designation "seaweeds." You may have eaten one of these multicellular red algae, *Porphyra* (Japanese "nori"), as crispy sheets or as a wrap for sushi (see Figure 28.19). The thalli of many red algae are filamentous, often branched and interwoven in lacy patterns. The base of the thallus is usually differentiated as a simple holdfast.

Red algae have especially diverse life cycles, and alternation of generations is common. But unlike other algae, they have no flagellated stages in their life cycle and depend on water currents to bring gametes together for fertilization.

Green Algae

The grass-green chloroplasts of **green algae** have an ultrastructure and pigment composition much like the chloroplasts of land plants. Molecular systematics and cellular morphology leave little doubt that green algae and land plants are closely related. In fact, some systematists now advocate including green algae in an expanded "plant" kingdom, Viridiplantae (from the Latin *viridis*, green). Phylogenetically, this change makes sense, since otherwise the green algae are a paraphyletic group.

Green algae are divided into two main groups, chlorophytes (from the Greek *chloros*, green) and charophytes. More than 7,000 species of chlorophytes have been identified. Most live in fresh water, but there are also many marine and some terrestrial species. The simplest chlorophytes are unicellular organisms such as *Chlamydomonas*, which resemble the gametes and zoospores of more complex chlorophytes. Various species of unicellular chlorophytes exist as plankton or inhabit damp soil. Some live symbiotically within other eukaryotes, contributing part of their photosynthetic output to the food supply of their hosts. Some chlorophytes have even adapted to one of the last habitats you might expect to find them: snow. For example, *Chlamydomonas nivalis* can form dense algal blooms on high-altitude glaciers and snowfields, where its reddish pigments produce an effect known as "watermelon snow" (Figure 28.20). These chlorophytes carry out photosynthesis despite subfreezing temperatures and intense visible and ultraviolet radiation. They are protected by the snow itself, which acts as a shield, and by radiation-blocking compounds in their cytoplasm. Other chlorophytes contain similar protective compounds in their cell wall or in a durable coat that surrounds the zygote.

Larger size and greater complexity evolved in chlorophytes by three different mechanisms:

1. The formation of colonies of individual cells, as seen in *Volvox* (see Figure 28.3) and in filamentous forms that contribute to the stringy masses known as pond scum
2. The formation of true multicellular bodies by cell division and differentiation, as seen in the seaweed *Ulva* (Figure 28.21a)
3. The repeated division of nuclei with no cytoplasmic division, as seen in the multinucleate filaments of *Caulerpa* (Figure 28.21b)

(a) *Ulva*, or sea lettuce. This edible seaweed has a multicellular thallus differentiated into leaflike blades. Its rootlike holdfast anchors the alga against turbulent waves and tides.

2 cm

◀ **Figure 28.20 Watermelon snow.** Carotenoid pigments in some snow-dwelling chlorophytes, such as *Chlamydomonas nivalis*, turn the snow red.

(b) *Caulerpa*, an intertidal chlorophyte. The branched filaments lack crosswalls and thus are multinucleate. In effect, the thallus is one huge "supercell."

▲ **Figure 28.21 Multicellular chlorophytes.**

Most chlorophytes have complex life cycles, with both sexual and asexual reproductive stages. Nearly all species of chlorophytes reproduce sexually by means of biflagellated gametes that have cup-shaped chloroplasts (Figure 28.22). Alternation of generations has evolved in the life cycles of chlorophytes, including *Ulva*, in which the alternate generations are isomorphic.

The other main group of green algae, the charophytes, are the algae most closely related to land plants. For that reason, we will discuss them along with plants in Chapter 29.

CONCEPT CHECK 28.5

1. Identify two ways in which red algae differ from brown algae.
2. Why is it accurate to say that *Ulva* has true multicellularity but *Caulerpa* does not?
3. **WHAT IF?** Suggest a possible reason why species in the green algal lineage were more likely to colonize land than species in the red algal lineage.

For suggested answers, see Appendix A.

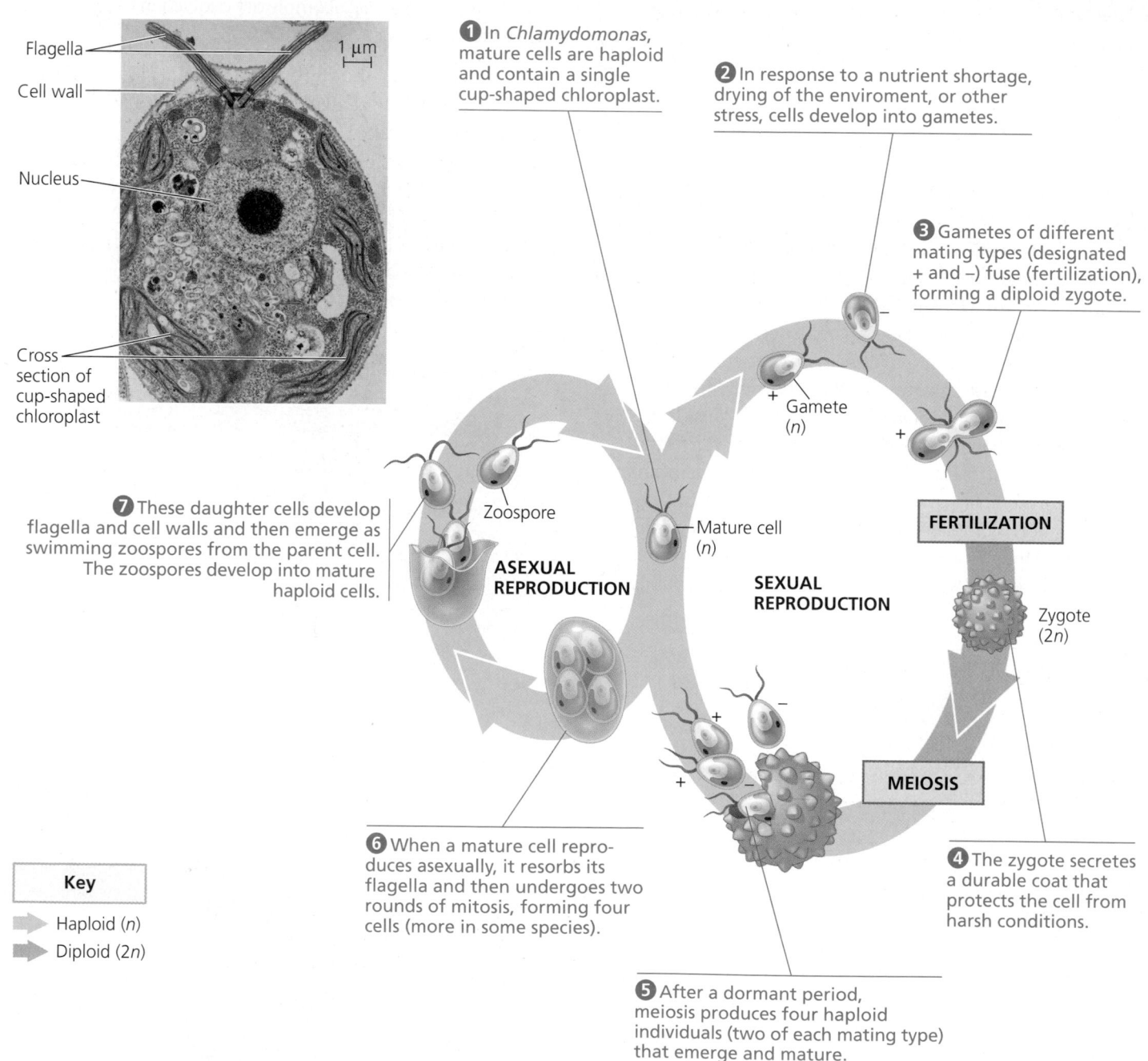

1 In *Chlamydomonas*, mature cells are haploid and contain a single cup-shaped chloroplast.

2 In response to a nutrient shortage, drying of the enviroment, or other stress, cells develop into gametes.

3 Gametes of different mating types (designated + and –) fuse (fertilization), forming a diploid zygote.

7 These daughter cells develop flagella and cell walls and then emerge as swimming zoospores from the parent cell. The zoospores develop into mature haploid cells.

6 When a mature cell reproduces asexually, it resorbs its flagella and then undergoes two rounds of mitosis, forming four cells (more in some species).

4 The zygote secretes a durable coat that protects the cell from harsh conditions.

5 After a dormant period, meiosis produces four haploid individuals (two of each mating type) that emerge and mature.

Flagella

Cell wall

Nucleus

Cross section of cup-shaped chloroplast

1 μm

Zoospore

ASEXUAL REPRODUCTION

SEXUAL REPRODUCTION

Gamete (n)

Mature cell (n)

FERTILIZATION

Zygote (2n)

MEIOSIS

Key

➡ Haploid (n)

➡ Diploid (2n)

▲ Figure 28.22 **The life cycle of *Chlamydomonas*, a unicellular chlorophyte.**
DRAW IT *Circle the stage(s) in the diagram in which clones are formed, producing additional new daughter cells that are genetically identical to the parent cell(s).*

Unikonts include protists that are closely related to fungi and animals

Unikonta is a recently proposed, extremely diverse supergroup of eukaryotes that includes animals, fungi, and some protists. There are two major clades of unikonts, the amoebozoans and the opisthokonts (animals, fungi, and closely related protist groups). Each of these two major clades is strongly supported by molecular systematics. The close relationship between amoebozoans and opisthokonts is more controversial. Support for this close relationship is provided by comparisons of myosin proteins and by several studies based on hundreds of genes, but not by other studies based on single genes.

Another controversy involving the unikonts concerns the root of the eukaryotic tree. Recall that the root of a phylogenetic tree anchors the tree in time: Branch points close to the root are the oldest. At present, the root of the eukaryotic tree is uncertain; thus, we do not know which group of eukaryotes was the first to diverge from other eukaryotes. Some hypotheses, such as the amitochondriate hypothesis described earlier, have been abandoned, but researchers have yet to agree on an alternative. If the root of the eukaryotic tree were known, scientists could infer characteristics of the common ancestor of all eukaryotes—information that would help to resolve some of the current debates about the five supergroups of eukaryotes.

In efforts to root the eukaryotic tree, phylogenics based on different sets of genes have provided conflicting results.

In a 2002 paper, Alexandra Stechmann and Thomas Cavalier-Smith, of Oxford University, described a different approach, results from which supported a radical new hypothesis about the root of the eukaryotic tree (**Figure 28.23**). According to their hypothesis, the unikonts were the first eukaryotes to diverge from other eukaryotes. This hypothesis proposes that animals

▼ Figure 28.23 **Inquiry**

What is the root of the eukaryotic tree?

EXPERIMENT   Responding to the difficulty in determining the root of the eukaryotic phylogenetic tree, Alexandra Stechmann and Thomas Cavalier-Smith, of Oxford University, proposed a new approach. They studied two genes, one for the enzyme dihydrofolate reductase (DHFR), the other for the enzyme thymidylate synthase (TS). Their approach took advantage of a rare evolutionary event: In some organisms, the DHFR and TS genes have fused, leading to the production of a single protein with both enzyme activities. Stechmann and Cavalier-Smith amplified (using PCR; see Figure 20.8) and sequenced DHFR and TS genes in nine species (one choanoflagellate; two amoebozoans; one euglenozoan; two chromalveolates; and three rhizarians). They combined their data with previously published data for species of bacteria, animals, plants, and fungi.

RESULTS   The bacteria studied all have separate DHFR and TS genes, suggesting that this is the ancestral condition (red dot on the tree below). Other taxa with separate genes are denoted by red type. Fused genes are a derived character, found in certain members (blue type) of the supergroups Excavata, Chromalveolata, Rhizaria, and Archaeplastida:

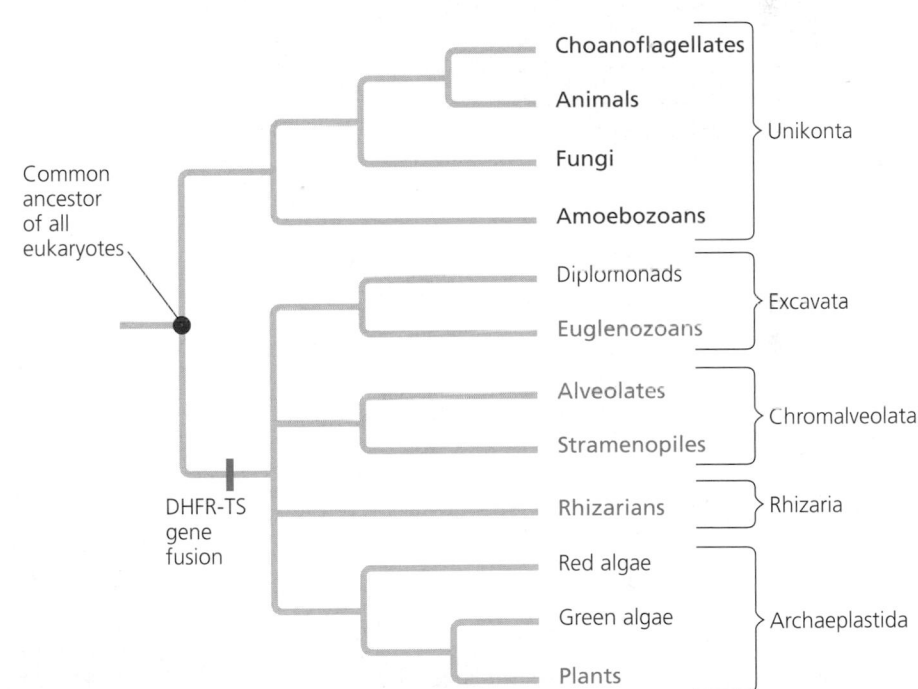

CONCLUSION   These results place the root of the tree between the unikonts and all other eukaryotes, suggesting that the unikonts may have been the first group of eukaryotes to diverge. Because this conclusion is based on only one trait—the fusion of the DHFR and TS genes—more data are needed to evaluate its validity.

SOURCE   A. Stechmann and T. Cavalier-Smith, Rooting the eukaryote tree by using a derived gene fusion, *Science* 297:89–91 (2002).

WHAT IF?   Stechmann and Cavalier-Smith wrote that their conclusions are "valid only if the genes fused just once and were never secondarily split." Why is this assumption critical to their approach?

and fungi belong to an early-diverging group of eukaryotes, while protists that lack typical mitochondria (such as the diplomonads and parabasalids) diverged much later in the history of life. The Stechmann and Cavalier-Smith hypothesis remains controversial and will require more supporting evidence to be widely accepted.

Amoebozoans

As already mentioned, **amoebozoans** form a clade that is well supported by molecular data. This clade includes many species of amoebas that have lobe- or tube-shaped, rather than thread-like, pseudopodia. Amoebozoans include slime molds, gymnamoebas, and entamoebas.

Slime Molds

Slime molds, or mycetozoans (from the Latin meaning "fungus animals"), were once thought to be fungi because, like fungi, they produce fruiting bodies that aid in spore dispersal. However, the resemblance between slime molds and fungi appears to be another example of evolutionary convergence. Molecular systematics places slime molds in Amoebozoa and suggests that they descended from unicellular ancestors. Slime molds have diverged into two main branches, plasmodial slime molds and cellular slime molds, distinguished in part by their unique life cycles.

Plasmodial Slime Molds Many **plasmodial slime molds** are brightly colored, often yellow or orange (**Figure 28.24**).

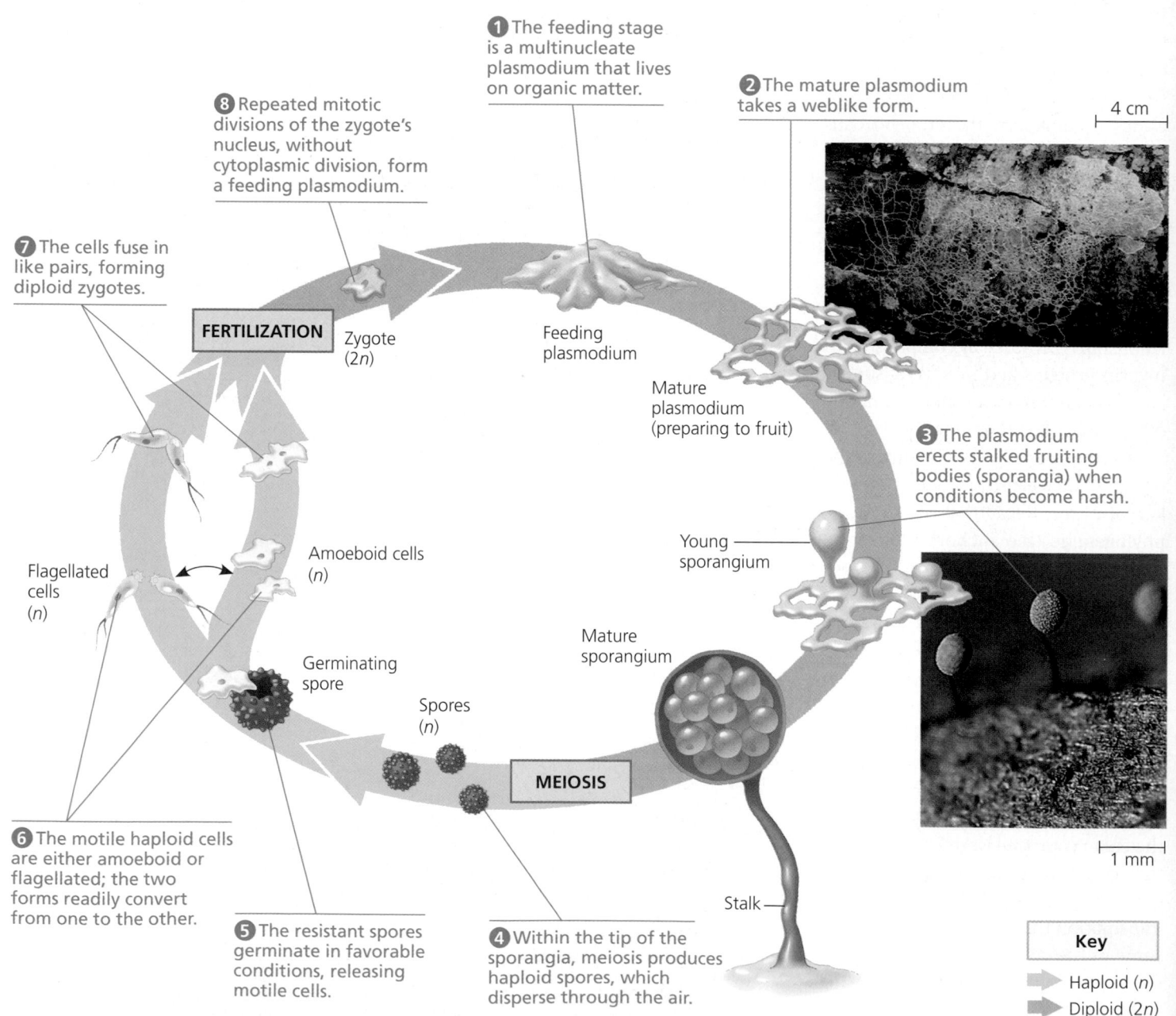

▲ **Figure 28.24 The life cycle of a plasmodial slime mold.** In most plasmodial slime molds, the diploid condition is the predominant part of the life cycle.

At one stage in their life cycle, they form a mass called a **plasmodium**, which may grow to a diameter of many centimeters. (Don't confuse a slime mold's plasmodium with the genus *Plasmodium*, which includes the parasitic apicomplexan that causes malaria.) Despite its size, the plasmodium is not multicellular; it is a single mass of cytoplasm that is undivided by plasma membranes and that contains many diploid nuclei. This "supercell" is the product of mitotic nuclear divisions that are not followed by cytokinesis.

Within the plasmodium, cytoplasm streams first one way, then the other, in pulsing flows that are beautiful to watch through a microscope. This cytoplasmic streaming apparently helps distribute nutrients and oxygen. The plasmodium extends pseudopodia through moist soil, leaf mulch, or rotting logs, engulfing food particles by phagocytosis as it grows. If the habitat begins to dry up or there is no food left, the plasmodium stops growing and differentiates into fruiting bodies, which function in sexual reproduction.

Cellular Slime Molds The life cycle of the protists called **cellular slime molds** can prompt us to question what it means to be an individual organism. The feeding stage of these organisms consists of solitary cells that function individually, but when food is depleted, the cells form an aggregate that functions as a unit **(Figure 28.25)**. Although this mass of cells superficially resembles a plasmodial slime mold, the cells remain separated by their individual plasma membranes. Cellular slime molds also differ from plasmodial slime molds in

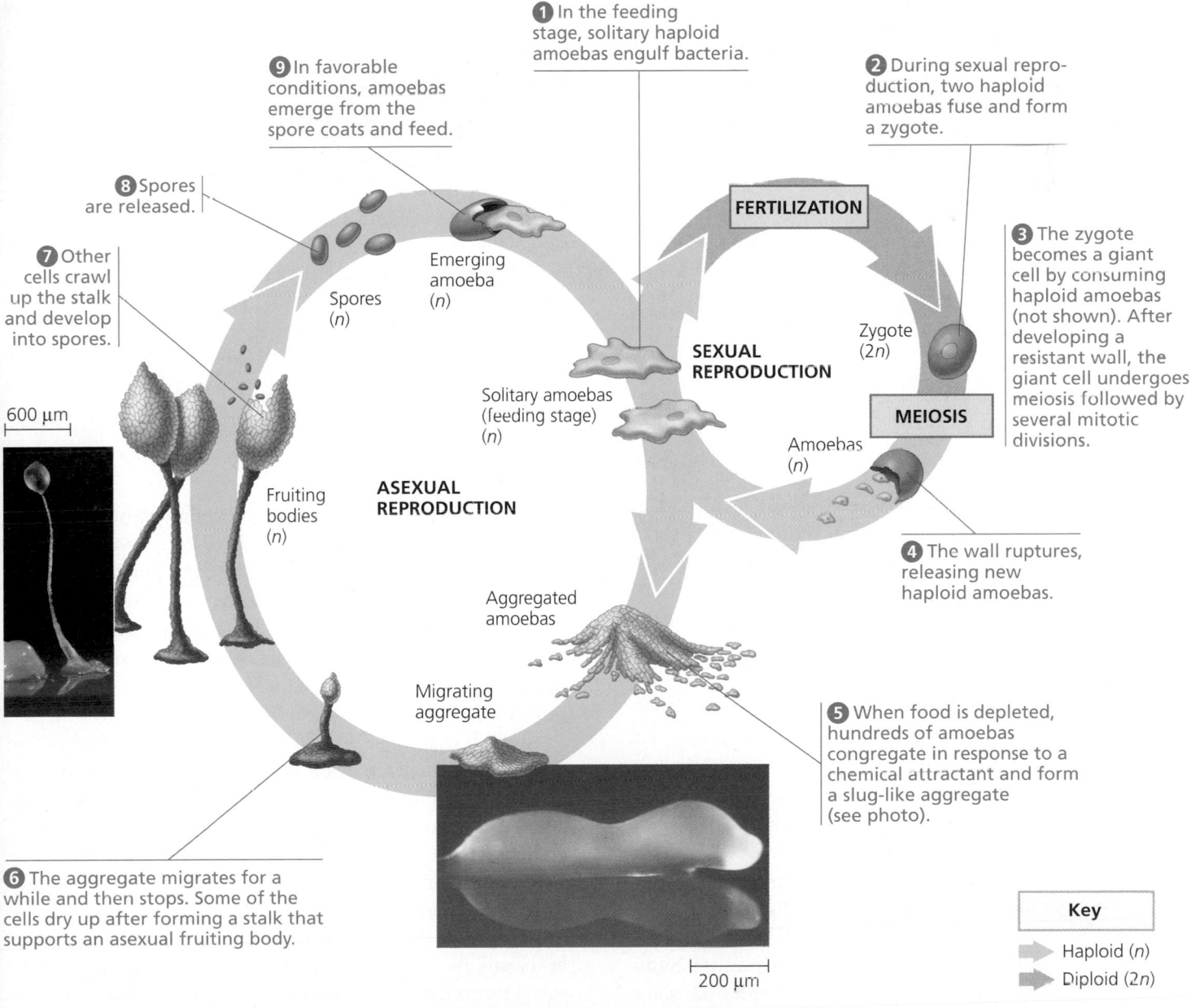

1 In the feeding stage, solitary haploid amoebas engulf bacteria.

2 During sexual reproduction, two haploid amoebas fuse and form a zygote.

9 In favorable conditions, amoebas emerge from the spore coats and feed.

8 Spores are released.

7 Other cells crawl up the stalk and develop into spores.

FERTILIZATION

3 The zygote becomes a giant cell by consuming haploid amoebas (not shown). After developing a resistant wall, the giant cell undergoes meiosis followed by several mitotic divisions.

Emerging amoeba (*n*)

Spores (*n*)

Zygote (2*n*)

SEXUAL REPRODUCTION

Solitary amoebas (feeding stage) (*n*)

MEIOSIS

Amoebas (*n*)

600 μm

Fruiting bodies (*n*)

ASEXUAL REPRODUCTION

4 The wall ruptures, releasing new haploid amoebas.

Aggregated amoebas

Migrating aggregate

5 When food is depleted, hundreds of amoebas congregate in response to a chemical attractant and form a slug-like aggregate (see photo).

6 The aggregate migrates for a while and then stops. Some of the cells dry up after forming a stalk that supports an asexual fruiting body.

Key

Haploid (*n*)

Diploid (2*n*)

200 μm

▲ **Figure 28.25 The life cycle of *Dictyostelium*, a cellular slime mold.** Cellular slime molds differ from plasmodial slime molds in being haploid organisms (only the zygote is diploid).

being haploid organisms (only the zygote is diploid) and in having fruiting bodies that function in asexual rather than sexual reproduction.

Dictyostelium discoideum, a cellular slime mold commonly found on forest floors, has become a model organism for studying the evolution of multicellularity. One line of research has focused on the slime mold's fruiting body stage. During this stage, the cells that form the stalk die as they dry out, while the spore cells at the top survive and have the potential to reproduce. Scientists have found that mutations to a single gene can turn individual *Dictyostelium* cells into "cheaters" that never become part of the stalk. Because these mutants gain a strong reproductive advantage over noncheaters, why don't all *Dictyostelium* cells cheat?

In 2003, scientists at Rice University and the University of Turin, Italy, discovered an answer to this question. Cheating mutants lack a protein on their cell surface, and noncheating cells can recognize this difference. Noncheaters preferentially aggregate with other noncheaters, thus depriving cheaters of the opportunity to exploit them. Such a recognition system may have been important in the evolution of multicellular eukaryotes such as animals and plants.

Gymnamoebas

Gymnamoebas constitute a large and varied group of amoebozoans. These unicellular protists are ubiquitous in soil as well as freshwater and marine environments. Most are heterotrophs that actively seek and consume bacteria and other protists (see Figure 28.3). Some gymnamoebas also feed on detritus (nonliving organic matter).

Entamoebas

Whereas most amoebozoans are free-living, those that belong to the genus *Entamoeba* are parasites. They infect all classes of vertebrates as well as some invertebrates. Humans are host to at least six species of *Entamoeba*, but only one, *E. histolytica*, is known to be pathogenic. *E. histolytica* causes amebic dysentery and is spread via contaminated drinking water, food, or eating utensils. Responsible for up to 100,000 deaths worldwide every year, the disease is the third-leading cause of death due to eukaryotic parasites, after malaria (see Figure 28.10) and schistosomiasis (see Figure 33.11).

Opisthokonts

Opisthokonts are an extremely diverse group of eukaryotes that includes animals, fungi, and several groups of protists. We will discuss the evolutionary history of fungi and animals in Chapters 31–34. Of the opisthokont protists, we will discuss the nucleariids in Chapter 31 because they are more closely related to fungi than they are to other protists. Similarly, we will discuss choanoflagellates in Chapter 32, since they are more closely related to animals than they are to other

protists. The nucleariids and choanoflagellates illustrate why scientists have abandoned the former kingdom Protista: A monophyletic group that included these single-celled eukaryotes would also have to include the multicellular animals and fungi that are closely related to them.

CONCEPT **28.7**

Protists play key roles in ecological relationships

Most protists are aquatic, and they are found almost anywhere there is water, including moist terrestrial habitats such as damp soil and leaf litter. In oceans, ponds, and lakes, many protists are bottom-dwellers that attach to rocks and other substrates or creep through the sand and silt. Other protists are important constituents of plankton. We'll focus here on two key roles that protists play in the varied habitats in which they live: that of symbiont and that of producer.

Symbiotic Protists

Many protists form symbiotic associations with other species. For example, photosynthetic dinoflagellates provide nourishment to their symbiotic partners, the coral polyps that build coral reefs. Coral reefs are highly diverse ecological communities. That diversity ultimately depends on corals—and on the mutualistic protist symbionts that provide corals with an essential source of energy. Corals support reef diversity by providing food to some species and habitat to many others.

Another example is termites, which cause over $3.5 billion in damage annually to wood homes in the United States. Unaided, the termites cannot digest wood. It is only the large populations of wood-digesting protists inhabiting these termites' gut that enable them to break down wood **(Figure 28.26)**.

Symbiotic protists also include parasites that have compromised the economies of entire countries. Consider the malaria-causing protist *Plasmodium*: Income levels in countries hard hit by malaria are 33% lower than in similar countries free of the disease. Protists can have similar devastating effects in natural communities. Massive fish kills have been attributed to *Pfiesteria*

◀ Figure 28.26 **A protist symbiont.** This organism is a hypermastigote, a member of a group of parabasalids that live in the gut of termites and certain cockroaches and enable the hosts to digest wood (SEM).

10 μm

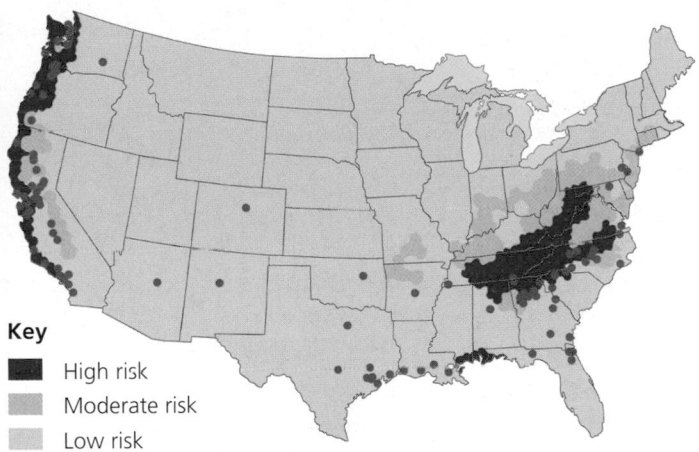

Key

■ High risk

■ Moderate risk

□ Low risk

•᛫• Nurseries with *P. ramorum* infections (2004) on other host plants (such as rhododendron).

▲ **Figure 28.27 Risk map for sudden oak death in the contiguous United States.** Sudden oak death (SOD) is caused by the parasitic oomycete *Phytophthora ramorum*. Since 1995, this disease has spread in the wild, killing more than 1 million trees in coastal California and southern Oregon.

shumwayae, a dinoflagellate parasite (see Figure 28.9) that attaches to its victims and eats their skin. Among species that parasitize plants, the oomycete protist *Phytophthora ramorum* has emerged as a major new forest pathogen. This species causes sudden oak death (SOD), a disease that affects oaks and other trees **(Figure 28.27)**.

Photosynthetic Protists

Many protists are important **producers**, organisms that use energy from light (or inorganic chemicals) to convert carbon dioxide to organic compounds. Producers form the base of ecological food webs. In aquatic communities, the main producers are photosynthetic protists and prokaryotes. All other organisms in the community depend on them for food, either directly (by eating them) or indirectly (for example, by eating an organism that ate a producer) **(Figure 28.28)**. Scientists estimate that up to one-quarter

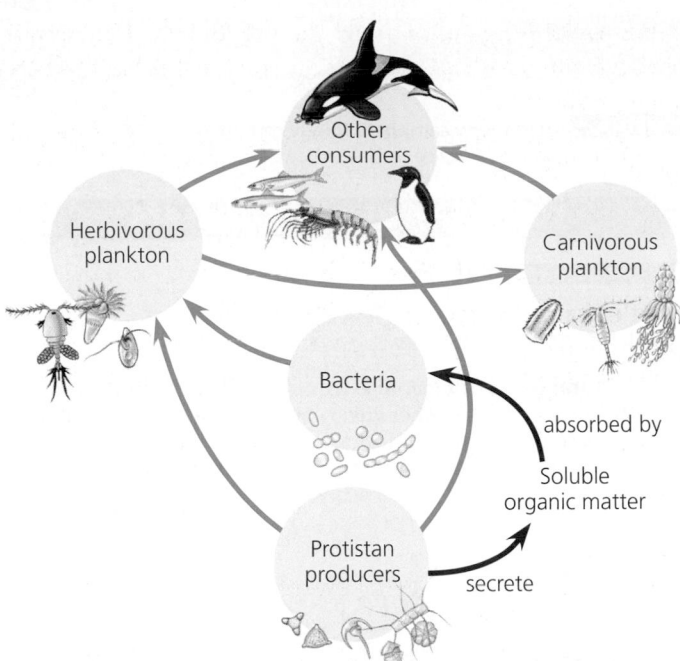

▲ **Figure 28.28 Protists are key producers in aquatic communities.** This simplified food web illustrates how organisms in an aquatic community depend directly or indirectly on photosynthetic protists for food. Blue arrows lead from food sources to the organisms that eat them.

of the world's photosynthesis is performed by diatoms, dinoflagellates, multicellular algae, and other protists.

Because producers form the foundation of food webs, factors that affect producers can dramatically affect their entire community. In aquatic environments, photosynthetic protists are often held in check by low concentrations of nitrogen, phosphorus, or iron. Various human actions can increase the concentrations of these elements in aquatic communities. For example, when fertilizer is applied to a field, some of the fertilizer may be washed by rainfall into a river that drains into a lake or ocean. When people add nutrients to aquatic communities in this or other ways, the abundance of photosynthetic protists can increase spectacularly. Such increases can alter the abundance of other species in the community, as we'll see in Chapter 55. Similar effects can occur on land, but there the base of food webs is occupied not by protists but by land plants, which we will discuss in Chapters 29 and 30.

MEDIA Go to **www.campbellbiology.com** for BioFlix 3-D Animations, MP3 Tutors, Videos, Practice Tests, an eBook, and more.

SUMMARY OF KEY CONCEPTS

CONCEPT 28.1

Most eukaryotes are single-celled organisms (pp. 575–579)

▶ **Structural and Functional Diversity in Protists** Protists are more diverse than all other eukaryotes and are no longer classified in a single kingdom. Most are unicellular. Protists include photoautotrophs, heterotrophs, and mixotrophs. Some species are exclusively asexual; others can reproduce sexually.

▶ **Endosymbiosis in Eukaryotic Evolution** Mitochondria and plastids are thought to be descendants of bacteria that were engulfed by other cells and became endosymbionts. The plastid-bearing lineage eventually evolved into red algae and green algae. Other protist groups evolved from secondary endosymbiosis events in which red algae or green algae were themselves engulfed.

▶ **Five Supergroups of Eukaryotes** In one hypothesis, eukaryotes are grouped into five monophyletic clades: Excavata, Chromalveolata, Rhizaria, Archaeplastida, and Unikonta.

MEDIA

Activity Tentative Phylogeny of Eukaryotes

Key Concept/Eukaryote Supergroup	Major Clades	Key Morphological Characteristics	Specific Examples
Concept 28.2 Excavates include protists with modified mitochondria and protists with unique flagella (pp. 580–581)	**Diplomonads and parabasalids**	Modified mitochondria	*Giardia, Trichomonas*
	Euglenozoans Kinetoplastids Euglenids	Spiral or crystalline rod inside flagella	*Trypanosoma, Euglena*
Concept 28.3 Chromalveolates may have originated by secondary endosymbiosis (pp. 582–589)	**Alveolates** Dinoflagellates Apicomplexans Ciliates	Membrane-bounded sacs (alveoli) beneath plasma membrane	*Pfiesteria, Plasmodium, Paramecium*
	Stramenopiles Diatoms Golden algae Brown algae Oomycetes	Hairy and smooth flagella	*Phytophthora, Laminaria*
Concept 28.4 Rhizarians are a diverse group of protists defined by DNA similarities (pp. 589–590)	**Forams**	Amoebas with threadlike pseudopodia and a porous shell	*Globigerina*
	Radiolarians	Amoebas with threadlike pseudopodia radiating from central body	
Concept 28.5 Red algae and green algae are the closest relatives of land plants (pp. 590–592—Archaeplastida)	**Red algae**	Phycoerythrin (accessory pigment)	*Porphyra*
	Green algae	Plant-type chloroplasts	*Chlamydomonas, Ulva*
	Land plants	(See Chapters 29 and 30.)	Mosses, ferns, conifers, flowering plants
Concept 28.6 Unikonts include protists that are closely related to fungi and animals (pp. 593–596)	**Amoebozoans** Slime molds Gymnamoebas Entamoebas	Amoebas with lobe-shaped pseudopodia	*Amoeba, Entamoeba, Dictyostelium*
	Opisthokonts	(Highly variable; see Chapters 31–34.)	Nucleariids, choanoflagellates, animals, fungi

Protists play key roles in ecological relationships (pp. 596–597)

▶ **Symbiotic Protists** Protists form a wide range of mutualistic and parasitic relationships that affect their symbiotic partners and many other members of the community.

▶ **Photosynthetic Protists** Photosynthetic protists are among the most important producers in aquatic communities. Because they are at the base of the food web, factors that affect photosynthetic protists affect many other species in the community.

MEDIA

Investigation What Kinds of Protists Do Various Habitats Support?

TESTING YOUR KNOWLEDGE

SELF-QUIZ

1. Plastids that are surrounded by more than two membranes are evidence of
   a. evolution from mitochondria.
   b. fusion of plastids.
   c. origin of the plastids from archaea.
   d. secondary endosymbiosis.
   e. budding of the plastids from the nuclear envelope.

2. Biologists suspect that endosymbiosis gave rise to mitochondria before plastids partly because
   a. the products of photosynthesis could not be metabolized without mitochondrial enzymes.
   b. all eukaryotes have mitochondria (or their remnants), whereas many eukaryotes do not have plastids.
   c. mitochondrial DNA is less similar to prokaryotic DNA than is plastid DNA.
   d. without mitochondrial CO_2 production, photosynthesis could not occur.
   e. mitochondrial proteins are synthesized on cytosolic ribosomes, whereas plastids utilize their own ribosomes.

3. Which group is *incorrectly* paired with its description?
   a. rhizarians—morphologically diverse group defined by DNA similarities
   b. diatoms—important producers in aquatic communities
   c. red algae—acquired plastids by secondary endosymbiosis
   d. apicomplexans—parasites with intricate life cycles
   e. diplomonads—protists with modified mitochondria

4. Based on the phylogenetic tree in Figure 28.3, which of the following statements is correct?
   a. The most recent common ancestor of Excavata is older than that of Chromalveolata.
   b. The most recent common ancestor of Chromalveolata is older than that of Rhizaria.
   c. The most recent common ancestor of red algae and land plants is older than that of nucleariids and fungi.
   d. The most basal (first to diverge) eukaryotic supergroup cannot be determined.
   e. Excavata is the most basal eukaryotic supergroup.

5. Which protists are in the same eukaryotic supergroup as land plants?
   a. green algae
   b. dinoflagellates
   c. red algae
   d. brown algae
   e. both a and c

6. In life cycles with an alternation of generations, multicellular haploid forms alternate with
   a. unicellular haploid forms.
   b. unicellular diploid forms.
   c. multicellular haploid forms.
   d. multicellular diploid forms.
   e. multicellular polyploid forms.

For Self-Quiz answers, see Appendix A.

MEDIA Visit **www.campbellbiology.com** for a Practice Test.

EVOLUTION CONNECTION

7. **DRAW IT** Medical researchers seek to develop drugs that can kill or restrict the growth of human pathogens yet have few harmful effects on patients. These drugs often work by disrupting the metabolism of the pathogen or by targeting its structural features.

   Draw and label a phylogenetic tree that includes an ancestral prokaryote and the following groups of organisms: Excavata, Chromalveolata, Rhizaria, Archaeplastida, and, within Unikonta, amoebozoans, animals, choanoflagellates, fungi, and nucleariids. Based on this tree, hypothesize whether it would be most difficult to develop drugs to combat human pathogens that are prokaryotes, protists, animals, or fungi. (You do not need to consider the evolution of drug resistance by the pathogen.)

SCIENTIFIC INQUIRY

8. Applying the "If . . . then" logic of science (see Chapter 1), what are a few of the predictions that arise from the hypothesis that plants evolved from green algae? Put another way, how could you test this hypothesis?

SCIENCE, TECHNOLOGY, AND SOCIETY

9. The ability of the pathogen *Plasmodium* to evade the human immune system is one reason developing a malaria vaccine is so difficult. Another reason is that less money is spent on malaria research than on research into diseases that affect far fewer people, such as cystic fibrosis. What are possible reasons for this imbalance in research effort?

Plant Diversity I: How Plants Colonized Land

▲ Figure 29.1 **How did plants change the world?**

OVERVIEW

The Greening of Earth

Looking at a lush landscape, such as the forest scene in **Figure 29.1**, it is difficult to imagine the terrestrial environment without any plants or other organisms. Yet for more than 3 billion years of Earth's history, the land surface was largely lifeless. Geochemical evidence suggests that thin coatings of cyanobacteria existed on land about 1.2 billion years ago. But it was only within the last 500 million years that small plants as well as fungi and animals joined them ashore. Finally, by about 370 million years ago, some plants appeared that could grow much taller, leading to the formation of the first forests (though with a very different set of species than those in Figure 29.1).

Since colonizing land, plants have diversified widely; today, there are more than 290,000 known plant species. Plants inhabit all but the harshest environments—some mountaintops, a few desert areas, and the polar regions. A few plant species, such as sea grasses, returned to aquatic habitats during their evolution, but most present-day plants live in terrestrial environments. Therefore, in this chapter we will refer to all plants as *land* plants, even those that are now aquatic, to distinguish them from algae, which are photosynthetic protists.

The presence of land plants has enabled other life-forms—including animals—to survive on land. Plant roots have created habitats for other organisms by stabilizing landscapes. Plants also supply oxygen and are the ultimate provider of most of the food eaten by terrestrial animals.

This chapter traces the first 100 million years of plant evolution, including the emergence of seedless plants such as mosses and ferns. Chapter 30 examines the later evolution of seed plants.

CONCEPT 29.1
Land plants evolved from green algae

As you read in Chapter 28, researchers have identified green algae called charophytes as the closest relatives of land plants. What is the evidence for this relationship, and what does it suggest about the algal ancestors of land plants?

Morphological and Molecular Evidence

Many key characteristics of land plants also appear in a variety of protists, primarily algae. For example, plants are multicellular, eukaryotic, photosynthetic autotrophs, as are brown, red, and certain green algae (see Chapter 28). Plants have cell walls made of cellulose, and so do green algae, dinoflagellates, and brown algae. And chloroplasts with chlorophylls *a* and *b* are present in green algae, euglenids, and a few dinoflagellates, as well as in plants.

However, the charophytes are the only algae that share the following four distinctive traits with land plants, strongly suggesting that they are the closest relatives of plants:

▶ **Rosette-shaped cellulose-synthesizing complexes.** The cells of both land plants and charophytes have circular, petal-shaped arrays of proteins in the plasma membrane **(Figure 29.2)**. These protein arrays synthesize the cellulose microfibrils of the cell wall. In contrast, noncharophyte algae have linear arrays of proteins that synthesize cellulose.

▶ **Peroxisome enzymes.** The peroxisomes (see Figure 6.19) of both land plants and charophytes contain enzymes that help minimize the loss of organic products as a result of

► **Figure 29.2 Rosette cellulose-synthesizing complexes.** These rings of proteins embedded in the plasma membrane are found only in land plants and charophyte algae (SEM).

30 nm

photorespiration (see Chapter 10). The peroxisomes of other algae lack these enzymes.

► **Structure of flagellated sperm.** In species of land plants that have flagellated sperm, the structure of the sperm closely resembles that of charophyte sperm.

► **Formation of a phragmoplast.** Particular details of cell division occur only in land plants and certain charophytes, including the genera *Chara* and *Coleochaete*. For example, in these organisms a group of microtubules known as the **phragmoplast** forms between the daughter nuclei of a dividing cell. A cell plate then develops in the middle of the phragmoplast, across the midline of the dividing cell (see Figure 12.10). The cell plate, in turn, gives rise to a new cross wall that separates the daughter cells.

Genetic evidence also supports the conclusion drawn from these four morphological and biochemical traits. Analyses of nuclear and chloroplast genes from a wide range of plants and algae indicate that charophytes—particularly *Chara* and *Coleochaete*—are the closest living relatives of land plants **(Figure 29.3)**. Note that this does not mean that plants are descended from these living algae; however, present-day charophytes may tell us something about what the algal ancestors of plants were like.

Adaptations Enabling the Move to Land

Many species of charophyte algae inhabit shallow waters around the edges of ponds and lakes, where they are subject to occasional drying. In such environments, natural selection favors individual algae that can survive periods when they are not submerged in water. In charophytes, a layer of a durable polymer called **sporopollenin** prevents exposed zygotes from drying out. A similar chemical adaptation is found in the tough sporopollenin walls that encase the spores of plants.

The accumulation of such traits by at least one population of charophyte ancestors probably enabled their descendants—the first land plants—to live permanently above the waterline. These evolutionary novelties opened a new frontier: a terrestrial habitat that offered enormous benefits. The bright sunlight was unfiltered by water and plankton; the atmosphere offered more plentiful carbon dioxide than did water; the soil was rich in mineral nutrients; and initially there were relatively few herbivores and pathogens. But these benefits were accompanied by challenges: a relative scarcity of water and a lack of structural support against gravity. (To appreciate why such support is important,

◄ *Chara* species, a pond organism

▼ *Coleochaete orbicularis*, a disk-shaped charophyte that also lives in ponds (LM)

5 mm

40 μm

▲ **Figure 29.3 Examples of charophytes, the closest algal relatives of land plants.**

picture how the soft body of a jellyfish sags when it is taken out of water.) Land plants diversified as adaptations evolved that enabled plants to thrive despite these challenges.

Today, what adaptations are unique to plants? The answer to this question depends on where you draw the boundary dividing land plants from algae **(Figure 29.4)**. Many biologists equate the kingdom Plantae with embryophytes (plants with embryos). Others propose that the boundaries of the plant kingdom should be expanded to include some or all of the green algae (kingdoms Streptophyta and Viridiplantae). Since the debate is ongoing, this text retains the embryophyte definition of the plant kingdom and uses Plantae as the formal name for the taxon. In this context, let's now identify the derived traits that separate land plants from their closest algal relatives.

Derived Traits of Plants

Many of the adaptations that appear to have emerged after land plants diverged from their algal relatives facilitated survival and reproduction on dry land. **Figure 29.5**, on the next two pages, depicts four key traits that appear in nearly all land plants but not in the charophyte algae. These four traits of land plants

ANCESTRAL ALGA

Red algae

Chlorophytes

Charophytes

Embryophytes

Viridiplantae

Streptophyta

Plantae

▲ **Figure 29.4 Three possible "plant" kingdoms.**

Exploring Derived Traits of Land Plants

Alternation of Generations and Multicellular, Dependent Embryos

The life cycles of all land plants alternate between two generations of multicellular organisms: gametophytes and sporophytes. As shown in the diagram, each generation gives rise to the other, a process called **alternation of generations**. This type of reproductive cycle evolved in various groups of algae but does not occur in the charophytes, the algae most closely related to land plants.

Take care not to confuse the alternation of generations in plants with the haploid and diploid stages in the life cycles of other sexually reproducing organisms (see Figure 13.6). In humans, for example, meiosis produces haploid gametes that unite, forming diploid zygotes that divide and become multicellular. The haploid stage is represented only by single-celled gametes. In contrast, alternation of generations is distinguished by the fact that the life cycle includes both multicellular haploid organisms and multicellular diploid organisms. The names of the two multicellular generations of the plant life cycle refer to the reproductive cells they produce. The haploid **gametophyte** ("gamete-producing plant") is named for its production by mitosis of haploid gametes—eggs and sperm—that fuse during fertilization, forming diploid zygotes. Mitotic division of the zygote produces a multicellular diploid **sporophyte** ("spore-producing plant"). Meiosis in a mature sporophyte produces haploid **spores**, reproductive cells that can develop into a new haploid organism without fusing with another cell. Mitotic division of the spore cell produces a new multicellular gametophyte, and the cycle begins again. In many seedless plants, such as the fern in the diagram, the gametophyte and sporophyte look like different types of plants, even though they are forms of the same species. In seed plants, the gametophytes are microscopic; the familiar plants we see are the sporophytes.

① The gametophyte produces haploid gametes by mitosis.

Gametophyte (*n*)

Gamete from another plant

⑤ The spores develop into multicellular haploid gametophytes.

Mitosis

Mitosis

n

n — Spore

Gamete

n

② Two gametes unite (fertilization) and form a diploid zygote.

MEIOSIS

FERTILIZATION

④ The sporophyte produces haploid spores by meiosis.

2*n* — Zygote

Mitosis

③ The zygote develops into a multicellular diploid sporophyte.

Sporophyte (2*n*)

Alternation of generations: five generalized steps

As part of a life cycle with alternation of generations, multicellular plant embryos develop from zygotes that are retained within tissues of the female parent (a gametophyte). The parental tissues provide the developing embryo with nutrients, such as sugars and amino acids. The embryo has specialized **placental transfer cells**, sometimes present in the adjacent maternal tissue as well, which enhance the transfer of nutrients from parent to embryo through elaborate ingrowths of the wall surface (plasma membrane and cell wall). This interface is analogous to the nutrient-transferring embryo-mother interface of eutherian (placental) mammals. The multicellular, dependent embryo of land plants is such a significant derived trait that land plants are also known as **embryophytes**.

2 μm

Embryo
Maternal tissue

Wall ingrowths
10 μm
Placental transfer cell (outlined in blue)

Embryo (LM) and placental transfer cell (TEM) of *Marchantia* (a liverwort)

Walled Spores Produced in Sporangia

Plant spores are haploid reproductive cells that can grow into multicellular haploid gametophytes by mitosis. The polymer sporopollenin makes the walls of plant spores tough and resistant to harsh environments. This chemical adaptation enables spores to be dispersed through dry air without harm.

The sporophyte has multicellular organs called **sporangia** (singular, *sporangium*) that produce the spores. Within a sporangium, diploid cells called **sporocytes**, or spore mother cells, undergo meiosis and generate the haploid spores. The outer tissues of the sporangium protect the developing spores until they are released into the air. Multicellular sporangia that produce spores with sporopollenin-enriched walls are key terrestrial adaptations of land plants. Although charophytes also produce spores, these algae lack multicellular sporangia, and their flagellated, water-dispersed spores lack sporopollenin.

Spores
Sporangium

Longitudinal section of *Sphagnum* sporangium (LM)

Sporophyte

Gametophyte

Sporophytes and sporangia of *Sphagnum* (a moss)

Multicellular Gametangia

Female gametophyte

Archegonium with egg

Antheridium with sperm

Male gametophyte

Archegonia and antheridia of *Marchantia* (a liverwort)

Another feature distinguishing early land plants from their algal ancestors was the production of gametes within multicellular organs called **gametangia**. The female gametangia are called **archegonia** (singular, *archegonium*). Each archegonium is a pear-shaped organ that produces a single nonmotile egg retained within the bulbous part of the organ (the top for the species shown here). Male gametangia, called **antheridia** (singular, *antheridium*), produce sperm and release them into the environment. In many groups of present-day plants, the sperm have flagella and swim to the eggs through water droplets or a film of water. Each egg is fertilized within an archegonium, where the zygote develops into an embryo. As you will see in Chapter 30, the gametophytes of seed plants are so reduced in size that the archegonia and antheridia have been lost in some lineages.

Apical Meristems

In terrestrial habitats, a photosynthetic organism finds essential resources in two very different places. Light and CO_2 are mainly available above ground; water and mineral nutrients are found mainly in the soil. Though plants cannot move from place to place, their roots and shoots can elongate, increasing exposure to environmental resources. This growth in length is sustained throughout the plant's life by the activity of **apical meristems**, localized regions of cell division at the tips of shoots and roots. Cells produced by apical meristems differentiate into the outer epidermis, which protects the body, and various types of internal tissues. Shoot apical meristems also generate leaves in most plants. Thus, the complex bodies of plants have specialized below- and aboveground organs.

Apical meristem of shoot

Developing leaves

Apical meristems of plant shoots and roots. The LMs are longitudinal sections at the tips of a shoot and root.

Shoot
100 μm

Apical meristem of root

Root
100 μm

are alternation of generations (along with an associated trait—multicellular, dependent embryos); walled spores produced in sporangia; multicellular gametangia; and apical meristems. We can infer that these traits were absent in the ancestor common to land plants and charophytes but instead evolved as derived traits of land plants. Note that some of these traits are not unique to plants, having evolved independently in other lineages. And not every land plant exhibits all four of these traits; certain lineages of plants have lost some traits over time.

In addition to the four traits shown in Figure 29.5, other derived traits that relate to terrestrial life have evolved in many plant species. For example, the epidermis in many species has a covering, the **cuticle**, which consists of polyester and wax polymers. Permanently exposed to the air, land plants run a far greater risk of desiccation (drying out) than their algal ancestors. The cuticle acts as waterproofing, helping prevent excessive water loss from the above-ground plant organs, while also providing some protection from microbial attack.

Early land plants lacked true roots and leaves. Without roots, how did these plants absorb nutrients from the soil? Fossils dating from 420 million years ago reveal an adaptation that may have aided early plants in nutrient uptake: They formed symbiotic associations with fungi similar in structure to beneficial associations observed today between plants and fungi. We'll describe these associations, called *mycorrhizae*, and their benefits to both plants and fungi in more detail in Chapter 31. For now, the main point is that mycorrhizal fungi form extensive networks of filaments through the soil, enabling them to absorb nutrients more effectively than a plant can on its own. The fungi transfer nutrients to their symbiotic plant partner—a benefit that may have helped plants without roots to colonize land.

Finally, many land plants produce molecules called *secondary compounds*, so named because they are products of secondary metabolic pathways—side branches off the primary metabolic pathways that produce the lipids, carbohydrates, amino acids, and other compounds common to all organisms. Secondary compounds include alkaloids, terpenes, tannins, and phenolics such as flavonoids. Various alkaloids, terpenes, and tannins have a bitter taste, strong odor, or toxic effect that helps defend against herbivores and parasites. Flavonoids absorb harmful UV radiation, and some other phenolics deter attack by pathogens. Humans also benefit from secondary compounds, many of which are used in spices, medicines, and other products.

The Origin and Diversification of Plants

Paleobotanists seeking the evolutionary origin of plants have long debated what constitutes the oldest fossil evidence of land plants. In the 1970s, researchers found fossil spores dating to the Ordovician period, up to 475 million years old. Although the fossil spores resemble those of living plants, they

(a) Fossilized spores. Unlike the spores of most living plants, which are single grains, these spores found in Oman are in groups of four (left; one hidden) and two (right).

(b) Fossilized sporophyte tissue. The spores were embedded in tissue that appears to be from plants.

▲ **Figure 29.6 Ancient plant spores and tissue** (colorized SEMs).

also have some striking differences. For example, spores of present-day plants are typically dispersed as single grains, but the fossil spores are fused together in groups of two or four. This difference raises the possibility that the fossil spores were not produced by plants, but by some extinct algal relative. Furthermore, the oldest known fragments of plant body tissues are 50 million years younger than the puzzling spores.

In 2003, scientists from Britain and the Middle Eastern country of Oman shed some light on this mystery when they extracted spores from 475-million-year-old rocks from Oman **(Figure 29.6a)**. Unlike previously discovered spores of this age, these were embedded in plant cuticle material that is similar to spore-bearing tissue in living plants **(Figure 29.6b)**. After uncovering other small fragments of tissue that clearly belonged to plants, the scientists concluded that the spores from Oman represent fossil plants rather than algae.

Whatever the precise age of the first land plants, those ancestral species gave rise to the vast diversity of living plants. **Table 29.1** summarizes the ten extant phyla in the taxonomic scheme used in this text. (Extant lineages are those that have surviving members, not only extinct ones.) As you read the rest of this section, look at Table 29.1 together with **Figure 29.7**, which reflects a view of plant phylogeny based on plant morphology, biochemistry, and genetics.

One way to distinguish plants is by whether or not they have an extensive system of **vascular tissue**, cells joined into tubes that transport water and nutrients throughout the plant body. Most plants have a complex vascular tissue system and are therefore called **vascular plants**. Plants that do not have an extensive transport system—liverworts, hornworts, and mosses—are described as "nonvascular" plants, even though

Table 29.1 Ten Phyla of Extant Plants

	Common Name	Estimated Number of Species
Nonvascular Plants (Bryophytes)		
Phylum Hepatophyta	Liverworts	9,000
Phylum Anthocerophyta	Hornworts	100
Phylum Bryophyta	Mosses	15,000
Vascular Plants		
Seedless Vascular Plants		
Phylum Lycophyta	Lycophytes	1,200
Phylum Pterophyta	Pterophytes	12,000
Seed Plants		
Gymnosperms		
Phylum Ginkgophyta	Ginkgo	1
Phylum Cycadophyta	Cycads	130
Phylum Gnetophyta	Gnetophytes	75
Phylum Coniferophyta	Conifers	600
Angiosperms		
Phylum Anthophyta	Flowering plants	250,000

some mosses do have simple vascular tissue. Nonvascular plants are often informally called **bryophytes** (from the Greek *bryon*, moss, and *phyton*, plant).

Although the term *bryophyte* is commonly used to refer to all nonvascular plants, debate continues over the relationships of liverworts, hornworts, and mosses to each other and to vascular plants. Whereas some molecular studies have concluded that bryophytes do not form a monophyletic group (a clade; see Figure 26.10), several recent analyses of amino acid sequences in chloroplasts assert that bryophytes do form a clade. Whether or not bryophytes are monophyletic, they share some derived traits with vascular plants, such as multicellular embryos and apical meristems, while lacking many innovations of vascular plants, such as roots and true leaves.

Vascular plants, which form a clade that comprises about 93% of all plant species, can be categorized further into smaller clades. Two of these clades are the **lycophytes** (club mosses and their relatives) and the **pterophytes** (ferns and their relatives). The plants in each of these clades lack seeds, which is why collectively the two clades are often informally called **seedless vascular plants**. However, notice in Figure 29.7 that seedless vascular plants are paraphyletic, not monophyletic. Groups such as the seedless vascular plants are sometimes referred to as a **grade**, a collection of organisms that share a common level of biological organization or adaptation.

1 Origin of land plants (about 475 mya)

2 Origin of vascular plants (about 420 mya)

3 Origin of extant seed plants (about 305 mya)

▲ **Figure 29.7 Highlights of plant evolution.** Several hypotheses about relationships between plant groups are actively under debate, including one proposing that bryophytes are a monophyletic group. The dotted lines indicate groups whose evolutionary relationships are unclear.

DRAW IT *Redraw this phylogeny assuming that bryophytes are a monophyletic group in which liverworts diverged first.*

Although grades can be informative by grouping organisms according to key biological features (such as lack of seeds), they can be misleading in other ways. Pterophytes, for example, share a more recent common ancestor with seed plants than with lycophytes. As a result, we would expect pterophytes and seed plants to share key traits not found in lycophytes—and they do, as you'll read.

A third clade of vascular plants consists of seed plants, which represent the vast majority of living plant species. A **seed** is an embryo packaged with a supply of nutrients inside a protective coat. Seed plants can be divided into two groups, gymnosperms and angiosperms, based on the absence or presence of enclosed chambers in which seeds mature. **Gymnosperms** (from the Greek *gymnos*, naked, and *sperm*, seed) are grouped together as "naked seed" plants because their seeds are not enclosed in chambers. Living gymnosperm species, the most familiar of which are the conifers, probably form a clade. **Angiosperms** (from the Greek *angion*, container) are a huge clade consisting of all flowering plants. Angiosperm seeds develop inside chambers called ovaries, which originate within flowers and mature into fruits. Nearly 90% of living plant species are angiosperms.

Note that the phylogeny depicted in Figure 29.7 focuses only on the relationships between extant plant lineages. Paleobotanists have also discovered fossils belonging to extinct plant lineages. Many of these fossils reveal intermediate steps in the emergence of the distinctive plant groups found on Earth today.

CONCEPT CHECK 29.1

1. Why do researchers identify charophytes rather than another group as the closest relatives of land plants?
2. Identify three derived traits that distinguish plants from charophytes *and* facilitate life on land. Explain.
3. **WHAT IF?** What would the human life cycle be like if we had alternation of generations? Assume that the multicellular diploid stage is similar in form to an adult human.

For suggested answers, see Appendix A.

CONCEPT 29.2
Mosses and other nonvascular plants have life cycles dominated by gametophytes

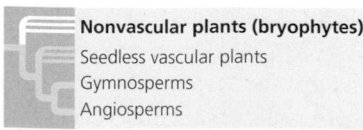

Nonvascular plants (bryophytes)
Seedless vascular plants
Gymnosperms
Angiosperms

The nonvascular plants (bryophytes) are represented today by three phyla of small herbaceous (nonwoody) plants: **liverworts** (phylum Hepatophyta), **hornworts** (phylum Anthocerophyta), and **mosses** (phylum Bryophyta).

Liverworts and hornworts are named for their shapes, plus the suffix *wort* (from the Anglo-Saxon for "herb"). Mosses are familiar to many people, although some plants commonly called "mosses" are not really mosses at all. These include Irish moss (a red seaweed), reindeer moss (a lichen), club mosses (seedless vascular plants), and Spanish mosses (lichens in some regions and flowering plants in others).

Note that the terms *Bryophyta* and *bryophyte* are not synonymous. Bryophyta is the formal taxonomic name for the phylum that consists solely of mosses. As mentioned earlier, the term *bryophyte* is used informally to refer to *all* nonvascular plants—liverworts, hornworts, and mosses. Systematists continue to debate the sequence in which the three phyla of bryophytes evolved.

Liverworts, hornworts, and mosses acquired many unique adaptations over the long course of their evolution. Nevertheless, living bryophytes likely reflect some traits of the earliest plants. The oldest known fossils of plant fragments, for example, include tissues very similar to those inside liverworts. Researchers hope to discover more parts of these ancient plants to see if this resemblance is reflected more broadly.

Bryophyte Gametophytes

Unlike vascular plants, in all three bryophyte phyla the gametophytes are the dominant stage of the life cycle: They are larger and longer-living than the sporophytes, as shown in the moss life cycle in **Figure 29.8**. Sporophytes are typically present only part of the time.

When bryophyte spores are dispersed to a favorable habitat, such as moist soil or tree bark, they may germinate and grow into gametophytes. Germinating moss spores, for example, characteristically produce a mass of green, branched, one-cell-thick filaments known as a **protonema** (plural, *protonemata*; from the Greek *proto*, first, and *nema*, threads). A protonema has a large surface area that enhances absorption of water and minerals. In favorable conditions, a protonema produces one or more "buds." (Note that when referring to nonvascular plants, we typically use quotation marks for structures similar to the buds, stems, and leaves of vascular plants because the definitions of these terms are based on vascular plant organs.) Each of these bud-like growths has an apical meristem that generates a gamete-producing structure known as a **gametophore** ("gamete bearer"). Together, a protonema and one or more gametophores make up the body of a moss gametophyte.

Bryophyte gametophytes generally form ground-hugging carpets, partly because their body parts are too thin to support a tall plant. A second constraint on the height of many bryophytes is the absence of vascular tissue, which would enable long-distance transport of water and nutrients. The thin structure of bryophyte organs makes it possible to distribute materials without specialized vascular tissue. Some mosses, however, such as the genus *Polytrichum*, have conducting tissues in the center of their "stems." A few of these mosses can grow as tall as 2 m as a result.

▼ **Figure 29.8 The life cycle of a moss.**

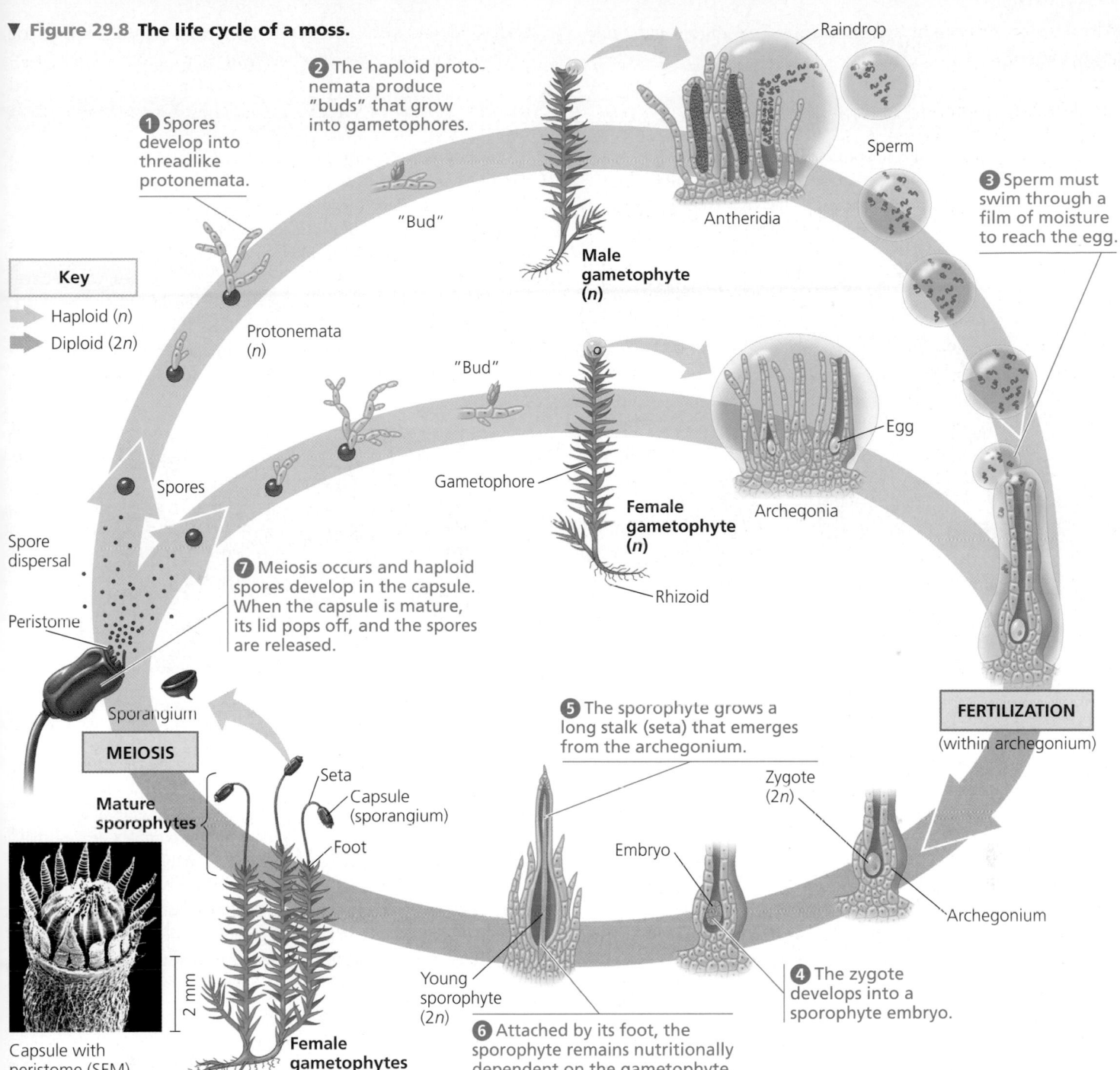

Key

→ Haploid (*n*)

→ Diploid (2*n*)

① Spores develop into threadlike protonemata.

② The haploid protonemata produce "buds" that grow into gametophores.

"Bud"

Male gametophyte (*n*)

Raindrop

Antheridia

Sperm

③ Sperm must swim through a film of moisture to reach the egg.

Protonemata (*n*)

Spores

"Bud"

Gametophore

Female gametophyte (*n*)

Rhizoid

Egg

Archegonia

Spore dispersal

⑦ Meiosis occurs and haploid spores develop in the capsule. When the capsule is mature, its lid pops off, and the spores are released.

Peristome

Sporangium

MEIOSIS

Mature sporophytes

Seta

Capsule (sporangium)

Foot

⑤ The sporophyte grows a long stalk (seta) that emerges from the archegonium.

FERTILIZATION

(within archegonium)

Zygote (2*n*)

Embryo

Archegonium

④ The zygote develops into a sporophyte embryo.

Young sporophyte (2*n*)

⑥ Attached by its foot, the sporophyte remains nutritionally dependent on the gametophyte.

Female gametophytes

2 mm

Capsule with peristome (SEM)

Phylogenetic analyses suggest that in these and some other bryophytes, conducting tissues similar to those of vascular plants arose independently by convergent evolution.

The gametophytes are anchored by delicate **rhizoids**, which are long, tubular single cells (in liverworts and hornworts) or filaments of cells (in mosses). Unlike roots, which are characteristic of vascular plants, rhizoids are not composed of tissues. Bryophyte rhizoids also lack specialized conducting cells and do not play a primary role in water and mineral absorption.

Mature gametophytes form gametangia that produce gametes and are covered by protective tissue. A gametophyte may have multiple gametangia. Eggs are produced singly in pear-shaped archegonia, whereas each antheridium produces many sperm. Some bryophyte gametophytes are bisexual, but in mosses the archegonia and antheridia are typically carried on separate female and male gametophytes. Flagellated sperm swim through a film of water toward eggs, entering the archegonia in response to chemical attractants. Eggs are not released but instead remain within the bases of archegonia. After fertilization, embryos are retained within the archegonia. Layers of placental transfer cells help transport nutrients to the embryos as they develop into sporophytes.

Exploring Bryophyte Diversity

Liverworts (Phylum Hepatophyta)

This phylum's common and scientific names (from the Latin *hepaticus*, liver) refer to the liver-shaped gametophytes of its members, such as *Marchantia*, shown below. In medieval times, their shape was thought to be a sign that the plants could help treat liver diseases. Some liverworts, including *Marchantia*, are described as "thalloid" because of the flattened shape of their gametophytes. (Recall from Chapter 28 that the body of a multicellular alga is called a thallus.) *Marchantia* gametangia are elevated on gametophores that look like miniature trees. You would need a magnifying glass to see the sporophytes, which have a short seta (stalk) with an oval or round capsule. Other liverworts, such as *Plagiochila*, below, are called "leafy" because their stemlike gametophytes have many leaflike appendages. There are many more species of leafy liverworts than thalloid liverworts.

Marchantia polymorpha,
a "thalloid" liverwort

Marchantia sporophyte (LM)

500 μm

Plagiochila deltoidea, a "leafy" liverwort

Hornworts (Phylum Anthocerophyta)

This phylum's common and scientific names (from the Greek *keras,* horn) refer to the long, tapered shape of the sporophyte. A typical sporophyte can grow to about 5 cm high. Unlike a liverwort or moss sporophyte, a hornwort sporophyte lacks a seta and consists only of a sporangium. The sporangium releases mature spores by splitting open, starting at the tip of the horn. The gametophytes, which are usually 1–2 cm in diameter, grow mostly horizontally and often have multiple sporophytes attached. Hornworts are frequently among the first species to colonize open areas with moist soils; a symbiotic relationship with nitrogen-fixing cyanobacteria contributes to their ability to do this (nitrogen is often in short supply in such areas).

An *Anthoceros* hornwort species

Sporophyte

Gametophyte

Mosses (Phylum Bryophyta)

Moss gametophytes, which range in height from less than 1 mm to up to 2 m, are less than 15 cm in most species. The familiar carpet of moss you observe consists mainly of gametophytes. The blades of their "leaves" are usually only one cell thick, but more complex "leaves" that have ridges coated with cuticle can be found on the common hairy-cap moss (*Polytrichum*, below) and its close relatives. Moss sporophytes are typically elongated and visible to the naked eye, with heights ranging up to about 20 cm. Though green and photosynthetic when young, they turn tan or brownish red when ready to release spores.

Polytrichum commune, hairy-cap moss

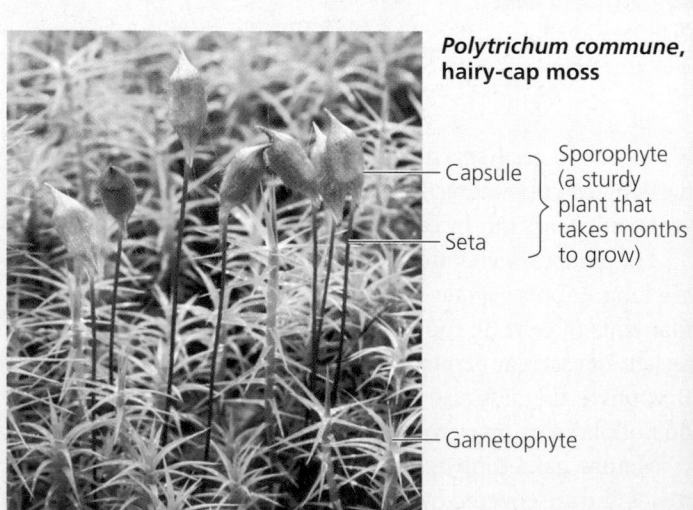

Capsule

Seta

Sporophyte (a sturdy plant that takes months to grow)

Gametophyte

Bryophyte sperm require a film of water to reach the eggs. Given this requirement, it is not surprising that many bryophyte species are found in moist habitats. The fact that sperm must swim through water to reach the egg also means that in species with separate male and female gametophytes (most mosses), sexual reproduction is likely to be more successful when individuals are located close to one another. Many bryophyte species can increase the number of individuals in a local area through various methods of asexual reproduction. For example, some mosses reproduce asexually by forming *brood bodies*, small plantlets that detach from the parent plant and grow into a new, genetically identical copy of their parent.

Bryophyte Sporophytes

Although bryophyte sporophytes are usually green and photosynthetic when young, they cannot live independently. They remain attached to their parental gametophytes, from which they absorb sugars, amino acids, minerals, and water.

Bryophytes have the smallest sporophytes of all extant plant groups, consistent with the hypothesis that larger sporophytes evolved only later, in the vascular plants. A typical bryophyte sporophyte consists of a foot, a seta, and a sporangium. Embedded in the archegonium, the **foot** absorbs nutrients from the gametophyte. The **seta** (plural, *setae*), or stalk, conducts these materials to the sporangium, also called a **capsule**, which uses them to produce spores by meiosis. One capsule can generate up to 50 million spores.

In most mosses, the seta becomes elongated, enhancing spore dispersal by elevating the capsule. Typically, the upper part of the capsule features a ring of interlocking, tooth-like structures known as the **peristome** (see Figure 29.8). These "teeth" open under dry conditions and close again when it is moist. This allows spores to be discharged gradually, via periodic gusts of wind that can carry them long distances.

Hornwort and moss sporophytes are larger and more complex than those of liverworts. Both hornwort and moss sporophytes also have specialized pores called **stomata** (singular, *stoma*), which are also found in all vascular plants. These pores support photosynthesis by allowing the exchange of CO_2 and O_2 between the outside air and the sporophyte interior (see Figure 10.3). Stomata are also the main avenues by which water evaporates from the sporophyte. In hot, dry conditions, the stomata close, minimizing water loss.

The fact that stomata are present in mosses and hornworts but absent in liverworts suggests three possible hypotheses for their evolution. If liverworts are the deepest-branching lineage of land plants, as in Figure 29.7, then stomata may have evolved once in the ancestor of hornworts, mosses, and vascular plants. If hornworts or mosses are the deepest-branching lineage, or if bryophytes are monophyletic, stomata may have evolved once and then been lost in the liverwort lineage. Finally, if hornworts are the deepest-branching lineage and mosses are the closest relatives of vascular plants, it is also possible that hornworts ac-quired stomata independently of mosses and vascular plants. This question is important to understanding plant evolution because stomata play a crucial role in the success of vascular plants, as you will learn in Chapter 36.

Figure 29.9, on the facing page, shows some examples of gametophytes and sporophytes in the bryophyte phyla.

The Ecological and Economic Importance of Mosses

Wind dispersal of their lightweight spores has distributed mosses throughout the world. These plants are particularly common and diverse in moist forests and wetlands. Some mosses colonize bare, sandy soil, where researchers have found they help retain nitrogen in the soil (**Figure 29.10**). Other

▼ **Figure 29.10** **Inquiry**

Can bryophytes reduce the rate at which key nutrients are lost from soils?

EXPERIMENT　　Soils in terrestrial ecosystems are often low in nitrogen, a nutrient that is required for normal plant growth. Richard Bowden, of Allegheny College, measured annual inputs (gains) and outputs (losses) of nitrogen in a sandy-soil ecosystem dominated by the moss *Polytrichum*. Nitrogen inputs to the ecosystem were measured from rainfall (dissolved ions such as nitrate, NO_3^-), biological N_2 fixation, and wind deposition. Nitrogen losses were measured in leached water (dissolved ions, such as NO_3^-) and gaseous emissions (such as NO_2 emitted by some bacteria). Bowden measured nitrogen losses for soils with *Polytrichum* and for soils where the moss had been removed two months before the experiment began.

RESULTS　　A total of 10.5 kg of nitrogen per hectare (kg/ha) entered the ecosystem each year. Little nitrogen was lost by gaseous emissions (0.10 kg/ha per year). The results of comparing nitrogen losses by leaching are shown below.

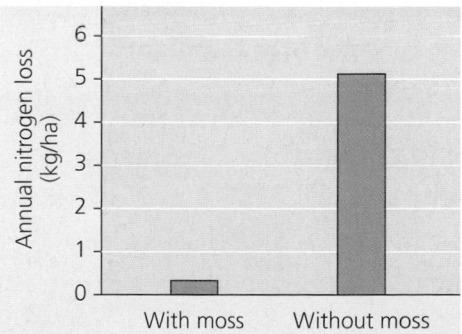

CONCLUSION　　The moss *Polytrichum* greatly reduced the loss of nitrogen by leaching in this ecosystem. Each year, the moss ecosystem retained over 95% of the 10.5 kg/ha of total nitrogen inputs (only 0.1 kg/ha and 0.3 kg/ha were lost to gaseous emissions and leaching, respectively).

SOURCE　　R. D. Bowden, Inputs, outputs, and accumulation of nitrogen in an early successional moss (*Polytrichum*) ecosystem, *Ecological Monographs* 61:207–223 (1991).

WHAT IF?　　How might the presence of *Polytrichum* affect plant species that typically colonize the sandy soils *after* the moss?

mosses inhabit such extreme environments as mountaintops, tundra, and deserts. Many mosses are able to live in very cold or dry habitats because they can survive the loss of most of their body water, then rehydrate when moisture is available. Few vascular plants can survive the same degree of desiccation.

One wetland moss genus, *Sphagnum*, or "peat moss," is especially widespread, forming extensive deposits of partially decayed organic material known as **peat (Figure 29.11a)**. Boggy regions dominated by this moss are called peatlands. *Sphagnum* does not decay readily, in part because of phenolic compounds embedded in its cell walls. The low temperature, pH, and oxygen level of peatlands also inhibit decay of moss—and other organisms. As a result, some peatlands have preserved corpses for thousands of years **(Figure 29.11b)**.

Peat has long been a fuel source in Europe and Asia, and it is still harvested for fuel today, notably in Ireland and Canada. In addition, peat moss is useful as a soil conditioner and for packing plant roots during shipment because it has large dead

(a) Peat being harvested from a peatland

(b) "Tollund Man," a bog mummy dating from 405–100 B.C.E.
The acidic, oxygen-poor conditions produced by *Sphagnum* can preserve human or other animal bodies for thousands of years.

▲ Figure 29.11 ***Sphagnum*, or peat moss: a bryophyte with economic, ecological, and archaeological significance.**

cells that can absorb roughly 20 times the moss's weight in water. Worldwide, an estimated 400 billion tons of organic carbon are stored in peat. These carbon reservoirs help stabilize atmospheric CO_2 concentrations (see Chapter 55). Current overharvesting of *Sphagnum* may reduce its beneficial ecological effects and contribute to global warming by releasing stored CO_2.

CONCEPT CHECK 29.2

1. How do bryophytes differ from other plants?
2. Give three examples of how structure fits function in bryophytes.
3. **WHAT IF?** For each hypothesis of stomatal evolution, label each gain and loss of stomata on the phylogenetic tree in Figure 29.7 (or a modified version).

For suggested answers, see Appendix A.

CONCEPT 29.3

Ferns and other seedless vascular plants were the first plants to grow tall

Nonvascular plants (bryophytes)
Seedless vascular plants
Gymnosperms
Angiosperms

During the first 100 million years of plant evolution, bryophytes or bryophyte-like plants were the prevalent vegetation. But it is vascular plants that dominate most landscapes today. Fossils and living seedless vascular plants can provide insights into plant evolution during the Devonian and Carboniferous periods, when vascular plants began to diversify but most groups of seed plants had not yet evolved. Fossils show that lycophytes, ferns, and other seedless vascular plants had well-developed vascular systems by the Devonian. As we'll see, this evolutionary innovation set the stage for vascular plants to grow taller than their bryophyte counterparts. As in nonvascular plants, however, the sperm of ferns and all other seedless vascular plants are flagellated and must swim through a film of water to reach eggs. In part because of these swimming sperm, seedless vascular plants today are most common in damp environments.

Origins and Traits of Vascular Plants

Fossils of the forerunners of present-day vascular plants date back about 420 million years. Unlike the nonvascular plants, these species had branched sporophytes that were not dependent on gametophytes for nutrition **(Figure 29.12)**. Although these ancestors of vascular plants grew no taller than about 50 cm, their branching made possible more complex bodies with multiple sporangia. As their bodies became

▶ Figure 29.12
Sporophytes of
Aglaophyton major,
an ancient relative of
present-day vascular
plants. This reconstruction
from fossils dating to about
420 million years ago exhibits
dichotomous (Y-shaped)
branching with sporangia at
the ends of the branches.
Sporophyte branching
characterizes living vascular
plants but is lacking in living
nonvascular plants
(bryophytes).

increasingly complex, competition for space and sunlight probably increased. As we'll see, that competition may have stimulated still more evolution in vascular plants.

The ancestors of vascular plants already had some derived traits of today's vascular plants, but they lacked roots and some other adaptations that evolved later. This section describes the main traits that characterize living vascular plants: life cycles with dominant sporophytes, transport in vascular tissues called xylem and phloem, and well-developed roots and leaves, including spore-bearing leaves called sporophylls.

Life Cycles with Dominant Sporophytes

Fossils suggest that the ancestors of vascular plants had gametophytes and sporophytes that were about equal in size. Among living vascular plants, however, the sporophyte (diploid) generation is the larger and more complex plant in the alternation of generations (**Figure 29.13**). In ferns, for example, the familiar leafy plants are the sporophytes. You

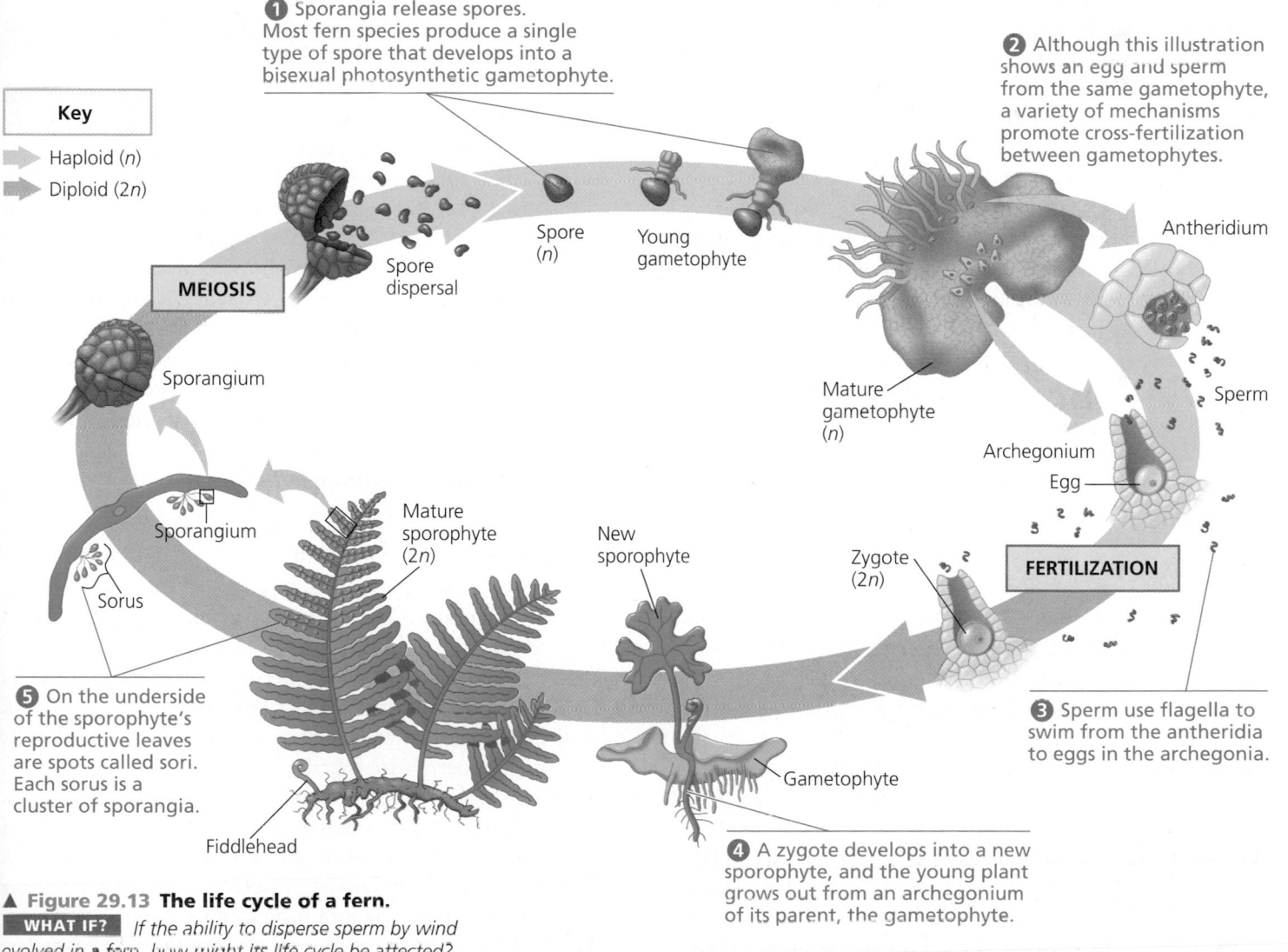

❶ Sporangia release spores. Most fern species produce a single type of spore that develops into a bisexual photosynthetic gametophyte.

❷ Although this illustration shows an egg and sperm from the same gametophyte, a variety of mechanisms promote cross-fertilization between gametophytes.

Key

→ Haploid (*n*)
➔ Diploid (2*n*)

Spore dispersal

MEIOSIS

Sporangium

Spore
(*n*)

Young
gametophyte

Antheridium

Mature
gametophyte
(*n*)

Sperm

Archegonium

Egg

Sporangium

Sorus

Mature
sporophyte
(2*n*)

New
sporophyte

Zygote
(2*n*)

FERTILIZATION

❺ On the underside of the sporophyte's reproductive leaves are spots called sori. Each sorus is a cluster of sporangia.

Fiddlehead

❸ Sperm use flagella to swim from the antheridia to eggs in the archegonia.

Gametophyte

❹ A zygote develops into a new sporophyte, and the young plant grows out from an archegonium of its parent, the gametophyte.

▲ **Figure 29.13 The life cycle of a fern.**
WHAT IF? *If the ability to disperse sperm by wind evolved in a fern, how might its life cycle be affected?*

would have to get down on your hands and knees and search the ground carefully to find fern gametophytes, which are tiny structures that often grow on or just below the soil surface. Until you have a chance to do that, you can study the sporophyte-dominant life cycle of seedless vascular plants in Figure 29.13, which uses a fern as an example. Then, for review, compare this life cycle with Figure 29.8, which represents a gametophyte-dominated life cycle typical of mosses and other nonvascular plants. In Chapter 30, you will see that gametophytes became even more reduced during the evolution of seed plants.

Transport in Xylem and Phloem

Vascular plants have two types of vascular tissue: xylem and phloem. **Xylem** conducts most of the water and minerals. The xylem of most vascular plants includes **tracheids**, tube-shaped cells that carry water and minerals up from roots (see Figure 35.10). (Tracheids have been lost in some highly specialized species, such as *Wolffia*, a tiny aquatic angiosperm.) Because nonvascular plants lack tracheids, vascular plants are sometimes referred to as tracheophytes. The water-conducting cells in vascular plants are *lignified;* that is, their cell walls are strengthened by the phenolic polymer **lignin**. The tissue called **phloem** has cells arranged into tubes that distribute sugars, amino acids, and other organic products (see Figure 35.10).

Lignified vascular tissue permitted vascular plants to grow tall. Their stems became strong enough to provide support against gravity, and they could transport water and mineral nutrients high above the ground. The ability to grow tall was a major evolutionary innovation: Tall plants could shade other plants, reducing their access to the sunlight needed for photosynthesis. This gave vascular plants a competitive edge over nonvascular plants, which rarely grow above 20 cm in height. Competition for light among vascular plants also increased, and taller growth forms were favored by natural selection—such as the treelike plants that formed the first forests about 370 million years ago.

Evolution of Roots

Lignified vascular tissue also provides benefits below ground. Instead of the rhizoids seen in bryophytes, roots evolved in almost all vascular plants. **Roots** are organs that absorb water and nutrients from the soil. Roots also anchor vascular plants, hence allowing the shoot system to grow taller.

Root tissues of living plants closely resemble stem tissues of early vascular plants preserved in fossils. This suggests that roots may have evolved from the lowest belowground portions of stems in ancient vascular plants. It is unclear whether roots evolved only once in the common ancestor of all vascular plants or independently in different lineages. Although the roots of living members of these lineages of vascular plants share many similarities, fossil evidence hints at convergent evolution. The oldest lycophyte fossils, for example, already displayed simple roots 400 million years ago, when the ancestors of ferns and seed plants still had none. Studying genes that control root development in different vascular plant species may help resolve this question.

Evolution of Leaves

Leaves increase the surface area of the plant body and serve as the primary photosynthetic organ of vascular plants. In terms of size and complexity, leaves can be classified as either microphylls or megaphylls. All of the lycophytes (the oldest lineage of present-day vascular plants)—and only the lycophytes—have **microphylls**, small, usually spine-shaped leaves supported by a single strand of vascular tissue. Almost all other vascular plants have **megaphylls**, leaves with a highly branched vascular system; a few species have reduced leaves that appear to have evolved from megaphylls. So named because they are typically larger than microphylls, megaphylls support greater photosynthetic productivity than microphylls as a result of the greater surface area served by their network of veins. Microphylls first appear in the fossil record 410 million years ago, but megaphylls do not emerge until about 370 million years ago, near the end of the Devonian period.

According to one model of leaf evolution, microphylls originated from sporangia located on the side of the stem **(Figure 29.14a)**. Megaphylls, by contrast, may have evolved from a series of branches lying close together on a stem. As one of these branches came to grow above, or *overtop*, the others, the lower branches became flattened and developed webbing that joined them to one another. These joined branches thus became a leaf attached to the branch that overtopped them **(Figure 29.14b)**. To better understand the origin of leaves, scientists are exploring genetic control of leaf development.

Sporophylls and Spore Variations

One milestone in the evolution of plants was the emergence of **sporophylls**, modified leaves that bear sporangia. Sporophylls vary greatly in structure. For example, fern sporophylls produce clusters of sporangia known as **sori** (singular, *sorus*), usually on the undersides of the sporophylls (see Figure 29.13). In many lycophytes and in most gymnosperms, groups of sporophylls form cone-like structures called **strobili** (from the Greek *strobilos*, cone). In Chapter 30, you will see how sporophylls form gymnosperm strobili and parts of angiosperm flowers.

Most seedless vascular plant species are **homosporous**: they have one type of sporangium that produces one type of spore, which typically develops into a bisexual gametophyte, as in most ferns. In contrast, a **heterosporous** species has two types of sporangia and produces two kinds of spores: Megasporangia on megasporophylls produce **megaspores**, which develop into female gametophytes; microsporangia on

(a) **Microphylls,** such as those of lycophytes, may have originated from sporangia supported by single, unbranched strands of vascular tissue.

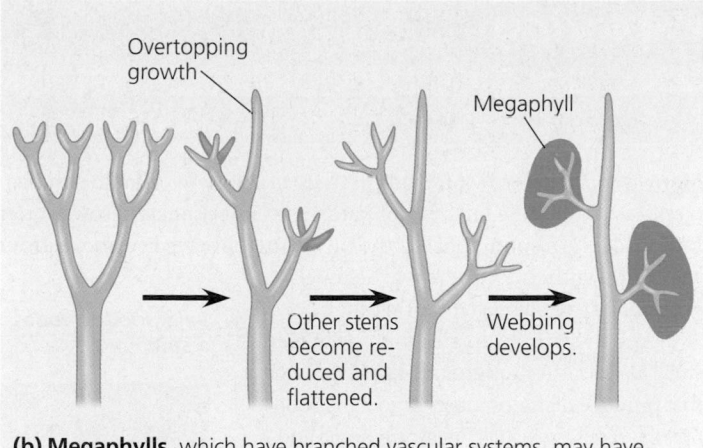

(b) **Megaphylls,** which have branched vascular systems, may have evolved by the fusion of branched stems.

▲ **Figure 29.14 Hypotheses for the evolution of leaves.**

microsporophylls produce **microspores,** which develop into male gametophytes. All seed plants and a few seedless vascular plants are heterosporous. The following diagram compares the two conditions:

Classification of Seedless Vascular Plants

As we noted earlier, biologists recognize two clades of living seedless vascular plants: the lycophytes (phylum Lycophyta) and the pterophytes (phylum Pterophyta). The Lycophytes include the club mosses, the spike mosses, and the quillworts. The pterophytes include the ferns, the horsetails, and the whisk ferns and their relatives. Because they differ greatly in appearance, the ferns, horsetails, and whisk ferns have long been considered separate phyla: phylum Pterophyta (ferns), phylum Sphenophyta (horsetails), and phylum Psilophyta (whisk ferns and a related genus). However, recent molecular comparisons provide convincing evidence that all three groups form a clade. Accordingly, many systematists now classify them together as

the phylum Pterophyta, as we do in this chapter. Others refer to these groups as three separate phyla within a clade.

Figure 29.15, on the next page, describes the two main groups of seedless vascular plants.

Phylum Lycophyta: Club Mosses, Spike Mosses, and Quillworts

Present-day species of lycophytes—the most ancient group of vascular plants—are relicts of a far more impressive past. By the Carboniferous period (359 to 299 million years ago), there were two evolutionary lineages of lycophytes: one consisting of small herbaceous plants and another consisting of giant woody treelike plants with diameters of more than 2 m and heights of more than 40 m. The giant "tree lycophytes" thrived for millions of years in moist swamps, but they became extinct when Earth's climate became drier at the end of the Carboniferous period. The small lycophytes survived, represented today by about 1,200 species. Though some are commonly called club mosses and spike mosses, they are not true mosses (which, as discussed earlier, are nonvascular plants).

Phylum Pterophyta: Ferns, Horsetails, and Whisk Ferns and Relatives

Ferns radiated extensively from their Devonian origins and grew alongside tree lycophytes and horsetails in the great Carboniferous swamp forests. Today, ferns are by far the most widespread seedless vascular plants, numbering more than 12,000 species. Though most diverse in the tropics, many ferns thrive in temperate forests, and some species are even adapted to arid habitats.

As mentioned earlier, ferns and other pterophytes are more closely related to seed plants than to lycophytes. As a result, pterophytes and seed plants share traits that are not

Exploring Seedless Vascular Plant Diversity

Lycophytes (Phylum Lycophyta)

Many lycophytes grow on tropical trees as epiphytes, plants that use other plants as a substrate but are not parasites. Other species grow on temperate forest floors. In some species, the tiny gametophytes live above ground and are photosynthetic. Others live below ground, nurtured by symbiotic fungi.

Sporophytes have upright stems with many small leaves, as well as ground-hugging stems that produce dichotomously branching roots. Spike mosses are usually relatively small and often grow horizontally. In many club mosses and spike mosses, sporophylls are clustered into club-shaped cones (strobili). Quillworts, named for their leaf shape, form a single genus that lives in marshy areas. Club mosses are all homosporous, whereas spike mosses and quillworts are all heterosporous. Spores of club mosses are released in clouds and are so rich in oil that magicians and photographers once ignited them to create smoke or flashes of light.

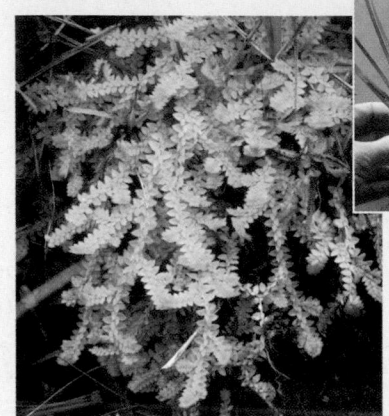

Selaginella apoda, a spike moss

Isoetes gunnii, a quillwort

2.5 cm

Strobili (clusters of sporophylls)

1 cm

Diphasiastrum tristachyum, a club moss

Pterophytes (Phylum Pterophyta)

Athyrium filix-femina, lady fern

25 cm

Equisetum arvense, field horsetail

Vegetative stem

Strobilus on fertile stem

1.5 cm

Psilotum nudum, a whisk fern

2.5 cm

Ferns

Unlike the lycophytes, ferns have mega-phylls (see Figure 29.14b). The sporophytes typically have horizontal stems that give rise to large leaves called fronds, often divided into leaflets. A frond grows as its coiled tip, the fiddlehead, unfurls.

Almost all species are homosporous. The gametophyte in some species shrivels and dies after the young sporophyte detaches itself. In most species, sporophytes have stalked sporangia with springlike devices that catapult spores several meters. Airborne spores can be carried far from their origin. Some species produce more than a trillion spores in a plant's lifetime.

Horsetails

The group's name refers to the brushy appearance of the stems, which have a gritty texture that made them historically useful as "scouring rushes" for pots and pans. Some species have separate fertile (cone-bearing) and vegetative stems. Horsetails are homosporous, with cones releasing spores that typically give rise to bisexual gametophytes.

Horsetails are also called arthrophytes ("jointed plants") because their stems have joints. Rings of small leaves or branches emerge from each joint, but the stem is the main photosynthetic organ. Large air canals carry oxygen to the roots, which often grow in waterlogged soil.

Whisk Ferns and Relatives

Like primitive vascular plant fossils, the sporophytes of whisk ferns (genus *Psilotum*) have dichotomously branching stems but no roots. Stems have scalelike outgrowths that lack vascular tissue and may have evolved as very reduced leaves. Each yellow knob on a stem consists of three fused sporangia. Species of the genus *Tmesipteris*, closely related to whisk ferns and found only in the South Pacific, also lack roots but have small, leaflike outgrowths in their stems, giving them a vine-like appearance. Both genera are homosporous, with spores giving rise to bisexual gametophytes that grow under-ground and are only about a centimeter long.

found in lycophytes, including over-topping growth (see Figure 29.14b), megaphyll leaves, and roots that can branch at various points along the length of an existing root (in lycophytes, by contrast, roots branch only at the growing tip of the root by forming a Y-shaped structure).

Horsetails were very diverse during the Carboniferous period, some growing as tall as 15 m. Today however, only about 15 species survive as a single, widely distributed genus, *Equisetum*, found in marshy places and along streams.

Psilotum (whisk ferns) and the closely related genus, *Tmesipteris*, form a clade consisting mainly of tropical epiphytes. Plants in these two genera, the only vascular plants lacking true roots, are called "living fossils" because of their striking resemblance to fossils of ancient relatives of living vascular plants (see Figures 29.12 and 29.15). However, much evidence, including analyses of DNA sequences and sperm structure, indicates that the genera *Psilotum* and *Tmesipteris* are closely related to ferns. This hypothesis suggests that their ancestor's true roots were lost during evolution. Today, plants in these two genera absorb water and nutrients through numerous absorptive rhizoids.

The Significance of Seedless Vascular Plants

The ancestors of living lycophytes, horsetails, and ferns, along with their extinct seedless vascular relatives, grew to great heights during the late Devonian and early Carboniferous, forming the first forests (Figure 29.16). How did their dramatic growth affect Earth and its other life? With the evolution of vascular tissue, roots, and leaves, these plants accelerated their rate of photosynthesis, dramatically increasing the removal of CO_2 from the atmosphere. Scientists estimate that CO_2 levels dropped by as much as a factor of five during the Carboniferous, causing global cooling that resulted in widespread glacier formation. Ancient CO_2 levels can be estimated in several ways. These include counting the number of stomata in fossil leaves (data from living species show that this number increases as CO_2 levels drop) and measuring carbon isotope levels in fossils of plankton. Different methods yield comparable results, suggesting that reconstructions of past climates are accurate.

The seedless vascular plants that formed the first forests eventually became coal. In the stagnant waters of Carboniferous swamps, dead plants did not completely decay. This or-

▲ **Figure 29.16 Artist's conception of a Carboniferous forest based on fossil evidence.** Most of the large plants with straight trunks are tree lycophytes. The shorter, spiky plant near the middle of the scene is a horsetail. Animals, including giant dragonflies like the one in the foreground, also thrived in the "coal forests" of the Carboniferous.

ganic material turned to thick layers of peat, later covered by the sea. Marine sediments piled on top, and over millions of years, heat and pressure converted the peat to coal. In fact, Carboniferous coal deposits are the most extensive ever formed. Coal was crucial to the Industrial Revolution, and people worldwide still burn 6 billion tons a year. It is ironic that coal, formed from plants that contributed to a global cooling, now contributes to global warming by returning carbon to the atmosphere (see Chapter 55).

Growing along with the seedless plants in Carboniferous swamps were primitive seed plants. Though seed plants were not dominant at that time, they rose to prominence after the swamps began to dry up at the end of the Carboniferous period. The next chapter traces the origin and diversification of seed plants, continuing our story of adaptation to life on land.

CONCEPT CHECK 29.3

1. List the key derived traits that are found in pterophytes and seed plants, but not in lycophytes.
2. How do the main similarities and differences between seedless vascular plants and nonvascular plants influence function in these plants?
3. **WHAT IF?** If (contrary to current evidence) lycophytes and pterophytes formed a clade, what could you conclude about how members of this clade gained (or lost) traits shared by pterophytes and seed plants?

For suggested answers, see Appendix A.

SUMMARY OF KEY CONCEPTS

CONCEPT 29.1

Land plants evolved from green algae (pp. 600–606)

▶ **Morphological and Molecular Evidence** Traits shared by plants and charophytes include rosette cellulose-synthesizing complexes, peroxisome enzymes, similarities in flagellated sperm structure, and formation of phragmoplasts during cell division. Similarities in nuclear and chloroplast genes also suggest that charophytes are the closest living relatives of land plants.

▶ **Adaptations Enabling the Move to Land** Sporopollenin and other traits allow charophytes to tolerate occasional drying along the edges of ponds and lakes. Such traits may have enabled the algal ancestors of plants to survive in terrestrial conditions, opening the way to the colonization of dry land. Although some biologists treat the plant kingdom as including some or all green algae, this textbook uses the embryophyte definition of kingdom Plantae.

▶ **Derived Traits of Plants** Derived traits that distinguish the clade of land plants from charophytes, their closest algal relatives, include the four shown here:

❶ Alternation of generations

❷ Apical meristems

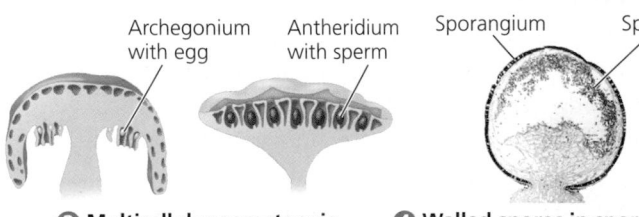

❸ Multicellular gametangia

❹ Walled spores in sporangia

▶ **The Origin and Diversification of Plants** Fossil evidence indicates that plants were on land at least 475 million years ago. Subsequently, plants diverged into several major groups, including nonvascular plants (bryophytes); seedless vascular plants, such as lycophytes and ferns; and the two groups of seed plants, gymnosperms and angiosperms.

MEDIA

Activity Terrestrial Adaptations of Plants
Activity Highlights of Plant Phylogeny

CONCEPT 29.2

Mosses and other nonvascular plants have life cycles dominated by gametophytes (pp. 606–610)

▶ The three phyla of bryophytes—liverworts, hornworts, and mosses—may not form a clade.

▶ **Bryophyte Gametophytes** Gametophytes are the dominant generation and are typically most visible, such as those that make up a carpet of moss. Rhizoids anchor gametophytes to the substrate on which they grow. The flagellated sperm produced by antheridia require a film of water to travel to the eggs in the archegonia.

▶ **Bryophyte Sporophytes** Sporophytes grow out of archegonia and are attached to and dependent on the haploid gametophytes for nourishment. Smaller and simpler than vascular plant sporophytes, they typically consist of a foot, seta (stalk), and sporangium.

▶ **The Ecological and Economic Importance of Mosses** Peat moss (*Sphagnum*) covers large regions known as peatlands and has many practical uses, including as a fuel.

MEDIA

Activity Moss Life Cycle

CONCEPT 29.3

Ferns and other seedless vascular plants were the first plants to grow tall (pp. 610–615)

▶ **Origins and Traits of Vascular Plants** Fossils of the forerunners of today's vascular plants date back about 420 million years and show that these small plants had independent, branching sporophytes. However, these ancestral species lacked other derived traits of living vascular plants, such as a life cycle with dominant sporophytes; lignified vascular tissue; well-developed roots and leaves; and sporophylls.

▶ **Classification of Seedless Vascular Plants** Seedless vascular plants include phylum Lycophyta (club mosses, spike mosses, and quillworts) and phylum Pterophyta (ferns, horsetails, and whisk ferns and relatives). Ancient lycophytes included both small herbaceous plants and large treelike plants. Present-day lycophytes are small herbaceous plants.

▶ **The Significance of Seedless Vascular Plants** Seedless vascular plants dominated the earliest forests. Their growth may have helped produce the major global cooling that characterized the end of the Carboniferous period. The decaying remnants of the first forests eventually became coal.

MEDIA

Activity Fern Life Cycle
Investigation What Are the Different Stages of a Fern Life Cycle?

SELF-QUIZ

1. Which of the following is *not* evidence that charophytes are the closest algal relatives of plants?
   a. similar sperm structure
   b. similarities in chloroplast shape
   c. similarities in cell wall formation during cell division
   d. genetic similarities in chloroplasts
   e. similarities in proteins that synthesize cellulose

2. Which of the following characteristics of plants is absent in their closest relatives, the charophyte algae?
   a. chlorophyll *b*
   b. cellulose in cell walls
   c. formation of a cell plate during cytokinesis
   d. sexual reproduction
   e. alternation of multicellular generations

3. Which of the following is *not* shared by all phyla of vascular plants?
   a. the development of seeds
   b. alternation of generations
   c. dominance of the diploid generation
   d. xylem and phloem
   e. the addition of lignin to cell walls

4. In plants, which of the following are produced by meiosis?
   a. haploid sporophytes   d. haploid spores
   b. haploid gametes   e. diploid spores
   c. diploid gametes

5. Microphylls are found in which of the following groups of plants?
   a. mosses   d. ferns
   b. liverworts   e. hornworts
   c. lycophytes

6. Which of the following is a land plant that produces flagellated sperm and has a sporophyte-dominated life cycle?
   a. moss   d. charophyte
   b. fern   e. hornwort
   c. liverwort

7. Suppose an efficient conducting system evolved in a moss that could transport water and other materials as high as a tall tree. Which of the following statements about "trees" of such a species would *not* be true?
   a. Fertilization would probably be more difficult.
   b. Spore dispersal distances might increase but probably would not decrease.
   c. Females could produce only one archegonium.
   d. Unless its body parts were strengthened, such a "tree" might flop over.
   e. Individuals could compete more effectively for access to light.

8. Identify each of the following structures as haploid or diploid:
   a. sporophyte   d. zygote
   b. spore   e. sperm
   c. gametophyte

For Self-Quiz answers, see Appendix A.

MEDIA Visit **www.campbellbiology.com** for a Practice Test.

EVOLUTION CONNECTION

9. **DRAW IT** Draw a phylogenetic tree that represents our current understanding of evolutionary relationships between a moss, a lycophyte, a fern, and a gymnosperm. Use a charophyte alga as the outgroup. (See Chapter 26 to review phylogenetic trees.) Label each branch point of the phylogeny with at least one derived character unique to the clade descended from the common ancestor represented by the branch point.

SCIENTIFIC INQUIRY

10. In April 1986, an accident at a nuclear power plant in Chernobyl, Ukraine, scattered radioactive fallout for hundreds of kilometers. In assessing the biological effects of the radiation, researchers found mosses to be especially valuable as organisms for monitoring the damage. Radiation damages organisms by causing mutations. Explain why the genetic effects of radiation can be observed sooner in bryophytes than in plants from other groups.

    Now imagine that you are conducting tests shortly after a nuclear accident. Using potted moss plants as your experimental organisms, design an experiment to test the hypothesis that the frequency of mutations decreases with the organism's distance from the source of radiation.

SCIENCE, TECHNOLOGY, AND SOCIETY

11. Nonvascular plants (bryophytes) and seedless vascular plants are common, and several of them have important economic and ecological uses. Nevertheless, very few are important agriculturally. Why? What attributes do they lack that make a plant useful in agriculture? What attributes limit their agricultural utility?

Plant Diversity II: The Evolution of Seed Plants

KEY CONCEPTS

30.1 Seeds and pollen grains are key adaptations for life on land

30.2 Gymnosperms bear "naked" seeds, typically on cones

30.3 The reproductive adaptations of angiosperms include flowers and fruits

30.4 Human welfare depends greatly on seed plants

OVERVIEW

Transforming the World

Continuing the saga of how plants have transformed Earth, this chapter follows the emergence and diversification of seed plants. Fossils and comparative studies of living plants offer clues about the origin of seed plants some 360 million years ago. As this new group of plants became established, they dramatically altered the course of plant evolution. We'll begin our exploration of how this occurred by looking at the innovation for which seed plants are named: seeds **(Figure 30.1)**.

A **seed** consists of an embryo and its food supply, surrounded by a protective coat. When mature, seeds are dispersed from their parent by wind or other means. Because it nourishes and protects the embryo—yet can move away from the mother plant—a seed is analogous to a detachable and mobile version of a pregnant woman's womb. As we'll see, seeds are a key adaptation that helped seed plants to become the dominant producers on land and to make up the vast majority of plant biodiversity today.

Seed plants have also had an enormous impact on human society. Starting about 13,000 years ago, humans began to cultivate wheat, figs, maize (commonly called corn in the United States), bananas, and other wild seed plants. This practice emerged independently in various parts of the world, including the Near East, East Asia, Africa, and the Americas. One piece of evidence, the well-preserved squash

seed in Figure 30.1, was found in a cave in Mexico and dates from between 8,000 and 10,000 years ago. This seed differs from wild squash seeds, suggesting that squash was being domesticated by that time. The domestication of seed plants, particularly angiosperms, produced the most important cultural change in human history, transforming most human societies from roving bands of hunter-gatherers to permanent settlements anchored by agriculture.

In this chapter, we will first examine the general characteristics of seed plants. Then we will look at the distinguishing features and evolution of gymnosperms and angiosperms.

CONCEPT 30.1

Seeds and pollen grains are key adaptations for life on land

We begin with an overview of terrestrial adaptations that seed plants added to those already present in nonvascular plants (bryophytes) and seedless vascular plants (see Chapter 29). In addition to seeds, the following are common to all seed plants: reduced gametophytes, heterospory, ovules, and pollen. As you'll read, these adaptations provided new ways for seed plants to cope with terrestrial conditions such as drought and exposure to the ultraviolet (UV) radiation in sunlight. Novel adaptations also freed seed plants from requiring water for fertilization, enabling reproduction to occur under a broader range of conditions than in seedless plants.

Advantages of Reduced Gametophytes

Mosses and other bryophytes have life cycles dominated by gametophytes, whereas ferns and other seedless vascular plants have sporophyte-dominated life cycles. The evolutionary trend

PLANT GROUP		
Mosses and other nonvascular plants	**Ferns and other seedless vascular plants**	**Seed plants (gymnosperms and angiosperms)**
Gametophyte Dominant	Reduced, independent (photosynthetic and free-living)	Reduced (usually microscopic), dependent on surrounding sporophyte tissue for nutrition
Sporophyte Reduced, dependent on gametophyte for nutrition	Dominant	Dominant
Example		

▲ **Figure 30.2 Gametophyte-sporophyte relationships in different plant groups.**

of gametophyte reduction continued further in the vascular plant lineage that led to seed plants. While the gametophytes of seedless vascular plants are visible to the naked eye, the gametophytes of seed plants are mostly microscopic.

This miniaturization allowed for an important evolutionary innovation in seed plants: Their tiny gametophytes can develop from spores retained within the sporangia of the parental sporophyte. This arrangement protects the delicate female (egg-containing) gametophytes from environmental stresses. The moist reproductive tissues of the sporophyte shield the gametophytes from UV radiation and protect against drying out. This relationship also enables the dependent gametophytes to obtain nutrients from the sporophyte. In contrast, the free-living gametophytes of seedless plants must fend for themselves. **Figure 30.2** contrasts the gametophyte-sporophyte relationships in nonvascular plants, seedless vascular plants, and seed plants.

Heterospory: The Rule Among Seed Plants

You read in Chapter 29 that nearly all seedless plants are homosporous—they produce one kind of spore, which usually gives

rise to a bisexual gametophyte. The closest relatives of seed plants are all homosporous, suggesting that seed plants had homosporous ancestors. At some point, seed plants or their ancestors became heterosporous: Megasporangia produce megaspores that give rise to female gametophytes, and microsporangia produce microspores that give rise to male gametophytes. Each megasporangium has a single functional megaspore, whereas each microsporangium contains vast numbers of microspores.

As we noted previously, the miniaturization of seed plant gametophytes likely contributed to the great success of this clade. Next we will look at the development of the female gametophyte within an ovule and the development of the male gametophyte in a pollen grain. Then we will follow the transformation of a fertilized ovule into a seed.

Ovules and Production of Eggs

Although a few species of seedless plants are heterosporous, seed plants are unique in retaining the megasporangium and megaspore within the parent sporophyte. A layer of sporophyte tissue called **integument** envelops and protects the megasporangium.

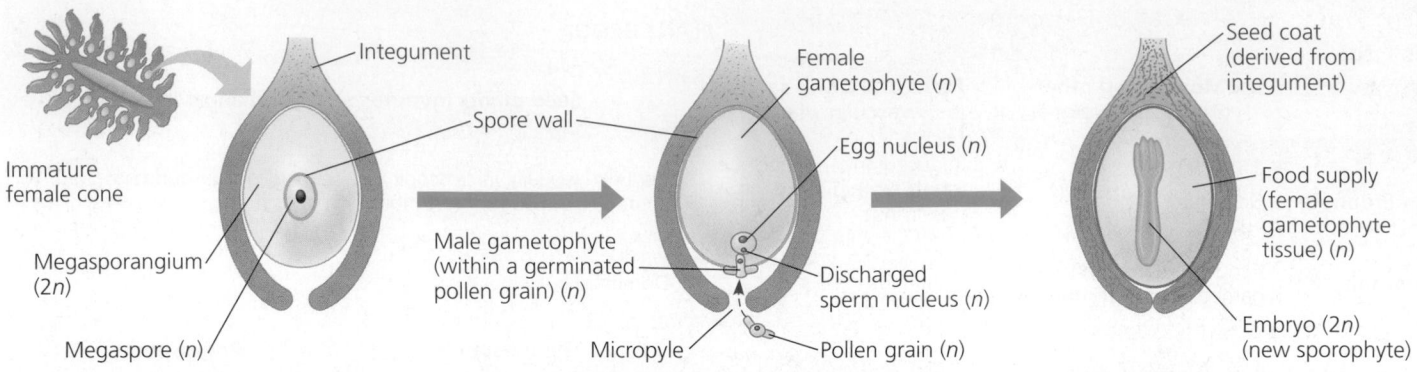

(a) Unfertilized ovule. In this longitudinal section through the ovule of a pine (a gymnosperm), a fleshy megasporangium is surrounded by a protective layer of tissue called an integument. (Angiosperms have two integuments.)

(b) Fertilized ovule. A megaspore develops into a multicellular female gametophyte. The micropyle, the only opening through the integument, allows entry of a pollen grain. The pollen grain contains a male gametophyte, which develops a pollen tube that discharges sperm, thereby fertilizing the egg.

(c) Gymnosperm seed. Fertilization initiates the transformation of the ovule into a seed, which consists of a sporophyte embryo, a food supply, and a protective seed coat derived from the integument.

▲ **Figure 30.3 From ovule to seed in a gymnosperm.**

? *A gymnosperm seed contains cells from how many different plant generations? Identify the cells and whether each is haploid or diploid.*

Gymnosperm megasporangia are surrounded by one integument, whereas those in angiosperms usually have two integuments. The whole structure—megasporangium, megaspore, and their integument(s)—is called an **ovule** (Figure 30.3a). Inside each ovule (from the Latin *ovulum*, little egg), a female gametophyte develops from a megaspore and produces one or more eggs.

Pollen and Production of Sperm

A microspore develops into a **pollen grain** that consists of a male gametophyte enclosed within the pollen wall. The tough pollen wall, which contains the polymer sporopollenin, protects a pollen grain as it is transported from the parent plant by wind, for example, or by hitchhiking on the body of an animal. The transfer of pollen to the part of a seed plant that contains the ovules is called **pollination**. If a pollen grain germinates (begins growing), it gives rise to a pollen tube that discharges sperm into the female gametophyte within the ovule, as shown in **Figure 30.3b**.

Recall that in nonvascular plants and seedless vascular plants such as ferns, free-living gametophytes release flagellated sperm that must swim through a film of water to reach eggs. The distance for this sperm transport rarely exceeds a few centimeters. By contrast, in seed plants a sperm-producing male gametophyte inside a pollen grain can be carried long distances by wind or by animals, eliminating the dependence on water for sperm transport. The sperm of seed plants also do not require motility because sperm are carried directly to the eggs by pollen tubes. Living gymnosperms provide evidence of the evolutionary transition to nonmotile sperm. The sperm of some gymnosperm species (such as ginkgos and cycads, depicted a little later in Figure 30.5) retain the ancient

flagellated condition, but flagella have been lost in the sperm of most gymnosperms and all angiosperms.

The Evolutionary Advantage of Seeds

If a sperm fertilizes an egg of a seed plant, the zygote grows into a sporophyte embryo. As shown in **Figure 30.3c**, the whole ovule develops into a seed: the embryo, along with a food supply, packaged within a protective coat derived from the integument(s).

Until the advent of seeds, the spore was the only protective stage in any plant life cycle. Moss spores, for example, may survive even if the local environment becomes too cold, too hot, or too dry for the mosses themselves to live. Their tiny size enables the moss spores to be dispersed in a dormant state to a new area, where they can germinate and give rise to new moss gametophytes if and when conditions are favorable enough for them to break dormancy. Spores were the main way that mosses and other seedless plants spread over Earth for the first 100 million years of plant life on land.

Although mosses and other seedless plants continue to be very successful today, seeds represent a major evolutionary innovation that contributed to the opening of new ways of life for seed plants. What advantages do seeds provide over spores? Spores are usually single-celled, whereas seeds have a multicellular layer of tissue, the seed coat, that provides extra protection to the embryo. Unlike spores, seeds also have a supply of stored food. This enables a seed to remain dormant for days, months, or even years after being released from the parent plant. (Most spores have much shorter lifetimes.) Under favorable conditions, the seed can then germinate, with its stored food providing critical support for growth as the sporophyte embryo emerges as a seedling. Some seeds land close to their parent sporophyte plant; others are transported long distances (up to hundreds of kilometers) by wind or animals.

CONCEPT CHECK 30.1

1. Contrast sperm delivery in seedless vascular plants with sperm delivery in seed plants.
2. What additional features of seed plants, not present in seedless plants, have contributed to the enormous success of seed plants on land?
3. **WHAT IF?** If seed plants were homosporous, what aspects of their reproduction would change? Explain.

For suggested answers, see Appendix A.

◀ **Figure 30.4 A progymnosperm.** *Archaeopteris*, which lived 380 million years ago, produced wood and was heterosporous, but it did not produce seeds. Growing up to 20 m tall, it had fernlike leaves.

CONCEPT **30.2**

Gymnosperms bear "naked" seeds, typically on cones

Nonvascular plants (bryophytes)
Seedless vascular plants
Gymnosperms
Angiosperms

Recall from Chapter 29 that gymnosperms are plants that have "naked" seeds that are not enclosed in ovaries. Their seeds are exposed on modified leaves (sporophylls) that usually form cones (strobili). (In contrast, angiosperm seeds are enclosed in fruits, which are mature ovaries.) We turn now to the origin of gymnosperms and other early seed plants.

Gymnosperm Evolution

Fossil evidence reveals that by late in the Devonian period (about 380 million years ago), some plants had begun to acquire adaptations characteristic of seed plants. For example, *Archaeopteris* was a heterosporous tree that had a woody stem (**Figure 30.4**). It did not, however, bear seeds. Such transitional species of seedless vascular plants are sometimes called **progymnosperms**.

The first seed-bearing plants to appear in the fossil record date from around 360 million years ago, more than 200 million years before the first angiosperm fossils. These early seed plants became extinct, as did several later lineages. Although the relationships between extinct and surviving lineages of seed plants remain uncertain, morphological and molecular evidence places the surviving lineages of seed plants into two monophyletic sister clades: the gymnosperms and the angiosperms (see Figure 29.7).

The earliest fossils of gymnosperms are about 305 million years old. These early gymnosperms lived in Carboniferous ecosystems still dominated by lycophytes, horsetails, ferns, and other seedless vascular plants. As the Carboniferous period gave way to the Permian, markedly drier climatic conditions favored the spread of gymnosperms. The flora and fauna changed dramatically, as many groups of organisms disappeared and others became prominent (see Chapter 25). Though most pronounced in the seas, the changeover also affected terrestrial life. For example, in the animal kingdom, amphibians decreased in diversity and were replaced by reptiles, which were especially well adapted to the arid conditions. Similarly, the lycophytes, horsetails, and ferns that dominated the Carboniferous swamps were largely replaced by gymnosperms, which were more suited to the drier climate. Gymnosperms have the key terrestrial adaptations found in all seed plants, such as seeds and pollen. In addition, some gymnosperms were particularly well suited to arid conditions because of the thick cuticles and relatively small surface areas of their needle-shaped leaves.

Geologists consider the end of the Permian period, about 251 million years ago, to be the boundary between the Paleozoic ("old life") and Mesozoic ("middle life") eras. Life changed profoundly as gymnosperms dominated terrestrial ecosystems throughout the Mesozoic, serving as the food supply for giant herbivorous dinosaurs. The Mesozoic era ended with mass extinctions of most of the dinosaurs and many other animal groups, and the planet gradually cooled. Although angiosperms now dominate most terrestrial ecosystems, many gymnosperms remain an important part of Earth's flora. For example, vast regions in northern latitudes are covered by forests of cone-bearing gymnosperms called **conifers**, which include spruce, pine, fir, and redwood (see Figure 52.21).

Of the ten plant phyla in the taxonomic scheme adopted by this textbook (see Table 29.1), four are gymnosperms: Cycadophyta, Ginkgophyta, Gnetophyta, and Coniferophyta. The relationships of these four phyla to each other are uncertain. **Figure 30.5**, on the next two pages, surveys the diversity of extant gymnosperms.

Exploring Gymnosperm Diversity

Phylum Cycadophyta

Cycads are the next largest group of gymnosperms after the conifers. They have large cones and palmlike leaves (true palm species are angiosperms). Only about 130 species survive today, but cycads thrived during the Mesozoic era, known as the age of cycads as well as the age of dinosaurs.

Cycas revoluta

Phylum Ginkgophyta

Ginkgo biloba is the only surviving species of this phylum. Also known as the maidenhair tree, it has deciduous fanlike leaves that turn gold in autumn. It is a popular ornamental tree in cities because it tolerates air pollution well. Landscapers often plant only pollen-producing trees because the fleshy seeds smell rancid as they decay.

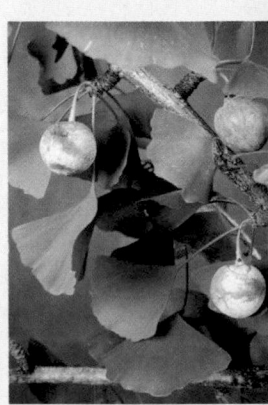

Phylum Gnetophyta

Plants in the phylum Gnetophyta, called gnetophytes, consist of three genera: *Gnetum*, *Ephedra*, and *Welwitschia*. Some species are tropical, whereas others live in deserts. Although very different in appearance, the genera are grouped together based on molecular data.

Welwitschia. This genus consists of one species, *Welwitschia mirabilis*, a plant that lives only in the deserts of southwestern Africa. Its straplike leaves are among the largest leaves known.

Ovulate cones

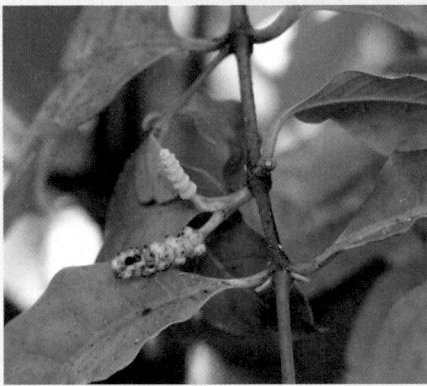

Gnetum. This genus includes about 35 species of tropical trees, shrubs, and vines, mainly native to Africa and Asia. Their leaves look similar to those of flowering plants, and their seeds look somewhat like fruits.

Ephedra. This genus includes about 40 species that inhabit arid regions worldwide. These desert shrubs, commonly called "Mormon tea," produce the compound ephedrine, which is used medicinally as a decongestant.

Phylum Coniferophyta is by far the largest of the gymnosperm phyla, consisting of about 600 species of conifers (from the Latin *conus*, cone, and *ferre*, to carry). Many are large trees, such as cypresses and redwoods. A few conifer species dominate vast forested regions of the Northern Hemisphere, where the growing season is relatively short because of latitude or altitude.

Most conifers are evergreens; they retain their leaves throughout the year. Even during winter, a limited amount of photosynthesis occurs on sunny days. When spring comes, conifers already have fully developed leaves that can take advantage of the sunnier, warmer days. Some conifers, such as the dawn redwood, tamarack, and larch, are deciduous trees that lose leaves each autumn.

Douglas fir. This evergreen tree (*Pseudotsuga menziesii*) provides more timber than any other North American tree species. Some uses include house framing, plywood, pulpwood for paper, railroad ties, and boxes and crates.

Common juniper. The "berries" of the common juniper (*Juniperus communis*) are actually ovule-producing cones consisting of fleshy sporophylls.

European larch. The needle-like leaves of this deciduous conifer (*Larix decidua*) turn yellow before they are shed in autumn. Native to the mountains of central Europe, including Switzerland's Matterhorn, depicted here, this species is extremely cold-tolerant, able to survive winter temperatures that plunge to −50°C.

Wollemi pine. A survivor of a conifer group once known only from fossils, living Wollemi pines (*Wollemia nobilis*) were discovered in 1994 in a national park only 150 km from Sydney, Australia. The species consists of just 40 known individuals in two small groves. The inset photo compares the leaves of this "living fossil" with actual fossils.

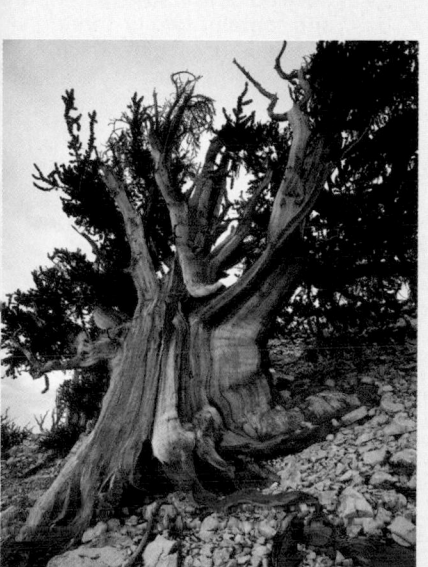

Bristlecone pine. This species (*Pinus longaeva*), which is found in the White Mountains of California, includes some of the oldest living organisms, reaching ages of more than 4,600 years. One tree (not shown here) is called Methuselah because it may be the world's oldest living tree. To protect the tree, scientists keep its location a secret.

Sequoia. This giant sequoia (*Sequoiadendron giganteum*) in California's Sequoia National Park weighs about 2,500 metric tons, equivalent to about 24 blue whales (the largest animals) or 40,000 people. The giant sequoia is one of the largest living organisms and also among the most ancient, with some individuals estimated to be between 1,800 and 2,700 years old. Their cousins, the coast redwoods (*Sequoia sempervirens*), grow to heights of more than 110 m (taller than the Statue of Liberty) and are found only in a narrow coastal strip of northern California and southern Oregon.

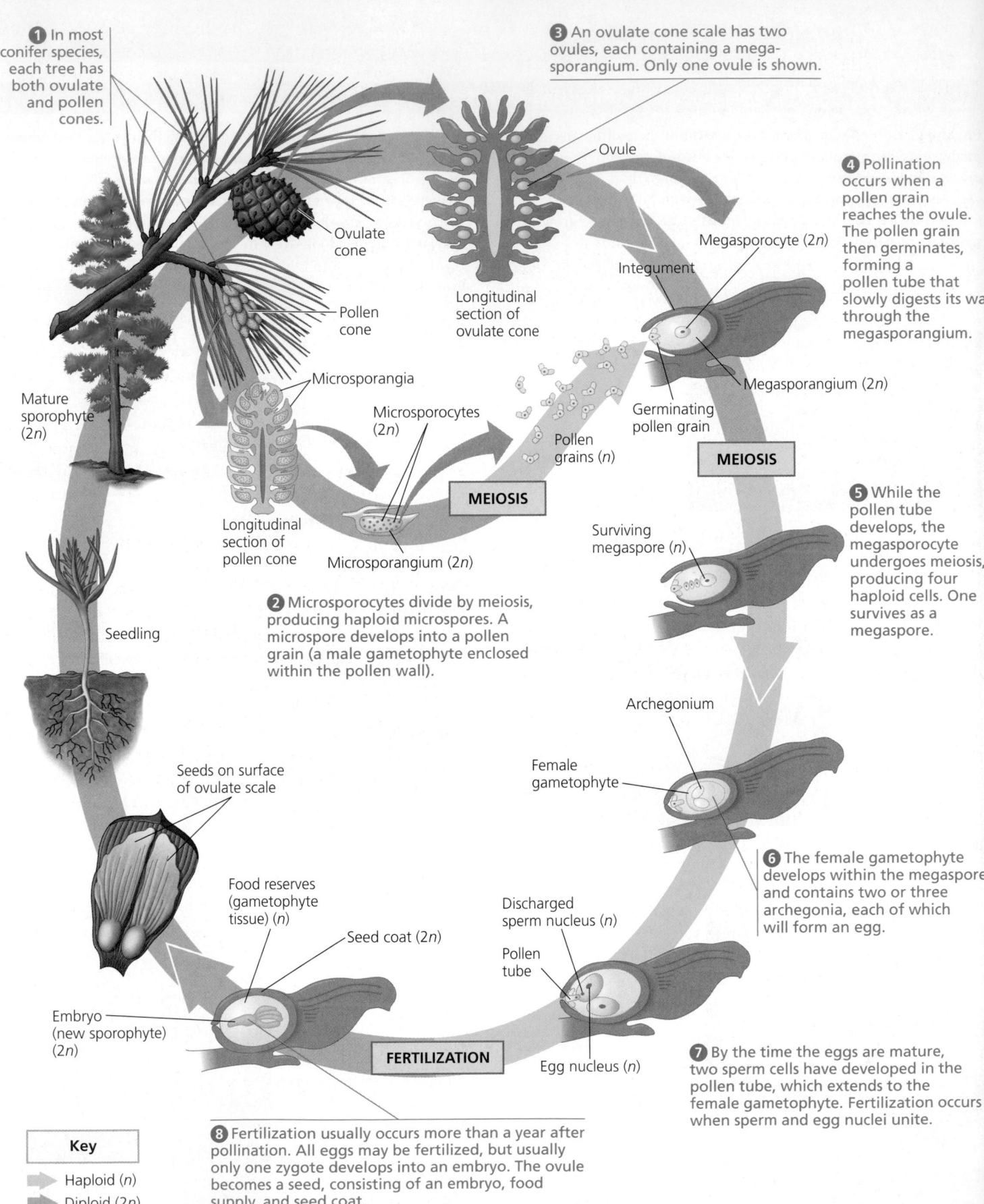

1 In most conifer species, each tree has both ovulate and pollen cones.

3 An ovulate cone scale has two ovules, each containing a mega-sporangium. Only one ovule is shown.

Ovule

Ovulate cone

Pollen cone

Longitudinal section of ovulate cone

4 Pollination occurs when a pollen grain reaches the ovule. The pollen grain then germinates, forming a pollen tube that slowly digests its wa[y] through the megasporangium.

Integument

Megasporocyte (2n)

Germinating pollen grain

Megasporangium (2n)

Mature sporophyte (2n)

Microsporangia

Microsporocytes (2n)

Pollen grains (n)

MEIOSIS

MEIOSIS

Longitudinal section of pollen cone

Microsporangium (2n)

2 Microsporocytes divide by meiosis, producing haploid microspores. A microspore develops into a pollen grain (a male gametophyte enclosed within the pollen wall).

Surviving megaspore (n)

5 While the pollen tube develops, the megasporocyte undergoes meiosis, producing four haploid cells. One survives as a megaspore.

Seedling

Archegonium

Female gametophyte

6 The female gametophyte develops within the megaspore and contains two or three archegonia, each of which will form an egg.

Seeds on surface of ovulate scale

Food reserves (gametophyte tissue) (n)

Seed coat (2n)

Discharged sperm nucleus (n)

Pollen tube

Embryo (new sporophyte) (2n)

FERTILIZATION

Egg nucleus (n)

7 By the time the eggs are mature, two sperm cells have developed in the pollen tube, which extends to the female gametophyte. Fertilization occurs when sperm and egg nuclei unite.

8 Fertilization usually occurs more than a year after pollination. All eggs may be fertilized, but usually only one zygote develops into an embryo. The ovule becomes a seed, consisting of an embryo, food supply, and seed coat.

Key

Haploid (n)

Diploid (2n)

▲ **Figure 30.6 The life cycle of a pine.**

The Life Cycle of a Pine: *A Closer Look*

As you read earlier, seed plant evolution has included three key reproductive adaptations: the increasing dominance of the sporophyte; the advent of the seed as a resistant, dispersible stage in the life cycle; and the appearance of pollen as an airborne agent that brings gametes together. **Figure 30.6**, on the facing page, shows how these adaptations come into play during the life cycle of a pine, a familiar conifer.

The pine tree is the sporophyte; its sporangia are located on scalelike structures packed densely in cones. Like all seed plants, conifers are heterosporous. In conifers, the two types of spores are produced by separate cones: small pollen cones and large ovulate cones. In most pine species, each tree has both types of cones. In pollen cones, microsporocytes (microspore mother cells) undergo meiosis, producing haploid microspores. Each microspore develops into a pollen grain containing a male gametophyte. In pines and other conifers, the yellow pollen is released in large amounts and carried by the wind, dusting everything in its path. Meanwhile, in ovulate cones, megasporocytes (megaspore mother cells) undergo meiosis and produce haploid megaspores inside the ovule. Surviving megaspores develop into female gametophytes, which are retained within the sporangia.

From the time young pollen and ovulate cones appear on the tree, it takes nearly three years for the male and female gametophytes to be produced and brought together and for mature seeds to form from the fertilized ovules. The scales of each ovulate cone then separate, and the seeds are dispersed by the wind. A seed that lands in a suitable environment then germinates, its embryo emerging as a pine seedling.

CONCEPT CHECK 30.2

1. Use examples from Figure 30.5 to describe how various gymnosperms are similar yet distinctive.
2. Explain how the pine life cycle (see Figure 30.6) reflects basic characteristics of seed plants.
3. **WHAT IF?** Does the hypothesis that gymnosperms and angiosperms are sister clades imply that these two lineages originated at the same time? Explain.

For suggested answers, see Appendix A.

CONCEPT 30.3

The reproductive adaptations of angiosperms include flowers and fruits

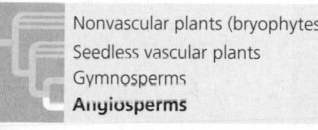
Nonvascular plants (bryophytes)
Seedless vascular plants
Gymnosperms
Angiosperms

Commonly known as flowering plants, angiosperms are seed plants that produce the reproductive structures called flowers and fruits. The name *angiosperm* (from the Greek *angion*, container) refers to seeds contained in fruits, the mature ovaries. Today, angiosperms are the most diverse and widespread of all plants, with more than 250,000 species (about 90% of all plant species).

Characteristics of Angiosperms

All angiosperms are classified in a single phylum, Anthophyta (from the Greek *anthos*, flower). Before considering the evolution of angiosperms, we will examine their key adaptations—flowers and fruits—and their roles in the angiosperm life cycle.

Flowers

The **flower** is an angiosperm structure specialized for sexual reproduction. In many angiosperm species, insects or other animals transfer pollen from one flower to the sex organs on another flower, which makes pollination more directed than the wind-dependent pollination of most gymnosperms. However, some angiosperms *are* wind-pollinated, particularly those species that occur in dense populations, such as grasses and tree species in temperate forests.

A flower is a specialized shoot that can have up to four rings of modified leaves (sporophylls) called floral organs: sepals, petals, stamens, and carpels **(Figure 30.7)**. Starting at the base of the flower are the **sepals**, which are usually green and enclose the flower before it opens (think of a rosebud). Interior to the sepals are the **petals**, which are brightly colored in most flowers and aid in attracting pollinators. Flowers that are wind-pollinated, however, generally lack brightly colored parts. In all angiosperms, the sepals and petals are sterile floral organs, meaning that they are not directly involved in reproduction. Within the petals are two whorls of fertile floral organs that produce spores, the stamens and carpels. **Stamens** produce

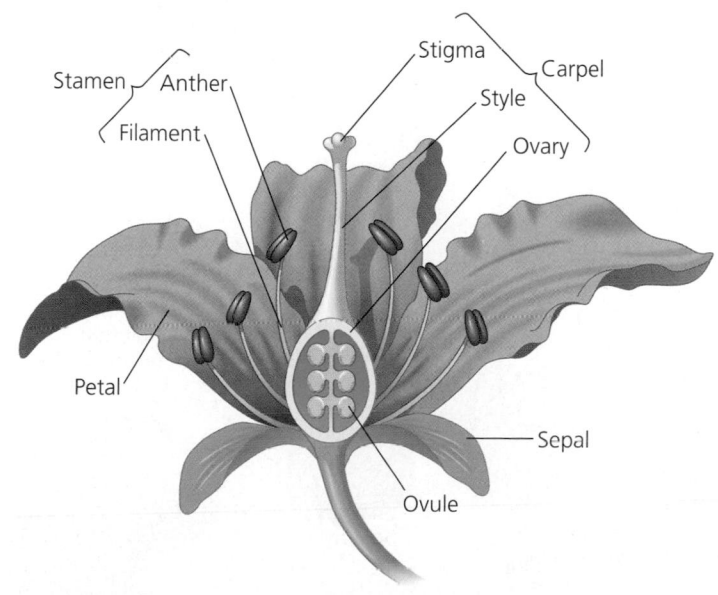

▲ Figure 30.7 **The structure of an idealized flower.**

microspores that develop into pollen grains containing male gametophytes. A stamen consists of a stalk called the **filament** and a terminal sac, the **anther**, where pollen is produced. **Carpels** make megaspores and their products, female gametophytes. Some flowers, such as pea blossoms, have a single carpel, while others, such as the magnolia on the cover of this book, have several separate carpels. At the tip of the carpel is a sticky **stigma** that receives pollen. A **style** leads from the stigma to the **ovary** at the base of the carpel; the ovary contains one or more ovules. If fertilized, an ovule develops into a seed.

Fruits

A **fruit** typically consists of a mature ovary, although it can include other flower parts as well. As seeds develop from ovules after fertilization, the wall of the ovary thickens. A pea pod is an example of a fruit, with seeds (mature ovules, the peas) encased in the ripened ovary (the pod).

Fruits protect dormant seeds and aid in their dispersal. Mature fruits can be either fleshy or dry **(Figure 30.8)**. Oranges,

plums, and grapes are examples of fleshy fruits, in which the wall of the ovary becomes soft during ripening. Dry fruits include beans, nuts, and grains. The dry, wind-dispersed fruits of grasses, harvested while on the plant, are major staple foods for humans. The cereal grains of wheat, rice, maize, and other grasses, though easily mistaken for seeds, are each actually a fruit with a dry outer covering (the former wall of the ovary) that adheres to the seed coat of the seed within.

Various adaptations of fruits help to disperse seeds **(Figure 30.9)**. The seeds of some flowering plants, such as dandelions and maples, are contained within fruits that function like parachutes or propellers, adaptations that enhance dispersal by wind. Some fruits, such as coconuts, are adapted to dispersal by water (see Figure 38.11). And many angiosperms rely on animals to carry seeds. Some of these plants have fruits modified as burrs that cling to animal fur (or the clothes of humans). Other angiosperms produce edible fruits, which are usually nutritious, sweet tasting, and vividly colored, advertising their ripeness. When an animal eats the fruit, it digests the fruit's fleshy part, but the tough seeds usually pass unharmed through the animal's digestive tract. Animals may deposit the seeds, along with a supply of natural fertilizer, many kilometers from where the fruit was eaten.

▼ Figure 30.8 **Some variations in fruit structure.**

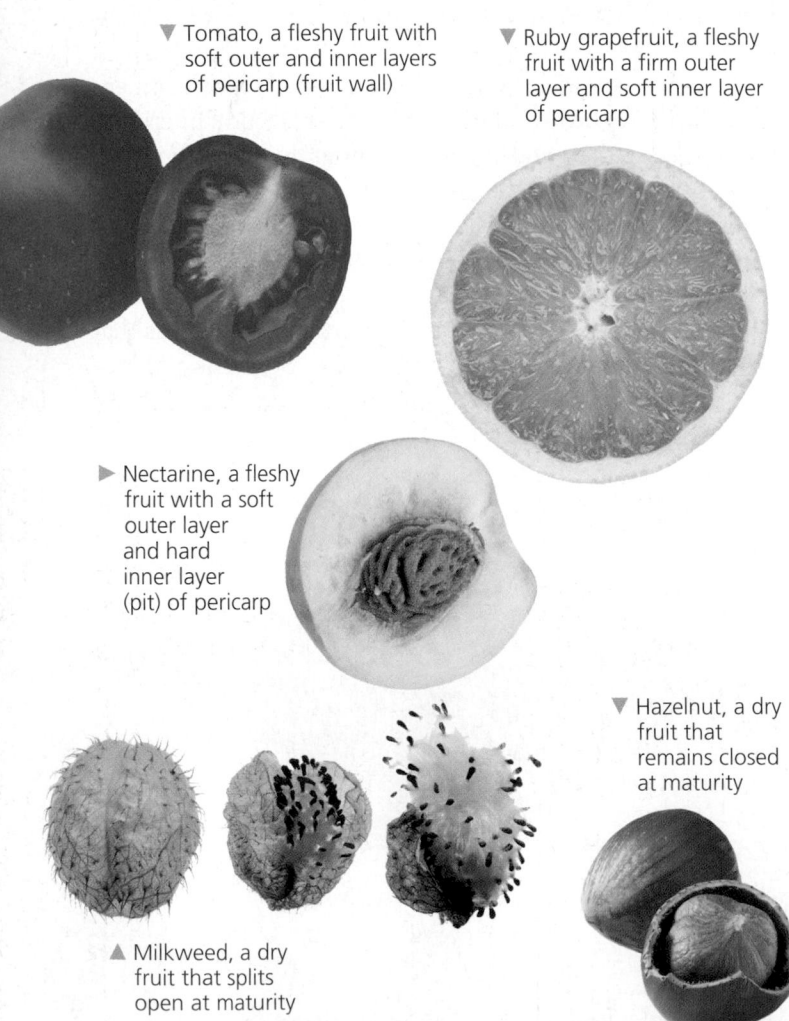

▼ Tomato, a fleshy fruit with soft outer and inner layers of pericarp (fruit wall)

▼ Ruby grapefruit, a fleshy fruit with a firm outer layer and soft inner layer of pericarp

▶ Nectarine, a fleshy fruit with a soft outer layer and hard inner layer (pit) of pericarp

▼ Hazelnut, a dry fruit that remains closed at maturity

▲ Milkweed, a dry fruit that splits open at maturity

▼ Figure 30.9 **Fruit adaptations that enhance seed dispersal.**

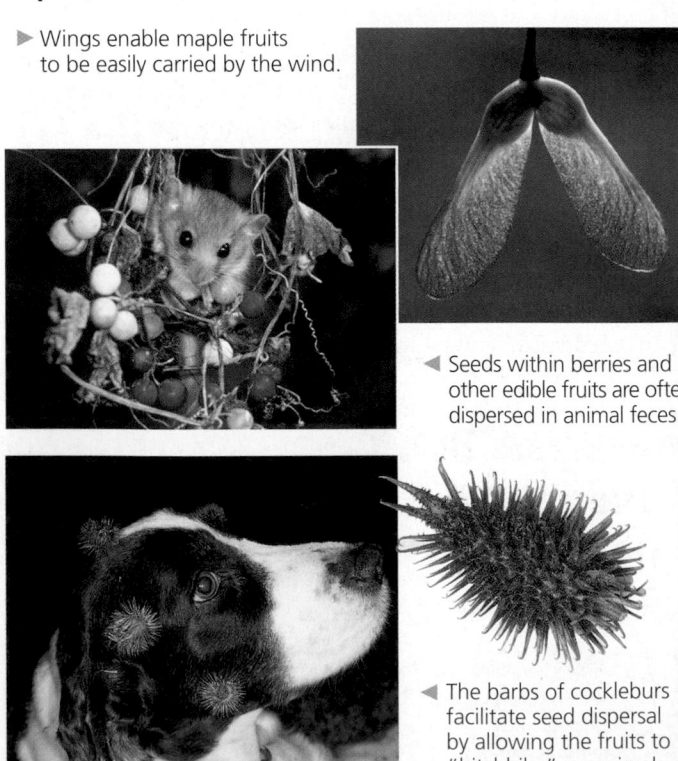

▶ Wings enable maple fruits to be easily carried by the wind.

◀ Seeds within berries and other edible fruits are often dispersed in animal feces.

◀ The barbs of cockleburs facilitate seed dispersal by allowing the fruits to "hitchhike" on animals.

The Angiosperm Life Cycle

You can follow a typical angiosperm life cycle in **Figure 30.10**. The flower of the sporophyte produces microspores that form male gametophytes and megaspores that form female gametophytes. The male gametophytes are in the pollen grains, which develop within microsporangia in the anthers. Each male gametophyte has two haploid cells: a *generative cell* that divides, forming two sperm, and a *tube cell* that pro-

duces a pollen tube. Each ovule, which develops in an ovary, contains a female gametophyte, also known as an **embryo sac**. The embryo sac consists of only a few cells, one of which is the egg. (We will discuss gametophyte development in more detail in Chapter 38.)

After its release from the anther, the pollen is carried to the sticky stigma at the tip of a carpel. Although some flowers self-pollinate, most have mechanisms that ensure **cross-pollination**, which in angiosperms is the transfer of pollen from an anther

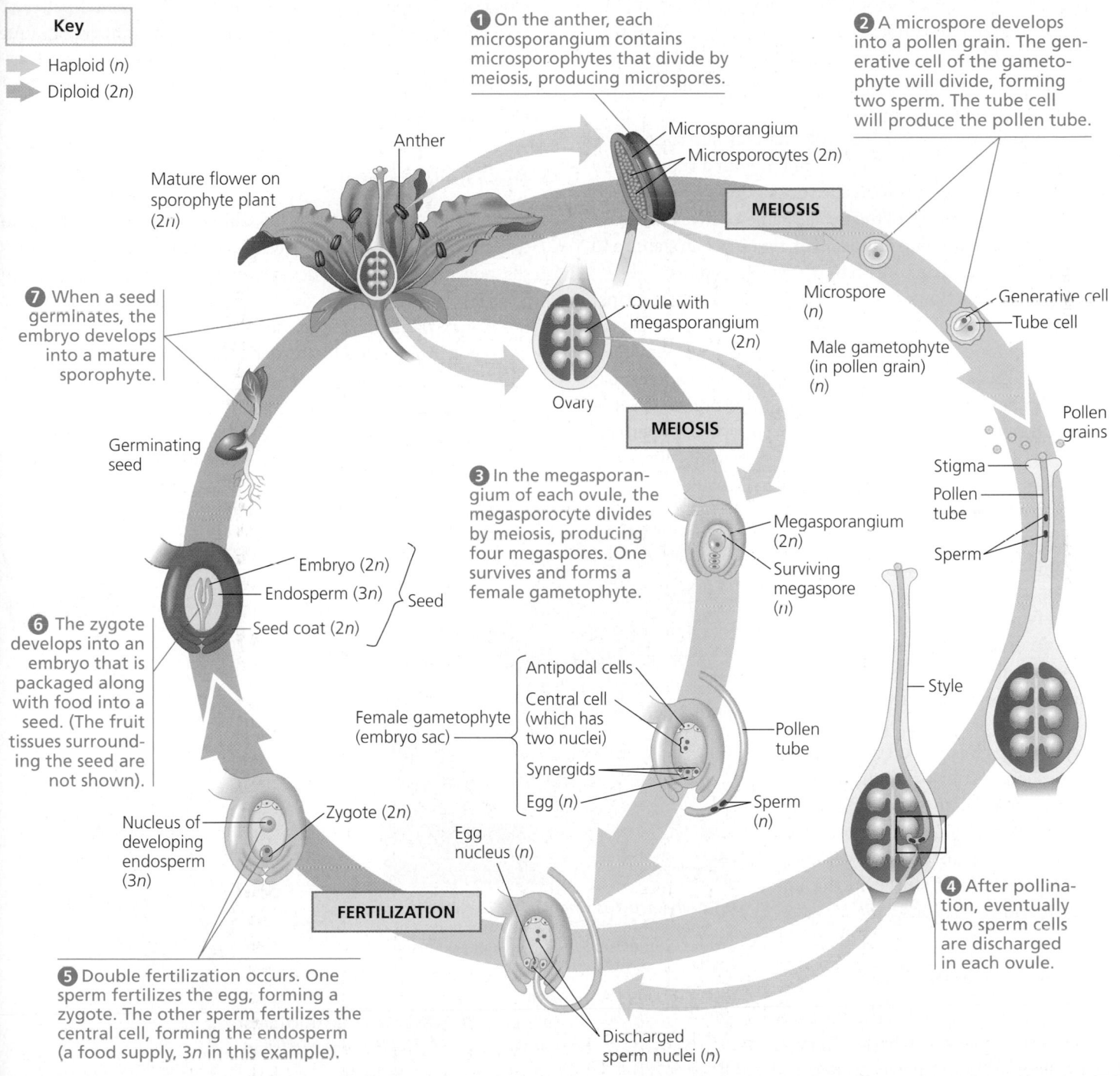

▲ **Figure 30.10 The life cycle of an angiosperm.**

of a flower on one plant to the stigma of a flower on another plant of the same species. Cross-pollination enhances genetic variability. In some cases, stamens and carpels of a single flower may mature at different times, or they may be so arranged that self-pollination is unlikely.

The pollen grain germinates after it adheres to the stigma of a carpel. The pollen grain's male gametophyte extends a pollen tube that grows down within the style of the carpel. After reaching the ovary, the pollen tube penetrates through the **micropyle**, a pore in the integuments of the ovule, and discharges two sperm cells into the female gametophyte (embryo sac). One sperm fertilizes the egg, forming a diploid zygote. The other sperm fuses with the two nuclei in the large central cell of the female gametophyte, producing a triploid cell. This type of **double fertilization**, in which one fertilization event produces a zygote and the other produces a triploid cell, is unique to angiosperms.

After double fertilization, the ovule matures into a seed. The zygote develops into a sporophyte embryo with a rudimentary root and one or two seed leaves called **cotyledons**. The fertilized nucleus of the central cell of the female gametophyte divides repeatedly and develops into **endosperm**, tissue rich in starch and other food reserves that nourish the developing embryo.

What is the function of double fertilization in angiosperms? One hypothesis is that double fertilization synchronizes the development of food storage in the seed with the development of the embryo. If a particular flower is not pollinated or sperm cells are not discharged into the embryo sac, fertilization does not occur, and neither endosperm nor embryo forms. So perhaps double fertilization is an adaptation that prevents flowering plants from squandering nutrients on infertile ovules.

Another type of double fertilization occurs in some gymnosperm species belonging to the phylum Gnetophyta. However, double fertilization in these species gives rise to two embryos rather than to an embryo and endosperm.

As you read earlier, the seed consists of the embryo, endosperm, and a seed coat derived from the integuments. An ovary develops into a fruit as its ovules become seeds. After being dispersed, a seed may germinate if environmental conditions are favorable. The coat ruptures and the embryo emerges as a seedling, using food stored in the endosperm and cotyledons.

Angiosperm Evolution

Clarifying the origin and early evolution of angiosperms—what Charles Darwin once called an "abominable mystery"— poses fascinating challenges to evolutionary biologists. Angiosperms originated at least 140 million years ago, and during the late Mesozoic, the major branches of the clade diverged from their common ancestor. By the mid-Cretaceous period (100 million years ago), angiosperms began to dominate many terrestrial ecosystems. Landscapes changed dramatically as conifers, cycads, and other gymnosperms gave way to flowering plants in many parts of the world.

The flowers and fruits of angiosperms distinguish them markedly from living gymnosperms, which makes the origins of angiosperms puzzling. To understand how the angiosperm body plan emerged, scientists are studying fossils, refining angiosperm phylogeny, and elucidating developmental patterns that underlie flowers and other angiosperm innovations. As we'll see, much progress has been made toward solving Darwin's mystery—but we still do not fully understand how angiosperms originated from earlier seed plants.

Fossil Angiosperms

In the late 1990s, scientists in China discovered several intriguing fossils of 125-million-year-old angiosperms. These fossils, now named *Archaefructus liaoningensis* and *Archaefructus sinensis* **(Figure 30.11)**, display both derived and ancestral traits. *Archaefructus sinensis,* for example, has anthers and also has seeds inside closed carpels but lacks petals and sepals. In 2002, scientists completed a phylogenetic comparison of *A. sinensis* with 173 living plants. (*Archaefructus liaoningensis* was not included because its fossils are not as well preserved.) The researchers concluded that *Archaefructus* ". . . may belong to the earliest-diverging group of angiosperms known."

(a) *Archaefructus sinensis*, **a 125-million-year-old fossil.** This species may represent the sister group to all other angiosperms.

(b) Artist's reconstruction of *Archaefructus sinensis*

▲ **Figure 30.11 A primitive flowering plant?**

If *Archaefructus* was indeed a very early angiosperm, that would suggest that the ancestors of flowering plants were herbaceous rather than woody. *Archaefructus* was discovered along with fish fossils and has bulbous structures that might be aquatic adaptations, implying that angiosperms may have originated as aquatic plants. The discoverers of *Archaefructus* have suggested that fast-growing herbaceous plants could have returned to water and thrived there, escaping competition with other seed plants and then later taking over the land.

More recently, however, some paleobotanists have disputed this interpretation. They cite examples of angiosperms from later-diverging lineages that became aquatic, and in which simpler flowers evolved that resemble the "primitive" flowers of *Archaefructus*. Such debates, typical whenever a seemingly transitional fossil is discovered, may be resolved when more fossils and other types of evidence emerge.

Angiosperm Phylogeny

To shed light on the body plan of early angiosperms, scientists have long sought to identify which seed plants, including fossil species, are most closely related to angiosperms. Molecular and morphological evidence suggests that living gymnosperms are a monophyletic group whose earliest lineages diverged from the ancestors of angiosperms about 305 million years ago. Note that this does not necessarily imply that angiosperms originated 305 million years ago—but that the most recent common ancestor of gymnosperms

and angiosperms lived at that time. Angiosperms may, in fact, be most closely related to extinct seed plants such as the group called Bennettitales, which had flowerlike structures that may have been pollinated by insects (**Figure 30.12a**). Systematists hope to resolve this issue through phylogenetic studies that combine data from fossil and living species of a wide range of seed plants.

Making sense of the origin of angiosperms also depends on working out the order in which angiosperm clades diverged from one another. Here, dramatic progress has been made in recent years. Molecular and morphological evidence suggests that *Amborella* and water lilies are living representatives of two of the most ancient angiosperm lineages (**Figure 30.12b**). This information has already proved useful as researchers seek to interpret new findings about plant development.

Developmental Patterns in Angiosperms

Additional clues about the origin of flowering plants are emerging from studies of plant development. For example, a 2006 study demonstrated that in *Amborella*, eggs form from precursor cells that differ from the egg precursor cells of most other living angiosperms. Intriguingly, the way in which eggs form in *Amborella* has similarities to how eggs form in gymnosperms—a possible link to the ancient common ancestor of gymnosperms and angiosperms. Other studies suggest that in a variety of early angiosperms (as well as in *Amborella*), the outer of the two protective integuments appears to be a modified leaf that originates

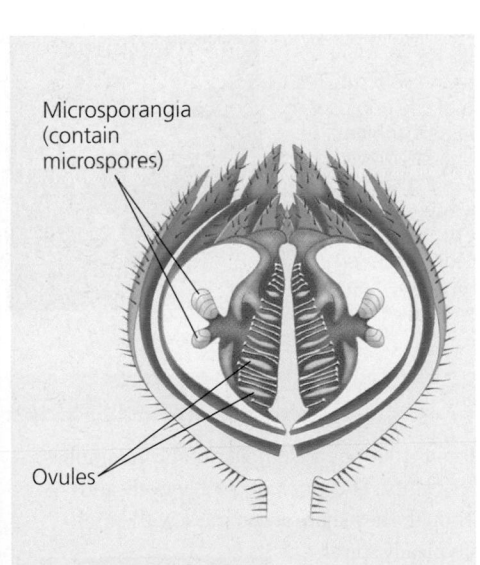

Microsporangia (contain microspores)

Ovules

(a) A possible ancestor of the angiosperms? This reconstruction shows a cross section through the flowerlike structures found in the Bennettitales, an extinct group of seed plants hypothesized to be more closely related to angiosperms than to gymnosperms.

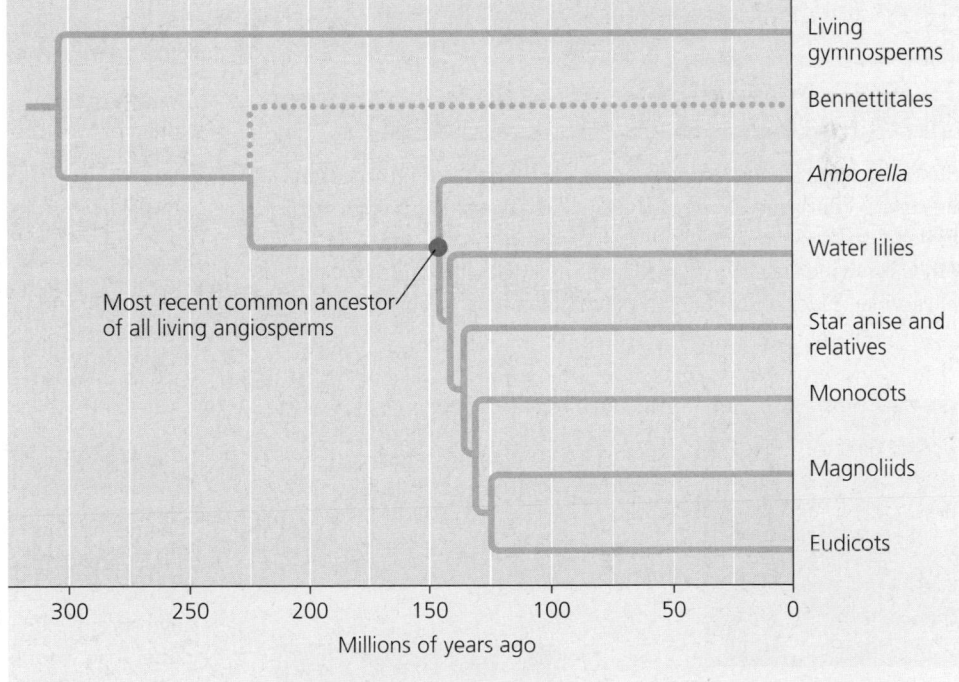

Living gymnosperms

Bennettitales

Amborella

Water lilies

Star anise and relatives

Monocots

Magnoliids

Eudicots

Most recent common ancestor of all living angiosperms

300   250   200   150   100   50   0
Millions of years ago

(b) Angiosperm phylogeny. This tree represents one current hypothesis of angiosperm evolutionary relationships, based on morphological and molecular evidence. Angiosperms originated at least 140 million years ago. The dotted line indicates the uncertain position of the Bennettitales, a possible sister group to the angiosperms.

▲ **Figure 30.12 Angiosperm evolutionary history.**
? *Would the branching order of the phylogeny in (b) necessarily have to be redrawn if a 150-million-year-old fossil monocot were discovered? Explain.*

separately from the inner integument. Because gymnosperms have only one integument, scientists are curious exactly how the second integument originated in angiosperms. Finally, in work that holds great promise for deepening our understanding of the origin of flowering plants, researchers are currently studying how genes that control flower development in angiosperms are expressed in a range of gymnosperm and angiosperm species (see Chapter 38).

Angiosperm Diversity

From their humble beginnings in the Mesozoic, angiosperms have diversified into more than 250,000 living species. Until the late 1990s, most systematists divided flowering plants into two groups, based partly on the number of cotyledons, or seed leaves, in the embryo. Species with one cotyledon were called **monocots**, and those with two were called **dicots**. Other features, such as flower and leaf structure, were also used to define the two groups. For example, monocots typically have parallel leaf veins (think of a grass blade), while the veins of most dicots have a netlike pattern (think of an oak leaf). Some examples of monocots are orchids, palms, and grain crops such as maize, wheat, and rice. Some examples of dicots are roses, peas, sunflowers, and maples.

Recent DNA studies, however, indicate that the monocot-dicot distinction does not completely reflect evolutionary relationships. Current research supports the hypothesis that monocots form a clade but reveals that the species traditionally called dicots are polyphyletic. The vast majority of species once categorized as dicots form a large clade, now known as **eudicots** ("true" dicots). The rest of the former dicots are now grouped into several small lineages. Three of these lineages are informally called **basal angiosperms** because they appear to include the flowering plants belonging to the oldest lineages. A fourth lineage, called the **magnoliids**, evolved later. **Figure 30.13** provides an overview of angiosperm diversity.

Evolutionary Links Between Angiosperms and Animals

Ever since they colonized land, animals have influenced the evolution of terrestrial plants, and vice versa. For example, herbivores can reduce a plant's reproductive success by eating its roots, leaves, or seeds. As a result, if a novel and effective defense against herbivores originates in a group of plants, those plants may be favored by natural selection—as will any herbivores that can overcome this new defense.

▼ Figure 30.13

Exploring Angiosperm Diversity

Basal Angiosperms

Surviving basal angiosperms are currently thought to consist of three lineages comprising only about 100 species. The oldest lineage seems to be represented by a single species, *Amborella trichopoda*. The other surviving lineages diverged later: a clade that includes water lilies and a clade consisting of the star anise and its relatives.

Amborella trichopoda. This small shrub, found only on the South Pacific island of New Caledonia, may be the sole survivor of a branch at the base of the angiosperm tree. *Amborella* lacks vessels, which are present in angiosperms in later-diverging lineages. Consisting of xylem cells arranged in continuous tubes, vessels transport water more efficiently than tracheids. Their absence in *Amborella* indicates they evolved after the lineage that gave rise to *Amborella* diverged.

Water lily (*Nymphaea "Rene Gerard"*). Water lilies are living members of a clade that may be predated only by the *Amborella* lineage.

Magnoliids

Magnoliids consist of about 8,000 species, most notably magnolias, laurels, and black pepper plants. They include both woody and herbaceous species. Although they share some traits with basal angiosperms, such as a typically spiral rather than whorled arrangement of floral organs, magnoliids are more closely related to eudicots and monocots.

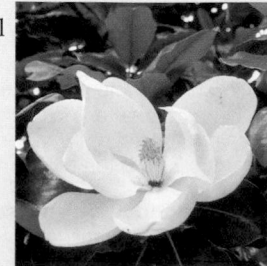

Southern magnolia (*Magnolia grandiflora*). This member of the magnolia family is a woody magnoliid. This variety of southern magnolia, called "Goliath," has flowers that measure up to about a foot across.

Star anise (*Illicium floridanum*). This species represents a third surviving lineage of basal angiosperms.

Monocots

More than one-quarter of angiosperm species are monocots—about 70,000 species. These examples represent some of the largest families.

Eudicots

More than two-thirds of angiosperm species are eudicots—roughly 170,000 species. Below is a sampling of eudicot floral diversity.

Orchid (*Lemboglossum rossii*)

Pygmy date palm (*Phoenix roebelenii*)

Lily (*Lilium "Enchantment"*)

Barley (*Hordeum vulgare*), a grass

Anther

Stigma

Filament

Ovary

Monocot Characteristics		Eudicot Characteristics
One cotyledon	**Embryos**	Two cotyledons
Veins usually parallel	**Leaf venation**	Veins usually netlike
Vascular tissue scattered	**Stems**	Vascular tissue usually arranged in ring
Root system usually fibrous (no main root)	**Roots**	Taproot (main root) usually present
Pollen grain with one opening	**Pollen**	Pollen grain with three openings
Floral organs usually in multiples of three	**Flowers**	Floral organs usually in multiples of four or five

California poppy (*Eschscholzia californica*)

Pyrenean oak (*Quercus pyrenaica*)

Dog rose (*Rosa canina*), a wild rose

Snow pea (*Pisum sativum*), a legume

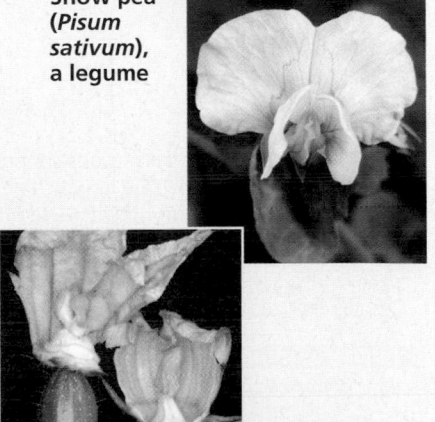

Zucchini (*Cucurbita pepo*) flowers

▼ Figure 30.14 **Inquiry**

Can flower shape influence speciation rate?

EXPERIMENT The shapes of bilaterally symmetrical flowers can force pollinators seeking nectar to enter the flower from certain directions only. This facilitates the placement of pollen on particular parts of the pollinator's body, which in turn can increase how effectively pollen is transferred between flowers of the same species. Such specificity in plant-pollinator relationships tends to decrease gene flow between diverging plant populations and hence could lead to increased rates of plant speciation. Risa Sargent, then at the University of British Columbia, tested this hypothesis by determining whether angiosperm families with bilaterally symmetrical flowers contain more species than do closely related families with radially symmetrical flowers. She took this approach:

1. Identify as many cases as possible in which a clade of one or more families with bilaterally symmetrical flowers is sister to a clade whose members have radially symmetrical flowers. By definition, such sister clades share an immediate common ancestor and hence had the same amount of time to form new species.

2. Determine the number of species in each pair of sister clades. The hypothesis would be supported if bilaterally symmetrical clades consistently have more species than their radially symmetrical sister clades.

RESULTS Sargent identified 19 pairs of sister clades that differed in flower shape. In 15 of these pairs, clades with bilateral symmetry had more species than did clades with radial symmetry.

CONCLUSION Sargent's results supported the hypothesis that flower shape affects the rate at which new species form, with bilateral symmetry promoting increased rates of speciation.

SOURCE R. D. Sargent, Floral symmetry affects speciation rates in angiosperms, *Proceedings of the Royal Society B: Biological Sciences* 271:603–608 (2004).

Inquiry in Action Read and analyze the original paper in *Inquiry in Action: Interpreting Scientific Papers*.

WHAT IF? Does this study show that flower shape is *correlated with* the rate at which new species form, or that flower shape is *responsible for* this rate? Explain.

Plant-pollinator and other mutually beneficial interactions can have similar effects. Consider the evolutionary impact of how flower petals are arranged. Flower petals can be symmetrical in one direction only (bilateral symmetry, as in the pea blossom in Figure 30.13), or they can be symmetrical in all directions (radial symmetry, as in the dog rose in Figure 30.13). On a flower with bilateral symmetry, an insect pollinator may be able to obtain nectar only when it approaches the flower from a certain direction. Such constraints can make it more likely that as an insect moves from flower to flower, pollen is placed on a part of the insect's body that will come into contact with the stigma of a flower of the same species.

Because of this specificity of pollen transfer, gene flow may be reduced more easily in diverging populations with bilateral symmetry than in populations with radial symmetry. As a result, researchers have hypothesized that speciation should occur more rapidly in flowers with bilateral symmetry than in flowers with radial symmetry (**Figure 30.14**). Working at the University of British Columbia, Risa Sargent tested this hypothesis and found that clades with bilaterally symmetrical flowers do indeed have more species than do closely related clades with radially symmetrical flowers. Overall, such effects of plant-pollinator interactions are thought to have contributed to the increasing dominance of flowering plants in the Cretaceous period, helping to make angiosperms of central importance in ecological communities and human societies.

CONCEPT CHECK 30.3

1. It has been said that an oak is an acorn's way of making more acorns. Write an explanation that includes these terms: sporophyte, gametophyte, ovule, seed, ovary, and fruit.

2. Compare and contrast a pine cone and a flower in terms of structure and function.

3. **WHAT IF?** If researchers discovered a 135-million-year-old fossil angiosperm that had woody tissues as well as sepals and petals, how would their findings affect current interpretations of *Archaefructus sinensis* fossils?

For suggested answers, see Appendix A.

CONCEPT 30.4

Human welfare depends greatly on seed plants

Throughout this unit, we are highlighting the ways in which humans depend on various organisms. In forests and on farms, seed plants are key sources of food, fuel, wood products, and medicine. Our reliance on them makes the preservation of plant diversity critical.

Products from Seed Plants

Most of our food comes from angiosperms. Just six crops—wheat, rice, maize, potatoes, cassava, and sweet potatoes—yield 80% of all the calories consumed by humans. We also depend on angiosperms to feed livestock: It takes 5–7 kg of grain to produce 1 kg of grain-fed beef.

Today's crops are the products of a relatively recent burst of genetic change, resulting from artificial selection after humans began domesticating plants approximately 13,000 years ago. To appreciate the scale of the transformation, note how the number and size of seeds in domesticated plants is greater than those of their wild relatives, as in the case of maize and teosinte (see Figure 38.16). At the genetic level, scientists can glean information about domestication by comparing the genes of crops with those of wild relatives. With maize, dramatic changes, such as increased cob size and loss of the hard coating around teosinte kernels, may have been initiated by as few as five mutations.

How did wild plants change so dramatically in such a relatively short time? For thousands of years, farmers have selected the seeds of plants with desirable traits (large fruits, for example) to plant for the next year's crops. Humans may also have selected the traits of some plants indirectly, as in the case of wild almonds. Almonds contain a bitter compound called amygdalin that repels birds and other animals. Amygdalin breaks down into cyanide, so eating a large number of wild almonds can be fatal. But mutations can reduce the level of amygdalin, making almonds sweet rather than bitter. Wild birds eat almonds from trees with such mutations. According to one hypothesis, humans may have observed birds eating the almonds and then eaten the almonds themselves—ultimately using such seeds to grow trees that produced sweeter, less dangerous almonds.

In addition to staple crops, flowering plants provide other edible products. Two of the world's most popular beverages come from tea leaves and coffee beans, and you can thank the tropical cacao tree for cocoa and chocolate. Spices are derived from various plant parts, such as flowers (cloves, saffron), fruits and seeds (vanilla, black pepper, mustard, cumin), leaves (basil, mint, sage), and even bark (cinnamon).

Many seed plants, both gymnosperms and angiosperms, are sources of wood, which is absent in all living seedless plants. Wood consists of an accumulation of tough-walled xylem cells (see Chapter 35). Wood is the primary source of fuel for much of the world, and wood pulp, typically derived from conifers such as fir and pine, is used to make paper. Worldwide, wood also remains the most widely used construction material.

For centuries, humans have also depended on seed plants for medicines. Many cultures have a long tradition of using herbal remedies, and scientific research has identified the relevant secondary compounds in many of these plants, leading to the synthesis of medicines. Willow leaves and bark, for instance, have been used since ancient times in pain-relieving remedies, in-

Table 30.1 A Sampling of Medicines Derived from Seed Plants

Compound	Source	Example of Use
Atropine	Belladonna plant	Pupil dilator in eye exams
Digitalin	Foxglove	Heart medication
Menthol	Eucalyptus tree	Ingredient in cough medicines
Morphine	Opium poppy	Pain reliever
Quinine	Cinchona tree (see below)	Malaria preventive
Taxol	Pacific yew	Ovarian cancer drug
Tubocurarine	Curare tree	Muscle relaxant during surgery
Vinblastine	Periwinkle	Leukemia drug

Cinchona bark, source of quinine

cluding prescriptions by the Greek physician Hippocrates. In the 1800s, scientists traced the willow's medicinal property to the chemical salicin. A synthesized derivative, acetylsalicylic acid, is what we call aspirin. Although modern chemistry facilitates laboratory synthesis, plants remain an important direct source of medicinal compounds. In the United States, for example, about 25% of prescription drugs contain one or more active ingredients extracted or derived from plants, typically from seed plants. Other ingredients were first discovered in seed plants and then synthesized artificially. **Table 30.1** lists some medicinal uses of secondary compounds of seed plants.

Threats to Plant Diversity

Although plants may be a renewable resource, plant diversity is not. The exploding human population and its demand for space and resources are extinguishing plant species at an extremely rapid rate. The problem is especially severe in the tropics, where more than half the human population lives and where population growth is fastest. Thirty-five million acres of tropical rain forest, an area nearly the size of Iowa, are cleared each year, a rate that would completely eliminate Earth's tropical forests within 100 to 150 years. The most common cause of this destruction is slash-and-burn clearing of forests for agricultural use (see Chapter 56). As forests disappear, so do thousands of plant species. Of course, once a species becomes extinct, it can never return.

The loss of plant species is often accompanied by the loss of insects and other rain forest animals. Researchers estimate that habitat destruction in rain forests and other ecosystems is pushing hundreds of species toward extinction each year. If current rates of loss in the tropics and elsewhere continue, scientists estimate that within the next 100 to 200 years, 50% or more of Earth's species will become extinct. Such losses would constitute a global mass extinction, rivaling the Permian and Cretaceous mass extinctions and forever changing the evolutionary history of land plants (and many other organisms).

Many people have ethical concerns about contributing to the extinction of living forms. In addition, there are practical reasons to be concerned about the loss of plant diversity. So far, we have explored the potential uses of only a tiny fraction of the more than 290,000 known plant species. For example, almost all our food is based on the cultivation of only about two dozen species of seed plants. And fewer than 5,000 plant species have been studied as potential sources of medicines. The tropical rain forest may be a medicine chest of healing plants that could be extinct before we even know they exist. If we begin to view rain forests and other ecosystems as living treasures that can regenerate only slowly, we may learn to harvest their products at sustainable rates. What else can we do to preserve plant diversity? Few questions are as important, as we'll explore more fully in Unit Eight (Ecology).

CONCEPT CHECK 30.4

1. Explain why plant diversity may be considered a non-renewable resource.
2. **WHAT IF?** How could phylogenies be used to improve the efficiency with which researchers search for novel medicines derived from seed plants?

For suggested answers, see Appendix A.

Chapter 30 Review

MEDIA Go to www.campbellbiology.com for BioFlix 3-D Animations, MP3 Tutors, Videos, Practice Tests, an eBook, and more.

SUMMARY OF KEY CONCEPTS

CONCEPT 30.1

Seeds and pollen grains are key adaptations for life on land (pp. 618–621)

Five Derived Traits of Seed Plants		
Reduced gametophytes	Microscopic male and female gametophytes (*n*) are nourished and protected by the sporophyte (2*n*)	Male gametophyte — Female gametophyte
Heterospory	Microspore (gives rise to a male gametophyte)	
	Megaspore (gives rise to a female gametophyte)	
Ovules	Ovule (gymnosperm) { Integument (2*n*) / Megaspore (*n*) / Megasporangium (2*n*) }	
Pollen	Pollen grains make water unnecessary for fertilization	
Seeds	Seeds: survive better than unprotected spores, can be transported long distances	{ Integument / Food supply / Embryo }

CONCEPT 30.2

Gymnosperms bear "naked" seeds, typically on cones (pp. 621–625)

▶ **Gymnosperm Evolution** Gymnosperms appear early in the plant fossil record and dominated Mesozoic terrestrial ecosystems. Living seed plants can be divided into two monophyletic groups: gymnosperms and angiosperms. Extant gymnosperms include cycads, *Ginkgo biloba*, gnetophytes, and conifers.

▶ **The Life Cycle of a Pine:** *A Closer Look* Dominance of the sporophyte generation, the development of seeds from fertilized ovules, and the role of pollen in transferring sperm to ovules are key features of a typical gymnosperm life cycle.

MEDIA

Activity Pine Life Cycle

CONCEPT 30.3

The reproductive adaptations of angiosperms include flowers and fruits (pp. 625–632)

▶ **Characteristics of Angiosperms** Flowers generally consist of four whorls of modified leaves: sepals, petals, stamens (which produce pollen), and carpels (which produce ovules). Ovaries ripen into fruits, which often carry seeds by wind, water, or animals to new locations.

▶ **Angiosperm Evolution** An adaptive radiation of angiosperms occurred during the Cretaceous period. Fossils, phylogenetic analyses, and developmental studies offer insights into the origin of flowers.

▶ **Angiosperm Diversity** Several groups of basal angiosperms have been identified. Other major clades of angiosperms include monocots, magnoliids, and eudicots.

▶ **Evolutionary Links Between Angiosperms and Animals** Pollination and other interactions between angiosperms and animals may have led to increased species diversity in both of these groups.

MEDIA

Activity Angiosperm Life Cycle
Investigation How Are Trees Identified by Their Leaves?

CONCEPT **30.4**

Human welfare depends greatly on seed plants (pp. 632–634)

▶ **Products from Seed Plants** Humans depend on seed plants for food, wood, and many medicines.

▶ **Threats to Plant Diversity** Destruction of habitat threatens the extinction of many plant species and the animal species they support.

TESTING YOUR KNOWLEDGE

SELF-QUIZ

1. Where in an angiosperm would you find a megasporangium?
   a. in the style of a flower
   b. inside the tip of a pollen tube
   c. enclosed in the stigma of a flower
   d. within an ovule contained within an ovary of a flower
   e. packed into pollen sacs within the anthers found on a stamen

2. A fruit is most commonly
   a. a mature ovary.
   b. a thickened style.
   c. an enlarged ovule.
   d. a modified root.
   e. a mature female gametophyte.

3. With respect to angiosperms, which of the following is *incorrectly* paired with its chromosome count?
   a. egg—*n*
   b. megaspore—2*n*
   c. microspore—*n*
   d. zygote—2*n*
   e. sperm—*n*

4. Which of the following is *not* a characteristic that distinguishes gymnosperms and angiosperms from other plants?
   a. alternation of generations
   b. ovules
   c. integuments
   d. pollen
   e. dependent gametophytes

5. Gymnosperms and angiosperms have the following in common *except*
   a. seeds.
   b. pollen.
   c. vascular tissue.
   d. ovaries.
   e. ovules.

6. **DRAW IT** Use the letters a–d to label where on the phylogenetic tree each of the following derived characters appeared.
   a. flowers
   b. embryos
   c. seeds
   d. vascular tissue

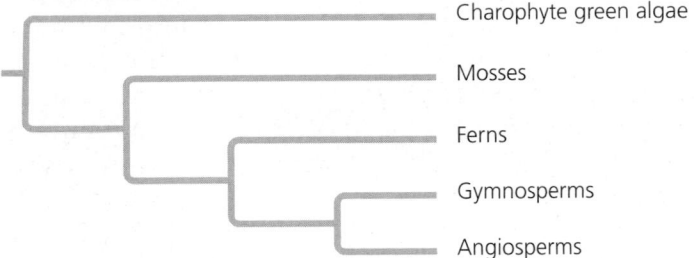

For Self-Quiz answers, see Appendix A.

MEDIA Visit **www.campbellbiology.com** for a Practice Test.

EVOLUTION CONNECTION

7. The history of life has been punctuated by several mass extinctions. For example, the impact of a meteorite may have wiped out most of the dinosaurs and many forms of marine life at the end of the Cretaceous period (see Chapter 25). Fossils indicate that plants were less severely affected by this and other mass extinctions. What adaptations may have enabled plants to withstand these disasters better than animals?

SCIENTIFIC INQUIRY

8. **DRAW IT** As will be described in detail in Chapter 38, the female gametophyte of angiosperms typically has seven cells, one of which, the central cell, is diploid. After double fertilization, the central cell develops into endosperm, which is triploid. Because all monocots, magnoliids, and eudicots have female gametophytes with seven cells and triploid endosperm, scientists assumed that this was the ancestral state for angiosperms. Consider, however, the following recent discoveries:
   ▶ Our understanding of angiosperm phylogeny has changed to that shown in Figure 30.12b.
   ▶ *Amborella* has eight-celled female gametophytes and triploid endosperm.
   ▶ Water lilies and star anise have four-celled female gametophytes and diploid endosperm.
   (a) Draw a phylogeny of the angiosperms (see Figure 30.12b), incorporating the data given above about the number of cells in female gametophytes and the ploidy of the endosperm. Assume that all of the star anise relatives have four-celled female gametophytes and diploid endosperm.
   (b) What does your labeled phylogeny suggest about the evolution of the female gametophyte and endosperm in angiosperms?

Fungi 31

OVERVIEW

Mighty Mushrooms

Hiking through the Malheur National Forest in eastern Oregon, you might notice a few clusters of honey mushrooms (*Armillaria ostoyae*) scattered here and there beneath the towering trees **(Figure 31.1)**. Though the trees appear to dwarf the mushrooms, as strange as it sounds, the reverse is actually true. All these mushrooms are just the aboveground portion of a single enormous fungus. Its subterranean network of filaments spreads through 965 hectares of the forest—more than the area of 1,800 football fields. Based on its current growth rate, scientists estimate that this fungus, which weighs hundreds of tons, has been growing for more than 1,900 years.

The inconspicuous honey mushrooms on the forest floor are a fitting symbol of the neglected grandeur of the kingdom Fungi. Most of us are barely aware of these eukaryotes beyond the occasional brush with athlete's foot or spoiled food. Yet fungi are a huge and important component of the biosphere. Their diversity is staggering: While about 100,000 species have been described, it is estimated that there are actually as many as 1.5 million species of fungi. Some fungi are exclusively single-celled, but most have complex multicellular bodies, which in many cases include the structures we know as mushrooms. This diversity has enabled fungi to colonize just about every

imaginable terrestrial habitat; airborne spores have even been found 160 km above ground.

Fungi are not only diverse and widespread, but they are also essential for the well-being of most terrestrial ecosystems. They break down organic material and recycle nutrients, allowing other organisms to assimilate essential chemical elements. Humans benefit from fungi's services to agriculture and forestry as well as their essential role in making products ranging from bread to antibiotics. But it is also true that some fungi cause diseases in plants and animals.

In this chapter, we will investigate the structure and evolutionary history of fungi, survey the members of kingdom Fungi, and discuss their ecological and commercial significance.

CONCEPT 31.1
Fungi are heterotrophs that feed by absorption

Despite their vast diversity, fungi share some key traits, most importantly the way they derive nutrition. In addition, many fungi grow by forming multicellular filaments, a body structure that plays an important role in how they obtain food.

Nutrition and Ecology

Like animals, fungi are heterotrophs—they cannot make their own food as plants and algae can. But unlike animals, fungi do not ingest (eat) their food. Instead, a fungus absorbs nutrients from the environment outside of its body. Many fungi accomplish this task by secreting powerful hydrolytic enzymes into their surroundings. These enzymes break down complex molecules to smaller organic compounds that the fungi can absorb into their bodies and use. Other fungi use enzymes to penetrate the walls of plant cells, enabling the fungi to absorb nutrients from the plant cell.

Collectively, the different enzymes found in various fungal species can digest compounds from a wide range of sources, living or dead. As a result, fungi take on many roles in ecological communities, with different species living as decomposers, parasites, or mutualists. Decomposer fungi break down and absorb nutrients from nonliving organic material, such as fallen logs, animal corpses, and the wastes of living organisms. Parasitic fungi absorb nutrients from the cells of living hosts. Some parasitic fungi are pathogenic, including species that infect human lungs and other species that are responsible for about 80% of plant diseases. Mutualistic fungi also absorb nutrients from a host organism, but they reciprocate with actions that benefit the host. For example, mutualistic fungi that live inside certain termite species use their enzymes to break down wood, as do mutualistic protists in other termite species (see Figure 28.26).

The versatile enzymes that enable fungi to digest a wide range of food sources are not the only reason for their ecological success. Another important factor is how their body structure increases the efficiency of nutrient absorption.

Body Structure

The most common fungal body structures are multicellular filaments and single cells (**yeasts**). Many species can grow as both filaments and yeasts, but even more grow only as filaments; relatively few species grow only as yeasts. Yeasts often inhabit moist environments, including plant sap and animal tissues, where there is a ready supply of soluble nutrients, such as sugars and amino acids. We'll discuss yeasts and their particular importance to humans later; here, we'll focus on the morphology of multicellular fungi.

Fungal Morphology

The morphology of multicellular fungi enhances their ability to grow into and absorb nutrients from their surroundings (**Figure 31.2**). The bodies of these fungi typically form a network of tiny filaments, which are called **hyphae** (singular, *hypha*). Hyphae consist of tubular cell walls surrounding the plasma membrane and cytoplasm of the cells. Unlike plant cell walls, which contain cellulose, fungal cell walls are strengthened by **chitin**. This strong but flexible nitrogen-containing polysaccharide is also found in the external skeletons of insects and other arthropods.

Fungal hyphae form an interwoven mass called a **mycelium** (plural, *mycelia*) that infiltrates the material on which the fungus feeds. A mycelium's structure maximizes its surface area-to-volume ratio,

making feeding more efficient. Just 1 cm³ of rich soil may contain as much as 1 km of hyphae with a total surface area of 300 cm² in contact with the soil. A fungal mycelium grows rapidly, as proteins and other materials synthesized by the fungus are channeled through cytoplasmic streaming to the tips of the extending hyphae. The fungus concentrates its energy and resources on adding hyphal length and thus overall absorptive surface area, rather than on increasing hyphal girth. Fungi are not motile in the typical sense of the word—they cannot run, swim, or fly in search of food or mates. However, as they grow, fungi can move into new places, swiftly extending the tips of their hyphae into previously unoccupied territory.

In most fungi, the hyphae are divided into cells by crosswalls, or **septa** (singular, *septum*) (**Figure 31.3a**). Septa generally have pores large enough to allow ribosomes, mitochondria, and even nuclei to flow from cell to cell. Some fungi lack septa (**Figure 31.3b**). Known as **coenocytic fungi**, these organisms

Reproductive structure. The mushroom produces tiny cells called spores.

Hyphae. The mushroom and its subterranean mycelium are a continuous network of hyphae.

Spore-producing structures

Mycelium

20 µm

▲ **Figure 31.2 Structure of a multicellular fungus.** The top photograph shows the sexual structures, in this case called mushrooms, of the penny bun fungus (*Boletus edulis*). The bottom photograph shows a mycelium growing on fallen conifer needles. The inset LM shows hyphae.

? *Although the mushrooms in the top photograph appear to be different individuals, could their DNA be identical? Explain.*

▶ **Figure 31.3 Two forms of hyphae.**

Nuclei

Cell wall

Pore

Septum

Cell wall

Nuclei

(a) Septate hypha

(b) Coenocytic hypha

consist of a continuous cytoplasmic mass having hundreds or thousands of nuclei. The coenocytic condition results from the repeated division of nuclei without cytokinesis. This description may remind you of the plasmodial slime molds you read about in Chapter 28, which also consist of cytoplasmic masses containing many nuclei. This similarity is one reason that slime molds were once classified as fungi; molecular data have since shown that slime molds and fungi belong to distinct clades.

Specialized Hyphae in Mycorrhizal Fungi

Some fungi have specialized hyphae that allow them to feed on living animals (**Figure 31.4a**). Other fungal species have specialized hyphae called **haustoria**, which the fungi use to extract nutrients from—or exchange nutrients with—their hosts (**Figure 31.4b**). Mutually beneficial relationships between such fungi and plant roots are called **mycorrhizae** (the term means "fungus roots").

(a) Hyphae adapted for trapping and killing prey. In *Arthrobotrys*, a soil fungus, portions of the hyphae are modified as hoops that can constrict around a nematode (roundworm) in less than a second. The fungus then penetrates its prey with hyphae and digests the prey's inner tissues (SEM).

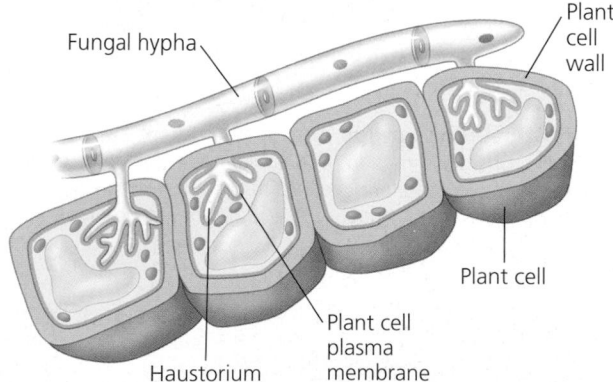

(b) Haustoria. Some mutualistic and parasitic fungi grow specialized hyphae called haustoria that can extract nutrients from living plant cells. Haustoria remain separated from a plant cell's cytoplasm by the plasma membrane of the plant cell (orange).

▲ **Figure 31.4 Specialized hyphae.**

Mycorrhizal fungi (fungi that form mycorrhizae) can improve delivery of phosphate ions and other minerals to plants because the vast mycelial networks of the fungi are more efficient than the plants' roots at acquiring these minerals from the soil. In exchange, the plants supply the fungi with organic nutrients such as carbohydrates. There are several types of mycorrhizal fungi. **Ectomycorrhizal fungi** (from the Greek *ektos*, out) form sheaths of hyphae over the surface of a root and also grow into the extracellular spaces of the root cortex (see Figure 37.12a). **Arbuscular mycorrhizal fungi** (from the Latin *arbor*, tree) extend their branching hyphae through the root cell wall and into tubes formed by invagination (pushing inward) of the root cell membrane (see Figure 37.12b).

Mycorrhizae are enormously important in natural ecosystems and agriculture. Almost all vascular plants have mycorrhizae and rely on their fungal partners for essential nutrients. Many studies have demonstrated the significance of mycorrhizae by comparing the growth of plants with and without them (see Figure 37.13). Foresters commonly inoculate pine seedlings with mycorrhizal fungi to promote growth. In the absence of human intervention, mycorrhizal fungi colonize soils by spore dispersal, a key component of how fungi reproduce and spread to new areas, as we discuss next.

CONCEPT CHECK 31.1

1. Compare and contrast the nutritional mode of a fungus with your own nutritional mode.
2. **WHAT IF?** Suppose a certain fungus is a mutualist that lives within its insect host, yet its ancestors were parasites that grew in and on the insect's body. What derived traits might you find in this mutualistic fungus?

For suggested answers, see Appendix A.

CONCEPT 31.2

Fungi produce spores through sexual or asexual life cycles

Most fungi propagate themselves by producing vast numbers of spores, either sexually or asexually. For example, puffballs, the reproductive structures of certain fungal species, may release trillions of spores in cloud-like bursts (see Figure 31.18). Spores can be carried long distances by wind or water. If they land in a moist place where there is food, they germinate, producing new mycelia. To appreciate how effective spores are at dispersing, leave a slice of melon exposed to the air. Even without a visible source of spores nearby, within a week or so, you will likely observe fuzzy mycelia growing from the microscopic spores constantly falling onto the melon.

Figure 31.5 generalizes the many different life cycles that can produce fungal spores. In this section, we will survey general

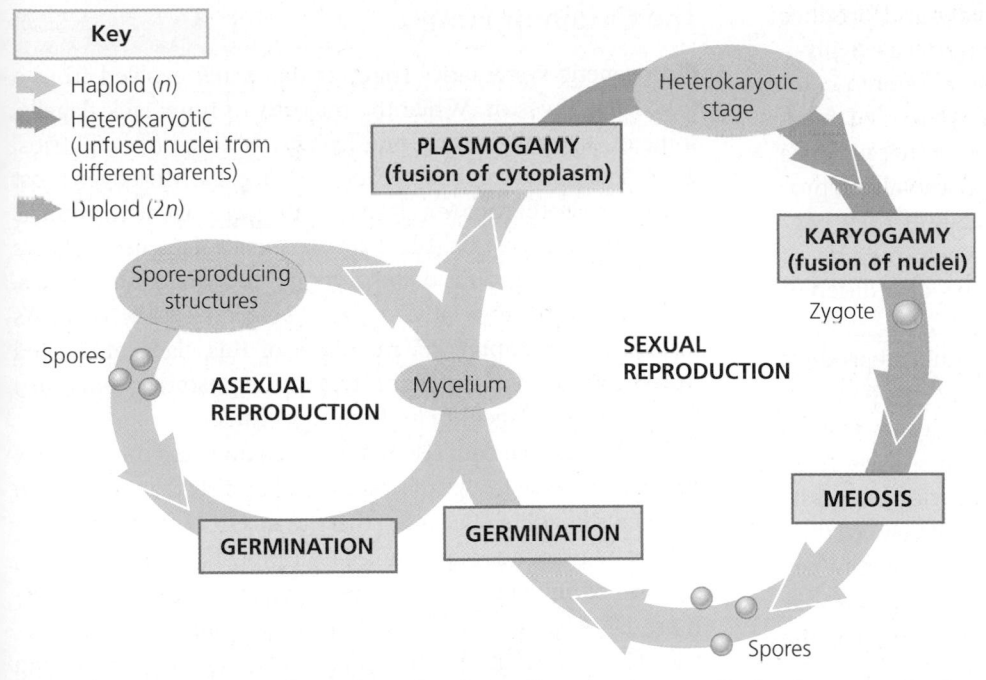

Hours, days, or (in some fungi) even centuries may pass between plasmogamy and the next stage in the sexual cycle, **karyogamy**. During karyogamy, the haploid nuclei contributed by the two parents fuse, producing diploid cells. Zygotes and other transient structures form during karyogamy, the only diploid stage in most fungi. Meiosis then restores the haploid condition, leading to the formation of spores that enable fungi to disperse.

The sexual processes of karyogamy and meiosis generate extensive genetic variation, a prerequisite for natural selection. (See Chapters 13 and 23 to review how sex can increase genetic diversity in a population.) The heterokaryotic condition also offers some of the advantages of diploidy, in that one haploid genome may compensate for harmful mutations in the other.

▲ **Figure 31.5 Generalized life cycle of fungi.** Many—but not all—fungi reproduce both sexually and asexually. Some reproduce only sexually, others only asexually.

aspects of the sexual and asexual life cycles of fungi. Later, we'll examine more closely the life cycles of specific fungi.

Sexual Reproduction

The nuclei of fungal hyphae and the spores of most fungal species are haploid, although many fungi have transient diploid stages that form during sexual life cycles. Generally, sexual reproduction begins when hyphae from two mycelia release sexual signaling molecules called **pheromones**. If the mycelia are of different mating types, the pheromones from each partner bind to receptors on the other, and the hyphae extend toward the source of the pheromones. When the hyphae meet, they fuse. In species with such a "compatibility test," this process contributes to genetic variation by preventing hyphae from fusing with other hyphae from the same mycelium or another genetically identical mycelium.

The union of the cytoplasms of two parent mycelia is known as **plasmogamy**. In most fungi, the haploid nuclei contributed by each parent do not fuse right away. Instead, parts of the fused mycelium contain coexisting, genetically different nuclei. Such a mycelium is said to be a **heterokaryon** (meaning "different nuclei"). In some species, the different nuclei may even exchange chromosomes and genes in a process similar to crossing over (see Chapter 13). In other species, the haploid nuclei pair off two to a cell, one from each parent. Such a mycelium is **dikaryotic** (meaning "two nuclei"). As a dikaryotic mycelium grows, the two nuclei in each cell divide in tandem without fusing. Because these cells retain two separate haploid nuclei, they differ from diploid cells, which have pairs of homologous chromosomes within a single nucleus.

Asexual Reproduction

In addition to sexual reproduction, many fungi can reproduce asexually. Some 20,000 fungal species are only known to reproduce asexually. As with sexual reproduction, the processes of asexual reproduction vary widely among fungi.

Many fungi reproduce asexually by growing as filamentous fungi that produce (haploid) spores by mitosis; such species are known informally as **molds** if they form visible mycelia. Depending on your housekeeping habits, you may have observed molds in your kitchen, forming furry carpets on fruit, bread, and other foods **(Figure 31.6)**. Molds typically

2.5 μm

▲ **Figure 31.6 *Penicillium*, a mold commonly encountered as a decomposer of food.** The bead-like clusters in the colorized SEM are conidia, structures involved in asexual reproduction.

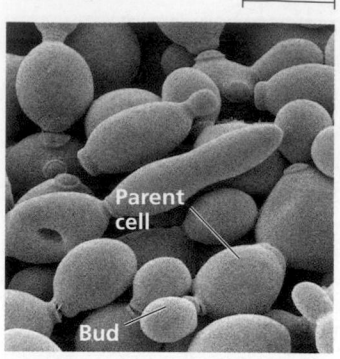

▲ **Figure 31.7 The yeast *Saccharomyces cerevisiae* in several stages of budding** (SEM).

grow rapidly and produce many spores asexually—enabling the fungi to colonize new sources of food. Many species that produce such spores can also reproduce sexually if they happen to contact a member of their species of a different mating type.

Other fungi reproduce asexually by growing as single-celled yeasts. Instead of producing spores, asexual reproduction in yeasts occurs by ordinary cell division or by the pinching of small "bud cells" off a parent cell (**Figure 31.7**). As already mentioned, some fungi that grow as yeasts can also grow as filamentous mycelia, depending on the availability of nutrients.

Many yeasts and filamentous fungi have no known sexual stage. Mycologists (biologists who study fungi) have traditionally called such fungi **deuteromycetes** (from the Greek *deutero*, second, and *mycete*, fungus). Whenever a sexual stage is discovered for a so-called deuteromycete, the species is reclassified in a particular phylum, depending on the type of sexual structures it forms. In addition to searching for little-known sexual stages of such unassigned fungi, mycologists can now use genetic techniques to determine the taxonomic status of a fungus.

CONCEPT CHECK 31.2

1. In terms of haploidy versus diploidy, how do the life cycles of humans and fungi differ?
2. **WHAT IF?** Suppose that you sample the DNA of two mushrooms on opposite sides of your yard and find that they are identical. Propose two hypotheses that could reasonably account for this result.

For suggested answers, see Appendix A.

CONCEPT 31.3

The ancestor of fungi was an aquatic, single-celled, flagellated protist

Data from both paleontology and molecular systematics offer insights into the early evolution of fungi. As a result, systematists now recognize that the kingdoms Fungi and Animalia are more closely related to each other than either is to plants or most other eukaryotes.

The Origin of Fungi

Phylogenetic systematics suggests that fungi evolved from a flagellated ancestor. While the majority of fungi lack flagella, some of the earliest-diverging lineages of fungi (the chytrids, discussed later in this chapter) do have flagella. Moreover, most of the protists that share a close common ancestor with animals and fungi also have flagella. DNA sequence data also indicate that these three groups of eukaryotes—the fungi, the animals, and their protistan relatives—form a clade (**Figure 31.8**). As discussed in Chapter 28, members of this clade are called **opisthokonts**, a name that refers to the posterior (*opistho-*) location of the flagellum in these organisms.

DNA sequence data also indicate that fungi are more closely related to several groups of single-celled protists than they are to other opisthokonts, suggesting that the ancestor of fungi was unicellular. One such group of unicellular protists, the **nucleariids**, consists of amoebas that feed on algae and bacteria. Furthermore, DNA evidence indicates that animals are more closely related to a *different* group of protists (the choanoflagellates) than they are to either fungi or nucleariids. Together, these results suggest that multicellularity must have evolved in animals and fungi independently, from different single-celled ancestors.

Based on molecular clock analysis (see Chapter 26), scientists have estimated that the ancestors of animals and fungi diverged into separate lineages about one billion years ago. However, the oldest undisputed fossils of fungi are only about 460 million years old (**Figure 31.9**). One possible explanation

▲ **Figure 31.8 Fungi and their close relatives.** Molecular evidence indicates that the nucleariids, a group of single-celled protists, are the closest living relatives of fungi. The three parallel lines leading to the chytrids indicate that this group may be paraphyletic.

▶ **Figure 31.9 Fossil fungal hyphae and spores from the Ordovician period (about 460 million years ago)** (LM).

Host cell nucleus

Developing microsporidian

Spore

10 μm

▲ **Figure 31.10 A eukaryotic cell infected by microsporidia.** A large vacuole inside this host eukaryotic cell contains spores and developing forms of the parasite *Encephalitozoon intestinalis* (TEM).

for this discrepancy is that the microscopic ancestors of today's terrestrial fungi fossilized poorly.

Are Microsporidia Closely Related to Fungi?

In addition to animals and protists such as the nucleariids, another group of organisms, the microsporidia, may be closely related to fungi. Microsporidia are unicellular parasites of animals and protists (**Figure 31.10**). They are often used to control insect pests. While microsporidia do not normally cause illness in humans, they do pose a risk to people with AIDS and other immune-compromised conditions.

In many ways, microsporidia are unlike most other eukaryotes. They do not have conventional mitochondria, for example. As a result, microsporidia have been something of a taxonomic mystery, thought by some researchers to be an ancient, deep-branching lineage of eukaryotes. In recent years, however, researchers have discovered that microsporidia actually have tiny organelles derived from mitochondria. Meanwhile, some molecular comparisons indicate that microsporidia are closely related to fungi, suggesting they are highly derived parasites. Other molecular evidence—including a 2006 analysis of DNA sequence data from six genes in nearly 200 fungal species—indicates that microsporidia may, in fact, be an early-diverging lineage of fungi. Additional genetic data from species belonging to early-diverging lineages of fungi are needed to resolve whether microsporidia are fungi or are a closely related but distinct group of organisms.

The Move to Land

Much of the fungal diversity we observe today may have originated during an adaptive radiation that began when multicellular plants and animals colonized land. For example, fossils of the earliest known vascular plants from the late Silurian period (420 million years ago) contain evidence of mycorrhizal relationships between plants and fungi. Plants probably existed in this beneficial relationship with fungi from the earliest periods of colonization of land.

CONCEPT CHECK **31.3**

1. Why are fungi classified as opisthokonts despite the fact that most fungi lack flagella?
2. Explain the evolutionary significance of the presence of mycorrhizae in the earliest vascular plants.
3. **WHAT IF?** If fungi had colonized land before plants, where might the fungi have lived? What might they have eaten?

For suggested answers, see Appendix A.

CONCEPT **31.4**

Fungi have radiated into a diverse set of lineages

The phylogeny of fungi is currently the subject of much research. In the past decade, molecular analyses have helped clarify the evolutionary relationships between fungal groups, although there are still areas of uncertainty. **Figure 31.11**, on the next page, presents a simplified version of one current hypothesis. In this section, we will survey each of the major fungal groups identified in this phylogenetic tree.

Chytrids

Chytrids
Zygomycetes
Glomeromycetes
Ascomycetes
Basidiomycetes

Fungi classified in the phylum Chytridiomycota, called **chytrids**, are ubiquitous in lakes and soil. Some of the approximately 1,000 chytrid species are decomposers, while others are parasites of protists, other fungi, plants, or animals. Still other chytrids are important mutualists. For example, anaerobic chytrids that live in the digestive tracts of sheep and cattle help to break down plant matter, thereby contributing significantly to the animals' growth.

Molecular evidence supports the hypothesis that chytrids diverged early in fungal evolution. Like other fungi, chytrids have cell walls made of chitin, and they also share certain key enzymes and metabolic pathways with other fungal groups. Some chytrids form colonies with hyphae, while others exist as single spherical cells. But chytrids are unique among fungi in having flagellated spores, called **zoospores** (**Figure 31.12**).

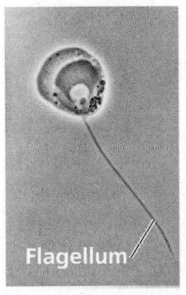

◄ **Figure 31.12 Flagellated chytrid zoospore** (TEM).

Flagellum

4 μm

Exploring Fungal Diversity

Most mycologists currently recognize five phyla of fungi, although at least the chytrids are probably paraphyletic (as indicated by the parallel lines).

Hyphae   25 μm

Chytrids (1,000 species)

In chytrids such as *Chytridium*, the globular fruiting body forms multicellular, branched hyphae (LM); other species are single-celled. Chytrids are thought to be one of the earliest fungal groups to diverge from other fungi.

Zygomycetes (1,000 species)

The hyphae of some zygomycetes, including this mold in the genus *Mucor* (LM), grow rapidly into foods such as fruits and bread. As such, the fungi may act as decomposers (if the food is not alive) or parasites; other species live as neutral (commensal) symbionts.

Fungal hypha

Glomeromycetes (160 species)

The glomeromycetes (arbuscular mycorrhizal fungi) are of great ecological importance. Many plants form mycorrhizal associations with these fungi. This LM shows glomeromycete hyphae (stained dark blue) within a plant root.

Ascomycetes (65,000 species)

Also called sac fungi, members of this diverse group are common to many marine, freshwater, and terrestrial habitats. The cup-shaped ascocarp (fruiting body) of the ascomycete shown here (*Aleuria aurantia*) gives this species its common name: orange peel fungus.

Basidiomycetes (30,000 species)

Often important as decomposers and ectomycorrhizal fungi, basidiomycetes, or club fungi, are unusual in having a long-lived, dikaryotic mycelium. The fruiting bodies—commonly called mushrooms—of this fly agaric (*Amanita muscaria*) are a familiar sight in coniferous forests of the Northern Hemisphere.

Until recently, systematists thought that fungi lost flagella only once in their history, after chytrids had diverged from other lineages. However, molecular data indicate that chytrids are a paraphyletic group: Some "chytrids" are actually more closely related to another fungal group, the zygomycetes, than they are to other chytrids. These data also suggest that flagella have been lost several times during the evolution of fungi.

Zygomycetes

Chytrids
Zygomycetes
Glomeromycetes
Ascomycetes
Basidiomycetes

There are approximately 1,000 known species of **zygomycetes** (fungi in the phylum Zygomycota). This diverse phylum includes the fast-growing molds responsible for causing foods such as bread, peaches, strawberries, and sweet potatoes to rot during storage. Other zygomycetes live as parasites or as commensal (neutral) symbionts of animals.

The life cycle of *Rhizopus stolonifer* (black bread mold) is fairly typical of zygomycetes (Figure 31.13). Its hyphae spread out over the food surface, penetrate it, and absorb nutrients. The hyphae are coenocytic, with septa found only where reproductive cells are formed. In the asexual phase, bulbous black sporangia develop at the tips of upright hyphae. Within each sporangium, hundreds of haploid spores develop and are dispersed through the air. Spores that happen to land on moist food germinate, growing into new mycelia. Some zygomycetes,

Key

➡ Haploid (*n*)
➡ Heterokaryotic (*n* + *n*)
➡ Diploid (2*n*)

1 Mycelia have various mating types (here designated +, with red nuclei, and –, with blue nuclei).

2 Neighboring mycelia of different mating types form hyphal extensions (gametangia), each of which encloses several haploid nuclei.

Mating type (+)

Mating type (–)

Gametangia with haploid nuclei

PLASMOGAMY

3 A zygosporangium forms, containing multiple haploid nuclei from the two parents.

Young zygosporangium (heterokaryotic)

100 μm

Zygosporangium

Rhizopus growing on bread

8 The spores germinate and grow into new mycelia.

SEXUAL REPRODUCTION

9 Mycelia can also reproduce asexually by forming sporangia that produce genetically identical haploid spores.

Dispersal and germination

7 The sporangium disperses genetically diverse haploid spores.

Sporangia

KARYOGAMY

4 The zygosporangium develops a rough, thick-walled coating that can resist harsh conditions for months.

Diploid nuclei

Sporangium

ASEXUAL REPRODUCTION

MEIOSIS

5 When conditions are favorable, karyogamy occurs, then meiosis.

Dispersal and germination

50 μm

Mycelium

6 The zygosporangium germinates into a sporangium on a short stalk.

▲ Figure 31.13 **The life cycle of the zygomycete *Rhizopus stolonifer* (black bread mold).**

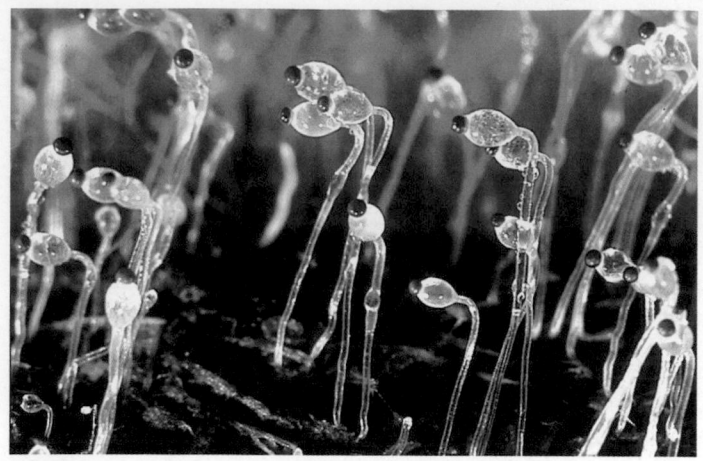

0.5 mm

▲ **Figure 31.14** *Pilobolus* **aiming its sporangia.** The spore-bearing hyphae of this zygomycete, which decomposes animal dung, bend toward light, where grass is likely to grow. The fungus then launches its sporangia in a jet of water as far as 2 m. Grazing animals ingest the fungi with the grass and then scatter the spores in feces.

such as *Pilobolus*, can actually "aim" and then shoot their sporangia toward bright light **(Figure 31.14)**.

If environmental conditions deteriorate—for instance, if the mold consumes all its food—*Rhizopus* may reproduce sexually. The parents in a sexual union are mycelia of different mating types that possess different chemical markers, although they may appear identical. Plasmogamy produces a sturdy structure called a **zygosporangium**, in which karyogamy and then meiosis occur. Note that while a zygosporangium represents the zygote (2*n*) stage in the life cycle, it is not a zygote in the usual sense (that is, a cell with one diploid nucleus). Rather, a zygosporangium is a multinucleate structure, first heterokaryotic with many haploid nuclei from the two parents, then with many diploid nuclei after karyogamy.

Zygosporangia are resistant to freezing and drying and are metabolically inactive. When conditions improve, a zygosporangium undergoes meiosis, germinates into a sporangium, and releases genetically diverse haploid spores that may colonize a new substrate.

Glomeromycetes

Chytrids
Zygomycetes
Glomeromycetes
Ascomycetes
Basidiomycetes

The **glomeromycetes**, fungi assigned to the phylum Glomeromycota, were formerly thought to be zygomycetes. But recent molecular studies, including a phylogenetic analysis of DNA sequence data from six genes in hundreds of fungal species, indicate that glomeromycetes form a separate clade (monophyletic group). In spite of their small numbers—only 160 species have been identified to date—the glomeromycetes are an ecologically significant group. Nearly all glomeromycetes form arbuscular mycorrhizae **(Figure 31.15)**. The tips of the hyphae that push into plant root cells branch into tiny treelike

2.5 μm

▲ **Figure 31.15** **Arbuscular mycorrhizae.** Glomeromycetes form arbuscular mycorrhizae with plant roots, supplying minerals and other nutrients to the roots. This SEM depicts the branched hyphae—an arbuscule—of *Glomus mosseae* bulging into a root cell by pushing in the membrane (the root has been treated to remove the cytoplasm).

structures known as arbuscules. About 90% of all plant species have such mutualistic partnerships with glomeromycetes.

Ascomycetes

Chytrids
Zygomycetes
Glomeromycetes
Ascomycetes
Basidiomycetes

Mycologists have described 65,000 species of **ascomycetes** (fungi in the phylum Ascomycota) from a wide variety of marine, freshwater, and terrestrial habitats. The defining feature of ascomycetes is the production of sexual spores in saclike **asci** (singular, *ascus*); thus, they are commonly called **sac fungi**. Unlike zygomycetes, most ascomycetes bear their sexual stages in

▼ The edible ascocarp of *Morchella esculenta*, the tasty morel, is often found under trees in orchards.

▼ *Tuber melanosporum* is a truffle species that forms ectomycorrhizae with trees. The ascocarp grows underground and emits a strong odor. These ascocarps have been dug up and the middle one sliced open.

▲ **Figure 31.16** **Ascomycetes (sac fungi).**

? *Ascomycetes vary greatly in morphology (see also Figure 31.11). How could you confirm that a fungus is an ascomycete?*

fruiting bodies, or **ascocarps**, which range in size from microscopic to macroscopic (**Figure 31.16**, on the facing page). The spore-forming asci are found in the ascocarps.

Ascomycetes vary in size and complexity from unicellular yeasts to elaborate cup fungi and morels (see Figure 31.16). They include some of the most devastating plant pathogens, which we will discuss later. However, many ascomycetes are important decomposers, particularly of plant material. More than 40% of all ascomycete species live with green algae or cyanobacteria in beneficial symbiotic associations called lichens. Some ascomycetes form mycorrhizae with plants. Many others live between mesophyll cells in leaves; some of these species release toxic compounds that help protect the plant from insects.

Although the life cycles of various ascomycete groups differ in the details of their reproductive structures and processes, we'll illustrate some common elements using the bread mold *Neurospora crassa* (**Figure 31.17**). Ascomycetes reproduce asexually by producing enormous numbers of asexual spores called **conidia** (singular, *conidium*). Conidia are not formed inside sporangia, as are the asexual spores of most zygomycetes. Rather, they are produced externally at the tips of specialized hyphae called conidiophores, often in clusters or long chains, from which they may be dispersed by the wind.

Conidia may also be involved in sexual reproduction, fusing with hyphae from a mycelium of a different mating type, as occurs in *Neurospora*. Fusion of two different mating types is

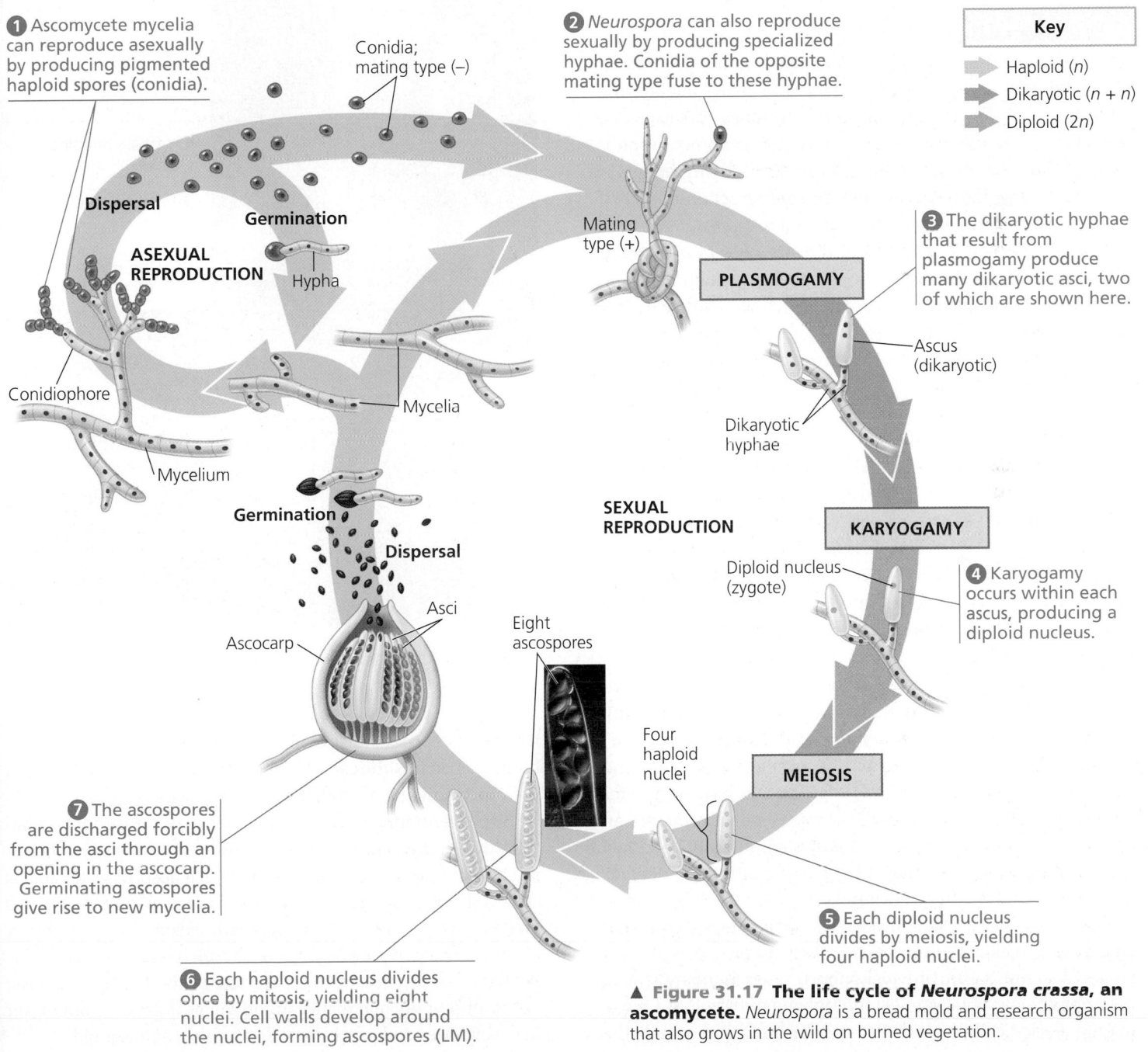

1 Ascomycete mycelia can reproduce asexually by producing pigmented haploid spores (conidia).

Conidia; mating type (–)

Dispersal

Germination

ASEXUAL REPRODUCTION

Hypha

Conidiophore

Mycelium

Mycelia

Germination

Dispersal

Ascocarp

Asci

7 The ascospores are discharged forcibly from the asci through an opening in the ascocarp. Germinating ascospores give rise to new mycelia.

6 Each haploid nucleus divides once by mitosis, yielding eight nuclei. Cell walls develop around the nuclei, forming ascospores (LM).

2 *Neurospora* can also reproduce sexually by producing specialized hyphae. Conidia of the opposite mating type fuse to these hyphae.

Mating type (+)

Key

Haploid (*n*)
Dikaryotic (*n* + *n*)
Diploid (2*n*)

PLASMOGAMY

3 The dikaryotic hyphae that result from plasmogamy produce many dikaryotic asci, two of which are shown here.

Ascus (dikaryotic)

Dikaryotic hyphae

SEXUAL REPRODUCTION

KARYOGAMY

Diploid nucleus (zygote)

4 Karyogamy occurs within each ascus, producing a diploid nucleus.

Eight ascospores

Four haploid nuclei

MEIOSIS

5 Each diploid nucleus divides by meiosis, yielding four haploid nuclei.

▲ **Figure 31.17 The life cycle of *Neurospora crassa*, an ascomycete.** *Neurospora* is a bread mold and research organism that also grows in the wild on burned vegetation.

followed by plasmogamy, resulting in the formation of dikaryotic cells, each with two haploid nuclei representing the two parents. The cells at the tips of these dikaryotic hyphae develop into many asci. Within each ascus, karyogamy combines the two parental genomes, and then meiosis forms four genetically different nuclei. This is usually followed by a mitotic division, forming eight ascospores. The ascospores develop in and are eventually discharged from the ascocarp.

In contrast to the life cycle of zygomycetes, the extended dikaryotic stage of ascomycetes (and also basidiomycetes) provides increased opportunity for genetic recombination. In *Neurospora*, for example, many dikaryotic cells can develop into asci, recombining genomes and resulting in a multitude of genetically different offspring from one mating event (see Figure 31.17).

Neurospora has a significant history in biological research. As we discussed in Chapter 17, biologists in the 1930s used *Neurospora* in research that led to the one gene–one enzyme hypothesis. Today, this ascomycete continues to serve as a model research organism; in 2003, its entire genome was published. With 10,000 genes, the genome of this tiny fungus is about three-fourths the size of the *Drosophila* genome and half the size of the human genome. The *Neurospora* genome is relatively compact, having few of the stretches of noncoding DNA that occupy much space in the genomes of humans and many other eukaryotes. In fact, there is evidence that *Neurospora* has a genomic defense system that prevents noncoding DNA such as transposons from accumulating.

Basidiomycetes

Chytrids
Zygomycetes
Glomeromycetes
Ascomycetes
Basidiomycetes

Approximately 30,000 species, including mushrooms, puffballs, and shelf fungi, are called **basidiomycetes** and are classified in the phylum Basidiomycota **(Figure 31.18)**. The phylum also includes mutualists that form mycorrhizae and two groups of destructive plant parasites: rusts and smuts. The name of the phylum derives from the **basidium** (Latin for "little pedestal"), a cell in which karyogamy occurs, followed immediately by meiosis. The club-like shape of the basidium also gives rise to the common name **club fungus**.

Basidiomycetes are important decomposers of wood and other plant material. Of all the fungi, certain basidiomycetes are the best at decomposing the complex polymer lignin, an abundant component of wood. Many shelf fungi break down the wood of weak or damaged trees and continue to decompose the wood after the tree dies.

The life cycle of a basidiomycete usually includes a long-lived dikaryotic mycelium **(Figure 31.19)**. As in ascomycetes, this extended dikaryotic stage provides opportunities for many genetic recombination events, in effect multiplying the result of a single mating. Periodically, in response to environmental stimuli, the

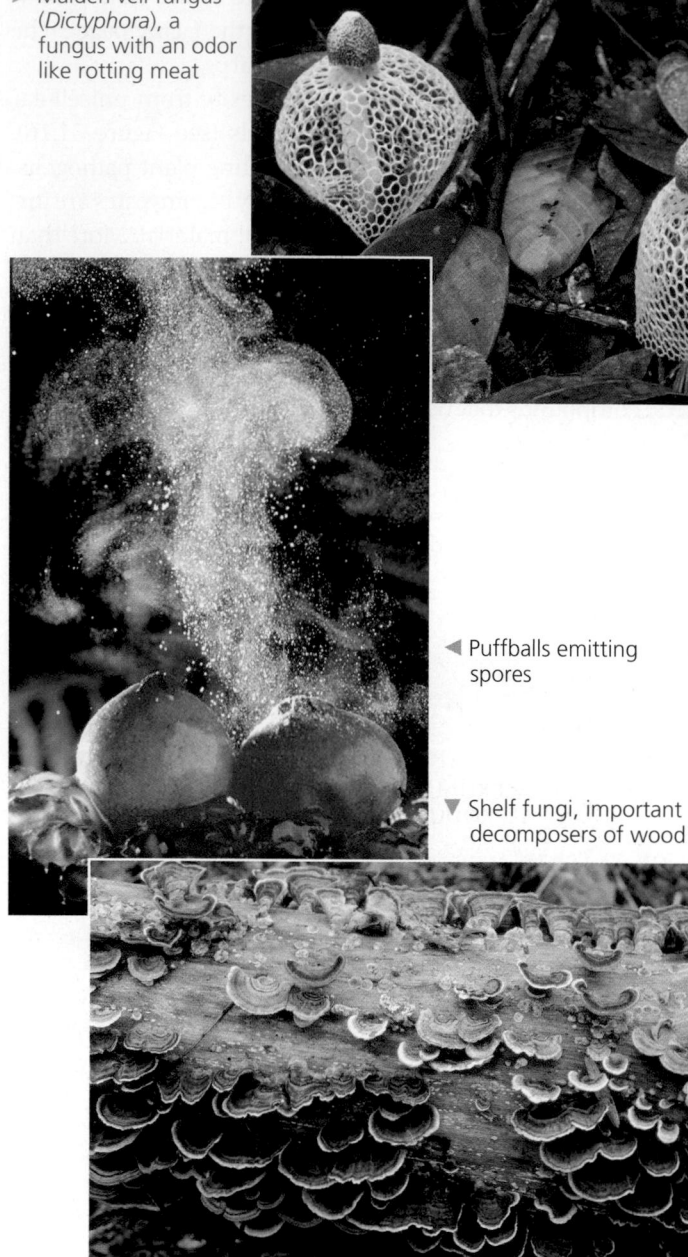

► Maiden veil fungus (*Dictyphora*), a fungus with an odor like rotting meat

◄ Puffballs emitting spores

▼ Shelf fungi, important decomposers of wood

▲ **Figure 31.18 Basidiomycetes (club fungi).**

mycelium reproduces sexually by producing elaborate fruiting bodies called **basidiocarps**. The common white mushrooms in the supermarket are familiar examples of a basidiocarp.

By concentrating growth in the hyphae of mushrooms, a basidiomycete mycelium can quickly erect its fruiting structures in just a few hours; a mushroom pops up as it absorbs water and as cytoplasm streams in from the dikaryotic mycelium. By this process, a ring of mushrooms, popularly called a "fairy ring," may appear literally overnight **(Figure 31.20)**. The mycelium below the fairy ring expands outward at a rate of about 30 cm per year, decomposing organic matter in the soil as it grows. Some giant fairy rings are produced by mycelia that are centuries old.

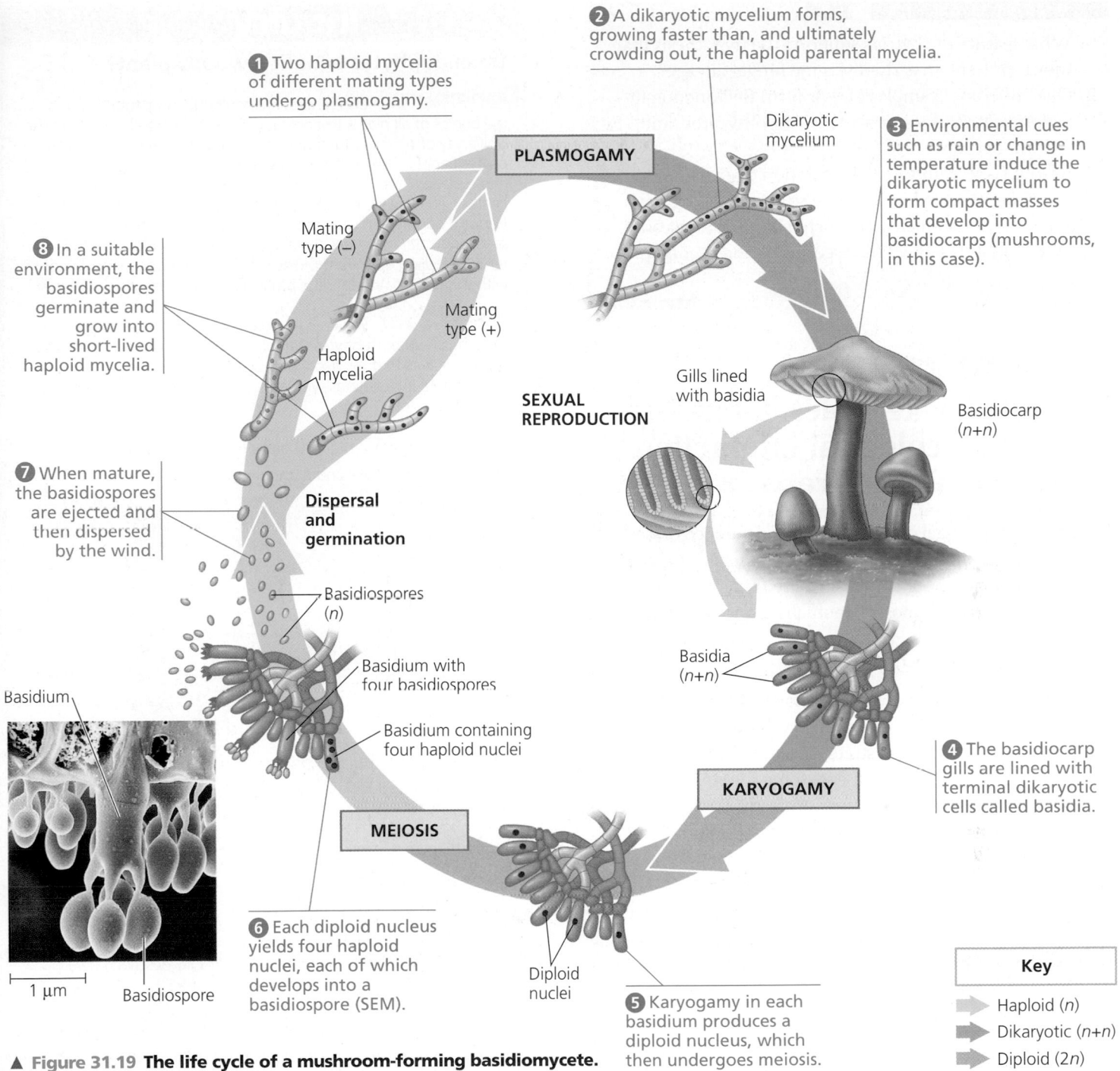

❶ Two haploid mycelia of different mating types undergo plasmogamy.

❷ A dikaryotic mycelium forms, growing faster than, and ultimately crowding out, the haploid parental mycelia.

❸ Environmental cues such as rain or change in temperature induce the dikaryotic mycelium to form compact masses that develop into basidiocarps (mushrooms, in this case).

❽ In a suitable environment, the basidiospores germinate and grow into short-lived haploid mycelia.

❼ When mature, the basidiospores are ejected and then dispersed by the wind.

PLASMOGAMY

Mating type (−)

Mating type (+)

Haploid mycelia

Dikaryotic mycelium

SEXUAL REPRODUCTION

Gills lined with basidia

Basidiocarp (n+n)

Dispersal and germination

Basidiospores (n)

Basidium with four basidiospores

Basidium containing four haploid nuclei

Basidia (n+n)

❹ The basidiocarp gills are lined with terminal dikaryotic cells called basidia.

KARYOGAMY

MEIOSIS

❻ Each diploid nucleus yields four haploid nuclei, each of which develops into a basidiospore (SEM).

Diploid nuclei

❺ Karyogamy in each basidium produces a diploid nucleus, which then undergoes meiosis.

Basidium

1 μm

Basidiospore

Key

Haploid (n)

Dikaryotic (n+n)

Diploid (2n)

▲ **Figure 31.19 The life cycle of a mushroom-forming basidiomycete.**

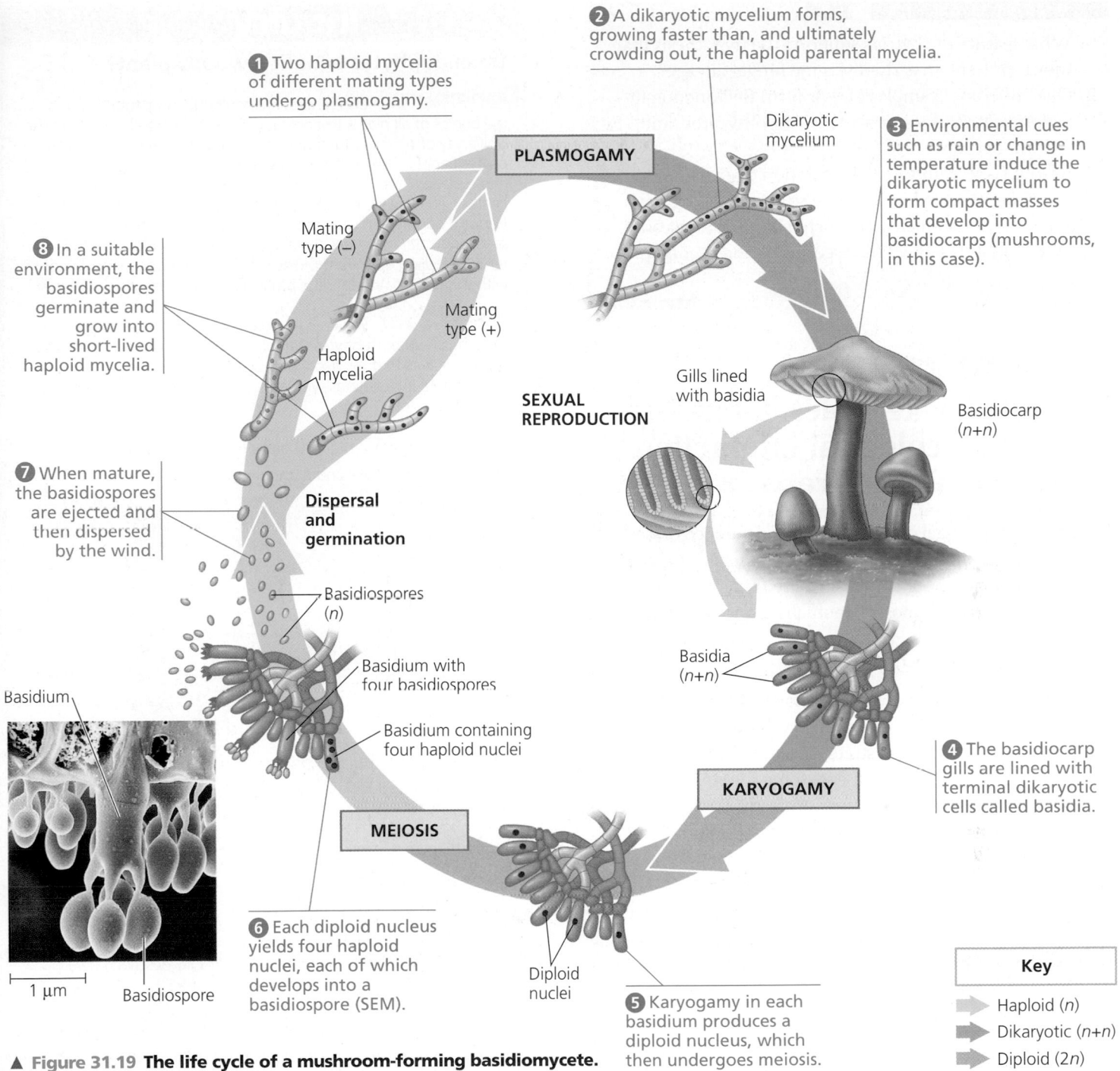

▲ **Figure 31.20 A fairy ring.** According to legend, these mushrooms spring up where fairies have danced in a ring on a moonlit night. (The text provides a biological explanation of how fairy rings form.)

The numerous basidia in a basidiocarp are the sources of sexual spores called basidiospores. After a mushroom forms, its cap supports and protects a large surface area of dikaryotic basidia on gills. During karyogamy, the two nuclei in each basidium fuse, producing a diploid nucleus (see Figure 31.19). This nucleus then undergoes meiosis, yielding four haploid nuclei. The basidium then grows four appendages, and one haploid nucleus enters each appendage and develops into a basidiospore. Large numbers of basidiospores are produced: The gills of a common white mushroom have a surface area of about 200 cm² and may release a billion basidiospores, which drop from the bottom of the cap and are blown away.

1. What feature of chytrids supports the hypothesis that they represent an early-diverging fungal lineage?
2. Give different examples of how form fits function in zygomycetes, glomeromycetes, ascomycetes, and basidiomycetes.
3. **WHAT IF?** Suppose that mutation of an ascomycete changed its life cycle so that plasmogamy, karyogamy, and meiosis occurred in quick succession. How might this affect the ascospores and ascocarp?

For suggested answers, see Appendix A.

CONCEPT 31.5
Fungi play key roles in nutrient cycling, ecological interactions, and human welfare

In our survey of fungal classification, we've touched on some of the ways fungi influence other organisms, including ourselves. We will now look more closely at these impacts, focusing on how fungi act as decomposers, mutualists, and pathogens.

Fungi as Decomposers

Fungi are well adapted as decomposers of organic material, including the cellulose and lignin of plant cell walls. In fact, almost any carbon-containing substrate—even jet fuel and house paint—can be consumed by at least some fungi. As you might expect, researchers are developing ways to use a variety of fungal species in bioremediation projects. In addition, fungi and bacteria are primarily responsible for keeping ecosystems stocked with the inorganic nutrients essential for plant growth. Without these decomposers, carbon, nitrogen, and other elements would remain tied up in organic matter. Plants and the animals that eat them could not exist because elements taken from the soil would not be returned (see Chapter 55). Without decomposers, life as we know it would cease.

Fungi as Mutualists

Fungi may form mutualistic relationships with plants, algae, cyanobacteria, and animals. All of these relationships have profound ecological effects.

Fungus-Plant Mutualisms

We've already considered the enormous importance of the mutualistic associations that most vascular plants form with mycorrhizal fungi. In addition, all plant species studied to date appear to harbor symbiotic **endophytes**, fungi that live inside leaves or other plant parts without causing harm. Most endophytes identified to date are ascomycetes. Endophytes have

---

▼ Figure 31.21 **Inquiry**

Do endophytes benefit a woody plant?

EXPERIMENT Endophytes are symbiotic fungi found within the bodies of all plants examined to date. A. Elizabeth Arnold at the University of Arizona, Tucson, and colleagues tested whether endophytes benefit the cacao tree (*Theobroma cacao*). This tree, whose name means "food of the gods" in Greek, is the source of the beans used to make chocolate, and it is cultivated throughout the tropics. Endophytes were added to the leaves of some cacao seedlings, but not others. (In cacao, endophytes colonize leaves after the seedling germinates.) The seedlings were then inoculated with a virulent pathogen, the protist *Phytophthora* (see Chapter 28).

RESULTS Fewer leaves were killed by the pathogen in seedlings with endophytes than in seedlings without endophytes. Among leaves that survived, pathogens damaged less of the leaf surface area in seedlings with endophytes than in seedlings without endophytes.

- Endophyte not present; pathogen present (E–P+)
- Both endophyte and pathogen present (E+P+)

CONCLUSION The presence of endophytes appears to benefit cacao trees by reducing the leaf mortality and damage caused by *Phytophthora*.

SOURCE A. E. Arnold et al., Fungal endophytes limit pathogen damage in a tropical tree, *Proceedings of the National Academy of Sciences* 100:15649–15654 (2003).

WHAT IF? Arnold and colleagues also performed control treatments. Suggest two controls they might have used, and explain how each would be helpful in interpreting the results described here.

---

been shown to benefit certain grasses and other nonwoody plants by making toxins that deter herbivores or by increasing host plant tolerance of heat, drought, or heavy metals. Seeking to discover how endophytes affect a woody plant, researchers tested whether leaf endophytes benefited seedlings of the cacao tree, *Theobroma cacao* (**Figure 31.21**). Their findings show that the endophytes of woody flowering plants can play an important role in defending against pathogens.

Fungus-Animal Symbioses

As mentioned earlier, some fungi share their digestive services with animals, helping break down plant material in the guts of cattle and other grazing mammals. Many species of ants take advantage of the digestive power of fungi by raising them in

▲ Figure 31.22 **Fungus-gardening insects.** These leaf-cutting ants depend on fungi to convert plant material to a form the insects can digest. The fungi, in turn, depend on the nutrients from the leaves the ants feed them.

comycete, but one glomeromycete and several basidiomycete lichens are known. The fungus usually gives a lichen its overall shape and structure, and tissues formed by hyphae account for most of the lichen's mass. The algae or cyanobacteria generally occupy an inner layer below the lichen surface **(Figure 31.24)**. The merger of fungus and alga or cyanobacterium is so complete that lichens are actually given scientific names as though they were single organisms. More than 13,500 species have been described, accounting for nearly one out of seven of all known fungi.

In most lichens that have been studied, each partner provides something the other could not obtain on its own. The algae provide carbon compounds; the cyanobacteria also fix nitrogen (see Chapter 27) and provide organic nitrogen. The fungi provide their photosynthetic partners with a suitable environment for growth. The physical arrangement of hyphae allows for gas

"farms." Leaf-cutter ants, for example, scour tropical forests in search of leaves, which they cannot digest on their own but carry back to their nests and feed to the fungi **(Figure 31.22)**. As the fungi grow, their hyphae develop specialized swollen tips that are rich in proteins and carbohydrates. The ants feed primarily on these nutrient-rich tips. In effect, the fungi break down plant leaves into substances the insects can digest, and they also detoxify plant defensive compounds that would otherwise kill or harm the ants. In some tropical forests, the fungi have helped these insects become the major consumers of leaves.

The evolution of such farmer ants and that of their fungal "crops" have been tightly linked for over 50 million years. The fungi have become so dependent on their caretakers that in many cases they can no longer survive without the ants, and vice versa.

Lichens

A **lichen** is a symbiotic association between a photosynthetic microorganism and a fungus in which millions of photosynthetic cells are held in a mass of fungal hyphae. Lichens grow on the surfaces of rocks, rotting logs, trees, and roofs in various forms **(Figure 31.23)**. The photosynthetic partners are unicellular or filamentous green algae or cyanobacteria. The fungal component is most often an as-

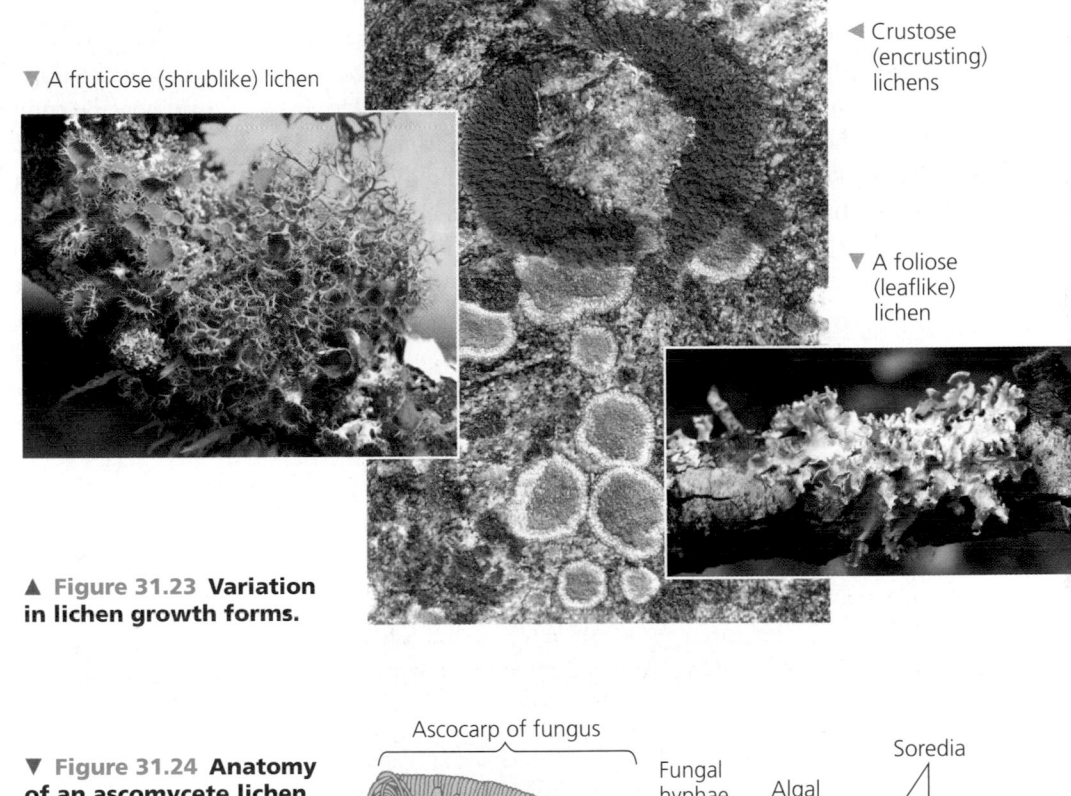

▼ A fruticose (shrublike) lichen

◀ Crustose (encrusting) lichens

▼ A foliose (leaflike) lichen

▲ Figure 31.23 **Variation in lichen growth forms.**

▼ Figure 31.24 **Anatomy of an ascomycete lichen** (colorized SEM).

Ascocarp of fungus

Fungal hyphae

Algal layer

Soredia

Algal cell

Fungal hyphae

20 μm

exchange, protects the photosynthetic partner, and retains water and minerals, most of which are absorbed either from airborne dust or from rain. The fungi also secrete acids, which aid in the uptake of minerals. Fungal pigments help shade the algae or cyanobacteria from intense sunlight. Some fungal compounds are toxic and prevent most lichens from being eaten by animals.

The fungi of many lichens reproduce sexually by forming ascocarps or basidiocarps. Lichen algae reproduce independently of the fungus by asexual cell division. As might be expected of "dual organisms," asexual reproduction as a symbiotic unit also occurs commonly, either by fragmentation of the parental lichen or by the formation of **soredia**, small clusters of hyphae with embedded algae (see Figure 31.24).

Lichens are important pioneers on newly cleared rock and soil surfaces, such as burned forests and volcanic flows. They break down the surface by physically penetrating and chemically attacking it, and they trap windblown soil. Nitrogen-fixing lichens also add organic nitrogen to some ecosystems. These processes make it possible for a succession of plants to grow (see Chapter 54).

As tough as lichens are, many do not stand up very well to air pollution. Their passive mode of mineral uptake from rain and moist air makes them particularly sensitive to sulfur dioxide and other airborne poisons. The death of sensitive lichens in an area can be an early warning that air quality is deteriorating.

Fungi as Pathogens

About 30% of the 100,000 known species of fungi make a living as parasites or pathogens, mostly of plants (**Figure 31.25**).

For example, *Cryphonectria parasitica*, the ascomycete fungus that causes chestnut blight, dramatically changed the landscape of the northeastern United States. Accidentally introduced on trees imported from Asia in the early 1900s, spores of the fungus enter cracks in the bark of American chestnut trees and produce hyphae, killing the tree. American chestnuts once were common in many forests in eastern North America, but now they typically persist only as sprouts from the stumps of former trees. Another ascomycete, *Fusarium circinatum*, causes pine pitch canker, a disease that threatens pines throughout the world. Fungi are also serious pests of food crops. Between 10% and 50% of the world's fruit harvest is lost each year to fungal attack. Grain crops also suffer major losses each year from fungi such as the basidiomycete *Puccinia graminis*, which causes black stem rust on wheat.

Some of the fungi that attack food crops are toxic to humans. For example, certain species of the ascomycete mold *Aspergillus* contaminate improperly stored grain and peanuts by secreting carcinogenic compounds called aflatoxins. Another example is the ascomycete *Claviceps purpurea*, which grows on rye plants, forming purple structures called ergots. If diseased rye is inadvertently milled into flour and then consumed, poisons from the ergots can cause ergotism, a condition characterized by gangrene, nervous spasms, burning sensations, hallucinations, and temporary insanity. An epidemic of ergotism around 944 C.E. killed more than 40,000 people in France. One compound that has been isolated from ergots is lysergic acid, the raw material from which the hallucinogen LSD is made.

(a) Corn smut on corn   (b) Tar spot fungus on maple leaves   (c) Ergots on rye

▲ Figure 31.25 **Examples of fungal diseases of plants.**

Animals are much less susceptible to parasitic fungi than are plants. Only about 50 fungal species are known to parasitize animals, but these few species do considerable damage. The general term for such a fungal infection is **mycosis**.

Skin mycoses include the disease ringworm, so named because it appears as circular red areas on the skin. The ascomycetes that cause ringworm can infect almost any skin surface. Most commonly, they grow on the feet, causing the intense itching and blisters known as athlete's foot. Though highly contagious, athlete's foot and other ringworm infections can be treated with fungicidal lotions and powders.

Systemic mycoses, by contrast, spread through the body and usually cause very serious illnesses. They are typically caused by inhaled spores. For example, coccidioidomycosis is a systemic mycosis that produces tuberculosis-like symptoms in the lungs. Each year, hundreds of cases in North America require treatment with antifungal drugs, without which the disease would be fatal.

Some mycoses are opportunistic, occurring only when a change in the body's microorganisms, chemical environment, or immune system allows fungi to grow unchecked. *Candida albicans*, for example, is one of the normal inhabitants of moist epithelia, such as the vaginal lining. Under certain circumstances, *Candida* can grow too rapidly and become pathogenic, leading to so-called "yeast infections." Many other opportunistic mycoses in humans have become more common in recent decades, due in part to AIDS, which compromises the immune system.

Over the past few years, the alleged dangers of indoor molds (including the ascomycete *Stachybotrys chartarum*) have been the subject of sensationalistic news reports. Indoor molds thrive in damp buildings and have been implicated in some studies as the cause of a wide variety of diseases. As a result, entire "sick buildings" have been abandoned. Yet there is no well-substantiated evidence linking the presence of indoor molds to these diseases. Many other factors—including bacteria and human-made chemicals—may explain some of the symptoms attributed to indoor molds.

Practical Uses of Fungi

The dangers posed by fungi should not overshadow the immense benefits we derive from these remarkable eukaryotes. We depend on their ecological services as decomposers and recyclers of organic matter. Without mycorrhizae, our agriculture would be far less productive.

Mushrooms are not the only fungi of interest for human consumption. The distinctive flavors of certain kinds of cheeses, including Roquefort and other blue cheeses, come from the fungi used to ripen them. The soft drink industry uses a species of *Aspergillus* to produce citric acid for colas. Morels and truffles, the edible fruiting bodies of various ascomycetes, are highly prized for their complex flavors (see Figure 31.16). These fungi can sell for several hundred dollars a pound. Truffles release strong odors that attract mammals and insects, which feed on them and disperse their spores. In some cases, the odors mimic the pheromones (sex attractants) of certain mammals. For example, several European truffles mimic the pheromones released by male pigs, which explains why *female* pigs have historically been used to help find these delicacies.

Humans have used yeasts to produce alcoholic beverages and raise bread for thousands of years. Under what are typically anaerobic conditions, yeasts ferment sugars to alcohol and CO_2, which leavens dough. Only relatively recently have the yeasts involved been separated into pure cultures for more controlled use. The yeast *Saccharomyces cerevisiae* is the most important of all cultured fungi (see Figure 31.7). It is available as many strains of baker's yeast and brewer's yeast.

Many fungi have great medical value as well. For example, a compound extracted from ergots is used to reduce high blood pressure and to stop maternal bleeding after childbirth. Some fungi produce antibiotics that are essential in treating bacterial infections. In fact, the first antibiotic discovered was penicillin, made by the ascomycete mold *Penicillium* (**Figure 31.26**). Other examples of pharmaceuticals derived from fungi include cholesterol-lowering drugs and cyclosporine, a drug used to suppress the immune system after organ transplants.

Fungi also figure prominently in research in molecular biology and biotechnology. Researchers use the yeast *Saccharomyces* to study the molecular genetics of eukaryotes because its cells are easy to culture and manipulate. Scientists are gaining insight into the genes involved in human diseases such as Parkinson's disease and Huntington's disease by examining the interactions of homologous genes in *Saccharomyces*.

Genetically modified fungi hold much promise. Although bacteria such as *Escherichia coli* can produce some useful proteins, they cannot synthesize glycoproteins because they lack enzymes that can attach carbohydrates to proteins. Fungi, on the other hand, do produce such enzymes. In 2003, scientists succeeded in engineering a strain of *S. cerevisiae* that produces human glycoproteins, including insulin-like growth factor. Such

▲ **Figure 31.26 Fungal production of an antibiotic.** The mold *Penicillium* produces an antibiotic that inhibits the growth of *Staphylococcus* bacteria, resulting in the clear area between the mold and the bacteria.

fungus-produced glycoproteins could treat people with medical conditions that prevent them from producing these compounds. Meanwhile, other researchers are sequencing the genome of the wood-digesting basidiomycete *Phanerochaete chrysosporium*, one of many "white rot" fungi. They hope to decipher the metabolic pathways by which white rot breaks down wood, with the goal of harnessing these pathways to produce paper pulp.

Having now completed our survey of the kingdom Fungi, we will turn in the remaining chapters of this unit to the closely related kingdom Animalia, to which we humans belong.

CONCEPT CHECK 31.5

1. What are some of the benefits that lichen algae can derive from their relationship with fungi?
2. What characteristics of pathogenic fungi result in their being efficiently transmitted?
3. **WHAT IF?** How might life on Earth differ from what we know today if no mutualistic relationships between fungi and other organisms had ever evolved?

For suggested answers, see Appendix A.

Chapter 31 Review

MEDIA Go to **www.campbellbiology.com** for BioFlix 3-D Animations, MP3 Tutors, Videos, Practice Tests, an eBook, and more.

SUMMARY OF KEY CONCEPTS

CONCEPT 31.1
Fungi are heterotrophs that feed by absorption (pp. 636–638)

▶ **Nutrition and Ecology** All fungi are heterotrophs (including decomposers and symbionts) that acquire nutrients by absorption. Many fungi secrete enzymes that break down complex molecules in food to smaller molecules that can be absorbed.

▶ **Body Structure** Most fungi grow as multicellular filaments; relatively few species grow exclusively as single-celled yeasts. In their multicellular form, fungi consist of mycelia, networks of branched hyphae adapted for absorption. Mycorrhizal fungi have specialized hyphae that enable them to form a mutually beneficial relationship with plants.

MEDIA
Activity Fungal Reproduction and Nutrition

CONCEPT 31.2
Fungi produce spores through sexual or asexual life cycles (pp. 638–640)

▶ **Sexual Reproduction** The sexual cycle involves cytoplasmic fusion (plasmogamy) and nuclear fusion (karyogamy), with an intervening heterokaryotic stage in which cells have haploid nuclei from two parents. The diploid phase resulting from karyogamy is short-lived and undergoes meiosis, producing haploid spores.

▶ **Asexual Reproduction** Many fungi can reproduce asexually as filamentous fungi or yeasts. DNA sequence data now allow mycologists to classify all fungi, even those lacking a known sexual morphology.

CONCEPT 31.3
The ancestor of fungi was an aquatic, single-celled, flagellated protist (pp. 640–641)

▶ **The Origin of Fungi** Molecular evidence supports the hypothesis that fungi and animals diverged from a common ancestor that was unicellular and had a flagellum.

▶ **Are Microsporidia Closely Related to Fungi?** Unicellular parasites called microsporidia may be protists that are closely related to fungi, or they may be an early-diverging fungal lineage.

▶ **The Move to Land** Fungi were among the earliest colonizers of land, probably as symbionts with early land plants.

CONCEPT 31.4
Fungi have radiated into a diverse set of lineages (pp. 641–648)

Fungal Phylum	Distinguishing Features of Morphology and Life Cycles	
Chytridiomycota (chytrids)	Flagellated spores	
Zygomycota (zygote fungi)	Resistant zygosporangium as sexual stage	
Glomeromycota (arbuscular mycorrhizal fungi)	Form arbuscular mycorrhizae with plants	
Ascomycota (sac fungi)	Sexual spores (ascospores) borne internally in sacs called asci; ascomycetes also produce vast numbers of asexual spores (conidia)	
Basidiomycota (club fungi)	Elaborate fruiting body (basidiocarp) containing many basidia that produce sexual spores (basidiospores)	

MEDIA
Activity Fungal Life Cycles

Fungi play key roles in nutrient cycling, ecological interactions, and human welfare (pp. 648–652)

▶ **Fungi as Decomposers** Fungi perform essential recycling of chemical elements between the living and nonliving world.

▶ **Fungi as Mutualists** Some endophytes help protect plants from herbivores and pathogens, while other fungi help certain animals digest plant tissue. Lichens are highly integrated symbiotic associations of fungi and algae or cyanobacteria.

▶ **Fungi as Pathogens** About 30% of all known fungal species are parasites, mostly of plants. Some fungi also cause human diseases.

▶ **Practical Uses of Fungi** Humans eat many fungi and use others to make cheeses, alcoholic beverages, and bread. Antibiotics produced by fungi treat bacterial infections. Genetic research on fungi is leading to applications in biotechnology.

MEDIA

Investigation How Does the Fungus *Pilobolus* Succeed as a Decomposer?

TESTING YOUR KNOWLEDGE

SELF-QUIZ

1. *All* fungi share which of the following characteristics?
   a. symbiotic
   b. heterotrophic
   c. flagellated
   d. pathogenic
   e. act as decomposers

2. Which feature seen in chytrids supports the hypothesis that they diverged earliest in fungal evolution?
   a. the absence of chitin within the cell wall
   b. coenocytic hyphae
   c. flagellated spores
   d. formation of resistant zygosporangia
   e. parasitic lifestyle

3. Which of the following cells or structures are associated with *asexual* reproduction in fungi?
   a. ascospores
   b. basidiospores
   c. zygosporangia
   d. conidiophores
   e. ascocarps

4. The adaptive advantage associated with the filamentous nature of fungal mycelia is primarily related to
   a. the ability to form haustoria and parasitize other organisms.
   b. avoiding sexual reproduction until the environment changes.
   c. the potential to inhabit almost all terrestrial habitats.
   d. the increased probability of contact between different mating types.
   e. an extensive surface area well suited for invasive growth and absorptive nutrition.

5. The photosynthetic symbiont of a lichen is often
   a. a moss.
   b. a green alga.
   c. a brown alga.
   d. an ascomycete.
   e. a small vascular plant.

6. Among the organisms listed here, which are thought to be the closest relatives of fungi?
   a. animals
   b. vascular plants
   c. mosses
   d. brown algae
   e. slime molds

For Self-Quiz answers, see Appendix A.

MEDIA Visit **www.campbellbiology.com** for a Practice Test.

EVOLUTION CONNECTION

7. The fungus-alga symbiosis that makes up lichens is thought to have evolved multiple times independently in different fungal groups. However, lichens fall into three well-defined growth forms (see Figure 31.23). What research could you perform to test the following hypotheses?
   Hypothesis 1: Crustose, foliose, and fruticose lichens each represent a monophyletic group.
   Hypothesis 2: Each lichen growth form represents convergent evolution by taxonomically diverse fungi.

SCIENTIFIC INQUIRY

8. **DRAW IT** The grass *Dichanthelium languinosum* lives in hot soils and houses fungi of the genus *Curvularia.* Regina Redman, of Montana State University, and colleagues performed field experiments to test the impact of *Curvularia* on the heat tolerance of this grass. They grew plants without (E−) and with (E+) *Curvularia* endophytes in soils of different temperatures and measured plant mass and the number of new shoots the plants produced. Draw a bar graph of the results for plant mass versus temperature and interpret it.

Soil Temp.	*Curvularia* Presence	Plant Mass (g)	Number of New Shoots
30°C	E−	16.2	32
	E+	22.8	60
35°C	E−	21.7	43
	E+	28.4	60
40°C	E−	8.8	10
	E+	22.2	37
45°C	E−	0	0
	E+	15.1	24

Source: R. S. Redman et al., Thermotolerance generated by plant/fungal symbiosis, *Science* 298:1581 (2002).

SCIENCE, TECHNOLOGY, AND SOCIETY

9. As you read in the chapter, the ascomycete fungus that causes chestnut blight and has killed an estimated 4 billion chestnut trees in North America was accidentally imported from Asia. More recently, the fungus *Discula destructiva*, introduced to eastern North America in the 1980s, has killed more than 80% of the eastern dogwood trees in some locations. Why are plants particularly vulnerable to fungi imported from other regions? What kinds of human activities might contribute to the spread of plant diseases? Do you think introductions of fungal plant pathogens are more or less likely to occur in the future? Why?

An Introduction to Animal Diversity

32

OVERVIEW

Welcome to Your Kingdom

Reading the last few chapters, you may have felt like a tourist among some unfamiliar organisms, such as slime molds, whisk ferns, and sac fungi. You probably are more at home with the topic introduced in this chapter—the animal kingdom, which of course includes yourself. But animal diversity extends far beyond humans and the dogs, cats, birds, and other animals we humans regularly encounter. For example, the diverse organisms in **Figure 32.1** are all animals, including those that appear to resemble lacy branches, thick stems, and curly leaves. To date biologists have identified 1.3 million extant (living) species of animals. Estimates of the actual number of animal species run far higher. This vast diversity encompasses a spectacular range of morphological variation, from corals to cockroaches to crocodiles.

In this chapter, we embark on a tour of the animal kingdom that will continue in the next two chapters. We will consider the characteristics that all animals share, as well as those that distinguish various taxonomic groups. This information is central to understanding animal phylogeny, a topic that is currently a lively arena of biological research and debate, as you will read.

CONCEPT 32.1

Animals are multicellular, heterotrophic eukaryotes with tissues that develop from embryonic layers

Constructing a good definition of an animal is not straightforward, as there are exceptions to nearly every criterion for distinguishing animals from other life-forms. However, several characteristics of animals, when taken together, sufficiently define the group for our discussion.

Nutritional Mode

Animals differ from both plants and fungi in their mode of nutrition. Plants are autotrophic eukaryotes capable of generating organic molecules through photosynthesis. Fungi are heterotrophs that grow on or near their food and that feed by absorption (often after they have released enzymes that digest the food outside their bodies). Unlike plants, animals cannot construct all of their own organic molecules and so, in most cases, they ingest them—either by eating other living organisms or by eating nonliving organic material. But unlike fungi, most animals do not feed by absorption; instead, animals ingest their food and then use enzymes to digest it within their bodies.

Cell Structure and Specialization

Animals are eukaryotes, and like plants and most fungi (but unlike most protists), animals are multicellular. In contrast to plants and fungi, however, animals lack the structural support of cell walls. Instead, animal cells are held together by structural proteins, the most abundant being collagen (see Figure 6.30), which is found only in animals.

Many animals have two types of specialized cells not seen in other multicellular organisms: muscle cells and nerve cells. In most animals, these cells are organized into muscle tissue and nervous tissue, respectively, and are responsible for moving the body and conducting nerve impulses. The ability to move and conduct nerve impulses underlies many of the adaptations that differentiate animals from plants and fungi, making muscle and nerve cells central to what it means to be an animal.

Reproduction and Development

Most animals reproduce sexually, and the diploid stage usually dominates the life cycle. In most species, a small, flagellated sperm fertilizes a larger, nonmotile egg, forming a diploid zygote. The zygote then undergoes **cleavage**, a succession of mitotic cell divisions without cell growth between division cycles. During the development of most animals, cleavage leads to the formation of a multicellular stage called a **blastula**, which in many animals takes the form of a hollow ball **(Figure 32.2)**. Following the blastula stage is the process of **gastrulation**, during which layers of embryonic tissues that will develop into adult body parts are produced. The resulting developmental stage is called a **gastrula**.

Some animals, including humans, develop directly into adults through transient stages of maturation, but the life cycles of many animals also include at least one larval stage. A **larva** is a sexually immature form of an animal that is morphologically distinct from the adult, usually eats different food, and may even have a different habitat than the adult, as in the case of the aquatic larva of a mosquito or a dragonfly. Animal larvae eventually undergo **metamorphosis**, a developmental transformation that turns the animal into a juvenile, which resembles an adult but is not yet sexually mature.

Although adult animals vary widely in morphology, the underlying genetic network that controls animal development is similar across a broad range of taxa. All eukaryotes have genes that regulate the expression of other genes, and many of these regulatory genes contain common sets of DNA sequences called *homeoboxes* (see Chapter 21). Animals share a unique homeobox-containing family of genes, known as *Hox* genes. *Hox* genes play important roles in the development of animal embryos, controlling the expression of dozens or even hundreds of other genes that influence animal morphology (see Chapter 25).

Sponges, which are among the simplest extant animals, have *Hox* genes that regulate formation of water channels in the body wall, a key feature of sponge morphology (see Chapter 33). In the ancestors of more complex animals, the *Hox* gene family underwent further duplications, yielding a more versatile "toolkit" for regulating development. In vertebrates, insects, and most other animals, *Hox* genes regulate patterning of the anterior-posterior (front-to-back) axis, as well as other aspects of development. The same conserved genetic network governs the development of both a fly and a human, despite their obvious differences and hundreds of millions of years of divergent evolution.

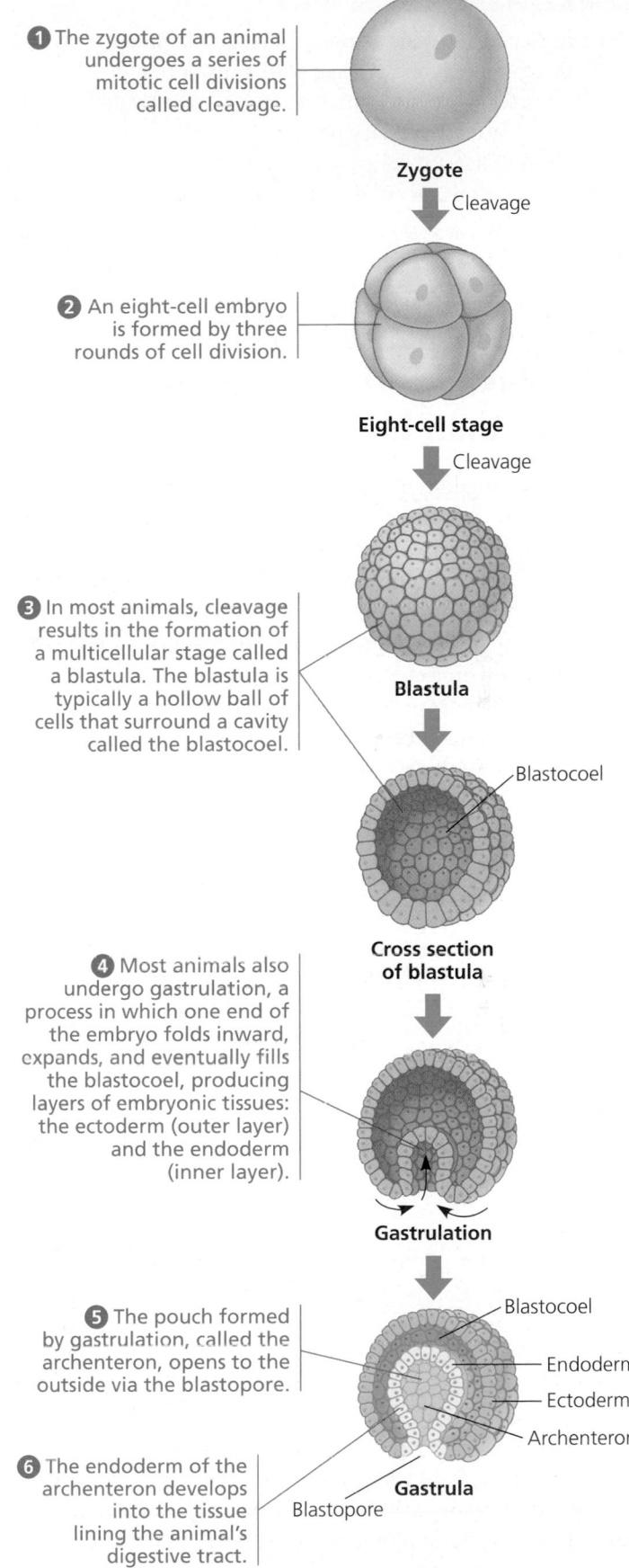

❶ The zygote of an animal undergoes a series of mitotic cell divisions called cleavage.

Zygote

Cleavage

❷ An eight-cell embryo is formed by three rounds of cell division.

Eight-cell stage

Cleavage

❸ In most animals, cleavage results in the formation of a multicellular stage called a blastula. The blastula is typically a hollow ball of cells that surround a cavity called the blastocoel.

Blastula

Blastocoel

Cross section of blastula

❹ Most animals also undergo gastrulation, a process in which one end of the embryo folds inward, expands, and eventually fills the blastocoel, producing layers of embryonic tissues: the ectoderm (outer layer) and the endoderm (inner layer).

Gastrulation

Blastocoel

❺ The pouch formed by gastrulation, called the archenteron, opens to the outside via the blastopore.

Endoderm

Ectoderm

Archenteron

❻ The endoderm of the archenteron develops into the tissue lining the animal's digestive tract.

Gastrula

Blastopore

▲ Figure 32.2 **Early embryonic development in animals.**

CONCEPT 32.2
The history of animals spans more than half a billion years

The animal kingdom includes not only the great diversity of living species, but also the even greater diversity of extinct ones. (Some paleontologists have estimated that 99% of all animal species are extinct.) Various studies suggest that this great diversity has its origins in evolutionary changes that occurred during the last billion years. For example, some estimates based on molecular clocks suggest that the ancestors of animals diverged from the ancestors of fungi about a billion years ago. Similar studies suggest that the common ancestor of living animals may have lived sometime between 675 and 875 million years ago.

To learn what this common ancestor may have been like, scientists have sought to identify protist groups that are closely related to animals. As shown in **Figure 32.3**, a combination of morphological and molecular evidence indicates that choanoflagellates are among the closest living relatives of animals. Based on such results, researchers hypothesize that the common ancestor of living animals may have been a stationary suspension feeder, similar to present-day choanoflagellates. In this section, we will survey the fossil evidence for how animals evolved from their distant common ancestor over four geologic eras (see Table 25.1 to review the geologic time scale.)

Neoproterozoic Era (1 Billion–542 Million Years Ago)

Despite the molecular data indicating an earlier origin of animals, the first generally accepted macroscopic fossils of animals range in age from 565 to 550 million years old. These fossils are members of an early group of multicellular eukaryotes, known collectively as the **Ediacaran biota**. These soft-bodied organisms were named for the Ediacara Hills of Australia, where they were first discovered **(Figure 32.4)**. Similar fossils have since been found on other continents. Some are sponges, while others may be related to living cnidarians. Still others of these fossil organisms have proved difficult to classify, as they do not seem to be closely related to any living animal or plant groups.

In addition to these macroscopic fossils, Neoproterozoic rocks have also yielded what may be microscopic signs of early animals. As you read in Chapter 25, 575-million-year-old microfossils discovered in China appear to exhibit the basic structural organization of present-day animal embryos. However, debate continues about whether the fossil embryos are animals

▼ Figure 32.3 **Three lines of evidence that choanoflagellates are closely related to animals.**

? *Are the data described in ❸ consistent with predictions that could be made from the evidence in ❶ and ❷? Explain.*

❶ Morphologically, choanoflagellate cells and the collar cells (or *choanocytes*) of sponges are almost indistinguishable.

Individual choanoflagellate

Collar cell (choanocyte)

❸ DNA sequence data indicate that choanoflagellates and animals are sister groups. In addition, signaling and adhesion genes previously known only from animals have been discovered in choanoflagellates.

❷ Similar collar cells have been identified in other animals, including cnidarians, flatworms, and echinoderms—but they have never been observed in non-choanoflagellate protists or in plants or fungi.

(a) Mawsonites spriggi   **(b) Spriggina floundersi**

▲ **Figure 32.4 Ediacaran fossils.** Fossils dating from 565–550 million years ago include animals **(a)** with simple, radial forms and **(b)** with many body segments.

or are members of extinct groups that are closely related to animals (but are not actually animals). Though older fossils of animals may be discovered in the future, the fossil record as it is known today strongly suggests that the end of the Neoproterozoic era was a time of increasing animal diversity.

Paleozoic Era (542–251 Million Years Ago)

Animal diversification appears to have accelerated dramatically from 535 to 525 million years ago, during the Cambrian period of the Paleozoic era—a phenomenon often referred to as the **Cambrian explosion** (see Chapter 25). In strata formed before the Cambrian explosion, only a few animal phyla can be recognized. But in strata that are 535 to 525 million years old, paleontologists have found the oldest fossils of about half of all extant animal phyla, including the first arthropods, chordates, and echinoderms. Many of these distinctive fossils—which include the first animals with hard mineralized skeletons—look quite different from most living animals **(Figure 32.5)**. But for the most part, paleontologists have established that these Cambrian fossils are members of extant animal phyla—or at least are close relatives.

What caused the Cambrian explosion? There are several current hypotheses. Some evidence suggests that new predator-prey relationships that emerged in the Cambrian period generated diversity through natural selection. Predators acquired novel adaptations, such as forms of locomotion that helped them catch prey, while prey species acquired new defenses, such as protective shells. Another hypothesis focuses on a rise in atmospheric oxygen that preceded the Cambrian explosion. Greater oxygen availability would have provided opportunities for animals with higher metabolic rates and larger body sizes to thrive. A third hypothesis proposes that the evolution of the *Hox* gene complex provided the developmental flexibility that resulted in variations in morphology. These hypotheses are not mutually exclusive, however; predator-prey relationships, atmospheric changes, and developmental flexibility may each have played a role.

▲ **Figure 32.5 A Cambrian seascape.** This artist's reconstruction depicts a diverse array of organisms found in fossils from the Burgess Shale site in British Columbia, Canada. The animals include *Pikaia* (swimming eel-like chordate), *Hallucigenia* (animal with toothpick-like spikes), *Anomalocaris* (large animal with anterior grasping limbs and a circular mouth), and *Marella* (arthropod swimming at left).

The Cambrian period was followed by the Ordovician, Silurian, and Devonian periods, when animal diversity continued to increase, although punctuated by episodes of mass extinctions (see Figure 25.14). Vertebrates (fishes) emerged as the top predators of the marine food web. By 460 million years ago, groups that diversified during the Cambrian period were making an impact on land. Arthropods began to adapt to terrestrial habitats, as indicated by the appearance of millipedes and centipedes. Fern galls—enlarged cavities that resident insects stimulate fern plants to form, providing protection for the insects—date back at least 302 million years, suggesting that insects and plants were influencing each other's evolution by that time.

Vertebrates made the transition to land around 360 million years ago and diversified into numerous terrestrial groups. Two of these survive today: the amphibians (such as frogs and salamanders) and the amniotes (reptiles and mammals). We will explore these groups, known collectively as the tetrapods, in more detail in Chapter 34.

Mesozoic Era (251–65.5 Million Years Ago)

No fundamentally new animal groups emerged during the Mesozoic era. But the animal phyla that had evolved during the Paleozoic now began to spread into new ecological habitats. In the oceans, the first coral reefs formed, providing other animals with new marine habitats. Some reptiles returned to the water and succeeded as large aquatic predators. On land, descent with modification in some tetrapods led to the origin of wings and other flight equipment in pterosaurs and birds. Large and small dinosaurs emerged, both as predators and herbivores. At the same time, the first mammals—tiny nocturnal insect-eaters—appeared on the scene. In addition, as you read in Chapter 30, flowering plants (angiosperms) and insects both underwent dramatic diversifications during the late Mesozoic.

Cenozoic Era (65.5 Million Years Ago to the Present)

Mass extinctions of both terrestrial and marine animals ushered in a new era, the Cenozoic. Among the groups of species that disappeared were the large, nonflying dinosaurs and the marine reptiles. The fossil record of the early Cenozoic documents the rise of large mammalian herbivores and predators as mammals began to exploit the vacated ecological niches. The global climate gradually cooled throughout the Cenozoic, triggering significant shifts in many animal lineages. Among primates, for example, some species in Africa adapted to the open woodlands and savannas that replaced the former dense forests. The ancestors of our own species were among those grassland apes.

CONCEPT CHECK 32.2

1. Put the following milestones in animal evolution in chronological order from oldest to most recent: (a) origin of mammals, (b) earliest evidence of terrestrial arthropods, (c) Ediacaran fauna, (d) extinction of large, nonflying dinosaurs.

2. **WHAT IF?** Suppose the most recent common ancestor of fungi and animals lived 1 billion years ago. If the first fungi lived 990 million years ago, would animals also have been alive at that time? Explain.

For suggested answers, see Appendix A.

CONCEPT 32.3

Animals can be characterized by "body plans"

Although animal species vary tremendously in morphology, their great diversity in form can be categorized into a relatively small number of major "body plans." A **body plan** is a set of morphological and developmental traits, integrated into a functional whole—the living animal. (Note that the term *plan* here is not meant to imply that animal forms are the result of conscious planning or invention.)

Like all features of organisms, animal body plans have evolved over time. Some of the evolutionary changes appear to have occurred early in the history of animal life. For example, recent research suggests that a key step in the molecular control of gastrulation has remained unchanged for more than 500 million years **(Figure 32.6)**. This early evolutionary innovation was of fundamental importance: Gastrulation explains why most

---

▼ Figure 32.6 Inquiry

Did β-catenin play an ancient role in the molecular control of gastrulation?

EXPERIMENT In most animals, gastrulation leads to the formation of three layers of embryonic cells. In several species, the protein β-catenin marks the site of gastrulation and activates the transcription of genes necessary for gastrulation. Athula Wikramanayake and Mark Martindale, of the University of Hawaii, and colleagues tested whether β-catenin also helps to control gastrulation in the sea anemone *Nematostella vectensis*. This species is in the phylum Cnidaria, a group that predates the origin of animals whose embryos form three layers of cells.

RESULTS

❶ In early stages of development, β-catenin (here labeled with green fluorescent protein) is found throughout the *N. vectensis* embryo.

100 µm

❷ By the 32-cell stage, β-catenin is concentrated on the side of the embryo where gastrulation will occur.

Site of gastrulation

❸ In the early gastrula stage, β-catenin activity (here stained a darker red) occurs in the inner layer of cells.

Site of gastrulation

❹ In embryos in which β-catenin activity is blocked (by a protein that binds to β-catenin), gastrulation does not occur.

CONCLUSION In *N. vectensis*, β-catenin helps to determine the site of gastrulation and is required for gastrulation to occur. The fossil record indicates that cnidarians diverged more than 500 million years ago from other species in which β-catenin is known to influence gastrulation, suggesting that β-catenin played an ancient role in the molecular control of gastrulation.

SOURCE A. H. Wikramanayake et al., An ancient role for nuclear β-catenin in the evolution of axial polarity and germ layer segregation, *Nature* 426:446–450 (2003).

WHAT IF? β-catenin binds to DNA, thereby stimulating the transcription of genes necessary for gastrulation. Based on this information, suggest a different experiment that could be used to confirm the results in step 4. What would be the purpose of performing such an experiment?

---

animals are not a hollow ball of cells. But other aspects of animal body plans may have changed many times as various animal lineages evolved and diversified. As you explore the major features of animal body plans, bear in mind that similar body forms may have evolved independently in two different lineages. Consider, for example, the group of invertebrate animals called gastropods (class Gastropoda). This group includes many species that lack shells and are referred to as slugs, along with many shelled species, such as snails. All slugs have a similar body plan and hence belong to the same *grade* (a group whose members share key biological features). However, phylogenetic studies show that several gastropod lineages independently lost their shells and became slugs. As illustrated by this example, a grade is not necessarily equivalent to a *clade* (a group that includes an ancestral species and all of its descendants).

Symmetry

One very basic way that animals can be categorized is by the type of symmetry of their bodies—or the absence of symmetry. Most sponges, for example, lack symmetry altogether. Among the animals that do have symmetrical bodies, symmetry can take different forms. Some animals exhibit **radial symmetry**, the form found in a flowerpot **(Figure 32.7a)**. Sea anemones, for example, have a top side (where the mouth is located) and a bottom side. But they have no front and back ends and no left and right sides.

The two-sided symmetry seen in a shovel is an example of **bilateral symmetry** **(Figure 32.7b)**. A bilateral animal has two axes of orientation: front to back and top to bottom.

(a) Radial symmetry. A radial animal, such as a sea anemone (phylum Cnidaria), does not have a left side and a right side. Any imaginary slice through the central axis divides the animal into mirror images.

(b) Bilateral symmetry. A bilateral animal, such as a lobster (phylum Arthropoda), has a left side and a right side. Only one imaginary cut divides the animal into mirror-image halves.

▲ **Figure 32.7 Body symmetry.** The flowerpot and shovel are included to help you remember the radial-bilateral distinction.

Thus, such animals have a **dorsal** (top) side and a **ventral** (bottom) side, as well as a left side and a right side and an **anterior** (front) end with a mouth and a **posterior** (back) end. Many animals with a bilaterally symmetrical body plan (such as arthropods and mammals) have sensory equipment concentrated at their anterior end, including a central nervous system ("brain") in the head—an evolutionary trend called **cephalization** (from the Greek *kephale*, head).

The symmetry of an animal generally fits its lifestyle. Many radial animals are sessile (living attached to a substrate) or planktonic (drifting or weakly swimming, such as jellyfish, more accurately called jellies). Their symmetry equips them to meet the environment equally well from all sides. In contrast, bilateral animals typically move actively from place to place. Most bilateral animals have a central nervous system that enables them to coordinate the complex movements involved in crawling, burrowing, flying, or swimming. Fossil evidence indicates that these two fundamentally different kinds of symmetry have been present for at least 550 million years.

Tissues

Animal body plans also vary according to the organization of the animal's tissues. True tissues are collections of specialized cells isolated from other tissues by membranous layers. Sponges and a few other groups lack true tissues. In all other animals, the embryo becomes layered through the process of gastrulation (see Figure 32.2). As development progresses, these concentric layers, called *germ layers*, form the various tissues and organs of the body. **Ectoderm**, the germ layer covering the surface of the embryo, gives rise to the outer covering of the animal and, in some phyla, to the central nervous system. **Endoderm**, the innermost germ layer, lines the developing digestive tube, or **archenteron**, and gives rise to the lining of the digestive tract (or cavity) and organs such as the liver and lungs of vertebrates.

Animals that have only these two germ layers are said to be **diploblastic**. Diploblasts include the animals called cnidarians (jellies and corals, for example) as well as the comb jellies (see Chapter 33). All bilaterally symmetrical animals have a third germ layer, called the **mesoderm**, between the ectoderm and endoderm. Thus, animals with bilateral symmetry are also said to be **triploblastic** (having three germ layers). In triploblasts, the mesoderm forms the muscles and most other organs between the digestive tract and the outer covering of the animal. Triploblasts include a broad range of animals, from flatworms to arthropods to vertebrates. (Although some diploblasts actually do have a third germ layer, it is not nearly as well developed as the mesoderm of animals considered to be triploblastic.)

Body Cavities

Most triploblastic animals possess a **body cavity**, a fluid- or air-filled space separating the digestive tract from the outer body wall. This body cavity is also known as a **coelom** (from the Greek *koilos*, hollow). A so-called "true" coelom forms from tissue derived from mesoderm. The inner and outer layers of tissue that surround the cavity connect dorsally and ventrally and form structures that suspend the internal organs. Animals that possess a true coelom are known as **coelomates** (Figure 32.8a).

Some triploblastic animals have a body cavity that is formed from mesoderm and endoderm (Figure 32.8b). Such a cavity is called a "pseudocoelom" (from the Greek *pseudo*, false), and animals that have one are **pseudocoelomates**. Despite its name, however, a pseudocoelom is not false; it is a fully functional body cavity. Finally, some triploblastic animals lack a body cavity altogether (Figure 32.8c). They are known collectively as **acoelomates** (from the Greek *a*, without).

A body cavity has many functions. Its fluid cushions the suspended organs, helping to prevent internal injury. In soft-bodied coelomates, such as earthworms, the coelom contains noncom-

pressible fluid that acts like a skeleton against which muscles can work. The cavity also enables the internal organs to grow and move independently of the outer body wall. If it were not for your coelom, for example, every beat of your heart or ripple of your intestine would warp your body's surface.

Current phylogenetic research suggests that true coeloms and pseudocoeloms have been gained or lost multiple times in the course of animal evolution. Thus, the terms *coelomates* and *pseudocoelomates* refer to grades, not clades.

Protostome and Deuterostome Development

Based on certain aspects of early development, many animals can be categorized as having one of two developmental modes: **protostome development** or **deuterostome development**. These modes can generally be distinguished by differences in cleavage, coelom formation, and fate of the blastopore.

Cleavage

A pattern in many animals with protostome development is **spiral cleavage**, in which the planes of cell division are diagonal to the vertical axis of the embryo; as seen in the eight-cell stage, smaller cells lie in the grooves between larger, underlying cells (Figure 32.9a, left). Furthermore, the so-called **determinate cleavage** of some animals with protostome development rigidly casts ("determines") the developmental fate of each embryonic cell very early. A cell isolated at the four-cell stage from a snail, for example, after repeated divisions will form an inviable embryo that lacks many parts.

In contrast to the spiral cleavage pattern, deuterostome development is predominantly characterized by **radial cleavage**. The cleavage planes are either parallel or perpendicular to the vertical axis of the embryo; as seen in the eight-cell stage, the tiers of cells are aligned, one directly above the other (see Figure 32.9a, right). Most animals with deuterostome development also have **indeterminate cleavage**, meaning that each cell produced by early cleavage divisions retains the capacity to develop into a complete embryo. For example, if the cells of a sea urchin embryo are isolated at the four-cell stage, each will form a complete larva. It is the indeterminate cleavage of the human zygote that makes identical twins possible. This characteristic also explains the developmental versatility of embryonic stem cells that may provide new ways to overcome a variety of diseases (see Chapter 20).

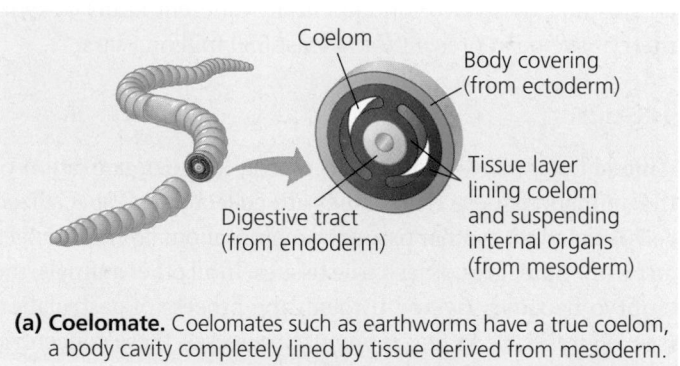

(a) Coelomate. Coelomates such as earthworms have a true coelom, a body cavity completely lined by tissue derived from mesoderm.

(b) Pseudocoelomate. Pseudocoelomates such as roundworms have a body cavity lined in part by tissue derived from mesoderm, but also by tissue derived from endoderm.

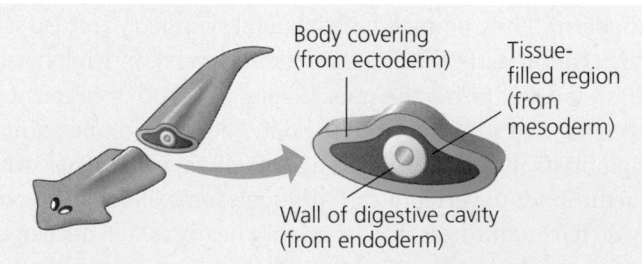

(c) Acoelomate. Acoelomates such as planarians lack a body cavity between the digestive cavity and outer body wall.

▲ **Figure 32.8 Body cavities of triploblastic animals.** The various organ systems of a triploblastic animal develop from the three germ layers that form in the embryo. Blue represents tissue derived from ectoderm, red from mesoderm, and yellow from endoderm.

Coelom Formation

Another difference between protostome and deuterostome development is apparent later in the process. During gastrulation, an embryo's developing digestive tube initially forms as a blind pouch, the archenteron, which becomes the gut (Figure 32.9b). As the archenteron forms in protostome development, initially solid masses of mesoderm split and form the coelom. In contrast, in deuterostome development, the mesoderm buds from the wall of the archenteron, and its cavity becomes the coelom.

These are useful general distinctions, though there are many variations and exceptions to these patterns.

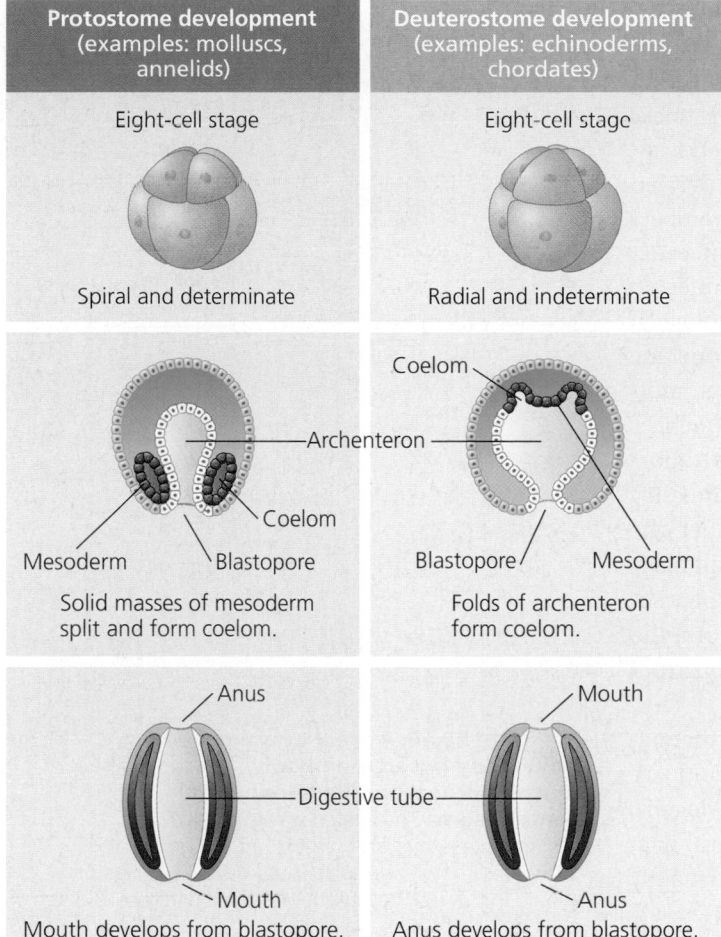

Protostome development (examples: molluscs, annelids)	Deuterostome development (examples: echinoderms, chordates)
Eight-cell stage	Eight-cell stage
Spiral and determinate	Radial and indeterminate

(a) Cleavage. In general, protostome development begins with spiral, determinate cleavage. Deuterostome development is characterized by radial, indeterminate cleavage.

(b) Coelom formation. Coelom formation begins in the gastrula stage. In protostome development, the coelom forms from splits in the mesoderm. In deuterostome development, the coelom forms from mesodermal outpocketings of the archenteron.

Archenteron

Coelom

Mesoderm — Blastopore

Solid masses of mesoderm split and form coelom.

Blastopore — Mesoderm

Folds of archenteron form coelom.

Key

Ectoderm
Mesoderm
Endoderm

(c) Fate of the blastopore. In protostome development, the mouth forms from the blastopore. In deuterostome development, the mouth forms from a secondary opening.

Anus

Digestive tube

Mouth

Mouth develops from blastopore.

Mouth

Anus

Anus develops from blastopore.

Fate of the Blastopore

Protostome and deuterostome development often differ in the fate of the **blastopore**, the indentation that during gastrulation leads to the formation of the archenteron (**Figure 32.9c**). After the archenteron develops, in most animals a second opening forms at the opposite end of the gastrula. Ultimately, the blastopore and this second opening become the two openings of the digestive tube (the mouth and the anus). In protostome development, the mouth generally develops from the first opening, the blastopore, and it is for this characteristic that the term *protostome* derives (from the Greek *protos*, first, and *stoma*, mouth). In deuterostome (from the Greek *deuteros*, second) development, the mouth is derived from the secondary opening, and the blastopore usually forms the anus.

CONCEPT CHECK 32.3

1. Distinguish the terms *grade* and *clade*.
2. Compare three aspects of the early development of a snail (a mollusc) and a human (a chordate).
3. **WHAT IF?** Evaluate this claim: Ignoring the details of their specific anatomy, worms, humans, and almost all other triploblasts are basically shaped like a doughnut.

For suggested answers, see Appendix A.

CONCEPT 32.4
New views of animal phylogeny are emerging from molecular data

Zoologists currently recognize about three dozen animal phyla. But the relationships between these phyla continue to be debated. Although it might be frustrating that the phylogenies in textbooks cannot be memorized as set-in-stone truths, the uncertainty inherent in these diagrams is a healthy reminder that science is an ongoing, dynamic process of inquiry.

Researchers have long based their hypotheses about animal phylogeny on morphological data. In the late 1980s, biologists also began to study the molecular systematics of animals. Additional clues about animal phylogeny have come from new studies of lesser-known phyla, along with fossil analyses that can help clarify which traits are ancestral in various animal groups and which are derived.

As you read in Chapter 26, phylogenetic systematists seek to classify organisms based on common descent. Their goal is to place organisms into groups that correspond to clades, each of which includes an ancestral species and all of its descendants. Based on cladistic methods, a phylogenetic tree takes shape as a hierarchy of clades nested within larger clades—the finer branches and the thicker branches of the tree, respectively. Clades are inferred from shared derived characters that are unique to members of the clade and their common ancestor. For example, a clade might be inferred from key anatomical and embryological similarities that researchers conclude are homologous. In recent years, molecular data such as DNA sequences have provided another source of information for inferring common ancestry and defining clades. But whether the data used are "traditional" morphological characters or "new" molecular sequences or a combination of both, the overall goal is the same—to reconstruct the evolutionary history of life.

To get a sense of the debates that occur in animal systematics, we'll compare a traditional view of animal phylogeny, based primarily on morphological data (Figure 32.10), with a view based mainly on molecular data (Figure 32.11).

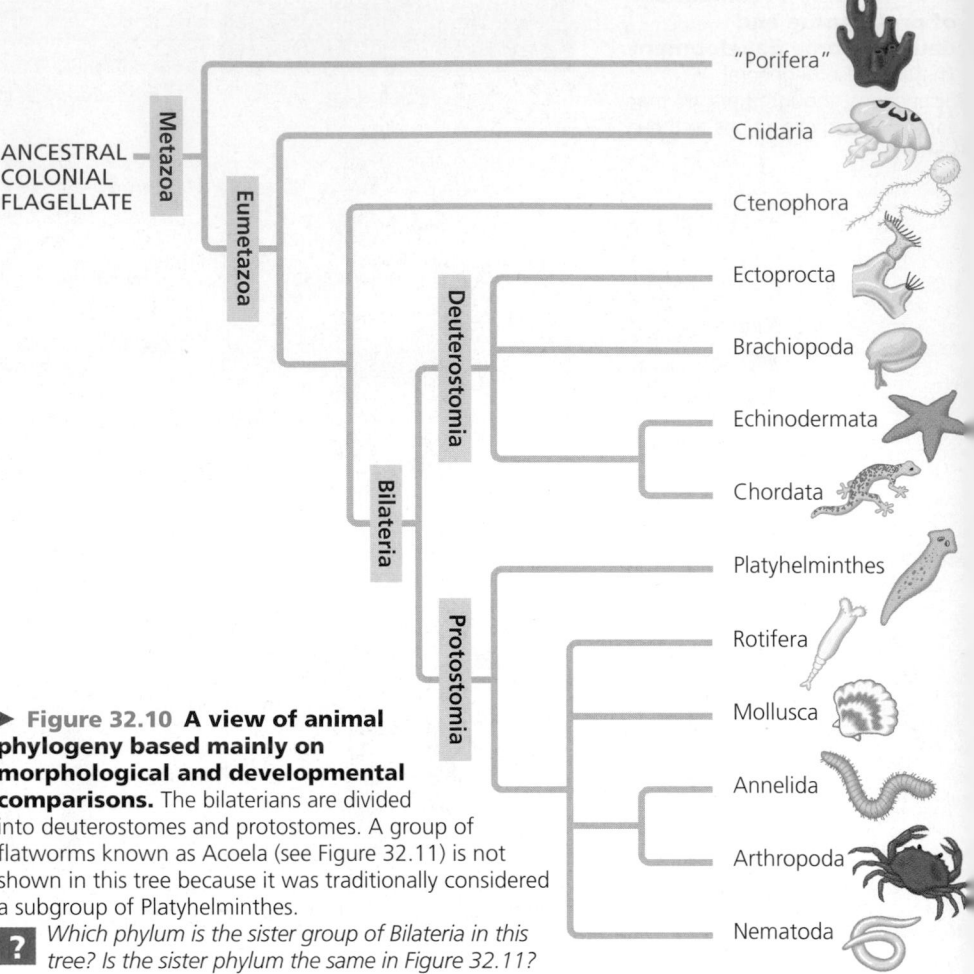

▶ **Figure 32.10 A view of animal phylogeny based mainly on morphological and developmental comparisons.** The bilaterians are divided into deuterostomes and protostomes. A group of flatworms known as Acoela (see Figure 32.11) is not shown in this tree because it was traditionally considered a subgroup of Platyhelminthes.

? *Which phylum is the sister group of Bilateria in this tree? Is the sister phylum the same in Figure 32.11?*

Points of Agreement

The morphological and molecular trees agree on a number of major features of animal phylogeny. After reading each point, see how the statement is reflected in the phylogenetic trees in Figures 32.10 and 32.11.

1. **All animals share a common ancestor.** Both trees indicate that the animal kingdom is monophyletic, representing a clade called Metazoa. In other words, if we could trace all extant and extinct animal lineages back to their origin, they would converge on a common ancestor.

2. **Sponges are basal animals.** Among the extant taxa, sponges (formerly, the phylum Porifera) branch from the base of both animal trees. Some molecular analyses suggest that sponges are paraphyletic, falling into at least the two phyla shown in Figure 32.11.

3. **Eumetazoa is a clade of animals with true tissues.** All animals except for sponges and a few other groups belong to a clade of **eumetazoans** ("true animals"). True tissues evolved in the common ancestor of living eumetazoans. Basal members of the eumetazoan clade include the phyla Ctenophora (comb jellies) and Cnidaria. These basal eumetazoans are diploblastic and generally feature radial symmetry.

4. **Most animal phyla belong to the clade Bilateria.** Bilateral symmetry and the presence of three germ layers are shared derived characters that help to define the clade Bilateria. This clade contains the majority of animal phyla, and its members are known as **bilaterians**. The Cambrian explosion was primarily a rapid diversification of the bilaterians.

5. **Chordates and some other phyla belong to the clade Deuterostomia.** The term *deuterostome* refers not only to a mode of animal development, but also to the members of a clade that includes vertebrates and other chordates. (Note, however, that the traditional and molecular views of animal phylogeny disagree as to which other phyla are also deuterostomes.)

Progress in Resolving Bilaterian Relationships

While evolutionary relationships inferred from traditional morphological data and molecular data are similar in many respects, there also are some differences. For example, the morphology-based tree in Figure 32.10 divides the bilaterians into two clades: deuterostomes and protostomes. This view assumes that these two modes of development reflect a

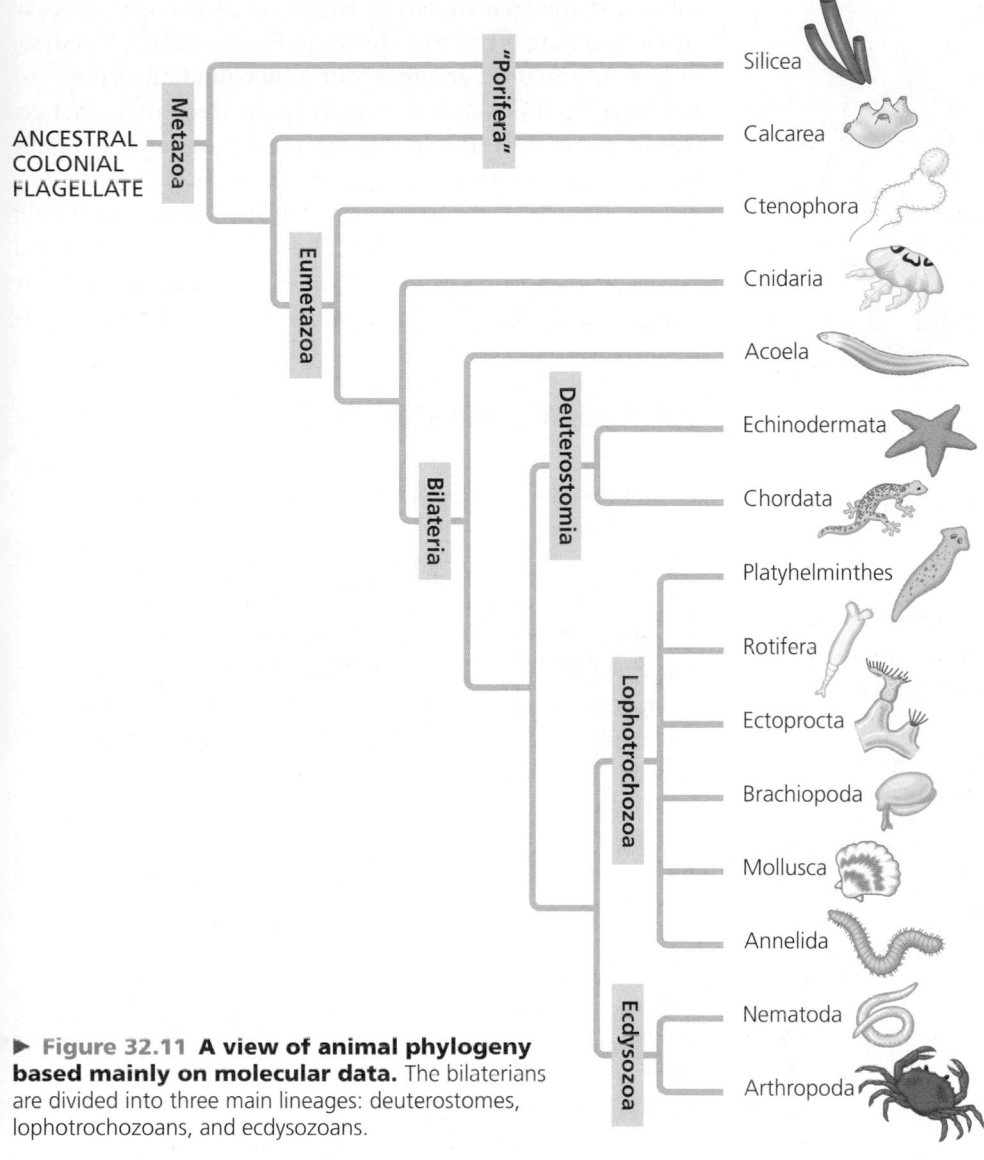

ANCESTRAL
COLONIAL
FLAGELLATE

Metazoa

"Porifera"

Silicea

Calcarea

Eumetazoa

Ctenophora

Cnidaria

Acoela

Bilateria

Deuterostomia

Echinodermata

Chordata

Platyhelminthes

Rotifera

Lophotrochozoa

Ectoprocta

Brachiopoda

Mollusca

Annelida

Ecdysozoa

Nematoda

Arthropoda

► **Figure 32.11 A view of animal phylogeny based mainly on molecular data.** The bilaterians are divided into three main lineages: deuterostomes, lophotrochozoans, and ecdysozoans.

phylogenetic pattern. Within the protostomes, Figure 32.10 indicates that arthropods (which include insects and crustaceans) are grouped with annelids. Both groups have segmented bodies (think of the tail of a lobster, which is an arthropod, and an earthworm, which is an annelid).

A different view has emerged from molecular phylogenies based on ribosomal genes, *Hox* genes, and dozens of other protein-coding nuclear genes, as well as mitochondrial genes. Collectively, these studies indicate that there are three major clades of bilaterally symmetrical animals: Deuterostomia, Lophotrochozoa, and Ecdysozoa (see Figure 32.11). In contrast to the traditional morphological view, the molecular phylogeny holds that the arthropods and annelids are not closely related to one another. Note also that Figure 32.11 includes a group of acoelomate flatworms (Acoela) not shown in Figure 32.10. Traditionally, acoel flatworms were classified with other flatworms in the phylum Platyhelminthes. However, recent research indicates that acoel flatworms are basal

bilaterians, not members of the phylum Platyhelminthes. Acoela's basal position suggests that the bilaterians may have descended from a common ancestor that resembled living acoel flatworms—that is, from an ancestor that had a simple nervous system, a saclike gut, and no excretory system.

As seen in Figure 32.11, the molecular phylogeny assigns the animal phyla that are not in Deuterostomia to two taxa rather than one: the **ecdysozoans** and the **lophotrochozoans**. The clade name Ecdysozoa refers to a characteristic shared by nematodes, arthropods, and some of the other ecdysozoan phyla that are not included in our survey. These animals secrete external skeletons (exoskeletons); the stiff covering of a cicada or cricket is an example. As the animal grows, it molts, squirming out of its old exoskeleton and secreting a larger one. The process of shedding the old exoskeleton is called *ecdysis* **(Figure 32.12)**. Though named for this characteristic, the clade was proposed based mainly on molecular data that support the common ancestry of its members. Furthermore, some taxa excluded from this clade by their molecular data, such as certain species of leeches, do in fact molt.

The name Lophotrochozoa refers to two different features observed in some animals belonging to this clade. Some lophotrochozoans, such as brachiopods, develop a structure called a **lophophore** (from the Greek *lophos*, crest, and *pherein*, to carry), a crown of ciliated tentacles that function in

◄ **Figure 32.12 Ecdysis.** This molting cicada is in the process of emerging from its old exoskeleton. The animal will now secrete a new, larger exoskeleton.

Lophophore

(a) An ectoproct, which has a lophophore (LM)

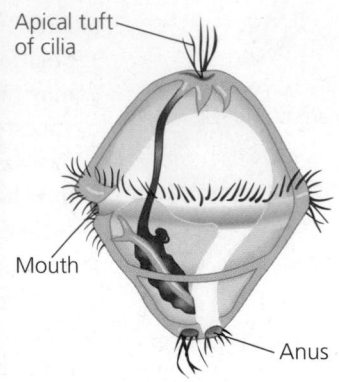

Apical tuft of cilia

Mouth

Anus

(b) Structure of a trochophore larva

▲ Figure 32.13 **Morphological characteristics found among lophotrochozoans.**

feeding (**Figure 32.13a**). Individuals in other phyla, including molluscs and annelids, go through a distinctive developmental stage called the **trochophore larva** (**Figure 32.13b**)—hence the name lophotrochozoan.

Future Directions in Animal Systematics

Like any area of scientific inquiry, animal systematics is a work in progress. At present, most (but not all) systematists think that the tree shown in Figure 32.11 is more strongly supported than is the tree shown in Figure 32.10. Of course, as new information emerges, our understanding of the evolutionary relationships shown in these trees may change. Researchers continue to conduct large-scale analyses of multiple genes across a wide sample of animal phyla. A better understanding of the relationships between these phyla will give scientists a clearer picture of how the diversity of animal body plans arose. In Chapters 33 and 34, we will take a closer look at the diverse phyla of extant animals and their evolutionary history.

Chapter 32 Review

SUMMARY OF KEY CONCEPTS

CONCEPT 32.1

Animals are multicellular, heterotrophic eukaryotes with tissues that develop from embryonic layers (pp. 654–656)

▶ **Nutritional Mode** Animals are heterotrophs that ingest their food.

▶ **Cell Structure and Specialization** Animals are multicellular eukaryotes. Their cells lack cell walls; instead, they are held together by structural proteins such as collagen. Nervous tissue and muscle tissue are unique to animals.

▶ **Reproduction and Development** In most animals, gastrulation follows the formation of the blastula and leads to the formation of embryonic tissue layers. All animals, and only animals, have *Hox* genes that regulate the development of body form. Although *Hox* genes have been highly conserved, they can produce a wide diversity of animal morphology.

CONCEPT 32.2

The history of animals spans more than half a billion years (pp. 656–658)

▶ **Neoproterozoic Era (1 Billion–542 Million Years Ago)** Early animal fossils include the Ediacaran fauna.

▶ **Paleozoic Era (542–251 Million Years Ago)** The Cambrian explosion marks the earliest fossil appearance of many major groups of living animals.

▶ **Mesozoic Era (251–65.5 Million Years Ago)** Dinosaurs were the dominant land vertebrates. Coral reefs emerged, providing marine habitats for other organisms.

▶ **Cenozoic Era (65.5 Million Years Ago to the Present)** Mammalian orders diversified during the Cenozoic.

CONCEPT 32.3

Animals can be characterized by "body plans" (pp. 658–661)

▶ **Symmetry** Animals may lack symmetry or may have radial or bilateral symmetry. Bilaterally symmetrical animals have dorsal and ventral sides, as well as anterior and posterior ends.

▶ **Tissues** Eumetazoan embryos may be diploblastic (having two germ layers) or triploblastic (having three germ layers).

► **Body Cavities** In triploblastic animals, a body cavity may be present or absent. A body cavity can be a pseudocoelom (derived from both mesoderm and endoderm) or a true coelom (derived only from mesoderm).

► **Protostome and Deuterostome Development** These two modes of development often differ in patterns of cleavage, coelom formation, and fate of the blastopore.

CONCEPT 32.4

New views of animal phylogeny are emerging from molecular data (pp. 661–664)

► **Points of Agreement**

► **Progress in Resolving Bilaterian Relationships**

► **Future Directions in Animal Systematics** Phylogenetic studies based on larger databases may provide further insights into animal evolutionary history.

MEDIA

Activity Animal Phylogenetic Tree
Investigation How Do Molecular Data Fit Traditional Phylogenies?

TESTING YOUR KNOWLEDGE

SELF-QUIZ

1. Among the characteristics unique to animals is
   a. gastrulation.
   b. multicellularity.
   c. sexual reproduction.
   d. flagellated sperm.
   e. heterotrophic nutrition.

2. The distinction between sponges and other animal phyla is based mainly on the absence versus the presence of
   a. a body cavity.
   b. a complete digestive tract.
   c. a circulatory system.
   d. true tissues.
   e. mesoderm.

3. Which of these is a point of conflict between the phylogenetic analyses presented in Figures 32.10 and 32.11?
   a. the monophyly of the animal kingdom
   b. the relationship of taxa of segmented animals to taxa of nonsegmented animals
   c. that sponges are basal animals
   d. that chordates are deuterostomes
   e. the monophyly of the bilaterians

4. Acoelomates are characterized by
   a. the absence of a brain.
   b. the absence of mesoderm.
   c. deuterostome development.
   d. a coelom that is not completely lined with mesoderm.
   e. a solid body without a cavity surrounding internal organs.

5. Which of the following was probably the *least* important factor in bringing about the Cambrian explosion?
   a. the emergence of predator-prey relationships among animals
   b. the accumulation of diverse adaptations, such as shells and different modes of locomotion
   c. the movement of animals onto land
   d. the evolution of *Hox* genes that controlled development
   e. the accumulation of sufficient atmospheric oxygen to support the more active metabolism of mobile animals

6. What is the main basis for placing the arthropods and nematodes in Ecdysozoa in one hypothesis of animal phylogeny?
   a. Animals in both groups are segmented.
   b. Animals in both groups undergo ecdysis.
   c. They both have radial, determinate cleavage, and their embryonic development is similar.
   d. Fossils reveal a common ancestor of the two phyla.
   e. Analysis of genes shows that their sequences are quite similar, and these sequences differ from those of the lophotrochozoans and deuterostomes.

For Self-Quiz answers, see Appendix A.

MEDIA Visit **www.campbellbiology.com** for a Practice Test.

EVOLUTION CONNECTION

7. Some scientists suggest that the phrase "Cambrian fizzle" might be more appropriate than "Cambrian explosion" to describe the diversification of animals during that geologic period. Other scientists have compared observing an explosion of animal diversity in Cambrian strata to monitoring Earth from a satellite and noticing the emergence of cities only when they are large enough to be visible from that distance. What do these views imply about the evolutionary history of animals during that time?

SCIENTIFIC INQUIRY

8. **DRAW IT** Redraw the eumetazoan portion of Figure 32.11. Using the information in the table below, label each branch that leads to a phylum with S, R, or I, depending on the cleavage pattern of its members. What is the ancestral cleavage pattern? How many times have cleavage patterns changed over the course of evolution? Explain.

Cleavage Pattern	Phyla
Spiral (S)	Mollusca, Platyhelminthes, Annelida
Idiosyncratic (I)	Acoela, Arthropoda
Radial (R)	All eumetazoan phyla not listed above

Invertebrates

33

OVERVIEW

Life Without a Backbone

At first glance, you might mistake the organism shown in **Figure 33.1** for some type of seaweed. But this colorful inhabitant of coral reefs is actually an animal, not an alga. Specifically, it is a species of segmented worm known as a Christmas tree worm (*Spirobranchus giganteus*). The two tree-shaped whorls are tentacles, which the worm uses for gas exchange and for filtering small food particles from the surrounding water. The tentacles emerge from a tube of calcium carbonate secreted by the worm that protects and supports its soft body. Light-sensitive structures on the tentacles can detect the shadow cast by a predator, triggering the worm to contract muscles that rapidly withdraw the tentacles into the tube.

Christmas tree worms are **invertebrates**—animals that lack a backbone. Invertebrates account for 95% of known animal species. They occupy almost every habitat on Earth, from the scalding water released by deep-sea hydrothermal vents to the rocky, frozen ground of Antarctica. Adaptation to these varied environments has produced an immense diversity of forms, ranging from a species consisting simply of a flat bilayer of cells to other species with silk-spinning glands, pivoting spines, dozens of jointed legs, or tentacles covered with suction cups, just to list a few.

In this chapter, we'll take a tour of the invertebrate world, using the phylogenetic tree in **Figure 33.2** as a guide. **Figure 33.3** on the next three pages, surveys 23 invertebrate phyla. As representatives of invertebrate diversity, many of those phyla are explored in more detail in the rest of this chapter.

▲ Figure 33.1 **What function do the red whorls of this organism have?**

▶ Figure 33.2 **Review of animal phylogeny.** Except for sponges (basal animals in phyla Calcarea and Silicea) and a few other groups, all animals have tissues and are in the clade Eumetazoa. Most animals are in the diverse clade Bilateria.

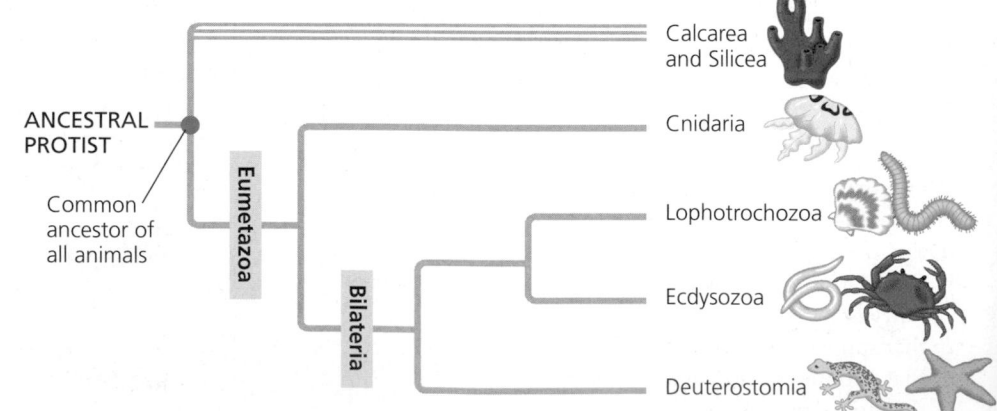

Exploring Invertebrate Diversity

Kingdom Animalia encompasses 1.3 million known species, and estimates of total species range far higher. Of the 23 phyla surveyed here, those illustrated with smaller-sized "preview" photographs are discussed more fully in this chapter or another.

Calcarea and Silicea (5,500 species)

Animals in these phyla are informally called "sponges." Sponges are sessile animals that lack true tissues. They live as suspension feeders, trapping particles that pass through the internal channels of their bodies (see Concept 33.1).

A sponge

Cnidaria (10,000 species)

Cnidarians include corals, jellies, and hydras. These animals have a diplobastic, radially symmetrical body plan that includes a gastrovascular cavity with a single opening that serves as both mouth and anus (see Concept 33.2).

A jelly

Acoela (400 species)

Acoel flatworms have a simple nervous system and a saclike gut, and thus had been placed in phylum Platyhelminthes. Molecular analyses, however, indicate Acoela is a separate lineage that diverged before the three main bilaterian clades (see Concept 32.4).

Acoel flatworms (LM)

Placozoa (1 species)

The single known species in this phylum, *Trichoplax adhaerens*, does not even look like an animal. It consists of a few thousand cells arranged in a double-layered plate. *Trichoplax* can reproduce by dividing into two individuals or by budding off many multicellular individuals.

A placozoan (LM)

Ctenophora (100 species)

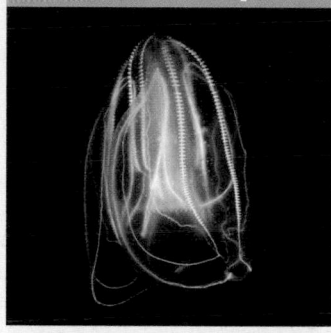

Ctenophores (comb jellies) are diploblastic and radially symmetrical like cnidarians, suggesting that both phyla diverged from other animals very early. Comb jellies make up much of the ocean's plankton. They have many distinctive traits, including eight "combs" of cilia that propel the animals through the water. When a small animal contacts the tentacles of some comb jellies, specialized cells burst open, covering the prey with sticky threads.

A ctenophore, or comb jelly

LOPHOTROCHOZOANS

Platyhelminthes (20,000 species)

Flatworms (including tapeworms, planarians, and flukes) have bilateral symmetry and a central nervous system that processes information from sensory structures. They have no body cavity or organs for circulation (see Concept 33.3).

A marine flatworm

Rotifera (1,800 species)

Despite their microscopic size, rotifers have specialized organ systems, including an alimentary canal (digestive tract). They feed on microorganisms suspended in water (see Concept 33.3).

A rotifer (LM)

Ectoprocta (4,500 species)

Ectoprocts (also known as bryozoans) live as sessile colonies and are covered by a tough exoskeleton (see Concept 33.3).

Ectoprocts

Brachiopoda (335 species)

Brachiopods, or lamp shells, may be easily mistaken for clams or other molluscs. However, most brachiopods have a unique stalk that anchors them to their substrate (see Concept 33.3).

A brachiopod

Continued on next page

Exploring Invertebrate Diversity

Acanthocephala (1,100 species)

Acanthocephalans (from the Greek *acanthias*, prickly, and *cephalo*, head) are called spiny-headed worms because of the curved hooks on the proboscis at the anterior end of their body. All species are parasites. Some acanthocephalans manipulate their intermediate hosts (generally arthropods) in ways that increase their chances of reaching their final hosts (generally vertebrates). For example, acanthocephalans that infect New Zealand mud crabs force their hosts to move to more visible areas on the beach, where the crabs are more likely to be eaten by birds, the worms' final hosts.

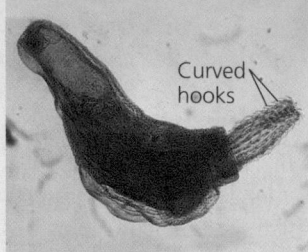
Curved hooks

An acanthocephalan (LM)

Cycliophora (1 species)

100 μm

A cycliophoran (colorized SEM)

The only known species of cycliophoran, *Symbion pandora*, was discovered in 1995 on the mouthparts of a lobster. This tiny, vase-shaped creature has a unique body plan and a particularly bizarre life cycle. Males impregnate females that are still developing in their mothers' bodies. The fertilized females then escape, settle elsewhere on the lobster, and release their offspring. The offspring apparently leave that lobster and search for another one to which they attach.

Nemertea (900 species)

Proboscis worms, or ribbon worms, swim through water or burrow in sand, extending a unique proboscis to capture prey. Like flatworms, they lack a true coelom. However, unlike flatworms, nemerteans have an alimentary canal and a closed circulatory system in which the blood is contained in vessels and hence is distinct from fluid in the body cavity.

A ribbon worm

Mollusca (93,000 species)

Molluscs (including snails, clams, squids, and octopuses) have a soft body that in many species is protected by a hard shell (see Concept 33.3).

An octopus

Annelida (16,500 species)

Annelids, or segmented worms, are distinguished from other worms by their body segmentation. Earthworms are the most familiar annelids, but the phylum also includes marine and freshwater species (see Concept 33.3).

A marine annelid

ECDYSOZOA

Loricifera (10 species)

Loriciferans (from the Latin *lorica*, corset, and *ferre*, to bear) are tiny animals that inhabit the deep-sea bottom. A loriciferan can telescope its head, neck, and thorax in and out of the lorica, a pocket formed by six plates surrounding the abdomen. Though the natural history of loriciferans is mostly a mystery, at least some species likely eat bacteria.

50 μm

A loriciferan (LM)

Priapula (16 species)

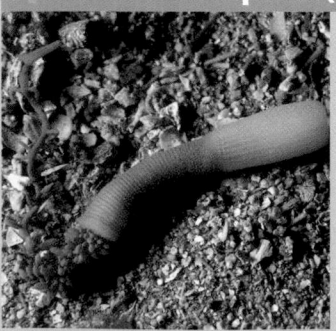

A priapulan

Priapulans are worms with a large, rounded proboscis at the anterior end. (They are named after Priapos, the Greek god of fertility, who was symbolized by a giant penis.) Ranging from 0.5 mm to 20 cm in length, most species burrow through seafloor sediments. Fossil evidence suggests that priapulans were among the major predators during the Cambrian period.

Tardigrada (800 species)

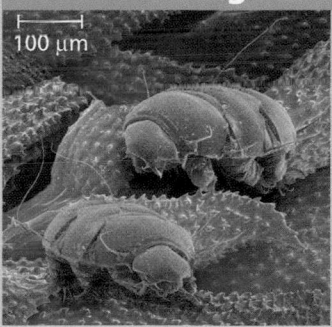

Tardigrades (from the Latin *tardus*, slow, and *gradus*, step) are sometimes called water bears for their rounded shape, stubby appendages, and lumbering, bearlike gait. Most tardigrades are less than 0.5 mm in length. Some live in oceans or fresh water, while others live on plants or animals. As many as 2 million tardigrades can be found on a square meter of

Tardigrades (colorized SEM)

moss. Harsh conditions may cause tardigrades to enter a state of dormancy; while dormant, they can survive temperatures as low as −272°C, close to absolute zero!

Onychophora (110 species)

Onychophorans, also called velvet worms, originated during the Cambrian explosion (see Chapter 32). Originally, they thrived in the ocean, but at some point they succeeded in colonizing land. Today they live only in humid forests. Onychophorans have fleshy antennae and several dozen pairs of saclike legs.

An onychophoran

Nematoda (25,000 species)

Roundworms are enormously abundant and diverse in the soil and in aquatic habitats; many species parasitize plants and animals. The most distinctive feature of roundworms is a tough cuticle that coats the body (see Concept 33.4).

A roundworm

Arthropoda (1,000,000 species)

The vast majority of known animal species, including insects, crustaceans, and arachnids, are arthropods. All arthropods have a segmented exoskeleton and jointed appendages (see Concept 33.4).

A scorpion (an arachnid)

DEUTEROSTOMIA

Hemichordata (85 species)

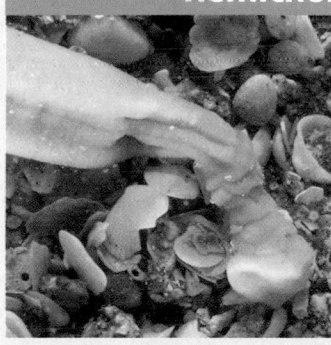

An acorn worm

Like echinoderms and chordates, hemichordates are members of the deuterostome clade (see Chapter 32). Hemichordates share some traits with other chordates, such as gill slits and a dorsal nerve cord. The largest group of hemichordates are the enteropneusts, or acorn worms. Acorn worms are marine and generally live buried in mud or under rocks; they may grow to more than 2 m in length.

Echinodermata (7,000 species)

Echinoderms, such as sand dollars, sea stars, and sea urchins, are aquatic animals in the deuterostome clade that are bilaterally symmetrical as larvae but not as adults. They move and feed by using a network of internal canals to pump water to different

A sea urchin

parts of their body (see Concept 33.5).

Chordata (52,000 species)

More than 90% of all known chordate species have backbones (and thus are vertebrates). However, the phylum Chordata also includes three groups of invertebrates: lancelets, tunicates, and hagfishes. See Chapter 34 for a full discussion of this phylum.

A tunicate

CONCEPT 33.1

Sponges are basal animals that lack true tissues

Calcarea and Silicea
Cnidaria
Lophotrochozoa
Ecdysozoa
Deuterostomia

Animals in the phyla Calcarea and Silicea are known informally as "sponges." (Previously, all sponges were placed in a single phylum, Porifera, now thought to be paraphyletic based on molecular data.) Among the simplest of animals, sponges are sedentary and were mistaken for plants by the ancient Greeks. They range in size from a few millimeters to a few meters and live in both fresh and marine waters. Sponges are **suspension feeders**: They capture food particles suspended in the water that passes through their body, which in some species resembles a sac perforated with pores. Water is drawn through the pores into a central cavity, the **spongocoel**, and then flows out of the sponge through a larger opening called the **osculum** (**Figure 33.4**). More complex sponges have folded body walls, and many contain branched water canals and several oscula.

Sponges are basal animals; that is, they represent a lineage that originates near the root of the phylogenetic tree of animals. Unlike nearly all other animals, sponges lack true tissues,

groups of similar cells that act as a functional unit and are isolated from other tissues by membranous layers. However, the sponge body does contain several different cell types. For example, lining the interior of the spongocoel are flagellated **choanocytes**, or collar cells (named for the membranous collar around the base of the flagellum). The similarity between choanocytes and the cells of choanoflagellates supports molecular evidence suggesting that animals evolved from a choanoflagellate-like ancestor (see Figure 32.3).

The body of a sponge consists of two layers of cells separated by a gelatinous region called the **mesohyl**. Wandering through the mesohyl are cells called **amoebocytes**, named for their use of pseudopodia. Amoebocytes have many functions. They take up food from the water and from choanocytes, digest it, and carry nutrients to other cells. They also manufacture tough skeletal fibers within the mesohyl. In some groups of sponges, these fibers are sharp spicules made from calcium carbonate or silica. Other sponges produce more flexible fibers composed of a protein called spongin; you may have seen these pliant skeletons being sold as fluffy brown bath sponges.

Most sponges are **hermaphrodites**, meaning that each individual functions as both male and female in sexual reproduction by producing sperm *and* eggs. Almost all sponges exhibit sequential hermaphroditism, functioning first as one sex and then as the other.

Azure vase sponge (*Callyspongia plicifera*)

⑤ Choanocytes. The spongocoel is lined with flagellated cells called choanocytes. By beating flagella, the choanocytes create a current that draws water in through the pores and out through the osculum.

Flagellum
Collar
Food particles in mucus
Choanocyte
Osculum
Phagocytosis of food particles
Amoebocyte

④ Spongocoel. Water passing through pores enters a cavity called the spongocoel.

③ Pores. Water enters the epidermis through pores formed by doughnut-shaped cells that span the body wall.

② Epidermis. The outer layer consists of tightly packed epidermal cells.

Water flow

Spicules

① Mesohyl. The wall of this sponge consists of two layers of cells separated by a gelatinous matrix, the mesohyl ("middle matter").

⑥ The movement of a choanocyte's flagellum also draws water through its collar of fingerlike projections. Food particles are trapped in the mucus coating the projections, engulfed by phagocytosis, and either digested or transferred to amoebocytes.

⑦ Amoebocytes. These cells can transport nutrients to other cells of the sponge body, produce materials for skeletal fibers (spicules), or become any type of sponge cell as needed.

▲ **Figure 33.4 Anatomy of a sponge.**

Sponge gametes arise from choanocytes or amoebocytes. Eggs reside in the mesohyl, but sperm are carried out of the sponge by the water current. Cross-fertilization results from some of the sperm being drawn into neighboring individuals. Fertilization occurs in the mesohyl, where the zygotes develop into flagellated, swimming larvae that disperse from the parent sponge. After settling on a suitable substrate, a larva develops into a sessile adult.

Sponges produce a variety of antibiotics and other defensive compounds. Researchers are now isolating these compounds, which hold promise for fighting human diseases. For example, a compound called cribrostatin isolated from marine sponges can kill penicillin-resistant strains of the bacterium *Streptococcus.* Other sponge-derived compounds are being tested as possible anticancer agents.

CONCEPT CHECK 33.1

1. Describe how sponges feed.
2. **WHAT IF?** Some molecular evidence suggests that the sister group of animals is not the choanoflagellates, but rather a group of parasitic protists, Mesomycetozoa. Given that these parasites lack collar cells, can this hypothesis be correct? Explain.

For suggested answers, see Appendix A.

CONCEPT 33.2

Cnidarians are an ancient phylum of eumetazoans

Calcarea and Silicea
Cnidaria
Lophotrochozoa
Ecdysozoa
Deuterostomia

All animals except sponges and a few other groups belong to the clade Eumetazoa, animals with true tissues (see Chapter 32). One of the oldest lineages in this clade is the phylum Cnidaria. Cnidarians have diversified into a wide range of sessile and motile forms, including hydras, corals, and jellies (commonly called "jellyfish"). Yet most cnidarians still exhibit the relatively simple, diploblastic, radial body plan that existed some 570 million years ago.

The basic body plan of a cnidarian is a sac with a central digestive compartment, the **gastrovascular cavity**. A single opening to this cavity functions as both mouth and anus. There are two variations on this body plan: the sessile polyp and the motile medusa **(Figure 33.5)**. **Polyps** are cylindrical forms that adhere to the substrate by the aboral end of their body (the end opposite the mouth) and extend their tentacles, waiting for prey. Examples of the polyp form include hydras and sea anemones. A **medusa** is a flattened, mouth-down version of the polyp. It moves freely in the water by a combination of passive drifting and contractions of its bell-shaped body. Medusae include free-swimming jellies. The tentacles of a jelly dangle

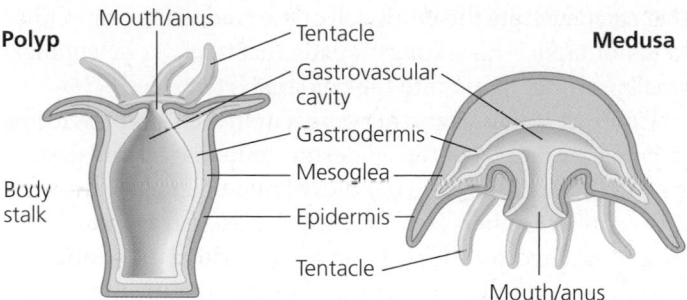

▲ Figure 33.5 **Polyp and medusa forms of cnidarians.** The body wall of a cnidarian has two layers of cells: an outer layer of epidermis (from ectoderm) and an inner layer of gastrodermis (from endoderm). Digestion begins in the gastrovascular cavity and is completed inside food vacuoles in the gastrodermal cells. Flagella on the gastrodermal cells keep the contents of the gastrovascular cavity agitated and help distribute nutrients. Sandwiched between the epidermis and gastrodermis is a gelatinous layer, the mesoglea.

from the oral surface, which points downward. Some cnidarians exist only as polyps or only as medusae; others have both a polyp stage and a medusa stage in their life cycle.

Cnidarians are carnivores that often use tentacles arranged in a ring around their mouth to capture prey and push the food into their gastrovascular cavity, where digestion begins. Any undigested remains are expelled through the mouth/anus. The tentacles are armed with batteries of **cnidocytes**, cells unique to cnidarians that function in defense and prey capture **(Figure 33.6)**. Cnidocytes contain cnidae (from the Greek *cnide*, nettle), capsule-like organelles that are capable of exploding outward and that give phylum Cnidaria its name. Specialized cnidae called **nematocysts** contain a stinging thread

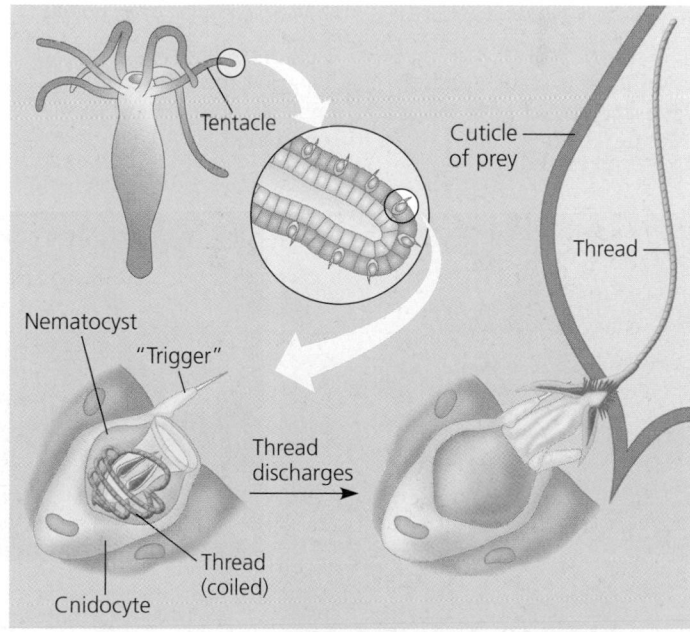

▲ Figure 33.6 **A cnidocyte of a hydra.** This type of cnidocyte contains a stinging capsule, the nematocyst, which contains a coiled thread. When a "trigger" is stimulated by touch or by certain chemicals, the thread shoots out, puncturing and injecting poison into prey.

that can penetrate the body wall of the cnidarian's prey. Other kinds of cnidae have long threads that stick to or entangle small prey that bump into the cnidarian's tentacles.

Contractile tissues and nerves occur in their simplest forms in cnidarians. Cells of the epidermis (outer layer) and gastrodermis (inner layer) have bundles of microfilaments arranged into contractile fibers (see Chapter 6). The gastrovascular cavity acts as a hydrostatic skeleton against which the contractile cells can work. When a cnidarian closes its mouth, the volume of the cavity is fixed, and contraction of selected cells causes the animal to change shape. Movements are coordinated by a nerve net. Cnidarians have no brain, and the noncentralized nerve net is associated with sensory structures that are distributed radially around the body. Thus, the animal can detect and respond to stimuli from all directions.

As summarized in **Table 33.1**, the phylum Cnidaria is divided into four major classes: Hydrozoa, Scyphozoa, Cubozoa, and Anthozoa **(Figure 33.7)**.

Table 33.1 Classes of Phylum Cnidaria

Class and Examples	Main Characteristics
Hydrozoa (Portuguese man-of-wars, hydras, *Obelia*, some corals; see Figures 33.7a and 33.8)	Most marine, a few freshwater; both polyp and medusa stages in most species; polyp stage often colonial
Scyphozoa (jellies, sea nettles; see Figure 33.7b)	All marine; polyp stage absent or reduced; free-swimming; medusae up to 2 m in diameter
Cubozoa (box jellies, sea wasps; see Figure 33.7c)	All marine; box-shaped medusae; complex eyes; potent venom
Anthozoa (sea anemones, most corals, sea fans; see Figure 33.7d)	All marine; medusa stage completely absent; most sessile; many colonial

Hydrozoans

Most hydrozoans alternate between polyp and medusa forms, as in the life cycle of *Obelia* (**Figure 33.8**). The polyp stage, a colony of interconnected polyps in the case of *Obelia*, is more conspicuous than the medusa. Hydras, among the few cnidarians found in fresh water, are unusual hydrozoans in that they exist only in polyp form. When environmental conditions are favorable, a hydra reproduces asexually by budding, forming outgrowths that pinch off from the parent and live independently (see Figure 13.2). When conditions deteriorate, hydras can reproduce sexually, forming resistant zygotes that remain dormant until conditions improve.

Scyphozoans

The medusa generally is the predominant stage in the life cycle of the class Scyphozoa. The medusae of most species live among the plankton as jellies. Most coastal scyphozoans go through a stage as small polyps during their life cycle, whereas those that live in the open ocean generally lack the polyp stage altogether.

Cubozoans

As their name (which means "cube animals") suggests, cubozoans have a box-shaped medusa stage. Cubozoans can be distinguished from scyphozoans in other significant ways, such as having complex eyes embedded in the fringe of their medusae. They are comparatively strong swimmers and as a result are less likely to be stranded on shore. Cubozoans, which generally live in tropical oceans, are often equipped with highly toxic cnidocytes. The sea wasp (*Chironex fleckeri*), a cubozoan that lives off the coast of northern Australia, is one of the deadliest organisms: Its sting causes intense pain and can lead to respiratory failure, cardiac arrest, and death within minutes. The poison of sea wasps isn't universally fatal, however; sea turtles have defenses against it, allowing them to eat the cubozoan in great quantities.

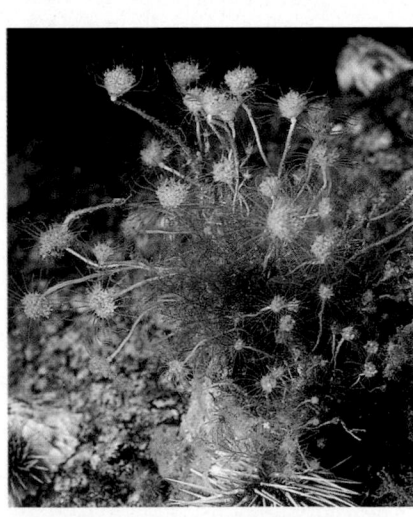

(a) These colonial polyps are members of class Hydrozoa.

(b) Many jellies (class Scyphozoa) are bioluminescent. Food captured by nematocyst-bearing tentacles is transferred to specialized oral arms (that lack nematocysts) for transport to the mouth.

(c) The sea wasp (*Chironex fleckeri*) is a member of class Cubozoa. Its poison, which can subdue fish and other large prey, is more potent than cobra venom.

(d) Sea anemones and other members of class Anthozoa exist only as polyps.

▲ **Figure 33.7 Cnidarians.**

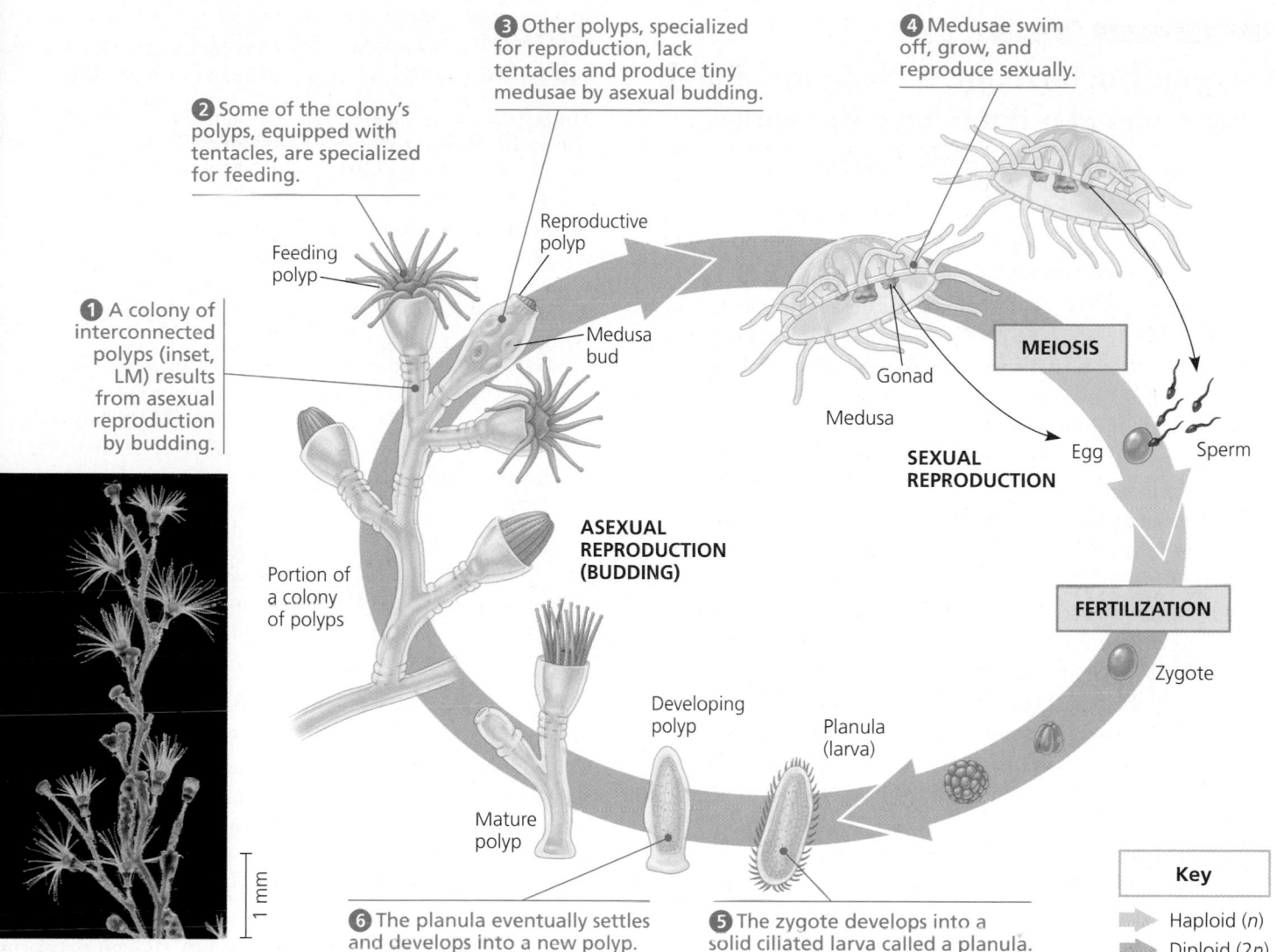

① **A colony of interconnected polyps (inset, LM) results from asexual reproduction by budding.**

② **Some of the colony's polyps, equipped with tentacles, are specialized for feeding.**

③ **Other polyps, specialized for reproduction, lack tentacles and produce tiny medusae by asexual budding.**

④ **Medusae swim off, grow, and reproduce sexually.**

Feeding polyp

Reproductive polyp

Medusa bud

Portion of a colony of polyps

MEIOSIS

Gonad

Medusa

SEXUAL REPRODUCTION

Egg

Sperm

ASEXUAL REPRODUCTION (BUDDING)

FERTILIZATION

Zygote

Developing polyp

Planula (larva)

Mature polyp

1 mm

⑥ **The planula eventually settles and develops into a new polyp.**

⑤ **The zygote develops into a solid ciliated larva called a planula.**

Key

Haploid (*n*)

Diploid (2*n*)

▲ **Figure 33.8 The life cycle of the hydrozoan *Obelia*.** The polyp stage is asexual, and the medusa stage is sexual; these two stages alternate, one producing the other. Do not confuse this with the alternation of generations that occurs in plants and some algae: In *Obelia*, both the polyp and the medusa are diploid organisms. Typical of animals, only the single-celled gametes are haploid. By contrast, plants have a multicellular haploid generation and a multicellular diploid generation.

WHAT IF? *Suppose that* Obelia *medusae and gametes were haploid, but all other stages were diploid. What aspects of its actual life cycle would have to change for this to occur?*

Anthozoans

Sea anemones (see Figure 33.7d) and corals belong to the class Anthozoa (meaning "flower animals"). These cnidarians occur only as polyps. Corals live as solitary or colonial forms, and many species secrete a hard external skeleton of calcium carbonate. Each polyp generation builds on the skeletal remains of earlier generations, constructing "rocks" with shapes characteristic of their species. It is these skeletons that we usually think of as coral.

Coral reefs are to tropical seas what rain forests are to tropical land areas: They provide habitat for a wealth of other species. Unfortunately, like rain forests, coral reefs are being destroyed at an alarming rate by human activity. Pollution and overfishing are major threats, and global warming (see Chapter 55) may also

be contributing to their demise by raising seawater temperatures above the narrow range in which corals thrive.

CONCEPT CHECK **33.2**

1. Compare and contrast the polyp and medusa forms of cnidarians.
2. Describe the structure and function of the stinging cells for which cnidarians are named.
3. **WHAT IF?** If the common ancestor of cnidarians were an open-ocean jelly, what might you infer about evolutionary trends in the relative importance of the polyp and medusa stages?

For suggested answers, see Appendix A.

Lophotrochozoans, a clade identified by molecular data, have the widest range of animal body forms

Calcarea and Silicea
Cnidaria
Lophotrochozoa
Ecdysozoa
Deuterostomia

The vast majority of animal species belong to the clade Bilateria, whose members exhibit bilateral symmetry and triploblastic development (see Chapter 32). Most bilaterians are also coelomates. While the sequence of bilaterian evolution is a subject of active investigation, most researchers think that the most recent common ancestor of living bilaterians probably existed in the late Proterozoic eon (about 575 million years ago). Most major groups of bilaterians first appeared in the fossil record during the Cambrian explosion.

As you read in Chapter 32, molecular evidence suggests that there are three major clades of bilaterally symmetrical animals: Lophotrochozoa, Ecdysozoa, and Deuterostomia. This section will focus on the first of these clades, the lophotrochozoans. Concepts 33.4 and 33.5 will explore the other two clades.

Although the clade Lophotrochozoa was identified by molecular data, its name comes from features found in some of its members. Some lophotrochozoans develop a structure called a *lophophore*, a crown of ciliated tentacles that functions in feeding, while others go through a distinctive stage called the *trochophore larva* (see Figure 32.13). Other members of the group have neither of these features. Few other unique morphological features are widely shared within the group—in fact, the lophotrochozoans are the most diverse bilaterian clade in terms of body plan. This diversity in form is reflected in the number of phyla classified in the group: Lophotrochozoa includes about 18 phyla, more than twice the number in any other clade of bilaterians.

We'll now introduce six lophotrochozoan phyla: the flatworms, rotifers, ectoprocts, brachiopods, molluscs, and annelids.

Flatworms

Flatworms (phylum Platyhelminthes) live in marine, freshwater, and damp terrestrial habitats. In addition to free-living forms, flatworms include many parasitic species, such as flukes and tapeworms. Flatworms are so named because they have thin bodies that are flattened dorsoventrally (between the dorsal and ventral surfaces); *platyhelminth* means "flat worm." (Note that *worm* is not a formal taxonomic name but a general term for animals with long, thin bodies.) The smallest flatworms are nearly microscopic free-living species, while some tapeworms are more than 20 m long.

Although flatworms undergo triploblastic development, they are acoelomates (animals that lack a body cavity). Their flat shape places all their cells close to water in the surrounding environment or in their gut. Because of this proximity to water, gas

Table 33.2 Classes of Phylum Platyhelminthes	
Class and Examples	**Main Characteristics**
Turbellaria (mostly free-living flatworms, such as *Dugesia*; see Figures 33.9 and 33.10)	Most marine, some freshwater, a few terrestrial; predators and scavengers; body surface ciliated
Monogenea (monogeneans)	Marine and freshwater parasites; most infect external surfaces of fishes; life history simple; ciliated larva starts infection on host
Trematoda (trematodes, also called flukes; see Figure 33.11)	Parasites, mostly of vertebrates; two suckers attach to host; most life cycles include intermediate and final hosts
Cestoda (tapeworms; see Figure 33.12)	Parasites of vertebrates; scolex attaches to host; proglottids produce eggs and break off after fertilization; no head or digestive system; life cycle with one or more intermediate hosts

exchange and the elimination of nitrogenous waste (ammonia) can occur by diffusion across the body surface. Flatworms have no organs specialized for gas exchange, and their relatively simple excretory apparatus functions mainly to maintain osmotic balance with their surroundings. This apparatus consists of **protonephridia**, networks of tubules with ciliated structures called *flame bulbs* that pull fluid through branched ducts opening to the outside (see Figure 44.11). Most flatworms have a gastrovascular cavity with only one opening. Though flatworms lack a circulatory system, the fine branches of the gastrovascular cavity distribute food directly to the animal's cells.

Flatworms are divided into four classes **(Table 33.2)**: Turbellaria (mostly free-living flatworms), Monogenea (monogeneans), Trematoda (trematodes, or flukes), and Cestoda (tapeworms).

Turbellarians

Turbellarians are nearly all free-living and mostly marine **(Figure 33.9)**. The best-known freshwater turbellarians are members of the genus *Dugesia*, commonly called **planarians**. Abundant in unpolluted ponds and streams, planarians prey on smaller animals or feed on dead animals. They move by using cilia on their ventral surface, gliding along a film of mucus they secrete. Some other turbellarians also use their muscles to swim through water with an undulating motion.

A planarian's head is equipped with a pair of light-sensitive eyespots and lateral flaps that function mainly to detect specific chemicals. The planarian nervous system is more complex and centralized than the nerve nets of cnidarians **(Figure 33.10)**. Experiments have shown that planarians can learn to modify their responses to stimuli.

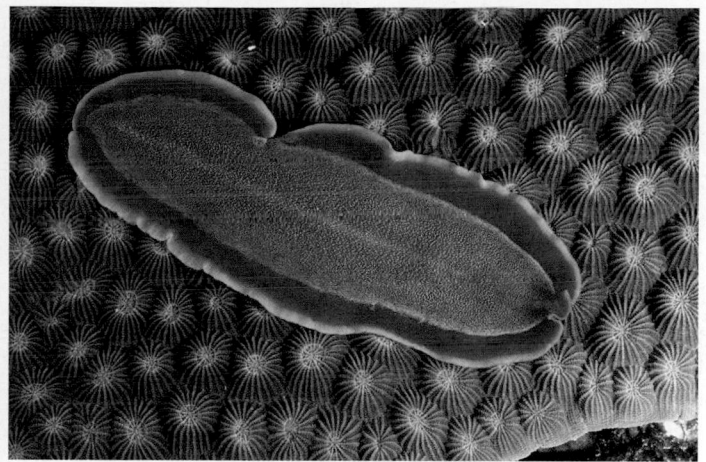

▲ Figure 33.9 **A marine flatworm (class Turbellaria).**

Some planarians can reproduce asexually through fission. The parent constricts roughly in the middle of its body, separating into a head end and a tail end; each end then regenerates the missing parts. Sexual reproduction also occurs. Planarians are hermaphrodites, and copulating mates typically cross-fertilize each other.

Monogeneans and Trematodes

Monogeneans and trematodes live as parasites in or on other animals. Many have suckers that attach to the internal organs or outer surfaces of the host animal. A tough covering helps protect the parasites within their hosts. Reproductive organs occupy nearly the entire interior of these worms.

As a group, trematodes parasitize a wide range of hosts, and most species have complex life cycles with alternating sexual and asexual stages. Many trematodes require an intermediate host in which larvae develop before infecting the final host (usually a vertebrate), where the adult worms live. For example, trematodes that parasitize humans spend part of their lives in snail hosts **(Figure 33.11)**. Around the world, some 200 million people are infected with blood flukes (*Schistosoma*) and suffer from schistosomiasis, a disease whose symptoms include pain, anemia, and dysentery.

Living within different hosts puts demands on trematodes that free-living animals don't face. A blood fluke, for instance, must evade the immune systems of both snails and humans. By mimicking the surface proteins of its hosts, the blood fluke creates a partial immunological camou-

▼ Figure 33.10 **Anatomy of a planarian, a turbellarian.**

Pharynx. The mouth is at the tip of a muscular pharynx. Digestive juices are spilled onto prey, and the pharynx sucks small pieces of food into the gastrovascular cavity, where digestion continues.

Digestion is completed within the cells lining the gastrovascular cavity, which has many fine subbranches that provide an extensive surface area.

Undigested wastes are egested through the mouth.

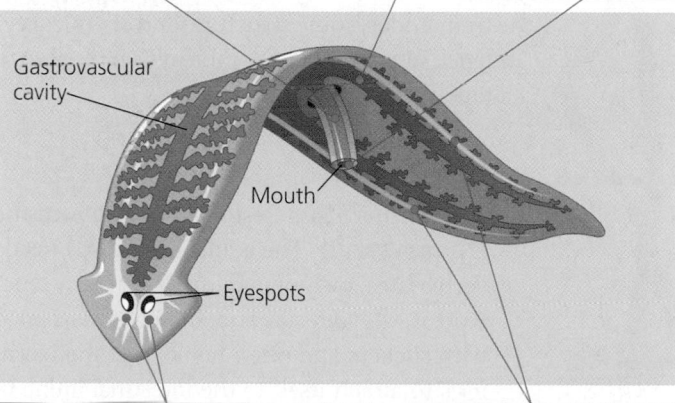

Gastrovascular cavity

Mouth

Eyespots

Ganglia. At the anterior end of the worm, near the main sources of sensory input, is a pair of ganglia, dense clusters of nerve cells.

Ventral nerve cords. From the ganglia, a pair of ventral nerve cords runs the length of the body.

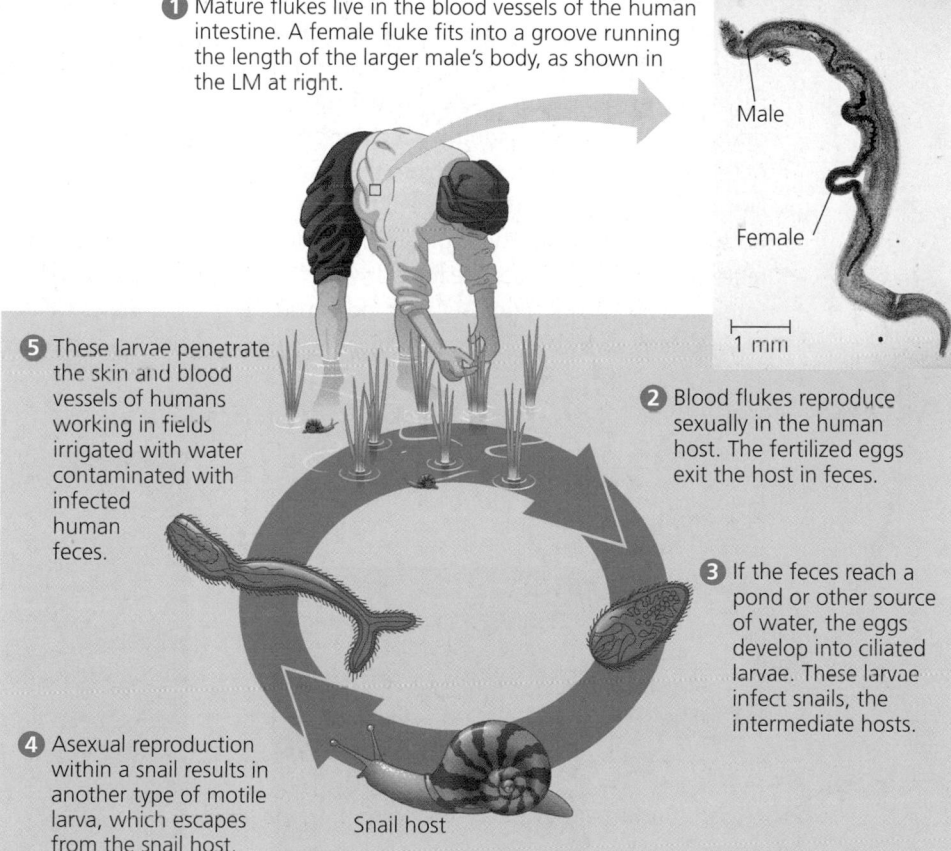

❶ Mature flukes live in the blood vessels of the human intestine. A female fluke fits into a groove running the length of the larger male's body, as shown in the LM at right.

Male

Female

1 mm

❷ Blood flukes reproduce sexually in the human host. The fertilized eggs exit the host in feces.

❸ If the feces reach a pond or other source of water, the eggs develop into ciliated larvae. These larvae infect snails, the intermediate hosts.

❹ Asexual reproduction within a snail results in another type of motile larva, which escapes from the snail host.

Snail host

❺ These larvae penetrate the skin and blood vessels of humans working in fields irrigated with water contaminated with infected human feces.

▲ Figure 33.11 **The life cycle of a blood fluke (*Schistosoma mansoni*), a trematode.**
WHAT IF? *Snails eat algae, whose growth is stimulated by nutrients found in fertilizer. How would the contamination of irrigation water with fertilizer likely affect the occurrence of schistosomiasis? Explain.*

flage for itself. It also releases molecules that manipulate the hosts' immune systems into tolerating the parasite's existence. These defenses are so effective that individual blood flukes can survive in humans for more than 40 years.

Most monogeneans, however, are external parasites of fish. The monogenean life cycle is relatively simple; a ciliated, free-swimming larva initiates the infection of a host fish. Although monogeneans have been traditionally aligned with the trematodes, some structural and chemical evidence suggests they are more closely related to tapeworms.

Tapeworms

Tapeworms (class Cestoda) are also parasitic (**Figure 33.12**). The adults live mostly inside vertebrates, including humans. In many tapeworms, the anterior end, or scolex, is armed with suckers and often hooks that the worm uses to attach itself to the intestinal lining of its host. Tapeworms lack a mouth and gastrovascular cavity; they absorb nutrients released by digestion in the host's intestine. Absorption occurs across the tapeworm's body surface.

Posterior to the scolex is a long ribbon of units called proglottids, which are little more than sacs of sex organs. After sexual reproduction, proglottids loaded with thousands of fertilized eggs are released from the posterior end of a tapeworm and leave the host's body in feces. In one type of life cycle, infected feces contaminate the food or water of intermediate hosts, such as pigs or cattle, and the tapeworm eggs develop into larvae

that encyst in muscles of these animals. A human acquires the larvae by eating undercooked meat contaminated with cysts, and the worms develop into mature adults within the human. Large tapeworms can block the intestines and rob enough nutrients from the human host to cause nutritional deficiencies. Doctors use an orally administered drug, niclosamide, to kill the adult worms.

Rotifers

Rotifers (phylum Rotifera) are tiny animals that inhabit freshwater, marine, and damp soil habitats. Ranging in size from about 50 μm to 2 mm, rotifers are smaller than many protists but nevertheless are multicellular and have specialized organ systems (**Figure 33.13**). In contrast to cnidarians and flatworms, which have a gastrovascular cavity, rotifers have an **alimentary canal**, a digestive tube with a separate mouth and anus. Internal organs lie within the pseudocoelom, a body cavity that is not completely lined by mesoderm (see Figure 32.8b). Fluid in the pseudocoelom serves as a hydrostatic skeleton (see Chapter 50). Movement of a rotifer's body distributes the fluid throughout the body, circulating nutrients.

The word *rotifer*, derived from Latin, means "wheel-bearer," a reference to the crown of cilia that draws a vortex of water into the mouth. Posterior to the mouth, a region of the digestive tract called the pharynx bears jaws called trophi that grind up food, mostly microorganisms suspended in the water.

Rotifers exhibit some unusual forms of reproduction. Some species consist only of females that produce more females from unfertilized eggs, a type of reproduction called **parthenogenesis**. Other species produce two types of eggs that develop by parthenogenesis. One type forms females while the other type (produced when conditions deteriorate) develops into simplified males that cannot even feed themselves. These males survive only long enough to fertilize eggs, which form resistant

Proglottids with reproductive structures

200 μm

Hooks

Scolex

Sucker

▲ **Figure 33.12 Anatomy of a tapeworm.** The inset shows a close-up of the scolex (colorized SEM).

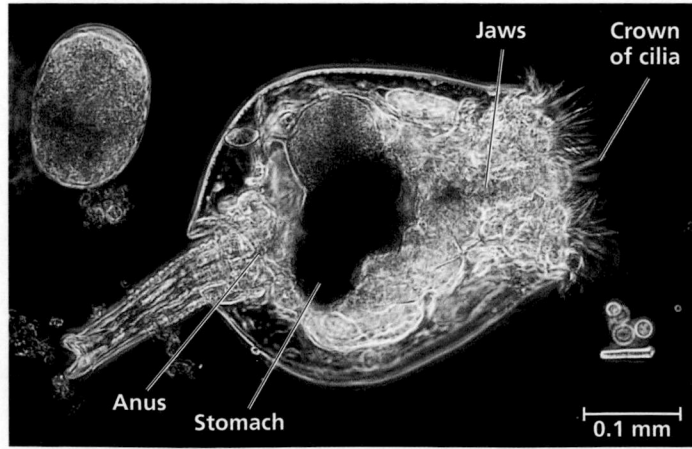

Jaws

Crown of cilia

Anus

Stomach

0.1 mm

▲ **Figure 33.13 A rotifer.** These pseudocoelomates, smaller than many protists, are generally more anatomically complex than flatworms (LM).

zygotes that can survive when a pond dries up. When conditions are favorable, the zygotes break dormancy and develop into a new female generation that reproduces by parthenogenesis until conditions become unfavorable again.

It is puzzling that so many rotifer species survive without males. The vast majority of animals and plants reproduce sexually at least some of the time, and sexual reproduction has certain advantages over asexual reproduction. For example, species that reproduce asexually tend to accumulate harmful mutations in their genomes faster than sexually reproducing species. As a result, asexual species should experience higher rates of extinction and lower rates of speciation.

Seeking to understand this unusual group, Nobel Prize-winning biologist Matthew Meselson, of Harvard University, has been studying a class of asexual rotifers named Bdelloidea. Some 360 species of bdelloid rotifers are known, and all of them reproduce by parthenogenesis without any males. Paleontologists have discovered bdelloid rotifers preserved in 35-million-year-old amber, and the morphology of these fossils resembles only the female form, with no evidence of males. By comparing the DNA of bdelloids with that of their closest sexually reproducing rotifer relatives, Meselson and his colleagues concluded that bdelloids have likely been asexual for much longer than 35 million years. How these animals manage to flout the general rule against long-lived asexuality remains a puzzle.

Lophophorates: Ectoprocts and Brachiopods

Bilaterians in the phyla Ectoprocta and Brachiopoda are among those known as lophophorates. These animals have a *lophophore*, a crown of ciliated tentacles that surround the mouth (see Figure 32.13a). As the cilia draw water toward the mouth, these tentacles trap suspended food particles. Other similarities, such as a U-shaped alimentary canal and the absence of a distinct head, reflect these organisms' sessile existence. In contrast to flatworms, which lack a body cavity, and rotifers, which have a pseudocoelom, lophophorates have a true coelom that is completely lined by mesoderm (see Figure 32.8a).

Ectoprocts (from the Greek *ecto*, outside, and *procta*, anus) are colonial animals that superficially resemble clumps of moss. (In fact, their common name, bryozoans, means "moss animals.") In most species, the colony is encased in a hard **exoskeleton** (external skeleton) studded with pores through which the lophophores extend (**Figure 33.14a**). Most ectoproct species live in the sea, where they are among the most widespread and numerous sessile animals. Several species are important reef builders. Ectoprocts also live in lakes and rivers. Colonies of the freshwater ectoproct *Pectinatella magnifica* grow on submerged sticks or rocks and can grow into a gelatinous, ball-shaped mass more than 10 cm across.

Brachiopods, or lamp shells, superficially resemble clams and other hinge-shelled molluscs, but the two halves of the bra-

(a) Ectoprocts, such as this sea mat (*Membranipora membranacea*), are colonial lophophorates.

(b) Brachiopods have a hinged shell. The two parts of the shell are dorsal and ventral.

▲ **Figure 33.14 Lophophorates.**

chiopod shell are dorsal and ventral rather than lateral, as in clams (**Figure 33.14b**). All brachiopods are marine. Most live attached to the seafloor by a stalk, opening their shell slightly to allow water to flow through the lophophore. The living brachiopods are remnants of a much richer past that included 30,000 species in the Paleozoic and Mesozoic eras. Some living brachiopods, such as those in the genus *Lingula*, are nearly identical to fossils of species that lived 400 million years ago.

Molluscs

Snails and slugs, oysters and clams, and octopuses and squids are all molluscs (phylum Mollusca). Most molluscs are marine, though some inhabit fresh water, and some snails and slugs live on land. Molluscs are soft-bodied animals (from the Latin *molluscus*, soft), but most secrete a hard protective shell made of calcium carbonate. Slugs, squids, and octopuses have a reduced internal shell or have lost their shell completely during their evolution.

Despite their apparent differences, all molluscs have a similar body plan (**Figure 33.15**, on the next page). Molluscs are coelomates, and their bodies have three main parts: a muscular **foot**, usually used for movement; a **visceral mass** containing most of the internal organs; and a **mantle**, a fold of tissue that drapes over the visceral mass and secretes a shell (if one is present). In many molluscs, the mantle extends beyond the visceral mass, producing a water-filled chamber, the **mantle cavity**, which houses the gills, anus, and excretory pores. Many molluscs feed by using a straplike rasping organ called a **radula** to scrape up food.

Most molluscs have separate sexes, and their gonads (ovaries or testes) are located in the visceral mass. Many snails, however, are hermaphrodites. The life cycle of many marine molluscs includes a ciliated larval stage, the trochophore (see Figure 32.13b),

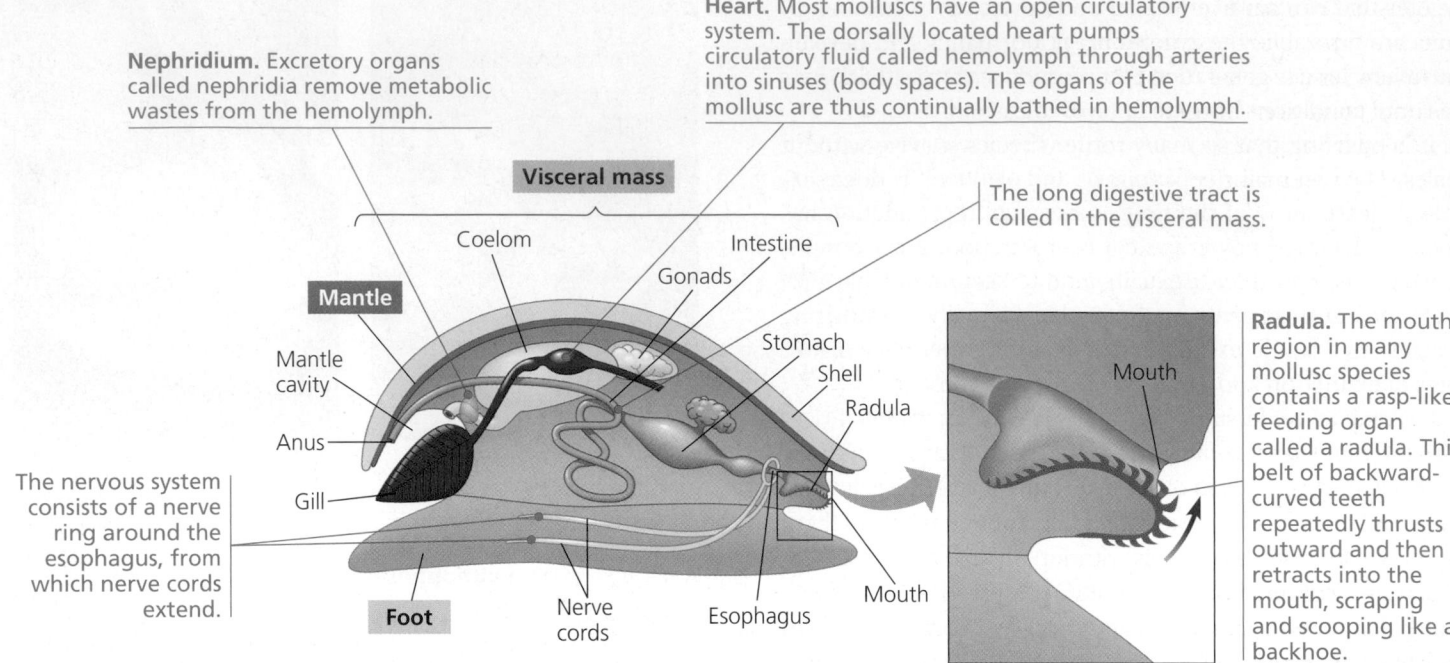

Nephridium. Excretory organs called nephridia remove metabolic wastes from the hemolymph.

Heart. Most molluscs have an open circulatory system. The dorsally located heart pumps circulatory fluid called hemolymph through arteries into sinuses (body spaces). The organs of the mollusc are thus continually bathed in hemolymph.

Visceral mass

Coelom

Intestine

The long digestive tract is coiled in the visceral mass.

Mantle

Gonads

Mantle cavity

Stomach

Shell

Radula

Anus

Gill

The nervous system consists of a nerve ring around the esophagus, from which nerve cords extend.

Foot

Nerve cords

Esophagus

Mouth

Mouth

Radula. The mouth region in many mollusc species contains a rasp-like feeding organ called a radula. This belt of backward-curved teeth repeatedly thrusts outward and then retracts into the mouth, scraping and scooping like a backhoe.

▲ **Figure 33.15 The basic body plan of a mollusc.**

Table 33.3 Major Classes of Phylum Mollusca	
Class and Examples	**Main Characteristics**
Polyplacophora (chitons; see Figure 33.16)	Marine; shell with eight plates; foot used for locomotion; radula; no head
Gastropoda (snails, slugs; see Figures 33.17 and 33.18)	Marine, freshwater, or terrestrial; head present; a symmetrical body, usually with a coiled shell; shell reduced or absent; foot for locomotion; radula
Bivalvia (clams, mussels, scallops, oysters; see Figures 33.19 and 33.20)	Marine and freshwater; flattened shell with two valves; head reduced; paired gills; no radula; most are suspension feeders; mantle forms siphons
Cephalopoda (squids, octopuses, cuttlefishes, chambered nautiluses; see Figure 33.21)	Marine; head surrounded by grasping tentacles, usually with suckers; shell external, internal, or absent; mouth with or without radula; locomotion by jet propulsion using siphon formed from foot

▲ **Figure 33.16 A chiton.** Note the eight-plate shell characteristic of molluscs in the class Polyplacophora.

Chitons

Chitons have an oval-shaped body and a shell divided into eight dorsal plates **(Figure 33.16)**. The chiton's body itself, however, is unsegmented. You can find these marine animals clinging to rocks along the shore during low tide. If you try to dislodge a chiton by hand, you will be surprised at how well its foot, acting as a suction cup, grips the rock. A chiton can also use its foot to creep slowly over the rock surface. Chitons use their radula to scrape algae off the rock surface.

Gastropods

About three-quarters of all living species of molluscs are gastropods **(Figure 33.17)**. Most gastropods are marine, but there are also many freshwater species. Some gastropods have adapted to life on land, including garden snails and slugs.

which is also characteristic of marine annelids (segmented worms) and some other lophotrochozoans.

The basic body plan of molluscs has evolved in various ways in the phylum's eight classes. We'll examine four of those classes here **(Table 33.3)**: Polyplacophora (chitons), Gastropoda (snails and slugs), Bivalvia (clams, oysters, and other bivalves), and Cephalopoda (squids, octopuses, cuttlefishes, and chambered nautiluses).

A distinctive characteristic of class Gastropoda is a developmental process known as **torsion**. As a gastropod embryo develops, its visceral mass rotates up to 180°, causing the animal's anus and mantle cavity to wind up above its head **(Figure 33.18)**. After torsion, some organs that were bilateral may be reduced in size, while others may be lost on one side of the body. Torsion should not be confused with the formation of a coiled shell, which is an independent developmental process.

Most gastropods have a single, spiraled shell into which the animal can retreat when threatened. The shell is often conical but is somewhat flattened in abalones and limpets. Many gastropods have a distinct head with eyes at the tips of tentacles. Gastropods move literally at a snail's pace by a rippling motion of their foot or by means of cilia, often leaving a trail of slime in their wake. Most gastropods use their radula to graze on algae or plants. Several groups, however, are predators, and their radula has become modified for boring holes in the shells of other molluscs or for tearing apart prey. In the cone snails, the teeth of the radula act as poison darts that are used to subdue prey.

Terrestrial snails lack the gills typical of most aquatic gastropods. Instead, the lining of their mantle cavity functions as a lung, exchanging respiratory gases with the air.

Bivalves

The molluscs of class Bivalvia include many species of clams, oysters, mussels, and scallops. Bivalves have a shell divided into two halves **(Figure 33.19)**. The halves are hinged at the mid-dorsal line, and powerful adductor muscles draw them tightly together to protect the animal's soft body. Bivalves have no distinct head, and the radula has been lost. Some bivalves have eyes and sensory tentacles along the outer edge of their mantle.

The mantle cavity of a bivalve contains gills that are used for gas exchange as well as feeding in most species **(Figure 33.20)**. Most bivalves are suspension feeders. They trap fine food particles in mucus that coats their gills, and cilia then convey those particles to the mouth. Water enters the mantle cavity through an incurrent siphon, passes over the gills, and then exits the mantle cavity through an excurrent siphon.

▲ **Figure 33.19 A bivalve.** This scallop has many eyes (dark blue spots) peering out from each half of its hinged shell.

(a) A land snail

▲ **Figure 33.17 Gastropods.**

(b) A sea slug. Nudibranchs, or sea slugs, lost their shell during their evolution.

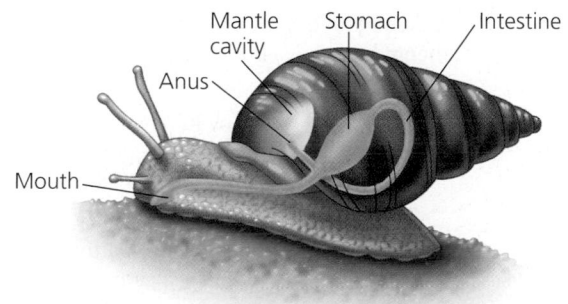

▲ **Figure 33.18 The results of torsion in a gastropod.** Because of torsion (twisting of the visceral mass) during embryonic development, the digestive tract is coiled and the anus is near the anterior end of the animal.

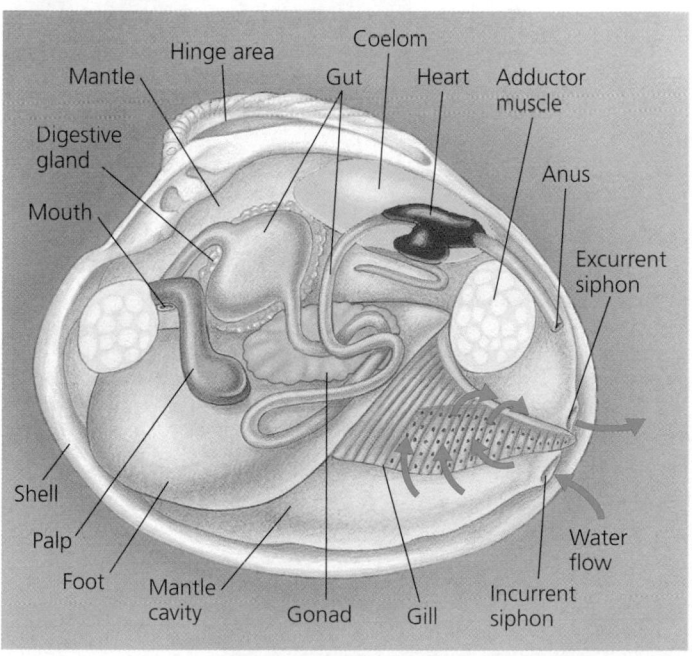

▲ **Figure 33.20 Anatomy of a clam.** Food particles suspended in water that enters through the incurrent siphon are collected by the gills and passed via cilia to the mouth.

Most bivalves lead sedentary lives, a characteristic suited to suspension feeding. Sessile mussels secrete strong threads that tether them to rocks, docks, boats, and the shells of other animals. However, clams can pull themselves into the sand or mud, using their muscular foot for an anchor, and scallops can skitter along the seafloor by flapping their shells, rather like the mechanical false teeth sold in novelty shops.

Cephalopods

Cephalopods are active predators (Figure 32.21). They use their tentacles to grasp prey, which they then bite with beak-like jaws and immobilize with a poison found in their saliva. The foot of a cephalopod has become modified into a muscular excurrent siphon and part of the tentacles. Squids dart about by drawing water into their mantle cavity and then firing a jet of water through the excurrent siphon; they steer by pointing the siphon in different directions. Octopuses use a similar mechanism to escape predators.

A mantle covers the visceral mass of cephalopods, but the shell is reduced and internal (in squids and cuttlefishes) or missing altogether (in many octopuses). One small group of shelled cephalopods, the chambered nautiluses, survives today.

Cephalopods are the only molluscs with a closed circulatory system. They also have well-developed sense organs and a complex brain. The ability to learn and behave in a complex manner is probably more critical to fast-moving predators than to sedentary animals such as clams.

The ancestors of octopuses and squids were probably shelled molluscs that took up a predatory lifestyle; the shell was lost in later evolution. Shelled cephalopods called **ammonites**, some of them as large as truck tires, were the dominant invertebrate predators of the seas for hundreds of millions of years until their disappearance during the mass extinction at the end of the Cretaceous period, 65.5 million years ago (see Chapter 25).

Most species of squid are less than 75 cm long, but some are considerably larger. The giant squid (*Architeuthis dux*) was for a long time the largest squid known, with a mantle up to 2.25 m long and a total length of 18 m. In 2003, however, a specimen of the rare species *Mesonychoteuthis hamiltoni* was caught near Antarctica; its mantle was 2.5 m long. Some biologists think that this specimen was a juvenile and estimate that adults of its species could be twice as large! Unlike *A. dux*, which has large suckers and small teeth on its tentacles, *M. hamiltoni* has two rows of sharp hooks at the ends of its tentacles that can deliver deadly lacerations.

It is likely that *A. dux* and *M. hamiltoni* spend most of their time in the deep ocean, where they may feed on large fishes. Remains of both giant squid species have been found in the stomachs of sperm whales, which are probably their only natural predator. In 2005, scientists reported the first observations of *A. dux* in the wild, photographed while attacking baited hooks at a depth of 900 m. *M. hamiltoni* has yet to be observed in nature. Overall, these marine giants remain among the great mysteries of invertebrate life.

Annelids

Annelida means "little rings," referring to the annelid body's resemblance to a series of fused rings. Annelids are segmented

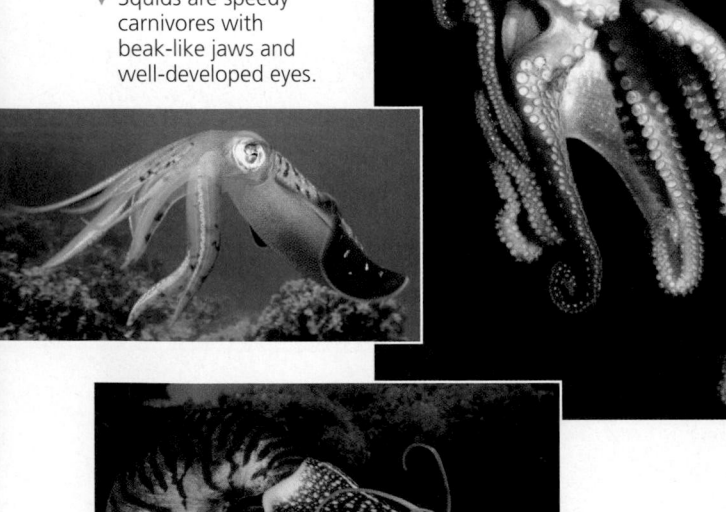

▶ Octopuses are considered among the most intelligent invertebrates.

▼ Squids are speedy carnivores with beak-like jaws and well-developed eyes.

◀ Chambered nautiluses are the only living cephalopods with an external shell.

▲ **Figure 33.21 Cephalopods.**

Table 33.4 **Classes of Phylum Annelida**	
Class and Examples	**Main Characteristics**
Oligochaeta (freshwater, marine, and terrestrial segmented worms; see Figure 33.22)	Reduced head; no parapodia, but chaetae present
Polychaeta (mostly marine segmented worms; see Figure 33.23)	Many have a well-developed head; each segment usually has parapodia with many chaetae; free-living
Hirudinea (leeches; see Figure 33.24)	Body usually flattened, with reduced coelom and segmentation; chaetae usually absent; suckers at anterior and posterior ends; parasites, predators, and scavengers

worms that live in the sea, in most freshwater habitats, and in damp soil. Annelids are coelomates, and they range in length from less than 1 mm to more than 3 m, the length of a giant Australian earthworm.

The phylum Annelida can be divided into three classes (Table 33.4, on the facing page): Oligochaeta (the earthworms and their relatives), Polychaeta (the polychaetes), and Hirudinea (the leeches).

Oligochaetes

Oligochaetes (from the Greek *oligos*, few, and *chaitē*, long hair) are named for their relatively sparse chaetae, or bristles made of chitin. This class of segmented worms includes the earthworms and a variety of aquatic species. Figure 33.22 provides a guided tour of the anatomy of an earthworm, which is representative of annelids. Earthworms eat their way through the soil, extracting

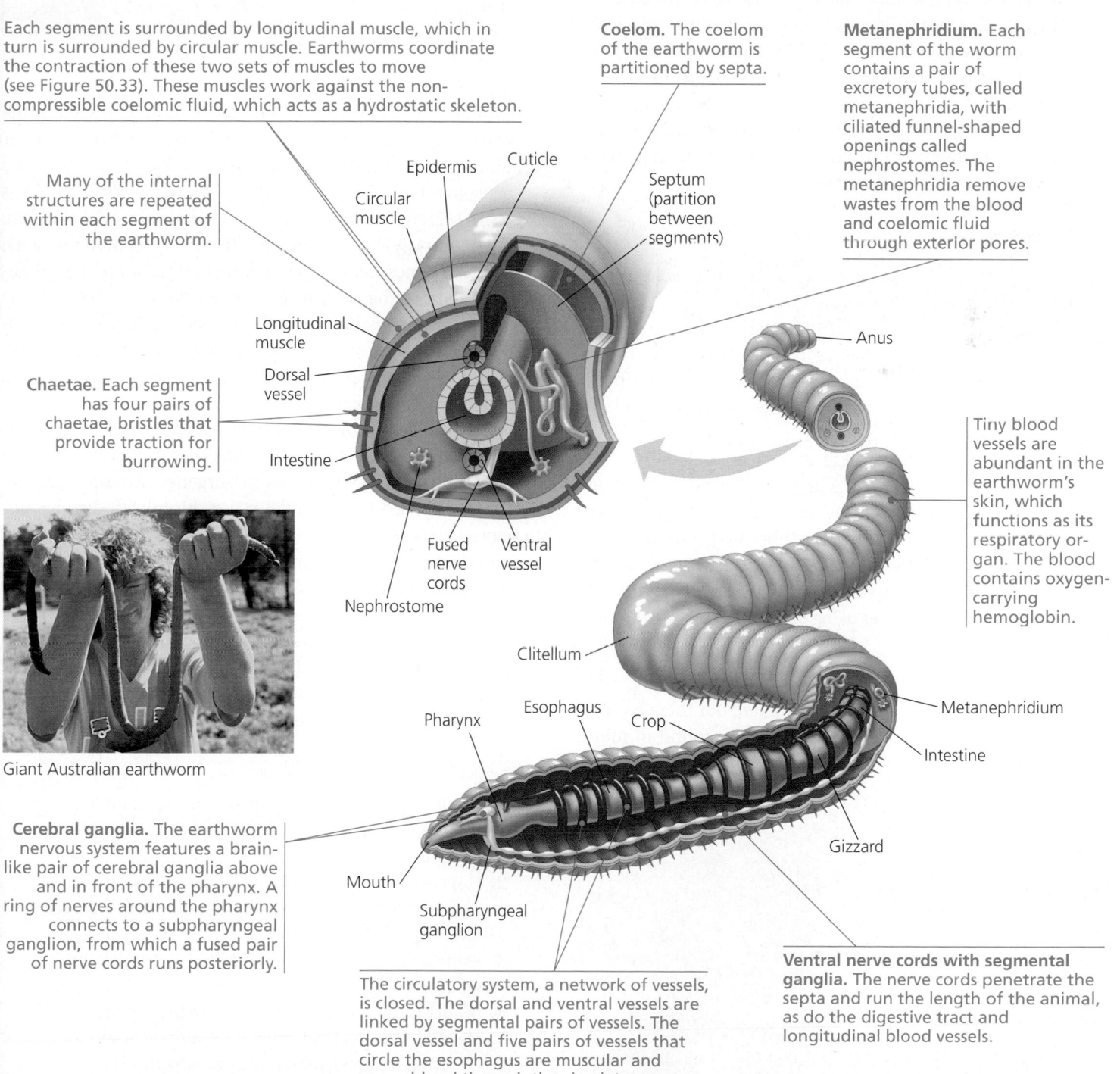

Each segment is surrounded by longitudinal muscle, which in turn is surrounded by circular muscle. Earthworms coordinate the contraction of these two sets of muscles to move (see Figure 50.33). These muscles work against the non-compressible coelomic fluid, which acts as a hydrostatic skeleton.

Coelom. The coelom of the earthworm is partitioned by septa.

Metanephridium. Each segment of the worm contains a pair of excretory tubes, called metanephridia, with ciliated funnel-shaped openings called nephrostomes. The metanephridia remove wastes from the blood and coelomic fluid through exterior pores.

Many of the internal structures are repeated within each segment of the earthworm.

Epidermis
Cuticle
Circular muscle
Septum (partition between segments)
Longitudinal muscle
Dorsal vessel
Anus

Chaetae. Each segment has four pairs of chaetae, bristles that provide traction for burrowing.

Intestine
Fused nerve cords
Ventral vessel
Nephrostome

Tiny blood vessels are abundant in the earthworm's skin, which functions as its respiratory organ. The blood contains oxygen-carrying hemoglobin.

Giant Australian earthworm

Clitellum

Pharynx
Esophagus
Crop
Metanephridium
Intestine

Cerebral ganglia. The earthworm nervous system features a brain-like pair of cerebral ganglia above and in front of the pharynx. A ring of nerves around the pharynx connects to a subpharyngeal ganglion, from which a fused pair of nerve cords runs posteriorly.

Mouth
Subpharyngeal ganglion
Gizzard

The circulatory system, a network of vessels, is closed. The dorsal and ventral vessels are linked by segmental pairs of vessels. The dorsal vessel and five pairs of vessels that circle the esophagus are muscular and pump blood through the circulatory system.

Ventral nerve cords with segmental ganglia. The nerve cords penetrate the septa and run the length of the animal, as do the digestive tract and longitudinal blood vessels.

▲ **Figure 33.22 Anatomy of an earthworm, an oligochaete.**

nutrients as the soil passes through the alimentary canal. Undigested material, mixed with mucus secreted into the canal, is eliminated as fecal castings through the anus. Farmers value earthworms because the animals till and aerate the earth, and their castings improve the texture of the soil. (Charles Darwin estimated that a single acre of British farmland contains about 50,000 earthworms, producing 18 tons of castings per year.)

Earthworms are hermaphrodites, but they cross-fertilize. Two earthworms mate by aligning themselves in opposite directions in such a way that they exchange sperm (see Figure 46.1), and then they separate. The received sperm are stored temporarily while an organ called the clitellum secretes a cocoon of mucus. The cocoon slides along the worm, picking up the eggs and then the stored sperm. The cocoon then slips off the worm's head and remains in the soil while the embryos develop. Some earthworms can also reproduce asexually by fragmentation followed by regeneration.

Polychaetes

Each segment of a polychaete has a pair of paddle-like or ridge-like structures called parapodia ("near feet") that function in locomotion (Figure 33.23). Each parapodium has numerous chaetae, so polychaetes usually have many more chaetae per segment than do oligochaetes. In many polychaetes, the parapodia are richly supplied with blood vessels and also function as gills.

Polychaetes make up a large and diverse class, most of whose members are marine. A few species drift and swim among the plankton, many crawl on or burrow in the seafloor, and many others live in tubes. Some tube-dwellers, such as the fan worms, build their tubes by mixing mucus with bits of sand and broken shells. Others, such as Christmas tree worms (see Figure 33.1), construct tubes using only their own secretions.

Leeches

The majority of leeches inhabit fresh water, but there are also marine species as well as terrestrial leeches found in moist vegetation. Leeches range in length from about 1 to 30 cm.

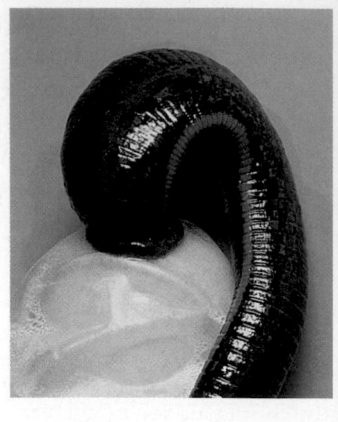
► **Figure 33.24 A leech.** A nurse applied this medicinal leech (*Hirudo medicinalis*) to a patient's sore thumb to drain blood from a hematoma (an abnormal accumulation of blood around an internal injury).

Many are predators that feed on other invertebrates, but some are parasites that suck blood by attaching temporarily to other animals, including humans (Figure 33.24). Some parasitic species use bladelike jaws to slit the skin of their host, whereas others secrete enzymes that digest a hole through the skin. The host is usually oblivious to this attack because the leech secretes an anesthetic. After making the incision, the leech secretes another chemical, hirudin, which keeps the blood of the host from coagulating near the incision. The parasite then sucks as much blood as it can hold, often more than ten times its own weight. After this gorging, a leech can last for months without another meal.

Until this century, leeches were frequently used for bloodletting. Today they are used to drain blood that accumulates in tissues following certain injuries or surgeries. Researchers have also investigated the potential use of hirudin to dissolve unwanted blood clots that form during surgery or as a result of heart disease. Several recombinant forms of hirudin have been developed, two of which were recently approved for clinical use.

As a group, Lophotrochozoa encompasses a remarkable range of body plans, as illustrated by members of such phyla as Rotifera, Ectoprocta, Mollusca, and Annelida. Next we'll explore the diversity of Ecdysozoa, a dominant presence on Earth in terms of sheer number of species.

CONCEPT CHECK 33.3

1. Explain how tapeworms can survive without a coelom, a mouth, a digestive system, or an excretory system.
2. How does the modification of the molluscan foot in gastropods and cephalopods relate to their respective lifestyles?
3. Annelid anatomy can be described as "a tube within a tube." Explain.
4. **WHAT IF?** Relatively few free-living lophotrochozoans live *on* land, above the surface of the soil. Focusing on gravity, hypothesize why this is so.

For suggested answers, see Appendix A.

► **Figure 33.23 A polychaete.** *Hesiolyra bergi* lives on the seafloor around deep-sea hydrothermal vents.

Parapodia

Ecdysozoans are the most species-rich animal group

Calcarea and Silicea
Cnidaria
Lophotrochozoa
Ecdysozoa
Deuterostomia

Although defined primarily by molecular evidence, the clade Ecdysozoa includes animals that shed a tough external coat (**cuticle**) as they grow; in fact, the group derives its name from this process, which is called **molting**, or ecdysis. Ecdysozoa consists of about eight animal phyla and contains more known species than all other protist, fungus, plant, and animal groups combined. Here we'll focus on the two largest ecdysozoan phyla, the nematodes and arthropods, which are among the most successful and abundant of all animal groups.

Nematodes

Some of the most ubiquitous animals, nematodes (phylum Nematoda), or roundworms, are found in most aquatic habitats, in the soil, in the moist tissues of plants, and in the body fluids and tissues of animals. In contrast to annelids, nematodes do not have segmented bodies. The cylindrical bodies of nematodes range from less than 1 mm to more than a meter in length, often tapering to a fine tip at the posterior end and to a more blunt tip at the anterior end (**Figure 33.25**). A nematode's body is covered by a tough cuticle; as the worm grows, it periodically sheds its old cuticle and secretes a new, larger one. Nematodes have an alimentary canal, though they lack a circulatory system. Nutrients are transported throughout the body via fluid in the pseudocoelom. The body wall muscles are all longitudinal, and their contraction produces a thrashing motion.

Nematodes usually reproduce sexually, by internal fertilization. In most species, the sexes are separate and females are larger than males. A female may deposit 100,000 or more fertilized eggs (zygotes) per day. The zygotes of most species are resistant cells that can survive harsh conditions.

Multitudes of nematodes live in moist soil and in decomposing organic matter on the bottoms of lakes and oceans. While 25,000 species are known, perhaps 20 times that number actually exist. It has been said that if nothing but nematodes remained on Earth, they would still preserve the outline of the planet and many of its features. These free-living worms play an important role in decomposition and nutrient cycling, but little is known about most species. One species of soil nematode, *Caenorhabditis elegans*, however, is very well studied and has become a model research organism in biology. Ongoing studies on *C. elegans* are revealing some of the mechanisms involved in aging in humans, among other findings.

Phylum Nematoda includes many significant agricultural pests that attack the roots of plants. Other species of nematodes parasitize animals. Humans are hosts to at least 50 nematode species, including various pinworms and hookworms. One notorious nematode is *Trichinella spiralis*, the worm that causes trichinosis (**Figure 33.26**). Humans acquire this nematode by eating raw or undercooked pork or other meat (including wild game such as bear or walrus) that has juvenile worms encysted in the muscle tissue. Within the human intestines, the juveniles develop into sexually mature adults. Females burrow into the intestinal muscles and produce more juveniles, which bore through the body or travel in lymphatic vessels to other organs, including skeletal muscles, where they encyst.

Parasitic nematodes have an extraordinary molecular toolkit that enables them to redirect some of the cellular functions of their hosts and thus evade their immune systems. Plant-parasitic nematodes inject molecules that induce the development of root cells, which then supply nutrients to the parasites. *Trichinella* controls the expression of specific muscle-cell genes that code for proteins that make the cell elastic enough to house the nematode. Additionally, the infected muscle cell releases signals that attract blood vessels, which

Encysted juveniles   Muscle tissue   50 μm

▲ **Figure 33.26 Juveniles of the parasitic nematode *Trichinella spiralis* encysted in human muscle tissue** (LM).

25 μm

▲ **Figure 33.25 A free-living nematode** (colorized SEM).

then supply the nematode with nutrients. These extraordinary parasites have been dubbed "animals that act like viruses."

Arthropods

Zoologists estimate that there are about a billion billion (10^{18}) arthropods living on Earth. More than 1 million arthropod species have been described, most of which are insects. In fact, two out of every three known species are arthropods, and members of the phylum Arthropoda can be found in nearly all habitats of the biosphere. By the criteria of species diversity, distribution, and sheer numbers, arthropods must be regarded as the most successful of all animal phyla.

Arthropod Origins

Biologists hypothesize that the diversity and success of **arthropods** is related to their body plan—their segmented bodies, hard exoskeleton, and jointed appendages (*arthropod* means "jointed feet"). The earliest fossils with this body plan are from the Cambrian explosion (535–525 million years ago), indicating that the arthropods are at least that old.

Along with arthropods, the fossil record of the Cambrian explosion contains many species of *lobopods*, an extinct group from which arthropods may have evolved. Lobopods such as *Hallucigenia* (see Figure 25.4) had segmented bodies, but most of their body segments were identical to one another. Early arthropods, such as the trilobites, also showed little variation from segment to segment **(Figure 33.27)**. As arthropods continued to evolve, the segments tended to fuse and become fewer, and the appendages became specialized for a variety of functions. These evolutionary changes resulted not only in great diversification but also in an efficient body plan that permits the division of labor among different body regions.

What genetic changes led to the increasing complexity of the arthropod body plan? Arthropods today have two unusual *Hox* genes, both of which influence segmentation. To test whether these genes could have driven the evolution of increased body segment diversity in arthropods, Sean Carroll (see pages 534–535) and colleagues studied *Hox* genes in onychophorans, close relatives of arthropods **(Figure 33.28)**.

▶ **Figure 33.27 A trilobite fossil.** Trilobites were common denizens of the shallow seas throughout the Paleozoic era but disappeared with the great Permian extinctions about 250 million years ago. Paleontologists have described about 4,000 trilobite species.

▼ **Figure 33.28 Inquiry**

Did the arthropod body plan result from new *Hox* genes?

EXPERIMENT How did the highly successful arthropod body plan arise? One hypothesis suggests that it resulted from the origin (by a gene duplication event) of two unusual *Hox* genes found in arthropods: *Ultrabithorax* (*Ubx*) and *abdominal-A* (*abd-A*). To test this hypothesis, Sean Carroll, of the University of Wisconsin, Madison, and colleagues turned to the onychophorans, a group of invertebrates closely related to arthropods. Unlike many living arthropods, onychophorans have a body plan in which most body segments are identical to one another. Thus, Carroll and colleagues reasoned that if the origin of the *Ubx* and *abd-A Hox* genes drove the evolution of body segment diversity in arthropods, these genes probably arose on the arthropod branch of the evolutionary tree:

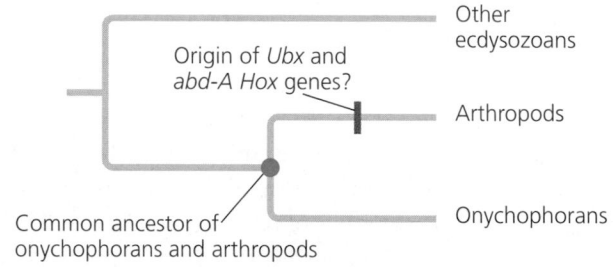

As the hypothesis depicted above suggests, *Ubx* and *abd-A* would not have been present in the common ancestor of arthropods and onychophorans, and hence, onychophorans should not have these genes. To find out whether this was the case, Carroll and colleagues examined the *Hox* genes of the onychophoran *Acanthokara kaputensis*.

RESULTS The onychophoran *A. kaputensis* has all arthropod *Hox* genes, including *Ubx* and *abd-A*.

Red indicates the body regions of this onychophoran embryo in which *Ubx* or *abd-A* genes were expressed. (The inset shows this area enlarged.)

Ant = antenna
J = jaws
L1–L15 = body segments

CONCLUSION Since *A. kaputensis,* an onychophoran, has the arthropod *Hox* genes, the evolution of increased body segment diversity in arthropods must not have been related to the origin of new *Hox* genes.

SOURCE J. K. Grenier, S. Carroll et al., Evolution of the entire arthropod *Hox* gene set predated the origin and radiation of the onychophoran/arthropod clade, *Current Biology* 7:547–553 (1997).

WHAT IF? If Carroll and colleagues had found that *A. kaputensis* did *not* have the *Ubx* and *abd-A Hox* genes, how would their conclusion have been affected? Explain.

Their results indicate that arthropod body plan diversity did *not* arise from the acquisition of new *Hox* genes. Instead, the evolution of body segment diversity in arthropods may have been driven by changes in the sequence or regulation of existing *Hox* genes. (See Chapter 25 for a discussion of how changes in form can result from changes in the sequence or regulation of developmental genes such as *Hox* genes.)

General Characteristics of Arthropods

Over the course of evolution, the appendages of some arthropods have become modified, specializing in functions such as walking, feeding, sensory reception, reproduction, and defense. **Figure 33.29** illustrates the diverse appendages and other arthropod characteristics of a lobster.

The body of an arthropod is completely covered by the cuticle, an exoskeleton constructed from layers of protein and the polysaccharide chitin. The cuticle can be thick and hard over some parts of the body and paper-thin and flexible over others, such as the joints. The rigid exoskeleton protects the animal and provides points of attachment for the muscles that move the appendages. But it also means that an arthropod cannot grow without occasionally shedding its exoskeleton and producing a larger one. This molting process is energetically expensive. A molting or recently molted arthropod is also vulnerable to predation and other dangers until its new, soft exoskeleton hardens.

When the arthropod exoskeleton first evolved in the sea, its main functions were probably protection and anchorage for muscles, but it later additionally enabled certain arthropods to live on land. The exoskeleton's relative impermeability to water helped prevent desiccation, and its strength solved the problem of support when arthropods left the buoyancy of wa-ter. Arthropods began to diversify on land following the colonization of land by plants in the early Paleozoic. Evidence includes a 428-million-year-old fossil of a millipede found in 2004 by an amateur fossil hunter in Scotland. Fossilized tracks of other terrestrial arthropods date from about 450 million years ago.

Arthropods have well-developed sensory organs, including eyes, olfactory (smell) receptors, and antennae that function in both touch and smell. Most sensory organs are concentrated at the anterior end of the animal.

Like many molluscs, arthropods have an **open circulatory system**, in which fluid called *hemolymph* is propelled by a heart through short arteries and then into spaces called sinuses surrounding the tissues and organs. (The term *blood* is generally reserved for fluid in a closed circulatory system.) Hemolymph reenters the arthropod heart through pores that are usually equipped with valves. The hemolymph-filled body sinuses are collectively called the *hemocoel*, which is not part of the coelom. Although arthropods are coelomates, in most species the coelom that forms in the embryo becomes much reduced as development progresses, and the hemocoel becomes the main body cavity in adults. Despite their similarity, the open circulatory systems of molluscs and arthropods probably arose independently.

A variety of specialized gas-exchange organs have evolved in arthropods. These organs allow the diffusion of respiratory gases in spite of the exoskeleton. Most aquatic species have gills with thin, feathery extensions that place an extensive surface area in contact with the surrounding water. Terrestrial arthropods generally have internal surfaces specialized for gas exchange. Most insects, for instance, have tracheal systems, branched air ducts leading into the interior from pores in the cuticle.

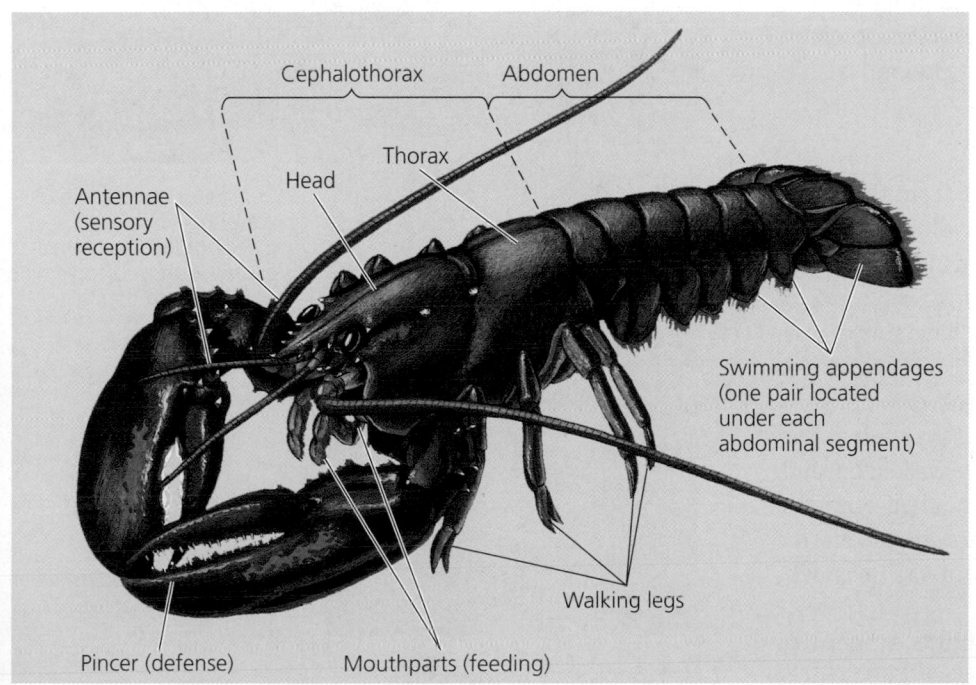

◀ **Figure 33.29 External anatomy of an arthropod.** Many of the distinctive features of arthropods are apparent in this dorsal view of a lobster, along with some uniquely crustacean characteristics. The body is segmented, but this characteristic is obvious only in the abdomen. The appendages (including antennae, pincers, mouthparts, walking legs, and swimming appendages) are jointed. The head bears a pair of compound (multilens) eyes, each situated on a movable stalk. The whole body, including appendages, is covered by an exoskeleton.

Cephalothorax | Abdomen
Thorax
Head
Antennae (sensory reception)
Swimming appendages (one pair located under each abdominal segment)
Walking legs
Pincer (defense)
Mouthparts (feeding)

Table 33.5 Subphyla of Phylum Arthropoda

Subphylum and Examples	Main Characteristics
Cheliceriformes (horseshoe crabs, spiders, scorpions, ticks, mites; see Figures 33.30–33.32)	Body having one or two main parts; six pairs of appendages (chelicerae, pedipalps, and four pairs of walking legs); mostly terrestrial or marine
Myriapoda (millipedes and centipedes; see Figures 33.33 and 33.34)	Distinct head bearing antennae and chewing mouthparts; terrestrial; millipedes are herbivorous and have two pairs of walking legs per trunk segment; centipedes are carnivorous and have one pair of walking legs per trunk segment and poison claws on first body segment
Hexapoda (insects, springtails; see Figures 33.35–33.37)	Body divided into head, thorax, and abdomen; antennae present; mouthparts modified for chewing, sucking, or lapping; three pairs of legs and usually two pairs of wings; mostly terrestrial
Crustacea (crabs, lobsters, crayfishes, shrimps; see Figures 33.29 and 33.38)	Body of two or three parts; antennae present; chewing mouthparts; three or more pairs of legs; mostly marine and freshwater

▲ **Figure 33.30 Horseshoe crabs (*Limulus polyphemus*).** Common on the Atlantic and Gulf coasts of the United States, these "living fossils" have changed little in hundreds of millions of years. They are surviving members of a rich diversity of cheliceriforms that once filled the seas.

▲ Scorpions have pedipalps that are pincers specialized for defense and the capture of food. The tip of the tail bears a poisonous stinger.

▲ Dust mites are ubiquitous scavengers in human dwellings but are harmless except to those people who are allergic to them (colorized SEM).

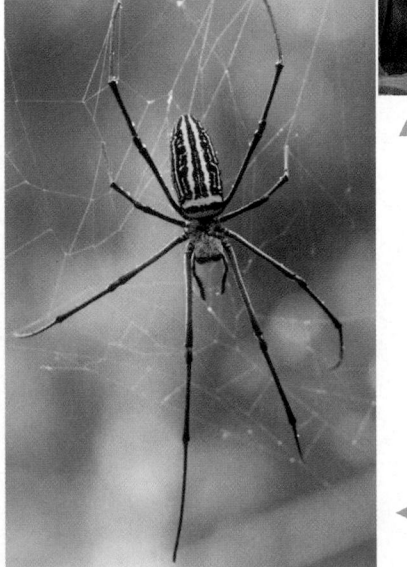

◄ Web-building spiders are generally most active during the daytime.

▲ **Figure 33.31 Arachnids.**

Morphological and molecular evidence suggests that living arthropods consist of four major lineages that diverged early in the evolution of the phylum **(Table 33.5)**: **cheliceriforms** (sea spiders, horseshoe crabs, scorpions, ticks, mites, and spiders); **myriapods** (centipedes and millipedes); **hexapods** (insects and their wingless, six-legged relatives); and **crustaceans** (crabs, lobsters, shrimps, barnacles, and many others).

Cheliceriforms

Cheliceriforms (subphylum Cheliceriformes; from the Greek *cheilos*, lips, and *cheir*, arm) are named for clawlike feeding appendages called **chelicerae**, which serve as pincers or fangs. Cheliceriforms have an anterior cephalothorax and a posterior abdomen. They lack antennae, and most have simple eyes (eyes with a single lens).

The earliest cheliceriforms were **eurypterids**, or water scorpions. These marine and freshwater predators grew up to 3 m long; it is thought that some species could have walked on land, much as land crabs do today. Most of the marine cheliceriforms, including all of the eurypterids, are extinct. Among the marine cheliceriforms that survive today are the sea spiders (pycnogonids) and horseshoe crabs **(Figure 33.30)**.

The bulk of modern cheliceriforms are **arachnids**, a group that includes scorpions, spiders, ticks, and mites **(Figure 33.31)**. Ticks and many mites are among a large group of parasitic arthropods. Nearly all ticks are bloodsucking parasites that live on the body surfaces of reptiles or mammals. Parasitic mites live on or in a wide variety of vertebrates, invertebrates, and plants.

Arachnids have a cephalothorax that has six pairs of appendages: the chelicerae; a pair of appendages called *pedipalps* that function in sensing, feeding, or reproduction; and four pairs of walking legs **(Figure 33.32)**. Spiders use their fang-like chelicerae, which are equipped with poison glands, to attack prey. As the chelicerae pierce the prey, the spider secretes digestive juices onto the prey's torn tissues. The food softens, and the spider sucks up the liquid meal.

In most spiders, gas exchange is carried out by **book lungs**, stacked platelike structures contained in an internal chamber (see Figure 33.32). The extensive surface area of these respiratory organs is a structural adaptation that enhances the exchange of O_2 and CO_2 between the hemolymph and air.

A unique adaptation of many spiders is the ability to catch insects by constructing webs of silk, a liquid protein produced by specialized abdominal glands. The silk is spun by organs called spinnerets into fibers that then solidify. Each spider engineers a web characteristic of its species and builds it perfectly on the first try. This complex behavior is apparently inherited. Various spiders also use silk in other ways: as droplines for rapid escape, as a cover for eggs, and even as "gift wrap" for food that males offer females during courtship. Many small spiders also extrude silk into the air and let themselves be transported by wind, a behavior known as "ballooning."

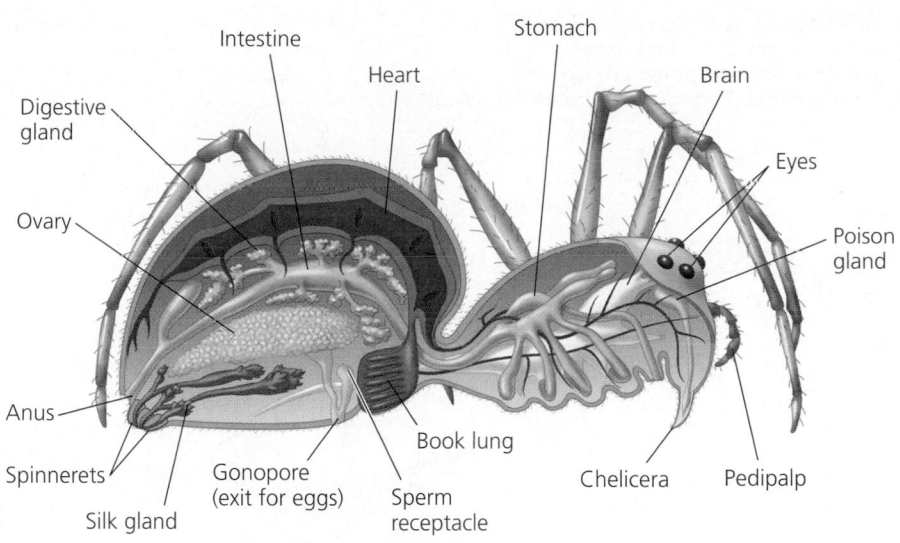

▲ Figure 33.32 **Anatomy of a spider.**

Myriapods

Millipedes and centipedes belong to the subphylum Myriapoda, the myriapods. All living myriapods are terrestrial. The myriapod head has a pair of antennae and three pairs of appendages modified as mouthparts, including the jaw-like **mandibles**.

Millipedes (class Diplopoda) have a large number of legs, though fewer than the thousand their name implies **(Figure 33.33)**. Each trunk segment is formed from two fused segments and bears two pairs of legs. Millipedes eat decaying leaves and other plant matter. They may have been among the earliest animals on land, living on mosses and primitive vascular plants.

Unlike millipedes, centipedes (class Chilopoda) are carnivores. Each segment of a centipede's trunk region has one pair of legs **(Figure 33.34)**. Centipedes have poison claws on their foremost trunk segment that paralyze prey and aid in defense.

▲ Figure 33.33 **A millipede.**

▲ Figure 33.34 **A centipede.**

The insect body has three regions: head, thorax, and abdomen. The segmentation of the thorax and abdomen are obvious, but the segments that form the head are fused.

Cerebral ganglion. The two nerve cords meet in the head, where the ganglia of several anterior segments are fused into a cerebral ganglion (brain, colored white below). The antennae, eyes, and other sense organs are concentrated on the head.

Heart. The insect heart drives hemolymph through an open circulatory system.

Compound eye

Antennae

Dorsal artery

Crop

Anus

Malpighian tubules. Metabolic wastes are removed from the hemolymph by excretory organs called Malpighian tubules, which are out-pocketings of the digestive tract.

Vagina

Ovary

Abdomen   Thorax   Head

Tracheal tubes. Gas exchange in insects is accomplished by a tracheal system of branched, chitin-lined tubes that infiltrate the body and carry oxygen directly to cells. The tracheal system opens to the outside of the body through spiracles, pores that can control air flow and water loss by opening or closing.

Nerve cords. The insect nervous system consists of a pair of ventral nerve cords with several segmental ganglia.

Insect mouthparts are formed from several pairs of modified appendages. The mouthparts include mandibles, which grasshoppers use for chewing. In other insects, mouthparts are specialized for lapping, piercing, or sucking.

▲ Figure 33.35 **Anatomy of a grasshopper, an insect.**

Insects

Insects and their relatives (subphylum Hexapoda) are more species-rich than all other forms of life combined. They live in almost every terrestrial habitat and in fresh water, and flying insects fill the air. Insects are rare, though not absent, in marine habitats, where crustaceans are the dominant arthropods. The internal anatomy of an insect includes several complex organ systems, which are highlighted in **Figure 33.35**.

The oldest insect fossils date from the Devonian period, which began about 416 million years ago. However, when flight evolved during the Carboniferous and Permian periods, it spurred an explosion in insect diversity. A fossil record of diverse insect mouthparts indicates that specialized feeding on gymnosperms and other Carboniferous plants also contributed to early adaptive radiations of insects. Later, a major increase in insect diversity appears to have been stimulated by the evolutionary expansion of flowering plants during the mid-Cretaceous period (about 90 million years ago). Although insect and plant diversity decreased during the Cretaceous mass extinction, both groups rebounded over the next 65 million years. Studies indicate that rebounds of particular insect groups often were associated with radiations of the flowering plants on which they fed.

Flight is obviously one key to the great success of insects. An animal that can fly can escape many predators, find food and mates, and disperse to new habitats much faster than an animal that must crawl about on the ground. Many insects have one or two pairs of wings that emerge from the dorsal side of the thorax. Because the wings are extensions of the cuticle and not true appendages, insects can fly without sacrificing any walking legs. By contrast, the flying vertebrates—birds and bats—have one of their two pairs of walking legs modified into wings, making some of these species clumsy on the ground.

Insect wings may have first evolved as extensions of the cuticle that helped the insect body absorb heat, only later becoming organs for flight. Other hypotheses suggest that wings allowed terrestrial insects to glide from vegetation to the ground or that they served as gills in aquatic insects. Still another hypothesis is that insect wings functioned for swimming before they functioned for flight.

Morphological and molecular data indicate that wings evolved only once in insects. Dragonflies, which have two similar pairs of wings, were among the first insects to fly. Several insect orders that evolved later than dragonflies have modified flight equipment. The wings of bees and wasps, for instance, are hooked together and move as a single pair. Butterfly wings operate in a similar fashion because the anterior pair overlaps the posterior wings. In beetles, the posterior wings function in flight, while the anterior ones are modified as covers that protect the flight wings when the beetle is walking on the ground or burrowing.

Many insects undergo metamorphosis during their development. In the **incomplete metamorphosis** of grasshoppers and some other insect groups, the young (called nymphs) resemble adults but are smaller, have different body proportions, and lack wings. The nymph undergoes a series of molts, each time looking more like an adult. With the final molt, the insect reaches full size, acquires wings, and becomes sexually mature. Insects with **complete metamorphosis** have larval stages specialized for eating and growing that are known by such names as caterpillar, maggot, or grub. The larval stage looks entirely different from the adult stage, which is specialized for dispersal and reproduction. Metamorphosis from the larval stage to the adult occurs during a pupal stage **(Figure 33.36)**.

Reproduction in insects is usually sexual, with separate male and female individuals. Adults come together and recognize each other as members of the same species by advertising with bright colors (as in butterflies), sound (as in crickets), or odors (as in moths). Fertilization is generally internal. In most species, sperm are deposited directly into the female's vagina at the time of copulation, though in some species the male deposits a sperm packet outside the female, and the female picks it up. An internal structure in the female called the spermatheca stores the sperm, usually enough to fertilize more than one batch of eggs. Many insects mate only once in a lifetime. After mating, a female often lays her eggs on an appropriate food source where the next generation can begin eating as soon as it hatches.

Insects are classified in more than 30 orders, 15 of which are presented in **Figure 33.37**, on the next two pages.

Animals as numerous, diverse, and widespread as insects are bound to affect the lives of most other terrestrial organisms, including humans. We depend on bees, flies, and many other insects to pollinate our crops and orchards. On the other hand, insects are carriers for many diseases, including African sleeping sickness (spread by tsetse flies that carry the protist *Trypanosoma*; see Figure 28.6) and malaria (spread by mosquitoes that carry the protist *Plasmodium*; see Figure 28.10). Furthermore, insects compete with humans for food. In parts of Africa, for instance, insects claim about 75% of the crops. In the United States, billions of dollars are spent each year on pesticides, spraying crops with massive doses of some of the deadliest poisons ever invented. Try as they may, not even humans have challenged the preeminence of insects and their arthropod kin. As Cornell University entomologist Thomas Eisner puts it: "Bugs are not going to inherit the Earth. They own it now. So we might as well make peace with the landlord."

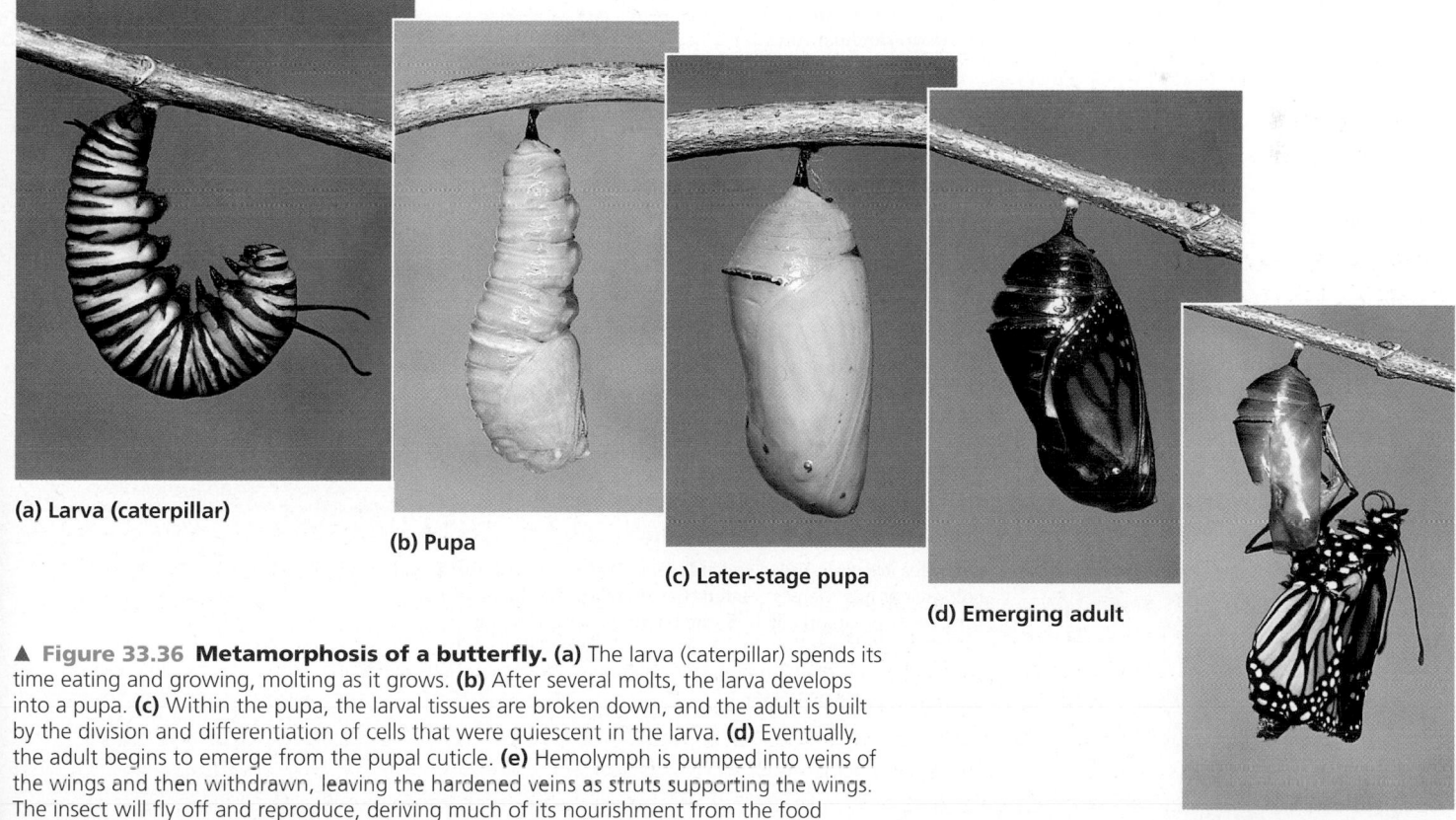

(a) Larva (caterpillar)

(b) Pupa

(c) Later-stage pupa

(d) Emerging adult

(e) Adult

▲ **Figure 33.36 Metamorphosis of a butterfly. (a)** The larva (caterpillar) spends its time eating and growing, molting as it grows. **(b)** After several molts, the larva develops into a pupa. **(c)** Within the pupa, the larval tissues are broken down, and the adult is built by the division and differentiation of cells that were quiescent in the larva. **(d)** Eventually, the adult begins to emerge from the pupal cuticle. **(e)** Hemolymph is pumped into veins of the wings and then withdrawn, leaving the hardened veins as struts supporting the wings. The insect will fly off and reproduce, deriving much of its nourishment from the food reserves stored by the feeding larva.

Exploring Insect Diversity

Order	Approximate Number of Species	Main Characteristics	Examples
Blattodea	4,000	Cockroaches have a dorsoventrally flattened body, with legs modified for rapid running. Forewings, when present, are leathery, whereas hind wings are fanlike. Fewer than 40 cockroach species live in houses; the rest exploit habitats ranging from tropical forest floors to caves and deserts.	German cockroach
Coleoptera	350,000	Beetles comprise the most species-rich order of insects. They have two pairs of wings, one of which is thick and stiff, the other membranous. They have an armored exoskeleton and mouthparts adapted for biting and chewing. Beetles undergo complete metamorphosis.	Japanese beetle
Dermaptera	1,200	Earwigs are generally nocturnal scavengers. Some species are wingless, while others have two pairs of wings, one of which is thick and leathery, the other membranous. Earwigs have biting mouthparts and large posterior pincers. They undergo incomplete metamorphosis.	Earwig
Diptera	151,000	Dipterans have one pair of wings; the second pair has become modified into balancing organs called halteres. Their mouthparts are adapted for sucking, piercing, or lapping. Dipterans undergo complete metamorphosis. Flies and mosquitoes are among the best-known dipterans, which live as scavengers, predators, and parasites.	Horsefly
Hemiptera	85,000	Hemipterans are so-called "true bugs," including bed bugs, assassin bugs, and chinch bugs. (Insects in other orders are sometimes erroneously called bugs.) Hemipterans have two pairs of wings, one pair partly leathery, the other membranous. They have piercing or sucking mouthparts and undergo incomplete metamorphosis.	Leaf-footed bug
Hymenoptera	125,000	Ants, bees, and wasps are generally highly social insects. They have two pairs of membranous wings, a mobile head, and chewing or sucking mouthparts. The females of many species have a posterior stinging organ. Hymenopterans undergo complete metamorphosis.	Cicada-killer wasp
Isoptera	2,000	Termites are widespread social insects that produce enormous colonies. It has been estimated that there are 700 kg of termites for every person on Earth! Some termites have two pairs of membranous wings, while others are wingless. They feed on wood with the aid of microbial symbionts carried in specialized chambers in their hindgut.	Termite

Order	Approximate Number of Species	Main Characteristics	Examples
Lepidoptera	120,000	Butterflies and moths are among the best-known insects. They have two pairs of wings covered with tiny scales. To feed, they uncoil a long proboscis. Most feed on nectar, but some species feed on other substances, including animal blood or tears.	Swallowtail butterfly
Odonata	5,000	Dragonflies and damselflies have two pairs of large, membranous wings. They have an elongated abdomen, large, compound eyes, and chewing mouthparts. They undergo incomplete metamorphosis and are active predators.	Dragonfly
Orthoptera	13,000	Grasshoppers, crickets, and their relatives are mostly herbivorous. They have large hind legs adapted for jumping, two pairs of wings (one leathery, one membranous), and biting or chewing mouthparts. Males commonly make courtship sounds by rubbing together body parts, such as a ridge on their hind legs. Orthopterans undergo incomplete metamorphosis.	Katydid
Phasmatodea	2,600	Stick insects and leaf insects are exquisite mimics of plants. The eggs of some species even mimic seeds of the plants on which the insects live. Their body is cylindrical or flattened dorsoventrally. They lack forewings but have fanlike hind wings. Their mouthparts are adapted for biting or chewing.	Stick insect
Phthiraptera	2,400	Commonly called sucking lice, these insects spend their entire life as an ectoparasite feeding on the hair or feathers of a single host. Their legs, equipped with clawlike tarsi, are adapted for clinging to their hosts. They lack wings and have reduced eyes. Sucking lice undergo incomplete metamorphosis.	Human body louse
Siphonaptera	2,400	Fleas are bloodsucking ectoparasites on birds and mammals. Their body is wingless and laterally compressed. Their legs are modified for clinging to their hosts and for long-distance jumping. They undergo complete metamorphosis.	Flea
Thysanura	450	Silverfish are small, wingless insects with a flattened body and reduced eyes. They live in leaf litter or under bark. They can also infest buildings, where they can become pests.	Silverfish
Trichoptera	7,100	The larvae of caddisflies live in streams, where they make houses from sand grains, wood fragments, or other material held together by silk. Adults have two pairs of hairy wings and chewing or lapping mouthparts. They undergo complete metamorphosis.	Caddisfly

Crustaceans

While arachnids and insects thrive on land, crustaceans, for the most part, have remained in marine and freshwater environments. Crustaceans (subphylum Crustacea) typically have highly specialized appendages. Lobsters and crayfishes, for instance, have a toolkit of 19 pairs of appendages (see Figure 33.29). The anteriormost appendages are antennae; crustaceans are the only arthropods with two pairs. Three or more pairs of appendages are modified as mouthparts, including the hard mandibles. Walking legs are present on the thorax, and, unlike insects, crustaceans also have appendages on their abdomen. A lost appendage can be regenerated at next molt.

Small crustaceans exchange gases across thin areas of the cuticle; larger species have gills. Nitrogenous wastes also diffuse through thin areas of the cuticle, but a pair of glands regulates the salt balance of the hemolymph.

Sexes are separate in most crustaceans. In the case of lobsters and crayfish, the male uses a specialized pair of abdominal appendages to transfer sperm to the reproductive pore of the female during copulation. Most aquatic crustaceans go through one or more swimming larval stages.

One of the largest groups of crustaceans (numbering about 10,000 species) is the **isopods**, which include terrestrial, freshwater, and marine species. Some isopod species are abundant in habitats at the bottom of the deep ocean. Among the terrestrial isopods are the pill bugs, or wood lice, common on the undersides of moist logs and leaves.

Lobsters, crayfishes, crabs, and shrimps are all relatively large crustaceans called **decapods (Figure 33.38a)**. The cuticle of decapods is hardened by calcium carbonate; the portion that covers the dorsal side of the cephalothorax forms a shield called the carapace. Most decapod species are marine. Crayfishes, however, live in fresh water, and some tropical crabs live on land.

Many small crustaceans are important members of marine and freshwater plankton communities. Planktonic crustaceans include many species of **copepods**, which are among the most numerous of all animals, as well as the shrimplike krill, which grow to about 5 cm long **(Figure 33.38b)**. A major food source for baleen whales (including blue whales, humpbacks, and right whales), krill are now being harvested in great numbers by humans for food and agricultural fertilizer. The larvae of many larger-bodied crustaceans are also planktonic.

Barnacles are a group of mostly sessile crustaceans whose cuticle is hardened into a shell containing calcium carbonate **(Figure 33.38c)**. Most barnacles anchor themselves to rocks, boat hulls, pilings, and other submerged surfaces. Their natural adhesive is as strong as synthetic glues. To feed, these barnacles extend appendages from their shell to strain food from the water. Barnacles were not recognized as crustaceans until the 1800s, when naturalists discovered that barnacle larvae resemble the larvae of other crustaceans. The remarkable mix of unique traits and crustacean homologies found in barnacles was a major inspiration to Charles Darwin as he developed his theory of evolution.

(a) Ghost crabs live on sandy ocean beaches worldwide. Primarily nocturnal, they take shelter in burrows during the day.

(b) Planktonic crustaceans known as krill are consumed in vast quantities by some whales.

(c) The jointed appendages projecting from the shells of these barnacles capture organisms and organic particles suspended in the water.

▲ **Figure 33.38 Crustaceans.**

CONCEPT CHECK 33.4

1. How do nematode and annelid body plans differ?
2. In contrast to our jaws, which move up and down, the mouthparts of arthropods move side to side. Explain this feature of arthropods in terms of the origin of their mouthparts.
3. Describe two adaptations that have enabled insects to thrive on land.
4. **WHAT IF?** Traditionally, annelids and arthropods were thought to be closely related because both groups show body segmentation. Yet molecular data indicate that annelids belong to one clade (Lophotrochozoa) and arthropods to another (Ecdysozoa). Could traditional and molecular hypotheses be tested by studying the expression of *Hox* genes that control body segmentation? Explain.

For suggested answers, see Appendix A.

CONCEPT 33.5

Echinoderms and chordates are deuterostomes

Calcarea and Silicea
Cnidaria
Lophotrochozoa
Ecdysozoa
Deuterostomia

Sea stars, sea urchins, and other echinoderms (phylum Echinodermata) may seem to have little in common with phylum Chordata, which includes the vertebrates—animals that have a backbone. In fact, however, echinoderms and chordates share features characteristic of a deuterostome mode of development, such as radial cleavage and formation of the mouth at the end of the embryo opposite the blastopore (see Figure 32.9). Molecular systematics has reinforced Deuterostomia as a clade of bilaterian animals. But molecular evidence also indicates that some animal phyla with members that have deuterostome developmental features, including ectoprocts and brachiopods, are not in the deuterostome clade (see Chapter 32). Hence, despite its name, the clade

Deuterostomia is defined primarily by DNA similarities—not developmental similarities.

Echinoderms

Sea stars and most other **echinoderms** (from the Greek *echin*, spiny, and *derma*, skin) are slow-moving or sessile marine animals. A thin epidermis covers an endoskeleton of hard calcareous plates. Most echinoderms are prickly from skeletal bumps and spines. Unique to echinoderms is the **water vascular system**, a network of hydraulic canals branching into extensions called **tube feet** that function in locomotion, feeding, and gas exchange **(Figure 33.39)**. Sexual reproduction of echinoderms usually involves separate male and female individuals that release their gametes into the water.

The internal and external parts of most adult echinoderms radiate from the center, often as five spokes. However, echinoderm larvae have bilateral symmetry. Furthermore, the symmetry of adult echinoderms is not truly radial. For example, the opening (madreporite) of a sea star's water vascular system is not central but shifted to one side.

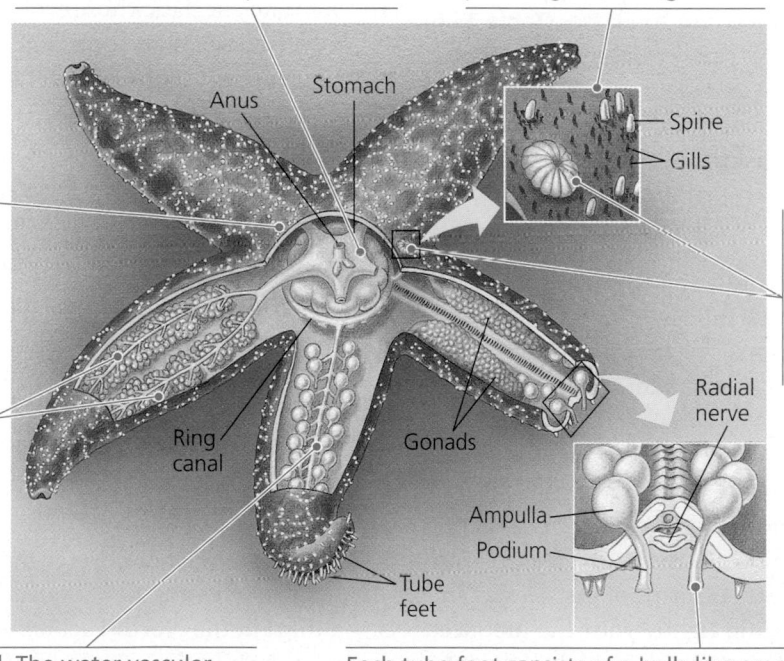

The surface of a sea star is covered by spines that help defend against predators, as well as by small gills that provide gas exchange.

A short digestive tract runs from the mouth on the bottom of the central disk to the anus on top of the disk.

Anus

Stomach

Spine

Gills

Central disk. The central disk has a nerve ring and nerve cords radiating from the ring into the arms.

Madreporite. Water can flow in or out of the water vascular system into the surrounding water through the madreporite.

Digestive glands secrete digestive juices and aid in the absorption and storage of nutrients.

Radial nerve

Ring canal

Gonads

Ampulla

Podium

Tube feet

Radial canal. The water vascular system consists of a ring canal in the central disk and five radial canals, each running in a groove down the entire length of an arm. Branching from each radial canal are hundreds of hollow, muscular tube feet filled with fluid.

Each tube foot consists of a bulb-like ampulla and a podium (foot portion). When the ampulla squeezes, water is forced into the podium, which expands and contacts the substrate. Adhesive chemicals are then secreted from the base of the podium, attaching it to the substrate. To detach the tube foot, de-adhesive chemicals are secreted and muscles in the podium contract, forcing water back into the ampulla and shortening the podium. As it moves, a sea star leaves an observable "footprint" of adhesive material on the substrate.

▲ Figure 33.39 **Anatomy of a sea star, an echinoderm.**

Table 33.6 Classes of Phylum Echinodermata

Class and Examples	Main Characteristics
Asteroidea (sea stars; see Figure 33.39 and Figure 33.40a)	Star-shaped body with multiple arms; mouth directed to substrate
Ophiuroidea (brittle stars; see Figure 33.40b)	Distinct central disk; long, flexible arms; incomplete digestive system
Echinoidea (sea urchins, sand dollars; see Figure 33.40c)	Roughly spherical or disk-shaped; no arms; five rows of tube feet, enabling slow movement; mouth ringed by complex, jaw-like structure
Crinoidea (sea lilies, feather stars; see Figure 33.40d)	Feathered arms surrounding upward-pointing mouth; suspension feeders
Holothuroidea (sea cucumbers; see Figure 33.40e)	Cucumber-shaped body; five rows of tube feet; tube feet around the mouth are modified as feeding tentacles; reduced skeleton; no spines
Concentricycloidea (sea daisies; see Figure 33.40f)	Armless, disk-shaped body ringed with small spines; incomplete digestive system; live on submerged wood

Living echinoderms are divided into six classes (Table 33.6; Figure 33.40): Asteroidea (sea stars), Ophiuroidea (brittle stars), Echinoidea (sea urchins and sand dollars), Crinoidea (sea lilies and feather stars), Holothuroidea (sea cucumbers), and Concentricycloidea (sea daisies).

Sea Stars

Sea stars have multiple arms radiating from a central disk, the undersurfaces of which bear tube feet. By a combination of muscular and chemical actions, the tube feet can attach to or detach from a substrate. The sea star adheres firmly to rocks or creeps along slowly as its tube feet extend, grip, release, extend, and grip again. Although the base of a sea star tube foot has a flattened disk that resembles a suction cup, the gripping action results from adhesive chemicals, not suction (see Figure 33.39). Sea stars also use their tube feet to grasp prey, such as clams and oysters. The arms of the sea star embrace the closed bivalve, clinging tightly with the tube feet. The sea star then turns part of its stomach inside out, everting it through its mouth and into the narrow opening between the halves of the bivalve's shell. The digestive system of the sea star secretes juices that begin digesting the soft body of the mollusc within its own shell.

Sea stars and some other echinoderms have considerable powers of regeneration. Sea stars can regrow lost arms, and

members of one genus can even regrow an entire body from a single arm if part of the central disk remains attached.

Brittle Stars

Brittle stars have a distinct central disk and long, flexible arms. They move primarily by lashing their arms in serpentine movements. The base of a brittle star tube foot lacks the flattened disk found in sea stars but does secrete adhesive chemicals. Hence, like sea stars and other echinoderms, brittle stars can use their tube feet to grip substrates. Some species are suspension feeders; others are predators or scavengers.

Sea Urchins and Sand Dollars

Sea urchins and sand dollars have no arms, but they do have five rows of tube feet that function in slow movement. Sea urchins also have muscles that pivot their long spines, which aid in locomotion as well as protection. The mouth of a sea urchin is ringed by highly complex, jaw-like structures that are well adapted to eating seaweed. Sea urchins are roughly spherical, whereas sand dollars are flat disks.

Sea Lilies and Feather Stars

Sea lilies live attached to the substrate by a stalk; feather stars crawl about by using their long, flexible arms. Both use their arms in suspension feeding. The arms encircle the mouth, which is directed upward, away from the substrate. Crinoidea is an ancient class whose evolution has been very conservative; fossilized sea lilies some 500 million years old are extremely similar to present-day members of the class.

Sea Cucumbers

On casual inspection, sea cucumbers do not look much like other echinoderms. They lack spines, and their endoskeleton is much reduced. They are also elongated in their oral-aboral axis, giving them the shape for which they are named and further disguising their relationship to sea stars and sea urchins. Closer examination, however, reveals that sea cucumbers have five rows of tube feet. Some of the tube feet around the mouth are developed as feeding tentacles.

Sea Daisies

Sea daisies were discovered in 1986, and only three species are known (one near New Zealand, a second in the Bahamas, and a third in the North Pacific). All live on submerged wood. A sea daisy's body is armless and is typically disk-shaped; it has a five-sided organization and measures less than a centimeter in diameter. The edge of the body is ringed with small spines. Sea daisies absorb nutrients through the membrane surrounding their body. The relationship of sea daisies to other echinoderms remains unclear; some systematists consider sea daisies the sister group of sea stars.

(a) A sea star (class Asteroidea)

(b) A brittle star (class Ophiuroidea)

(c) A sea urchin (class Echinoidea)

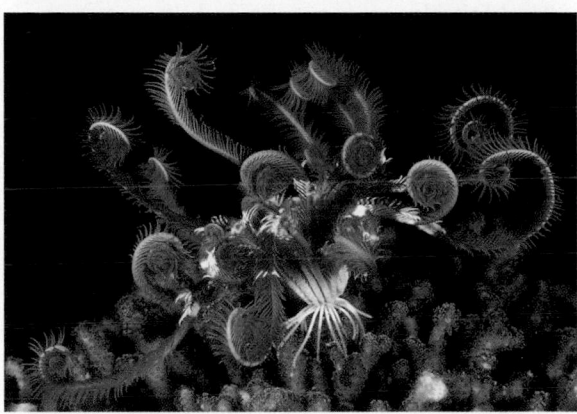

(d) A feather star (class Crinoidea)

(e) A sea cucumber (class Holothuroidea)

(f) A sea daisy (class Concentricycloidea)

▲ Figure 33.40 **Echinoderms.**

Chordates

Phylum Chordata consists of two subphyla of invertebrates as well as the hagfishes and the vertebrates. Chordates are bilaterally symmetrical coelomates with segmented bodies. The close relationship between echinoderms and chordates does not mean that one phylum evolved from the other. In fact, echinoderms and chordates have evolved independently of one another for at least 500 million years. We will trace the phylogeny of chordates in Chapter 34, focusing on the history of vertebrates.

CONCEPT CHECK   **33.5**

1. Describe how sea star tube feet attach to substrates.
2. Are characteristics shared by a sea star and a sea daisy homologous or analogous? Explain.
3. **WHAT IF?**   The insect *Drosophila melanogaster* and the nematode *Caenorhabditis elegans* are prominent model organisms. Are these species the most appropriate invertebrates for making inferences about humans and other vertebrates in Deuterostomia? Explain.

For suggested answers, see Appendix A.

Chapter 33 Review

SUMMARY OF KEY CONCEPTS

The table below summarizes the groups of animals surveyed in this chapter.

Selected Animal Phyla

Key Concept				Phylum		Description
Concept 33.1 **Sponges are basal animals that lack true tissues** (pp. 670–671)	Metazoa			Calcarea, Silicea (sponges)		Lack true tissues; have choanocytes (collar cells—flagellated cells that ingest bacteria and tiny food particles)
Concept 33.2 **Cnidarians are an ancient phylum of eumetazoans** (pp. 671–673)		Eumetazoa		Cnidaria (hydras, jellies, sea anemones, corals)		Unique stinging structures (nematocysts) housed in specialized cells (cnidocytes); diploblastic; radially symmetrical; gastrovascular cavity (digestive compartment with a single opening)
Concept 33.3 **Lophotrochozoans, a clade identified by molecular data, have the widest range of animal body forms** (pp. 674–682)			Bilateria / Lophotrochozoa	Platyhelminthes (flatworms)		Dorsoventrally flattened, unsegmented acoelomates; gastrovascular cavity or no digestive tract
				Rotifera (rotifers)		Pseudocoelomates with alimentary canal (digestive tube with mouth and anus); jaws (trophi) in pharynx; head with ciliated crown
				Lophophorates: Ectoprocta, Brachiopoda		Coelomates with lophophores (feeding structures bearing ciliated tentacles)
				Mollusca (clams, snails, squids)		Coelomates with three main body parts (muscular foot, visceral mass, mantle); coelom reduced; most have hard shell made of calcium carbonate
				Annelida (segmented worms)		Coelomates with segmented body wall and internal organs (except digestive tract, which is unsegmented)
Concept 33.4 **Ecdysozoans are the most species-rich animal group** (pp. 683–692) **MEDIA** Investigation How Are Insect Species Identified?			Ecdysozoa	Nematoda (roundworms)		Cylindrical, unsegmented pseudocoelomates with tapered ends; no circulatory system; undergo ecdysis
				Arthropoda (crustaceans, insects, spiders)		Coelomates with segmented body, jointed appendages, and exoskeleton made of protein and chitin
Concept 33.5 **Echinoderms and chordates are deuterostomes** (pp. 693–695) **MEDIA** Activity Characteristics of Invertebrates			Deuterostomia	Echinodermata (sea stars, sea urchins)		Coelomates with bilaterally symmetrical larvae and five-part body organization as adults; unique water vascular system; endoskeleton
				Chordata (lancelets, tunicates, vertebrates)		Coelomates with notochord; dorsal, hollow nerve cord; pharyngeal slits; post-anal tail (see Chapter 34)

SELF-QUIZ

1. Which two main clades branch from the most recent common ancestor of the eumetazoans?
   a. Calcarea and Silicea
   b. Lophotrochozoa and Ecdysozoa
   c. Cnidaria and Bilateria
   d. Rotifera and Deuterostomia
   e. Deuterostomia and Bilateria

2. A land snail, a clam, and an octopus all share
   a. a mantle.
   b. a radula.
   c. gills.
   d. embryonic torsion.
   e. distinct cephalization.

3. Which phylum is characterized by animals that have a segmented body?
   a. Cnidaria
   b. Platyhelminthes
   c. Silicea
   d. Arthropoda
   e. Mollusca

4. Which of the following characteristics is probably *most* responsible for the great diversification of insects on land?
   a. segmentation
   b. antennae
   c. eyes
   d. bilateral symmetry
   e. exoskeleton

5. The water vascular system of echinoderms
   a. functions as a circulatory system that distributes nutrients to body cells.
   b. functions in locomotion, feeding, and gas exchange.
   c. is bilateral in organization, even though the adult animal is not bilaterally symmetrical.
   d. moves water through the animal's body during suspension feeding.
   e. is analogous to the gastrovascular cavity of flatworms.

6. Which of the following combinations of phylum and description is *incorrect?*
   a. Echinodermata—bilateral symmetry as a larva, coelom present
   b. Nematoda—roundworms, pseudocoelomate
   c. Cnidaria—radial symmetry, polyp and medusa body forms
   d. Platyhelminthes—flatworms, gastrovascular cavity, acoelomate
   e. Calcarea—gastrovascular cavity, coelom present

For Self-Quiz answers, see Appendix A.

MEDIA Visit **www.campbellbiology.com** for a Practice Test.

EVOLUTION CONNECTION

7. **DRAW IT** Draw a phylogenetic tree of Bilateria that includes the ten phyla of bilaterians discussed in detail in this chapter. Label each branch that leads to a phylum with a C, P, or A, depending on whether members of the phylum are coelomates (C), pseudocoelomates (P), or acoelomates (A). Use your labeled tree to answer the following questions:
   (a) For each of the three major clades of bilaterians, what (if anything) can be inferred about whether the common ancestor of the clade had a true coelom?
   (b) To what extent has the presence of a true coelom in animals changed over the course of evolution?

SCIENTIFIC INQUIRY

8. A marine biologist has dredged up an unknown animal from the seafloor. Describe some of the characteristics she should look at to determine the phylum to which the animal should be assigned.

SCIENCE, TECHNOLOGY, AND SOCIETY

9. Construction of a dam and irrigation canals in an African country has enabled farmers to increase the amount of food they can grow. In the past, crops were planted only after spring floods; the fields were too dry the rest of the year. Now fields can be watered year-round. But improved crop yields have had an unexpected cost—a tremendous increase in the incidence of schistosomiasis. Imagine that your Peace Corps assignment is to help local health officials control the disease. Reviewing the blood fluke life cycle in Figure 33.11, why do you think the irrigation project increased the incidence of schistosomiasis? It is difficult and expensive to control this disease with drugs. Suggest three other methods that could be tried to prevent people from becoming infected.

Vertebrates

KEY CONCEPTS

34.1 Chordates have a notochord and a dorsal, hollow nerve cord

34.2 Craniates are chordates that have a head

34.3 Vertebrates are craniates that have a backbone

34.4 Gnathostomes are vertebrates that have jaws

34.5 Tetrapods are gnathostomes that have limbs

34.6 Amniotes are tetrapods that have a terrestrially adapted egg

34.7 Mammals are amniotes that have hair and produce milk

34.8 Humans are mammals that have a large brain and bipedal locomotion

OVERVIEW

Half a Billion Years of Backbones

Early in the Cambrian period, some 530 million years ago, an immense variety of animals inhabited Earth's oceans. Predators used sharp claws and mandibles to skewer their prey. Many animals had protective spikes or armor as well as modified mouthparts that enabled their bearers to filter food from the water. Worms slithered in the bottom muck, feeding on organic matter. Amidst this bustle, it would have been easy to overlook certain slender, 3-cm-long creatures gliding through the water **(Figure 34.1)**: *Myllokunmingia fengjiaoa*. Although lacking armor and appendages, these animals would leave behind a remarkable legacy. They gave rise to one of the most successful groups of animals ever to swim, walk, slither, or fly: the **vertebrates**, which derive their name from vertebrae, the series of bones that make up the vertebral column, or backbone.

For nearly 200 million years, vertebrates were restricted to the oceans, but about 360 million years ago, the evolution of limbs in one lineage of vertebrates set the stage for these vertebrates to colonize land. There they diversified into amphibians, reptiles (including birds), and mammals.

There are approximately 52,000 species of vertebrates, a relatively small number compared to, say, the 1 million insect species on Earth. But what vertebrates lack in species diversity they make up for in *disparity*, showing a wide range of differences in characteristics such as body mass. Vertebrates include the heaviest animals ever to walk on land, plant-eating dinosaurs as massive as 40,000 kg (more than 13 pickup trucks). They also include the biggest animal ever to exist on Earth, the blue whale, which can exceed a mass of 100,000 kg. On the other end of the spectrum, a fish discovered in 2004 is just 8.4 mm long and has a mass roughly 100 billion times smaller than that of a blue whale.

In this chapter, you will learn about current hypotheses regarding the origins of vertebrates from invertebrate ancestors. We will track the evolution of the vertebrate body plan, from a notochord to a head to a mineralized skeleton. We'll also explore the major groups of vertebrates (both living and extinct), as well as the evolutionary history of our own species.

CONCEPT 34.1

Chordates have a notochord and a dorsal, hollow nerve cord

Vertebrates are members of the phylum Chordata, the chordates. **Chordates** are bilaterian (bilaterally symmetrical) animals, and within Bilateria, they belong to the clade of animals known as Deuterostomia (see Chapter 32). The best-known deuterostomes, aside from vertebrates, are the echinoderms, the group that includes sea stars and sea urchins. However, as shown in **Figure 34.2**, two groups of invertebrate deuterostomes, the cephalochordates and the urochordates, are more closely related

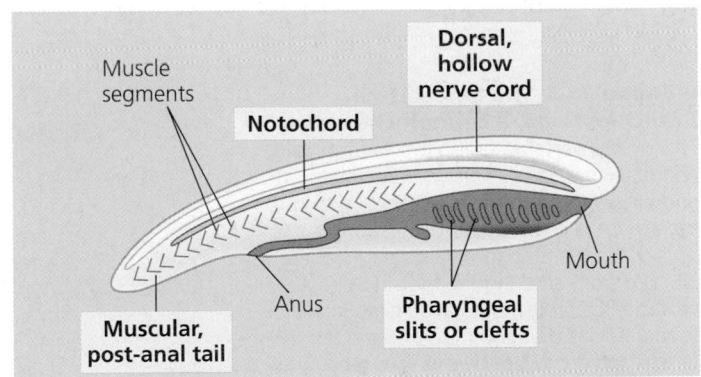

▲ **Figure 34.2 Phylogeny of living chordates.** This phylogenetic hypothesis shows the major clades of chordates in relation to the other main deuterostome clade, Echinodermata (see Chapter 33). For selected clades, some of the derived characters are listed; for example, all chordates, and only chordates, have a notochord.

to vertebrates than to other invertebrates. Along with the hagfishes and the vertebrates, they make up the chordates.

Derived Characters of Chordates

All chordates share a set of derived characters, though many species possess some of these traits only during embryonic development. **Figure 34.3** illustrates four key characters of chordates: a notochord; a dorsal, hollow nerve cord; pharyngeal slits or clefts; and a muscular, post-anal tail.

Notochord

Chordates are named for a skeletal structure, the notochord, present in all chordate embryos as well as in some adult chordates. The **notochord** is a longitudinal, flexible rod located between the digestive tube and the nerve cord. It is composed of large, fluid-filled cells encased in fairly stiff, fibrous tissue. The notochord provides skeletal support throughout most of the length of a chordate, and in larvae or adults that retain it, it also provides a firm but flexible structure against which

▲ **Figure 34.3 Chordate characteristics.** All chordates possess the four highlighted structural trademarks at some point during their development.

muscles can work during swimming. In most vertebrates, a more complex, jointed skeleton develops around the ancestral notochord, and the adult retains only remnants of the embryonic notochord. In humans, the notochord is reduced to gelatinous disks sandwiched between the vertebrae.

Dorsal, Hollow Nerve Cord

The nerve cord of a chordate embryo develops from a plate of ectoderm that rolls into a tube located dorsal to the notochord. The resulting dorsal, hollow nerve cord is unique to chordates. Other animal phyla have solid nerve cords, and in most cases they are ventrally located. The nerve cord of a chordate embryo develops into the central nervous system: the brain and spinal cord.

Pharyngeal Slits or Clefts

The digestive tube of chordates extends from the mouth to the anus. The region just posterior to the mouth is the pharynx. In all chordate embryos, a series of pouches separated by grooves forms along the sides of the pharynx. In most chordates, these grooves (known as **pharyngeal clefts**) develop into slits that open to the outside of the body. These **pharyngeal slits** allow water entering the mouth to exit the body without passing through the entire digestive tract. Pharyngeal slits function as suspension-feeding devices in many invertebrate chordates. In vertebrates (with the exception of vertebrates with limbs, the tetrapods), these slits and the structures that support them have been modified for gas exchange and are known as gill slits. In tetrapods, the pharyngeal clefts do not develop into slits. Instead, they play an important role in the development of parts of the ear and other structures in the head and neck.

Muscular, Post-Anal Tail

Chordates have a tail that extends posterior to the anus, although in many species it is greatly reduced during embryonic development. In contrast, most nonchordates have a digestive tract that extends nearly the whole length of the body. The chordate tail contains skeletal elements and muscles, and it helps propel many aquatic species in the water.

Lancelets

| Cephalochordata |
| Urochordata |
| Myxini |
| Petromyzontida |
| Chondrichthyes |
| Actinopterygii |
| Actinistia |
| Dipnoi |
| Amphibia |
| Reptilia |
| Mammalia |

The animals called **lancelets** (Cephalochordata) get their name from their bladelike shape (**Figure 34.4**). As larvae, lancelets develop a notochord, a dorsal, hollow nerve cord, numerous pharyngeal slits, and a post-anal tail. The larvae feed on plankton in the water column, alternating between upward swimming and passive sinking. As the larvae sink, they trap plankton and other suspended particles in their pharynx.

Adult lancelets can reach 5 cm in length. They retain key chordate traits, closely resembling the idealized chordate shown in Figure 34.3. Following metamorphosis, an adult lancelet swims down to the seafloor and wriggles backward into the sand, leaving only its anterior end exposed. Cilia draw seawater into the lancelet's mouth. A net of mucus secreted across the pharyngeal slits removes tiny food particles as the water passes through the slits, and the trapped food enters the intestine. The pharynx and pharyngeal slits play a minor role in gas exchange, which occurs mainly across the external body surface.

A lancelet frequently leaves its burrow to swim to a new location. Though feeble swimmers, these invertebrate chordates display, in a simple form, the swimming mechanism of fishes. Coordinated contraction of muscles arranged like rows of chevrons (<<<<) along the sides of the notochord flexes the notochord, producing side-to-side undulations that thrust the

▶ **Figure 34.4 The lancelet *Branchiostoma*, a cephalochordate.** This small invertebrate displays all four main chordate characters. Water enters the mouth and passes through the pharyngeal slits into the atrium, a chamber that vents to the outside via the atriopore; large particles are blocked from entering the mouth by tentacle-like projections called cirri. Smaller food particles that enter are trapped by mucus and are swept by cilia into the digestive tract. The serially arranged segmental muscles produce the lancelet's undulatory (wavelike) swimming movements.

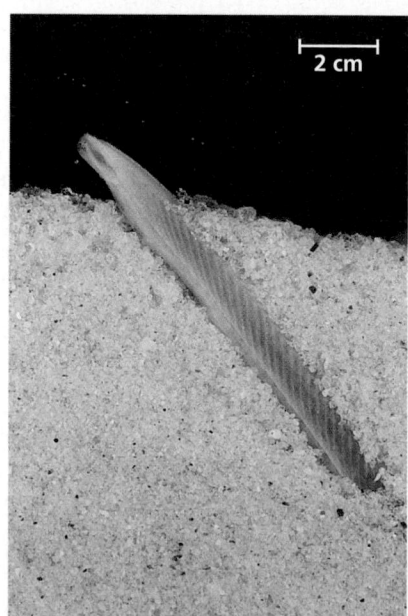

body forward. This serial arrangement of muscles is evidence of the lancelet's segmentation. The muscle segments develop from blocks of mesoderm called *somites*, which are found along each side of the notochord in all chordate embryos.

Globally, lancelets are rare, but in a few regions (including Tampa Bay, along the Florida coast) they occasionally reach densities in excess of 5,000 individuals per square meter.

Tunicates

Cephalochordata
Urochordata
Myxini
Petromyzontida
Chondrichthyes
Actinopterygii
Actinistia
Dipnoi
Amphibia
Reptilia
Mammalia

Contrary to what was formerly thought, recent molecular studies suggest that the **tunicates** (Urochordata) are more closely related to other chordates than are lancelets. The chordate characters of tunicates are most apparent during their larval stage, which may be as brief as a few minutes. In many species, the larva uses its tail muscles and notochord to swim through water in search of a suitable substrate on which it can settle, guided by cues it receives from light- and gravity-sensitive cells.

Once a tunicate has settled on a substrate, it undergoes a radical metamorphosis in which many of its chordate characters disappear. Its tail and notochord are resorbed; its nervous system degenerates; and its remaining organs rotate 90°. As an adult, a tunicate draws in water through an incurrent siphon; the water then passes through the pharyngeal slits into a chamber called the atrium and exits through an excurrent siphon **(Figure 34.5)**. Food particles are filtered from the water by a mucous net and transported by cilia to the esophagus. The anus empties into the excurrent siphon. Some tunicate species shoot a jet of water through their excurrent siphon when attacked, earning them the informal name of "sea squirts."

The degenerate adult stage of tunicates appears to have evolved only after the tunicate lineage branched off from other chordates. Even the tunicate larva appears to be highly derived, rather than a faithful reproduction of the body plan of early chordates. For example, tunicates have 9 *Hox* genes, whereas all other chordates studied to date—including the early-diverging lancelets—share a set of 13 *Hox* genes. The apparent loss of 4 *Hox* genes during their evolution indicates that tunicates have an unusual developmental program with different genetic controls than other chordates.

Early Chordate Evolution

Although lancelets and tunicates are relatively obscure animals, they occupy key positions in the history of life. Possessing many—but not all—of the derived characters shared by vertebrates, they can provide clues about the evolutionary origin of vertebrates.

As you have read, lancelets display a number of chordate characters as adults, and their lineage branches from the base of the chordate phylogenetic tree. These findings suggest that the ancestral chordate may have looked something like a lancelet—that is, it had an anterior end with a mouth; a notochord; a dorsal, hollow nerved cord; pharyngeal slits; and a post-anal tail. As for tunicates, their genome has been completely sequenced and can be used to identify genes likely to have been present in early chordates. Researchers taking this approach have suggested that ancestral chordates had genes

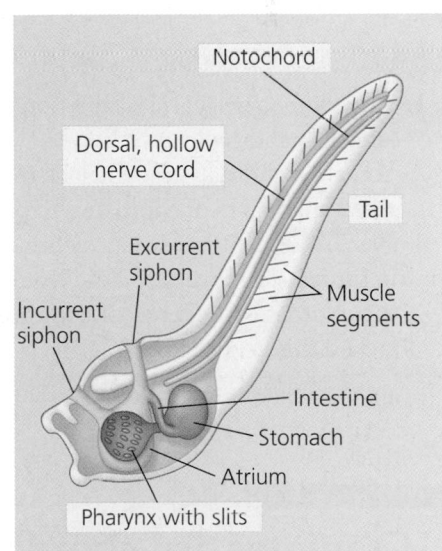

(a) An adult tunicate, or sea squirt, is a sessile animal (photo is approximately life-sized).

(b) In the adult, prominent pharyngeal slits function in suspension feeding, but other chordate characters are not obvious.

(c) A tunicate larva is a free-swimming but nonfeeding "tadpole" in which all four chief characters of chordates are evident.

▲ **Figure 34.5 A tunicate, a urochordate.**

▲ **Figure 34.6 Expression of developmental genes in lancelets and vertebrates.** *Hox* genes (including *BF1, Otx,* and *Hox3*) control the development of major regions of the vertebrate brain. These genes are expressed in the same anterior-to-posterior order in lancelets and vertebrates.

associated with vertebrate organs such as the heart and thyroid gland. These genes are found in tunicates and vertebrates but are absent from nonchordate invertebrates. In contrast, tunicates lack many genes that in vertebrates are associated with the long-range transmission of nerve impulses. This result suggests that such genes arose in an early vertebrate and are unique to the vertebrate evolutionary lineage.

Finally, research on lancelets has revealed important clues about the evolution of the chordate brain. Rather than a full-fledged brain, lancelets have only a slightly swollen tip on the anterior end of their dorsal nerve cord. But the same *Hox* genes that organize major regions of the forebrain, midbrain, and hindbrain of vertebrates express themselves in a corresponding pattern in this small cluster of cells in the lancelet's nerve cord **(Figure 34.6)**. This suggests that the vertebrate brain is an elaboration of an ancestral structure similar to the lancelet's simple nerve cord tip.

CONCEPT CHECK 34.1

1. How do pharyngeal slits function during feeding in lancelets and tunicates?
2. You are a chordate, yet you lack most of the main derived characters of chordates. Explain.
3. **WHAT IF?** Suppose lancelets lacked a gene found in tunicates and vertebrates. Would this imply that the chordates' most recent common ancestor also lacked this gene? Explain.

For suggested answers, see Appendix A.

CONCEPT 34.2
Craniates are chordates that have a head

After the evolution of the basic chordate body plan, that seen in lancelets and tunicates, the next major transition in chordate

evolution was the appearance of a head. Chordates with a head are known as **craniates** (from the word *cranium,* skull). The origin of a head—consisting of a brain at the anterior end of the dorsal nerve cord, eyes and other sensory organs, and a skull—enabled chordates to coordinate more complex movement and feeding behaviors. (Note that heads evolved independently in other animal lineages as well, as described in Chapter 33.)

Derived Characters of Craniates

Living craniates share a set of derived characters that distinguish them from other chordates. On a genetic level, they possess two clusters of *Hox* genes (lancelets and tunicates have only one). Other important families of genes that produce signaling molecules and transcription factors are also duplicated in craniates. This additional genetic complexity may have made it possible for craniates to develop more complex morphologies than those of tunicates and lancelets.

One feature unique to craniates is the **neural crest**, a collection of cells that appears near the dorsal margins of the closing neural tube in an embryo **(Figure 34.7)**. Neural crest cells disperse throughout the body, where they give rise to a variety of structures, including teeth, some of the bones and cartilage of the skull, the inner layer of skin (dermis) of the facial region, several types of neurons, and the sensory capsules in which eyes and other sense organs develop.

In aquatic craniates, the pharyngeal clefts evolved into gill slits. Unlike the pharyngeal slits of lancelets, which are used primarily for suspension feeding, gill slits are associated with muscles and nerves that allow water to be pumped through

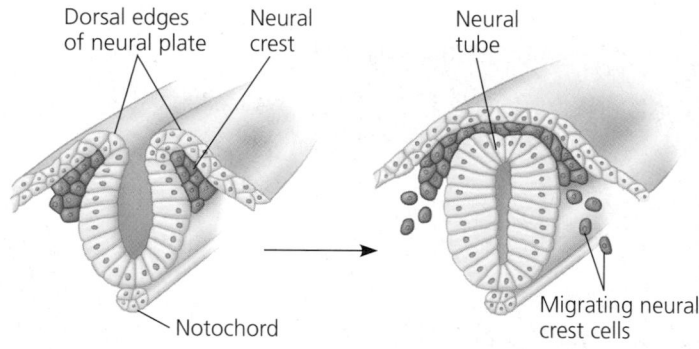

(a) The neural crest consists of bilateral bands of cells near the margins of the embryonic folds that form the neural tube.

(b) Neural crest cells migrate to distant sites in the embryo.

(c) The migrating neural crest cells give rise to some of the anatomical structures unique to vertebrates, including some of the bones and cartilage of the skull.

▲ **Figure 34.7 The neural crest, embryonic source of many unique craniate characters.**

the slits. This pumping can assist in sucking in food, and it facilitates gas exchange. (In terrestrial craniates, the pharyngeal clefts develop into other structures, as we'll explain later.)

Craniates, which are more active than tunicates and lancelets, also have a higher metabolic rate and a much more extensive muscular system. Muscles lining their digestive tract aid digestion by moving food through the tract. Craniates also have a heart with at least two chambers, red blood cells with hemoglobin, and kidneys that remove waste products from the blood.

The Origin of Craniates

In the late 1990s, paleontologists working in China discovered a vast supply of fossils of early chordates that appear to straddle the transition to craniates. The fossils were formed during the Cambrian explosion 530 million years ago, when many groups of animals were diversifying (see Chapter 32).

The most primitive of the fossils are the 3-cm-long *Haikouella* **(Figure 34.8)**. In many ways, *Haikouella* resembled a lancelet. Its mouth structure indicates that, like lancelets, it probably was a suspension feeder. However, *Haikouella* also had some of the characters of craniates. For example, it had a large and well-formed brain, small eyes, and muscle segments along the body as do the vertebrate fishes. It also had respiratory gills in its pharynx, which all the more-basal chordates lack. However, *Haikouella* did not have a skull or ear organs, suggesting that these characters emerged with further innovations to the chordate nervous system.

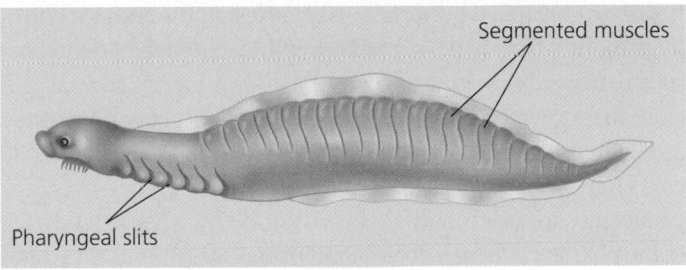

Segmented muscles

Pharyngeal slits

▲ **Figure 34.8 Fossil of an early chordate.** Discovered in 1999 in southern China, *Haikouella* had eyes and a brain but lacked a skull, a derived trait of craniates. The colors in the illustration are fanciful.

In other Cambrian rocks, paleontologists have found fossils of more advanced chordates, such as *Myllokunmingia* (see Figure 34.1). About the same size as *Haikouella*, *Myllokunmingia* had ear capsules and eye capsules, parts of the skull that surround these organs. Based on these and other characters, paleontologists have identified *Myllokunmingia* as a true craniate.

Hagfishes

Cephalochordata
Urochordata
Myxini
Petromyzontida
Chondrichthyes
Actinopterygii
Actinistia
Dipnoi
Amphibia
Reptilia
Mammalia

The least derived craniate lineage that still survives is Myxini, the hagfishes **(Figure 34.9)**. Hagfishes have a skull made of cartilage, but they lack jaws and vertebrae. They swim in a snakelike fashion by using their segmental muscles to exert force against their notochord, which they retain in adulthood as a strong, flexible rod of cartilage. Hagfishes have a small brain, eyes, ears, and a nasal opening that connects with the pharynx. Their mouths contain tooth-like formations made of the protein keratin.

All of the 30 living species of hagfishes are marine. Measuring up to 60 cm in length, most are bottom-dwelling scavengers that feed on worms and sick or dead fish. Rows of slime glands on a hagfish's flanks secrete a substance that absorbs water, forming a slime that may repulse other scavengers when a hagfish is feeding (see Figure 34.9). When attacked by a predator, a hagfish can produce several liters of slime in less than a minute. The slime coats the gills of the attacking fish, sending it into retreat or even suffocating it. Several teams of biologists and engineers are investigating the properties of hagfish slime in hopes of producing an artificial slime that could act as a space-filling gel. Such a gel might be used, for instance, to curtail bleeding during surgery.

Slime glands

▲ **Figure 34.9 A hagfish.**

1. What characteristics do hagfishes have that lancelets and tunicates lack?
2. Which extinct chordate is more closely related to humans, *Myllokunmingia* or *Haikouella*? Explain your answer.
3. **WHAT IF?** In several different animal lineages, organisms with heads first appeared roughly 530 million years ago. Does this finding constitute proof that having a head is favored by natural selection? Explain.

For suggested answers, see Appendix A.

▲ **Figure 34.10 A sea lamprey.** Most lampreys use their mouth (enlarged, right) and tongue to bore a hole in the side of a fish. The lamprey then ingests the blood and other tissues of its host.

CONCEPT 34.3
Vertebrates are craniates that have a backbone

During the Cambrian period, a lineage of craniates gave rise to vertebrates. With a more complex nervous system and a more elaborate skeleton than those of their ancestors, vertebrates became more efficient at two essential tasks: capturing food and avoiding being eaten.

Derived Characters of Vertebrates

After vertebrates branched off from other craniates, they underwent another gene duplication, this one involving a group of transcription factor genes called the *Dlx* family. The resulting additional genetic complexity may be associated with innovations in the vertebrate nervous system and skeleton, including a more extensive skull and a backbone composed of vertebrae. In some vertebrates, the vertebrae are little more than small prongs of cartilage arrayed dorsally along the notochord. In the majority of vertebrates, however, the vertebrae enclose the spinal cord and have taken over the mechanical roles of the notochord. Aquatic vertebrates also acquired dorsal, ventral, and anal fins stiffened by fin rays, which provide thrust and steering control when swimming after prey or away from predators. Faster swimming was supported by other adaptations, including a more efficient gas exchange system in the gills.

Lampreys

Cephalochordata
Urochordata
Myxini
Petromyzontida
Chondrichthyes
Actinopterygii
Actinistia
Dipnoi
Amphibia
Reptilia
Mammalia

Lampreys (Petromyzontida) represent the oldest living lineage of vertebrates. Like hagfishes, lampreys may offer clues to early chordate evolution but have also acquired unique characters.

There are about 35 species of lampreys inhabiting vari-

ous marine and freshwater environments (**Figure 34.10**). Most are parasites that feed by clamping their round, jawless mouth onto the flank of a live fish. They then use their rasping tongue to penetrate the skin of the fish and ingest the fish's blood.

As larvae, lampreys live in freshwater streams. The larva is a suspension feeder that resembles a lancelet and spends much of its time partially buried in sediment. Some species of lampreys feed only as larvae; following several years in streams, they mature sexually, reproduce, and die within a few days. Most lampreys, however, migrate to the sea or lakes as they mature into adults. Sea lampreys (*Petromyzon marinus*) have invaded the Great Lakes over the past 170 years and have devastated a number of fisheries there.

The skeleton of lampreys is made of cartilage. Unlike the cartilage found in most vertebrates, lamprey cartilage contains no collagen. Instead, it is a stiff protein matrix. The notochord of lampreys persists as the main axial skeleton in the adult, as it does in hagfishes. However, lampreys also have a cartilaginous pipe around their rodlike notochord. Along the length of this pipe, pairs of cartilaginous projections related to vertebrae extend dorsally, partially enclosing the nerve cord.

Fossils of Early Vertebrates

After the ancestors of lampreys branched off from other vertebrates during the Cambrian period, many other lineages of vertebrates emerged. Like lampreys, the early members of these lineages lacked jaws, but the resemblance stopped there.

Conodonts were slender, soft-bodied vertebrates with prominent eyes controlled by numerous muscles. At the anterior end of their mouth, they had a set of barbed hooks made of dental tissues that were *mineralized* (composed of minerals such as calcium that provide rigidity) (**Figure 34.11**). Most conodonts were 3–10 cm in length, although some may have been as long as 30 cm. They probably hunted with the help of their large eyes, impaling prey on their mouth hooks. The food was then passed back to the pharynx, where a different set of dental elements sliced and crushed the food.

Conodonts were extremely abundant for over 300 million years. Their fossilized dental elements are so plentiful that they

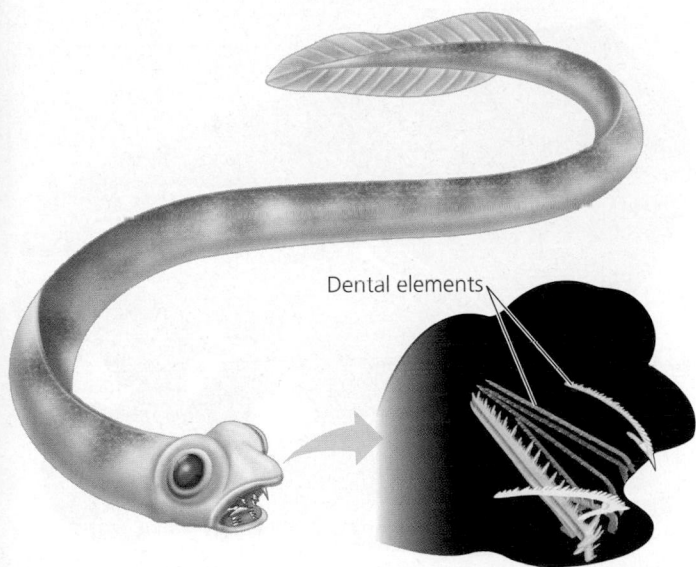

▲ Figure 34.11 A conodont. Conodonts were early vertebrates that lived from the late Cambrian until the late Triassic. Unlike lampreys, conodonts had mineralized mouthparts, which they used for either predation or scavenging.

Dental elements

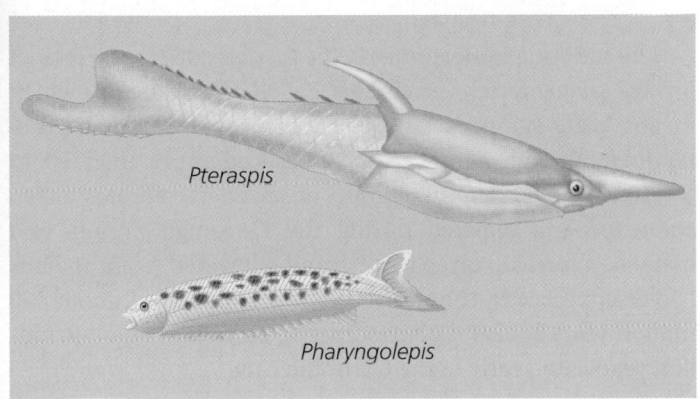

Pteraspis

Pharyngolepis

▲ Figure 34.12 Jawless armored vertebrates. *Pteraspis* and *Pharyngolepis* were two of many genera of jawless vertebrates that emerged during the Ordovician, Silurian, and Devonian periods.

have been used for decades by petroleum geologists as guides to the age of rock layers in which they search for oil. (These elements also gave conodonts their name, which means "cone teeth.")

Vertebrates with additional innovations emerged during the Ordovician, Silurian, and Devonian periods. These vertebrates had paired fins and an inner ear with two semicircular canals that provided a sense of balance. Although they, too, lacked jaws, they had a muscular pharynx, which they may have used to suck in bottom-dwelling organisms or detritus. They were also armored with mineralized bone, which covered varying amounts of their body **(Figure 34.12)**. The armor, which in some species included spines, may have offered protection from predators. Although there were many species of these jawless, armored swimming vertebrates, they all became extinct by the end of the Devonian period.

Origins of Bone and Teeth

The human skeleton is heavily mineralized bone, whereas cartilage plays a fairly minor role. But this was a later development in the history of vertebrates. As we've seen, the vertebrate skeleton evolved initially as a structure made of unmineralized cartilage. Its mineralization began only after lampreys diverged from other vertebrates.

What initiated the process of mineralization in vertebrates? One hypothesis is that mineralization was associated with a transition in feeding mechanisms. Early chordates probably were suspension feeders, like lancelets, but over time they became larger and were therefore able to ingest larger particles, including some small animals. The earliest known mineralized structures in vertebrates—conodont dental elements—were an adaptation that may have allowed these animals to become scavengers and predators. The armor seen in later jawless vertebrates was derived from dental mineralization. Thus, mineralization of the vertebrate body may have begun in the mouth. Only in more derived vertebrates did the endoskeleton begin to mineralize, starting with the skull. As you'll learn in the next section, more recent lineages of vertebrates underwent even further mineralization.

CONCEPT CHECK 34.3

1. How are differences in the anatomy of lampreys and conodonts reflected in each animal's feeding method?
2. **WHAT IF?** Suggest key roles that mineralized bone might have played in early vertebrates.

For suggested answers, see Appendix A.

CONCEPT 34.4
Gnathostomes are vertebrates that have jaws

Hagfishes and lampreys are survivors from the early Paleozoic era, when jawless craniates were common. Since then, jawless vertebrates have been far outnumbered by jawed vertebrates, known as **gnathostomes**. Living gnathostomes are a diverse group that includes sharks and their relatives, ray-finned fishes, lobe-fins, amphibians, reptiles (including birds), and mammals.

Derived Characters of Gnathostomes

Gnathostomes ("jaw mouth") are named for their jaws, hinged structures that, especially with the help of teeth, enable gnathostomes to grip food items firmly and slice them. According to one hypothesis, gnathostome jaws evolved by modification of the skeletal rods that had previously supported the

▶ **Figure 34.13 Hypothesis for the evolution of vertebrate jaws.** The skeleton of the jaws and their supports may have evolved from two pairs of skeletal rods (red and green) located between gill slits near the mouth. Pairs of rods anterior to those that formed the jaws were either lost or incorporated into the cranium or jaws.

Gill slits · Cranium · Mouth · Skeletal rods

0.5 m

▲ **Figure 34.14 Fossil of an early gnathostome.** The placoderm *Dunkleosteus* grew up to 10 m in length. A 2006 analysis of its jaw structure concluded that *Dunkleosteus* could exert a force of 8,000 pounds per square inch at the tip of its jaws.

anterior pharyngeal (gill) slits **(Figure 34.13)**. The remaining gill slits, no longer required for suspension feeding, remained as the major sites of respiratory gas exchange with the external environment.

Gnathostomes share other derived characters besides jaws. The common ancestors of all gnathostomes underwent an additional duplication of *Hox* genes, such that the single cluster present in early chordates became four. Other gene clusters also duplicated, and together these genetic changes probably allowed further complexity in the development of gnathostome embryos. The gnathostome forebrain is enlarged compared to that of other craniates, mainly in association with enhanced senses of smell and vision. An additional characteristic of aquatic gnathostomes (early versions of which were present in the head shields of some jawless vertebrates) is the **lateral line system**. These organs, which form a row along each side of the body, are sensitive to vibrations in the surrounding water.

Fossil Gnathostomes

Gnathostomes appeared in the fossil record in the mid-Ordovician period, about 470 million years ago, and steadily became more diverse. Their success probably lies in two features of their anatomy: Their paired fins and tail allowed them to swim efficiently after prey, and their jaws enabled them to grab prey or simply bite off chunks of flesh.

The earliest gnathostomes in the fossil record are an extinct lineage of armored vertebrates called **placoderms**, which means "plate-skinned." Most placoderms were less than a meter long, though some giants measured more than 10 m **(Figure 34.14)**. Another group of jawed vertebrates called **acanthodians** radiated during the Devonian period, and many new forms evolved in fresh and salt water. Acanthodians had disappeared by the end of the Devonian period, about 360 million years ago, and placoderms became extinct a few million years later, early in the Carboniferous.

Chondrichthyans (Sharks, Rays, and Their Relatives)

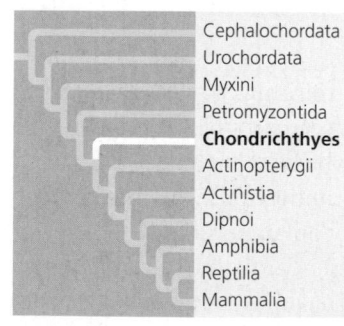

Cephalochordata
Urochordata
Myxini
Petromyzontida
Chondrichthyes
Actinopterygii
Actinistia
Dipnoi
Amphibia
Reptilia
Mammalia

Sharks, rays, and their relatives include some of the biggest and most successful vertebrate predators in the oceans. They belong to the clade Chondrichthyes, which means "cartilage fish." As their name indicates, the **chondrichthyans** have a skeleton composed predominantly of cartilage, though often impregnated with calcium.

When the name Chondrichthyes was first coined in the 1800s, scientists thought that chondrichthyans represented an early stage in the evolution of the vertebrate skeleton and that mineralization had evolved only in more derived lineages (such as "bony fishes"). However, as conodonts and armored jawless vertebrates demonstrate, the mineralization of the vertebrate skeleton had already begun before the chondrichthyan lineage branched off from other vertebrates. Moreover, bonelike tissues have been found in early chondrichthyans, such as the fin skeleton of a shark that lived in the Carboniferous period. Traces of bone can also be found in living chondrichthyans—in their scales, at the base of their teeth, and, in some sharks, in a thin layer on the surface of their vertebrae. Such findings strongly suggest that the restricted distribution of bone in the chondrichthyan body is a derived condition, emerging after chondrichthyans diverged from other gnathostomes.

There are about 750 species of living chondrichthyans. The largest and most diverse group consists of the sharks, rays, and skates (Figure 34.15a and b). A second group is composed of a few dozen species of ratfishes, or chimaeras (Figure 34.15c).

Most sharks have a streamlined body and are swift swimmers, but they do not maneuver very well. Powerful movements of the trunk and the caudal (tail) fin propel them forward. The dorsal fins function mainly as stabilizers, and the paired pectoral (fore) and pelvic (hind) fins provide lift when the shark swims. Although a shark gains buoyancy by storing a large amount of oil in its huge liver, the animal is still more dense than water, and if it stops swimming it sinks. Continual swimming also ensures that water flows into the shark's mouth and out through the gills, where gas exchange occurs (sharks do not have lungs). However, some sharks and many skates and rays spend a good deal of time resting on the seafloor. When resting, they use muscles of their jaws and pharynx to pump water over the gills.

The largest sharks and rays are suspension feeders that consume plankton. Most sharks, however, are carnivores that swallow their prey whole or use their powerful jaws and sharp teeth to tear flesh from animals too large to swallow in one piece. Sharks have several rows of teeth that gradually move to the front of the mouth as old teeth are lost. The digestive tract of many sharks is proportionately shorter than that of many other vertebrates. Within the shark intestine is a *spiral valve*, a corkscrew-shaped ridge that increases surface area and prolongs the passage of food through the digestive tract.

Acute senses are adaptations that go along with the active, carnivorous lifestyle of sharks. Sharks have sharp vision but cannot distinguish colors. The nostrils of sharks, like those of most aquatic vertebrates, open into dead-end cups. They function only for olfaction (smelling), not for breathing. Sharks also have a pair of regions in the skin of their head that can detect electric fields generated by the muscle contractions of nearby animals. Like all (nonmammalian) aquatic vertebrates, sharks have no eardrums, structures that terrestrial vertebrates use to transmit sound waves in air to the auditory organs. Sound reaches a shark through water, and the animal's entire body transmits the sound to the hearing organs of the inner ear.

Shark eggs are fertilized internally. The male has a pair of claspers on its pelvic fins that transfer sperm into the reproductive tract of the female. Some species of sharks are **oviparous**; they lay eggs that hatch outside the mother's body. These sharks

(a) Blacktip reef shark (*Carcharhinus melanopterus*). Fast swimmers with acute senses, sharks have paired pectoral and pelvic fins.

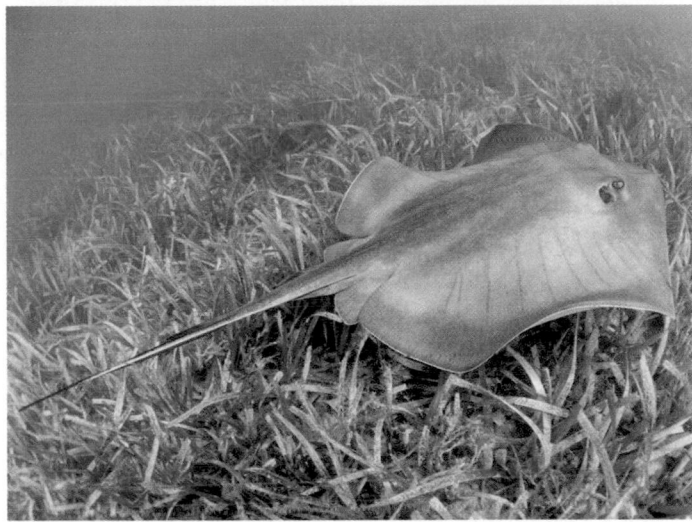

(b) Southern stingray (*Dasyatis americana*). Most rays are bottom-dwellers that feed on molluscs and crustaceans. Some rays cruise in open water and scoop food into their gaping mouth.

(c) Spotted ratfish (*Hydrolagus colliei*). Ratfishes, or chimaeras, typically live at depths greater than 80 m and feed on shrimps, molluscs, and sea urchins. Some species have a poisonous spine at the front of their first dorsal fin.

▲ **Figure 34.15 Chondrichthyans.**

release their eggs after encasing them in protective coats. Other species are **ovoviviparous**; they retain the fertilized eggs in the oviduct. Nourished by the egg yolk, the embryos develop into young that are born after hatching within the uterus. A few species are **viviparous**; the young develop within the uterus and obtain nourishment prior to birth by receiving nutrients from the mother's blood through a yolk sac placenta, by absorbing a nutritious fluid produced by the uterus, or by eating other eggs. The reproductive tract of the shark empties along with the excretory system and digestive tract into the **cloaca**, a common chamber that has a single opening to the outside.

Although rays are closely related to sharks, they have adopted a very different lifestyle. Most rays are bottom-dwellers that feed by using their jaws to crush molluscs and crustaceans. They have a flattened shape and use their greatly enlarged pectoral fins like water wings to propel themselves through the water. The tail of many rays is whiplike and, in some species, bears venomous barbs that function in defense.

Morphologically, chondrichthyans have changed little in over 300 million years. Today, however, they are severely threatened with overfishing: A recent report indicated that shark stocks in the northwest Atlantic had declined 75% over a 15-year period.

Ray-Finned Fishes and Lobe-Fins

The vast majority of vertebrates belong to the clade of gnathostomes called Osteichthyes. Like many other taxonomic names, the name Osteichthyes ("bony fish") was coined long before the advent of phylogenetic systematics. When it was originally defined, the group excluded tetrapods, but we now know that such a taxon would actually be paraphyletic (see Figure 34.2). Therefore, systematists

today include tetrapods along with bony fishes in the clade Osteichthyes. Clearly, the name of the group does not accurately describe all of its members.

Unlike chondrichthyans, nearly all living **osteichthyans** have an ossified (bony) endoskeleton with a hard matrix of calcium phosphate. As discussed earlier, several lines of evidence suggest that the common ancestor of both chondrichthyans and osteichthyans was already highly ossified and that chondrichthyans subsequently lost much of this bone. However, some scientists dispute this conclusion, and until more fossils of early chondrichthyans and osteichthyans are unearthed, the question will remain open.

In this section, we'll discuss the aquatic osteichthyans known informally as fishes. Most fishes breathe by drawing water over four or five pairs of gills located in chambers covered by a protective bony flap called the **operculum (Figure 34.16)**. Water is drawn into the mouth, through the pharynx, and out between the gills by movement of the operculum and contraction of muscles surrounding the gill chambers.

Most fishes can control their buoyancy with an air sac known as a **swim bladder**. Movement of gases from the blood to the swim bladder increases buoyancy, making the animal rise; transfer of gas back to the blood causes the animal to sink. Charles Darwin proposed that the lungs of tetrapods evolved from swim bladders, but, strange as it may sound, the opposite seems to be true. Osteichthyans in many early-branching lineages have lungs, which they use to breathe air as a supplement to gas exchange in their gills. The weight of evidence indicates that lungs arose in early osteichthyans; later, swim bladders evolved from lungs in some lineages.

In nearly all fishes, the skin is covered by flattened, bony scales that differ in structure from the tooth-like scales of sharks. Glands in the skin secrete a slimy mucus over the skin, an adaptation that reduces drag during swimming. Like the ancient aquatic gnathostomes mentioned earlier, fishes have a lateral line system, which is evident as a row of tiny pits in the skin on either side of the body.

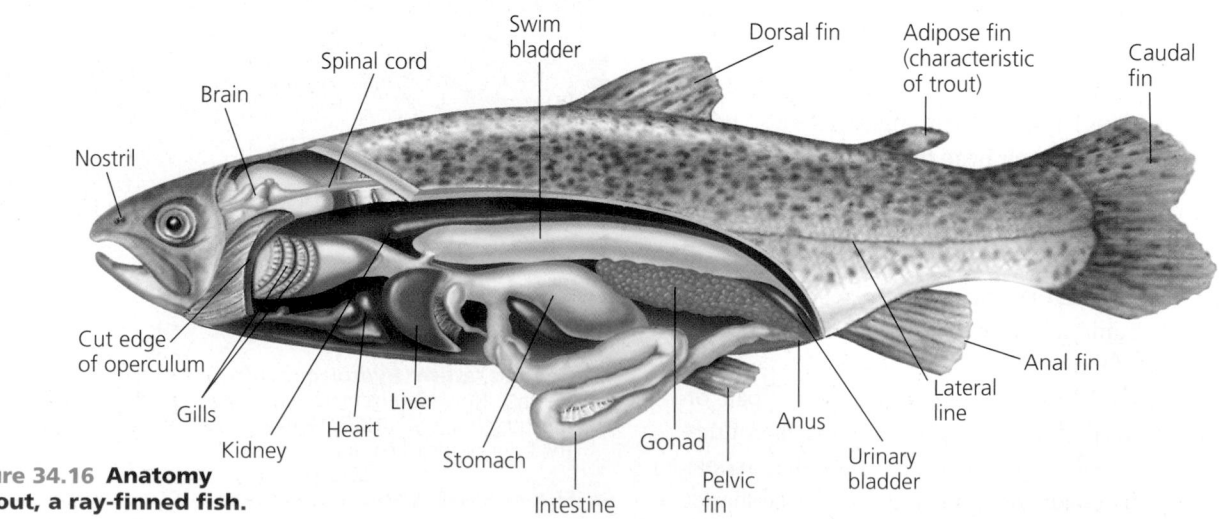

▲ **Figure 34.16 Anatomy of a trout, a ray-finned fish.**

The details of fish reproduction vary extensively. Most species are oviparous, reproducing by external fertilization after the female sheds large numbers of small eggs. However, internal fertilization and birthing characterize other species.

Ray-Finned Fishes

Nearly all the aquatic osteichthyans familiar to us are among the over 27,000 species of **ray-finned fishes** (Actinopterygii) **(Figure 34.17)**. The fins, supported mainly by bony rays for which the group is named, are modified for maneuvering, defense, and other functions.

(a) Yellowfin tuna (*Thunnus albacares*), a fast-swimming, schooling fish that is commercially important worldwide

(b) Clownfish (*Amphiprion ocellaris*), a mutualistic symbiont of sea anemones

(c) Sea horse (*Hippocampus ramulosus*), unusual in the animal kingdom in that the male carries the young during their embryonic development

(d) Fine-spotted moray eel (*Gymnothorax dovii*), a predator that ambushes prey from crevices in its coral reef habitat

▲ **Figure 34.17 Ray-finned fishes (class Actinopterygii).**

Ray-finned fishes appear to have originated in fresh water and spread to the seas. (Adaptations that address the osmotic problems associated with the move to salt water are discussed in Chapter 44.) Numerous species of ray-finned fishes returned to fresh water at some point in their evolution. Some of them, including salmon and certain trout, replay their evolutionary round-trip from fresh water to seawater and back to fresh water during their life cycle.

Ray-finned fishes serve as a major source of protein for humans, who have harvested them for thousands of years. However, industrial-scale fishing operations appear to have driven some of the world's biggest fisheries to collapse. For example, after decades of abundant harvests, in the 1990s the catch of cod (*Gadus morhua*) in the northwest Atlantic plummeted to just 5% of its historic maximum, bringing codfishing there to a near halt. Despite ongoing restrictions on the fishery, cod populations have yet to recover to sustainable levels. Ray-finned fishes also face other pressures from humans, such as the diversion of rivers by dams. Changing water flow patterns can hamper the fishes' ability to obtain food and interferes with migratory pathways and spawning grounds.

Lobe-Fins

Ray-finned fishes evolved during the Devonian period, along with another major lineage of osteichthyans, the **lobe-fins** (Sarcopterygii). The key derived character of lobe-fins is the presence of rod-shaped bones surrounded by a thick layer of muscle in their pectoral and pelvic fins. During the Devonian, many lobe-fins lived in brackish waters, such as in coastal wetlands. There they probably used their lobed fins to swim and "walk" underwater across the substrate. Some Devonian lobe-fins were gigantic predators. It is not uncommon to find spike-shaped fossils of Devonian lobe-fin teeth as big as your thumb.

By the end of the Devonian period, lobe-fin diversity was dwindling, and today only three lineages survive. One lineage, the coelacanths (Actinistia), was thought to have become extinct 75 million years ago **(Figure 34.18)**. However,

▲ **Figure 34.18 A coelacanth (*Latimeria*).** These lobe-fins were found living off the coasts of southern Africa and Indonesia.

in 1938, fishermen caught a living coelacanth off the Comoros Islands in the western Indian Ocean. Coelacanths were found only in that area until 1999, when a second population was identified in the eastern Indian Ocean, near Indonesia. The Indonesian population may represent a second species.

The second lineage of living lobe-fins, the lungfishes (Dipnoi), is represented today by six species in three genera, all of which are found in the Southern Hemisphere. Lungfishes evolved in the ocean but today are found only in fresh water, generally in stagnant ponds and swamps. They surface to gulp air into lungs connected to their pharynx. Lungfishes also have gills, which are the main organs for gas exchange in Australian lungfishes. When ponds shrink during the dry season, some lungfishes can burrow into the mud and estivate (wait in a state of torpor; see Chapter 40).

The third lineage of lobe-fins that survives today is far more diverse than the coelacanths or the lungfishes. During the mid-Devonian, these organisms adapted to life on land and gave rise to vertebrates with limbs and feet, called tetrapods—a lineage that includes humans. The tetrapod clade is the topic of the next section.

CONCEPT CHECK 34.4

1. What derived characters do sharks and tuna share? What are some characteristics that distinguish tuna from sharks?
2. Describe key adaptations of aquatic gnathostomes.
3. **WHAT IF?** Imagine we could replay the history of life. Is it possible that a group of vertebrates that colonized land could have arisen from aquatic gnathostomes other than the lobe-fins? Explain.

For suggested answers, see Appendix A.

CONCEPT 34.5
Tetrapods are gnathostomes that have limbs

One of the most significant events in vertebrate history took place about 360 million years ago, when the fins of some lobe-fins evolved into the limbs and feet of tetrapods. Until then, all vertebrates had shared the same basic fishlike anatomy. After tetrapods moved onto land, they took on many new forms, from leaping frogs to flying eagles to bipedal humans.

Derived Characters of Tetrapods

The most significant character of **tetrapods** gives the group its name, which means "four feet" in Greek. In place of pectoral and pelvic fins, tetrapods have limbs that can support their

weight on land and feet with digits that allow them to transmit muscle-generated forces to the ground when they walk.

Life on land brought numerous other changes to the tetrapod body plan. In tetrapods, the head is separated from the body by a neck that originally had one vertebra on which the skull could move up and down. Later, with the origin of a second vertebra in the neck, the head could also swing from side to side. The bones of the pelvic girdle, to which the hind legs are attached, are fused to the backbone, permitting forces generated by the hind legs against the ground to be transferred to the rest of the body. Living tetrapods do not have gill slits; during embryonic development, the pharyngeal clefts instead give rise to parts of the ears, certain glands, and other structures.

As you will see, some of these characters were dramatically altered or lost in various lineages of tetrapods. In birds, for example, the pectoral limbs became wings, and in whales, the entire body converged toward a fishlike shape.

The Origin of Tetrapods

As you have read, the Devonian coastal wetlands were home to a wide range of lobe-fins. Those that entered particularly shallow, oxygen-poor water could use their lungs to breathe air. Some species probably used their stout fins to help them move across logs or the muddy bottom. Thus, the tetrapod body plan did not evolve "out of nowhere" but was simply a modification of a preexisting body plan.

In one lineage of lobe-fins, the fins became progressively more limb-like while the rest of the body retained adaptations for aquatic life. Consider *Acanthostega*, which lived in Greenland 365 million years ago and had fully formed legs, ankles, and digits (**Figure 34.19**). This species was a close relative of tetrapods, yet it also retained adaptations for the water. It had

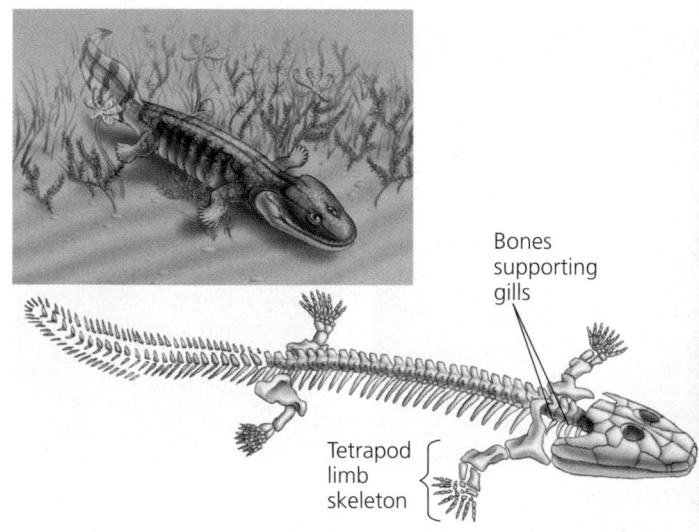

Bones supporting gills

Tetrapod limb skeleton

▲ **Figure 34.19 *Acanthostega*, a Devonian relative of tetrapods.** Along with the derived appendages of tetrapods, *Acanthostega* retained primitive aquatic adaptations, such as gills.

bones that supported gills, and its tail contained rays supporting a delicate fin that propelled it through water. Its pectoral and pelvic girdles and vertebrae were too weak to carry its body on land: *Acanthostega* may have slithered out of the water from time to time, but for the most part it was aquatic.

Extraordinary fossil discoveries over the past 20 years have allowed paleontologists to reconstruct with confidence the origin of tetrapods **(Figure 34.20)**. A great diversity of tetrapods emerged during the Devonian and Carboniferous periods, and some species reached 2 m in length. Judging from the morphology and locations of their fossils, most of these early tetrapods probably remained tied to the water, a feature they share with some members of a group of living tetrapods called amphibians.

Amphibians

Cephalochordata
Urochordata
Myxini
Petromyzontida
Chondrichthyes
Actinopterygii
Actinistia
Dipnoi
Amphibia
Reptilia
Mammalia

The **amphibians** (class Amphibia) are represented today by about 6,150 species of salamanders (order Urodela, "tailed ones"), frogs (order Anura, "tail-less ones"), and caecilians (order Apoda, "legless ones").

There are only about 550 species of urodeles. Some are entirely aquatic, but others live on land as adults or throughout life. Most salamanders that live on land walk with

▲ **Figure 34.20 The origin of tetrapods.** The white bars on the branches of this diagram place known fossils in time; arrowheads indicate lineages that extend to today. The drawings of extinct forms are based on fossilized skeletons, but the colors are fanciful.

WHAT IF? *If the most recent common ancestor of Hynerpeton and later tetrapods originated 380 million years ago, what range of dates would include the origin of amphibians?*

Ray-finned fishes

Coelacanths

Lungfishes

Eusthenopteron

Panderichthys

Tiktaalik

Elginerpeton

Metaxygnathus

Acanthostega

Ichthyostega

Hynerpeton

Greerpeton

Amphibians

Amniotes

PALEOZOIC			
Silurian	Devonian	Carboniferous	Permian

430   415   400   385   370   355   340   325   310   295   280   265   0

Time (millions of years ago)

(a) Order Urodela. Urodeles (salamanders) retain their tail as adults.

(b) Order Anura. Anurans, such as this poison dart frog, lack a tail as adults.

(c) Order Apoda. Apodans, or caecilians, are legless, mainly burrowing amphibians.

▲ **Figure 34.21 Amphibians.**

a side-to-side bending of the body, a trait inherited from the early terrestrial tetrapods **(Figure 34.21a)**. Paedomorphosis is common among aquatic salamanders; the axolotl, for instance, retains larval features even when it is sexually mature (see Figure 25.20).

Anurans, numbering about 5,420 species, are more specialized than urodeles for moving on land **(Figure 34.21b)**. Adult frogs use their powerful hind legs to hop along the terrain. A frog nabs insects and other prey by flicking out its long, sticky tongue, which is attached to the front of the mouth. Frogs display a great variety of adaptations that help them avoid being eaten by larger predators. Their skin glands secrete distasteful or even poisonous mucus. Many poisonous species have bright coloration, which predators apparently associate with danger (see Figure 54.5b). Other frogs have color patterns that camouflage them (see Figure 54.5a).

Apodans, the caecilians (about 170 species), are legless and nearly blind, and superficially they resemble earthworms **(Figure 34.21c)**. Their absence of legs is a secondary adaptation, as they evolved from a legged ancestor. Caecilians inhabit tropical areas, where most species burrow in moist forest soil. A few South American species live in freshwater ponds and streams.

Amphibian (derived from *amphibious*, meaning "both ways of life") refers to the life stages of many frog species that live first in water and then on land **(Figure 34.22)**. The larval stage of a frog, called a tadpole, is usually an aquatic herbivore with gills, a lateral line system resembling that of aquatic vertebrates, and a long, finned tail. The tadpole initially lacks

(a) The tadpole is an aquatic herbivore with a fishlike tail and internal gills.

(b) During metamorphosis, the gills and tail are resorbed, and walking legs develop. The adult frog will live on land.

▲ **Figure 34.22 The "dual life" of a frog (*Rana temporaria*).**

(c) The adults return to water to mate. The male grasps the female, stimulating her to release eggs. The eggs are laid and fertilized in water. They have a jelly coat but lack a shell and would desiccate in air.

legs; it swims by undulating its tail. During the metamorphosis that leads to the "second life," the tadpole develops legs, lungs, a pair of external eardrums, and a digestive system adapted to a carnivorous diet. At the same time, the gills disappear; the lateral line system also disappears in most species. The young frog crawls onto shore and becomes a terrestrial hunter. In spite of their name, however, many amphibians do not live a dual—aquatic and terrestrial—life. There are some strictly aquatic or strictly terrestrial frogs, salamanders, and caecilians. Moreover, salamander and caecilian larvae look much like the adults, and typically both the larvae and the adults are carnivorous.

Most amphibians are found in damp habitats such as swamps and rain forests. Even those adapted to drier habitats spend much of their time in burrows or under moist leaves, where humidity is high. Amphibians generally rely heavily on their moist skin for gas exchange with the environment. Some terrestrial species lack lungs and breathe exclusively through their skin and oral cavity.

Fertilization is external in most amphibians; the male grasps the female and spills his sperm over the eggs as the female sheds them (see Figure 34.22c). Amphibians typically lay their eggs in water or in moist environments on land. The eggs lack a shell and dehydrate quickly in dry air. Some amphibian species lay vast numbers of eggs in temporary pools, and egg mortality is high. In contrast, other species lay relatively few eggs and display various types of parental care. Depending on the species, either males or females may house eggs on their back (Figure 34.23), in their mouth, or even in their stomach. Certain tropical tree frogs stir their egg masses into moist, foamy nests that resist drying. There

are also some ovoviviparous and viviparous species that retain the eggs in the female reproductive tract, where embryos can develop without drying out.

Many amphibians exhibit complex and diverse social behaviors, especially during their breeding seasons. Frogs are usually quiet, but the males of many species vocalize to defend their breeding territory or to attract females. In some species, migrations to specific breeding sites may involve vocal communication, celestial navigation, or chemical signaling.

Over the past 25 years, zoologists have documented a rapid and alarming decline in amphibian populations in locations throughout the world. There appear to be several causes, including habitat loss, the spread of a fungal (chytrid) pathogen, climate change, and pollution. These and other factors have not only reduced populations, they have led to extinctions. A 2004 study indicates that since 1980, at least 9 amphibian species have become extinct. An additional 113 species have not been seen since that time and are considered "possibly extinct."

▲ **Figure 34.23 A mobile nursery.** A female pygmy marsupial frog, *Flectonotus pygmaeus,* incubates her eggs in a pouch of skin on her back, helping to protect the eggs from predators. When the eggs hatch, the female deposits the tadpoles in water where they begin life on their own.

CONCEPT CHECK **34.5**

1. Describe the origin of tetrapods and identify some of their key derived traits.
2. Some amphibians never leave the water, whereas others can survive in relatively dry terrestrial environments. Contrast the adaptations that facilitate these two lifestyles.
3. **WHAT IF?** Scientists think that amphibian populations may provide an early warning system of environmental problems. What features of amphibians might make them particularly sensitive to environmental problems?

For suggested answers, see Appendix A.

CONCEPT **34.6**
Amniotes are tetrapods that have a terrestrially adapted egg

The **amniotes** are a group of tetrapods whose extant members are the reptiles (including birds) and mammals (**Figure 34.24**, on the next page). During their evolution, amniotes acquired a number of new adaptations to life on land.

Derived Characters of Amniotes

Amniotes are named for the major derived character of the clade, the **amniotic egg**, which contains four specialized membranes: the amnion, the chorion, the yolk sac, and the allantois

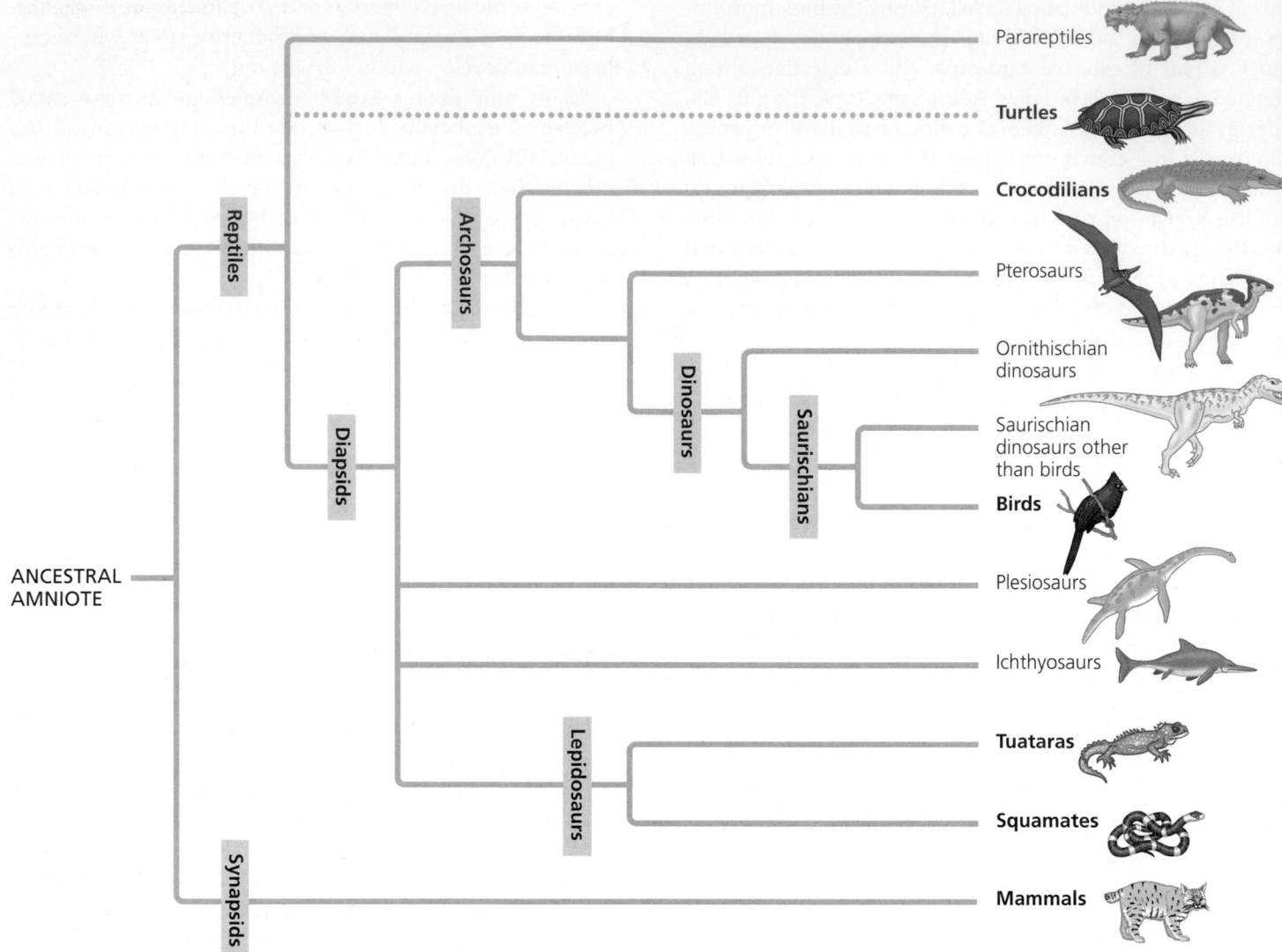

▲ **Figure 34.24 A phylogeny of amniotes.** Extant groups are named at the tips of the branches in boldface type. The dotted line of the turtle branch indicates the uncertain relationship of turtles to other reptiles. Turtles may be a sister group to parareptiles (as indicated by some morphological data), or they may be diapsids more closely related to lepidosaurs (as indicated by other morphological analyses) or to archosaurs (as indicated by many molecular studies).

(Figure 34.25). Called *extraembryonic membranes* because they are not part of the body of the embryo itself, these membranes develop from tissue layers that grow out from the embryo. The amniotic egg is named for the amnion, which encloses a compartment of fluid that bathes the embryo and acts as a hydraulic shock absorber. The other membranes in the egg function in gas exchange, the transfer of stored nutrients to the embryo, and waste storage. The amniotic egg was a key evolutionary innovation for terrestrial life: It allowed the embryo to develop on land in its own private "pond," hence reducing the dependence of tetrapods on an aqueous environment for reproduction.

In contrast to the shell-less eggs of amphibians, the amniotic eggs of most reptiles and some mammals have a shell. The shells of bird eggs are calcareous (made of calcium carbonate) and inflexible, while the eggshells of many other reptiles are leathery and flexible. Either kind of shell significantly slows dehydration of the egg in air, an adaptation that helped amniotes to occupy a wider range of terrestrial habitats than amphibians, their closest living relatives. (Seeds played a similar role in the evolution of land plants, as we discussed in Chapter 30.) Most mammals have dispensed with the eggshell over the course of their evolution, and the embryo avoids desiccation by developing within the mother's body.

Amniotes acquired other key adaptations to life on land. For example, amniotes use their rib cage to ventilate their lungs. This method is more efficient than throat-based ventilation, which amphibians use as a supplement to breathing through

Extraembryonic membranes

Allantois. The allantois is a disposal sac for certain metabolic wastes produced by the embryo. The membrane of the allantois also functions with the chorion as a respiratory organ.

Chorion. The chorion and the membrane of the allantois exchange gases between the embryo and the air. Oxygen and carbon dioxide diffuse freely across the shell.

Amnion. The amnion protects the embryo in a fluid-filled cavity that cushions against mechanical shock.

Yolk sac. The yolk sac contains the yolk, a stockpile of nutrients. Blood vessels in the yolk sac membrane transport nutrients from the yolk into the embryo. Other nutrients are stored in the albumen ("egg white").

◀ **Figure 34.25 The amniotic egg.** The embryos of reptiles and mammals form four extraembryonic membranes: the amnion, chorion, yolk sac, and allantois. This diagram shows these membranes in the shelled egg of a reptile.

Embryo

Amniotic cavity with amniotic fluid

Yolk (nutrients)

Shell

Albumen

their skin. The increased efficiency of rib cage ventilation may have allowed amniotes to abandon breathing through their skin and develop less permeable skin, thereby conserving water.

Early Amniotes

The most recent common ancestor of living amphibians and amniotes likely lived about 370 million years ago. No fossils of amniotic eggs have been found from that time, which is not surprising given how delicate they are. Thus, it is not yet possible to say when the amniotic egg evolved, although it must have existed in the last common ancestor of living amniotes, which all have amniotic eggs.

What is evident from fossils of early amniotes and their closest relatives is that they could live in drier environments than did the first tetrapods. Some early amniotes were herbivores, as evidenced by their grinding teeth and other features; others were clearly predators.

Reptiles

Cephalochordata
Urochordata
Myxini
Petromyzontida
Chondrichthyes
Actinopterygii
Actinistia
Dipnoi
Amphibia
Reptilia
Mammalia

The **reptile** clade includes tuataras, lizards, snakes, turtles, crocodilians, and birds, along with a number of extinct groups, such as plesiosaurs and ichthyosaurs (see Figure 34.24). Because all of the living reptile lineages are highly derived,

none can serve as a straightforward model for the earliest reptiles, which lived some 320 million years ago. Nevertheless, comparative studies allow us to infer some of the derived characters that likely distinguished early reptiles from other tetrapods.

For example, unlike amphibians, reptiles have scales that contain the protein keratin (as does a human nail). Scales help protect the animal's skin from desiccation and abrasion. In addition, most reptiles lay their shelled eggs on land (**Figure 34.26**). Fertilization must occur internally, before the eggshell is secreted. Many species of snakes and lizards are viviparous; in such species, the extraembryonic membranes form a kind

▲ **Figure 34.26 Hatching reptiles.** These bushmaster snakes (*Lachesis muta*) are breaking out of their parchment-like shells, a common type of shell among living reptiles other than birds.

of placenta that enables the embryo to obtain nutrients from its mother.

Reptiles such as lizards and snakes are sometimes described as "cold-blooded" because they do not use their metabolism extensively to control their body temperature. However, they do regulate their body temperature by using behavioral adaptations. For example, many lizards bask in the sun when the air is cool and seek shade when the air is too warm. A more accurate description of these reptiles is to say that they are **ectothermic**, which means that they absorb external heat as their main source of body heat. (This topic is discussed in more detail in Chapter 40.) By warming themselves directly with solar energy rather than through the metabolic breakdown of food, an ectothermic reptile can survive on less than 10% of the food energy required by a mammal of the same size. The reptile clade is not entirely ectothermic; birds are **endothermic**, capable of maintaining body temperature through metabolic activity.

The Origin and Evolutionary Radiation of Reptiles

The oldest reptilian fossils, found in rocks from Nova Scotia, date from the late Carboniferous period, about 310 million years ago. One of the first major groups of reptiles to emerge were the **parareptiles**, which were mostly large, stocky, quadrupedal herbivores. Some parareptiles had plates on their skin that may have provided them with defense against predators. Parareptiles died out by about 200 million years ago, at the end of the Triassic period.

As parareptiles were dwindling, another ancient clade of reptiles, the **diapsids**, was diversifying. One of the most obvious derived characters of diapsids is a pair of holes on each side of the skull, behind the eye socket. The diapsids are composed of two main lineages. One lineage gave rise to the **lepidosaurs**, which include tuataras, lizards, and snakes. This lineage also produced a number of marine reptiles, including the giant mosasaurs. Some of these marine species rivaled today's whales in length; all of them are extinct. (We'll say more about living lepidosaurs shortly.)

The other diapsid lineage, the **archosaurs**, produced the crocodilians (which we'll discuss later), pterosaurs, and dinosaurs. **Pterosaurs**, which originated in the late Triassic, were the first tetrapods to exhibit flapping flight. The pterosaur wing was completely different from the wings of birds and bats. It consisted of a collagen-strengthened membrane that stretched between the trunk or hind leg and a very long digit on the foreleg. Well-preserved fossils show evidence of muscles, blood vessels, and nerves in the wing membranes, suggesting that pterosaurs could dynamically adjust their membranes to assist their flight.

The smallest pterosaurs were no bigger than a sparrow, and the largest had a wingspan of nearly 11 m. They appear to have converged on many of the ecological roles later played by birds; some were insect-eaters, others grabbed fish out of the ocean,

and still others filtered small animals through thousands of fine needle-like teeth. But by the end of the Cretaceous period 65 million years ago, pterosaurs had become extinct.

On land, the **dinosaurs** diversified into a vast range of shapes and sizes, from bipeds the size of a pigeon to 45-m-long quadrupeds with necks long enough to let them browse the tops of trees. One lineage of dinosaurs, the ornithischians, were herbivores; they included many species with elaborate defenses against predators, such as tail clubs and horned crests. The other main lineage of dinosaurs, the saurischians, included the long-necked giants and a group called the **theropods**, which were bipedal carnivores. Theropods included the famous *Tyrannosaurus rex* as well as the ancestors of birds.

There is continuing debate about the metabolism of dinosaurs. Some researchers have pointed out that the Mesozoic climate over much of the dinosaurs' range was relatively warm and consistent, and they have suggested that the low surface-to-volume ratios of large dinosaurs combined with behavioral adaptations such as basking may have been sufficient for an ectotherm to maintain a suitable body temperature. However, some anatomical evidence supports the hypothesis that at least some dinosaurs were endotherms. Furthermore, paleontologists have found fossils of dinosaurs in both Antarctica and the Arctic; although the climate in these areas was milder when dinosaurs existed than it is today, it was cool enough that small dinosaurs may have had difficulty maintaining a high body temperature through ectothermy. The dinosaur that gave rise to birds was *certainly* endothermic, as are all birds.

Traditionally, dinosaurs were considered slow, sluggish creatures. Since the early 1970s, however, fossil discoveries and research have led to the conclusion that many dinosaurs were agile, fast moving, and, in some cases, social. Paleontologists have also discovered evidence that some dinosaurs built nests and brooded their eggs, as birds do today (see Figure 26.17).

All dinosaurs except birds became extinct by the end of the Cretaceous period. Their extinction may have been caused at least in part by the asteroid or comet impact you read about in Chapter 25. Some analyses of the fossil record are consistent with this idea in that they show a sudden decline in dinosaur diversity at the end of the Cretaceous. However, other analyses indicate that the number of dinosaur species had begun to decline several million years before the Cretaceous ended. Further fossil discoveries and new analyses will be needed to resolve this debate.

Lepidosaurs

One surviving lineage of lepidosaurs is represented by two species of lizard-like reptiles called tuataras (**Figure 34.27a**). Fossil evidence indicates that tuatara relatives lived at least

220 million years ago. These organisms thrived on many continents well into the Cretaceous period, reaching up to a meter in length. Today, however, tuataras are found only on 30 islands off the coast of New Zealand. When humans arrived in New Zealand 750 years ago, the rats that accompanied them devoured tuatara eggs, eventually eliminating the reptiles on the main islands. The tuataras that remain on the out-lying islands are about 50 cm long and feed on insects, small lizards, and bird eggs and chicks. They can live to be over 100 years old. Their future survival depends on whether their remaining habitats are kept rat-free.

The other major living lineage of lepidosaurs consists of the lizards and snakes, or squamates, which number about 7,900 species. Lizards are the most numerous and diverse reptiles (apart from birds) alive today (Figure 34.27b). Most lizards are small; the Jaragua lizard, discovered in the Dominican Republic in 2001, is only 16 mm long—small enough to fit comfortably on a dime. In contrast, the Komodo dragon of Indonesia can reach a length of 3 m. It hunts deer and other large prey, delivering pathogenic bacteria with its bite. As its wounded prey weakens from the infection, the lizard slowly stalks it.

Snakes are legless lepidosaurs whose closest living relatives include the Komodo dragon (Figure 34.27c). Today, some species of snakes retain vestigial pelvic and limb bones, which provide evidence of their ancestry.

Despite their lack of legs, snakes are quite proficient at moving on land, most often by producing waves of lateral bending that pass from head to tail. Force exerted by the bends against solid objects pushes the snake forward. Snakes can also move by gripping the ground with their belly scales at several points along the body, while the scales at intervening points are lifted slightly off the ground and pulled forward.

Snakes are carnivorous, and a number of adaptations aid them in hunting and eating prey. They have acute chemical sensors, and though they lack eardrums, they are sensitive to ground vibrations, which helps them detect the movements of prey. Heat-detecting organs between the eyes and nostrils of pit vipers, including rattlesnakes, are sensitive to minute temperature changes, enabling these night hunters to locate warm animals. Poisonous snakes inject their toxin through a pair of sharp, hollow or grooved teeth. The flicking tongue is not poisonous but helps fan odors toward olfactory (smell) organs on the roof of the mouth. Loosely articulated jawbones and elastic skin enable most snakes to swallow prey larger than the diameter of the snake's head (see Figure 23.14).

▼ Figure 34.27 **Extant reptiles (other than birds).**

(a) Tuatara (*Sphenodon punctatus*)

(b) Australian thorny devil lizard (*Moloch horridus*)

(c) Wagler's pit viper (*Tropidolaemus wagleri*)

(d) Eastern box turtle (*Terrapene carolina carolina*)

(e) American alligator (*Alligator mississippiensis*)

Turtles

Turtles are one of the most distinctive group of reptiles alive today. All turtles have a boxlike shell made of upper and lower shields that are fused to the vertebrae, clavicles (collarbones), and ribs (Figure 34.27d). Most of the 307 known species of turtles have a hard shell, providing excellent defense against predators. The earliest fossils of turtles, dating from about 220 million years ago, have fully developed shells. In the absence of transitional fossils, clues to the origin of the turtle shell can be found in molecular data. Molecular analyses to date suggest that turtles are closely related to crocodiles and other Triassic archosaurs—organisms that had bony plates along their backbones and sometimes over their bodies. These plates may have become more extensive in the ancestors of turtles, over time resulting in a shell. If turtles are not closely related to archosaurs (the legend of Figure 34.24 discusses other possible relationships), new fossil discoveries will be needed to shed light on the origin of the turtle shell.

The earliest turtles could not retract their head into their shell, but mechanisms for doing so evolved independently in two separate branches of turtles. The side-necked turtles (pleurodires) fold their neck horizontally, while the vertical-necked turtles (cryptodires) fold their neck vertically.

Some turtles have adapted to deserts, and others live almost entirely in ponds and rivers. Still others have returned to the sea. Sea turtles have a reduced shell and enlarged forelimbs that function as flippers. They include the largest living turtles, the deep-diving leatherbacks, which can exceed a mass of 1,500 kg and feed on jellies. Leatherbacks and other sea turtles are endangered by being caught in fishing nets, as well as by development of the beaches where the turtles lay their eggs.

Alligators and Crocodiles

Alligators and crocodiles (collectively called crocodilians) belong to a lineage that reaches back to the late Triassic (Figure 34.27e). The earliest members of this lineage were small terrestrial quadrupeds with long, slender legs. Later species became larger and adapted to aquatic habitats, breathing air through their upturned nostrils. Some Mesozoic crocodilians grew as long as 12 m and may have attacked dinosaurs and other prey at the water's edge.

The 23 known species of living crocodilians are confined to warm regions of the globe. Alligators in the southeastern United States have made a comeback after spending years on the endangered species list.

Birds

There are about 10,000 species of birds in the world. Like crocodilians, birds are archosaurs, but almost every feature of their anatomy has been modified in their adaptation to flight.

Derived Characters of Birds Many of the characters of birds are adaptations that facilitate flight, including weight-saving modifications that make flying more efficient. For example, birds lack a urinary bladder, and the females of most species have only one ovary. The gonads of both females and males are usually small, except during the breeding season, when they increase in size. Living birds are also toothless, an adaptation that trims the weight of the head.

A bird's most obvious adaptations for flight are its wings and feathers (Figure 34.28). Feathers are made of the protein β-keratin, which is also found in the scales of other reptiles. The shape and arrangement of the feathers form the wings into airfoils, and they illustrate some of the same principles of aerodynamics as the wings of an airplane. Power for flapping the wings comes from contractions of large pectoral (breast) muscles anchored to a keel on the sternum (breastbone). Some birds, such as eagles and hawks, have wings adapted for soaring on air currents and flap their wings only occasionally (see Figure 34.28); other birds, including hummingbirds, must flap continuously to stay aloft. Among the fastest birds are the appropriately named swifts, which can fly up to 170 km/hr.

Flight provides numerous benefits. It enhances hunting and scavenging; many birds consume flying insects, an abundant, highly nutritious food resource. Flight also provides ready escape from earthbound predators and enables some birds to migrate great distances to exploit different food resources and seasonal breeding areas.

Flying requires a great expenditure of energy from an active metabolism. Birds are endothermic; they use their own metabolic heat to maintain a high, constant body temperature. Feathers and in some species a layer of fat provide insulation that enables birds to retain body heat. The lungs have tiny tubes leading to and from elastic air sacs that improve airflow and oxygen uptake. This efficient respiratory system and a circulatory system with a four-chambered heart keep tissues well supplied with oxygen and nutrients, supporting a high rate of metabolism.

Flight also requires both acute vision and fine muscle control. Birds have excellent eyesight. The visual and motor areas of the brain are well developed, and the brain is proportionately larger than those of amphibians and nonbird reptiles.

Birds generally display very complex behaviors, particularly during breeding season, when they engage in elaborate courtship rituals. Because eggs have shells by the time they are laid, fertilization must be internal. Copulation usually involves contact between the mates' vents, the openings to their cloacas. After eggs are laid, the avian embryo must be kept warm through brooding by the mother, the father, or both, depending on the species.

The Origin of Birds Cladistic analyses of birds and of reptilian fossils indicate that birds belong to the group of bipedal saurischians called theropods. Since the late 1990s, Chinese paleontologists have unearthed a spectacular trove of feathered theropod fossils that are shedding light on the origin of birds.

Finger 1

(b) Bone structure

(a) Wing

Palm

Finger 2

Finger 3

Forearm

Wrist

Shaft

Vane

Shaft

Barb

Barbule

Hook

(c) Feather structure

◀ **Figure 34.28 Form fits function: the avian wing and feather. (a)** A wing is a remodeled version of the tetrapod forelimb. **(b)** The bones of many birds have a honeycombed internal structure and are filled with air. **(c)** A feather consists of a central air-filled shaft, from which radiate the vanes. The vanes are made up of barbs, which bear small branches called barbules. Birds have contour feathers and downy feathers. Contour feathers are stiff and contribute to the aerodynamic shapes of the wings and body. Their barbules have hooks that cling to barbules on neighboring barbs. When a bird preens, it runs the length of each contour feather through its bill, engaging the hooks and uniting the barbs into a precise shape. Downy feathers lack hooks, and the free-form arrangement of their barbs produces a fluffiness that provides insulation by trapping air.

Several species of dinosaurs closely related to birds had feathers with vanes, and a wider range of species had filamentous feathers. Such findings imply that feathers evolved long before powered flight. Among the possible functions of these early feathers were insulation, camouflage, and courtship display.

How did flight evolve in the theropods? In one scenario, feathers may have enabled small, running dinosaurs chasing prey or escaping predators to gain extra lift as they jumped into the air. Or, small dinosaurs could have gained traction as they ran up hills by flapping their feathered fore limbs—a behavior seen in some birds today. In a third scenario, some dinosaurs could have climbed trees and glided, aided by feathers. Whether birds took to the air from the ground up or the trees down, an essential question being studied by scientists ranging from paleontologists to engineers is how their efficient flight stroke evolved.

By 150 million years ago, feathered theropods had evolved into birds. *Archaeopteryx*, which was discovered in a German limestone quarry in 1861, remains the earliest known bird **(Figure 34.29)**. It had feathered wings but retained ancestral characters such as teeth, clawed digits in its wings, and a long tail. *Archaeopteryx* flew well at high speeds, but unlike a present-day bird, it could not take off from a standing position. Fossils of later birds from the Cretaceous show a gradual loss of certain ancestral dinosaur features, such as teeth and clawed forelimbs, as well as the acquisition of innovations found in extant birds, including a short tail covered by a fan of feathers.

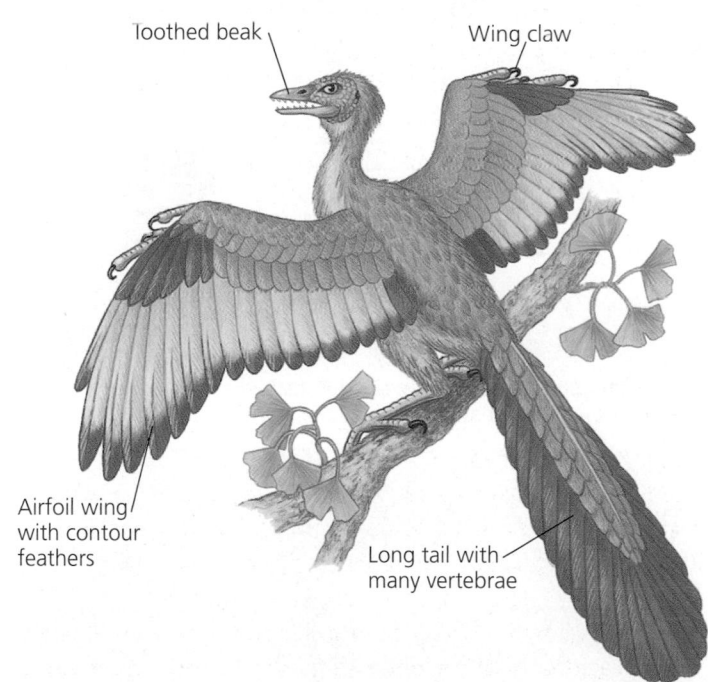

Toothed beak

Wing claw

Airfoil wing with contour feathers

Long tail with many vertebrae

▲ **Figure 34.29 Artist's reconstruction of *Archaeopteryx*, the earliest known bird.** Fossil evidence indicates that *Archaeopteryx* was capable of powered flight but retained many characters of nonbird dinosaurs.

Living Birds Clear evidence of Neornithes, the clade that includes the 28 orders of living birds, can be found before the Cretaceous-Paleogene boundary 65.5 million years ago. Several

(a) Emu. This ratite lives in Australia.

(b) Mallards. Like many bird species, the mallard exhibits pronounced color differences between the sexes.

(c) Laysan albatrosses. Like most birds, Laysan albatrosses have specific mating behaviors, such as this courtship ritual.

(d) Barn swallows. The barn swallow is a member of the order Passeriformes. Species in this order are called perching birds because the toes of their feet can lock around a branch or wire, enabling the bird to rest in place for long periods.

▲ **Figure 34.30 A small sample of living birds.**

groups of living and extinct birds include one or more flightless species. The **ratites** (order Struthioniformes), which consist of the ostrich, rhea, kiwi, cassowary, and emu, are all flightless. In ratites (from the Latin *ratitus*, flat-bottomed), the sternal keel is absent, and the pectoral muscles are not greatly enlarged **(Figure 34.30a)**. Penguins make up the flightless order Sphenisciformes, but, like flying birds, they have powerful pectoral muscles. They use these muscles to "fly" in the water: As they swim, they flap their flipper-like wings in a manner that resembles the flight stroke of a more typical bird. Certain species of rails, ducks, and pigeons are also flightless.

Although the demands of flight have rendered the general body forms of many flying birds similar to one another, experienced bird-watchers can distinguish species by their profile, flying style, behavior, colors, and beak shape **(Figure 34.30b–d)**. During avian evolution, the beak has taken on a variety of shapes suited to different diets. Foot structure, too, shows considerable variation. Various birds use their feet for perching on branches, grasping food, defense, swimming or walking, and even courtship (see Figure 24.4e).

CONCEPT CHECK 34.6

1. Describe three key amniote adaptations for life on land.
2. Identify four avian adaptations for flight.
3. **WHAT IF?** Suppose turtles are more closely related to lepidosaurs than to other reptiles. Redraw Figure 34.24 to show this relationship, and mark the node that represents the most recent common ancestor shared by all living reptiles. Defining the reptile clade as consisting of all descendants of that ancestor, list the reptiles.

For suggested answers, see Appendix A.

CONCEPT 34.7

Mammals are amniotes that have hair and produce milk

Cephalochordata
Urochordata
Myxini
Petromyzontida
Chondrichthyes
Actinopterygii
Actinistia
Dipnoi
Amphibia
Reptilia
Mammalia

The reptiles we have been discussing represent one of two great lineages of amniotes. The other amniote lineage is our own, the **mammals** (class Mammalia). Today, there are more than 5,300 known species of mammals on Earth.

Derived Characters of Mammals

The distinctive character from which mammals derive their name is their mammary glands, which produce milk for offspring. All mammalian mothers nourish their young with milk, a balanced diet rich in fats, sugars, proteins, minerals, and vitamins. Hair, another mammalian characteristic, and a fat layer under the skin help the body retain heat. Like birds, mammals are endothermic, and most have a high metabolic rate. Efficient respiratory and circulatory systems (including a four-chambered heart) support a mammal's metabolism. A sheet of muscle called the diaphragm helps ventilate the lungs.

Like birds, mammals generally have a larger brain than other vertebrates of equivalent size, and many species are capable learners. And as in birds, the relatively long duration of parental care extends the time for offspring to learn important survival skills by observing their parents.

Differentiated teeth are another important mammalian trait. Whereas the teeth of reptiles are generally uniform in size and shape, the jaws of mammals bear a variety of teeth with sizes and shapes adapted for chewing many kinds of foods. Humans, like most mammals, have teeth modified for shearing (incisors and canine teeth) and for crushing and grinding (premolars and molars; see Figure 41.18).

Early Evolution of Mammals

Mammals belong to a group of amniotes known as **synapsids**. Early nonmammalian synapsids lacked hair, had a sprawling gait, and laid eggs. A distinctive characteristic of synapsids is the single temporal fenestra, a hole behind the eye socket on each side of the skull. Humans retain this feature; your jaw muscles pass through the temporal fenestra and anchor on your temple. Fossil evidence shows that the jaw was remodeled as mammalian features arose gradually in successive lineages of earlier synapsids (see Figure 25.6). In addition, two of the bones that formerly made up the jaw joint were incorporated into the mammalian middle ear **(Figure 34.31)**.

Synapsids evolved into large herbivores and carnivores during the Permian period, and for a time they were the dominant tetrapods. However, the Permian-Triassic extinctions took a heavy toll on them, and their diversity fell during the Triassic. Increasingly mammal-like synapsids emerged by the end of the Triassic 200 million years ago. While not true mammals, these synapsids had acquired a number of the derived characters that distinguish mammals from other amniotes. They were small and probably hairy, and they likely fed on insects at night. Their bones show that they grew faster than other synapsids, suggesting that they probably had a relatively high metabolic rate; however, they still laid eggs.

During the Jurassic period, the first true mammals arose and diversified into a number of lineages, many of which are extinct. Yet throughout the Mesozoic era, most mammals remained about the size of today's shrews. One possible explanation for their small size is that dinosaurs already occupied ecological niches of large-bodied animals.

By the early Cretaceous, the three major lineages of living mammals emerged: monotremes (egg-laying mammals), marsupials (mammals with a pouch), and eutherians (placental mammals). After the extinction of large dinosaurs, pterosaurs, and marine reptiles during the late Cretaceous period, mammals underwent an adaptive radiation, giving rise to large predators and herbivores as well as flying and aquatic species.

◀ **Figure 34.31 The evolution of the mammalian ear bones.** *Biarmosuchus* was an early synapsid, a lineage that eventually gave rise to the mammals. Bones that transmit sound in the ear of mammals arose from the modification of bones in the jaw of nonmammalian synapsids.

Key

- Articular
- Quadrate
- Dentary
- Squamosal

(a) In *Biarmosuchus*, the articular and quadrate bones formed the jaw joint.

Present-day reptile **Present-day mammal**

(b) During the evolutionary remodeling of the mammalian skull, a new jaw joint formed between the dentary and squamosal bones (see Figure 25.6). No longer used in the jaw, the quadrate and articular bones became incorporated into the middle ear as two of the three bones that transmit sound from the eardrum to the inner ear.

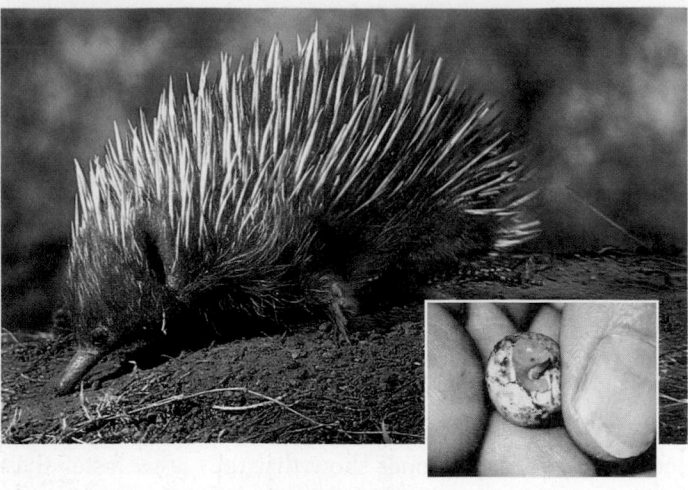

▲ Figure 34.32 **Short-beaked echidna (*Tachyglossus aculeatus*), an Australian monotreme.** Monotremes have hair and produce milk, but they lack nipples. Monotremes are the only mammals that lay eggs (inset).

(a) A young brushtail possum. The young of marsupials are born very early in their development. They finish their growth while nursing from a nipple (in their mother's pouch in most species).

(b) Long-nosed bandicoot. Most bandicoots are diggers and burrowers that eat mainly insects but also some small vertebrates and plant material. Their rear-opening pouch helps protect the young from dirt as the mother digs. Other marsupials, such as kangaroos, have a pouch that opens to the front.

▲ Figure 34.33 **Australian marsupials.**

Monotremes

Monotremes are found only in Australia and New Guinea and are represented by one species of platypus and four species of echidnas (spiny anteaters). Monotremes lay eggs, a character that is ancestral for amniotes and retained in most reptiles (**Figure 34.32**). Like all mammals, monotremes have hair and produce milk, but they lack nipples. Milk is secreted by glands on the belly of the mother. After hatching, the baby sucks the milk from the mother's fur.

Marsupials

Opossums, kangaroos, and koalas are examples of **marsupials**. Both marsupials and eutherians share derived characters not found among monotremes. They have higher metabolic rates and nipples that provide milk, and they give birth to live young. The embryo develops inside the uterus of the female's reproductive tract. The lining of the uterus and the extraembryonic membranes that arise from the embryo form a **placenta**, a structure in which nutrients diffuse into the embryo from the mother's blood.

A marsupial is born very early in its development and completes its embryonic development while nursing. In most species, the nursing young are held within a maternal pouch called a marsupium (**Figure 34.33a**). A red kangaroo, for instance, is about the size of a honeybee at its birth, just 33 days after fertilization. Its back legs are merely buds, but its front legs are strong enough for it to crawl from the exit of its mother's reproductive tract to a pouch that opens to the front of her body, a journey that lasts a few minutes. In other species, the marsupium opens to the rear of the mother's body; in bandicoots this protects the young as their mother burrows in the dirt (**Figure 34.33b**).

Marsupials existed worldwide during the Mesozoic era, but today they are found only in the Australian region and in North and South America. The biogeography of marsupials is an example of the interplay between biological and geologic evolution (see Chapter 25). After the breakup of the supercontinent Pangaea, South America and Australia became island continents, and their marsupials diversified in isolation from the eutherians that began an adaptive radiation on the northern continents. Australia has not been in contact with another continent since early in the Cenozoic era, about 65 million years ago. In Australia, convergent evolution has resulted in a diversity of marsupials that resemble eutherians in similar ecological roles in other parts of the world (**Figure 34.34**). In contrast, although South America had a diverse marsupial fauna throughout the Paleogene, it has experienced several migrations of eutherians. One of the most important migrations occurred about 3 million years ago, when North and South America joined at the Panamanian isthmus and extensive two-way traffic of animals took place over

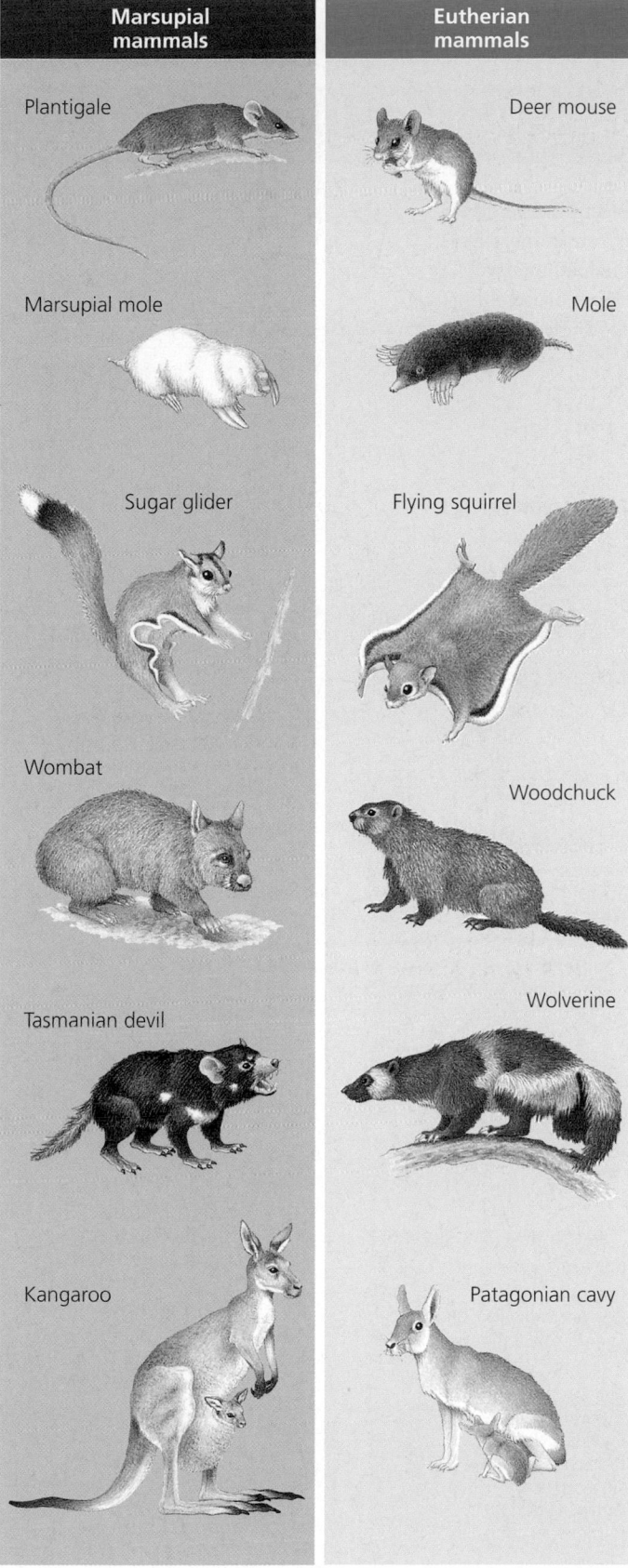

Marsupial mammals	Eutherian mammals
Plantigale	Deer mouse
Marsupial mole	Mole
Sugar glider	Flying squirrel
Wombat	Woodchuck
Tasmanian devil	Wolverine
Kangaroo	Patagonian cavy

▲ **Figure 34.34 Evolutionary convergence of marsupials and eutherians (placental mammals).** (Drawings are not to scale.)

the land bridge. Today, only three families of marsupials live outside the Australian region, and the only marsupials found in the wild in North America are a few species of opossum.

Eutherians (Placental Mammals)

Eutherians are commonly called placental mammals because their placentas are more complex than those of marsupials. Eutherians have a longer pregnancy than marsupials. Young eutherians complete their embryonic development within the uterus, joined to their mother by the placenta. The eutherian placenta provides an intimate and long-lasting association between the mother and her developing young.

The major groups of living eutherians are thought to have diverged from one another in a burst of evolutionary change. The timing of this burst is uncertain: It is dated to 100 million years ago by molecular data and 60 million years ago by morphological data. **Figure 34.35**, on the next two pages, explores the major eutherian orders and their possible phylogenetic relationships with each other as well as with the monotremes and marsupials.

Primates

The mammalian order Primates includes the lemurs, the tarsiers, the monkeys, and the apes. Humans are members of the ape group.

Derived Characters of Primates Most primates have hands and feet adapted for grasping, and their digits have flat nails instead of the narrow claws of other mammals. There also are other characteristic features of the hands and feet, such as skin ridges on the fingers (which account for human fingerprints). Relative to other mammals, primates have a large brain and short jaws, giving them a flat face. Their forward-looking eyes are close together on the front of the face. Primates also exhibit relatively well-developed parental care and complex social behavior.

The earliest known primates were tree-dwellers, and many of the characteristics of primates are adaptations to the demands of living in the trees. Grasping hands and feet allow primates to hang onto tree branches. All living primates, except humans, have a big toe that is widely separated from the other toes, enabling them to grasp branches with their feet. All primates also have a thumb that is relatively moveable and separate from the fingers, but monkeys and apes have a fully **opposable thumb**; that is, they can touch the ventral surface (fingerprint side) of the tip of all four fingers with the ventral surface of the thumb of the same hand. In monkeys and apes other than humans, the opposable thumb functions in a grasping "power grip." In humans, a distinctive bone structure at the base of the thumb allows it to be used for more precise manipulation. The unique dexterity of humans represents descent with modification from our tree-dwelling ancestors. Arboreal maneuvering also requires excellent eye-hand coordination. The overlapping

Exploring Mammalian Diversity

Phylogenetic Relationships of Mammals

Evidence from numerous fossils and molecular analyses indicates that monotremes diverged from other mammals about 180 million years ago and that marsupials diverged from eutherians (placental mammals) about 140 million years ago. Molecular systematics has helped to clarify the evolutionary relationships between the eutherian orders, though there is still no broad consensus on a phylogenetic tree. One current hypothesis, represented by the tree shown below, clusters the eutherian orders into four main clades.

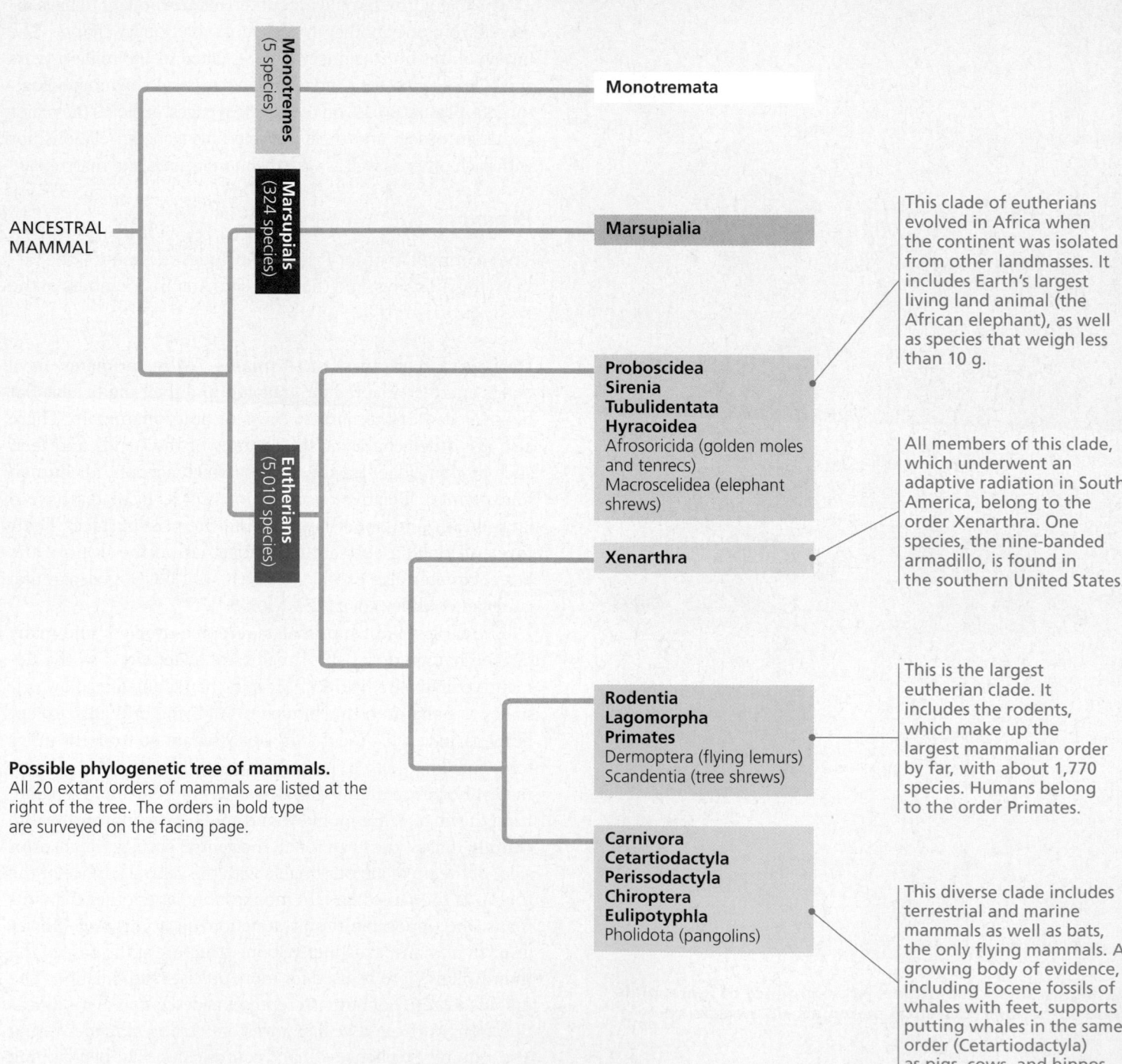

Possible phylogenetic tree of mammals.
All 20 extant orders of mammals are listed at the right of the tree. The orders in bold type are surveyed on the facing page.

This clade of eutherians evolved in Africa when the continent was isolated from other landmasses. It includes Earth's largest living land animal (the African elephant), as well as species that weigh less than 10 g.

All members of this clade, which underwent an adaptive radiation in South America, belong to the order Xenarthra. One species, the nine-banded armadillo, is found in the southern United States.

This is the largest eutherian clade. It includes the rodents, which make up the largest mammalian order by far, with about 1,770 species. Humans belong to the order Primates.

This diverse clade includes terrestrial and marine mammals as well as bats, the only flying mammals. A growing body of evidence, including Eocene fossils of whales with feet, supports putting whales in the same order (Cetartiodactyla) as pigs, cows, and hippos.

Orders and Examples	Main Characteristics	Orders and Examples	Main Characteristics
Monotremata Platypuses, echidnas Echidna	Lay eggs; no nipples; young suck milk from fur of mother	**Marsupialia** Kangaroos, opossums, koalas Koala	Embryo completes development in pouch on mother
Proboscidea Elephants African elephant	Long, muscular trunk; thick, loose skin; upper incisors elongated as tusks	**Tubulidentata** Aardvarks Aardvark	Teeth consisting of many thin tubes cemented together; eats ants and termites
Sirenia Manatees, dugongs Manatee	Aquatic; finlike forelimbs and no hind limbs; herbivorous	**Hyracoidea** Hyraxes Rock hyrax	Short legs; stumpy tail; herbivorous; complex, multichambered stomach
Xenarthra Sloths, anteaters, armadillos Tamandua	Reduced teeth or no teeth; herbivorous (sloths) or carnivorous (anteaters, armadillos)	**Rodentia** Squirrels, beavers, rats, porcupines, mice Red squirrel	Chisel-like, continuously growing incisors worn down by gnawing; herbivorous
Lagomorpha Rabbits, hares, picas Jackrabbit	Chisel-like incisors; hind legs longer than forelegs and adapted for running and jumping; herbivorous	**Primates** Lemurs, monkeys, chimpanzees, gorillas, humans Golden lion tamarin	Opposable thumbs; forward-facing eyes; well-developed cerebral cortex; omnivorous
Carnivora Dogs, wolves, bears, cats, weasels, otters, seals, walruses Coyote	Sharp, pointed canine teeth and molars for shearing; carnivorous	**Perissodactyla** Horses, zebras, tapirs, rhinoceroses Indian rhinoceros	Hooves with an odd number of toes on each foot; herbivorous
Cetartiodactyla **Artiodactyls** Sheep, pigs, cattle, deer, giraffes Bighorn sheep	Hooves with an even number of toes on each foot; herbivorous	**Chiroptera** Bats Frog-eating bat	Adapted for flight; broad skinfold that extends from elongated fingers to body and legs; carnivorous or herbivorous
Cetaceans Whales, dolphins, porpoises Pacific white-sided porpoise	Aquatic; streamlined body; paddle-like forelimbs and no hind limbs; thick layer of insulating blubber; carnivorous	**Eulipotyphla** "Core insecti-vores": some moles, some shrews Star-nosed mole	Diet consists mainly of insects and other small invertebrates

visual fields of the two forward-facing eyes enhance depth perception, an obvious advantage when brachiating (traveling by swinging from branch to branch in trees).

► **Figure 34.36 Coquerel's sifakas (*Propithecus verreauxi coquereli*), a type of lemur.**

Living Primates There are three main groups of living primates: (1) the lemurs of Madagascar **(Figure 34.36)** and the lorises and pottos of tropical Africa and southern Asia; (2) the tarsiers, which live in Southeast Asia; and (3) the **anthropoids**, which include monkeys and apes and are found worldwide. The first group—lemurs, lorises, and pottos—probably resemble early arboreal primates. The oldest known anthropoid fossils, discovered in China in mid-Eocene strata about 45 million years old, indicate that tarsiers are more closely related to anthropoids than to the lemur group **(Figure 34.37)**. You can see in Figure 34.37 that monkeys do not constitute a monophyletic group.

Both New and Old World monkeys are thought to have originated in Africa or Asia. The fossil record indicates that New World monkeys first colonized South America roughly 25 million years ago. By that time, South America and Africa had drifted apart, and monkeys may have reached South America by rafting on logs or other debris from Africa. What is certain is that New World monkeys and Old World monkeys underwent separate adaptive radiations during their many millions of years of separation **(Figure 34.38)**. All species of New World monkeys are arboreal, whereas Old World monkeys include ground-dwelling as well as arboreal species. Most monkeys in both groups are diurnal (active during the day) and usually live in bands held together by social behavior.

ANCESTRAL PRIMATE

Lemurs, lorises, and pottos

Tarsiers

New World monkeys

Old World monkeys

Gibbons

Orangutans

Gorillas

Chimpanzees and bonobos

Humans

Anthropoids

▲ **Figure 34.37 A phylogenetic tree of primates.** The fossil record indicates that anthropoids began diverging from other primates about 50 million years ago. New World monkeys, Old World monkeys, and apes (the clade that includes gibbons, orangutans, gorillas, chimpanzees, and humans) have been evolving as separate lineages for over 20 million years. The lineages leading to humans branched off from other apes sometime between 5 and 7 million years ago.

? *Taxonomists currently recognize two species in the genus Pan: chimpanzees and bonobos. Some scientists have commented that visitors from outer space would likely consider humans a third species in this genus. Is the phylogeny shown here consistent with that view?*

60   50   40   30   20   10   0

Time (millions of years ago)

▼ **Figure 34.38 New World monkeys and Old World monkeys.**

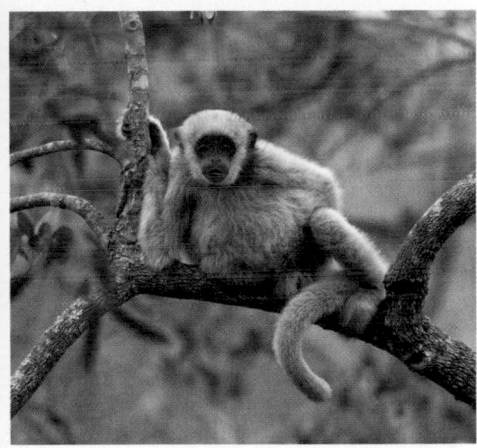

(a) New World monkeys, such as spider monkeys (shown here), squirrel monkeys, and capuchins, have a prehensile tail and nostrils that open to the sides.

(b) Old World monkeys lack a prehensile tail, and their nostrils open downward. This group includes macaques (shown here), mandrils, baboons, and rhesus monkeys.

The other group of anthropoids consists of primates informally called apes **(Figure 34.39)**. The ape group includes the genera *Hylobates* (gibbons), *Pongo* (orangutans), *Gorilla* (gorillas), *Pan* (chimpanzees and bonobos), and *Homo* (humans). The apes diverged from Old World monkeys about 20–25 million years ago. Today, nonhuman apes are found exclusively in tropical regions of the Old World. With the exception of gibbons, living apes are larger than either New or Old World monkeys. All living apes have relatively long arms, short legs, and no tail. Although all nonhuman apes spend time in trees, only gibbons and orangutans are primarily arboreal. Social organization varies among the apes; gorillas and chimpanzees are highly social. Finally, compared to other primates, apes have a larger brain in proportion to their body size, and their behavior is more flexible. These two characteristics are especially prominent in the next group we'll consider, the hominins.

(a) Gibbons, such as this Muller's gibbon, are found only in southeastern Asia. Their very long arms and fingers are adaptations for brachiating (swinging by the arms from branch to branch).

(b) Orangutans are shy apes that live in the rain forests of Sumatra and Borneo. They spend most of their time in trees; note the foot adapted for grasping and the opposable thumb.

(c) Gorillas are the largest apes; some males are almost 2 m tall and weigh about 200 kg. Found only in Africa, these herbivores usually live in groups of up to about 20 individuals.

(d) Chimpanzees live in tropical Africa. They feed and sleep in trees but also spend a great deal of time on the ground. Chimpanzees are intelligent, communicative, and social.

(e) Bonobos are in the same genus (*Pan*) as chimpanzees but are smaller. They survive today only in the African nation of Congo.

▲ **Figure 34.39 Nonhuman apes.**

1. Contrast monotremes, marsupials, and eutherians in terms of how they bear young.
2. Identify at least five derived traits of primates.
3. **WHAT IF?** Develop a hypothesis to explain why the diversity of mammals increased in the Cenozoic. Your explanation should consider mammalian adaptations as well as factors such as mass extinctions and continental drift.

For suggested answers, see Appendix A.

CONCEPT 34.8

Humans are mammals that have a large brain and bipedal locomotion

In our tour of Earth's biodiversity, we come at last to our own species, *Homo sapiens*, which is about 200,000 years old. When you consider that life has existed on Earth for at least 3.5 billion years, we are clearly evolutionary newcomers.

Derived Characters of Humans

Many characters distinguish humans from other apes. Most obviously, humans stand upright and are bipedal (walk on two legs). Humans have a much larger brain and are capable of language, symbolic thought, and the manufacture and use of complex tools. Humans also have reduced jawbones and jaw muscles, along with a shorter digestive tract.

At the molecular level, the list of derived characters of humans is growing as scientists compare the genomes of humans and chimpanzees. Although the two genomes are 99% identical, a disparity of 1% can translate into a large number of differences in a genome that contains 3 billion base pairs. Furthermore, changes in a small number of genes can have large effects. This point was highlighted by recent results showing that humans and chimpanzees differ in the expression of 19 regulatory genes. These genes turn other genes on and off and hence may account for many differences between humans and chimpanzees.

Bear in mind that such genomic differences—and whatever derived phenotypic traits they code for—separate humans from other *living* apes. But many of these new characters first emerged in our ancestors, long before our own species appeared. We will consider some of these ancestors to see how these characters originated.

The Earliest Hominins

The study of human origins is known as **paleoanthropology**. Paleoanthropologists have unearthed fossils of approximately 20 extinct species that are more closely related to humans than to chimpanzees. These species are known as **hominins (Figure 34.40)**. (Although a majority of anthropologists now use the term *hominin*, its older synonym, *hominid*, continues to be used by some). Since 1994, fossils of four hominin species dating from more than 4 million years ago have been discovered. The oldest of these hominins, *Sahelanthropus tchadensis*, lived about 6–7 million years ago.

Sahelanthropus and other early hominins shared some of the derived characters of humans. For example, they had reduced canine teeth, and some fossils suggest that they had relatively flat faces. They also show signs of having been more upright and bipedal than other apes. One clue to their upright stance can be found in the foramen magnum, the hole at the base of the skull through which the spinal cord exits. In chimpanzees, the foramen magnum is relatively far back on the skull, while in early hominins (and in humans), it is located underneath the skull. This position allows us to hold our head directly over our body, as apparently early hominins did as well. Leg bones of *Australopithecus anamensis*, a hominin that lived 4.5–4 million years ago, also suggest that early hominins were increasingly bipedal. (We will return to the subject of bipedalism later.)

Note that the characters that distinguish humans from other living apes did not all evolve in tight unison. While early hominins were showing signs of bipedalism, their brains remained small—about 400–450 cm^3 in volume, compared with an average of 1,300 cm^3 for *Homo sapiens*. The earliest hominins were also small overall (the 4.5-million-year-old *Ardipithecus ramidus* is estimated to have weighed only 40 kg) but had relatively large teeth and a lower jaw that projected beyond the upper part of their face. (Humans, in contrast, have a relatively flat face; compare your own face with those of the chimpanzees in Figure 34.39d.)

It's important to avoid two common misconceptions when considering these early hominins. One is to think of them as chimpanzees. Chimpanzees represent the tip of a separate branch of evolution, and they acquired derived characters of their own after they diverged from their common ancestor with humans.

Another misconception is to think of human evolution as a ladder leading directly from an ancestral ape to *Homo sapiens*. This error is often illustrated as a parade of fossil species that become progressively more like ourselves as they march across the page. If human evolution is a parade, it is a very disorderly one, with many groups breaking away to wander other evolutionary paths. At times, several hominin species coexisted. These species often differed in skull shape, body size, and diet (as inferred from their teeth). Ultimately, all but one lineage—the one that gave rise to *Homo sapiens*—ended in extinction. But when the characteristics of all hominins that lived over the past 6 million years are considered, *H. sapiens* appears not as the end result of a straight evolutionary path, but rather as the only surviving member of a highly branched evolutionary tree.

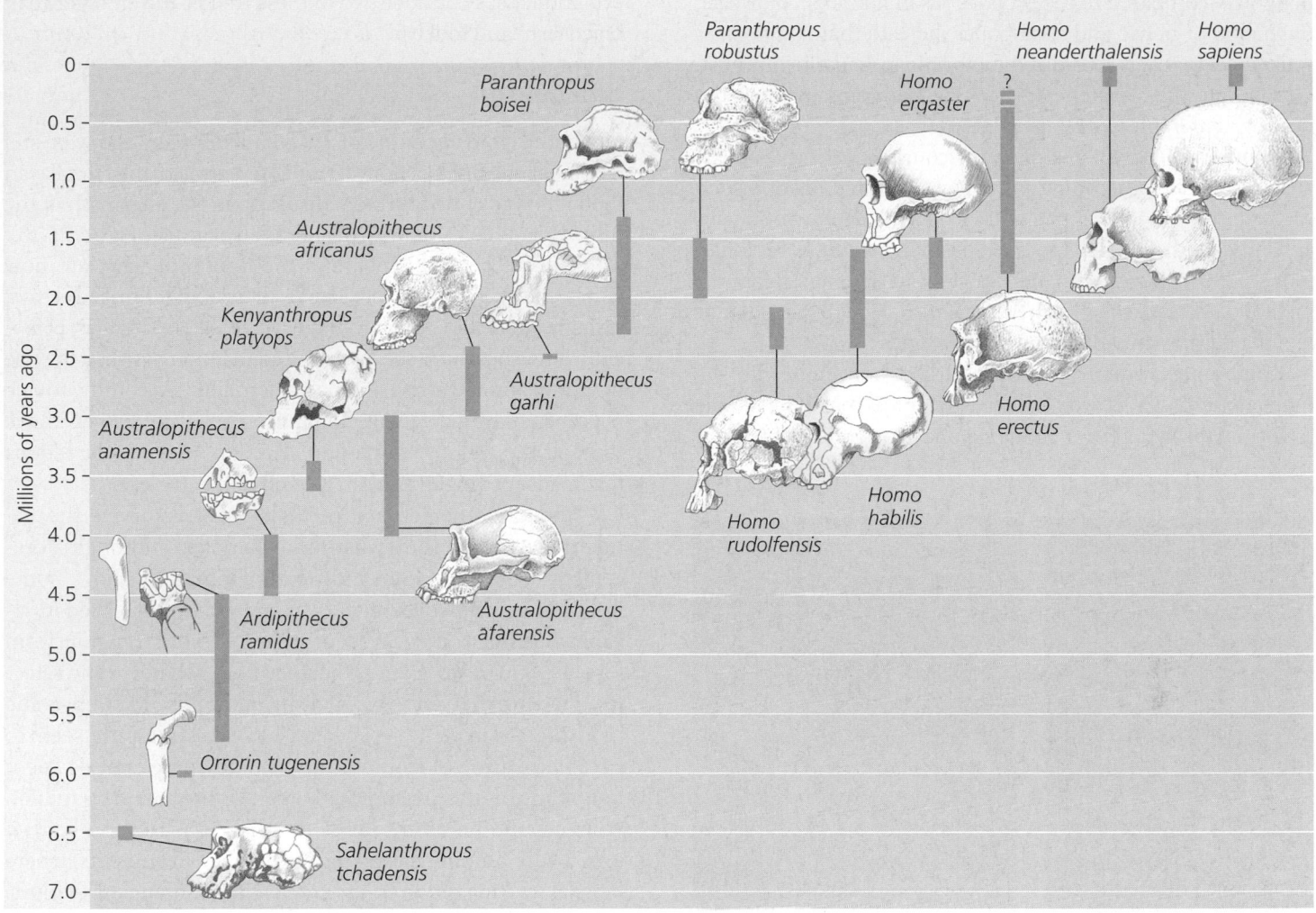

▲ Figure 34.40 A timeline for some selected hominin species. Most of these fossils come from sites in eastern and southern Africa. Note that at most times in hominin history, two or more hominin species were contemporaries. Some of the species are controversial, reflecting phylogenetic debates about the interpretation of skeletal details and biogeography.

Australopiths

The fossil record indicates that hominin diversity increased dramatically between 4 million and 2 million years ago. Many of the hominins from this period are collectively called australopiths. Their phylogeny remains unresolved on many points, but as a group, they are almost certainly paraphyletic. *Australopithecus anamensis*, mentioned earlier, links the australopiths to older hominins such as *Ardipithecus ramidus*.

Australopiths got their name from the 1924 discovery in South Africa of *Australopithecus africanus* ("southern ape of Africa"), which lived between 3 and 2.4 million years ago. With the discovery of more fossils, it became clear that *A. africanus* walked fully erect (was bipedal) and had human-like hands and teeth. However, its brain was only about one-third the size of the brain of a present-day human.

In 1974, in the Afar region of Ethiopia, paleoanthropologists discovered a 3.2-million-year-old *Australopithecus* skeleton that was 40% complete. "Lucy," as the fossil was named, was short—only about 1 m tall. Lucy and similar fossils have been considered sufficiently different from *Australopithecus africanus* to be designated as a separate species, *Australopithecus afarensis* (for the Afar region). Fossils discovered in the early 1990s show that *A. afarensis* existed as a species for at least 1 million years.

At the risk of oversimplifying, one could say that *A. afarensis* had fewer of the derived characters of humans above the neck than below. Lucy's head was the size of a softball, indicating a brain size about the same as that of a chimpanzee of Lucy's body size. *A. afarensis* skulls also have a long lower jaw. Skeletons of *A. afarensis* suggest these hominins were capable of arboreal locomotion, with arms that were relatively long in proportion to body size (compared to the proportions in humans). However, fragments of pelvic and skull bones indicate that *A. afarensis* walked on two legs. Fossilized footprints in Laetoli, Tanzania, corroborate the skeletal evidence that hominins living at the time of *A. afarensis* were bipedal (Figure 34.41).

Another lineage of australopiths consisted of the "robust" australopiths. These hominins, which included species such as *Paranthropus boisei*, had sturdy skulls with powerful jaws and large teeth, adapted for grinding and chewing hard, tough foods. They contrast with the "gracile" (slender) australopiths, including *A. afarensis* and *A. africanus*, which had lighter feeding equipment adapted for softer foods.

Combining evidence from the earliest hominins with the much richer fossil record of later australopiths makes it possible to formulate hypotheses about significant trends in hominin evolution. Let's consider two of these trends: the emergence of bipedalism and tool use.

Bipedalism

Our anthropoid ancestors of 30–35 million years ago were still tree-dwellers. But by about 10 million years ago, the Himalayan mountain range had formed, thrust up in the aftermath of the Indian plate's collision with the Eurasian plate (see Figure 25.13). The climate became drier, and the forests of what are now Africa and Asia contracted. The result was an increased area of savanna (grassland) habitat, with fewer trees. For decades, paleo-anthropologists have seen a strong connection between the rise of savannas and the rise of bipedal hominins. According to one hypothesis, tree-dwelling hominins could no longer move through the canopy, so natural selection favored adaptations that made moving over open ground more efficient.

Although some elements of this hypothesis survive, the picture now appears somewhat more complex. Although all recently discovered fossils of early hominins show some indications of bipedalism, none of these hominins lived in savannas. Instead, they lived in mixed habitats ranging from forests to open woodlands. Furthermore, whatever the selective pressure that led to bipedalism, hominins did not become more bipedal in a simple, linear fashion. Australopiths seem to have had various locomotor styles, and some species spent more time on the ground than others. Only about 1.9 million years ago did hominins begin to walk long distances on two legs. These hominins lived in more arid environments, where bipedal walking requires less energy than walking on all fours.

Tool Use

As you read earlier, the manufacture and use of complex tools is a derived behavioral character of humans. Determining the origin of tool use in hominin evolution is one of paleoanthropology's great challenges. Other apes are capable of surprisingly sophisticated tool use. Orangutans, for example, can fashion sticks into probes for retrieving insects from their nests. Chimpanzees are even more adept, using rocks to smash open food and putting leaves on their feet to walk over thorns. It's likely that early hominins were capable of this sort of simple tool use, but finding fossils of modified sticks or leaves that were used as shoes is practically impossible.

The oldest generally accepted evidence of tool use by hominins is 2.5-million-year-old cut marks on animal bones found in Ethiopia. These marks suggest that hominins cut flesh from the bones of animals using stone tools. Interestingly, the hominins whose fossils were found near the site where the bones were discovered had a relatively small brain. If these hominins, which have been named *Australopithecus garhi*, were indeed the creators of the stone tools used on the bones, that would suggest that stone tool use originated before the evolution of large brains in hominins.

(a) Lucy, a 3.24-million-year-old skeleton, represents the hominin species *Australopithecus afarensis.*

(b) The Laetoli footprints, more than 3.5 million years old, confirm that upright posture evolved quite early in hominin history.

(c) An artist's reconstruction of what *A. afarensis* may have looked like.

▲ **Figure 34.41 Upright posture predates an enlarged brain in human evolution.**

Early *Homo*

The earliest fossils that paleoanthropologists place in our genus, *Homo*, are those of the species *Homo habilis*. These fossils, ranging in age from about 2.4 to 1.6 million years, show clear signs of certain derived hominin characters above the neck. Compared to the australopiths, *H. habilis* had a shorter jaw and a larger brain volume, about 600–750 cm³. Sharp stone tools have also been found with some fossils of *H. habilis* (the name means "handy man").

Fossils from 1.9 to 1.5 million years ago mark a new stage in hominin evolution. A number of paleoanthropologists recognize these fossils as those of a distinct species, *Homo ergaster*. *Homo ergaster* had a substantially larger brain than *H. habilis* (over 900 cm³), as well as long, slender legs with hip joints well adapted for long-distance walking **(Figure 34.42)**. The fingers were relatively short and straight, suggesting that *H. ergaster* did not climb trees like earlier hominins. *Homo ergaster* fossils have been discovered in far more arid environments than earlier hominins and have been associated with more sophisticated stone tools. Its

◄ **Figure 34.42 Fossil and artist's reconstruction of *Homo ergaster*.** This 1.7-million-year-old fossil from Kenya belongs to a young male *Homo ergaster*. This individual was tall, slender, and fully bipedal, and he had a relatively large brain.

smaller teeth also suggest that *H. ergaster* either ate different foods than australopiths (more meat and less plant material) or prepared some of its food before chewing, perhaps by cooking or mashing the food.

Homo ergaster marks an important shift in the relative sizes of the sexes. In primates, a size difference between males and females is a major component of sexual dimorphism (see Chapter 23). On average, male gorillas and orangutans weigh about twice as much as females of their species. In chimpanzees and bonobos, males are only about 1.35 times as heavy as females, on average. In *Australopithecus afarensis*, males were 1.5 times as heavy as females. But in early *Homo*, sexual dimorphism was significantly reduced, and this trend continues through our own species: Human males average about 1.2 times the weight of females.

The reduced sexual dimorphism may offer some clues to the social systems of extinct hominins. In extant primates, extreme sexual dimorphism is associated with intense male-male competition for multiple females. In species that undergo more pair-bonding (including our own), sexual dimorphism is less dramatic. Male and female *H. ergaster* may therefore have engaged in more pair-bonding than earlier hominins did. This shift may have been associated with long-term care of the young by both parents. Human babies depend on their parents for food and protection much longer than do the young of other apes.

Fossils now generally recognized as *H. ergaster* were originally considered early members of another species, *Homo erectus*, and some paleoanthropologists still hold this position. *Homo erectus* originated in Africa and was the first hominin to migrate out of Africa. The oldest fossils of hominins outside Africa, dating back 1.8 million years, were discovered in 2000 in the former Soviet Republic of Georgia. *Homo erectus* eventually migrated as far as the Indonesian archipelago. Comparisons of *H. erectus* fossils with humans and studies of human DNA indicate that *H. erectus* became extinct sometime after 200,000 years ago.

Neanderthals

In 1856, miners discovered some mysterious human fossils in a cave in the Neander Valley in Germany. The 40,000-year-old fossils belonged to a thick-boned hominin with a prominent brow. The hominin was named *Homo neanderthalensis* and is commonly called a Neanderthal. Neanderthals were living in Europe and the Near East by 200,000 years ago, but never spread outside that region. They had a brain as large as that of present-day humans, buried their dead, and made hunting tools from stone and wood. But despite their adaptations and culture, Neanderthals apparently became extinct about 28,000 years ago.

At one time, many paleoanthropologists considered Neanderthals to be a stage in the evolution of *Homo erectus* into *Homo sapiens*. Now most have abandoned this view. One reason for this change concerns evidence from the analysis of mitochondrial DNA (**Figure 34.43**). The results suggest that Neanderthals may have contributed little to the gene pool of *H. sapiens*. However, preliminary results from a 2006 study that compared Neanderthal and human nuclear DNA appear to be consistent with limited gene flow between the two species. In addition, some researchers have argued that evidence of gene flow can be found in fossils that show a mixture of *H. sapiens* and Neanderthal characteristics. Further genetic analyses and fossil discoveries will be needed to resolve the ongoing debate over the extent of genetic exchange between the two species.

Homo Sapiens

Evidence from fossils, archaeology, and DNA studies has led to a compelling hypothesis about how our own species, *Homo sapiens*, emerged and spread around the world.

Fossil evidence indicates that the ancestors of humans originated in Africa. Older species (perhaps *H. ergaster* or *H. erectus*) gave rise to later species, ultimately including *H. sapiens*. Furthermore, the oldest known fossils of our own species have been found at two different sites in Ethiopia and include specimens that are 195,000 and 160,000 years old (**Figure 34.44**). These early humans lacked the heavy browridges of *H. erectus* and Neanderthals and were more slender than other hominins.

The Ethiopian fossils support inferences about the origin of humans from molecular evidence. As you saw in Figure 34.43, DNA analyses indicate that all living humans are more closely related to one another than to Neanderthals. Other studies on human DNA show that Europeans and Asians share a relatively recent common ancestor and that many African lineages branched off more ancient positions on the human family tree. These findings strongly suggest that all living humans have ancestors that originated as *H. sapiens* in Africa, which is further supported by analysis of mitochondrial DNA and Y chromosomes from members of various human populations.

The oldest fossils of *H. sapiens* outside Africa are from the Middle East and date back about 115,000 years. Studies of the human Y chromosome suggest that humans spread beyond Africa in one or more waves, first into Asia and then to Europe and Australia. The date of the first arrival of humans in the New World is uncertain, although the oldest generally accepted evidence puts that date at sometime before 15,000 years ago.

New findings continually update our understanding of the evolution of *H. sapiens*. For example, in 2004, researchers reported an astonishing find: skeletal remains of adult hominins dating from just 18,000 years ago and representing a previously unknown species, which they named *Homo floresiensis*. Discovered in a limestone cave on the Indonesian island of Flores, the individuals were much shorter and had a much smaller brain volume than *H. sapiens*—more similar, in fact, to an australopith. The researchers who discovered these fossils argue that the skeletons also display many derived traits, including skull thickness and proportions and teeth shape, suggesting the species is descended from the larger *H. erectus*. Not convinced, some researchers argued that the fossils represent a small *H. sapiens* who had a deformed, miniature brain, a condition called microcephaly.

However, a 2007 study found that the wrist bones of the Flores fossils are similar in shape to those of nonhuman apes and early hominins, but different from those of Neanderthals and of

---

▼ **Figure 34.43** **Inquiry**

Did Neanderthals give rise to European humans?

EXPERIMENT   People have long been fascinated by Neanderthals and their relationship to *Homo sapiens*. Several fossils discovered in Europe have been interpreted by some researchers as showing a mixture of Neanderthal and human features, leading to the suggestion that European humans bred with or descended from Neanderthals. Igor Ovchinnikov and William Goodwin, then at the University of Glasgow, and their team used genetic methods to assess the relationship between Neanderthals and *H. sapiens*. The team extracted mitochondrial DNA (mtDNA) from a Neanderthal fossil (Neanderthal 1) and compared its sequence to an mtDNA sequence that other researchers had obtained three years earlier from a different Neanderthal fossil (Neanderthal 2). Mitochondrial DNA sequences were also obtained for a number of living humans from Europe, Africa, and Asia. The researchers then used Neanderthal and *H. sapiens* mtDNA sequences to construct a phylogenetic tree for Neanderthals and humans; data from chimpanzees were used to root the tree. This approach permitted the researchers to test the following hypothesis:

Hypothesis: Neanderthals gave rise to European humans.

Expected phylogeny:

```
         ┌─────────── Chimpanzees
 ────────┤
         │   ┌─────── Neanderthals
         └───┤
             │   ┌─── Living Europeans
             └───┤
                 └─── Other living humans
```

RESULTS   The two Neanderthal mtDNA sequences differed at 3.5% of the bases, whereas on average, the Neanderthal and *H. sapiens* mtDNA differed at 24% of the bases. The phylogenetic analysis yielded the following tree:

```
         ┌─────────── Chimpanzees
 ────────┤
         │   ┌─────── Neanderthal 1
         └───┤
             │   ┌─── Neanderthal 2
             └───┤
                 └─── European and other
                     living humans
```

CONCLUSION   The Neanderthals form one clade, and living humans form another, separate clade. Thus, it is not likely that Neanderthals gave rise to European humans. More generally, the results suggest that Neanderthals contributed little to the *H. sapiens* gene pool.

SOURCE   I. V. Ovchinnikov et al., Molecular analysis of Neanderthal DNA from the northern Caucasus, *Nature* 404:490–493 (2000).

WHAT IF?   DNA obtained from fossils can break down over time (obscuring the original sequence) or be contaminated by the DNA of other organisms. Do you think it is likely that these potential sources of error could have significantly affected the results obtained in this study? Explain.

▶ **Figure 34.44 A 160,000-year-old fossil of *Homo sapiens*.** This skull, discovered in Ethiopia in 2003, differs little from the skulls of living humans.

▲ **Figure 34.45 Art, a human hallmark.** The engravings on this 77,000-year-old piece of ochre, discovered in South Africa's Blombos Cave, are among the earliest signs of symbolic thought in humans.

H. sapiens. These researchers concluded that the Flores fossils represent a species whose lineage branched off before the origin of the clade that includes Neanderthals and humans. If further evidence supports the designation of *H. floresiensis* as a new hominin, one intriguing explanation for this species' apparent "shrinkage" is that isolation on the island may have resulted in selection for greatly reduced size. Such dramatic size reduction is well studied in other dwarf mammalian species that are endemic to islands; these include primitive pygmy elephants found in the same vicinity as the *H. floresiensis* specimen. Compelling questions that may yet be answered from the cache of anthropological and archeological finds on Flores include how *H. floresiensis* originated and whether it ever encountered *H. sapiens*, which also lived in Indonesia during the late Pleistocene.

The rapid expansion of our species (and the replacement of Neanderthals) may have been spurred by changes in human cognition as *H. sapiens* evolved in Africa. Evidence of sophisticated thought in *H. sapiens* includes a 2002 discovery in South Africa of 77,000-year-old art—geometric markings made on pieces of ochre **(Figure 34.45)**. And in 2004, archaeologists working in southern and eastern Africa found 75,000-year-old ostrich eggs and snail shells with holes neatly drilled through them. By 36,000 years ago, humans were producing spectacular cave paintings (see Figure 56.25a).

Clues to the cognitive transformation of humans can also be found within the human genome. For example, the gene *FOXP2* is thought to play a key role in human language. People who inherit mutated versions of the gene suffer from language impediments and have reduced activity in Broca's area in the brain (see Chapters 21 and 49). In 2002, geneticists compared the *FOXP2* gene in humans with the homologous gene in other mammals. They concluded that the gene experienced intense natural selection after the ancestors of humans and chimpanzees diverged. By comparing mutations in regions flanking the gene, the researchers estimated that this bout of natural selection occurred within the past 200,000 years. Of course, the human capacity for lan-

guage involves many regions of the brain, and it is almost certain that many other genes are essential for language. But the evolution of *FOXP2* may be one genetic clue as to how our own species came to play its unique role in the world.

Our discussion of humans brings this unit on biological diversity to an end. But this organization isn't meant to imply that life consists of a ladder leading from lowly microorganisms to lofty humanity. Biological diversity is the product of branching phylogeny, not ladderlike "progress," however we choose to measure it. The fact that there are more species of ray-finned fishes alive today than all other vertebrates combined is a clear indication that our finned relatives are not outmoded underachievers that failed to leave the water. The tetrapods—amphibians, reptiles, and mammals—are derived from one lineage of lobe-finned vertebrates. As tetrapods diversified on land, fishes continued their branching evolution in the greatest portion of the biosphere's volume. Similarly, the ubiquity of diverse prokaryotes throughout the biosphere today is a reminder of the enduring ability of these relatively simple organisms to keep up with the times through adaptive evolution. Biology exalts life's diversity, past and present.

CONCEPT CHECK 34.8

1. Identify some characters that distinguish and contrast apes and hominins.
2. Provide an example in which different features of organisms in the hominin evolutionary lineage evolved at different rates.
3. **WHAT IF?** Some genetic studies suggest that the most recent common ancestor of *Homo sapiens* that lived outside of Africa spread from Africa about 50,000 years ago. Compare this date to the dates of fossils given in the text. Can both the genetic results and the dates ascribed to the fossils be correct? Explain.

For suggested answers, see Appendix A.

MEDIA Go to **www.campbellbiology.com** for BioFlix 3-D Animations, MP3 Tutors, Videos, Practice Tests, an eBook, and more.

SUMMARY OF KEY CONCEPTS

Key Concept			Clade		Description
Concept 34.1 Chordates have a notochord and a dorsal, hollow nerve cord (pp. 698–702)	**Chordates:** notochord; dorsal, hollow nerve cord; pharyngeal slits; post-anal tail		Cephalochordata (lancelets)		Basal chordates; marine suspension feeders that exhibit four key derived characters of chordates
			Urochordata (tunicates)		Marine suspension feeders; larvae display the derived traits of chordates
Concept 34.2 Craniates are chordates that have a head (pp. 702–704)		**Craniates:** two *Hox* gene clusters, neural crest	Myxini (hagfishes and relatives)		Jawless marine organisms; have head that includes a skull and brain, eyes, and other sensory organs
Concept 34.3 Vertebrates are craniates that have a backbone (pp. 704–705)		**Vertebrates:** *Dlx* genes duplication, backbone of vertebrae	Petromyzontida (lampreys)		Jawless vertebrates; typically feed by attaching to a live fish and ingesting its blood
Concept 34.4 Gnathostomes are vertebrates that have jaws (pp. 705–710)		**Gnathostomes:** hinged jaws, four *Hox* gene clusters	Chondrichthyes (sharks, rays, skates, ratfishes)		Aquatic gnathostomes; have cartilaginous skeleton secondarily evolved from an ancestral mineralized skeleton
		Osteichthyans: bony skeleton	Actinopterygii (ray-finned fishes)		Aquatic gnathostomes; have bony skeleton and maneuverable fins supported by rays
		Lobe-fins: muscular fins or limbs	Actinistia (coelacanths)		Ancient lineage of aquatic lobe-fins still surviving in Indian Ocean
			Dipnoi (lungfishes)		Freshwater lobe-fins with both lungs and gills; sister group of tetrapods
Concept 34.5 Tetrapods are gnathostomes that have limbs (pp. 710–713)		**Tetrapods:** four limbs, neck, fused pelvic girdle	Amphibia (salamanders, frogs, caecilians)		Have four limbs descended from modified fins; most have moist skin that functions in gas exchange; many live both in water (as larvae) and on land (as adults)
Concept 34.6 Amniotes are tetrapods that have a terrestrially adapted egg (pp. 713–720) **MEDIA** **Investigation** How Does Bone Structure Shed Light on the Origin of Birds?		**Amniotes:** amniotic egg, rib-cage ventilation	Reptilia (tuataras, lizards and snakes, turtles, crocodilians, birds)		One of two groups of living amniotes; have amniotic eggs and rib-cage ventilation, which are key adaptations for life on land
Concept 34.7 Mammals are amniotes that have hair and produce milk (pp. 720–728) **MEDIA** **Activity** Characteristics of Chordates **Activity** Primate Diversity			Mammalia (monotremes, marsupials, eutherians)		Evolved from synapsid ancestors; include egg-laying monotremes (echidnas, platypus); pouched marsupials (such as kangaroos, opossums); and eutherians (placental mammals such as rodents, primates)

CONCEPT 34.8

Humans are mammals that have a large brain and bipedal locomotion (pp. 728–733)

▶ **Derived Characters of Humans** Humans are bipedal and have a larger brain and reduced jaw compared to other apes.

▶ **The Earliest Hominins** Hominins—humans and species that are more closely related to humans than to chimpanzees—originated in Africa at least 6–7 million years ago. Early hominins had a small brain but probably walked upright.

▶ **Australopiths** Australopiths lived 4–2 million years ago. Some species walked upright and had human-like hands and teeth.

▶ **Bipedalism** Hominins began to walk long distances on two legs about 1.9 million years ago.

▶ **Tool Use** The oldest evidence of tool use—cut marks on animal bones—is 2.5 million years old.

▶ **Early *Homo*** *Homo ergaster* was the first fully bipedal, large-brained hominin. *Homo erectus* was the first hominin to leave Africa.

▶ **Neanderthals** Neanderthals lived in Europe and the Near East about 200,000—28,000 years ago.

▶ ***Homo Sapiens*** *Homo sapiens* appeared in Africa by about 195,000 years ago. Its spread to other continents about 115,000 years ago may have been preceded by genetic changes that enabled language and other aspects of cognition. Research into the origins and contemporaries of *Homo sapiens* is a lively area.

MEDIA
Activity Human Evolution

TESTING YOUR KNOWLEDGE

SELF-QUIZ

1. Vertebrates and tunicates share
   a. jaws adapted for feeding.
   b. a high degree of cephalization.
   c. the formation of structures from the neural crest.
   d. an endoskeleton that includes a skull.
   e. a notochord and a dorsal, hollow nerve cord.

2. Some animals that lived 530 million years ago resembled lancelets but had a brain and a skull. These animals may represent
   a. the first chordates.
   b. a "missing link" between urochordates and cephalochordates.
   c. early craniates.
   d. marsupials.
   e. nontetrapod gnathostomes.

3. Which of the following could be considered the most recent common ancestor of living tetrapods?
   a. a sturdy-finned, shallow-water lobe-fin whose appendages had skeletal supports similar to those of terrestrial vertebrates
   b. an armored, jawed placoderm with two pairs of appendages
   c. an early ray-finned fish that developed bony skeletal supports in its paired fins
   d. a salamander that had legs supported by a bony skeleton but moved with the side-to-side bending typical of fishes
   e. an early terrestrial caecilian whose legless condition had evolved secondarily

4. Mammals and living birds share all of the following characteristics *except*
   a. endothermy.

   b. descent from a common amniotic ancestor.
   c. a dorsal, hollow nerve cord.
   d. an archosaur common ancestor.
   e. an amniotic egg.

5. Unlike eutherians, *both* monotremes and marsupials
   a. lack nipples.
   b. have some embryonic development outside the mother's uterus.
   c. lay eggs.
   d. are found in Australia and Africa.
   e. include only insectivores and herbivores.

6. Which clade does *not* include humans?
   a. synapsids   d. craniates
   b. lobe-fins   e. osteichthyans
   c. diapsids

7. As hominins diverged from other primates, which of the following appeared first?
   a. reduced jawbones   d. the making of stone tools
   b. language   e. an enlarged brain
   c. bipedal locomotion

For Self-Quiz answers, see Appendix A.

MEDIA Visit www.campbellbiology.com for a Practice Test.

EVOLUTION CONNECTION

8. Identify one characteristic that qualifies humans for membership in each of the following clades: eukaryotes, animals, deuterostomes, chordates, vertebrates, gnathostomes, amniotes, mammals, primates.

SCIENTIFIC INQUIRY

9. **DRAW IT** As a consequence of size alone, organisms that are large tend to have larger brains than organisms that are small. However, some organisms have brains that are considerably larger than expected for an animal of their size. There are high costs associated with the development and maintenance of brains that are large relative to body size.

   (a) The fossil record documents trends in which brains that are large relative to body size evolved in certain lineages, including hominins. In such lineages, what can you infer about the relative magnitude of the costs and benefits of large brains?

   (b) Hypothesize how natural selection might favor the evolution of large brains despite the high maintenance costs of such brains.

   (c) Data for 14 bird species are listed below. Graph the data, placing deviation from expected brain size on the x-axis and mortality rate on the y-axis. What can you conclude about the relationship between brain size and mortality?

Deviation from Expected Brain Size*	-2.4	-2.1	2.0	-1.8	-1.0	0.0	0.3	0.7	1.2	1.3	2.0	2.3	3.0	3.2
Mortality Rate	0.9	0.7	0.5	0.9	0.4	0.7	0.8	0.4	0.8	0.3	0.6	0.6	0.3	0.6

*Negative values indicate brain sizes smaller than expected, positive values indicate brain sizes larger than expected.
Source: D. Sol et al., Big-brained birds survive better in nature, *Proceedings of the Royal Society B* 274:763–769 (2007).

6

Plant Form and Function

AN INTERVIEW WITH

Patricia C. Zambryski

Pat Zambryski opened the door to genetic engineering in plants by discovering how the bacterium *Agrobacterium tumefaciens* transfers DNA into the plants it infects, and her lab continues to provide insights into this process. She also has a second major research area: plasmodesmata, the channels through plant cell walls. Her work in this area is shedding light on cell-to-cell communication, plant development, and defenses against pathogens. Dr. Zambryski grew up in Montreal, Canada, where she graduated from McGill University, and she earned her Ph.D. from the University of Colorado. After postdoctoral research at the University of California, San Francisco (UCSF), she spent five years as a senior investigator at Ghent University in Belgium. A member of the National Academy of Sciences, Dr. Zambryski is currently a professor of plant and microbial biology at the University of California, Berkeley.

What were the subjects of your early research, leading up to your work with *Agrobacterium*?
In grad school at the University of Colorado, I worked on bacteriophage T4. To learn how to evaluate data and pose new questions in biology, it's good to work with a simple system like a phage or bacterium because you can do an experiment in one day and get the answer quickly. Especially in those days, before genetic engineering, if you were working with a multicellular eukaryote, a research project could take a long, long time. I used gel electrophoresis to separate and identify all the different proteins that this phage made, and I determined that specific groups of proteins were made at different times during infection.

Then I went to UCSF to do a post-doc. I was interested in working with animal tumor viruses. But after a few years I realized that

there were thousands of people in that field—all working on the same small viruses, with tiny genomes that encoded just a few proteins! And I didn't feel like I could contribute something novel with so many people working on the same thing.

At the time, there was a powerful new method for using two-dimensional electrophoresis to separate all the proteins from cell extracts, and I was looking at the proteins made in a number of different biological systems. I was invited to visit a lab at Ghent University to use these 2-D gels to try to figure out what might be the gene product that enabled *Agrobacterium tumefaciens* to cause tumors in plants. While I was there, it occurred to me that this would be a very good biological system to study. Little was known about it, and it was a fascinating system of genetic transfer from a prokaryote to a eukaryote. So I got involved with tumors after all—but tumors in plants rather than animals!

It had already been discovered that there was a piece of DNA that *Agrobacterium* transferred into the plant it infected, but we didn't know the exact composition of that DNA, the nature of its borders with surrounding DNA, or how the transfer happened. Meanwhile, back at UCSF, people were just starting to do DNA cloning using phage lambda. When I returned there, my project was to clone the piece of *Agrobacterium* DNA that was inserted into the plant genome—the T DNA—and find out what the ends of the T DNA were.

I would spend summers in Ghent learning the biology of *Agrobacterium* and then return to UCSF to work on cloning the T DNA. Finally, after one summer, I decided to stay, and I spent the next five years at Ghent University. That's where a really big thing happened. I had figured out what the T-DNA ends were, and in Ghent I discovered that *any* DNA inserted between these ends (by recombinant DNA technology) would be transferred to plant cells and stably integrated into their genomes. It was the birth of genetic engineering in plants. [See Figure 20.25 to review how T DNA is used.]

For the genetic engineering of plants, how does the *Agrobacterium* system compare with a "gene gun"?
People generally prefer to use the *Agrobacterium* system because all the DNA carried between the ends of the T element is precisely integrated into the plant cell's DNA. *Agrobacterium* DNA transfer is more precise and significantly more efficient than shooting foreign DNA into plant cells using a gene gun, which fires tiny pellets coated with DNA. But for plants that are not susceptible to *Agrobacterium* infection, you have to use a gene gun.

What have you been studying recently in *Agrobacterium*?
Bacteria have various molecular systems that allow them to transport things out of the cell (secretion) or take things up. A major focus of our current research is one specific bacterial secretion system, called type IV, which is used by *Agrobacterium*. This system is used for translocating both DNA, as in bacterial conjugation, and proteins. In *Agrobacterium*, generation of a transferable T-DNA segment and expression of the type IV secretion system have evolved to occur only in the presence of a wounded plant cell. The wounded cell then is the recipient for DNA and protein transport. It turns out that type IV secretion systems are also used to secrete toxins into host cells by bacteria that are pathogenic for humans, such as those that cause whooping cough, stomach ulcers, and Legionnaires' disease. The system probably evolved first as a bacterial conjugation system and later developed the ability to transfer DNA and proteins to eukaryotic hosts, causing disease. Recall that in nature *Agrobacterium* causes disease—tumorous growths on plants.

How did you become interested in plasmodesmata, your other major area of research?
Although my background was mostly in microbiology, I was hired by a plant biology department, here at Berkeley. So I said to

myself, this is cool—maybe I should do some experiments with plants! But knowing almost nothing about plants, I decided to work on something about which little was known. So I started to work on plasmodesmata because I thought I could contribute to the field of plant intercellular communication. I didn't want to start with a well-studied system like photosynthesis!

What are plasmodesmata, and what is currently known about their function?

When adjacent plant cells need to communicate, information must be transferred across the thick cell walls that lie outside the plasma membrane. Plasmodesmata are plant-specific communication channels that span the cell walls and link the cytoplasm of adjacent cells; the plasma membrane of the two cells is continuous in these places. At first, it was thought that plasmodesmata were a fixed size, with apertures so narrow that only ions and small molecules such as sugars and hormones could pass through. However, it was also known that plant viruses could commandeer plasmodesmata, and it was discovered that these viruses encode proteins that open the channels enough to allow passage of the virus.

The big breakthrough in recent years has been the discovery that, even in plants not infected with a virus, the apertures of plasmodesmata are dynamic. And the apertures can open wide enough to allow the transport not only of small molecules but also of macromolecules such as RNA or protein. Also, the aperture size can change during development, both during embryonic development and during the development of new tissues and organs from regions of mature plants called meristems. This discovery has tremendous implications for how plant development proceeds. Immature tissues such as those found in embryos and meristems have very dilated plasmodesmata, suggesting that plasmodesma-mediated communication between cells is likely to be involved in the initiation and coordination of developmental processes.

What do you want to find out about plasmodesmata now?

We want to understand how the structure and function of plasmodesmata are regulated, both during embryonic development and in the life of the mature plant. To get at this, we have been searching for the genes that are responsible for this regulation. We've collected mutants that are deficient in regulating transport between cells of the embryo. We reasoned that we could not screen for mutants in mature plants because plasmodesmata are so important that any mutant would be a dead plant. Thus, we assay plasmodesmata function in so-called embryo defective lines that can be propagated as heterozygotes. The seedpods of heterozygote plants contain both wild-type and homozygous mutant embryos that develop enough to allow us to assay for plasmodesma-mediated transport. Once we identify the gene products affected by the mutations, we can study how these proteins affect the regulation of plasmodesmata in older plants, as well.

Fluorescent tracers are key tools in our research. Tracers of small molecular weight can move from cell to cell during all embryonic stages. However, larger tracers move freely only during the earlier stages. That means there is "down regulation" of plasmodesma apertures during embryonic development. So we used the large fluorescent tracers in a genetic screen for mutants that continued to traffic it at late embryonic stages. We screened 5,000 mutants in this way to find about 10 embryo-defective mutants of the sort we were looking for! Now we're cloning the genes affected, trying to identify their products, and seeing how they affect plasmodesmata.

How does the regulation of plasmodesma size benefit the plant?

In a tiny embryo, it makes sense for all the cells to be in communication with each other so that development is properly coordinated. Then, as cells differentiate and tissues and organs develop, groups of cells with related functions need to be in communication. Later, as cells and tissues develop unique functions, they may lose communication with adjacent regions. Cell differentiation occurs by regulation of gene expression, but development requires another layer of control on top of that—the control of what gene products can move cell to cell via plasmodesmata, which in turn coordinates development throughout the plant body.

Why do you and most other plant molecular biologists use *Arabidopsis thaliana* as a research organism?

You can grow thousands of these small plants in a small space, and they go from seed to seed in six weeks. *Arabidopsis* has a small genome, less than one twentieth the size of the corn or human genomes, making it easy to clone its genes. Its genome has been sequenced. The genetics are fabulous. Almost every gene has been tagged by T-DNA insertions to make mutants with particular phenotypes and to facilitate cloning of their affected genes. This plant is very convenient to work with for those reasons and more.

Along with laboratory research, do you enjoy teaching?

When I started teaching, I taught only graduate students, but I've found that I really enjoy teaching undergraduates, too. I teach a class with no prerequisites called "The Secret Life of Plants." I want the students to realize that plants are absolutely critical to our lives and also interesting in their own right. I want students to have enough understanding of science to read the popular press and form decisions about important issues such as global warming and genetically modified organisms (GMOs). We talk about basic biology that is unique to plants, but also about global warming, GMOs, biofuels, and medicinal plants, among other applied topics. Teaching that course is one of the most rewarding things I do.

I want the students to realize that plants are absolutely critical to our lives and also interesting in their own right.

Inquiry in Action

Learn about an experiment by Pat Zambryski and colleagues in Inquiry Figure 36.22 on page 782.

Jane Reece (left) and Pat Zambryski

737

35 Plant Structure, Growth, and Development

▲ Figure 35.1 **Why does this plant have two types of leaves?**

KEY CONCEPTS

35.1 The plant body has a hierarchy of organs, tissues, and cells

35.2 Meristems generate cells for new organs

35.3 Primary growth lengthens roots and shoots

35.4 Secondary growth adds girth to stems and roots in woody plants

35.5 Growth, morphogenesis, and differentiation produce the plant body

OVERVIEW

Plastic Plants?

Although the graceful fanwort (*Cabomba caroliniana*) **(Figure 35.1)** is an attractive addition to many aquariums, its most striking feature is its extreme *developmental plasticity*—its ability to alter its form in response to local environmental conditions. The underwater leaves are feathery, an adaptation that protects them from damage by lessening their resistance to moving water. In contrast, the surface leaves are pads that aid in flotation. Both leaf types have genetically identical cells, but dissimilar environments result in the turning on or off of different genes during leaf development. Such extreme developmental plasticity is much more common in plants than in animals and may help compensate for plants' inability to escape adverse conditions by moving.

In addition to structural responses by an individual plant to a specific environment, entire species have by natural selection accumulated adaptations in **morphology**, or external form, that vary little among plants within the species. For example, most cactus species, regardless of local environment, have leaves that are so highly reduced—to spines—that the stems are the primary photosynthetic organs. This adaptation in leaf morphology enhances the survival and reproductive success of cacti because with reduced leaf surface areas, these desert plants lose less water.

Both genetic and environmental factors influence form in plants and animals, but the effect of environment is greater in plants. Consequently, plants typically vary much more within a species than do animals. All lions, for example, have four legs and are roughly the same size at maturity. In contrast, ginkgo trees vary greatly in the numbers, sizes, and positions of their roots, branches, and leaves. Lacking mobility, plants must be adapted to their environment in other ways. Thus, plant form is central to understanding how plants compete in nature.

This chapter focuses on how the body of a plant is formed, setting the stage for the rest of this unit on plant biology. Chapters 29 and 30 described the evolution and characteristics of nonvascular plants, seedless vascular plants, gymnosperms, and angiosperms (flowering plants). Here, in Unit Six, we'll focus primarily on vascular plants—especially angiosperms, because they account for about 90% of plant species and are of great importance to humans. As the world's population increases, the need for plants to supply food, fuel, fiber, medicine, lumber, and paper has never been greater, heightening the importance of understanding how plants grow and develop.

CONCEPT 35.1

The plant body has a hierarchy of organs, tissues, and cells

Plants, like most animals, have organs composed of different tissues, which in turn are composed of cells of different types. A **tissue** is a group of cells with a common function, structure, or both. An **organ** consists of several types of tissues that together carry out particular functions. In looking at the hierarchy of plant organs, tissues, and cells, we begin with organs because they are the most familiar and easily observed plant structures. As you learn about the hierarchy of plant structure, keep in mind how natural selection has produced plant forms, at all levels of organization, that fit plant function.

The Three Basic Plant Organs: Roots, Stems, and Leaves

The basic morphology of most vascular plants reflects their evolutionary history as terrestrial organisms that inhabit and draw resources from two very different environments—below ground and above ground. They must absorb water and minerals from below the ground surface and CO_2 and light from above the ground surface. The ability to acquire these resources arose from the evolution of three basic organs—roots, stems, and leaves. These organs form a **root system** and a **shoot system**, the latter consisting of stems and leaves **(Figure 35.2)**. With few exceptions, angiosperms and other vascular plants rely completely on both systems for survival. Roots are typically nonphotosynthetic and starve unless *photosynthates*, the sugars and other carbohydrates produced during photosynthesis, are imported from the shoot system. Conversely, the shoot system depends on the water and minerals that roots absorb from the soil.

Vegetative growth—production of nonreproductive leaves, stems, and roots—is only one stage in a plant's life. Many plants also undergo reproductive growth. In angiosperms, reproductive shoots bear flowers, which are composed of leaves that are highly modified for sexual reproduction. Later in this chapter, we'll discuss the transition from vegetative shoot formation to reproductive shoot formation.

In describing plant organs, we'll draw examples mainly from the two major groups of angiosperms: monocots and eudicots (see Figure 30.13).

Roots

A **root** is a multicellular organ that anchors a vascular plant in the soil, absorbs minerals and water, and often stores carbohydrates. Most eudicots and gymnosperms have a *taproot system*, consisting of one main vertical root, the **taproot**, that develops from an embryonic root. The taproot gives rise to **lateral roots**, also called branch roots (see Figure 35.2). In many angiosperms, the taproot stores sugars and starches that the plant will consume during flowering and fruit production. For this reason, root crops such as carrots, turnips, and beets are harvested before they flower. Taproot systems generally penetrate deeply and are therefore well adapted to deep soils where the groundwater is not close to the surface.

In seedless vascular plants and in most monocots, such as grasses, the embryonic root dies and does not give rise to a main root. Instead, many small roots grow from the stem. Such roots are said to be *adventitious* (from the Latin *adventicus*, extraneous), a term describing a plant organ that grows in an unusual location, such as roots arising from stems or leaves. Each small root forms its own lateral roots. The result is a *fibrous root system*—a mat of generally thin roots spreading out below the soil surface, with no root functioning as the main one (see Figure 30.13). Fibrous root systems usually do not penetrate deeply and are therefore best adapted to shallow soils or regions where rainfall is light and does not moisten the soil much below the surface layer. Most grasses have shallow roots, concentrated in the upper few centimeters of the soil. Because these shallow roots hold the topsoil in place, grass makes excellent ground cover for preventing erosion.

Although the entire root system helps anchor a plant, in most plants the absorption of water and minerals occurs primarily near the tips of roots, where vast numbers of tiny **root hairs** increase the surface area of the root enormously **(Figure 35.3)**.

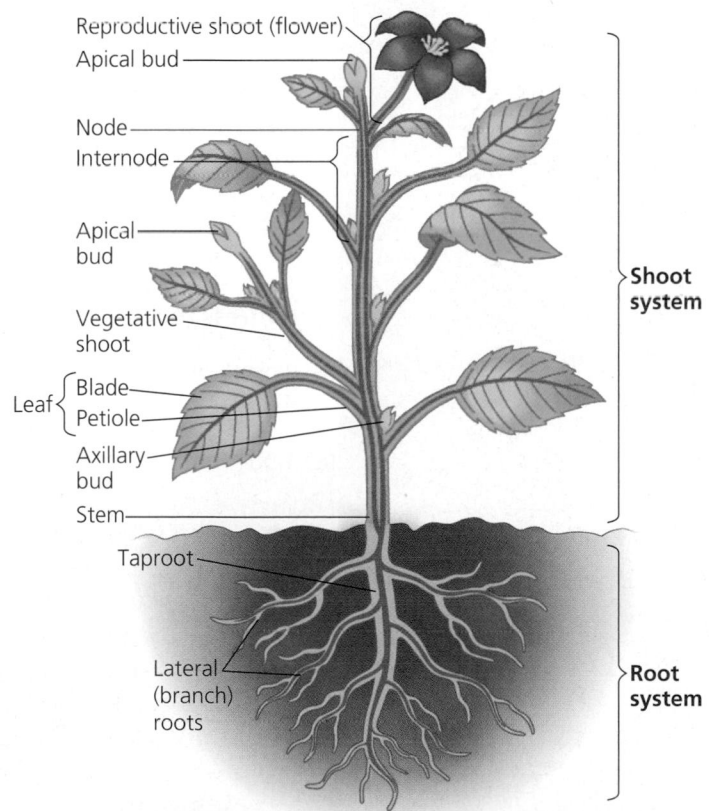

▲ **Figure 35.2 An overview of a flowering plant.** The plant body is divided into a root system and a shoot system, connected by vascular tissue (purple strands in this diagram) that is continuous throughout the plant. The plant shown is an idealized eudicot.

Labels for Figure 35.2:
- Reproductive shoot (flower)
- Apical bud
- Node
- Internode
- Apical bud
- Vegetative shoot
- Leaf { Blade, Petiole }
- Axillary bud
- Stem
- Shoot system
- Taproot
- Lateral (branch) roots
- Root system

◄ **Figure 35.3 Root hairs of a radish seedling.** Root hairs grow by the thousands just behind the tip of each root. By increasing the root's surface area, they greatly enhance the absorption of water and minerals from the soil.

Root hairs are short-lived and constantly replaced. A root hair is a thin, tubular extension of a root epidermal cell. It should not be confused with a lateral root, which is a multicellular organ. Despite their great surface area, root hairs, unlike lateral roots, contribute little to plant anchorage. Their main function is absorption.

Many plants have modified roots (Figure 35.4). Some of these arise from roots, and others are adventitious, developing from stems or, in rare cases, leaves. Some modified roots provide more support and anchorage, whereas others store water and nutrients or absorb oxygen from the air.

Stems

A **stem** is an organ consisting of an alternating system of **nodes**, the points at which leaves are attached, and **internodes**, the stem segments between nodes (see Figure 35.2). In the upper angle (axil) formed by each leaf and the stem is an **axillary bud**, a structure that can form a lateral shoot, commonly called a branch. Most axillary buds of a young shoot are dormant (not growing). Thus, elongation of a young shoot is usually concentrated near the shoot tip, which consists of an **apical bud**, or terminal bud, with developing leaves and a compact series of nodes and internodes.

The proximity of the axillary buds to the apical bud is partly responsible for their dormancy. The inhibition of axillary buds by an apical bud is called **apical dominance**. By concentrating resources on elongation, the evolutionary adaptation of

▼ **Figure 35.4 Modified roots.**

◀ **Prop roots.** The aerial roots of maize (corn) are examples of prop roots, so named because they support tall, top-heavy plants. All roots of a mature maize plant are adventitious after the original roots die. The emerging roots shown here will eventually penetrate the soil.

▶ **Storage roots.** Many plants, such as the common beet, store food and water in their roots.

◀ **"Strangling" aerial roots.** The seeds of this strangler fig germinate in the branches of tall trees of other species and send numerous aerial roots to the ground. These snake-like roots gradually wrap around the host tree and objects such as this Cambodian temple ruin. Eventually, the host tree dies of shading by the fig leaves.

▼ **Buttress roots.** Aerial roots that look like buttresses support the tall trunks of some tropical trees, such as this ceiba tree in Central America.

▲ **Pneumatophores.** Also known as air roots, pneumatophores are produced by trees such as mangroves that inhabit tidal swamps. By projecting above the water's surface, they enable the root system to obtain oxygen, which is lacking in the thick, waterlogged mud.

apical dominance increases the plant's exposure to light. If an animal eats the end of the shoot, or if shading results in the light being more intense to the side of a plant than directly above, axillary buds break dormancy; that is, they start growing. A growing axillary bud gives rise to a lateral shoot, complete with its own apical bud, leaves, and axillary buds. Removing the apical bud usually stimulates the growth of axillary buds, resulting in more lateral shoots. That is why pruning trees and shrubs and pinching back houseplants will make them bushier.

Some plants have stems with additional functions such as food storage and asexual reproduction. These modified stems, which include rhizomes, bulbs, stolons, and tubers, are often mistaken for roots (**Figure 35.5**).

▼ Figure 35.5 **Modified stems.**

▼ **Rhizomes.** The base of this iris plant is an example of a rhizome, a horizontal shoot that grows just below the surface. Vertical shoots emerge from axillary buds on the rhizome.

▶ **Bulbs.** Bulbs are vertical underground shoots consisting mostly of the enlarged bases of leaves that store food. You can see the many layers of modified leaves attached to the short stem by slicing an onion bulb lengthwise.
Storage leaves
Stem

▶ **Stolons.** Shown here on a strawberry plant, stolons are horizontal shoots that grow along the surface. These "runners" enable a plant to reproduce asexually, as plantlets form at nodes along each runner.
Stolon

◀ **Tubers.** Tubers, such as these red potatoes, are enlarged ends of rhizomes or stolons specialized for storing food. The "eyes" of a potato are clusters of axillary buds that mark the nodes.

Leaves

In most vascular plants, the **leaf** is the main photosynthetic organ, although green stems also perform photosynthesis. Leaves vary extensively in form but generally consist of a flattened **blade** and a stalk, the **petiole**, which joins the leaf to the stem at a node (see Figure 35.2). Grasses and many other monocots lack petioles; instead, the base of the leaf forms a sheath that envelops the stem.

Monocots and eudicots differ in the arrangement of **veins**, the vascular tissue of leaves. Most monocots have parallel major veins that run the length of the blade. Eudicots generally have a branched network of major veins (see Figure 30.13).

In identifying angiosperms according to structure, taxonomists rely mainly on floral morphology, but they also use variations in leaf morphology, such as leaf shape, the branching pattern of veins, and the spatial arrangement of leaves. **Figure 35.6** illustrates a difference in leaf shape: simple versus compound. Many

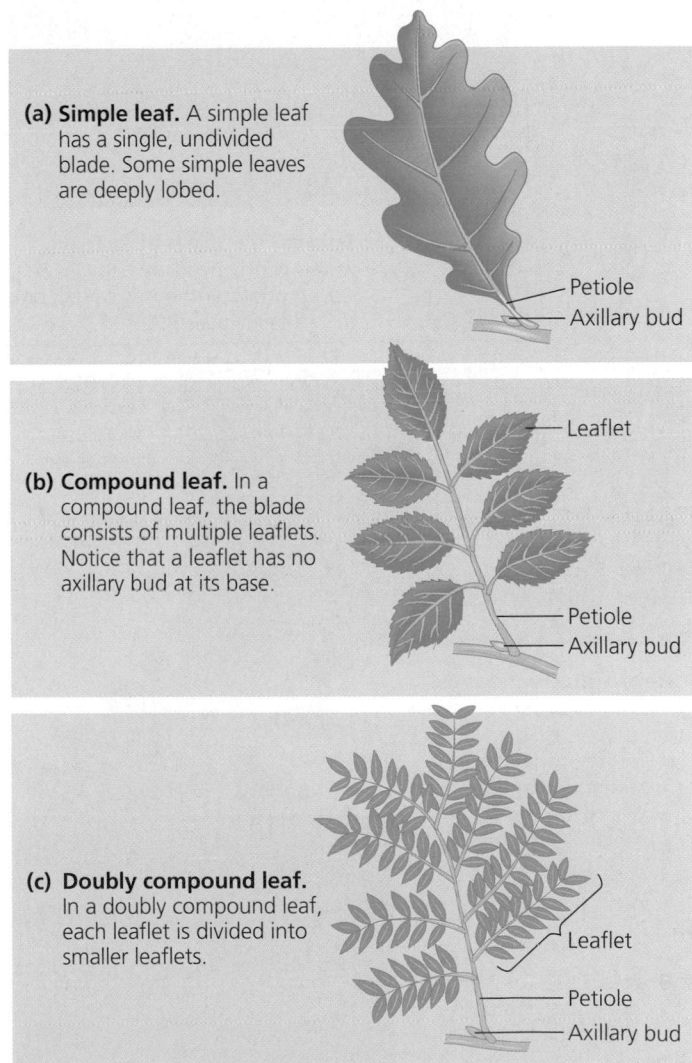

(a) **Simple leaf.** A simple leaf has a single, undivided blade. Some simple leaves are deeply lobed.
Petiole
Axillary bud

(b) **Compound leaf.** In a compound leaf, the blade consists of multiple leaflets. Notice that a leaflet has no axillary bud at its base.
Leaflet
Petiole
Axillary bud

(c) **Doubly compound leaf.** In a doubly compound leaf, each leaflet is divided into smaller leaflets.
Leaflet
Petiole
Axillary bud

▲ Figure 35.6 **Simple versus compound leaves.** One can distinguish simple leaves from compound leaves by looking for axillary buds. Leaves have axillary buds; leaflets do not.

very large leaves are compound or doubly compound. This structural adaptation may enable large leaves to withstand strong wind with less tearing. It may also confine some pathogens (disease-causing organisms and viruses) that invade the leaf to a single leaflet, rather than allowing them to spread to the entire leaf.

Almost all leaves are specialized for photosynthesis. However, some species have leaves with adaptations that enable them to perform additional functions, such as support, protection, storage, or reproduction (**Figure 35.7**).

▼ Figure 35.7 **Modified leaves.**

► **Tendrils.** The tendrils by which this pea plant clings to a support are modified leaves. After it has "lassoed" a support, a tendril forms a coil that brings the plant closer to the support. Tendrils are typically modified leaves, but some tendrils are modified stems, as in grapevines.

◄ **Spines.** The spines of cacti, such as this prickly pear, are actually leaves; photosynthesis is carried out by the fleshy green stems.

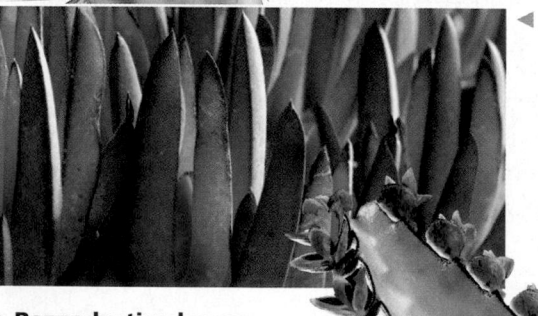

◄ **Storage leaves.** Most succulents, such as this ice plant, have leaves modified for storing water.

► **Reproductive leaves.** The leaves of some succulents, such as *Kalanchoë daigremontiana*, produce adventitious plantlets, which fall off the leaf and take root in the soil.

► **Bracts.** Often mistaken for petals, the red parts of the poinsettia are actually modified leaves called bracts that surround a group of flowers. Such brightly colored leaves attract pollinators.

Dermal, Vascular, and Ground Tissues

Each plant organ—root, stem, or leaf—has dermal, vascular, and ground tissues. Each of these three categories forms a **tissue system**, a functional unit connecting all of the plant's organs. Although each tissue system is continuous throughout the plant, specific characteristics of the tissues and their spatial relationships to one another vary in different organs (**Figure 35.8**).

The **dermal tissue system** is the plant's outer protective covering. Like our skin, it forms the first line of defense against physical damage and pathogens. In nonwoody plants, it is usually a single tissue called the **epidermis**, a layer of tightly packed cells. In leaves and most stems, the **cuticle**, a waxy coating on the epidermal surface, helps prevent water loss. In woody plants, protective tissues called **periderm** replace the epidermis in older regions of stems and roots. In addition to protecting the plant from water loss and disease, the epidermis has specialized characteristics in each organ. For example, a root hair is an extension of an epidermal cell near the tip of a root. *Trichomes*, hairlike outgrowths of the shoot epidermis, reduce water loss and reflect excess light. They can also provide defense against insects by forming a barrier or by secreting sticky fluids and toxic

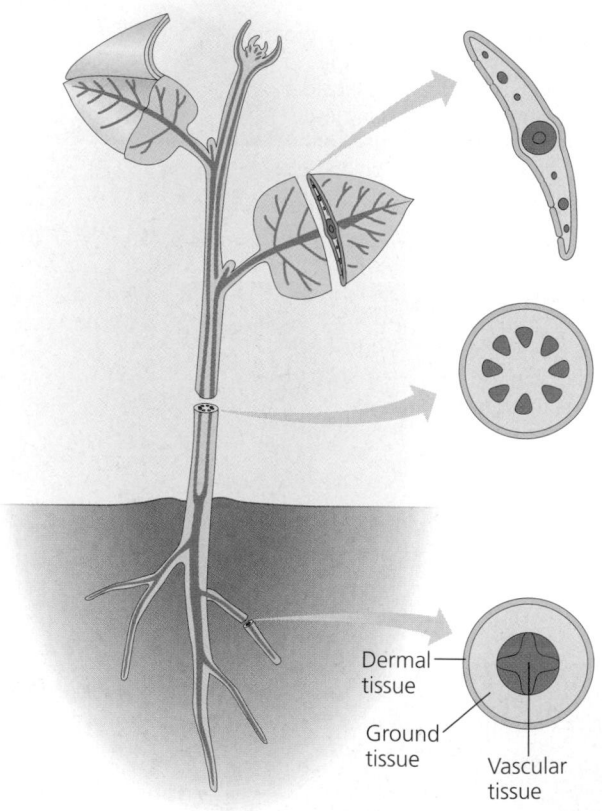

Dermal tissue

Ground tissue

Vascular tissue

▲ Figure 35.8 **The three tissue systems.** The dermal tissue system (blue) provides a protective cover for the entire body of a plant. The vascular tissue system (purple), which transports materials between the root and shoot systems, is also continuous throughout the plant, but is arranged differently in each organ. The ground tissue system (yellow), which is responsible for most of the plant's metabolic functions, is located between the dermal tissue and the vascular tissue in each organ.

compounds. For instance, the trichomes on aromatic leaves such as mint secrete oils that protect the plants from herbivores and disease. **Figure 35.9** describes an investigation of the relationship between trichome density on soybean pods and damage by beetles.

▼ Figure 35.9 Inquiry

Do soybean pod trichomes deter herbivores?

EXPERIMENT Bean leaf beetles (*Cerotoma trifurcata*) feed on developing legume pods, causing pod scarring and decreased seed quality. W. K. Lam and L. P. Pedigo, of Purdue University, investigated whether the stiff trichomes on soybean pods (*Glycine max*) physically deter these beetles. The researchers placed hungry beetles in muslin bags and sealed the bags around the pods of adjacent plants expressing different pod hairiness. The amount of damage to the pods was assessed after 24 hours.

Very hairy pod (10 trichomes/ mm²)   Slightly hairy pod (2 trichomes/ mm²)   Bald pod (no trichomes)

RESULTS Beetle damage to very hairy soybean pods was much lower compared with the other pod types.

Very hairy pod: 10% damage   Slightly hairy pod: 25% damage   Bald pod: 40% damage

CONCLUSION Soybean pod trichomes protect against beetle damage.

SOURCE W. F. Lam and L. P. Pedigo, Effect of trichome density on soybean pod feeding by adult bean leaf beetles (Coleoptera: Chrysomelidae), *Journal of Economic Entomology* 94(6):1459–1463 (2001).

WHAT IF? The pod trichomes of most soybean varieties are white, but some varieties have tawny-colored trichomes. Suppose that the effects of trichome density on beetle feeding were observed only in tawny-haired varieties. What might this finding suggest about how these trichomes deter beetles?

The **vascular tissue system** carries out long-distance transport of materials between the root and shoot systems. The two types of vascular tissues are xylem and phloem. **Xylem** conducts water and dissolved minerals upward from roots into the shoots. **Phloem** transports sugars, the products of photosynthesis, from where they are made (usually the leaves) to where they are needed—usually roots and sites of growth, such as developing leaves and fruits. The vascular tissue of a root or stem is collectively called the **stele** (the Greek word for "pillar"). The arrangement of the stele varies, depending on the species and organ. In angiosperms, for example, the root stele is a solid central *vascular cylinder* of xylem and phloem, whereas the stele of stems and leaves consists of *vascular bundles*, separate strands containing xylem and phloem (see Figure 35.8). Both xylem and phloem are composed of a variety of cell types, including cells that are highly specialized for transport or support.

Tissues that are neither dermal nor vascular are part of the **ground tissue system**. Ground tissue that is internal to the vascular tissue is known as **pith**, and ground tissue that is external to the vascular tissue is called **cortex**. The ground tissue system is not just filler. It includes various cells specialized for functions such as storage, photosynthesis, and support.

Common Types of Plant Cells

Like any multicellular organism, a plant is characterized by cellular differentiation, the specialization of cells in structure and function. Cellular differentiation may involve changes both in the cytoplasm and its organelles and in the cell wall. **Figure 35.10**, on the next two pages, focuses on the major types of plant cells: parenchyma cells, collenchyma cells, sclerenchyma cells, the water-conducting cells of the xylem, and the sugar-conducting cells of the phloem. Notice the structural adaptations in the different cells that make their specific functions possible. You may also wish to review Figures 6.9 and 6.28, which show basic plant cell structure.

CONCEPT CHECK 35.1

1. How does the vascular tissue system enable leaves and roots to function together in supporting growth and development of the whole plant?

2. When you eat the following, what plant structure are you consuming? (a) brussels sprouts; (b) celery sticks; (c) onions; (d) carrot sticks

3. Characterize the role of each of the three tissue systems in a leaf.

4. Describe at least three specializations in plant organs and plant cells that are adaptations to life on land.

5. **WHAT IF?** If humans were photoautotrophs, making food by capturing light energy for photosynthesis, how might our anatomy be different?

For suggested answers, see Appendix A.

Exploring Examples of Differentiated Plant Cells

Parenchyma Cells

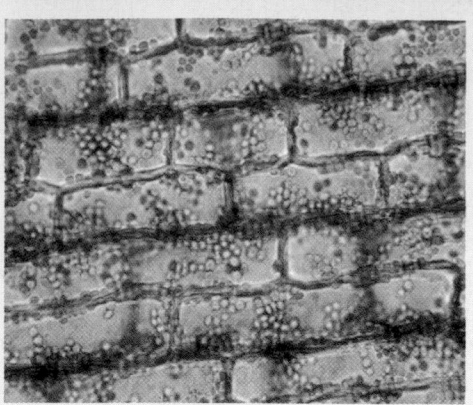

Parenchyma cells in *Elodea* leaf, with chloroplasts (LM)

60 μm

Mature **parenchyma cells** have primary walls that are relatively thin and flexible, and most lack secondary walls. (See Figure 6.28 to review primary and secondary cell walls.) When mature, parenchyma cells generally have a large central vacuole. Diagrams of "typical" plant cells often depict parenchyma cells because they are the least specialized structurally. Parenchyma cells perform most of the metabolic functions of the plant, synthesizing and storing various organic products. For example, photosynthesis occurs within the chloroplasts of parenchyma cells in the leaf. Some parenchyma cells in stems and roots have colorless plastids that store starch. The fleshy tissue of many fruits is composed mainly of parenchyma cells. Most parenchyma cells retain the ability to divide and differentiate into other types of plant cells under particular conditions—during wound repair, for example. It is even possible for scientists to grow an entire plant from a single parenchyma cell.

Collenchyma Cells

5 μm

Collenchyma cells (in *Helianthus* stem) (LM)

Grouped in strands or cylinders, **collenchyma cells** help support young parts of the plant shoot. Collenchyma cells have thicker primary walls than parenchyma cells, though the walls are unevenly thickened. Young stems and petioles often have strands of collenchyma cells just below their epidermis (for example, the "strings" of a celery stalk, which is a petiole). Collenchyma cells lack secondary walls, and the hardening agent lignin is absent from their primary walls. Therefore, these cells provide flexible support without restraining growth. At maturity, collenchyma cells are living and flexible, elongating with the stems and leaves they support—unlike sclerenchyma cells, which we discuss next.

Sclerenchyma Cells

5 μm

Sclereid cells in pear (LM)

25 μm

Cell wall

Fiber cells (cross section from ash tree) (LM)

Also functioning as supporting elements in the plant, but with thick secondary walls that are usually strengthened by lignin, **sclerenchyma cells** are much more rigid than collenchyma cells. Mature sclerenchyma cells cannot elongate, and they occur in regions of the plant that have stopped growing in length. Sclerenchyma cells are so specialized for support that many are dead at functional maturity, but they produce secondary walls before the protoplast (the living part of the cell) dies. The rigid walls remain as a "skeleton" that supports the plant, in some cases for hundreds of years.

Two types of sclerenchyma cells, known as **sclereids** and **fibers**, are specialized entirely for support and strengthening. Sclereids, which are shorter than fibers and irregular in shape, have very thick, lignified secondary walls. Sclereids impart the hardness to nutshells and seed coats and the gritty texture to pear fruits. Fibers, which are usually arranged in threads, are long, slender, and tapered. Some are used commercially, such as hemp fibers for making rope and flax fibers for weaving into linen.

Water-Conducting Cells of the Xylem

The two types of water-conducting cells, **tracheids** and **vessel elements**, are tubular, elongated cells that are dead at functional maturity. Tracheids are found in the xylem of nearly all vascular plants. In addition to tracheids, most angiosperms, as well as a few gymnosperms and a few seedless vascular plants, have vessel elements. When the living cellular contents of a tracheid or vessel element disintegrate, the cell's thickened walls remain behind, forming a nonliving conduit through which water can flow. The secondary walls of tracheids and vessel elements are often interrupted by pits, thinner regions where only primary walls are present (see Figure 6.28 to review primary and secondary walls). Water can migrate laterally between neighboring cells through pits.

Tracheids are long, thin cells with tapered ends. Water moves from cell to cell mainly through the pits, where it does not have to cross thick secondary walls. The secondary walls of tracheids are hardened with lignin, which prevents collapse under the tensions of water transport and also provides support.

Vessel elements are generally wider, shorter, thinner walled, and less tapered than the tracheids. They are aligned end to end, forming long micropipes known as **vessels**. The end walls of the vessel elements have perforation plates that enable water to flow freely through the vessels.

Vessel   Tracheids   100 μm

Tracheids and vessels (colorized SEM)

Perforation plate

Vessel element

Pits

Vessel elements, with perforated end walls

Tracheids

Sugar-Conducting Cells of the Phloem

Unlike the water-conducting cells of the xylem, the sugar-conducting cells of the phloem are alive at functional maturity. In seedless vascular plants and gymnosperms, sugars and other organic nutrients are transported through long, narrow cells called sieve cells. In the phloem of angiosperms, these nutrients are transported through sieve tubes, which consist of chains of cells called **sieve-tube elements**, or sieve-tube members.

Though alive, sieve-tube elements lack a nucleus, ribosomes, a distinct vacuole, and cytoskeletal elements. This reduction in cell contents enables nutrients to pass more easily through the cell. The end walls between sieve-tube elements, called **sieve plates**, have pores that facilitate the flow of fluid from cell to cell along the sieve tube. Alongside each sieve-tube element is a nonconducting cell called a **companion cell**, which is connected to the sieve-tube element by numerous channels, plasmodesmata (see Figure 6.28). The nucleus and ribosomes of the companion cell serve not only that cell itself but also the adjacent sieve-tube element. In some plants, companion cells in leaves also help load sugars into the sieve-tube elements, which then transport the sugars to other parts of the plant.

MEDIA

BioFlix Visit **www.campbellbiology.com** for the BioFlix 3-D Animation called Tour of a Plant Cell.

3 μm

Sieve-tube element (left) and companion cell: cross section (TEM)

Sieve-tube elements: longitudinal view (LM)

Sieve plate

Companion cells

Sieve-tube elements

Plasmodesma

Sieve plate

Nucleus of companion cell

Sieve-tube elements: longitudinal view

30 μm

10 μm

Sieve plate with pores (SEM)

CONCEPT 35.2
Meristems generate cells for new organs

So far, we have looked at the structure and arrangement of plant tissues and cells in mature organs. How does this organization arise? A major difference between plants and most animals is that plant growth is not limited to an embryonic or juvenile period. Instead, growth occurs throughout the plant's life, a process known as **indeterminate growth**. At any given time, a typical plant consists of embryonic, developing, and mature organs. Except for dormant periods, most plants grow continuously. In contrast, most animals and some plant organs—such as most leaves, thorns, and flowers—undergo **determinate growth**; that is, they stop growing after reaching a certain size.

Although plants continue to grow throughout their lives, they do die, of course. Based on the length of their life cycle, flowering plants can be categorized as annuals, biennials, or perennials. **Annuals** complete their life cycle—from germination to flowering to seed production to death—in a single year or less. Many wildflowers are annuals, as are most staple food crops, including legumes and cereal grains such as wheat and rice. **Biennials** generally require two growing seasons to complete their life cycle, flowering and fruiting only in their second year. Radishes and carrots are biennials, though they are usually harvested after the first year. **Perennials** live many years and include trees, shrubs, and some grasses. Some buffalo grass of the North American plains is thought to have been growing for 10,000 years from seeds that sprouted at the close of the last ice age. When a peren-

nial dies, it is usually not from old age but from an infection or some environmental trauma, such as fire or severe drought.

Plants are capable of indeterminate growth because they have perpetually embryonic tissues called **meristems**. There are two main types: apical meristems and lateral meristems **(Figure 35.11)**. **Apical meristems**, located at the tips of roots and shoots and in the axillary buds of shoots, provide additional cells that enable the plant to grow in length, a process known as **primary growth**. Primary growth allows roots to extend throughout the soil and shoots to increase their exposure to light. In herbaceous (nonwoody) plants, primary growth produces all, or almost all, of the plant body. Woody plants, however, also grow in girth in the parts of stems and roots that no longer grow in length. This growth in thickness, known as **secondary growth**, is caused by the activity of **lateral meristems** called the vascular cambium and cork cambium. These cylinders of dividing cells extend along the length of roots and stems. The **vascular cambium** adds layers of vascular tissue called secondary xylem (wood) and secondary phloem. The **cork cambium** replaces the epidermis with the thicker, tougher periderm.

The cells within meristems divide relatively frequently, generating additional cells. Some of these new cells remain in the meristem and produce more cells, while others differentiate and are incorporated into tissues and organs of the growing plant. Cells that remain as sources of new cells are called *initials*. The new cells displaced from the meristem, called *derivatives*, continue to divide until the cells they produce become specialized within developing tissues.

The relationship between primary and secondary growth is clearly seen in the winter twig of a deciduous tree. At the shoot

▲ Figure 35.11 **An overview of primary and secondary growth.**

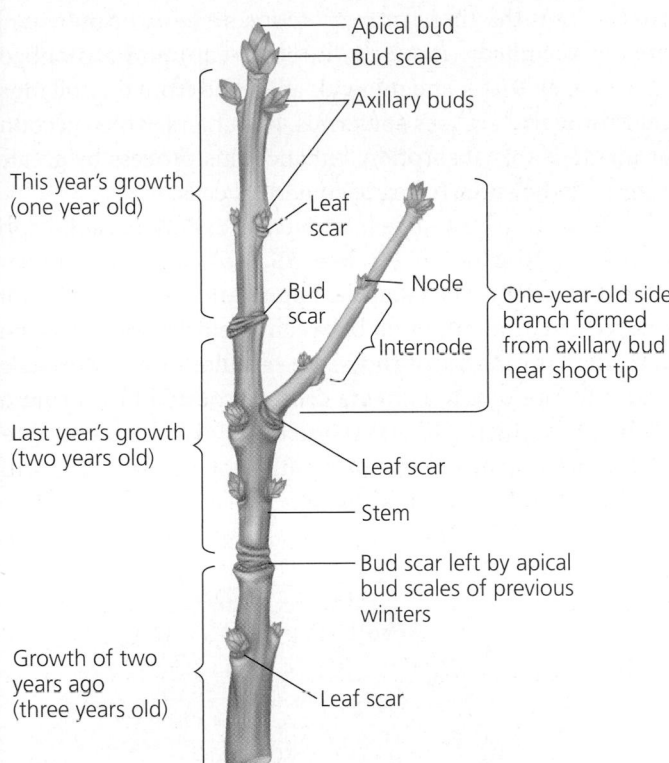

▲ Figure 35.12 **Three years' growth in a winter twig.**

Apical bud
Bud scale
Axillary buds

This year's growth
(one year old)

Leaf
scar

Bud
scar

Node

Internode

One-year-old side
branch formed
from axillary bud
near shoot tip

Last year's growth
(two years old)

Leaf scar

Stem

Bud scar left by apical
bud scales of previous
winters

Growth of two
years ago
(three years old)

Leaf scar

tip is the dormant apical bud, enclosed by scales that protect its apical meristem (**Figure 35.12**). In spring, the bud sheds its scales and begins a new spurt of primary growth, producing a series of nodes and internodes. Along each growth segment, nodes are marked by scars that were left when leaves fell. Above each leaf scar is an axillary bud or a branch formed by an axillary bud. Farther down the twig are bud scars from the whorls of scales that enclosed the apical bud during the previous winter. During each growing season, primary growth extends the shoots, and secondary growth thickens the parts that formed in previous years.

CONCEPT CHECK 35.2

1. Distinguish between primary and secondary growth.
2. Cells in lower layers of your skin divide and replace dead cells sloughed from the surface. Why is it inaccurate to compare such regions of cell division to a plant meristem?
3. Roots and stems grow indeterminately, but leaves do not. How might this benefit the plant?
4. **WHAT IF?** Suppose a gardener picks some radishes and finds that they are too small. Since radishes are biennials, the gardener leaves the remaining plants in the ground, thinking that they will grow larger during their second year. Is this a good idea? Explain.

For suggested answers, see Appendix A.

CONCEPT 35.3
Primary growth lengthens roots and shoots

As you have learned, primary growth is growth in length, produced by apical meristems. Collectively, the results of this growth are called the **primary plant body**. In herbaceous plants, it is usually the entire plant. In woody plants, it consists only of the youngest parts, which are not yet woody. Although apical meristems lengthen both roots and shoots, there are differences in the primary growth of these two systems.

Primary Growth of Roots

The tip of a root is covered by a thimble-like **root cap**, which protects the delicate apical meristem as the root pushes through the abrasive soil during primary growth. The root cap also secretes a polysaccharide slime that lubricates the soil around the tip of the root. Growth occurs just behind the tip in three zones of cells at successive stages of primary growth. Moving away from the tip, they are the zones of cell division, elongation, and differentiation (**Figure 35.13**).

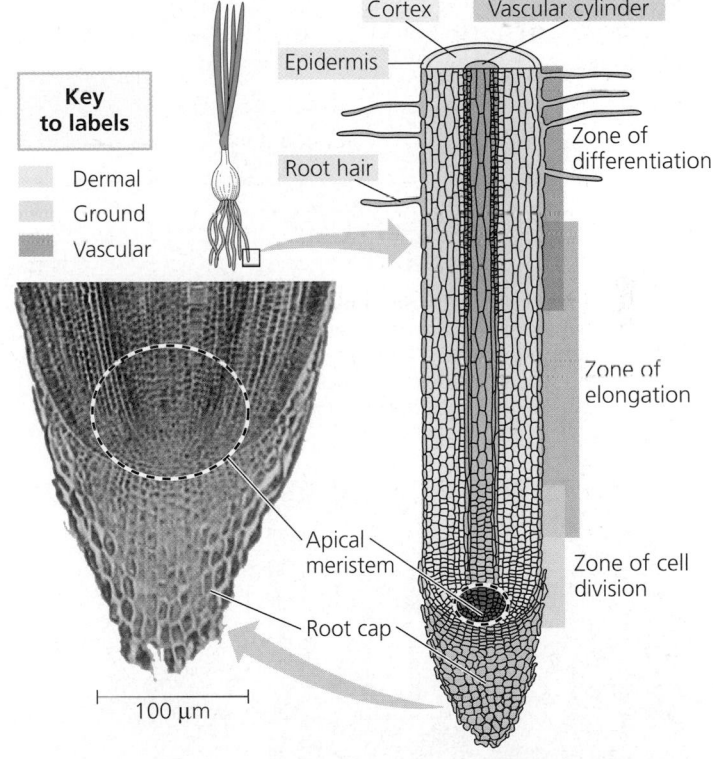

Cortex
Vascular cylinder
Epidermis

Key to labels

Dermal
Ground
Vascular

Root hair

Zone of
differentiation

Zone of
elongation

Apical
meristem

Root cap

Zone of cell
division

100 μm

▲ Figure 35.13 **Primary growth of a root.** The light micrograph and diagram reveal the anatomical features of the tip of an onion root. Mitosis is concentrated in the zone of cell division, where the apical meristem and its immediate growth products are located. The apical meristem also maintains the root cap by generating new cells that replace those that are sloughed off. Most lengthening of the root occurs in the zone of elongation. Cells become functionally mature in the zone of differentiation. The zones grade into one another without sharp boundaries.

The three zones grade together, with no sharp boundaries. The *zone of cell division* includes the root apical meristem and its derivatives. New root cells are produced in this region, including the root cap. Typically, about a millimeter behind the tip of the root is the *zone of elongation*, where root cells elongate, sometimes to more than ten times their original length. Cell elongation in this zone pushes the tip farther into the soil. Meanwhile, the root apical meristem keeps adding cells to the younger end of the zone of elongation. Even before the root cells finish lengthening, many begin specializing in structure and function. In the *zone of differentiation*, or zone of maturation, cells complete their differentiation and become distinct cell types.

The primary growth of a root produces its epidermis, ground tissue, and vascular tissue. **Figure 35.14** shows in cross section the three primary tissue systems in the young roots of a eudicot (*Ranunculus*, buttercup) and a monocot (*Zea*, maize). Water and minerals absorbed from the soil must enter through the root's epidermis. Root hairs, which account for much of this absorption, enhance this process by greatly increasing the surface area of epidermal cells.

In most roots, the stele is a vascular cylinder, a solid core of xylem and phloem **(Figure 35.14a)**. In most eudicot roots, the xylem has a starlike appearance and the phloem occupies the indentations between the arms of the xylem "star." In many monocot roots, the vascular tissue consists of a central core of parenchyma cells surrounded by a ring of xylem and a ring of phloem **(Figure 35.14b)**. The central region is often called pith but should not be confused with stem pith, which is ground tissue.

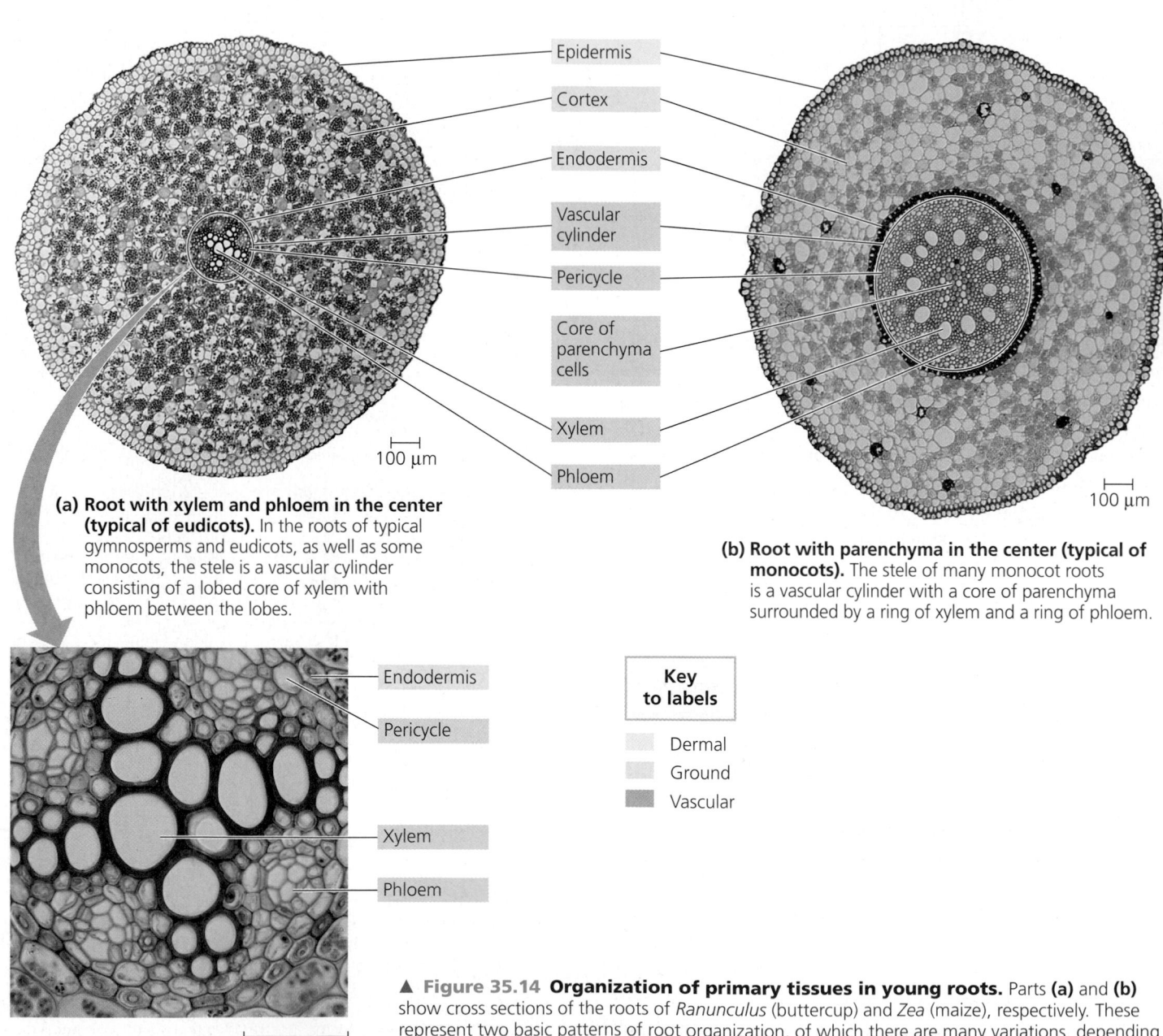

Epidermis

Cortex

Endodermis

Vascular cylinder

Pericycle

Core of parenchyma cells

Xylem

Phloem

100 μm

(a) Root with xylem and phloem in the center (typical of eudicots). In the roots of typical gymnosperms and eudicots, as well as some monocots, the stele is a vascular cylinder consisting of a lobed core of xylem with phloem between the lobes.

(b) Root with parenchyma in the center (typical of monocots). The stele of many monocot roots is a vascular cylinder with a core of parenchyma surrounded by a ring of xylem and a ring of phloem.

100 μm

Endodermis

Pericycle

Xylem

Phloem

50 μm

Key to labels

   Dermal

   Ground

   Vascular

▲ **Figure 35.14 Organization of primary tissues in young roots.** Parts **(a)** and **(b)** show cross sections of the roots of *Ranunculus* (buttercup) and *Zea* (maize), respectively. These represent two basic patterns of root organization, of which there are many variations, depending on the plant species (all LMs).

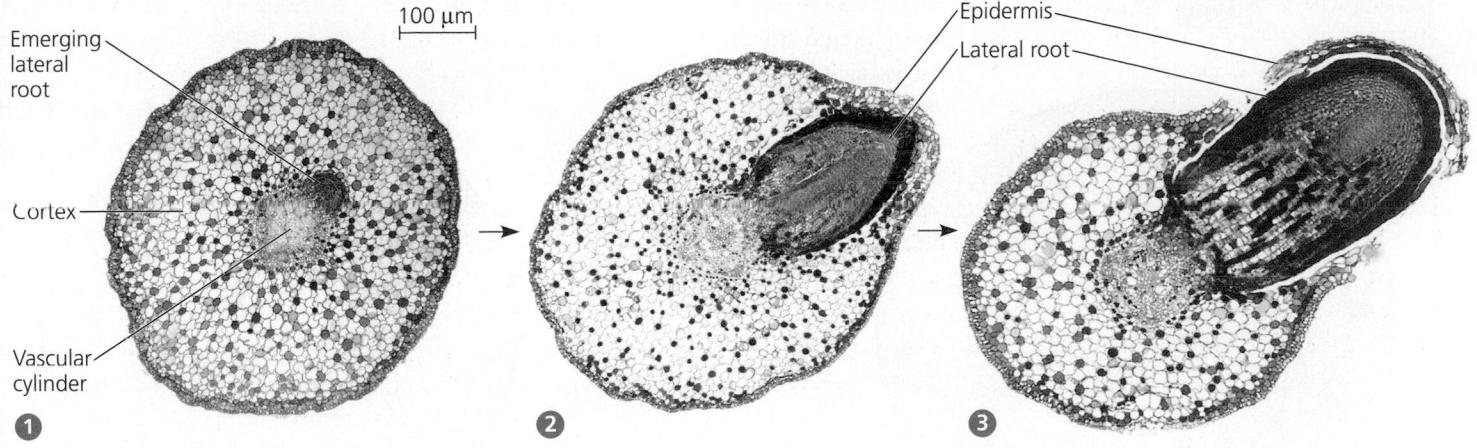

▲ Figure 35.15 **The formation of a lateral root.** A lateral root originates in the pericycle, the outermost layer of the vascular cylinder of a root, and grows out through the cortex and epidermis. In this series of light micrographs, the view of the original root is a cross section, while the view of the lateral root is a longitudinal section.

The ground tissue of roots, consisting mostly of parenchyma cells, fills the cortex, the region between the vascular cylinder and epidermis. Cells within the ground tissue store carbohydrates, and their plasma membranes absorb water and minerals from the soil. The innermost layer of the cortex is called the **endodermis**, a cylinder one cell thick that forms the boundary with the vascular cylinder. As you will see in Chapter 36, the endodermis is a selective barrier that regulates passage of substances from the soil into the vascular cylinder.

Lateral roots arise from the **pericycle**, the outermost cell layer in the vascular cylinder, which is adjacent to and just inside the endodermis (see Figure 35.14). A lateral root pushes through the cortex and epidermis until it emerges from the established root **(Figure 35.15)**. A lateral root cannot originate near the root's surface because its vascular system must be continuous with the vascular cylinder at the center of the established root.

Primary Growth of Shoots

A shoot apical meristem is a dome-shaped mass of dividing cells at the shoot tip **(Figure 35.16)**. Leaves develop from **leaf primordia** (singular, *primordium*), finger-like projections along the sides of the apical meristem. Axillary buds develop from islands of meristematic cells left by the apical meristem at the bases of the leaf primordia. Axillary buds can form lateral shoots at some later time (see Figure 35.12).

Within a bud, leaf primordia are spaced close together because the internodes are very short. Most shoot elongation is due to the lengthening of internode cells below the shoot tip. In some plants, including grasses, a few leaf cells are produced by areas of meristematic tissue separated from the apical meristem. These areas, called *intercalary meristems*, remain at the base of leaf blades and stem internodes. This morphological feature helps grasses tolerate grazing because the elevated part of the leaf blade can be removed without stopping growth.

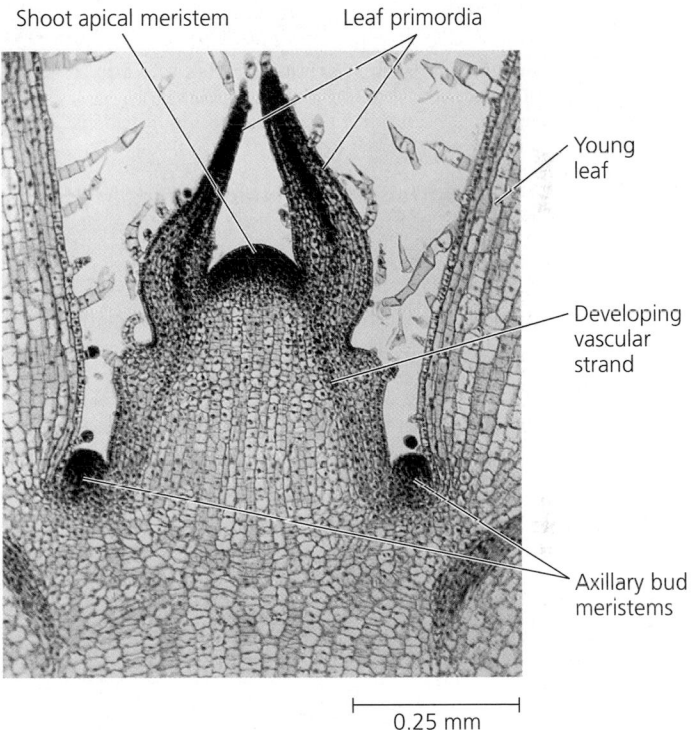

▲ Figure 35.16 **The shoot tip.** Leaf primordia arise from the flanks of the dome of the apical meristem. This is a longitudinal section of the shoot tip of *Coleus* (LM).

Tissue Organization of Stems

The epidermis covers stems as part of the continuous dermal tissue system. Vascular tissue runs the length of a stem in vascular bundles. Unlike lateral roots, which arise from vascular tissue deep within a root and disrupt the vascular cambium, cortex, and epidermis as they emerge (see Figure 35.15), lateral shoots develop from axillary bud meristems on the stem's surface and disrupt no other tissues (see Figure 35.16). The vascular bundles of the stem converge with the root's vascular cylinder in a zone of transition located near the soil surface.

Phloem   Xylem

Sclerenchyma
(fiber cells)

Ground tissue
connecting
pith to cortex

Ground
tissue

Pith

Epidermis

Epidermis

Cortex

Vascular
bundle

Vascular
bundles

**Key
to labels**

Dermal

Ground

Vascular

1 mm

1 mm

**(a) Cross section of stem with vascular bundles forming a
ring (typical of eudicots).** Ground tissue toward the
inside is called pith, and ground tissue toward the outside is
called cortex (LM).

**(b) Cross section of stem with scattered vascular bundles
(typical of monocots).** In such an arrangement, ground tissue is
not partitioned into pith and cortex (LM).

▲ **Figure 35.17 Organization of primary tissues in young stems.**

? *Why aren't the terms* pith *and* cortex *used to describe the ground tissue of monocot stems?*

In most eudicot species, the vascular tissue consists of vascular bundles arranged in a ring **(Figure 35.17a)**. The xylem in each vascular bundle is adjacent to the pith, and the phloem in each bundle is adjacent to the cortex. In most monocot stems, the vascular bundles are scattered throughout the ground tissue, rather than forming a ring **(Figure 35.17b)**. In the stems of both monocots and eudicots, the ground tissue consists mostly of parenchyma cells. However, collenchyma cells just beneath the epidermis strengthen many stems. Sclerenchyma cells, especially fiber cells, also provide support in those parts of the stems that are no longer elongating.

Tissue Organization of Leaves

Figure 35.18 provides an overview of leaf structure. The epidermal barrier is interrupted by **stomata** (singular, *stoma*), which allow gas exchange between the surrounding air and the photosynthetic cells inside the leaf. In addition to regulating CO_2 uptake for photosynthesis, stomata are major avenues for the evaporative loss of water. The term *stoma* can refer to the stomatal pore or to the entire stomatal complex consisting of a pore flanked by two **guard cells**, which regulate the opening and closing of the pore. We'll discuss stomata in detail in Chapter 36.

The ground tissue of a leaf, a region called the **mesophyll** (from the Greek *mesos*, middle, and *phyll*, leaf), is sandwiched between the upper and lower epidermal layers. Mes-

ophyll consists mainly of parenchyma cells specialized for photosynthesis. The leaves of many eudicots have two distinct areas: palisade mesophyll and spongy mesophyll. The *palisade mesophyll* consists of one or more layers of elongated parenchyma cells on the upper part of the leaf. The *spongy mesophyll* is below the palisade mesophyll. These parenchyma cells are more loosely arranged, with a labyrinth of air spaces through which CO_2 and oxygen circulate around the cells and up to the palisade region. The air spaces are particularly large in the vicinity of stomata, where gas exchange with the outside air occurs.

The vascular tissue of each leaf is continuous with the vascular tissue of the stem. *Leaf traces*, connections from vascular bundles in the stem, pass through petioles and into leaves. Veins are the leaf's vascular bundles, which subdivide repeatedly and branch throughout the mesophyll. This network brings xylem and phloem into close contact with the photosynthetic tissue, which obtains water and minerals from the xylem and loads its sugars and other organic products into the phloem for transport to other parts of the plant. The vascular structure also functions as a skeleton that reinforces the shape of the leaf. Each vein is enclosed by a protective *bundle sheath*, consisting of one or more layers of cells, usually parenchyma cells. Bundle sheath cells are particularly prominent in leaves of plants that undergo C_4 photosynthesis (see Chapter 10). Unlike stems and roots, leaves rarely undergo secondary growth, which is the topic of the next section.

▼ Figure 35.18 **Leaf anatomy.**

Key to labels
▢ Dermal
▢ Ground
▢ Vascular

Cuticle

Sclerenchyma fibers

Stoma

Bundle-sheath cell

Xylem
Phloem

Guard cells

Vein

Cuticle

(a) Cutaway drawing of leaf tissues

Guard cells
Stomatal pore
Epidermal cell

50 µm

(b) Surface view of a spiderwort (*Tradescantia*) leaf (LM)

Upper epidermis
Palisade mesophyll
Spongy mesophyll
Lower epidermis

100 µm

Vein   Air spaces   Guard cells

(c) Cross section of a lilac (*Syringa*) leaf (LM)

CONCEPT CHECK 35.3

1. Describe how roots and shoots differ in branching.
2. Contrast primary growth in roots and shoots.
3. When grazing animals are removed from grasslands, eudicots often replace grasses. Suggest a reason why.
4. **WHAT IF?** If a leaf is vertically oriented, would you expect its mesophyll to be divided into spongy and palisade layers? Explain.

For suggested answers, see Appendix A.

For suggested answers, see Appendix A.

CONCEPT 35.4

Secondary growth adds girth to stems and roots in woody plants

As you have seen, primary growth arises from apical meristems and involves the production and elongation of roots, stems, and leaves. In contrast, secondary growth, the growth in thickness produced by lateral meristems, occurs in stems and roots of woody plants, but rarely in leaves. The **secondary plant body** consists of the tissues produced by the vascular cambium and cork cambium. The vascular cambium adds secondary xylem (wood) and secondary phloem, increasing vascular flow and support for the shoot system. The cork cambium produces a tough,

thick covering consisting mainly of wax-impregnated cells that protect the stem from water loss and from invasion by insects, bacteria, and fungi. All gymnosperm species and many eudicot species have secondary growth, but it is rare in monocots.

Primary growth and secondary growth occur simultaneously. As primary growth adds leaves and lengthens stems and roots in the younger regions of a plant, secondary growth thickens stems and roots in older regions where primary growth has stopped. The process is similar in shoots and roots. **Figure 35.19**, on the next page, provides an overview of growth in a woody stem.

The Vascular Cambium and Secondary Vascular Tissue

The vascular cambium is a cylinder of meristematic cells, often only one cell thick. It increases in circumference and also adds layers of secondary xylem to its interior and secondary phloem to its exterior. Each layer has a larger diameter than the previous layer (see Figure 35.19). In this way, the vascular cambium thickens roots and stems.

In a typical woody stem, the vascular cambium consists of a continuous cylinder of undifferentiated parenchyma cells, located outside the pith and primary xylem and to the inside of the cortex and primary phloem. In a typical woody root, the vascular cambium forms to the exterior of the primary xylem and interior to the primary phloem and pericycle.

(a) Primary and secondary growth in a two-year-old stem

Epidermis
Cortex
Primary phloem
Vascular cambium
Primary xylem
Pith

Periderm (mainly cork cambia and cork)
Primary phloem
Secondary phloem
Vascular cambium
Secondary xylem
Primary xylem
Pith

1
Pith
Primary xylem
Vascular cambium
Primary phloem
Epidermis
Cortex

3 Vascular ray
Growth
Primary xylem
Secondary xylem
Vascular cambium
Secondary phloem
Primary phloem
First cork cambium
4
Cork

Growth
6
Secondary xylem (two years of production)
Vascular cambium
Secondary phloem
7 Most recent cork cambium
5
9 Bark
8 Layers of periderm
Cork

1 Primary growth from the activity of the apical meristem is nearing completion. The vascular cambium has just formed.

2 Although primary growth continues in the apical bud, only secondary growth occurs in this section. The stem thickens as the vascular cambium forms secondary xylem to the inside and secondary phloem to the outside.

3 Some initials of the vascular cambium give rise to vascular rays (see next page).

4 As the vascular cambium's diameter increases, the secondary phloem and other tissues external to the cambium can't keep pace because their cells no longer divide. As a result, these tissues, including the epidermis, will eventually rupture. A second lateral meristem, the cork cambium, develops from parenchyma cells in the cortex. The cork cambium produces cork cells, which replace the epidermis.

5 In year 2 of secondary growth, the vascular cambium produces more secondary xylem and phloem, and the cork cambium produces more cork.

6 As the stem's diameter increases, the outermost tissues exterior to the cork cambium rupture and are sloughed off.

7 In many cases, the cork cambium re-forms deeper in the cortex. When none of the cortex is left, the cambium develops from phloem parenchyma cells.

8 Each cork cambium and the tissues it produces form a layer of periderm.

9 Bark consists of all tissues exterior to the vascular cambium.

▲ **Figure 35.19 Primary and secondary growth of a stem.** The progress of secondary growth can be tracked by examining the sections through sequentially older parts of the stem.

? *How does the vascular cambium cause some tissues to rupture?*

Secondary phloem
Vascular cambium
Bark
Secondary xylem { Late wood, Early wood }
Cork cambium } Periderm
Cork
0.5 mm
Vascular ray   Growth ring
(b) Cross section of a three-year-old *Tilia* (linden) stem (LM)
0.5 mm

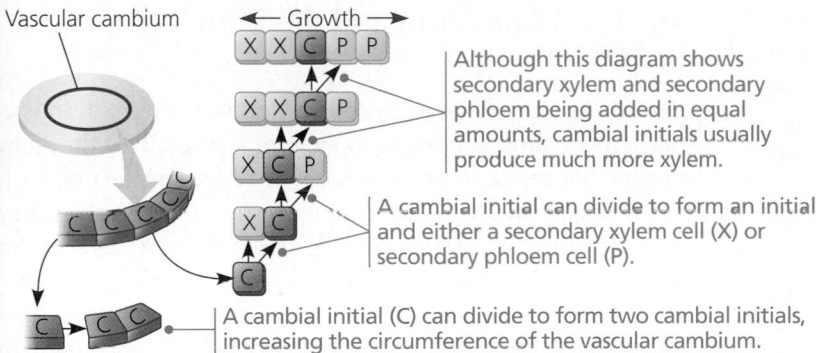

Vascular cambium ←— Growth —→

Although this diagram shows secondary xylem and secondary phloem being added in equal amounts, cambial initials usually produce much more xylem.

A cambial initial can divide to form an initial and either a secondary xylem cell (X) or secondary phloem cell (P).

A cambial initial (C) can divide to form two cambial initials, increasing the circumference of the vascular cambium.

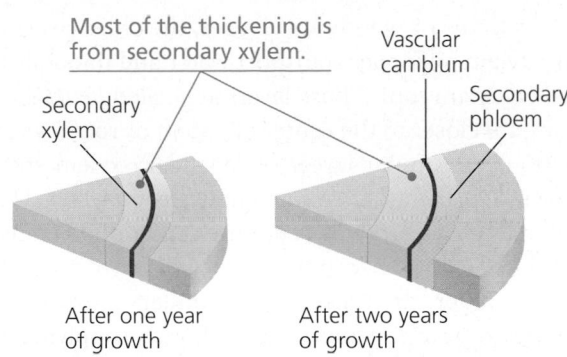

Most of the thickening is from secondary xylem.

Vascular cambium

Secondary xylem

Secondary phloem

After one year of growth

After two years of growth

▲ **Figure 35.20 Secondary growth produced by the vascular cambium.**

Viewed in cross section, the vascular cambium appears as a ring of initials. As these meristematic cells divide, they increase the circumference of the vascular cambium and also add secondary xylem to the inside of the cambium and secondary phloem to the outside **(Figure 35.20)**. Some initials are elongated and are oriented with their long axis parallel to the axis of the stem or root. They produce cells such as the tracheids, vessel elements, and fibers of the xylem, as well as the sieve-tube elements, companion cells, parenchyma, and fibers of the phloem. The other initials are shorter and are oriented perpendicular to the axis of the stem or root. They produce *vascular rays*—radial files of cells that connect the secondary xylem with the secondary phloem. The cells of a vascular ray move water and nutrients between the secondary xylem and phloem, store carbohydrates, and aid in wound repair.

As secondary growth continues over many years, layers of secondary xylem (wood) accumulate, consisting mainly of tracheids, vessel elements, and fibers (see Figure 35.10). Gymnosperms have only tracheids, whereas almost all angiosperms have both tracheids and vessel elements. The walls of secondary xylem cells are heavily lignified and account for the hardness and strength of wood. In temperate regions, wood that develops early in the spring, known as early wood, usually consists of secondary xylem cells with relatively large diameters and thin cell walls (see Figure 35.19b). This structure maximizes delivery of water to new, growing leaves. Wood produced later in the growing season, during late summer or early fall, is known as late wood. It is composed of thick-walled cells that do not transport as much water but contribute more to stem support.

In temperate regions, the vascular cambium becomes dormant during winter, and after growth resumes in spring, there is a marked contrast between the large cells of the new early wood and the smaller cells of the late wood of the previous growing season. A year's growth appears as a distinct ring in cross sections of most tree trunks and roots. Therefore, researchers can estimate a tree's age by counting its annual rings. *Dendrochronology* (from the Greek *dendron,* trees) is the science of analyzing tree ring growth patterns. Rings can vary in thicknesses, depending on seasonal growth. Trees grow well in

▼ **Figure 35.21** **Research Method**

Using Dendrochronology to Study Climate

APPLICATION   Dendrochronology, the science of analyzing tree rings, is useful in studying climate change. Most scientists attribute recent global warming to the burning of fossil fuels and release of CO_2 and other greenhouse gases, whereas a minority think it is a natural variation. Studying climate patterns requires comparing past and present temperatures, but instrumental climate records span only the last two centuries and apply only to some regions. By examining growth rings of Mongolian conifers dating back to the mid-1500s, G. C. Jacoby and Rosanne D'Arrigo, of the Lamont-Doherty Earth Observatory, and colleagues sought to learn whether Mongolia experienced similar warm periods in the past.

TECHNIQUE   Researchers can analyze patterns of rings in living and dead trees. They can even study wood used for building long ago by matching samples with those from naturally situated specimens of overlapping age. Core samples, each about the diameter of a pencil, are taken from the bark to the center of the trunk. Each sample is dried and sanded to reveal the rings. By comparing, aligning, and averaging many samples from the Mongolian conifers, the researchers compiled a chronology. In this way, the trees served as a chronicle of environmental change.

RESULTS

This graph summarizes a composite record of ring-width indexes for the Mongolian conifers from 1550 to 1993. Higher indexes indicate wider rings and warmer temperatures. The highest growth period was from 1974 to 1993, and 17 of the 20 highest-growth years occurred since 1946, suggesting unusual warming during the 1900s.

wet and warm years but may grow hardly at all in cold or dry years. Because a thick ring indicates a warm year and a thin ring indicates a cold or dry one, scientists can use ring patterns to study climate changes **(Figure 35.21)**.

As a tree or woody shrub ages, the older layers of secondary xylem no longer transport water and minerals (a solution called xylem sap). These layers are called *heartwood* because they are closer to the center of a stem or root (Figure 35.22). The newest, outer layers of secondary xylem still transport xylem sap and are therefore known as *sapwood*. That is why a large tree can survive even if the center of its trunk is hollow (Figure 35.23). Because each new layer of secondary xylem has a larger circumference, secondary growth enables the xylem to transport more sap each year, supplying an increasing number of leaves. Heartwood is generally darker than sapwood because of resins and other compounds that permeate the cell cavities and help protect the core of the tree from fungi and wood-boring insects.

Only the youngest secondary phloem, closest to the vascular cambium, functions in sugar transport. As a stem or root increases in circumference, the older secondary phloem is sloughed off, which is why secondary phloem does not accumulate as extensively as does secondary xylem.

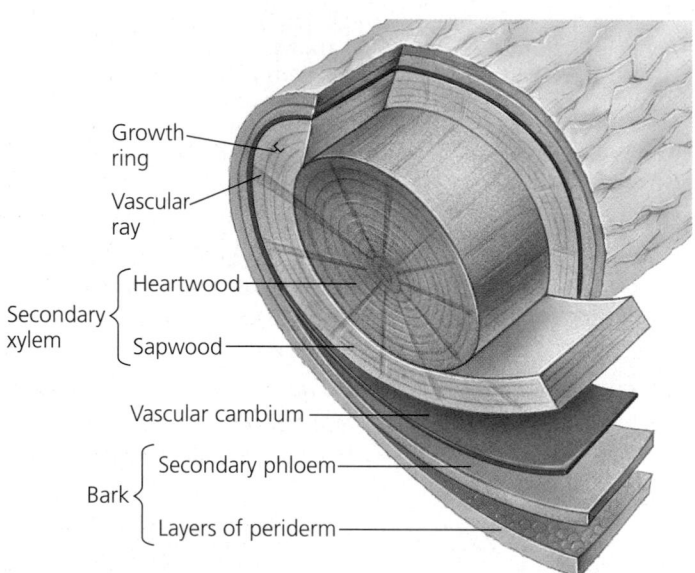

▲ Figure 35.22 **Anatomy of a tree trunk.**

◄ Figure 35.23 **Is this tree living or dead?** The Wawona Sequoia tunnel in Yosemite National Park in California was cut in 1881 as a tourist attraction. This giant sequoia (*Sequoiadendron giganteum*) lived for another 88 years before it fell during a severe winter. It was 71.3 m tall and estimated to be 2,100 years old. Though conservation policies today would forbid the mutilation of such an important specimen, the Wawona Sequoia did teach a valuable botanical lesson: Trees do not need heartwood to survive.

The Cork Cambium and the Production of Periderm

During the early stages of secondary growth, the epidermis is pushed outward, causing it to split, dry, and fall off the stem or root. It is replaced by two tissues produced by the first cork cambium, a cylinder of dividing cells that arises in the outer cortex of stems (see Figure 35.19a) and in the outer layer of the pericycle in roots. One tissue, called *phelloderm*, is a thin layer of parenchyma cells that forms to the interior of the cork cambium. The other tissue consists of cork cells that accumulate to the exterior of the cork cambium. As cork cells mature, they deposit a waxy material called *suberin* in their walls and then die. The cork tissue then functions as a barrier that helps protect the stem or root from water loss, physical damage, and pathogens. Each cork cambium and the tissues it produces comprise a layer of periderm.

Because cork cells have suberin and are usually compacted together, most of the periderm is impermeable to water and gases, unlike the epidermis. In most plants, therefore, water and minerals are absorbed primarily in the youngest parts of roots. The older parts of roots anchor the plant and transport water and solutes between the soil and shoots. Dotting the periderm are small, raised areas called **lenticels**, in which there is more space between cork cells, enabling living cells within a woody stem or root to exchange gases with the outside air. Lenticels often appear as slits, as shown in Figure 35.19a.

The thickening of a stem or root often splits the first cork cambium, which loses its meristematic activity and differentiates into cork cells. A new cork cambium forms to the inside, resulting in another layer of periderm. As this process continues, older layers of periderm are sloughed off, as you can see in the cracked, peeling bark of many tree trunks.

Many people think that bark is only the protective outer covering of a woody stem or root. Actually, **bark** includes all tissues external to the vascular cambium. In an outward direction, its main components are the secondary phloem (produced by the vascular cambium), the most recent periderm, and all the older layers of periderm (see Figure 35.22).

CONCEPT CHECK **35.4**

1. A sign is hammered into a tree 2 m from the tree's base. If the tree is 10 m tall and elongates 1 m each year, how high will the sign be after 10 years?
2. Stomata and lenticels are both involved in gas exchange. Why do stomata need to be able to close, but lenticels do not?
3. Would you expect a tropical tree to have distinct growth rings? Why or why not?
4. **WHAT IF?** If a complete ring of bark is removed around a tree trunk (a process called girdling), the tree usually dies. Explain why.

For suggested answers, see Appendix A.

CONCEPT 35.5

Growth, morphogenesis, and differentiation produce the plant body

So far, we have described the development of the plant body from meristems. Here we will move from a description of plant growth and development to the mechanisms that underlie these processes.

Consider that a typical small plant may consist of billions of cells—some large, some small, some highly specialized and others not. The growth that occurs during the life of the plant results from both cell division and cell expansion. But what controls these two processes? Why do leaves stop growing upon reaching a certain size, whereas the cells of apical meristems keep dividing? Also, what controls cell specialization and the development of recognizable tissues and organs? Leaves arise from nodes; roots usually do not. Epidermis forms on the exterior of the leaf, and vascular tissue in the interior—never vice versa.

Each cell in the plant contains the same set of genes. The different patterns of gene expression among various cells cause the cellular differentiation that creates a diversity of cell types (see Chapter 18). Other processes lead to the development of body form and organization, called **morphogenesis**. The three developmental processes of growth, morphogenesis, and cellular differentiation act in concert to produce the body of a plant.

Molecular Biology: Revolutionizing the Study of Plants

Modern molecular techniques are helping plant biologists explore how growth, morphogenesis, and cellular differentiation give rise to a plant. In the current renaissance in plant biology, new laboratory methods and a focus on model organisms have catalyzed a research explosion. A major research focus is *Arabidopsis thaliana*, a weed of the mustard family that is small enough to allow researchers to cultivate thousands of plants in a few square meters of lab space. Its short generation span, about six weeks from germination to flowering, makes *Arabidopsis* an excellent model for genetic studies. It also has among the smallest genomes of all known plants. *Arabidopsis* was the first plant to have its entire genome sequenced—a six-year, multinational effort **(Figure 35.24)**. More recently, rice, a species of poplar, the common grape, and maize have had their entire genomes sequenced, too.

Arabidopsis has about 26,700 protein-encoding genes, but many of these are duplicates. There are probably fewer than 15,000 different types of genes, a number similar to that found in the fly *Drosophila*. Determining the function of many *Arabidopsis* genes has greatly expanded our understanding of plant

▲ **Figure 35.24** ***Arabidopsis thaliana* gene functions.** Due to its small size, rapid life cycle, and small genome, *Arabidopsis* was the first plant to have its entire genome sequenced (containing about 26,700 genes). The pie chart represents the proportion of *Arabidopsis* genes in different functional categories. (Data from TAIR, The *Arabidopsis* Information Resource, 2007.)

development. To fill the gaps in our knowledge, plant biologists have launched an ambitious quest to determine the function of every one of the plant's genes. Toward this goal, they are attempting to create mutants for every gene in the genome of this species. We will discuss some of these mutants shortly, as we take a closer look at the molecular mechanisms that underlie growth, morphogenesis, and cellular differentiation. By identifying each gene's function and tracking every biochemical pathway, researchers aim to establish a blueprint for how plants develop, a major goal of systems biology. It may one day be possible to create a computer-generated "virtual plant" that enables researchers to visualize which plant genes are activated in different parts of the plant during the entire course of development.

Growth: Cell Division and Cell Expansion

By increasing cell number, cell division in meristems increases the potential for growth. However, it is cell expansion, particularly cell elongation, that accounts for increase in size. The process of plant cell division is described more fully in Chapter 12 (see Figure 12.10), and Chapter 39 discusses the process of cell elongation (see Figure 39.8). Here we are more concerned with how these processes contribute to plant form.

The Plane and Symmetry of Cell Division

The plane (direction) and symmetry of cell division are immensely important in determining plant form. Imagine a single cell that is ready to undergo mitosis. If the planes of division of its descendants are parallel to the plane of the first cell division, a single file of cells will be produced **(Figure 35.25a)**. At the other extreme, if the planes vary randomly, a disorganized clump of cells results. Meanwhile, even though chromosomes are allocated to daughter cells equally during mitosis, the cytoplasm may divide asymmetrically. *Asymmetrical cell division*, in which one daughter cell receives more cytoplasm than the other during mitosis, is fairly common in plant cells and usually signals a key event in development. For example, the formation of guard cells typically involves both an asymmetrical cell division and a change in the plane of cell division. An epidermal cell divides asymmetrically, forming a large cell that remains an unspecialized epidermal cell and a small cell that becomes the guard cell "mother cell." Guard cells form when this small mother cell divides in a plane perpendicular to the first cell division **(Figure 35.25b)**.

The plane in which a cell divides is determined during late interphase. The first sign of this spatial orientation is a rearrangement of the cytoskeleton. Microtubules in the cytoplasm become concentrated into a ring that is called the **preprophase band (Figure 35.26)**. The band disappears before metaphase, but it predicts the future plane of cell division. The "imprint" consists of an ordered array of actin microfilaments that remain after the microtubules disperse.

Orientation of Cell Expansion

Before discussing how cell expansion contributes to plant form, it is useful to consider the difference in cell expansion between plants and animals. Animal cells grow mainly by synthesizing protein-rich cytoplasm, a metabolically expensive process. Growing plant cells also produce additional protein-rich material in their cytoplasm, but water uptake typically accounts for about 90% of expansion. Most of this water is packaged in the large central vacuole. Vacuolar sap is very dilute and nearly devoid of the energetically expensive macromolecules that are found in great abundance in the rest of the cytoplasm. Large vacuoles are therefore a "cheap" way of filling space, enabling a plant to grow rapidly and economically. Bamboo shoots, for instance, can elongate more than 2 m per week. Rapid extensibility of shoots and roots was an important evolutionary adaptation that increased their exposure to light and soil.

In a growing cell, enzymes weaken the cross-links in the cell wall, allowing it to expand as water diffuses into the vacuole by osmosis. Loosening of the wall occurs when hydrogen ions secreted by the cell activate cell wall enzymes that break the

(a) Cell divisions in the same plane produce a single file of cells, whereas cell divisions in three planes give rise to a cube.

(b) An asymmetrical cell division precedes the development of epidermal guard cells, the cells that border stomata (see Figure 35.18).

▲ **Figure 35.25 The plane and symmetry of cell division influence development of form.**

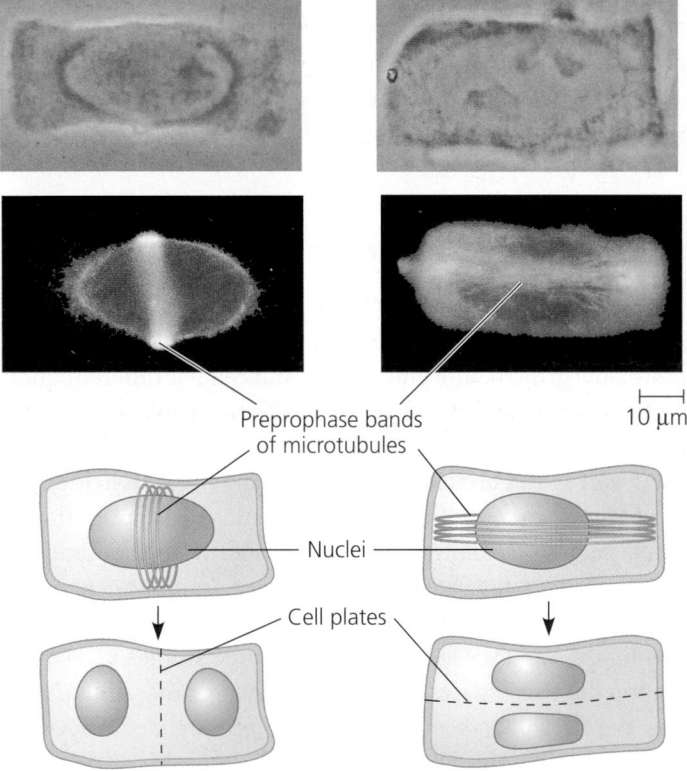

▲ **Figure 35.26 The preprophase band and the plane of cell division.** The location of the preprophase band predicts the plane of cell division. Although the cells shown on the left and right are similar in shape, they will divide in different planes. Each cell is represented by two light micrographs, one (top) unstained and the other (bottom) stained with a fluorescent dye that binds specifically to microtubules. The stained microtubules form a "halo" (preprophase band) around the nucleus in the outer cytoplasm.

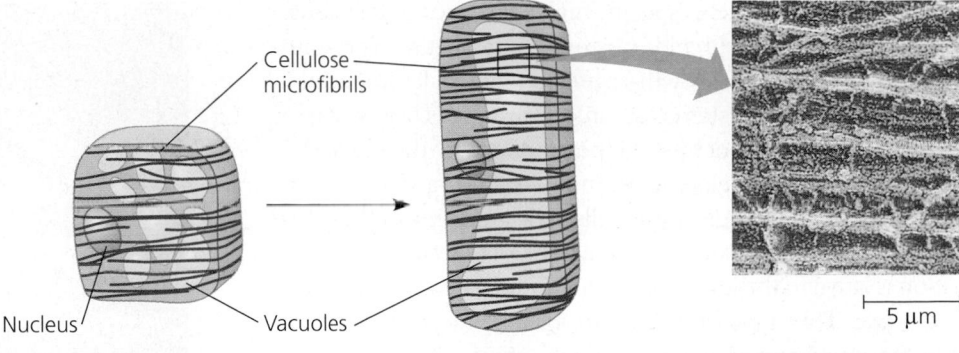

▶ **Figure 35.27 The orientation of plant cell expansion.** Growing plant cells expand mainly through water uptake. In a growing cell, enzymes weaken cross-links in the cell wall, allowing it to expand as water diffuses into the vacuole by osmosis; at the same time, more microfibrils are made. The orientation of cell growth is mainly in the plane perpendicular to the orientation of cellulose microfibrils in the wall. The microfibrils are embedded in a matrix of other (noncellulose) polysaccharides, some of which form the cross-links visible in the micrograph (TEM).

Cellulose microfibrils

Nucleus

Vacuoles

5 μm

cross-links between polymers in the wall. This reduces constraint on the turgid cell, which can take up more water and expand. Small vacuoles, which accumulate most of this water, coalesce and form the cell's central vacuole.

Plant cells rarely expand equally in all directions. Their greatest expansion is usually oriented along the plant's main axis. For example, cells near the tip of the root may elongate up to 20 times their original length, with relatively little increase in width. The orientation of cellulose microfibrils in the innermost layers of the cell wall causes this differential growth. The microfibrils do not stretch, so the cell expands mainly perpendicular to the "grain" of the microfibrils, as shown in **Figure 35.27**.

As with the plane of cell division, microtubules play a key role in regulating the plane of cell expansion. It is the orientation of microtubules in the cell's outermost cytoplasm that determines the orientation of cellulose microfibrils, the basic structural units of the cell wall.

Microtubules and Plant Growth

Studies of *fass* mutants of *Arabidopsis* have confirmed the importance of cytoplasmic microtubules in cell division and expansion. The *fass* mutants have unusually squat cells with seemingly random planes of cell division. Their roots and stems have no ordered cell files and layers. Despite these abnormalities, *fass* mutants develop into tiny adult plants, but their organs are compressed longitudinally **(Figure 35.28)**.

The stubby form and disorganized tissue arrangement can be traced to the abnormal organization of microtubules. During interphase, the microtubules are randomly positioned, and preprophase bands do not form prior to mitosis (see Figure 35.26). As a result, there is no orderly "grain" of cellulose microfibrils in the cell wall to determine the direction of elongation (see Figure 35.27). This defect gives rise to cells that expand in all directions and divide haphazardly without respect to orientation.

Morphogenesis and Pattern Formation

A plant's body is more than a collection of dividing and expanding cells. Morphogenesis must occur for development to proceed properly; that is, cells must be organized into multicellular

arrangements of tissues and organs. The development of specific structures in specific locations is called **pattern formation**.

Many developmental biologists postulate that pattern formation is determined by **positional information** in the form of signals that continuously indicate to each cell its location within a developing structure. According to this hypothesis, each cell within a developing organ responds to positional information from neighboring cells by differentiating into a particular cell type, oriented in a particular way. Biologists have accumulated

0.3 mm

(b) *fass* seedling

2 mm

(a) Wild-type seedling

2 mm

(c) Mature *fass* mutant

▲ **Figure 35.28 The *fass* mutant of *Arabidopsis* confirms the importance of cytoplasmic microtubules in plant growth.** The squat body of the *fass* mutant results from cell division and cell elongation being oriented randomly instead of in the direction of the normal plant axis.

evidence that gradients of specific molecules, such as hormones, proteins, or mRNAs, provide positional information. For example, the diffusion of a growth-regulating molecule produced in the shoot apical meristem may "inform" the cells below of their distance from the shoot tip. Cells possibly "gauge" their radial positions within the developing organ by detecting a second chemical signal from the outermost cells. The gradients of these two substances would be sufficient for each cell to "get a fix" on its position relative to the longitudinal and radial axes of the developing organ. This hypothesis of diffusible chemical signals is just one that developmental biologists are testing.

One type of positional information is associated with **polarity**, the condition of having structural or chemical differences at opposite ends of an organism. Plants typically have an axis, with a root end and a shoot end. Such polarity is most obvious in morphological differences, but it is also manifest in physiological properties, including the unidirectional movement of the hormone auxin (see Chapter 39) and the emergence of adventitious roots and shoots from "cuttings." Adventitious roots form within the root end of a stem cutting, and adventitious shoots arise from the shoot end of a root cutting.

The first division of a plant zygote is normally asymmetrical, initiating polarization of the plant body into shoot and root. Once this polarity has been induced, it becomes exceedingly difficult to reverse experimentally. Therefore, the proper establishment of axial polarity is a critical step in a plant's morphogenesis. In the *gnom* mutant of *Arabidopsis*, the establishment of polarity is defective. The first cell division of the zygote is abnormal because it is symmetrical, and the resulting ball-shaped plant has neither roots nor leaves **(Figure 35.29)**.

Morphogenesis in plants, as in other multicellular organisms, is often under the control of homeotic genes, master regulatory genes that mediate many of the major events in an individual's development, such as the initiation of an organ (see Chapter 21). For example, the protein product of the homeotic gene *KNOTTED-1*, found in many plant species, is important in the development of leaf morphology, including the production of compound leaves. If the *KNOTTED-1* gene

▲ Figure 35.30 **Overexpression of a homeotic gene in leaf formation.** *KNOTTED-1* is a homeotic gene involved in leaf and leaflet formation. An increase in its expression in tomato plants results in leaves that are "super-compound" (right) compared with normal leaves (left).

is expressed in greater quantity in the genome of tomato plants, the normally compound leaves become "super-compound" **(Figure 35.30)**.

Gene Expression and Control of Cellular Differentiation

Cells of a developing organism can synthesize different proteins and diverge in structure and function even though they share a common genome. If a mature cell removed from a root or leaf can dedifferentiate in tissue culture and give rise to the diverse cell types of a plant, then it must possess all the genes necessary to make any kind of plant cell (see Figure 20.16). This means that cellular differentiation depends, to a large extent, on the control of gene expression—the regulation of transcription and translation, resulting in the production of specific proteins. Researchers are beginning to unravel the molecular mechanisms that switch specific genes on and off at critical times during cellular differentiation (see Chapter 18).

The activation or inactivation of specific genes involved in cellular differentiation depends, to a large extent, on positional information—where a particular cell is located relative to other cells. For example, two distinct cell types are formed in the root epidermis of *Arabidopsis*: root hair cells and hairless epidermal cells. Cell fate is associated with the position of the epidermal cells. The immature epidermal cells that are in contact with two underlying cells of the root cortex differentiate into root hair cells, whereas the immature epidermal cells in contact with only one cortical cell differentiate into mature hairless cells. Differential expression of a homeotic gene called *GLABRA-2* (from the Latin *glaber*, bald) is required for appropriate root hair distribution. Researchers have demonstrated this by coupling the *GLABRA-2* gene to a "reporter gene" that causes every cell expressing *GLABRA-2* in the root to turn pale blue following a certain treatment **(Figure 35.31)**. The *GLABRA-2* gene is normally expressed only in epidermal cells that will not develop root hairs.

◀ Figure 35.29 **Establishment of axial polarity.** The normal *Arabidopsis* seedling (left) has a shoot end and a root end. In the *gnom* mutant (right), the first division of the zygote was not asymmetrical; as a result, the plant is ball-shaped and lacks leaves and roots. The defect in *gnom* mutants has been traced to an inability to transport the hormone auxin in a polar manner.

When epidermal cells border a single cortical cell, the homeotic gene *GLABRA-2* is selectively expressed, and these cells will remain hairless. (The blue color in this light micrograph indicates cells in which *GLABRA-2* is expressed.)

Cortical cells

├20 μm┤

Here an epidermal cell borders two cortical cells. *GLABRA-2* is not expressed, and the cell will develop a root hair.

The root cap cells external to the epidermal layer will be sloughed off before root hairs emerge.

▲ **Figure 35.31 Control of root hair differentiation by a homeotic gene** (LM).

WHAT IF? *What would the roots look like if GLABRA-2 were rendered dysfunctional by a mutation?*

Location and a Cell's Developmental Fate

In the process of shaping an organ, patterns of cell division and cell expansion affect the differentiation of cells by placing them in specific locations relative to other cells. Thus, positional information underlies all the processes of development: growth, morphogenesis, and differentiation. One way to study the relationships among these processes is *clonal analysis*, in which the cell lineages derived from each cell in an apical meristem are mapped during organ development. Researchers use mutations to distinguish a specific meristematic cell from the neighboring cells in the shoot tip. All cells derived from the mutant cell by cell division will thereby be "marked." For example, a single cell in the meristem may have a mutation that prevents chlorophyll synthesis. This cell and all of its descendants will be "albino," and they will appear as a linear file of "albino" cells running down the long axis of the otherwise green shoot.

How early is a cell's developmental fate determined by its position in an embryonic structure? To some extent, the developmental fates of cells in the shoot tip are predictable very early. For example, clonal analysis has shown that almost all the cells derived from the outermost meristematic cells become part of the dermal tissue. However, we cannot pinpoint which meristematic cells will give rise to specific tissues and organs. Apparently random changes in rates and planes of cell division can reorganize the meristem. For example, the outermost cells *usually* divide perpendicularly to the surface of the shoot tip, adding cells to the surface layer. Occasionally, however, one of the outermost cells divides parallel to the surface of the shoot tip, placing one daughter cell beneath the surface,

among cells derived from different lineages. Such exceptions indicate that meristematic cells are not dedicated early to forming specific tissues and organs. Instead, the cell's *final* position in an emerging organ determines what kind of cell it will become.

Shifts in Development: Phase Changes

Multicellular organisms generally pass through developmental phases. In humans, these are infancy, childhood, adolescence, and adulthood, with puberty as the dividing line between the nonreproductive and reproductive phases. Plants also pass through phases, developing from a juvenile phase to an adult vegetative phase to an adult reproductive phase. In animals, these developmental changes take place throughout the entire organism, such as when a larva develops into an adult animal. In contrast, plant developmental phases occur within a single region, the shoot apical meristem. The morphological changes that arise from these transitions in shoot apical meristem activity are called **phase changes**. During the transition from a juvenile phase to an adult phase, the most obvious morphological changes typically occur in leaf size and shape **(Figure 35.32)**. Juvenile

Leaves produced by adult phase of apical meristem

Leaves produced by juvenile phase of apical meristem

▲ **Figure 35.32 Phase change in the shoot system of** *Acacia koa.* This native of Hawaii has compound juvenile leaves, consisting of many small leaflets, and simple mature "leaves" (technically, highly modified petioles). This dual foliage reflects a phase change in the development of the apical meristem of each shoot. Once a node forms, the developmental phase—juvenile or adult—is fixed; that is, compound leaves do not mature into simple leaves.

nodes and internodes retain their juvenile status even after the shoot continues to elongate and the shoot apical meristem has changed to the adult phase. Therefore, any *new* leaves that develop on branches that emerge from axillary buds at juvenile nodes will also be juvenile, even though the apical meristem of the stem's main axis may have been producing mature nodes for years.

Phase changes are examples of developmental plasticity. The transition from juvenile to adult leaves is only one type of phase change. The transition in the fanwort (see Figure 35.1) from feathery underwater leaves to fan-shaped floating leaves is another example. Next we'll examine a common but nevertheless remarkable phase change—the transition of a vegetative shoot apical meristem into a floral meristem.

Genetic Control of Flowering

Flower formation involves a phase change from vegetative growth to reproductive growth. This transition is triggered by a combination of environmental cues, such as day length, and internal signals, such as hormones. (You will learn more about the roles of these signals in flowering in Chapter 39.) Unlike vegetative growth, which is indeterminate, floral growth is determinate: The production of a flower by a shoot apical meristem stops the primary growth of that shoot. The transition from vegetative growth to flowering is associated with the switching on of floral **meristem identity genes**. The protein products of these genes are transcription factors that regulate the genes required for the conversion of the indeterminate vegetative meristems to determinate floral meristems.

When a shoot apical meristem is induced to flower, the relative position of each primordium determines its development into a specific type of floral organ—a sepal, petal, stamen, or carpel (see Figure 30.7 to review basic flower structure). Viewed from above, the floral organs develop in four concentric circles, or whorls: Sepals form the fourth (outermost) whorl; petals form the third; stamens form the second; and carpels form the first (innermost) whorl. Plant biologists have identified several **organ identity genes** that regulate the development of this characteristic floral pattern. Organ identity genes, also called plant homeotic genes, code for transcription factors. Positional information determines which organ identity genes are expressed in a particular floral organ primordium. The result is the development of an emerging floral primordium into a specific floral organ. And just as a mutation in a fruit fly homeotic gene can cause legs to grow in place of antennae

(see Figure 18.18), a mutation in a plant organ identity gene can cause abnormal floral development, such as petals growing in place of stamens, as shown in **Figure 35.33**.

By studying mutants with abnormal flowers, researchers have identified and cloned three classes of floral organ identity genes, and their studies are beginning to reveal how these genes function. The **ABC model** of flower formation, diagrammed in **Figure 35.34a**, identifies how these three classes of genes direct the formation of the four types of floral organs. According to the ABC model, each class of organ identity genes is switched on in two specific whorls of the floral meristem. Normally, *A* genes are switched on in the two outer whorls (sepals and petals); *B* genes are switched on in the two middle whorls (petals and stamens); and *C* genes are switched on in the two inner whorls (stamens and carpels). Sepals arise from those parts of the floral meristems in which only *A* genes are active; petals arise where *A* and *B* genes are active; stamens where *B* and *C* genes are active; and carpels where only *C* genes are active. The ABC model can account for the phenotypes of mutants lacking *A*, *B*, or *C* gene activity, with one addition: Where gene *A* activity is present, it inhibits *C*, and vice versa. If either *A* or *C* is missing, the other takes its place. **Figure 35.34b** shows the floral patterns of mutants lacking each of the three classes of organ identity

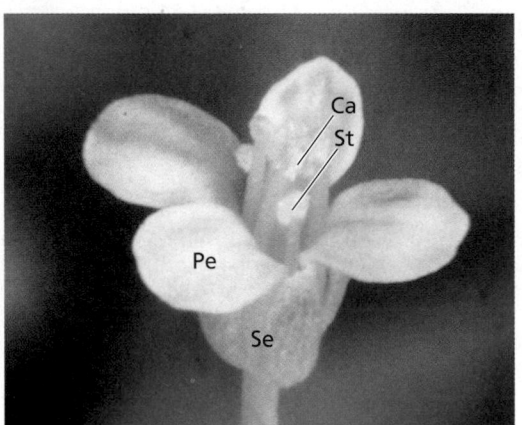

(a) Normal *Arabidopsis* flower. *Arabidopsis* normally has four whorls of flower parts: sepals (Se), petals (Pe), stamens (St), and carpels (Ca).

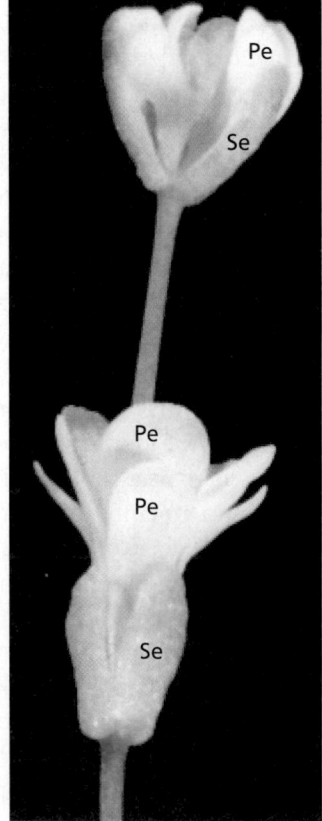

(b) Abnormal *Arabidopsis* flower. Researchers have identified several mutations of organ identity genes that cause abnormal flowers to develop. This flower has an extra set of petals in place of stamens and an internal flower where normal plants have carpels.

▶ **Figure 35.33 Organ identity genes and pattern formation in flower development.**

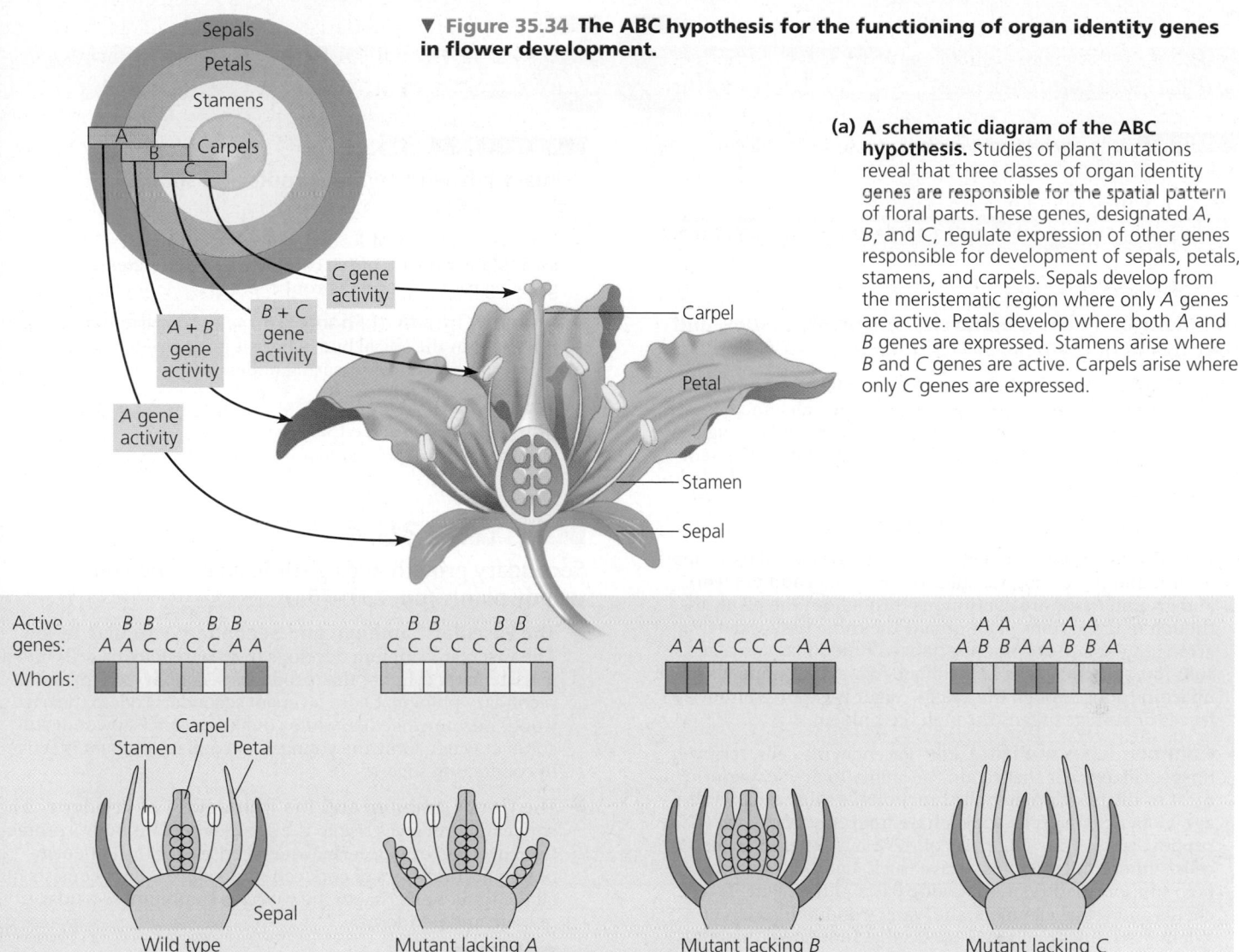

▼ **Figure 35.34 The ABC hypothesis for the functioning of organ identity genes in flower development.**

(a) A schematic diagram of the ABC hypothesis. Studies of plant mutations reveal that three classes of organ identity genes are responsible for the spatial pattern of floral parts. These genes, designated *A*, *B*, and *C*, regulate expression of other genes responsible for development of sepals, petals, stamens, and carpels. Sepals develop from the meristematic region where only *A* genes are active. Petals develop where both *A* and *B* genes are expressed. Stamens arise where *B* and *C* genes are active. Carpels arise where only *C* genes are expressed.

(b) Side view of flowers with organ identity mutations. The phenotype of mutants lacking a functional *A*, *B*, or *C* organ identity gene can be explained by combining the model in part (a) with the rule that if *A* or *C* activity is missing, the other activity occurs through all four whorls.

genes and depicts how the model accounts for the floral phenotypes. By constructing such hypotheses and designing experiments to test them, researchers are tracing the genetic basis of plant development.

In dissecting the plant to examine its parts, as we have done in this chapter, we must remember that the whole plant functions as an integrated organism. In the following chapters, you'll learn more about how materials are transported within vascular plants (Chapter 36), how plants obtain nutrients (Chapter 37), how plants reproduce (Chapter 38, focusing on flowering plants), and how plant functions are coordinated (Chapter 39). Remembering that structure fits function and that plant anatomy and physiology reflect evolutionary adaptations to the challenges of living on land will enhance your understanding of plants.

CONCEPT CHECK 35.5

1. What attributes of the weed *Arabidopsis thaliana* make it such a useful research organism?
2. How can two cells in a plant have vastly different structures even though they have the same genome?
3. Explain how the *fass* mutation in *Arabidopsis* results in a stubby plant rather than a normal elongated one.
4. **WHAT IF?** In some species, such as the magnolia on the cover of this book, sepals look like petals, and both are collectively called "tepals." Suggest an extension to the ABC model that could hypothetically account for the origin of tepals.

For suggested answers, see Appendix A

SUMMARY OF KEY CONCEPTS

CONCEPT 35.1

The plant body has a hierarchy of organs, tissues, and cells (pp. 738–745)

▶ **The Three Basic Plant Organs: Roots, Stems, and Leaves** Roots anchor the plant, absorb and conduct water and minerals, and store food. Shoots consist of stems, leaves, and (in angiosperms) flowers. Leaves are attached to the nodes of the stem and are the primary organs of photosynthesis. Axillary buds, located in axils of leaves and stems, give rise to shoot branches. Plant organs may be modified for specialized functions.

▶ **Dermal, Vascular, and Ground Tissues** Dermal tissue (epidermis and periderm), vascular tissue (xylem and phloem), and ground tissue are continuous throughout the plant, although in the various plant organs the three tissues differ in arrangement and in some specialized functions. Vascular tissues integrate the parts of the plant. Water and minerals move up from roots through the xylem. Sugar is exported from leaves or storage organs through the phloem.

▶ **Common Types of Plant Cells** Parenchyma cells, relatively unspecialized cells that retain the ability to divide, perform most of the plant's metabolic functions of synthesis and storage. Collenchyma cells, which have unevenly thickened walls, support young, growing parts of the plant. Sclerenchyma cells—fibers and sclereids—have thick, lignified walls that help support mature, nongrowing parts of the plant. Tracheids and vessel elements, the water-conducting cells of xylem, have thick walls and are dead at functional maturity. Sieve-tube elements are the sugar-transporting cells of phloem in angiosperms. Though alive at functional maturity, sieve-tube elements depend on neighboring companion cells.

MEDIA
BioFlix 3-D Animation Tour of a Plant Cell

CONCEPT 35.2

Meristems generate cells for new organs (pp. 746–747)

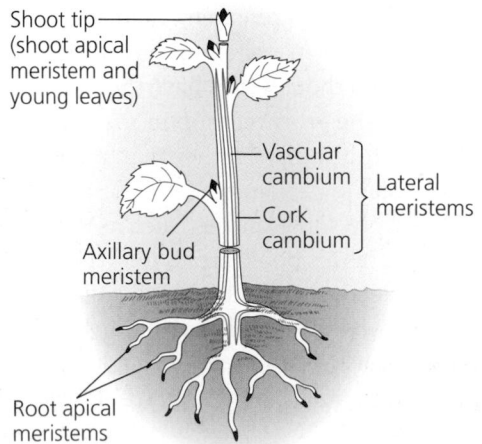

Shoot tip (shoot apical meristem and young leaves)

Vascular cambium
Cork cambium
Lateral meristems

Axillary bud meristem

Root apical meristems

CONCEPT 35.3

Primary growth lengthens roots and shoots (pp. 747–751)

▶ **Primary Growth of Roots** The root apical meristem is located near the tip of the root, where it generates cells for the growing root axis and the root cap.

▶ **Primary Growth of Shoots** The apical meristem of a shoot is located in the apical bud, where it gives rise to a repetition of internodes and leaf-bearing nodes.

MEDIA
Activity Root, Stem, and Leaf Sections
Investigation What Are Functions of Monocot Tissues?

CONCEPT 35.4

Secondary growth adds girth to stems and roots in woody plants (pp. 751–754)

▶ **The Vascular Cambium and Secondary Vascular Tissue** The vascular cambium develops from parenchyma cells into a meristematic cylinder that produces secondary xylem and secondary phloem. Older layers of secondary xylem (heartwood) become inactive, while younger layers (sapwood) still conduct water. Only the youngest secondary phloem is active in conducting sugars.

▶ **The Cork Cambium and the Production of Periderm** The cork cambium gives rise to the secondary plant body's protective covering, or periderm, which consists of the cork cambium plus the layers of cork cells it produces. Bark consists of all the tissues external to the vascular cambium: secondary phloem and periderm.

MEDIA
Activity Primary and Secondary Growth

CONCEPT 35.5

Growth, morphogenesis, and differentiation produce the plant body (pp. 755–761)

▶ **Molecular Biology: Revolutionizing the Study of Plants** New techniques and model systems, including *Arabidopsis*, are catalyzing progress in understanding plants. *Arabidopsis* was the first plant to have its genome sequenced.

▶ **Growth: Cell Division and Cell Expansion** Cell division and cell expansion are the primary determinants of growth and form. A preprophase band determines where a cell plate will form in a dividing cell. Cytoskeleton orientation affects the direction of cell elongation by controlling the orientation of cellulose microfibrils in the cell wall.

▶ **Morphogenesis and Pattern Formation** Development of tissues and organs in specific locations depends on cells responding to positional information, such as polarity. Homeotic genes often control morphogenesis.

▶ **Gene Expression and Control of Cellular Differentiation** Despite having identical genomes, plant cells differentiate because of differential gene activation.

- ► **Location and a Cell's Developmental Fate** The way in which a plant cell differentiates is determined largely by the cell's position in the developing plant body.

- ► **Shifts in Development: Phase Changes** Internal or environmental cues may cause a plant to switch from one developmental phase to another—for example, from developing juvenile leaves to developing mature leaves. Such morphological changes are called phase changes.

- ► **Genetic Control of Flowering** Research on organ identity genes in developing flowers provides a model system for studying pattern formation. The ABC model identifies how three classes of organ identity genes control formation of sepals, petals, stamens, and carpels.

TESTING YOUR KNOWLEDGE

SELF-QUIZ

1. Which structure is *incorrectly* paired with its tissue system?
   a. root hair—dermal tissue
   b. palisade mesophyll—ground tissue
   c. guard cell—dermal tissue
   d. companion cell—ground tissue
   e. tracheid—vascular tissue

2. In a root, a vessel element completes its development in which area of growth?
   a. zone of cell division   d. root cap
   b. zone of elongation   e. apical meristem
   c. zone of differentiation

3. Heartwood and sapwood consist of
   a. bark.   d. secondary phloem.
   b. periderm.   e. cork.
   c. secondary xylem.

4. Which of the following is *not* part of an older tree's bark?
   a. cork   d. secondary xylem
   b. cork cambium   e. secondary phloem
   c. lenticels

5. The phase change of an apical meristem from the juvenile to the mature vegetative phase is often revealed by
   a. a change in the morphology of the leaves produced.
   b. the initiation of secondary growth.
   c. the formation of lateral roots.
   d. a change in the orientation of preprophase bands and cytoplasmic microtubules in lateral meristems.
   e. the activation of floral meristem identity genes.

6. Which of the following arise from meristematic activity?
   a. secondary xylem   d. tubers
   b. leaves   e. all of the above
   c. dermal tissue

7. Pinching off the tops of snapdragons causes the plants to make many more flowers than they would if left alone. Why does the removal of the top cause more flowers to form?
   a. Removal of an apical meristem causes a phase transition from vegetative to floral development.

b. Removal of an apical meristem causes cell division to become disorganized, as in the *fass* mutant of *Arabidopsis*.
c. Removal of an apical meristem allows more nutrients to be delivered to floral meristems.
d. Removal of an apical meristem causes outgrowth of lateral buds that produce extra branches, which ultimately produce flowers.
e. Removal of an apical meristem allows the periderm to produce new lateral branches.

8. Which of these are *not* produced by the vascular cambium?
   a. sclerenchyma cells   d. root hairs
   b. parenchyma cells   e. vessel elements
   c. sieve-tube elements

9. The type of mature cell that a particular embryonic plant cell will become appears to be determined mainly by
   a. the selective loss of genes.
   b. the cell's final position in a developing organ.
   c. the cell's pattern of migration.
   d. the cell's age.
   e. the cell's particular meristematic lineage.

10. Based on the ABC model, what would be the structure of a flower that had normal expression of genes *A* and *C* and expression of gene *B* in all four whorls?
    a. carpel-petal-petal-carpel
    b. stamen-stamen-petal-petal
    c. sepal-carpel-carpel-sepal
    d. sepal-sepal-carpel-carpel
    e. carpel-carpel-carpel-carpel

11. **DRAW IT** On this cross section from a woody eudicot, label a growth ring, late wood, early wood, and a vessel element. Then draw an arrow in the pith-to-cork direction.

For Self-Quiz answers, see Appendix A.

MEDIA Visit **www.campbellbiology.com** for a Practice Test.

EVOLUTION CONNECTION

12. Evolutionary biologists have coined the term *exaptation* to describe a common occurrence in the evolution of life: A limb or organ originally has a particular function but later fulfills a new function. What are some examples of exaptations in plant organs?

SCIENTIFIC INQUIRY

13. Write a paragraph explaining why mutants are useful for investigating the regulation of plant development. Include at least one specific example.

Resource Acquisition and Transport in Vascular Plants

▲ Figure 36.1 **Plants or pebbles?**

OVERVIEW

Underground Plants

The Kalahari Desert of southern Africa receives only about 20 cm of precipitation a year, almost exclusively during the summer months, when daytime temperatures reach a scorching 35–45°C (95–113°F). Many animals escape the desert heat by seeking shelter underground. A peculiar genus of perennial plants called stone plants (*Lithops*) has a similar, mostly subterranean lifestyle (**Figure 36.1**). Except for the tips of two succulent leaves that are exposed to the surface, a stone plant lives entirely below ground. Each leaf tip has a region of clear, lens-like cells that allow light to penetrate to the photosynthetic tissues underground. These adaptations enable stone plants to conserve moisture and avoid the potentially harmful temperatures and high light intensities of the desert.

The remarkable growth habit of *Lithops* reminds us that the success of plants depends largely on their ability to gather and conserve resources from their environment. Through natural selection, many plant species have become highly proficient in acquiring resources that are especially limited in their environment, but there are often trade-offs in such specializations. For example, the mostly subterranean lifestyle of stone plants

is good for the net acquisition of water but not for photosynthesis. As a result, stone plants grow very slowly.

This chapter begins by examining structural features of shoot and root systems that increase their efficiency in acquiring resources. Resource acquisition, however, is not the end of the story but only the beginning. Once acquired, resources must be transported to those parts of the plant where they are needed. The transport of materials, therefore, is critical for the integrated functioning of the whole plant. A central theme of this chapter is how three basic transport mechanisms—diffusion, active transport, and bulk flow—work together in vascular plants to transfer water, minerals, and the products of photosynthesis (sugars).

CONCEPT 36.1

Land plants acquire resources both above and below ground

Land plants typically inhabit two worlds—above ground, where their shoot systems acquire sunlight and CO_2, and below ground, where their root systems acquire water and minerals. Without adaptations that allow acquisition and transport of these resources from these dual sites, plants could not have colonized land.

The algal ancestors of land plants absorbed water, minerals, and CO_2 directly from the water in which they lived. Transport in these algae was relatively simple because each cell was close to the source of these substances. The earliest land plants were nonvascular plants that grew photosynthetic shoots above the shallow fresh water in which they lived. These leafless shoots had waxy cuticles and few stomata, which allowed them to avoid excessive water loss while still permitting gas exchange for photosynthesis. The anchoring and absorbing functions of early land plants were assumed by the base of the stem or by threadlike rhizoids (see Figure 29.8).

As land plants evolved and increased in number, competition for light, water, and nutrients intensified. Taller plants with broad, flat appendages had an advantage in absorbing light. This increase in surface area, however, resulted in more evaporation and therefore a greater need for water. Larger shoots also required more anchorage. These needs favored the production of multicellular, branching roots. Meanwhile, as greater shoot heights further separated the top of the photosynthetic shoot from the nonphotosynthetic parts below ground, natural selection favored plants capable of efficient long-distance transport of water, minerals, and products of photosynthesis.

The evolution of vascular tissue consisting of xylem and phloem made possible the development of extensive root and shoot systems that carry out long-distance transport (see Figure 35.10). The xylem transports water and minerals from roots to shoots. The phloem transports products of photosynthesis from where they are made or stored to where they are needed. **Figure 36.2** provides an overview of resource acquisition and transport in a vascular plant.

Because plant success depends on photosynthesis, evolution has resulted in many mechanisms for acquiring light from the sun, CO_2 from the air, and water from the ground. Perhaps just as important, land plants must minimize evaporative loss of water, particularly in environments where water is scarce. The adaptations of each species represent compromises between enhancing photosynthesis and minimizing water loss in the species' particular habitat. Later in the chapter, we'll discuss how plants minimize water loss. Here, we'll examine how the basic architecture of shoots and roots helps plants acquire resources.

Shoot Architecture and Light Capture

In shoot systems, stems serve as supporting structures for leaves and as conduits for the transport of water and nutrients. Variations in shoot systems arise largely from the form and arrangement of leaves, the outgrowth of axillary buds, and the relative growth in stem length and thickness.

Leaf size and structure account for much of the outward diversity we see in plant form. Leaves range in length from the minuscule 1.3-mm leaves of the pygmy weed (*Crassula erecta*), a native weed of dry, sandy regions in the western United States, to the 20-m leaves of the palm *Raphia regalis*, a native of African rain forests. These species represent extreme examples of a general correlation observed between water availability and leaf size. The largest leaves are generally found in tropical rain forests, and the smallest are usually found in dry or very cold environments, where liquid water is scarce and evaporative loss from leaves is potentially more problematic.

The arrangement of leaves on a stem, known as **phyllotaxy**, is an architectural feature of immense importance in light capture.

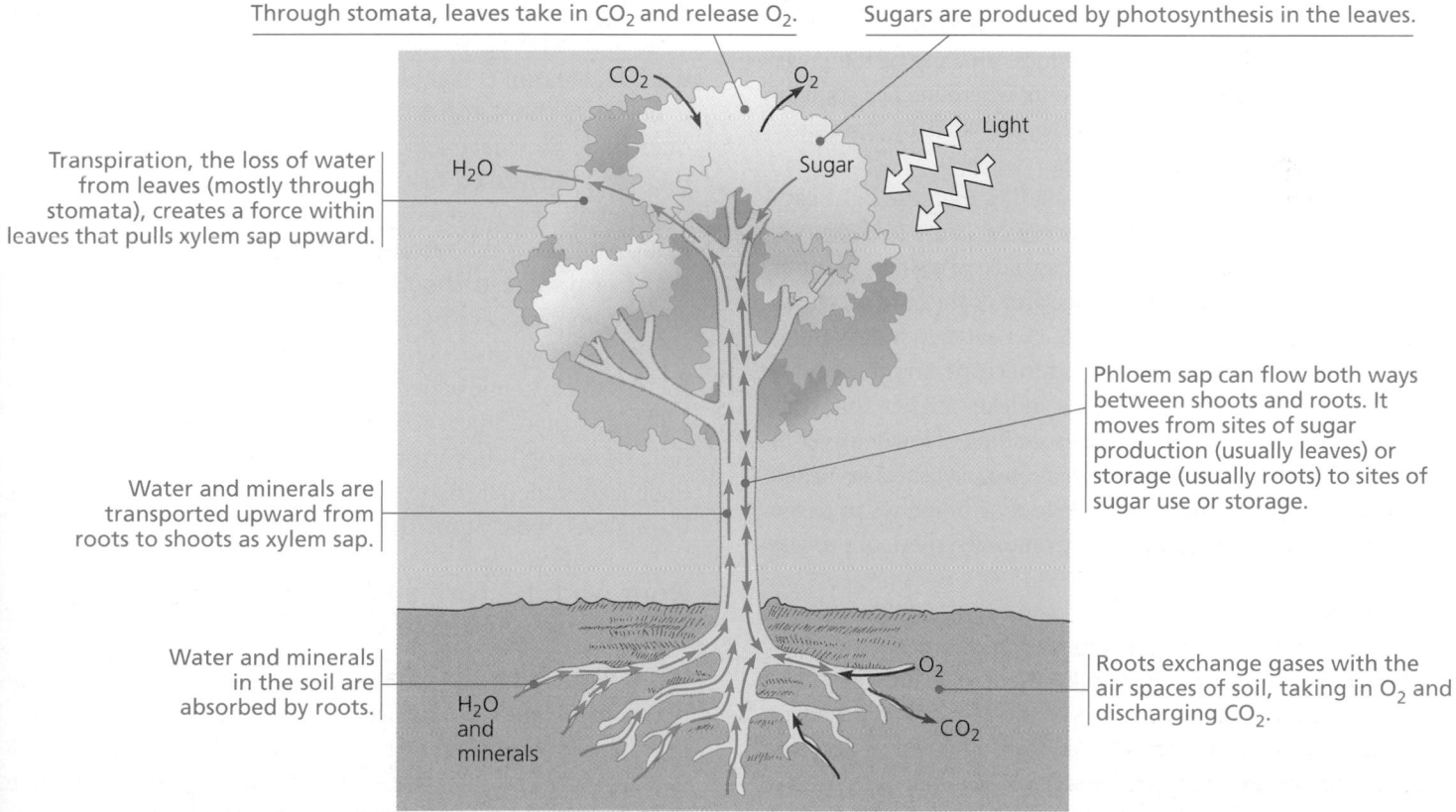

Through stomata, leaves take in CO_2 and release O_2.

Sugars are produced by photosynthesis in the leaves.

CO_2

O_2

Light

Transpiration, the loss of water from leaves (mostly through stomata), creates a force within leaves that pulls xylem sap upward.

H_2O

Sugar

Phloem sap can flow both ways between shoots and roots. It moves from sites of sugar production (usually leaves) or storage (usually roots) to sites of sugar use or storage.

Water and minerals are transported upward from roots to shoots as xylem sap.

Water and minerals in the soil are absorbed by roots.

H_2O and minerals

O_2

CO_2

Roots exchange gases with the air spaces of soil, taking in O_2 and discharging CO_2.

▲ Figure 36.2 **An overview of resource acquisition and transport in a vascular plant.**

▲ **Figure 36.3 Emerging phyllotaxy of Norway spruce.** This SEM, taken from above a shoot tip, shows the pattern of emergence of leaves. The leaves are numbered, with 1 being the youngest. (Some numbered leaves are not visible in the close-up.)

? *With your finger, trace the progression of leaf emergence, starting with leaf number 29. What is the pattern?*

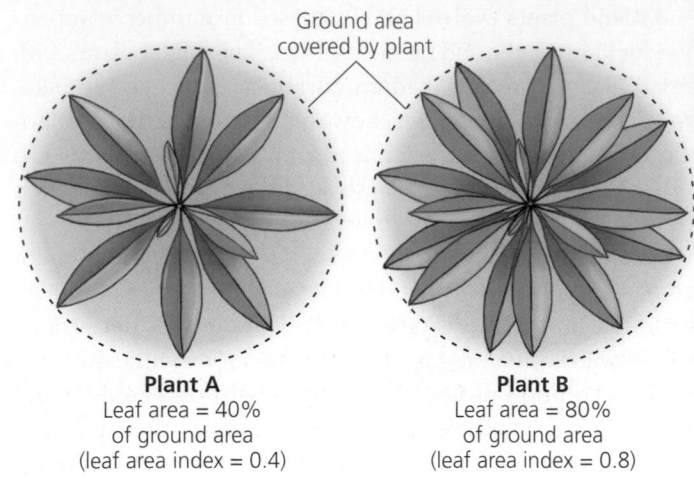

▲ **Figure 36.4 Leaf area index.** The leaf area index of a single plant is the ratio of the total area of the top surfaces of the leaves to the area of ground covered by the plant, as shown in this illustration of two plants viewed from the top.

? *Would a higher leaf area index always increase the amount of photosynthesis? Explain.*

Phyllotaxy is determined by the shoot apical meristem and is specific to each species **(Figure 36.3)**. A species may have one leaf per node (alternate, or spiral, phyllotaxy), two leaves per node (opposite phyllotaxy), or more (whorled phyllotaxy). Most angiosperms have alternate phyllotaxy, with leaves arranged in an ascending spiral around the stem, each successive leaf emerging about 137.5° from the site of the previous one. Why 137.5°? Mathematical analyses suggest that this angle allows each leaf to get the maximum exposure to light and reduces shading of the lower leaves by those above. In environments where intense sunlight can harm leaves, the greater shading provided by oppositely arranged leaves may be advantageous.

Plant features that reduce self-shading increase light capture. A useful measurement in this regard is the *leaf area index,* the ratio of the total upper leaf surface of a single plant or an entire crop divided by the surface area of the land on which the plant or crop grows **(Figure 36.4)**. Leaf area index values of up to 7 are common for many mature crops, and there is little agricultural benefit to leaf area indexes higher than this value. Adding more leaves increases shading of lower leaves to the point that they respire more than photosynthesize. When this happens, the nonproductive leaves or branches undergo programmed cell death and are eventually shed, a process called *self-pruning.*

Another factor affecting light capture is leaf orientation. Some plants have horizontally oriented leaves; others, such as grasses, have leaves that are vertically oriented. In low-light conditions, horizontal leaves capture sunlight much more effectively than vertical leaves. In grasslands or other sunny regions, however, horizontal orientation may expose upper leaves to intense light, injuring leaves and reducing photosynthesis. But if a plant's leaves are nearly vertical, light rays are essentially paral-

lel to the leaf surfaces, so no leaf receives too much light, and light penetrates more deeply to the lower leaves.

Some other factors that contribute greatly to the outward appearance and ecological success of plants are bud outgrowth and stem elongation. Carbon dioxide and sunlight are resources that are more effectively exploited by branching. However, some plants, such as palms, generally do not branch, whereas others, such as grasses, have short stems with many branches. Why is there so much variation in shoot architecture? The reason is that plants have a finite amount of energy to devote to shoot growth. If they put most of that energy into branching, they have less to devote toward growing tall, and they are at increased risk of being shaded by taller plants. If they put all of their energy into being tall, they are not optimally exploiting the resources above ground. Natural selection has produced shoot architectures that optimize light absorption in the ecological niche plants naturally occupy.

Plant species also vary in stem thickness. Most tall plants require thick stems, which enable greater vascular flow to the leaves and mechanical support for them. Vines are an exception, relying on other structures (usually other plants) to raise their leaves higher. In woody plants, stems become thicker through secondary growth (see Figure 35.11).

Root Architecture and Acquisition of Water and Minerals

Just as carbon dioxide and sunlight are resources exploited by the shoot system, soil contains resources mined by the root system. The evolution of root branching enabled land plants to more effectively acquire water and nutrients from the soil, while also providing strong anchorage. The tallest plant species, including gymnosperms and eudicots, are typically anchored by strong taproot systems with numerous branches (see Figure 35.2). Although there are exceptions, such as palms, most monocots do not reach treelike heights because their fibrous root systems do not anchor a tall plant as strongly as a taproot system (see Figure 30.13).

Recent evidence suggests that physiological mechanisms reduce competition within the root system of a plant. Cuttings from the stolons of buffalo grass (*Buchloe dactyloides*) developed fewer and shorter roots in the presence of cuttings from the same plant than they did in the presence of cuttings from another buffalo grass plant. Moreover, when cuttings from the same node were separated, their root systems eventually began competing with each other. Although the mechanism underlying this ability to distinguish self from nonself is unknown, avoiding competition between roots of the same plant for the same limited pool of resources certainly seems beneficial.

Evolution of mutualistic associations between roots and fungi was a critical step in the successful colonization of land by plants, especially given the poorly developed soils available at that time. The very specialized mutualistic associations between roots and fungi are called **mycorrhizae** (Figure 36.5). About 80% of extant land plant species form mycorrhizal associations (discussed in Chapters 31 and 37). Mycorrhizal hyphae endow the fungus and plant roots with an enormous surface area for absorbing water and minerals, particularly phosphate. As much as 3 m of hyphae can extend from each centimeter along a root's length, facilitating access to a far greater volume of soil than the root alone could penetrate.

Once acquired, resources must be transported to other parts of the plant that need them. In the next section, we'll examine the processes that enable resources such as water, minerals, and sugars to be transported throughout the plant.

2.5 mm

▲ **Figure 36.5 A mycorrhiza, a mutualistic association of fungi and roots.** The white mycelium of the fungus ensheathes these roots of a pine tree. The branched, club-shaped roots are often characteristic of this association. The fungal hyphae provide an extensive surface area for the absorption of water and minerals.

CONCEPT 36.2

Transport occurs by short-distance diffusion or active transport and by long-distance bulk flow

Like animals, plants need to transport water and nutrients from one part of their body to another. How do they do this without a pumping mechanism like a heart? To answer this question, we must first look at the basic transport processes of plants.

Transport begins with the absorption of resources by plant cells. As in any organism, the selective permeability of the plasma membrane controls the movement of substances into and out of the cell. We examined the transport of solutes and water across plasma membranes in detail in Chapter 7. Here we'll review diffusion and active transport in the context of short-distance transport in plant cells, and then we'll look at long-distance transport through bulk flow.

Diffusion and Active Transport of Solutes

Recall from Chapter 7 that a solute tends to diffuse down its electrochemical gradient, the combined effect of the solute's concentration gradient and the voltage (charge difference) across the membrane. Diffusion across a membrane is called *passive transport* because it happens without the cell directly using metabolic energy. *Active transport* is the pumping of a solute across a membrane against its electrochemical gradient. It is called "active" because the cell must expend energy, usually in the form of ATP, to transport a solute counter to the net direction in which the solute diffuses.

Most solutes cannot diffuse across the phospholipid bilayer of the membrane directly. Instead, they must pass through **transport proteins** embedded in the membrane. Transport proteins involved in active transport require energy to function,

▲ **Figure 36.6 Proton pumps provide energy for solute transport.** By pumping H$^+$ out of the cell, proton pumps produce an H$^+$ gradient and a charge separation called a membrane potential. These two forms of potential energy can drive the transport of solutes.

whereas those engaged in passive transport do not. In some cases, transport proteins bind selectively to a solute on one side of the membrane and then change shape, releasing the solute on the opposite side. Other transport proteins provide selective channels across the membrane. For example, membranes of most plant cells have potassium channels that allow potassium ions (K$^+$) to pass but not other cations, such as sodium (Na$^+$). Some channels are gated, opening or closing in response to stimuli such as chemicals, pressure, or voltage. Later in this chapter, we'll discuss how K$^+$ channels in guard cells function in opening and closing stomata.

In active transport in plant cells, the most important transport proteins are **proton pumps**, which use energy from ATP to pump protons (H$^+$) out of the cell. This movement results in an H$^+$ gradient (proton gradient), with a higher H$^+$ concentration outside the cell than inside (**Figure 36.6**). The H$^+$ gradient across the membrane is a form of potential (stored) energy, and the flow of H$^+$ back into the cell can be harnessed to do work. The movement of H$^+$ out of the cell also makes the inside of the cell negative in charge relative to the outside. This charge separation across the membrane contributes to a voltage called a **membrane potential**, another form of potential energy that can be harnessed to perform cellular work.

Plant cells use the energy in the H$^+$ gradient and membrane potential to drive the active transport of many different solutes. For example, the membrane potential generated by proton pumps contributes to the absorption of K$^+$ by root cells (**Figure 36.7a**). In the mechanism called **cotransport**, a transport protein couples the diffusion of one solute (H$^+$) with active transport of another (NO$_3^-$ in **Figure 36.7b**).

The "coattail" effect of cotransport is also responsible for absorption of neutral solutes, such as the sugar sucrose, by plant cells (**Figure 36.7c**). A sucrose-H$^+$ cotransporter couples movement of sucrose against its concentration gradient with movement of H$^+$ down its electrochemical gradient.

Diffusion of Water (Osmosis)

To survive, plants must balance water absorption and loss. The net absorption or loss of water by a cell occurs by **osmosis**, the

(a) Membrane potential and cation uptake

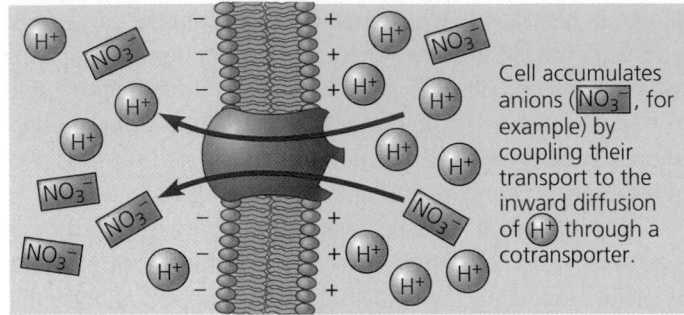

(b) Cotransport of an anion with H$^+$

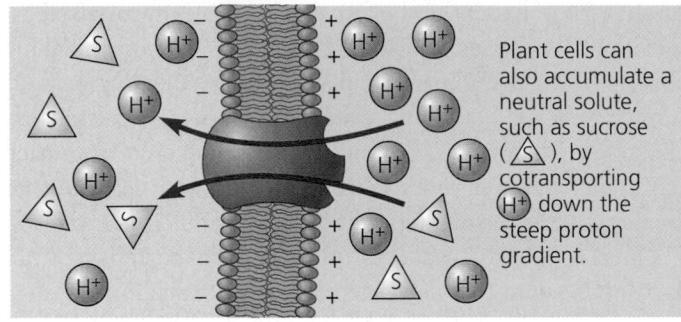

(c) Cotransport of a neutral solute with H$^+$

▲ **Figure 36.7 Solute transport in plant cells.**

diffusion of water across a membrane (see Figure 7.12). What determines the direction of water movement? In an animal cell, if the plasma membrane is impermeable to the solutes, water will move from the solution with the lower solute concentration to the solution with the higher solute concentration. But a plant cell has an almost rigid cell wall, which adds another factor that affects osmosis: the physical pressure of the cell wall pushing back against the expanding protoplast (the living part of the cell, consisting of the nucleus, cytoplasm, and plasma membrane). The combined effects of solute concentration and physical pressure are incorporated into a quantity called the **water potential**.

Water potential determines the direction of water movement. The primary idea to keep in mind is that free water—water that is not bound to solutes or surfaces—moves *from regions of higher water potential to regions of lower water potential* if there is no barrier to its flow. For example, if a plant cell is immersed in a solution that has a higher water potential than the cell, water will move into the cell. As it moves, water can perform work, such as cell expansion. The word *potential* in the term *water potential* refers to water's potential energy—water's capacity to perform work when it moves from a region of higher water potential to a region of lower water potential.

Water potential is abbreviated by the Greek letter ψ (psi, pronounced "sigh"). Plant biologists measure ψ in units of pressure called **megapascals** (abbreviated **MPa**). Physicists have assigned the value of zero ($\psi = 0$ MPa) to the water potential of pure water in a container open to the atmosphere under standard conditions (at sea level and at room temperature). One MPa is equal to about 10 atmospheres of pressure. (An atmosphere is the pressure exerted at sea level by the volume of air extending through the entire height of the atmosphere—about 1 kg of pressure per square centimeter.) The internal pressure of a plant cell is approximately 0.5 MPa, about twice the air pressure inside an inflated car tire.

How Solutes and Pressure Affect Water Potential

Both pressure and solute concentration can affect water potential, as expressed in the *water potential equation*:

$$\psi = \psi_S + \psi_P$$

where ψ is the water potential, ψ_S is the solute potential (osmotic potential), and ψ_P is the pressure potential. The **solute potential** (ψ_S) of a solution is proportional to its molarity. Solute potential is also called **osmotic potential** because solutes affect the direction of osmosis. Solutes are dissolved chemicals, which in plants are typically mineral ions and sugars. By definition, the ψ_S of pure water is 0. But what happens when solutes are added? The solutes bind water molecules, reducing the number of free water molecules and lowering the capacity of the water to move and do work. Thus, adding solutes always

lowers water potential, and the ψ_S of a solution is always negative. A 0.1 M solution of a sugar, for example, has a ψ_S of -0.23 MPa.

Pressure potential (ψ_P) is the physical pressure on a solution. Unlike ψ_S, ψ_P can be positive or negative relative to atmospheric pressure. For example, the water in the nonliving xylem cells (tracheids and vessel elements) of a plant is often under a negative pressure potential (tension) of less than -2 MPa. Conversely, much like the air in a balloon, the water in living cells is usually under positive pressure. Specifically, the cell contents press the plasma membrane against the cell wall, and the cell wall, in turn, presses against the protoplast, producing what is called **turgor pressure**.

Measuring Water Potential

Now let's put the water potential equation to use. We'll apply it to an artificial model and then to a living plant cell.

A U-shaped tube can be used to demonstrate water movement across a selectively permeable membrane (**Figure 36.8**). As you consider this model, keep in mind the key point: *Water moves from regions of higher water potential to regions of lower water potential.* The two arms of the U-tube are separated by a membrane (shown as a vertical dashed line) that is permeable to water but not to solutes. If the right arm of the tube contains a 0.1 M solution ($\psi_S = -0.23$ MPa) and the left arm contains pure water ($\psi_S = 0$), and there is no physical pressure (that is, $\psi_P = 0$), the water potential ψ is equal to ψ_S. Thus, the ψ of the right arm is -0.23 MPa, whereas the ψ of the left arm (pure water) is 0 MPa. Because water moves from regions of higher water potential to regions of lower water potential, the net water movement will be from the left arm of the tube to

(a)

0.1 M solution

Pure water

H₂O →

$\psi_P = 0$ $\psi_P = 0$
$\psi_S = 0$ $\psi_S = -0.23$
$\psi = 0$ MPa $\psi = -0.23$ MPa

(b)

Positive pressure

H₂O

$\psi_P = 0$ $\psi_P = 0.23$
$\psi_S = 0$ $\psi_S = -0.23$
$\psi = 0$ MPa $\psi = 0$ MPa

(c)

Increased positive pressure

← H₂O

$\psi_P = 0$ $\psi_P = 0.30$
$\psi_S = 0$ $\psi_S = -0.23$
$\psi = 0$ MPa $\psi = 0.07$ MPa

(d)

Negative pressure (tension)

← H₂O

$\psi_P = -0.30$ $\psi_P = 0$
$\psi_S = 0$ $\psi_S = -0.23$
$\psi = -0.30$ MPa $\psi = -0.23$ MPa

▲ **Figure 36.8 Water potential and water movement: an artificial model.** In this U-shaped apparatus, a membrane separates pure water (left arm) from a 0.1 M solution (right arm) containing a solute that cannot pass freely across the membrane. The values for ψ, ψ_S, and ψ_P in the left and right arms of the U-tube are given for *initial* conditions, *before* any net movement of water. **(a)** If no pressure is applied, ψ_S determines net movement of water. **(b)** Positive pressure (increased ψ_P) on the right raises ψ on the right, here making ψ the same in both arms, so eventually there is no net water movement. **(c)** Further increasing positive pressure on the right causes net water movement to the left. **(d)** Negative pressure reduces ψ_P. In this case, negative pressure on the left decreases ψ on the left, causing net water movement to the left.

the right arm, as shown in Figure 36.8a. But applying a positive physical pressure of +0.23 MPa to the solution in the right arm raises its water potential from a negative value to 0 MPa (ψ = −0.23 + 0.23). As shown in Figure 36.8b, there is now no net flow of water between this pressurized solution and the compartment of pure water. If we increase ψ_P to +0.30 MPa in the right arm, as in Figure 36.8c, then the solution has a water potential of +0.07 MPa (ψ = −0.23 + 0.30), and this solution will actually *lose* water to a compartment containing pure water. Whereas applying positive pressure increases ψ, applying negative pressure (tension) reduces ψ, as shown in Figure 36.8d. In this case, a negative pressure potential of −0.30 MPa reduces the ψ of the water compartment enough so that water is drawn from the solution on the right side.

Now let's consider how water potential affects absorption and loss of water by a living plant cell. First, imagine a cell that is **flaccid** (limp) as a result of losing water. The cell has a ψ_P of 0 MPa. Suppose this flaccid cell is bathed in a solution of higher solute concentration (more negative solute potential) than the cell itself **(Figure 36.9a)**. Since the external solution has the lower (more negative) water potential, water diffuses out of the cell. The cell's protoplast undergoes **plasmolysis**—that is, it shrinks and pulls away from the cell wall. If we place the same flaccid cell in pure water (ψ = 0 MPa) **(Figure 36.9b)**, the cell, because it contains solutes, has a lower water potential than the water, and water enters the cell by osmosis. The contents of the cell begin to swell and press the plasma membrane against the cell wall. The partially elastic wall, exerting turgor pressure, pushes back against the pressurized protoplast. When this pressure is enough to offset the tendency for water to enter because of the solutes in the cell, then ψ_P and ψ_S are equal, and ψ = 0. This matches the

water potential of the extracellular environment: in this example, 0 MPa. A dynamic equilibrium has been reached, and there is no further net movement of water.

In contrast to a flaccid cell, a walled cell with a greater solute concentration than its surroundings is **turgid**, or very firm. When turgid cells in a nonwoody tissue push against each other, the tissue is stiffened. The effects of turgor loss are seen during **wilting**, when leaves and stems droop as a result of cells losing water **(Figure 36.10)**.

▲ **Figure 36.10 A wilted *Impatiens* plant regains its turgor when watered.**

Initial flaccid cell:
$$\psi_P = 0$$
$$\psi_S = -0.7$$
$$\psi = -0.7 \text{ MPa}$$

0.4 *M* sucrose solution:
$$\psi_P = 0$$
$$\psi_S = -0.9$$
$$\psi = -0.9 \text{ MPa}$$

Pure water:
$$\psi_P = 0$$
$$\psi_S = 0$$
$$\psi = 0 \text{ MPa}$$

Plasmolyzed cell at osmotic equilibrium with its surroundings
$$\psi_P = 0$$
$$\psi_S = -0.9$$
$$\psi = -0.9 \text{ MPa}$$

Turgid cell at osmotic equilibrium with its surroundings
$$\psi_P = 0.7$$
$$\psi_S = -0.7$$
$$\psi = 0 \text{ MPa}$$

(a) Initial conditions: cellular ψ > environmental ψ. The cell loses water and plasmolyzes. After plasmolysis is complete, the water potentials of the cell and its surroundings are the same.

(b) Initial conditions: cellular ψ < environmental ψ. There is a net uptake of water by osmosis, causing the cell to become turgid. When this tendency for water to enter is offset by the back pressure of the elastic wall, water potentials are equal for the cell and its surroundings. (The volume change of the cell is exaggerated in this diagram.)

▲ **Figure 36.9 Water relations in plant cells.** In these experiments, identical cells, initially flaccid, are placed in two environments. (Protoplasts of flaccid cells are in contact with their walls but lack turgor pressure.) Blue arrows indicate initial net water movement.

Aquaporins: Facilitating Diffusion of Water

A difference in water potential determines the *direction* of water movement across membranes, but how do water molecules actually cross the membranes? Water molecules are small enough to diffuse across the phospholipid bilayer, even though the middle zone is hydrophobic (see Figure 7.2), but their movement is too rapid to be explained by unaided diffusion. Indeed, transport proteins called **aquaporins** facilitate the diffusion (see Chapter 7). These selective channels, which have been found most commonly in plants, affect the *rate* at which water diffuses down its water potential gradient. Evidence is accumulating that the rate of water movement through these proteins is regulated by phosphorylation of the aquaporin proteins, which can be induced by increases in cytoplasmic calcium ions or decreases in cytoplasmic pH. Recent evidence suggests that aquaporins may also facilitate absorption of CO_2 by plant cells.

Three Major Pathways of Transport

Transport within plants is also regulated by the compartmental structure of plant cells (**Figure 36.11a**). Outside the protoplast is a cell wall (see Figures 6.9 and 6.28), consisting of a mesh of polysaccharides through which mineral ions diffuse readily. Because every plant cell is separated from its neighboring cells by cell walls, ions can diffuse across a tissue (or be carried passively by water flow) entirely through the **apoplast** (**Figure 36.11b**), the continuum formed by cell walls, extracellular spaces, and the dead interiors of tracheids and vessels. However, it is the plasma membrane that directly controls the traffic of molecules into and out of the protoplast. Just as the cell walls form a continuum, so does the cytosol of cells, collectively referred to as the **symplast** (see Figure 36.11b). The cytoplasmic channels called **plasmodesmata** connect the cytoplasm of neighboring cells.

The compartmental structure of plant cells provides three routes for short-distance transport within a plant tissue or organ: the apoplastic, symplastic, and transmembrane routes (see Figure 36.11b). In the apoplastic route, water and solutes move along the continuum of cell walls and extracellular spaces. In the symplastic route, water and solutes move along the continuum of cytosol within a plant tissue. This route requires only one crossing of a plasma membrane. After entering one cell, substances can move from cell to cell via plasmodesmata. In the transmembrane route, water and solutes move out of one cell, across the cell wall, and into the neighboring cell, which may pass them to the next cell in the same way. The transmembrane route requires repeated crossings of plasma membranes as water and solutes exit one cell and enter the next. Substances may use more than one route. Scientists are debating which route, if any, is responsible for the most transport.

Bulk Flow in Long-Distance Transport

Diffusion and active transport are fairly efficient for short-distance transport within a cell and between cells. However, these processes are much too slow to function in long-distance transport within a plant. Although diffusion from one end of a cell to the other takes just seconds, diffusion from the roots to the top of a giant redwood would take decades or longer. Instead, long-distance transport occurs through **bulk flow**, the movement of a fluid driven by pressure.

Within tracheids and vessel elements of the xylem and within the sieve-tube elements (also called sieve-tube members) of the phloem, water and dissolved solutes move together in the same direction by bulk flow. The structures of these conducting cells of the xylem and phloem help to make bulk flow possible. If you have ever dealt with a partially clogged drain, you know that the volume of flow depends on the pipe's diameter. Clogs reduce the effective diameter of the drainpipe. Such experiences help us

(a) Cell compartments. The cell wall, cytosol, and vacuole are the three main compartments of most mature plant cells.

(b) Transport routes between cells. At the tissue level, there are three pathways: the transmembrane, symplastic, and apoplastic routes. Substances can transfer from one pathway to another.

▲ **Figure 36.11 Cell compartments and routes for short-distance transport.**

understand how the structures of plant cells specialized for bulk flow fit their function. As you learned in Chapter 35, mature tracheids and vessel elements are dead cells and therefore have no cytoplasm, and the cytoplasm of sieve-tube elements is almost devoid of internal organelles (see Figure 35.10). Like unplugging a kitchen drain, loss of cytoplasm in a plant's "plumbing" allows for efficient bulk flow through the xylem and phloem. Bulk flow is also enhanced by the perforation plates at the ends of vessel elements and the porous sieve plates connecting sieve-tube elements.

Diffusion, active transport, and bulk flow act in concert to transport resources throughout the whole plant. For example, bulk flow due to a pressure difference is the mechanism of long-distance transport of sugars in the phloem, but active transport of sugar at the cellular level maintains this pressure difference. In the next three sections, we'll examine in more detail the transport of water and minerals from roots to shoots, the control of evaporation, and the transport of sugars.

CONCEPT CHECK 36.2

1. If a plant cell immersed in distilled water has a ψ_S of -0.7 MPa and a ψ of 0 MPa, what is the cell's ψ_P? If you put it in an open beaker of solution that has a ψ of -0.4 MPa, what would be its ψ_P at equilibrium?
2. How would an aquaporin deficiency affect a plant cell's ability to adjust to new osmotic conditions?
3. How would the long-distance transport of water be affected if vessel elements and tracheids were alive at maturity? Explain.
4. **WHAT IF?** What would happen if you put plant protoplasts in pure water? Explain.

For suggested answers, see Appendix A.

CONCEPT 36.3

Water and minerals are transported from roots to shoots

Picture yourself struggling to carry a very large container of water up several flights of stairs. Then consider the fact that water within a plant is transported effortlessly against the force of gravity. Up to 800 L (800 kg or 1,760 lb) of water reach the top of an average-sized tree every day. But trees and other plants have no pumping mechanism. So how is this feat accomplished? To answer this question, we'll follow each step in the journey of water and minerals from the tips of roots to the tips of shoots.

Absorption of Water and Minerals by Root Cells

Although all living plant cells absorb nutrients across their plasma membranes, the cells near the tips of roots are partic-

ularly important because most of the water and mineral absorption occurs there. In this region, the epidermal cells are permeable to water, and many are differentiated into root hairs, modified cells that account for much of the absorption of water by roots (see Figure 35.3). The root hairs absorb the soil solution, which consists of water molecules and dissolved mineral ions that are not bound tightly to soil particles. The soil solution flows into the hydrophilic walls of epidermal cells and passes freely along the cell walls and the extracellular spaces into the root cortex. This flow enhances the exposure of the cells of the cortex to the soil solution, providing a much greater membrane surface area for absorption than the surface area of the epidermis alone. Although the soil solution usually has a low mineral concentration, active transport enables roots to accumulate essential minerals, such as K^+, to concentrations hundreds of times higher than in the soil.

Transport of Water and Minerals into the Xylem

Water and minerals that pass from the soil into the root cortex cannot be transported to the rest of the plant until they enter the xylem of the stele, or vascular cylinder. The **endodermis**, the innermost layer of cells in the root cortex, surrounds the stele and functions as a last checkpoint for the selective passage of minerals from the cortex into the vascular tissue (**Figure 36.12**). Minerals already in the symplast when they reach the endodermis continue through the plasmodesmata of endodermal cells and pass into the stele. These minerals were already screened by the plasma membrane they had to cross to enter the symplast in the epidermis or cortex. Those minerals that reach the endodermis via the apoplast encounter a dead end that blocks their passage into the stele. This barrier, located in the transverse and radial walls of each endodermal cell, is the **Casparian strip**, a belt made of suberin, a waxy material impervious to water and dissolved minerals (see Figure 36.12). Thus, water and minerals cannot cross the endodermis and enter the vascular tissue via the apoplast. The Casparian strip forces water and minerals that are passively moving through the apoplast to cross the plasma membrane of an endodermal cell and enter the stele via the symplast.

The endodermis, with its Casparian strip, ensures that no minerals can reach the vascular tissue of the root without crossing a selectively permeable plasma membrane. The endodermis also prevents solutes that have accumulated in the xylem from leaking back into the soil solution. The structure of the endodermis and its strategic location fit its function as an apoplastic barrier between the cortex and the stele. The endodermis helps roots to transport certain minerals preferentially from the soil into the xylem.

The last segment in the soil-to-xylem pathway is the passage of water and minerals into the tracheids and vessel elements of the xylem. These water-conducting cells lack protoplasts when mature and therefore are part of the apoplast. Endodermal cells, as well as living cells within the stele, discharge minerals

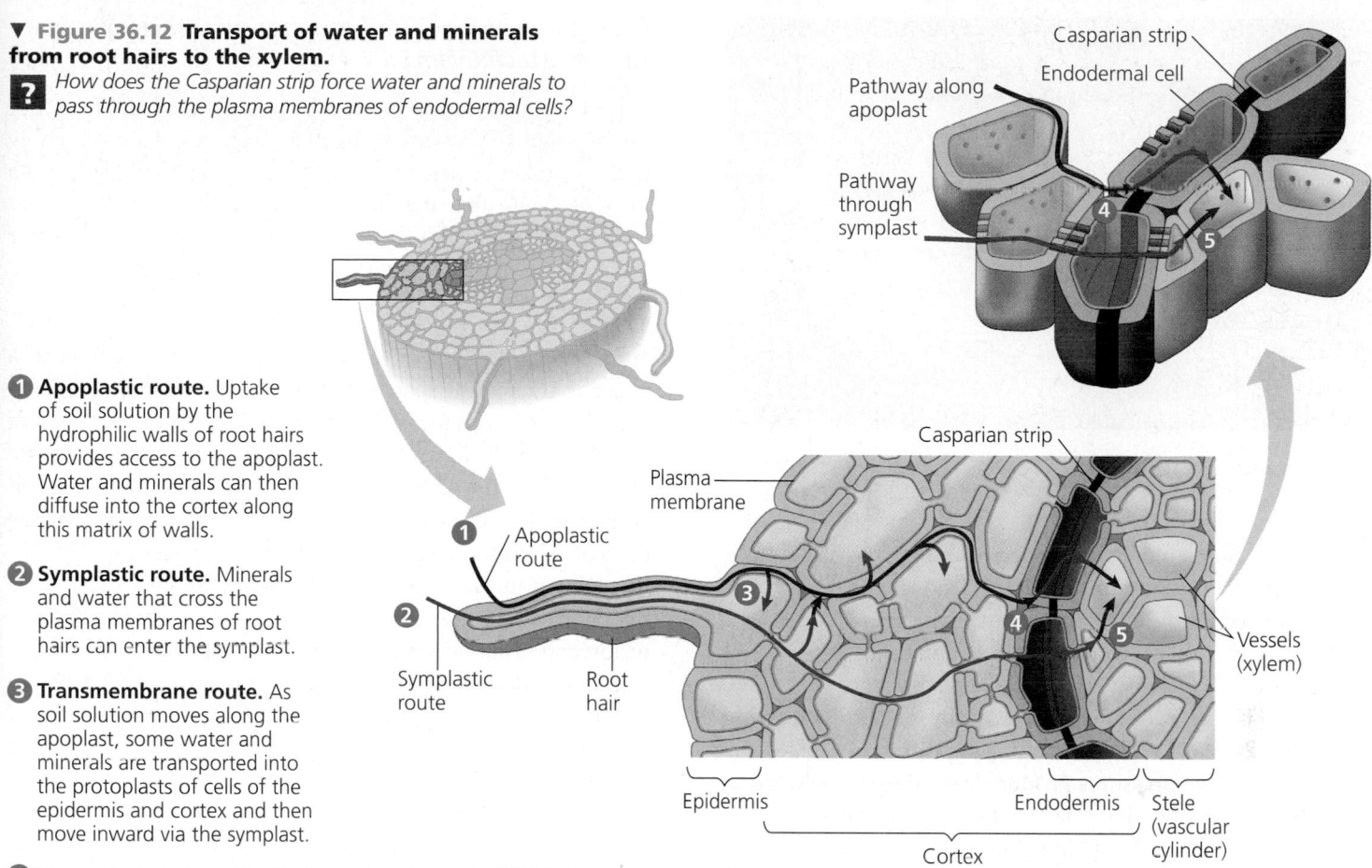

▼ Figure 36.12 Transport of water and minerals from root hairs to the xylem.

? *How does the Casparian strip force water and minerals to pass through the plasma membranes of endodermal cells?*

❶ Apoplastic route. Uptake of soil solution by the hydrophilic walls of root hairs provides access to the apoplast. Water and minerals can then diffuse into the cortex along this matrix of walls.

❷ Symplastic route. Minerals and water that cross the plasma membranes of root hairs can enter the symplast.

❸ Transmembrane route. As soil solution moves along the apoplast, some water and minerals are transported into the protoplasts of cells of the epidermis and cortex and then move inward via the symplast.

❹ The endodermis: controlled entry to the stele. Within the transverse and radial walls of each endodermal cell is the Casparian strip, a belt of waxy material (purple band) that blocks the passage of water and dissolved minerals. Only minerals already in the symplast or entering that pathway by crossing the plasma membrane of an endodermal cell can detour around the Casparian strip and pass into the stele, the vascular cylinder.

❺ Transport in the xylem. Endodermal cells and also living cells within the stele discharge water and minerals into their walls (apoplast). The xylem vessels then transport the water and minerals upward into the shoot system.

from their protoplasts into their own cell walls. Both diffusion and active transport are involved in this transfer of solutes from symplast to apoplast, and the water and minerals are now free to enter the tracheids and vessels, where they are transported to the shoot system by bulk flow.

Bulk Flow Driven by Negative Pressure in the Xylem

Water and minerals from the soil enter the plant through the epidermis of roots, cross the root cortex, and pass into the stele. From there the **xylem sap**, the water and dissolved minerals in the xylem, gets transported long distances by bulk flow to the veins that branch throughout each leaf.

As noted earlier, bulk flow is much faster than diffusion or active transport. Peak velocities in the transport of xylem sap can range from 15 to 45 m/hr for trees with wide vessels. Leaves depend on this efficient delivery system for their supply of water. Plants lose an astonishing amount of water by **transpiration**, the loss of water vapor from leaves and other aerial parts of the plant. Consider the example of maize (commonly called corn in the

United States). A single plant transpires 60 L (60 kg) of water during a growing season. A maize crop growing at a typical density of 60,000 plants per hectare transpires almost 4 million L of water per hectare every growing season (about 400,000 gallons of water per acre per growing season). Unless the transpired water is replaced by water transported up from the roots, the leaves will wilt, and the plants will eventually die. The flow of xylem sap also brings mineral nutrients to the shoot system.

Xylem sap rises to heights of more than 100 m in the tallest trees. Is the sap mainly *pushed* upward from the roots, or is it mainly *pulled* upward by the leaves? Let's evaluate the relative contributions of these two mechanisms.

Pushing Xylem Sap: Root Pressure

At night, when there is almost no transpiration, root cells continue pumping mineral ions into the xylem of the stele. Meanwhile, the endodermis helps prevent the ions from leaking out. The resulting accumulation of minerals lowers the water potential within the stele. Water flows in from the root cortex, generating **root pressure**, a push of xylem sap. The root pressure

▲ **Figure 36.13 Guttation.** Root pressure is forcing excess water from this strawberry leaf.

sometimes causes more water to enter the leaves than is transpired, resulting in **guttation**, the exudation of water droplets that can be seen in the morning on the tips or edges of some plant leaves **(Figure 36.13)**. Guttation fluid should not be confused with dew, which is condensed atmospheric moisture.

In most plants, root pressure is a minor mechanism driving the ascent of xylem sap, at most pushing water only a few meters. The positive pressures produced are simply too weak to overcome the gravitational force of the water column in the xylem, particularly in tall plants. Many plants do not generate any root pressure. Even in plants that display guttation, root pressure cannot keep pace with transpiration after sunrise. For the most part, xylem sap is not pushed from below by root pressure but pulled by the leaves themselves.

Pulling Xylem Sap: The Transpiration-Cohesion-Tension Mechanism

Material can be moved upward by positive pressure from below or negative pressure from above. Here we'll focus on how water is pulled by negative pressure potential in the xylem. As we investigate this mechanism of transport, we'll see that transpiration provides the pull and that the cohesion of water due to hydrogen bonding transmits the pull along the entire length of the xylem to the roots.

Transpirational Pull Stomata on a leaf's surface lead to a maze of internal air spaces that expose the mesophyll cells to the CO_2 they need for photosynthesis. The air in these spaces is saturated with water vapor because it is in contact with the moist walls of the cells. On most days, the air outside the leaf is drier; that is, it has a lower water potential than the air inside the leaf. Therefore, water vapor in the air spaces of a leaf diffuses down its water potential gradient and exits the leaf via the stomata. It is this loss of water vapor from the leaf by diffusion and evaporation that we call transpiration.

But how does loss of water vapor from the leaf translate into a pulling force for upward movement of water through a plant? The negative pressure potential that causes water to move up through the xylem develops at the surface of mesophyll cell walls in the leaf **(Figure 36.14)**. The cell wall acts like a very fine capillary network. Water adheres to the cellulose microfibrils and other hydrophilic components of the cell wall. As water evaporates from the water film that covers the cell walls of mesophyll cells, the air-water interface retreats farther into the cell wall. Because of the high surface tension of water, the curvature of the

❺ Water from the xylem is pulled into the surrounding cells and air spaces to replace the water that was lost.

❹ The increased surface tension shown in step ❸ pulls water from surrounding cells and air spaces.

❸ The evaporation of the water film causes the air-water interface to retreat farther into the cell wall and to become more curved. This curvature increases the surface tension and the rate of transpiration.

Microfibrils in cell wall of mesophyll cell

❷ At first, the water vapor lost by transpiration is replaced by evaporation from the water film that coats mesophyll cells.

Cuticle
Upper epidermis
Xylem
Mesophyll
Air space
Lower epidermis
Cuticle
Stoma
Microfibril (cross section)
Water film
Air-water interface

❶ In transpiration, water vapor (shown as blue dots) diffuses from the moist air spaces of the leaf to the drier air outside via stomata.

▲ **Figure 36.14 Generation of transpirational pull.** Negative pressure (tension) at the air-water interface in the leaf is the basis of transpirational pull, which draws water out of the xylem.

interface induces a tension, or negative pressure potential, in the water. As more water evaporates from the cell wall, the curvature of the air-water interface increases and the pressure of the water becomes more negative. Water molecules from the more hydrated parts of the leaf are then pulled toward this area to reduce the tension. These pulling forces are transferred to the xylem because each water molecule is cohesively bound to the next by hydrogen bonds. Thus, transpirational pull depends on several of the properties of water discussed in Chapter 3: adhesion, cohesion, and surface tension.

The role of negative pressure potential in transpiration is consistent with the water potential equation because negative pressure potential (tension) *lowers* water potential (see Figure 36.8d). Because water moves from areas of higher water potential to areas of lower water potential, the more negative pressure potential at the air-water interface causes water in xylem cells to be "pulled" into mesophyll cells, which lose water to the air spaces, where it diffuses out through stomata. In this way, the negative water potential of leaves provides the "pull" in transpirational pull.

Cohesion and Adhesion in the Ascent of Xylem Sap The transpirational pull on xylem sap is transmitted all the way from the leaves to the root tips and even into the soil solution (**Figure 36.15**). Cohesion and adhesion facilitate this long-distance transport by bulk flow. The cohesion of water due to hydrogen bonding makes it possible to pull a column of xylem sap from above without the water molecules separating. Water molecules exiting the xylem in the leaf tug on adjacent water molecules, and this pull is relayed, molecule by molecule, down the entire column of water in the xylem. Meanwhile, the strong adhesion of water molecules (again by hydrogen bonds) to the hydrophilic walls of xylem cells helps offset the downward force of gravity.

The upward pull on the sap creates tension within the xylem vessels and tracheids, which are like elastic pipes. Positive pressure causes an elastic pipe to swell, whereas tension pulls the walls of the pipe inward. On a warm day, a decrease in the diameter of a tree trunk can even be measured. As transpirational pull puts the vessels and tracheids under ten-

sion, their thick secondary walls prevent them from collapsing, much as wire rings maintain the shape of a vacuum-cleaner hose. The tension produced by transpirational pull lowers water potential in the root xylem to such an extent that water flows passively from the soil, across the root cortex, and into the stele.

Transpirational pull can extend down to the roots only through an unbroken chain of water molecules. Cavitation, the formation of a water vapor pocket, breaks the chain. It is more common in wide vessels than in tracheids and can occur during drought stress or when xylem sap freezes in winter. The air bubbles resulting from cavitation expand and block water channels of the xylem. The rapid expansion of air bubbles produces

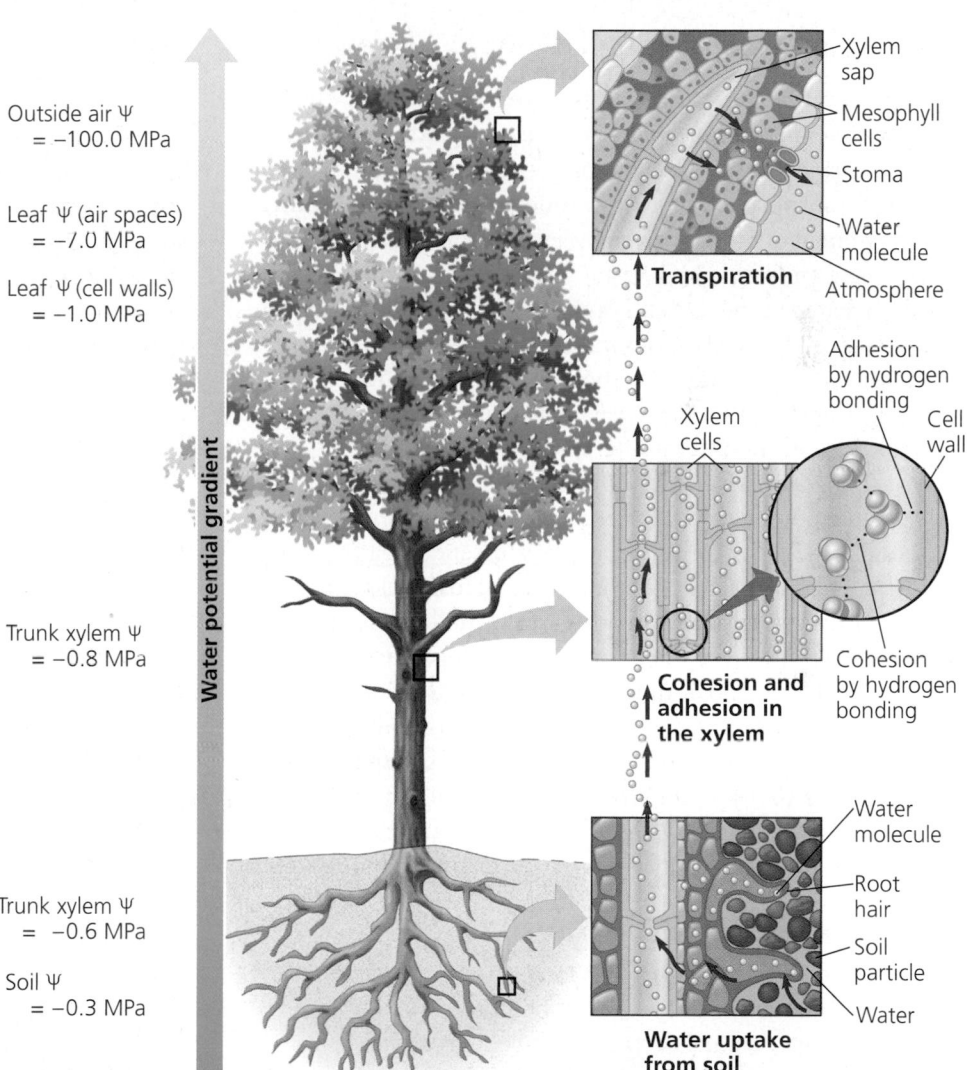

▲ **Figure 36.15 Ascent of xylem sap.** Hydrogen bonding forms an unbroken chain of water molecules extending from leaves to the soil. The force driving the ascent of xylem sap is a gradient of water potential (ψ). For bulk flow over long distance, the ψ gradient is due mainly to a gradient of the pressure potential (ψ_P). Transpiration results in the ψ_P at the leaf end of the xylem being lower than the ψ_P at the root end. The ψ values shown at the left are a "snapshot." During daylight, they may vary, but the direction of the ψ gradient remains the same.

 MEDIA ***BioFlix*** Visit
www.campbellbiology.com
for the BioFlix 3-D Animation on
Water Transport in Plants.

clicking noises that can be heard by placing sensitive microphones at the surface of the stem.

Root pressure enables small plants to refill blocked vessels in spring. In trees, though, root pressure is insufficient to push water to the top, so a vessel with a water vapor pocket usually cannot function in xylem sap transport. However, the chain of molecules can detour around the pocket through pits between adjacent tracheids or vessels. In addition, secondary growth adds a layer of new xylem each year. Only the youngest, outermost secondary xylem transports water. Although the older secondary xylem no longer transports water, it does provide support for the tree (see Figure 35.22).

Xylem Sap Ascent by Bulk Flow: *A Review*

The transpiration-cohesion-tension mechanism that transports xylem sap against gravity is an excellent example of how physical principles apply to biological processes. In the long-distance transport of water from roots to leaves by bulk flow, the movement of fluid is driven by a water potential difference at opposite ends of xylem tissue. The water potential difference is created at the leaf end of the xylem by the evaporation of water from leaf cells. Evaporation lowers the water potential at the air-water interface, thereby generating the negative pressure (tension) that pulls water through the xylem.

Bulk flow in the xylem differs from diffusion in some key ways. First, it is driven by differences in pressure potential (ψ_P); solute potential (ψ_S) is not a factor. Therefore, the water potential gradient within the xylem is essentially a pressure gradient. Also, the flow does not occur across plasma membranes of living cells, but instead within hollow, dead cells. Furthermore, it moves the entire solution together—not just water or solutes—and at much greater speed than diffusion.

The plant expends no energy to lift xylem sap by bulk flow. Instead, the absorption of sunlight drives most of transpiration by causing water to evaporate from the moist walls of mesophyll cells and by lowering the water potential in the air spaces within a leaf. Thus, the ascent of xylem sap is ultimately solar powered.

Stomata help regulate the rate of transpiration

Leaves generally have large surface areas and high surface-to-volume ratios. The large surface area enhances light absorption for photosynthesis. The high surface-to-volume ratio aids in CO_2 absorption during photosynthesis as well as in the release of O_2 as a by-product of photosynthesis. Upon diffusing through the stomata, CO_2 enters a honeycomb of air spaces formed by the spongy mesophyll cells (see Figure 35.18). Because of the irregular shapes of these cells, the leaf's internal surface area may be 10 to 30 times greater than the external surface area.

Although large surface areas and high surface-to-volume ratios increase the rate of photosynthesis, they also increase water loss by way of the stomata. Thus, a plant's tremendous requirement for water is largely a negative consequence of the shoot system's need for ample gas exchange for photosynthesis. By opening and closing the stomata, guard cells help balance the plant's requirement to conserve water with its requirement for photosynthesis (**Figure 36.16**).

Stomata: Major Pathways for Water Loss

About 95% of the water a plant loses escapes through stomata, although these pores account for only 1–2% of the external leaf surface. The waxy cuticle limits water loss through the remaining surface of the leaf. Each stoma is flanked by a pair of guard cells. Guard cells control the diameter of the stoma by changing shape, thereby widening or narrowing the gap between the guard cell pair. Under the same environmental conditions, the amount of water lost by a leaf depends largely on the number of stomata and the average size of their pores.

The stomatal density of a leaf, which may be as high as 20,000 per square centimeter, is under both genetic and environmental control. For example, as a result of evolution by

▲ **Figure 36.16** **An open stoma (left) and closed stoma (LMs).**

natural selection, desert plants have lower stomatal densities than do marsh plants. Stomatal density, however, is a developmentally plastic feature of many plants. High light exposures and low CO_2 levels during leaf development lead to increased density in many species. By measuring stomatal density of leaf fossils, scientists have gained insight into the levels of atmospheric CO_2 in past climates. A recent British survey found that stomatal density of many woodland species has decreased since 1927, when a similar survey was made. This survey is consistent with other findings that atmospheric CO_2 levels increased dramatically during the 1900s.

Mechanisms of Stomatal Opening and Closing

When guard cells take in water from neighboring cells by osmosis, they become more turgid. In most angiosperm species, the cell walls of guard cells are uneven in thickness, and the cellulose microfibrils are oriented in a direction that causes the guard cells to bow outward when turgid (**Figure 36.17a**). This bowing outward increases the size of the pore between the guard cells. When the cells lose water and become flaccid, they become less bowed, and the pore closes.

The changes in turgor pressure in guard cells result primarily from the reversible absorption and loss of K^+. Stomata open when guard cells actively accumulate K^+ from neighboring epidermal cells (**Figure 36.17b**). The flow of K^+ across the plasma membrane of the guard cell is coupled to the generation of a membrane potential by proton pumps. Stomatal opening correlates with active transport of H^+ out of the guard cell. The resulting voltage (membrane potential) drives K^+ into the cell through specific membrane channels (see Figure 36.7a). The absorption of K^+ causes the water potential to become more negative within the guard cells, and the cells become more turgid as water enters by osmosis. Because most of the K^+ and water are stored in the vacuole, the vacuolar membrane also plays a role in regulating guard cell dynamics. Stomatal closing results from a loss of K^+ from guard cells to neighboring cells, which leads to an osmotic loss of water. Aquaporins also help regulate the osmotic swelling and shrinking of guard cells.

Stimuli for Stomatal Opening and Closing

In general, stomata are open during the day and closed at night, preventing the plant from losing water under conditions when photosynthesis cannot occur. At least three cues contribute to stomatal opening at dawn: light, CO_2 depletion, and an internal "clock" in guard cells.

The light stimulates guard cells to accumulate K^+ and become turgid. This response is triggered by illumination of blue-light receptors in the plasma membrane of guard cells. Activation of these receptors stimulates the activity of proton pumps in the plasma membrane of the guard cells, in turn promoting absorption of K^+.

Guard cells turgid/Stoma open   Guard cells flaccid/Stoma closed

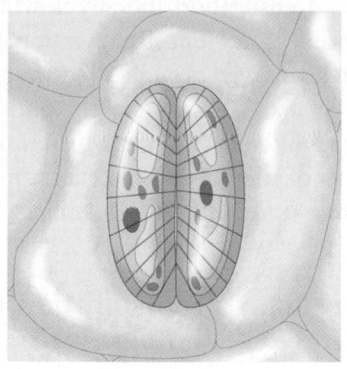

(a) Changes in guard cell shape and stomatal opening and closing (surface view). Guard cells of a typical angiosperm are illustrated in their turgid (stoma open) and flaccid (stoma closed) states. The radial orientation of cellulose microfibrils in the cell walls causes the guard cells to increase more in length than width when turgor increases. Since the two guard cells are tightly joined at their tips, they bow outward when turgid, causing the stomatal pore to open.

(b) Role of potassium in stomatal opening and closing. The transport of K^+ (potassium ions, symbolized here as red dots) across the plasma membrane and vacuolar membrane causes the turgor changes of guard cells. The uptake of anions, such as malate and chloride ions (not shown), also contributes to guard cell swelling.

▲ **Figure 36.17 Mechanisms of stomatal opening and closing.**

The stomata also open in response to depletion of CO_2 within the leaf's air spaces as a result of photosynthesis. As CO_2 concentrations decrease during the day, the stomata progressively open if sufficient water is supplied to the leaf.

A third cue, the internal "clock" in the guard cells, ensures that stomata continue their daily rhythm of opening and closing. This rhythm occurs even if a plant is kept in a dark location. All eukaryotic organisms have internal clocks that regulate cyclic processes. Cycles with intervals of approximately 24 hours are called **circadian rhythms**, which you'll learn more about in Chapter 39.

Environmental stresses, such as droughts, can cause stomata to close during the daytime. When the plant has a water deficiency, guard cells may lose turgor and close stomata. In addition, a hormone called abscisic acid, produced in roots and leaves in response to water deficiency, signals guard cells to close stomata. This response reduces wilting but also restricts CO_2 absorption, thereby slowing photosynthesis. Since turgor is necessary for cell elongation, growth ceases. These are some reasons why droughts reduce crop yields.

Guard cells control the photosynthesis-transpiration compromise on a moment-to-moment basis by integrating a variety of internal and external stimuli. Even the passage of a cloud or a transient shaft of sunlight through a forest can affect the rate of transpiration.

Effects of Transpiration on Wilting and Leaf Temperature

As long as most stomata remain open, transpiration is greatest on a day that is sunny, warm, dry, and windy because these environmental factors increase evaporation. If transpiration cannot pull sufficient water to the leaves, the shoot becomes slightly wilted as cells lose turgor pressure (see Figure 36.10). Although plants respond to such mild drought stress by rapidly closing stomata, some evaporative water loss still occurs through the cuticle. Under prolonged drought conditions, leaves can become severely wilted and irreversibly injured.

Transpiration also results in evaporative cooling, which can lower a leaf's temperature by as much as 10°C compared with the surrounding air. This cooling prevents the leaf from reaching temperatures that could denature enzymes involved in photosynthesis and other metabolic processes.

Adaptations That Reduce Evaporative Water Loss

Plants that are adapted to deserts and other regions with little moisture are called **xerophytes** (from the Greek *xero*, dry). The stone plants in Figure 36.1 are an example. **Figure 36.18**

▼ Figure 36.18 **Some xerophytic adaptations.**

▶ Ocotillo (*Fouquieria splendens*) is common in the southwestern region of the United States and northern Mexico. It is leafless during most of the year, thereby avoiding excessive water loss (right). Immediately after a heavy rainfall, it produces small leaves (below and inset). As the soil dries, the leaves quickly shrivel and die.

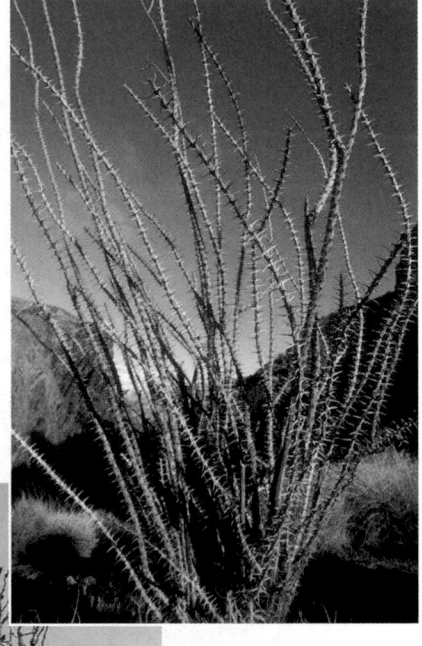

▼ Oleander (*Nerium oleander*), shown in the inset, is commonly found in arid climates. Its leaves have a thick cuticle and multiple-layered epidermal tissue that reduce water loss. Stomata are recessed in cavities called "crypts," an adaptation that reduces the rate of transpiration by protecting the stomata from hot, dry wind. Trichomes help minimize transpiration by breaking up the flow of air, allowing the chamber of the crypt to have a higher humidity than the surrounding atmosphere (LM).

Cuticle   Upper epidermal tissue

100 μm

Trichomes   Crypt   Stomata   Lower epidermal
("hairs")   tissue

▶ This is a close-up view of stems of old man cactus (*Cephalocereus senilis*), a Mexican desert plant. The long, white, hairlike bristles help reflect the sun.

shows others. Rain comes infrequently in deserts, but when it arrives the vegetation is transformed. Many species of desert plants avoid drying out by completing their short life cycles during the brief rainy seasons. Longer-lived species have unusual physiological or morphological adaptations that enable them to withstand the harsh desert conditions. Xerophytes are also found in other environments where access to liquid fresh water is problematic, such as frozen regions and seashores. Many xerophytes, such as cacti, have highly reduced leaves that resist excessive water loss; they carry out photosynthesis mainly in their stems. The stems of many xerophytes are fleshy because they store water for use during prolonged dry periods. Another adaptation to arid habitats is crassulacean acid metabolism (CAM), a specialized form of photosynthesis found in succulents of the family Crassulaceae and several other families (see Figure 10.20). Because the leaves of CAM plants take in CO_2 at night, the stomata can remain closed during the day, when evaporative stresses are greater.

As we have seen, plants face a dilemma: how to acquire as much CO_2 from the air as they can and at the same time retain as much water as possible. Stomata are the most important mediators of the conflicting demands of CO_2 acquisition and water retention.

CONCEPT CHECK 36.4

1. What are the stimuli that control the opening and closing of stomata?
2. The pathogenic fungus *Fusicoccum amygdali* secretes a toxin called fusicoccin that activates the plasma membrane proton pumps of plant cells and leads to uncontrolled water loss. Suggest a mechanism by which the activation of proton pumps could lead to severe wilting.
3. **WHAT IF?** If you buy cut flowers, why might the florist recommend cutting the stems underwater and then transferring the flowers to a vase while the cut ends are still wet?

For suggested answers, see Appendix A.

CONCEPT 36.5

Sugars are transported from leaves and other sources to sites of use or storage

You have read how water and minerals are absorbed by root cells, transported through the endodermis, released into the vessels and tracheids of the xylem, and carried to the tops of plants by the bulk flow driven by transpiration. However, transpiration cannot meet all the long-distance transport needs of the plant. The flow of water and minerals from soil to roots to leaves is largely in a direction opposite to the direction necessary for transporting sugars from mature leaves to lower parts of the plants, such as root tips that require large amounts of sugars for energy and growth. It is another tissue—the phloem—that transports the products of photosynthesis, a process called **translocation**.

Movement from Sugar Sources to Sugar Sinks

In angiosperms, the specialized cells that are conduits for translocation are the sieve-tube elements. Arranged end to end, they form long sieve tubes (see Figure 35.10). Between these cells are sieve plates, structures that allow the flow of sap along the sieve tube.

Phloem sap, the aqueous solution that flows through sieve tubes, differs markedly from xylem sap. By far the most prevalent solute in phloem sap is sugar, typically sucrose in most species. The sucrose concentration may be as high as 30% by weight, giving the sap a syrupy thickness. Phloem sap may also contain amino acids, hormones, and minerals.

In contrast to the unidirectional transport of xylem sap from roots to leaves, phloem sap moves from sites of sugar production to sites of sugar use or storage (see Figure 36.2). A **sugar source** is a plant organ that is a net producer of sugar, by photosynthesis or by breakdown of starch. A **sugar sink** is an organ that is a net consumer or depository of sugar. Growing roots, buds, stems, and fruits are sugar sinks. Although expanding leaves are sugar sinks, fully grown leaves, if well illuminated, are sugar sources. A storage organ, such as a tuber or a bulb, may be a source or a sink, depending on the season. When stockpiling carbohydrates in the summer, it is a sugar sink. After breaking dormancy in the spring, it is a sugar source because its starch is broken down to sugar, which is carried to the growing shoot tips.

Sinks usually receive sugar from the nearest sugar sources. The upper leaves on a branch, for example, may export sugar to the growing shoot tip, whereas the lower leaves may export sugar to the roots. A growing fruit may monopolize the sugar sources that surround it. For each sieve tube, the direction of transport depends on the locations of the sugar source and sugar sink that are connected by that tube. Therefore, neighboring sieve tubes may carry sap in opposite directions if they originate and end in different locations.

Sugar must be transported, or loaded, into sieve-tube elements before being exported to sugar sinks. In some species, it moves from mesophyll cells to sieve-tube elements via the symplast, passing through plasmodesmata. In other species, it moves by symplastic and apoplastic pathways. In maize leaves, for example, sucrose diffuses through the symplast from photosynthetic mesophyll cells into small veins. Much of it then moves into the apoplast and is accumulated by nearby sieve-tube elements, either directly or through companion cells

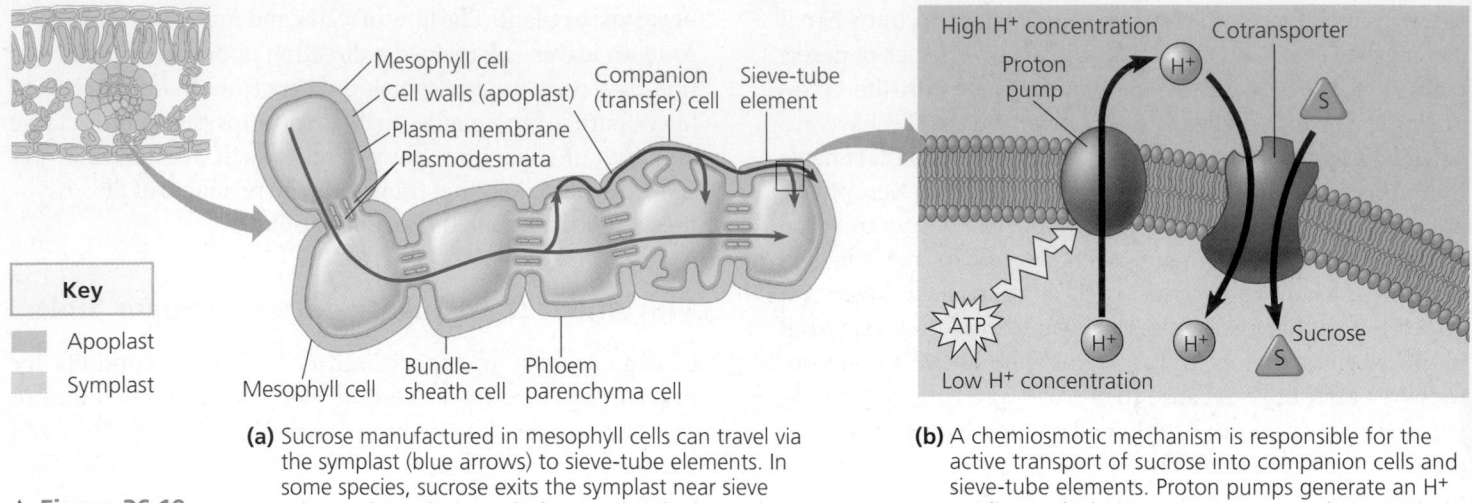

Key

Apoplast

Symplast

(a) Sucrose manufactured in mesophyll cells can travel via the symplast (blue arrows) to sieve-tube elements. In some species, sucrose exits the symplast near sieve tubes and travels through the apoplast (red arrow). It is then actively accumulated from the apoplast by sieve-tube elements and their companion cells.

(b) A chemiosmotic mechanism is responsible for the active transport of sucrose into companion cells and sieve-tube elements. Proton pumps generate an H⁺ gradient, which drives sucrose accumulation with the help of a cotransport protein that couples sucrose transport to the diffusion of H⁺ back into the cell.

▲ **Figure 36.19 Loading of sucrose into phloem.**

(Figure 36.19a). In some plants, the walls of the companion cells feature many ingrowths, enhancing solute transfer between apoplast and symplast. Such modified cells are called **transfer cells** (see Figure 29.5).

In many plants, sugar movement into the phloem requires active transport because sucrose is more concentrated in sieve-tube elements and companion cells than in mesophyll. Proton pumping and cotransport enable sucrose to move from mesophyll cells to sieve-tube elements **(Figure 36.19b)**.

Sucrose is unloaded at the sink end of a sieve tube. The process varies by species and organ. However, the concentration of free sugar in the sink is always lower than in the sieve tube because the unloaded sugar is consumed during growth and metabolism of the cells of the sink or converted to insoluble polymers such as starch. As a result of this sugar concentration gradient, sugar molecules diffuse from the phloem into the sink tissues, and water follows by osmosis.

Bulk Flow by Positive Pressure: The Mechanism of Translocation in Angiosperms

Phloem sap flows from source to sink at rates as great as 1 m/hr, much faster than diffusion or cytoplasmic streaming, the circular flow of cytoplasm within cells. In studying angiosperms, researchers have concluded that phloem sap moves through a sieve tube by bulk flow driven by positive pressure, known as *pressure flow* **(Figure 36.20)**. The building of pressure at the source end and reduction of that pressure at the sink end cause water to flow from source to sink, carrying the sugar along.

The pressure flow hypothesis explains why phloem sap flows from source to sink, and experiments build a strong case for pressure flow as the mechanism of translocation in angiosperms **(Figure 36.21)**. However, studies using electron microscopes suggest that in nonflowering vascular plants, the pores between phloem cells may be too small or obstructed to permit pressure

❶ Loading of sugar (green dots) into the sieve tube at the source reduces water potential inside the sieve-tube elements. This causes the tube to take up water by osmosis.

❷ This uptake of water generates a positive pressure that forces the sap to flow along the tube.

❸ The pressure is relieved by the unloading of sugar and the consequent loss of water at the sink.

❹ In leaf-to-root translocation, xylem recycles water from sink to source.

▲ **Figure 36.20 Bulk flow by positive pressure (pressure flow) in a sieve tube.**

flow. Thus, it is not known if the model applies to all other vascular plants.

Sinks vary in energy demands and capacity to unload sugars. Sometimes there are more sinks than can be supported by sources. In such cases, a plant might abort some flowers, seeds, or fruits—a phenomenon called *self-thinning*. Removing sinks can also be a horticulturally useful practice. For example, since large apples command a much better price than small ones, growers sometimes remove flowers or young fruits so that their trees produce fewer but larger apples.

▼ Figure 36.21 Inquiry

Does phloem sap contain more sugar near sources than sinks?

EXPERIMENT   The pressure flow hypothesis predicts that phloem sap near sources should have a higher sugar content than phloem sap near sinks. To test this aspect of the hypothesis, S. Rogers and A. J. Peel, at the University of Hull in England, used aphids that feed on phloem sap. An aphid probes with a hypodermic-like mouthpart called a stylet that penetrates a sieve-tube element. As sieve-tube pressure forced out phloem into the stylets, the researchers separated the aphids from the stylets, which then acted as taps exuding sap for hours. Researchers measured the sugar concentration of sap from stylets at different points between a source and sink.

Aphid feeding

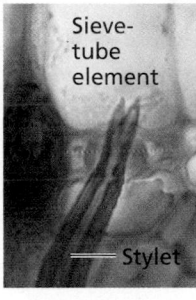

├─ 25 μm ─┤

Sieve-tube element

Stylet in sieve-tube element

Stylet

Sap droplet

Separated stylet exuding sap

Sap droplet

RESULTS   The closer the stylet was to a sugar source, the higher its sugar concentration was.

CONCLUSION   The results of such experiments support the pressure flow hypothesis, which predicts that sugar concentrations should be higher in sieve tubes closer to sugar sources.

SOURCE   S. Rogers and A. J. Peel, Some evidence for the existence of turgor pressure in the sieve tubes of willow (*Salix*), *Planta* 126, no. 3:259–267 (1975).

WHAT IF?   Spittle bugs are xylem sap feeders that use strong muscles to pump xylem sap through their guts. Could you isolate xylem sap from the excised stylets of spittle bugs?

CONCEPT CHECK 36.5

1. Compare and contrast the forces that move phloem sap and xylem sap over long distance.
2. Identify plant organs that are sugar sources, organs that are sugar sinks, and organs that might be either. Explain.
3. Why can xylem transport water and minerals using dead cells, whereas phloem requires living cells?
4. **WHAT IF?**   Apple growers in Japan sometimes make a nonlethal spiral slash around the bark of trees destined for removal after the growing season. This practice makes the apples sweeter. Why?

For suggested answers, see Appendix A.

CONCEPT 36.6
The symplast is highly dynamic

Although we have been discussing transport in mostly physical terms, almost like the flow of solutions through pipes, plant transport is a dynamic process. That is, the transport needs of a plant cell typically change during its development. A leaf, for example, may begin as a sugar sink but spend most of its life as a sugar source. Also, environmental changes may trigger marked responses in plant transport processes. Water stress may activate signal transduction pathways that greatly alter the membrane transport proteins governing the overall transport of water and minerals. Because the symplast is living tissue, it is largely responsible for the dynamic changes in plant transport processes.

Plasmodesmata: Continuously Changing Structures

Plasmodesmata provide an example of the dynamic nature of the symplast. Biologists formerly thought of plasmodesmata as unchanging pore-like structures, based mostly on the static images from electron microscopy. Recently, however, new techniques have revealed that plasmodesmata are highly dynamic structures that can change in permeability and number. They can open or close rapidly in response to changes in turgor pressure, cytoplasmic calcium levels, or cytoplasmic pH. Although some form during cytokinesis, they can also form much later. Moreover, loss of function is common during differentiation. For example, as a leaf matures from a sink to a source, its plasmodesmata either close or are eliminated, causing phloem unloading to cease.

Early studies by plant physiologists and pathologists came to differing conclusions regarding pore sizes of plasmodesmata. Physiologists injected fluorescent probes of different molecular sizes into cells and recorded whether the molecules passed into adjacent cells. Based on these observations, they concluded that the pore sizes were approximately 2.5 nm—too small for macromolecules such as proteins to pass. In contrast, pathologists provided electron micrographs showing evidence of passage of viral particles with diameters of 10 nm or greater. One hypothesis to explain these discordant findings was that viruses can greatly dilate plasmodesmata.

Subsequently, it was learned that plant viruses produce *viral movement proteins* that do cause plasmodesmata to dilate, enabling viral RNA to pass between cells. More recent evidence shows that plant cells themselves regulate plasmodesmata as part of a dynamic communication network. Viruses subvert this network by mimicking the cell's regulators of plasmodesmata.

A high degree of cytoplasmic interconnectedness exists only within certain groups of cells and tissues, known as *symplastic domains*. Informational molecules, such as proteins and RNAs, coordinate development between cells within each symplastic domain. If symplastic communication is altered by mutation, development can be grossly affected, as was shown by Patricia Zambryski and colleagues at the University of California, Berkeley (Figure 36.22). (See the interview on pages 736–737.)

Electrical Signaling in the Phloem

Rapid, long-distance electrical signaling through the phloem is another dynamic feature of the symplast. Electrical signaling has been studied extensively in plants that have rapid leaf movements, such as the sensitive plant (*Mimosa pudica*) and Venus flytrap (*Dionaea muscipula*). However, its role in other species is less clear. Some studies have revealed that a stimulus in one part of a plant can trigger an electrical signal in the phloem that affects another part, such as eliciting a change in gene transcription, respiration, photosynthesis, phloem unloading, or hormonal levels. Thus, the phloem can serve a nerve-like function, allowing for swift electrical communication between widely separated organs.

Phloem: An Information Superhighway

In addition to transporting sugars and conducting electrical signals, the phloem is a "superhighway" for the systemic transport of macromolecules and viruses. **Systemic** changes are those that spread throughout the body, affecting many or all of the body's systems or organs. Macromolecules translocated through the phloem include proteins and various types of RNA that enter the sieve tubes through plasmodesmata. Although plasmodesmata are often likened to the gap junctions between animal cells, their ability to traffic proteins and RNA is unique.

Systemic communication through the phloem helps integrate the functions of the whole plant. One classic example is the delivery of a flower-inducing signal from leaves to vegetative meristems. Another is a defensive response to localized infection, in which signals traveling through the phloem activate defense genes in noninfected tissues.

The coordinated transport of materials and information is central to plant survival. Plants acquire only so many resources in the course of their lifetimes. If these resources are not distributed and used in an optimal manner, the plant will not be able to compete well. Ultimately, the successful acquisition and conservation of resources and the integrated functioning of the whole plant are the most critical determinants of whether the plant will compete successfully.

CONCEPT CHECK 36.6

1. What factors influence symplastic communication?
2. How do plasmodesmata differ from gap junctions?
3. **WHAT IF?** If plants were genetically modified to be unresponsive to viral movement proteins, would this be a good way to prevent spread of infection? Explain.

For suggested answers, see Appendix A.

▼ Figure 36.22 **Inquiry**

Do alterations in symplastic communication affect plant development?

EXPERIMENT Patricia Zambryski and colleagues at the University of California, Berkeley, loaded large and small fluorescent probes at the base of the cotyledon and the root tip of developing *Arabidopsis* embryos. Studies of wild-type embryos had revealed a period in the middle of embryogenesis when symplastic transport of the large probes ceased but transport of small probes continued. The researchers screened for mutants that still transported the large probes during this period and then analyzed their growth into seedlings. The light micrographs below contrast the movement of the large probes (green fluorescence) in a wild-type embryo and mutant embryo.

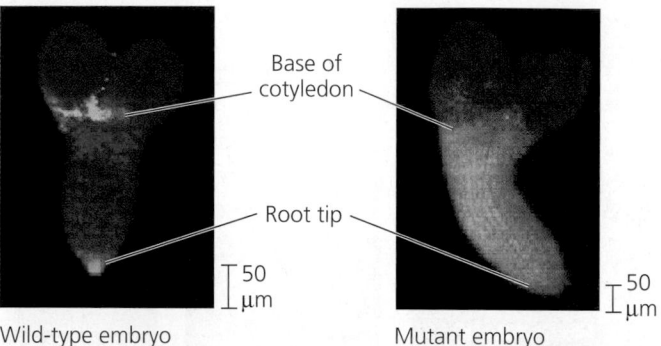

Base of cotyledon

Root tip

Wild-type embryo   Mutant embryo

RESULTS As shown in the scanning electron micrograph on the left, about half of the cell files in the wild type consisted of differentiated cells without root hairs (examples marked with yellow Xs). The mutant seedlings were developmentally retarded, with less cell differentiation than the wild-type seedlings. All cell files in a mutant seedling's root epidermis developed root hairs (examples marked with red circles).

 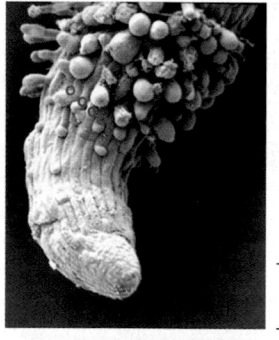

Wild-type seedling root tip   Mutant seedling root tip

CONCLUSION Isolation of the mutant and demonstration of its altered development support the hypothesis that maintaining symplastic domains is critical for proper plant development.

SOURCE I. Kim, F. Hempel, K. Sha, J. Pfluger, and P. Zambryski, Identification of a developmental transition in plasmodesmatal function during embryogenesis in *Arabidopsis thaliana, Development* 125:1261–1272 (2002).

WHAT IF? Suppose it was found that the mutation caused overproduction of an enzyme that cleaved the fluorescent molecule off the large probe midway through embryogenesis. Would you interpret the results differently?

Chapter 36 Review

SUMMARY OF KEY CONCEPTS

CONCEPT 36.1
Land plants acquire resources both above and below ground (pp. 764–767)

▶ **Shoot Architecture and Light Capture** Arrangement and size of leaves, branching, and stem thickness help shoots acquire CO_2 and light.

▶ **Root Architecture and Acquisition of Water and Minerals** Elongation, branching, and mycorrhizae help roots mine the soil for water and minerals.

CONCEPT 36.2
Transport occurs by short-distance diffusion or active transport and by long-distance bulk flow (pp. 767–772)

▶ **Diffusion and Active Transport of Solutes** Diffusion is the spontaneous movement down concentration gradients. Transport proteins aid diffusion across membranes. Proton pumps generate an H^+ gradient used to transport solutes.

▶ **Diffusion of Water (Osmosis)** Osmosis is the spontaneous movement of free water down its concentration gradient. Water flows across membranes from regions with higher water potential (ψ) to regions with lower ψ. Solutes decrease ψ. Pressure may increase or decrease ψ.

▶ **Three Major Pathways of Transport** The symplast is the cytoplasmic continuum linked by plasmodesmata. The apoplast is the continuum of cell walls and extracellular spaces.

▶ **Bulk Flow in Long-Distance Transport** Bulk flow is due to pressure differences at opposite ends of vessel elements and tracheids (for xylem sap) or sieve tubes (for phloem sap).

CONCEPT 36.3
Water and minerals are transported from roots to shoots (pp. 772–776)

▶ **Absorption of Water and Minerals by Root Cells** Root hairs and the extensive surface area of cortical cell membranes enhance uptake of water and minerals.

▶ **Transport of Water and Minerals into the Xylem** Water can cross the cortex via the symplast or apoplast, but minerals moving via the apoplast must finally cross the selective membranes of endodermal cells. The Casparian strip blocks apoplastic transfer of minerals to the stele.

▶ **Bulk Flow Driven by Negative Pressure in the Xylem** Transpiration lowers ψ in the leaf by producing a negative pressure potential (tension). This low ψ draws water from the xylem. Cohesion and adhesion of water transmit the pulling force to the roots.

▶ **Xylem Sap Ascent by Bulk Flow: *A Review*** Transpiration maintains movement of xylem sap against gravity.

CONCEPT 36.4
Stomata help regulate the rate of transpiration (pp. 776–779)

▶ **Stomata: Major Pathways for Water Loss** Guard cells widen or narrow the diameter of stomatal pores. Genetic and environmental factors influence stomatal density.

▶ **Mechanisms of Stomatal Opening and Closing** When guard cells take up K^+, they bow outward, widening the pore. Stomatal closing involves the loss of K^+.

▶ **Stimuli for Stomatal Opening and Closing** Stomatal aperture is controlled by light, CO_2, water availability, the hormone abscisic acid, and circadian rhythm.

▶ **Effects of Transpiration on Wilting and Leaf Temperature** If water lost by transpiration is not replaced by absorption from roots, the plant will wilt. Cooling by transpiration can lower leaf temperature.

▶ **Adaptations That Reduce Evaporative Water Loss** Reduced leaves and CAM photosynthesis are examples of adaptations to arid environments.

CONCEPT 36.5
Sugars are transported from leaves and other sources to sites of use or storage (pp. 779–781)

▶ **Movement from Sugar Sources to Sugar Sinks** Mature leaves are the main sources, though storage organs can be seasonal sources. Meristems and developing fruits and seeds are examples of sinks. Phloem loading and unloading depend on active transport of sucrose. Sucrose is cotransported with H^+, which diffuses down a gradient generated by proton pumps.

▶ **Bulk Flow by Positive Pressure: The Mechanism of Translocation in Angiosperms** Loading of sugar at the source and unloading at the sink maintain a pressure difference that keeps sap flowing through a sieve tube.

CONCEPT 36.6
The symplast is highly dynamic (pp. 781–782)

▶ **Plasmodesmata: Continuously Changing Structures** Plasmodesmata can change in number. When dilated, they can provide a passageway for macromolecules such as RNA and proteins.

▶ **Electrical Signaling in the Phloem** The phloem can conduct nerve-like electrical signals that propagate through the symplast and help to integrate whole-plant function.

▶ **Phloem: An Information Superhighway** Phloem helps integrate whole-plant function by transporting proteins, RNAs, and other macromolecules over long distances.

TESTING YOUR KNOWLEDGE

SELF-QUIZ

1. Which of the following does *not* affect self-shading?
   - a. leaf area index
   - b. phyllotaxy
   - c. self-pruning
   - d. stem thickness
   - e. leaf orientation

2. What would enhance water uptake by a plant cell?
   - a. decreased ψ of the surrounding solution
   - b. an increase in pressure exerted by the cell wall
   - c. the loss of solutes from the cell
   - d. an increase in ψ of the cytoplasm
   - e. positive pressure on the surrounding solution

3. A plant cell with a ψ_S of -0.65 MPa maintains a constant volume when bathed in a solution that has a ψ_S of -0.30 MPa and is in an open container. The cell has a
   - a. ψ_P of $+0.65$ MPa.
   - b. ψ of -0.65 MPa.
   - c. ψ_P of $+0.35$ MPa.
   - d. ψ_P of $+0.30$ MPa.
   - e. ψ of 0 MPa.

4. Which structure or compartment is *not* part of the apoplast?
   - a. the lumen of a xylem vessel
   - b. the lumen of a sieve tube
   - c. the cell wall of a mesophyll cell
   - d. an extracellular air space
   - e. the cell wall of a root hair

5. Which of the following is an adaptation that enhances the uptake of water and minerals by roots?
   - a. mycorrhizae
   - b. cavitation
   - c. active uptake by vessels
   - d. rhythmic contractions by cortical cells
   - e. pumping through plasmodesmata

6. Which of the following is *not* part of the transpiration-cohesion-tension mechanism for the ascent of xylem sap?
   - a. loss of water from the mesophyll cells, which initiates a pull of water molecules from neighboring cells
   - b. transfer of transpirational pull from one water molecule to the next, due to cohesion by hydrogen bonds
   - c. hydrophilic walls of tracheids and vessels that help maintain the column of water against gravity
   - d. active pumping of water into the xylem of roots
   - e. lowering of ψ in the surface film of mesophyll cells due to transpiration

7. Photosynthesis ceases when leaves wilt, mainly because
   - a. the chlorophyll of wilting leaves breaks down.
   - b. flaccid mesophyll cells are incapable of photosynthesis.
   - c. stomata close, preventing CO_2 from entering the leaf.
   - d. photolysis, the water-splitting step of photosynthesis, cannot occur when there is a water deficiency.
   - e. accumulation of CO_2 in the leaf inhibits enzymes.

8. Stomata open when guard cells
   - a. sense an increase in CO_2 in the air spaces of the leaf.
   - b. open because of a decrease in turgor pressure.
   - c. become more turgid because of an addition of K^+, followed by the osmotic entry of water.
   - d. close aquaporins, preventing uptake of water.
   - e. accumulate water by active transport.

9. Movement of phloem sap from a source to a sink
   - a. occurs through the apoplast of sieve-tube elements.
   - b. may translocate sugars from the breakdown of stored starch in a root up to developing shoots.
   - c. depends on tension, or negative pressure potential.
   - d. depends on pumping water into sieve tubes at the source.
   - e. results mainly from diffusion.

10. Which of these is *not* transported via the symplast?
    - a. sugars
    - b. mRNA
    - c. DNA
    - d. proteins
    - e. viruses

11. **DRAW IT** Trace the uptake of water and minerals from root hairs to the vessels in a root, following a symplastic route and an apoplastic route. Label the routes.

For Self-Quiz answers, see Appendix A.

MEDIA Visit **www.campbellbiology.com** for a Practice Test.

EVOLUTION CONNECTION

12. Large brown algae called kelps can grow as tall as 25 m. Kelps consist of a holdfast anchored to the ocean floor, blades that float at the surface and collect light, and a long stalk connecting the blades to the holdfast (see Figure 28.15). Specialized cells in the stalk, although nonvascular, transport sugar. Suggest a reason why these structures analogous to sieve-tube elements might have evolved in kelps.

SCIENTIFIC INQUIRY

13. Tomato and cotton plants wilt within a few hours of flooding their roots. Flooding leads to low oxygen conditions, increases in cytoplasmic calcium, and decreases in cytoplasmic pH. Suggest a hypothesis to explain how it leads to wilting.

SCIENCE, TECHNOLOGY, AND SOCIETY

14. In the arid southwestern United States, there has been growing criticism of water use for lawns and golf courses. Should such use be limited or even banned? Explain.

Soil and Plant Nutrition

KEY CONCEPTS

37.1 Soil is a living, finite resource
37.2 Plants require essential elements to complete their life cycle
37.3 Plant nutrition often involves relationships with other organisms

OVERVIEW

"The Nation that Destroys Its Soil Destroys Itself"

President Franklin D. Roosevelt wrote these words in 1937 in referring to an ecological and human disaster that ravaged the southwestern Great Plains, a region that came to be called the Dust Bowl. The series of devastating dust storms was caused by a massive drought and decades of inappropriate farming techniques. Before the arrival of farmers, the Great Plains had been covered by hardy grasses that held the soil in place in spite of recurring droughts and torrential rains. But in the late 1800s and early 1900s, many homesteaders settled in the region, planting wheat and raising cattle. These land uses left the soil exposed to erosion by winds. A few years of drought made the problem worse. During the 1930s, huge quantities of fertile soil were blown away in "black blizzards," rendering millions of hectares of farmland useless (Figure 37.1). In one of the worst dust storms, clouds of dust blew eastward to Chicago, where soil fell like snow, and even reached as far east as New York City and Washington, D.C. Hundreds of thousands of people in the Dust Bowl region were forced to abandon their homes and land, a plight immortalized in John Steinbeck's novel *The Grapes of Wrath*.

Soil mismanagement in various forms has been a recurrent problem throughout human history and continues to this day.

▲ Figure 37.1 **Could this happen again?**

More than 30% of the world's farmland has reduced productivity stemming from poor soil conditions, such as chemical contamination, mineral deficiencies, acidity, salinity, and poor drainage. As the world's population continues to grow, the demand for food increases. Because soil quality is a major determinant of crop yield, the need to manage soil resources prudently has never been greater.

Healthy soil improves plant growth by enhancing plant **nutrition**, the process by which an organism takes in and makes use of food substances. As discussed in Chapter 36, plants obtain nutrients from both the atmosphere and the soil. Using sunlight as an energy source, plants produce organic nutrients by reducing carbon dioxide to sugars through the process of photosynthesis. Land plants also take up water and various mineral nutrients from the soil through their root systems. In this chapter, we discuss the basic physical properties of soils and the factors that govern soil quality. We then explore why certain inorganic nutrients are essential for plant function. Finally, we examine some nutritional adaptations that have evolved in plants, often in relationships with other organisms.

CONCEPT 37.1
Soil is a living, finite resource

The upper layers of the soil, from which plants absorb nearly all of the water and minerals they require, contain a wide range of living organisms that interact with each other and with the physical environment. This complex ecosystem may take centuries to form but can be destroyed by human mismanagement in just a few years. To understand why soil must be conserved and why particular plants grow where they do, we must appreciate the basic physical properties of soil: its texture and composition.

Soil Texture

The texture of soil depends on the sizes of its particles. Soil particles can range from coarse sand (0.02–2 mm in diameter) to silt (0.002–0.02 mm) to microscopic clay particles (less than 0.002 mm). These different-sized particles arise ultimately from the weathering of rock. Water freezing in the crevices of rocks causes mechanical fracturing, and weak acids in the soil break rocks down chemically. When organisms penetrate the rock, they accelerate breakdown by chemical and mechanical means. Plant roots, for example, secrete acids that dissolve the rock, and their growth in fissures leads to mechanical fracturing. The mineral particles released by weathering become mixed with living organisms and **humus**, the remains of dead organisms and other organic matter, forming **topsoil**. The topsoil and other distinct soil layers, or **soil horizons**, are often visible where there is a road cut or deep hole (**Figure 37.2**). The topsoil, or A horizon, can range in depth from millimeters to meters. We focus mostly on the properties of topsoil because it is the most important soil layer for the growth of most plants.

In the topsoil, plants are nourished by the soil solution, the water and dissolved minerals in the pores between soil particles. The pores also contain air pockets. After a heavy rainfall, water drains away from the larger spaces in the soil, but smaller spaces retain water because water molecules are attracted to the negatively charged surfaces of clay and other soil particles.

The topsoils that are the most fertile—supporting the most abundant growth—are **loams**, which are composed of roughly equal amounts of sand, silt, and clay. Loamy soils have enough small silt and clay particles to provide ample surface area for the adhesion and retention of minerals and water. Meanwhile, the large spaces between sand particles enable efficient diffusion of oxygen to the roots. Sandy soils generally don't retain enough water to support vigorous plant growth, and clayey soils tend to retain too much water. When soil does not drain adequately, the air is replaced by water, and the roots suffocate from lack of oxygen. Typically, the most fertile topsoils have pores that are about half water and half air, providing a good balance between aeration, drainage, and water storage capacity. The physical properties of soils can be adjusted by adding soil amendments, such as peat moss, compost, manure, or sand.

Topsoil Composition

A soil's composition encompasses its inorganic (mineral) and organic chemical components. The organic components include the many life-forms that inhabit the soil.

Inorganic Components

The surface charges of soil particles determine their ability to bind many nutrients. Most soil particles are negatively charged. Positively charged ions (cations)—such as potassium (K^+), calcium (Ca^{2+}), and magnesium (Mg^{2+})—adhere to these particles and are therefore not easily lost by *leaching*, the percolation of water through the soil. Roots, however, do not absorb mineral cations directly from soil particles. Instead, they become available in the soil solution, through **cation exchange**. In this process, mineral cations are displaced from soil particles by other cations, particularly H^+, and enter the soil solution, which is then absorbed by root hairs (**Figure 37.3**). A soil's capacity to exchange cations is determined by the number of

The A horizon is the topsoil, a mixture of broken-down rock of various textures, living organisms, and decaying organic matter.

The B horizon contains much less organic matter than the A horizon and is less weathered.

The C horizon, composed mainly of partially broken-down rock, serves as the "parent" material for the upper layers of soil.

▲ **Figure 37.2 Soil horizons.**

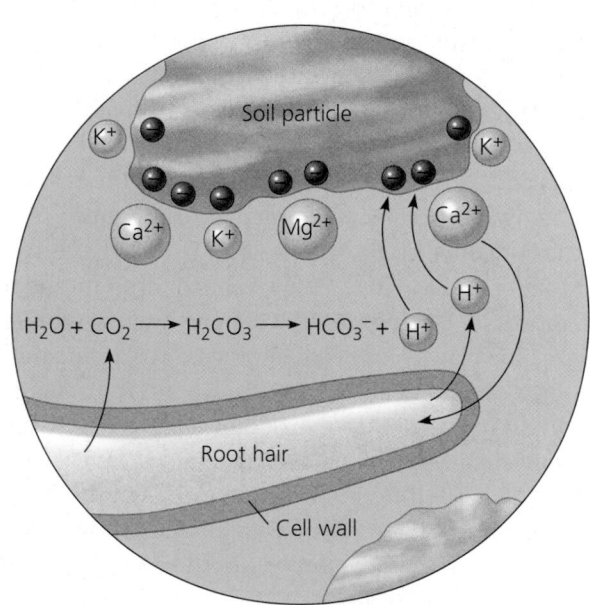

▲ **Figure 37.3 Cation exchange in soil.**
? *Which are more likely to be leached from the soil by heavy rains—cations or anions? Explain.*

cation adhesion sites and by the pH. Soils with higher capacities generally have a larger reserve of mineral nutrients.

Negatively charged ions (anions)—such as the plant nutrients nitrate (NO_3^-), phosphate ($H_2PO_4^-$), and sulfate (SO_4^{2-})—are not bound tightly to the negatively charged soil particles and are therefore easily released. During heavy rain or irrigation, they are leached into the groundwater, making them unavailable for uptake by roots.

Organic Components

Humus is a major organic component of topsoil, consisting of organic material produced by the decomposition of dead organisms, feces, fallen leaves, and other organic matter by bacteria and fungi. Humus prevents clay particles from packing together and forms a crumbly soil that retains water but is still porous enough to aerate roots adequately. Humus also increases the soil's capacity to exchange cations and serves as a reservoir of mineral nutrients that return gradually to the soil as microorganisms decompose the organic matter.

Topsoil is also home to an astonishing number and variety of organisms. A teaspoon of topsoil has about 5 billion bacteria that cohabit with fungi, algae and other protists, insects, earthworms, nematodes, and plant roots. The activities of all these organisms affect the soil's physical and chemical properties. Earthworms, for example, consume organic matter and derive their nutrition from the bacteria and fungi growing on this material. They excrete wastes and move large amounts of material to the soil surface. In addition, they move organic matter into deeper layers of the soil. In effect, earthworms mix and clump the soil particles, allowing for better gaseous diffusion and retention of water. Plant roots also affect soil texture and composition. For example, by binding the soil, they reduce erosion, and by excreting acids, they lower soil pH.

Soil Conservation and Sustainable Agriculture

Ancient farmers recognized that yields on a particular plot of land decreased over the years. Moving to uncultivated areas, they observed the same pattern of reduced yields over time. Eventually, they realized that soil—if fertilized—was a renewable resource that enabled crops to be cultivated season after season at a fixed location. This sedentary agriculture facilitated a new way of life. Humans began to build permanent dwellings—the first villages. They also stored food for use between harvests,

and food surpluses enabled some members of these early communities to specialize in nonfarming occupations. In short, soil management, by fertilization and other practices, helped prepare the way for the establishment of modern societies.

In this section, we'll discuss how farmers irrigate and modify soil to maintain good crop yields. The goal is **sustainable agriculture**, a commitment embracing a variety of farming methods that are conservation minded, environmentally safe, and profitable. We will also examine how problems such as erosion, soil compaction, and soil contamination are causing global soil degradation.

Irrigation

Because water is often the limiting factor in plant growth, perhaps no technology has increased crop yield as much as irrigation. However, irrigation is a huge drain on freshwater resources. Globally, about 75% of all freshwater use is devoted to agriculture. Many rivers in the southwestern United States have been reduced to trickles by the diversion of water for irrigation. The primary source of irrigation water, however, is not surface waters, such as rivers and lakes, but underground water reserves called *aquifers*. In some parts of the world, the rate of water removal is exceeding the natural refilling of the aquifers. The result is *land subsidence*, a gradual settling or sudden sinking of Earth's surface (**Figure 37.4**). Land subsidence alters drainage patterns, causes damage to humanmade structures, promotes loss of underground springs, and increases the risk of flooding.

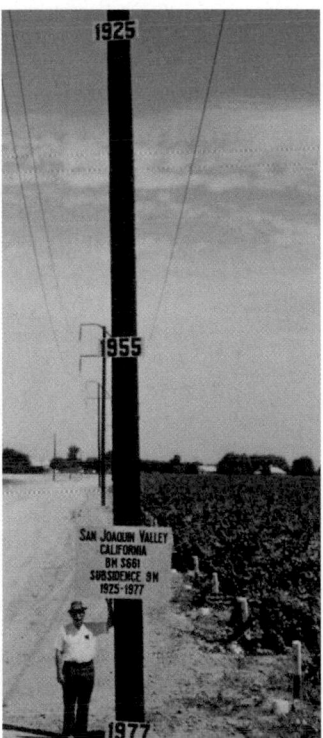

◄ To emphasize the dramatic effects of land subsidence in California's San Joaquin Valley, geologist Joseph F. Poland (shown here in 1977) had signs posted to represent approximate altitudes of the land surface in 1925 and 1955.

▲ Sudden land subsidence resulting from the overuse of groundwater for irrigation triggered the formation of this sinkhole in Florida.

▲ **Figure 37.4 Land subsidence caused by excessive removal of groundwater.**

Irrigation, particularly from groundwater, can also lead to soil *salinization*—formation of soil too salty for cultivating plants. Salts dissolved in irrigation water accumulate in the soil as the water evaporates, making the water potential of the soil solution more negative. The water potential gradient from soil to roots is lowered, reducing water uptake (see Chapter 36).

Many forms of irrigation, such as the flooding of fields, are wasteful because much of the water evaporates. In order to use water efficiently, farmers must understand the water-holding capacity of their soil, the water needs of their crops, and the appropriate irrigation technology. One popular technology is *drip irrigation*, the slow release of water to soil and plants from perforated plastic tubing placed directly at the root zone. Because drip irrigation requires less water and reduces salinization, it is used in many arid agricultural regions.

Fertilization

In natural ecosystems, mineral nutrients are usually recycled by the decomposition of dead organic material and by the excretion of animal wastes. Agriculture, however, is unnatural. The lettuce in your salad, for example, contains minerals extracted from a farmer's field. As you excrete wastes, these minerals are now deposited far from their original source. Over many harvests, the farmer's field will become depleted of nutrients if they are not restored. Nutrient depletion is a major cause of global soil degradation. Farmers must reverse nutrient depletion by **fertilization**, the addition of mineral nutrients to the soil.

Today, most farmers in industrialized nations use fertilizers containing minerals that are either mined or prepared by energy-intensive processes. These fertilizers are usually enriched in nitrogen (N), phosphorus (P), and potassium (K)—the nutrients most commonly deficient in depleted soils. You may have seen fertilizers labeled with a three-number code, called the N-P-K ratio. A fertilizer marked "15-10-5," for instance, is 15% N (as ammonium or nitrate), 10% P (as phosphoric acid), and 5% K (as the mineral potash).

Manure, fishmeal, and compost are called "organic" fertilizers because they are of biological origin and contain decomposing organic material. Before plants can use organic material, however, it must be decomposed into the inorganic nutrients that roots can absorb. Whether from organic fertilizer or a chemical factory, the minerals a plant extracts are in the same form. However, organic fertilizers release them gradually, whereas minerals in commercial fertilizers are immediately available but may not be retained by the soil for long. Minerals not absorbed by roots are often leached from the soil by rainwater or irrigation. To make matters worse, mineral runoff into lakes may lead to explosions in algal populations that can deplete oxygen levels and decimate fish populations.

Adjusting Soil pH

Soil pH is another important factor influencing mineral availability because it affects cation exchange and the chemical form of minerals. Depending on the soil pH, a particular mineral may be bound too tightly to clay particles or may be in a chemical form that the plant cannot absorb. Most plants prefer slightly acidic soil because the high H^+ concentrations can displace positively charged minerals from soil particles, making them more available for absorption. Adjusting soil pH for optimal crop growth is tricky because a change in H^+ concentration may make one mineral more available but another mineral less available. At pH 8, for instance, plants can absorb calcium, but iron is almost completely unavailable. The soil pH should be matched to a crop's mineral needs. If the soil is too alkaline, adding sulfate will lower the pH. Soil that is too acidic can be adjusted by adding lime (calcium carbonate or calcium hydroxide).

When the soil pH dips to 5 or lower, toxic aluminum ions (Al^{3+}) become more soluble and are absorbed by roots, stunting root growth and preventing the uptake of calcium, a needed plant nutrient. Some plants can cope with high Al^{3+} levels by secreting organic anions that bind the Al^{3+} and render it harmless. However, low soil pH and Al^{3+} toxicity continue to pose serious problems, especially in tropical regions, where growing populations and food production pressures are often most acute.

Controlling Erosion

As happened most dramatically in the Dust Bowl, water and wind erosion can remove considerable amounts of topsoil. Erosion is a major cause of soil degradation because soil nutrients are carried far away by wind and streams. To limit erosion, farmers can take precautions such as planting rows of trees as windbreaks, terracing hillside crops, and cultivating in a contour pattern **(Figure 37.5)**. Crops such as alfalfa and wheat provide good ground cover and protect the soil better

▲ **Figure 37.5 Contour tillage.** These crops in Wisconsin are planted in rows that go around, rather than up and down, the hills. Contour tillage helps slow water runoff and topsoil erosion after heavy rains.

than maize and other crops that are usually planted in more widely spaced rows.

Erosion can also be reduced by a plowing technique called **no-till agriculture**. In traditional plowing, the entire field is tilled, or turned over. Although this practice helps control weeds, it also disrupts the meshwork of roots that holds the soil in place, leading to increased surface runoff and erosion. In no-till agriculture, a specialized plow creates narrow furrows for seeds and fertilizer. In this way, the field can be seeded with minimal disturbance of the soil, while also requiring less fertilizer.

Preventing Soil Compaction

Large heavy farm equipment causes a problem called soil compaction: Soil particles are pressed together, reducing pore space between them. Heavily compacted soils contain few large pores and have reduced rates of water absorption and drainage because the small pores that remain are less effective in moving water through the soil. Compaction also slows down gas exchange between roots and the soil. In addition, compaction reduces root growth by making it harder for them to penetrate the soil, thereby decreasing absorption of water and nutrients. The best cure for soil compaction is to avoid it by not farming soil that is too wet and by redesigning agricultural equipment with more and broader tires to redistribute the weight.

Phytoremediation

Some land areas are unfit for cultivation because toxic heavy metals or organic pollutants have contaminated the soil or groundwater. Traditionally, soil remediation, the detoxification of contaminated soils, has focused on nonbiological technologies, such as removing and storing contaminated soil in landfills, but these techniques are very costly and often disrupt the landscape. **Phytoremediation** is a nondestructive biotechnology that harnesses some plants' ability to extract soil pollutants and concentrate them in portions of the plant that can be easily removed for safe disposal. For example, alpine pennycress (*Thlaspi caerulescens*) can accumulate zinc in its shoots at concentrations 300 times higher than most plants can tolerate. The shoots can then be harvested and the contaminating zinc removed. Such plants show promise for cleaning up areas contaminated by smelters, mining operations, or nuclear testing. Phytoremediation is one form of the more general technology of bioremediation, which also includes the use of prokaryotes and protists to detoxify polluted sites (see Chapters 27 and 56).

In this section, we have discussed the importance of soil conservation for sustainable agriculture. Mineral nutrients are major factors contributing to soil fertility, but which minerals are most important, and why do plants need them? These are the topics of the next section.

CONCEPT CHECK 37.1

1. Explain how the phrase "too much of a good thing" can apply to watering and fertilizing plants.
2. Some lawn mowers collect clippings for easy disposal and to prevent clumps from inhibiting photosynthesis. What is a possible drawback of this practice with respect to plant nutrition?
3. **WHAT IF?** How would adding clay to loamy soil affect the soil's capacity to exchange cations and retain water? Explain.

For suggested answers, see Appendix A.

CONCEPT 37.2
Plants require essential elements to complete their life cycle

Watch a large plant grow from a tiny seed, and you cannot help wondering where all the plant mass comes from. Aristotle hypothesized that plants "ate" soil because they were seen to arise from the ground. In the 1640s, the Belgian physiologist Jan Baptista van Helmont tested the hypothesis that plants grow by consuming soil. He planted a small willow in a pot that contained 90.9 kg of soil. After five years, the plant weighed 76.8 kg, but only 0.06 kg of soil had disappeared from the pot. He concluded that the willow had grown mainly from the water he had added. A century later, the English physiologist Stephen Hales, armed with knowledge from recent advances in physics and chemistry that air is a substance with mass, postulated that plants are nourished mostly by air.

There is some truth to all three hypotheses because soil, water, and air all contribute to plant growth. The water content of a plant can be measured by comparing the mass of plant material before and after it is dried. Typically, 80–90% of a plant's fresh mass is water. We can also analyze the chemical composition of the dry residue. Organic substances generally account for about 96% of the dry mass. Thus, the inorganic nutrients from the soil, although essential for plant survival, contribute very little to the plant's total mass. The majority of a plant's dry mass is derived neither from water nor from soil minerals but from the CO_2 that is assimilated from the air during photosynthesis. Water also supplies most of the hydrogen atoms and some of the oxygen atoms incorporated into organic compounds by photosynthesis (see Figure 10.4). Most of the organic material of plants is carbohydrate, including the cellulose of cell walls. Thus, the components of carbohydrates—carbon, oxygen, and hydrogen—are the most abundant elements in a dried plant. Because many macromolecules contain nitrogen, sulfur, or phosphorus, these elements are also relatively abundant in plants.

Macronutrients and Micronutrients

The inorganic substances in plants contain more than 50 chemical elements. In studying the chemical composition of plants, we must distinguish elements that are essential from those that are merely present in the plant. A chemical element is considered an **essential element** only if it is required for a plant to complete its life cycle and produce another generation.

To determine which chemical elements are essential, researchers use **hydroponic culture**, in which plants are grown in mineral solutions instead of soil (**Figure 37.6**). Such studies have helped identify 17 essential elements needed by all plants (**Table 37.1**). Hydroponic culture is also used on a small scale to grow some greenhouse crops.

Nine of the essential elements are called **macronutrients** because plants require them in relatively large amounts. Six of these are the major components of organic compounds forming a plant's structure: carbon, oxygen, hydrogen, nitrogen, phosphorus, and sulfur. The other three macronutrients are potassium, calcium, and magnesium. Of all the mineral nutrients, nitrogen contributes the most to plant growth and crop yields. Plants require nitrogen as a component of proteins, nucleic acids, chlorophyll, and other important organic molecules.

The remaining eight essential elements are known as **micronutrients** because plants need them in tiny quantities. They are chlorine, iron, manganese, boron, zinc, copper, nickel, and molybdenum. In some cases, sodium may be a ninth essential micronutrient: Plants that use the C_4 and CAM pathways of photosynthesis (see Chapter 10) require sodium ions to regenerate phosphophenolpyruvate, which is the CO_2 acceptor in these two types of carbon fixation.

Micronutrients function in plants mainly as cofactors, nonprotein helpers in enzymatic reactions (see Chapter 8). Iron, for example, is a metallic component of cytochromes, the proteins in the electron transport chains of chloroplasts and mitochondria. It is because micronutrients generally play catalytic roles that plants need only tiny quantities. The requirement for molybdenum, for instance, is so modest that there is only one atom of this rare element for every 60 million atoms of hydrogen in dried plant material. Yet a deficiency of molybdenum or any other micronutrient can weaken or kill a plant.

Symptoms of Mineral Deficiency

The symptoms of a deficiency depend partly on the mineral's function as a nutrient. For example, a deficiency of magnesium, a component of chlorophyll, causes *chlorosis*, yellowing of the leaves. In some cases, the relationship between a mineral deficiency and its symptoms is less direct. For instance, iron deficiency can cause chlorosis even though chlorophyll contains no iron, because iron ions are required as a cofactor in one of the enzymatic steps of chlorophyll synthesis.

Mineral deficiency symptoms depend not only on the role of the nutrient but also on its mobility within the plant. If a nutrient

Hydroponic Culture

APPLICATION In hydroponic culture, plants are grown in mineral solutions without soil. One use of hydroponic culture is to identify essential elements in plants.

TECHNIQUE Plant roots are bathed in aerated solutions of known mineral composition. Aerating the water provides the roots with oxygen for cellular respiration. (Note: The flasks would normally be opaque to prevent algal growth.) A mineral, such as potassium, can be omitted to test whether it is essential.

Control: Solution containing all minerals

Experimental: Solution without potassium

RESULTS If the omitted mineral is essential, mineral deficiency symptoms occur, such as stunted growth and discolored leaves. By definition, the plant would not be able to complete its life cycle. Deficiencies of different elements may have different symptoms, which can aid in diagnosing mineral deficiencies in soil.

moves about freely, symptoms appear first in older organs because young, growing tissues have more "drawing power" for nutrients that are in short supply. For example, magnesium is relatively mobile and is shunted preferentially to young leaves. Therefore, a plant deficient in magnesium first shows signs of chlorosis in its older leaves. The mechanism for preferential routing is the source-to-sink translocation in phloem, as minerals move along with sugars to the growing tissues (see Figure 36.20). In contrast, a deficiency of a mineral that is relatively immobile affects young parts of the plant first. Older tissues may have adequate amounts that they retain during periods of short supply. For example, iron does not move freely within a plant, and an iron deficiency causes yellowing of young leaves before any effect on older leaves is visible. The mineral requirements of a plant may also change with the time of the year and the age of the plant. Young seedlings, for example, rarely show mineral deficiency symptoms because their mineral requirements are met largely by minerals released from stored reserves in the seed itself.

Table 37.1 Essential Elements in Plants

Element	Form Available to Plants	% Mass in Dry Tissue	Major Functions
Macronutrients			
Carbon	CO_2	45%	Major component of plant's organic compounds
Oxygen	CO_2	45%	Major component of plant's organic compounds
Hydrogen	H_2O	6%	Major component of plant's organic compounds
Nitrogen	NO_3^-, NH_4^+	1.5%	Component of nucleic acids, proteins, hormones, chlorophyll, coenzymes
Potassium	K^+	1.0%	Cofactor that functions in protein synthesis; major solute functioning in water balance; operation of stomata
Calcium	Ca^{2+}	0.5%	Important in formation and stability of cell walls and in maintenance of membrane structure and permeability; activates some enzymes; regulates many responses of cells to stimuli
Magnesium	Mg^{2+}	0.2%	Component of chlorophyll; activates many enzymes
Phosphorus	$H_2PO_4^-$, HPO_4^{2-}	0.2%	Component of nucleic acids, phospholipids, ATP, several coenzymes
Sulfur	SO_4^{2-}	0.1%	Component of proteins, coenzymes
Micronutrients			
Chlorine	Cl^-	0.01%	Required for water-splitting step of photosynthesis; functions in water balance
Iron	Fe^{3+}, Fe^{2+}	0.01%	Component of cytochromes; activates some enzymes
Manganese	Mn^{2+}	0.005%	Active in formation of amino acids; activates some enzymes; required for water-splitting step of photosynthesis
Boron	$H_2BO_3^-$	0.002%	Cofactor in chlorophyll synthesis; may be involved in carbohydrate transport and nucleic acid synthesis; role in cell wall function
Zinc	Zn^{2+}	0.002%	Active in formation of chlorophyll; activates some enzymes
Copper	Cu^+, Cu^{2+}	0.001%	Component of many redox and lignin-biosynthetic enzymes
Nickel	Ni^{2+}	0.001%	Cofactor for an enzyme functioning in nitrogen metabolism
Molybdenum	MoO_4^{2-}	0.0001%	Essential for mutualistic relationship with nitrogen-fixing bacteria; cofactor in nitrate reduction

Deficiencies of phosphorus, potassium, and especially nitrogen are most common. Micronutrient shortages are less common and tend to occur in certain geographic regions because of differences in soil composition. The symptoms of a mineral deficiency may vary between species but are often distinctive enough for a plant physiologist or farmer to diagnose the cause **(Figure 37.7)**. One way to confirm a diagnosis is to analyze the mineral content of the plant or soil. The amount of a micronutrient needed to correct a deficiency is usually quite small. For example, a zinc deficiency in fruit trees can usually be cured by hammering a few zinc nails into each tree trunk.

Healthy

Phosphate-deficient

Potassium-deficient

Nitrogen-deficient

▶ **Figure 37.7 The most common mineral deficiencies, as seen in maize leaves.** Mineral deficiency symptoms may vary in different species. In maize, phosphate-deficient plants have reddish purple margins, particularly in young leaves. Potassium-deficient maize plants exhibit "firing," or drying, along tips and margins of older leaves. Nitrogen deficiency is evident in a yellowing that starts at the tip and moves along the center (midrib) of older leaves.

Moderation is important because overdoses of many nutrients can be detrimental or toxic to plants. Too much nitrogen, for example, can lead to excessive vine growth in tomato plants at the expense of good fruit production.

Improving Plant Nutrition by Genetic Modification: Some Examples

In exploring plant nutrition so far, we have discussed how farmers use irrigation, fertilization, and other means to tailor the soil to fit the needs of a crop. An opposite approach involves tailoring the plant by genetic engineering to better fit the soil. Here we highlight a few examples of how genetic engineering is improving plant nutrition and fertilizer usage.

Resistance to Aluminum Toxicity

As previously discussed, aluminum in acidic soils damages roots and greatly reduces crop yields. The major mechanism of aluminum resistance is the secretion of organic acids (such as malic acid and citric acid) by roots. These acids bind to free aluminum ions and lower aluminum levels in the soil. Luis Herrera-Estrella and colleagues, at the Research and Advanced Studies Center in Mexico, altered tobacco and papaya plants by introducing a citrate synthase gene from a bacterium into the plants' genomes. The resulting overproduction of citric acid increased aluminum resistance in these two crops.

Flood Tolerance

Waterlogged soil not only deprives roots of oxygen but also can injure plants as ethanol and other toxic products of alcoholic fermentation by soil microbes accumulate. In Asian countries, flooding during the monsoon season often destroys rice crops. Although most varieties of rice die after being submerged for a week, some types can survive weeks of flooding. A gene called *Submergence 1A-1* (*Sub1A-1*) is the main source of submergence tolerance in flood-resistant rice. Sub1A-1 proteins regulate the expression of genes that are normally activated under anaerobic conditions, such as those that code for alcohol dehydrogenase, an enzyme that breaks down ethanol. The heightened expression of *Sub1A-1* in flooding-intolerant varieties of rice increased the alcohol dehydrogenase levels of the plants and conferred tolerance to submergence.

Smart Plants

Agricultural researchers are developing ways to maintain crop yields while reducing fertilizer use. One approach is to genetically engineer "smart" plants that signal when a nutrient deficiency is imminent—but *before* damage has occurred. One type of smart plant takes advantage of a promoter (a DNA sequence that indicates where the transcription of a gene starts) that more readily binds RNA polymerase (the transcription enzyme) when the phosphorus content of the plant's tissues begins to decline. This promoter is linked to a

No phosphorus deficiency | Beginning phosphorus deficiency | Well-developed phosphorus deficiency

▲ **Figure 37.8 Deficiency warnings from "smart" plants.** Some plants have been genetically modified to signal an impending nutrient deficiency before irreparable damage occurs. For example, after laboratory treatments, the research plant *Arabidopsis* develops a blue color in response to an imminent phosphate deficiency.

"reporter" gene that leads to production of a light blue pigment in the leaf cells **(Figure 37.8)**. When leaves of these smart plants develop a blue tinge, the farmer knows it is time to add phosphate-containing fertilizer.

So far, you have learned that soil, to support vigorous plant growth, must have an adequate supply of mineral nutrients, sufficient aeration, good water-holding capacity, low salinity, and a pH near neutrality. It must also be free of toxic concentrations of minerals and other chemicals. These physical and chemical features of soil, however, are just half the story. To understand soil fully, we must also consider its living components.

CONCEPT CHECK 37.2

1. Explain how Table 37.1 supports Stephen Hales's hypothesis.
2. Are some essential elements more important than others? Explain.
3. **WHAT IF?** The element silicon (Si) is absorbed by plants and increases the quality and yield of agricultural crops. Would this be sufficient evidence to consider it an essential plant nutrient?

For suggested answers, see Appendix A.

CONCEPT 37.3

Plant nutrition often involves relationships with other organisms

To this point, we have portrayed plants as exploiters of soil resources. But plants and soil have a two-way relationship. Dead plants provide much of the energy needed by soil-dwelling microorganisms, while secretions from living roots support a wide variety of microbes in the near-root environment. Here we'll focus on some mutualistic, or mutually beneficial, relationships between plants and soil bacteria or fungi. Then we'll look at some unusual plants that form nonmutualistic relationships with other plants or, in a few cases, with animals.

Soil Bacteria and Plant Nutrition

Some beneficial bacteria are found predominantly in the **rhizosphere**, the soil layer that is bound to the plant's roots. Others are decomposers, deriving nutrition from decaying organic material (humus) in the topsoil. Yet another class of important nitrogen-providing bacteria grow inside roots.

Rhizobacteria

Rhizobacteria are soil bacteria with especially large populations in the rhizosphere. Different soils vary greatly in the types and number of rhizobacteria they harbor. Microbial activity within a plant's rhizosphere is 10 to 100 times higher than in unbound soil because the roots secrete nutrients such as sugars, amino acids, and organic acids. Up to 20% of a plant's photosynthetic production fuels the organisms in this miniature ecosystem. As a result of diverse plant-microbe interactions, the composition of this microbial population often differs greatly from the surrounding soil and the rhizospheres of other plant species. Each rhizosphere contains a unique and complex cocktail of root secretions and microbial products.

Some rhizobacteria, known as *plant-growth-promoting rhizobacteria*, enhance plant growth by a variety of mechanisms. Some produce chemicals that stimulate plant growth. Others produce antibiotics that protect roots from disease. Still others absorb toxic metals or make nutrients more available to roots. Inoculation of seeds with plant-growth-promoting rhizobacteria can increase crop yield and reduce the need for fertilizers and pesticides. How do the bacteria benefit by interacting with plants? Root secretions supply most of the energy in the rhizosphere, so bacterial adaptations that help a plant thrive and secrete nutrients also help the bacteria.

Bacteria in the Nitrogen Cycle

Plants also have mutualistic relationships with several groups of bacteria that help make nitrogen more available. From a global perspective, no mineral nutrient is more limiting to plant growth than nitrogen, which is required in large amounts as a component of proteins and nucleic acids. The **nitrogen cycle**, discussed in Chapter 55, describes transformations of nitrogen and nitrogenous compounds in nature. Here we focus on processes leading directly to nitrogen assimilation by plants.

Unlike other soil minerals, ammonium ions (NH_4^+) and nitrate ions (NO_3^-) are not derived from the weathering of rocks. Although lightning produces small amounts of NO_3^- that get carried to the soil in rain, most soil nitrogen comes from the activity of bacteria **(Figure 37.9)**. *Ammonifying bacteria*, which are usually decomposers living in humus-rich soil, release ammonia (NH_3) by breaking down proteins and other organic compounds in humus. *Nitrogen-fixing bacteria* convert gaseous nitrogen (N_2) into NH_3, in a process we'll discuss shortly. In either case, the NH_3 produced picks up another H^+ in the soil solution to form NH_4^+, which plants can absorb. However, plants acquire nitrogen mainly in the form of NO_3^-. Soil NO_3^- is largely formed by a two-step process called *nitrification*, which consists of the oxidation of NH_3 to nitrite (NO_2^-), followed by oxidation of nitrite to nitrate (NO_3^-). Different types of *nitrifying bacteria* mediate each step. After the roots absorb NO_3^-, a plant enzyme reduces it back to NH_4^+, which other enzymes incorporate into amino acids and other organic compounds. Most plant species export nitrogen from roots to shoots via the xylem as NO_3^- or organic compounds synthesized in the roots. Some soil nitrogen is lost, particularly in anaerobic soils, when denitrifying bacteria convert NO_3^- to N_2, which diffuses into the atmosphere.

▲ **Figure 37.9 The roles of soil bacteria in the nitrogen nutrition of plants.** Ammonium is made available to plants by two types of soil bacteria: those that fix atmospheric N_2 (nitrogen-fixing bacteria) and those that decompose organic material (ammonifying bacteria). Although plants absorb some ammonium from the soil, they absorb mainly nitrate, which is produced from ammonium by nitrifying bacteria. Plants reduce nitrate back to ammonium before incorporating the nitrogen into organic compounds.

Nitrogen-Fixing Bacteria: A Closer Look

Although Earth's atmosphere is 79% nitrogen, plants cannot use free gaseous nitrogen (N_2) because there is a triple bond between the two nitrogen atoms, making the molecule almost inert. For atmospheric N_2 to be of use to plants, it must be reduced to NH_3 by a process called **nitrogen fixation**. All N_2-fixing organisms are prokaryotes, and some that carry out this process are free living (see Figure 37.9). In the particular case of N_2 fixation by the bacterium *Rhizobium,* the bacteria form an intimate association with the roots of legume plants (such as peas, soybeans, alfalfa, and clover) and markedly alter root structure. Although *Rhizobium* bacteria can be free living in the soil, they cannot fix N_2 in their free state, nor can legume roots fix N_2 without the bacteria.

The conversion of N_2 to NH_3 is a complicated, multistep process, but the reactants and products in nitrogen fixation can be summarized as follows:

$$N_2 + 8\,e^- + 8\,H^+ + 16\,ATP \rightarrow 2\,NH_3 + H_2 + 16\,ADP + 16\,\textcircled{P}_i$$

The enzyme complex nitrogenase catalyzes the entire reaction sequence, which reduces N_2 to NH_3 by adding electrons and H^+. Because the process of nitrogen fixation requires eight ATP molecules for each NH_3 synthesized, nitrogen-fixing bacteria require a rich supply of carbohydrates from decaying material, root secretions, or (in the case of *Rhizobium*) the vascular tissue of roots.

The specialized mutualism between *Rhizobium* bacteria and legume roots involves dramatic changes in root structure. Along a legume's roots are swellings called **nodules** composed of plant cells that have been "infected" by *Rhizobium* ("root living") bacteria (**Figure 37.10a**). Inside the nodule, *Rhizobium* bacteria assume a form called **bacteroids**, which are contained within vesicles formed in the root cell (**Figure 37.10b**). Legume-*Rhizobium* relationships generate more usable nitrogen for plants than all industrial fertilizers used today, and the mutualism provides the right amount of nitrogen at the right time at virtually no cost to the farmer. In addition to supplying the legume with nitrogen, this nitrogen fixation significantly reduces spending on fertilizers for subsequent crops.

The location of the bacteroids inside living, nonphotosynthetic cells is conducive to nitrogen fixation, which requires an anaerobic environment. Lignified external layers of root nodules also limit gas exchange. Some root nodules appear reddish because of a molecule called leghemoglobin (*leg-* for "legume"), an iron-containing protein that binds reversibly to oxygen (it is similar to the hemoglobin in human red blood cells). This protein is an oxygen "buffer," reducing the concentration of free oxygen and thereby providing an anaerobic environment for nitrogen fixation while regulating the oxygen supply for the intense cellular respiration required to produce ATP for nitrogen fixation.

Each legume species is associated with a particular strain of *Rhizobium.* **Figure 37.11** describes how a root nodule develops after bacteria enter through an "infection thread." The symbiotic relationship between a legume and nitrogen-fixing bacteria is mutualistic in that the bacteria supply the host plant with fixed nitrogen while the plant provides the bacteria with carbohydrates and other organic compounds. The root nodules use most of the ammonium produced to make amino

(a) Pea plant root. The bumps on this pea plant root are nodules containing *Rhizobium* bacteria. The bacteria fix nitrogen and obtain photosynthetic products supplied by the plant.

Nodules

Roots

(b) Bacteroids in a soybean root nodule. In this TEM, a cell from a root nodule of soybean is filled with bacteroids in vesicles. The cells on the left are uninfected.

Bacteroids within vesicle

5 μm

◀ **Figure 37.10 Root nodules on legumes.** The coordinated activities of the legume and the *Rhizobium* bacteria depend on a chemical dialogue between the mutualistic partners.

? *How is the relationship between legume plants and* Rhizobium *bacteria mutualistic?*

① Roots emit chemical signals that attract *Rhizobium* bacteria. The bacteria then emit signals that stimulate root hairs to elongate and to form an infection thread by an invagination of the plasma membrane.

Rhizobium bacteria

Infection thread

Dividing cells in root cortex

Bacteroid

Infected root hair

② The bacteria penetrate the cortex within the infection thread. Cells of the cortex and pericycle begin dividing, and vesicles containing the bacteria bud into cortical cells from the branching infection thread. This process results in the formation of bacteroids.

Dividing cells in pericycle

Developing root nodule

Bacteroid

③ Growth continues in the affected regions of the cortex and pericycle, and these two masses of dividing cells fuse, forming the nodule.

④ The nodule develops vascular tissue that supplies nutrients to the nodule and carries nitrogenous compounds into the vascular cylinder for distribution throughout the plant.

Nodule vascular tissue

Bacteroid

▲ **Figure 37.11 Development of a soybean root nodule.**
? *What plant tissue systems are modified by nodulation?*

acids, which are then transported up to the shoot through the xylem.

How does a legume species recognize a certain strain of *Rhizobium* among the many bacterial strains in the soil? And how does an encounter with that specific *Rhizobium* strain lead to development of a nodule? These two questions have led researchers to uncover a chemical dialogue between the bacteria and the root. Each partner responds to chemical signals from the other by expressing certain genes whose products contribute to nodule formation. By understanding the molecular biology underlying the formation of root nodules, researchers hope to learn how to induce *Rhizobium* uptake and nodule formation in crop plants that do not normally form such nitrogen-fixing mutualistic relationships.

Nitrogen Fixation and Agriculture

The agricultural benefits of mutualistic nitrogen fixation underlie most types of **crop rotation**. In this practice, a non-legume such as maize is planted one year, and the following year alfalfa or some other legume is planted to restore the concentration of fixed nitrogen in the soil. To ensure that the legume encounters its specific *Rhizobium* strain, the seeds are soaked in a culture of the bacteria or dusted with bacterial spores before sowing. Instead of being harvested, the legume crop is often plowed under so that it will decompose as "green manure," reducing the need for manufactured fertilizers.

Many plant families besides legumes include species that benefit from mutualistic nitrogen fixation. For example, alder trees and certain tropical grasses host gram-positive bacteria of the actinomycete group (see Figure 27.18). Rice, a crop of great commercial importance, benefits indirectly from mutualistic nitrogen fixation. Rice farmers culture a free-floating aquatic fern, *Azolla*, which has mutualistic cyanobacteria that fix nitrogen. The growing rice eventually shades and kills the *Azolla*, and decomposition of this nitrogen-rich organic material increases the paddy's fertility.

Fungi and Plant Nutrition

Certain species of soil fungi also form mutualistic relationships with roots and play a major role in plant nutrition. **Mycorrhizae** ("fungus roots") are mutualistic associations of roots and fungi (see Figures 31.15 and 36.5). The host plant provides the fungus with a steady supply of sugar. Meanwhile, the fungus increases the surface area for water uptake and also supplies the plant with phosphate and other minerals absorbed from the soil. The fungi of mycorrhizae also secrete growth factors that stimulate roots to grow and branch, as well as antibiotics that help protect the plant from pathogens in the soil.

Mycorrhizae are not oddities; they are formed by most plant species. In fact, this plant-fungus mutualism might have been one of the evolutionary adaptations that helped plants initially colonize land (see Chapter 29). Indeed, fossilized roots from some of the earliest plants include mycorrhizae. In early terrestrial ecosystems, the soil was probably poor in nutrients. The fungi of mycorrhizae, which are more efficient at absorbing minerals than the roots themselves, would have helped nourish the pioneering plants.

The Two Main Types of Mycorrhizae

The major mutualistic symbioses of fungi and plants consist of two types: ectomycorrhizae and arbuscular mycorrhizae (sometimes called endomycorrhizae). In **ectomycorrhizae**, the mycelium (mass of branching hyphae; see Chapter 31) forms a dense sheath, or mantle, over the surface of the root **(Figure 37.12a)**. Fungal hyphae extend from the mantle into the soil, greatly increasing the surface area for water and min-

eral absorption. Hyphae also grow into the root cortex. These hyphae do not penetrate the root cells but form a network in the apoplast, or extracellular space, that facilitates nutrient exchange between the fungus and the plant. Compared with "uninfected" roots, ectomycorrhizae are generally thicker, shorter, and more branched. They typically do not form root hairs, which would be superfluous given the extensive surface area of the fungal mycelium. About 10% of plant families have species that form ectomycorrhizae, and the vast majority of these species are woody, including members of the pine, spruce, oak, walnut, birch, willow, and eucalyptus families.

In contrast, **arbuscular mycorrhizae** do not have a dense mantle ensheathing the root **(Figure 37.12b)**. Mycorrhizal associations start when microscopic soil hyphae respond to the presence of a root by growing toward it, establishing contact, and growing along its surface. Hyphae penetrate between epidermal cells and then enter the root cortex. These hyphae digest small patches of the cortical cell walls, but they do not actually pierce the plasma membrane and enter the cytoplasm. Instead, a hypha grows into a tube formed by invagination of the root cell's membrane. The process is analogous to poking a finger gently into a balloon without popping it; your finger is like the fungal hypha, and the balloon skin is like the root cell's membrane. After the fungal hyphae have penetrated in this way, some branch densely, forming structures called arbuscules ("little trees"), which are important sites of nutrient transfer between the fungus and the

(a) Ectomycorrhizae. The mantle of the fungal mycelium ensheathes the root. Fungal hyphae extend from the mantle into the soil, absorbing water and minerals, especially phosphate. Hyphae also extend into the extracellular spaces of the root cortex, providing extensive surface area for nutrient exchange between the fungus and its host plant.

Mantle (fungal sheath)

Epidermis　Cortex　Mantle (fungal sheath)

Endodermis

Fungal hyphae between cortical cells

100 μm

(colorized SEM)

(b) Arbuscular mycorrhizae (endomycorrhizae). No mantle forms around the root, but microscopic fungal hyphae extend into the root. Within the root cortex, the fungus makes extensive contact with the plant through branching of hyphae that form arbuscules, providing an enormous surface area for nutrient swapping. The hyphae penetrate the cell walls, but not the plasma membranes, of cells within the cortex.

Fungal hyphae

Root hair

Epidermis　Cortex

Cortical cells

Endodermis

Fungal vesicle

Casparian strip

Arbuscules

Plasma membrane

10 μm

(LM, stained specimen)

▲ Figure 37.12 **Mycorrhizae.**

plant. Within the hyphae themselves, oval vesicles may form, possibly serving as food storage sites for the fungus. To the unaided eye, arbuscular mycorrhizae look like "normal" roots with root hairs, but a microscope reveals a mutualistic relationship of enormous importance to plant nutrition. Arbuscular mycorrhizae are much more common than ectomycorrhizae and are found in over 85% of plant species, including crop plants such as maize, wheat, and legumes.

Agricultural and Ecological Importance of Mycorrhizae

Roots can form mycorrhizal symbioses only if exposed to the appropriate species of fungus. In most ecosystems, these fungi are present in the soil, and seedlings develop mycorrhizae. But if seeds are collected in one environment and planted in foreign soil, the plants may show signs of malnutrition (particularly phosphorus deficiency) resulting from the absence of mycorrhizal partners. Treating seeds with spores of mycorrhizal fungi can sometimes help seedlings to form mycorrhizae and improve crop yield.

Mycorrhizal associations are also important in understanding ecological relationships. Invasive exotic plants sometimes colonize areas by disrupting interactions between native organisms. For example, garlic mustard (*Alliaria petiolata*), introduced into New England from Europe during the 1800s, has invaded woodlands throughout the eastern and middle United States, suppressing tree seedlings and other native plants. Kristina Stinson, of Harvard University, and colleagues have produced compelling evidence that its invasive properties may be related to an ability to slow the growth of other plant species by preventing the growth of arbuscular mycorrhizal fungi (**Figure 37.13**).

Epiphytes, Parasitic Plants, and Carnivorous Plants

Almost all plant species have mutualistic symbiotic relationships with soil fungi or bacteria or both. Though rarer, there are also plant species with nutritional adaptations that use other organisms in nonmutualistic ways. **Figure 37.14**, on the next page, provides an overview of three unusual adaptations: epiphytes, parasitic plants, and carnivorous plants.

CONCEPT CHECK 37.3

1. Why is the study of the rhizosphere critical to understanding plant nutrition?
2. How do soil bacteria and mycorrhizae contribute to plant nutrition?
3. **WHAT IF?** A peanut farmer finds that the older leaves of his plant are turning yellow following a long period of wet weather. Suggest a reason why.

For suggested answers, see Appendix A.

▼ **Figure 37.13** **Inquiry**

Does the invasive weed garlic mustard disrupt mutualistic associations between native tree seedlings and arbuscular mycorrhizal fungi?

EXPERIMENT Kristina Stinson, of Harvard University, and colleagues investigated the effect of invasive garlic mustard on the growth of native tree seedlings and associated mycorrhizal fungi. In one experiment, they grew seedlings of three North American trees—sugar maple, red maple, and white ash—in four different soils. Two of the soil samples were collected from a location where garlic mustard was growing, and one of these samples was sterilized. The other two soil samples were collected from a location devoid of garlic mustard, and one was then sterilized. After four months of growth, the researchers harvested the shoots and roots and determined the dried biomass. The roots were also analyzed for percent colonization by arbuscular mycorrhizal fungi.

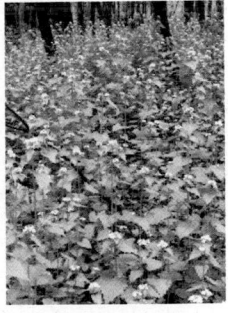

RESULTS Native tree seedlings grew more slowly and were less able to form mycorrhizal associations when grown either in sterilized soil or in unsterilized soil collected from a location that had been invaded by garlic mustard.

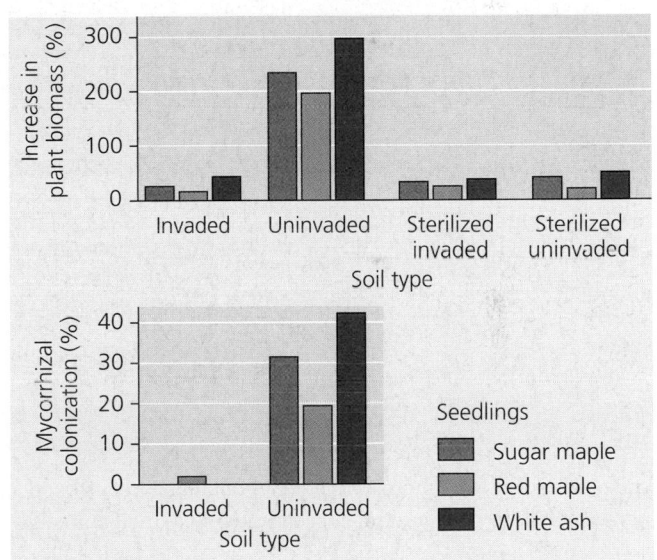

CONCLUSION The data support the hypothesis that garlic mustard suppresses growth of native trees by affecting the soil in a way that disrupts mutualistic associations between the trees and arbuscular mycorrhizal fungi.

SOURCE K. A. Stinson et al., Invasive plant suppresses the growth of native tree seedlings by disrupting belowground mutualisms, *PLoS Biol* (*Public Library of Science: Biology*) 4(5): e140 (2006).

Inquiry in Action Read and analyze the original paper in *Inquiry in Action: Interpreting Scientific Papers.*

WHAT IF? What effect would applying inorganic phosphate to soil invaded by garlic mustard have on the plant's ability to outcompete native species?

Exploring Unusual Nutritional Adaptations in Plants

Epiphytes

An **epiphyte** (from the Greek *epi,* upon, and *phyton,* plant) nourishes itself but grows on another plant, usually anchored to branches or trunks of living trees. Epiphytes absorb water and minerals from rain, mostly through leaves rather than roots. Some examples are staghorn ferns, bromeliads, and many orchids.

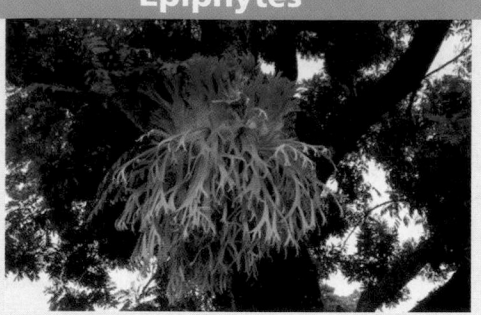

Staghorn fern, an epiphyte. This tropical fern (genus *Platycerium*) grows on large rocks, cliffs, and trees. It has two types of fronds: branched fronds resembling antlers and circular fronds that form a collar around the base of the fern.

Parasitic Plants

Unlike epiphytes, parasitic plants absorb sugars and minerals from their living hosts, although some parasitic species are photosynthetic.

Many species have roots that function as haustoria, nutrient-absorbing projections that enter the host plant.

Mistletoe, a photosynthetic parasite. Tacked above doorways during the holiday season, mistletoe (genus *Phoradendron*) lives in nature as a parasite on oaks and other trees.

Host's phloem

Dodder

Haustoria

Dodder, a nonphotosynthetic parasite. Dodder (genus *Cuscuta*), the orange "strings" on this pickleweed, draws its nutrients from the host. The cross section shows haustoria tapping the host's phloem (LM).

Indian pipe, a nonphotosynthetic parasite. Also called the ghost flower, this species (*Monotropa uniflora*) absorbs nutrients from the fungal hyphae of mycorrhizae of green plants.

Carnivorous Plants

Carnivorous plants are photosynthetic but obtain some nitrogen and minerals by killing and digesting insects and other small animals.

Carnivorous plants live in acid bogs and other habitats where soils are poor in nitrogen and other minerals. Various insect traps consist of modified leaves, usually equipped with glands that secrete digestive enzymes. Fortunately for animals, such turnabouts are rare!

Venus flytrap. Triggered by electrical impulses from sensory hairs, two leaf lobes close in half a second. Despite its common name, *Dionaea muscipula* usually catches ants and grasshoppers.

Pitcher plants. *Nepenthes, Sarracenia,* and other genera have water-filled funnels. The insects drown and are digested by enzymes.

Sundews. Sundews (genus *Drosera*) exude a sticky fluid that glitters like dew. Insects get stuck to the leaf hairs, which enfold the prey.

SUMMARY OF KEY CONCEPTS

CONCEPT 37.1

Soil is a living, finite resource (pp. 785–789)

▶ **Soil Texture** Particles of various sizes derived from the breakdown of rock are found in soil. Soil particle size affects the availability of water, oxygen, and minerals in the soil.

▶ **Topsoil Composition** A soil's composition refers to its inorganic and organic components. Topsoil is a complex ecosystem teeming with bacteria, fungi, protists, animals, and the roots of plants.

▶ **Soil Conservation and Sustainable Agriculture** Some agricultural practices can deplete the mineral content of soil, tax water reserves, and promote erosion. The goal of soil conservation is to minimize this damage.

MEDIA

Activity How Plants Obtain Minerals from Soil
Investigation How Does Acid Precipitation Affect Mineral Deficiency?
GraphIt! Global Soil Degradation

CONCEPT 37.2

Plants require essential elements to complete their life cycle (pp. 789–792)

▶ **Macronutrients and Micronutrients** Macronutrients, elements required in relatively large amounts, include carbon, oxygen, hydrogen, nitrogen, and other major ingredients of organic compounds. Micronutrients, elements required in very small amounts, typically have catalytic functions as cofactors of enzymes.

▶ **Symptoms of Mineral Deficiency** Deficiency of a mobile nutrient usually affects older organs more than younger ones; the reverse is true for nutrients that are less mobile within a plant. Macronutrient deficiencies are most common, particularly deficiencies of nitrogen, phosphorus, and potassium.

▶ **Improving Plant Nutrition by Genetic Modification: Some Examples** Rather than tailoring the soil to match the plant, genetic engineers are tailoring the plant to match the soil.

CONCEPT 37.3

Plant nutrition often involves relationships with other organisms (pp. 792–798)

▶ **Soil Bacteria and Plant Nutrition** Many soil bacteria are decomposers, living on decaying organic material. Other soil bacteria, called rhizobacteria, derive their energy from the rhizosphere, a microbe-enriched ecosystem intimately associated with roots. Plant secretions support the energy needs of the rhizosphere. Some rhizobacteria produce antibiotics, whereas others make nutrients more available for plants. Most are free-living, but some live inside plants.

Plants satisfy most of their huge needs for nitrogen from the bacterial decomposition of humus and the fixation of gaseous nitrogen.

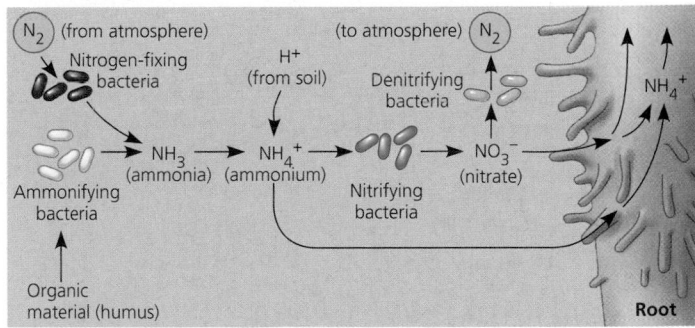

Nitrogen-fixing bacteria convert atmospheric N_2 to nitrogenous minerals that plants can absorb as a nitrogen source for organic synthesis. The most efficient mutualism between plants and nitrogen-fixing bacteria occurs in the nodules formed by *Rhizobium* bacteria growing in the roots of legumes. These bacteria obtain sugar from the plant and supply the plant with fixed nitrogen. In agriculture, legume crops are rotated with other crops to restore nitrogen to the soil.

▶ **Fungi and Plant Nutrition** Mycorrhizae are mutualistic associations of fungi and roots. The fungal hyphae of both ectomycorrhizae and arbuscular mycorrhizae absorb water and minerals, which they supply to their plant hosts.

▶ **Epiphytes, Parasitic Plants, and Carnivorous Plants** Epiphytes grow on the surfaces of other plants but acquire water and minerals from rain. Parasitic plants absorb nutrients from host plants. Carnivorous plants supplement their mineral nutrition by digesting animals.

MEDIA

Activity The Nitrogen Cycle

TESTING YOUR KNOWLEDGE

SELF-QUIZ

1. Most of the mass of organic material of a plant comes from
   a. water.
   b. carbon dioxide.
   c. soil minerals.
   d. atmospheric oxygen.
   e. nitrogen.

2. Micronutrients are needed in very small amounts because
   a. most of them are mobile in the plant.
   b. most serve mainly as cofactors of enzymes.
   c. most are supplied in large enough quantities in seeds.
   d. they play only a minor role in the growth and health of the plant.
   e. only the most actively growing regions of the plants require micronutrients.

3. The rhizosphere would best be described as
   a. legume root swellings that are involved in nitrogen fixation.
   b. the part of the topsoil that supplies carbohydrates to plants.
   c. soil that is bound to roots and differs from the surrounding soil in containing many more microbes.
   d. the spherical soil horizon in which roots typically grow.
   e. all of the living organisms that inhabit the soil.

4. Some of the problems associated with intensive irrigation include all but
   a. mineral runoff.
   b. overfertilization.
   c. land subsidence.
   d. aquifer depletion.
   e. soil salinization.

5. A mineral deficiency is likely to affect older leaves more than younger leaves if
   a. the mineral is a micronutrient.
   b. the mineral is very mobile within the plant.
   c. the mineral is required for chlorophyll synthesis.
   d. the mineral is a macronutrient.
   e. the older leaves are in direct sunlight.

6. Two groups of tomatoes were grown under laboratory conditions, one with humus added to the soil and one a control without humus. The leaves of the plants grown without humus were yellowish (less green) compared with those of the plants grown in humus-enriched soil. The best explanation for this difference is that
   a. the healthy plants used the food in the decomposing leaves of the humus for energy to make chlorophyll.
   b. the humus made the soil more loosely packed, so water penetrated more easily to the roots.
   c. the humus contained minerals such as magnesium and iron, needed for the synthesis of chlorophyll.
   d. the heat released by the decomposing leaves of the humus caused more rapid growth and chlorophyll synthesis.
   e. the healthy plants absorbed chlorophyll from the humus.

7. The specific relationship between a legume and its mutualistic *Rhizobium* strain probably depends on
   a. each legume having a chemical dialog with a fungus.
   b. each *Rhizobium* strain having a form of nitrogenase that works only in the appropriate legume host.
   c. each legume being found where the soil has only the *Rhizobium* specific to that legume.
   d. specific recognition between the chemical signals and signal receptors of the *Rhizobium* strain and legume species.
   e. destruction of all incompatible *Rhizobium* strains by enzymes secreted from the legume's roots.

8. Mycorrhizae enhance plant nutrition mainly by
   a. absorbing water and minerals through the fungal hyphae.
   b. providing sugar to the root cells, which have no chloroplasts of their own.
   c. converting atmospheric nitrogen to ammonia.
   d. enabling the roots to parasitize neighboring plants.
   e. stimulating the development of root hairs.

9. We would expect the greatest difference in plant health between two groups of plants of the same species, one group with mycorrhizae and one group without mycorrhizae, in an environment
   a. where nitrogen-fixing bacteria are abundant.
   b. that has soil with poor drainage.
   c. that has hot summers and cold winters.
   d. in which the soil is relatively deficient in mineral nutrients.
   e. that is near a body of water, such as a pond or river.

10. Carnivorous adaptations of plants mainly compensate for soil that has a relatively low content of
    a. potassium.
    b. nitrogen.
    c. calcium.
    d. water.
    e. phosphate.

11. **DRAW IT** Draw a simple sketch of cation exchange, showing a root hair, a soil particle with anions, and a hydrogen ion displacing a mineral cation.

For Self-Quiz answers, see Appendix A.

MEDIA Visit www.campbellbiology.com for a Practice Test.

EVOLUTION CONNECTION

12. Imagine taking the plant out of the picture in Figure 37.9. Write a paragraph explaining how soil bacteria could sustain the recycling of nitrogen *before* land plants evolved.

SCIENTIFIC INQUIRY

13. Acid precipitation has an abnormally high concentration of hydrogen ions (H^+). One effect of acid precipitation is to deplete the soil of nutrients such as calcium (Ca^{2+}), potassium (K^+), and magnesium (Mg^{2+}). Suggest a hypothesis to explain how acid precipitation washes these nutrients from the soil. How might you test your hypothesis?

SCIENCE, TECHNOLOGY, AND SOCIETY

14. About 10% of U.S. cropland is irrigated. Agriculture is by far the biggest user of water in arid western states, including Colorado, Arizona, and California. As the populations of these states grow, there is ongoing conflict between cities and farm regions over water. To ensure adequate water supplies for urban growth, cities are buying water rights from farmers. This is often the least expensive way to obtain more water, and it is possible for some farmers to make more money by selling water rights than by growing crops. Discuss the possible consequences of this trend. Is this the best way to allocate water? Why or why not?

38
Angiosperm Reproduction and Biotechnology

KEY CONCEPTS

38.1 Flowers, double fertilization, and fruits are unique features of the angiosperm life cycle

38.2 Flowering plants reproduce sexually, asexually, or both

38.3 Humans modify crops by breeding and genetic engineering

OVERVIEW

Flowers of Deceit

Male wasps of the species *Campsoscolia ciliata* often attempt to copulate with the flowers of the Mediterranean orchid *Ophrys speculum* **(Figure 38.1)**. During this encounter, a sac of pollen becomes glued to the insect's body. Eventually frustrated, the wasp flies off and deposits the pollen onto another *Ophrys* flower that has become the object of his misplaced ardor. *Ophrys* flowers offer no reward such as nectar to the male wasps, only sexual frustration. So what makes the male wasps so enamored of this orchid? The traditional answer has been that the shape of the orchid's largest petal and the frill of orange bristles around it vaguely resemble the female wasp. These visual cues, however, are only part of the deception: *Ophrys* orchids also emit chemicals with a scent similar to that produced by sexually receptive female wasps.

This orchid and its wasp pollinators are one example of the amazing ways in which angiosperms (flowering plants) reproduce sexually with spatially distant members of their own species. Sex, however, is not their only means of reproduction. Many species also reproduce asexually, creating offspring that are genetically identical to the parent.

An unusual aspect of the orchid and wasp example is that the insect does not profit from interacting with the flower. In fact, by wasting time and energy trying to copulate with it, the wasp is probably rendered less fit. More typically, a plant lures an animal pollinator to its flowers not with offers of sex but with rewards of energy-rich nectar or pollen. Thus, both plant and pollinator benefit; that is, the symbiotic relationship is mutualistic. Participating in mutualistic relationships with other organisms is very common in the plant kingdom. In fact, in recent evolutionary times, some flowering plants have formed mutualistic relationships with an animal that not only disperses their seeds but also provides the plants with water and mineral nutrients and vigorously protects them from encroaching competitors, pathogens, and predators. In return for these favors, the animal typically gets to eat a fraction of the plants' seeds and fruits. The plant symbionts involved in these remarkable mutualistic interactions are called crops; the animal symbionts are called humans.

Since the origins of crop domestication over 10,000 years ago, plant breeders have genetically manipulated the traits of a few hundred wild angiosperm species by artificial selection, transforming them into the crops we grow today. Genetic engineering has dramatically increased the variety of ways and the speed with which we can now modify plants.

In Chapters 29 and 30, we approached plant reproduction from an evolutionary perspective, tracing the descent of land plants from algal ancestors. Here, we'll explore the reproductive biology of flowering plants in much greater detail because they are the most important group of plants in most terrestrial ecosystems and in agriculture. After discussing the sexual and asexual reproduction of angiosperms, we'll examine the role of humans in genetically altering crop species, as well as the controversies surrounding modern plant biotechnology.

CONCEPT 38.1
Flowers, double fertilization, and fruits are unique features of the angiosperm life cycle

The life cycles of plants are characterized by an alternation of generations, in which multicellular haploid (n) and diploid ($2n$)

generations take turns producing each other (see Figures 29.5 and 30.10). The diploid plant, the sporophyte, produces haploid spores by meiosis. These spores divide by mitosis, giving rise to the multicellular gametophytes, the male and female haploid plants that produce gametes (sperm and eggs). **Fertilization**, the fusion of gametes, results in diploid zygotes, which divide by mitosis and form new sporophytes. In angiosperms, the sporophyte is the dominant generation: It is larger, more conspicuous, and longer-lived than the gametophyte. Over the course of seed plant evolution, gametophytes became reduced in size and wholly dependent on the sporophyte for nutrients. Angiosperm gametophytes are the most reduced of all plants, consisting of only a few cells. **Figure 38.2** reviews the angiosperm life cycle, which is shown in more detail in Figure 30.10. The key derived traits of the angiosperm life cycle can be remembered as the "three Fs"—*f*lowers, double *f*ertilization, and *f*ruits. Since angiosperms, along with gymnosperms, are seed plants, a knowledge of seed structure and function is also critical to understanding the angiosperm life cycle.

Flower Structure and Function

Flowers, the reproductive shoots of angiosperm sporophytes, are typically composed of four whorls of modified leaves called floral organs, which are separated by short internodes. Unlike vegetative shoots, flowers are determinate shoots. That is, they cease growing after the flower and fruit are formed.

Floral organs—**sepals, petals, stamens**, and **carpels**—are attached to a part of the stem called the **receptacle**. Stamens and carpels are reproductive organs, whereas sepals and petals are sterile. Sepals, which enclose and protect the floral bud before it opens, are usually green and more leaflike in appearance than the other floral organs. In many species, petals are more brightly colored than sepals and advertise the flower to insects and other pollinators.

A stamen consists of a stalk called the *filament* and a terminal structure called the **anther**; within the anther are chambers called microsporangia (pollen sacs) that produce pollen. A carpel has an **ovary** at its base and a long, slender neck called the **style**. At the top of the style is a generally sticky structure called the **stigma** that serves as a landing platform for pollen. Within the ovary are one or more **ovules**; the number of ovules depends on the species. The flower shown in Figure 38.2 has a single carpel, but many species have multiple carpels. In most species, two or more are fused into a single structure; the result is an ovary with two or more chambers, each containing one or more ovules. The term **pistil** is sometimes used to refer to a single carpel or a group of fused carpels.

Complete flowers have all four basic floral organs (see Figure 38.2a). Some species have **incomplete flowers**, lacking sepals, petals, stamens, or carpels. For example, most grass flowers lack petals. Some incomplete flowers are sterile, lacking functional stamens and carpels; others are *unisexual*, lacking either stamens or carpels. Flowers also vary in size, shape, color, odor, organ arrangement, and time of opening. Some are borne singly, while others are arranged in showy clusters called **inflorescences**. For example, a sunflower's central disk consists of hundreds of tiny incomplete flowers, and what look like petals are actually sterile flowers (see Figure 1.3). Much of floral diversity represents adaptation to specific pollinators.

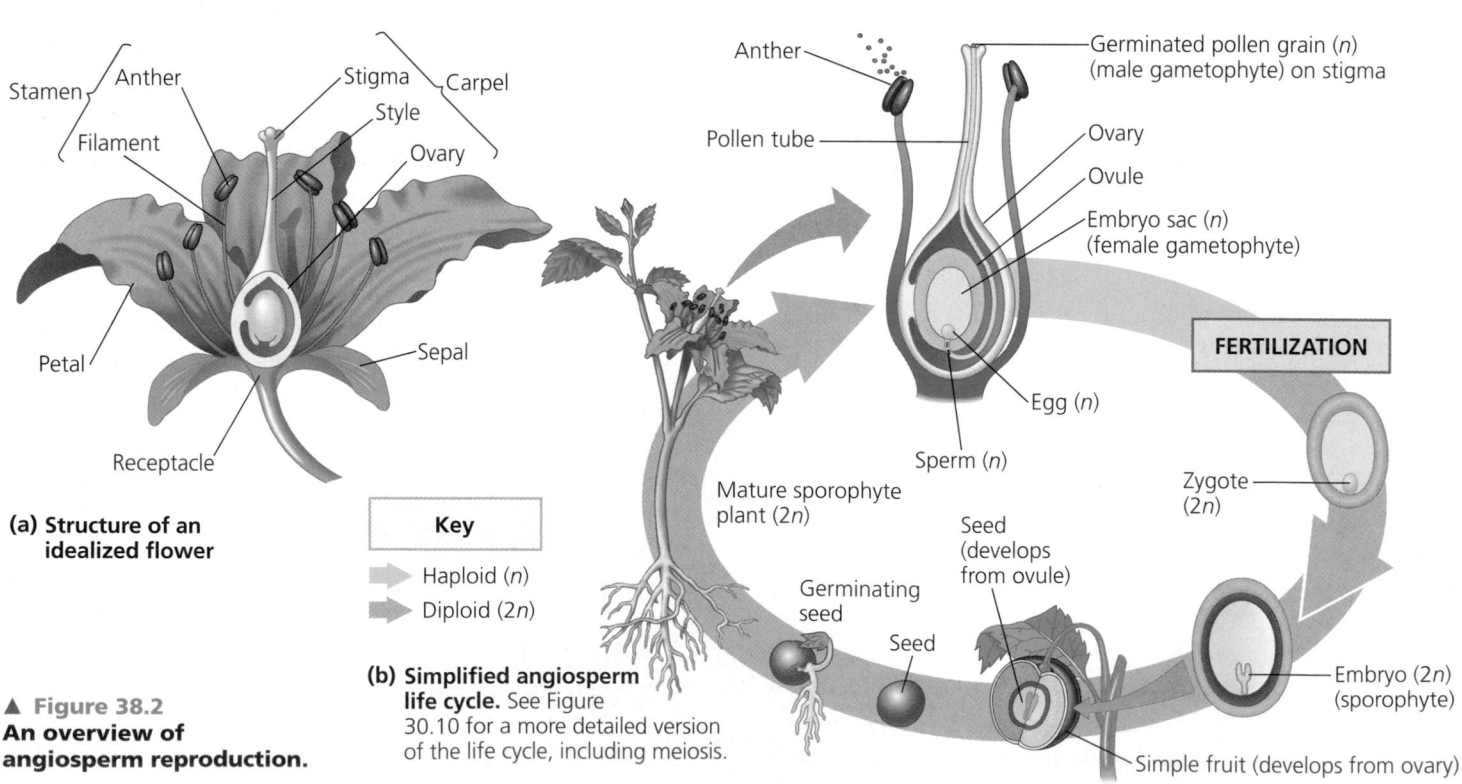

(a) Structure of an idealized flower

Key
- Haploid (*n*)
- Diploid (*2n*)

(b) Simplified angiosperm life cycle. See Figure 30.10 for a more detailed version of the life cycle, including meiosis.

▲ **Figure 38.2**
An overview of angiosperm reproduction.

Development of Male Gametophytes in Pollen Grains

Each anther contains four microsporangia, also known as pollen sacs. Within the microsporangia are many diploid cells called microsporocytes, or microspore mother cells **(Figure 38.3a)**. Each microsporocyte undergoes meiosis, forming four haploid **microspores**, each of which eventually gives rise to a haploid male gametophyte. Each microspore then undergoes mitosis, producing a male gametophyte consisting of only two cells: the *generative cell* and the *tube cell*. Together, these two cells and the spore wall constitute a **pollen grain**. The spore wall, which consists of material produced by both the microspore and the anther, usually exhibits an elaborate pattern unique to the species. During maturation of the male gametophyte, the generative cell passes into the tube cell and the spore wall is completed. The tube cell now has a completely free-standing cell inside it. After the microsporangium breaks open and releases the pollen, a pollen grain may be transferred to a receptive surface of a stigma. There, the tube cell produces the **pollen tube**, a long cellular protuberance that delivers sperm to the female gametophyte. Pollen tubes can grow very quickly, at rates of 1 cm/hr or more. As a pollen tube elongates through the style, the generative cell usually divides and produces two sperm cells, which remain inside the tube cell (see Figure 30.10). The pollen tube grows through the style and into the ovary, where it releases the sperm cells in the vicinity of the female gametophyte.

Development of Female Gametophytes (Embryo Sacs)

Among angiosperm species, there are over 15 variations in the development of the female gametophyte, also known as an **embryo sac**. We'll focus on just one. The entire process occurs within the carpel's ovary, in a tissue within each ovule called the megasporangium. Two *integuments* (layers of protective sporophytic tissue that will develop into the seed coat) surround each megasporangium except at a gap called the *micropyle*. Female gametophyte development begins when one cell in the megasporangium of each ovule, the *megasporocyte* (or megaspore mother cell), enlarges and undergoes meiosis, producing four haploid **megaspores (Figure 38.3b)**. Only one megaspore survives; the others disintegrate.

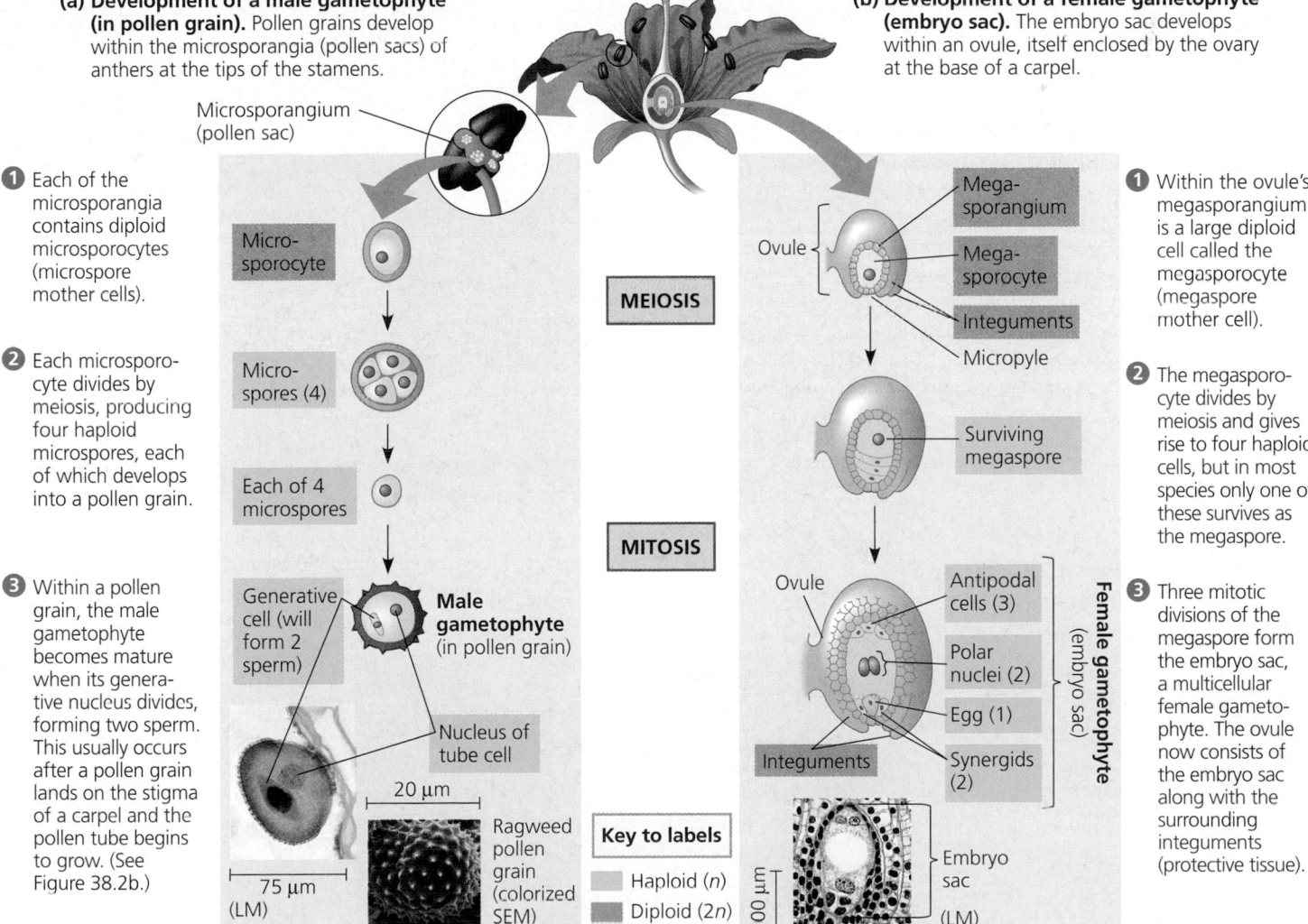

(a) Development of a male gametophyte (in pollen grain). Pollen grains develop within the microsporangia (pollen sacs) of anthers at the tips of the stamens.

(b) Development of a female gametophyte (embryo sac). The embryo sac develops within an ovule, itself enclosed by the ovary at the base of a carpel.

Microsporangium (pollen sac)

1 Each of the microsporangia contains diploid microsporocytes (microspore mother cells).

2 Each microsporocyte divides by meiosis, producing four haploid microspores, each of which develops into a pollen grain.

3 Within a pollen grain, the male gametophyte becomes mature when its generative nucleus divides, forming two sperm. This usually occurs after a pollen grain lands on the stigma of a carpel and the pollen tube begins to grow. (See Figure 38.2b.)

Microsporocyte

Microspores (4)

Each of 4 microspores

Generative cell (will form 2 sperm)

Male gametophyte (in pollen grain)

Nucleus of tube cell

20 μm

75 μm (LM)

Ragweed pollen grain (colorized SEM)

MEIOSIS

MITOSIS

Key to labels

Haploid (*n*)
Diploid (2*n*)

Ovule

Mega-sporangium

Mega-sporocyte

Integuments

Micropyle

Surviving megaspore

Ovule

Antipodal cells (3)

Polar nuclei (2)

Egg (1)

Synergids (2)

Integuments

Female gametophyte (embryo sac)

Embryo sac

100 μm

(LM)

1 Within the ovule's megasporangium is a large diploid cell called the megasporocyte (megaspore mother cell).

2 The megasporocyte divides by meiosis and gives rise to four haploid cells, but in most species only one of these survives as the megaspore.

3 Three mitotic divisions of the megaspore form the embryo sac, a multicellular female gametophyte. The ovule now consists of the embryo sac along with the surrounding integuments (protective tissue).

▲ **Figure 38.3 The development of male and female gametophytes in angiosperms.**

The surviving megaspore continues to grow, and its nucleus divides by mitosis three times without cytokinesis, resulting in one large cell with eight haploid nuclei. Membranes then partition this mass into a multicellular female gametophyte—the embryo sac. Three of the cells within the embryo sac are near the micropyle: the egg cell and two cells called synergids. The synergids flank the egg cell and help attract and guide the pollen tube to the embryo sac. At the opposite end of the embryo sac are three antipodal cells of unknown function. The remaining two nuclei, called polar nuclei, are not partitioned into separate cells but instead share the cytoplasm of the large central cell of the embryo sac. The ovule, which will eventually become a seed, now consists of the embryo sac and two surrounding integuments.

▼ Figure 38.4

Exploring Flower Pollination

Some angiosperm species can self-pollinate, but such species are limited to inbreeding in nature. Most angiosperm species rely on a living (biotic) or nonliving (abiotic) pollinating agent that can move pollen from the anther of a stamen of a flower on one plant to the stigma of a carpel of a flower on another plant. Approximately 80% of all angiosperm pollination is biotic, employing animal go-betweens. Among abiotically pollinated species, 98% rely on wind and 2% on water.

Abiotic Pollination by Wind

About 20% of all angiosperm species are wind-pollinated. Since their reproductive success does not depend on attracting pollinators, there was no selective pressure favoring colorful or scented flowers. Accordingly, the evolution of wind-pollinated species has resulted in flowers that are often small, green, and inconspicuous, and they produce neither nectar nor scent. Most temperate trees and grasses are wind-pollinated. The flowers of hazel (*Corylus avellana* shown here) and many other temperate, wind-pollinated trees appear in the early spring, when leaves are not present to interfere with pollen movement. The relative inefficiency of wind pollination is compensated for by production of copious amounts of pollen grains. Wind tunnel studies reveal that wind pollination is often more efficient than it appears because floral structures can create eddy currents that aid in pollen capture.

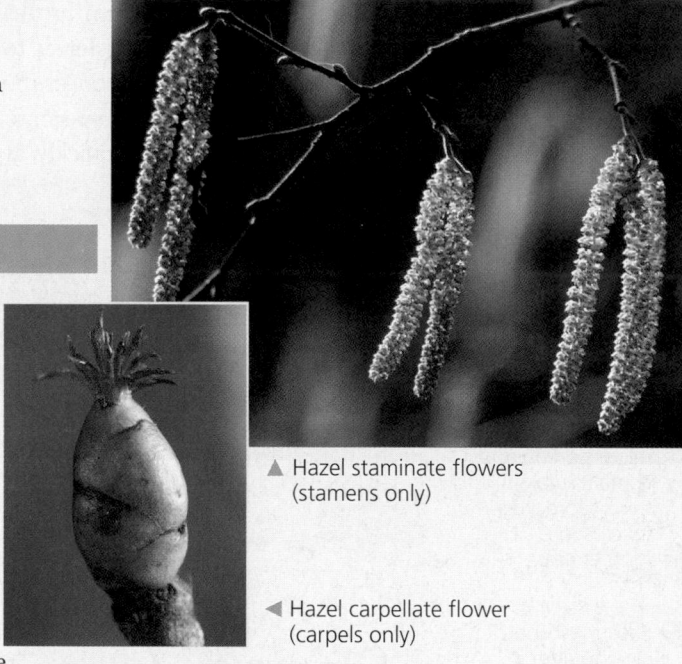

▲ Hazel staminate flowers (stamens only)

◀ Hazel carpellate flower (carpels only)

Pollination by Bees

About 65% of all flowering plants require insects for pollination; the percentage is even greater for major crops. Bees are the most important insect pollinators, and there is great concern in Europe and North America that honeybee populations have shrunk. Pollinating bees depend on nectar and pollen for food. Typically, bee-pollinated flowers have a delicate, sweet fragrance. Bees are attracted to bright colors, primarily yellow and blue. Red appears dull to them, but they can see ultraviolet radiation. Many bee-pollinated flowers, such as the common dandelion (*Taraxacum vulgare*), have markings called "nectar guides" that help insects locate the nectaries but are only visible to human eyes under ultraviolet light.

▲ Common dandelion under normal light

▶ Common dandelion under ultraviolet light

Pollination

In angiosperms, **pollination** is the transfer of pollen from an anther to a stigma. It is accomplished by wind, water, or animals **(Figure 38.4)**. In wind-pollinated species, including grasses and many trees, the release of enormous quantities of pollen compensates for the randomness of dispersal by the wind. At certain times of the year, the air is loaded with pollen grains, as anyone who is plagued with pollen allergies can attest. Some species of aquatic plants rely on water to disperse pollen. Most angiosperm species, however, depend on insects, birds, or other animal pollinators to transfer pollen directly from one flower to another flower. If pollination is successful, a pollen grain produces a pollen tube, which then grows down into the ovary via the style.

Pollination by Moths and Butterflies

Moths and butterflies detect odors, and the flowers they pollinate are often sweetly fragrant. Butterflies perceive many bright colors, but moth-pollinated flowers are usually white or yellow, which stand out in low light (as at night). A yucca plant (shown here) is typically pollinated by a single species of moth with appendages that pack pollen onto the stigma. The moth then deposits eggs directly into the ovary. The larvae eat some developing seeds, but this cost is outweighed by the benefit of an efficient and reliable pollinator. If a moth deposits too many eggs, the flower aborts and drops off, selecting against individuals that overexploit the plant.

▲ Moth on yucca flower

Anther

Stigma

Pollination by Flies

Fly-pollinated flowers are reddish and fleshy, with an odor like rotten meat. Blowflies visiting carrion flowers (*Stapelia* species) mistake the flower for a rotting corpse and lay their eggs on it. In the process, the blowflies become dusted with pollen that they carry to other flowers. When the eggs hatch, the larvae find no carrion to eat and therefore die.

Fly egg

▲ Blowfly on carrion flower

Pollination by Birds

Bird-pollinated flowers, such as poro flowers, are usually large and bright red or yellow, but they have little odor. Since birds often do not have a well-developed sense of smell, there was no selective pressure favoring scent production. However, the flowers produce copious nectar that helps meet the high energy demands of the pollinating birds. Nectar is a sugary solution produced by nectaries at the base of many flowers. Nectar's primary function is to "reward" the pollinator. The petals of such flowers often fuse, forming a bent floral tube that fits the curved beak of the bird.

▲ Hummingbird drinking nectar of poro flower

Pollination by Bats

Bat-pollinated flowers, like moth-pollinated flowers, are light-colored and aromatic, attracting their nocturnal pollinators. The lesser long-nosed bat (*Leptonycteris curasoae yerbabuenae*) feeds on the nectar and pollen of agave and cactus flowers in the southwestern United States and Mexico. In feeding, the bats transfer pollen from plant to plant. Long-nosed bats are on the federal list of endangered species.

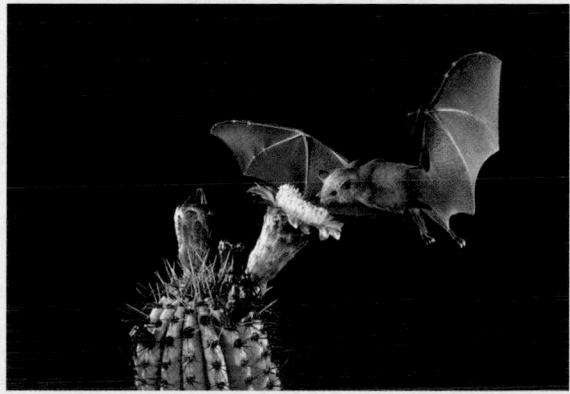
▲ Long-nosed bat feeding on cactus flower at night

> **?** *What are the benefits and dangers to a plant of having a highly specific animal pollinator?*

Double Fertilization

At the time of pollination, the living pollen grain typically consists of only the tube cell and the generative cell. After a pollen grain lands on a suitable stigma, it absorbs water and germinates by producing a pollen tube, which grows between the cells of the style toward the ovary **(Figure 38.5)**. The nucleus of the generative cell divides by mitosis and forms two sperm. Directed by a chemical attractant produced by the two synergids flanking the egg, the tip of the pollen tube enters the ovule through the micropyle and discharges its two sperm near or within the female gametophyte (embryo sac). A gradient in gamma-aminobutyric acid (GABA), a chemical that functions as a neurotransmitter in animal cells, may be the critical signal for attracting the pollen tube **(Figure 38.6)**.

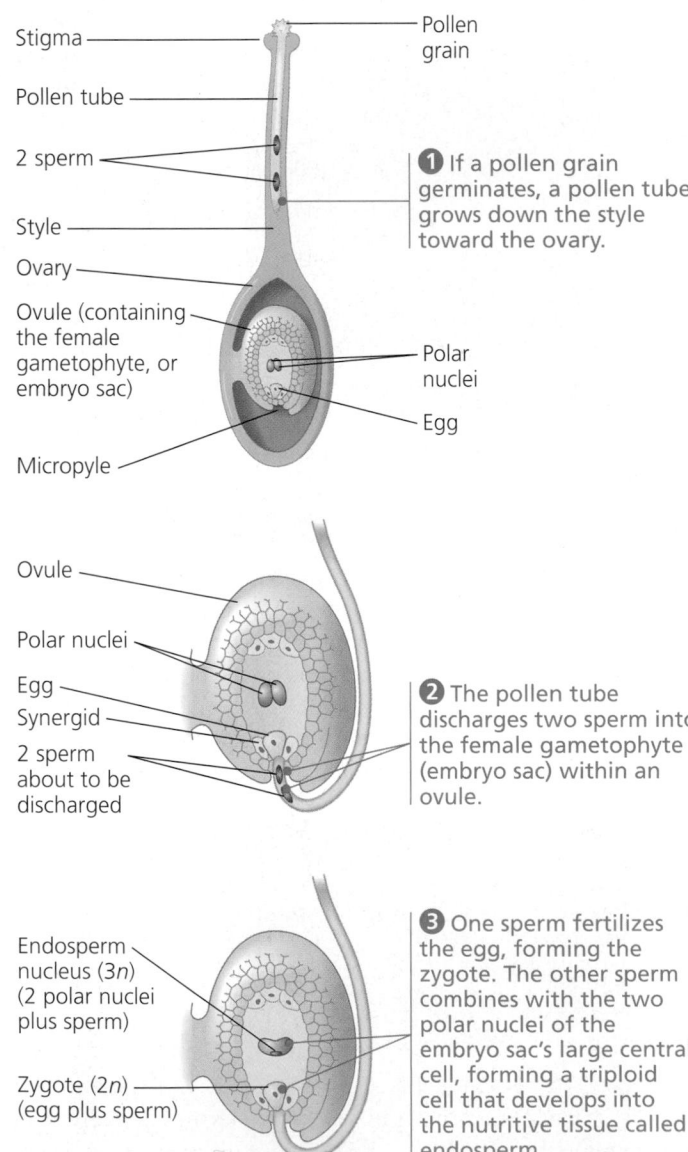

▲ **Figure 38.5 Growth of the pollen tube and double fertilization.**

Upon reaching the female gametophyte, one sperm fertilizes the egg, forming the zygote. The other sperm combines with the two polar nuclei, forming a triploid (3*n*) nucleus in the center of the large central cell of the female gametophyte. This large cell will give rise to the **endosperm**, a food-storing tissue of the seed. The union of two sperm cells with different nuclei of the female gametophyte is called **double fertilization**. Dou-

---

▼ **Figure 38.6** **Inquiry**

Do GABA gradients play a role in directing pollen tubes to the eggs in *Arabidopsis*?

EXPERIMENT Researchers at the University of Chicago found an *Arabidopsis* mutant (carrying a mutation called *pop2*) that failed to produce viable seeds because pollen tubes couldn't seem to "find" the egg. In wild-type *Arabidopsis*, the pollen tubes (thick red lines in the LMs below) have little trouble finding the egg, but in *pop2* mutants none of the numerous pollen tubes turn down the seed stalk toward the micropyle and the egg. The *pop2* mutation was mapped, and the wild-type allele was identified as coding for a protein related to gamma-aminobutyric acid (GABA) transaminase, an enzyme that breaks down GABA. The researchers tested the hypothesis that GABA plays a role in pollen tube guidance by measuring GABA levels in the flowers of *pop2* and wild-type flowers and by examining the effects of GABA on pollen tube growth *in vitro*.

Wild-type *Arabidopsis*	*pop2* mutant *Arabidopsis*
	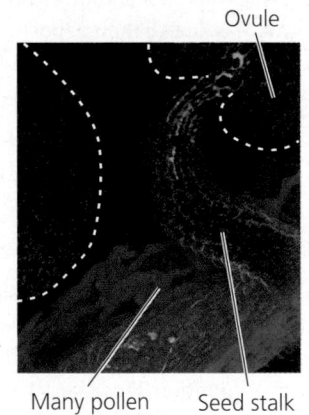

RESULTS GABA levels were 113-fold higher in *pop2* flowers than in wild-type flowers. Other intermediates in the GABA pathway were unaffected by *pop2*. Measurements of GABA content in wild-type flowers revealed a gradient from the stigma (low) to the ovary (high), but this gradient was disrupted in the *pop2* mutant. *In vitro*, GABA stimulated pollen tube growth, although vast excesses were inhibitory.

CONCLUSION A GABA gradient helps guide the pollen tube to the egg in *Arabidopsis* flowers.

SOURCE R. Palinivelu et al., Pollen tube growth and guidance is regulated by POP2, an *Arabidopsis* gene that controls GABA levels, *Cell* 114: 47–59 (2003).

WHAT IF? What phenotypic effects would occur in a mutant that could not synthesize any GABA in its flowers?

ble fertilization ensures that the endosperm will develop only in ovules where the egg has been fertilized, thereby preventing angiosperms from squandering nutrients.

The tissues surrounding the female gametophyte have prevented researchers from directly observing fertilization in plants grown under normal conditions. Scientists have, however, isolated sperm from germinated pollen grains and eggs from female gametophytes and have observed the merging of plant gametes *in vitro* (in an artificial environment). The first cellular event that takes place after gamete fusion is an increase in the levels of cytoplasmic calcium ions (Ca^{2+}) in the egg, as also occurs during animal gamete fusion (see Chapter 47). Another similarity to animals is the establishment of a block to *polyspermy*, the fertilization of an egg by multiple sperm. Thus, sperm cannot fuse with zygotes even *in vitro*. In maize (*Zea mays*), for example, this barrier to polyspermy is established as early as 45 seconds after the initial sperm fusion with the egg.

Seed Development, Form, and Function

After double fertilization, each ovule develops into a seed, and the ovary develops into a fruit enclosing the seed(s). As the embryo develops from the zygote, the seed stockpiles proteins, oils, and starch to varying degrees, depending on the species. This is why seeds are such major sugar sinks—sites of sugar use and storage (see Chapter 36). Initially, these nutrients are stored in the seed's endosperm, although later in seed development, the main nutrient-storage sites for most species are the swelling cotyledons, or seed leaves, of the embryo.

Endosperm Development

Endosperm usually develops before the embryo does. After double fertilization, the triploid nucleus of the ovule's central cell divides, forming a multinucleate "supercell" that has a milky consistency. This liquid mass, the endosperm, becomes multicellular when cytokinesis partitions the cytoplasm by forming membranes between the nuclei. Eventually, these "naked" cells produce cell walls, and the endosperm becomes solid. Coconut "milk" and "meat" are examples of liquid and solid endosperm, respectively. The white fluffy part of popcorn is also solid endosperm.

In grains and most other species of monocots, as well as many eudicots, the endosperm stores nutrients that can be used by the seedling after germination. In other eudicot seeds (including those of beans), the food reserves of the endosperm are completely exported to the cotyledons before the seed completes its development; consequently, the mature seed lacks endosperm.

Embryo Development

The first mitotic division of the zygote splits the fertilized egg into a basal cell and a terminal cell (Figure 38.7). The termi-

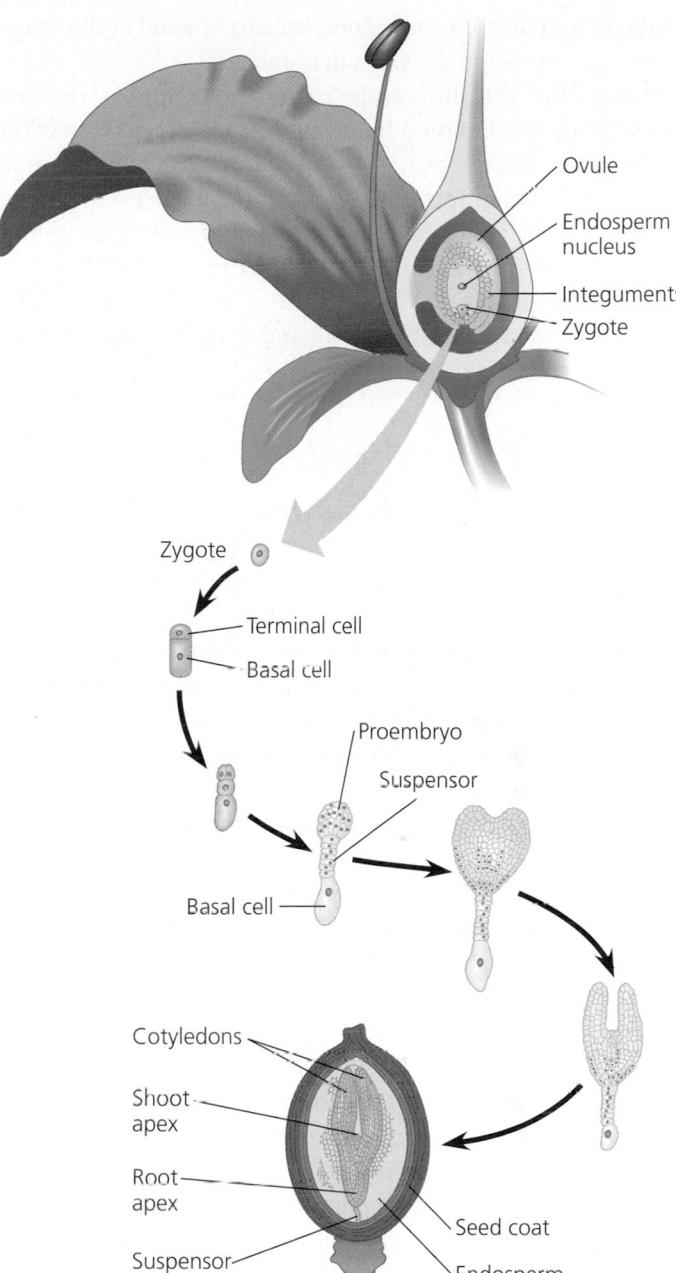

▲ **Figure 38.7 The development of a eudicot plant embryo.** By the time the ovule becomes a mature seed and the integuments harden and thicken into the seed coat, the zygote has given rise to an embryonic plant with rudimentary organs.

nal cell eventually gives rise to most of the embryo. The basal cell continues to divide, producing a thread of cells called the *suspensor*, which anchors the embryo to the parent plant. The suspensor helps in transferring nutrients to the embryo from the parent plant and, in some species of plants, from the endosperm. As the suspensor elongates, it pushes the embryo deeper into the nutritive and protective tissues. Meanwhile, the terminal cell divides several times and forms a spherical proembryo (early embryo) attached to the suspensor. The cotyledons begin to form as bumps on the proembryo. A eudicot, with its two cotyledons, is heart-shaped at this stage. Only one cotyledon develops in monocots.

Soon after the rudimentary cotyledons appear, the embryo elongates. Cradled between the two cotyledons is the embryonic shoot apex, which includes the shoot apical meristem. At the opposite end of the embryo's axis, where the suspensor attaches, is the embryonic root apex, which includes the root apical meristem. After the seed germinates—indeed, for the rest of the plant's life—the apical meristems at the tips of shoots and roots sustain primary growth (see Figure 35.11).

Structure of the Mature Seed

During the last stages of its maturation, the seed dehydrates until its water content is only about 5–15% of its weight. The embryo, which is surrounded by a food supply (cotyledons, endosperm, or both), enters **dormancy**; that is, it stops growing and its metabolism nearly ceases. The embryo and its food supply are enclosed by a hard, protective **seed coat** formed from the integuments of the ovule. In some species, dormancy is imposed by the presence of an intact seed coat rather than by the embryo itself.

You can take a closer look at one type of eudicot seed by splitting open the seed of a common garden bean. The embryo consists of an elongate structure, the embryonic axis, attached to fleshy cotyledons **(Figure 38.8a)**. Below where the cotyledons are attached, the embryonic axis is called the **hypocotyl** (from the Greek *hypo*, under). The hypocotyl terminates in the **radicle**, or embryonic root. The portion of the embryonic axis above where the cotyledons are attached and below the first pair of miniature leaves is the **epicotyl** (from the Greek *epi*, on, over). The epicotyl, young leaves, and shoot apical meristem are collectively called the *plumule*.

The cotyledons of the common garden bean are packed with starch before the seed germinates because they absorbed carbohydrates from the endosperm when the seed was developing. However, the seeds of some eudicot species, such as castor beans (*Ricinus communis*), retain their food supply in the endosperm and have very thin cotyledons **(Figure 38.8b)**. The cotyledons absorb nutrients from the endosperm and transfer them to the rest of the embryo when the seed germinates.

The embryo of a monocot has a single cotyledon **(Figure 38.8c)**. Members of the grass family, including maize and wheat, have a specialized cotyledon called a *scutellum* (from the Latin *scutella*, small shield, a reference to its shape). The scutellum, which has a large surface area, is pressed against the endosperm, from which it absorbs nutrients during germination. The embryo of a grass seed is enclosed by two protective sheaths: a **coleoptile**, which covers the young shoot, and a **coleorhiza**, which covers the young root.

(a) Common garden bean, a eudicot with thick cotyledons. The fleshy cotyledons store food absorbed from the endosperm before the seed germinates.

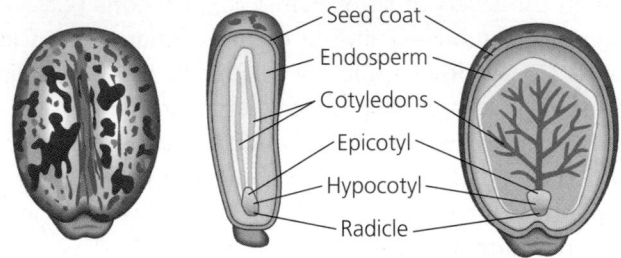

(b) Castor bean, a eudicot with thin cotyledons. The narrow, membranous cotyledons (shown in edge and flat views) absorb food from the endosperm when the seed germinates.

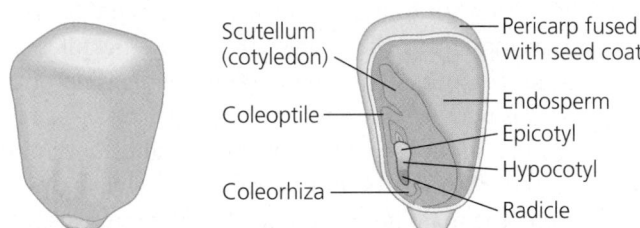

(c) Maize, a monocot. Like all monocots, maize has only one cotyledon. Maize and other grasses have a large cotyledon called a scutellum. The rudimentary shoot is sheathed in a structure called the coleoptile, and the coleorhiza covers the young root.

▲ **Figure 38.8 Seed structure.**

Seed Dormancy: An Adaptation for Tough Times

Dormancy (from the Latin word meaning "to sleep") is a condition of extremely low metabolic rate and suspension of growth and development. Environmental conditions required to break dormancy vary among species. Seeds of some species germinate as soon as they are in a suitable environment. Others remain dormant, even if sown in a favorable place, until an environmental cue causes them to break dormancy.

The requirement for specific cues to break seed dormancy increases the chances that germination will occur at a time and place most advantageous to the seedling. Seeds of many desert plants, for instance, germinate only after a substantial rainfall. If they were to germinate after a mild drizzle, the soil might soon become too dry to support the seedlings. Where natural fires are common, many seeds require intense heat or smoke to break dormancy; seedlings are therefore most abundant after fire has cleared away competing vegetation. Where winters are harsh, seeds may require extended exposure to cold. Seeds sown during summer or fall do not germinate until the following spring, ensuring a long growth season before the next winter. Some small seeds, such as those of some lettuce varieties, require light for germination and will break dormancy only if buried shallow enough for the seedlings to poke through the soil surface. Some seeds have coats that must be weakened by chemical attack as they pass through an animal's digestive tract and thus are usually carried a considerable distance before being defecated.

The length of time a dormant seed remains viable and capable of germinating varies from a few days to decades or even longer, depending on the plant species and environmental conditions. Most seeds are durable enough to last a year or two until conditions are favorable for germinating. Thus, the soil has a bank of ungerminated seeds that may have accumulated for several years. This is one reason vegetation reappears so rapidly after a fire, drought, flood, or other environmental disruption.

Seed Germination and Seedling Development

Germination depends on **imbibition**, the uptake of water due to the low water potential of the dry seed. Imbibing water causes the seed to expand and rupture its coat and also triggers metabolic changes in the embryo that enable it to resume growth. Following hydration, enzymes begin digesting the storage materials of the endosperm or cotyledons, and the nutrients are transferred to the growing regions of the embryo.

The first organ to emerge from the germinating seed is the radicle, the embryonic root. Next, the shoot tip must break through the soil surface. In garden beans and many other eudicots, a hook forms in the hypocotyl, and growth pushes the hook above ground **(Figure 38.9a)**. Stimulated by light, the hypocotyl straightens, raising the cotyledons and epicotyl. Thus, the delicate shoot tip and bulky cotyledons are pulled upward rather than being pushed tip-first through the abrasive soil. The epicotyl now spreads its first foliage leaves, which are true leaves, as distinguished from the cotyledons, or seed leaves. The foliage leaves expand, become green, and begin making food by photosynthesis. The cotyledons shrivel and fall away from the seedling, their food reserves having been exhausted by the germinating embryo.

Some monocots, such as maize and other grasses, use a different method for breaking ground when they germinate **(Figure 38.9b)**. The coleoptile, the sheath enclosing and protecting the embryonic shoot, pushes upward through the soil and into the air. The shoot tip then grows straight up through

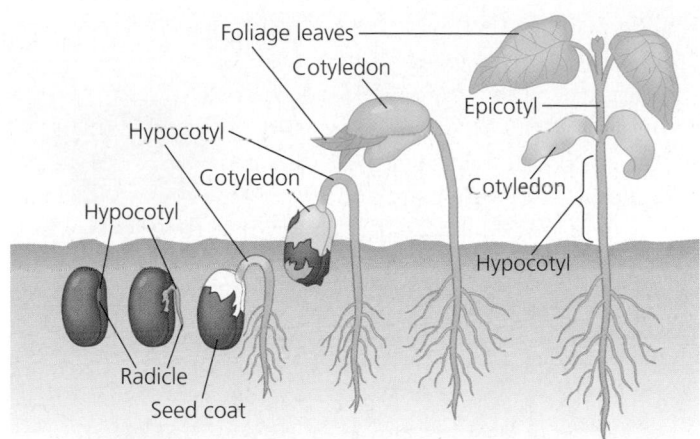

(a) Common garden bean. In common garden beans, straightening of a hook in the hypocotyl pulls the cotyledons from the soil.

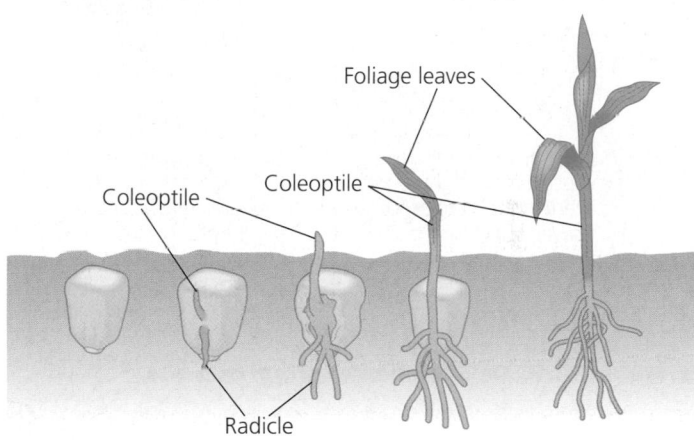

(b) Maize. In maize and other grasses, the shoot grows straight up through the tube of the coleoptile.

▲ **Figure 38.9 Two common types of seed germination.**

? *How do bean and maize seedlings protect their shoot systems as they push through the soil?*

the tunnel provided by the tubular coleoptile and eventually breaks out through the coleoptile's tip.

Fruit Form and Function

While the seeds are developing from ovules, the ovary of the flower is developing into a **fruit**, which protects the enclosed seeds and, when mature, aids in their dispersal by wind or animals. Fertilization triggers hormonal changes that cause the ovary to begin its transformation into a fruit. If a flower has not been pollinated, fruit typically does not develop, and the entire flower usually withers and falls away.

During fruit development, the ovary wall becomes the pericarp, the thickened wall of the fruit. As the ovary grows, the other parts of the flower usually wither and are shed. For example, the pointed tip of a pea pod is the withered remains of the pea flower's stigma.

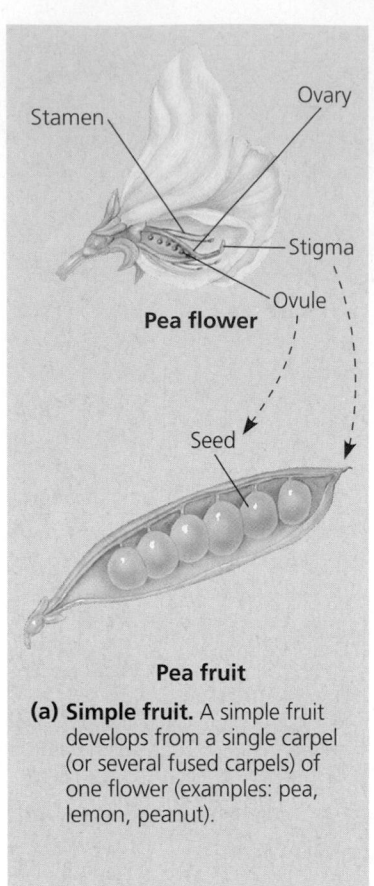

Pea flower

Pea fruit

(a) Simple fruit. A simple fruit develops from a single carpel (or several fused carpels) of one flower (examples: pea, lemon, peanut).

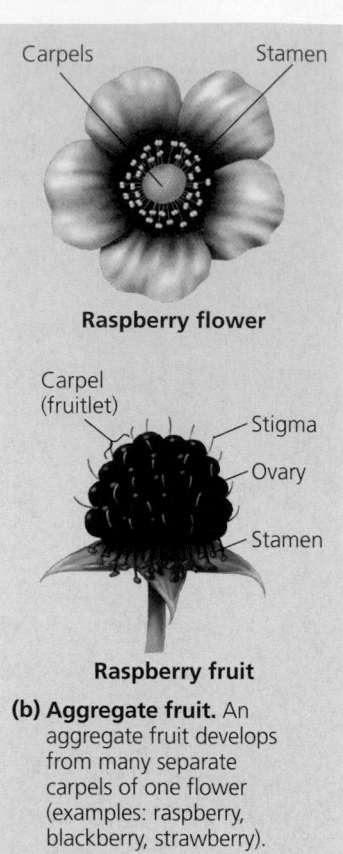

Raspberry flower

Raspberry fruit

(b) Aggregate fruit. An aggregate fruit develops from many separate carpels of one flower (examples: raspberry, blackberry, strawberry).

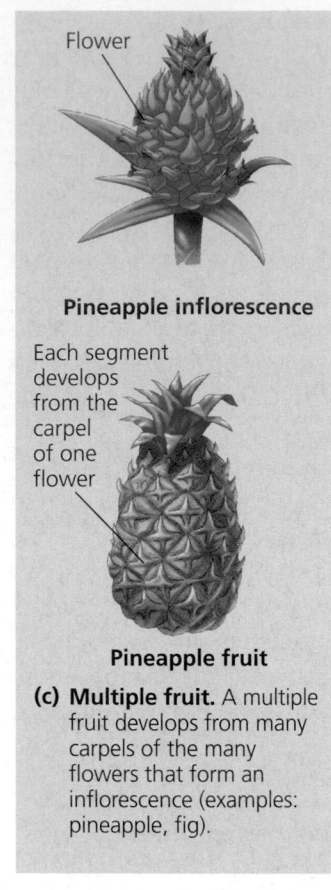

Pineapple inflorescence

Each segment develops from the carpel of one flower

Pineapple fruit

(c) Multiple fruit. A multiple fruit develops from many carpels of the many flowers that form an inflorescence (examples: pineapple, fig).

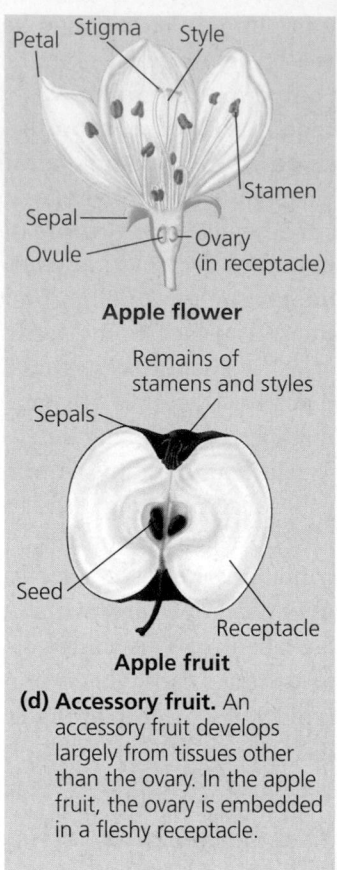

Apple flower

Apple fruit

(d) Accessory fruit. An accessory fruit develops largely from tissues other than the ovary. In the apple fruit, the ovary is embedded in a fleshy receptacle.

▲ **Figure 38.10 Developmental origin of fruits.**

Fruits are classified into several types, depending on their developmental origin. Most fruits are derived from a single carpel or several fused carpels and are called **simple fruits (Figure 38.10a)**. Some simple fruits are dry, such as a pea pod or a nut, whereas others are fleshy, such as a nectarine (see Figure 30.8). An **aggregate fruit** results from a single flower that has more than one separate carpel, each forming a small fruit **(Figure 38.10b)**. These "fruitlets" are clustered together on a single receptacle, as in a raspberry. A **multiple fruit** develops from an inflorescence, a group of flowers tightly clustered together. When the walls of the many ovaries start to thicken, they fuse together and become incorporated into one fruit, as in a pineapple **(Figure 38.10c)**.

In some angiosperms, other floral parts in addition to ovaries contribute to what we commonly call the fruit. Such fruits are called **accessory fruits**. In apple flowers, for example, the ovary is embedded in the receptacle, and the fleshy part of this simple fruit is derived mainly from the enlarged receptacle; only the apple core develops from the ovary **(Figure 38.10d)**. Another example is the strawberry, an aggregate fruit consisting of an enlarged receptacle embedded with tiny one-seeded fruits.

A fruit usually ripens about the same time that its seeds complete their development. Whereas the ripening of a dry fruit, such as a soybean pod, involves the aging and drying out of fruit tissues, the process in a fleshy fruit is more elab-

orate. Complex interactions of hormones result in an edible fruit that entices animals that help spread the seeds. The fruit's "pulp" becomes softer as a result of enzymes digesting components of the cell walls. The color usually changes from green to another color, such as red, orange, or yellow. The fruit becomes sweeter as organic acids or starch molecules are converted to sugar, which may reach a concentration of as much as 20% in a ripe fruit. **Figure 38.11** examines some mechanisms of fruit dispersal in more detail.

In this section, you have learned about the unique features of sexual reproduction in angiosperms—flowers, fruits, and double fertilization. As you will learn in the next section, many angiosperms also reproduce asexually.

CONCEPT CHECK 38.1

1. Distinguish between pollination and fertilization.
2. What is the advantage of seed dormancy?
3. Explain why the four types of fruits described in Figure 38.10 are not completely separate categories.
4. **WHAT IF?** If flowers had shorter styles, pollen tubes would more easily reach the embryo sac. Suggest an explanation for why very long styles have nevertheless evolved in most flowering plants.

For suggested answers, see Appendix A.

Exploring Fruit and Seed Dispersal

A plant's life depends on finding fertile ground. But a seed that falls and sprouts beneath the parent plant stands little chance of competing successfully for nutrients. To prosper, seeds must be widely dispersed. Plants use biotic dispersal agents as well as abiotic agents such as water and wind.

Dispersal by Water

▶ Some buoyant seeds and fruits can survive months or years at sea. In coconut, the seed embryo and fleshy white "meat" (endosperm) are within a hard layer (endocarp) surrounded by a thick and buoyant fibrous husk.

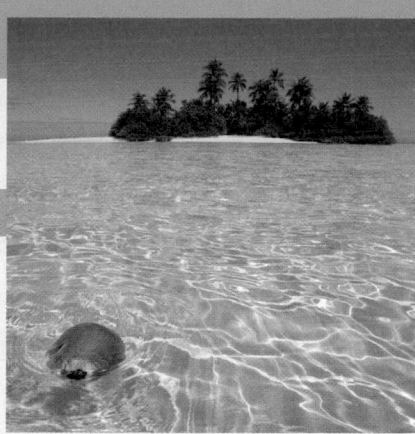

Dispersal by Wind

▶ The winged seed of the tropical Asian climbing gourd *Alsomitra macrocarpa* glides through the air of the rain forest in wide circles when released.

▶ Some seeds and fruits have "parachutes" with an umbrella-like crown of intricately branched hairs, often produced in puffy clusters, such as these dandelion seeds. The slightest gust carries them aloft.

▶ The winged fruits of maples spin like helicopter blades, slowing descent and increasing the chance of being carried farther by horizontal winds.

▶ Some tumbleweeds break off at the ground and tumble across the terrain, scattering their seeds.

Dispersal by Animals

▶ The sharp, tack-like spines on the fruits of puncture vine (*Tribulus terrestris*) can pierce bicycle tires and injure animals, including humans. When these painful "tacks" are removed and discarded, the seeds are dispersed.

◀ Seeds in edible fruits are often dispersed in feces, such as the black bear feces shown here. Such dispersal may carry seeds far from the parent plant.

▶ Ants are chemically attracted to seeds with food bodies rich in fatty acids, amino acids, and sugars. The ants carry the seed to their underground nest, where the food body (the lighter-colored portion shown here) is removed and fed to larvae. Due to the seed's size, unwieldy shape, or hard coating, the remainder is usually left intact in the nest, where it germinates.

▶ Some animals, such as squirrels, hoard seeds or fruits in underground caches. If the animal dies or forgets the cache's location, the seeds may germinate.

CONCEPT 38.2
Flowering plants reproduce sexually, asexually, or both

Imagine chopping off your finger and watching it develop into an exact copy of you. If this could actually occur, it would be an example of **asexual reproduction**, in which offspring are derived from a single parent without genetic recombination. The result would be a clone, an asexually produced, genetically identical organism. Asexual reproduction is common in angiosperms, as well as in other plants, and for some plant species it is the predominant mode of reproduction.

Mechanisms of Asexual Reproduction

Asexual reproduction in plants is typically an extension of the capacity for indeterminate growth. Plants, remember, have meristems, tissues of dividing, undifferentiated cells that can sustain or renew growth indefinitely. In addition, parenchyma cells throughout the plant can divide and differentiate into more specialized types of cells, enabling plants to regenerate lost parts. Detached vegetative fragments of some plants can develop into whole offspring; a severed stem, for instance, may develop adventitious roots and become a whole plant. Such **fragmentation**, the separation of a parent plant into parts that develop into whole plants, is one of the most common modes of asexual reproduction. The adventitious plantlets on *Kalanchoë* leaves exemplify an unusual type of fragmentation (see Figure 35.7). In another form of asexual reproduction in some species, the root system of a single parent gives rise to many adventitious shoots that become separate shoot systems. The result is a clone formed by asexual reproduction from one parent **(Figure 38.12)**. Such asexual propagation has produced the oldest of all known plant clones, a ring of

▲ **Figure 38.12 Asexual reproduction in aspen trees.** Some aspen groves, such as those shown here, actually consist of thousands of trees descended by asexual reproduction. Each grove of trees derives from the root system of one parent. Notice that genetic differences between groves descended from different parents result in different timing for the development of fall color and the loss of leaves.

creosote bushes in the Mojave Desert of California, estimated to be at least 12,000 years old.

An entirely different mechanism of asexual reproduction has evolved in dandelions and some other plants. These plants can sometimes produce seeds without pollination or fertilization. This asexual production of seeds is called **apomixis** (from the Greek words meaning "away from the act of mixing") because there is no joining or, indeed, production of sperm and egg. Instead, a diploid cell in the ovule gives rise to the embryo, and the ovules mature into seeds, which in the dandelion are dispersed by windblown fruits. Thus, these plants clone themselves by an asexual process but have the advantage of seed dispersal, usually associated with sexual reproduction. Introducing apomixis into hybrid crops is a goal of great interest to plant breeders because apomixis would allow hybrid plants to pass on their desirable genomes intact to their offspring.

Advantages and Disadvantages of Asexual Versus Sexual Reproduction

An important advantage of asexual reproduction is that there is no need for a pollinator. This may be beneficial in situations where plants of the same species are sparsely distributed and unlikely to be visited by the same pollinator. Asexual reproduction also allows the plant to pass on all of its genetic legacy intact to its progeny. In contrast, when reproducing sexually, a plant passes on only half of its alleles. If a plant is superbly suited to a stable environment, asexual reproduction can be advantageous. A vigorous plant that is well adapted to its environment can clone many copies of itself, and if the environmental circumstances remain stable, these clones will also be genetically well adapted to the same environmental conditions under which the parent flourished.

Generally, the clones produced by asexual reproduction are not as frail as seedlings produced by sexual reproduction. The clones usually arise from mature vegetative fragments from the parent plant, which is why asexual reproduction in plants is also known as **vegetative reproduction**. In contrast, seed germination is a precarious stage in a plant's life. The tough seed gives rise to a fragile seedling that is exposed to predators, parasites, wind, and other hazards. In the wild, only a small fraction of seedlings endure long enough to become parents themselves. Production of enormous numbers of seeds compensates for the odds against individual survival and gives natural selection ample genetic variations to screen. However, this is a very expensive means of reproduction in terms of the resources consumed in flowering and fruiting.

Sexual reproduction generates variation in offspring and populations and can therefore be advantageous in unstable environments where evolving pathogens and fluctuating variables affect survival and reproductive success. In contrast, the genotypic uniformity of asexually produced plants puts them at great risk of local extinction if there is a catastrophic environmental change, such as a new strain of disease. Moreover, seeds (which are almost always produced sexually) facilitate the dispersal of offspring to more distant locations. Finally, seed dormancy allows growth to be suspended until environmental conditions become more favorable.

While the great advantage of sexual reproduction is that it increases the genetic diversity of offspring, some flowers, such as garden peas, self-fertilize. This process, called "selfing," can be a desirable attribute in some crop plants because it ensures that a seed will develop. In many angiosperm species, however, mechanisms have evolved that make it difficult or impossible for a flower to fertilize itself, as we'll discuss next.

Mechanisms That Prevent Self-Fertilization

The various mechanisms that prevent self-fertilization contribute to genetic variety by ensuring that sperm and eggs come from different parents. In the case of **dioecious** species, plants cannot self-fertilize because different individuals have either staminate flowers (lacking carpels) or carpellate flowers (lacking stamens) **(Figure 38.13a)**. Other plants have flowers with functional stamens and carpels that mature at different times or are structurally arranged in such a way that it is unlikely that an animal pollinator could transfer pollen from an anther to a stigma of the same flower **(Figure 38.13b)**. However, the most common anti-selfing mechanism in flowering plants is **self-incompatibility**, the ability of a plant to reject its own pollen and sometimes the pollen of closely related individuals. If a pollen grain lands on a stigma of a flower on the same plant, a biochemical block prevents the pollen from completing its development and fertilizing an egg.

Researchers are unraveling the molecular mechanisms involved in self-incompatibility. This plant response is analogous to the immune response of animals in that both are based on the ability to distinguish the cells of "self" from those of "nonself." The key difference is that the animal immune system rejects nonself, as when the system mounts a defense against a pathogen or rejects a transplanted organ (see Chapter 43). Self-incompatibility in plants, in contrast, is a rejection of self.

Recognition of "self" pollen is based on genes for self-incompatibility, called *S*-genes. In the gene pool of a plant population, there can be dozens of alleles of an *S*-gene. If a pollen grain has an allele that matches an allele of the stigma on which it lands, the pollen tube fails to grow. Depending on the species, self-recognition blocks pollen tube growth by one of two molecular mechanisms: gametophytic self-incompatibility or sporophytic self-incompatibility.

In gametophytic self-incompatibility, the *S*-allele in the pollen genome governs the blocking of fertilization. For example, an S_1 pollen grain from an S_1S_2 parental sporophyte will fail to fertilize eggs of an S_1S_2 flower but will fertilize an S_2S_3 flower. An S_2 pollen grain will not fertilize either flower. Self-recognition of this kind involves the enzymatic destruction of RNA within a pollen tube. RNA-hydrolyzing enzymes are produced by the style and enter the pollen tube. If the pollen tube is a "self" type, these enzymes destroy its RNA.

In sporophytic self-incompatibility, fertilization is blocked by *S*-allele gene products in tissues of the parental sporophyte that adhere to the pollen wall. For example, neither an S_1 nor S_2 pollen grain from an S_1S_2 parental sporophyte will fertilize eggs of an S_1S_2 flower or S_2S_3 flower, due to the S_1S_2 parental tissue attached to the pollen grain wall. Sporophytic incompatibility involves a signal transduction pathway in epidermal cells of the stigma that prevents germination of the pollen grain.

Some crops, such as peas, maize, and tomatoes, routinely self-pollinate with satisfactory results. However, plant breeders frequently hybridize different varieties of a crop plant to combine the best traits of the varieties and counter the loss of vigor that can often result from excessive inbreeding (see Chapter 14). To obtain hybrid seeds, plant breeders today must prevent self-fertilization either by laboriously removing the anthers from the parent plants that provide the seeds or by developing male-sterile plants. The latter option is increasingly common. Eventually, it may also be possible to impose self-incompatibility genetically on crop species that are normally self-compatible. Basic research on mechanisms of self-incompatibility may thus have agricultural applications.

 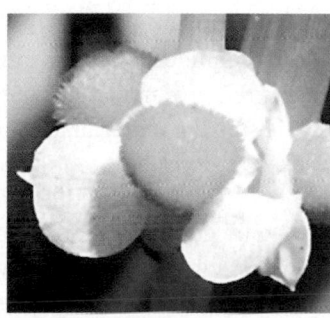

(a) Some species, such as *Sagittaria latifolia* (common arrowhead), are dioecious, having plants that produce only staminate flowers (left) or carpellate flowers (right).

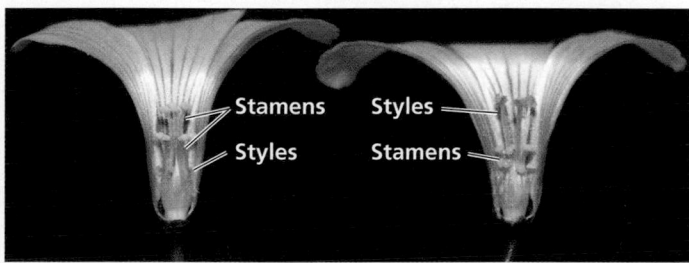

Thrum flower   Pin flower

(b) Some species, such as *Oxalis alpina* (alpine woodsorrel), produce two types of flowers on different individuals: "thrums," which have short styles and long stamens, and "pins," which have long styles and short stamens. An insect foraging for nectar would collect pollen on different parts of its body; thrum pollen would be deposited on pin stigmas, and vice versa.

▲ **Figure 38.13 Some floral adaptations that prevent self-fertilization.**

Vegetative Propagation and Agriculture

With the objective of improving crops and ornamental plants, humans have devised various methods for asexual propagation of angiosperms. Most of these methods are based on the ability of plants to form adventitious roots or shoots.

Clones from Cuttings

Most houseplants, woody ornamentals, and orchard trees are asexually reproduced from plant fragments called cuttings. In some cases, shoot cuttings are used. At the cut end of the shoot, a mass of dividing, undifferentiated cells called a **callus** forms, and adventitious roots then develop from the callus. If the shoot fragment includes a node, then adventitious roots form without a callus stage. Some plants, including African violets, can be propagated from single leaves rather than stems. For other plants, cuttings are taken from specialized storage stems. For example, a potato can be cut up into several pieces, each with a vegetative bud, or "eye," that regenerates a whole plant.

Grafting

In a modification of vegetative reproduction from cuttings, a twig or bud from one plant can be grafted onto a plant of a closely related species or a different variety of the same species. Grafting makes it possible to combine the best qualities of different species or varieties into a single plant. The graft is usually done when the plant is young. The plant that provides the root system is called the **stock**; the twig grafted onto the stock is referred to as the **scion**. For example, scions from French varieties of vines that produce superior wine grapes are grafted onto root stocks of American varieties, which are more resistant to certain soil pathogens. The genes of the scion determine the quality of the fruit, so the quality is not diminished by the genetic makeup of the stock. In some cases of grafting, however, the stock can alter the characteristics of the shoot system that develops from the scion. For example, dwarf fruit trees, which allow for easier harvesting of the fruit, are made by grafting normal twigs onto stocks of dwarf varieties that retard the vegetative growth of the shoot system. Because seeds are produced by the part of the plant derived from the scion, they give rise to plants of the scion species when planted.

Test-Tube Cloning and Related Techniques

Plant biologists have adopted *in vitro* methods to create and clone novel plant varieties. It is possible to grow whole plants by culturing small pieces of tissue cut from the parent or even single parenchyma cells on an artificial medium containing nutrients and hormones **(Figure 38.14a)**. The cultured cells divide and form an undifferentiated callus. When the hormonal balance is manipulated in the culture medium, the callus can sprout shoots and roots with fully differentiated cells

(a) Just a few parenchyma cells from a carrot gave rise to this callus, a mass of undifferentiated cells.

(b) The callus differentiates into an entire plant, with leaves, stems, and roots.

▲ **Figure 38.14 Test-tube cloning of carrots.** (See also Figure 20.16.)

(Figure 38.14b). The test-tube plantlets can then be transferred to soil, where they continue their growth. A single plant can be cloned into thousands of copies by dividing calluses as they grow. This method is now used for propagating orchids and also a wide variety of horticulturally important trees and shrubs.

Plant tissue culture also facilitates genetic engineering. Most techniques for the introduction of foreign genes into plants require small pieces of plant tissue or single plant cells as the starting material. In plant biology, the term **transgenic** is used to describe genetically modified (GM) organisms that have been engineered to express a gene from another species. Test-tube culture makes it possible to regenerate GM plants from a single plant cell into which the foreign DNA has been incorporated. The techniques of genetic engineering are discussed in more detail in Chapter 20.

Some researchers couple a technique known as **protoplast fusion** with tissue culture methods to invent new plant varieties that can be cloned. Protoplasts are plant cells with their cell walls removed by treatment with enzymes (cellulases and pectinases) isolated from fungi **(Figure 38.15)**. Before protoplasts

◄ **Figure 38.15 Protoplasts.** These wall-less plant cells are prepared by treating cells or tissues with wall-degrading enzymes isolated from certain types of fungi. Researchers can fuse protoplasts from different species to make hybrids and can also culture the hybrid cells to produce a new plant (LM).

50 μm

are cultured, they can be screened for mutations that may improve the plant's agricultural value. In some cases, it is possible to fuse two protoplasts from different plant species that would otherwise be reproductively incompatible and then culture the hybrid protoplasts. Each protoplast can regenerate a wall and eventually form a hybrid plantlet. One success of this method is a hybrid between a potato and a wild relative called black nightshade. The nightshade is resistant to an herbicide commonly used to kill weeds. The hybrids are also resistant, making it possible to "weed" a field with the herbicide without killing potato plants.

The *in vitro* culturing of plant cells and tissues is fundamental to most types of plant biotechnology. The other basic process is the production of transgenic plants through various methods of genetic engineering. In the next section, we take a closer look at plant biotechnology.

▲ **Figure 38.16 Maize: a product of artificial selection.**
Modern maize (bottom) was derived from teosinte (top). Teosinte kernels are tiny, and each row has a husk that must be removed to get at the kernel. The seeds are loose at maturity, allowing dispersal, which probably made harvesting difficult for early farmers. Neolithic farmers selected for larger cob and kernel size as well as the permanent attachment of seeds to the cob and the encasing of the entire cob by a tough husk.

CONCEPT CHECK 38.2

1. Explain how both asexual and sexual "strategies" contribute to the reproductive success of plants.
2. The seedless banana, the world's most popular fruit, is losing the battle against two fungal epidemics. Why do such epidemics generally pose a greater risk to asexually propagated crops?
3. Given the seeming disadvantages of selfing as a reproductive "strategy" in nature, it is surprising that about 20% of angiosperm species primarily rely on selfing. Although fairly common in nature, self-fertilization has been called an "evolutionary dead end." Suggest a reason why selfing might be selected for in nature and yet still be an evolutionary dead end.
4. **WHAT IF?** Potatoes (*Solanum tuberosum*) and tomatoes (*Solanum lycopersicum*) are fairly closely related species. If you managed to cross the two, would it be possible to have a hybrid that makes potato-like tubers and tomato-like fruits on the same plant?

For suggested answers, see Appendix A.

CONCEPT 38.3

Humans modify crops by breeding and genetic engineering

Humans have intervened in the reproduction and genetic makeup of plants since the dawn of agriculture. Indeed, it is no exaggeration to say that maize is an unnatural monster created by humans. Left on its own in nature, maize would soon become extinct for the simple reason that it cannot spread its seeds. Maize kernels are not only permanently attached to the central axis (the "cob") but also permanently protected by tough, overlapping leaf sheathes (the "husk") **(Figure 38.16)**. These attributes arose by artificial selection by humans. (See Chapter 22 to review the basic concept of artificial selection.) Despite having no understanding of the scientific principles underlying plant breeding, Neolithic (late Stone Age) humans domesticated most of our crop species over a relatively short period about 10,000 years ago. But genetic modification began long before humans started altering crops by artificial selection. For example, the wheat species we rely on for much of our food evolved by the natural hybridization between different species of grasses. Such hybridization is common in plants and has long been exploited by breeders to introduce genetic variation for artificial selection and crop improvement.

Plant Breeding

The art of recognizing valuable traits is important in plant breeding. Breeders scrutinize their fields carefully and travel to other countries searching for domesticated varieties or wild relatives with desirable traits. Such traits occasionally arise spontaneously through mutation, but the natural rate of mutation is too slow and unreliable to produce all the mutations that breeders would like to study. Breeders sometimes hasten mutations by treating large batches of seeds or seedlings with X-rays, radiation, or chemicals.

When a desirable trait is identified in a wild species, the wild species is crossed with a domesticated variety. Generally, those progeny that have inherited the desirable trait from the wild parent have also inherited many traits that are not desirable for agriculture. The progeny that express the desired trait are again crossed with members of the domesticated species and their progeny examined for the desired trait. This process is continued until the progeny with the desired wild trait resemble the original domesticated parent in their other agricultural attributes.

While most breeders cross-pollinate plants of a single species, some breeding methods rely on hybridization between two distant species of the same genus. For example, a cross between two species of the genus *Musa* produced the familiar Cavendish banana. Distant crosses often result in the abortion of the hybrid seed during development. Very often the embryo begins to develop, but the endosperm does not. Hybrid embryos are sometimes rescued by surgically removing them from the ovule and culturing them *in vitro*.

Less commonly, distant hybridization is carried out between members of two different genera. A cross between wheat (*Triticum aestivum*) and rye (*Secale cereale*), for example, produced a novel grain called triticale, which contains a copy of all the chromosomes from both species. When triticale was first produced in the 1870s, it was considered little more than a botanical oddity. In the mid-1900s, however, plant breeders realized that triticale could potentially be developed into a crop with the yield and quality of bread wheat and with rye's tolerance of cold stress, moisture stress, and acidic soils. The early triticales were plagued with problems. These tall, late-maturing plants tended to fall over, were partially sterile, and were low yielding. They typically produced shriveled seeds that germinated poorly and were of poor quality for milling and baking. But through continued artificial selection, these problems were overcome, and triticale is now grown on more than 1 million hectares worldwide (1 ha = 2.47 acres). Some 600,000 ha are on the sandy, acidic soils of Poland, where the grain is used primarily for animal feed. It is nutritionally superior to rye, and the flour blends better with wheat in the baking of bread. Triticale grows well on *marginal land*, agriculturally inferior land that usually yields a poor return. If we are to feed the burgeoning world population in the 21st century, such marginal lands will have to become increasingly productive.

Plant Biotechnology and Genetic Engineering

Plant biotechnology has two meanings. In the general sense, it refers to innovations in the use of plants (or substances obtained from plants) to make products of use to humans—an endeavor that began in prehistory. In a more specific sense, biotechnology refers to the use of GM organisms in agriculture and industry. Indeed, in the last two decades, genetic engineering has become such a powerful force that the terms *genetic engineering* and *biotechnology* have become synonymous in the media.

Unlike traditional plant breeders, modern plant biotechnologists, using techniques of genetic engineering, are not limited to the transfer of genes between closely related species or varieties of the same species. For example, traditional breeding techniques could not be used to insert a desired gene from daffodil into rice because the many intermediate species between rice and daffodil and their common ancestor are extinct. In theory, if breeders had the intermediate species, over the course of several centuries they could probably introduce a daffodil gene into rice by traditional hybridization and breeding methods. With genetic engineering, however, such gene transfers can be done more quickly and without the need for intermediate species.

In the remainder of this chapter, we expand on discussions in Chapter 20 by examining the prospects and the controversies surrounding the use of genetically modified crops. The advocates of plant biotechnology believe that the genetic engineering of crop plants is the key to overcoming some of the most pressing problems of the 21st century, including world hunger and fossil fuel dependency.

Reducing World Hunger and Malnutrition

Currently, 800 million people on Earth suffer from nutritional deficiencies, with 40,000 dying each day of malnutrition, half of them children. There is much disagreement about the causes of such hunger. Some argue that food shortages arise from inequities in distribution and that the dire poor simply cannot afford food. Others regard food shortages as evidence that the world is overpopulated—that the human species has exceeded the carrying capacity of the planet (see Chapter 53). Whatever the social and demographic causes of malnutrition, increasing food production is a humane objective. Because land and water are the most limiting resources, the best option is to increase yields on the available land. Indeed, there is very little "extra" land that can be farmed, especially if the few remaining pockets of wilderness are to be preserved. Based on conservative estimates of population growth, farmers will have to produce 40% more grain per hectare to feed the human population in 2030. Plant biotechnology can help make these crop yields possible.

The commercial use of transgenic crops has been one of the most dramatic examples of rapid technology adoption in the history of agriculture. These crops include varieties and hybrids of cotton, maize, and potatoes that contain genes from the bacterium *Bacillus thuringiensis*. These "transgenes" encode a protein (*Bt* toxin) that is toxic to insect pests. The use of such plant varieties greatly reduces the need for chemical insecticides. The *Bt* toxin used in crops is produced in the plant as a harmless protoxin that only becomes toxic if activated by alkaline conditions, such as occur in the guts of insects. Because vertebrates have highly acidic stomachs, protoxin consumed by humans or farm animals is destroyed without becoming active.

Considerable progress has also been made in developing transgenic plants of cotton, maize, soybeans, sugar beets, and wheat that tolerate certain herbicides. The cultivation of these plants may reduce production costs by enabling farmers to "weed" crops with herbicides that do not damage the transgenic crop plants instead of by heavy tillage, which can cause soil erosion. Researchers are also engineering plants with enhanced resistance to disease. In one case, a transgenic papaya

◀ **Figure 38.17 Genetically modified papaya.** A ring spot virus has devastated papaya cultivation worldwide. However, a transgenic papaya variety rescued the industry in Hawaii. The genetically engineered papaya on the left is more resistant to ring spot virus than the nontransgenic papaya on the right.

Genetically modified rice

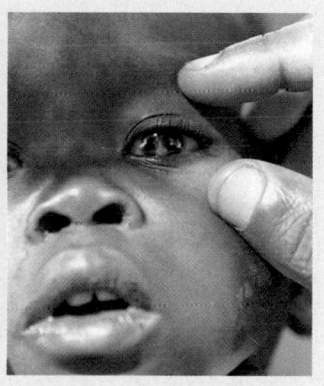

Ordinary rice

▲ **Figure 38.18 "Golden Rice" and prevention of blindness associated with vitamin A deficiency.** Some 250,000 to 500,000 children go blind each year because of vitamin A deficiencies. The onset of blindness, indicated by a cloudy white spot in the eye, is a sign of severe underlying health problems: More than half of these children die within a year of becoming blind. The golden color and increased nutritional value of Golden Rice are attributable to its ability to make beta-carotene (provitamin A).

resistant to a ring spot virus was introduced into Hawaii, thereby saving its papaya industry (**Figure 38.17**).

The nutritional quality of plants is also being improved. "Golden Rice," a transgenic variety carrying two daffodil genes, produces grain containing beta-carotene, a precursor of vitamin A. This rice was developed to prevent the blindness that occurs in those of the world's poor whose diet is deficient in vitamin A (**Figure 38.18**). Recently, scientists have developed a new variety with much more beta-carotene than the original.

Reducing Fossil Fuel Dependency

Global sources of inexpensive fossil fuels, particularly oil, are rapidly being depleted. Moreover, climatologists attribute global warming mostly to the rampant burning of fossil fuels, such as coal and oil, and the resulting release of greenhouse gases. How

can the world meet its energy demands in the 21st century in an economical and nonpolluting way? In certain localities, wind or solar power may become economically viable, but such alternative energy sources are unlikely to fill all the energy demands of the planet. Many scientists predict that the biomass from extremely fast-growing plants, such as switchgrass (*Panicum virgatum*) and poplar (*Populus trichocarpa*), could produce a sizable fraction of the world's energy needs in the not-too-distant future.

Under optimal conditions, poplars can grow 3–4 m each year, and switchgrass grows well under a wide variety of conditions found in regions where most types of agriculture are not economically viable. Scientists do not envisage the plant biomass being burned directly. Instead, the polymers in cell walls, such as cellulose and hemicellulose, which constitute the most abundant organic compounds on Earth, would be broken down into sugars by enzymatic reactions. These sugars, in turn, would be fermented into alcohol and distilled to yield **biofuels**.

The use of biofuels from plant biomass would reduce the net emission of the greenhouse gas CO_2. Whereas burning fossil fuels increases atmospheric CO_2 concentrations, biofuel crops reabsorb by photosynthesis the CO_2 emitted when biofuels are burned, creating a cycle that is carbon neutral. Plant breeders are trying to genetically engineer faster-growing poplar trees that produce more readily convertible biomass.

Biofuel technology does have its critics. For example, ecologist David Pimentel, of Cornell University, and geo-engineer Tad Patzek, of UC Berkeley, have published estimates that more energy may be required to produce biofuels than would be produced from combustion of these products. Biofuel advocates, in turn, have questioned the accuracy of the data underlying these estimates.

The Debate over Plant Biotechnology

Much of the debate about GM organisms in agriculture is political, social, economic, or ethical and outside the scope of this book. But we *should* consider the biological concerns about GM crops. There are some biologists, particularly ecologists, who are concerned about the unknown risks associated with the release of GM organisms (GMOs) into the environment. The debate centers on the extent to which GMOs could harm human health or the environment. Those who want to proceed more slowly with agricultural biotechnology (or end it) are concerned about the unstoppable nature of the "experiment." If a drug trial produces unanticipated harmful results, the trial is stopped. But we may not be able to stop the "trial" of introducing novel organisms into the biosphere.

Chapter 20 introduced the key concerns regarding biotechnology in general. Here we take a closer look at some issues as they relate to plant biotechnology. Laboratory and field studies continue to examine the possible consequences of using GM crops, including the effects on human health and nontarget organisms and the potential for transgene escape.

Issues of Human Health

Many GMO opponents worry that genetic engineering may inadvertently transfer allergens, molecules to which some humans are allergic, from a species that produces an allergen to a plant used for food. However, biotechnologists are engaged in removing genes that encode allergenic proteins from soybeans and other crops. So far, there is no credible evidence that GM plants specifically designed for human consumption have adverse effects on human health. In fact, some GM foods are potentially healthier than non-GM foods. For example, *Bt* maize (the transgenic variety with the *Bt* toxin) contains 90% less of a cancer-causing and birth defect–causing mycotoxin than non-*Bt* maize. Called fumonisin, this toxin is highly resistant to degradation and has been found in alarmingly high concentrations in some batches of processed maize products, ranging from cornflakes to beer. Fumonisin is produced by a fungus (*Fusarium*) that infects insect-damaged maize. Because *Bt* maize generally suffers less insect damage than non-GM maize, it contains much less fumonisin.

Nevertheless, because of health concerns, GMO opponents lobby for the clear labeling of all foods containing products of GMOs. Some also argue for strict regulations against the mixing of GM foods with non-GM foods during food transport, storage, and processing. Biotechnology advocates, however, note that similar demands were not made when "transgenic" crops produced by traditional plant-breeding techniques were put on the market. There are, for example, some commercially grown varieties of wheat derived by traditional plant-breeding techniques that contain entire chromosomes (and thousands of genes) from rye.

Possible Effects on Nontarget Organisms

Many ecologists are concerned that the growing of GM crops might have unforeseen effects on nontarget organisms. One laboratory study indicated that the larvae (caterpillars) of monarch butterflies responded adversely and even died after eating milkweed leaves (their preferred food) heavily dusted with pollen from transgenic *Bt* maize. This study has since been discredited and affords a good example of the self-correcting nature of science. As it turns out, when the original researchers shook the male maize inflorescences onto the milkweed leaves in the laboratory, the filaments of stamens, opened microsporangia, and other floral parts also rained onto the leaves. Subsequent research found that it was these other floral parts, *not* the pollen, that contained *Bt* toxin in high concentrations. Unlike pollen, these floral parts would not be carried by the wind to neighboring milkweed plants when shed under natural field conditions. Only one *Bt* maize line, accounting for less than 2% of commercial *Bt* maize production (and now discontinued), produced pollen with high *Bt* toxin concentrations.

In considering the negative effects of *Bt* pollen on monarch butterflies, one must also weigh the effects of an alternative to the cultivation of *Bt* maize—the spraying of non-*Bt* maize with chemical pesticides. Recent studies have shown that such spraying was much more harmful to nearby monarch populations than was *Bt* maize production. Although the effects of *Bt* maize pollen on monarch butterfly larvae appear to be minor, the controversy has emphasized the need for accurate field testing of all GM crops and the importance of targeting gene expression to specific tissues to improve safety.

Addressing the Problem of Transgene Escape

Perhaps the most serious concern raised about GM crops is the possibility of the introduced genes escaping from a transgenic crop into related weeds through crop-to-weed hybridization. The fear is that the spontaneous hybridization between a crop engineered for herbicide resistance and a wild relative might give rise to a "superweed" that would have a selective advantage over other weeds in the wild and would be much more difficult to control in the field. Some crops *do* hybridize with weedy relatives, and crop-to-weed transgene escape is a possibility. Its likelihood depends on the ability of the crop and weed to hybridize and on how the transgenes affect the overall fitness of the hybrids. A desirable crop trait—a dwarf phenotype, for example—might be disadvantageous to a weed growing in the wild. In other instances, there are no weedy relatives nearby with which to hybridize; soybean, for example, has no wild relatives in the United States. However, canola, sorghum, and many other crops do hybridize readily with weeds.

Many different strategies are being pursued with the goal of preventing transgene escape. For example, if male sterility could be engineered into plants, these plants would still produce seeds and fruit if pollinated by nearby nontransgenic plants, but they would produce no viable pollen. A second approach involves genetically engineering apomixis into transgenic crops. When a seed is produced by apomixis, the embryo and endosperm develop without fertilization. The transfer of this trait to transgenic crops would therefore minimize the possibility of transgene escape via pollen because plants could be male-sterile without compromising seed or fruit production. A third approach is to engineer the transgene into the chloroplast DNA of the crop. Chloroplast DNA in many plant species is inherited strictly from the egg, so transgenes in the chloroplast cannot be transferred by pollen (see Chapter 15 to review maternal inheritance). A fourth approach for preventing transgene escape is to genetically engineer flowers that develop normally but fail to open. Consequently, self-pollination would occur, but pollen would be unlikely to escape from the flower. This solution would require modifications to flower design. Several floral genes have been identified that could be manipulated to this end.

The continuing debate about GMOs in agriculture exemplifies one of this textbook's recurring ideas: the relationship of science and technology to society. Technological advances almost always involve some risk of unintended outcomes. In plant biotechnology, zero risk is probably unattainable. Therefore, scientists and the public must assess on a case-by-case basis the possible benefits of transgenic products versus the risks that society is willing to take. The best scenario is for these discussions and decisions to be based on sound scientific information and rigorous testing rather than on reflexive fear or blind optimism.

CONCEPT CHECK **38.3**

1. Compare traditional plant-breeding methods with genetic engineering.
2. Explain some benefits and risks of GM crops.
3. Why does *Bt* maize have less fumonisin than non-GM maize?
4. **WHAT IF?** In a few species, chloroplast genes are inherited only from sperm. How might this affect efforts to prevent transgene escape?

For suggested answers, see Appendix A.

Chapter 38 Review

MEDIA Go to **www.campbellbiology.com** for BioFlix 3-D Animations, MP3 Tutors, Videos, Practice Tests, an eBook, and more.

SUMMARY OF KEY CONCEPTS

CONCEPT 38.1

Flowers, double fertilization, and fruits are unique features of the angiosperm life cycle (pp. 801–811)

▶ The sporophyte, the dominant generation, produces spores that develop within flowers into male gametophytes (in pollen grains) and female gametophytes (embryo sacs).

▶ **Flower Structure and Function** Flowers function in sexual reproduction. The four floral organs are sepals, petals, stamens, and carpels. Pollen develops from microspores within the microsporangia of anthers; female gametophytes develop from megaspores within ovules. Pollination, which precedes fertilization, is the placing of pollen on the stigma of a carpel.

▶ **Double Fertilization**
The pollen tube discharges two sperm into the female gametophyte; one sperm fertilizes the egg, while the other combines with the polar nuclei, giving rise to food-storing endosperm.

Endosperm nucleus (3n) (2 polar nuclei plus sperm)

Zygote (2n) (egg plus sperm)

▶ **Seed Development, Form, and Function** The seed coat encloses the embryo along with a food supply stocked in either the endosperm or the cotyledons. Seed dormancy ensures that seeds germinate only when conditions for seedling survival are optimal. The breaking of dormancy often requires environmental cues, such as temperature or lighting changes.

▶ **Fruit Form and Function** The fruit protects the enclosed seeds and aids in wind dispersal or in the attraction of seed-dispersing animals.

MEDIA

MP3 Tutor From Flower to Fruit
Activity Angiosperm Life Cycle
Investigation What Tells Desert Seeds When to Germinate?
Activity Seed and Fruit Development

CONCEPT 38.2

Flowering plants reproduce sexually, asexually, or both (pp. 812–815)

▶ **Mechanisms of Asexual Reproduction** Modes of asexual reproduction include fragmentation and the production of adventitious shoots.

▶ **Advantages and Disadvantages of Asexual Versus Sexual Reproduction** Asexual reproduction enables successful clones to spread; sexual reproduction generates the genetic variation that makes evolutionary adaptation possible.

▶ **Mechanisms That Prevent Self-Fertilization** Some plants reject pollen that has an *S*-gene matching an allele in the stigma cells. Recognition of "self" pollen triggers a signal transduction pathway leading to a block in growth of a pollen tube.

▶ **Vegetative Propagation and Agriculture** Cloning plants from cuttings is an ancient practice. Plants can be cloned from single cells, which can be genetically manipulated before being allowed to develop into a plant.

CONCEPT 38.3

Humans modify crops by breeding and genetic engineering (pp. 815–819)

▶ **Plant Breeding** Interspecific hybridization of plants is common in nature and has been used by breeders, ancient and modern, to introduce new genes into crops. After two plants are successfully hybridized, plant breeders select those progeny that have the desired traits.

▶ **Plant Biotechnology and Genetic Engineering** In genetic engineering, genes from unrelated organisms are incorporated into plants. Genetically modified (GM) plants have the potential of increasing the quality and quantity of food worldwide and may also become increasingly important as biofuels.

▶ **The Debate over Plant Biotechnology** There are concerns about the unknown risks of releasing GM organisms into the environment, but the potential benefits of transgenic crops need to be considered.

MEDIA

Activity Making Decisions About DNA Technology: Golden Rice

SELF-QUIZ

1. A plant that has small, green petals is most likely to be
   a. bee-pollinated.
   b. bird-pollinated.
   c. bat-pollinated.
   d. wind-pollinated.
   e. moth-pollinated.

2. A seed develops from
   a. an ovum.
   b. a pollen grain.
   c. an ovule.
   d. an ovary.
   e. an embryo.

3. A fruit is
   a. a mature ovary.
   b. a mature ovule.
   c. a seed plus its integuments.
   d. a fused carpel.
   e. an enlarged embryo sac.

4. Double fertilization means that
   a. flowers must be pollinated twice to yield fruits and seeds.
   b. every egg must receive two sperm to produce an embryo.
   c. one sperm is needed to fertilize the egg, and a second sperm is needed to fertilize the polar nuclei.
   d. the egg of the embryo sac is diploid.
   e. every sperm has two nuclei.

5. Some dioecious species have the XY genotype for male and XX for female. After double fertilization, what would be the genotypes of the embryos and endosperm nuclei?
   a. embryo X and endosperm XX or embryo Y and endosperm XY
   b. embryo XX and endosperm XX or embryo XY and endosperm XY
   c. embryo XX and endosperm XXX or embryo XY and endosperm XYY
   d. embryo XX and endosperm XXX or embryo XY and endosperm XXY
   e. embryo XY and endosperm XXX or embryo XX and endosperm XXY

6. Which statement concerning grafting is correct?
   a. Stocks and scions refer to twigs of different species.
   b. Stocks come from vines, but scions come from trees.
   c. Stocks provide root systems for grafting.
   d. Grafting creates new species.
   e. Stocks and scions must come from unrelated species.

7. Plant biotechnologists use protoplast fusion mainly to
   a. culture plant cells *in vitro*.
   b. asexually propagate desirable plant varieties.
   c. introduce bacterial genes into a plant genome.
   d. study the early events following fertilization.
   e. produce new hybrid species.

8. The basal cell from the zygote's first division develops into
   a. the suspensor that anchors the embryo and transfers nutrients.
   b. the proembryo.
   c. the endosperm that nourishes the developing embryo.
   d. the root apex of the embryo.
   e. two cotyledons in eudicots, but one in monocots.

9. The development of *Bt* crops raises concerns because
   a. *Bt* crops have been shown to be toxic to humans.
   b. pollen from these crops is harmful to monarch butterfly larvae in the field.
   c. if genes for *Bt* toxin "escape" to related weed species, the hybrid weeds could have harmful ecological effects.
   d. *Bacillus thuringiensis* is a pathogen of humans.
   e. *Bt* toxin reduces the nutritional quality of crops.

10. "Golden Rice" is a transgenic variety that
    a. is resistant to various herbicides, making it practical to weed rice fields with those herbicides.
    b. is resistant to a virus that commonly attacks rice fields.
    c. includes bacterial genes that produce a toxin that reduces damage from insect pests.
    d. produces larger, golden grains that increase crop yields.
    e. contains daffodil genes that increase vitamin A content.

11. **DRAW IT** Draw and label the parts of a flower.

For Self-Quiz answers, see Appendix A.

MEDIA Visit **www.campbellbiology.com** for a Practice Test.

EVOLUTION CONNECTION

12. With respect to sexual reproduction, some plant species are fully self-fertile, others are fully self-incompatible, and some exhibit a "mixed strategy" with partial self-incompatibility. These reproductive strategies differ in their implications for evolutionary potential. How, for example, might a self-incompatible species fare as a small founder population or remnant population in a severe population bottleneck (see Chapter 23), as compared with a self-fertile species?

SCIENTIFIC INQUIRY

13. Critics of GM foods have argued that foreign genes may disturb normal cellular functioning, causing unexpected and potentially harmful substances to appear inside cells. Toxic intermediary substances that normally occur in very small amounts may arise in larger amounts, or new substances may appear. The disruption may also lead to loss of substances that help maintain normal metabolism. If you were your nation's chief scientific advisor, how would you respond to these criticisms?

    Biological Inquiry: A Workbook of Investigative Cases Explore GM crops further with the case "Corn Under Construction."

SCIENCE, TECHNOLOGY, AND SOCIETY

14. Humans have engaged in genetic manipulation for millennia, producing plant and animal varieties through selective breeding and hybridization processes that significantly modify the genomes of organisms. Why do you think modern genetic engineering, which often entails introducing or modifying only one or a few genes, has met with so much public opposition? Should some forms of genetic engineering be of greater concern than others? Explain.

Plant Responses to Internal and External Signals

▲ Figure 39.1 **Can flowers tell you the time of day?**

OVERVIEW

Stimuli and a Stationary Life

Carolus Linnaeus, the father of taxonomy, was a keen naturalist and observer of plants. Linnaeus noted that certain plants opened and closed their flowers at particular times of the day, with these times varying from species to species. Therefore, one could deduce the approximate time of day according to which species had opened or closed its flowers. If the times of opening and closing were arranged in sequence, they could serve as a kind of floral clock, or *horologium florae*, as Linnaeus called it. **Figure 39.1** shows a modern simplified representation as a 12-hour clock face. Why does the timing vary? The time at which flowers open presumably reflects the time when their insect pollinators are most active, just one of many environmental factors that a plant must sense to compete successfully. Contrary to the common notion of plants as being almost inanimate, a plant's morphology and physiology are constantly tuned to its surroundings by complex interactions between environmental stimuli and internal signals.

This chapter focuses on how plants respond to external and internal cues. At the organismal level, plants and animals respond to environmental stimuli by very different means. Animals, being mobile, respond mainly by behavioral mechanisms, moving toward positive stimuli and away from negative stimuli. Being stationary, a plant generally responds to environmental cues by adjusting its individual pattern of growth and development. For this reason, plants of the same species vary in body form much more than do animals of the same species. Before a plant can initiate growth responses to environmental signals, it must first detect the change in its environment. At the cellular level, the processes by which plants perceive environmental changes are as complex as those used by animal cells and are often homologous to them.

CONCEPT 39.1

Signal transduction pathways link signal reception to response

All organisms receive specific signals and respond to them in ways that enhance survival and reproductive success. For example, bees, which have UV-sensitive photoreceptors in their eyes, can discern nectar-guiding patterns on flower petals—patterns that are completely invisible to humans (see Figure 38.4). Plants, too, have cellular receptors that they use to detect important changes in their internal or external environments, whether the change is an increase in the concentration of a growth hormone, an injury from a caterpillar munching on leaves, or a decrease in day length as winter approaches.

For a stimulus to elicit a response, an organism must have cells with an appropriate receptor, a molecule affected by the stimulus. For example, humans' inability to see UV-reflecting floral patterns is due to our eyes lacking UV photoreceptors. Upon receiving a stimulus, a receptor initiates a signal transduction pathway, a series of biochemical steps that couples reception to response (see Chapter 11 to review general concepts of signal transduction). Plants are sensitive to a wide range of stimuli, each initiating a specific signal transduction pathway.

(a) Before exposure to light. A dark-grown potato has tall, spindly stems and nonexpanded leaves—morphological adaptations that enable the shoots to penetrate the soil. The roots are short, but there is little need for water absorption because little water is lost by the shoots.

(b) After a week's exposure to natural daylight. The potato plant begins to resemble a typical plant with broad green leaves, short sturdy stems, and long roots. This transformation begins with the reception of light by a specific pigment, phytochrome.

▲ **Figure 39.2 Light-induced de-etiolation (greening) of dark-grown potatoes.**

▲ **Figure 39.3 Review of a general model for signal transduction pathways.** As discussed in Chapter 11, a hormone or other kind of stimulus interacting with a specific receptor protein can trigger the sequential activation of relay proteins and also the production of second messengers that participate in the pathway. The signal is passed along, ultimately bringing about cellular responses. In this diagram, the receptor is on the surface of the target cell; in other cases, the stimulus interacts with receptors inside the cell.

Consider a forgotten potato in the back corner of a kitchen cupboard. This modified underground stem, or tuber, has sprouted shoots from its "eyes" (axillary buds). These shoots, however, scarcely resemble those of a typical plant. Instead of sturdy stems and broad green leaves, these plants have ghostly pale stems and unexpanded leaves, as well as short, stubby roots **(Figure 39.2a)**. These morphological adaptations for growing in darkness, collectively referred to as **etiolation**, make sense if we consider that a young potato plant in nature usually encounters continuous darkness when sprouting underground. Under these circumstances, expanded leaves would be a hindrance to soil penetration and would be damaged as the shoots pushed through the soil. Because the leaves are unexpanded and underground, there is little evaporative loss of water and little requirement for an extensive root system to replace the water lost by transpiration. Moreover, the energy expended in producing green chlorophyll would be wasted because there is no light for photosynthesis. Instead, a potato plant growing in the dark allocates as much energy as possible to elongating its stems. This adaptation enables the shoots to break ground before the nutrient reserves in the tuber are exhausted. The etiolation response is one example of how a plant's morphology and physiology are tuned to its surroundings by complex interactions between environmental and internal signals.

When a shoot reaches the sunlight, the plant undergoes profound changes, collectively called **de-etiolation** (informally known as greening). Stem elongation slows; leaves expand; roots elongate; and the shoot produces chlorophyll. In short, it begins to resemble a typical plant **(Figure 39.2b)**. In this section, we will use this de-etiolation response as an example of how a plant cell's reception of a signal—in this case, light—is transduced into a response (greening). Along the

way, we will explore how studies of mutants provide insights into the molecular details of the stages of cell-signal processing: reception, transduction, and response **(Figure 39.3)**.

Reception

Signals are first detected by receptors, proteins that undergo changes in shape in response to a specific stimulus. The receptor involved in de-etiolation is a type of *phytochrome*, a photoreceptor that we'll examine more closely later in the chapter. Unlike most receptors, which are built into the plasma membrane, the phytochrome that functions in the de-etiolation response is located in the cytoplasm. Researchers demonstrated the requirement for phytochrome in de-etiolation through studies of the tomato, a close relative of the potato. The *aurea* mutant tomato, which has lower-than-normal levels of phytochrome, greens less than wild-type tomatoes when exposed to light. (The name *aurea* comes from the Latin for "gold-colored." In the absence of chlorophyll, the yellow plant pigments called carotenoids are more obvious.) Researchers produced a normal de-etiolation response in individual *aurea* leaf cells by injecting phytochrome from other plants and then exposing the cells to light. Such experiments indicate that phytochrome functions in light detection during de-etiolation.

Transduction

Receptors can be sensitive to very weak environmental or chemical signals. Some de-etiolation responses are triggered by extremely low levels of light. For example, light levels equivalent to a few seconds of moonlight are sufficient to slow stem elongation in dark-grown oat seedlings. How is the information from these extremely weak signals amplified, and how is their reception transduced into a specific response by the plant? The answer is **second messengers**—small molecules and ions in the cell that amplify the signal and transfer it from the receptor to other proteins that carry out the response. In de-etiolation, for example, each activated phytochrome molecule may give rise to hundreds of molecules of a second messenger, each of which may lead to the activation of hundreds of molecules of a specific enzyme. By such mechanisms, a second messenger in a signal transduction pathway rapidly amplifies the signal. In Chapter 11, we discussed several kinds of second messengers in general (see Figures 11.11 and 11.13). Here, we examine the particular roles of second messengers in de-etiolation. Refer to **Figure 39.4** frequently as you read the following description of this complex process.

Light causes phytochrome to undergo a change in shape that leads to increases in levels of the second messengers cyclic GMP (cGMP) and Ca^{2+}. One function of GMP is the activation of protein kinases, a diverse class of enzymes that influence the activation of other proteins by phosphorylation, a modification in which a phosphate group is attached to the protein at a specific site. Injection of cGMP into *aurea* tomato leaf cells induces a partial de-etiolation response,

even without the addition of phytochrome, via the upper pathway in the figure. Changes in cytosolic Ca^{2+} levels also play an important role in phytochrome signal transduction. The concentration of Ca^{2+} is generally very low in the cytosol (about $10^{-7} M$). But phytochrome activation can open Ca^{2+} channels and lead to a transient 100 fold increase in cytosolic Ca^{2+} levels. In other cases of signal transduction, both cGMP and cytosolic Ca^{2+} can influence the activity of specific ion channels, cytoskeletal proteins, and enzymes, including protein kinases.

Response

Ultimately, a signal transduction pathway leads to regulation of one or more cellular activities. In most cases, these responses involve the increased activity of particular enzymes. There are two main mechanisms by which a signaling pathway can enhance an enzymatic step in a biochemical pathway: transcriptional regulation and post-translational modification. Transcriptional regulation increases or decreases synthesis of the mRNA that codes for the enzyme. Post-translational modification activates existing enzyme molecules.

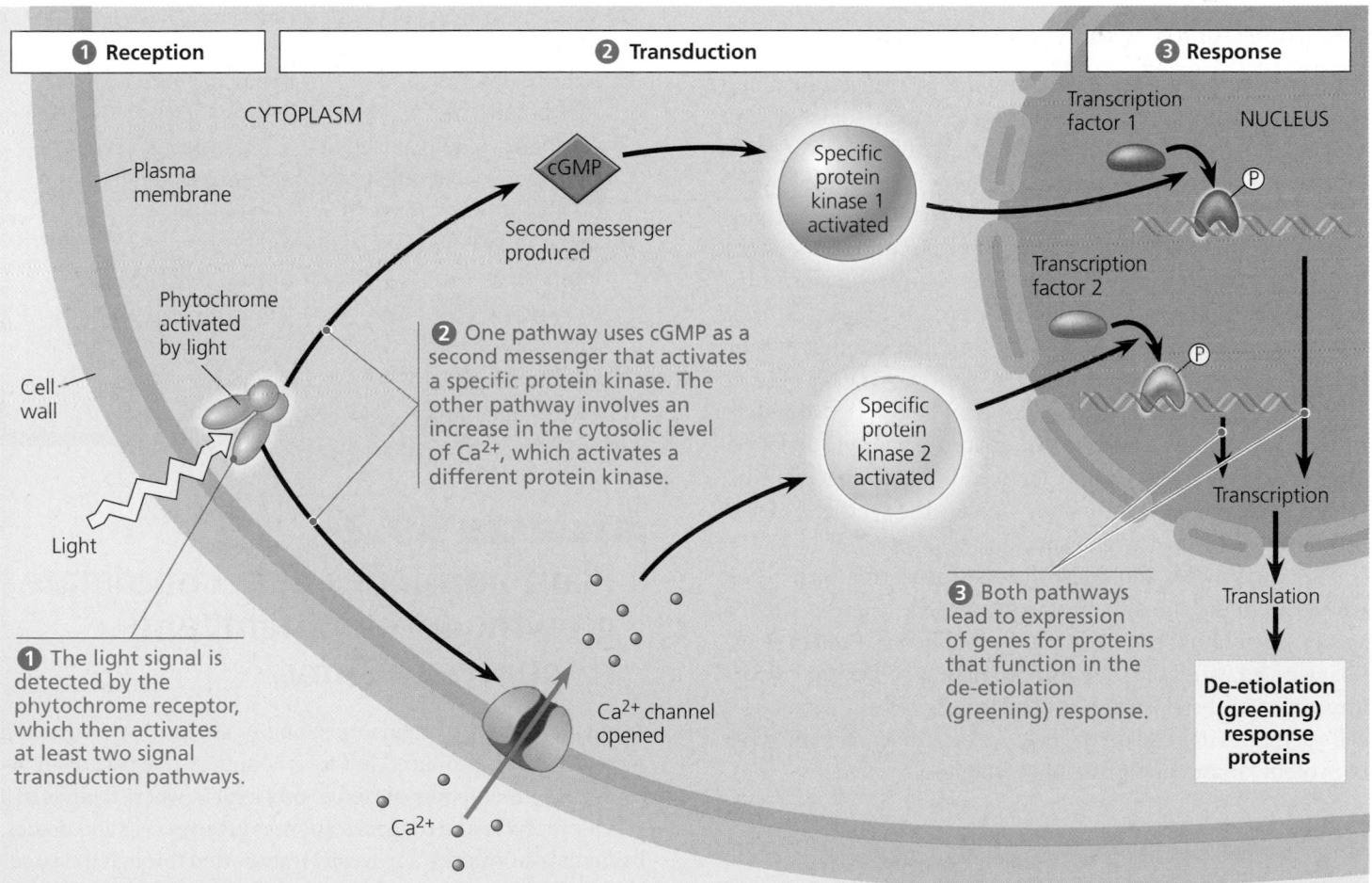

▲ **Figure 39.4 An example of signal transduction in plants: the role of phytochrome in the de-etiolation (greening) response.**

Transcriptional Regulation

As discussed in Chapter 18, the proteins we call *specific transcription factors* bind to specific regions of DNA and control the transcription of specific genes (see Figure 18.9). In the case of phytochrome-induced de-etiolation, several such transcription factors are activated by phosphorylation in response to the appropriate light conditions. The activation of some of these transcription factors depends on cGMP, whereas the activation of others requires Ca^{2+}.

The mechanism by which a signal promotes a new developmental course may depend on transcription factors that are activators (which *increase* transcription of specific genes) or repressors (which *decrease* transcription) or both. For example, consider *Arabidopsis* mutants that, except for their pale color, have a light-grown morphology when grown in the dark; they have expanded leaves and short, sturdy stems but are not green because the final step in chlorophyll production requires light directly. These mutants have defects in a repressor that inhibits the expression of other genes normally activated by light. When the repressor is eliminated by mutation, the pathway that it normally blocks proceeds. Thus, these mutants appear to have been grown in the light, except for their pale color.

Post-Translational Modification of Proteins

Although the syntheses of new proteins by transcription and translation are important molecular events associated with de-etiolation, so are post-translational modifications of existing proteins. Most often, existing proteins are modified by the phosphorylation of specific amino acids, which alters the protein's hydrophobicity and activity. Many second messengers, including cGMP, and some receptors themselves, including some forms of phytochrome, activate protein kinases directly. Often, one protein kinase will phosphorylate another protein kinase, which then phosphorylates another, and so on (see Figure 11.9). Such kinase cascades may link initial stimuli to responses at the level of gene expression, usually via the phosphorylation of transcription factors. By such mechanisms, many signal pathways ultimately regulate the synthesis of new proteins, usually by turning specific genes on or off.

Signal pathways must also have a means for turning off when the initial signal is no longer present, such as when a sprouting potato is put back into the cupboard. Protein phosphatases, enzymes that dephosphorylate specific proteins, are important in these "switch-off" processes. At any moment, a cell's activities depend on the balance of activity of many types of protein kinases and protein phosphatases.

De-Etiolation ("Greening") Proteins

What types of proteins are either newly transcribed or activated by phosphorylation during the de-etiolation process? Many are enzymes that function in photosynthesis directly; others are enzymes involved in supplying the chemical precursors necessary for chlorophyll production; still others affect the levels of plant hormones that regulate growth. For example, the levels of auxin and brassinosteroids, hormones that enhance stem elongation, decrease following phytochrome activation. That decrease explains the slowing of stem elongation that accompanies de-etiolation.

We have discussed the signal transduction involved in the de-etiolation response of a potato plant in some detail to give you a sense of the complexity of biochemical changes that underlie this one process. Every plant hormone and every environmental stimulus triggers one or more signal transduction pathways of comparable complexity. As with the *aurea* mutant tomato, techniques of molecular biology combined with genetic studies of mutants are helping researchers identify these various pathways. But molecular biology builds on a long history of careful physiological and biochemical investigations into how plants work. As you will read in the next section, classical experiments provided the first clues that transported signaling molecules called hormones are internal regulators of plant growth.

CONCEPT CHECK **39.1**

1. What are the morphological differences between dark- and light-grown plants?
2. Explain how etiolation helps a seedling compete successfully.
3. Cycloheximide is a drug that inhibits protein synthesis. Predict what effect cycloheximide would have on de-etiolation.
4. **WHAT IF?** The sexual dysfunction drug Viagra inhibits an enzyme that breaks down cyclic GMP. If tomato leaf cells have a similar enzyme, would applying Viagra cause a normal de-etiolation of *aurea* mutant tomato leaves?

For suggested answers, see Appendix A.

CONCEPT **39.2**

Plant hormones help coordinate growth, development, and responses to stimuli

A **hormone**, in the original meaning of the term, is a signaling molecule that is produced in tiny amounts by one part of an organism's body and transported to other parts, where it binds to a specific receptor and triggers responses in target cells and tissues. In animals, hormones are usually transported through the circulatory system, a criterion often included in definitions of the term.

The hormone concept originated from studies of animals and was adopted by plant physiologists in the early 1900s. Many modern plant biologists, however, argue that it is too limiting to describe plant physiological processes using the narrow definitions established by animal physiologists. For example, plants don't have blood or a circulatory system to transport hormone-like signaling molecules. Moreover, some signaling molecules that are considered plant hormones act only locally. Finally, there are some signaling molecules in plants, such as sucrose, which typically occur in plants at concentrations that are hundreds of thousands times greater than a typical hormone. Nevertheless, they are transported through plants and activate signal transduction pathways that greatly alter the functioning of plants in a manner similar to a hormone. Thus, many plant biologists prefer the broader term *plant growth regulator* to describe organic compounds, either natural or synthetic, that modify or control one or more specific physiological processes within a plant. At this point in time, the terms *plant hormone* and *plant growth regulator* are used about equally, but for historical continuity we will use the term *plant hormone* and adhere to the criterion that plant hormones are active at very low concentrations.

Virtually every aspect of plant growth and development is under hormonal control to some degree. A single hormone can regulate an amazingly diverse array of cellular and developmental processes. Conversely, multiple hormones can influence a single process.

The Discovery of Plant Hormones

The idea that chemical messengers exist in plants emerged from a series of classic experiments on how stems respond to light. As you know, the shoot of a houseplant on a windowsill grows toward light. If you rotate the plant, it soon reorients its growth until its leaves again face the window. Any growth response that results in plant organs curving toward or away from stimuli is called a **tropism** (from the Greek *tropos*, turn). The growth of a shoot toward light or away from it is called **phototropism**; the former is positive phototropism, the latter negative phototropism.

In a forest or other natural ecosystem where plants may be crowded, phototropism directs growing seedlings toward the sunlight that powers photosynthesis. What is the mechanism for this adaptive response? Much of what is known about phototropism has been learned from studies of grass seedlings, particularly oats. The shoot of a sprouting grass seedling is enclosed in a sheath called the coleoptile (see Figure 38.9b), which grows straight upward if the seedling is kept in the dark or if it is illuminated uniformly from all sides. If the growing coleoptile is illuminated from one side, it grows toward the light. This response results from a differential growth of cells on opposite sides of the coleoptile; the cells on the darker side elongate faster than the cells on the brighter side.

Charles Darwin and his son Francis conducted some of the earliest experiments on phototropism in the late 1800s **(Figure 39.5)**. They observed that a grass seedling could bend toward light only if the tip of the coleoptile was present. If the

▼ Figure 39.5 **Inquiry**

What part of a grass coleoptile senses light, and how is the signal transmitted?

EXPERIMENT   In 1880, Charles and Francis Darwin removed and covered parts of grass coleoptiles to determine what part senses light. In 1913, Peter Boysen-Jensen separated coleoptiles with different materials to determine how the signal for phototropism is transmitted.

RESULTS

Control

Darwin and Darwin: Phototropism occurs only when the tip is illuminated.

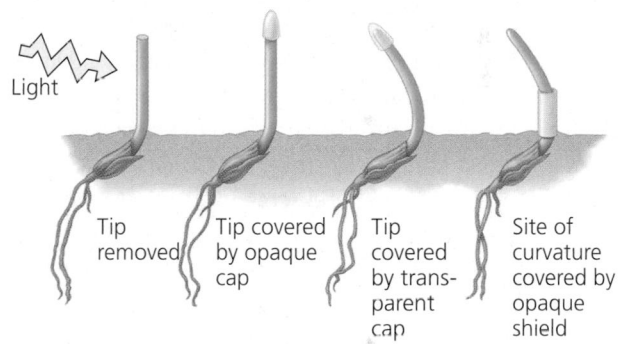

Boysen-Jensen: Phototropism occurs when the tip is separated by a permeable barrier but not an impermeable barrier.

CONCLUSION   The Darwins' experiment suggested that only the tip of the coleoptile senses light. The phototropic bending, however, occurred at a distance from the site of light perception (the tip). Boysen-Jensen's results suggested that the signal for the bending is a light-activated mobile chemical.

SOURCE   C. R. Darwin, The power of movement in plants, John Murray, London (1880). P. Boysen-Jensen, Concerning the performance of phototropic stimuli on the *Avena* coleoptile, *Berichte der Deutschen Botanischen Gesellschaft* (Reports of the German Botanical Society) 31:559–566 (1913).

WHAT IF?   How could you experimentally determine which colors of light cause the most phototropic bending?

tip was removed, the coleoptile did not curve. The seedling also failed to grow toward light if the tip was covered with an opaque cap; but neither a transparent cap over the tip nor an opaque shield placed below the coleoptile tip prevented the phototropic response. It was the tip of the coleoptile, the Darwins concluded, that was responsible for sensing light. However, they noted that the differential growth response that led to curvature of the coleoptile occurred some distance below the tip. The Darwins postulated that some signal was transmitted downward from the tip to the elongating region of the coleoptile. A few decades later, the Danish scientist Peter Boysen-Jensen demonstrated that the signal was a mobile chemical substance. He separated the tip from the remainder of the coleoptile by a cube of gelatin, which prevented cellular contact but allowed chemicals to pass. These seedlings responded normally, bending toward light. However, if the tip was experimentally separated from the lower coleoptile by an impermeable barrier, such as the mineral mica, no phototropic response occurred.

In 1926, Frits Went, a Dutch graduate student, extracted the chemical messenger for phototropism by modifying the experiments of Boysen-Jensen (**Figure 39.6**). Went removed the coleoptile tip and placed it on a cube of agar, a gelatinous material. The chemical messenger from the tip, Went reasoned, should diffuse into the agar, and the agar block should then be able to substitute for the coleoptile tip. Went placed the agar blocks on decapitated coleoptiles that were kept in the dark. A block that was centered on top of the coleoptile caused the stem to grow straight upward. However, when the block was placed off center, the coleoptile began to bend away from the side with the agar block, as though growing toward light. Went concluded that the agar block contained a chemical produced in the coleoptile tip, that this chemical stimulated growth as it passed down the coleoptile, and that a coleoptile curved toward light because of a higher concentration of the growth-promoting chemical on the darker side of the coleoptile. For this chemical messenger, or hormone, Went chose the name auxin (from the Greek *auxein*, to increase). Auxin was later purified by Kenneth Thimann, at the California Institute of Technology, and its chemical structure found to be indoleacetic acid (IAA).

The classical hypothesis for what causes grass coleoptiles to grow toward light, based on the work of the Darwins, Boysen-Jensen, and Went, is that an asymmetrical distribution of auxin moving down from the coleoptile tip causes cells on the darker side to elongate faster than cells on the brighter side. But studies of phototropism by organs other than grass coleoptiles provide less support for this idea. There is no evidence that illumination from one side causes asymmetrical distribution of auxin in stems of sunflowers or other eudicots. There *is*, however, asymmetrical distribution of certain substances that may act as growth *inhibitors*, and these substances are more concentrated on the lighted side of a stem.

▼ Figure 39.6 **Inquiry**

Does asymmetrical distribution of a growth-promoting chemical cause a coleoptile to grow toward the light?

EXPERIMENT In 1926, Frits Went's experiment identified how a growth-promoting chemical causes a coleoptile to grow toward light. He placed coleoptiles in the dark and removed their tips, putting some tips on agar cubes that he predicted would absorb the growth-promoting chemical. On a control coleoptile, he placed a cube that lacked the chemical. On others, he placed cubes containing the chemical, either centered on top of the coleoptile to distribute the chemical evenly or offset to increase the concentration on one side.

RESULTS The coleoptile grew straight if the growth-promoting chemical was distributed evenly. If the chemical was distributed unevenly, the coleoptile curved away from the side with the cube, as if growing toward light, even though it was grown in the dark.

Excised tip placed on agar cube

Growth-promoting chemical diffuses into agar cube

Agar cube with chemical stimulates growth

Control (agar cube lacking chemical) has no effect

Control

Offset cubes cause curvature

CONCLUSION Went concluded that a coleoptile curved toward light because its dark side had a higher concentration of the growth-promoting chemical, which he named auxin.

SOURCE F. Went, A growth substance and growth, *Recueils des Travaux Botaniques Néerlandais* (Collections of Dutch Botanical Works) 25:1–116 (1928).

WHAT IF? Triiodobenzoic acid (TIBA) inhibits auxin transport. If a tiny agar bead containing TIBA were placed off center on the tip of an intact coleoptile, which way would the coleoptile bend: toward the side with the bead or away from it? Explain.

A Survey of Plant Hormones

The early studies on phototropism that we have just discussed provided the basis for subsequent research on plant hormones. **Table 39.1** previews some major classes of plant hormones: auxin, cytokinins, gibberellins, brassinosteroids, abscisic acid, and ethylene. Many molecules in plants that function in defense against pathogens are probably plant hormones as well. (These molecules will be discussed later in the chapter.)

Plant hormones are produced in very low concentrations, but a tiny amount of hormone can have a profound effect on the growth and development of a plant organ. This implies that the hormonal signal must be amplified in some way. A hormone may act by altering the expression of genes, by affecting the activity of existing enzymes, or by changing properties of membranes. Any of these actions could redirect the metabolism and development of a cell responding to a small number of hormone molecules. Signal transduction pathways amplify the hormonal signal and connect it to a cell's specific responses.

In general, hormones control plant growth and development by affecting the division, elongation, and differentiation of cells. Some hormones also mediate shorter-term physiological responses of plants to environmental stimuli. Each hormone has multiple effects, depending on its site of action, its concentration, and the developmental stage of the plant.

Response to a hormone usually depends not so much on the amount of that hormone as on its relative concentration compared with other hormones. It is hormonal balance, rather than hormones acting in isolation, that may control growth and development. These interactions will become apparent in the following survey of hormone function.

Auxin

The term **auxin** is used for any chemical substance that promotes elongation of coleoptiles, although auxins have multiple

Table 39.1 Overview of Plant Hormones

Hormone	Where Produced or Found in Plant	Major Functions
Auxin (IAA)	Shoot apical meristems and young leaves are the primary sites of auxin synthesis. Root apical meristems also produce auxin, although the root depends on the shoot for much of its auxin. Developing seeds and fruits contain high levels of auxin, but it is unclear whether it is newly synthesized or transported from maternal tissues.	Stimulates stem elongation (low concentration only); promotes the formation of lateral and adventitious roots; regulates development of fruit; enhances apical dominance; functions in phototropism and gravitropism; promotes vascular differentiation; retards leaf abscission.
Cytokinins	These are synthesized primarily in roots and transported to other organs, although there are many minor sites of production as well.	Regulate cell division in shoots and roots; modify apical dominance and promote lateral bud growth; promote movement of nutrients into sink tissues; stimulate seed germination; delay leaf senescence.
Gibberellins	Meristems of apical buds and roots, young leaves, and developing seeds are the primary sites of production.	Stimulate stem elongation, pollen development, pollen tube growth, fruit growth, and seed development and germination; regulate sex determination and the transition from juvenile to adult phases.
Brassinosteroids	These compounds are present in all plant tissues, although different intermediates predominate in different organs. Internally produced brassinosteroids act near the site of synthesis.	Promote cell expansion and cell division in shoots; promote root growth at low concentrations; inhibit root growth at high concentrations; promote xylem differentiation and inhibit phloem differentiation; promote seed germination and pollen tube elongation.
Abscisic acid (ABA)	Almost all plant cells have the ability to synthesize abscisic acid, and its presence has been detected in every major organ and living tissue; may be transported in the phloem or xylem.	Inhibits growth; promotes stomatal closure during drought stress; promotes seed dormancy and inhibits early germination; promotes leaf senescence; promotes desiccation tolerance.
Ethylene	This gaseous hormone can be produced by almost all parts of the plant. It is produced in high concentrations during senescence, leaf abscission, and the ripening of some types of fruits. Synthesis is also stimulated by wounding and stress.	Promotes ripening of many types of fruit, leaf abscission, and the triple response in seedlings (inhibition of stem elongation, promotion of lateral expansion, and horizontal growth); enhances the rate of senescence; promotes root and root hair formation; promotes flowering in the pineapple family.

functions in flowering plants. The natural auxin in plants is indoleacetic acid, or IAA, but several other compounds, including some synthetic ones, have auxin activity. Throughout this chapter, however, the term *auxin* is used specifically to refer to IAA. Although IAA was the first plant hormone to be discovered, much remains to be learned about auxin signal transduction and the regulation of auxin biosynthesis.

Auxin is transported down the stem from the shoot apex at a speed of about 10 mm/hr, much too fast for diffusion, although slower than translocation in phloem. Auxin seems to be transported directly through parenchyma tissue, from one cell to the next. In the shoot, it moves only from tip to base, not in the reverse direction. This unidirectional transport of auxin is called polar transport. Polar transport has nothing to do with gravity; experiments have shown that auxin travels upward when a stem or coleoptile segment is placed upside down. Rather, the polarity of auxin movement is attributable to the polar distribution of auxin transport protein in the cells. Concentrated at the basal end of a cell, the auxin transporters move the hormone out of the cell. The auxin can then enter the apical end of the neighboring cell (**Figure 39.7**). Auxin has a variety of effects, including stimulating cell elongation and lateral root formation.

The Role of Auxin in Cell Elongation

Although auxin affects several aspects of plant development, one of its chief functions is to stimulate elongation of cells within young developing shoots. The apical meristem of a shoot is a major site of auxin synthesis. As auxin from the shoot apex moves down to the region of cell elongation (see Figure 35.16), the hormone stimulates cell growth, probably by binding to a receptor in the plasma membrane. Auxin stimulates growth only over a certain concentration range, from about 10^{-8} to 10^{-4} M. At higher concentrations, auxin may inhibit cell elongation, probably by inducing production of ethylene, a hormone that generally inhibits elongation. We will return to this hormonal interaction when we discuss ethylene.

According to a model called the *acid growth hypothesis*, proton pumps play a major role in the growth response of cells to auxin. In a shoot's region of elongation, auxin stimulates the plasma membrane's proton (H^+) pumps. This pumping of H^+ increases the voltage across the membrane (membrane potential) and lowers the pH in the cell wall within minutes (**Figure 39.8**). Acidification of the wall activates enzymes called **expansins** that break the cross-links (hydrogen bonds) between cellulose microfibrils and other cell wall constituents, loosening the wall's fabric. (Expansins can even weaken the integrity of filter paper made of pure cellulose.) Increasing the membrane potential enhances ion uptake into the cell, which causes osmotic uptake of water and increased turgor. Increased turgor and increased cell wall plasticity enable the cell to elongate.

Auxin also rapidly alters gene expression, causing cells in the region of elongation to produce new proteins within min-

utes. Some of these proteins are short-lived transcription factors that repress or activate the expression of other genes. For sustained growth after this initial spurt, cells must make more cytoplasm and wall material. Auxin also stimulates this sustained growth response.

Lateral and Adventitious Root Formation

Auxins are used commercially in the vegetative propagation of plants by cuttings. Treating a detached leaf or stem with rooting powder containing auxin often causes adventitious roots to form near the cut surface. Auxin is also involved in the branching of roots. Researchers found that an *Arabidopsis* mutant that exhibits extreme proliferation of lateral roots has an auxin concentration 17-fold higher than normal.

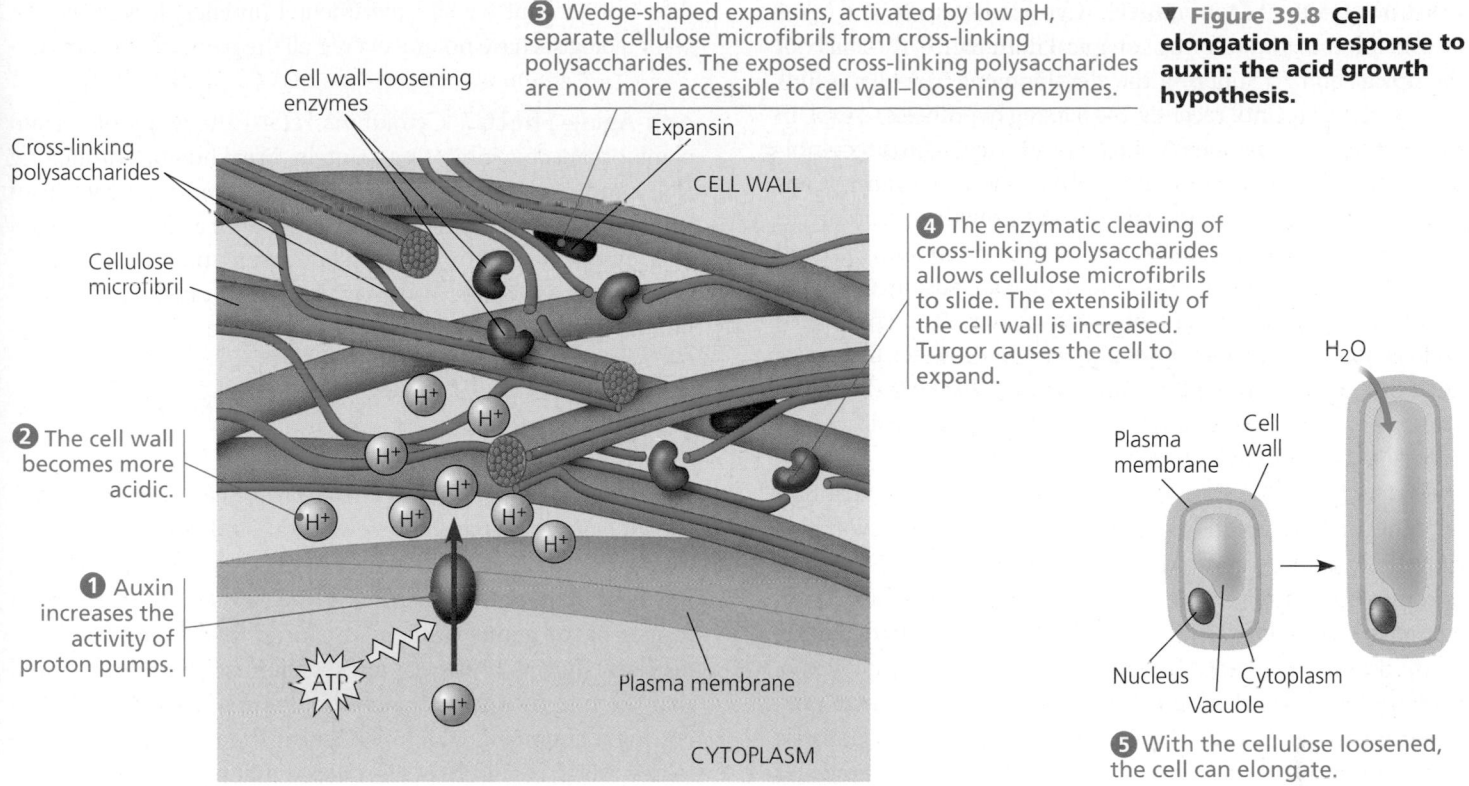

③ Wedge-shaped expansins, activated by low pH, separate cellulose microfibrils from cross-linking polysaccharides. The exposed cross-linking polysaccharides are now more accessible to cell wall–loosening enzymes.

Cell wall–loosening enzymes

Expansin

Cross-linking polysaccharides

Cellulose microfibril

CELL WALL

④ The enzymatic cleaving of cross-linking polysaccharides allows cellulose microfibrils to slide. The extensibility of the cell wall is increased. Turgor causes the cell to expand.

② The cell wall becomes more acidic.

① Auxin increases the activity of proton pumps.

ATP

H^+

Plasma membrane

CYTOPLASM

H_2O

Plasma membrane

Cell wall

Nucleus

Cytoplasm

Vacuole

⑤ With the cellulose loosened, the cell can elongate.

▼ **Figure 39.8 Cell elongation in response to auxin: the acid growth hypothesis.**

Auxins as Herbicides   Certain synthetic auxins, including 2,4-dichlorophenoxyacteic acid (2,4-D), are widely used as herbicides. Monocots, such as maize and turfgrass, can rapidly inactivate such synthetic auxins. However, eudicots cannot and therefore die from hormonal overdose. Spraying cereal fields or turf with 2,4-D eliminates eudicot (broadleaf) weeds.

Other Effects of Auxin   In addition to stimulating cell elongation during primary growth, auxin affects secondary growth by increasing cambial activity and influencing the differentiation of cambial initials (see Figure 35.20).

Developing seeds produce auxin, which promotes fruit growth. In greenhouses, seed production is often poor because of the lack of insect pollinators, resulting in poorly developed tomato fruits. However, spraying synthetic auxins on greenhouse-grown tomato vines induces normal fruit development without pollination, making the greenhouse-cultivated tomato fruits commercially viable.

Cytokinins

Trial-and-error attempts to find chemical additives that would enhance the growth and development of plant cells in tissue culture led to the discovery of **cytokinins**. In the 1940s, Johannes van Overbeek, working at the Cold Spring Harbor Laboratory in New York, found he could stimulate the growth of plant embryos by adding coconut milk, the liquid endosperm of a coconut's giant seed, to his culture medium. A decade later, Folke Skoog and Carlos O. Miller, at the University of Wisconsin,

Madison, induced cultured tobacco cells to divide by adding degraded DNA samples. The active ingredients of both experimental additives turned out to be modified forms of adenine, a component of nucleic acids. These growth regulators were named cytokinins because they stimulate cytokinesis, or cell division. The most common natural cytokinin is zeatin, so named because it was discovered first in maize (*Zea mays*). Although much remains to be learned about cytokinin synthesis and signal transduction, the effects of cytokinins on cell division and differentiation, apical dominance, and aging are well documented.

Control of Cell Division and Differentiation   Cytokinins are produced in actively growing tissues, particularly in roots, embryos, and fruits. Cytokinins produced in roots reach their target tissues by moving up the plant in the xylem sap. Acting in concert with auxin, cytokinins stimulate cell division and influence the pathway of differentiation. The effects of cytokinins on cells growing in tissue culture provide clues about how this class of hormones may function in an intact plant. When a piece of parenchyma tissue from a stem is cultured in the absence of cytokinins, the cells grow very large but do not divide. But if cytokinins are added along with auxin, the cells divide. Cytokinins alone have no effect. The ratio of cytokinins to auxin controls cell differentiation. When the concentrations of these two hormones are at certain levels, the mass of cells continues to grow, but it remains a cluster of undifferentiated cells called a callus (see Figure 38.14). If cytokinin levels increase, shoot buds develop from the callus. If auxin levels increase, roots form.

Control of Apical Dominance Cytokinins, auxin, and other factors interact in the control of apical dominance, the ability of the apical bud to suppress the development of axillary buds **(Figure 39.9a)**. Until recently, the leading hypothesis to explain the hormonal regulation of apical dominance—the direct inhibition hypothesis—proposed that auxin and cytokinins act antagonistically in regulating axillary bud growth. According to this view, auxin transported down the shoot from the apical bud directly inhibits axillary buds from growing, causing a shoot to lengthen at the expense of lateral branching. Meanwhile, cytokinins entering the shoot system from roots counter the action of auxin by signaling axillary buds to begin growing. Thus, the ratio of auxin and cytokinins was viewed as the critical factor in controlling axillary bud inhibition.

Many observations are consistent with the direct inhibition hypothesis. If the apical bud, the primary source of auxin, is removed, the inhibition of axillary buds is removed and the plant becomes bushier **(Figure 39.9b)**. Applying auxin to the cut surface of the decapitated shoot resuppresses the growth of the lateral buds **(Figure 39.9c)**. Mutants that overproduce cytokinins or plants treated with cytokinins also tend to be bushier than normal. However, one prediction of the direct inhibition hypothesis *not* supported by experiment is that decapitation, by removing the primary source of auxin, should lead to a decrease in the auxin levels of axillary buds. Biochemical studies have in fact revealed the opposite: Auxin levels actually *increase* in the axillary buds of decapitated plants. The direct inhibition hypothesis, therefore, does not account for all experimental findings. It is likely that plant biologists have not uncovered all the pieces of this puzzle.

Anti-Aging Effects Cytokinins retard the aging of certain plant organs by inhibiting protein breakdown, stimulating RNA and protein synthesis, and mobilizing nutrients from surrounding tissues. If leaves removed from a plant are dipped in a cytokinin solution, they stay green much longer than otherwise. Cytokinins also slow the deterioration of leaves on intact plants. Because of this anti-aging effect, florists use cytokinin sprays to keep cut flowers fresh.

Gibberellins

In the early 1900s, farmers in Asia noticed that some rice seedlings in their paddies grew so tall and spindly that they toppled over before they could mature and flower. In 1926, Japanese plant pathologist Ewiti Kurosawa discovered that a fungus of the genus *Gibberella* caused this "foolish seedling disease." By the 1930s, Japanese scientists had determined that the fungus caused hyperelongation of rice stems by secreting a chemical, which was given the name **gibberellin**. In the 1950s, researchers discovered that plants also produce gibberellins (GAs). Since that time, scientists have identified more than 100 different gibberellins that occur naturally in plants, although a much smaller number occur in each plant species. "Foolish rice" seedlings, it seems, suffer from an overdose of gibberellins normally found in plants in lower concentrations. Gibberellins have a variety of effects, such as stem elongation, fruit growth, and seed germination.

Stem Elongation The major sites of gibberellin production are roots and young leaves. Gibberellins stimulate stem and leaf growth but have little effect on roots. In stems, they stimulate cell elongation *and* cell division. One hypothesis proposes that they activate enzymes that loosen cell walls, facilitating entry of expansin proteins. Thus, gibberellins act in concert with auxin to promote stem elongation.

The effects of gibberellins in enhancing stem elongation are evident when certain dwarf (mutant) varieties of plants are treated with gibberellins. For instance, some dwarf pea plants (including the variety Mendel studied; see Chapter 14) grow tall if treated with gibberellins. But there is often no response if the gibberellins are applied to wild-type plants. Apparently, these plants already produce

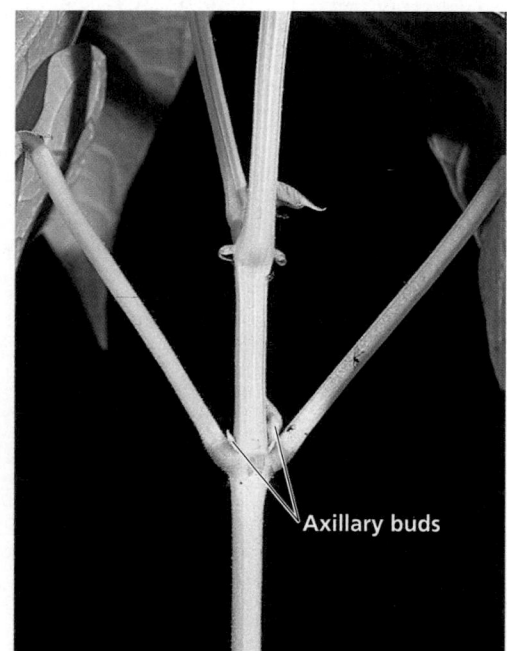

(a) Apical bud intact (not shown in photo)

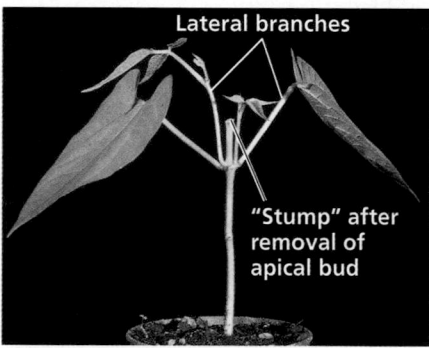

Lateral branches

"Stump" after removal of apical bud

(b) Apical bud removed

(c) Auxin added to decapitated stem

Axillary buds

▲ **Figure 39.9 Apical dominance. (a)** The inhibition of growth of axillary buds, possibly influenced by auxin from the apical bud, favors elongation of the shoot's main axis. **(b)** Removal of the apical bud from the same plant enables lateral branches to grow. **(c)** Applying a gelatin capsule containing auxin to the stump prevents the lateral branches from growing.

an optimal dose of the hormone. The most dramatic example of gibberellin-induced stem elongation is *bolting*, rapid growth of the floral stalk (**Figure 39.10a**).

Fruit Growth   In many plants, both auxin and gibberellins must be present in order for fruit to develop. The most important commercial application of gibberellins is in the spray-ing of Thompson seedless grapes (**Figure 39.10b**). The hormone makes the individual grapes grow larger, a trait valued by the consumer. The gibberellin sprays also make the internodes of the grape bunch elongate, allowing more space for the individual grapes. By enhancing air circulation between the grapes, this increase in space also makes it harder for yeasts and other microorganisms to infect the fruits.

Germination   The embryo of a seed is a rich source of gibberellins. After water is imbibed, the release of gibberellins from the embryo signals the seed to break dormancy and germinate. Some seeds that require particular environmental conditions to germinate, such as exposure to light or low temperatures, break dormancy if they are treated with gibberellins. Gibberellins support the growth of cereal seedlings by stimulating the synthesis of digestive enzymes such as α-amylase that mobilize stored nutrients (**Figure 39.11**).

Brassinosteroids

Brassinosteroids are steroids and therefore chemically similar to cholesterol and the sex hormones of animals. They induce cell elongation and division in stem segments and seedlings at concentrations as low as 10^{-12} *M*. They also retard leaf abscission (leaf drop) and promote xylem differentiation. These effects are so qualitatively similar to those of auxin that it took several years for plant physiologists to determine that brassinosteroids were not types of auxins.

Evidence from molecular biology established brassinosteroids as plant hormones. Joanne Chory and colleagues at the Salk Institute in San Diego were interested in mutant *Arabidopsis* with morphological features similar to those of light-grown plants, even though the mutants were grown in the dark. The researchers discovered that the mutation affects a gene that normally codes for an enzyme similar to one involved in steroid synthesis in mammals. They also found that this brassinosteroid-deficient mutant could be restored to the wild-type phenotype by applying brassinosteroids in the lab.

Abscisic Acid

In the 1960s, one research group studying the chemical changes that precede bud dormancy and leaf abscission in deciduous trees and another team investigating chemical changes preceding abscission of cotton fruits isolated the same compound, **abscisic acid (ABA)**.

(b) The Thompson seedless grape bunch on the left is from an untreated control vine. The bunch on the right is growing from a vine that was sprayed with gibberellin during fruit development.

(a) Some plants develop in a rosette form, low to the ground with very short internodes, as in the *Arabidopsis* plant shown at the left. As the plant switches to reproductive growth, a surge of gibberellins induces bolting: Internodes elongate rapidly, elevating floral buds that develop at stem tips (right).

◀ **Figure 39.10 Effects of gibberellins on stem elongation and fruit growth.**

❶ After a seed imbibes water, the embryo releases gibberellin (GA), which sends a signal to the aleurone, the thin outer layer of the endosperm.

❷ The aleurone responds to GA by synthesizing and secreting digestive enzymes that hydrolyze nutrients stored in the endosperm. One example is α-amylase, which hydrolyzes starch.

❸ Sugars and other nutrients absorbed from the endosperm by the scutellum (cotyledon) are consumed during growth of the embryo into a seedling.

Aleurone
Endosperm
GA
GA
Water
Scutellum (cotyledon)
α-amylase
Radicle
Sugar

▲ **Figure 39.11 Mobilization of nutrients by gibberellins during the germination of grain seeds such as barley.**

Ironically, ABA is no longer thought to play a primary role in bud dormancy or leaf abscission, but it is very important in other functions. Unlike the growth-stimulating hormones we have studied so far—auxin, cytokinins, gibberellins, and brassinosteroids—ABA *slows* growth. ABA often antagonizes the actions of growth hormones, and the ratio of ABA to one or more growth hormones determines the final physiological outcome. We will consider here two of ABA's many effects: seed dormancy and drought tolerance.

Seed Dormancy Seed dormancy increases the likelihood that seeds will germinate only when there are sufficient amounts of light, temperature, and moisture for the seedlings to survive (see Chapter 38). What prevents seeds dispersed in autumn from germinating immediately, only to die in the winter? What mechanisms ensure that such seeds do not germinate until spring? For that matter, what prevents seeds from germinating in the dark, moist interior of the fruit? The answer to these questions is ABA. The levels of ABA may increase 100-fold during seed maturation. The high levels of ABA in maturing seeds inhibit germination and induce the production of certain proteins that help the seeds withstand the extreme dehydration that accompanies maturation.

Many types of dormant seeds germinate when ABA is removed or inactivated. The seeds of some desert plants break dormancy only when heavy rains wash ABA out of them. Other seeds require light or prolonged exposure to cold to inactivate ABA. Often, the ratio of ABA to gibberellins determines whether the seed remains dormant or germinates, and adding ABA to seeds that are primed to germinate makes them dormant again. Inactivated ABA or low levels of ABA can lead to precocious (early) germination **(Figure 39.12)**. For example, a maize mutant with grains that germinate while still on the cob lacks a functional transcription factor required for ABA to induce expression of certain genes. Precocious germination of red mangrove seeds, due to low ABA levels, is actually an adaptation that helps the young seedlings to plant themselves in the soft mud below the parent tree.

Drought Tolerance ABA is the primary internal signaling molecule that enables plants to withstand drought. When a plant begins to wilt, ABA accumulates in leaves and causes stomata to close rapidly, reducing transpiration and preventing further water loss. By affecting second messengers such as calcium, ABA causes potassium channels in the plasma membrane of guard cells to open, leading to a massive loss of potassium ions from the cells. The accompanying osmotic loss of water reduces guard cell turgor and leads to closing of the stomatal pores (see Figure 36.17). In some cases, water shortage stresses the root system before the shoot system, and ABA transported from roots to leaves may function as an "early warning system." Many mutants that are especially prone to wilting are deficient in ABA production.

◀ Red mangrove (*Rhizophora mangle*) seeds produce only low levels of ABA, and their seeds germinate while still on the tree. In this case, early germination is a useful adaptation. When released, the radicle of the dart-like seedling deeply penetrates the soft mudflats in which the mangroves grow.

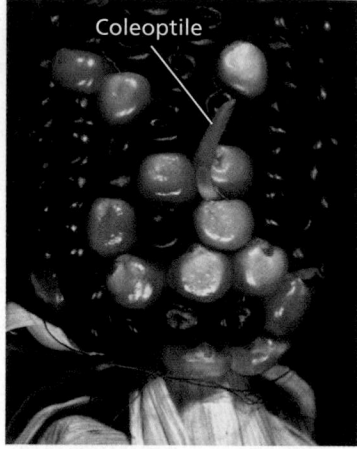

Coleoptile

▲ Precocious germination in this maize mutant is caused by lack of a functional transcription factor required for ABA action.

▲ **Figure 39.12 Precocious germination of wild-type mangrove and mutant maize seeds.**

Ethylene

During the 1800s, when coal gas was used as fuel for streetlights, leakage from gas pipes caused nearby trees to drop leaves prematurely. In 1901, the Russian scientist Dimitry Neljubow demonstrated that the gas **ethylene** was the active factor in the coal gas. The idea that ethylene is a plant hormone was not widely accepted, however, until the advent of gas chromatography simplified identification.

Plants produce ethylene in response to stresses such as drought, flooding, mechanical pressure, injury, and infection. Ethylene is also produced during fruit ripening and programmed cell death and in response to high concentrations of externally applied auxin. Indeed, many effects previously ascribed to auxin, such as inhibition of root elongation, may be due to auxin-induced ethylene production. We will focus here on four of ethylene's many effects: response to mechanical stress, senescence, leaf abscission, and fruit ripening.

The Triple Response to Mechanical Stress Imagine a pea seedling pushing upward through the soil, only to come up against a stone. As it pushes against the obstacle, the stress in its delicate tip induces the seedling to produce ethylene. The hormone then instigates a growth maneuver known as the **triple response** that enables the shoot to avoid the obstacle. The three parts of this response are a slowing of stem elongation, a thickening of the stem (which makes it stronger), and a curvature that causes the stem to start growing horizontally. As the effects of the initial ethylene pulse lessen, the stem resumes vertical growth. If it again contacts a barrier, another burst of ethylene is released, and horizontal growth resumes. However, if the upward touch detects no solid object, then ethylene production decreases, and the stem, now clear of the obstacle, resumes its normal upward growth. It is ethylene that induces the stem to grow horizontally rather than the physical obstruction itself; when ethylene is applied to normal seedlings growing free of physical impediments, they still undergo the triple response (Figure 39.13).

Studies of *Arabidopsis* mutants with abnormal triple responses are an example of how biologists identify a signal transduction pathway. Scientists isolated ethylene-insensitive (*ein*) mutants, which fail to undergo the triple response after exposure to ethylene (Figure 39.14a). Some types of *ein* mutants are insensitive to ethylene because they lack a functional ethylene receptor. Mutants of a different sort undergo the triple response even out of soil, in the air, where there are no physical obstacles. Some of these mutants have a regulatory defect that causes them to produce ethylene at rates 20 times normal. The phenotype of such ethylene-overproducing (*eto*) mutants can be restored to wild-type by treating the seedlings with inhibitors of ethylene synthesis. Other mutants, called constitutive triple-response (*ctr*) mutants, undergo the triple response in air but do not respond to inhibitors of ethylene synthesis (Figure 39.14b). (Constitutive genes are genes that are continually expressed in all cells of an organism.) In *ctr* mutants, ethylene signal transduction is permanently turned on, even though ethylene is not present.

The affected gene in *ctr* mutants codes for a protein kinase. The fact that this mutation *activates* the ethylene response suggests that the normal kinase product of the wild-type allele is a *negative* regulator of ethylene signal transduction. Here is one hypothesis for how the pathway works in wild-type plants: Binding of the hormone ethylene to the ethylene receptor leads to inactivation of the kinase; and inactivation of this negative regulator allows synthesis of the proteins required for the triple response.

Senescence Consider the shedding of a leaf in autumn or the death of an annual after flowering. Or think about the final step in differentiation of a vessel element, when its living contents are destroyed, leaving a hollow tube behind. Such events involve **senescence**—the programmed death of certain cells or organs or the entire plant. Cells, organs, and plants genetically programmed to die on a schedule do not simply shut down cellular machinery and await death. Instead, at the molecular level, the onset of programmed cell death, called **apoptosis**, is a very busy time in a cell's life, requiring new gene expression (see Figure 11.19). During apoptosis, newly formed enzymes break down many chemical components, including chlorophyll, DNA, RNA, proteins, and membrane

▲ Figure 39.13 **The ethylene-induced triple response.** In response to ethylene, a gaseous plant hormone, germinating pea seedlings grown in the dark undergo the triple response—slowing of stem elongation, stem thickening, and horizontal stem growth. The response is greater with increased ethylene concentration.

Ethylene concentration (parts per million)

0.00   0.10   0.20   0.40   0.80

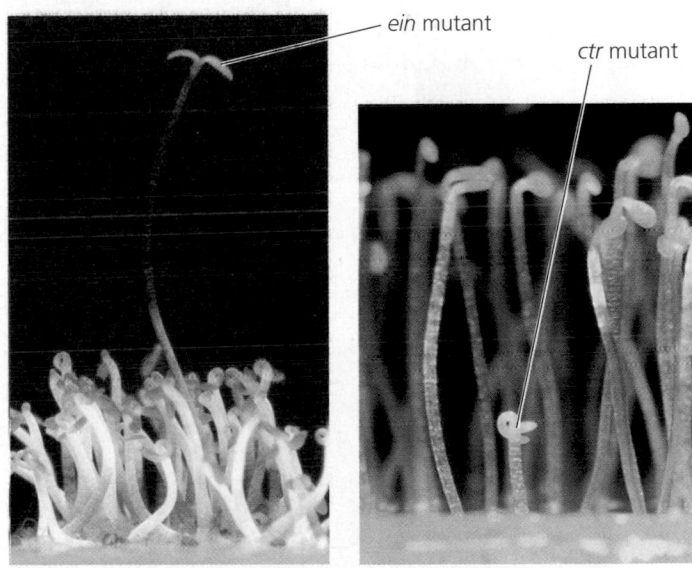

ein mutant

ctr mutant

(a) *ein* **mutant.** An ethylene-insensitive (*ein*) mutant fails to undergo the triple response in the presence of ethylene.

(b) *ctr* **mutant.** A constitutive triple-response (*ctr*) mutant undergoes the triple response even in the absence of ethylene.

▲ Figure 39.14 **Ethylene triple-response *Arabidopsis* mutants.**

lipids. The plant salvages many of the breakdown products. A burst of ethylene is almost always associated with the programmed destruction of cells, organs, or the whole plant.

Leaf Abscission The loss of leaves from deciduous trees helps prevent desiccation during seasonal periods of climatic stress that severely limit the availability of water to the roots. Before dying leaves abscise, many essential elements are salvaged from them and stored in stem parenchyma cells. These nutrients are recycled back to developing leaves the following spring. Autumn leaf color is due to newly made red pigments as well as yellow and orange carotenoids (see Chapter 10) that were already present in the leaf and are rendered visible by the breakdown of the dark green chlorophyll in autumn.

When an autumn leaf falls, the breaking point is an abscission layer that develops near the base of the petiole (Figure 39.15). The small parenchyma cells of this layer have very thin walls, and there are no fiber cells around the vascular tissue. The abscission layer is further weakened when enzymes hydrolyze polysaccharides in the cell walls. Finally, the weight of the leaf, with the help of wind, causes a separation within the abscission layer. Even before the leaf falls, a layer of cork forms a protective scar on the twig side of the abscission layer, preventing pathogens from invading the plant.

A change in the ratio of ethylene to auxin controls abscission. An aging leaf produces less and less auxin, rendering the cells of the abscission layer more sensitive to ethylene. As the influence of ethylene on the abscission layer prevails, the cells produce enzymes that digest the cellulose and other components of cell walls.

0.5 mm

Protective layer   Abscission layer

Stem   Petiole

▲ **Figure 39.15 Abscission of a maple leaf.** Abscission is controlled by a change in the ratio of ethylene to auxin. The abscission layer is seen in this longitudinal section as a vertical band at the base of the petiole. After the leaf falls, a protective layer of cork becomes the leaf scar that helps prevent pathogens from invading the plant (LM).

Fruit Ripening Immature fleshy fruits are generally tart, hard, and green—features that help protect the developing seeds from herbivores. After ripening, the mature fruits help *attract* animals that disperse the seeds (see Figures 30.8 and 30.9). In many cases, a burst of ethylene production in the fruit triggers the ripening process. The enzymatic breakdown of cell wall components softens the fruit, and the conversion of starches and acids to sugars makes the fruit sweet. The production of new scents and colors helps advertise ripeness to animals, which eat the fruits and disperse the seeds.

A chain reaction occurs during ripening: Ethylene triggers ripening, and ripening triggers more ethylene production—a rare example of positive feedback in physiology (see Figure 1.13). The result is a huge burst in ethylene production. Because ethylene is a gas, the signal to ripen spreads from fruit to fruit. If you pick or buy green fruit, you may be able to speed ripening by storing the fruit in a paper bag, allowing ethylene to accumulate. On a commercial scale, many kinds of fruits are ripened in huge storage containers in which ethylene levels are enhanced. In other cases, fruit producers take measures to slow ripening caused by natural ethylene. Apples, for instance, are stored in bins flushed with carbon dioxide. Circulating the air prevents ethylene from accumulating, and carbon dioxide inhibits synthesis of new ethylene. Stored in this way, apples picked in autumn can still be shipped to grocery stores the following summer.

Given the importance of ethylene in the postharvest physiology of fruits, the genetic engineering of ethylene signal transduction pathways has potential commercial applications. For example, by engineering a way to block the transcription of one of the genes required for ethylene synthesis, molecular biologists have created tomato fruits that ripen on demand. These fruits are picked while green and will not ripen unless ethylene gas is added. As such methods are refined, they will reduce spoilage of fruits and vegetables, a problem that ruins almost half the produce harvested in the United States.

Systems Biology and Hormone Interactions

As we have discussed, plant responses often involve the interactions of many hormones and their signal transduction pathways. The study of hormone interactions can be a complex problem. For example, flooding of deepwater rice leads to a 50-fold increase in internal ethylene levels and rapid stem elongation. But ethylene's role in this response is a small part of the story. Flooding also leads to an increase in sensitivity to gibberellins that is mediated by a decrease in ABA levels. Thus, stem elongation results from an interaction of these three hormones and their signal transduction pathways.

Imagine yourself as a molecular biologist assigned the task of genetically engineering a deepwater rice plant so that it grows even faster when submerged. Would the best molecular target for genetic manipulation be an enzyme that inactivates ABA? An enzyme that produces more gibberellins? An ethylene receptor? It is difficult to predict. And this is by no means an unusual problem. Virtually every plant response discussed in this chapter is of comparable complexity. Because of this pervasive and unavoidable issue of complex interactions, many plant biologists are promoting a new, systems-based approach to plant biology.

Chapter 1 provided a general description of systems biology, which attempts to discover and understand biological properties that emerge from the interactions of many system elements (for example, mRNAs, proteins, hormones, and metabolites). Using genomic techniques, biologists can now identify all the genes in a plant. As of early 2008, the genomes of several plant species have been sequenced, including the research plant *Arabidopsis*, rice (*Oryza sativa*), a species of poplar (*Populus trichocarpa*), grape (*Vitus vinifera*), and maize (*Zea mays*). Moreover, using microarray and proteomic techniques (see Chapters 20 and 21), scientists can determine which genes are activated or inactivated during development or in response to an environmental change. However, simply identifying all the genes and proteins (system elements) in an organism is comparable to listing all the parts of an airplane. Although such a list provides a catalog of components, it is not sufficient for understanding the complexity underlying the integrated system. What plant biologists really need to know is how all these system elements interact.

A systems-based approach may greatly alter how plants are studied. One vision is laboratories equipped with high-throughput robotic scanners that record which genes in a plant's genome are activated in which cells and under what conditions. New hypotheses and avenues of research will emerge from analysis of these comprehensive data sets. Ultimately, one goal of systems biology is to model an entire living plant. Armed with such detailed knowledge, a biologist attempting to genetically engineer faster stem elongation in rice could proceed much more efficiently. The ability to model a living plant could make it possible to predict the result of a genetic manipulation before setting foot in the laboratory.

CONCEPT CHECK 39.2

1. Suggest a physiological reason for the old adage "One bad apple spoils the bunch."
2. Suggest a reason why cut flowers such as carnations are often treated with cytokinins prior to shipping.
3. Fusicoccin is a fungal toxin that stimulates the plasma membrane H^+ pumps of plant cells. How may it affect the growth of isolated stem sections?
4. **WHAT IF?** If a plant has the double mutation *ctr* and *ein*, what would be its triple-response phenotype? Explain your answer.

For suggested answers, see Appendix A.

CONCEPT 39.3
Responses to light are critical for plant success

Light is an especially important environmental factor in the lives of plants. In addition to being required for photosynthesis, light cues many key events in plant growth and development. Effects of light on plant morphology are what plant biologists call **photomorphogenesis**. Light reception also allows plants to measure the passage of days and seasons.

Plants can detect not only the presence of light but also its direction, intensity, and wavelength (color). A graph called an **action spectrum** depicts the relative effectiveness of different wavelengths of radiation in driving a particular process. For example, the action spectrum for photosynthesis has two peaks, one in red light and one in blue light (see Figure 10.9b). This is because chlorophyll absorbs light primarily in the red and blue portions of the visible spectrum. Action spectra are useful in studying *any* process that depends on light, such as phototropism **(Figure 39.16)**. By

(a) This action spectrum illustrates that only light wavelengths below 500 nm (blue and violet light) induce curvature.

(b) These photographs of coleoptiles were taken before and after 90-minute exposures to light sources of the colors indicated.

▲ **Figure 39.16 Action spectrum for blue-light-stimulated phototropism in maize coleoptiles.** Phototropic bending toward light is controlled by phototropin, a photoreceptor sensitive to blue and violet light, particularly blue light.

comparing action spectra of various plant responses, researchers determine which responses are mediated by the same photoreceptor (pigment). They also compare action spectra with absorption spectra of pigments; a close correspondence for a given pigment suggests that the pigment is the photoreceptor mediating the response. Action spectra reveal that red and blue light are the most important colors in regulating a plant's photomorphogenesis. These observations led researchers to two major classes of light receptors: **blue-light photoreceptors** and **phytochromes**, photoreceptors that absorb mostly red light.

Blue-Light Photoreceptors

Blue light initiates a variety of responses in plants, including phototropism, the light-induced opening of stomata (see Figure 36.16), and the light-induced slowing of hypocotyl elongation that occurs when a seedling breaks ground. The biochemical identity of the blue-light photoreceptor was so elusive that in the 1970s, plant physiologists began to call this putative receptor "cryptochrome" (from the Greek *kryptos*, hidden, and *chrom*, pigment). In the 1990s, molecular biologists analyzing *Arabidopsis* mutants found that plants use at least three different types of pigments to detect blue light. *Cryptochromes*, molecular relatives of DNA repair enzymes, are involved in the blue-light-induced inhibition of stem elongation that occurs, for example, when a seedling first emerges from the soil. *Phototropin* is a protein kinase involved in mediating phototropic curvatures, such as those studied in grass seedlings by the Darwins, and in chloroplast movements in response to light. There is currently much debate about whether phototropin or a carotenoid-based photoreceptor called *zeaxanthin* is the major blue-light photoreceptor involved in blue-light-mediated stomatal opening.

Phytochromes as Photoreceptors

When introducing signal transduction in plants earlier in the chapter, we discussed the role of the plant pigments called phytochromes in the de-etiolation process. Phytochromes regulate many plant responses to light. Let's look at two more examples: seed germination and shade avoidance.

Phytochromes and Seed Germination

Studies of seed germination led to the discovery of phytochromes. Because of limited nutrient reserves, many types of seeds, especially small ones, germinate only when the light environment and other conditions are near optimal. Such seeds often remain dormant for many years until light conditions change. For example, the death of a shading tree or the plowing of a field may create a favorable light environment.

In the 1930s, scientists at the U.S. Department of Agriculture determined the action spectrum for light-induced germination of lettuce seeds. They exposed water-swollen seeds to a few minutes of monochromatic (single-colored) light of various

▼ **Figure 39.17** Inquiry

How does the order of red and far-red illumination affect seed germination?

EXPERIMENT Scientists at the U.S. Department of Agriculture briefly exposed batches of lettuce seeds to red light or far-red light to test the effects on germination. After the light exposure, the seeds were placed in the dark, and the results were compared with control seeds that were not exposed to light.

RESULTS The bar below each photo indicates the sequence of red light exposure, far-red light exposure, and darkness. The germination rate increased greatly in groups of seeds that were last exposed to red light (left). Germination was inhibited in groups of seeds that were last exposed to far-red light (right).

Dark (control)

Red | Dark

Red | Far-red | Dark

Red | Far-red | Red | Dark

Red | Far-red | Red | Far-red

CONCLUSION Red light stimulated germination, and far-red light inhibited germination. The final light exposure was the determining factor. The effects of red and far-red light were reversible.

SOURCE H. Borthwick et al., A reversible photoreaction controlling seed germination, *Proceedings of the National Academy of Sciences, USA* 38:662–666 (1952).

WHAT IF? Phytochrome responds faster to red light than to far-red. If the seeds had been placed in white light instead of the dark after their red and far-red light treatments, would the results have been different?

wavelengths and then stored the seeds in the dark. After two days, the researchers counted the number of seeds that had germinated under each light regimen. They found that red light of wavelength 660 nm increased the germination percentage of lettuce seeds maximally, whereas far-red light—that is, light of wavelengths near the upper edge of human visibility (730 nm)—*inhibited* germination compared with dark controls (**Figure 39.17**). What happens when the lettuce seeds are subjected to a flash of red

Two identical subunits. Each subunit has two domains.

Chromophore

Photoreceptor activity. In each subunit, one domain, which functions as the photoreceptor, is covalently bonded to a nonprotein pigment, or chromophore.

Kinase activity. The other domain has protein kinase activity. The photoreceptor domains interact with the kinase domains, linking light reception to cellular responses triggered by the kinase.

▲ **Figure 39.18 Structure of a phytochrome.**

light followed by a flash of far-red light or, conversely, to far-red light followed by red light? The *last* flash of light determines the seeds' response. In other words, the effects of red and far-red light are reversible.

The photoreceptors responsible for the opposing effects of red and far-red light are phytochromes. A phytochrome has two identical subunits, each consisting of a polypeptide component covalently bonded to a nonpolypeptide *chromophore*, the light-absorbing part of the subunit (**Figure 39.18**). So far, researchers have identified five phytochromes in *Arabidopsis*, each with a slightly different polypeptide component.

The chromophore of a phytochrome is photoreversible, reverting back and forth between two isomeric forms, depending on the color of light provided (see Figure 4.7 to review isomers). In its P_r isomer form, a phytochrome absorbs red (r) light maximally, whereas in its P_{fr} isomer form, it absorbs far-red (fr) light:

Red light

$$P_r \rightleftharpoons P_{fr}$$

Far-red light

▶ **Figure 39.19 Phytochrome: a molecular switching mechanism.** Absorption of red light causes the P_r to change to the P_{fr}. Far-red light reverses this conversion. In most cases, it is the P_{fr} form of the pigment that switches on physiological and developmental responses in the plant.

This $P_r \rightleftharpoons P_{fr}$ interconversion is a switching mechanism that controls various light-induced events in the life of the plant (**Figure 39.19**). P_{fr} is the form of phytochrome that triggers many of a plant's developmental responses to light. For example, P_r in lettuce seeds exposed to red light is converted to P_{fr}, stimulating the cellular responses that lead to germination. When red-illuminated seeds are then exposed to far-red light, the P_{fr} is converted back to P_r, inhibiting the germination response.

How does phytochrome switching explain light-induced germination in nature? Plants synthesize phytochrome as P_r, and if seeds are kept in the dark, the pigment remains almost entirely in the P_r form (see Figure 39.19). Sunlight contains both red light and far-red light, but the conversion to P_{fr} is faster than the conversion to P_r. Therefore, the ratio of P_{fr} to P_r increases in the sunlight. When seeds are exposed to adequate sunlight, the production and accumulation of P_{fr} will trigger their germination.

Phytochromes and Shade Avoidance

The phytochrome system also provides the plant with information about the *quality* of light. Because sunlight includes both red and far-red radiation, during the day the $P_r \rightleftharpoons P_{fr}$ interconversion reaches a dynamic equilibrium, with the ratio of the two phytochrome forms indicating the relative amounts of red and far-red light. This sensing mechanism enables plants to adapt to changes in light conditions. Consider, for example, the "shade avoidance" response of a tree that requires relatively high light intensity. If other trees in a forest shade this tree, the phytochrome ratio shifts in favor of P_r because the forest canopy screens out more red light than far-red light. This is because the chlorophyll pigments in the leaves of the canopy absorb red light and allow far-red light to pass. The shift in the ratio of red to far-red light induces the tree to allocate more of its resources to growing taller. In contrast, direct sunlight increases the proportion of P_{fr}, which stimulates branching and inhibits vertical growth.

In addition to helping plants detect light, phytochrome helps a plant to keep track of the passage of days and seasons. To understand phytochrome's role in these timekeeping processes, we must first examine the nature of the plant's internal clock.

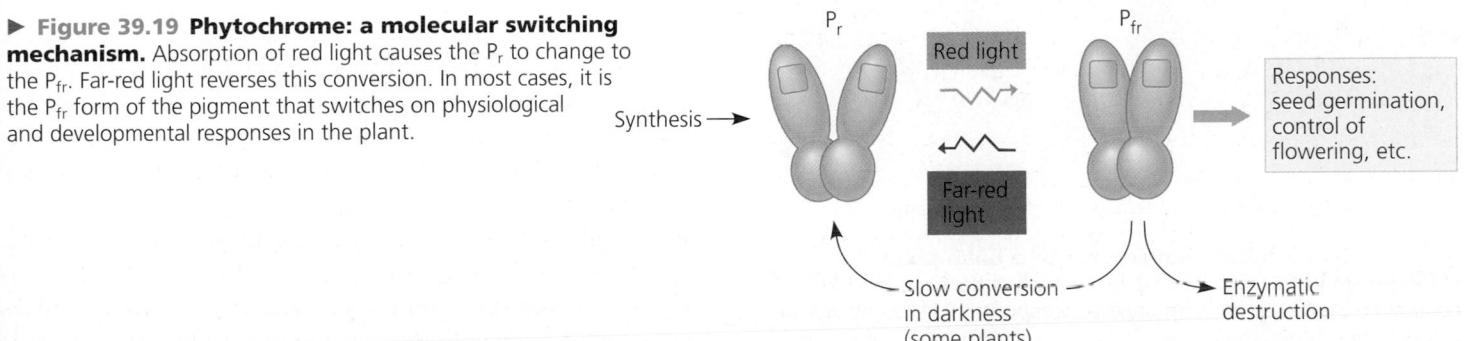

P_r P_{fr}

Red light

Synthesis →

Far-red light

Responses: seed germination, control of flowering, etc.

Slow conversion in darkness (some plants)

Enzymatic destruction

Biological Clocks and Circadian Rhythms

Many plant processes, such as transpiration and the synthesis of certain enzymes, oscillate during the course of a day. Some of these cyclic variations are responses to the changes in light levels, temperature, and relative humidity that accompany the 24-hour cycle of day and night. One can control these external factors by growing plants in growth chambers under rigidly maintained conditions of light, temperature, and humidity. But even under artificially constant conditions, many physiological processes in plants, such as the opening and closing of stomata and the production of photosynthetic enzymes, continue to oscillate with a frequency of about 24 hours. For example, many legumes lower their leaves in the evening and raise them in the morning (Figure 39.20). A bean plant continues these "sleep movements" even if kept in constant light or constant darkness; the leaves are not simply responding to sunrise and sunset. Such cycles, with a frequency of about 24 hours and not directly controlled by any known environmental variable, are called **circadian rhythms** (from the Latin *circa*, approximately, and *dies*, day), and they are common to all eukaryotic life. Your pulse rate, blood pressure, temperature, rate of cell division, blood cell count, alertness, urine composition, metabolic rate, sex drive, and response to medications all fluctuate in a circadian manner.

Current research indicates that the molecular "gears" of the circadian clock are internal, rather than a daily response to some subtle but pervasive environmental cycle, such as geomagnetism or cosmic radiation. Organisms, including plants and humans, continue their rhythms even when placed in deep mine shafts or when orbited in satellites, conditions that alter these subtle geophysical periodicities. However, daily signals from the environment can entrain (set) the circadian clock to a period of precisely 24 hours.

If an organism is kept in a constant environment, its circadian rhythms deviate from a 24-hour period (a period is the duration of one cycle). These free-running periods, as they are called, vary from about 21 to 27 hours, depending on the particular rhythmic response. The sleep movements of bean plants, for instance, have

a period of 26 hours when the plants are kept in the free-running condition of constant darkness. Deviation of the free-running period from exactly 24 hours does not mean that biological clocks drift erratically. Free-running clocks are still keeping perfect time, but they are not synchronized with the outside world.

How do biological clocks work? In attempting to answer this question, we must distinguish between the clock and the rhythmic processes it controls. For example, the leaves of the bean plant in Figure 39.20 are the clock's "hands" but are not the essence of the clock itself. If bean leaves are restrained for several hours and then released, they will reestablish the position appropriate for the time of day. We can interfere with a biological rhythm, but the underlying clockwork continues.

Researchers are tracing the clock to a molecular mechanism that may be common to all eukaryotes. A leading hypothesis is that biological timekeeping may depend on the synthesis of a protein that regulates its own production through feedback control. This protein may be a transcription factor that inhibits transcription of the gene that encodes the transcription factor itself. The concentration of this transcription factor may increase during the first half of the circadian cycle and then decline during the second half as a result of inhibiting its own production.

Researchers have recently used a novel technique to identify clock mutants of *Arabidopsis*. One prominent circadian rhythm in plants is the daily production of certain photosynthesis-related proteins. Molecular biologists traced the cause of this rhythm to the promoter that initiates the transcription of the genes for these photosynthesis proteins. To identify clock mutants, scientists spliced the gene for an enzyme responsible for the bioluminescence of fireflies, called luciferase, to the promoter. When the biological clock turned on the promoter in the *Arabidopsis* genome, it also turned on the production of luciferase. The plants began to glow with a circadian periodicity. Clock mutants were then isolated by selecting specimens that glowed for a longer or shorter time than normal. The genes altered in some of these mutants affect proteins that normally bind photoreceptors. Perhaps these particular mutations disrupt a light-dependent mechanism that sets the biological clock.

The Effect of Light on the Biological Clock

As we have discussed, the free-running period of the circadian rhythm of bean leaf movements is 26 hours. Consider a bean plant placed at dawn in a dark cabinet for 72 hours: Its leaves would not rise again until 2 hours after natural dawn on the second day, 4 hours after natural dawn on the third day, and so on. Shut off from environmental cues, the plant becomes desynchronized. Desynchronization happens to humans when we cross several time zones in an airplane; when we reach our destination, the clocks on the wall are not synchronized with our internal clocks. All eukaryotes are probably prone to jet lag.

Noon   Midnight

▲ Figure 39.20 **Sleep movements of a bean plant (*Phaseolus vulgaris*).** The movements are caused by reversible changes in the turgor pressure of cells on opposing sides of the pulvini, motor organs of the leaf.

The factor that entrains the biological clock to precisely 24 hours every day is light. Both phytochrome and blue-light photoreceptors can entrain circadian rhythms in plants, but our understanding of how phytochrome does this is more complete. The mechanism involves turning cellular responses on and off by means of the $P_r \rightleftharpoons P_{fr}$ switch.

Consider again the photoreversible system in Figure 39.19. In darkness, the phytochrome ratio shifts gradually in favor of the P_r form, partly as a result of turnover in the overall phytochrome pool. The pigment is synthesized in the P_r form, and enzymes destroy more P_{fr} than P_r. In some plant species, P_{fr} present at sundown slowly converts to P_r. In darkness, there is no means for the P_r to be reconverted to P_{fr}, but upon illumination, the P_{fr} level suddenly increases again as P_r is rapidly converted. This increase in P_{fr} each day at dawn resets the biological clock: Bean leaves reach their most extreme night position 16 hours after dawn.

In nature, interactions between phytochrome and the biological clock enable plants to measure the passage of night and day. The relative lengths of night and day, however, change over the course of the year (except at the equator). Plants use this change to adjust activities in synchrony with the seasons.

Photoperiodism and Responses to Seasons

Imagine the consequences if a plant produced flowers when pollinators were not present or if a deciduous tree produced leaves in the middle of winter. Seasonal events are of critical importance in the life cycles of most plants. Seed germination, flowering, and the onset and breaking of bud dormancy are all stages that usually occur at specific times of the year. The environmental stimulus that plants use most often to detect the time of year is the photoperiod, the relative lengths of night and day. A physiological response to photoperiod, such as flowering, is called **photoperiodism**.

Photoperiodism and Control of Flowering

An early clue to how plants detect seasons came from a mutant variety of tobacco, Maryland Mammoth, which grew tall but failed to flower during summer. It finally bloomed in a greenhouse in December. After trying to induce earlier flowering by varying temperature, moisture, and mineral nutrition, researchers learned that the shortening days of winter stimulated this variety to flower. If the plants were kept in light-tight boxes so that lamps could manipulate "day" and "night," flowering occurred only if the day length was 14 hours or shorter. It did not flower during summer because at Maryland's latitude, the summer days were too long.

The researchers called Maryland Mammoth a **short-day plant** because it apparently required a light period *shorter* than a critical length to flower. Chrysanthemums, poinsettias, and some soybean varieties are also short-day plants, which generally flower in late summer, fall, or winter. Another group

of plants flower only when the light period is *longer* than a certain number of hours. These **long-day plants** generally flower in late spring or early summer. Spinach, for example, flowers when days are 14 hours or longer. Radishes, lettuce, irises, and many cereal varieties are also long-day plants. **Day-neutral plants**, such as tomatoes, rice, and dandelions, are unaffected by photoperiod and flower when they reach a certain stage of maturity, regardless of day length.

Critical Night Length In the 1940s, researchers learned that flowering and other responses to photoperiod are actually controlled by night length, not day length. Many of these scientists worked with cocklebur (*Xanthium strumarium*), a short-day plant that flowers only when days are 16 hours or shorter (and nights are at least 8 hours long). These researchers found that if the daytime portion of the photoperiod is broken by a brief exposure to darkness, there is no effect on flowering. However, if the nighttime part of the photoperiod is interrupted by even a few minutes of dim light, cocklebur will not flower, and this turned out to be true for other short-day plants as well **(Figure 39.21a)**. Cocklebur is unresponsive to day length, but it requires at least 8 hours of continuous darkness to flower. Short-day plants are really long-night plants, but the older term is embedded firmly in the jargon of plant physiology. Similarly, long-day plants are actually short-night plants. A long-day plant grown on photoperiods of long nights that would not normally induce flowering will flower if the period of continuous darkness is interrupted by a few minutes of light **(Figure 39.21b)**. Notice that we distinguish long-day from short-day plants *not* by

(a) **Short-day (long-night) plant.** Flowers when night exceeds a critical dark period. A flash of light interrupting the dark period prevents flowering.

Light · Flash · Darkness

Critical · of
dark period · light

(b) **Long-day (short-night) plant.** Flowers only if the night is shorter than a critical dark period. A brief flash of light artificially interrupts a long dark period, thereby inducing flowering.

Flash
of
light

▲ Figure 39.21 **Photoperiodic control of flowering.**

an absolute night length but by whether the critical night length sets a maximum (long-day plants) or minimum (short-day plants) number of hours of darkness required for flowering. In both cases, the actual number of hours in the critical night length is specific to each species of plant.

Red light is the most effective color in interrupting the nighttime portion of the photoperiod. Action spectra and photoreversibility experiments show that phytochrome is the pigment that detects the red light (**Figure 39.22**). For example, if a flash of red (R) light during the dark period is followed by a flash of far-red (FR) light, then the plant detects no interruption of night length. As in the case of phytochrome-mediated seed germination, red/far-red photoreversibility occurs.

Plants detect night length very precisely; some short-day plants will not flower if night is even 1 minute shorter than the critical length. Some plant species always flower on the same day each year. It appears that plants use their biological clock, entrained by night length with the help of phytochrome, to tell the season of the year. The floriculture (flower-growing) industry applies this knowledge to produce flowers out of season. Chrysanthemums, for instance, are short-day plants that normally bloom in fall, but their blooming can be stalled until Mother's Day in May by punctuating each long night with a flash of light, thus turning one long night into two short nights.

Some plants bloom after a single exposure to the photoperiod required for flowering. Other species need several successive days of the appropriate photoperiod. Still other plants respond to a photoperiod only if they have been previously exposed to some other environmental stimulus, such as a period of cold temperatures. Winter wheat, for example, will not flower unless it has been exposed to several weeks of temperatures below 10°C. The use of pretreatment with cold to induce flowering is called **vernalization** (from the Latin for "spring"). Several weeks after winter wheat is vernalized, a photoperiod with long days (short nights) induces flowering.

A Flowering Hormone?

Although flowers form from apical or axillary bud meristems, it is leaves that detect changes in photoperiod and produce signaling molecules that cue buds to develop as flowers. In many short-day and long-day plants, exposing just one leaf to the appropriate photoperiod is enough to induce flowering. Indeed, as long as one leaf is left on the plant, photoperiod is detected and floral buds are induced. If all leaves are removed, the plant is insensitive to photoperiod.

Classic experiments revealed that the floral stimulus could move across a graft from an induced plant to a noninduced plant and trigger flowering in the latter. Moreover, the flowering stimulus appears to be the same for short-day and long-day plants, despite the differing photoperiodic conditions required for leaves to send this signal (**Figure 39.23**). The hypothetical signaling molecule for flowering, called **florigen**, is still unidentified after 70 years, possibly because plant scientists had focused on small hormone-like molecules. As discussed in Chapter 36, large macromolecules, such as mRNA and proteins, can move by the

▲ **Figure 39.22 Reversible effects of red and far-red light on photoperiodic response.** A flash of red (R) light shortens the dark period. A subsequent flash of far-red (FR) light cancels the red flash's effect.

? *How would a single flash of full-spectrum light affect each plant?*

▲ **Figure 39.23 Experimental evidence for a flowering hormone.** If grown individually under short-day conditions, a short-day plant will flower and a long-day plant will not. However, both will flower if grafted together and exposed to short days. This result indicates that a flower-inducing substance (florigen) is transmitted across grafts and induces flowering in both short-day and long-day plants.

WHAT IF? *If flowering were inhibited in both parts of the grafted plants, what would you conclude?*

symplastic route via plasmodesmata (see Figure 36.11) and regulate plant development. Could florigen be a macromolecule? Plant biologists are now excited about this possibility. *Arabidopsis* is a long-day plant that requires a functional *CONSTANS* gene to flower under long days. Brian Ayre and Robert Turgeon, of Cornell University, noted that *Arabidopsis* plants flowered only when *CONSTANS* was expressed in the leaf, a finding consistent with the observation that florigen is made only in leaves. They provided further evidence for a role for the CONSTANS protein in floral signaling when they grafted *Arabidopsis* plants that contained no CONSTANS protein onto plants synthesizing CONSTANS in their leaves. This elegant experiment showed that CONSTANS, or another factor that it interacts with, can move through the graft junction to signal flowering in the parts of the plant that formerly were devoid of the protein. More recent evidence suggests that CONSTANS turns on a gene called *FLOWERING LOCUS T (FT)* in the leaf and that the FT protein travels to the shoot apical meristem and initiates flowering.

Meristem Transition and Flowering

Whatever combination of environmental cues (such as photoperiod or vernalization) and internal signaling molecules (such as the FT protein) is necessary for flowering, the outcome is the transition of a bud's meristem from a vegetative state to a flowering state. This transition requires changes in the expression of genes that regulate pattern formation. Meristem identity genes that induce the bud to form a flower instead of a vegetative shoot must first be switched on. Then the organ identity genes that specify the spatial organization of the floral organs—sepals, petals, stamens, and carpels—are activated in the appropriate regions of the meristem (see Figure 35.34). Research on flower development is progressing rapidly, and one goal is to identify the signal transduction pathways that link such cues as photoperiod and hormonal changes to the gene expression required for flowering.

CONCEPT 39.4
Plants respond to a wide variety of stimuli other than light

Plants can neither migrate to a watering hole when water is scarce nor seek shelter from wind. A seed landing upside down in the soil cannot maneuver itself into an upright position. Because of their immobility, plants must adjust to a wide range of environmental circumstances through developmental and physiological mechanisms, and natural selection has refined these responses. Light is so important in the life of a plant that we devoted the entire previous section to a plant's reception of and response to this one environmental factor. In this section, we examine responses to some of the other environmental stimuli that a plant commonly encounters.

Gravity

Because plants are solar-powered organisms, it is not surprising that mechanisms for growing toward sunlight have evolved. But what environmental cue does the shoot of a young seedling use to grow upward when it is completely underground and there is no light for it to detect? Similarly, what environmental factor prompts the young root to grow downward? The answer to both questions is gravity.

Place a plant on its side, and it adjusts its growth so that the shoot bends upward and the root curves downward. In their responses to gravity, or **gravitropism**, roots display positive gravitropism **(Figure 39.24a)** and shoots exhibit negative

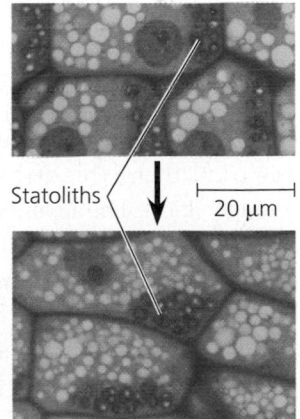

Statoliths   20 μm

(a) Over the course of hours, a horizontally oriented primary root of maize bends gravitropically until its growing tip becomes vertically oriented (LMs).

(b) Within minutes after the root is placed horizontally, plastids called statoliths begin settling to the lowest sides of root cap cells. This settling may be the gravity-sensing mechanism that leads to redistribution of auxin and differing rates of elongation by cells on opposite sides of the root (LMs).

▲ **Figure 39.24 Positive gravitropism in roots: the statolith hypothesis.**

gravitropism. Gravitropism occurs as soon as a seed germinates, ensuring that the root grows into the soil and the shoot grows toward sunlight, regardless of how the seed is oriented when it lands. Auxin plays a key role in gravitropism.

Plants may detect gravity by the settling of **statoliths**, specialized plastids containing dense starch grains, to the lower portions of cells (**Figure 39.24b**, on the previous page). In roots, statoliths are located in certain cells of the root cap. According to one hypothesis, the aggregation of statoliths at the low points of these cells triggers redistribution of calcium, which causes lateral transport of auxin within the root. The calcium and auxin accumulate on the lower side of the root's zone of elongation. Because these chemicals are dissolved, they do not respond to gravity but must be actively transported to one side of the root. At high concentration, auxin inhibits cell elongation, an effect that slows growth on the root's lower side. The more rapid elongation of cells on the upper side causes the root to curve as it grows. This tropism continues until the root grows straight down.

Plant physiologists are refining the "falling statolith" hypothesis of root gravitropism, based on new experiments. For example, mutants of *Arabidopsis* and tobacco that lack statoliths are still capable of gravitropism, though the response is slower than in wild-type plants. It could be that the entire cell helps the root sense gravity by mechanically pulling on proteins that tether the protoplast to the cell wall, stretching the proteins on the "up" side and compressing the proteins on the "down" side of the root cells. Dense organelles, in addition to starch granules, may also contribute by distorting the cytoskeleton as they are pulled by gravity. Statoliths, because of their density, may enhance gravitational sensing by a mechanism that works more slowly in their absence.

Mechanical Stimuli

A tree growing on a windy mountain ridge usually has a shorter, stockier trunk than a tree of the same species growing in a more sheltered location. The advantage of this stunted morphology is that it enables the plant to hold its ground against strong gusts of wind. The term **thigmomorphogenesis** (from the Greek *thigma*, touch) refers to the changes in form that result from mechanical perturbation. Plants are very sensitive to mechanical stress: Even the act of measuring the length of a leaf with a ruler alters its subsequent growth. Rubbing the stems of a young plant a couple of times daily results in plants that are shorter than controls (**Figure 39.25**). Mechanical stimulation activates a signal transduction pathway involving an increase in cytosolic Ca^{2+} that mediates the activation of specific genes, some of which code for proteins that affect cell wall properties.

Some plant species have become, over the course of their evolution, "touch specialists." Acute responsiveness to mechanical stimuli is an integral part of these plants' "life strategies."

▲ Figure 39.25 **Altering gene expression by touch in** *Arabidopsis*. The shorter plant on the left was rubbed twice a day. The untouched plant (right) grew much taller.

Most vines and other climbing plants have tendrils that coil rapidly around supports (see Figure 35.7). These grasping organs usually grow straight until they touch something; the contact stimulates a coiling response caused by differential growth of cells on opposite sides of the tendril. This directional growth in response to touch is called **thigmotropism**, and it allows the vine to take advantage of whatever mechanical supports it comes across as it climbs upward toward a forest canopy.

Other examples of touch specialists are plants that undergo rapid leaf movements in response to mechanical stimulation. For example, when the compound leaf of the sensitive plant *Mimosa pudica* is touched, it collapses and its leaflets fold together (**Figure 39.26**). This response, which takes only a second or two, results from a rapid loss of turgor in cells within pulvini, specialized motor organs located at the joints of the leaf. The motor cells suddenly become flaccid after stimulation because they lose potassium, which causes water to leave the cells by osmosis. It takes about 10 minutes for the cells to regain their turgor and restore the "unstimulated" form of the leaf. The function of the sensitive plant's behavior invites speculation. Perhaps by folding its leaves and reducing its surface area when jostled by strong winds, the plant conserves water. Or perhaps because the collapse of the leaves exposes thorns on the stem, the rapid response of the sensitive plant discourages herbivores.

A remarkable feature of rapid leaf movements is the mode of transmission of the stimulus through the plant. If one leaflet on a sensitive plant is touched, first that leaflet responds, then the adjacent leaflet responds, and so on, until all the leaflet pairs have folded together. From the point of stimulation, the signal that produces this response travels at a speed of about 1 cm/sec. An electrical impulse, traveling at the same rate, can

(a) Unstimulated state (leaflets spread apart)   **(b) Stimulated state (leaflets folded)**

Leaflets after stimulation

Pulvinus (motor organ)

Side of pulvinus with flaccid cells

Side of pulvinus with turgid cells

Vein

0.5 μm

(c) Cross section of a leaflet pair in the stimulated state (LM). The curvature of a pulvinus (motor organ) is caused when motor cells on one side of the pulvinus lose water and become flaccid while cells on the opposite side retain their turgor.

▲ **Figure 39.26 Rapid turgor movements by the sensitive plant (*Mimosa pudica*).**

be detected by attaching electrodes to the leaf. These impulses, called **action potentials**, resemble nerve impulses in animals, though the action potentials of plants are thousands of times slower. Action potentials, which have been discovered in many species of algae and plants, may be widely used as a form of internal communication. For example, in the Venus flytrap (*Dionaea muscipula*), action potentials are transmitted from sensory hairs in the trap to the cells that respond by closing the trap (see Figure 37.14). In the case of *Mimosa pudica*, more violent stimuli, such as touching a leaf with a hot needle, causes *all* the leaves and leaflets on a plant to droop, but this systemic response involves the spread of signaling molecules released from the injured area to other parts of the shoot.

Environmental Stresses

Occasionally, certain factors in the environment change severely enough to have a potentially adverse effect on a plant's survival, growth, and reproduction. Environmental stresses, such as flooding, drought, or extreme temperatures, can have a devastating impact on crop yields in agriculture. In natural

ecosystems, plants that cannot tolerate an environmental stress either will succumb or will be outcompeted by other plants, and they will become locally extinct. Thus, environmental stresses are an important factor in determining the geographic ranges of plants. Here, we will consider some of the more common **abiotic** (nonliving) stresses that plants encounter. In the last section of this chapter, we will examine the defensive responses of plants to common **biotic** (living) stresses, such as pathogens and herbivores.

Drought

On a bright, warm, dry day, a plant may be stressed by a water deficiency because it is losing water by transpiration faster than the water can be restored by uptake from the soil. Prolonged drought can stress crops and the plants of natural ecosystems for weeks or months. Severe water deficit, of course, will kill a plant, as you may know from experience with neglected houseplants. But plants have control systems that enable them to cope with less extreme water deficits.

Many of a plant's responses to water deficit help the plant conserve water by reducing the rate of transpiration. Water deficit in a leaf causes guard cells to lose turgor, a simple control mechanism that slows transpiration by closing stomata (see Figure 36.17). Water deficit also stimulates increased synthesis and release of abscisic acid in the leaf; this hormone helps keep stomata closed by acting on guard cell membranes. Leaves respond to water deficit in several other ways. Because cell expansion is a turgor-dependent process, water deficits inhibit the growth of young leaves, as does the accumulation of abscisic acid. This response minimizes the transpirational loss of water by slowing the increase in leaf surface. When the leaves of many grasses and other plants wilt from a water deficit, they roll into a shape that reduces transpiration by exposing less leaf surface to dry air and wind. Although these leaf responses conserve water, they reduce photosynthesis, which is one reason why a drought diminishes crop yield.

Root growth also responds to water deficit. During a drought, the soil usually dries from the surface down. This inhibits the growth of shallow roots, partly because cells cannot maintain the turgor required for elongation. Deeper roots surrounded by soil that is still moist continue to grow. Thus, the root system proliferates in a way that maximizes exposure to soil water.

Flooding

Too much water is also a problem for a plant. An overwatered houseplant may suffocate because the soil lacks the air spaces that provide oxygen for cellular respiration in the roots. Some plants are structurally adapted to very wet habitats. For example, the submerged roots of mangroves, which inhabit coastal marshes, are continuous with aerial roots exposed to oxygen (see Figure 35.4). But how do less specialized plants cope with oxygen deprivation in waterlogged soils? Oxygen deprivation stimulates the production of ethylene, which causes some cells in the root cortex to undergo apoptosis. The destruction of these cells creates air tubes that function as "snorkels," providing oxygen to the submerged roots (Figure 39.27).

Salt Stress

An excess of sodium chloride or other salts in the soil threatens plants for two reasons. First, by lowering the water potential of the soil solution, salt can cause a water deficit in plants even though the soil has plenty of water. As the water potential of the soil solution becomes more negative, the water potential gradient from soil to roots is lowered, thereby reducing water uptake (see Chapter 36). The second problem with saline soil is that sodium and certain other ions are toxic to plants when their concentrations are relatively high. The selectively permeable membranes of root cells impede the uptake of most harmful ions, but this only aggravates the problem of acquiring water from soil that is rich in solutes. Many plants can respond to moderate soil salinity by producing solutes that are well tolerated at high concentrations: These mostly organic compounds keep the water potential of cells more negative than that of the soil solution without ad-

mitting toxic quantities of salt. However, most plants cannot survive salt stress for long. The exceptions are halophytes, salt-tolerant plants with adaptations such as salt glands that pump salts out across the leaf epidermis.

Heat Stress

As is true for other organisms, excessive heat harms and even kills a plant by denaturing its enzymes and damaging its metabolism. One function of transpiration is evaporative cooling. On a warm day, for example, the temperature of a leaf may be 3–10°C below the ambient air temperature. Hot, dry weather also tends to dehydrate many plants; the closing of stomata in response to this stress conserves water but then sacrifices evaporative cooling. This dilemma is one reason why very hot, dry days take a toll on most plants.

Most plants have a backup response that enables them to survive heat stress. Above a certain temperature—about 40°C for most plants in temperate regions—plant cells begin synthesizing **heat-shock proteins**, which help protect other proteins from heat stress. This response also occurs in heat-stressed animals and microorganisms. Some heat-shock proteins are chaperone proteins (chaperonins), which function in unstressed cells as temporary scaffolds that help other proteins fold into their functional shapes (see Chapter 5). In their roles as heat-shock proteins, perhaps these molecules bind to other proteins and help prevent their denaturation.

Cold Stress

One problem plants face when the temperature of the environment falls is a change in the fluidity of cell membranes. Recall from Chapter 7 that a biological membrane is a fluid mosaic, with proteins and lipids moving laterally in the plane of the membrane. When a membrane cools below a critical point, it loses its fluidity as the lipids become locked into crystalline structures. This alters solute transport across the membrane and also adversely affects the functions of membrane proteins. Plants respond to cold stress by altering the lipid composition of their membranes. For example, membrane lipids increase in their proportion of unsaturated fatty acids, which have shapes that help keep membranes fluid at lower temperatures by impeding crystal formation (see Figure 7.5b). Such membrane modification requires from several hours to days, which is one reason why unseasonably cold temperatures are generally more stressful to plants than the more gradual seasonal drop in air temperature.

Vascular cylinder

Air tubes

Epidermis

100 μm

(a) Control root (aerated)

100 μm

(b) Experimental root (nonaerated)

▲ **Figure 39.27 A developmental response of maize roots to flooding and oxygen deprivation. (a)** A cross section of a control root grown in an aerated hydroponic medium. **(b)** A root grown in a nonaerated hydroponic medium. Ethylene-stimulated apoptosis (programmed cell death) creates the air tubes (SEMs).

Freezing is a more severe version of cold stress. At sub-freezing temperatures, ice forms in the cell walls and intercellular spaces of most plants. The cytosol generally does not freeze at the cooling rates encountered in nature because it contains more solutes than the very dilute solution found in the cell wall, and solutes lower the freezing point of a solution. The reduction in liquid water in the cell wall caused by ice formation lowers the extracellular water potential, causing water to leave the cytoplasm. The resulting increase in the concentration of ions in the cytoplasm is harmful and can lead to cell death. Whether the cell survives depends largely on how well it resists dehydration. In regions with cold winters, native plants are adapted to cope with freezing stress. For example, before the onset of winter, the cells of many frost-tolerant species increase cytoplasmic levels of specific solutes, such as sugars, that are well tolerated at high concentrations and that help reduce the loss of water from the cell during extracellular freezing. The unsaturation of membrane lipids also increases, thereby maintaining proper levels of membrane fluidity.

CONCEPT 39.5
Plants respond to attacks by herbivores and pathogens

Plants do not exist in isolation but interact with many other species in their communities. Some interspecific interactions—for example, the associations of plants with fungi in mycorrhizae (see Figure 37.12) or with pollinators (see Figure 38.4)—are mutually beneficial. Most of a plant's interactions with other organisms, however, do not benefit the plant. As primary producers, plants are at the base of most food webs and are subject to attack by a wide range of plant-eating (herbivorous) animals. A plant is also subject to infection by diverse viruses, bacteria, and fungi that can damage tissues or even kill the plant. Plants counter these threats with defense systems that deter herbivory and prevent infection or combat pathogens that infect the plant.

Defenses Against Herbivores

Herbivory—animals eating plants—is a stress that plants face in any ecosystem. Plants prevent excessive herbivory by using both physical defenses, such as thorns, and chemical defenses, such as the production of distasteful or toxic compounds. For example, some plants produce an unusual amino acid called *canavanine*, named for one of its sources, the jackbean (*Canavalia ensiformis*). Canavanine resembles arginine, one of the 20 amino acids that organisms incorporate into their proteins. If an insect eats a plant containing canavanine, the molecule is incorporated into the insect's proteins in place of arginine. Because canavanine is different enough from arginine to adversely affect the shape and hence the function of the proteins, the insect dies.

Some plants even "recruit" predatory animals that help defend the plant against specific herbivores. For example, insects called parasitoid wasps inject their eggs into their prey, including caterpillars feeding on plants (see Figure 54.1). The eggs hatch within the caterpillars, and the larvae eat through their organic containers from the inside out. The plant, which benefits from the destruction of the herbivorous caterpillars, has an active role in this drama. A leaf damaged by caterpillars releases volatile compounds that attract parasitoid wasps. The stimulus for this response is a combination of physical damage to the leaf caused by the munching caterpillar and a specific compound in the caterpillar's saliva (**Figure 39.28**).

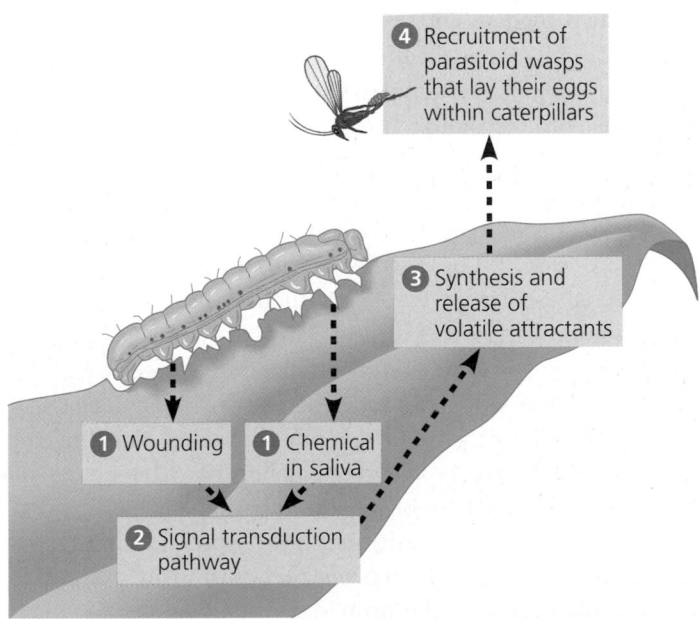

▲ Figure 39.28 **A maize leaf "recruiting" a parasitoid wasp as a defensive response to an armyworm caterpillar, an herbivore.**

The volatile molecules a plant releases in response to herbivore damage can also function as an "early warning system" for nearby plants of the same species. For example, lima bean plants infested with spider mites release a cocktail of volatile chemicals, including methyljasmonic acid, that signal "news" of the attack to neighboring, noninfested lima bean plants. In response to these chemicals, noninfested lima bean leaves express defense genes. Volatile chemicals released from leaves that are mechanically wounded in experiments do not have the same effect. As a result of the activation of specific genes by these released volatile chemicals, noninfested neighbors become less susceptible to spider mites and more attractive to another species of mite that preys on spider mites. Iris Kappers and her colleagues at Wageningen University, in the Netherlands, transgenically engineered *Arabidopsis* plants to produce two volatile chemicals that normally are not made by *Arabidopsis* but which have been found to attract carnivorous predatory mites in other plants. The predatory mites were now also attracted to the genetically modified *Arabidopsis*, a finding that could have implications for the genetic engineering of insect resistance in crop plants.

Defenses Against Pathogens

A plant's first line of defense against infection is the physical barrier presented by the epidermis of the primary plant body and the periderm of the secondary plant body (see Figure 35.19). This first defense system, however, is not impenetrable. Viruses, bacteria, and the spores and hyphae of fungi can still enter the plant through wounds or through the natural openings in the epidermis, such as stomata. Once a pathogen invades, the plant mounts a chemical attack as a second line of defense that destroys the pathogens and prevents their spread from the site of infection. This second defense system is enhanced by the plant's ability to recognize certain pathogens.

Plants can recognize invading pathogens and defend against them. Successful pathogens cause disease because they evade recognition or suppress the host's defense mechanisms. Pathogens against which a plant has little specific defense are said to be **virulent** pathogens. They are the exceptions, for if they were not, then hosts and pathogens would soon perish together. A kind of "compromise" has evolved between plants and most of their pathogens. In such cases, the pathogen gains enough access to its host to enable it to perpetuate itself without severely damaging or killing the plant. Strains of pathogens that only mildly harm but do not kill the host plant are said to be **avirulent** pathogens.

Gene-for-gene recognition is a widespread form of plant disease resistance that involves recognition of pathogen-derived molecules by the protein products of specific plant disease resistance (*R*) genes. There are many pathogens, and plants have many *R* genes—*Arabidopsis* has at least several

hundred. An R protein usually recognizes only a single corresponding pathogen molecule that is encoded by one of a pathogen's avirulence (*Avr*) genes. Despite their name, Avr proteins are harmful to the plant; they are thought to redirect the host's metabolism to the advantage of the pathogen. The recognition of pathogen-derived molecules called *elicitors* by R proteins triggers signal transduction pathways leading to the activation of an arsenal of defense responses. These include the **hypersensitive response**—the genetically programmed death of infected cells—as well as tissue reinforcement and antibiotic production at the infection site. Pathogen invasion can also trigger **systemic acquired resistance**, a long-lasting systemic response that primes the plant for resisting a broad spectrum of pathogens. Local and systemic responses to pathogens require extensive genetic reprogramming and commitment of cellular resources. Therefore, a plant activates these defenses only after detecting an invading pathogen.

The Hypersensitive Response

The hypersensitive response is a defense response that causes cell and tissue death near the infection site, thereby restricting the spread of a pathogen. After the cells at the infection site mount a chemical defense and seal off the area, they destroy themselves. The hypersensitive response is initiated when pathogen elicitors bind to R proteins, altering the selective permeability of the plasma membrane and stimulating the production of *phytoalexins*, which are toxic compounds with general fungicidal and bactericidal properties. The hypersensitive response also induces production of *PR proteins* (pathogenesis-related proteins), many of which are enzymes that hydrolyze components in the cell walls of the pathogens. Infection also stimulates the cross-linking of molecules within the cell wall and the deposition of lignin, responses that set up a local barricade that slows the spread of the pathogen to other parts of the plant.

We can see the result of a hypersensitive response as lesions on a leaf. As "sick" as such a leaf appears, it will still survive, and its defensive response will help protect the rest of the plant (**Figure 39.29**).

Systemic Acquired Resistance

The hypersensitive response is localized and specific, a containment response based on gene-for-gene (*R-Avr*) recognition between host and pathogen. However, as noted previously, pathogen invasions can also produce signaling molecules that "sound the alarm" of infection to the whole plant. The resulting systemic acquired resistance, which is associated with the systemic expression of defense genes, is nonspecific, providing protection against a diversity of pathogens that lasts for days. The search for a signaling molecule that moves from the infection site to elicit the systemic acquired resistance led to the

④ Before they die, infected cells release the signaling molecule methylsalicylic acid.

③ In a hypersensitive response, plant cells produce anti-microbial molecules, seal off infected areas by modifying their walls, and then destroy themselves. This localized response produces lesions and protects other parts of an infected leaf.

② The identification in step ① triggers a signal transduction pathway.

① Specific resistance is based on the binding of molecules from the pathogen to receptors in plant cells.

Signal

④

③ Hypersensitive response

② Signal transduction pathway

①

Avirulent pathogen

R-Avr recognition and hypersensitive response

⑤

Signal transduction pathway ⑥

⑦ Acquired resistance

Systemic acquired resistance

⑤ The signaling molecule is distributed to the rest of the plant.

⑥ In cells remote from the infection site, methyl salicylate is converted to salicylic acid, which initiates a signal transduction pathway.

⑦ Systemic acquired resistance is activated: the production of molecules that help protect the cell against a diversity of pathogens for several days.

▲ **Figure 39.29 Defense responses against an avirulent pathogen.**

identification of *methylsalicylic acid* as the most likely candidate. Methylsalicylic acid is produced around the infection site and carried by the phloem throughout the plant, where it is converted to **salicylic acid** in areas remote from the sites of infection. Salicylic acid activates a signal transduction pathway that induces the production of PR proteins and resistance to pathogen attack (see Figure 39.29).

A modified form of salicylic acid, acetylsalicylic acid, is the active ingredient in aspirin. Centuries before aspirin was sold as a pain reliever, some cultures had learned that chewing the bark of a willow tree (*Salix*) would lessen the pain of a toothache or headache. With the discovery of systemic acquired resistance, biologists have finally learned one function of salicylic acid in plants. Aspirin is a natural medicine in the plants that produce it, but with effects entirely different from the medicinal action in humans who consume the drug.

Plant biologists investigating disease resistance and other evolutionary adaptations of plants are getting to the heart of how a plant responds to internal and external signals. These scientists, along with thousands of other plant biologists working on other questions and millions of students experimenting with plants in biology courses, are all extending a centuries-old tradition of curiosity about the green organisms that feed the biosphere.

CONCEPT CHECK 39.5

1. What are some drawbacks of spraying fields with general-purpose insecticides?
2. Chewing insects mechanically damage plants and lessen the surface area of leaves for photosynthesis. In addition, these insects make plants more vulnerable to pathogen attack. Suggest a reason why.
3. Many fungal pathogens get their food by causing plant cells to become leaky, thereby releasing nutrients into the intercellular spaces. Would it benefit the fungus to kill the host plant in a way that results in all the nutrients leaking out?
4. **WHAT IF?** Suppose a scientist finds that a population of plants growing in a breezy location is more prone to herbivory by insects than a population of the same species growing in a sheltered area. Suggest a hypothesis to account for this observation.

For suggested answers, see Appendix A.

MEDIA Go to **www.campbellbiology.com** for BioFlix 3-D Animations, MP3 Tutors, Videos, Practice Tests, an eBook, and more.

SUMMARY OF KEY CONCEPTS

CONCEPT 39.1

Signal transduction pathways link signal reception to response (pp. 821–824)

CONCEPT 39.2

Plant hormones help coordinate growth, development, and responses to stimuli (pp. 824–835)

▶ **The Discovery of Plant Hormones** Researchers discovered auxin by identifying the compound responsible for transmitting a signal downward through coleoptiles, from the tips to the elongating regions, during phototropism.

▶ **A Survey of Plant Hormones** Auxin, produced primarily in the apical meristem of the shoot, stimulates cell elongation in different target tissues. Cytokinins stimulate cell division. Gibberellins, produced in roots and young leaves, stimulate growth in leaves and stems. Brassinosteroids, chemically similar to the sex hormones of animals, induce cell elongation and division. Abscisic acid maintains dormancy in seeds. Ethylene helps control fruit ripening.

▶ **Systems Biology and Hormone Interactions** Interactions between hormones and their signal transduction pathways make it difficult to predict what effect a genetic manipulation will have on a plant. Systems biology seeks a comprehensive understanding of plants that will permit successful modeling of plant functions.

MEDIA

Activity Leaf Abscission
Investigation What Plant Hormones Affect Organ Formation?

CONCEPT 39.3

Responses to light are critical for plant success (pp. 835–841)

▶ **Blue-Light Photoreceptors** Various blue-light photoreceptors control the responses of hypocotyl elongation, stomatal opening, and phototropism.

▶ **Phytochromes as Photoreceptors**

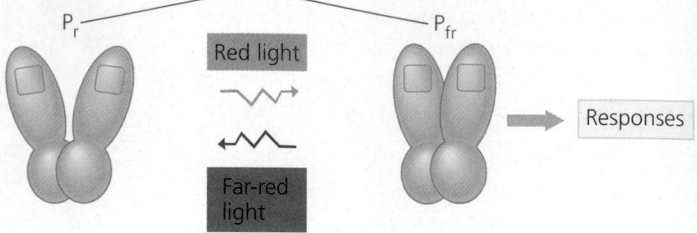

Photoreversible states of phytochrome

▶ **Biological Clocks and Circadian Rhythms** Free-running circadian cycles are approximately 24 hours long but are entrained to exactly 24 hours by the day/night cycle.

▶ **The Effect of Light on the Biological Clock** Phytochrome conversion marks sunrise and sunset, providing the clock with environmental cues.

▶ **Photoperiodism and Responses to Seasons** Some developmental processes, including flowering in many species, require a certain photoperiod. A critical night length sets a minimum (in short-day plants) or maximum (in long-day plants) number of hours of darkness required for flowering.

MEDIA

Activity Flowering Lab

CONCEPT 39.4

Plants respond to a wide variety of stimuli other than light (pp. 841–845)

▶ **Gravity** Gravitropism is a growth response to gravity. Roots show positive gravitropism, and stems show negative gravitropism. Plastids called statoliths may enable plant roots to detect gravity.

▶ **Mechanical Stimuli** Growth in response to touch is called thigmotropism. Rapid leaf movements involve transmission of electrical impulses called action potentials.

▶ **Environmental Stresses** During drought, plants respond to water deficit by reducing transpiration. Enzymatic destruction of cells creates air tubes that help plants survive oxygen deprivation during flooding. Plants respond to salt stress by producing solutes tolerated at high concentrations, keeping the water potential of cells more negative than the soil solution. Heat-shock proteins help plants survive heat stress. Altering lipid composition of membranes is a response to cold stress.

CONCEPT 39.5

Plants respond to attacks by herbivores and pathogens (pp. 845–847)

▶ **Defenses Against Herbivores** In addition to physical defenses such as thorns, plants defend themselves chemically by producing distasteful or toxic compounds, as well as airborne attractants that bring animals that destroy herbivores.

▶ **Defenses Against Pathogens** A pathogen is avirulent if it has a specific *Avr* gene corresponding to a particular *R* allele in the host plant. A hypersensitive response against an avirulent pathogen seals off the infection and destroys both pathogen and host cells in the region of the infection. Systemic acquired resistance is a generalized defense response in organs distant from the infection site.

SELF-QUIZ

1. Which of the following does *not* occur in a signal transduction pathway?
   a. stimulation of the receptor by a relay molecule
   b. production of second messengers such as cGMP
   c. expression of specific genes
   d. activation of protein kinases
   e. phosphorylation of transcription factors

2. Auxin enhances cell elongation in all of these ways *except*
   a. increased uptake of solutes.
   b. gene activation.
   c. acidification of the cell wall, causing denaturation of growth-inhibiting cell wall proteins.
   d. increased activity of plasma membrane proton pumps.
   e. cell wall loosening.

3. Charles and Francis Darwin discovered that
   a. auxin is responsible for phototropic curvature.
   b. auxin can pass through agar.
   c. light destroys auxin.
   d. light is perceived by the tips of coleoptiles.
   e. red light is most effective in causing phototropic curvatures.

4. Which hormone is *incorrectly* paired with its function?
   a. auxin—promotes stem growth through cell elongation
   b. cytokinins—initiate programmed cell death
   c. gibberellins—stimulate seed germination
   d. abscisic acid—promotes seed dormancy
   e. ethylene—inhibits cell elongation

5. The hormone that helps plants respond to drought is
   a. auxin.   d. ethylene.
   b. gibberellin.   e. abscisic acid.
   c. cytokinin.

6. The signaling molecule for flowering might be released earlier than normal in a long-day plant exposed to flashes of
   a. far-red light during the night.
   b. red light during the night.
   c. red light followed by far-red light during the night.
   d. far-red light during the day.
   e. red light during the day.

7. If a long-day plant has a critical night length of 9 hours, which 24-hour cycle would prevent flowering?
   a. 16 hours light/8 hours dark
   b. 14 hours light/10 hours dark
   c. 15.5 hours light/8.5 hours dark
   d. 4 hours light/8 hours dark/4 hours light/8 hours dark
   e. 8 hours light/8 hours dark/light flash/8 hours dark

8. If a scientist discovers an *Arabidopsis* mutant that does not store starch in plastids but has normal gravitropic bending, what aspect of our understanding of gravitropism would need to be reevaluated?
   a. the role of auxin in gravitropism
   b. the role of calcium in gravitropism
   c. the role of statoliths in gravitropism
   d. the role of light in gravitropism
   e. the role of differential growth in gravitropic bending

9. How may a plant respond to *severe* heat stress?
   a. by orienting leaves to increase evaporative cooling
   b. by producing ethylene, which kills some cortex cells and creates air tubes for ventilation
   c. by initiating a systemic acquired resistance response
   d. by increasing the proportion of unsaturated fatty acids in cell membranes, reducing their fluidity
   e. by producing heat-shock proteins, which may protect the plant's proteins from denaturing

10. In systemic acquired resistance, salicylic acid probably
    a. destroys pathogens directly.
    b. activates defenses throughout the plant before infection spreads.
    c. closes stomata, thus preventing the entry of pathogens.
    d. activates heat-shock proteins.
    e. sacrifices infected tissues by hydrolyzing cells.

11. **DRAW IT** Indicate the response to each condition by drawing a straight seedling or one with the triple response.

	Control	Ethylene added	Ethylene synthesis inhibitor
Wild-type			
Ethylene insensitive (*ein*)			
Ethylene overproducing (*eto*)			
Constitutive triple response (*ctr*)			

For Self-Quiz answers, see Appendix A.

EVOLUTION CONNECTION

12. Coevolution is defined as the evolution of reciprocal adaptations in two species, with each species adapting its interaction with the other. In this context, explain the coevolutionary relationship between a plant and an avirulent pathogen.

SCIENTIFIC INQUIRY

13. A plant biologist observed a peculiar pattern when a tropical shrub was attacked by caterpillars. After a caterpillar ate a leaf, it would skip over nearby leaves and attack a leaf some distance away. Simply removing a leaf did not deter caterpillars from eating nearby leaves. The biologist suspected that an insect-damaged leaf sent out a chemical that signaled nearby leaves. How could the researcher test this hypothesis?

SCIENCE, TECHNOLOGY, AND SOCIETY

14. Describe how our knowledge about the control systems of plants is being applied to agriculture or horticulture, giving three examples.

Animal Form and Function

AN INTERVIEW WITH

Masashi Yanagisawa

While still in graduate school, Masashi Yanagisawa became famous for discovering endothelins, local regulators that are the most potent constrictors of blood vessels known. Later he discovered orexins, which regulate food intake and wakefulness. He received his M.D. and Ph.D. degrees from the University of Tsukuba, Japan. Since 1996, Dr. Yanagisawa has been a professor and Howard Hughes Medical Institute Investigator at the University of Texas Southwestern Medical Center at Dallas, where he holds the Patrick E. Haggerty Distinguished Chair in Basic Biomedical Science. The recipient of many awards, he is also a member of the National Academy of Sciences.

How did you get to be a medical scientist?
Even as a small child, I wanted to be a scientist. And in Japan, you really have to decide what you want to do before college; it's a European-style system. My decision to enter medical school, which is a 6-year undergraduate program there, was influenced by something my father told me. He said—this was the late 1970s—that biology would be very exciting in the coming era and that if I wanted to do biology, going to medical school was not a bad choice. I believed him, and I decided to go to medical school.

Until then, basic biology hadn't genuinely excited me, partly because of a bias at that time in Japan, where biology was regarded as a science discipline for "humanities people." And high-school biology mostly meant traditional taxonomy and lots of memorization. But in medical school, I was exposed to cutting-edge biology and found it very exciting, and I did some informal research internships that confirmed my interest in basic research. Clinical medicine excited me as well—it's impressive to see a patient improve dramatically.

The decision about what to do after medical school was probably the most difficult I've faced in my life. Should I continue with clinical training or go directly into basic research? An experience I

had toward the end of medical school helped me make up my mind. When I was on rotation in the OB-GYN department, there was a patient—a young woman—suffering from a terminal case of ovarian cancer. Her abdominal cavity was full of cancer cells; no surgery could help. The doctors were discussing how aggressively to treat her with chemotherapy. At that time in Japan, most terminal cancer patients were not told of their condition. So this patient didn't know about her own condition and certainly didn't know about her options. Immediately after that, I had a chance to go to Australia in an exchange program, and there I was assigned to surgery and oncology. Their philosophy was totally different: The patient was at the center. The young me was very moved. If I had been a more aggressive person, I might have decided to try to change clinical practice in Japan, but I wasn't like that. I just decided not to go through clinical training, but instead to enroll in a Ph.D. program in pharmacology.

Why did you choose pharmacology?
Actually, pharmacology itself didn't matter. I was considering various programs all over Japan, but eventually I realized that I wanted to work under Tomoh Masaki, who happened to be a professor in pharmacology at Tsukuba. It was his open style of running his lab that appealed to me. I felt I could be a semi-independent researcher in his lab. My first research project was in Masaki's lifelong research area, the biochemistry of contractile proteins in muscles. My specific goal was to clone the gene for the large polypeptide subunit of the muscle protein myosin. I was sent off to another institution for almost a year to learn DNA cloning and other molecular techniques.

I finished the myosin project, but I strongly wanted to do something more medically oriented. So I started to look for an interesting topic. Many researchers were talking about a newly identified factor made by the endothelium (lining) of blood vessels that caused the vessel walls to relax. This was clearly a hot topic. I went to the library to browse through the scientific literature. (Remember, this was the pre-Internet era, so browsing meant actually

flipping pages—very time-consuming!) I was lucky to find one abstract describing a mysterious vascular constricting factor that was secreted into culture medium when endothelial cells were cultured. This seemed interesting—and a promising research topic for me because the abstract authors hadn't gone on to identify the factor. I thought I could do this. In my lab and neighboring labs, I had all the techniques and teachers I needed for the project.

The great thing about my mentor, Masaki, is that he supported me in this project, even though it was outside his field; he gave me half a year to try it. Amazingly, within a few months I had purified the factor, a 21-amino-acid peptide. When I sequenced the peptide, it turned out to be previously unknown. When we injected the peptide into rats, their blood pressure shot up, because their blood vessels were being constricted. We called the peptide endothelin. It's a local regulator, a signaling molecule that acts on muscle cells lying just outside the blood-vessel endothelium. Endothelin recognizes its target cells by means of specific receptor proteins on the target cell surface. The binding of endothelin, the "ligand," to its receptor triggers a signal-transduction pathway that leads to muscle cell contraction. I stayed on as a post-doc and cloned the gene for the endothelin receptor, which is a G protein-coupled receptor (GPCR). [See Chapter 11 to review cell signaling.]

How did all the publicity arising from your work influence your career path?
My endothelin discoveries had attracted attention to me. I realized that I wanted to be in the United States, which seemed to be the center of the world for biology. I also wanted more independence as a researcher. Unfortunately, to be head of a laboratory in Japan, you had to be a full professor, which meant 37 years old at least. I was then about 27, and 10 years seemed too long to wait! This department offered me a lot of support, and it was an easy decision to come here.

What did you work on once you got here?
I wanted to learn more about how endothelin functioned, so we genetically engineered strains

of mice each lacking a component of the endothelin system—"knock-out" mice. We got some surprising results. The effects of endothelin go way beyond the vascular system. We learned that this protein has a fundamental role in certain stages of embryonic development. In the embryo, it's made by cells derived from a structure called the neural crest and is necessary for normal development of the intestine and several other organs. In adults, genes for endothelins (there are actually several) and their receptors are expressed in many, many places, and they seem to be doing a variety of things outside the vascular system.

Let's talk about the orphan receptor project, which led to orexin. Why is your approach called "reverse" pharmacology?

In the past, scientists usually went from the discovery of an intercellular signaling molecule, such as a hormone, to the eventual discovery of its receptor and the pathway leading to the response in target cells. For example, insulin was discovered years ago as a blood sugar-lowering hormone, and it was only later that the insulin receptor and the cellular pathway were identified. But the sequencing of the human genome has made the reverse approach possible. Now we can directly identify the genes for receptor proteins, especially for GPCRs, which all have very similar sequences. The human genome has more than 1,000 such genes. Many encode sensory receptors, especially for smell, but there are probably 400 or so encoding receptors that sense something internally. Out of these receptors, the ligands of more than 100 haven't been identified yet—these are the "orphan" receptors.

The genes encoding the ligands we're interested in—the peptides called neuropeptides because they are often made by neurons—can be extremely hard to find. We decided to search for novel neuropeptides that, like endothelin,

had GPCRs. We developed a strategy to screen orphan receptors for peptide ligands—and we had beginners' luck. Orexin was found as the ligand for one of the first receptors we tested.

How did you find out what orexin did in the body?

The first clue was that both the orexin gene and its receptor gene are expressed only in the brain, and orexin is produced by neurons located only in the lateral hypothalamus. This part of the brain was known to play a role in appetite, which was immediately very exciting. Our next experiment was to inject orexin into the brains of mice, which then ate much more than the control mice. Shortly afterwards, we discovered that when you withhold a mouse's food, more orexin mRNA is made in its lateral hypothalamus. So that seemed to be the story: The animal gets hungry, somehow signals to its orexin neurons, more orexin is made, and the animal eats more. We got the name orexin from the Greek word for appetite.

Next, as usual, we engineered mice with the orexin gene or orexin receptor gene knocked out. Our hypothesis was that a mouse without orexin would have less appetite and become leaner. But we were wrong. It turned out that the mice lacking orexin were, if anything, chubbier. Now we know the reason was that orexin knock-out mice had a reduced appetite but also an even more reduced metabolic rate, so the net effect was that they became fatter.

That's when my instinct as a whole-animal physiologist kicked in. The orexin system must be doing something more important than the subtle effect we'd seen, I thought. Then I realized that observing the mice during the day was probably a mistake. Physiological research is usually done in the daytime for human convenience. But mice are nocturnal, so observing them during the day and concluding anything

about their behavior is like sneaking into someone's home at night and concluding that humans are a lazy, sleepy species. So to observe the eating behavior of our mice at night, we set up a night-vision camera. And we discovered a weird phenomenon: A mouse would be running around, and all of a sudden it would fall to the side and stop moving for a minute or two and then suddenly get up and behave as if nothing had happened.

This strange behavior and subsequent tests told us that the mice had the sleep disorder called narcolepsy, which until then had been a mystery. People with narcolepsy have normal 24-hour sleep-wake cycles, but their wakeful periods are fragmented, and they go into REM sleep suddenly and inappropriately. My standard joke is this: When I'm giving a boring seminar in a dimly lit room, it's normal for a few in the audience to doze off. But if I start to doze off during my own talk, that's abnormal. That kind of thing can happen to a narcolepsy patient without medication. What's fundamentally abnormal is the regulation of sleep-state transitions. It turns out that people with narcolepsy don't have orexin-secreting neurons; these neurons disappear during adolescence, presumably from an autoimmune attack. Their orexin genes are OK.

So what's the connection between appetite regulation and sleep regulation?

It's well known that when animals are hungry they are more active; that's an important physiological adaptation. When an animal is hungry, it has to go out and hunt or seek for food, while protecting itself from danger. In the lab, if you don't feed a mouse, it becomes more awake and active. But an orexin-deficient animal doesn't do that, suggesting that orexin may be a crucial part of a connection between the brain's roles in regulating feeding and sleep.

What advice do you have for students aspiring to be biologists?

I always say that identifying a good research question is more difficult than solving it. The question should be important and feasible to answer. Something else I tell my students is this: In every class you attend, try to ask at least one meaningful question. If you can't come up with one, then you're not taking the class seriously enough. That's a mode of study very different from just knowledge absorption. To be a scientist, you have to question everything.

Our hypothesis was that a mouse without orexin would have less appetite and become leaner. But we were wrong.

Inquiry in Action

Learn about an experiment by Masashi Yanagisawa and colleagues in Inquiry Figure 42.12 on page 908.

Left to right: Steve Wasserman, Masashi Yanagisawa, Jane Reece

Basic Principles of Animal Form and Function

KEY CONCEPTS

40.1 Animal form and function are correlated at all levels of organization

40.2 Feedback control loops maintain the internal environment in many animals

40.3 Homeostatic processes for thermoregulation involve form, function, and behavior

40.4 Energy requirements are related to animal size, activity, and environment

OVERVIEW

Diverse Forms, Common Challenges

The outer ears of the jackrabbit (*Lepus alleni*) in **Figure 40.1** are thin and remarkably large. They provide this hare with an acute sense of hearing, a primary defense against predators. The ears also help the jackrabbit shed excess heat. Blood flowing through each ear's network of vessels transfers heat to the surrounding air. At times, however, blood flow in the ear could be a liability. When the air is hot, blood passing through the ears could absorb heat, raising body temperature to dangerous levels. So how does a big-eared jackrabbit survive in the midday desert heat? To answer this question, we need to look more closely at the biological form, or **anatomy**, of the animal.

Over the course of its life, a jackrabbit faces the same fundamental challenges as any other animal, whether hydra, hawk, or human. All animals must obtain oxygen and nutrients, fight off infection, and produce offspring. Given that they share these basic requirements, why do species vary so enormously in makeup, complexity, organization, and appearance? The answer is that natural selection favors, over many generations, the variations appearing in a population that best meet the animal's needs. The solutions to the chal-

lenges of survival vary among environments and species, but for the jackrabbit and other animals, they frequently result in a close match of form to function.

Because form and function are correlated, examining anatomy often provides clues to **physiology**—biological function. In the case of the jackrabbit, researchers noted that its large pink-tinged ears turn pale when the air temperature exceeds 40°C (104°F), the normal temperature of the jackrabbit's body. The color change reflects a temporary narrowing of blood vessels in response to a hot environment. With their blood supply reduced, the ears can absorb heat without overheating the rest of the body. When the air cools, blood flow resumes, and the large ears again help release excess heat.

In this chapter, we will begin our study of animal form and function by examining the levels of organization in the animal body and the systems for coordinating the activities of distinct body parts. Next, we will discuss how animals regulate their internal environment, using body temperature regulation to introduce and illustrate the concept of homeostasis. Finally, we will explore how anatomy and physiology relate to an animal's interactions with the environment and its management of energy use.

CONCEPT 40.1
Animal form and function are correlated at all levels of organization

An animal's size and shape are fundamental aspects of form that significantly affect the way an animal interacts with its environment. Although we may refer to size and shape as elements of a "body plan" or "design," this does not imply a process of conscious invention. The body plan of an animal is the result of a pattern of development programmed by the genome, itself the product of millions of years of evolution.

Physical Constraints on Animal Size and Shape

Many different body plans have arisen during the course of evolution, but the variations fall within certain bounds. Physical laws that govern strength, diffusion, movement, and heat exchange limit the range of animal forms.

As an example of how physical laws constrain evolution, let's consider how some properties of water limit the possible shapes for animals that are fast swimmers. Water is about a thousand times denser than air and also far more viscous. Thus, any bump on an animal's body surface that causes drag impedes a swimmer more than it would a runner or flyer. Tuna and other fast ray-finned fishes can swim at speeds up to 80 km/hr (50 mph). Sharks, penguins, dolphins, and seals are also fast swimmers. As apparent in the examples in **Figure 40.2**, such animals share a streamlined body contour: a shape that is fusiform, meaning tapered on both ends. The similar shape found in these speedy fishes, birds, and mammals is an example of convergent evolution (see Chapter 22). Natural selection often shapes similar adaptations when diverse organisms face the same environmental challenge, such as the resistance of water to fast travel.

Physical laws also influence animal body plans with regard to maximum size. As body dimensions increase, thicker skeletons are required to maintain adequate strength. This limitation affects internal skeletons, such as those of vertebrates, as well as external skeletons, such as those of insects and other arthropods. In addition, as bodies increase in size, the muscles required for locomotion must represent an ever-larger fraction of the total body mass. At some point, mobility becomes limited. By consid-ering the fraction of body mass in leg muscles and the effective force such muscles generate, scientists can estimate maximum running speed for a wide range of body plans. Such calculations indicate that the dinosaur *Tyrannosaurus rex*, over 6 m tall, probably could reach speeds of 30 km/hr (19 mph), as fast as a professional soccer player but not quite the thunderous sprint depicted in the movie *Jurassic Park*.

Exchange with the Environment

Animals need to exchange materials with their environment, and this need imposes limitations on their body plans (as it does for all other multicellular organisms). Exchange occurs as substances dissolved in an aqueous medium move across the plasma membrane of each cell. The rates of exchange for nutrients, waste products, and gases are proportional to membrane surface area. In contrast, the amount of material that must be exchanged to sustain life is proportional to volume.

The opportunity for exchange is strongly influenced by cell number. A single-celled organism, such as the amoeba in **Figure 40.3a**, has a sufficient membrane surface area in contact with its environment to carry out all necessary exchange. In contrast, an animal is composed of many cells, each with its own plasma membrane across which exchange must occur. A multicellular organization therefore works only if every cell has access to a suitable aqueous environment, either inside or outside of the animal's body.

Many animals with a simple internal organization have body plans that enable direct exchange between the external environment and nearly all cells. For example, a pond-dwelling hydra, which has a saclike body plan, has a body wall only two cell layers thick **(Figure 40.3b)**. Because its gastrovascular cavity

(a) Tuna

(b) Penguin

(c) Seal

▲ **Figure 40.2 Convergent evolution in fast swimmers.**

(a) Single cell

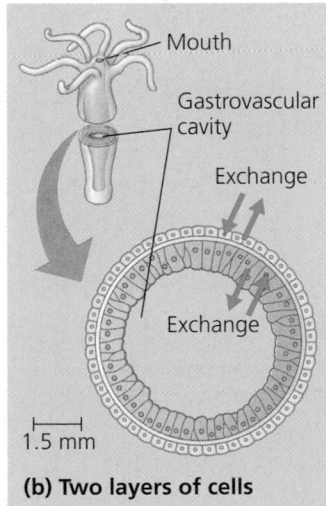

(b) Two layers of cells

▲ Figure 40.3 **Contact with the environment. (a)** In a single-celled organism, such as an amoeba, the entire surface area contacts the environment. **(b)** Although all animals are multicellular, some have a simple organization in which all or nearly all cells contact the environment. For example, a hydra's body consists of two layers of cells. As fluid moves in and out of the hydra's mouth, every body cell can exchange material directly with the aqueous environment.

opens to the external environment, both the outer and inner layers of cells are constantly bathed by pond water. Another common design that maximizes exposure to the surrounding medium is a flat body shape. Consider, for instance, a parasitic tapeworm, which can reach several meters in length (see Figure 33.12). A thin, flat shape places most cells of the worm in direct contact with its specialized environment—the nutrient-rich intestinal fluid of a vertebrate host.

Most animals have a much more complex internal organization than that of a hydra or a tapeworm. Composed of compact masses of cells, these animals have outer surfaces that are relatively small compared with their volumes. As cell number increases, the ratio of the outer surface area of the animal to its total volume steadily decreases (see Figure 6.8). As an extreme comparison, the ratio of outer surface to volume for a whale is hundreds of thousands of times smaller than that for a water flea (*Daphnia*). Nevertheless, every cell in the whale must be bathed in fluid and have access to oxygen, nutrients, and other resources. How is this accomplished?

In whales and most other animals, extensively branched or folded surfaces are the evolutionary adaptation that enables sufficient exchange with the environment **(Figure 40.4)**. In almost all cases, these surfaces lie within the body, protecting delicate exchange tissues from abrasion or dehydration and allowing for streamlined body contours. In humans, the digestive, respiratory, and circulatory systems rely on exchange surfaces within the body that in each system have a total area more than 25 times that of the skin.

Internal body fluids link exchange surfaces to body cells. In all animals, the spaces between cells are filled with fluid, often called **interstitial fluid** (from the Latin for "stand between"). Complex body plans also include a circulatory fluid, such as blood. Exchange between the interstitial fluid and circulatory fluid enables cells throughout the body to obtain nutrients and get rid of wastes (see Figure 40.4).

Despite the greater challenges of exchange with the environment, complex body plans have distinct benefits over simple ones. For example, an external skeleton can protect against

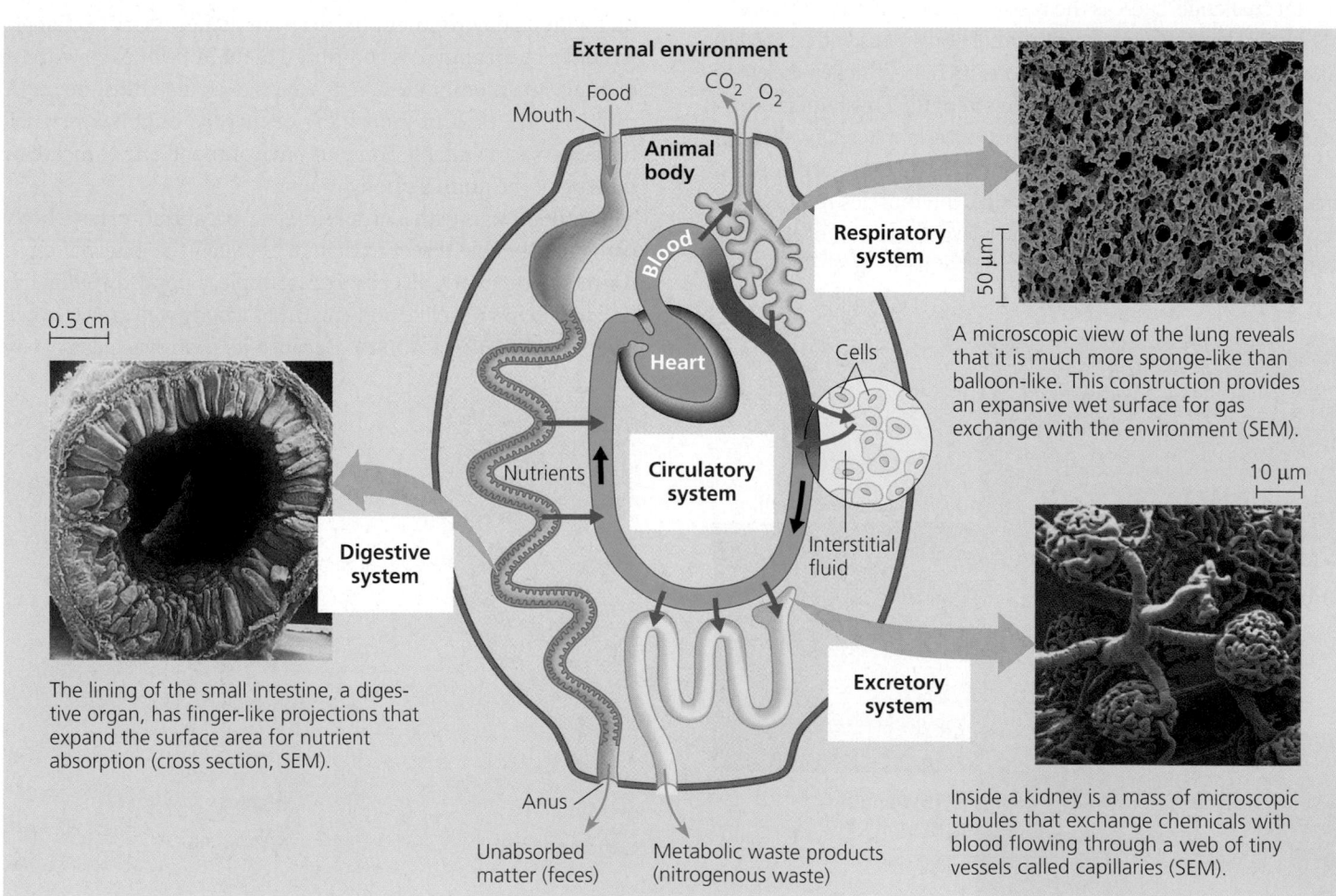

The lining of the small intestine, a digestive organ, has finger-like projections that expand the surface area for nutrient absorption (cross section, SEM).

A microscopic view of the lung reveals that it is much more sponge-like than balloon-like. This construction provides an expansive wet surface for gas exchange with the environment (SEM).

Inside a kidney is a mass of microscopic tubules that exchange chemicals with blood flowing through a web of tiny vessels called capillaries (SEM).

▲ **Figure 40.4 Internal exchange surfaces of complex animals.** This diagram provides an overview of chemical exchange between an animal body and the environment. Most animals have surfaces that are specialized for exchanging chemicals with the surroundings. These exchange surfaces are usually internal but are connected to the environment via openings on the body surface (the mouth, for example). The exchange surfaces are finely branched or folded, giving them a very large area. The digestive, respiratory, and excretory systems all have such exchange surfaces. The circulatory system carries chemicals transported across these surfaces throughout the body.

? *In what sense are exchange surfaces such as the lining of the digestive system both internal and external?*

predators, and sensory organs can provide detailed information on the animal's surroundings. Internal digestive organs can break down food gradually, controlling the release of stored energy. In addition, specialized filtration systems can adjust the composition of the internal fluid that bathes the animal's body cells. In this way, an animal can maintain a relatively stable internal environment while living in a variable external environment. A complex body plan is especially advantageous for animals living on land, where the external environment may be highly variable.

Hierarchical Organization of Body Plans

Cells form an animal's body through their emergent properties. Recall from Chapter 1 that emergent properties arise through successive levels of structural and functional organization. Cells are organized into **tissues**, groups of cells of similar appearance and a common function. In all but the simplest animals (such as sponges), different tissues are further organized into functional units called **organs**. Groups of organs that work together provide an additional level of organization and coordination and make up an **organ system (Table 40.1)**. Thus, for example, the skin is an organ of the integumentary system, which protects against infection and helps regulate body temperature.

Organs often contain tissues with distinct physiological roles. In some cases, the roles are different enough that we consider the organ to belong to more than one organ system. The pancreas, for instance, produces enzymes critical to the function of the digestive system and also regulates the level of sugar in the blood as a vital part of the endocrine system.

Just as viewing the hierarchy of the body's organization from the "bottom up" (from cells to organ systems) reveals emergent properties that underlie organ systems, a view of the hierarchy from the "top down" makes clear the multilayered basis of specialization. Consider the digestive system, which in humans consists of the mouth, pharynx, esophagus, stomach, small and large intestines, accessory organs, and anus. Each organ has specific roles in digestion. One important function of the stomach, for example, is to initiate the breakdown of proteins. This process requires a churning powered by stomach muscles, as well as digestive juices secreted by the stomach lining. Production of digestive juices, in turn, requires several highly specialized cell types, one of which generates concentrated hydrochloric acid.

The specialization characteristic of complex body plans is based on varied combinations of a limited set of cell and tissue types. For example, lungs and blood vessels have distinct functions but are lined by tissues that are of the same basic type and therefore share many properties. To introduce these shared properties, we next survey the major tissue types in vertebrates. In later chapters, we'll discuss how the tissues described here contribute to the functions of each organ system.

Tissue Structure and Function

Animal tissues fall into four main categories: epithelial tissue, connective tissue, muscle tissue, and nervous tissue. We explore the structure and function of each type in **Figure 40.5** and in the accompanying text, on the next four pages.

Table 40.1 **Organ Systems: Their Main Components and Functions in Mammals**		
Organ System	**Main Components**	**Main Functions**
Digestive	Mouth, pharynx, esophagus, stomach, intestines, liver, pancreas, anus	Food processing (ingestion, digestion, absorption, elimination)
Circulatory	Heart, blood vessels, blood	Internal distribution of materials
Respiratory	Lungs, trachea, other breathing tubes	Gas exchange (uptake of oxygen; disposal of carbon dioxide)
Immune and lymphatic	Bone marrow, lymph nodes, thymus, spleen, lymph vessels, white blood cells	Body defense (fighting infections and cancer)
Excretory	Kidneys, ureters, urinary bladder, urethra	Disposal of metabolic wastes; regulation of osmotic balance of blood
Endocrine	Pituitary, thyroid, pancreas, adrenal, and other hormone-secreting glands	Coordination of body activities (such as digestion and metabolism)
Reproductive	Ovaries or testes, and associated organs	Reproduction
Nervous	Brain, spinal cord, nerves, sensory organs	Coordination of body activities; detection of stimuli and formulation of responses to them
Integumentary	Skin and its derivatives (such as hair, claws, skin glands)	Protection against mechanical injury, infection, drying out; thermoregulation
Skeletal	Skeleton (bones, tendons, ligaments, cartilage)	Body support, protection of internal organs, movement
Muscular	Skeletal muscles	Locomotion and other movement

Epithelial Tissue

Occurring as sheets of cells, **epithelial tissue** covers the outside of the body and lines organs and cavities within the body. The close packing of epithelial cells, often involving tight junctions (see Figure 6.32), enables epithelial tissue to function as a barrier against mechanical injury, pathogens, and fluid loss. The cells of an epithelial tissue, or **epithelium** (plural, *epithelia*), also form active interfaces with the environment. For example, the epithelium that lines the nasal passages has a critical function in olfaction, the sense of smell.

Epithelial cell shape may be *cuboidal* (like dice), *columnar* (like bricks standing on end), or *squamous* (like floor tiles). In addition, cells may be arranged in a *simple epithelium* (single cell layer), a *stratified epithelium* (multiple tiers of cells), or a *pseudostratified epithelium* (a single layer of cells varying in height). As shown in Figure 40.5, different cell shapes and arrangements correlate with distinct functions. For example, columnar epithelia, which have cells with relatively large cytoplasmic volumes, are often located where secretion or active absorption is important.

▼ Figure 40.5

Exploring Structure and Function in Animal Tissues

Epithelial Tissue

Cuboidal epithelium, with dice-shaped cells specialized for secretion, makes up the epithelium of kidney tubules and many glands, including the thyroid gland and salivary glands.

Simple columnar epithelium lines the intestines. This epithelium secretes digestive juices and absorbs nutrients.

Pseudostratified ciliated columnar epithelium forms a mucous membrane that lines portions of the respiratory tract of many vertebrates. The beating cilia move the film of mucus along the surface.

Stratified squamous epithelium regenerates rapidly by cell division near the basal lamina (see below). The new cells are pushed outward, replacing cells that are sloughed off. This epithelium is commonly found on surfaces subject to abrasion, such as the outer skin and linings of the esophagus, anus, and vagina.

Simple squamous epithelium, which is thin and leaky, functions in the exchange of material by diffusion. This type of epithelium lines blood vessels and the air sacs of the lungs, where diffusion of nutrients and gases is critical.

Apical surface

Basal surface

Basal lamina

40 μm

All epithelia are polarized, meaning that they have two different sides. The *apical* surface faces the lumen (cavity) or outside of the organ and is therefore exposed to fluid or air. It is this surface that is often covered with specialized projections. For example, the epithelium of the small intestine is covered with microvilli, projections that increase the surface area available for absorbing nutrients (see Figure 40.4). The opposite side of each epithelium is the *basal* surface. The basal surface is attached to a *basal lamina*, a dense mat of extracellular matrix, which separates the epithelium from the underlying tissue.

(All photos in figure are LMs.)

Connective Tissue

The most common functions of **connective tissues** are to bind and support other tissues in the body (see Figure 40.5). Connective tissue consists of a sparse population of cells scattered through an extracellular matrix. The matrix generally consists of a web of fibers embedded in a uniform foundation that may be liquid, jellylike, or solid. This variation in matrix structure is reflected in the six major types of connective tissue in vertebrates: loose connective tissue, cartilage, fibrous connective tissue, adipose tissue, blood, and bone.

Connective tissue fibers, which are made of protein, are of three kinds: collagenous, elastic, and reticular. *Collagenous fibers* provide strength combined with flexibility. They are made of collagen, probably the most abundant protein in the animal kingdom. Collagenous fibers are nonelastic and do not tear easily when pulled lengthwise. *Elastic fibers* are easily stretched but are also resilient, snapping back to their original length when tension is released. Shaped as long threads, elastic fibers are made of a protein called elastin. *Reticular fibers* are very thin and branched. Composed of collagen and continuous with collagenous fibers,

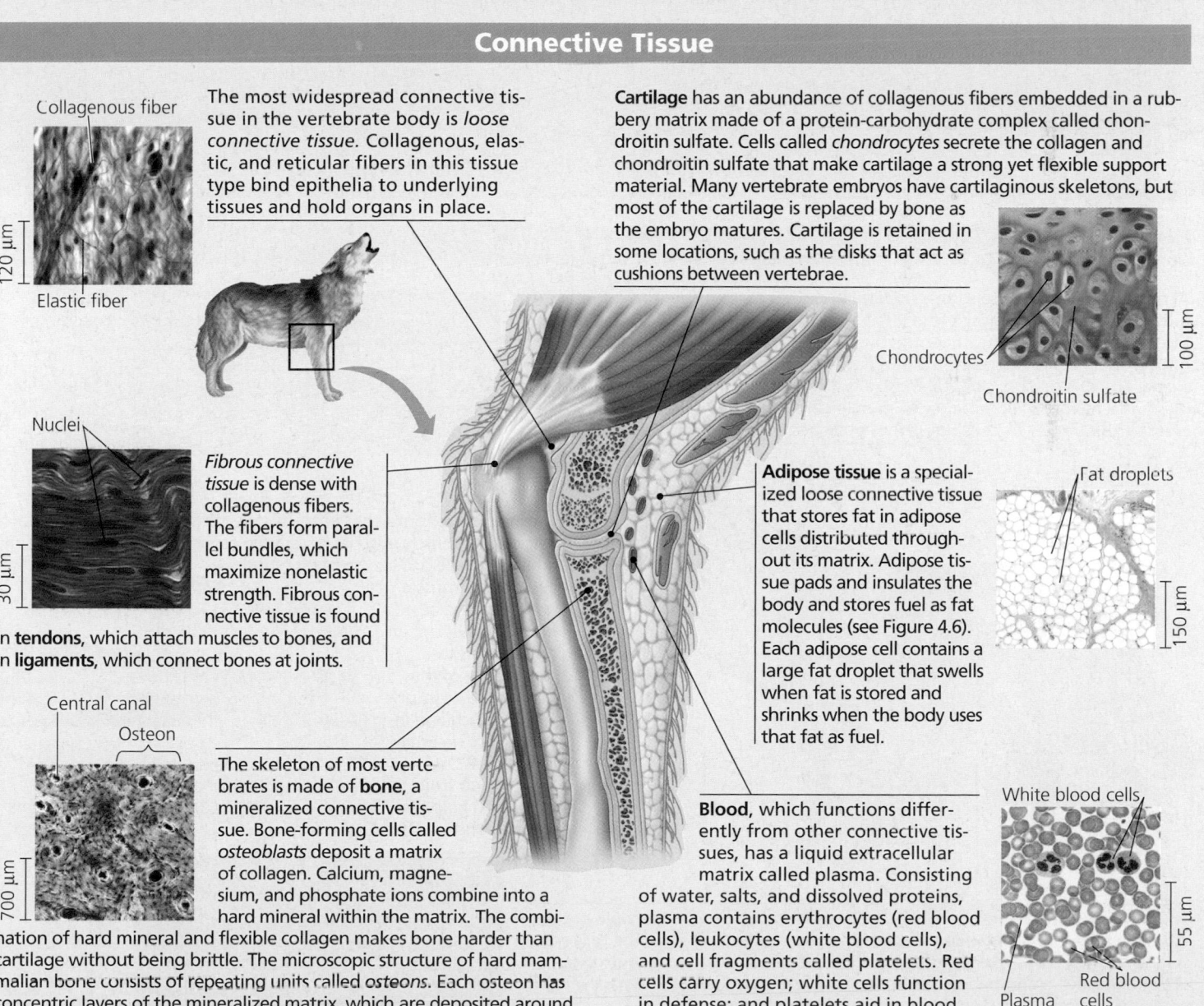

Connective Tissue

Collagenous fiber

120 μm

Elastic fiber

The most widespread connective tissue in the vertebrate body is *loose connective tissue*. Collagenous, elastic, and reticular fibers in this tissue type bind epithelia to underlying tissues and hold organs in place.

Nuclei

30 μm

Fibrous connective tissue is dense with collagenous fibers. The fibers form parallel bundles, which maximize nonelastic strength. Fibrous connective tissue is found in **tendons**, which attach muscles to bones, and in **ligaments**, which connect bones at joints.

Central canal

Osteon

700 μm

The skeleton of most vertebrates is made of **bone**, a mineralized connective tissue. Bone-forming cells called *osteoblasts* deposit a matrix of collagen. Calcium, magnesium, and phosphate ions combine into a hard mineral within the matrix. The combination of hard mineral and flexible collagen makes bone harder than cartilage without being brittle. The microscopic structure of hard mammalian bone consists of repeating units called *osteons*. Each osteon has concentric layers of the mineralized matrix, which are deposited around a central canal containing blood vessels and nerves.

Cartilage has an abundance of collagenous fibers embedded in a rubbery matrix made of a protein-carbohydrate complex called chondroitin sulfate. Cells called *chondrocytes* secrete the collagen and chondroitin sulfate that make cartilage a strong yet flexible support material. Many vertebrate embryos have cartilaginous skeletons, but most of the cartilage is replaced by bone as the embryo matures. Cartilage is retained in some locations, such as the disks that act as cushions between vertebrae.

Chondrocytes

100 μm

Chondroitin sulfate

Adipose tissue is a specialized loose connective tissue that stores fat in adipose cells distributed throughout its matrix. Adipose tissue pads and insulates the body and stores fuel as fat molecules (see Figure 4.6). Each adipose cell contains a large fat droplet that swells when fat is stored and shrinks when the body uses that fat as fuel.

Fat droplets

150 μm

Blood, which functions differently from other connective tissues, has a liquid extracellular matrix called plasma. Consisting of water, salts, and dissolved proteins, plasma contains erythrocytes (red blood cells), leukocytes (white blood cells), and cell fragments called platelets. Red cells carry oxygen; white cells function in defense; and platelets aid in blood clotting.

White blood cells

55 μm

Plasma

Red blood cells

Continued on next page

they form a tightly woven fabric that joins connective tissue to adjacent tissues. If you pinch a fold of skin on the back of your hand, the collagenous and reticular fibers prevent the tissue from being pulled far from the bone; the elastic fibers then restore the skin to its original shape when you release your grip.

The connective tissue that holds many tissues and organs together and in place contains scattered cells of varying function. Of these cells, two types predominate: fibroblasts and macrophages. **Fibroblasts** secrete the protein ingredients of the extracellular fibers. **Macrophages** are cells that roam the maze of fibers, engulfing both foreign particles and the debris of dead cells by phagocytosis (see Chapter 6).

Muscle Tissue

The tissue responsible for nearly all types of body movement is **muscle tissue**. All muscle cells consist of filaments containing the proteins actin and myosin, which together enable mus-

cles to contract. Muscle is the most abundant tissue in many animals, and muscle activity accounts for much of the energy-consuming cellular work in an active animal. Figure 40.5 shows the three types of muscle tissue in the vertebrate body: skeletal, cardiac, and smooth muscle.

Nervous Tissue

The function of **nervous tissue** is to sense stimuli and transmit signals in the form of nerve impulses from one part of the animal to another. Nervous tissue contains **neurons**, or nerve cells, which have extensions called axons that are uniquely specialized to transmit nerve impulses (see Figure 40.5). It also includes different forms of **glial cells**, or glia, which help nourish, insulate, and replenish neurons. In many animals, a concentration of nervous tissue forms a brain, an information-processing center. As we will discuss next, neurons have a critical role in managing many of the animal's physiological functions.

▼ **Figure 40.5 (continued)**

Exploring Structure and Function in Animal Tissues

Muscle Tissue

Attached to bones by tendons, **skeletal muscle** is responsible for voluntary movements. Skeletal muscle consists of bundles of long cells called muscle fibers. The arrangement of contractile units, or sarcomeres, along the length of the fibers gives the cells a striped (striated) appearance under the microscope. For this reason, skeletal muscle is also called *striated muscle*. Adult mammals have a fixed number of muscle cells; building muscle does not increase the number of cells but rather enlarges those already present.

Multiple nuclei

Muscle fiber

Sarcomere

100 μm

Cardiac muscle forms the contractile wall of the heart. It is striated like skeletal muscle and has contractile properties similar to those of skeletal muscle. Unlike skeletal muscle, however, cardiac muscle carries out an unconscious task: contraction of the heart. Cardiac muscle fibers branch and interconnect via intercalated disks, which relay signals from cell to cell and help synchronize the heartbeat.

Nucleus

Intercalated disk

50 μm

Smooth muscle, so named because it lacks striations, is found in the walls of the digestive tract, urinary bladder, arteries, and other internal organs. The cells are spindle-shaped. Controlled by different kinds of nerves than those controlling skeletal muscles, smooth muscles are responsible for involuntary body activities, such as churning of the stomach or constriction of arteries.

Nucleus

Muscle fibers

25 μm

Coordination and Control

An animal's tissues, organs, and organ systems must act in conjunction with one another. For example, during long dives the harbor seal in Figure 40.2 slows its heart rate, collapses its lungs, and lowers its body temperature while propelling itself forward with its hind flippers. Coordinating activity across an animal's body in this way requires communication. What signals are used? How do the signals move within the body? There are two sets of answers to these questions, reflecting the two major systems for control and coordination: the endocrine system and the nervous system (**Figure 40.6**). In the endocrine system, signaling molecules released into the bloodstream by endocrine cells reach all locations in the body. In the nervous system, neurons transmit information between specific locations.

The signaling molecules broadcast throughout the body by the endocrine system are called **hormones**. Different hormones cause distinct effects, and only cells that have receptors for a particular hormone respond (**Figure 40.6a**). Depending on which cells have receptors for that hormone, the hormone may have an effect in just a single location or in sites throughout the body. Cells, in turn, can express more than one receptor type. Thus, cells in the ovaries and testes are regulated not only by sex hormones but also by metabolic hormones. Such hormones include insulin, which controls the level of glucose in the blood by binding to and regulating virtually every cell outside of the brain.

Hormones are relatively slow acting. It takes many seconds for insulin and other hormones to be released into the bloodstream and be carried throughout the body. Hormone effects are often long-lasting, however, because hormones remain in the bloodstream and target tissue for seconds, minutes, or even hours.

Nervous Tissue

Nerve cells (neurons) are the basic units of the nervous system. A neuron consists of a cell body and two or more extensions called dendrites and axons. Dendrites transmit signals from their tips toward the rest of the neuron. Axons, which are often bundled together into nerves, transmit signals toward another neuron or toward an effector, a structure such as a muscle cell that carries out a body response. The supporting glial cells help neurons function properly.

Glial cells

40 µm

Dendrites
Cell body
Axon

(Fluorescent LM)

Axons

Blood vessel

(Confocal LM)

15 µm

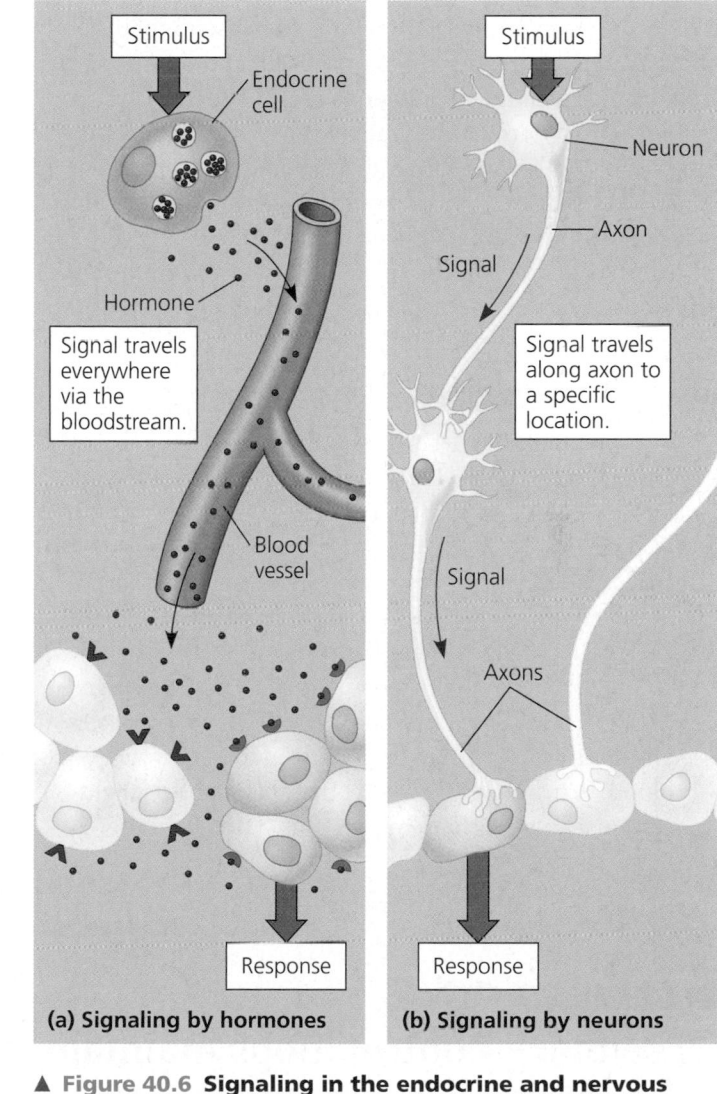

(a) **Signaling by hormones**

Stimulus
Endocrine cell
Hormone
Signal travels everywhere via the bloodstream.
Blood vessel
Response

(b) **Signaling by neurons**

Stimulus
Neuron
Axon
Signal
Signal travels along axon to a specific location.
Signal
Axons
Response

▲ Figure 40.6 **Signaling in the endocrine and nervous systems.** Endocrine cells secrete specific hormones—signaling molecules (shown as red dots)—into the bloodstream. Only cells expressing the corresponding receptor receive and respond to the signal. Nerve cells (neurons) generate signals that travel along axons. Only cells that form a specialized junction with the axon of an activated neuron receive and respond to the signal.

In the nervous system, a signal is not broadcast throughout the entire body. Instead, each signal, called a nerve impulse, travels to a target cell along a dedicated communication line, consisting mainly of the neuron extensions called axons (**Figure 40.6b**). Four types of cells receive nerve impulses: other neurons, muscle cells, endocrine cells, and exocrine cells. Unlike the endocrine system, the nervous system conveys information by the *pathway* the signal takes. For example, a person can distinguish different musical notes because each note's frequency activates different neurons connecting the ear to the brain.

Signaling in the nervous system usually involves more than one type of signal. Nerve impulses travel within axons, sometimes over long distances, as changes in voltage. But in many cases, passing signals from one neuron to another involves very short-range chemical signals. Overall, transmission is extremely fast; nerve impulses take only a fraction of a second to reach the target and last only a fraction of a second.

Because the two major communication systems of the body differ in signal type, transmission, speed, and duration, they are adapted to different functions. The endocrine system is well suited for coordinating gradual changes that affect the entire body, such as growth and development, reproduction, metabolic processes, and digestion. The nervous system is well suited for directing immediate and rapid responses to the environment, especially in controlling fast locomotion and behavior. Both systems contribute to maintaining a stable internal environment, our next topic of discussion.

CONCEPT CHECK 40.1

1. What properties are shared by all types of epithelia?
2. Under what temperature conditions would it benefit a jackrabbit to flatten its ears against its body? Explain.
3. **WHAT IF?** Suppose you are standing at the edge of a cliff and you suddenly slip—you barely manage to keep your balance to keep from falling. As your heart races, you feel a burst of energy, due in part to a surge of blood into dilated (widened) vessels in your muscles and an upward spike in the level of glucose in your blood. Why might you expect that this "fight-or-flight" response requires both the nervous system and the endocrine system?

For suggested answers, see Appendix A.

CONCEPT 40.2
Feedback control loops maintain the internal environment in many animals

Imagine that your body temperature soared every time you took a hot shower or drank a freshly brewed cup of coffee.

Managing the state of the internal environment is a major challenge for the animal body. Faced with environmental fluctuations, animals manage their internal environment by either regulating or conforming.

Regulating and Conforming

An animal is said to be a **regulator** for a particular environmental variable if it uses internal control mechanisms to regulate internal change in the face of external fluctuation. For example, the river otter in **Figure 40.7** is a regulator for temperature, keeping its body at a temperature that is largely independent of that of the water in which it swims.

An animal is said to be a **conformer** for a particular environmental variable if it allows its internal condition to conform to external changes in the variable. For instance, the largemouth bass in Figure 40.7 conforms to the temperature of the lake in which it lives. As the water warms or cools, so do the cells of the bass. Some animals conform to more constant environments. For example, many marine invertebrates, such as spider crabs of the genus *Libinia*, let their internal solute concentration conform to the relatively stable solute concentration (salinity) of their ocean environment.

Regulating and conforming represent extremes on a continuum. An animal may regulate some internal conditions while allowing others to conform to the environment. For example, even though the bass conforms to the temperature of the surrounding water, the solute concentration in its blood

▲ Figure 40.7 **The relationship between body and environmental temperatures in an aquatic temperature regulator and an aquatic temperature conformer.** The river otter regulates its body temperature, keeping it stable across a wide range of environmental temperatures. The largemouth bass, meanwhile, allows its internal environment to conform to the water temperature.

and interstitial fluid differs from the solute concentration of the fresh water in which it lives. This difference occurs because the fish's anatomy and physiology enable it to regulate internal changes in solute concentration. (You will learn more about the mechanisms of this regulation in Chapter 44.)

Homeostasis

The steady body temperature of a river otter and the stable concentration of solutes in a freshwater bass are examples of **homeostasis**, which means "steady state," or internal balance. In achieving homeostasis, animals maintain a relatively constant internal environment even when the external environment changes significantly.

Like many animals, humans exhibit homeostasis for a range of physical and chemical properties. For example, the human body maintains a fairly constant body temperature of about 37°C (98.6°F) and a pH of the blood and interstitial fluid within 0.1 pH unit of 7.4. The body also regulates the solute concentration of glucose in the bloodstream so that it does not fluctuate for long from about 90 mg of glucose per 100 mL of blood.

Mechanisms of Homeostasis

Before exploring homeostasis in animals, let's first consider a nonliving example: the regulation of room temperature (Figure 40.8). Let's assume we want to keep a house at 20°C (68°F), a comfortable temperature for normal activity. We adjust a control device—the thermostat—to 20°C and allow a thermometer in the thermostat to monitor temperature. If the room temperature falls below 20°C, the thermostat responds by turning on the heating system. Heat is produced until the room reaches 20°C, at which point the thermostat switches off the heater. Whenever the temperature in the room again drifts below 20°C, the thermostat activates another heating cycle.

Like a home heating system, an animal achieves homeostasis by maintaining a variable, such as body temperature or solute concentration, at or near a particular value, or **set point**. Fluctuations in the variable above or below the set point serve as the **stimulus**. A receptor, or **sensor**, detects the stimulus and triggers a **response**, a physiological activity that helps return the variable to the set point. In the home heating example, a drop in temperature below the set point acts as a stimulus, the thermometer serves as the sensor, and the heater produces the response.

Feedback Loops in Homeostasis

Like the regulatory circuit shown in Figure 40.8, homeostasis in animals relies largely on **negative feedback**, a response that reduces, or "damps," the stimulus. For example, when you exercise vigorously, you produce heat, which increases body temperature. Your nervous system detects this increase and

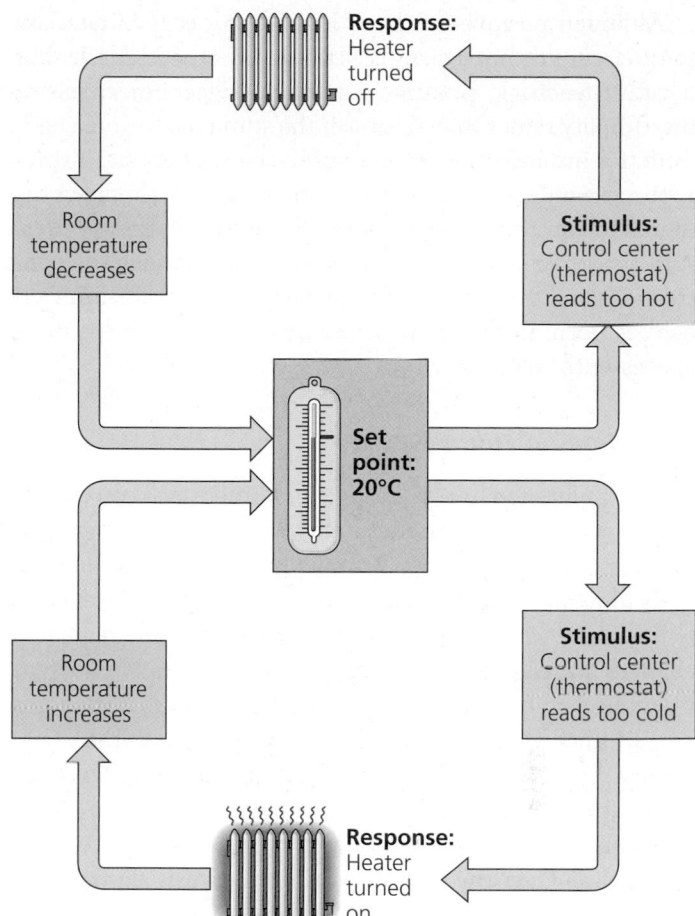

▲ **Figure 40.8 A nonliving example of negative feedback: control of room temperature.** Regulating room temperature depends on a control center (a thermostat) that detects temperature change and activates mechanisms that reverse that change.

? *How would adding an air conditioner to the system contribute to homeostasis?*

triggers sweating. As you sweat, the evaporation of moisture from your skin cools your body, helping return your body temperature to its set point.

Homeostasis is a dynamic equilibrium, the interplay between external factors that tend to change the internal environment and internal control mechanisms that oppose such changes. Note that physiological responses to stimuli are not instantaneous, just as switching on a furnace does not immediately warm a house. As a result, homeostasis reduces but doesn't eliminate changes in the internal environment. Additional fluctuation occurs if a variable has a **normal range**—an upper and lower limit—rather than a single set point. This is equivalent to a heating system that begins producing heat when the room temperature drops to 19°C (66°F) and stops heating when the temperature reaches 21°C (70°F). Regardless of whether there is a set point or a normal range, homeostasis is enhanced by mechanisms that reduce fluctuations, such as insulation in the case of temperature and physiological buffers in the case of pH.

Although positive-feedback loops also occur in animals, these circuits do not usually contribute to homeostasis. Unlike negative feedback, **positive feedback** triggers mechanisms that amplify rather than diminish the stimulus. During childbirth, for instance, the pressure of the baby's head against receptors near the opening of the mother's uterus stimulates the uterus to contract. These contractions result in greater pressure against the opening of the uterus, heightening the contractions and thereby causing even greater pressure, until the baby is born. In this way, the positive feedback helps drive processes to completion.

Alterations in Homeostasis

The set points and normal ranges for homeostasis can change under various circumstances. In fact, so-called *regulated changes* in the internal environment are essential to normal body functions. For example, many animals have a lower body temperature when asleep than when awake. Some regulated changes are associated with a particular stage in life, such as the radical shift in hormone balance that occurs during puberty. Other regulated changes are cyclic, such as the variation in hormone levels responsible for women's menstrual cycles (see Figure 46.14). Over the short term, homeostatic mechanisms maintain the set point in effect during a particular interval. Over the longer term, homeostasis allows regulated change in the set point and therefore in the body's internal environment.

One way in which the normal range of homeostasis may change is through **acclimatization**, the process by which an animal adjusts to changes in its external environment. For example, when an elk or other mammal moves from sea level to a much higher elevation, changes that occur over several days facilitate activity at lowered oxygen concentrations. These changes include increased blood flow in the lungs and increased production of red blood cells that carry oxygen. Note that acclimatization, a temporary change during an animal's lifetime, should not be confused with adaptation, a process of change in a population brought about by natural selection acting over many generations.

CONCEPT CHECK 40.2

1. Is it accurate to define homeostasis as a constant internal environment? Explain.
2. Describe the difference between negative feedback and positive feedback.
3. **WHAT IF?** If you were deciding where to locate the thermostat in a house, what considerations would govern your decision? How do these factors relate to the location of many homeostatic control sensors in the human brain?

For suggested answers, see Appendix A.

CONCEPT 40.3

Homeostatic processes for thermoregulation involve form, function, and behavior

In this section, we will examine the regulation of body temperature as an example of how form and function work together in regulating an animal's internal environment. Later chapters in this unit will discuss other physiological systems involved in maintaining homeostasis.

Thermoregulation is the process by which animals maintain an internal temperature within a tolerable range. Thermoregulation is critical to survival because most biochemical and physiological processes are very sensitive to changes in body temperature. For every 10°C (18°F) decrease in temperature, the rates of most enzyme-mediated reactions decrease two- to threefold. Increases in temperatures speed up reactions but cause some proteins to become less active. For instance, the oxygen carrier molecule hemoglobin becomes less effective at binding oxygen as temperature increases. Membranes can also change properties, becoming increasingly fluid or rigid as temperatures rise or fall, respectively.

Each animal species has an optimal temperature range. Thermoregulation helps keep body temperature within that optimal range, enabling cells to function effectively even as the external temperature fluctuates.

Endothermy and Ectothermy

Internal metabolism and the external environment provide the sources of heat for thermoregulation. Birds and mammals are mainly **endothermic**, meaning that they are warmed mostly by heat generated by metabolism. A few nonavian reptiles, some fishes, and many insect species are also mainly endothermic. In contrast, amphibians, lizards, snakes, turtles, many fishes, and most invertebrates are mainly **ectothermic**, meaning that they gain most of their heat from external sources.

Animals that are mainly endothermic are known as endotherms; those that are mainly ectothermic are known as ectotherms. Keep in mind, though, that endothermy and ectothermy are not mutually exclusive modes of thermoregulation. For example, a bird is mainly endothermic, but it may warm itself in the sun on a cold morning, much as an ectothermic lizard does.

Endothermic animals can maintain stable body temperatures even in the face of large environmental temperature fluctuations. For example, few ectotherms are active in the below-freezing weather that prevails during winter over much of Earth's surface, but many endotherms function very well in these conditions **(Figure 40.9a)**. In a cold environment, an endotherm generates enough heat to keep its body substantially warmer than its surroundings. In a hot environment, endothermic vertebrates have

(a) A walrus, an endotherm

(b) A lizard, an ectotherm

▲ **Figure 40.9 Endothermy and ectothermy.**

mechanisms for cooling the body, enabling them to withstand heat loads that are intolerable for most ectotherms.

Because their heat source is largely environmental, ectotherms generally need to consume much less food than endotherms of equivalent size—an advantage if food supplies are limited. Ectotherms also usually tolerate larger fluctuations in their internal temperatures. Although ectotherms do not generate enough heat for thermoregulation, many adjust body temperature by behavioral means, such as seeking out shade or basking in the sun **(Figure 40.9b)**. Overall, ectothermy is an effective and successful strategy in most environments, as shown by the abundance and diversity of ectothermic animals.

Variation in Body Temperature

Animals can have either a variable or a constant body temperature. An animal whose body temperature varies with its environment is called a *poikilotherm* (from the Greek *poikilos*, varied). In contrast, a *homeotherm* has a relatively constant body temperature. For example, the largemouth bass is a poikilotherm, and the river otter is a homeotherm (see Figure 40.7).

From the descriptions of ectotherms and endotherms, it might seem that all ectotherms are poikilothermic and all endotherms are homeothermic. Actually, there is no fixed relationship between the source of heat and the stability of body temperature. For example, many ectothermic marine fishes and invertebrates inhabit waters with such stable temperatures that their body temperature varies less than that of endotherms such as humans and other mammals. Conversely, the body temperature of a few endotherms varies considerably. For example, bats and hummingbirds may periodically enter an inactive state in which they maintain a lower body temperature.

It is a common misconception that ectotherms are "cold-blooded" and endotherms are "warm-blooded." Ectotherms do not necessarily have low body temperatures. In fact, when sitting in the sun, many ectothermic lizards have higher body temperatures than mammals. Thus, the terms *cold-blooded* and *warm-blooded* are misleading and have been dropped from the scientific vocabulary.

Balancing Heat Loss and Gain

Thermoregulation depends on an animal's ability to control the exchange of heat with its environment. Any organism, like any object, exchanges heat by four physical processes: conduction, convection, radiation, and evaporation. **Figure 40.10** distinguishes these processes, which account for the flow of heat

Radiation is the emission of electromagnetic waves by all objects warmer than absolute zero. Radiation can transfer heat between objects that are not in direct contact, as when a lizard absorbs heat radiating from the sun.

Evaporation is the removal of heat from the surface of a liquid that is losing some of its molecules as gas. Evaporation of water from a lizard's moist surfaces that are exposed to the environment has a strong cooling effect.

Convection is the transfer of heat by the movement of air or liquid past a surface, as when a breeze contributes to heat loss from a lizard's dry skin, or blood moves heat from the body core to the extremities.

Conduction is the direct transfer of thermal motion (heat) between molecules of objects in direct contact with each other, as when a lizard sits on a hot rock.

▲ **Figure 40.10 Heat exchange between an organism and its environment.**

Epidermis

Dermis

Hypodermis

Adipose tissue

Blood vessels

Hair

Sweat pore

Muscle

Nerve

Sweat gland

Oil gland

Hair follicle

▲ **Figure 40.11 Mammalian integumentary system.** The skin and its derivatives serve important functions in mammals, including protection and thermoregulation.

both within an organism and between an organism and its external environment. Note that heat is always transferred from an object of higher temperature to one of lower temperature.

The essence of thermoregulation is maintaining rates of heat gain that equal rates of heat loss. Animals do this through mechanisms that either reduce heat exchange overall or that favor heat exchange in a particular direction. In mammals, several of these mechanisms involve the **integumentary system**, the outer covering of the body, consisting of the skin, hair, and nails (claws or hooves in some species). A key organ of this system is the skin, which consists of the epidermis and the dermis **(Figure 40.11)**. The epidermis is the outermost layer of skin and is composed mostly of dead epithelial cells that continually flake and fall off. New cells pushing up from lower layers replace the cells that are lost. The inner layer, the dermis, contains hair follicles, oil and sweat glands, muscles, nerves, and blood vessels. Beneath the skin lies the hypodermis, a layer of adipose tissue that includes fat-storing cells as well as blood vessels.

Insulation

A major thermoregulatory adaptation in mammals and birds is insulation, which reduces the flow of heat between an animal and its environment. Sources of insulation include hair, feathers, and layers of fat formed by adipose tissue.

Many animals that rely on insulation to reduce overall heat exchange also adjust their insulating layers to help thermoregulate. Most land mammals and birds, for example, react to cold by raising their fur or feathers. This action traps a thicker layer of air,

thereby increasing the insulating power of the fur or feather layer. To repel water that would reduce the insulating capacity of feathers or fur, some animals secrete oily substances, such as the oils that birds apply to their feathers during preening. Lacking feathers or fur, humans must rely primarily on fat for insulation. "Goose bumps" are a vestige of hair raising inherited from our furry ancestors.

Insulation plays a particularly important role in thermoregulation by marine mammals, such as whales and walruses. These animals swim in water colder than their body core temperature, and many species spend at least part of the year in nearly freezing polar seas. The problem of thermoregulation is made worse by the fact that the transfer of heat to water occurs 50 to 100 times more rapidly than heat transfer to air. Just under the skin, marine mammals have a very thick layer of insulating fat called blubber. The insulation blubber provides is so effective that marine mammals maintain body core temperatures of about 36–38°C (97–100°F) without requiring much more food energy than land mammals of similar size.

Circulatory Adaptations

Circulatory systems provide a major route for heat flow between the interior and exterior of the body. Adaptations that regulate the extent of blood flow near the body surface or that trap heat within the body core play a significant role in thermoregulation.

In response to changes in the temperature of their surroundings, many animals alter the amount of blood (and hence heat) flowing between their body core and their skin. Nerve signals that relax the muscles of the vessel walls result in *vasodilation*, an increase in the diameter of superficial blood vessels (those near the body surface). As a consequence of the increase in vessel diameter, blood flow in the skin is elevated. In endotherms, vasodilation usually warms the skin and increases the transfer of body heat to the environment by radiation, conduction, and convection (see Figure 40.10). The reverse process, *vasoconstriction*, reduces blood flow and heat transfer by decreasing the diameter of superficial vessels. It is vasoconstriction in blood vessels of the ear that allows the jackrabbit shown in Figure 40.1 to avoid overheating on hot desert days.

Like endotherms, some ectotherms control heat exchange by regulating blood flow. For example, when the marine iguana of the Galápagos Islands swims in the cold ocean, its superficial blood vessels will undergo vasoconstriction. This process routes more blood to the central core of the body, conserving body heat.

In many birds and mammals, reduction of heat loss relies on **countercurrent exchange**, the flow of adjacent fluids in opposing directions that maximizes transfer rates of heat or solutes. Heat transfer involves an antiparallel arrangement of blood vessels called a *countercurrent heat exchanger*. When tissues are organized this way, arteries and veins are located adjacent to each other. As warm blood passes through arteries, it transfers heat to the colder blood returning from the extremities in the veins. Because the arteries and veins have countercurrent blood flow—blood flowing in opposite directions—heat transfer occurs along the entire length of the exchanger. **Figure 40.12** illustrates countercurrent heat exchange in a goose and dolphin.

Certain sharks, bony fishes, and insects also use countercurrent heat exchange. Although most sharks and fishes are temperature conformers, countercurrent heat exchangers are found in some large, powerful swimmers, including great white sharks, bluefin tuna, and swordfish. By keeping the main swimming muscles several degrees warmer than tissues near the animal's surface, this adaptation enables the vigorous, sustained activity that is characteristic of these animals. Similarly, many endothermic insects (bumblebees, honeybees, and some moths) have a countercurrent exchanger that helps maintain a high temperature in the thorax, where flight muscles are located.

In controlling heat gain and loss, some species regulate the extent of blood flow to the countercurrent exchanger. By allowing blood to pass through the heat exchanger or diverting it to other blood vessels, these animals alter the rate of heat loss as their physiological state or environment changes. For example, insects flying in hot weather run the risk of overheating because of the large amount of heat produced by working flight muscles. In some species, the countercurrent mechanism can be "shut down," allowing muscle-produced heat to be lost from the thorax to the abdomen and then to the environment.

Cooling by Evaporative Heat Loss

Many mammals and birds live in places where thermoregulation requires cooling as well as warming. If environmental temperature is above body temperature, animals gain heat from the environment as well as from metabolism, and evaporation is the only way to keep body temperature from rising rapidly. Terrestrial animals lose water by evaporation across the skin and when they breathe. Water absorbs considerable heat when it evaporates (see Chapter 3); this heat is carried away from the body surface with the water vapor.

Canada goose   Bottlenose dolphin

Artery   Vein

❶ 35°C   ❸ 33°
30°   27°
20°   18°
10°   9°
❷

Blood flow

❶
❸   Vein
Artery
❸
❷

❶ Arteries carrying warm blood down the legs of a goose or the flippers of a dolphin are in close contact with veins conveying cool blood in the opposite direction, back toward the trunk of the body. This arrangement facilitates heat transfer from arteries to veins (black arrows) along the entire length of the blood vessels.

❷ Near the end of the leg or flipper, where arterial blood has been cooled to far below the animal's core temperature, the artery can still transfer heat to the even colder blood of an adjacent vein. The blood in the veins continues to absorb heat as it passes warmer and warmer blood traveling in the opposite direction in the arteries.

❸ As the blood in the veins approaches the center of the body, it is almost as warm as the body core, minimizing the heat lost as a result of supplying blood to body parts immersed in cold water.

In the flippers of a dolphin, each artery is surrounded by several veins in a countercurrent arrangement, allowing efficient heat exchange between blood in the arteries and veins.

▲ **Figure 40.12 Countercurrent heat exchangers.** A countercurrent exchange system traps heat in the body core, thus reducing heat loss from the extremities, particularly when they are immersed in cold water or in contact with ice or snow. In essence, heat in the arterial blood emerging from the body core is transferred directly to the returning venous blood instead of being lost to the environment.

Thermoregulation in some animals is aided by adaptations that can greatly augment this cooling effect. Panting is important in birds and many mammals. Some birds have a pouch richly supplied with blood vessels in the floor of the mouth; fluttering the pouch increases evaporation. Pigeons, for example, can use evaporative cooling to keep body temperature close to 40°C (104°F) in air temperatures as high as 60°C (140°F), as long as they have sufficient water. Sweating or bathing moistens the skin and enhances evaporative cooling. Many terrestrial mammals have sweat glands controlled by the nervous system (see Figure 40.11).

Behavioral Responses

Both endotherms and ectotherms control body temperature through behavioral responses. Many ectotherms maintain a nearly constant body temperature through relatively simple behaviors. More extreme behavioral adaptations in some animals include hibernation or migration to a more suitable climate.

All amphibians and most reptiles other than birds are ectothermic. Therefore, these organisms control body temperature mainly by behavior. When exposed to air, most amphibians lose heat rapidly by evaporation from their moist body surfaces, making it difficult to keep sufficiently warm. However, an amphibian can maintain a satisfactory body temperature simply by moving to a location where solar heat is available. When the surroundings are too warm, amphibians seek shady spots or other cooler microenvironments.

Like amphibians, reptiles other than birds use behavior as their dominant means of thermoregulation. When cold, they seek warm places, orienting themselves toward heat sources and expanding the portion of their body surface exposed to the heat source (see Figure 40.9b). When hot, they move to cool areas or turn in another direction. Many reptiles keep their body temperatures very stable over the course of a day by shuttling back and forth between warm and cool spots.

Many terrestrial invertebrates can adjust internal temperature by the same behavioral mechanisms used by vertebrate ectotherms. The desert locust, for example, must reach a certain temperature to become active, and on cold days it orients in a direction that maximizes the absorption of sunlight. Other terrestrial invertebrates have certain postures that enable them to maximize or minimize their absorption of heat from the sun (Figure 40.13).

Honeybees use a thermoregulatory mechanism that depends on social behavior. In cold weather, they increase heat production and huddle together, thereby retaining heat. They maintain a relatively constant temperature by changing how densely they huddle. Individuals move between the cooler outer edges of the cluster and the warmer center, thus circulating and distributing the heat. Even when huddling, honeybees must expend considerable energy to keep warm during long periods of cold weather, and this is the main function of storing large quantities of fuel in the hive in the form of honey.

◀ **Figure 40.13**
Thermoregulatory behavior in a dragonfly. This dragonfly's "obelisk" posture is an adaptation that minimizes the amount of body surface exposed to the sun. This posture helps reduce heat gain by radiation.

Honeybees also control the temperature of their hive by transporting water to the hive in hot weather and fanning with their wings, promoting evaporation and convection. Thus, a colony of honeybees uses many of the mechanisms of thermoregulation seen in individual organisms.

Adjusting Metabolic Heat Production

Because endotherms generally maintain body temperatures considerably higher than that of the environment, they must counteract constant heat loss. Endotherms can vary heat production to match changing rates of heat loss. For example, heat production—*thermogenesis*—is increased by such muscle activity as moving or shivering. In some mammals, certain hormones can cause mitochondria to increase their metabolic activity and produce heat instead of ATP. This *nonshivering thermogenesis* takes place throughout the body, but some mammals also have a tissue called *brown fat* in the neck and between the shoulders that is specialized for rapid heat production. Through shivering and nonshivering thermogenesis, mammals and birds in cold environments can increase their metabolic heat production by as much as five to ten times the levels that occur in warm conditions. For example, chickadees, birds with a body mass of only 20 g, can remain active and hold body temperature nearly constant at 40°C (104°F) in environmental temperatures as low as −40°C (−40°F), as long as they have adequate food.

A few large reptiles become endothermic in particular circumstances. In the early 1960s, Herndon Dowling, at the Bronx Zoo in New York, documented this phenomenon for a female Burmese python (*Python molurus bivittatus*). Placing temperature-recording devices along the snake's coils, Dowling found that the snake maintained a body temperature roughly 6°C (10°F) above that of the surrounding air during the month when she was incubating eggs. Where did the heat come from? To answer this question, Dowling carried out studies together with a graduate student, Allen Vinegar, and his research supervisor, Victor Hutchison (Figure 40.14). What they found was that pythons, like mammals, can generate heat

How does a Burmese python generate heat while incubating eggs?

EXPERIMENT Herndon Dowling and colleagues at the Bronx Zoo in New York observed that when a female Burmese python incubated eggs by wrapping her body around them, she raised her body temperature and frequently contracted the muscles in her coils. To learn if the contractions were elevating her body temperature, they placed the python and her eggs in a chamber. They varied the chamber's temperature and monitored the python's muscle contractions and her oxygen uptake, a measure of her rate of cellular respiration.

RESULTS The python's oxygen consumption increased when the temperature in the chamber decreased. Her oxygen consumption also changed with the rate of muscle contraction:

CONCLUSION Because oxygen consumption generates heat through cellular respiration and increases linearly with the rate of muscle contraction, the researchers concluded that the muscle contractions, a form of shivering, were the source of the Burmese python's elevated body temperature.

SOURCE V. H. Hutchison, H.G. Dowling, and A. Vinegar, Thermoregulation in a brooding female Indian python, *Python molurus bivittatus*, *Science* 151:694–696 (1966).

WHAT IF? Suppose you varied air temperature and measured oxygen consumption for a female Burmese python without a clutch of eggs. Since she would not show shivering behavior, how would the snake's oxygen consumption vary with environmental temperature?

through spasmodic muscle contraction—in other words, shivering. These findings and others have led to new insights into thermoregulation in reptiles and contributed to the idea, still under debate, that certain groups of dinosaurs were endothermic (see Chapter 34).

As mentioned earlier, many species of flying insects, such as bees and moths, are endothermic—the smallest of all endotherms. The capacity of such endothermic insects to elevate body temperature depends on powerful flight muscles, which

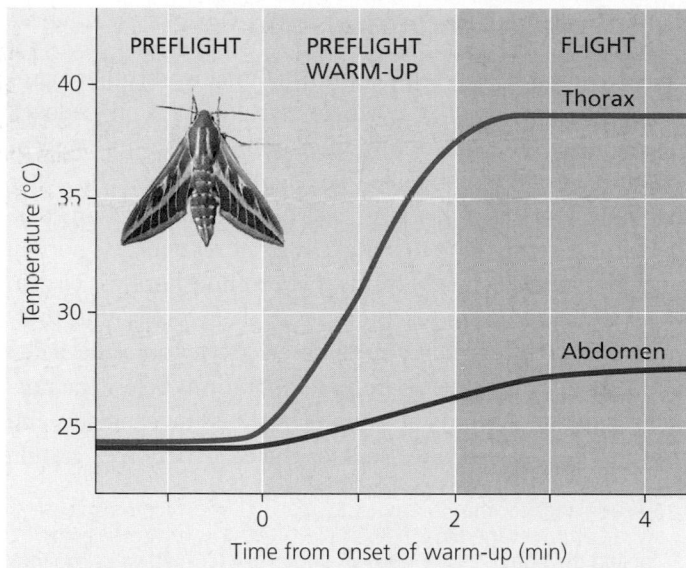

▲ **Figure 40.15 Preflight warm-up in the hawkmoth.** The hawkmoth (*Manduca sexta*) is one of many insect species that use a shivering like mechanism for preflight warm-up of thoracic flight muscles. Warming up helps these muscles produce enough power to let the animal take off. Once airborne, flight muscle activity maintains a high thoracic temperature.

generate large amounts of heat when operating. Many endothermic insects warm up by shivering before taking off. As they contract their flight muscles in synchrony, only slight wing movements occur, but considerable heat is produced. Chemical reactions, and hence cellular respiration, speed up in the warmed-up flight "motors," enabling these insects to fly even on cold days or at night **(Figure 40.15)**.

Acclimatization in Thermoregulation

Acclimatization contributes to thermoregulation across many animal species. In birds and mammals, acclimatization to seasonal temperature changes often includes adjusting the amount of insulation—by growing a thicker coat of fur in the winter and shedding it in the summer, for example. These changes help endotherms keep a constant body temperature throughout the year.

Acclimatization in ectotherms often includes adjustments at the cellular level. Cells may produce variants of enzymes that have the same function but different optimal temperatures. Also, the proportions of saturated and unsaturated lipids in membranes may change; unsaturated lipids help keep membranes fluid at lower temperatures (see Figure 7.5). Some ectotherms that experience subzero body temperatures protect themselves by producing "antifreeze" compounds that prevent ice formation in the cells. In the Arctic and Southern (Antarctic) oceans, these compounds in the body fluids of certain fishes enable survival where water temperatures can be as low as −2°C (28°F), below the freezing point of unprotected body fluids (about −1°C, or 30°F).

Physiological Thermostats and Fever

The regulation of body temperature in humans and other mammals is brought about by a complex system based on feedback mechanisms. The sensors for thermoregulation are concentrated in a brain region called the **hypothalamus**. The hypothalamus contains a group of nerve cells that functions as a thermostat, responding to body temperatures outside a normal range by activating mechanisms that promote heat loss or gain **(Figure 40.16)**. Warm receptors signal the hypothalamic thermostat when temperatures increase; cold receptors signal when temperatures decrease. At body temperatures below the normal range, the thermostat inhibits heat loss mechanisms and activates heat-saving ones such as the constriction of certain blood vessels and the raising of fur, while stimulating heat-generating mechanisms (shivering and nonshivering thermogenesis). In response to elevated body temperature, the thermostat shuts down heat retention mechanisms and promotes body cooling by vasodilation, sweating, or panting. Because the same blood vessel supplies the hypothalamus and ears, an ear thermometer records the temperature detected by the hypothalmic thermostat.

In the course of certain bacterial and viral infections, mammals and birds develop fever, an elevated body temperature. A variety of experiments have shown that fever reflects an increase in the set point for the biological thermostat. For example, artificially raising the temperature of the hypothalamus in an infected animal reduces fever in the rest of the body.

Although only endotherms develop fever, lizards exhibit a related response. When infected with certain bacteria, the desert iguana (*Dipsosaurus dorsalis*) seeks a warmer environment and then maintains a body temperature that is elevated by 2–4°C (4–7°F). Similar observations in fishes, amphibians, and even cockroaches indicate broad evolutionary conservation of this response to certain infections.

Having explored thermoregulation in depth, we'll now consider some other energy-consuming processes and the different ways that animals allocate, use, and conserve energy.

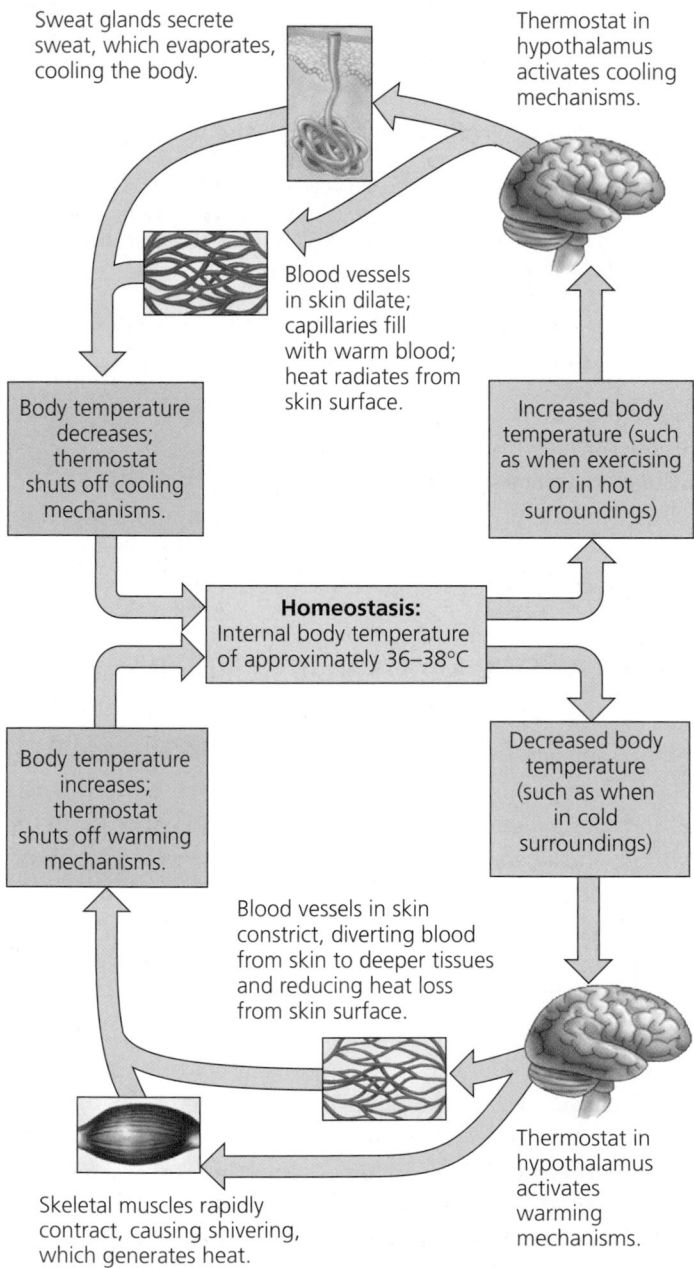

▲ **Figure 40.16 The thermostatic function of the hypothalamus in human thermoregulation.**

Sweat glands secrete sweat, which evaporates, cooling the body.

Thermostat in hypothalamus activates cooling mechanisms.

Blood vessels in skin dilate; capillaries fill with warm blood; heat radiates from skin surface.

Body temperature decreases; thermostat shuts off cooling mechanisms.

Increased body temperature (such as when exercising or in hot surroundings)

Homeostasis: Internal body temperature of approximately 36–38°C

Body temperature increases; thermostat shuts off warming mechanisms.

Decreased body temperature (such as when in cold surroundings)

Blood vessels in skin constrict, diverting blood from skin to deeper tissues and reducing heat loss from skin surface.

Thermostat in hypothalamus activates warming mechanisms.

Skeletal muscles rapidly contract, causing shivering, which generates heat.

CONCEPT CHECK 40.3

1. What mode of heat exchange is involved in "wind chill," when moving air feels colder than still air at the same temperature?
2. Flowers differ in how much sunlight they absorb. Why might this matter to a hummingbird seeking nectar on a cool morning?
3. **WHAT IF?** Suppose at the end of a hard run on a hot day you find that there are no drinks left in the cooler. If, out of desperation, you dunk your head into the cooler, how might the ice-cold water affect the rate at which your body temperature returns to normal?

For suggested answers, see Appendix A.

CONCEPT 40.4
Energy requirements are related to animal size, activity, and environment

Like other organisms, animals require chemical energy for growth, repair, activity, and reproduction. The overall flow and transformation of energy in an animal—its **bioenergetics**—determines nutritional needs and is related to an animal's size, activity, and environment.

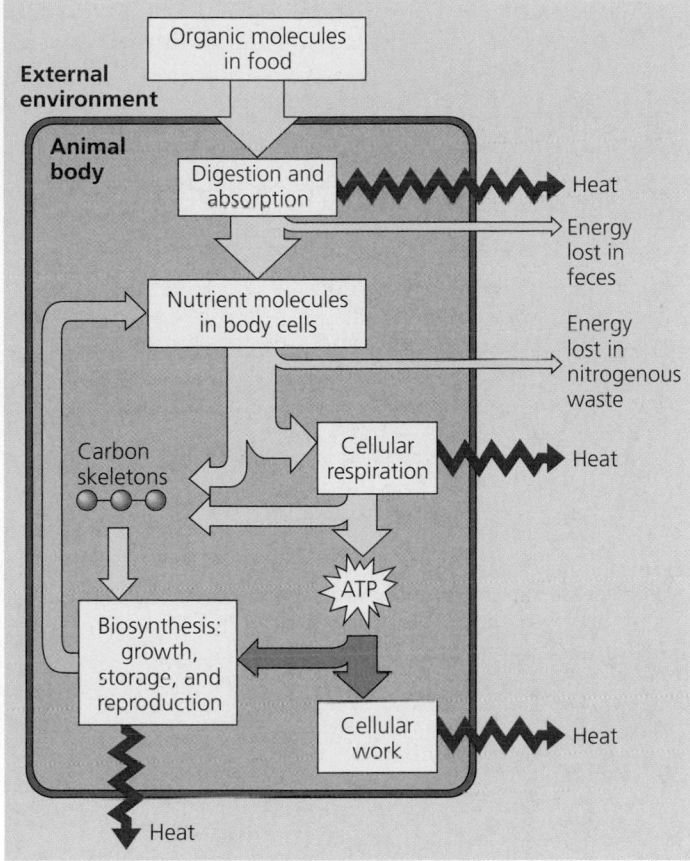

▲ **Figure 40.17 Bioenergetics of an animal: an overview.**

Energy Allocation and Use

As we have discussed in other chapters, organisms can be classified by how they obtain chemical energy. Most autotrophs, such as plants, use light energy to build energy-rich organic molecules and then use those organic molecules for fuel. Heterotrophs, such as animals, must obtain their chemical energy from food, which contains organic molecules synthesized by other organisms.

Animals use chemical energy harvested from the food they eat to fuel metabolism and activity **(Figure 40.17)**. Food is digested by enzymatic hydrolysis (see Figure 5.2b), and nutrients are absorbed by body cells. Most energy-containing molecules are used to generate ATP. ATP produced by cellular respiration and fermentation (see Chapter 9) powers cellular work, enabling cells, organs, and organ systems to perform the functions that keep an animal alive. Energy in the form of ATP is also used in biosynthesis, which is needed for body growth and repair, synthesis of storage material such as fat, and production of gametes. The production and use of ATP generates heat, which the animal eventually gives off to its surroundings.

Quantifying Energy Use

How much of the total energy an animal obtains from food does it need just to stay alive? How much energy must be ex-

▲ **Figure 40.18 Measuring rate of oxygen consumption in a running pronghorn.** A researcher collects respiratory data from a pronghorn running on a treadmill at 40 km/hr.

pended to walk, run, swim, or fly from one place to another? What fraction of the energy intake is used for reproduction? Physiologists answer such questions by measuring the rate at which an animal uses chemical energy and how this rate changes in different circumstances.

The amount of energy an animal uses in a unit of time is called its **metabolic rate**—the sum of all the energy-requiring biochemical reactions over a given time interval. Energy is measured in joules or in calories (cal) and kilocalories (kcal). (A kilocalorie equals 1,000 calories. The unit Calorie, with a capital C, as used by many nutritionists, is actually a kilocalorie.)

Metabolic rate can be determined in several ways. Because nearly all of the chemical energy used in cellular respiration eventually appears as heat, metabolic rate can be measured by monitoring an animal's rate of heat loss. For this approach, researchers use a calorimeter, which is a closed, insulated chamber equipped with a device that records an animal's heat loss. Metabolic rate can also be determined from the amount of oxygen consumed or carbon dioxide produced by an animal's cellular respiration **(Figure 40.18)**. To calculate metabolic rate over longer periods, researchers record the rate of food consumption, the energy content of the food (about 4.5–5 kcal per gram of protein or carbohydrate and about 9 kcal per gram of fat), and the chemical energy lost in waste products (feces and nitrogenous waste).

Minimum Metabolic Rate and Thermoregulation

Animals must maintain a minimum metabolic rate for basic functions such as cell maintenance, breathing, and heartbeat. Researchers measure this minimum metabolic rate differently for endotherms and ectotherms. The minimum metabolic rate of a nongrowing endotherm that is at rest, has an empty stomach, and is not experiencing stress is called the **basal metabolic rate (BMR)**. BMR is measured under a "comfortable" temperature range—a range that requires no generation or shedding of heat above the minimum. The minimum metabolic rate of ectotherms is determined at a specific temperature because changes in the environmental temperature alter body temperature and therefore metabolic rate. The metabolic rate of a fasting, nonstressed ectotherm at rest at a particular temperature is called its **standard metabolic rate (SMR)**.

Comparisons of minimum metabolic rates reveal that endothermy and ectothermy have distinct energy costs. The BMR for humans averages 1,600–1,800 kcal per day for adult males and 1,300–1,500 kcal per day for adult females. These BMRs are about equivalent to the rate of energy use by a 75-watt light bulb. In contrast, SMR calculations reveal that an American alligator at rest consumes only about 60 kcal per day at 20°C (68°F). Since this represents less than ½₀ the energy used by a comparably sized adult human, the lower energetic requirement of ectothermy is readily apparent.

Influences on Metabolic Rate

Metabolic rate is affected by many factors besides whether the animal is an endotherm or an ectotherm. Some key factors are age, sex, size, activity, temperature, and nutrition. Here we'll examine the effects of size and activity.

Size and Metabolic Rate

An intriguing, yet largely unanswered, question in animal biology has to do with the relationship between body size and metabolic rate. Larger animals have more body mass and therefore require more chemical energy. Remarkably, the relationship between overall metabolic rate and body mass is constant across a wide range of sizes and forms, as illustrated for various mammals in **Figure 40.19a**. For creatures ranging in size from bacteria to blue whales, metabolic rate is roughly proportional to body mass to the three-quarter power ($m^{3/4}$).

The relationship of metabolic rate to size profoundly affects energy consumption by body cells and tissues. As shown in **Figure 40.19b**, the energy it takes to maintain each gram of body weight is inversely related to body size. Each gram of a mouse, for instance, requires about 20 times as many calories as a gram of an elephant, even though the whole elephant uses far more calories than the whole mouse. The smaller animal's higher metabolic rate per gram demands a greater rate of oxygen delivery. Correlated with its higher metabolic rate per gram, the smaller animal has a higher breathing rate, blood volume (relative to its size), and heart rate. Also, it must eat much more food per unit of body mass.

The reason for the inverse relationship of metabolic rate per unit of body mass to body size is still a subject of debate. One hypothesis is that for endotherms the smaller the animal, the greater the energy cost of maintaining a stable body tem-

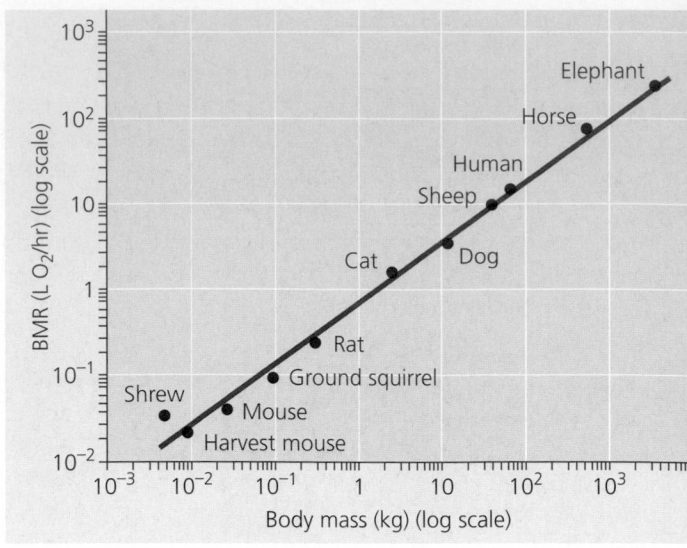

(a) Relationship of basal metabolic rate (BMR) to body size for various mammals. From shrew to elephant, size increases 1 millionfold.

(b) Relationship of BMR per kilogram of body mass to body size for the same mammals as in (a).

▲ **Figure 40.19 The relationship of metabolic rate to body size.**

perature. In effect, the smaller an animal is, the greater its surface-to-volume ratio is and thus the faster it loses heat to (or gains heat from) the surroundings. Logical as this hypothesis seems, it does not explain the fact that the inverse relationship between metabolic rate per gram and size is also observed in ectotherms, which do not use metabolic heat to maintain body temperature.

Bioenergetic considerations associated with body size provide a clear example of how trade-offs shape the evolution of body plans. As body size becomes smaller, each gram of tissue increases in energy cost. As body size increases, energy costs per gram of tissue lessen, but an ever-larger fraction of body tissue is required for exchange, support, and locomotion.

Activity and Metabolic Rate

For both ectotherms and endotherms, activity greatly affects metabolic rate. Even a person reading quietly at a desk or an insect twitching its wings consumes energy beyond the BMR or SMR. Maximum metabolic rates (the highest rates of ATP use) occur during peak activity, such as lifting heavy weights, sprinting, or high-speed swimming. In general, the maximum metabolic rate an animal can sustain is inversely related to the duration of activity.

For most terrestrial animals, the average daily rate of energy consumption is 2 to 4 times BMR (for endotherms) or SMR (for ectotherms). Humans in most developed countries have an unusually low average daily metabolic rate of about 1.5 times BMR—an indication of their relatively sedentary lifestyles.

Energy Budgets

As we have seen, the ways in which animals use the chemical energy of food depend on environment, behavior, size, and thermoregulation. To understand how these influences affect bioenergetics in animal bodies, let's consider typical annual energy "budgets" of four terrestrial vertebrates varying in size and thermoregulatory strategy: a 60-kg female human, a 4-kg male Adélie penguin, a 25-g (0.025-kg) female deer mouse, and a 4-kg female eastern indigo snake **(Figure 40.20)**. Reproduction is included in these energy budgets because it can greatly influence energy allocation and is critical to species survival.

The female human, an endothermic mammal, spends the largest fraction of her annual energy budget for BMR and relatively little for activity and thermoregulation. The small amount of growth, about 1%, is equivalent to adding about 1 kg of body fat or 5–6 kg of other tissues. (Growth is not shown in the budgets for the penguin and deer mouse because these animals don't typically gain weight year to year after they are adults.) The cost of

nine months of pregnancy and several months of breast-feeding is only 5–8% of the mother's annual energy requirements.

A male penguin spends the largest fraction of his energy for activity because he must swim to catch food. Being well insulated and fairly large, he has relatively low costs of thermoregulation in spite of living in the cold Antarctic. His reproductive costs, about 6% of annual energy expenditures, come mainly from incubating eggs (brooding) and bringing food to his chicks. Like most birds, penguins do not grow after they become adults.

Despite living in a temperate climate, the female deer mouse spends a large fraction of her energy budget for temperature regulation. Because of the high surface-to-volume ratio that goes with small size, deer mice lose body heat rapidly and must constantly generate metabolic heat to maintain body temperature.

In contrast with these endothermic animals, the ectothermic snake has no thermoregulation costs. Like most snakes, she grows continuously throughout her life. In the example in Figure 40.20, the snake added about 750 g of new body tissue in a year. She also produced about 650 g of eggs. The snake's economical ectothermic strategy is revealed by her very low energy expenditure, only ¼₀ the energy expended by the similarly sized endothermic penguin.

For all the animals in Figure 40.20, locomotion and other activities are a major part of the energy budget. Some animals can conserve energy by temporarily decreasing their activity to a very low level, a process we will consider next.

Torpor and Energy Conservation

Despite their many adaptations for homeostasis, animals may encounter conditions that severely challenge their abilities to balance their heat, energy, and materials budgets. For example, at certain seasons or times of day, temperatures may be extremely high or low, or food may be unavailable. **Torpor**, a physiological

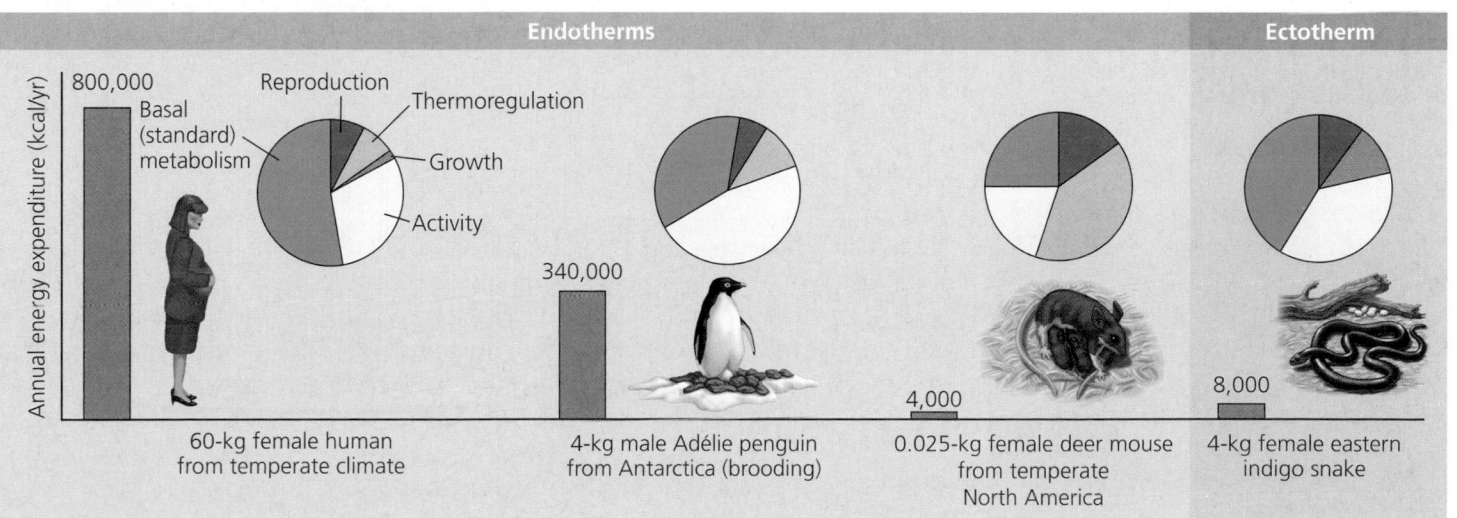

▲ **Figure 40.20 Energy budgets for four animals.** The slices of the pie charts indicate annual energy expenditures for various functions.

state in which activity is low and metabolism decreases, is an adaptation that enables animals to save energy while avoiding difficult and dangerous conditions.

Hibernation is long-term torpor that is an adaptation to winter cold and food scarcity. When vertebrate endotherms (birds and mammals) enter hibernation, their body temperatures decline as their body's thermostat is turned down. The temperature reduction may be dramatic: Some hibernating mammals cool to as low as 1–2°C (34–35°F), and a few even drop slightly below 0°C (32°F) in a supercooled (unfrozen) state. The resulting energy savings are huge; metabolic rates during hibernation can be much lower than if the animal attempted to maintain normal body temperatures of 36–38°C (97–100°F). Consider, for example, a Belding's ground squirrel (*Spermophilus beldingi*) living in the high mountains of California (**Figure 40.21**). Instead of spending 150 kcal per day to maintain body temperature in winter weather, a hibernating squirrel spends an average of only 5–8 kcal per day. As a result, hibernators such as the ground squirrel can survive through the winter on limited supplies of energy stored in the body tissues or as food cached in a burrow. Similarly, the slow metabolism and inactivity of *estivation*, or summer torpor, enables animals to survive long periods of high temperatures and scarce water supplies.

Many small mammals and birds exhibit a daily torpor that seems to be adapted to feeding patterns. For instance, some bats feed at night and go into torpor in daylight. Chickadees and hummingbirds feed during the day and often go into torpor on cold nights; the body temperature of chickadees drops as much as 10°C (18°F) at night, and the temperature of hummingbirds can fall 25°C (45°F) or more. All endotherms that use daily torpor are relatively small; when active, they have high metabolic rates and thus very high rates of energy consumption.

From discussing body shape to considering energy conservation, this chapter has focused on the whole animal. We explored common tissue types that make up organs and organ systems. We also investigated how body plans provide for exchange, how size affects metabolic rate, and how some animals maintain a constant internal environment. For much of the rest of this unit, we'll see how specialized organs and organ systems enable animals to meet the basic challenges of life.

CONCEPT CHECK 40.4

1. If a mouse and a small lizard of the same mass (both at rest) were placed in experimental chambers under identical environmental conditions, which animal would consume oxygen at a higher rate? Explain.
2. Which animal must eat a larger proportion of its weight in food each day: a house cat or an African lion caged in a zoo? Explain.
3. **WHAT IF?** If you monitored energy allocation in the penguin in Figure 40.20 for just a few months, the "growth" category might now be a significant part of the pie chart, even though adult penguins don't change in size from year to year. What limitation in such energy budget studies does this lead you to consider?

For suggested answers, see Appendix A.

▶ **Figure 40.21 Body temperature and metabolism during hibernation in Belding's ground squirrels.**
WHAT IF? *Propose two different hypotheses about the environmental change that triggers hibernation. Then suppose that, during one year, the outside temperatures dropped steadily a month earlier than normal. For each hypothesis, what effect on the timing of hibernation would you expect?*

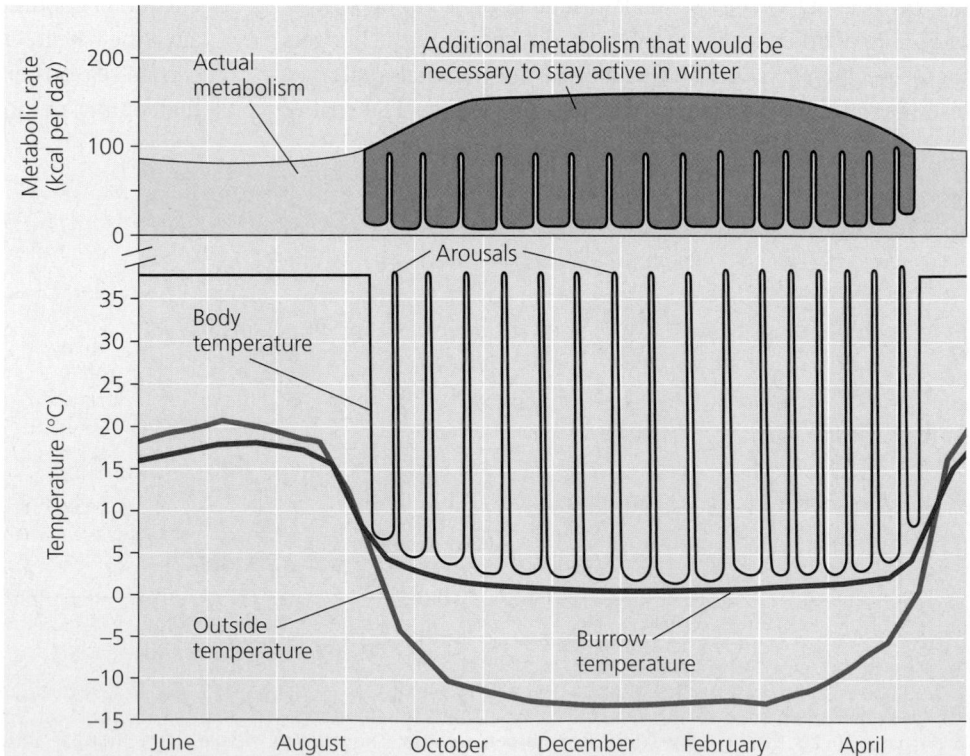

MEDIA Go to www.campbellbiology.com for BioFlix 3-D Animations, MP3 Tutors, Videos, Practice Tests, an eBook, and more.

SUMMARY OF KEY CONCEPTS

CONCEPT 40.1
Animal form and function are correlated at all levels of organization (pp. 852–860)

▶ **Physical Constraints on Animal Size and Shape** The ability to perform certain actions, such as fast swimming, depends on an animal's size and shape. Convergent evolution reflects different species' independent adaptations to a similar environmental challenge.

▶ **Exchange with the Environment** Each cell of an animal must have access to an aqueous environment. Simple two-layered sacs and flat shapes maximize exposure to the surrounding medium. More complex body plans have highly folded internal surfaces specialized for exchanging materials.

▶ **Hierarchical Organization of Body Plans** Animals are composed of cells. Groups of cells with a common structure and function make up tissues. Different tissues make up organs, which together make up organ systems.

▶ **Tissue Structure and Function** Epithelial tissue covers the outside of the body and lines internal organs and cavities. Connective tissues bind and support other tissues. Muscle tissue contracts in response to nerve signals. Nervous tissue transmits nerve signals throughout the animal.

▶ **Coordination and Control** The endocrine and nervous systems function as the two means of communication between distinct locations in the body. The endocrine system broadcasts signaling molecules called hormones everywhere via the bloodstream, but only certain cells are responsive. The nervous system uses dedicated cellular circuits involving electrical and chemical signals to send information to specific locations.

MEDIA

Activity Overview of Animal Tissues
Activity Epithelial Tissue
Activity Connective Tissue
Activity Muscle Tissue
Activity Nervous Tissue

CONCEPT 40.2
Feedback control loops maintain the internal environment in many animals (pp. 860–862)

▶ **Regulating and Conforming** Animals cope with environmental fluctuations by regulating certain internal variables while allowing others to conform to external changes.

▶ **Homeostasis** Homeostasis describes an animal's internal steady state. It is a balance between external changes and the animal's internal control mechanisms that oppose the changes. The interstitial fluid surrounding an animal's cells is usually very different from the external environment. Homeostatic mechanisms moderate changes in the internal environ-

ment and usually involve negative feedback. These mechanisms enable regulated change.

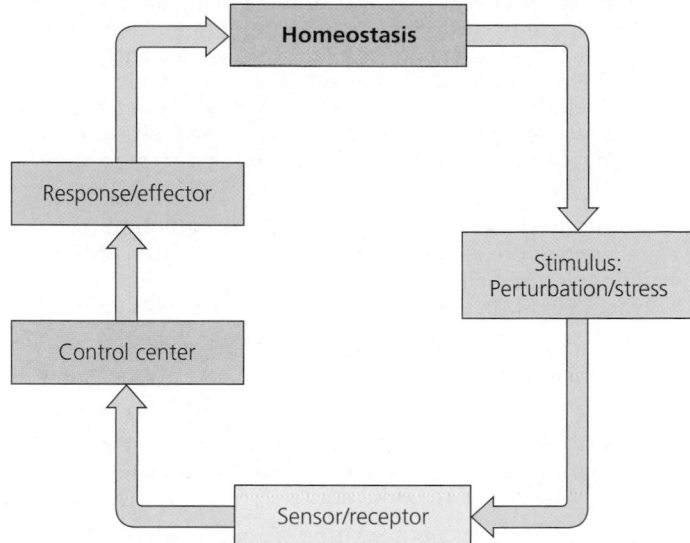

Regulated change in the internal environment is essential to normal body functions. Acclimatization involves temporary changes in homeostasis in response to alterations in the environment.

MEDIA

Activity Regulation: Negative and Positive Feedback

CONCEPT 40.3
Homeostatic processes for thermoregulation involve form, function, and behavior (pp. 862–868)

▶ An animal maintains its internal temperature within a tolerable range by processes of thermoregulation.

▶ **Endothermy and Ectothermy** Endotherms are warmed mostly by heat generated by metabolism. Ectotherms get most of their heat from external sources. Endothermy requires an animal to expend more energy.

▶ **Variation in Body Temperature** Body temperature varies in poikilotherms and is relatively constant in homeotherms.

▶ **Balancing Heat Loss and Gain** Conduction, convection, radiation, and evaporation account for heat exchange. Thermoregulation involves physiological and behavioral adjustments that balance heat gain and loss. Insulation, vasodilation, vasoconstriction, and countercurrent heat exchange alter the rate of heat exchange. Panting, sweating, and bathing increase evaporation, cooling the body. Both ectotherms and endotherms adjust the rate of heat exchange with their surroundings by behavioral responses. Some animals can even adjust their rate of metabolic heat production.

▶ **Acclimatization in Thermoregulation** Many mammals and birds adjust the amount of body insulation in response to changes in environmental temperature. Ectotherms undergo a variety of changes at the cellular level to acclimatize to shifts in temperature.

▶ **Physiological Thermostats and Fever** Mammals regulate their body temperature by complex negative-feedback mechanisms that involve several organ systems, including the nervous, circulatory, and integumentary systems.

Energy requirements are related to animal size, activity, and environment (pp. 868–872)

▶ **Energy Allocation and Use** Animals obtain chemical energy from food, storing it for short-term use in ATP.

▶ **Quantifying Energy Use** An animal's metabolic rate is the total amount of energy it uses in a unit of time. Metabolic rates for birds and mammals, which maintain a fairly constant body temperature using metabolic heat (endothermy), are generally higher than those for most fishes, nonavian reptiles, amphibians, and invertebrates, which rely mostly on external sources of heat for maintaining body temperature (ectothermy).

▶ **Minimum Metabolic Rate and Thermoregulation** Under similar conditions and for animals of the same size, BMR, the minimum metabolic rate of endotherms, is substantially higher than SMR, the standard metabolic rate of ectotherms.

▶ **Influences on Metabolic Rate** Minimum metabolic rate per gram is inversely related to body size among similar animals. Activity increases metabolic rate.

▶ **Energy Budgets** Animals use energy for basal (or standard) metabolism, activity, homeostasis (such as temperature regulation), growth, and reproduction.

▶ **Torpor and Energy Conservation** Torpor involves a decrease in metabolic rate, conserving energy during environmental extremes. Animals may enter torpor in winter (hibernation), summer (estivation), or during sleep periods (daily torpor).

MEDIA

Investigation How Does Temperature Affect Metabolic Rate in *Daphnia*?

TESTING YOUR KNOWLEDGE

SELF-QUIZ

1. Compared with a smaller cell, a larger cell of the same shape has
   a. less surface area.
   b. less surface area per unit of volume.
   c. the same surface-to-volume ratio.
   d. a smaller average distance between its mitochondria and the external source of oxygen.
   e. a smaller cytoplasm-to-nucleus ratio.

2. The epithelium best adapted for a body surface subject to abrasion is
   a. simple squamous.   d. stratified columnar.
   b. simple cuboidal.   e. stratified squamous.
   c. simple columnar.

3. Which of the following is not an adaptation for reducing the rate of heat exchange between an animal and its environment?
   a. feathers or fur
   b. vasoconstriction
   c. nonshivering thermogenesis
   d. countercurrent heat exchanger
   e. blubber or fat layer

4. Which of the following animals uses the highest percent of its energy budget for homeostatic regulation?
   a. a hydra   d. a desert insect
   b. a marine jelly (an invertebrate)   e. a desert bird
   c. a snake in a temperate forest

5. Consider the energy budgets for a human, an elephant, a penguin, a mouse, and a snake. The _____ would have the highest total annual energy expenditure, and the _____ would have the highest energy expenditure per unit mass.
   a. elephant; mouse   d. mouse; snake
   b. elephant; human   e. penguin; mouse
   c. human; penguin

6. An animal's inputs of energy and materials would exceed its outputs
   a. if the animal is an endotherm, which must always take in more energy because of its high metabolic rate.
   b. if it is actively foraging for food.
   c. if it is hibernating.
   d. if it is growing and increasing its mass.
   e. never; homeostasis makes these energy and material budgets always balance.

7. **DRAW IT** Draw a model of the control loop(s) required for driving an automobile at a fairly constant speed over a hilly road. Assuming that either the driver or a cruise control device is the control center, indicate each feature that represents a sensor, input, or response.

For Self-Quiz answers, see Appendix A.

MEDIA Visit **www.campbellbiology.com** for a Practice Test.

EVOLUTION CONNECTION

8. The biologist C. Bergmann noted that mammals and birds living at higher latitudes are on average larger and bulkier than related species found at lower latitudes. Suggest an evolutionary hypothesis for this observation.

SCIENTIFIC INQUIRY

9. Eastern tent caterpillars (*Malacosoma americanum*) live in large groups in silk nests, or tents, which they build in trees. They are among the first insects to be active in early spring, when daily temperature fluctuates from freezing to very hot. Over the course of a day, they display striking differences in behavior: Early in the morning, they rest in a tightly packed group on the tent's east-facing surface. In midafternoon, they are on its undersurface, each caterpillar hanging by a few of its legs. Propose a hypothesis to explain this behavior. How could you test it?

SCIENCE, TECHNOLOGY, AND SOCIETY

10. Medical researchers are investigating artificial substitutes for various human tissues. Why might artificial blood or skin be useful? What characteristics would these substitutes need in order to function well in the body? Why do real tissues work better? Why not use the real tissues if they work better? What other artificial tissues might be useful? What problems do you anticipate in developing and applying them?

Animal Nutrition

41

▲ Figure 41.1 **How does a lean fish help a bear make fat?**

OVERVIEW

The Need to Feed

Dinnertime has arrived for the Kodiak bear in **Figure 41.1** (and for the salmon, though in quite a different sense). The skin, muscles, and other parts of the fish will be chewed into pieces, broken down by acid and enzymes in the bear's digestive system, and finally absorbed as small molecules into the body of the bear. Such a process is what is meant by animal **nutrition**: food being taken in, taken apart, and taken up.

Although a diet of fish plucked from a waterfall is not common, all animals eat other organisms—dead or alive, piecemeal or whole. Unlike plants, animals rely on their food for both the energy and the organic molecules used to assemble new molecules, cells, and tissues. Despite this shared need, animals have diverse diets. **Herbivores**, such as cattle, parrotfish, and termites, dine mainly on plants or algae. **Carnivores**, such as sharks, hawks, and spiders, mostly eat other animals. Bears and other **omnivores** (from the Latin *omni*, all) don't in fact eat everything, but they do regularly consume animals as well as plants or algae. We humans are typically omnivores, as are cockroaches and crows.

The terms *herbivore*, *carnivore*, and *omnivore* represent the kinds of food an animal usually eats. Keep in mind, however, that most animals are opportunistic feeders, eating foods outside their standard diet when their usual foods aren't available. For example, deer are herbivores, but in addition to feeding on grass and other plants, they occasionally eat insects, worms, or bird eggs. Note as well that microorganisms are an unavoidable "supplement" in every animal's diet.

Animals must eat. But to survive and reproduce, they must also balance their consumption, storage, and use of food. Bats, for example, store energy, largely in the form of body fat, for periods of hibernation. Eating too little food, too much food, or the wrong mixture of foods can endanger an animal's health. In this chapter, we will survey the nutritional requirements of animals, explore some of the diverse evolutionary adaptations for obtaining and processing food, and investigate the regulation of energy intake and expenditure.

CONCEPT 41.1

An animal's diet must supply chemical energy, organic molecules, and essential nutrients

The activities of cells, tissues, organs, and whole animals depend on sources of chemical energy in the diet. This energy, after being converted to ATP, powers processes ranging from DNA replication and cell division to vision and flight. To meet the continuous requirement for ATP, animals ingest and digest nutrients, such as carbohydrates, proteins, and lipids, for use in cellular respiration and energy storage.

In addition to providing fuel for ATP production, an animal's diet must supply the raw materials needed for biosynthesis. To build the complex molecules it needs to grow, maintain itself, and reproduce, an animal must obtain two types of organic precursors from its food. Animals need a source of organic carbon (such as sugar) and a source of organic nitrogen (usually amino acids from the digestion of protein). Starting with these materials, animals can construct a great variety of organic molecules.

The materials that an animal's cells require but cannot synthesize are called **essential nutrients**. Obtained from dietary sources, these nutrients include both minerals and preassembled organic molecules. Some nutrients are essential for all animals, whereas others are needed only by certain species. For instance, ascorbic acid (vitamin C) is an essential nutrient for humans and other primates, guinea pigs, and some birds and snakes, but not for most other animals.

Overall, an adequate diet thus satisfies three nutritional needs: chemical energy for cellular processes, organic building blocks for carbohydrates and other macromolecules, and essential nutrients.

Essential Nutrients

There are four classes of essential nutrients: essential amino acids, essential fatty acids, vitamins, and minerals.

Essential Amino Acids

Animals require 20 amino acids to make proteins. The majority of animal species can synthesize about half of these amino acids, as long as their diet includes organic nitrogen. The remaining amino acids must be obtained from food in prefabricated form and are therefore called **essential amino acids**. Most animals, including adult humans, require eight amino acids in their diet (infants also need a ninth, histidine).

A diet that provides insufficient amounts of one or more essential amino acids causes protein deficiency, the most common type of malnutrition among humans. The victims are usually children, who, if they survive infancy, often have impaired physical and sometimes mental development.

The proteins in animal products such as meat, eggs, and cheese are "complete," which means that they provide all the essential amino acids in their proper proportions. In contrast, most plant proteins are "incomplete," being deficient in one or more essential amino acids. Corn (maize), for example, is deficient in tryptophan and lysine, whereas beans are lacking in methionine. To prevent protein deficiency, vegetarian diets must therefore include combinations of plant products that together provide all of the essential amino acids **(Figure 41.2)**.

Some animals have adaptations that help them through periods when their bodies demand extraordinary amounts of protein. In penguins, for example, muscle protein provides a

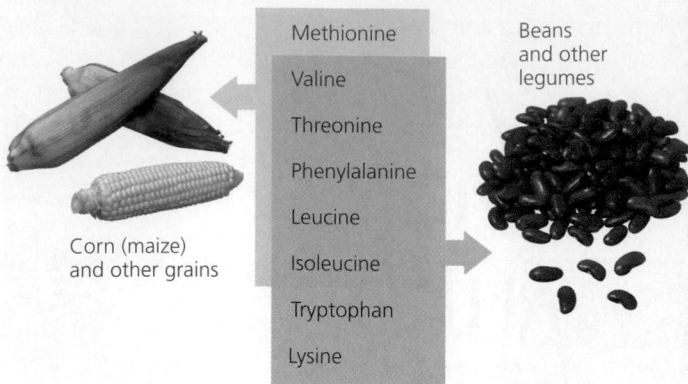

Methionine
Valine
Threonine
Phenylalanine
Leucine
Isoleucine
Tryptophan
Lysine

Corn (maize) and other grains

Beans and other legumes

▲ **Figure 41.2 Essential amino acids from a vegetarian diet.** In combination, corn and beans provide an adult human with all essential amino acids.

▲ **Figure 41.3 Storing protein for growth.** Penguins, such as this Adélie from Antarctica, must make an abundance of new protein when they molt (grow new feathers). Because of the temporary loss of their insulating coat of feathers, penguins cannot swim—or feed—when molting. What is the source of amino acids for production of feather protein? Before molting, a penguin greatly increases its muscle mass. The penguin then breaks down the extra muscle protein, which supplies the amino acids for growing new feathers.

source of amino acids for making new proteins when feathers are replaced after molting **(Figure 41.3)**.

Essential Fatty Acids

Animals can synthesize most, but not all, of the fatty acids they need. The **essential fatty acids**, the ones they cannot make, are certain fatty acids that are unsaturated (containing one or more double bonds; see Figure 5.12). For example, humans require linoleic acid to make some membrane phospholipids. Because seeds, grains, and vegetables in the diets of humans and other animals generally furnish ample quantities of essential fatty acids, deficiencies in this class of nutrients are rare.

Vitamins

Vitamins are organic molecules with diverse functions that are required in the diet in very small amounts. Vitamin B$_2$, for example, is converted in the body to FAD, a coenzyme used in many metabolic processes, including cellular respiration (see Figure 9.12). For humans, 13 essential vitamins have been identified. Depending on the vitamin, the required amount ranges from about 0.01 to 100 mg per day.

Vitamins are classified as water-soluble or fat-soluble (Table 41.1). The water-soluble vitamins include the B complex, which are compounds that generally function as coenzymes, and vitamin C, which is required to produce connective tissue.

Among the fat-soluble vitamins are vitamin A, which is incorporated into visual pigments of the eye, and vitamin K, which functions in blood clotting. Another is vitamin D, which aids in calcium absorption and bone formation. Our dietary requirement for vitamin D is variable because we synthesize this vitamin from other molecules when the skin is exposed to sunlight.

For people with poorly balanced diets, taking vitamin supplements that provide recommended daily levels is certainly reasonable. It is much less clear whether massive doses of vitamins confer any health benefits or are, in fact, safe. Moderate overdoses of water-soluble vitamins are probably harmless because excesses of these vitamins are excreted in urine. However, excesses of

Table 41.1 Vitamin Requirements of Humans

Vitamin	Major Dietary Sources	Major Functions in the Body	Symptoms of Deficiency or Extreme Excess
Water-Soluble Vitamins			
Vitamin B$_1$ (thiamine)	Pork, legumes, peanuts, whole grains	Coenzyme used in removing CO$_2$ from organic compounds	Beriberi (nerve disorders, emaciation, anemia)
Vitamin B$_2$ (riboflavin)	Dairy products, meats, enriched grains, vegetables	Component of coenzymes FAD and FMN	Skin lesions such as cracks at corners of mouth
Niacin (B$_3$)	Nuts, meats, grains	Component of coenzymes NAD$^+$ and NADP$^+$	Skin and gastrointestinal lesions, nervous disorders **Liver damage**
Vitamin B$_6$ (pyridoxine)	Meats, vegetables, whole grains	Coenzyme used in amino acid metabolism	Irritability, convulsions, muscular twitching, anemia **Unstable gait, numb feet, poor coordination**
Pantothenic acid (B$_5$)	Most foods: meats, dairy products, whole grains, etc.	Component of coenzyme A	Fatigue, numbness, tingling of hands and feet
Folic acid (folacin) (B$_9$)	Green vegetables, oranges, nuts, legumes, whole grains	Coenzyme in nucleic acid and amino acid metabolism	Anemia, birth defects **May mask deficiency of vitamin B$_{12}$**
Vitamin B$_{12}$	Meats, eggs, dairy products	Coenzyme in nucleic acid metabolism; maturation of red blood cells	Anemia, nervous system disorders
Biotin	Legumes, other vegetables, meats	Coenzyme in synthesis of fat, glycogen, and amino acids	Scaly skin inflammation, neuromuscular disorders
Vitamin C (ascorbic acid)	Fruits and vegetables, especially citrus fruits, broccoli, cabbage, tomatoes, green peppers	Used in collagen synthesis (such as for bone, cartilage, gums); antioxidant; aids in detoxification; improves iron absorption	Scurvy (degeneration of skin, teeth, blood vessels), weakness, delayed wound healing, impaired immunity **Gastrointestinal upset**
Fat-Soluble Vitamins			
Vitamin A (retinol)	Provitamin A (beta-carotene) in deep green and orange vegetables and fruits; retinal in dairy products	Component of visual pigments; maintenance of epithelial tissues; antioxidant; helps prevent damage to cell membranes	Blindness and increased death rate **Headache, irritability, vomiting, hair loss, blurred vision, liver and bone damage**
Vitamin D	Dairy products, egg yolk; also made in human skin in presence of sunlight	Aids in absorption and use of calcium and phosphorus; promotes bone growth	Rickets (bone deformities) in children, bone softening in adults **Brain, cardiovascular, and kidney damage**
Vitamin E (tocopherol)	Vegetable oils, nuts, seeds	Antioxidant; helps prevent damage to cell membranes	Degeneration of the nervous system
Vitamin K (phylloquinone)	Green vegetables, tea; also made by colon bacteria	Important in blood clotting	Defective blood clotting **Liver damage and anemia**

fat-soluble vitamins are deposited in body fat, so overconsumption may result in accumulating toxic levels of these compounds.

Minerals

Dietary **minerals** are inorganic nutrients, such as zinc and potassium, that are usually required in small amounts—from less than 1 mg to about 2,500 mg per day **(Table 41.2)**. Mineral requirements vary among animal species. For example, humans and other vertebrates require relatively large quantities of calcium and phosphorus for building and maintaining bone. In addition, calcium is necessary for the functioning of nerves and muscles, and phosphorus is an ingredient of ATP and nucleic acids. Iron is a component of the cytochromes that function in cellular respiration (see Figure 9.13) and of hemoglobin, the oxygen-binding protein of red blood cells. Many minerals are cofactors built into the structure of enzymes; magnesium, for example, is present in enzymes that split ATP. Vertebrates need iodine to make thyroid hormones, which regulate metabolic rate. Sodium, potassium, and chloride ions are important in the functioning of nerves and in maintaining osmotic balance between cells and the surrounding body fluid.

Table 41.2 Mineral Requirements of Humans

Mineral	Major Dietary Sources	Major Functions in the Body	Symptoms of Deficiency*
Calcium (Ca)	Dairy products, dark green vegetables, legumes	Bone and tooth formation, blood clotting, nerve and muscle function	Retarded growth, possibly loss of bone mass
Phosphorus (P)	Dairy products, meats, grains	Bone and tooth formation, acid-base balance, nucleotide synthesis	Weakness, loss of minerals from bone, calcium loss
Sulfur (S)	Proteins from many sources	Component of certain amino acids	Symptoms of protein deficiency
Potassium (K)	Meats, dairy products, many fruits and vegetables, grains	Acid-base balance, water balance, nerve function	Muscular weakness, paralysis, nausea, heart failure
Chlorine (Cl)	Table salt	Acid-base balance, formation of gastric juice, nerve function, osmotic balance	Muscle cramps, reduced appetite
Sodium (Na)	Table salt	Acid-base balance, water balance, nerve function	Muscle cramps, reduced appetite
Magnesium (Mg)	Whole grains, green leafy vegetables	Cofactor; ATP bioenergetics	Nervous system disturbances
Iron (Fe)	Meats, eggs, legumes, whole grains, green leafy vegetables	Component of hemoglobin and of electron carriers in energy metabolism; enzyme cofactor	Iron-deficiency anemia, weakness, impaired immunity
Fluorine (F)	Drinking water, tea, seafood	Maintenance of tooth (and probably bone) structure	Higher frequency of tooth decay
Zinc (Zn)	Meats, seafood, grains	Component of certain digestive enzymes and other proteins	Growth failure, skin abnormalities, reproductive failure, impaired immunity
Copper (Cu)	Seafood, nuts, legumes, organ meats	Enzyme cofactor in iron metabolism, melanin synthesis, electron transport	Anemia, cardiovascular abnormalities
Manganese (Mn)	Nuts, grains, vegetables, fruits, tea	Enzyme cofactor	Abnormal bone and cartilage
Iodine (I)	Seafood, dairy products, iodized salt	Component of thyroid hormones	Goiter (enlarged thyroid)
Cobalt (Co)	Meats and dairy products	Component of vitamin B_{12}	None, except as B_{12} deficiency
Selenium (Se)	Seafood, meats, whole grains	Enzyme cofactor; antioxidant functioning in close association with vitamin E	Muscle pain, possibly heart muscle deterioration
Chromium (Cr)	Brewer's yeast, liver, seafood, meats, some vegetables	Involved in glucose and energy metabolism	Impaired glucose metabolism
Molybdenum (Mo)	Legumes, grains, some vegetables	Enzyme cofactor	Disorder in excretion of nitrogen-containing compounds

Minerals from Calcium through Magnesium are grouped as "Greater than 200 mg per day required."

*All of these minerals are also harmful when consumed in excess.

Ingesting large amounts of some minerals can upset homeostatic balance and cause toxic side effects. For example, liver damage due to iron overload affects as much as 10% of the population in some regions of Africa where the water supply is especially iron-rich. Many individuals in these regions have a genetic alteration in mineral metabolism that increases the toxic effects of iron overload. In a different example, excess salt (sodium chloride) is not toxic but can contribute to high blood pressure. This is a particular problem in the United States, where the typical person consumes enough salt to provide about 20 times the required amount of sodium. Packaged (prepared) foods often contain large amounts of sodium chloride, even if they do not taste very salty.

Dietary Deficiencies

Diets that fail to meet basic needs can lead to either under-nourishment or malnourishment. **Undernourishment** is the result of a diet that consistently supplies less chemical energy than the body requires. In contrast, **malnourishment** is the long-term absence from the diet of one or more essential nutrients. Both have negative impacts on health and survival.

Undernourishment

When an animal is undernourished, a series of events unfold: The body uses up stored fat and carbohydrates; the body begins breaking down its own proteins for fuel; muscles begin to decrease in size; and the brain may become protein-deficient. If energy intake remains less than energy expenditures, the animal will eventually die. Even if a seriously undernourished animal survives, some of the damage may be irreversible.

Because adequate amounts of just a single staple such as rice or corn can provide sufficient calories, human undernourishment is most common when drought, war, or another crisis severely disrupts the food supply. In sub-Saharan Africa, where the AIDS epidemic has crippled both rural and urban communities, approximately 200 million children and adults cannot obtain enough food.

Sometimes undernourishment occurs within well-fed populations as a result of eating disorders. For example, anorexia nervosa leads individuals, usually female, to starve themselves compulsively.

Malnourishment

The potential effects of malnourishment include deformities, disease, and even death. For example, cattle, deer, and other herbivores may develop fragile bones if they graze on plants growing in soil that lacks phosphorus. Some grazing animals obtain the missing nutrients by consuming concentrated sources of salt or other minerals **(Figure 41.4)**. Among carnivores, recent experiments reveal that spiders can adjust for dietary deficiencies by switching to prey that restores nutritional balance.

▲ **Figure 41.4 Obtaining essential nutrients by eating antlers.** A caribou, an arctic herbivore, chews on discarded antlers from another animal. Because antlers contain calcium phosphate, this behavior is common among herbivores living where soils and plants are deficient in phosphorus. Animals require phosphorus to make ATP, nucleic acids, phospholipids, and components of bones.

Like other animals, humans sometimes suffer from malnourishment. Among populations subsisting on simple rice diets, individuals are often afflicted with vitamin A deficiency, which can cause blindness or death. To overcome this problem, scientists have engineered a strain of rice to synthesize beta-carotene, the orange-colored source of vitamin A that is abundant in carrots. The potential benefit of this "Golden Rice" is enormous because, at present, 1 to 2 million young children worldwide die every year from vitamin A deficiency.

Assessing Nutritional Needs

Determining the ideal diet for the human population is an important but difficult problem for scientists. As objects of study, people present many challenges. Unlike laboratory animals, humans are genetically diverse. They also live in settings far more varied than the stable and uniform environment that scientists use to facilitate comparisons in laboratory experiments. Ethical concerns present an additional barrier. For example, it is not acceptable to investigate the nutritional needs of children in a way that might harm a child's growth or development.

The methods used to study human nutrition have changed dramatically over time. To avoid harming others, several of the researchers who discovered vitamins a century ago used themselves as subject animals. Today, an important approach is the study of genetic defects that disrupt food uptake, storage, or use. For example, a genetic disorder called hemochromatosis causes iron buildup in the absence of any abnormal iron consumption or exposure. Fortunately, this common disorder is remarkably easy to treat: Drawing blood regularly removes enough iron from the body to restore homeostasis. By studying the defective genes that can cause the disease, scientists have learned a great deal about the regulation of iron absorption.

Many insights into human nutrition have come from *epidemiology*, the study of human health and disease at the population level. By tracking the causes and distribution of a disease among many individuals, epidemiologists can identify potential nutritional strategies for preventing and controlling diseases and disorders. For example, researchers discovered that dietary intake of the vitamin folic acid substantially reduces the frequency of neural tube defects, which are a serious and sometimes fatal type of birth defect.

Neural tube defects occur when tissue fails to enclose the developing brain and spinal cord. In the 1970s, studies revealed that these defects were more frequent in children born to women of low socioeconomic status. Richard Smithells, of the University of Leeds, thought that malnutrition among these women might be responsible. As described in **Figure 41.5**, he found that vitamin supplementation greatly reduced the risk of neural tube defects. In other studies, he obtained evidence that

folic acid (B_9) was the specific vitamin responsible, a finding confirmed by other researchers. Based on this evidence, the FDA in 1998 began to require that folic acid be added to enriched grain products used to make bread, cereals, and other foods. Follow-up studies have documented the effectiveness of this program in reducing the frequency of neural tube defects. Thus, at a time when microsurgery and sophisticated diagnostic imaging dominate the headlines, simple dietary changes such as folic acid supplements or consumption of Golden Rice may be among the greatest contributors to human health.

CONCEPT CHECK **41.1**

1. All 20 amino acids are needed to make animal proteins. Why aren't they all essential to animal diets?
2. Explain why vitamins are required in much smaller amounts than carbohydrates.
3. **WHAT IF?** If a zoo animal shows signs of malnutrition, how might a researcher determine which nutrient is lacking?

For suggested answers, see Appendix A.

CONCEPT **41.2**

The main stages of food processing are ingestion, digestion, absorption, and elimination

In this section, we turn from nutritional requirements to the mechanisms by which animals process food. Food processing can be divided into four distinct stages: ingestion, digestion, absorption, and elimination. The first stage, **ingestion**, is the act of eating. Food can be ingested in many liquid and solid forms. **Figure 41.6** surveys and classifies the principal feeding mechanisms that have evolved among animals. Given the variation in food sources, it is not surprising that strategies for extracting resources from food also differ widely among animal species. We will focus, however, on the shared processes, pausing periodically to consider some adaptations to particular diets or environments.

In **digestion**, the second stage of food processing, food is broken down into molecules small enough for the body to absorb. This stage is necessary because animals cannot directly use the proteins, carbohydrates, nucleic acids, fats, and phospholipids in food. One problem is that these molecules are too large to pass through membranes and enter the cells of the animal. In addition, the large molecules in food are not all identical to those the animal needs for its particular tissues and functions. When large molecules in food are broken down into their components, however, the animal can use these smaller mol-

---

▼ **Figure 41.5** **Inquiry**

Can diet influence the frequency of birth defects?

EXPERIMENT Richard Smithells, of the University of Leeds, examined the effect of vitamin supplementation on the risk of neural tube defects. Women who had had one or more babies with such a defect were put into two study groups. The experimental group consisted of those who were planning a pregnancy and began taking a multivitamin at least four weeks before attempting conception. The control group, who were not given vitamins, included women who declined them and women who were already pregnant. The numbers of neural tube defects resulting from the pregnancies were recorded for each group.

RESULTS

Group	Number of infants/fetuses studied	Infants/fetuses with a neural tube defect
Vitamin supplements (experimental group)	141	1 (0.7%)
No vitamin supplements (control group)	204	12 (5.9%)

CONCLUSION This study provided evidence that vitamin supplementation protects against neural tube defects, at least in pregnancies after the first. Follow-up trials demonstrated that folic acid alone provided an equivalent protective effect.

SOURCE R.W. Smithells et al., Possible prevention of neural tube defects by periconceptional vitamin supplementation, *Lancet* 339–340 (1980).

Inquiry in Action Read and analyze the original paper in *Inquiry in Action: Interpreting Scientific Papers.*

WHAT IF? Subsequent studies were designed to learn if folic acid supplements prevent neural tube defects during first-time pregnancies. To determine the required number of subjects, what additional information did the researchers need?

Exploring Four Main Feeding Mechanisms of Animals

Suspension Feeders

Baleen

Many aquatic animals are **suspension feeders**, which sift small food particles from the water. For example, attached to the upper jaw of this humpback whale are comb-like plates called baleen, which strain small invertebrates and fish from enormous volumes of water. Clams and oysters are also suspension feeders. They use their gills to trap tiny morsels; cilia then sweep the food particles to the mouth in a film of mucus.

Substrate Feeders

Substrate feeders are animals that live in or on their food source. This leaf miner caterpillar, the larva of a moth, is eating through the soft tissue of an oak leaf, leaving a dark trail of feces in its wake. Some other substrate feeders include maggots (fly larvae), which burrow into animal carcasses.

Caterpillar   Feces

Fluid Feeders

Fluid feeders suck nutrient-rich fluid from a living host. This mosquito has pierced the skin of its human host with hollow, needle-like mouthparts and is consuming a blood meal (colorized SEM). Similarly, aphids are fluid feeders that tap the phloem sap of plants. In contrast to such parasites, some fluid feeders actually benefit their hosts. For example, hummingbirds and bees move pollen between flowers as they fluid-feed on nectar.

Bulk Feeders

Most animals, including humans, are **bulk feeders**, which eat relatively large pieces of food. Their adaptations include tentacles, pincers, claws, poisonous fangs, jaws, and teeth that kill their prey or tear off pieces of meat or vegetation. In this amazing scene, a rock python is beginning to ingest a gazelle it has captured and killed. Snakes cannot chew their food into pieces and must swallow it whole—even if the prey is much bigger than the diameter of the snake. They can do so because the lower jaw is loosely hinged to the skull by an elastic ligament that permits the mouth and throat to open very wide. After swallowing its prey, which may take more than an hour, the python will spend two weeks or more digesting its meal.

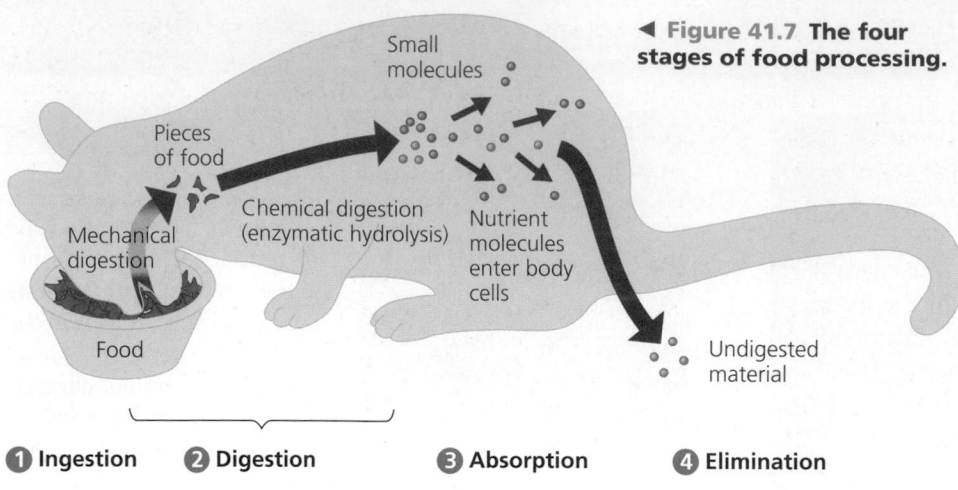

◀ **Figure 41.7 The four stages of food processing.**

Small molecules

Pieces of food

Mechanical digestion

Chemical digestion (enzymatic hydrolysis)

Nutrient molecules enter body cells

Food

Undigested material

1 Ingestion   **2** Digestion   **3** Absorption   **4** Elimination

ecules to assemble the large molecules it needs. For example, although fruit flies and humans have very different diets, both convert proteins in their food to the same 20 amino acids from which they assemble all of the proteins specific for their species.

Recall from Chapter 5 that a cell makes a macromolecule or fat by linking together smaller components; it does so by removing a molecule of water for each new covalent bond formed. Chemical digestion by enzymes reverses this process by breaking bonds with the addition of water (see Figure 5.2). This splitting process is called **enzymatic hydrolysis**. A variety of enzymes catalyze the digestion of large molecules in food. Polysaccharides and disaccharides are split into simple sugars; proteins are broken down into amino acids; and nucleic acids are cleaved into nucleotides. Enzymatic hydrolysis also releases fatty acids and other components from fats and phospholipids. Such chemical digestion is typically preceded by mechanical digestion—by chewing, for instance. Mechanical digestion breaks food into smaller pieces, increasing the surface area available for chemical processes.

The last two stages of food processing occur after the food is digested. In the third stage, **absorption**, the animal's cells take up (absorb) small molecules such as amino acids and simple sugars. **Elimination** completes the process as undigested material passes out of the digestive system. **Figure 41.7** reviews the four stages of food processing.

Digestive Compartments

In our overview of food processing, we have seen that digestive enzymes hydrolyze the same biological materials (such as proteins, fats, and carbohydrates) that make up the bodies of the animals themselves. How, then, are animals able to digest food without digesting their own cells and tissues? The evolutionary adaptation found across a wide range of animal species is the processing of food within specialized compartments. Such compartments can be intracellular, in the form of food vacuoles, or extracellular, as in digestive organs and systems.

Intracellular Digestion

Food vacuoles—cellular organelles in which hydrolytic enzymes break down food—are the simplest digestive compartments. The hydrolysis of food inside vacuoles, called **intracellular digestion**, begins after a cell engulfs solid food by phagocytosis or liquid food by pinocytosis (see Figure 7.20). Newly formed food vacuoles fuse with lysosomes, organelles containing hydrolytic enzymes. This fusion of organelles brings food together with the enzymes, allowing digestion to occur safely within a compartment enclosed by a protective membrane. A few animals, such as sponges, digest their food entirely by this intracellular mechanism (see Figure 33.4).

Extracellular Digestion

In most animals, at least some hydrolysis occurs by **extracellular digestion**, the breakdown of food in compartments that are continuous with the outside of the animal's body. Having one or more extracellular compartments for digestion enables an animal to devour much larger sources of food than can be ingested by phagocytosis.

Many animals with relatively simple body plans have a digestive compartment with a single opening **(Figure 41.8)**. This pouch, called a **gastrovascular cavity**, functions in digestion as well as in the distribution of nutrients throughout the body (hence the *vascular* part of the term). The carnivorous

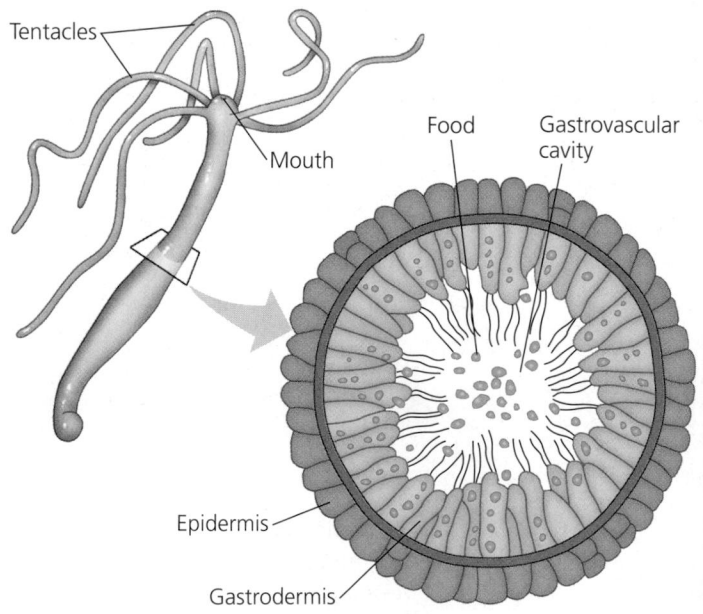

Tentacles

Mouth

Food

Gastrovascular cavity

Epidermis

Gastrodermis

▲ **Figure 41.8 Digestion in a hydra.** Digestion begins in the gastrovascular cavity and is completed intracellularly after small food particles are engulfed by specialized cells of the gastrodermis.

cnidarians called hydras provide a good example of how a gastrovascular cavity works. A hydra uses its tentacles to stuff captured prey through its mouth into its gastrovascular cavity. Specialized gland cells of the hydra's gastrodermis, the tissue layer that lines the cavity, then secrete digestive enzymes that break the soft tissues of the prey into tiny pieces. Other cells of the gastrodermis engulf these food particles, and most of the actual hydrolysis of macromolecules occurs intracellularly, as in sponges. After a hydra has digested its meal, undigested materials that remain in the gastrovascular cavity, such as exoskeletons of small crustaceans, are eliminated through the same opening by which food entered. Many flatworms also have a gastrovascular cavity with a single opening (see Figure 33.10).

In contrast with cnidarians and flatworms, most animals have a digestive tube extending between two openings, a mouth and an anus. Such a tube is called a **complete digestive tract** or, more commonly, an **alimentary canal**. Because food moves along the alimentary canal in a single direction, the tube can be organized into specialized compartments that carry out digestion and nutrient absorption in a stepwise fashion (**Figure 41.9**). An animal with an alimentary canal can ingest food while earlier meals are still being digested, a feat that is likely to be difficult or inefficient for animals with gastrovascular cavities. In the next section, we'll explore the spatial and functional organization of an alimentary canal.

CONCEPT CHECK 41.2

1. Distinguish the overall structure of a gastrovascular cavity from that of an alimentary canal.
2. In what sense are nutrients from a recently ingested meal not really "inside" your body prior to the absorption stage of food processing?
3. **WHAT IF?** Thinking in broad terms, what similarities can you identify between digestion in an animal body and the breakdown of gasoline in an automobile? (You don't have to know about auto mechanics.)

For suggested answers, see Appendix A.

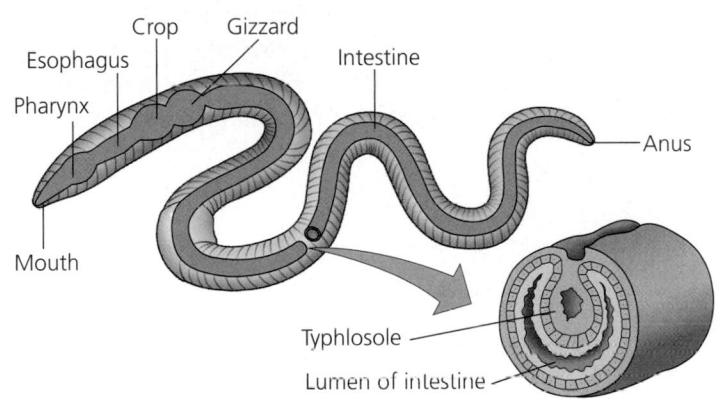

(a) Earthworm. The alimentary canal of an earthworm includes a muscular pharynx that sucks food in through the mouth. Food passes through the esophagus and is stored and moistened in the crop. Mechanical digestion occurs in the muscular gizzard, which pulverizes food with the aid of small bits of sand and gravel. Further digestion and absorption occur in the intestine, which has a dorsal fold, the typhlosole, that increases the surface area for nutrient absorption.

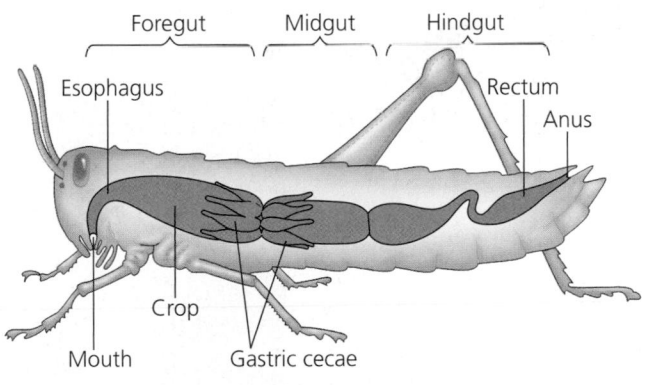

(b) Grasshopper. A grasshopper has several digestive chambers grouped into three main regions: a foregut, with an esophagus and crop; a midgut; and a hindgut. Food is moistened and stored in the crop, but most digestion occurs in the midgut. Gastric cecae, (singular, ceca), pouches extending from the beginning of the midgut, function in digestion and absorption.

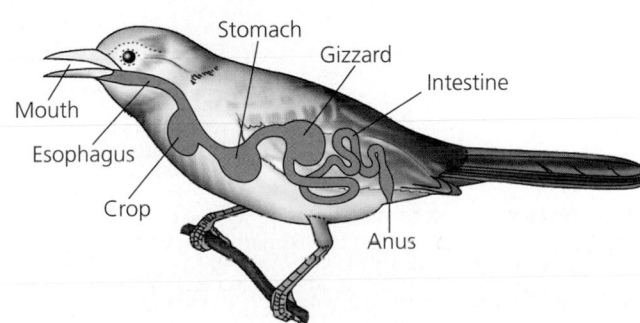

(c) Bird. Many birds have three separate chambers—the crop, stomach, and gizzard—where food is pulverized and churned before passing into the intestine. A bird's crop and gizzard function very much like those of an earthworm. In most birds, chemical digestion and absorption of nutrients occur in the intestine.

▲ Figure 41.9 **Variation in alimentary canals.**

Organs specialized for sequential stages of food processing form the mammalian digestive system

Because most animals, including mammals, have an alimentary canal, we can use the mammalian digestive system as a representative example of the general principles of food processing. In mammals, the digestive system consists of the alimentary canal and various accessory glands that secrete digestive juices through ducts into the canal **(Figure 41.10)**. The accessory glands of the mammalian digestive system are three pairs of salivary glands, the pancreas, the liver, and the gallbladder.

Food is pushed along the alimentary canal by **peristalsis**, alternating waves of contraction and relaxation in the smooth muscles lining the canal. It is peristalsis that enables us to process and digest food even while lying down. At some of the junctions between specialized compartments, the muscular layer forms ringlike valves called **sphincters**. Acting like drawstrings to close off the alimentary canal, sphincters regulate the passage of material between compartments.

Using the human digestive system as a model, let's now follow a meal through the alimentary canal. As we do so, we'll ex-amine in more detail what happens to the food in each digestive compartment along the way.

The Oral Cavity, Pharynx, and Esophagus

Ingestion and the initial steps of digestion occur in the mouth, or **oral cavity**. Mechanical digestion begins as teeth of various shapes cut, smash, and grind food, making the food easier to swallow and increasing its surface area. Meanwhile, the presence of food stimulates a nervous reflex that causes the **salivary glands** to deliver saliva through ducts to the oral cavity. Saliva may also be released before food enters the mouth, triggered by a learned association between eating and the time of day, a cooking odor, or another stimulus.

Saliva initiates chemical digestion while also protecting the oral cavity. **Amylase**, an enzyme in saliva, hydrolyzes starch (a glucose polymer from plants) and glycogen (a glucose polymer from animals) into smaller polysaccharides and the disaccharide maltose. Mucin, a slippery glycoprotein (carbohydrate-protein complex) in saliva, protects the lining of the mouth from abrasion. Mucin also lubricates food for easier swallowing. Additional components of saliva include buffers, which help prevent tooth decay by neutralizing acid, and antibacterial agents (such as lysozyme; see Figure 5.19), which protect against microorganisms that enter the mouth with food.

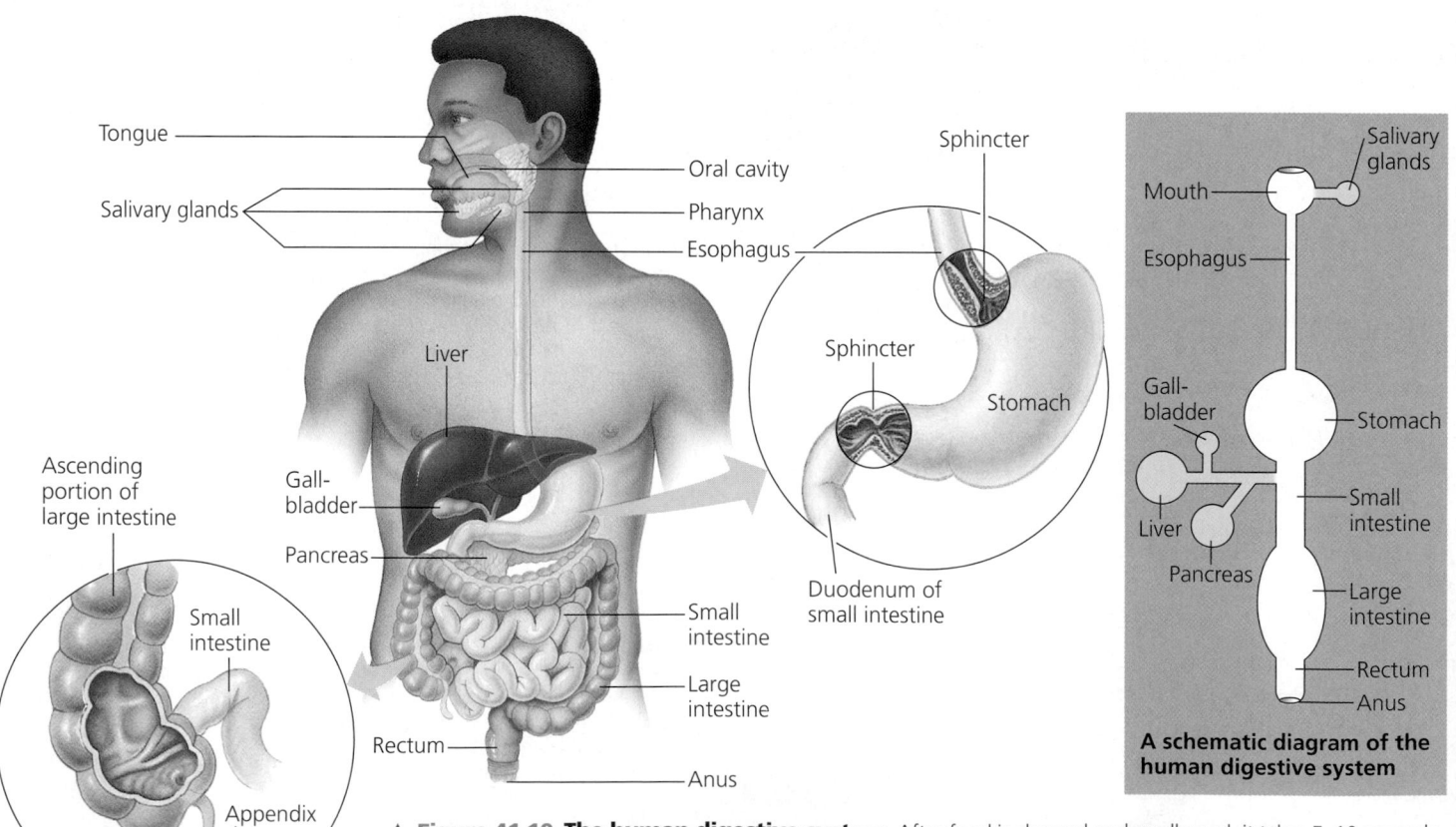

▲ **Figure 41.10 The human digestive system.** After food is chewed and swallowed, it takes 5–10 seconds for it to pass down the esophagus and into the stomach, where it spends 2–6 hours being partially digested. Final digestion and nutrient absorption occur in the small intestine over a period of 5–6 hours. In 12–24 hours, any undigested material passes through the large intestine, and feces are expelled through the anus.

Much as a doorman screens and assists people entering a building, the tongue aids digestive processes by evaluating ingested material and then enabling its further passage. When food arrives at the oral cavity, the tongue plays a critical role in distinguishing which foods should be processed further (see Chapter 50 for a discussion of the sense of taste). After food is deemed acceptable and chewing commences, tongue movements manipulate the food, helping shape it into a ball called a **bolus**. During swallowing, the tongue provides further help, pushing the bolus to the back of the oral cavity and into the pharynx.

The **pharynx**, or throat region, opens to two passageways: the esophagus and the trachea (windpipe). The **esophagus** connects to the stomach, whereas the trachea leads to the lungs. Swallowing must therefore be carefully choreographed to keep food from entering and blocking the airway. When you swallow, a flap of cartilage called the *epiglottis* prevents food from entering the trachea by covering the *glottis*—the vocal cords and the opening between them. Guided by the movements of the *larynx*, the upper part of the respiratory tract, this swallowing mechanism directs each bolus into the entrance of the esophagus (**Figure 41.11**, steps 1–4). If the swallowing reflex fails, food or liquids can reach the windpipe and cause choking, a blockage of the trachea. The resulting lack of airflow into the lungs can be fatal if the material is not dislodged by vigorous coughing or a forced upward thrust of the diaphragm (the Heimlich maneuver).

The esophagus contains both striated and smooth muscle (see Figure 40.5). The striated muscle is situated at the top of the esophagus and is active during swallowing. Throughout the rest of the esophagus, smooth muscle functions in peristalsis. The rhythmic cycles of contraction move each bolus to the stomach (see Figure 41.11, step 6). As with other parts of the digestive system, the form of the esophagus fits its function and varies among species. For example, fishes have no lungs to bypass and therefore have a very short esophagus. And it will come as no surprise that giraffes have a very long esophagus.

Digestion in the Stomach

The **stomach** is located just below the diaphragm in the upper abdominal cavity. A few nutrients are absorbed from the stomach into the bloodstream, but the stomach primarily stores food and continues digestion. With accordion-like folds and a very elastic wall, it can stretch to accommodate about 2 L of food and fluid. The stomach secretes a digestive fluid called **gastric juice** and mixes this secretion with the food through a churning action. This mixture of ingested food and digestive juice is called **chyme**.

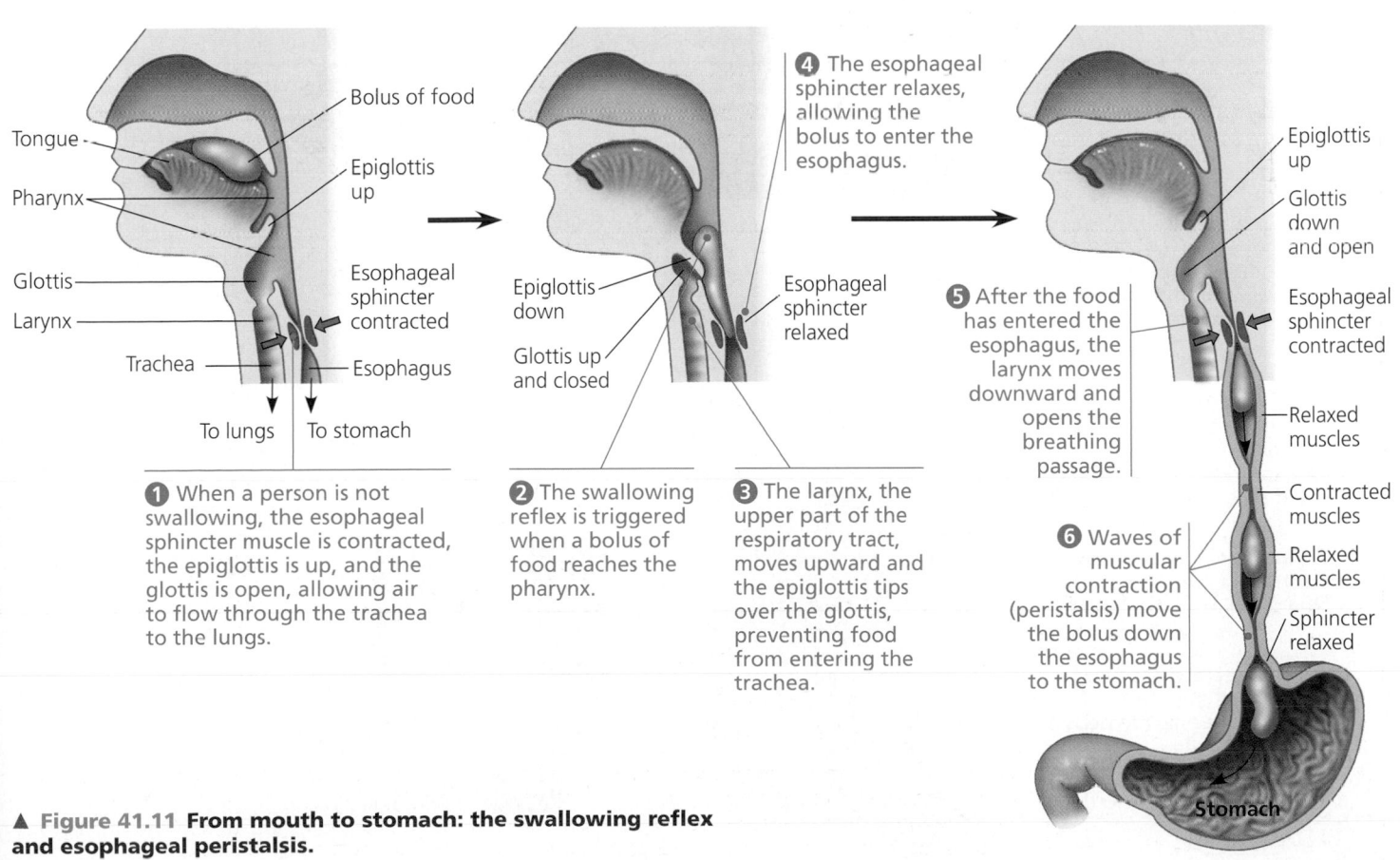

▲ Figure 41.11 **From mouth to stomach: the swallowing reflex and esophageal peristalsis.**

Chemical Digestion in the Stomach

Two components of gastric juice carry out chemical digestion. One is hydrochloric acid (HCl), which disrupts the extracellular matrix that binds cells together in meat and plant material. The concentration of HCl is so high that the pH of gastric juice is about 2, acidic enough to dissolve iron nails. This low pH not only kills most bacteria but also denatures (unfolds) proteins in food, increasing exposure of their peptide bonds. The exposed bonds are attacked by the second component of gastric juice—a **protease**, or protein-digesting enzyme, called **pepsin**. Unlike most enzymes, pepsin works best in a strongly acidic environment. By breaking peptide bonds, it cleaves proteins into smaller polypeptides. Further digestion to individual amino acids occurs in the small intestine.

Why doesn't gastric juice destroy the stomach cells that make it? The answer is that the ingredients of gastric juice are kept inactive until they are released into the lumen (cavity) of the stomach. The components of gastric juice are produced by cells in the gastric glands of the stomach (**Figure 41.12**). *Parietal cells* secrete hydrogen and chloride ions, which form hydrochloric acid (HCl). Using an ATP-driven pump, the parietal cells expel hydrogen ions into the lumen at very high concentration. There the hydrogen ions combine with chloride ions that diffuse into the lumen through specific membrane channels. Meanwhile, *chief cells* release pepsin into the lumen in an inactive form called **pepsinogen**. HCl converts pepsinogen to active pepsin by clipping off a small portion of the molecule and exposing its active site. Through these processes, both HCl and pepsin form in the lumen of the stomach, not within the cells of the gastric glands.

After hydrochloric acid converts a small amount of pepsinogen to pepsin, a second chemical process helps activate the remaining pepsinogen. Pepsin, like HCl, can clip pepsinogen to expose the enzyme's active site. This generates more pepsin, which activates more pepsinogen, forming more active enzyme. This series of events is an example of positive feedback.

When HCl and pepsin form within the stomach lumen, why aren't the cells that line the stomach damaged? Actually, these cells are vulnerable to gastric juice as well as to acid-tolerant pathogens in food. However, the stomach lining protects against self-digestion by secreting **mucus**, a viscous and slippery mixture of glycoproteins, cells, salts, and water. In addition, cell division adds a new epithelial layer every three days, replacing cells

▶ **Figure 41.12 The stomach and its secretions.** The micrograph (colorized SEM) shows a gastric pit on the interior surface of the stomach, through which digestive juices are secreted.

5 μm

Interior surface of stomach. The interior surface of the stomach wall is highly folded and dotted with pits leading into tubular gastric glands.

Gastric gland. The gastric glands have three types of cells that secrete different components of the gastric juice: mucus cells, chief cells, and parietal cells.

Mucus cells secrete mucus, which lubricates and protects the cells lining the stomach.

Chief cells secrete pepsinogen, an inactive form of the digestive enzyme pepsin.

Parietal cells secrete hydrochloric acid (HCl).

Esophagus

Sphincter

Stomach

Sphincter

Small intestine

Folds of epithelial tissue

Epithelium

Pepsinogen → Pepsin (active enzyme)

HCl

H⁺

Cl⁻

Chief cell

Parietal cell

❶ Pepsinogen and HCl are secreted into the lumen of the stomach.

❷ HCl converts pepsinogen to pepsin.

❸ Pepsin then activates more pepsinogen, starting a chain reaction. Pepsin begins the chemical digestion of proteins.

eroded by digestive juices. Despite these defenses, damaged areas of the stomach lining called gastric ulcers may appear. For decades, scientists thought they were caused by psychological stress and resulting excess acid secretion. In 1982, however, researchers Barry Marshall and Robin Warren, at Royal Perth Hospital in Australia, reported that infection by the acid-tolerant bacterium *Helicobacter pylori* causes ulcers. They also demonstrated that an antibiotic treatment could cure most gastric ulcers. For these findings, they were awarded the Nobel Prize in 2005.

Stomach Dynamics

Chemical digestion by gastric juice is accompanied by the churning action of the stomach. This coordinated series of muscle contractions and relaxations mixes the stomach contents about every 20 seconds. As a result of mixing and enzyme action, what begins as a recently swallowed meal becomes the acidic, nutrient-rich broth known as chyme. Most of the time, the stomach is closed off at both ends (see Figure 41.10). The sphincter between the esophagus and the stomach normally opens only when a bolus arrives. Occasionally, however, a person experiences acid reflux, a backflow of chyme from the stomach into the lower end of the esophagus. The resulting irritation of the esophagus is commonly but inaccurately called "heartburn."

The sphincter located where the stomach opens to the small intestine helps regulate the passage of chyme into the small intestine, allowing only one squirt at a time. The mixture of acid, enzyme, and partially digested food typically leaves the stomach 2–6 hours after a meal.

Digestion in the Small Intestine

Most enzymatic hydrolysis of macromolecules from food occurs in the **small intestine (Figure 41.13)**. Over 6 m long in

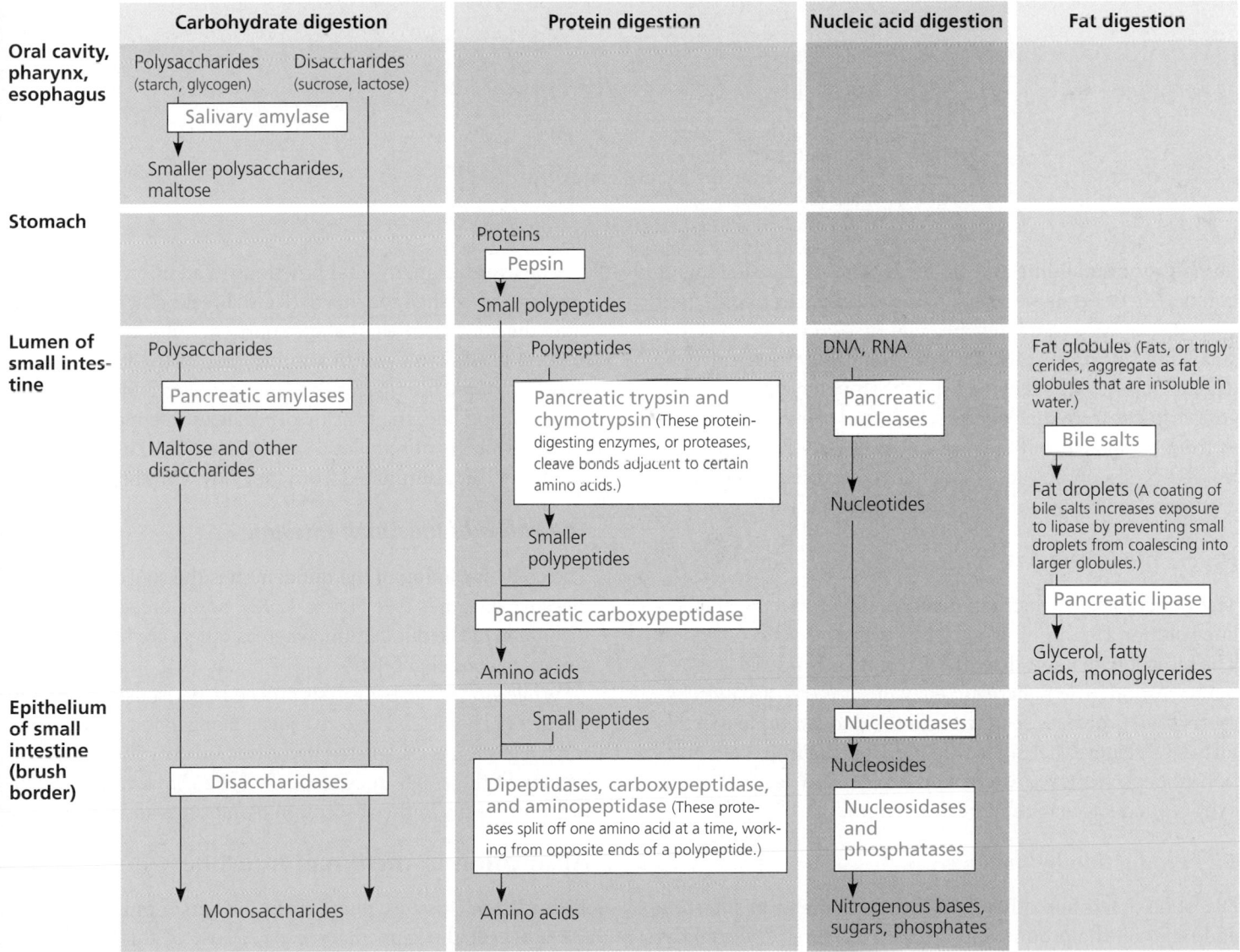

▲ **Figure 41.13 Enzymatic hydrolysis in the human digestive system.**
? *Pepsin is resistant to the denaturing effect of the low pH environment of the stomach. Thinking about the different digestive processes that occur in the small intestine, what adaptation do you think the digestive enzymes in that compartment share?*

► **Figure 41.14 Hormonal control of digestion.** Many animals go for long intervals between meals and do not need their digestive systems to be active continuously. Hormones released by the stomach and duodenum help ensure that digestive secretions are present only when needed. Like all hormones, they are transported through the bloodstream. In the case of gastrin, the target is the organ that secretes the hormone.

Liver

Gallbladder   **Bile**

Secretin and CCK

CCK +

Duodenum of small intestine

Secretin +

CCK +

When chyme rich in fats enters the duodenum, **secretin** and **CCK** inhibit peristalsis and acid secretion by the stomach, thereby slowing digestion.

Stomach

Gastrin +

Gastrin circulates via the bloodstream back to the stomach, where it stimulates production of gastric juices.

Pancreas

Secretin stimulates the pancreas to release sodium bicarbonate, which neutralizes chyme.

Key
+ Stimulation
− Inhibition

Amino acids or fatty acids trigger the release of **cholecystokinin (CCK),** which stimulates release of enzymes from the pancreas and of bile from the gallbladder.

humans, the small intestine is the alimentary canal's longest compartment. Its name refers to its small diameter, compared with that of the large intestine. The first 25 cm or so of the small intestine forms the **duodenum**, a major crossroad in digestion. It is here that chyme from the stomach mixes with digestive juices from the pancreas, liver, and gallbladder, as well as from gland cells of the intestinal wall itself. Hormones released by the stomach and duodenum control the digestive secretions into the alimentary canal **(Figure 41.14)**.

Pancreatic Secretions

The **pancreas** aids chemical digestion by producing an alkaline solution rich in bicarbonate as well as several enzymes. The bicarbonate neutralizes the acidity of chyme and acts as a buffer. Among the pancreatic enzymes are trypsin and chymotrypsin, proteases secreted into the duodenum in inactive forms (see Figure 41.13). In a chain reaction similar to activation of pepsin, they are activated when safely located in the extracellular space within the duodenum.

Bile Production by the Liver

Digestion of fats and other lipids begins in the small intestine and relies on the production of **bile**, a mixture of substances that is made in the **liver**. Bile contains bile salts, which act as detergents (emulsifiers) that aid in digestion and absorption of lipids. Bile is stored and concentrated in the **gallbladder**.

The liver has many vital functions in addition to bile production. As we shall see shortly, it also breaks down toxins that enter the body and helps balance nutrient utilization. Bile production itself is integral to another task of the liver: the destruction of red blood cells that are no longer fully functional. In producing bile, the liver incorporates some pigments that are by-products of red blood cell disassembly. These bile pigments are then eliminated from the body with the feces.

Secretions of the Small Intestine

The epithelial lining of the duodenum is the source of several digestive enzymes (see Figure 41.13). Some are secreted into the lumen of the duodenum, whereas others are bound to the surface of epithelial cells.

While enzymatic hydrolysis proceeds, peristalsis moves the mixture of chyme and digestive juices along the small intestine. Most digestion is completed in the duodenum. The remaining regions of the small intestine, called the *jejunum* and *ileum*, function mainly in the absorption of nutrients and water.

Absorption in the Small Intestine

To reach body tissues, nutrients in the lumen must first cross the lining of the alimentary canal. Most of this absorption occurs in the small intestine. This organ has a huge surface area—300 m^2, roughly the size of a tennis court. Large folds in the lining have finger-like projections called **villi**. In turn, each

Vein carrying blood to hepatic portal vein (see next page)

Muscle layers

Villi

Large circular folds

Key

→ Nutrient absorption

Intestinal wall

Blood capillaries

Epithelial cells

Lacteal (see below)

Lymph vessel

Villi

Microvilli (brush border) at apical (lumenal) surface

Lumen

Basal surface

Epithelial cells

▲ **Figure 41.15 The structure of the small intestine.**

❓ *Tapeworms sometimes infect humans, anchoring themselves to the wall of the small intestine. Based on how digestion is compartmentalized along the alimentary canal, what digestive functions would you expect these parasites to have?*

epithelial cell of a villus has on its apical surface many microscopic appendages, or **microvilli**, that are exposed to the intestinal lumen **(Figure 41.15)**. The many side-by-side microvilli give the intestinal epithelium a brush-like appearance—reflected in the name *brush border*. The enormous surface area presented by microvilli is an adaptation that greatly increases the total capacity for nutrient absorption.

Depending on the nutrient, transport across the epithelial cells can be passive or active. The sugar fructose, for example, moves by facilitated diffusion down its concentration gradient from the lumen of the small intestine into the epithelial cells. From there, fructose exits the basal surface and is absorbed into microscopic blood vessels, or capillaries, at the core of each villus. Other nutrients, including amino acids, small peptides, vitamins, and most glucose molecules, are pumped against concentration gradients by the epithelial cells of the villus. This active transport allows much more absorption of nutrients than would be possible with passive diffusion alone.

Although many nutrients leave the intestine through the bloodstream, some products of fat (triglyceride) digestion take a different path. After being absorbed by epithelial cells, fatty acids and monoglycerides (glycerol joined to a single fatty acid) are recombined into triglycerides within those cells. These fats are then coated with phospholipids, cholesterol, and proteins, forming water-soluble globules called **chylomicrons (Figure 41.16)**. These globules are too large to pass through the membranes of capillaries. Instead, they are transported into a **lacteal**, a vessel at the core of each villus (see Figures 41.15 and 41.16). Lacteals are part of the vertebrate lymphatic system, which is a network of vessels that are filled with a clear fluid called lymph. Starting

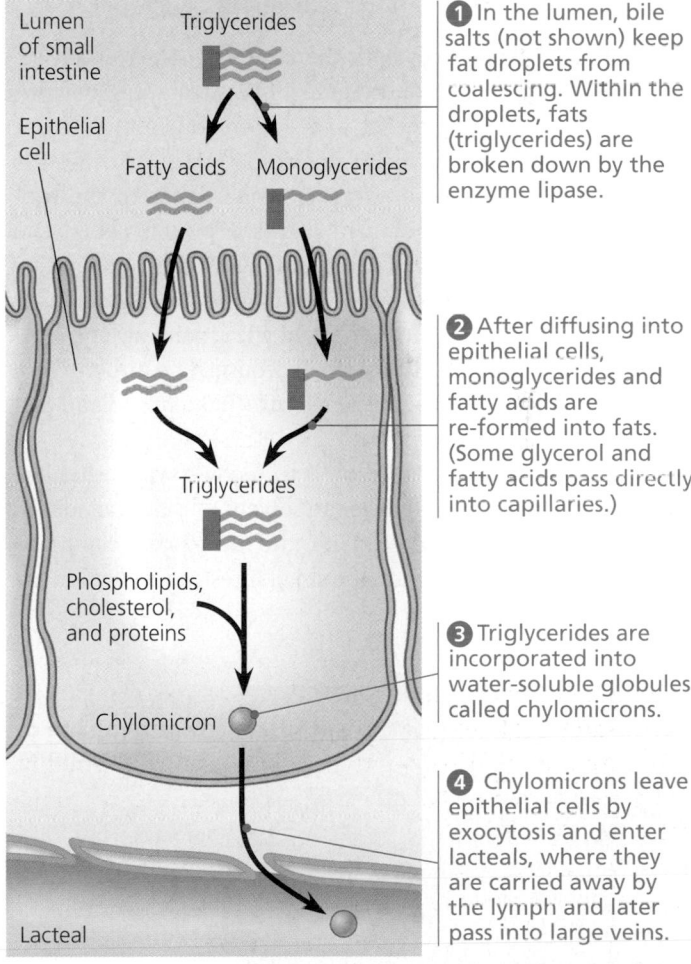

Lumen of small intestine

Triglycerides

Epithelial cell

Fatty acids **Monoglycerides**

Triglycerides

Phospholipids, cholesterol, and proteins

Chylomicron

Lacteal

❶ In the lumen, bile salts (not shown) keep fat droplets from coalescing. Within the droplets, fats (triglycerides) are broken down by the enzyme lipase.

❷ After diffusing into epithelial cells, monoglycerides and fatty acids are re-formed into fats. (Some glycerol and fatty acids pass directly into capillaries.)

❸ Triglycerides are incorporated into water-soluble globules called chylomicrons.

❹ Chylomicrons leave epithelial cells by exocytosis and enter lacteals, where they are carried away by the lymph and later pass into large veins.

▲ **Figure 41.16 Absorption of fats.** Because fats are insoluble in water, adaptations are needed to digest and absorb them. Bile salts maintain a small droplet size, exposing more surface for enzymatic hydrolysis to fatty acids and monoglycerides. These molecules can diffuse into epithelial cells, where fats are reassembled and incorporated into water-soluble chylomicrons that enter the bloodstream via the lymphatic system.

at the lacteals, lymph containing the chylomicrons passes into the larger vessels of the lymphatic system and eventually into large veins that return the blood to the heart.

In contrast with the lacteals, the capillaries and veins that carry nutrient-rich blood away from the villi all converge into the **hepatic portal vein**, a blood vessel that leads directly to the liver. From the liver, blood travels to the heart and then to other tissues and organs. This arrangement serves two major functions. First, it allows the liver to regulate distribution of nutrients to the rest of the body. Because the liver can interconvert many organic molecules, blood that leaves the liver may have a very different nutrient balance than the blood that entered via the hepatic portal vein. For example, blood exiting the liver usually has a glucose concentration very close to 90 mg per 100 mL, regardless of the carbohydrate content of a meal. Second, the arrangement allows the liver to remove toxic substances before the blood circulates broadly. The liver is the primary site for the detoxification of many organic molecules, including drugs, that are foreign to the body.

Absorption in the Large Intestine

The alimentary canal ends with the **large intestine**, which includes the colon, cecum, and rectum. The small intestine connects to the large intestine at a T-shaped junction, where a sphincter controls the movement of material. One arm of the T is the 1.5-m-long **colon (Figure 41.17)**, which leads to the rectum and anus. The other arm forms a pouch called the **cecum** (see Figure 41.10). The cecum is important for fermenting ingested material, especially in animals that eat large amounts of plant material. Compared with many other mammals, humans have a relatively small cecum. The **appendix**, a finger-like extension of the human cecum, has a minor and dispensable role in immunity.

A major function of the colon is to recover water that has entered the alimentary canal as the solvent of digestive juices. About 7 L of fluid are secreted into the lumen of the alimentary canal each day. Together, the small intestine and colon re-

absorb about 90% of the water that enters the alimentary canal. Since there is no biological mechanism for active transport of water, water absorption in the colon occurs by osmosis that results when ions, particularly sodium, are pumped out of the lumen.

The **feces**, the wastes of the digestive system, become increasingly solid as they are moved along the colon by peristalsis. It takes approximately 12–24 hours for material to travel the length of the colon. If the lining of the colon is irritated—by a viral or bacterial infection, for instance—less water than normal may be reabsorbed, resulting in diarrhea. The opposite problem, constipation, occurs when the feces move along the colon too slowly. An excess of water is reabsorbed, and therefore the feces become compacted.

A rich flora of mostly harmless bacteria resides in the human colon, contributing approximately one-third of the dry weight of feces. One inhabitant is *Escherichia coli*, a favorite research organism of molecular biologists (see Chapter 18). Because *E. coli* is so common in human digestive systems, its presence in lakes and streams is a useful indicator of contamination by untreated sewage. Within the intestine, *E. coli* and other bacteria live on unabsorbed organic material. As by-products of their metabolism, many colon bacteria generate gases, including methane and hydrogen sulfide, which has an offensive odor. These gases and ingested air are expelled through the anus. Some of the bacteria produce vitamins, such as biotin, vitamin K, and several B vitamins, including folic acid. These vitamins, absorbed into the blood, supplement our dietary intake of vitamins.

Besides bacteria, feces contain undigested material, including cellulose fiber. Although it has no caloric value to humans, fiber helps move food along the alimentary canal.

The terminal portion of the large intestine is the **rectum**, where feces are stored until they can be eliminated. Between the rectum and the anus are two sphincters, the inner one being involuntary and the outer one being voluntary. Periodically (once a day or so in most individuals), strong contractions of the colon create an urge to defecate.

We have followed a meal from one opening (the mouth) of the alimentary canal to the other (the anus). Next we'll see how some digestive adaptations may have evolved.

◀ **Figure 41.17**
Digital image of a human colon. This CAT scan image was produced by integrating two-dimensional sectional views of the large intestine.

CONCEPT CHECK **41.3**

1. In the zero-gravity environment of space, how does food swallowed by an astronaut reach his or her stomach?
2. What step in food processing occurs more readily for fats than for proteins and carbohydrates?
3. **WHAT IF?** Some early experiments involved obtaining samples of digestive juices and observing digestion outside the body. If you mixed gastric juice with crushed food, how far would the process of digestion proceed?

For suggested answers, see Appendix A.

Evolutionary adaptations of vertebrate digestive systems correlate with diet

The digestive systems of mammals and other vertebrates are variations on a common plan, but there are many intriguing adaptations, often associated with the animal's diet. To highlight how form fits function, we'll examine a few of them.

Some Dental Adaptations

Dentition, an animal's assortment of teeth, is one example of structural variation reflecting diet. Consider the dentition of carnivorous, herbivorous, and omnivorous mammals in **Figure 41.18**. The evolutionary adaptation of teeth for processing different kinds of food is one of the major reasons mammals have been so successful. Nonmammalian vertebrates generally have less specialized dentition, but there are interesting exceptions. For example, poisonous snakes, such as rattlesnakes, have fangs, modified teeth that inject venom into prey. Some fangs are hollow, like syringes, whereas others drip the poison along grooves on the surfaces of the teeth. Other teeth are absent. Combined with an elastic ligament that permits the mouth to open very wide, these anatomical adaptations allow prey to be swallowed whole, as in the astonishing scene in Figure 41.6.

Stomach and Intestinal Adaptations

Large, expandable stomachs are common in carnivorous vertebrates, which may go for a long time between meals and must eat as much as they can when they do catch prey. A 200-kg African lion can consume 40 kg of meat in one meal!

The length of the vertebrate digestive system is also correlated with diet. In general, herbivores and omnivores have longer alimentary canals relative to their body size than do carnivores (**Figure 41.19**). Vegetation is more difficult to digest than meat because it contains cell walls. A longer digestive tract furnishes more time for digestion and more surface area for the absorption of nutrients.

Incisors **Canines** **Premolars** **Molars**

(a) Carnivore. Carnivores, such as members of the dog and cat families, generally have pointed incisors and canines that can be used to kill prey and rip or cut away pieces of flesh. The jagged premolars and molars crush and shred food.

(b) Herbivore. In contrast, herbivorous mammals, such as horses and deer, usually have teeth with broad, ridged surfaces that grind tough plant material. The incisors and canines are generally modified for biting off pieces of vegetation. In some herbivorous mammals, canines are absent.

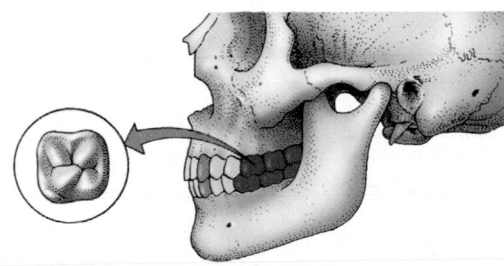

(c) Omnivore. Humans, being omnivores adapted for eating both vegetation and meat, have a relatively unspecialized dentition consisting of 32 permanent (adult) teeth. From the midline to the back along one side of one jaw, there are two bladelike incisors for biting, a pointed canine for tearing, two premolars for grinding, and three molars for crushing.

▲ **Figure 41.18 Dentition and diet.**

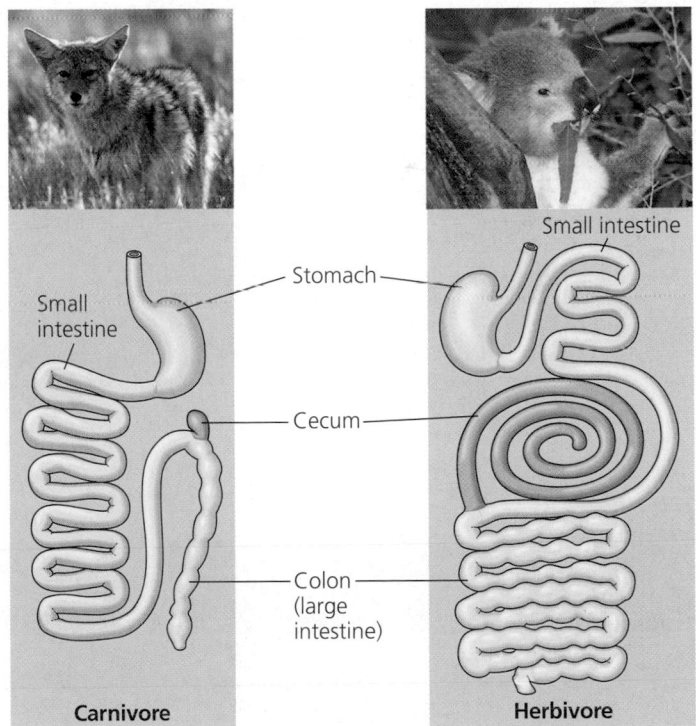

Small intestine Stomach Small intestine Cecum Colon (large intestine)

Carnivore Herbivore

▲ **Figure 41.19 The alimentary canals of a carnivore (coyote) and herbivore (koala).** Although these two mammals are about the same size, the koala's intestines are much longer, enhancing processing of fibrous, protein-poor eucalyptus leaves from which it obtains virtually all its food and water. Extensive chewing chops the leaves into tiny pieces, increasing exposure to digestive juices. In the long cecum, symbiotic bacteria convert the shredded leaves to a more nutritious diet.

Mutualistic Adaptations

Some digestive adaptations involve mutualistic symbiosis, a mutually beneficial interaction between two species (see Chapter 54). For example, microorganisms help herbivores digest plants. Much of the chemical energy in herbivore diets comes from the cellulose of plant cell walls, but animals do not produce enzymes that hydrolyze cellulose. Instead, many vertebrates (as well as termites, whose wood diets are largely cellulose) house large populations of mutualistic bacteria and protists in fermentation chambers in their alimentary canals. These microorganisms have enzymes that can digest cellulose to simple sugars and other compounds that the animal can absorb. In many cases, the microorganisms also use the sugars from digested cellulose to produce a variety of nutrients essential to the animal, such as vitamins and amino acids.

The location of mutualistic microbes in alimentary canals varies, depending on the type of herbivore. For example:

▶ The hoatzin, an herbivorous bird that lives in the South American rain forests, has a large, muscular crop (an esophageal pouch; see Figure 41.9) that houses mutualistic microorganisms. Hard ridges in the wall of the crop grind plant leaves into small fragments, and the microorganisms break down cellulose.

▶ Horses and many other herbivorous mammals house mutualistic microorganisms in a large cecum, the pouch where the small and large intestines connect.

▶ In rabbits and some rodents, mutualistic bacteria live in the large intestine as well as in the cecum. Since most nutrients are absorbed in the small intestine, nourishing by-products of fermentation by bacteria in the large intestine are initially lost with the feces. Rabbits and rodents recover these nutrients by *coprophagy* (from the Greek, meaning "dung eating"), feeding on some of their feces and then passing the food through the alimentary canal a second time. The familiar rabbit "pellets," which are not reingested, are the feces eliminated after food has passed through the digestive tract twice.

▶ The koala, an Australian marsupial, also has an enlarged cecum, where mutualistic bacteria ferment finely shredded eucalyptus leaves (see Figure 41.19).

▶ The most elaborate adaptations for an herbivorous diet have evolved in the animals called **ruminants**, which include deer, sheep, and cattle **(Figure 41.20)**.

1 **Rumen.** When the cow first chews and swallows a mouthful of grass, boluses (green arrows) enter the rumen.

Intestine

2 **Reticulum.** Some boluses also enter the reticulum. In both the rumen and the reticulum, mutualistic prokaryotes and protists (mainly ciliates) go to work on the cellulose-rich meal. As by-products of their metabolism, the microorganisms secrete fatty acids. The cow periodically regurgitates and rechews the cud (red arrows), which further breaks down the fibers, making them more accessible to further microbial action.

Esophagus

4 **Abomasum.** The cud, containing great numbers of microorganisms, finally passes to the abomasum for digestion by the cow's own enzymes (black arrows).

3 **Omasum.** The cow then reswallows the cud (blue arrows), which moves to the omasum, where water is removed.

▲ **Figure 41.20 Ruminant digestion.** The stomach of a ruminant has four chambers. Because of the microbial action in the chambers, the diet from which a ruminant actually absorbs its nutrients is much richer than the grass the animal originally eats. In fact, a ruminant eating grass or hay obtains many of its nutrients by digesting the mutualistic microorganisms, which reproduce rapidly enough in the rumen to maintain a stable population.

Although we have focused our discussion on vertebrates, adaptations related to digestion are also widespread among other animals. Some of the most remarkable examples are the giant tubeworms that live at deep-sea hydrothermal vents (see Figure 52.18). These worms, which thrive at pressures as high as 260 atmospheres in water that reaches a remarkable 400°C (752°F), have no mouth or digestive system. Instead, they rely entirely on mutualistic bacteria to generate energy and nutrients from the carbon dioxide, oxygen, hydrogen sulfide, and nitrate available at the vents. Thus, for invertebrates and vertebrates alike, mutualistic symbiosis has evolved as a general strategy for expanding the sources of nutrition available to animals.

Having examined how animals optimize their extraction of nutrients from food, we will next turn to the challenge of balancing the use of these nutrients.

CONCEPT CHECK 41.4

1. What are the two advantages of a longer alimentary canal for processing plant material that is difficult to digest?
2. What features of an animal's digestive system make it an attractive habitat for mutualistic microorganisms?
3. **WHAT IF?** "Lactose-intolerant" people have a shortage of lactase, the enzyme that breaks down lactose in milk. As a result, they sometimes develop cramps, bloating, or diarrhea after consuming dairy products. Suppose such a person ate yogurt, which contains bacteria that produce lactase. Why might you expect that eating yogurt would provide at best only temporary relief of the symptoms?

For suggested answers, see Appendix A.

CONCEPT 41.5

Homeostatic mechanisms contribute to an animal's energy balance

As discussed in Chapter 40, the energy obtained from food balances the expenditure of energy for metabolism, activity, and storage. In concluding our overview of nutrition, we'll examine some ways in which animals achieve this balance.

Energy Sources and Stores

In deriving energy from their diet, animals make use of certain fuel sources before others. Nearly all of an animal's ATP generation is based on the oxidation of energy-rich organic molecules—carbohydrates, proteins, and fats—in cellular respiration. Although any of these substances can be used as fuel, most animals "burn" proteins only after exhausting their supply of carbohydrates and fats. Fats are especially rich in energy; oxi-

Insulin enhances the transport of glucose into body cells and stimulates the liver and muscle cells to store glucose as glycogen. As a result, blood glucose level drops.

The pancreas secretes the hormone insulin into the blood.

Stimulus: Blood glucose level rises after eating.

Homeostasis: 90 mg glucose/ 100 mL blood

Stimulus: Blood glucose level drops below set point.

Glucagon promotes the breakdown of glycogen in the liver and the release of glucose into the blood, increasing blood glucose level.

The pancreas secretes the hormone glucagon into the blood.

▲ **Figure 41.21 Homeostatic regulation of cellular fuel.** After a meal is digested, glucose and other monomers are absorbed into the blood from the digestive tract. The human body regulates the use and storage of glucose, a major cellular fuel. Notice that these regulatory loops are examples of the negative feedback control described in Chapter 40.

dizing a gram of fat liberates about twice the energy liberated from a gram of carbohydrate or protein.

When an animal takes in more energy-rich molecules than it breaks down, the excess is converted to storage molecules. In humans, the primary sites of storage are liver and muscle cells. Excess energy from the diet is stored there in the form of glycogen, a polymer made up of many glucose units (see Figure 5.6b). When fewer calories are taken in than are expended—perhaps because of sustained heavy exercise or lack of food—glycogen is oxidized. The hormones insulin and glucagon maintain glucose homeostasis by tightly regulating glycogen synthesis and breakdown (**Figure 41.21**).

Adipose (fat) cells represent a secondary site of energy storage in the body. If glycogen depots are full and caloric intake exceeds caloric expenditure, the excess is usually stored as fat. When more energy is required than is generated from the diet, the human body generally expends liver glycogen first and then draws on muscle glycogen and fat. Most healthy people have enough stored fat to sustain them through several weeks without food.

100 µm

◀ **Figure 41.22 Fat cells from the abdomen of a human.** Strands of connective tissue (yellow) hold the fat-storing adipose cells in place (colorized SEM).

Overnourishment and Obesity

Overnourishment, the consumption of more calories than the body needs for normal metabolism, causes obesity, the excessive accumulation of fat (Figure 41.22). Obesity, in turn, contributes to a number of health problems, including the most common type of diabetes (type 2), cancer of the colon and breast, and cardiovascular disease that can lead to heart attacks and strokes. It is estimated that obesity is a factor in about 300,000 deaths per year in the United States alone.

Researchers have discovered several homeostatic mechanisms that help regulate body weight. Operating as feedback circuits, these mechanisms control the storage and metabolism of fat. Several hormones regulate long-term and short-term appetite by affecting a "satiety center" in the brain (Figure 41.23). A network of neurons relays and integrates information from the digestive system to regulate hormone release.

Mutations that cause mice to be chronically obese played a key role in advancing our understanding of the satiety pathway. Mice with mutations in the *ob* or *db* gene eat voraciously and become much more massive than normal. Doug Coleman, a researcher at the Jackson Laboratory in Maine, investigated how *ob* and *db* mutations disrupt normal control of appetite (Figure 41.24). Based on his experiments, Coleman deduced that the *ob* gene is required to produce the satiety factor, and the *db* gene is required to respond to the factor.

Cloning of the *ob* gene led to the demonstration that it produces a hormone, now known as leptin (from the Greek *lepto*, thin). The *db* gene encodes the leptin receptor. Leptin and the leptin receptor are key components of the circuitry that regulates appetite over the long term. Leptin is a product of adipose cells, so levels rise when body fat increases, cuing the

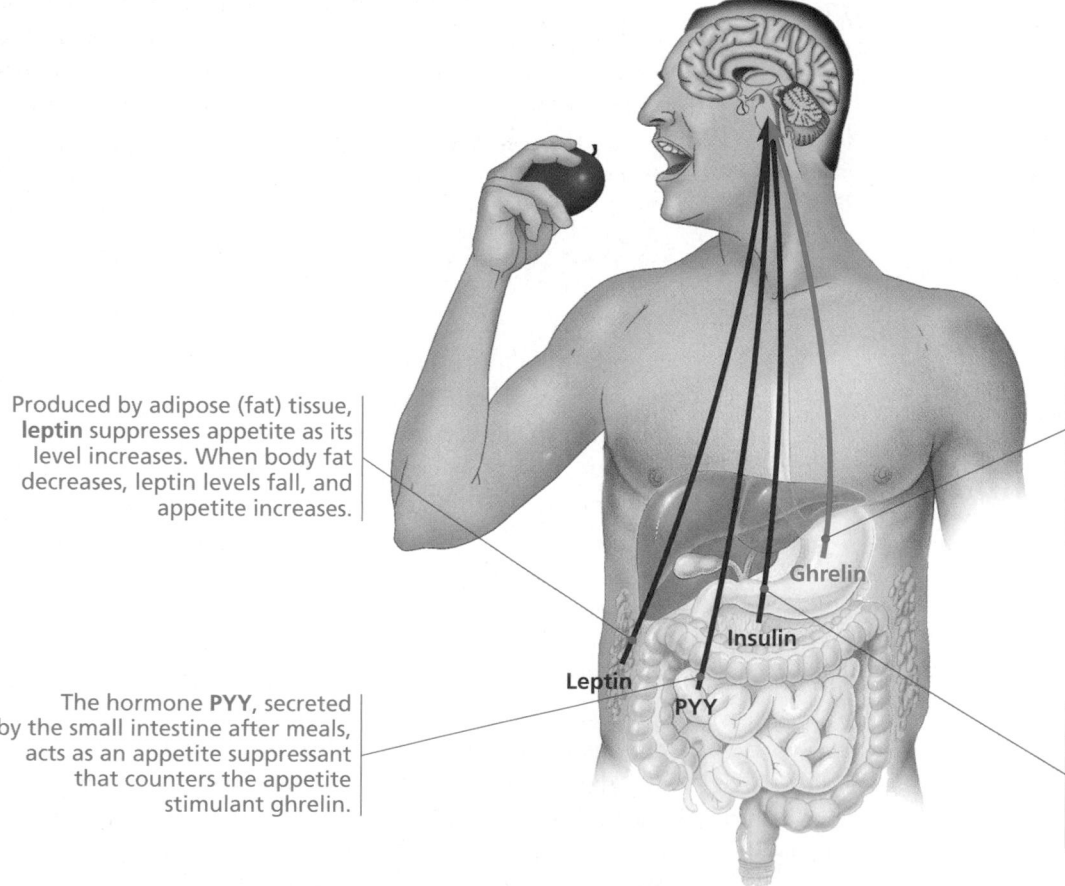

Produced by adipose (fat) tissue, **leptin** suppresses appetite as its level increases. When body fat decreases, leptin levels fall, and appetite increases.

Secreted by the stomach wall, **ghrelin** is one of the signals that triggers feelings of hunger as mealtimes approach. In dieters who lose weight, ghrelin levels increase, which may be one reason it's so hard to stay on a diet.

Ghrelin

Insulin

Leptin

PYY

The hormone **PYY**, secreted by the small intestine after meals, acts as an appetite suppressant that counters the appetite stimulant ghrelin.

A rise in blood sugar level after a meal stimulates the pancreas to secrete **insulin** (see Figure 41.21). In addition to its other functions, insulin suppresses appetite by acting on the brain.

▲ **Figure 41.23 A few of the appetite-regulating hormones.** Secreted by various organs and tissues, the hormones reach the brain via the bloodstream. The hormones act on a region of the brain that in turn controls the "satiety center," which generates the nervous impulses that make us feel either hungry or satiated ("full"). The green arrow indicates an appetite stimulant; red arrows represent appetite suppressants.

▼ Figure 41.24 Inquiry

What are the roles of the *ob* and *db* genes in appetite regulation?

EXPERIMENT Margaret Dickie, Katherine Hummel, and Doug Coleman, of the Jackson Laboratory in Bar Harbor, Maine, discovered that mice with a mutant *ob* gene or a mutant *db* gene eat voraciously and grow much more massive than mice with the wild-type (nonmutant) forms of both genes (designated *ob+, db+*).

Obese mouse with mutant *ob* gene (left) next to wild-type mouse.

To explore further the roles of the two genes, Coleman measured the body masses of pairs of young mice with various genotypes and then surgically linked the circulatory systems of each pair. This procedure ensured that any factor circulating in the bloodstream of either mouse would be transferred to the other. After several weeks, he again measured the mass of each mouse.

RESULTS

Genotype pairing (red type indicates mutant genes; bar indicates pairing)	Average body mass (g)	
	Starting	Ending
ob+, db+ | *ob+, db+*	20.3 20.8	23.6 21.4
ob, db+ | *ob, db+*	27.6 26.6	47.0 44.0
ob, db+ | *ob+, db+*	29.4 22.5	39.8 25.5
ob, db+ | *ob+, db*	33.7 30.3	18.8 33.2

CONCLUSION Because an *ob* mouse gains less weight when surgically joined with an *ob+* mouse than when joined with an *ob* mouse, Coleman concluded that the *ob* mouse fails to make a satiety factor but can respond to the factor when it is present. To explain the weight loss in an *ob* mouse that receives circulating factors from a *db* mouse, he reasoned that the *db* mutation blocks the response to the satiety factor but not its production. Subsequent molecular studies demonstrated the validity of both parts of Coleman's conclusion. The *ob+* gene product is leptin, the satiety factor, whereas the *db+* gene product is the leptin receptor. Thus, mice with the *ob* mutation cannot produce leptin, and mice with the *db* mutation produce leptin but cannot respond to it.

SOURCE D. L. Coleman, Effects of parabiosis of obese with diabetes and normal mice. *Diabetologia* 9:294–298 (1973).

WHAT IF? Suppose you collected blood from a wild-type mouse and a *db* mouse. Which would you expect to have a higher concentration of leptin, the satiety factor, and why?

---

brain to suppress appetite (see Figure 41.23). Conversely, loss of fat decreases leptin levels, signaling the brain to increase appetite. In this way, the feedback signals provided by leptin maintain body fat levels within a set range.

Our understanding of leptin may lead to treatments for obesity, but uncertainties remain. For one thing, leptin has complex functions, including a role in how the nervous system develops. Also, most obese people have an abnormally high leptin level, which somehow fails to elicit a response from the brain's satiety center. Clearly, there is much to learn in this important area of human physiology.

Obesity and Evolution

Though fat hoarding can be a health liability, it may have been an advantage in our evolutionary past. Our ancestors on the African savanna were hunter-gatherers who probably survived mainly on seeds and other plant products, a diet only occasionally supplemented by hunting game or scavenging meat from animals killed by other predators. In such a feast or-famine existence, natural selection may have favored those individuals with a physiology that induced them to gorge on rich, fatty foods on those rare occasions when such treats were abundantly available. Such individuals with genes promoting the storage of high-energy molecules during feasts may have been more likely than their thinner friends to survive famines. So perhaps our present-day taste for fats is partly an evolutionary vestige of less nutritious times.

The relationship between fat storage and evolutionary adaptation in animals is sometimes complex. Consider the plump offspring of the seabirds called petrels (**Figure 41.25**). Their parents must fly long distances to find food. Most of the food that they bring to their chicks is very rich in lipids. The fact that fat has twice as many calories per gram as other

▲ **Figure 41.25 A plump petrel.** Too heavy to fly, the petrel chick (right) will have to lose weight before it takes wing. In the meantime, its stored fat provides energy during times when its parent fails to bring enough food.

fuels minimizes the number of foraging trips. However, growing baby petrels need lots of protein for building new tissues, and there is relatively little in their oily diet. To get all the protein they need, young petrels have to consume many more calories than they burn in metabolism and consequently become obese. Their fat depots nevertheless help them survive periods when parents cannot find enough food. When food is not scarce, chicks at the end of the growth period weigh much more than their parents. The youngsters must then fast for several days to lose enough weight to be capable of flight.

In the next chapter, we'll see that obtaining food, digesting it, and absorbing nutrients are parts of a larger story. Provisioning the body also involves distributing nutrients (circulation) and exchanging respiratory gases with the environment.

CONCEPT CHECK **41.5**

1. Explain how people can become obese even if their intake of dietary fat is relatively low compared with carbohydrate intake.
2. After reviewing Figure 41.23, explain how PYY and leptin complement each other in regulating body weight.
3. **WHAT IF?** Suppose you were studying two groups of obese people with genetic abnormalities in the leptin pathway. In one group, the leptin levels are abnormally high; in the other group, they are abnormally low. How would each group's leptin levels change if both groups were placed on a low-calorie diet for an extended period? Explain.

For suggested answers, see Appendix A.

Chapter 41 Review

MEDIA Go to www.campbellbiology.com for BioFlix 3-D Animations, MP3 Tutors, Videos, Practice Tests, an eBook, and more.

SUMMARY OF KEY CONCEPTS

▶ Animals have diverse diets. Herbivores mainly eat plants; carnivores mainly eat other animals; and omnivores eat both. Animals must balance consumption, storage, and use of food.

CONCEPT **41.1**

An animal's diet must supply chemical energy, organic molecules, and essential nutrients (pp. 875–880)

▶ Animals need fuel to produce ATP, carbon skeletons for biosynthesis, and essential nutrients—nutrients that must be supplied in preassembled form.

▶ **Essential Nutrients** Essential nutrients include essential amino acids, essential fatty acids, vitamins, and minerals. Essential amino acids are those an animal cannot synthesize. Essential fatty acids are unsaturated. Vitamins are organic molecules required in small amounts. Minerals are inorganic nutrients, usually required in small amounts.

▶ **Dietary Deficiencies** Undernourished animals have diets deficient in calories. Malnourished animals are missing one or more essential nutrients.

▶ **Assessing Nutritional Needs** Studies of genetic defects and the study of disease at the population level help researchers determine human dietary requirements.

MEDIA
Activity Analyzing Food Labels

CONCEPT **41.2**

The main stages of food processing are ingestion, digestion, absorption, and elimination (pp. 880–883)

▶ Food processing in animals involves ingestion (eating), digestion (enzymatic breakdown of large molecules), absorption (uptake of nutrients by cells), and elimination (passage of undigested materials out of the body in feces).

▶ Suspension feeders sift small particles from the water. Substrate feeders eat as they tunnel through their food. Fluid feeders suck nutrient-rich fluids from a living host. Most animals are bulk feeders, eating large pieces of food.

▶ **Digestive Compartments** In intracellular digestion, food particles are engulfed by endocytosis and digested within food vacuoles that have fused with lysosomes. Most animals use extracellular digestion: Enzymatic hydrolysis occurs outside cells in a gastrovascular cavity or alimentary canal.

MEDIA
Activity Feeding Mechanisms of Animals

CONCEPT **41.3**

Organs specialized for sequential stages of food processing form the mammalian digestive system (pp. 884–890)

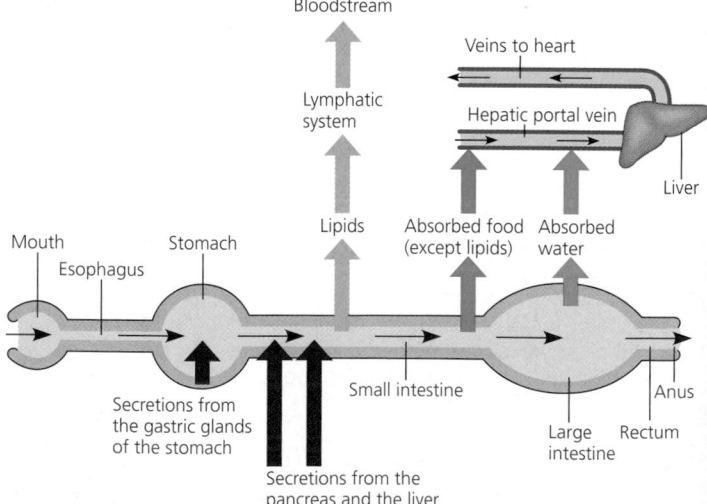

MEDIA
MP3 Tutor The Human Digestive System
Activity Digestive System Function
Investigation What Role Does Amylase Play in Digestion?
Activity Hormonal Control of Digestion

CONCEPT 41.4

Evolutionary adaptations of vertebrate digestive systems correlate with diet (pp. 891–893)

▶ **Some Dental Adaptations** Dentition generally correlates with diet.

▶ **Stomach and Intestinal Adaptations** Herbivores generally have longer alimentary canals than carnivores, reflecting the longer time needed to digest vegetation.

▶ **Mutualistic Adaptations** Many herbivores have fermentation chambers where microorganisms digest cellulose.

CONCEPT 41.5

Homeostatic mechanisms contribute to an animal's energy balance (pp. 893–896)

▶ **Energy Sources and Stores** Vertebrates store excess calories as glycogen in the liver and muscles and as fat. These energy stores can be tapped when an animal expends more calories than it consumes.

▶ **Overnourishment and Obesity** Overnourishment, the consumption of more calories than the body needs for normal metabolism, can lead to the serious health problem of obesity. Several hormones regulate appetite by affecting the brain's satiety center. Studies of the hormone leptin may lead to treatments for obesity.

▶ **Obesity and Evolution** The problem of maintaining a healthy weight partly stems from our evolutionary past, when fat hoarding may have been important for survival.

MEDIA
Activity Case Studies of Nutritional Disorders

TESTING YOUR KNOWLEDGE

SELF-QUIZ

1. Individuals whose diet consists primarily of corn would likely become
   a. obese.
   b. anorexic.
   c. overnourished.
   d. undernourished.
   e. malnourished.

2. Which of the following animals is *incorrectly* paired with its feeding mechanism?
   a. lion—substrate feeder
   b. baleen whale—suspension feeder
   c. aphid—fluid feeder
   d. clam—suspension feeder
   e. snake—bulk feeder

3. The mammalian trachea and esophagus both connect to the
   a. large intestine.
   b. stomach.
   c. pharynx.
   d. rectum.
   e. epiglottis.

4. Which of the following enzymes works most effectively at a very low pH?
   a. salivary amylase
   b. trypsin
   c. pepsin
   d. pancreatic amylase
   e. pancreatic lipase

5. Which of the following organs is *incorrectly* paired with its function?
   a. stomach—protein digestion
   b. oral cavity—starch digestion
   c. large intestine—bile production
   d. small intestine—nutrient absorption
   e. pancreas—enzyme production

6. After surgical removal of an infected gallbladder, a person must be especially careful to restrict dietary intake of
   a. starch.
   b. protein.
   c. sugar.
   d. fat.
   e. water.

7. The mutualistic microorganisms that help nourish a ruminant live mainly in specialized regions of the
   a. large intestine.
   b. liver.
   c. small intestine.
   d. pharynx.
   e. stomach.

8. If you were to jog a mile a few hours after lunch, which stored fuel would you probably tap?
   a. muscle proteins
   b. muscle and liver glycogen
   c. fat stored in the liver
   d. fat stored in adipose tissue
   e. blood proteins

9. **DRAW IT** Make a flowchart of the events that occur after partially digested food leaves the stomach. Use the following terms: bicarbonate secretion, circulation, decrease in acid, secretin secretion, increase in acid, signal detection. Next to each term, indicate the compartment(s) involved. You may use a term more than once.

For Self-Quiz answers, see Appendix A.

MEDIA Visit **www.campbellbiology.com** for a Practice Test.

EVOLUTION CONNECTION

10. The human esophagus and trachea share a passage leading from the mouth and nasal passages. After reviewing vertebrate evolution in Chapter 34, explain the historical (evolutionary) basis for this "imperfect" anatomy.

SCIENTIFIC INQUIRY

11. In adult populations of northern European origin, the disorder called hemochromatosis causes excess iron uptake from food and affects one in 200 individuals. Men are ten times more likely to suffer symptoms than are women. Given that only women menstruate, devise a hypothesis for the difference in the disease between the two genders.

Biological Inquiry: A Workbook of Investigative Cases Explore several mammalian mechanisms for starch digestion in the case "Galloper's Gut."

Circulation and Gas Exchange

▲ Figure 42.1 **How does a feathery fringe help this animal survive?**

OVERVIEW

Trading Places

The animal in **Figure 42.1** may look like a creature from a science fiction film, but it's actually an axolotl, a salamander native to shallow ponds in central Mexico. The feathery red appendages jutting out from the head of this albino adult are gills. Although external gills are uncommon in adult animals, they help satisfy the need shared by all animals to exchange substances with their environment.

Exchange between an axolotl or any other animal and its surroundings ultimately occurs at the cellular level. The resources that animal cells require, such as nutrients and oxygen (O_2), enter the cytoplasm by crossing the plasma membrane. Metabolic by-products, such as carbon dioxide (CO_2), exit the cell by crossing the same membrane. In unicellular organisms, exchange occurs directly with the external environment. For most multicellular organisms, however, direct exchange between every cell and the environment is not possible. Instead, these organisms rely on specialized systems that carry out exchange with the environment and that transport materials between sites of exchange and the rest of the body.

The reddish color and branching structure of the axolotl's gills reflect the intimate association between exchange and transport. Tiny blood vessels lie close to the surface of each filament in the gills. Across this surface, there is a net diffusion of O_2 from the surrounding water into the blood and of CO_2 from the blood into the water. The short distances involved allow diffusion to be rapid. Pumping of the axolotl's heart propels the oxygen-rich blood from the gill filaments to all other tissues of the body. There, more short-range exchange occurs, involving nutrients and O_2 as well as CO_2 and other wastes.

Because internal transport and gas exchange are functionally related in most animals, not just axolotls, we will examine both circulatory and respiratory systems in this chapter. We will explore the remarkable variation in form and organization of these systems by considering examples from a number of species. We will also highlight the roles of circulatory and respiratory systems in maintaining homeostasis under a range of physiological and environmental stresses.

CONCEPT 42.1

Circulatory systems link exchange surfaces with cells throughout the body

The molecular trade that animals carry out with their environment—gaining O_2 and nutrients while shedding CO_2 and other waste products—must ultimately involve every cell in the body. As you learned in Chapter 7, small, nonpolar molecules such as O_2 and CO_2 can move between cells and their immediate surroundings by diffusion. But diffusion is very slow for distances of more than a few millimeters. That's because the time it takes for a substance to diffuse from one place to another is proportional to the *square* of the distance. For example, if it takes 1 second for a given quantity of glucose to diffuse 100 μm, it will take 100 seconds for the same quantity to diffuse 1 mm, and almost 3 hours to diffuse 1 cm. This relationship between diffusion time and distance places a substantial constraint on the body plan of any animal.

Given that diffusion is rapid only over small distances, how does each cell of an animal participate in exchange? Natural selection has resulted in two general solutions to this problem. The first solution is a body size and shape that keep many or all cells in direct contact with the environment. Each cell can thus exchange materials directly with the surrounding medium. This type of body plan is found only in certain invertebrates, including sponges, cnidarians, and flatworms. The second solution, found in all other animals, is a circulatory system that moves fluid between each cell's immediate surroundings and the tissues where exchange with the environment occurs.

Gastrovascular Cavities

Let's begin by looking at animals that lack a distinct circulatory system. In hydras and other cnidarians, a central gastrovascular cavity functions both in digestion and in the distribution of substances throughout the body. As was shown for a hydra in Figure 41.8, a single opening maintains continuity between the fluid inside the cavity and the water outside. As a result, both the inner and outer tissue layers are bathed by fluid. Only the cells of the inner layer have direct access to nutrients, but since the body wall is a mere two cells thick, the nutrients must diffuse only a short distance to reach the cells of the outer layer. Thin branches of a hydra's gastrovascular cavity extend into the animal's tentacles. Some cnidarians, such as jellies, have gastrovascular cavities with a much more elaborate branching pattern **(Figure 42.2a)**.

Planarians and most other flatworms also survive without a circulatory system. Their combination of a gastrovascular cavity and a flat body is well suited for exchange with the environment **(Figure 42.2b)**. A flat body optimizes diffusional exchange by increasing surface area and minimizing diffusion distances.

Open and Closed Circulatory Systems

For animals with many cell layers, diffusion distances are too great for adequate exchange of nutrients and wastes by a gastrovascular cavity. In these organisms, a circulatory system minimizes the distances that substances must diffuse to enter or leave a cell. By transporting fluid throughout the body, the circulatory system functionally connects the aqueous environment of the body cells to the organs that exchange gases, absorb nutrients, and dispose of wastes. In mammals, for example, O_2 from inhaled air diffuses across only two layers of cells in the lungs before reaching the blood. The circulatory system, powered by the heart, then carries the oxygen-rich blood to all parts of the body. As the blood streams throughout the body tissues in tiny blood vessels, O_2 in the blood again diffuses only a short distance before entering the interstitial fluid that directly bathes the cells.

A circulatory system has three basic components: a circulatory fluid, a set of interconnecting tubes, and a muscular pump, the **heart**. The heart powers circulation by using metabolic energy to elevate the hydrostatic pressure of the circulatory fluid, which then flows through a circuit of vessels and back to the heart.

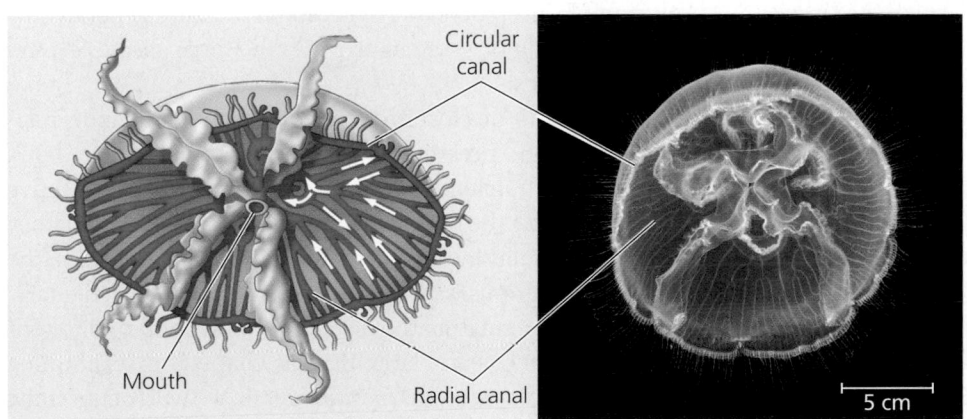

(a) The moon jelly *Aurelia*, a cnidarian. The jelly is viewed here from its underside (oral surface). The mouth leads to an elaborate gastrovascular cavity that consists of radial arms (canals) leading to and from a circular canal. Ciliated cells lining the canals circulate fluid within the cavity as indicated by the arrows.

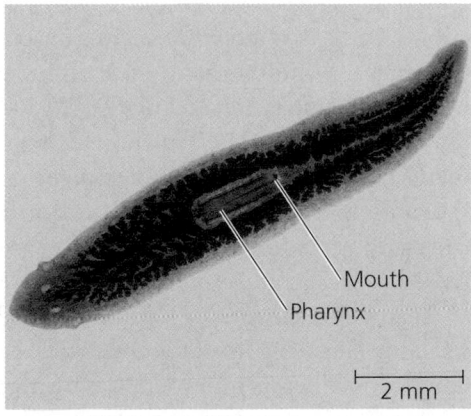

(b) The planarian *Dugesia*, a flatworm. The mouth and pharynx on the ventral side lead to the highly branched gastrovascular cavity, stained dark brown in this specimen (LM).

▲ **Figure 42.2 Internal transport in gastrovascular cavities.**

WHAT IF? Suppose a gastrovascular cavity were open at two ends, with fluid entering one end and leaving the other. How would this affect the gastrovascular cavity's function?

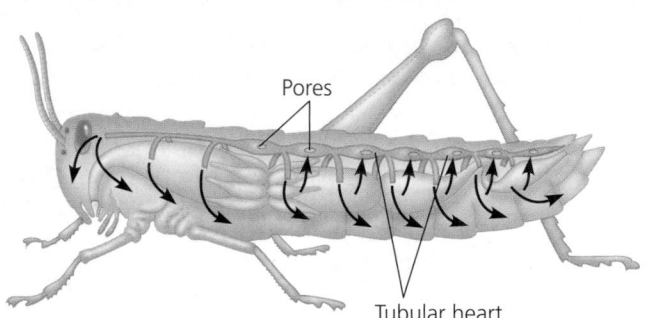

Pores

Tubular heart

(a) An open circulatory system. In an open circulatory system, such as that of a grasshopper, the circulatory fluid, called hemolymph, is the same as interstitial fluid. The heart pumps hemolymph through vessels into sinuses, fluid-filled spaces where materials are exchanged between the hemolymph and cells. Hemolymph returns to the heart through pores, which are equipped with valves that close when the heart contracts.

Dorsal vessel (main heart)

Auxiliary hearts   Ventral vessels

(b) A closed circulatory system. Closed circulatory systems circulate blood entirely within vessels, so the blood is distinct from the interstitial fluid. Chemical exchange occurs between the blood and the interstitial fluid, as well as between the interstitial fluid and body cells. In an earthworm, the dorsal vessel functions as the main heart, pumping blood forward by peristalsis. Near the worm's anterior end, five pairs of vessels loop around the digestive tract and function as auxillary hearts.

▲ **Figure 42.3 Open and closed circulatory systems.**

Arthropods and most mollusks have an **open circulatory system**, in which the circulatory fluid bathes the organs directly **(Figure 42.3a)**. In these animals, the circulatory fluid, called **hemolymph**, is also the interstitial fluid. Contraction of one or more hearts pumps the hemolymph through the circulatory vessels into interconnected sinuses, spaces surrounding the organs. Within the sinuses, chemical exchange occurs between the hemolymph and body cells. Relaxation of the heart draws hemolymph back in through pores, and body movements help circulate the hemolymph by periodically squeezing the sinuses. The open circulatory system of larger crustaceans, such as lobsters and crabs, includes a more extensive system of vessels as well as an accessory pump.

In a **closed circulatory system**, blood is confined to vessels and is distinct from the interstitial fluid **(Figure 42.3b)**. One or more hearts pump blood into large vessels that branch into smaller ones coursing through the organs. Materials are exchanged between the smallest vessels and the interstitial fluid bathing the cells. Annelids (including earthworms), cephalopods (including squids and octopuses), and all vertebrates have closed circulatory systems.

The fact that both open and closed circulatory systems are widespread among animals suggests that there are advantages to each system. The lower hydrostatic pressures associated with open circulatory systems make them less costly than closed systems in terms of energy expenditure. In some invertebrates, open circulatory systems serve additional functions. For example, in spiders, the hydrostatic pressure generated by the open circulatory system provides the force used to extend the animal's legs.

The benefits of closed circulatory systems include relatively high blood pressures, which enable the effective delivery of O_2 and nutrients to the cells of larger and more active animals. Among the molluscs, for instance, closed circulatory systems are found in the largest and most active species, the squids and octopuses. Closed systems are also particularly well suited to regulating the distribution of blood to different organs, as you'll learn later in this chapter. In examining closed circulatory systems in more detail, we will focus on the vertebrates.

Organization of Vertebrate Circulatory Systems

The closed circulatory system of humans and other vertebrates is often called the **cardiovascular system**. Blood circulates to and from the heart through an amazingly extensive network of vessels: The total length of blood vessels in an average human adult is twice Earth's circumference at the equator!

Arteries, veins, and capillaries are the three main types of blood vessels. Within each type, blood flows in only one direction. **Arteries** carry blood away from the heart to organs throughout the body. Within organs, arteries branch into **arterioles**, small vessels that convey blood to the capillaries. **Capillaries** are microscopic vessels with very thin, porous walls. Networks of these vessels, called **capillary beds**, infiltrate each tissue, passing within a few cell diameters of every cell in the body. Across the thin walls of capillaries, chemicals, including dissolved gases, are exchanged by diffusion between the blood and the interstitial fluid around the tissue cells. At their "downstream" end, capillaries converge into **venules**, and venules converge into **veins**, the vessels that carry blood back to the heart.

Arteries and veins are distinguished by the *direction* in which they carry blood, not by the O_2 content or other characteristics of the blood they contain. Arteries carry blood from the heart *toward* capillaries, and veins return blood to the heart *from* capillaries. There is one exception: the portal veins, which carry blood between pairs of capillary beds. The hepatic portal vein, for example, carries blood from capillary beds in the digestive system to capillary beds in the liver (see Chapter 41). From the liver, blood passes into the hepatic veins, which conduct blood toward the heart.

Natural selection has modified the cardiovascular systems of different vertebrates in accordance with their level of activity. For example, animals with higher metabolic rates generally have more complex circulatory systems and more powerful hearts than animals with lower metabolic rates. Similarly, within an animal, the complexity and number of blood vessels in a particular organ correlate with that organ's metabolic requirements.

The hearts of all vertebrates contain two or more muscular chambers. The chambers that receive blood entering the heart are called **atria** (singular, *atrium*). The chambers responsible for pumping blood out of the heart are called **ventricles**. The number of chambers and the extent to which they are separated from one another differ substantially among groups of vertebrates, as we will discuss next. These important differences reflect the close fit of form to function.

Single Circulation

In bony fishes, rays, and sharks, the heart consists of two chambers: an atrium and a ventricle. The blood passes through the heart once in each complete circuit, an arrangement called **single circulation (Figure 42.4)**. Blood entering the heart collects in the atrium before transfer to the ventricle. Contraction of the ventricle pumps blood to the gills, where there is a net diffusion of O_2 into the blood and of CO_2 out of the blood. As

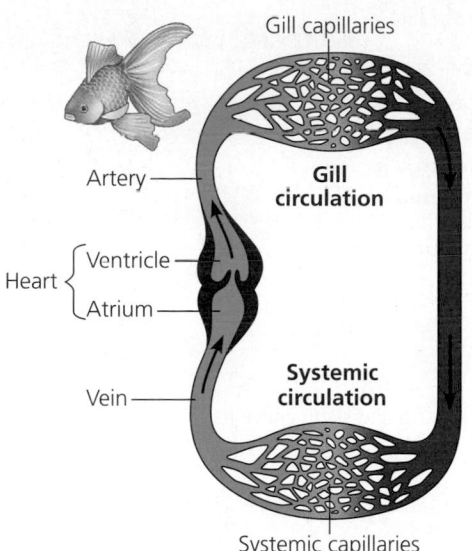

▲ **Figure 42.4 Single circulation in fishes.** Fishes have a two-chambered heart and a single circuit of blood flow.

blood leaves the gills, the capillaries converge into a vessel that carries oxygen-rich blood to capillary beds throughout the body. Blood then returns to the heart.

In single circulation, blood that leaves the heart passes through two capillary beds before returning to the heart. When blood flows through a capillary bed, blood pressure drops substantially, for reasons we will explain shortly. The drop in blood pressure in the gills of a bony fish, ray, or shark limits the rate of blood flow in the rest of the animal's body. As the animal swims, however, the contraction and relaxation of its muscles help accelerate the relatively sluggish pace of circulation.

Double Circulation

As shown in **Figure 42.5**, on the next page, the circulatory systems of amphibians, reptiles, and mammals have two distinct circuits, an arrangement called **double circulation**. The pumps for the two circuits serve different tissues but are combined into a single organ, the heart. Having both pumps within a single heart simplifies coordination of the pumping cycles.

One pump, the right side of the heart, delivers oxygen-poor blood to the capillary beds of the gas exchange tissues, where there is a net movement of O_2 into the blood and of CO_2 out of the blood. This part of the circulation is called a **pulmonary circuit** if the capillary beds involved are all in the lungs, as in reptiles and mammals. It is called a **pulmocutaneous circuit** if it includes capillaries in both the lungs and the skin, as in many amphibians.

After the oxygen-enriched blood leaves the gas exchange tissues, it enters the other pump, the left side of the heart. Contraction of the heart propels this blood to capillary beds in organs and tissues throughout the body. Following the exchange of O_2 and CO_2, as well as nutrients and waste products, the

Exploring Double Circulation in Vertebrates

Amphibians

Amphibians have a three-chambered heart and two circuits of blood flow: pulmocutaneous and systemic.

Reptiles (Except Birds)

Lizards, snakes, and turtles have a three-chambered heart, with a septum partially dividing the single ventricle. In crocodilians, the septum is complete and the heart is four-chambered.

Mammals and Birds

Mammals and birds have a four-chambered heart. In birds, the major vessels near the heart are slightly different than shown, but the pattern of double circulation is essentially the same.

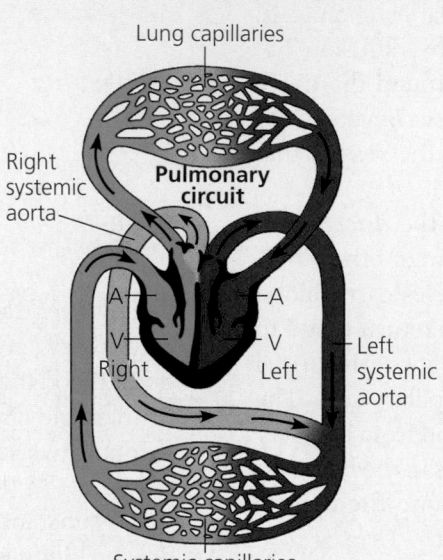

Systemic circuits include all body tissues except the primary gas exchange tissues. Note that circulatory systems are depicted as if the animal is facing you: The right side of the heart is shown on the left, and vice versa.

now oxygen-poor blood returns to the heart, completing the **systemic circuit**.

Double circulation provides a vigorous flow of blood to the brain, muscles, and other organs because the heart repressurizes the blood destined for these tissues after it passes through the capillary beds of the lungs or skin. Indeed, blood pressure is often much higher in the systemic circuit than in the gas exchange circuit. This contrasts sharply with single circulation, in which, as you read earlier, blood flows directly from the respiratory organs to other organs, under reduced pressure.

Adaptations of Double Circulatory Systems

Having considered the general properties of double circulation, let's examine the adaptations found in the hearts of different vertebrate groups that have this type of circulation. As you read, refer to the illustrations in Figure 42.5.

Amphibians   Frogs and other amphibians have a heart with three chambers: two atria and one ventricle. A ridge within the ventricle diverts most (about 90%) of the oxygen-

poor blood from the right atrium into the pulmocutaneous circuit and most of the oxygen-rich blood from the left atrium into the systemic circuit. When underwater, a frog adjusts its circulation, for the most part shutting off blood flow to its temporarily ineffective lungs. Blood flow continues to the skin, which acts as the sole site of gas exchange while the frog is submerged.

Reptiles (Except Birds)   Turtles, snakes, and lizards have a three-chambered heart, with a septum partially dividing the ventricle into separate right and left chambers. In alligators, caimans, and other crocodilians, the septum is complete, but the pulmonary and systemic circuits are connected where the arteries exit the heart. When a crocodilian is underwater, arterial valves divert most of the blood flow from the pulmonary circuit to the systemic circuit through this connection.

Mammals and Birds   In all mammals and birds, the ventricle is completely divided, such that there are two atria and two ventricles. The left side of the heart receives and pumps only oxygen-rich blood, while the right side receives and pumps only oxygen-poor blood.

A powerful four-chambered heart is a key adaptation that supports the endothermic way of life characteristic of mammals and birds. Endotherms use about ten times as much energy as equal-sized ectotherms; therefore, their circulatory systems need to deliver about ten times as much fuel and O_2 to their tissues (and remove ten times as much CO_2 and other wastes). This large traffic of substances is made possible by separate and independently powered systemic and pulmonary circuits and by large hearts that pump the necessary volume of blood. As we discussed in Chapter 34, mammals and birds descended from different tetrapod ancestors, and their four-chambered hearts evolved independently—an example of convergent evolution.

CONCEPT CHECK 42.1

1. How is the flow of hemolymph through an open circulatory system similar to the flow of water through an outdoor fountain?
2. Three-chambered hearts with incomplete septa were once viewed as being less adapted to circulatory function than mammalian hearts. What advantage of such hearts did this viewpoint overlook?
3. **WHAT IF?** The heart of a human fetus has a hole between the left and right ventricles. In some cases, this hole does not close completely before birth. If the hole weren't surgically corrected, how would it affect the O_2 content of the blood entering the systemic circuit from the heart?

For suggested answers, see Appendix A.

CONCEPT 42.2

Coordinated cycles of heart contraction drive double circulation in mammals

The timely delivery of O_2 to the body's organs is critical: Brain cells, for example, die within just a few minutes if their O_2 supply is interrupted. How does the mammalian cardiovascular system meet the body's continuous but variable demand for O_2? To answer this question, we need to consider how the parts of the system are arranged and how each part functions.

Mammalian Circulation

Let's first examine the overall organization of the mammalian cardiovascular system, beginning with the pulmonary circuit. (The circled numbers refer to corresponding locations in **Figure 42.6**). ❶ Contraction of the right ventricle pumps

blood to the lungs via ❷ the pulmonary arteries. As the blood flows through ❸ capillary beds in the left and right lungs, it loads O_2 and unloads CO_2. Oxygen-rich blood returns from the lungs via the pulmonary veins to ❹ the left atrium of the heart. Next, the oxygen-rich blood flows into ❺ the left ventricle, which pumps the oxygen-rich blood out to body tissues through the systemic circuit. Blood leaves the left ventricle via ❻ the aorta, which conveys blood to arteries leading throughout the body. The first branches from the aorta are the coronary arteries (not shown), which supply blood to the heart muscle itself. Then branches lead to ❼ capillary beds in the head and arms (forelimbs). The aorta then descends into the abdomen, supplying oxygen-rich blood to arteries leading to ❽ capillary beds in the abdominal organs and legs (hind limbs). Within the capillaries, there is a net diffusion of O_2 from the blood to the tissues and of CO_2 produced by cellular respiration into the blood. Capillaries rejoin, forming venules, which convey blood to veins. Oxygen-poor blood from the head, neck, and forelimbs is channeled into a large vein, ❾ the superior vena cava. Another large vein, ❿ the inferior vena cava, drains blood from the trunk and hind limbs. The two venae cavae empty their blood into ⓫ the right atrium, from which the oxygen-poor blood flows into the right ventricle.

▲ **Figure 42.6 The mammalian cardiovascular system: an overview.** Note that the dual circuits operate simultaneously, not in the serial fashion that the numbering in the diagram suggests. The two ventricles pump almost in unison; while some blood is traveling in the pulmonary circuit, the rest of the blood is flowing in the systemic circuit.

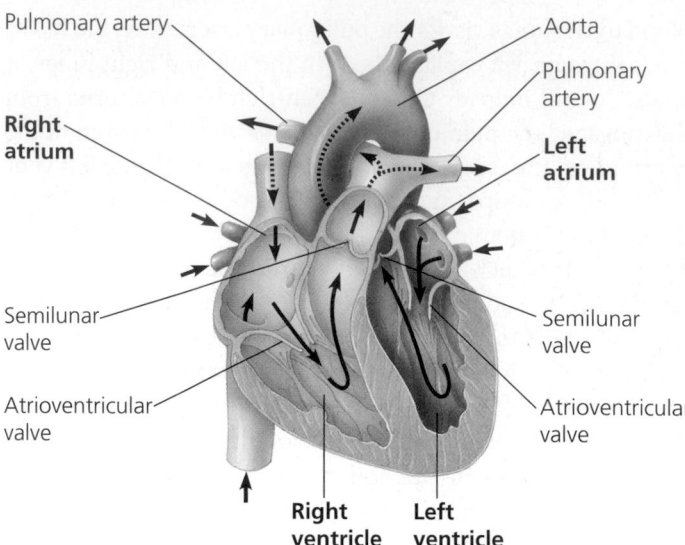

Pulmonary artery

Aorta

Pulmonary artery

Right atrium

Left atrium

Semilunar valve

Semilunar valve

Atrioventricular valve

Atrioventricular valve

Right ventricle

Left ventricle

▲ **Figure 42.7 The mammalian heart: a closer look.** Notice the locations of the valves, which prevent backflow of blood within the heart. Also notice how the atria and left and right ventricles differ in the thickness of their muscular walls.

The Mammalian Heart: *A Closer Look*

Using the human heart as an example, let's now take a closer look at how the mammalian heart works (**Figure 42.7**). Located behind the sternum (breastbone), the human heart is about the size of a clenched fist and consists mostly of cardiac muscle (see Figure 40.5). The two atria have relatively thin walls and serve as collection chambers for blood returning to the heart. Much of the blood entering the atria flows into the ventricles while all heart chambers are relaxed. Contraction of the atria transfers the remainder before the ventricles begin to contract. The ventricles have thicker walls and contract much more forcefully than the atria—especially the left ventricle, which pumps blood to all body organs through the systemic circuit. Although the left ventricle contracts with greater force than the right ventricle, it pumps the same volume of blood as the right ventricle during each contraction.

The heart contracts and relaxes in a rhythmic cycle. When it contracts, it pumps blood; when it relaxes, its chambers fill with blood. One complete sequence of pumping and filling is referred to as the **cardiac cycle**. The contraction phase of the cycle is called **systole**, and the relaxation phase is called **diastole** (**Figure 42.8**). The volume of blood each ventricle pumps per minute is the **cardiac output**. Two factors determine cardiac output: the rate of contraction, or **heart rate** (number of beats per minute), and the **stroke volume**, the amount of blood pumped by a ventricle in a single contraction. The average stroke volume in humans is about 70 mL. Multiplying this stroke volume by a resting heart rate of 72 beats per minute yields a cardiac output of 5 L/min—about equal to the total volume of blood in the human body. During heavy exercise, cardiac output increases as much as fivefold.

Four valves in the heart prevent backflow and keep blood moving in the correct direction (see Figures 42.7 and 42.8). Made of

flaps of connective tissue, the valves open when pushed from one side and close when pushed from the other. An **atrioventricular (AV) valve** lies between each atrium and ventricle. The AV valves are anchored by strong fibers that prevent them from turning inside out. Pressure generated by the powerful contraction of the ventricles closes the AV valves, keeping blood from flowing back into the atria. **Semilunar valves** are located at the two exits of the heart: where the aorta leaves the left ventricle and where the pulmonary artery leaves the right ventricle. These valves are pushed open by the pressure generated during contraction of the ventricles. When the ventricles relax, pressure built up in the aorta closes the semilunar valves and prevents significant backflow. You can follow these events either with a stethoscope or by pressing your ear tightly against the chest of a friend (or a friendly dog). The sound pattern is "lub-dup, lub-dup, lub-dup." The first heart sound ("lub") is created by the recoil of blood against the closed AV valves. The second sound ("dup") is produced by the recoil of blood against the closed semilunar valves.

If blood squirts backward through a defective valve, it may produce an abnormal sound called a **heart murmur**. Some

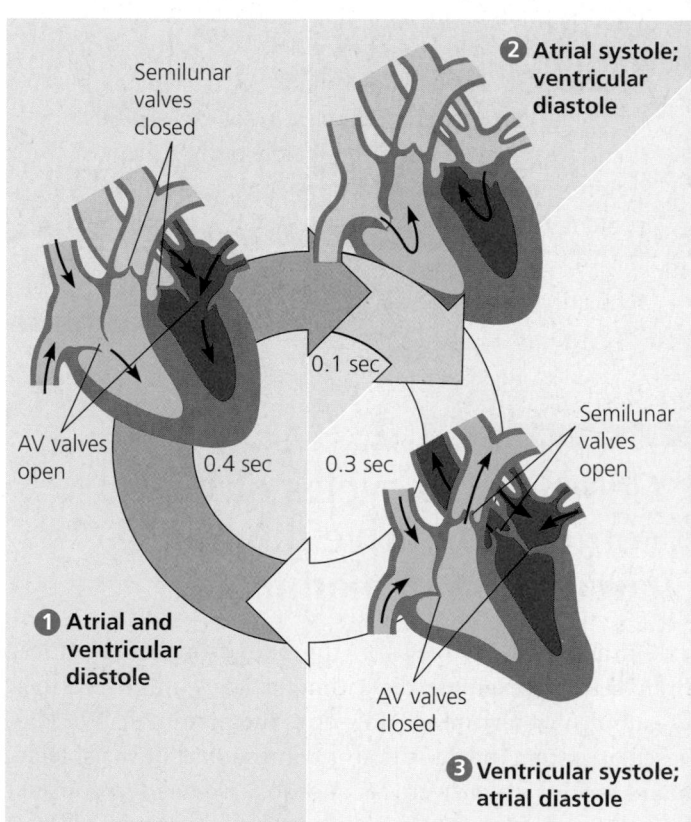

① Atrial and ventricular diastole

② **Atrial systole; ventricular diastole**

③ **Ventricular systole; atrial diastole**

Semilunar valves closed

AV valves open

Semilunar valves open

AV valves closed

0.1 sec

0.4 sec

0.3 sec

▲ **Figure 42.8 The cardiac cycle.** For an adult human at rest with a heart rate of about 72 beats per minute, one complete cardiac cycle takes about 0.8 second. ① During a relaxation phase (atria and ventricles in diastole), blood returning from the large veins flows into the atria and ventricles through the AV valves. ② A brief period of atrial systole then forces all blood remaining in the atria into the ventricles. ③ During the remainder of the cycle, ventricular systole pumps blood into the large arteries through the semilunar valves. Note that during all but 0.1 second of the cardiac cycle, the atria are relaxed and are filling with blood returning via the veins.

people are born with heart murmurs; in others, the valves may be damaged by infection (from rheumatic fever, for instance). When a valve defect is severe enough to endanger health, surgeons may implant a mechanical replacement valve. However, not all heart murmurs are caused by a defect, and most valve defects do not reduce the efficiency of blood flow enough to warrant surgery.

Maintaining the Heart's Rhythmic Beat

In vertebrates, the heartbeat originates in the heart itself. Some cardiac muscle cells are autorhythmic, meaning they contract and relax repeatedly without any signal from the nervous system. You can even see these rhythmic contractions in tissue that has been removed from the heart

▲ **Figure 42.9 The control of heart rhythm.** The sequence of electrical events in the heart is shown at the top; the corresponding components of an electrocardiogram (ECG) are highlighted below in gold. In step 4, the portion of the ECG to the right of the gold "spike" represents electrical activity that reprimes the ventricles for the next round of contraction.

and placed in a dish in the laboratory! Because each of these cells has its own intrinsic contraction rhythm, how are their contractions coordinated in the intact heart? The answer lies in a group of autorhythmic cells located in the wall of the right atrium, near where the superior vena cava enters the heart. This cluster of cells is called the **sinoatrial (SA) node**, or *pacemaker*, and it sets the rate and timing at which all cardiac muscle cells contract. (In contrast to vertebrates, some arthropods have pacemakers located in the nervous system, outside the heart.)

The SA node generates electrical impulses much like those produced by nerve cells. Because cardiac muscle cells are electrically coupled through gap junctions (see Figure 6.32), impulses from the SA node spread rapidly within heart tissue. In addition, these impulses generate currents that are conducted to the skin via body fluids. The medical test called an **electrocardiogram** (**ECG** or, sometimes, **EKG**) uses electrodes placed on the skin to detect and record these currents. The resulting graph has a characteristic shape that represents the stages in the cardiac cycle (**Figure 42.9**).

Impulses from the SA node first spread rapidly through the walls of the atria, causing both atria to contract in unison. During atrial contraction, the impulses originating at the SA node reach other autorhythmic cells that are located in the wall between the left and right atria. These cells form a relay point called the **atrioventricular (AV) node**. Here the impulses are delayed for about 0.1 second before spreading to the walls of the ventricles. This delay allows the atria to empty completely before the ventricles contract. Then, the signals from the AV node are conducted throughout the ventricular walls by specialized muscle fibers called bundle branches and Purkinje fibers.

Physiological cues alter heart tempo by regulating the SA node. Two sets of nerves, the sympathetic and parasympathetic nerves, are largely responsible for this regulation. These nerves

function like the spurs and reins used in riding a horse: One set speeds up the pacemaker, and the other set slows it down. For example, when you stand up and start walking, the sympathetic nerves increase your heart rate, an adaptation that enables your circulatory system to provide the additional O_2 needed by the muscles that are powering your activity. If you then sit down and relax, the parasympathetic nerves decrease your heart rate, an adaptation that conserves energy. Hormones secreted into the blood also influence the pacemaker. For instance, epinephrine, the "fight-or-flight" hormone secreted by the adrenal glands, causes the heart rate to increase. A third type of input that affects the pacemaker is body temperature. An increase of only 1°C raises the heart rate by about 10 beats per minute. This is the reason your heart beats faster when you have a fever.

Having examined the operation of the circulatory pump, we turn in the next section to the forces and structures that influence blood flow in the vessels of each circuit.

CONCEPT CHECK 42.2

1. Explain why blood in the pulmonary veins has a higher O_2 concentration than blood in the venae cavae, which are also veins.
2. Why is it important that the AV node delay the electrical impulse moving from the SA node and the atria to the ventricles?
3. **WHAT IF?** After exercising regularly for several months, you find that your resting heart rate has decreased. Given that your body now requires fewer cardiac cycles in a given time, what other change in the function of your heart at rest would you expect to find? Explain.

For suggested answers, see Appendix A.

Patterns of blood pressure and flow reflect the structure and arrangement of blood vessels

The vertebrate circulatory system enables blood to deliver oxygen and nutrients and remove wastes throughout the body. In doing so, the circulatory system relies on a branching network of vessels much like the plumbing system that delivers fresh water to a city and removes its wastes. Furthermore, the same physical principles that govern the operation of plumbing systems apply to the functioning of blood vessels.

Blood Vessel Structure and Function

Blood vessels contain a central lumen (cavity) lined with an **endothelium**, a single layer of flattened epithelial cells. The smooth surface of the endothelium minimizes resistance to the flow of blood. Surrounding the endothelium are layers of tissue that differ among capillaries, arteries, and veins, reflecting the specialized functions of these vessels.

Capillaries are the smallest blood vessels, having a diameter only slightly greater than that of a red blood cell (**Figure 42.10**). Capillaries also have very thin walls, which consist of just the endothelium and its basal lamina. This structural organization facilitates the exchange of substances between the blood in capillaries and the interstitial fluid.

The walls of arteries and veins have a more complex organization than those of capillaries. Both arteries and veins have two layers of tissue surrounding the endothelium: an outer layer of connective tissue containing elastic fibers, which allow the vessel to stretch and recoil, and a middle layer containing smooth muscle and more elastic fibers. However, arteries and veins differ in important ways. For a given blood vessel diameter, an artery has a wall about three times as thick as that of a vein (see Figure 42.10). The thicker walls of arteries are very strong, accommodating blood pumped at high pressure by the heart, and their elastic recoil helps maintain blood pressure when the heart relaxes between con-

tractions. Signals from the nervous system and hormones circulating in the blood act on the smooth muscles in arteries, controlling blood flow to different parts of the body. The thinner-walled veins convey blood back to the heart at a lower velocity and pressure. Valves in the veins maintain a unidirectional flow of blood in these vessels (see Figure 42.10).

Blood Flow Velocity

To understand how blood vessel diameter influences blood flow, consider how water flows through a thick hose connected to a faucet. When the faucet is turned on, water flows at the same velocity everywhere in the hose. However, if a narrow nozzle is attached to the end of the hose, the water will exit the nozzle at a much greater velocity. Because water doesn't compress under pressure, the volume of water moving through the nozzle in a given time must be the same as the volume moving through the rest of the hose. The cross-sectional area of the nozzle is smaller than that of the hose, so the water speeds up in the nozzle.

▼ Figure 42.10 **The structure of blood vessels.**

Artery   Vein

SEM   100 μm

Endothelium

Smooth muscle

Connective tissue

Artery

Basal lamina

Capillary

Valve

Endothelium

Smooth muscle

Connective tissue

Vein

Arteriole

Venule

15 μm

Red blood cell

Capillary

LM

An analogous situation exists in the circulatory system, but blood *slows* as it moves from arteries to arterioles to capillaries. Why? The reason is that the number of capillaries is enormous. Each artery conveys blood to so many capillaries that the *total* cross-sectional area is much greater in capillary beds than in the arteries or any other part of the circulatory system (Figure 42.11). The result is a dramatic decrease in velocity from the arteries to the capillaries: Blood travels 500 times slower in the capillaries (about 0.1 cm/sec) than in the aorta (about 48 cm/sec).

The reduced velocity of blood flow in capillaries is critical to the function of the circulatory system. Capillaries are the only vessels with walls thin enough to permit the transfer of substances between the blood and interstitial fluid. The slower flow of blood through these tiny vessels allows time for exchange to occur. After passing through the capillaries, the blood speeds up as it enters the venules and veins, which have smaller total cross-sectional areas (see Figure 42.11).

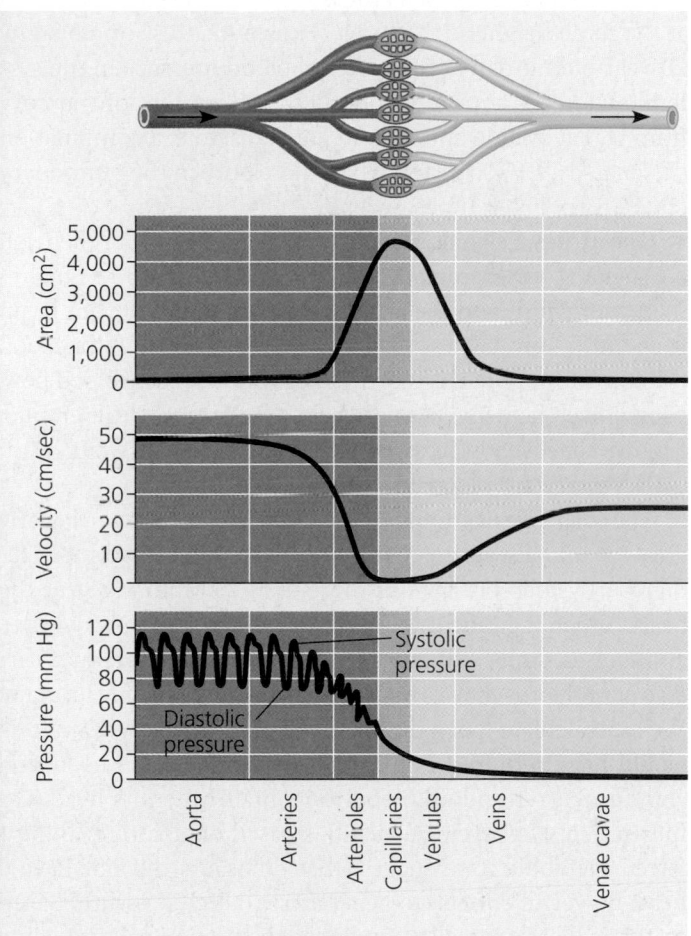

▲ **Figure 42.11 The interrelationship of cross-sectional area of blood vessels, blood flow velocity, and blood pressure.** Owing to an increase in total cross-sectional area, blood flow velocity decreases markedly in the arterioles and is lowest in the capillaries. Blood pressure, the main force driving blood from the heart to the capillaries, is highest in the aorta and other arteries.

Blood Pressure

Blood, like all fluids, flows from areas of higher pressure to areas of lower pressure. Contraction of a heart ventricle generates blood pressure, which exerts a force in all directions. The force directed lengthwise in an artery causes the blood to flow away from the heart, the site of highest pressure. The force exerted against the elastic wall of an artery stretches the wall, and the recoil of arterial walls plays a critical role in maintaining blood pressure, and hence blood flow, throughout the cardiac cycle. Once the blood enters the millions of tiny arterioles and capillaries, the narrow diameter of these vessels generates substantial resistance to flow. This resistance dissipates much of the pressure generated by the pumping heart by the time the blood enters the veins.

Changes in Blood Pressure During the Cardiac Cycle

Arterial blood pressure is highest when the heart contracts during ventricular systole. The pressure at this time is called **systolic pressure** (see Figure 42.11). The spikes in blood pressure caused by the powerful contractions of the ventricles stretch the arteries. By placing your fingers on your wrist, you can feel a **pulse**—the rhythmic bulging of the artery walls with each heartbeat. The surge of pressure is partly due to the narrow openings of arterioles impeding the exit of blood from the arteries. Thus, when the heart contracts, blood enters the arteries faster than it can leave, and the vessels stretch from the rise in pressure. During diastole, the elastic walls of the arteries snap back. As a consequence, there is a lower but still substantial blood pressure when the ventricles are relaxed (**diastolic pressure**). Before enough blood has flowed into the arterioles to completely relieve pressure in the arteries, the heart contracts again. Because the arteries remain pressurized throughout the cardiac cycle (see Figure 42.11), blood continuously flows into arterioles and capillaries.

Regulation of Blood Pressure

Blood pressure fluctuates over two different time scales. The first is the oscillation in arterial blood pressure during each cardiac cycle (see bottom graph in Figure 42.11). Blood pressure also fluctuates on a longer time scale in response to signals that change the state of smooth muscles in arteriole walls. For example, physical or emotional stress can trigger nervous and hormonal responses that cause smooth muscles in arteriole walls to contract, a process called **vasoconstriction**. When that happens, the arterioles narrow, thereby increasing blood pressure upstream in the arteries. When the smooth muscles relax, the arterioles undergo **vasodilation**, an increase in diameter that causes blood pressure in the arteries to fall.

Vasoconstriction and vasodilation are often coupled to changes in cardiac output that also affect blood pressure. This coordination of regulatory mechanisms maintains adequate blood flow as the body's demands on the circulatory system change. During heavy exercise, for example, the arterioles in working muscles dilate, causing a greater flow of oxygen-rich blood to the muscles. By itself, this increased flow to the muscles

would cause a drop in blood pressure (and therefore blood flow) in the body as a whole. However, cardiac output increases at the same time, maintaining blood pressure and supporting the necessary increase in blood flow.

Recent experiments have identified the molecules that serve as signals for vasodilation and vasoconstriction. Three scientists in the United States—Robert Furchgott, Louis Ignarro, and Ferid Murad—demonstrated that the gas nitric oxide (NO) serves as a major inducer of vasodilation in the cardiovascular system. Their research was honored with a Nobel Prize in 1998. Independent studies by Masashi Yanagisawa, then a graduate student at the University of Tsukuba in Japan, identified a peptide, **endothelin**, as a potent inducer of vasoconstriction **(Figure 42.12)**. As discussed in the interview with Dr. Yanagisawa on pages 850–851, his findings led to fundamental discoveries about signals that regulate not only blood vessel diameter but also the embryonic development of the digestive system.

Blood Pressure and Gravity

Blood pressure is generally measured for an artery in the arm at the same height as the heart **(Figure 42.13)**. For a healthy 20-year-old human at rest, arterial blood pressure in the systemic circuit is typically about 120 millimeters of mercury (mm Hg) at systole and 70 mm Hg at diastole, a combination designated 120/70. (Arterial blood pressure in the pulmonary circuit is six to ten times lower.)

Gravity has a significant effect on blood pressure. When you are standing, for example, your head is roughly 0.35 m higher than your chest, and the arterial blood pressure in your brain is about 27 mm Hg less than that near your heart. If the blood pressure in your brain is too low to provide adequate blood flow, you will likely faint. By causing your body to collapse to the ground, fainting effectively places your head at the level of your heart, quickly increasing blood flow to your brain.

The challenge of pumping blood against gravity is particularly great for animals with very long necks. A giraffe, for example, requires a systolic pressure of more than 250 mm Hg near the heart. When a giraffe lowers its head to drink, one-way valves and sinuses, along with feedback mechanisms that reduce cardiac output, prevent this high pressure from damaging its brain. We can calculate that a dinosaur with a neck nearly 10 m long would have required even greater systolic pressure—nearly 760 mm Hg—to pump blood to its brain when its head was fully raised. However, calculations based on anatomy and inferred metabolic rate suggest that dinosaurs did not have a heart powerful enough to generate such high pressure. Based on this evidence as well as studies of neck bone structure, some biologists have concluded that the long-necked dinosaurs fed close to the ground rather than on high foliage.

Gravity is also a consideration for blood flow in veins, especially those in the legs. Although blood pressure in veins is relatively low, several mechanisms assist the return of venous blood to the heart. First, rhythmic contractions of smooth muscles in

---

▼ Figure 42.12 Inquiry

How do endothelial cells control vasoconstriction?

EXPERIMENT   In 1988, Masashi Yanagisawa set out to identify the endothelial factor that triggers vasoconstriction in mammals. He isolated endothelial cells from blood vessels and grew them in liquid medium. Then he collected the liquid, which contained substances secreted by the cells. Next, he bathed a small piece of an artery in the liquid. The artery tissue contracted, indicating that the cells grown in culture had secreted a factor that causes vasoconstriction. Using biochemical procedures, Yanagisawa separated the substances in the fluid on the basis of size, charge, and other properties. He then tested each substance for its ability to cause arterial contraction. After several separation steps and many tests, he purified the vasoconstriction factor.

RESULTS   The vasoconstriction factor, which Yanagisawa named **endothelin**, is a peptide that contains 21 amino acids. Two disulfide bridges between cysteines stabilize the peptide structure.

Using the amino acid sequence of the peptide as a guide, Yanagisawa identified the endothelin gene. The polypeptide encoded by the gene is much longer than endothelin, containing 203 amino acids. The amino acids in endothelin extend from position 53 (Cys) to position 73 (Trp) in the longer polypeptide:

Yanagisawa also showed that treating endothelial cells with other substances already known to promote vasoconstriction, such as the hormone epinephrine, led to increased production of endothelin mRNA.

CONCLUSION   Endothelial cells produce and translate endothelin mRNA in response to signals, such as hormones, that circulate in the blood. The resulting polypeptide is cleaved to form active endothelin, the substance that triggers vasoconstriction. Yanagisawa and colleagues subsequently demonstrated that endothelial cells also make the enzyme that catalyzes this cleavage.

SOURCE   M. Yanagisawa et al., A novel potent vasoconstrictor peptide produced by vascular endothelial cells, *Nature* 332:411–415 (1988).

WHAT IF?   Given what you know about epithelial tissue organization (see Figure 40.5) and the function of endothelin, what would you predict about the location of endothelin secretion with regard to endothelial cell surfaces?

1 A sphygmomanometer, an inflatable cuff attached to a pressure gauge, measures blood pressure in an artery. The cuff is inflated until the pressure closes the artery, so that no blood flows past the cuff. When this occurs, the pressure exerted by the cuff exceeds the pressure in the artery.

Blood pressure reading: 120/70

Pressure in cuff greater than 120 mm Hg

Pressure in cuff drops below 120 mm Hg

Pressure in cuff below 70 mm Hg

Rubber cuff inflated with air

120

120

70

Artery closed

Sounds audible in stethoscope

Sounds stop

2 The cuff is allowed to deflate gradually. When the pressure exerted by the cuff falls just below that in the artery, blood pulses into the forearm, generating sounds that can be heard with the stethoscope. The pressure measured at this point is the systolic pressure.

3 The cuff is allowed to deflate further, just until the blood flows freely through the artery and the sounds below the cuff disappear. The pressure at this point is the diastolic pressure.

▲ **Figure 42.13 Measurement of blood pressure.** Blood pressure is recorded as two numbers separated by a slash. The first number is the systolic pressure; the second is the diastolic pressure.

the walls of venules and veins aid in the movement of the blood. Second, and more important, the contraction of skeletal muscles during exercise squeezes blood through the veins toward the heart **(Figure 42.14)**. This is why periodically walking up and down the aisle during a long airplane flight helps prevent potentially dangerous blood clots from forming in veins. Third, the change in pressure within the thoracic (chest) cavity during inhalation causes the venae cavae and other large veins near the heart to expand and fill with blood.

In rare instances, runners and other athletes can suffer heart failure if they stop vigorous exercise abruptly. When the leg muscles suddenly cease contracting and relaxing, less blood returns to the heart, which continues to beat rapidly. If the heart is weak or damaged, this inadequate blood flow may cause the heart to malfunction. To reduce the risk of stressing the heart excessively, athletes are encouraged to follow hard exercise with moderate activity, such as walking, to "cool down" until their heart rate approaches its resting level.

Direction of blood flow in vein (toward heart)

Valve (open)

Skeletal muscle

Valve (closed)

▲ **Figure 42.14 Blood flow in veins.** Skeletal muscle contraction squeezes and constricts veins. Flaps of tissue within the veins act as one-way valves that keep blood moving only toward the heart. If you sit or stand too long, the lack of muscular activity may cause your feet to swell as blood pools in your veins.

Capillary Function

At any given time, only about 5–10% of the body's capillaries have blood flowing through them. However, each tissue has many capillaries, so every part of the body is supplied with blood at all times. Capillaries in the brain, heart, kidneys, and liver are usually filled to capacity, but at many other sites the blood supply varies over time as blood is diverted from one destination to another. For example, blood flow to the skin is regulated to help control body temperature, and blood supply to the digestive tract increases after a meal. During strenuous exercise, blood is diverted from the digestive tract and supplied more generously to skeletal muscles and skin. This is one reason why exercising heavily immediately after eating a big meal may cause indigestion.

Given that capillaries lack smooth muscles, how is blood flow in capillary beds altered? There are two mechanisms, both of which rely on signals that regulate flow into capillaries. One mechanism involves contraction of the smooth muscle in the wall of an arteriole, which reduces the vessel's diameter and decreases blood flow to the adjoining capillary beds. When the smooth muscle relaxes, the arterioles dilate, allowing blood to enter the capillaries. The other mechanism for altering flow,

(a) Sphincters relaxed

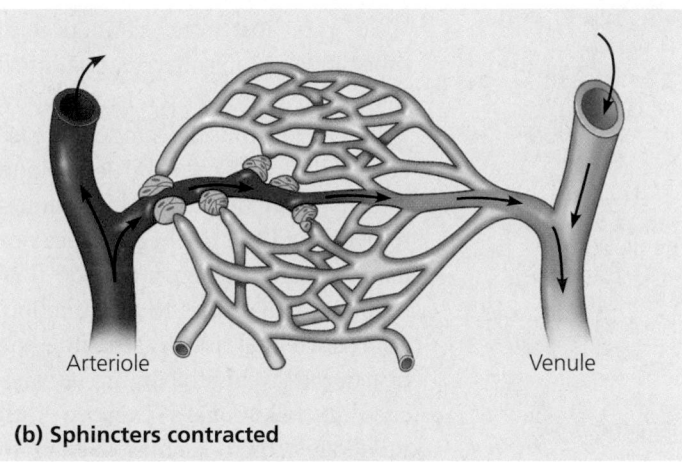

(b) Sphincters contracted

▲ **Figure 42.15 Blood flow in capillary beds.** Precapillary sphincters regulate the passage of blood into capillary beds. Some blood flows directly from arterioles to venules through capillaries called thoroughfare channels, which are always open.

shown in **Figure 42.15**, involves the action of *precapillary sphincters*, rings of smooth muscle located at the entrance to capillary beds. The signals that regulate blood flow include nerve impulses, hormones traveling throughout the bloodstream, and chemicals produced locally. For example, the chemical histamine released by cells at a wound site causes smooth muscle relaxation, dilating blood vessels and increasing blood flow. The dilated vessels also provide disease-fighting white blood cells greater access to invading microorganisms.

As you have read, the critical exchange of substances between the blood and interstitial fluid takes place across the thin endothelial walls of the capillaries. Some substances are carried across the endothelium in vesicles that form on one side by endocytosis and release their contents on the opposite side by exocytosis. Small molecules, such as O_2 and CO_2, simply diffuse across the endothelial cells or through the openings within and between adjoining cells. These openings also provide the route for transport of small solutes such as sugars, salts, and urea, as well as for bulk flow of fluid into tissues driven by blood pressure within the capillary.

▲ **Figure 42.16 Fluid exchange between capillaries and the interstitial fluid.** This diagram shows a hypothetical capillary in which osmotic pressure is constant along its length. At the arterial end, where blood pressure exceeds osmotic pressure, fluid flows out of the capillary into the interstitial fluid. At the venous end, the blood pressure is less than osmotic pressure, and fluid flows from the interstitial fluid into the capillary. In many capillaries, blood pressure may be higher or lower than osmotic pressure throughout the entire length of the capillary.

While blood pressure tends to drive fluid out of the capillaries, the presence of blood proteins tends to pull fluid back into the capillaries. Many blood proteins (and all blood cells) are too large to pass readily through the endothelium, and they remain in the capillaries. The proteins, especially albumin, create an osmotic pressure difference between the capillary interior and the interstitial fluid. In places where the blood pressure is greater than the osmotic pressure difference, there is a net loss of fluid from the capillaries. In contrast, where the osmotic pressure difference exceeds the blood pressure, there is a net movement of fluid from the tissues into the capillaries **(Figure 42.16)**.

Fluid Return by the Lymphatic System

Throughout the body, only about 85% of the fluid that leaves the capillaries because of blood pressure reenters them as a result of osmotic pressure. Each day, this imbalance results in a loss of about 4 L of fluid from capillaries to the surrounding tissues. There is also some leakage of blood proteins, even though the capillary wall is not very permeable to large molecules. The lost fluid and proteins return to the blood via the **lymphatic system**, which includes a network of tiny vessels intermingled among capillaries of the cardiovascular system. After entering the lymphatic system by diffusion, the fluid is called **lymph**; its composition is about the same as that of interstitial fluid. The lymphatic system drains into large veins of the circulatory system at the base of the neck (see Figure 43.7). As you read in Chapter 41, this joining of the lymphatic and circulatory systems functions in the transfer of lipids from the small intestine to the blood.

The movement of lymph from peripheral tissues to the heart relies on much the same mechanisms that assist blood flow in veins. Lymph vessels, like veins, have valves that prevent the backflow of fluid. Rhythmic contractions of the vessel walls help draw fluid into the small lymphatic vessels. In addition, skeletal muscle contractions play a role in moving lymph.

Disorders that interfere with the lymphatic system highlight its role in maintaining proper fluid distribution in the body. Disruptions in the movement of lymph often cause edema, swelling resulting from the excessive accumulation of fluid in tissues. Severe blockage of lymph flow, as occurs when certain parasitic worms lodge in lymph vessels, results in extremely swollen limbs or other body parts, a condition known as elephantiasis.

Along a lymph vessel are organs called **lymph nodes**. By filtering the lymph and by housing cells that attack viruses and bacteria, lymph nodes play an important role in the body's defense. Inside each lymph node is a honeycomb of connective tissue with spaces filled by white blood cells. When the body is fighting an infection, these cells multiply rapidly, and the lymph nodes become swollen and tender (which is why your doctor may check for swollen lymph nodes in your neck, armpits, or groin when you feel sick). Because lymph nodes have filtering and surveillance functions, doctors may examine the lymph nodes of cancer patients to detect the spread of diseased cells.

In recent years, evidence has appeared suggesting that the lymphatic system also has a role in harmful immune responses, such as those responsible for asthma. Because of these and other findings, the lymphatic system, largely ignored until the 1990s, has become a very active and promising area of biomedical research.

CONCEPT CHECK 42.3

1. What is the primary cause of the low velocity of blood flow through capillaries?
2. What short-term changes in cardiovascular function might best enable skeletal muscles to help an animal escape from a dangerous situation?
3. **WHAT IF?** If you had additional hearts distributed throughout your body, what would be one likely advantage and one likely disadvantage?

For suggested answers, see Appendix A.

Blood components function in exchange, transport, and defense

As we discussed earlier, the fluid transported by an open circulatory system is continuous with the fluid that surrounds all of the body cells and therefore has the same composition. In contrast, the fluid in a closed circulatory system can be much more highly specialized, as is the case for the blood of vertebrates.

Blood Composition and Function

Vertebrate blood is a connective tissue consisting of cells suspended in a liquid matrix called **plasma**. Dissolved in the plasma are ions and proteins that, together with the blood cells, function in osmotic regulation, transport, and defense. Separating the components of blood using a centrifuge reveals that cellular elements (cells and cell fragments) occupy about 45% of the volume of blood (**Figure 42.17**, on the next page). The remainder is plasma.

Plasma

Among the many solutes in plasma are inorganic salts in the form of dissolved ions, sometimes referred to as blood electrolytes (see Figure 42.17). Although plasma is about 90% water, the dissolved salts are an essential component of the blood. Some of these ions buffer the blood, which in humans normally has a pH of 7.4. Salts are also important in maintaining the osmotic balance of the blood. In addition, the concentration of ions in plasma directly affects the composition of the interstitial fluid, where many of these ions have a vital role in muscle and nerve activity. To serve all of these functions, plasma electrolytes must be kept within narrow concentration ranges, a homeostatic function we will explore in Chapter 44.

Plasma proteins act as buffers against pH changes, help maintain the osmotic balance between blood and interstitial fluid, and contribute to the blood's viscosity (thickness). Particular plasma proteins have additional functions. The immunoglobulins, or antibodies, help combat viruses and other foreign agents that invade the body (see Chapter 43). Others are escorts for lipids, which are insoluble in water and can travel in blood only when bound to proteins. A third group of plasma proteins are clotting factors that help plug leaks when blood vessels are injured. (The term *serum* refers to blood plasma from which these clotting factors have been removed.)

Plasma also contains a wide variety of other substances in transit from one part of the body to another, including nutrients, metabolic wastes, respiratory gases, and hormones. Plasma has a much higher protein concentration than interstitial fluid, although the two fluids are otherwise similar. (Capillary walls, remember, are not very permeable to proteins.)

Plasma 55%

Constituent	Major functions
Water	Solvent for carrying other substances
Ions (blood electrolytes)	
Sodium	Osmotic balance, pH buffering, and regulation of membrane permeability
Potassium	
Calcium	
Magnesium	
Chloride	
Bicarbonate	
Plasma proteins	
Albumin	Osmotic balance pH buffering
Fibrinogen	Clotting
Immunoglobulins (antibodies)	Defense
Substances transported by blood	
Nutrients (such as glucose, fatty acids, vitamins)	
Waste products of metabolism	
Respiratory gases (O_2 and CO_2)	
Hormones	

Separated blood elements

Cellular elements 45%

Cell type	Number per µL (mm³) of blood	Functions
Erythrocytes (red blood cells)	5–6 million	Transport oxygen and help transport carbon dioxide
Leukocytes (white blood cells)	5,000–10,000	Defense and immunity
Basophil		
Eosinophil		
Lymphocyte		
Neutrophil		
Monocyte		
Platelets	250,000–400,000	Blood clotting

▲ **Figure 42.17 The composition of mammalian blood.**

Cellular Elements

Suspended in blood plasma are two classes of cells: red blood cells, which transport O_2, and white blood cells, which function in defense (see Figure 42.17). Blood also contains **platelets**, fragments of cells that are involved in the clotting process.

Erythrocytes Red blood cells, or **erythrocytes**, are by far the most numerous blood cells. Each microliter (µL, or mm³) of human blood contains 5–6 million red cells, and there are about 25 trillion of these cells in the body's 5 L of blood. Their main function is O_2 transport, and their structure is closely related to this function. Human erythrocytes are small disks (7–8 µm in diameter) that are biconcave—thinner in the center than at the edges. This shape increases surface area, enhancing the rate of diffusion of O_2 across their plasma membranes. Mature mammalian erythrocytes lack nuclei. This unusual characteristic leaves more space in these tiny cells for **hemoglobin**, the iron-containing protein that transports O_2 (see Figure 5.21). Erythrocytes also lack mitochondria and generate their ATP exclusively by anaerobic metabolism. Oxygen transport would be less efficient if erythrocytes were aerobic and consumed some of the O_2 they carry.

Despite its small size, an erythrocyte contains about 250 million molecules of hemoglobin. Because each molecule of hemoglobin binds up to four molecules of O_2, one erythrocyte can transport about a billion O_2 molecules. As erythrocytes pass through the capillary beds of lungs, gills, or other respiratory organs, O_2 diffuses into the erythrocytes and binds to hemoglobin. In the systemic capillaries, O_2 dissociates from hemoglobin and diffuses into body cells.

Leukocytes The blood contains five major types of white blood cells, or **leukocytes**. Their function is to fight infections. Some are phagocytic, engulfing and digesting microorganisms as well as debris from the body's own dead cells. As we will see in Chapter 43, other leukocytes, called lymphocytes, develop into specialized B cells and T cells that mount immune responses against foreign substances. Normally, 1 µL of human blood contains about 5,000–10,000 leukocytes; their numbers increase temporarily whenever the body is fighting an infection. Unlike erythrocytes, leukocytes are also found outside the circulatory system, patrolling both interstitial fluid and the lymphatic system.

Platelets Platelets are pinched-off cytoplasmic fragments of specialized bone marrow cells. They are about 2–3 µm in diameter and have no nuclei. Platelets serve both structural and molecular functions in blood clotting.

① The clotting process begins when the endothelium of a vessel is damaged, exposing connective tissue in the vessel wall to blood. Platelets adhere to collagen fibers in the connective tissue and release a substance that makes nearby platelets sticky.

② The platelets form a plug that provides emergency protection against blood loss.

③ This seal is reinforced by a clot of fibrin when vessel damage is severe. Fibrin is formed via a multistep process: Clotting factors released from the clumped platelets or damaged cells mix with clotting factors in the plasma, forming an activation cascade that converts a plasma protein called prothrombin to its active form, thrombin. Thrombin itself is an enzyme that catalyzes the final step of the clotting process, the conversion of fibrinogen to fibrin. The threads of fibrin become interwoven into a clot (see colorized SEM below).

Collagen fibers

Platelet releases chemicals that make nearby platelets sticky

Platelet plug

Clotting factors from:
  Platelets
  Damaged cells
  Plasma (factors include calcium, vitamin K)

Prothrombin → Thrombin

Fibrinogen → Fibrin

Fibrin clot

Red blood cell

5 μm

▲ Figure 42.18 **Blood clotting.**

Blood Clotting

The occasional cut or scrape is not life-threatening because blood components seal the broken blood vessels. A break in a blood vessel wall exposes proteins that attract platelets and initiate coagulation, the conversion of liquid components of blood to a solid clot. The coagulant, or sealant, circulates in an inactive form called fibrinogen. Clotting involves the conversion of fibrinogen to its active form, **fibrin**, which aggregates into threads that form the framework of the clot. The formation of fibrin is the last step in a series of reactions triggered by the release of clotting factors from platelets **(Figure 42.18)**. A genetic mutation that affects any step of the clotting process causes hemophilia, a disease characterized by excessive bleeding and bruising from even minor cuts and bumps.

Anticlotting factors in the blood normally prevent spontaneous clotting in the absence of injury. Sometimes, however, clots form within a blood vessel, blocking the flow of blood. Such a clot is called a **thrombus**. We will explore how a thrombus forms and the danger that it poses later in this chapter.

Stem Cells and the Replacement of Cellular Elements

Erythrocytes, leukocytes, and platelets all develop from a common source: multipotent **stem cells** that are dedicated to replenishing the body's blood cell populations **(Figure 42.19)**.

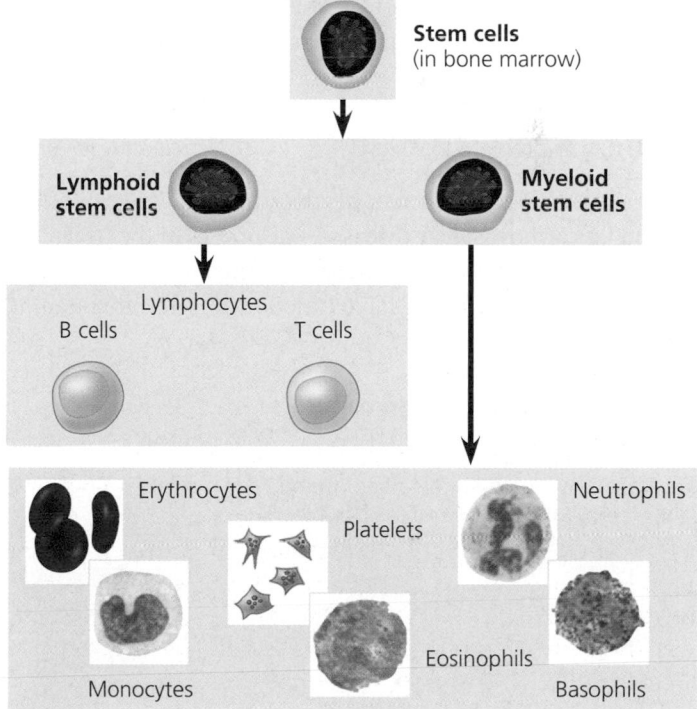

Stem cells (in bone marrow)

Lymphoid stem cells

Myeloid stem cells

Lymphocytes
B cells   T cells

Erythrocytes   Neutrophils
          Platelets

Monocytes   Eosinophils
                     Basophils

▲ Figure 42.19 **Differentiation of blood cells.** Some of the multipotent stem cells differentiate into lymphoid stem cells, which then develop into B cells and T cells, two types of lymphocytes that function in the immune response (see Chapter 43). All other blood cells differentiate from myeloid stem cells.

The stem cells that produce blood cells are located in the red marrow of bones, particularly the ribs, vertebrae, sternum, and pelvis. Multipotent stem cells are so named because they have the ability to form multiple types of cells—in this case, the myeloid and lymphoid cell lineages. When any stem cell divides, one daughter cell remains a stem cell while the other takes on a specialized function.

Throughout a person's life, erythrocytes, leukocytes, and platelets formed from stem cell divisions replace the worn-out cellular elements of blood. Erythrocytes, for example, usually circulate for only three to four months before being replaced; the old cells are consumed by phagocytic cells in the liver and spleen. The production of new erythrocytes involves recycling of materials, such as the use of iron scavenged from old erythrocytes in new hemoglobin molecules.

A negative-feedback mechanism, sensitive to the amount of O_2 reaching the body's tissues via the blood, controls erythrocyte production. If the tissues do not receive enough O_2, the kidneys synthesize and secrete a hormone called **erythropoietin (EPO)** that stimulates erythrocyte production. If the blood is delivering more O_2 than the tissues can use, the level of EPO falls and erythrocyte production slows. Physicians use synthetic EPO to treat people with health problems such as anemia, a condition of lower-than-normal hemoglobin levels. Some athletes inject themselves with EPO to increase their erythrocyte levels, although this practice, a form of blood doping, has been banned by the International Olympic Committee and other sports organizations. In recent years, a number of well-known runners and cyclists have tested positive for EPO-related drugs and have forfeited both their records and their right to participate in future competitions.

Cardiovascular Disease

More than half of all human deaths in the United States are caused by cardiovascular diseases—disorders of the heart and blood vessels. Cardiovascular diseases range from a minor disturbance of vein or heart valve function to a life-threatening disruption of blood flow to the heart or brain. The tendency to develop particular cardiovascular diseases is inherited but is also strongly influenced by lifestyle. Smoking, lack of exercise, and a diet rich in animal fat each increase the risk of a number of cardiovascular diseases.

Atherosclerosis

One reason cardiovascular diseases cause so many deaths is that they often aren't detected until they disrupt critical blood flow. An example is **atherosclerosis**, the hardening of the arteries by accumulation of fatty deposits. Healthy arteries have a smooth inner lining that reduces resistance to blood flow. Damage or infection can roughen the lining and lead to inflammation. Leukocytes are attracted to the damaged lining and begin to take up lipids, including cholesterol. A fatty deposit, called a plaque, grows steadily, incorporating fibrous connective tissue and additional cholesterol. As the plaque grows, the walls of the artery become thick and stiff, and the obstruction of the artery increases **(Figure 42.20)**.

Atherosclerosis sometimes produces warning signs. Partial blockage of the coronary arteries, which supply oxygen-rich blood to the heart muscle, may cause occasional chest pain, a condition known as angina pectoris. The pain is most likely to be felt when the heart is laboring hard during physical or emotional stress, and it signals that part of the heart is not receiving enough O_2. However, many people with atherosclerosis are completely unaware of their condition until catastrophe strikes.

Heart Attacks and Stroke

If unrecognized and untreated, the result of atherosclerosis is often a heart attack or a stroke. A **heart attack**, also called a *myocardial infarction*, is the damage or death of cardiac muscle tissue resulting from blockage of one or more coronary arteries. Because the coronary arteries are small in diameter, they are especially vulnerable to obstruction. Such blockage can destroy cardiac muscle quickly because the constantly beating heart muscle cannot survive long without O_2. If the

▶ **Figure 42.20 Atherosclerosis.** These light micrographs contrast **(a)** a cross section of a normal (healthy) artery with **(b)** that of an artery partially blocked by an atherosclerotic plaque. Plaques consist mostly of fibrous connective tissue and smooth muscle cells infiltrated with lipids.

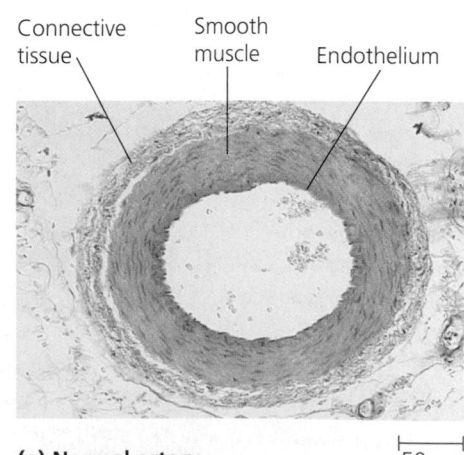

Connective tissue   Smooth muscle   Endothelium

(a) Normal artery   50 μm

Plaque

(b) Partly clogged artery   250 μm

heart stops beating, the victim may nevertheless survive if a heartbeat is restored by cardiopulmonary resuscitation (CPR) or some other emergency procedure within a few minutes of the attack. A **stroke** is the death of nervous tissue in the brain due to a lack of O_2. Strokes usually result from rupture or blockage of arteries in the head. The effects of a stroke and the individual's chance of survival depend on the extent and location of the damaged brain tissue.

Heart attacks and strokes frequently result from a thrombus that clogs an artery. A key step in thrombus formation is the rupture of plaques by an inflammatory response, analogous to the body's response to a cut infected by bacteria (see Figure 43.8). A fragment released by plaque rupture is swept along in the bloodstream, sometimes lodging in an artery. The thrombus may originate in a coronary artery or an artery in the brain, or it may develop elsewhere in the circulatory system and reach the heart or brain via the bloodstream.

Treatment and Diagnosis of Cardiovascular Disease

One major contributor to atherosclerosis is cholesterol. Cholesterol travels in the blood plasma mainly in the form of particles consisting of thousands of cholesterol molecules and other lipids bound to a protein. One type of particle—**low-density lipoprotein (LDL)**, often called "bad cholesterol"—is associated with the deposition of cholesterol in arterial plaques. Another type—**high-density lipoprotein (HDL)**, or "good cholesterol"—appears to reduce the deposition of cholesterol. Exercise decreases the LDL/HDL ratio. Smoking and consumption of certain processed vegetable oils called *trans* fats (see Chapter 5) have the opposite effect. Many individuals at high risk for cardiovascular disease are treated with drugs called statins, which lower LDL levels and thereby reduce the frequency of heart attacks.

The recent recognition that inflammation has a central role in atherosclerosis and thrombus formation is changing the diagnosis and treatment of cardiovascular disease. For example, aspirin, which blocks the inflammatory response, has been found to help prevent the recurrence of heart attacks and stroke. Researchers have also focused attention on C-reactive protein (CRP), which is produced by the liver and found in the blood during episodes of acute inflammation. Like a high level of LDL cholesterol, the presence of significant amounts of CRP in blood is a useful predictor of cardiovascular disease.

Hypertension (high blood pressure) is yet another contributor to heart attack and stroke as well as other health problems. According to one hypothesis, chronic high blood pressure damages the endothelium that lines the arteries, promoting plaque formation. The usual definition of hypertension in adults is a systolic pressure above 140 mm Hg or a diastolic pressure above 90 mm Hg. Fortunately, hypertension is simple to diagnose and can usually be controlled by dietary changes, exercise, medication, or a combination of these approaches.

CONCEPT **42.5**

Gas exchange occurs across specialized respiratory surfaces

In the remainder of this chapter, we will focus on the process of **gas exchange**. Although this process is often called respiratory exchange or respiration, it should not be confused with the energy transformations of cellular respiration. Gas exchange is the uptake of molecular O_2 from the environment and the discharge of CO_2 to the environment.

Partial Pressure Gradients in Gas Exchange

To understand the driving forces for gas exchange, we must calculate **partial pressure**, which is simply the pressure exerted by a particular gas in a mixture of gases. To do so, we need to know the pressure that the mixture exerts and the fraction of the mixture represented by a particular gas. Let's consider O_2 as an example. At sea level, the atmosphere exerts a downward force equal to that of a column of mercury (Hg) 760 mm high. Therefore, atmospheric pressure at sea level is 760 mm Hg. Since the atmosphere is 21% O_2 by volume, the partial pressure of O_2 is 0.21×760, or about 160 mm Hg. This value is called the *partial pressure* of O_2 (abbreviated P_{O_2}) because it is the portion of atmospheric pressure contributed by O_2. The partial pressure of CO_2, P_{CO_2}, is much less, only 0.29 mm Hg at sea level.

Calculating partial pressure for a gas dissolved in liquid, such as water, is also straightforward. When water is exposed to air, the amount of a gas that dissolves in the water is proportional to its partial pressure in the air and its solubility in water. Equilibrium is reached when gas molecules enter and leave the solution at the same rate. At equilibrium, the partial pressure of the gas in the solution equals the partial pressure of the gas in the air. Therefore, the P_{O_2} in water exposed to air at sea level must be 160 mm Hg, the same as that in the atmosphere. However, the *concentrations* of O_2 in the air and water differ substantially because O_2 is much less soluble in water than in air.

Once we have calculated partial pressures, we can readily predict the net result of diffusion at gas exchange surfaces: A gas always diffuses from a region of higher partial pressure to a region of lower partial pressure.

Respiratory Media

The conditions for gas exchange vary considerably, depending on whether the respiratory medium—the source of O_2—is air or water. As already noted, O_2 is plentiful in air, making up about 21% of Earth's atmosphere by volume. Compared to water, air is much less dense and less viscous, so it is easier to move and to force through small passageways. As a result, breathing air is relatively easy and need not be particularly efficient. Humans, for example, extract only about 25% of the O_2 in the air we inhale.

Gas exchange with water as the respiratory medium is much more demanding. The amount of O_2 dissolved in a given volume of water varies but is always less than in an equivalent volume of air: Water in many marine and freshwater habitats contains only 4–8 mL of dissolved O_2 per liter, a concentration roughly 40 times less than in air. The warmer and saltier the water is, the less dissolved O_2 it can hold. Water's lower O_2 content, greater density, and greater viscosity mean that aquatic animals such as fishes and lobsters must expend considerable energy to carry out gas exchange. In the context of these challenges, adaptations have evolved that in general enable aquatic animals to be very efficient in gas exchange. Many of these adaptations involve the organization of the surfaces dedicated to exchange.

Respiratory Surfaces

Specialization for gas exchange is apparent in the structure of the respiratory surface, the part of an animal's body where gas exchange occurs. Like all living cells, the cells that carry out gas exchange have a plasma membrane that must be in contact with an aqueous solution. Respiratory surfaces are therefore always moist.

The movement of O_2 and CO_2 across moist respiratory surfaces takes place entirely by diffusion. The rate of diffusion is proportional to the surface area across which it occurs and inversely proportional to the square of the distance through which molecules must move. In other words, gas exchange is fast when the area for diffusion is large and the path for diffusion is short. As a result, respiratory surfaces tend to be large and thin.

The structure of a respiratory surface depends mainly on the size of the animal and whether it lives in water or on land, but it is also influenced by metabolic demands for gas exchange. Thus, an endotherm generally has a larger area of respiratory surface than a similar-sized ectotherm.

In some relatively simple animals, such as sponges, cnidarians, and flatworms, every cell in the body is close enough to the external environment that gases can diffuse quickly between all

Parapodium (functions as gill)

(a) Marine worm. Many polychaetes (marine worms of the phylum Annelida) have a pair of flattened appendages called parapodia on each body segment. The parapodia serve as gills and also function in crawling and swimming.

Gills

(b) Crayfish. Crayfish and other crustaceans have long, feathery gills covered by the exoskeleton. Specialized body appendages drive water over the gill surfaces.

Coelom

Gills

Tube foot

(c) Sea star. The gills of a sea star are simple tubular projections of the skin. The hollow core of each gill is an extension of the coelom (body cavity). Gas exchange occurs by diffusion across the gill surfaces, and fluid in the coelom circulates in and out of the gills, aiding gas transport. The surfaces of a sea star's tube feet also function in gas exchange.

▲ Figure 42.21 **Diversity in the structure of gills, external body surfaces that function in gas exchange.**

cells and the environment. In many animals, however, the bulk of the body's cells lack immediate access to the environment. The respiratory surface in these animals is a thin, moist epithelium that constitutes a respiratory organ.

The skin serves as a respiratory organ in some animals, including earthworms and some amphibians. Just below the skin, a dense network of capillaries facilitates the exchange of gases between the circulatory system and the environment. Because the respiratory surface must remain moist, earthworms and many other skin-breathers can survive for extended periods only in damp places.

The general body surface of most animals lacks sufficient area to exchange gases for the whole organism. The solution is a respiratory organ that is extensively folded or branched, thereby enlarging the available surface area for gas exchange. Gills, tracheae, and lungs are three such organs.

Gills in Aquatic Animals

Gills are outfoldings of the body surface that are suspended in the water. As illustrated in **Figure 42.21**, on the facing page, the distribution of gills over the body can vary considerably. Regardless of their distribution, gills often have a total surface area much greater than that of the rest of the body.

Movement of the respiratory medium over the respiratory surface, a process called **ventilation**, maintains the partial pressure gradients of O_2 and CO_2 across the gill that are necessary for gas exchange. To promote ventilation, most gill-bearing an-

imals either move their gills through the water or move water over their gills. For example, crayfish and lobsters have paddle-like appendages that drive a current of water over the gills, whereas mussels and clams move water with cilia. Octopuses and squids ventilate their gills by taking in and ejecting water, with the side benefit of locomotion by jet propulsion. Fishes use the motion of swimming or coordinated movements of the mouth and gill covers to ventilate their gills. In both cases, a current of water enters the mouth, passes through slits in the pharynx, flows over the gills, and then exits the body **(Figure 42.22)**.

The arrangement of capillaries in a fish gill allows for **countercurrent exchange**, the exchange of a substance or heat between two fluids flowing in opposite directions. In a fish gill, this process maximizes gas exchange efficiency. Because blood flows in the direction opposite to that of water passing over the gills, at each point in its travel blood is less saturated with O_2 than the water it meets (see Figure 42.22). As blood enters a gill capillary, it encounters water that is completing its passage through the gill. Depleted of much of its dissolved O_2, this water nevertheless has a higher P_{O_2} than the incoming blood, and O_2 transfer takes place. As the blood continues its passage, its P_{O_2} steadily increases, but so does that of the water it encounters, since each successive position in the blood's travel corresponds to an earlier position in the water's passage over the gills. Thus, a partial pressure gradient favoring the diffusion of O_2 from water to blood exists along the entire length of the capillary.

Anatomy of gills

Gill arch

Water flow

Operculum

Gill arch

Gill filament organization

Blood vessels

Gill filaments

Fluid flow through gill filament

Oxygen-poor blood

Oxygen-rich blood

Lamella

Water flow between lamellae

Blood flow through capillaries in lamella

Countercurrent exchange

P_{O_2} (mm Hg) in water

150 120 90 60 30

Net diffusion of O_2 from water to blood

140 110 80 50 20

P_{O_2} (mm Hg) in blood

▲ **Figure 42.22 The structure and function of fish gills.** A fish continuously pumps water through its mouth and over gill arches, using coordinated movements of the jaws and operculum (gill cover) for this ventilation. (A swimming fish can simply open its mouth and let water flow past its gills.) Each gill arch has two rows of gill filaments, composed of flattened plates called lamellae. Blood flowing through capillaries within the lamellae picks up O_2 from the water. Notice that the countercurrent flow of water and blood maintains a partial pressure gradient down which O_2 diffuses from the water into the blood over the entire length of a capillary.

Countercurrent exchange mechanisms are remarkably efficient. In the fish gill, more than 80% of the O_2 dissolved in the water is removed as it passes over the respiratory surface. Countercurrent exchange also contributes to temperature regulation (see Chapter 40) and to the functioning of the mammalian kidney, as we will see in Chapter 44.

Gills are generally unsuitable for an animal living on land. An expansive surface of wet membrane exposed directly to air currents in the environment would lose too much water by evaporation. Furthermore, the gills would collapse as their fine filaments, no longer supported by water, would cling together. In most terrestrial animals, respiratory surfaces are enclosed within the body, exposed to the atmosphere through narrow tubes.

Tracheal Systems in Insects

Although the most familiar respiratory structure among terrestrial animals is the lung, the most common is actually the **tracheal system** of insects. Made up of air tubes that branch throughout the body, this system is one variation on the theme of an internal respiratory surface. The largest tubes, called tracheae, open to the outside **(Figure 42.23a)**. The finest branches extend close to the surface of nearly every cell, where gas is exchanged by diffusion across the moist epithelium that lines the tips of the tracheal branches **(Figure 42.23b)**. Because the tracheal system brings air within a very short distance of virtually all body cells in an insect, it can transport O_2 and CO_2 without the participation of the animal's open circulatory system.

For small insects, diffusion through the tracheae brings in enough O_2 and removes enough CO_2 to support cellular respiration. Larger insects meet their higher energy demands by ventilating their tracheal systems with rhythmic body movements that compress and expand the air tubes like bellows. For example, an insect in flight has a very high metabolic rate, consuming 10 to 200 times more O_2 than it does at rest. In many flying insects, alternating contraction and relaxation of the flight muscles pumps air rapidly through the tracheal system. The flight muscle cells are packed with mitochondria that support the high metabolic rate, and the tracheal tubes supply each of these ATP-generating organelles with ample O_2 **(Figure 42.23c)**. Thus, adaptations of tracheal systems are directly related to bioenergetics.

Lungs

Unlike tracheal systems, which branch throughout the insect body, **lungs** are localized respiratory organs. Representing an infolding of the body surface, they are typically subdivided into numerous pockets. Because the respiratory surface of a lung is not in direct contact with all other parts of the body, the gap must be bridged by the circulatory system, which transports gases between the lungs and the rest of the body. Lungs have evolved in organisms with open circulatory systems, such as spiders and land snails, as well as in vertebrates.

Among vertebrates that lack gills, the use of lungs for gas exchange varies. Amphibian lungs, when present, are relatively small and lack an extensive surface for exchange. Amphibians

▼ Figure 42.23 **Tracheal systems.**

(a) The respiratory system of an insect consists of branched internal tubes that deliver air directly to body cells. Rings of chitin reinforce the largest tubes, called tracheae, keeping them from collapsing. Enlarged portions of tracheae form air sacs near organs that require a large supply of oxygen.

(b) Air enters the tracheae through openings on the insect's body surface and passes into smaller tubes called tracheoles. The tracheoles are closed, and their terminal ends contain fluid (blue-gray). When the animal is active and using more O_2, most of the fluid is withdrawn into the body. This increases the surface area of air-filled tracheoles in contact with cells.

(c) The micrograph above shows cross sections of tracheoles in a tiny piece of insect flight muscle (TEM). Each of the numerous mitochondria in the muscle cells lies within about 5 μm of a tracheole.

2.5 μm

▼ **Figure 42.24 The mammalian respiratory system.** From the nasal cavity and pharynx, inhaled air passes through the larynx, trachea, and bronchi to the bronchioles, which end in microscopic alveoli lined by a thin, moist epithelium. Branches of the pulmonary arteries convey oxygen-poor blood to the alveoli; branches of the pulmonary veins transport oxygen-rich blood from the alveoli back to the heart. The left micrograph shows the dense capillary bed that envelops the alveoli. The right micrograph is a cutaway view of alveoli.

Nasal cavity

Pharynx

Larynx

(Esophagus)

Trachea

Right lung

Bronchus

Bronchiole

Diaphragm

Left lung

Heart

Branch of pulmonary vein (oxygen-rich blood)

Terminal bronchiole

Branch of pulmonary artery (oxygen-poor blood)

Alveoli

SEM   50 μm   Colorized SEM   50 μm

instead rely heavily on diffusion across other body surfaces, such as the skin, to carry out gas exchange. In contrast, most reptiles (including all birds) and all mammals depend entirely on lungs for gas exchange. Turtles are an exception; they supplement lung breathing with gas exchange across moist epithelial surfaces continuous with their mouth or anus. Lungs and air breathing have evolved in a few aquatic vertebrates (including lungfishes) as adaptations to living in oxygen-poor water or to spending part of their time exposed to air (for instance, when the water level of a pond recedes).

In general, the size and complexity of lungs are correlated with an animal's metabolic rate (and hence its rate of gas exchange). For example, the lungs of endotherms have a greater area of exchange surface than those of similar-sized ectotherms.

Mammalian Respiratory Systems: A Closer Look

In mammals, a system of branching ducts conveys air to the lungs, which are located in the thoracic cavity **(Figure 42.24)**. Air enters through the nostrils and is then filtered by hairs, warmed, humidified, and sampled for odors as it flows through a maze of spaces in the nasal cavity. The nasal cavity leads to the pharynx, an intersection where the paths for air and food cross. When food is swallowed, the **larynx** (the upper part of the respiratory tract) moves upward and tips the

epiglottis over the glottis (the opening of the **trachea**, or windpipe). This allows food to go down the esophagus to the stomach (see Figure 41.11). The rest of the time, the glottis is open, enabling breathing.

From the larynx, air passes into the trachea. Cartilage reinforcing the walls of both the larynx and the trachea keeps this part of the airway open. In most mammals, the larynx also functions as a voice box. Exhaled air rushes by the **vocal cords**, a pair of elastic bands of muscle in the larynx. Sounds are produced when muscles in the voice box are tensed, stretching the cords so they vibrate. High-pitched sounds result from tightly stretched cords vibrating rapidly; low-pitched sounds come from less tense cords vibrating slowly.

From the trachea fork two **bronchi** (singular, *bronchus*), one leading to each lung. Within the lung, the bronchi branch repeatedly into finer and finer tubes called **bronchioles**. The entire system of air ducts has the appearance of an inverted tree, the trunk being the trachea. The epithelium lining the major branches of this respiratory tree is covered by cilia and a thin film of mucus. The mucus traps dust, pollen, and other particulate contaminants, and the beating cilia move the mucus upward to the pharynx, where it can be swallowed into the esophagus. This process, sometimes referred to as the "mucus escalator," plays a critical role in cleansing the respiratory system.

Gas exchange occurs in **alveoli** (singular, *alveolus*; see Figure 42.24), air sacs clustered at the tips of the tiniest bronchioles. Human lungs contain millions of alveoli, which together have a surface area of about 100 m², fifty times that of the skin. Oxygen in the air entering the alveoli dissolves in the moist film lining their inner surfaces and rapidly diffuses across the epithelium into a web of capillaries that surrounds each alveolus. Carbon dioxide diffuses in the opposite direction, from the capillaries across the epithelium of the alveolus and into the air space.

Alveoli are so small that specialized secretions are required to relieve the surface tension in the fluid that coats their surface. These secretions, called **surfactants**, contain a mixture of phospholipids and proteins. In their absence, the alveoli collapse, blocking the entry of air. A lack of lung surfactants is a major problem for human babies born very prematurely. Surfactants typically appear in the lungs after 33 weeks of embryonic development. Among infants born before week 28, half suffer serious respiratory distress. Artificial surfactants are now used routinely to treat such preterm infants.

Lacking cilia or significant air currents to remove particles from their surface, alveoli are highly susceptible to contamination. White blood cells patrol alveoli, engulfing foreign particles. However, if too much particulate matter reaches the alveoli, the defenses can break down, leading to diseases that reduce the efficiency of gas exchange. Coal miners and other workers exposed to large amounts of dust from rock are susceptible to silicosis, a disabling, irreversible, and sometimes fatal lung disease. Cigarette smoke also brings damaging particulates into the alveoli.

Having surveyed the route that air follows when we breathe, we will turn next to the process of breathing itself.

CONCEPT CHECK 42.5

1. Why is the position of lung tissues *within* the body an advantage for terrestrial animals?
2. After a heavy rain, earthworms come to the surface. How would you explain this behavior in terms of an earthworm's requirements for gas exchange?
3. **WHAT IF?** The walls of alveoli contain elastic fibers that allow the alveoli to expand and contract with each breath. If alveoli lost their elasticity, how might gas exchange be affected? Explain.

For suggested answers, see Appendix A.

CONCEPT 42.6

Breathing ventilates the lungs

Like fishes, terrestrial vertebrates rely on ventilation to maintain high O₂ and low CO₂ concentrations at the gas exchange surface. The process that ventilates lungs is **breathing**, the alter-

nating inhalation and exhalation of air. A variety of mechanisms for moving air in and out of lungs have evolved, as we will see by considering breathing in amphibians, mammals, and birds.

How an Amphibian Breathes

An amphibian such as a frog ventilates its lungs by **positive pressure breathing**, inflating the lungs with forced airflow. During the first stage of inhalation, muscles lower the floor of an amphibian's oral cavity, drawing in air through its nostrils. Next, with the nostrils and mouth closed, the floor of the oral cavity rises, forcing air down the trachea. During exhalation, air is forced back out by the elastic recoil of the lungs and by compression of the muscular body wall. When male frogs puff themselves up in aggressive or courtship displays, they disrupt this breathing cycle, taking in air several times without allowing any release.

How a Mammal Breathes

Unlike amphibians, mammals employ **negative pressure breathing**—pulling, rather than pushing, air into their lungs (Figure 42.25). Using muscle contraction to actively expand the thoracic cavity, mammals lower air pressure in their lungs below that of the air outside their body. Because gas flows from a region of higher pressure to a region of lower pressure, air rushes through the nostrils and mouth and down the breathing tubes to the alveoli. During exhalation, the muscles controlling the thoracic cavity relax, and the volume of the cavity is reduced. The increased air pressure in the alveoli forces air up the breathing tubes and out of the body. Thus, inhalation is always active and requires work, whereas exhalation is usually passive.

Expanding the thoracic cavity during inhalation involves the animal's rib muscles and the **diaphragm**, a sheet of skeletal muscle that forms the bottom wall of the cavity. Contracting the rib muscles expands the rib cage, the front wall of the thoracic cavity, by pulling the ribs upward and the sternum outward. At the same time, the diaphragm contracts, expanding the thoracic cavity downward. The effect of the descending diaphragm is similar to that of a plunger being drawn out of a syringe.

Within the thoracic cavity, a double membrane surrounds the lungs. The inner layer of this membrane adheres to the outside of the lungs, and the outer layer adheres to the wall of the thoracic cavity. A thin space filled with fluid separates the two layers. Surface tension in the fluid causes the two layers to stick together like two plates of glass separated by a film of water: The layers can slide smoothly past each other, but they cannot be pulled apart easily. Consequently, the volume of the thoracic cavity and the volume of the lungs change in unison.

Depending on activity level, additional muscles may be recruited to aid breathing. The rib muscles and diaphragm are sufficient to change lung volume when a mammal is at rest. During exercise, other muscles of the neck, back, and chest increase the volume of the thoracic cavity by raising the rib cage. In kangaroos and some other species, locomotion causes a

▲ Figure 42.25 Negative pressure breathing. A mammal breathes by changing the air pressure within its lungs relative to the pressure of the outside atmosphere.

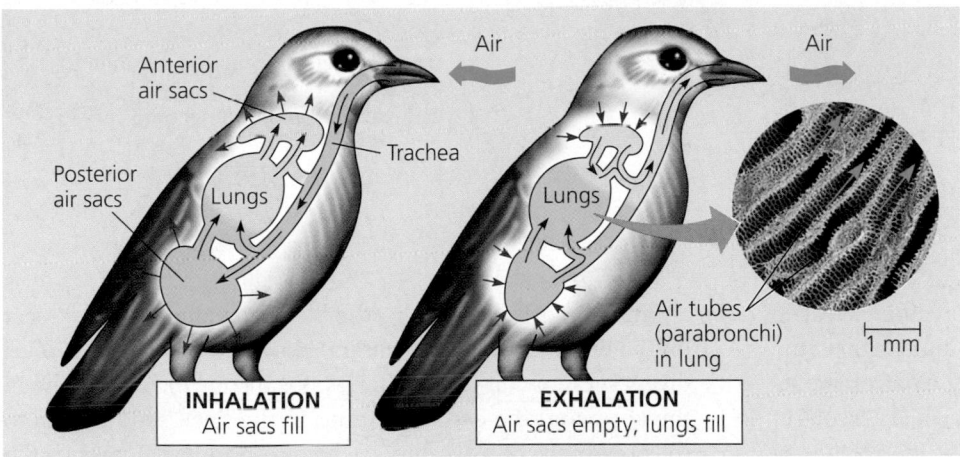

▲ Figure 42.26 The avian respiratory system. Inflation and deflation of the air sacs (red arrows) ventilates the lungs, forcing air in one direction through tiny parallel tubes in the lungs called parabronchi (inset, SEM). During inhalation, both sets of air sacs inflate. The posterior sacs fill with fresh air (blue) from the outside, while the anterior sacs fill with stale air (gray) from the lungs. During exhalation, both sets of air sacs deflate, forcing air from the posterior sacs into the lungs, and air from the anterior sacs out of the system via the trachea. Gas exchange occurs across the walls of the parabronchi. Two cycles of inhalation and exhalation are required for the air to pass all the way through the system and out of the bird.

rhythmic movement of organs in the abdomen, including the stomach and liver. The result is a piston-like pumping motion that pushes and pulls on the diaphragm, further increasing the volume of air moved in and out of the lungs.

The volume of air inhaled and exhaled with each breath is called **tidal volume**. It averages about 500 mL in resting humans. The tidal volume during maximal inhalation and exhalation is the **vital capacity**, which is about 3.4 L and 4.8 L for college-age women and men, respectively. The air that remains after a forced exhalation is called the **residual volume**. As we age, our lungs lose their resilience, and residual volume increases at the expense of vital capacity.

Because the lungs in mammals do not completely empty with each breath, and because inhalation occurs through the same airways as exhalation, each inhalation mixes fresh air with oxygen-depleted residual air. As a result, the maximum P_{O_2} in alveoli is always considerably less than in the atmosphere.

How a Bird Breathes

Ventilation is both more efficient and more complex in birds than in mammals. When birds breathe, they pass air over the gas exchange surface in only one direction. Furthermore, incoming, fresh air does not mix with air that has already carried out gas exchange. To bring fresh air to their lungs, birds use eight or nine air sacs situated on either side of the lungs (Figure 42.26). The air sacs do not function directly in gas exchange but act as bellows that keep air flowing through the lungs. Instead of alveoli, which are dead ends, the sites of gas exchange in bird lungs are tiny channels called *parabronchi*. Passage of air through the entire system—lungs and air sacs—requires two cycles of inhalation and exhalation. In some passageways, the direction in which air moves alternates (see Figure 42.26). Within the parabronchi, however, air always flows in the same direction.

Because the air in a bird's lungs is renewed with every exhalation, the maximum P_{O_2} in the lungs is higher in birds than in mammals. This is one reason birds function better than mammals at high altitude. For example, humans have great difficulty obtaining enough O_2 when climbing Earth's highest peaks, such as Mount Everest (8,850 m), in the Himalayas. But bar-headed geese and several other bird species easily fly over the Himalayas during migration.

Control of Breathing in Humans

Although you can voluntarily hold your breath or breathe faster and deeper, most of the time your breathing is regulated by involuntary mechanisms. These control mechanisms ensure that gas exchange is coordinated with blood circulation and with metabolic demand.

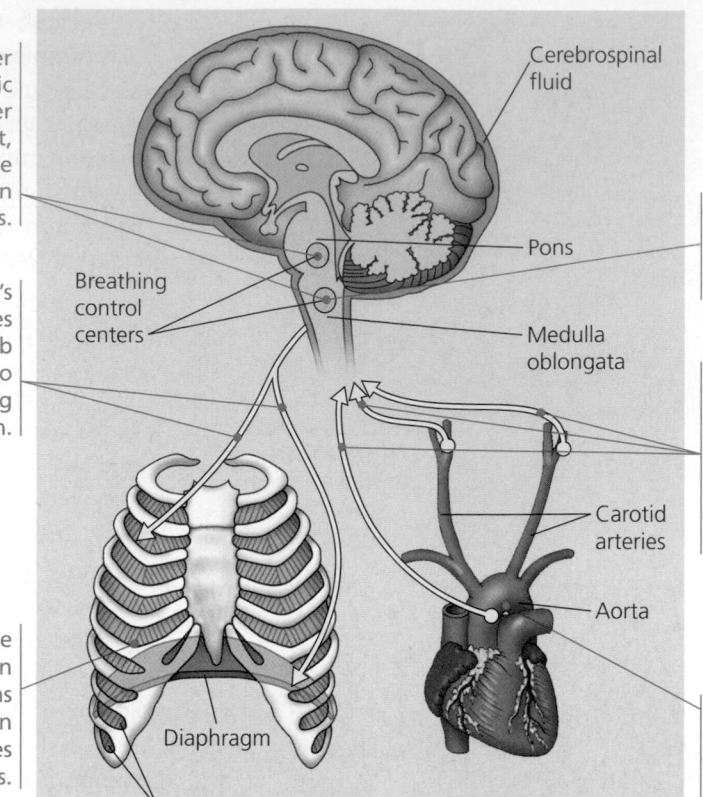

① A breathing control center in the medulla sets the basic rhythm, and a control center in the pons moderates it, smoothing out the transitions between inhalations and exhalations.

② Nerves from the medulla's control center send impulses to the diaphragm and rib muscles, stimulating them to contract and causing inhalation.

③ In a person at rest, these nerve impulses result in about 10 to 14 inhalations per minute. Between inhalations, the muscles relax and the person exhales.

Cerebrospinal fluid

Pons

Breathing control centers

Medulla oblongata

Carotid arteries

Aorta

Diaphragm

Rib muscles

④ Sensors in the medulla detect changes in the pH (reflecting CO_2 concentration) of the blood and cerebrospinal fluid bathing the surface of the brain.

⑤ Sensors in major blood vessels detect changes in blood pH and send nerve impulses to the medulla. In response, the medulla's control center alters the rate and depth of breathing, increasing both if CO_2 levels rise or decreasing both if CO_2 levels fall.

⑥ Other sensors in the aorta and carotid arteries signal the medulla to increase the breathing rate when O_2 levels in the blood become very low.

▲ Figure 42.27 **Automatic control of breathing.**

Networks of neurons that regulate breathing, called **breathing control centers**, are located in two brain regions, the medulla oblongata and the pons (**Figure 42.27**). Control circuits in the medulla establish the breathing rhythm, while neurons in the pons regulate its tempo. (The number and location of the circuits in the medulla is a subject of active research.) When you breathe deeply, a negative-feedback mechanism prevents the lungs from overexpanding: During inhalation, sensors that detect stretching of the lung tissue send nerve impulses to the control circuits in the medulla, inhibiting further inhalation.

In regulating breathing, the medulla uses the pH of the surrounding tissue fluid as an indicator of blood CO_2 concentration. The reason pH can be used in this way is that blood CO_2 is the main determinant of the pH of *cerebrospinal fluid*, the fluid surrounding the brain and spinal cord. Carbon dioxide diffuses from the blood to the cerebrospinal fluid, where it reacts with water and forms carbonic acid (H_2CO_3). The H_2CO_3 can then dissociate into a bicarbonate ion (HCO_3^-) and a hydrogen ion (H^+):

$$CO_2 + H_2O \rightleftharpoons H_2CO_3 \rightleftharpoons HCO_3^- + H^+$$

Increased metabolic activity, such as occurs during exercise, lowers pH by increasing the concentration of CO_2 in the blood. In response, the medulla's control circuits increase the depth and rate of breathing. Both remain high until the excess CO_2 is eliminated in exhaled air and pH returns to a normal value.

The O_2 concentration in the blood usually has little effect on the breathing control centers. However, when the O_2 level drops very low (at high altitudes, for instance), O_2 sensors in the aorta and the carotid arteries in the neck send signals to the breathing control centers, which respond by increasing the breathing rate.

Breathing control is effective only if it is coordinated with control of the cardiovascular system so that ventilation is matched to blood flow through alveolar capillaries. During exercise, for instance, an increased breathing rate, which enhances O_2 uptake and CO_2 removal, is coupled with an increase in cardiac output.

CONCEPT CHECK 42.6

1. How does an increase in the CO_2 concentration in the blood affect the pH of cerebrospinal fluid?
2. A slight decrease in blood pH causes the heart's pacemaker to speed up. What is the function of this control mechanism?
3. **WHAT IF?** Suppose that you broke a rib in a fall. If the broken end of the rib tore a small hole in the membranes surrounding your lungs, what effect on lung function would you expect?

For suggested answers, see Appendix A.

CONCEPT 42.7

Adaptations for gas exchange include pigments that bind and transport gases

The high metabolic demands of many animals necessitate the exchange of large quantities of O_2 and CO_2. Here we'll examine how blood molecules called respiratory pigments facilitate this exchange through their interaction with O_2 and CO_2. We will also investigate physiological adaptations that enable animals to be active under conditions of high metabolic load or very limiting P_{O_2}. As a basis for exploring these topics, let's summarize the basic gas exchange circuit in humans.

Coordination of Circulation and Gas Exchange

The partial pressures of O_2 and CO_2 in the blood vary at different points in the circulatory system, as shown in **Figure 42.28**. Blood arriving at the lungs via the pulmonary arteries has a lower P_{O_2} and a higher P_{CO_2} than the air in the alveoli. As blood enters the alveolar capillaries, CO_2 diffuses from the blood to the air in the alveoli. Meanwhile, O_2 in the air dissolves in the fluid that coats the alveolar epithelium and diffuses into the blood. By the time the blood leaves the lungs in the pulmonary veins, its P_{O_2} has been raised and its P_{CO_2} has been lowered. After returning to the heart, this blood is pumped through the systemic circuit.

In the tissue capillaries, gradients of partial pressure favor the diffusion of O_2 out of the blood and CO_2 into the blood. These gradients exist because cellular respiration in the mitochondria of cells near each capillary removes O_2 from and adds CO_2 to the surrounding interstitial fluid. After the blood unloads O_2 and loads CO_2, it is returned to the heart and pumped to the lungs again.

Although this description faithfully characterizes the driving forces for gas exchange in different tissues, it omits the critical role of the specialized carrier proteins we will discuss next.

Respiratory Pigments

The low solubility of O_2 in water (and thus in blood) poses a problem for animals that rely on the circulatory system to deliver O_2. For example, a person requires almost 2 L of O_2 per minute during intense exercise, and all of it must be carried in the blood from the lungs to the active tissues. At normal body temperature and air pressure, however, only 4.5 mL of O_2 can dissolve into a liter of blood in the lungs. Even if 80% of the dissolved O_2 were delivered to the tissues (an unrealistically high percentage), the heart would still need to pump 555 L of blood per minute!

In fact, animals transport most of their O_2 bound to certain proteins called **respiratory pigments**. Respiratory pigments circulate with the blood or hemolymph and are often contained within specialized cells. The pigments greatly increase the amount of O_2 that can be carried in the circulatory fluid (to about 200 mL of O_2 per liter in mammalian blood). In our

(a) Oxygen

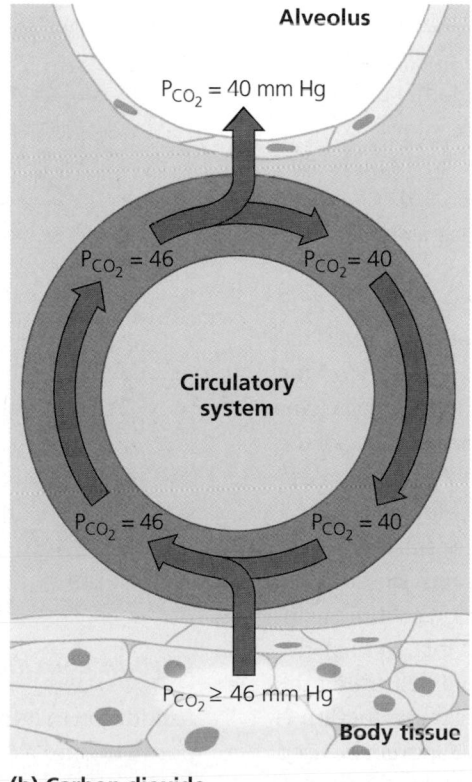

(b) Carbon dioxide

◄ **Figure 42.28 Loading and unloading of respiratory gases.**

WHAT IF? *If you consciously forced more air out of your lungs each time you exhaled, how would that affect the values shown in these diagrams?*

example of an exercising human with an O_2 delivery rate of 80%, the presence of respiratory pigments reduces the cardiac output necessary for O_2 transport to a manageable 12.5 L of blood per minute.

A variety of respiratory pigments have evolved among the animal taxa. With a few exceptions, these molecules have a distinctive color (hence the term *pigment*) and consist of a protein bound to a metal. One example is the blue pigment *hemocyanin*, which has copper as its oxygen-binding component and is found in arthropods and many molluscs. The respiratory pigment of almost all vertebrates and many invertebrates is hemoglobin. In vertebrates, it is contained in the erythrocytes.

Hemoglobin

Vertebrate hemoglobin consists of four subunits (polypeptide chains), each with a cofactor called a heme group that has an iron atom at its center. Each iron atom binds one molecule of O_2; hence, a single hemoglobin molecule can carry four molecules of O_2. Like all respiratory pigments, hemoglobin binds O_2 reversibly, loading O_2 in the lungs or gills and unloading it in other parts of the body. This process depends on cooperativity between the hemoglobin subunits (see Chapter 8). When O_2 binds to one subunit, the others change shape slightly, increasing their affinity for O_2. When four O_2 molecules are bound and one subunit unloads its O_2, the other three subunits more readily unload, as an associated shape change lowers their affinity for O_2.

β Chains

Iron
Heme

α Chains
Hemoglobin

Cooperativity in O_2 binding and release is evident in the dissociation curve for hemoglobin **(Figure 42.29a)**. Over the range of P_{O_2} where the dissociation curve has a steep slope, even a slight change in P_{O_2} causes hemoglobin to load or unload a substantial amount of O_2. Notice that the steep part of the curve corresponds to the range of P_{O_2} found in body tissues. When cells in a particular location begin working harder—during exercise, for instance—P_{O_2} dips in their vicinity as the O_2 is consumed in cellular respiration. Because of the effect of subunit cooperativity, a slight drop in P_{O_2} causes a relatively large increase in the amount of O_2 the blood unloads.

The production of CO_2 during cellular respiration promotes the unloading of O_2 by hemoglobin in active tissues. As we have seen, CO_2 reacts with water, forming carbonic acid, which lowers the pH of its surroundings. Low pH, in turn, decreases the affinity of hemoglobin for O_2, an effect called the **Bohr shift (Figure 42.29b)**. Thus, where CO_2 production is greater, hemoglobin releases more O_2, which can then be used to support more cellular respiration.

(a) P_{O_2} and hemoglobin dissociation at pH 7.4. The curve shows the relative amounts of O_2 bound to hemoglobin exposed to solutions with different P_{O_2}. At a P_{O_2} of 100 mm Hg, typical in the lungs, hemoglobin is about 98% saturated with O_2. At a P_{O_2} of 40 mm Hg, common in the vicinity of tissues at rest, hemoglobin is about 70% saturated. Hemoglobin can release additional O_2 to metabolically very active tissues, such as muscle tissue during exercise.

(b) pH and hemoglobin dissociation. Because hydrogen ions affect the shape of hemoglobin, a drop in pH shifts the O_2 dissociation curve toward the right (the Bohr shift). At a given P_{O_2}, say 40 mm Hg, hemoglobin gives up more O_2 at pH 7.2 than at pH 7.4, the normal pH of human blood. The pH decreases in very active tissues because the CO_2 produced by cellular respiration reacts with water, forming carbonic acid. Hemoglobin then releases more O_2, which supports the increased cellular respiration in the active tissues.

▲ **Figure 42.29 Dissociation curves for hemoglobin at 37°C.**

Carbon Dioxide Transport

In addition to its role in O_2 transport, hemoglobin helps transport CO_2 and assists in buffering the blood—that is, preventing harmful changes in pH. Only about 7% of the CO_2 released by respiring cells is transported in solution in blood plasma. Another 23% binds to the amino ends of the hemoglobin polypeptide chains, and about 70% is transported in the blood in the form of bicarbonate ions (HCO_3^-).

As shown in **Figure 42.30**, carbon dioxide from respiring cells diffuses into the blood plasma and then into erythrocytes. There the CO_2 reacts with water (assisted by the enzyme carbonic anhydrase) and forms H_2CO_3, which dissociates into H^+ and HCO_3^-. Most of the H^+ binds to hemoglobin and other proteins, minimizing the change in blood pH. The HCO_3^- diffuses into the plasma.

When blood flows through the lungs, the relative partial pressures of CO_2 favor the diffusion of CO_2 out of the blood. As CO_2 diffuses into alveoli, the amount of CO_2 in the blood decreases. This decrease shifts the chemical equilibrium in favor of the conversion of HCO_3^- to CO_2, enabling further net diffusion of CO_2 into alveoli.

Elite Animal Athletes

For some animals, such as long-distance runners and migratory birds and mammals, the O_2 demands of daily activities would overwhelm the capacity of a typical respiratory system. Other animals, such as diving mammals, are capable of being active underwater for extended periods without breathing. What evolutionary adaptations enable these animals to perform such feats?

The Ultimate Endurance Runner

The elite animal marathon runner may be the pronghorn, an antelope-like mammal native to the grasslands of North America. Second only to the cheetah in top speed for a land vertebrate, pronghorns are capable of running as fast as 100 km/hr and can sustain an average speed of 65 km/hr over long distances.

Stan Lindstedt and his colleagues at the University of Wyoming and the University of Bern were curious about how pronghorns achieve their combination

1. Carbon dioxide produced by body tissues diffuses into the interstitial fluid and the plasma.

2. Over 90% of the CO_2 diffuses into red blood cells, leaving only 7% in the plasma as dissolved CO_2.

3. Some CO_2 is picked up and transported by hemoglobin.

4. However, most CO_2 reacts with water in red blood cells, forming carbonic acid (H_2CO_3), a reaction catalyzed by carbonic anhydrase contained within red blood cells.

5. Carbonic acid dissociates into a bicarbonate ion (HCO_3^-) and a hydrogen ion (H^+).

6. Hemoglobin binds most of the H^+ from H_2CO_3, preventing the H^+ from acidifying the blood and thus preventing the Bohr shift.

7. Most of the HCO_3^- diffuses into the plasma, where it is carried in the bloodstream to the lungs.

8. In the lungs, HCO_3^- diffuses from the plasma into red blood cells, combining with H^+ released from hemoglobin and forming H_2CO_3.

9. Carbonic acid is converted back to CO_2 and water. CO_2 is also unloaded from hemoglobin.

10. CO_2 diffuses into the plasma and the interstitial fluid.

11. CO_2 diffuses into the alveolar space, from which it is expelled during exhalation. The reduction of CO_2 concentration in the plasma drives the breakdown of H_2CO_3 into CO_2 and water in the red blood cells (see step 9), a reversal of the reaction that occurs near body tissues (see step 4).

▲ **Figure 42.30 Carbon dioxide transport in the blood.**
? *In what three forms is CO_2 transported in the bloodstream?*

of exceptional speed and endurance. The researchers exercised pronghorns on a treadmill to estimate their maximum rate of O_2 consumption (see Figure 40.18). The results were surprising: Pronghorns consume O_2 at three times the rate predicted for an average animal of their size. Normally, as animals increase in size, their rate of O_2 consumption per gram of body mass declines. One gram of shrew tissue, for example, consumes as much O_2 in a day as a gram of elephant tissue consumes in an entire month. But the rate of O_2 consumption per gram of tissue by a pronghorn turned out to be as high as that of a 10-g mouse!

What adaptations enable the pronghorn to consume O_2 at such a high rate? To answer this question, Lindstedt and his colleagues compared various physiological characteristics of pronghorns with those of domestic goats, which lack great speed and endurance (Figure 42.31). They concluded that the pronghorn's unusually high O_2 consumption rate results from enhancements of normal physiological mechanisms at each stage of O_2 metabolism. These enhancements are the result of natural selection, perhaps exerted by the predators that have chased pronghorns across the open plains of North America for more than 4 million years.

Diving Mammals

Animals vary greatly in their ability to temporarily inhabit environments in which there is no access to their normal respiratory medium—for example, when an air-breather swims underwater. Whereas most humans, even well-trained divers, cannot hold their breath longer than 2 or 3 minutes or swim deeper than 20 m, the Weddell seal of Antarctica routinely plunges to 200–500 m and remains there for about 20 minutes (sometimes for more than an hour). (Humans can remain submerged for comparable periods, but only with the aid of specialized gear and compressed air tanks.) Some sea turtles, whales, and other species of seals make even more impressive dives. Elephant seals can reach depths of 1,500 m—almost a mile—and stay submerged for as long as 2 hours! One elephant seal carrying a recording device spent 40 days at sea, diving almost continuously with no surface period longer than 6 minutes.

One adaptation of diving mammals to prolonged stays underwater is an ability to store large amounts of O_2. Compared with humans, the Weddell seal can store about twice as much O_2 per kilogram of body mass. About 36% of our total O_2 is in our lungs, and 51% is in our blood. In contrast, the Weddell seal holds only about 5% of its O_2 in its relatively small lungs (and may exhale before diving, which reduces buoyancy), stockpiling 70% in the blood. The seal has about twice the volume of blood per kilogram of body mass as a human. Diving mammals also have a high concentration of an oxygen-storing

▼ Figure 42.31 **Inquiry**

What is the basis for the pronghorn's unusually high rate of O_2 consumption?

EXPERIMENT   Stan Lindstedt and colleagues had demonstrated that the pronghorn's maximal rate of O_2 consumption (V_{O_2} max) is five times that of a domestic goat, a similar-sized mammal adapted to climbing rather than running. To discover the physiological basis for this difference, they measured the following parameters in both animals: lung capacity (a measure of O_2 uptake), cardiac output (a measure of O_2 delivery), muscle mass, and muscle mitochondrial volume. (The last two parameters are measures of the muscles' potential O_2 use.)

RESULTS

CONCLUSION   The dramatic difference in V_{O_2} max between the pronghorn and the goat reflects comparable differences at each stage of O_2 metabolism: uptake, delivery, and use.

SOURCE   S. L. Lindstedt et al., Running energetics in the pronghorn antelope, *Nature* 353:748–750 (1991).

WHAT IF?   Suppose you measured V_{O_2} max among a large group of humans. To what extent would you expect those with the highest values to be the fastest runners?

protein called **myoglobin** in their muscles. The Weddell seal can store about 25% of its O_2 in muscle, compared with only 13% in humans.

Diving mammals not only have a relatively large O_2 stockpile but also have adaptations that conserve O_2. They swim with little muscular effort and glide passively upward or downward by changing their buoyancy. Their heart rate and O_2 consumption rate decrease during a dive. At the same time, regulatory mechanisms route most blood to the brain, spinal cord, eyes, adrenal glands, and, in pregnant seals, the placenta. Blood supply to the muscles is restricted or, during the longest dives, shut off altogether. During dives of more than about 20 minutes, a Weddell seal's muscles deplete the O_2 stored in myoglobin and then derive their ATP from fermentation instead of respiration (see Chapter 9).

The unusual abilities of the Weddell seal and other air-breathing divers to power their bodies during long dives showcase two related themes in our study of organisms—the response to environmental challenges over the short term by physiological adjustments and over the long term as a result of natural selection.

Chapter 42 Review

SUMMARY OF KEY CONCEPTS

CONCEPT 42.1

Circulatory systems link exchange surfaces with cells throughout the body (pp. 898–903)

▶ **Gastrovascular Cavities** Gastrovascular cavities in small animals with simple body plans mediate exchange between the environment and cells that can be reached by short-range diffusion.

▶ **Open and Closed Circulatory Systems** Because diffusion is slow over all but short distances, most complex animals have internal transport systems. These systems circulate fluid between cells and the organs that exchange gases, nutrients, and wastes with the outside environment. In the open circulatory systems of arthropods and most molluscs, the circulating fluid bathes the organs directly. Closed systems circulate fluid in a closed network of pumps and vessels.

▶ **Organization of Vertebrate Circulatory Systems** In vertebrates, blood flows in a closed cardiovascular system consisting of blood vessels and a two- to four-chambered heart. Arteries convey blood to capillaries, the sites of chemical exchange between blood and interstitial fluid. Veins return blood from capillaries to the heart. Fishes, rays, and sharks have a single pump in their circulation. Air-breathing vertebrates have two pumps combined in a single heart. Variations in ventricle number and separation reflect adaptations to different environments and metabolic needs.

CONCEPT 42.2

Coordinated cycles of heart contraction drive double circulation in mammals (pp. 903–905)

▶ **Mammalian Circulation** Heart valves dictate a one-way flow of blood through the heart. The right ventricle pumps blood to the lungs, where it loads O_2 and unloads CO_2. Oxygen-rich blood from the lungs enters the heart at the left atrium and is pumped to the body tissues by the left ventricle. Blood returns to the heart through the right atrium.

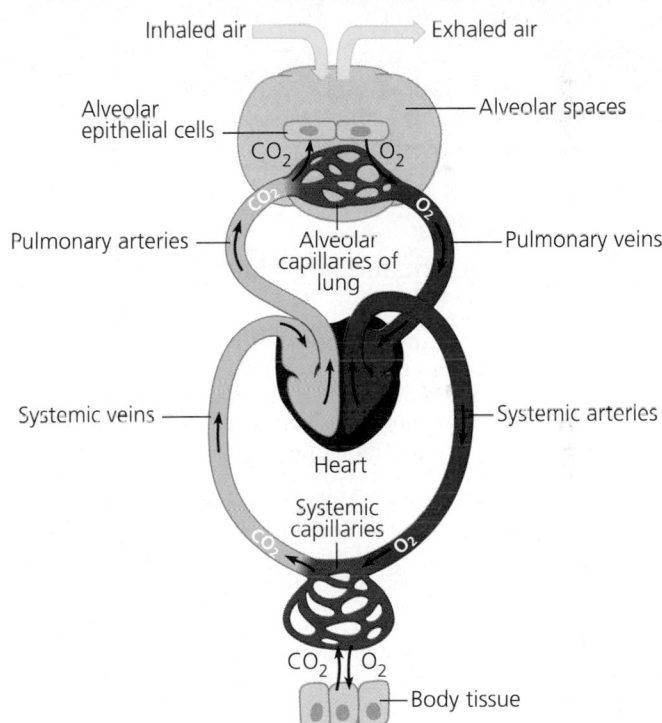

▶ **The Mammalian Heart: A Closer Look** The pulse is a measure of the number of times the heart beats each minute. The cardiac cycle, one complete sequence of the heart's pumping and filling, consists of a period of contraction, called systole, and a period of relaxation, called diastole. Cardiac output is the volume of blood pumped by each ventricle per minute.

▶ **Maintaining the Heart's Rhythmic Beat** Impulses originating at the sinoatrial (SA) node (pacemaker) of the right atrium pass to the atrioventricular (AV) node. After a delay, they are conducted along the bundle branches and Purkinje fibers. The pacemaker is influenced by nerves, hormones, and body temperature.

MEDIA
Activity Mammalian Cardiovascular System Structure

Patterns of blood pressure and flow reflect the structure and arrangement of blood vessels (pp. 906–911)

▶ **Blood Vessel Structure and Function** Capillaries have narrow diameters and thin walls that facilitate exchange. Arteries contain thick elastic walls that maintain blood pressure. Veins contain one-way valves that contribute to the return of blood to the heart.

▶ **Blood Flow Velocity** Physical laws governing the movement of fluids through pipes influence blood flow and blood pressure. The velocity of blood flow varies in the circulatory system, being lowest in the capillary beds as a result of their large total cross-sectional area.

▶ **Blood Pressure** Blood pressure is altered by changes in cardiac output and by variable constriction of arterioles.

▶ **Capillary Function** Transfer of substances between the blood and the interstitial fluid occurs across the thin walls of capillaries.

▶ **Fluid Return by the Lymphatic System** The lymphatic system returns fluid to the blood and parallels the circulatory system in its extent and its mechanisms for fluid flow under low hydrostatic pressure. It also plays a vital role in defense against infection.

> **MEDIA**
> **Activity** Path of Blood Flow in Mammals
> **Activity** Mammalian Cardiovascular System Function
> **Biology Labs On-Line** CardioLab

CONCEPT 42.4

Blood components function in exchange, transport, and defense (pp. 911–915)

▶ **Blood Composition and Function** Whole blood consists of cellular elements (cells and cell fragments called platelets) suspended in a liquid matrix called plasma. Plasma proteins influence blood pH, osmotic pressure, and viscosity and function in lipid transport, immunity (antibodies), and blood clotting (fibrinogen). Red blood cells, or erythrocytes, transport O_2. Five types of white blood cells, or leukocytes, function in defense against microbes and foreign substances in the blood. Platelets function in blood clotting, a cascade of reactions that converts plasma fibrinogen to fibrin.

▶ **Cardiovascular Disease** The deposition of lipids and tissues on the lining of arteries is a prime contributor to cardiovascular disease that can result in life-threatening damage to the heart or brain.

> **MEDIA**
> **Investigation** How Is Cardiovascular Fitness Measured?

CONCEPT 42.5

Gas exchange occurs across specialized respiratory surfaces (pp. 915–920)

▶ **Partial Pressure Gradients in Gas Exchange** At all sites of gas exchange, gases diffuse from where their partial pressures are higher to where they are lower.

▶ **Respiratory Media** Air is more conducive to gas exchange because of its higher O_2 content, lower density, and lower viscosity.

▶ **Respiratory Surfaces** Animals require large, moist respiratory surfaces for the adequate diffusion of O_2 and CO_2 between their cells and the respiratory medium, either air or water.

▶ **Gills in Aquatic Animals** Gills are outfoldings of the body surface specialized for gas exchange in water. The effectiveness of gas exchange in some gills, including those of fishes, is increased by ventilation and countercurrent flow of blood and water.

▶ **Tracheal Systems in Insects** The tracheae of insects are tiny, branching tubes that penetrate the body, bringing O_2 directly to cells.

▶ **Lungs** Spiders, land snails, and most terrestrial vertebrates have internal lungs. In mammals, air inhaled through the nostrils passes through the pharynx into the trachea, bronchi, bronchioles, and dead-end alveoli, where gas exchange occurs.

> **MEDIA**
> **Activity** The Human Respiratory System

CONCEPT 42.6

Breathing ventilates the lungs (pp. 920–922)

▶ **How an Amphibian Breathes** An amphibian ventilates its lungs by positive pressure breathing, which forces air down the trachea.

▶ **How a Mammal Breathes** Mammals ventilate their lungs by negative pressure breathing, which pulls air into the lungs. Lung volume increases as the rib muscles and diaphragm contract.

▶ **How a Bird Breathes** Besides lungs, birds have eight or nine air sacs that act as bellows, keeping air flowing through the lungs in one direction only. Every exhalation completely renews the air in the lungs.

▶ **Control of Breathing in Humans** Control centers in the medulla oblongata and pons of the brain regulate the rate and depth of breathing. Sensors detect the pH of cerebrospinal fluid (reflecting CO_2 concentration in the blood), and the medulla adjusts breathing rate and depth to match metabolic demands. Secondary control over breathing is exerted by sensors in the aorta and carotid arteries that monitor blood levels of O_2 and CO_2 and blood pH.

CONCEPT 42.7

Adaptations for gas exchange include pigments that bind and transport gases (pp. 923–927)

▶ **Coordination of Circulation and Gas Exchange** In the lungs, gradients of partial pressure favor the diffusion of O_2 into the blood and CO_2 out of the blood. The opposite situation exists in the rest of the body.

▶ **Respiratory Pigments** Respiratory pigments transport O_2, greatly increasing the amount of O_2 that blood or hemolymph can carry. Many arthropods and molluscs have copper-containing hemocyanin; vertebrates and a wide variety of invertebrates have hemoglobin. Hemoglobin also helps transport CO_2 and assists in buffering.

▶ **Elite Animal Athletes** The pronghorn's high O_2 consumption rate underlies its ability to run at high speeds over long distances. Deep-diving air-breathers stockpile O_2 and deplete it slowly.

TESTING YOUR KNOWLEDGE

SELF-QUIZ

1. Which of the following respiratory systems is not closely associated with a blood supply?
   a. the lungs of a vertebrate
   b. the gills of a fish
   c. the tracheal system of an insect
   d. the skin of an earthworm
   e. the parapodia of a polychaete worm

2. Blood returning to the mammalian heart in a pulmonary vein drains first into the
   a. vena cava.
   b. left atrium.
   c. right atrium.
   d. left ventricle.
   e. right ventricle.

3. Pulse is a direct measure of
   a. blood pressure.
   b. stroke volume.
   c. cardiac output.
   d. heart rate.
   e. breathing rate.

4. The conversion of fibrinogen to fibrin
   a. occurs when fibrinogen is released from broken platelets.
   b. occurs within red blood cells.
   c. is linked to hypertension and may damage artery walls.
   d. is likely to occur too often in an individual with hemophilia.
   e. is the final step of a clotting process that involves multiple clotting factors.

5. In negative pressure breathing, inhalation results from
   a. forcing air from the throat down into the lungs.
   b. contracting the diaphragm.
   c. relaxing the muscles of the rib cage.
   d. using muscles of the lungs to expand the alveoli.
   e. contracting the abdominal muscles.

6. When you hold your breath, which of the following blood gas changes first leads to the urge to breathe?
   a. rising O_2
   b. falling O_2
   c. rising CO_2
   d. falling CO_2
   e. rising CO_2 and falling O_2

7. Compared with the interstitial fluid that bathes active muscle cells, blood reaching these cells in arteries has a
   a. higher P_{O_2}.
   b. higher P_{CO_2}.
   c. greater bicarbonate concentration.
   d. lower pH.
   e. lower osmotic pressure.

8. Which of the following reactions prevails in red blood cells traveling through alveolar capillaries? (Hb = hemoglobin)
   a. $Hb + 4 O_2 \rightarrow Hb(O_2)_4$
   b. $Hb(O_2)_4 \rightarrow Hb + 4 O_2$
   c. $CO_2 + H_2O \rightarrow H_2CO_3$
   d. $H_2CO_3 \rightarrow H^+ + HCO_3^-$
   e. $Hb + 4 CO_2 \rightarrow Hb(CO_2)_4$

9. **DRAW IT** Draw a pair of simple diagrams comparing the essential features of single and double circulation.

For Self-Quiz answers, see Appendix A.

EVOLUTION CONNECTION

10. One of the many mutant opponents that the movie monster Godzilla contends with is Mothra, a giant mothlike creature with a wingspan of several dozen feet. Science fiction creatures like these can be critiqued on the grounds of biomechanical and physiological principles. What problems of respiration and gas exchange would Mothra face? The largest insects that have ever lived are Paleozoic dragonflies with half-meter wingspans. Why do you think truly giant insects are improbable?

SCIENTIFIC INQUIRY

11. The hemoglobin of a human fetus differs from adult hemoglobin. Compare the dissociation curves of the two hemoglobins in the graph below. Propose a hypothesis for the *function* of this difference between these two versions of hemoglobin.

SCIENCE, TECHNOLOGY, AND SOCIETY

12. Hundreds of studies have linked smoking with cardiovascular and lung disease. According to most health authorities, smoking is the leading cause of preventable, premature death in the United States. Antismoking and health groups have proposed that cigarette advertising in all media be banned entirely. What are some arguments in favor of a total ban on cigarette advertising? What are arguments in opposition? Do you favor or oppose such a ban? Defend your position.

43

The Immune System

▲ Figure 43.1 **How do immune cells of animals recognize foreign cells?**

KEY CONCEPTS

43.1 In innate immunity, recognition and response rely on shared traits of pathogens

43.2 In acquired immunity, lymphocyte receptors provide pathogen-specific recognition

43.3 Acquired immunity defends against infection of body cells and fluids

43.4 Disruptions in immune system function can elicit or exacerbate disease

OVERVIEW

Reconnaissance, Recognition, and Response

Animals are constantly under attack by **pathogens**, infectious agents that cause disease. For a pathogen, an animal body is a nearly ideal habitat, offering a ready source of nutrients, a protected setting for growth and reproduction, and a means of transport to new hosts and environments. Seizing this opportunity, pathogens—mostly viruses, bacteria, protists, and fungi—infect a wide range of animals, including humans. In response, animals fight back in various ways. Dedicated immune cells patrol the body fluids of most animals, searching out and destroying foreign cells. For example, as shown in the colorized scanning electron micrograph in **Figure 43.1**, an immune cell called a macrophage (blue) engulfs a yeast cell (green). Additional responses to infection take many forms, including proteins that punch holes in bacterial membranes or block viruses from entering body cells. These and other defenses make up an **immune system**, which enables an animal to avoid or limit many infections.

An animal's most basic defense against pathogens is a barrier. An outer covering, such as skin or a shell, provides a significant obstacle to invasion by the microbes that are present

on the body. Sealing off the entire body surface is impossible, however, because gas exchange, nutrition, and reproduction require openings to the environment. Additional barrier defenses, such as chemical secretions that trap or kill microbes, guard the body's entrances and exits.

If a pathogen breaches the barrier defenses and enters the animal's body, the problem of how to fend off attack changes substantially. Housed within the body fluids and tissues, the invader is no longer an outsider. To fight pathogens within the body, the animal's immune system must detect foreign particles and cells. In other words, an immune system must carry out recognition, distinguishing nonself from self.

In identifying pathogens, animal immune systems use receptors that specifically bind molecules from foreign cells or viruses. There are two general strategies for such molecular recognition, each forming the basis for a particular system for immunity. One defense system, **innate immunity**, is found in all animals. Innate immune responses are active immediately upon infection and are the same whether or not the pathogen has been encountered previously. Innate immunity includes the barrier defenses (for example, skin), as well as defenses that combat pathogens after they enter the body (see, for example, Figure 43.1). The activation of many of these internal defenses relies on recognition of pathogens. Innate immune cells produce a small preset group of receptor proteins that accomplish this task. Each innate immune receptor binds a molecule or structure that is absent from animal bodies but is common to a large class of microbes. In this way, innate immune systems detect a very broad range of pathogens.

A second defense system, found only in vertebrates, is **acquired immunity**, also known as *adaptive immunity*. Acquired (adaptive) immune responses are activated after innate immune defenses take effect and develop more slowly. The name *acquired* reflects the fact that this immune response is enhanced by previous exposure to the infecting pathogen. Ex-

Pathogens
(microorganisms
and viruses)

INNATE IMMUNITY	Barrier defenses:
• Recognition of traits shared by broad ranges of pathogens, using a small set of receptors • Rapid response	Skin Mucous membranes Secretions
	Internal defenses: Phagocytic cells Antimicrobial proteins Inflammatory response Natural killer cells

ACQUIRED IMMUNITY	Humoral response:
• Recognition of traits specific to particular pathogens, using a vast array of receptors • Slower response	Antibodies defend against infection in body fluids. **Cell-mediated response:** Cytotoxic lymphocytes defend against infection in body cells.

▲ **Figure 43.2 Overview of animal immunity.** Immune responses in animals can be divided into innate and acquired immunity. Some components of innate immunity contribute to activation of acquired immune defenses.

amples of acquired responses include the synthesis of proteins that inactivate a bacterial toxin and the targeted killing of a virally infected body cell. Animals with acquired immunity produce a large arsenal of receptors. Each acquired immune receptor recognizes a feature typically found only on a particular part of a particular molecule in a particular microbe. Accordingly, an acquired immune system detects pathogens with tremendous specificity.

Figure 43.2 provides an overview of the basic properties of innate and acquired immune systems. In this chapter, you will learn how each type of immune system protects animals from disease. You will also examine how pathogens can avoid or overwhelm an immune system and how defects in an immune system can imperil an animal's health.

In innate immunity, recognition and response rely on shared traits of pathogens

Innate immune systems are found among all animals (as well as in plants). In exploring innate immunity, we will begin with invertebrates, which repel and fight infection with only this type of immune system. We will then turn to vertebrates,

in which innate immunity serves both as an immediate defense against infection and as the foundation for acquired immune defenses.

Innate Immunity of Invertebrates

The great success of insects in terrestrial and water habitats teeming with diverse assortments of microbes highlights the effectiveness of an innate immune system. In each of these environments, insects rely on their exoskeleton as a first line of defense against infection. Composed largely of the polysaccharide chitin, the exoskeleton provides an effective barrier defense against most pathogens. A chitin-based barrier is also present in the insect intestine, where it blocks infection by many microbes ingested with food. **Lysozyme**, an enzyme that digests microbial cell walls, and a low pH further protect the insect digestive system.

Any pathogen that breaches an insect's barrier defenses encounters a number of internal immune defenses. Immune cells called *hemocytes* circulate within the hemolymph, the insect equivalent of blood. Some hemocytes carry out a cellular defense called **phagocytosis**, the ingestion and digestion of bacteria and other foreign substances (**Figure 43.3**). Other hemocytes trigger the production of chemicals that kill microbes and help entrap multicellular parasites. Encounters with pathogens in the hemolymph also cause hemocytes and certain other cells to secrete *antimicrobial peptides*. The antimicrobial peptides circulate throughout

❶ Pseudopodia surround microbes.

Microbes

PHAGOCYTIC CELL

❷ Microbes are engulfed into cell.

❸ Vacuole containing microbes forms.

Vacuole

Lysosome containing enzymes

❹ Vacuole and lysosome fuse.

❺ Toxic compounds and lysosomal enzymes destroy microbes.

❻ Microbial debris is released by exocytosis.

▲ **Figure 43.3 Phagocytosis.** This schematic depicts events in the ingestion and destruction of a microbe by a typical phagocytic cell.

▲ **Figure 43.4 An inducible innate immune response.** These fruit flies were engineered to express the green fluorescent protein (GFP) gene upon activation of the innate immune response. The fly on the top was injected with bacteria; the fly on the bottom was stabbed but not infected. Only the infected fly activates antimicrobial peptide genes, expresses GFP, and glows a bright green under fluorescent light.

the body of the insect **(Figure 43.4)** and inactivate or kill fungi and bacteria by disrupting their plasma membranes.

In recognizing foreign cells, immune response cells of insects rely on unique molecules in the outer layers of fungi and bacteria. Fungal cell walls contain certain unique polysaccharides, while bacterial cell walls have polymers containing combinations of sugars and amino acids not found in animal cells. Such macromolecules serve as identity tags in the process of pathogen recognition. Insect immune cells secrete specialized recognition proteins, each of which binds to the macromolecule specific to a particular type of fungus or bacterium.

Immune responses are distinct for different classes of pathogens. For example, when the fungus *Neurospora crassa* infects a fruit fly, pieces of the fungal cell wall bind a recognition protein that activates the protein Toll, a receptor on the surface of immune response cells. Signal transduction from the Toll receptor to the cell nucleus leads to synthesis of a particular set of antimicrobial peptides. If the fly is infected by the bacterium *Micrococcus luteus*, a different recognition protein is activated, and the fly produces a different set of antimicrobial peptides.

Because fruit flies secrete many different antimicrobial peptides in response to a single infection, it is difficult to study the activity of any one peptide. To get around this problem, Bruno Lemaitre and fellow researchers in France used modern genetic techniques to reprogram the fly immune system **(Figure 43.5)**. They found that the synthesis of a single

▼ Figure 43.5 **Inquiry**

Can a single antimicrobial peptide protect fruit flies against infection?

EXPERIMENT In 2002, Bruno Lemaitre and colleagues in France devised a novel strategy to test the function of a single antimicrobial peptide. They began with a mutant fruit fly strain in which pathogens are recognized but the signaling that would normally trigger innate immune responses is blocked. As a result, the mutant flies do not make any antimicrobial peptides. The researchers then genetically engineered some of the mutant fruit flies to express significant amounts of a single antimicrobial peptide, either drosomycin or defensin. The scientists infected the various flies with the fungus *Neurospora crassa* and monitored survival over a five-day period. They repeated the procedure for infection by the bacterium *Micrococcus luteus*.

RESULTS

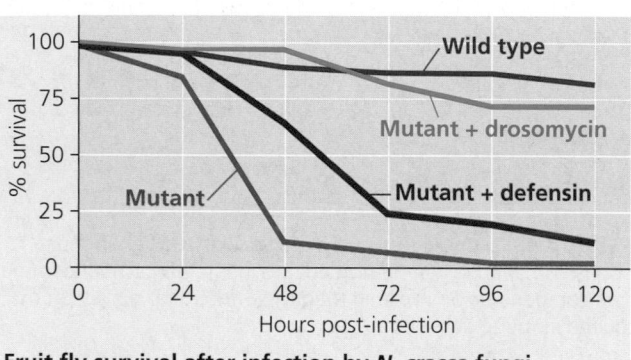

Fruit fly survival after infection by *N. crassa* fungi

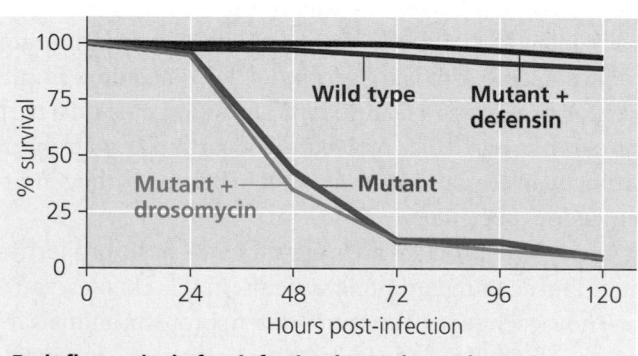

Fruit fly survival after infection by *M. luteus* bacteria

CONCLUSION Each of the two antimicrobial peptides provided a protective immune response. Furthermore, the different peptides defended against different pathogens. Drosomycin was effective against *N. crassa*, and defensin was effective against *M. luteus*.

SOURCE P. Tzou, J. Reichhart, and B. Lemaitre, Constitutive expression of a single antimicrobial peptide can restore wild-type resistance to infection in immunodeficient *Drosophila* mutants, *Proceedings of the National Academy of Sciences, USA* 99:2152 (2002).

WHAT IF? Even if a particular antimicrobial peptide showed no beneficial effect in such an experiment, why might it still be beneficial to flies?

antimicrobial peptide in the fly's body can provide an effective and specific immune defense against a particular pathogen.

Innate Immunity of Vertebrates

In vertebrates, innate immune defenses coexist with the more recently evolved system of acquired immunity. We'll focus here on mammals because most of the recent discoveries regarding vertebrate innate immunity have come from studies of mice and humans. First we'll outline the innate defenses that are similar to those found among invertebrates: barrier defenses, phagocytosis, and antimicrobial peptides. Then we'll examine two unique aspects of vertebrate innate immunity: the inflammatory response and natural killer cells.

Barrier Defenses

In mammals, epithelial tissues block the entry of many pathogens. These barrier defenses include not only the skin but also the mucous membranes lining the digestive, respiratory, urinary, and reproductive tracts. Certain cells of the mucous membranes produce *mucus*, a viscous fluid that enhances defenses by trapping microbes and other particles. In the trachea, ciliated epithelial cells sweep mucus and any entrapped microbes upward, helping prevent infection of the lungs. Saliva, tears, and mucous secretions that bathe various exposed epithelia provide a washing action that also inhibits colonization by microbes.

Beyond their physical role in inhibiting microbe entry, body secretions create an environment that is hostile to many microbes. Lysozyme in saliva, mucous secretions, and tears destroys susceptible bacteria as they enter the upper respiratory tract or the openings around the eyes. Microbes in food or water and those in swallowed mucus must also contend with the acidic environment of the stomach, which kills most microorganisms before they can enter the intestines. Similarly, secretions from sebaceous (oil) glands and sweat glands give human skin a pH ranging from 3 to 5, acidic enough to prevent the growth of many microorganisms.

Cellular Innate Defenses

Pathogens that make their way into the body are subject to detection by phagocytic white blood cells (leukocytes). These cells recognize microbes using receptors that are very similar to the Toll receptor of insects. Each mammalian **Toll-like receptor**, or **TLR**, recognizes fragments of molecules characteristic of a set of pathogens **(Figure 43.6)**. For example, TLR4, located on immune cell plasma membranes, recognizes lipopolysaccharide, a type of molecule found on the surface of many bacteria. Similarly, TLR3, on the inner surface of vesicles formed by endocytosis, is the sensor for double-stranded RNA, a form of nucleic acid characteristic of certain viruses. In each case, the recognized macromol-

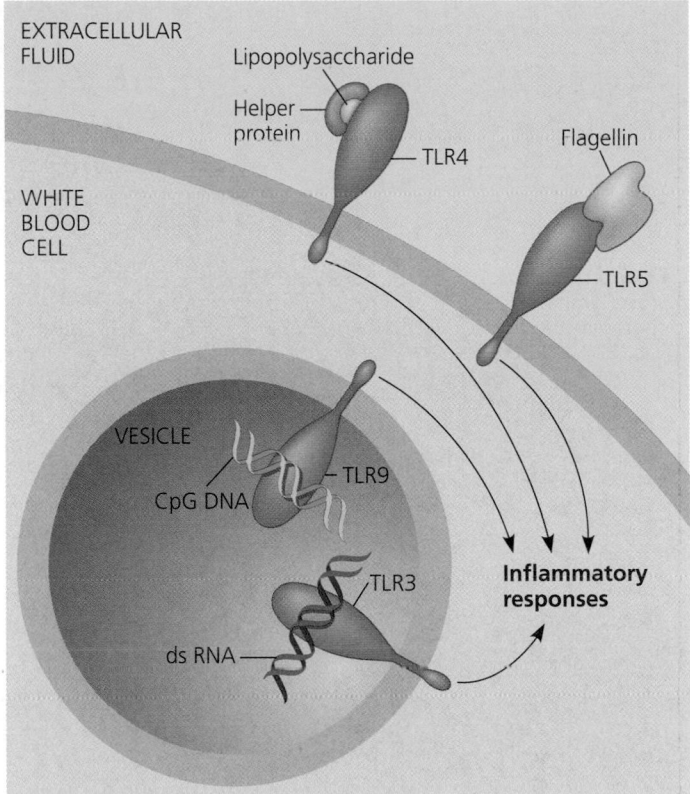

▲ **Figure 43.6 TLR signaling.** Each human Toll-like receptor (TLR) recognizes a molecular pattern characteristic of a group of pathogens. Lipopolysaccharide, flagellin, CpG DNA (DNA containing unmethylated CG sequences), and double-stranded (ds) RNA are all found in microorganisms or viruses, but not in animal cells. Together with other recognition and response factors, TLR proteins trigger internal innate immune defenses.

? *Some TLR proteins are on the cell surface, whereas others are inside vesicles. Suggest a possible benefit of this distribution.*

ecule is normally absent from the vertebrate body and is an essential component of a class of microbes.

As in insects, recognition by a TLR triggers a series of internal defenses, beginning with phagocytosis. A white blood cell recognizes and engulfs invading microbes, trapping them in a vacuole. The vacuole then fuses with a lysosome (see Figure 43.3), leading to destruction of the microbes in two ways. First, nitric oxide and other gases produced in the lysosome poison the engulfed microbes. Second, lysozyme and other enzymes degrade microbial components.

The most abundant phagocytic cells in the mammalian body are **neutrophils** (see Figure 42.17). Signals from infected tissues attract neutrophils, which then engulf and destroy microbes. **Macrophages** ("big eaters"), like the one shown in Figure 43.1, provide an even more effective phagocytic defense. Some of these large phagocytic cells migrate throughout the body, while others reside permanently in various organs and tissues. Macrophages in the spleen, lymph nodes, and other tissues of the lymphatic system are particularly well positioned to combat pathogens. Microbes in the blood become trapped in the spleen,

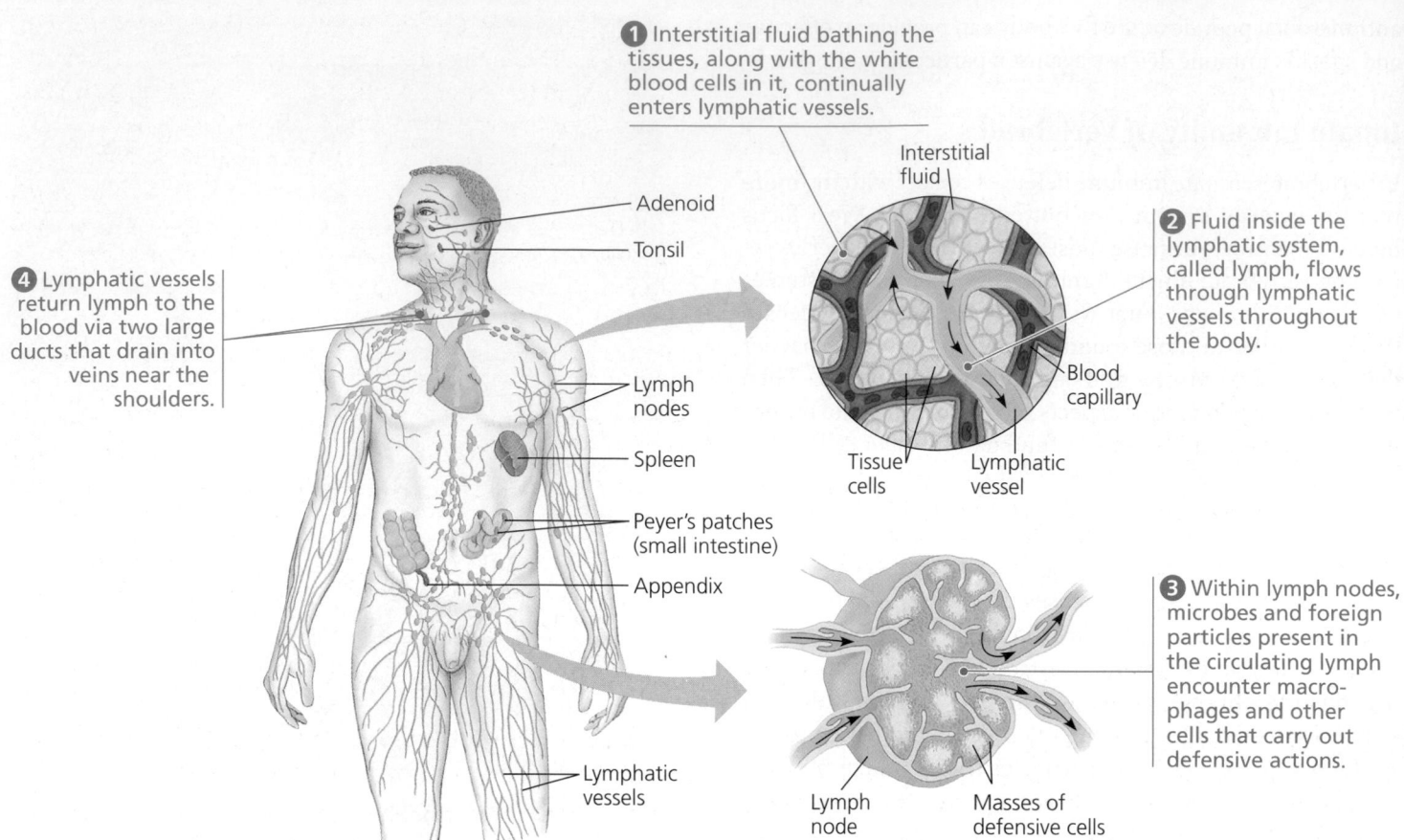

① Interstitial fluid bathing the tissues, along with the white blood cells in it, continually enters lymphatic vessels.

Adenoid

Tonsil

④ Lymphatic vessels return lymph to the blood via two large ducts that drain into veins near the shoulders.

Lymph nodes

Spleen

Peyer's patches (small intestine)

Appendix

Lymphatic vessels

Interstitial fluid

② Fluid inside the lymphatic system, called lymph, flows through lymphatic vessels throughout the body.

Blood capillary

Tissue cells

Lymphatic vessel

③ Within lymph nodes, microbes and foreign particles present in the circulating lymph encounter macrophages and other cells that carry out defensive actions.

Lymph node

Masses of defensive cells

▲ **Figure 43.7 The human lymphatic system.** The lymphatic system consists of lymphatic vessels, through which lymph travels, and various structures that trap "foreign" molecules and particles. These structures include the adenoids, tonsils, lymph nodes, spleen, Peyer's patches, and appendix. Steps 1–4 trace the flow of lymph.

whereas microbes in interstitial fluid flow into lymph and are trapped in lymph nodes. In either location, they encounter resident macrophages. **Figure 43.7** provides an overview of the lymphatic system and its role in the body's defenses.

Two other types of phagocytes—eosinophils and dendritic cells—play more limited roles in innate defense. **Eosinophils** have low phagocytic activity but are important in defending against multicellular invaders, such as parasitic worms. Rather than engulfing such parasites, eosinophils position themselves against the parasite's body and then discharge destructive enzymes that damage the invader. **Dendritic cells** populate tissues that are in contact with the environment. They mainly stimulate development of acquired immunity against microbes they encounter, a function we will explore later in this chapter.

Antimicrobial Peptides and Proteins

Pathogen recognition in mammals triggers the production and release of a variety of peptides and proteins that attack microbes or impede their reproduction. Some of these defense molecules function like the antimicrobial peptides of insects, damaging broad groups of pathogens by disrupting membrane integrity. Others, including the interferons and complement proteins, are unique to vertebrate immune systems.

Interferons are proteins that provide innate defense against viral infections. Virus-infected body cells secrete interferons, inducing nearby uninfected cells to produce substances that inhibit viral reproduction. In this way, interferons limit the cell-to-cell spread of viruses in the body, helping control viral infections such as colds and influenza. Some white blood cells secrete a different type of interferon that helps activate macrophages, enhancing their phagocytic ability. Pharmaceutical companies now mass-produce interferons by recombinant DNA technology for treating certain viral infections, such as hepatitis C.

The **complement system** consists of roughly 30 proteins in blood plasma that function together to fight infections. These proteins circulate in an inactive state and are activated by substances on the surface of many microbes. Activation results in a cascade of biochemical reactions leading to lysis (bursting) of invading cells. The complement system also functions in inflammation, our next topic, as well as in the acquired defenses discussed later in the chapter.

Inflammatory Responses

The pain and swelling that alert you to a splinter under your skin are the result of a local **inflammatory response**, the changes brought about by signaling molecules released upon injury or infection. One important inflammatory signaling molecule is **histamine**, which is stored in **mast cells**, connective tissue cells that store chemicals in granules for secretion. **Figure 43.8** summarizes the progression of events in local inflammation, starting with infection from a splinter. Histamine released by mast cells at sites of tissue damage triggers nearby blood vessels to dilate and become more permeable. Activated macrophages and other cells discharge additional signaling molecules that further promote blood flow to the injured site. The resulting increase in local blood supply causes the redness and heat typical of inflammation (from the Latin *inflammare*, to set on fire). Capillaries engorged with blood leak fluid into neighboring tissues, causing swelling.

During inflammation, cycles of signaling and response transform the infection site. Enhanced blood flow to the injury site helps deliver antimicrobial proteins. Activated complement proteins promote further release of histamine and help attract phagocytes. Nearby endothelial cells secrete signaling molecules that attract neutrophils and macrophages. Taking advantage of increased vessel permeability to enter injured tissues, these cells carry out additional phagocytosis and inactivation of microbes. The result is an accumulation of *pus*, a fluid rich in white blood cells, dead microbes, and cell debris.

A minor injury causes local inflammation, but severe tissue damage or infection may lead to a response that is systemic (throughout the body)—such as an increased production of white blood cells. Cells in injured or infected tissue often secrete molecules that stimulate the release of additional neutrophils from the bone marrow. In a severe infection, such as meningitis or appendicitis, the number of white blood cells in the blood may increase several-fold within a few hours.

Another systemic inflammatory response is fever. Some toxins produced by pathogens, as well as substances called *pyrogens* released by activated macrophages, can reset the body's thermostat to a higher temperature (see Chapter 40). The benefits of the resulting fever are still a subject of debate. One hypothesis is that an elevated body temperature may enhance phagocytosis and, by speeding up chemical reactions, accelerate tissue repair.

Certain bacterial infections can induce an overwhelming systemic inflammatory response, leading to a life-threatening condition called *septic shock*. Characterized by very high fever, low blood flow, and low blood pressure, septic shock occurs most often in the very old and the very young. It is fatal in more than one-third of cases.

Natural Killer Cells

Natural killer (NK) cells help recognize and eliminate certain diseased cells in vertebrates. With the exception of red blood cells, all cells in the body normally have on their surface a protein called a class I MHC molecule (we will say much more about this molecule shortly). Following viral infection or conversion to a cancerous state, cells sometimes stop expressing this protein. The NK cells that patrol the body attach to such stricken cells and release chemicals that lead to cell death, inhibiting further spread of the virus or cancer.

  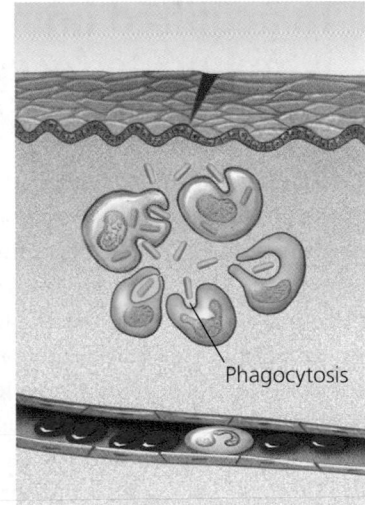

1 Activated macrophages and mast cells at the injury site release signaling molecules that act on nearby capillaries.

2 The capillaries widen and become more permeable, allowing fluid containing antimicrobial peptides to enter the tissue. Signaling molecules released by immune cells attract additional phagocytic cells.

3 Phagocytic cells digest pathogens and cell debris at the site, and the tissue heals.

▲ **Figure 43.8 Major events in a local inflammatory response.**

Innate Immune System Evasion by Pathogens

Adaptations have evolved in some pathogens that enable them to avoid destruction by phagocytic cells. For example, the outer capsule that surrounds certain bacteria hides the polysaccharides of their cell walls, preventing recognition. One such bacterium, *Streptococcus pneumoniae*, played a critical role in the discovery that DNA can convey genetic information (see Figure 16.2). Among bacteria that do not avoid recognition, some are resistant to breakdown within lysosomes following phagocytosis. One example is the bacterium that causes tuberculosis (TB). Rather than being destroyed within the host's cells, such microbes grow and reproduce, effectively hidden from the innate immune defenses of the body. These and other mechanisms that prevent destruction by the innate immune system make the microbes that possess them substantial pathogenic threats: TB kills more than a million people a year worldwide.

CONCEPT 43.2
In acquired immunity, lymphocyte receptors provide pathogen-specific recognition

Vertebrates are unique among animals in having acquired immunity in addition to innate immunity. B cells and T cells, types of white blood cells called **lymphocytes** (see Figure 42.17), are critical for this acquired immune defense. Like all blood cells, lymphocytes originate from stem cells in the bone marrow. Lymphocytes that migrate from the bone marrow to the **thymus**, an organ in the thoracic cavity above the heart, mature into **T cells** ("T" for thymus). Lymphocytes that mature in the bone marrow develop as **B cells**. (The "B" stands for the bursa of Fabricius, a bird organ where B cells were first discovered. But you can think of "B" as standing for bone marrow, where B cells mature in most vertebrates.)

B cells and T cells recognize and inactivate foreign cells and molecules. Both types of cells also contribute to *immunological memory*, an enhanced response to a foreign molecule encoun-

tered previously. Immunological memory, which can persist for many decades, is responsible for the protection we obtain against chickenpox and many other diseases from either a prior infection or vaccination. Its existence was apparent to the Greek historian Thucydides almost 2,400 years ago: He noted that individuals who had recovered from the plague could safely care for those who were sick or dying, "for the same man was never attacked twice—never at least fatally."

Although B cells and T cells function only in the acquired immune system, innate immunity and acquired immunity are not independent. At the start of an infection, signaling molecules from phagocytic cells carrying out innate immune responses activate lymphocytes, setting the stage for the slower-developing acquired response. For example, as macrophages and dendritic cells ingest microbes, these phagocytic cells secrete **cytokines**, proteins that help recruit and activate lymphocytes. Macrophages and dendritic cells also have a direct role in pathogen recognition by B cells and T cells, as you will see shortly.

Acquired Immunity: *An Overview*

The basic facts of acquired immunity can be summarized by the following set of statements. Each B cell or T cell has on its surface many receptor proteins that can each bind a particular foreign molecule. The receptor proteins on a single lymphocyte are all the same, but there are millions of lymphocytes in the body that differ in the foreign molecules that their receptors recognize. When an animal is infected, B and T cells with receptors that can recognize the microbe are activated for particular roles in the immune response. In the activation process, the B and T cells interact with fragments of microbes displayed on the surface of cells. Activated lymphocytes undergo cell division, with a set of daughter cells being set aside to fight any future infections of the host by the same microbe. Some T cells assist in activating other lymphocytes. Other T cells detect and kill infected host cells. Specialized B cells secrete soluble receptor proteins that attack foreign molecules and cells circulating in body fluids.

Although the preceding paragraph is a fair summary of acquired immunity, it raises many questions: How are millions of different receptors made? How does infection activate the very lymphocytes that fight that infection? How does the immune system distinguish self from nonself? The answers to these questions and others will become clear as we explore acquired immunity in more detail, beginning with the process of recognition.

Antigen Recognition by Lymphocytes

Any foreign molecule that is specifically recognized by lymphocytes and elicits a response from them is called an **antigen**. Most antigens are large molecules, either proteins or polysaccharides. Some antigens, such as toxins secreted by bacteria, are released into the extracellular fluid. Many other antigens protrude from the surface of pathogens or other foreign cells.

B cells and T cells recognize antigens using the antigen-specific receptors embedded in their plasma membranes **(Figure 43.9)**. A single B or T lymphocyte has about 100,000 of these **antigen receptors** on its surface. B cells sometimes give rise to *plasma cells* that secrete a soluble form of the antigen receptor. This secreted protein is called an **antibody**, or **immunoglobulin (Ig)**.

Antigen receptors and antibodies recognize just a small, accessible portion of an antigen that is called an **epitope**, or *antigenic determinant*. A single antigen usually has several different epitopes, each capable of inducing a response from a lymphocyte that recognizes the epitope **(Figure 43.10)**.

All the antigen receptors on a single lymphocyte are identical; that is, they recognize the same epitope. Each of the body's lymphocytes thus displays *specificity* for a particular epitope. Consequently, each lymphocyte defends against any pathogen that produces molecules containing that epitope.

The Antigen Receptors of B Cells and T Cells

Each **B cell receptor** for an antigen is a Y-shaped molecule consisting of four polypeptide chains: two identical **heavy chains** and two identical **light chains**, with disulfide bridges linking chains together (Figure 43.9a). A transmembrane region near one end of each heavy chain anchors the receptor in the cell's plasma membrane. A short tail region at the end of the heavy chain extends into the cytoplasm.

(a) A B cell receptor consists of two identical heavy chains and two identical light chains linked by disulfide bridges.

(b) A T cell receptor consists of one α chain and one β chain linked by a disulfide bridge.

▲ **Figure 43.9 Antigen receptors on lymphocytes.** All the antigen receptors on a particular B cell or T cell are identical and bind identical antigens. The variable (V) regions of receptors vary extensively from cell to cell, accounting for the different binding specificities of individual lymphocytes; the constant (C) regions vary little or not at all.

▶ **Figure 43.10 Epitopes (antigenic determinants).** Only small, specific regions on antigens, called epitopes, are bound by the antigen receptors on lymphocytes and by secreted antibodies. In this example, three different antibody molecules bind to different epitopes on the same large antigen molecule. Note that epitopes and antigen-binding sites are typically irregular in shape, as illustrated for the antibody molecule on the left, but are often represented in a simplified, symmetrical manner, as illustrated for the antibodies on the right.

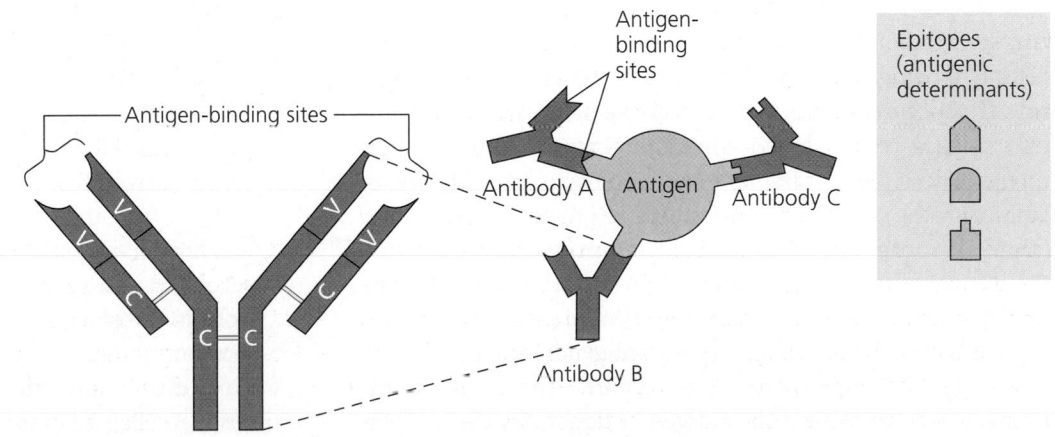

The light and heavy chains each have a *constant (C) region*, where amino acid sequences vary little among the receptors present on different B cells. The C region includes the cytoplasmic tail and transmembrane region of the heavy chain and all of the disulfide bridges. Within the two tips of the Y shape, the light and heavy chains each have a *variable (V) region*, so named because its amino acid sequence varies extensively from one B cell to another. Together, parts of a heavy-chain V region and a light-chain V region form an asymmetrical binding site for an antigen. As shown in Figure 43.9a, each B cell receptor has two identical antigen-binding sites.

Antibodies have the same overall organization as B cell receptors, except that they lack the transmembrane region and cytoplasmic tail (see Figures 43.9 and 43.10). As a result, antibodies are secreted rather than membrane-bound, a difference associated with distinct functions that we will discuss shortly.

Each **T cell receptor** for an antigen consists of two different polypeptide chains, an α *chain* and a β *chain*, linked by a disulfide bridge (Figure 43.9b). Despite having two rather than four chains, T cell receptors have many features in common with B cell receptors. Near the base of the T cell receptor is a transmembrane region that anchors the molecule in the cell's plasma membrane. At the outer tip of the molecule, the α and β chain variable (V) regions form a single antigen-binding site. The remainder of the molecule is made up of the constant (C) regions.

B cell and T cell receptors have closely related but distinct functions. Both types of receptors bind to antigens via noncovalent bonds that stabilize the interaction between an epitope and the binding surface. In this manner, B cell receptors recognize and bind to an intact antigen, whether that antigen is free or on the surface of a pathogen. In contrast, T cell receptors bind only to antigen fragments that are displayed, or *presented*, on the surface of host cells. Each of the genes in a group called the **major histocompatibility complex (MHC)** produces a host cell protein that can present an antigen fragment to T cell receptors in this way. The simultaneous interaction of an antigen fragment, an MHC molecule, and a T cell receptor is a central event in acquired immunity and is our next topic.

The Role of the MHC

Antigen recognition by T cells begins with a pathogen either infecting or being engulfed by a host cell. Once the pathogen is inside a host cell, enzymes in the cell cleave the pathogen proteins into smaller pieces, called peptide antigens or antigen fragments. These antigen fragments then bind to an MHC molecule inside the cell. Movement of the MHC molecule and bound fragment to the cell surface results in **antigen presentation**, the display of the antigen fragment on the cell surface (Figure 43.11). If an antigen-presenting cell encounters a T cell, the receptors on the T cell can bind to the antigen fragment.

Antigen presentation by MHC proteins either activates immune responses against the antigen or targets for destruction

▲ **Figure 43.11 Antigen presentation by an MHC molecule.** A class I MHC molecule extending from the plasma membrane displays a bound antigen fragment for recognition by the antigen receptor of a lymphocyte. The enlarged view is of the MHC surface that binds and presents an antigen fragment.

an infected cell displaying the antigen fragment. The type of cell that presents the antigen determines which kind of response occurs. When a phagocyte or lymphocyte that has engulfed a pathogen displays an antigen, it signals the immune system that an infection is under way. The immune system responds by increasing its response to that antigen and the pathogen that produces it. When a cell that has been invaded by a pathogen displays an antigen, it signals the immune system that the cell is infected. The immune system responds by eliminating such cells, disrupting further spread of the infection.

To recognize the type of cell displaying an antigen, the immune system relies on two classes of MHC molecules:

▶ **Class I MHC molecules** are found on almost all cells of the body (the notable exceptions being non-nucleated cells, such as red blood cells). Class I MHC molecules bind to peptide fragments of foreign antigens synthesized within the cell. Any body cell that becomes infected or cancerous can synthesize foreign antigens and display antigen fragments by virtue of its class I MHC molecules (Figure 43.12a). Class I MHC molecules displaying bound antigen fragments are recognized by a subgroup of T cells called **cytotoxic T cells**. The term *cytotoxic* refers to their use of toxic gene products to kill infected cells.

▶ **Class II MHC molecules** are made by just a few cell types, mainly dendritic cells, macrophages, and B cells. In these cells, class II MHC molecules typically bind to antigen fragment derived from foreign materials that have been internalized through phagocytosis or endocytosis (Figure 43.12b). Dendritic cells, macrophages, and B cells are known as **antigen-presenting cells** because of their key role in displaying such internalized antigens. Antigen-presenting cells display antigens for recognition by cytotoxic T cells and **helper T cells**, a group of T cells that assist both B cells and cytotoxic T cells.

◀ **Figure 43.12 The interaction of T cells with antigen-presenting cells.**
(a) Class I MHC molecules display fragments of antigens to cytotoxic T cells.
(b) Class II MHC molecules display fragments of antigens to both cytotoxic T cells and, as shown here, helper T cells.

In both (a) and (b), the T cell receptor binds with an MHC molecule–antigen fragment complex. Class I MHC molecules are made by most nucleated cells, whereas class II MHC molecules are made primarily by antigen-presenting cells (macrophages, dendritic cells, and B cells).

Infected cell

Antigen fragment

❶ A fragment of foreign protein (antigen) inside the cell associates with the components of an MHC molecule on the endoplasmic reticulum and is transported to the cell surface.

Class I MHC molecule

T cell receptor

❷ The combination of MHC molecule and antigen fragment is recognized by a T cell.

(a) **Cytotoxic T cell**

Microbe

Antigen-presenting cell

Antigen fragment

Class II MHC molecule

T cell receptor

(b) **Helper T cell**

Lymphocyte Development

Now that you know how lymphocytes recognize antigens, let's consider three major properties of the acquired immune system. First, the tremendous diversity of receptors ensures that even pathogens never before encountered will be recognized as foreign. Second, this ability to recognize vast numbers of foreign molecules coexists with a lack of reactivity against the molecules that make up the animal's own cells and tissues. Third, the response to an antigen that has been encountered previously is stronger and more rapid than the initial response—a feature called immunological memory.

Three events in a lymphocyte's life provide the basis for receptor diversity, lack of self-reactivity, and immunological memory. The first two events take place as a lymphocyte matures. The third important event happens when a mature lymphocyte encounters and binds a specific antigen. Let's consider these three events in the order in which they occur.

Generation of Lymphocyte Diversity by Gene Rearrangement

Differences in the amino acid sequence of the variable region account for the specificity of antigen receptors on lymphocytes. Recall that a single B or T cell displays about 100,000 antigen receptors, all identical. If we randomly selected any two B cells or T cells, it is highly unlikely that they would have the same antigen receptor. Instead, the variable regions at the tip of a particular antigen receptor would differ in their amino acid sequence from one cell to the other. Because the variable regions form the antigen-binding site, a particular amino acid sequence generates specificity for a certain epitope.

Each person has more than 1 million different B cells and 10 million different T cells, each with a particular antigen-binding specificity. Yet there are only about 20,500 protein-coding genes in the human genome. How, then, do we generate such remarkable diversity in antigen receptors? The answer lies in a

variety of combinations. Think of selecting a car with a choice of three interior colors and six exterior colors. There are 18 (3×6) color combinations to consider. Similarly, by combining variable elements, the immune system assembles many different receptors from a much smaller collection of parts.

To understand the origin of receptor diversity, let's consider an immunoglobulin (Ig) gene that encodes the light chain of secreted antibodies (immunoglobulins) and membrane-bound B cell receptors. Although we'll analyze only a single Ig light-chain gene, all B cell antigen receptor and T cell antigen receptor genes undergo very similar transformations.

The capacity to generate diversity is built into the structure of the Ig light-chain gene. A receptor light chain is encoded by three gene segments: a variable (V) segment, a joining (J) segment, and a constant (C) segment. The V and J segments together encode the variable region of the receptor chain, while the C segment encodes the entire constant region. DNA sequencing reveals that the light-chain gene contains a single C segment, 40 different V segments, and 5 different J segments. These alternative copies of the V and J segments are arranged within the gene in a series (**Figure 43.13**, on the next page). Because a functional gene is built from one copy of each type of segment, the pieces can be combined in 200 (40 $V \times 5 J \times 1 C$) different ways. (The number of different heavy-chain genes is even greater.)

Assembling a functional light-chain gene requires rearranging the DNA. Early in B cell development, a set of enzymes collectively called recombinase links one V gene segment to one J gene segment. This recombination event eliminates the long stretch of DNA between the segments, forming a single exon that is part V and part J. Because there is only an intron between the J and C DNA segments, no further DNA rearrangement is required. Instead, the J and C segments will be joined after transcription by splicing out the intervening RNA (see Figure 17.10 to review RNA splicing).

Recombinase acts randomly, linking any one of the 40 V gene segments to any one of the 5 J gene segments. Heavy-chain genes

◀ **Figure 43.13**
Immunoglobulin (antibody) gene rearrangement. The joining of randomly selected V and J gene segments (V_{39} and J_5 in this example) results in a functional gene that encodes the light-chain polypeptide of a B cell receptor. Transcription, splicing, and translation result in a light chain that combines with a polypeptide produced from an independently rearranged heavy-chain gene to form a functional receptor. Mature B cells (and T cells) are exceptions to the generalization that all body cells have exactly the same DNA.

undergo a similar rearrangement. In any given cell, however, only one light-chain gene and one heavy-chain gene are rearranged. Furthermore, the rearrangements are permanent and are passed on to the daughter cells when the lymphocyte divides.

After both the light- and heavy-chain genes have rearranged, antigen receptors can be synthesized. The rearranged genes are transcribed, and the transcripts are processed for translation. Following translation, the light chain and heavy chain assemble together, forming an antigen receptor (see Figure 43.13). Each pair of randomly rearranged heavy and light chains results in a different antigen-binding surface. For the total population of B cells in a human body, the number of such combinations has been calculated as 1.65×10^6. Furthermore, mutations introduced during VJ recombination add additional variation, making the number of possible antigen-binding specificities even greater.

Origin of Self-Tolerance

Because antigen receptor genes are randomly rearranged, some immature lymphocytes produce receptors specific for epitopes on the body's own molecules. If these self-reactive lymphocytes were not eliminated or inactivated, the immune system could not distinguish self from nonself and would attack body proteins, cells, and tissues. Instead, as lymphocytes mature in the bone marrow or thymus, their antigen receptors are tested for self-reactivity. Lymphocytes with receptors specific for the body's own molecules are typically either de-

stroyed by apoptosis or rendered nonfunctional, leaving only those that react to foreign molecules. Since the body normally lacks mature lymphocytes that can react against its own components, the immune system is said to exhibit *self-tolerance*. As you will read later, failure of self-tolerance can lead to autoimmune diseases, such as multiple sclerosis.

Amplifying Lymphocytes by Clonal Selection

Because the body contains an enormous variety of antigen receptors, only a tiny fraction are specific for the epitopes on a given antigen. As a result, it is very rare for an antigen to encounter a lymphocyte with a receptor specific for that antigen. How, then, can the acquired immune response be so effective? The answer lies in the changes in cell number and behavior triggered by the binding of antigen to lymphocyte.

The binding of an antigen receptor to its specific antigen initiates events that activate the lymphocyte. Activated B cells or T cells amplify the response by dividing many times, forming two types of clones: effector cells and memory cells. **Effector cells**, which are short-lived, attack the antigen and any pathogens producing that antigen. **Memory cells**, which are long-lived but less numerous, bear receptors specific for the antigen.

The proliferation of a lymphocyte into a clone of cells in response to binding an antigen is called **clonal selection (Figure 43.14)**. This concept is so fundamental to understanding acquired immunity that it is worth restating: The presentation of an antigen to specific receptors on a lymphocyte

B cells that differ in antigen specificity

Antigen molecules bind to the antigen receptors of only one of the three B cells shown.

Antigen receptor

The selected B cell proliferates, forming a clone of identical cells bearing receptors for the antigen.

Some proliferating cells develop into long-lived memory cells that can respond rapidly upon subsequent exposure to the same antigen.

Antibody molecules

Some proliferating cells develop into short-lived plasma cells that secrete antibodies specific for the antigen.

Clone of memory cells

Clone of plasma cells

▲ **Figure 43.14 Clonal selection of B cells.** In response to its specific antigen and immune cell signals, a B cell divides and forms a clone of cells. Some of these cells become memory B cells; others become antibody-secreting plasma cells. T cells specific for the antigen undergo a similar process, generating memory T cells and effector T cells. Lymphocytes with a different antigen specificity (represented in this figure by different shapes and colors of the receptors) do not respond.

leads to repeated rounds of cell division. The result is a clonal population of thousands of cells, all specific for that antigen.

Prior exposure to an antigen alters the speed, strength, and duration of the immune response. The production of effector cells from a clone of lymphocytes during the first exposure to an antigen represents the **primary immune response**. The primary response peaks about 10 to 17 days after the initial exposure. During this time, selected B cells generate antibody-secreting effector B cells, called **plasma cells**, and selected T cells are activated to their effector forms, consisting of helper cells and cytotoxic cells. If an individual is exposed again to the same antigen, the response is faster (typically peaking only 2 to 7 days after exposure), of greater magnitude, and more prolonged. This is the **secondary immune response**. Measures of antibody concentrations in blood serum over time clearly show the difference between primary and secondary immune responses **(Figure 43.15)**.

The secondary immune response relies on the reservoir of T and B memory cells generated following initial exposure to an antigen. Because these cells are long-lived, they provide the basis for immunological memory that can span many decades. If and when an antigen is encountered again, memory cells specific for that antigen enable the rapid formation of large clones of effector cells and thus a greatly enhanced immune defense.

Although the processes for antigen recognition, clonal selection, and immunological memory are similar for B cells and T cells, these two classes of lymphocytes fight infection in different ways and in different settings, as we will explore next.

Primary immune response to antigen A produces antibodies to A.

Secondary immune response to antigen A produces antibodies to A; **primary immune response** to antigen B produces antibodies to B.

Antibodies to A

Antibodies to B

Exposure to antigen A

Exposure to antigens A and B

Time (days)

▲ **Figure 43.15 The specificity of immunological memory.** Long-lived memory cells generated in the primary response to antigen A give rise to a heightened secondary response to the same antigen, but do not affect the primary response to a different antigen (B).

1. **DRAW IT** Sketch a B cell receptor. Label the V and C regions of the light and heavy chains. Now mark the positions of the antigen-binding sites, disulfide bridges, and transmembrane regions. How do the positions of these features relate to the location of the variable and constant regions?

2. Explain two advantages of having memory cells when a pathogen is encountered for a second time.

3. **WHAT IF?** If both copies of a light-chain gene and a heavy-chain gene recombined in each B cell, how would this affect B cell development?

For suggested answers, see Appendix A.

CONCEPT **43.3**
Acquired immunity defends against infection of body cells and fluids

Acquired immunity is based on both a humoral immune response and a cell-mediated immune response **(Figure 43.16)**. The **humoral immune response** involves the activation and clonal selection of effector B cells, which secrete antibodies that circulate in the blood and lymph. The humoral response is so named because blood and lymph were long ago called body humors. It is also called the antibody-mediated response because of the key role of antibodies. The predominant **cell-mediated immune response** involves the activation and

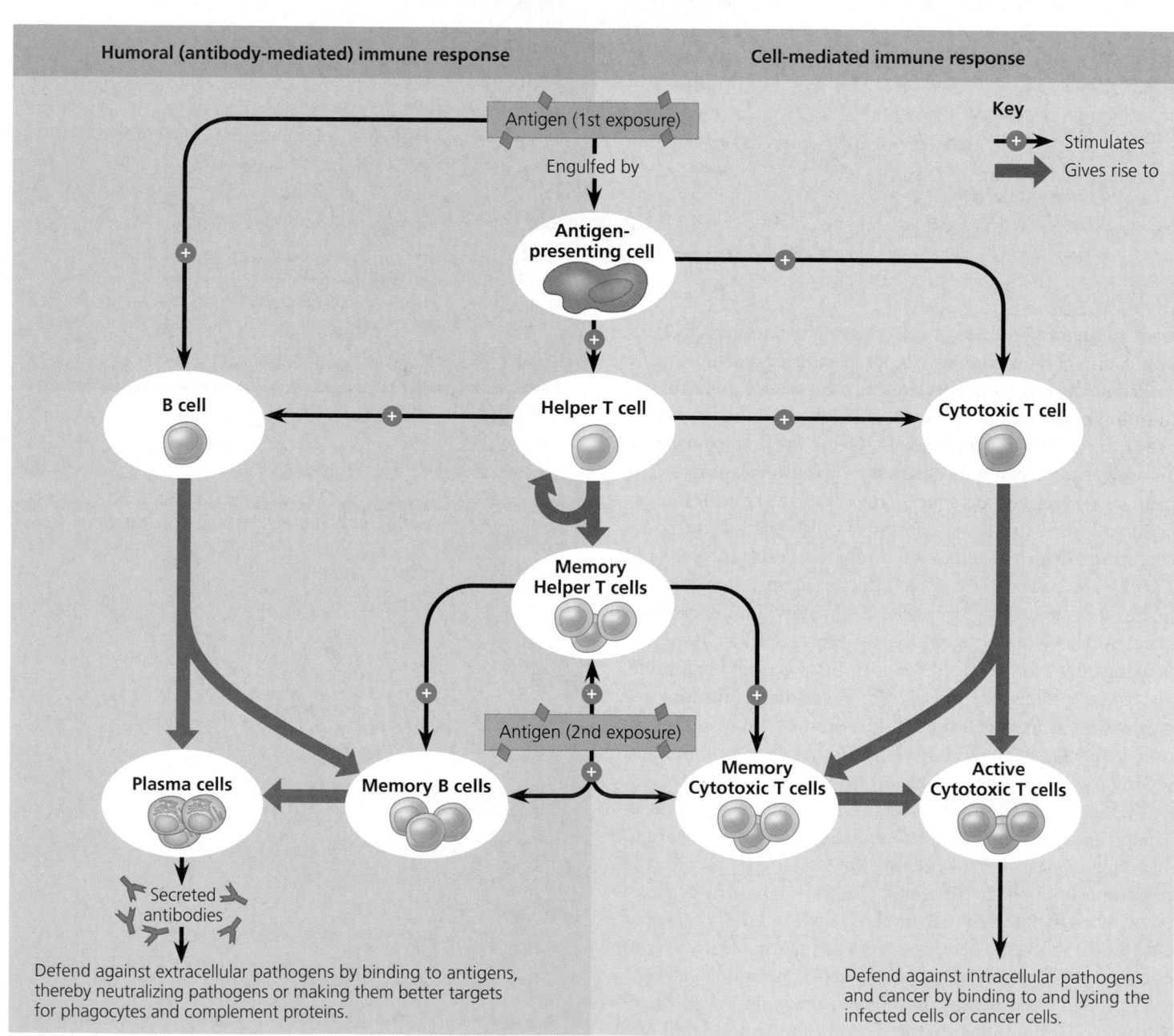

▲ **Figure 43.16 An overview of the acquired immune response.**

? *Identify each black or brown arrow as representing part of the primary or secondary response.*

clonal selection of cytotoxic T cells, which identify and destroy the target cells. A third population of lymphocytes, the helper T cells, aids both responses. As we examine the cellular interactions that underlie the acquired immune response, you can refer to the diagram in Figure 43.16 to appreciate how these interactions work together.

Helper T Cells: A Response to Nearly All Antigens

Activated by encounters with antigen-presenting cells, helper T cells play a central role in enhancing humoral and cell-mediated responses. The helper T cell proliferates after interacting with antigen fragments displayed by antigen-presenting cells (usually dendritic cells). The resulting clone of cells differentiates into activated helper T cells and memory helper T cells. Activated helper T cells secrete cytokines that stimulate the activation of nearby B cells and cytotoxic T cells.

A helper T cell and the antigen-presenting cell displaying its specific epitope have a complex interaction (Figure 43.17). The T cell receptors on the surface of the helper T cell bind to the antigen fragment that is held by a class II MHC molecule on the antigen-presenting cell. At the same time, a protein called **CD4**, found on the surface of most helper T cells, binds to the class II MHC molecule. CD4 helps keep the helper T cell and antigen-presenting cell joined. As the two cells interact, signals in the form of cytokines are exchanged in both directions. For example, cytokines secreted from a dendritic cell act in combination with the antigen to stimulate the helper T cell, causing it to produce its own set of cytokines. The net result is activation of the helper T cell.

The three principal types of antigen-presenting cells—dendritic cells, macrophages, and B cells—interact with helper T cells in different contexts. Dendritic cells are particularly important in triggering a primary immune response. They serve as sentinels in the epidermis and other tissues frequently exposed to foreign antigens. After dendritic cells capture antigens, they migrate from the infection site to lymphoid tissues. There they present antigens, via class II MHC molecules, to helper T cells (see Figure 43.17). Macrophages play the key role in initiating a secondary immune response by presenting antigens to memory helper T cells, while the humoral response relies mainly on B cells to present antigens to helper T cells.

Cytotoxic T Cells: A Response to Infected Cells

Cytotoxic T cells are the effector cells in a cell-mediated immune response. To become active, they require signaling molecules from helper T cells as well as interaction with an antigen-presenting cell. Once activated, they can eliminate cancerous body cells and body cells infected by viruses or other intracellular pathogens. Fragments of nonself proteins synthesized in such target cells associate with class I MHC molecules and are displayed on the cell surface, where they can be recognized by cytotoxic T cells (Figure 43.18, on the next page). A surface protein called **CD8**, found on most cytotoxic T cells, enhances the interaction between a target cell and a cytotoxic T cell. Binding of CD8 to a class I MHC molecule helps keep the two cells in contact while the cytotoxic T cell is activated. Thus, the roles of class I MHC molecules and CD8 are similar to those of class II MHC molecules and CD4.

The targeted destruction of an infected cell by a cytotoxic T cell involves the secretion of proteins that cause cell rupture and cell death (see Figure 43.18). The death of the infected cell not only deprives the pathogen of a place to reproduce but also exposes it to circulating antibodies, which mark it for disposal. After destroying an infected cell, the cytotoxic T cell may move on and kill other cells infected with the same pathogen.

1 After an antigen-presenting cell engulfs and degrades a bacterium, it displays bacterial antigen fragments (peptides) complexed with a class II MHC molecule on the cell surface. A specific helper T cell binds to the displayed complex via its TCR with the aid of CD4. This interaction promotes secretion of cytokines by the antigen-presenting cell.

Antigen-presenting cell

Bacterium

Antigen fragment

Class II MHC molecule

CD4

TCR (T cell receptor)

Helper T cell

2 Proliferation of the helper T cell, stimulated by cytokines from both the antigen-presenting cell and the helper T cell itself, gives rise to a clone of activated helper T cells (not shown), all with receptors for the same MHC-antigen fragment complex.

Cytokines

Humoral immunity (secretion of antibodies by plasma cells)

B cell

Cell-mediated immunity (attack on infected cells)

Cytotoxic T cell

3 Following proliferation, helper T cells secrete other cytokines, which help activate B cells and cytotoxic T cells.

▲ Figure 43.17 **The central role of helper T cells in humoral and cell-mediated immune responses.**

① An activated cytotoxic T cell binds to a class I MHC–antigen fragment complex on a target cell via its TCR with the aid of the protein CD8.

② The T cell releases perforin molecules, which form pores in the target cell membrane, and granzymes, enzymes that break down proteins. Granzymes enter the target cell by endocytosis.

③ The granzymes initiate apoptosis within the target cell, leading to fragmentation of the nucleus and cytoplasm and eventual cell death. The released cytotoxic T cell can attack other target cells.

▲ **Figure 43.18 The killing action of cytotoxic T cells.** An activated cytotoxic T cell releases molecules that make pores in a target cell's membrane and enzymes that break down proteins, promoting the cell's death.

① After an antigen-presenting cell engulfs and degrades a bacterium, it displays an antigen fragment (peptide) complexed with a class II MHC molecule. A helper T cell that recognizes the complex is activated with the aid of cytokines secreted from the antigen-presenting cell, forming a clone of activated helper T cells (not shown).

② A B cell with receptors for the same peptide internalizes the antigen and displays it on the cell surface in a complex with a class II MHC protein. An activated helper T cell bearing receptors specific for the displayed antigen fragment binds to the B cell. This interaction, with the aid of cytokines from the T cell, activates the B cell.

③ The activated B cell proliferates and differentiates into antibody-secreting plasma cells and memory B cells. The secreted antibodies are specific for the same bacterial antigen that initiated the response.

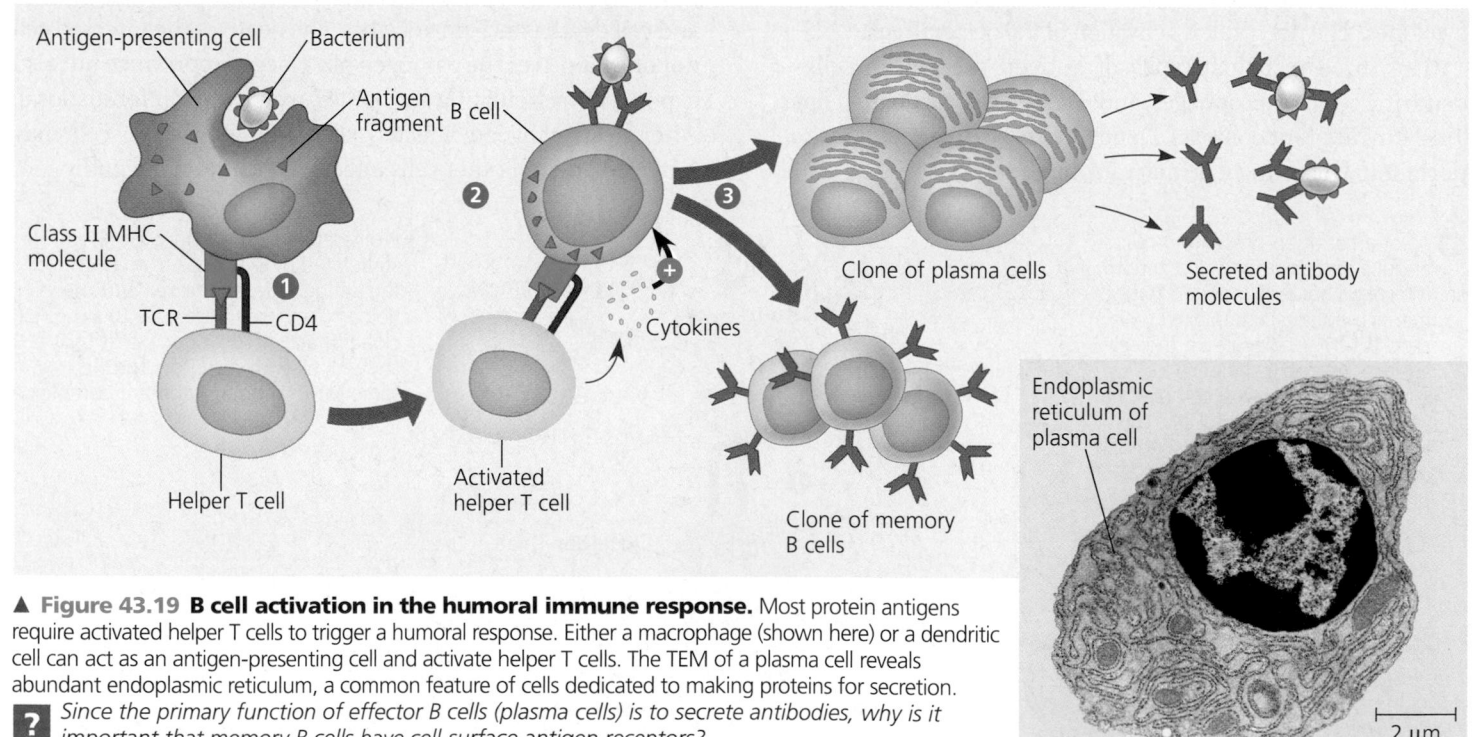

▲ **Figure 43.19 B cell activation in the humoral immune response.** Most protein antigens require activated helper T cells to trigger a humoral response. Either a macrophage (shown here) or a dendritic cell can act as an antigen-presenting cell and activate helper T cells. The TEM of a plasma cell reveals abundant endoplasmic reticulum, a common feature of cells dedicated to making proteins for secretion.

? *Since the primary function of effector B cells (plasma cells) is to secrete antibodies, why is it important that memory B cells have cell-surface antigen receptors?*

B Cells: A Response to Extracellular Pathogens

The secretion of antibodies by clonally selected B cells is the hallmark of the humoral response **(Figure 43.19)**. Activation of this response typically involves B cells and helper T cells, as well as proteins on the surface of bacteria. As depicted in Figure 43.19, B cell activation by an antigen is aided by cytokines secreted from helper T cells that have encountered the same antigen. Stimulated by both an antigen and cytokines, the B cell proliferates and differentiates into a clone of antibody-secreting plasma cells and a clone of memory B cells.

The pathway for antigen processing and display in B cells differs from that in other antigen-presenting cells. A macrophage or dendritic cell can present fragments from a wide variety of protein antigens, whereas a B cell presents only the antigen to which it specifically binds. When an antigen first binds to receptors on the surface of a B cell, the cell takes in a few of the foreign molecules by receptor-mediated endocytosis (see Figure 7.20). The B cell then presents an MHC-antigen fragment complex to a helper T cell. This achieves the direct cell-to-cell contact that is usually critical to B cell activation (see step 2 in Figure 43.19).

B cell activation leads to a robust humoral response: An activated B cell gives rise to a clone of thousands of plasma cells, each of which secretes approximately 2,000 antibody molecules every second of the cell's 4- to 5-day life span. Furthermore, most antigens recognized by B cells contain multiple epitopes. An exposure to a single antigen therefore normally activates a variety of B cells, with different clones of plasma cells directed against different epitopes on the common antigen.

For antigens, including polysaccharides, that contact multiple receptors on a single cell, a B cell response can occur without the involvement of cytokines or helper T cells. Although such responses generate no memory B cells, they play an important role in defending against many bacteria.

Antibody Classes

For a given B cell, the antibodies produced differ from the B cell receptor only in the constant (C) region of the heavy chain. In place of a transmembrane region and cytoplasmic tail, the heavy chain contains sequences that determine where the antibody is distributed and how it mediates antigen disposal.

The five major types of heavy-chain C regions determine five major classes of antibodies. **Figure 43.20** summarizes the structures and functions of these antibody classes. Changes in the heavy-chain gene that switch B cells from production of one antibody class to another occur only in response to antigen stimulation and to specific regulatory signals from T cells.

The power of antibody specificity and antigen-antibody binding has been harnessed in laboratory research and clinical diagnosis. Some antibody tools are *polyclonal*: They are the products of many different clones of B cells, each specific for a different epitope. Antibodies produced following exposure to a microbial antigen are polyclonal. In contrast, other antibody tools are *monoclonal*: They are prepared from a single clone of B cells grown in culture. All the **monoclonal antibodies** produced by such a culture are identical and specific for the same epitope on an antigen. Monoclonal antibodies are particularly

Class of Immuno-globulin (Antibody)	Distribution	Function
IgM (pentamer) — J chain	First Ig class produced after initial exposure to antigen; then its concentration in the blood declines	Promotes neutralization and cross-linking of antigens; very effective in complement system activation (see Figure 43.21)
IgG (monomer)	Most abundant Ig class in blood; also present in tissue fluids	Promotes opsonization, neutralization, and cross-linking of antigens; less effective in activation of complement system than IgM (see Figure 43.21) Only Ig class that crosses placenta, thus conferring passive immunity on fetus
IgA (dimer) — J chain, Secretory component	Present in secretions such as tears, saliva, mucus, and breast milk	Provides localized defense of mucous membranes by cross-linking and neutralization of antigens (see Figure 43.21) Presence in breast milk confers passive immunity on nursing infant
IgE (monomer)	Present in blood at low concentrations	Triggers release from mast cells and basophils of histamine and other chemicals that cause allergic reactions (see Figure 43.23)
IgD (monomer) — Transmembrane region	Present primarily on surface of B cells that have not been exposed to antigens	Acts as antigen receptor in the antigen-stimulated proliferation and differentiation of B cells (clonal selection)

▲ **Figure 43.20 The five antibody, or immunoglobulin (Ig), classes.** All antibody classes consist of similar Y-shaped molecules in which the tail region determines the distribution and functions characteristic of each class. IgM and IgA antibodies contain a J chain (unrelated to the *J* gene segment) that helps hold the subunits together. As an IgA antibody is secreted across a mucous membrane, it acquires a secretory component that protects it from cleavage by enzymes.

useful for tagging specific molecules. For example, home pregnancy kits use monoclonal antibodies to detect human chorionic gonadotropin (HCG). Because HCG is produced as soon as an embryo implants in the uterus (see Chapter 46), the presence of this hormone in a woman's urine provides a reliable indicator for a very early stage of pregnancy.

The Role of Antibodies in Immunity

The binding of antibodies to antigens can interfere with pathogen function in many ways, some of which are diagrammed in **Figure 43.21**. In the simplest of these, *neutralization*, antibodies bind to surface proteins of a virus or bacterium, thereby blocking the pathogen's ability to infect a host cell. Similarly, antibodies sometimes bind to and neutralize toxins released in body fluids. In a process called *opsonization*, the antibodies bound to antigens present a readily recognized structure for macrophages and therefore increase phagocytosis. Because each antibody has two antigen-binding sites, antibodies can also facilitate phagocytosis by linking bacterial cells, virus particles, or antigens into aggregates.

Antibodies sometimes work together with the proteins of the complement system to dispose of pathogens. (The name *complement* reflects the fact that these proteins increase the effectiveness of antibody-directed attacks on bacteria.) Binding of antigen-antibody complexes on a microbe or foreign cell to one of the complement proteins triggers a cascade in which each protein of the complement system activates the next. Ultimately, activated complement proteins generate a *membrane attack complex* that forms a pore in the membrane of the foreign cell. Ions and water rush into the cell, causing it to swell and lyse (see Figure 43.21, right). Whether activated as part of innate or acquired defenses, this cascade of complement protein activity results in the lysis of microbes and produces factors that promote inflammation or stimulate phagocytosis.

When antibodies facilitate phagocytosis (see Figure 43.21, middle), they also help fine-tune the humoral immune response. Recall that phagocytosis enables macrophages and dendritic cells to present antigens to and stimulate helper T cells, which in turn stimulate the very B cells whose antibodies contribute to phagocytosis. This positive feedback between the innate and acquired immune systems contributes to a coordinated, effective response to infection.

Although antibodies are the cornerstones of the response in body fluids, there is also a mechanism by which they can bring about the death of infected body cells. When a virus uses a cell's biosynthetic machinery to produce viral proteins, these viral products can appear on the cell surface. If antibodies specific for epitopes on these viral proteins bind the exposed proteins, the presence of bound antibody at the cell surface can recruit a natural killer cell. The NK cell then releases proteins that cause the infected cell to undergo apoptosis.

Viral neutralization	Opsonization	Activation of complement system and pore formation
Antibodies bound to antigens on the surface of a virus neutralize it by blocking its ability to bind to a host cell.	Binding of antibodies to antigens on the surface of bacteria promotes phagocytosis by macrophages.	Binding of antibodies to antigens on the surface of a foreign cell activates the complement system. / Following activation of the complement system, the membrane attack complex forms pores in the foreign cell's membrane, allowing water and ions to rush in. The cell swells and eventually lyses.

▲ **Figure 43.21 Antibody-mediated mechanisms of antigen disposal.** The binding of antibodies to antigens marks microbes, foreign particles, and soluble antigens for inactivation or destruction.

Active and Passive Immunization

Our discussion of acquired immunity has to this point focused on the defenses that arise when a particular microbe infects the body. In response to infection, clones of memory cells form, providing **active immunity**. In contrast, a distinct type of immunity results when the IgG antibodies of a pregnant woman cross the placenta to her fetus. The transferred antibodies are poised to immediately help destroy any pathogens for which they are specific. This protection is called **passive immunity** because the antibodies provided by the mother guard against microbes that have never infected the newborn. Because passive immunity does not involve the recipient's B and T cells, it persists only as long as the transferred antibodies last (a few weeks to a few months). However, IgA antibodies are passed from a mother to her infant in breast milk **(Figure 43.22)**. These antibodies provide additional protection against infection while the infant's immune system develops.

Both active immunity and passive immunity can be induced artificially. Active immunity can develop from the introduction of antigens into the body through **immunization**, often called **vaccination**. The virus causing cowpox, a mild disease usually seen in cows, was used over two centuries ago as the first vaccine (from the Latin *vacca*, cow). Vaccination with cowpox was significant because it enhanced the immune response to the closely related and far more dangerous smallpox virus. Today, many sources of antigen are used to make vaccines, including inactivated bacterial toxins, killed microbes, parts of microbes, weakened microbes that generally do not cause illness, and even genes encoding microbial proteins. Because all of these agents induce a primary immune response and immunological memory, an encounter with the pathogen from which the vaccine was derived triggers a rapid and strong secondary response.

Vaccination programs have been successful against many infectious diseases that once killed, crippled, or incapacitated large numbers of people. A worldwide vaccination campaign led to eradication of smallpox in the late 1970s. In industrialized countries, routine active immunization of infants and children has dramatically reduced the incidence of sometimes devastating diseases, such as polio, measles, and whooping cough. Unfortunately, not all pathogens are easily managed by vaccination. Furthermore, some vaccines are not readily available in impoverished areas of the globe. Even in developed countries, the failure of some parents to immunize children with available vaccines has led to sporadic outbreaks of serious but fully preventable diseases. For example, a decline in vaccination rates within the former Soviet Union led to an outbreak of diphtheria during the mid-1990s that resulted in over 5,000 deaths.

In artificial passive immunization, antibodies from an immune animal are injected into a nonimmune animal. For example, humans bitten by venomous snakes are sometimes

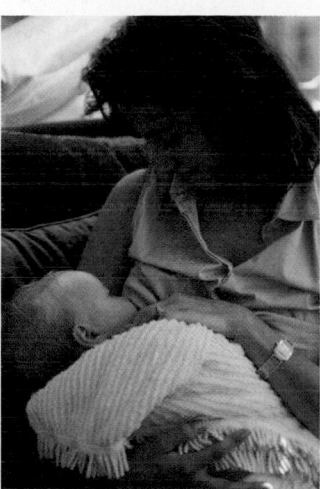

treated with antivenin, a serum from sheep or horses that have been immunized against the venom of one or more species of poisonous snakes. When injected immediately after a snakebite, the antibodies in antivenin can neutralize toxins in the venom before the toxins do massive damage.

Immune Rejection

Like pathogens, cells from another person can be recognized and attacked by immune defenses. For example, skin transplanted from one person to a genetically nonidentical person will look healthy for a week or so but will then be destroyed (rejected) by the recipient's immune response. (It remains something of a puzzle why a pregnant woman does not reject her fetus as nonself tissue.) Keep in mind that the body's hostile reaction to a transplant of other tissues or whole organs or to an incompatible blood transfusion is the expected reaction of a healthy immune system exposed to foreign antigens.

Blood Groups

To avoid harmful immune reactions in human blood transfusions, ABO blood groups must be taken into account. As discussed in Chapter 14, red blood cells are designated as type A if they have A antigen molecules on their surface. Similarly, the B antigen is found on type B red blood cells; both A and B antigens are found on type AB red blood cells; and neither antigen is found on type O red blood cells (see Figure 14.11).

To understand how ABO blood groups affect transfusions, let's consider the immune response of someone with type A blood. It turns out that certain bacteria normally present in the body have epitopes very similar to the A and B blood group antigens. By responding to the bacterial epitope similar to B antigen, a person with type A blood makes antibodies that can react with B antigen. No antibodies are made against the bacterial epitope similar to A antigen, since lymphocytes reactive with self antigens are inactivated or eliminated during development. If the person with type A blood receives a transfusion of type B blood, that person's anti-B antibodies cause an immediate and devastating transfusion reaction. The transfused red blood cells undergo lysis, which can lead to chills, fever, shock, and kidney malfunction. By the same token, anti-A antibodies in the donated type B blood can act against the recipient's type A red blood cells.

Tissue and Organ Transplants

In the case of tissue and organ transplants, or grafts, it is MHC molecules that stimulate the immune response that leads to rejection. Each vertebrate species has many different alleles for each class I and class II MHC gene, enabling presentation of antigen fragments that vary in shape and charge. This diversity of MHC molecules almost guarantees that no two people, except identical twins, will have exactly the same set. Thus, in the vast majority of graft and transplant recipients, some MHC molecules on the donated tissue are foreign to the recipient. To minimize rejection, physicians try to use donor tissue bearing MHC molecules that match those of the recipient as closely as possible. In addition, the recipient takes medicines that suppress immune responses. However, these medicines can leave the recipient more susceptible to infections during the course of treatment.

In a bone marrow transplant between individuals, the problem of rejection is reversed: The donor tissue can reject the recipient's body tissues. Bone marrow transplants are used to treat leukemia and other cancers as well as various hematological (blood cell) diseases. Prior to receiving transplanted bone marrow, the recipient is typically treated with radiation to eliminate his or her own bone marrow cells, thus destroying the source of abnormal cells. This treatment effectively obliterates the recipient's immune system, leaving little chance of graft rejection. However, lymphocytes in the donated marrow may react against the recipient. This *graft versus host reaction* is limited if the MHC molecules of the donor and recipient are well matched. Bone marrow donor programs continually seek volunteers because the great variability of MHC molecules makes a diverse pool of donors essential.

CONCEPT CHECK 43.3

1. If a child were born without a thymus, what cells and functions would be deficient? Explain.
2. Treatment of antibodies with a particular protease clips the heavy chains in half, releasing the two arms of the Y-shaped molecule. How might the antibodies continue to function?
3. **WHAT IF?** Suppose that a snake handler bitten by a particular venomous snake species was treated with antivenin. Why might the treatment for a second such bite be different?

For suggested answers, see Appendix A.

CONCEPT 43.4
Disruptions in immune system function can elicit or exacerbate disease

Although acquired immunity offers significant protection against a wide range of pathogens, it is not fail-safe. In this last section of the chapter, we'll first examine the problems that arise when the acquired immune system is blocked or misregulated. We'll then turn to some of the evolutionary adaptations of pathogens that diminish the effectiveness of host immune responses.

Exaggerated, Self-Directed, and Diminished Immune Responses

The highly regulated interplay among lymphocytes, body cells, and foreign substances generates an immune response that provides extraordinary protection against many pathogens. When allergic, autoimmune, or immunodeficiency disorders disrupt this delicate balance, the effects are frequently severe and sometimes life-threatening.

Allergies

Allergies are exaggerated (hypersensitive) responses to certain antigens called **allergens**. The most common allergies involve antibodies of the IgE class (see Figure 43.20). Hay fever, for instance, occurs when plasma cells secrete IgE antibodies specific for antigens on the surface of pollen grains **(Figure 43.23)**. Some of these antibodies attach by their base to mast cells in connective tissues. Later, when pollen grains again enter the body, they attach to the antigen-binding sites of IgE on the surface of mast cells. Interaction with the large pollen grains cross-links adjacent IgE molecules, inducing the mast cell to release histamine and other inflammatory agents from granules (vesicles), a process called *degranulation.* Recall that histamine causes dilation and increased permeability of small blood vessels. Such vascular changes lead to typical allergy symptoms: sneezing, runny nose, tearing eyes, and smooth muscle contractions that can result in breathing difficulty. Drugs called antihistamines diminish allergy symptoms (and inflammation) by blocking receptors for histamine.

An acute allergic response sometimes leads to *anaphylactic shock*, a whole-body, life-threatening reaction that can occur within seconds of exposure to an allergen. Anaphylactic shock develops when widespread mast cell degranulation triggers abrupt dilation of peripheral blood vessels, causing a precipitous drop in blood pressure. Death may occur within minutes. Allergic responses to bee venom or penicillin can lead to anaphylactic shock in people who are extremely allergic to these substances. Likewise, people very allergic to peanuts, fish, or other foods can die from ingesting only tiny amounts of these

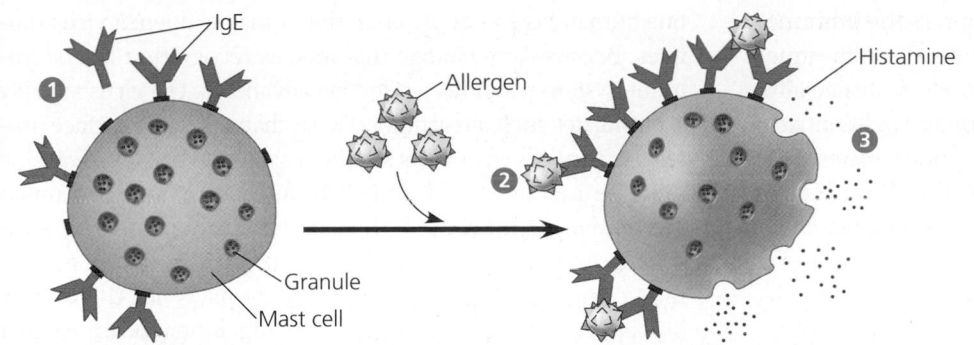

① IgE antibodies produced in response to initial exposure to an allergen bind to receptors on mast cells.

② On subsequent exposure to the same allergen, IgE molecules attached to a mast cell recognize and bind the allergen.

③ Degranulation of the cell, triggered by cross-linking of adjacent IgE molecules, releases histamine and other chemicals, leading to allergy symptoms.

▲ **Figure 43.23 Mast cells, IgE, and the allergic response.**

allergens. People with severe hypersensitivities often carry syringes containing the hormone epinephrine, which counteracts this allergic response.

Autoimmune Diseases

In some people, the immune system turns against particular molecules of the body, causing an **autoimmune disease**. This loss of self-tolerance can take many forms. In *systemic lupus erythematosus*, commonly called *lupus*, the immune system generates antibodies against histones and DNA released by the normal breakdown of body cells. These self-reactive antibodies cause skin rashes, fever, arthritis, and kidney dysfunction. Another antibody-mediated autoimmune disease, *rheumatoid arthritis*, leads to damage and painful inflammation of the cartilage and bone of joints (**Figure 43.24**). In *Type 1 diabetes mellitus*, the insulin-producing beta cells of the pancreas are the targets of autoimmune cytotoxic T cells. The most common chronic neurological disorder in developed countries is an autoimmune disease—*multiple sclerosis*. In this disease, T cells infiltrate the central nervous system, leading to destruction of the myelin sheath that surrounds parts of many neurons (see Figure 48.12).

Gender, genetics, and environment all influence susceptibility to autoimmune disorders. For example, members of certain families show an increased susceptibility to particular autoimmune disorders. In addition, many autoimmune diseases afflict females more often than

▲ **Figure 43.24 X-ray of a hand deformed by rheumatoid arthritis.**

males. Women are two to three times as likely as men to suffer from multiple sclerosis and rheumatoid arthritis and nine times more likely to develop lupus. There has been substantial progress in the field of autoimmunity. For example, we now know that regulatory T cells ordinarily help prevent attack by any self-reactive lymphocytes that remain functional in adults. Nevertheless, much remains to be learned about these often devastating disorders.

Exertion, Stress, and the Immune System

Many forms of exertion and stress influence immune system function. Consider, for example, susceptibility to the common cold and other infections of the upper respiratory tract. Moderate exercise improves immune system function and significantly reduces the risk of these infections. In contrast, exercise to the point of exhaustion leads to more frequent infections and to more severe symptoms. Studies of marathon runners support the conclusion that exercise intensity is the critical variable. Such runners get sick less often than their more sedentary peers during training, a time of moderate exertion, but have a marked increase in illness in the period immediately following the grueling race itself. Similarly, psychological stress has been shown to disrupt immune system regulation by altering the interplay of the hormonal, nervous, and immune systems.

Immunodeficiency Diseases

A disorder in which the ability of an immune system to protect against pathogens is defective or absent is called an **immunodeficiency**. An *inborn immunodeficiency* results from a genetic or developmental defect in the immune system. An *acquired immunodeficiency* develops later in life following exposure to chemical or biological agents. Whatever its cause and nature, an immunodeficiency can lead to frequent and recurrent infections and increased susceptibility to certain cancers.

Inborn immunodeficiencies result from defects in the development of various immune system cells or defects in the production of specific proteins, such as antibodies or the proteins of the complement system. Depending on the specific genetic defect, either innate or acquired defenses—or both—may be impaired. In severe combined immunodeficiency (SCID), functional lymphocytes are rare or absent. Lacking an acquired immune response, SCID patients are susceptible to recurrent infections, such as pneumonia and meningitis, that can cause death in infancy. Treatments include bone marrow and stem cell transplantation.

Exposure to certain agents can cause immunodeficiencies that develop later in life. Drugs used to fight autoimmune diseases or prevent transplant rejection suppress the immune system, leading to an immunodeficient state. The immune system is also suppressed by certain cancers, especially Hodgkin's disease, which damages the lymphatic system. Acquired immunodeficiencies range from temporary states that may arise from physiological stress to the devastating **acquired immunodeficiency syndrome**, or **AIDS**, which is caused by a virus. We will discuss AIDS further in the next section, which focuses on how pathogens escape the acquired immune response.

Acquired Immune System Evasion by Pathogens

Just as immune systems that ward off pathogens have evolved in animals, mechanisms that thwart immune responses have evolved in pathogens. Using human pathogens as examples, we'll examine some common mechanisms: antigenic variation, latency, and direct attack on the immune system.

Antigenic Variation

One mechanism for escaping the body's defenses is for a pathogen to alter how it appears to the immune system. Immunological memory is a record of the foreign epitopes an animal has encountered. If the pathogen that expressed those epitopes no longer does so, it can reinfect or remain in a host without triggering the rapid and robust response that memory cells provide. Such changes in epitope expression, which are called *antigenic variation*, are regular events for some viruses and parasites. The parasite that causes sleeping sickness (trypanosomiasis) provides one example. By periodically switching at random among 1,000 different versions of the protein found over its entire surface, this pathogen can persist in the body without facing an effective acquired immune response **(Figure 43.25)**.

Antigenic variation is the major reason the influenza, or "flu," virus remains a major public health problem. As it replicates in

▲ **Figure 43.25 Antigenic variation in the parasite that causes sleeping sickness.** Blood samples taken from a patient during a chronic infection of sleeping sickness reveal cyclic variation in the surface coat protein of the parasite. The infection has become chronic because this weekly variation allows the parasite to evade the acquired immune response.

one human host after another, the human influenza virus mutates. Because any change that lessens recognition by the immune system provides a selective advantage, the virus steadily accumulates such alterations. These changes in the surface proteins of the influenza virus are the reason that a new flu vaccine must be manufactured and distributed each year. Of much greater danger, however, is the fact that the human virus occasionally exchanges genes with influenza viruses that infect domesticated animals, such as pigs or chickens. When this occurs, influenza can take on such a radically different appearance that none of the memory cells in the human population completely recognize the new strain. Such an event caused the influenza outbreak of 1918–1919, which killed more than half a million people in the United States. Worldwide more than 20 million people died, a greater number than had died in World War I. Today, a very potent form of an avian influenza virus poses the threat of another devastating outbreak (see Chapter 54).

Latency

Some viruses remain in a host without activating immune defenses, ceasing production of viral products targeted by lymphocytes. In this largely inactive state called *latency*, there are typically no free virus particles. Instead, the viral genome persists in the nuclei of infected cells, either as a separate small DNA molecule or as a copy integrated into the host genome. Latency typically persists until conditions arise that are favorable for viral transmission or unfavorable for host survival. Such circumstances trigger the synthesis and release of particles that can infect new hosts.

Herpes simplex viruses, which establish themselves in human sensory neurons, provide a good example of latency. The type 1 virus causes most oral herpes infections, whereas the type 2 virus is responsible for most cases of genital herpes. Because sensory neurons express relatively few MHC I molecules, the infected cells are inefficient at presenting viral antigens to circulating lymphocytes. Stimuli such as fever, emotional stress, or menstruation reactivate the virus and infection of surrounding epithelial tissues. Activation of the type 1 virus can result in blisters around the mouth that are inaccurately called "cold" sores. The type 2 virus can cause genital sores, but people infected with either type 1 or type 2 virus often lack any apparent symptoms. Infections of the type 2 virus, which is sexually transmitted, pose a serious threat to the babies of infected mothers and can increase transmission of HIV, the virus that causes AIDS.

Attack on the Immune System: HIV

The human immunodeficiency virus (HIV), the pathogen that causes AIDS, both escapes and attacks the acquired immune response. Once introduced into the body, HIV infects helper T cells with high efficiency. To infect these cells, the virus binds specifically to the cell's CD4 molecules. However, HIV also infects some cell types that have low levels of CD4, including macrophages and brain cells. Within the cell, the HIV RNA genome is reverse-transcribed, and the product DNA is integrated into the host cell's genome. In this form, the viral genome can direct production of new virus particles (see Figure 19.8).

Although the body responds to HIV with an aggressive immune response sufficient to eliminate most viral infections, some HIV invariably escapes. One reason HIV persists is antigenic variation. The virus mutates at a very high rate during replication. Altered proteins on the surface of some mutated viruses prevent recognition and elimination by the immune system. Such viruses survive, proliferate, and mutate further. The virus thus evolves within the body. The continued presence of HIV is also helped by latency. When the viral DNA integrates into the chromosome of an infected cell but does not produce new virus proteins or particles, it is shielded from surveillance by the immune system. This inactive, or latent, viral DNA is also protected from antiviral agents currently used against HIV because they attack only actively replicating viruses.

Over time, an untreated HIV infection not only avoids the acquired immune response but also abolishes it (Figure 43.26). The damaging effects of viral reproduction and cell death triggered by the virus leads to loss of T cells, impairing both humoral and cell-mediated immune responses. The result is a susceptibility to infections and cancers that a healthy immune system would most of the time defeat. For example, *Pneumocystis carinii* is a common fungus that does not cause disease in healthy individuals but can result in severe pneumonia in people with AIDS. Likewise, the Kaposi's sarcoma herpes virus causes a cancer among AIDS patients that is extremely rare in individuals not infected with HIV. Such opportunistic diseases, as well as nerve damage and body wasting, are the primary cause of death in AIDS patients.

At present, HIV infection cannot be cured, although certain drugs can slow HIV reproduction and the progression to AIDS. Mutations that occur in each round of viral reproduction can generate strains of HIV that are drug resistant. The impact of such viral drug resistance is reduced by the use of a combination of drugs; viruses newly resistant to one drug can be defeated by another. But the appearance of strains resistant to multiple drugs reduces the effectiveness of multidrug "cocktails" in some patients. Frequent mutations in HIV surface antigen genes also have hampered efforts to develop an effective vaccine. Worldwide, the AIDS epidemic continues to grow. In 2006, more than 2.5 million people died of AIDS, with the disease now being the leading cause of death in Africa.

Transmission of HIV requires the transfer of virus particles or infected cells from person to person via body fluids such as semen or blood. Unprotected sex (that is, without a condom) and transmission via HIV-contaminated needles (typically among intravenous drug users) account for nearly all HIV infections. The virus can enter the body through the mucosal linings of the vagina, vulva, penis, or rectum during intercourse or via the mouth during oral sex. The likelihood of transmission is increased by factors that may damage these linings, especially other sexually transmitted infections that cause ulcers or inflammation. People infected with HIV transmit the disease most readily in the first few weeks of infection, before they express HIV-specific antibodies that can be detected in a blood test.

Cancer and Immunity

The relationship between the immune response and cancer remains only partially understood. It is clear that the frequency of certain cancers increases when the immune response is impaired. This observation has led to the suggestion that the immune system normally attacks body cells that become cancerous. However, there is an alternative explanation. Impairment of the immune response leaves the body open to infection, which causes inflammatory responses. Inflammation, in turn, is now known to be a condition contributing to the development of many cancers. Therefore, it may be that the immune system does not fight cancer effectively, and its impairment leads to increased cancer as the result of increased inflammation. Determining how cancer and immunity are linked and whether passive or active immunization can be used to fight cancer remain active areas of investigation.

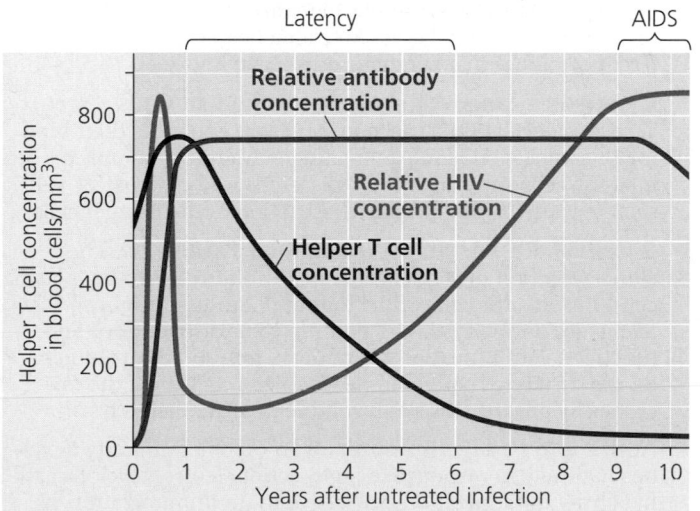

▲ **Figure 43.26 The progress of an untreated HIV infection.**

CONCEPT CHECK 43.4

1. In myasthenia gravis, antibodies bind to and block acetylcholine receptors at neuromuscular junctions, preventing muscle contraction. Is this disease best classified as an immunodeficiency disease, an autoimmune disease, or an allergic reaction? Explain.

2. People with herpes simplex type 1 viruses often get mouth sores when they have a cold or similar infection. How might this location benefit the virus?

3. **WHAT IF?** How would a macrophage deficiency likely affect a person's innate and acquired defenses?

For suggested answers, see Appendix A.

SUMMARY OF KEY CONCEPTS

CONCEPT 43.1

In innate immunity, recognition and response rely on shared traits of pathogens (pp. 931–936)

▶ **Innate Immunity of Invertebrates** Invertebrates are protected by physical and chemical barriers as well as cell-based defenses. In insects, microbes that penetrate barrier defenses are ingested by cells in the hemolymph that also release antimicrobial peptides. Activation of innate immune responses to a pathogen class relies on recognition proteins.

▶ **Innate Immunity of Vertebrates** Intact skin and mucous membranes form barriers to microbes. Mucus produced by membrane cells, the low pH of the skin and stomach, and degradation by lysozyme also deter pathogens. Microbes that penetrate barrier defenses are ingested by phagocytes, which help trigger an inflammatory response. Complement proteins, interferons, and other antimicrobial proteins also act against microbes. In local inflammation, histamine and other chemicals released from injured cells promote changes in blood vessels that allow fluid, more phagocytes, and antimicrobial proteins to enter tissues. Natural killer (NK) cells can induce the death of virus-infected cells.

▶ **Innate Immune System Evasion by Pathogens** The outer capsule of some bacteria prevents recognition. Some bacteria are resistant to breakdown within lysosomes.

CONCEPT 43.2

In acquired immunity, lymphocyte receptors provide pathogen-specific recognition (pp. 936–942)

▶ Acquired immunity relies on lymphocytes that arise from stem cells in the bone marrow and complete their maturation in the bone marrow (B cells) or in the thymus (T cells).

▶ **Acquired Immunity:** *An Overview* Lymphocytes have cell-surface receptors for foreign molecules. All receptor proteins on a single lymphocyte are the same, but there are millions of lymphocytes in the body that differ in the foreign molecules that their receptors recognize. Upon infection, B and T cells specific for the microbe are activated. Some T cells help other lymphocytes; others kill infected host cells. B cells produce soluble receptor proteins that inhibit foreign molecules and cells. Some activated lymphocytes defend against future infections by the same microbe.

▶ **Antigen Recognition by Lymphocytes** Variable regions of receptors bind to small regions of an antigen (epitopes). B cells recognize epitopes in intact antigens. T cells recognize epitopes in small antigen fragments (peptides) complexed with cell-surface proteins called major histocompatibility (MHC) molecules. Class I MHC molecules, located on all nucleated cells, display antigen fragments to cytotoxic T cells. Class II MHC molecules, located mainly on dendritic cells, macrophages, and B cells (antigen-presenting cells), display antigen fragments to helper T cells and cytotoxic T cells.

▶ **Lymphocyte Development**

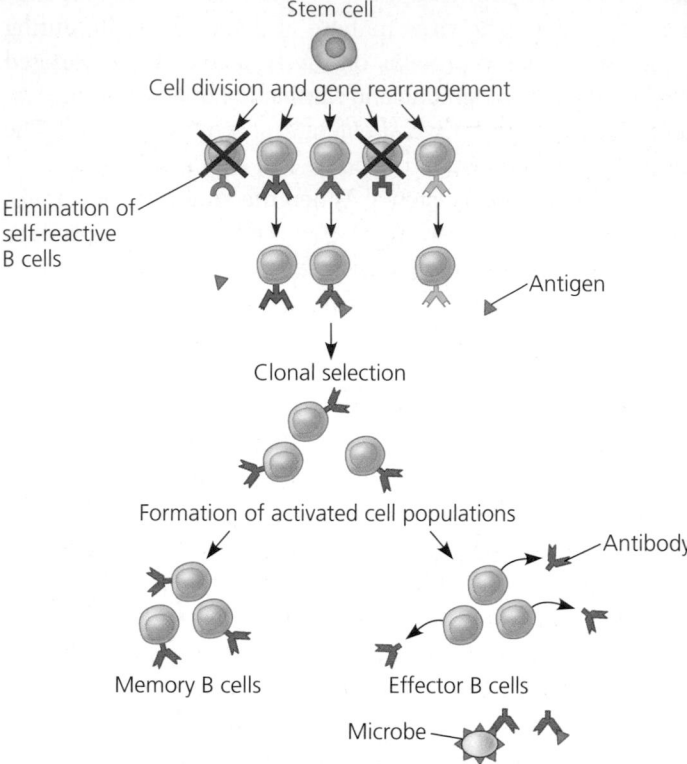

CONCEPT 43.3

Acquired immunity defends against infection of body cells and fluids (pp. 942–948)

▶ Infection of body fluids and infection of body cells are subject to humoral and cell-mediated responses, respectively.

▶ **Helper T Cells: A Response to Nearly All Antigens** Helper T cells make CD4, a surface protein that enhances their binding to class II MHC molecule–antigen fragment complexes on antigen-presenting cells. Activated helper T cells secrete different cytokines that stimulate other lymphocytes.

▶ **Cytotoxic T Cells: A Response to Infected Cells** Cytotoxic T cells make CD8, a surface protein that enhances their binding to class I MHC molecule–antigen fragment complexes on infected cells and cancerous cells. Activated cytotoxic T cells secrete proteins that initiate destruction of their target cells.

▶ **B Cells: A Response to Extracellular Pathogens** The clonal selection of B cells generates antibody-secreting plasma cells, the effector cells of the humoral immune response. The five major antibody classes differ in their distributions and functions within the body. Binding of antibodies to antigens on the surface of pathogens leads to elimination of the microbes by phagocytosis and complement-mediated lysis.

▶ **Active and Passive Immunization** Active immunity develops naturally in response to an infection; it also develops artificially by immunization (vaccination). In immunization, a nonpathogenic form of a microbe or part of a microbe elicits an immune response to and immunological memory for that microbe. Passive immunity, which provides immediate, short-term protection, is conferred naturally when IgG crosses the placenta from mother to fetus or when IgA passes from mother to infant in breast milk. It also can be conferred artificially by injecting antibodies into a nonimmune person.

▶ **Immune Rejection** Certain antigens on red blood cells determine whether a person has type A, B, AB, or O blood. Because antibodies to nonself blood antigens already exist in the body, transfusion with incompatible blood leads to destruction of the transfused cells. MHC molecules are responsible for stimulating the rejection of tissue grafts and organ transplants. The chances of successful transplantation are increased if the donor and recipient MHC tissue types are well matched and if immunosuppressive drugs are given to the recipient. Lymphocytes in bone marrow transplants may cause a graft versus host reaction in recipients.

MEDIA
MP3 Tutor The Human Immune System
Activity Immune Responses

CONCEPT **43.4**

Disruptions in immune system function can elicit or exacerbate disease (pp. 948–951)

▶ **Exaggerated, Self-Directed, and Diminished Immune Responses** In localized allergies, IgE attached to receptors on mast cells induces the cells to release histamine and other mediators that cause vascular changes and allergic symptoms. Loss of normal self-tolerance can lead to autoimmune diseases, such as multiple sclerosis. Inborn immunodeficiencies result from hereditary or congenital defects that interfere with innate, humoral, or cell-mediated defenses. AIDS is an acquired immunodeficiency caused by the human immunodeficiency virus (HIV).

▶ **Acquired Immune System Evasion by Pathogens** Pathogens use antigenic variation, latency, and direct assault on the immune system to thwart immune responses. HIV infection destroys helper T cells, leaving the patient prone to disease due to deficient humoral and cell-mediated immunity.

▶ **Cancer and Immunity** Although cancers are more common with immunodeficiencies, it is unclear whether this reflects reduced immune response or an increase in infections that contribute to cancer development through inflammation.

MEDIA
Activity HIV Reproductive Cycle
Investigation What Causes Infections in AIDS Patients?
Investigation Why Do AIDS Rates Differ Across the U.S.?

TESTING YOUR KNOWLEDGE

SELF-QUIZ

1. Which of these is *not* part of insect immunity?
   a. enzyme activation of microbe-killing chemicals
   b. activation of natural killer cells
   c. phagocytosis by hemocytes
   d. production of antimicrobial peptides
   e. a protective exoskeleton

2. What is a characteristic of early stages of local inflammation?
   a. anaphylactic shock
   b. fever
   c. attack by cytotoxic T cells
   d. release of histamine
   e. antibody- and complement-mediated lysis of microbes

3. An epitope associates with which part of an antibody?
   a. the antibody-binding site
   b. the heavy-chain constant regions only
   c. variable regions of a heavy chain and light chain combined
   d. the light-chain constant regions only
   e. the antibody tail

4. Which of the following is *not* true about helper T cells?
   a. They function in cell-mediated and humoral responses.
   b. They are activated by polysaccharide fragments.
   c. They bear surface CD4 molecules.
   d. They are subject to infection by HIV.
   e. When activated, they secrete cytokines.

5. Which statement best describes the difference in responses of effector B cells (plasma cells) and cytotoxic T cells?
   a. B cells confer active immunity; cytotoxic T cells confer passive immunity.
   b. B cells kill viruses directly; cytotoxic T cells kill virus-infected cells.
   c. B cells secrete antibodies against a virus; cytotoxic T cells kill virus-infected cells.
   d. B cells accomplish the cell-mediated response; cytotoxic T cells accomplish the humoral response.
   e. B cells respond the first time the invader is present; cytotoxic T cells respond subsequent times.

6. Which of the following results in long-term immunity?
   a. the passage of maternal antibodies to a developing fetus
   b. the inflammatory response to a splinter
   c. the injection of serum from people immune to rabies
   d. the administration of the chicken pox vaccine
   e. the passage of maternal antibodies to a nursing infant

7. HIV targets include all of the following except
   a. macrophages.   b. cytotoxic T cells.   c. helper T cells.
   d. cells bearing CD4.   e. brain cells.

8. **DRAW IT** Consider a pencil-shaped protein with two epitopes, Y (the "eraser" end) and Z (the "point" end). They are recognized by antibodies A1 and A2, respectively. Draw and label a picture showing the antibodies linking proteins into a complex that could trigger endocytosis by a macrophage.

For Self-Quiz answers, see Appendix A.

MEDIA Visit **www.campbellbiology.com** for a Practice Test.

EVOLUTION CONNECTION

9. Describe one invertebrate defense mechanism and discuss how it is an evolutionary adaptation retained in vertebrates.

SCIENTIFIC INQUIRY

10. To test for tuberculosis in AIDS patients, why wouldn't you inject purified bacterial antigen and assess signs of immune system reaction several days later?

   Biological Inquiry: A Workbook of Investigative Cases Explore the immune response to flu pathogens with the case "Pandemic Flu (Past and Possible)."

44 Osmoregulation and Excretion

▲ Figure 44.1 **How does an albatross drink saltwater without ill effect?**

OVERVIEW

A Balancing Act

With a wingspan that can reach 3.5 m, the largest of any living bird, a wandering albatross (*Diomedea exulans*) soaring over the ocean is hard not to notice (Figure 44.1). Yet the albatross commands attention for more than just its size. This massive bird remains at sea day and night throughout the year, returning to land only to reproduce. A human with only seawater to drink would die of dehydration, but under the same conditions the albatross thrives.

In surviving without fresh water, the albatross relies on **osmoregulation**, the general process by which animals control solute concentrations and balance water gain and loss. In the fluid environment of cells, tissues, and organs, osmoregulation is essential. For physiological systems to function properly, the relative concentrations of water and solutes must be kept within fairly narrow limits. In addition, ions such as sodium and calcium must be maintained at concentrations that permit normal activity of muscles, neurons, and other body cells. Osmoregulation is thus a process of homeostasis.

A number of strategies for water and solute control have evolved, reflecting the varied and often severe osmoregulatory challenges presented by an animal's surroundings. Desert animals live in an environment that can quickly deplete their body water. Despite a quite different environment, albatrosses and other marine animals also face the potential problem of dehydration. Success in such circumstances depends critically on conserving water and, for marine birds and bony fishes, eliminating excess salts. In contrast, freshwater animals live in an environment that threatens to flood and dilute their body fluids. These organisms survive by limiting water uptake, conserving solutes, and absorbing salts from their surroundings.

In safeguarding their internal fluid environment, animals must also deal with a hazardous metabolite produced by the dismantling of proteins and nucleic acids. Breakdown of *nitrogenous* (nitrogen-containing) molecules releases ammonia, a very toxic compound. Several different mechanisms have evolved for **excretion**, the process that rids the body of nitrogenous metabolites and other waste products. Because systems for excretion and osmoregulation are structurally and functionally linked in many animals, we will consider both of these processes in this chapter.

CONCEPT 44.1

Osmoregulation balances the uptake and loss of water and solutes

Just as thermoregulation depends on balancing heat loss and gain (see Chapter 40), regulating the chemical composition of body fluids depends on balancing the uptake and loss of water and solutes. This process of osmoregulation is based largely on controlled movement of solutes between internal fluids and the external environment. Because water follows solutes by osmosis, the net effect is to regulate both solute and water content.

Osmosis and Osmolarity

All animals—regardless of phylogeny, habitat, or type of waste produced—face the same need for osmoregulation. Over time,

Hyperosmotic side:
Higher solute concentration
Lower free H₂O concentration

Hypoosmotic side:
Lower solute concentration
Higher free H₂O concentration

▲ **Figure 44.2 Solute concentration and osmosis.**

water uptake and loss must balance. If water uptake is excessive, animal cells swell and burst; if water loss is substantial, they shrivel and die (see Figure 7.13).

Water enters and leaves cells by osmosis. Recall from Chapter 7 that osmosis, a special case of diffusion, is the movement of water across a selectively permeable membrane. It occurs whenever two solutions separated by the membrane differ in osmotic pressure, or **osmolarity** (total solute concentration expressed as molarity, or moles of solute per liter of solution). The unit of measurement for osmolarity used in this chapter is milliOsmoles per liter (mOsm/L); 1 mOsm/L is equivalent to a total solute concentration of $10^{-3}\ M$. The osmolarity of human blood is about 300 mOsm/L, while seawater has an osmolarity of about 1,000 mOsm/L.

If two solutions separated by a selectively permeable membrane have the same osmolarity, they are said to be *isoosmotic*. Under these conditions, water molecules continually cross the membrane, but they do so at equal rates in both directions. In other words, there is no *net* movement of water by osmosis between isoosmotic solutions. When two solutions differ in osmolarity, the one with the greater concentration of solutes is said to be *hyperosmotic*, and the more dilute solution is said to be *hypoosmotic* (**Figure 44.2**). Water flows by osmosis from a hypoosmotic solution to a hyperosmotic one.*

Osmotic Challenges

An animal can maintain water balance in two ways. One is to be an **osmoconformer**, which is isoosmotic with its surroundings. The second is to be an **osmoregulator**, which controls its internal osmolarity independent of that of its environment.

---

* In this chapter, we use the terms *isoosmotic*, *hypoosmotic*, and *hyperosmotic*, which refer specifically to osmolarity, instead of the more familiar terms *isotonic*, *hypotonic*, and *hypertonic*. The latter set of terms applies to the response of animal cells—whether they swell or shrink—in solutions of known solute concentrations.

▲ **Figure 44.3 Sockeye salmon (*Oncorhynchus nerka*), euryhaline osmoregulators.**

All osmoconformers are marine animals. Because an osmoconformer's internal osmolarity is the same as that of its environment, there is no tendency to gain or lose water. Many osmoconformers live in water that has a stable composition and hence have a constant internal osmolarity.

Osmoregulation enables animals to live in environments that are uninhabitable for osmoconformers, such as freshwater and terrestrial habitats. It also allows many marine animals to maintain an internal osmolarity different from that of seawater. To survive in a hypoosmotic environment, an osmoregulator must discharge excess water. In a hyperosmotic environment, an osmoregulator must instead take in water to offset osmotic loss.

Most animals, whether osmoconformers or osmoregulators, cannot tolerate substantial changes in external osmolarity and are said to be **stenohaline** (from the Greek *stenos*, narrow, and *halos*, salt). In contrast, **euryhaline** animals (from the Greek *eurys*, broad), which include certain osmoconformers and osmoregulators, can survive large fluctuations in external osmolarity. Many barnacles and mussels covered and uncovered by ocean tides are euryhaline osmoconformers; familiar examples of euryhaline osmoregulators are the striped bass and the various species of salmon (**Figure 44.3**).

Next we'll examine some adaptations for osmoregulation that have evolved in marine, freshwater, and terrestrial animals.

Marine Animals

Most marine invertebrates are osmoconformers. Their osmolarity (the sum of the concentrations of all dissolved substances) is the same as that of seawater. They therefore face no substantial challenges in water balance. However, because they differ considerably from seawater in the concentrations of *specific* solutes, they must actively transport these solutes to maintain homeostasis.

Many marine vertebrates and some marine invertebrates are osmoregulators. For most of these animals, the ocean is a strongly dehydrating environment. For example, marine bony

Gain of water and salt ions from food

Excretion of salt ions from gills

Osmotic water **loss** through gills and other parts of body surface

Key

Water

Salt

SALT WATER

Gain of water and salt ions from drinking seawater

Excretion of salt ions and small amounts of water in scanty urine from kidneys

(a) Osmoregulation in a saltwater fish

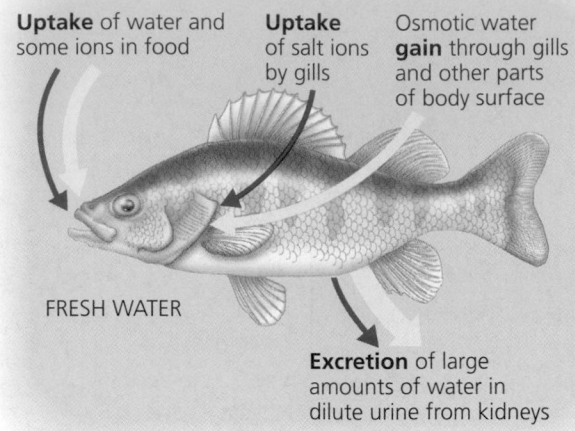

Uptake of water and some ions in food

Uptake of salt ions by gills

Osmotic water **gain** through gills and other parts of body surface

FRESH WATER

Excretion of large amounts of water in dilute urine from kidneys

(b) Osmoregulation in a freshwater fish

▲ **Figure 44.4 Osmoregulation in marine and freshwater bony fishes: a comparison.**

fishes, such as the cod in **Figure 44.4a**, constantly lose water by osmosis. Such fishes balance the water loss by drinking large amounts of seawater. They then make use of both their gills and kidneys to rid themselves of salts. In the gills, specialized *chloride cells* actively transport chloride ions (Cl$^-$) out, and sodium ions (Na$^+$) follow passively. In the kidneys, excess calcium, magnesium, and sulfate ions are excreted with the loss of only small amounts of water.

A distinct osmoregulatory strategy evolved in marine sharks and most other chondrichthyans (cartilaginous animals; see Chapter 34). Like bony fishes, sharks have an internal salt concentration much less than that of seawater, so salt tends to diffuse into their bodies from the water, especially across their gills. Unlike bony fishes, however, marine sharks are not hypoosmotic to seawater. The explanation is that shark tissue contains high concentrations of urea, a nitrogenous waste product of protein and nucleic acid metabolism (see Figure 44.9). Their body fluids also contain trimethylamine oxide (TMAO), an organic molecule that protects proteins from damage by urea. Together, the salts, urea, TMAO, and other compounds maintained in the body fluids of sharks result in an osmolarity very close to that of seawater. For this reason, sharks are often considered osmoconformers. However, because the solute concentration in their body fluids is actually somewhat greater than 1,000 mOsm/L, water slowly *enters* the shark's body by osmosis and in food (sharks do not drink). This small influx of water is disposed of in urine produced by the shark's kidneys. The urine also removes some of the salt that diffuses into the shark's body; the rest is lost in feces or is excreted by an organ called the rectal gland.

Freshwater Animals

The osmoregulatory problems of freshwater animals are the opposite of those of marine animals. The body fluids of fresh-

water animals must be hyperosmotic because animal cells cannot tolerate salt concentrations as low as those of lake or river water. Having internal fluids with an osmolarity higher than that of their surroundings, freshwater animals face the problem of gaining water by osmosis and losing salts by diffusion. Many freshwater animals, including fishes, solve the problem of water balance by drinking almost no water and excreting large amounts of very dilute urine. At the same time, salts lost by diffusion and in the urine are replenished by eating. Freshwater fishes, such as the perch in **Figure 44.4b**, also replenish salts by uptake across the gills. Chloride cells in the gills of the fish actively transport Cl$^-$ into the body, and Na$^+$ follows.

Salmon and other euryhaline fishes that migrate between seawater and fresh water undergo dramatic changes in osmoregulatory status. While living in the ocean, salmon carry out osmoregulation like other marine fishes by drinking seawater and excreting excess salt from their gills. When they migrate to fresh water, salmon cease drinking and begin to produce large amounts of dilute urine. At the same time, their gills start taking up salt from the dilute environment—just like fishes that spend their entire lives in fresh water.

Animals That Live in Temporary Waters

Extreme dehydration, or *desiccation*, is fatal for most animals. However, a few aquatic invertebrates that live in temporary ponds and in films of water around soil particles can lose almost all their body water and survive. These animals enter a dormant state when their habitats dry up, an adaptation called **anhydrobiosis** ("life without water"). Among the most striking examples are the tardigrades, or water bears **(Figure 44.5)**. Less than 1 mm long, these tiny invertebrates are found in marine, freshwater, and moist terrestrial environments. In their active, hydrated state, they contain about 85% water by weight, but they can dehydrate to less than 2% water and survive in an

(a) Hydrated tardigrade

(b) Dehydrated tardigrade

▲ **Figure 44.5 Anhydrobiosis.** Tardigrades (water bears) inhabit temporary ponds and droplets of water in soil and on moist plants (SEMs).

inactive state, dry as dust, for a decade or more. Just add water, and within hours the rehydrated tardigrades are moving about and feeding.

Anhydrobiosis requires adaptations that keep cell membranes intact. Researchers are just beginning to learn how tardigrades survive drying out, but studies of anhydrobiotic roundworms (phylum Nematoda) show that desiccated individuals contain large amounts of sugars. In particular, a disaccharide called trehalose seems to protect the cells by replacing the water that is normally associated with proteins and membrane lipids. Many insects that survive freezing in the winter also use trehalose as a membrane protectant, as do some plants resistant to desiccation.

Land Animals

The threat of dehydration is a major regulatory problem for terrestrial plants and animals. Humans, for example, die if they lose as little as 12% of their body water (desert camels can withstand approximately twice that level of dehydration). Adaptations that reduce water loss are key to survival on land. Much as a waxy cuticle contributes to the success of land plants, the body coverings of most terrestrial animals help prevent dehydration. Examples are the waxy layers of insect exoskeletons, the shells of land snails, and the layers of dead, keratinized skin cells covering most terrestrial vertebrates, including humans. Many terrestrial animals, especially desert-dwellers, are nocturnal, which reduces evaporative water loss because of the lower temperature and higher relative humidity of night air.

Despite these and other adaptations, most terrestrial animals lose water through many routes: in urine and feces, across their skin, and from moist surfaces in gas exchange organs. Land animals maintain water balance by drinking and eating moist foods and by producing water metabolically through cellular respiration. A number of desert animals, including many insect-eating birds and other reptiles, are well

▲ **Figure 44.6 Water balance in two terrestrial mammals.** Kangaroo rats, which live in the American Southwest, eat mostly dry seeds and do not drink water. A kangaroo rat gains water mainly from cellular metabolism and loses water mainly by evaporation during gas exchange. In contrast, a human gains water in food and drink and loses the largest fraction of it in urine.

enough adapted for minimizing water loss that they can survive without drinking. A noteworthy example is the kangaroo rat: It loses so little water that 90% is replaced by water generated metabolically (**Figure 44.6**); the remaining 10% comes from the small amount of water in its diet of seeds.

Energetics of Osmoregulation

When an animal maintains an osmolarity difference between its body and the external environment, there is an energy cost. Because diffusion tends to equalize concentrations in a system, osmoregulators must expend energy to maintain the osmotic gradients that cause water to move in or out. They do so by using active transport to manipulate solute concentrations in their body fluids.

The energy cost of osmoregulation depends on how different an animal's osmolarity is from its surroundings, how easily water and solutes can move across the animal's surface, and how much work is required to pump solutes across the membrane. Osmoregulation accounts for 5% or more of the resting metabolic rate of many freshwater and marine bony fishes. For brine shrimp, small crustaceans that live in Utah's Great Salt Lake and other extremely salty lakes, the gradient between internal and external osmolarity is very large, and the cost of osmoregulation is correspondingly high—as much as 30% of the resting metabolic rate.

The energy cost to an animal of maintaining water and salt balance is minimized by a body fluid composition adapted to the salinity of the animal's habitat. Comparing closely related species reveals that the body fluids of most freshwater animals have lower solute concentrations than the body fluids of their marine relatives. For instance, whereas marine molluscs have body fluids with a solute concentration of approximately 1,000 mOsm/L, some freshwater mussels maintain the solute concentration of their body fluids as low as 40 mOsm/L. The reduced osmotic difference between body fluids and the surrounding environment (about 1,000 mOsm/L for seawater and 0.5–15 mOsm/L for fresh water) decreases the energy the animal expends for osmoregulation.

Transport Epithelia in Osmoregulation

The ultimate function of osmoregulation is to maintain the composition of the cellular contents, but most animals do this indirectly by managing the composition of an internal body fluid that bathes the cells. In insects and other animals with an open circulatory system, this fluid is the hemolymph (see Chapter 42). In vertebrates and other animals with a closed circulatory system, the cells are bathed in an interstitial fluid that contains a mixture of solutes controlled indirectly by the blood. Maintaining the composition of such fluids depends on structures ranging from cells that regulate solute movement to complex organs, such as the vertebrate kidney.

In most animals, osmotic regulation and metabolic waste disposal rely on one or more kinds of **transport epithelium**— one or more layers of specialized epithelial cells that regulate solute movements. Transport epithelia move specific solutes in controlled amounts in specific directions. Transport epithelia are typically arranged into complex tubular networks with extensive surface areas. Some transport epithelia face the outside environment directly, while others line channels connected to the outside by an opening on the body surface.

The transport epithelium that enables the albatross to survive on seawater remained undiscovered for many years. Some scientists suggested that marine birds do not actually drink water, asserting that although the birds take water into their mouths they do not swallow. Questioning this idea, Knut Schmidt-Nielsen and colleagues carried out a simple but informative experiment **(Figure 44.7)**.

As Schmidt-Nielsen demonstrated, the adaptation that enables the albatross and other marine birds to maintain internal salt balance is a specialized nasal gland. In removing excess sodium chloride from the blood, the nasal gland relies on countercurrent exchange **(Figure 44.8)**. Recall from Chapter 40 that countercurrent exchange occurs between two fluids separated by one or more membranes and flowing in opposite directions. In the albatross's nasal gland, the net result is the secretion of fluid much saltier than the ocean. Thus, even though drinking seawater brings in a lot of salt, the bird achieves a net gain of wa-

ter. By contrast, humans who drink a given volume of seawater must use a greater volume of water to excrete the salt load, with the result that they become dehydrated.

Transport epithelia that function in maintaining water balance also often function in disposal of metabolic wastes. We will see examples of this coordinated function in our upcoming consideration of earthworm and insect excretory systems as well as the vertebrate kidney.

▼ **Figure 44.7** Inquiry

How do seabirds eliminate excess salt from their bodies?

EXPERIMENT   Knut Schmidt-Nielsen and colleagues, at the Mount Desert Island Laboratory, Maine, gave captive marine birds nothing but seawater to drink. However, only a small amount of the salt the birds consumed appeared in their urine. The remainder was concentrated in a clear fluid dripping from the tip of the birds' beaks. Where did this salty fluid come from? The researchers focused their attention on the nasal glands, a pair of structures found in the heads of all birds. The nasal glands of seabirds are much larger than those of land birds, and Schmidt-Nielsen hypothesized that the nasal glands function in salt elimination. To test this hypothesis, the researchers inserted a thin tube through the duct leading to a nasal gland and withdrew fluid.

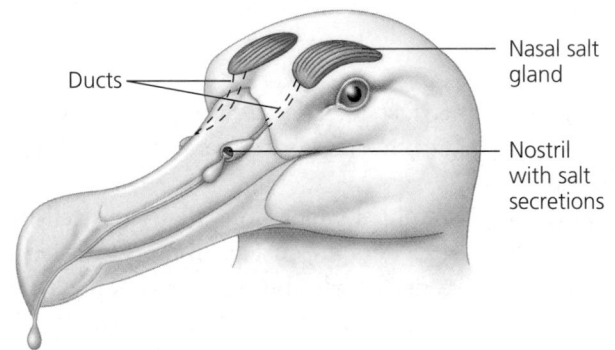

Ducts

Nasal salt gland

Nostril with salt secretions

RESULTS   The fluid drawn from the nasal glands of the captive marine birds was a nearly pure solution of NaCl. The salt concentration was 5%, nearly twice as salty as seawater (and many times saltier than human tears). Control samples of fluid drawn from other glands in the head revealed no other location of high salt concentration.

CONCLUSION   Marine birds utilize their nasal glands to eliminate excess salt from the body. It is these organs that make life at sea possible for species such as gulls and albatrosses. Similar structures, called salt glands, provide the identical function in sea turtles and marine iguanas.

SOURCE   K. Schmidt-Nielsen et al., Extrarenal salt excretion in birds, *American Journal of Physiology* 193:101–107 (1958).

WHAT IF?   The nasal glands enable marine birds to eliminate excess salt they gain from consuming prey as well as from drinking salt water. How would the type of animal prey that a marine bird eats influence how much salt it needs to eliminate?

(a) This cut-away diagram shows one of several thousand secretory tubules in a salt-excreting gland. Each tubule is lined by a transport epithelium surrounded by capillaries, and drains into a central duct.

(b) The secretory cells actively transport salt (NaCl) from the blood into the tubules. Blood flows counter to the flow of salt secretion. By maintaining a concentration gradient of salt in the tubule (aqua), this counter-current system enhances salt transfer from the blood to the lumen of the tubule.

▲ **Figure 44.8 Countercurrent exchange in salt-excreting nasal glands.**

CONCEPT CHECK 44.1

1. The movement of salt from the surrounding water to the blood of a freshwater fish requires the expenditure of energy in the form of ATP. Why?
2. Why aren't any freshwater animals osmoconformers?
3. **WHAT IF?** Researchers found that a camel standing in the sun required much more water when its fur was shaved off, although its body temperature remained the same. What can you conclude about the relationship between osmoregulation and the insulation provided by fur?

For suggested answers, see Appendix A.

CONCEPT 44.2

An animal's nitrogenous wastes reflect its phylogeny and habitat

Because most metabolic wastes must be dissolved in water to be excreted from the body, the type and quantity of waste products may have a large impact on an animal's water balance. In this regard, some of the most significant waste products are the

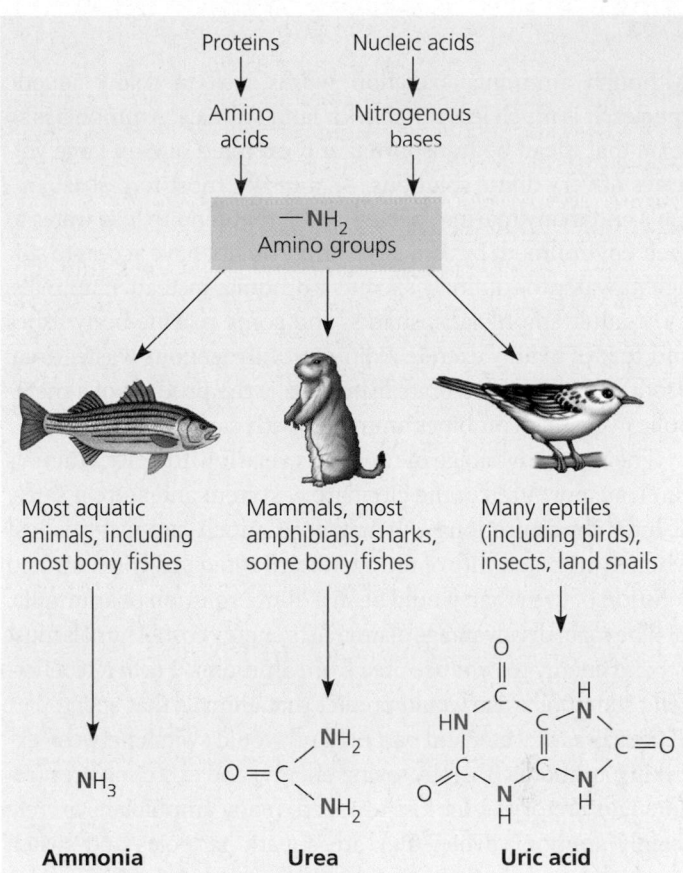

▲ **Figure 44.9 Nitrogenous wastes.**

nitrogenous breakdown products of proteins and nucleic acids (**Figure 44.9**). When proteins and nucleic acids are broken apart for energy or converted to carbohydrates or fats, enzymes remove nitrogen in the form of **ammonia** (NH_3). Ammonia is very toxic, in part because its ion, ammonium (NH_4^+), interferes with oxidative phosphorylation. Although some animals excrete ammonia directly, many species expend energy to convert it to less toxic compounds prior to excretion.

Forms of Nitrogenous Waste

Animals excrete nitrogenous wastes as ammonia, urea, or uric acid. These different forms vary significantly in their toxicity and the energy costs of producing them.

Ammonia

Because ammonia can be tolerated only at very low concentrations, animals that excrete nitrogenous wastes as ammonia need access to lots of water. Therefore, ammonia excretion is most common in aquatic species. Being highly soluble, ammonia molecules easily pass through membranes and are readily lost by diffusion to the surrounding water. In many invertebrates, ammonia release occurs across the whole body surface. In fishes, most of the ammonia is lost as NH_4^+ across the epithelium of the gills; the kidneys excrete only minor amounts of nitrogenous waste.

Urea

Although ammonia excretion works well in many aquatic species, it is much less suitable for land animals. Ammonia is so toxic that it can be transported and excreted only in large volumes of very dilute solutions. As a result, most terrestrial animals and many marine species (those that tend to lose water to their environment by osmosis) simply do not have access to sufficient water to routinely excrete ammonia. Instead, mammals, most adult amphibians, sharks, and some marine bony fishes and turtles mainly excrete a different nitrogenous waste, **urea**. Produced in the vertebrate liver, urea is the product of a metabolic cycle that combines ammonia with carbon dioxide.

The main advantage of urea is its very low toxicity. Animals can transport urea in the circulatory system and store it safely at high concentrations. Furthermore, much less water is lost when a given quantity of nitrogen is excreted in a concentrated solution of urea than would be in a dilute solution of ammonia.

The main disadvantage of urea is its energy cost: Animals must expend energy to produce urea from ammonia. From a bioenergetic standpoint, we would predict that animals that spend part of their lives in water and part on land would switch between excreting ammonia (thereby saving energy) and excreting urea (reducing excretory water loss). Indeed, many amphibians excrete mainly ammonia when they are aquatic tadpoles and switch largely to urea excretion when they become land-dwelling adults.

Uric Acid

Insects, land snails, and many reptiles, including birds, excrete **uric acid** as their primary nitrogenous waste. Uric acid is relatively nontoxic and does not readily dissolve in water. It therefore can be excreted as a semisolid paste with very little water loss. This is a great advantage for animals with little access to water, but there is a cost: Uric acid is even more energetically expensive to produce than urea, requiring considerable ATP for synthesis from ammonia.

Many animals, including humans, produce a small amount of uric acid as a product of purine breakdown. Diseases that disrupt this process reflect the problems that can arise when a metabolic product is insoluble. For example, a genetic defect in purine metabolism predisposes dalmatian dogs to form uric acid stones in their bladder. Humans may develop *gout*, a painful inflammation of the joints caused by deposits of uric acid crystals. Meals containing purine-rich animal tissues can increase the inflammation. Some dinosaurs appear to have been similarly affected: Fossilized bones of the carnivore *Tyrannosaurus rex* exhibit joint damage characteristic of gout.

The Influence of Evolution and Environment on Nitrogenous Wastes

In general, the kind of nitrogenous wastes excreted depend on an animal's evolutionary history and habitat, especially the availability of water. For example, terrestrial turtles (which often live in dry areas) excrete mainly uric acid, whereas aquatic turtles excrete both urea and ammonia. In addition, reproductive mode seems to have been an important factor in determining which type of nitrogenous waste has become the major form during the evolution of a particular group of animals. For example, soluble wastes can diffuse out of a shell-less amphibian egg or be carried away from a mammalian embryo by the mother's blood. However, the shelled eggs produced by birds and other reptiles are permeable to gases but not to liquids, which means that soluble nitrogenous wastes released by an embryo would be trapped within the egg and could accumulate to dangerous levels. (Although urea is much less harmful than ammonia, it does become toxic at very high concentrations.) The evolution of uric acid as a waste product conveyed a selective advantage because it precipitates out of solution and can be stored within the egg as a harmless solid left behind when the animal hatches.

Regardless of the type of nitrogenous waste, the amount produced by an animal is coupled to the energy budget. Endotherms, which use energy at high rates, eat more food and produce more nitrogenous waste than ectotherms. The amount of nitrogenous waste is also linked to diet. Predators, which derive much of their energy from protein, excrete more nitrogen than animals that rely mainly on lipids or carbohydrates as energy sources.

Having surveyed the forms of nitrogenous waste and their interrelationship with evolutionary lineage, habitat, and energy consumption, we will turn next to the processes and systems animals use to excrete these and other wastes.

CONCEPT CHECK **44.2**

1. What advantage does uric acid offer as a nitrogenous waste in arid environments?
2. **WHAT IF?** Suppose a bird and a human are both suffering from gout. Why might reducing the amount of purine in the diet help the human much more than the bird?

For suggested answers, see Appendix A.

CONCEPT **44.3**

Diverse excretory systems are variations on a tubular theme

Whether an animal lives on land, in salt water, or in fresh water, water balance depends on the regulation of solute movement between internal fluids and the external environment. Much of this movement is handled by excretory systems. These systems are central to homeostasis because they dispose of metabolic wastes and control body fluid composition. Before we describe particular excretory systems, let's consider the basic process of excretion.

Excretory Processes

Animals across a wide range of species produce a fluid waste called urine through the basic steps shown in **Figure 44.10**. In the first step, body fluid (blood, coelomic fluid, or hemolymph) is brought in contact with the selectively permeable membrane of a transport epithelium. In most cases, hydrostatic pressure (blood pressure in many animals) drives a process of **filtration**. Cells, as well as proteins and other large molecules, cannot cross the epithelial membrane and remain in the body fluid. In contrast, water and small solutes, such as salts, sugars, amino acids, and nitrogenous wastes, cross the membrane, forming a solution called the **filtrate**.

The filtrate is converted into a waste fluid by the specific transport of materials into or out of the filtrate. The process of selective **reabsorption** recovers useful molecules and water from the filtrate and returns them to the body fluids. Valuable solutes—including glucose, certain salts, vitamins, hormones, and amino acids—are reabsorbed by active transport. Nonessential solutes and wastes are left in the filtrate or are added to it by selective **secretion**, which also occurs by active transport. The pumping of various solutes adjusts the osmotic movement of water into or out of the filtrate. In the last step—excretion—the processed filtrate is released from the body as urine.

Survey of Excretory Systems

The systems that perform the basic excretory functions vary widely among animal groups. However, they are generally built on a complex network of tubules that provide a large surface area for the exchange of water and solutes, including nitrogenous wastes. We'll examine the excretory systems of flatworms, earthworms, insects, and vertebrates as examples of evolutionary variations on tubule networks.

Protonephridia

Flatworms (phylum Platyhelminthes), which lack a coelom or body cavity, have excretory systems called protonephridia (singular, *protonephridium*). The **protonephridia** form a network of dead-end tubules connected to external openings. As shown in **Figure 44.11**, the tubules branch throughout the body. Cellular units called flame bulbs cap the branches of each protonephridium. Formed from a tubule cell and a cap cell, each flame bulb has a tuft of cilia projecting into the tubule. During filtration, the beating of the cilia draws water and solutes from the interstitial fluid through the flame bulb, releasing filtrate into the tubule network. (The moving cilia resemble a flickering flame; hence the name *flame bulb.*) The processed filtrate then moves outward through the tubules and empties as urine into the external environment. The urine excreted by freshwater flatworms has a low solute concentration, helping to balance the osmotic uptake of water from the environment.

1 Filtration. The excretory tubule collects a filtrate from the blood. Water and solutes are forced by blood pressure across the selectively permeable membranes of a cluster of capillaries and into the excretory tubule.

Capillary

Filtrate

Excretory tubule

2 Reabsorption. The transport epithelium reclaims valuable substances from the filtrate and returns them to the body fluids.

3 Secretion. Other substances, such as toxins and excess ions, are extracted from body fluids and added to the contents of the excretory tubule.

Urine

4 Excretion. The altered filtrate (urine) leaves the system and the body.

▲ **Figure 44.10 Key functions of excretory systems: an overview.** Most excretory systems produce a filtrate by pressure-filtering body fluids and then modify the filtrate's contents. This diagram is modeled after the vertebrate excretory system.

▶ **Figure 44.11**
Protonephridia: the flame bulb system of a planarian. Protonephridia are branching internal tubules that function mainly in osmoregulation.

Nucleus of cap cell

Cilia

Interstitial fluid filters through membrane where cap cell and tubule cell interlock.

Tubule cell

Flame bulb

Tubule

Tubules of protonephridia

Opening in body wall

Protonephridia are also found in rotifers, some annelids, molluscs larvae, and lancelets (see Figure 34.4). Among these animals, the function of the protonephridia varies. In the freshwater flatworms, protonephridia serve mainly in osmoregulation. Most metabolic wastes diffuse out of the animal across the body surface or are excreted into the gastrovascular cavity and eliminated through the mouth (see Figure 33.10). However, in some parasitic flatworms, which are isoosmotic to the surrounding fluids of their host organisms, the main function of protonephridia is the disposal of nitrogenous wastes. Natural selection has thus adapted protonephridia to distinct tasks in different environments.

Metanephridia

Most annelids, such as earthworms, have **metanephridia** (singular, *metanephridium*), excretory organs that open internally to the coelom (Figure 44.12). Each segment of a worm has a pair of metanephridia, which are immersed in coelomic fluid and enveloped by a capillary network. A ciliated funnel surrounds the internal opening. As the cilia beat, fluid is drawn into a collecting tubule, which includes a storage bladder that opens to the outside.

The metanephridia of an earthworm have both excretory and osmoregulatory functions. As urine moves along the tubule, the transport epithelium bordering the lumen reabsorbs most solutes and returns them to the blood in the capillaries. Nitrogenous wastes remain in the tubule and are excreted to the outside. Earthworms inhabit damp soil and usually experience a net uptake of water by osmosis through their skin. Their metanephridia balance the water influx by producing urine that is dilute (hypoosmotic to body fluids).

Malpighian Tubules

Insects and other terrestrial arthropods have organs called **Malpighian tubules** that remove nitrogenous wastes and also function in osmoregulation (Figure 44.13). The Malpighian tubules extend from dead-end tips immersed in hemolymph (circulatory fluid) to openings into the digestive tract. The filtration step common to other excretory systems is absent. Instead, the transport epithelium that lines the tubules secretes certain solutes, including nitrogenous wastes, from the hemolymph into the lumen of the tubule. Water follows the solutes into the tubule by osmosis, and the fluid then passes into the rectum. There, most solutes are pumped back into the hemolymph, and water reabsorption by osmosis follows. The nitrogenous wastes—mainly insoluble uric acid—are eliminated as nearly dry matter along with the feces. Capable of conserving water very effectively, the insect excretory system is a key adaptation contributing to these animals' tremendous success on land.

Kidneys

In vertebrates and some other chordates, a specialized organ called the kidney functions in both osmoregulation and excretion. Like the excretory organs of most animal phyla, kidneys consist of tubules. The numerous tubules of these compact organs are arranged in a highly organized manner and closely associated with a network of capillaries. The vertebrate

Coelom

Capillary network

① – ④:
Components of a metanephridium

① Internal opening

② Collecting tubule

③ Bladder

④ External opening

▲ **Figure 44.12 Metanephridia of an earthworm.** Each segment of the worm contains a pair of metanephridia, which collect coelomic fluid from the adjacent anterior segment. (Only one metanephridium of each pair is shown here.)

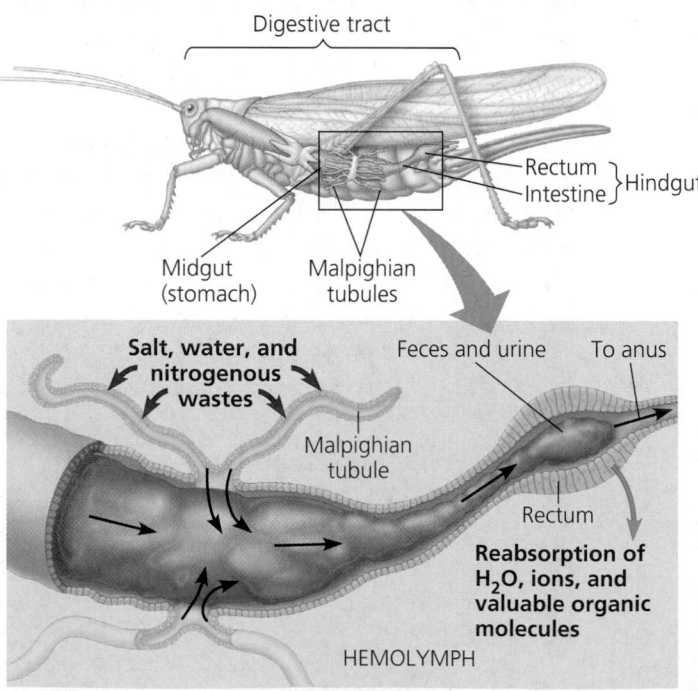

Digestive tract

Rectum
Intestine } Hindgut

Midgut (stomach)   Malpighian tubules

Salt, water, and nitrogenous wastes

Feces and urine   To anus

Malpighian tubule

Rectum

Reabsorption of H_2O, ions, and valuable organic molecules

HEMOLYMPH

▲ **Figure 44.13 Malpighian tubules of insects.** Malpighian tubules are outpocketings of the digestive tract that remove nitrogenous wastes and function in osmoregulation.

excretory system also includes ducts and other structures that carry urine from the tubules out of the kidney and, eventually, the body.

Vertebrate kidneys are typically nonsegmented. But hagfishes, which are invertebrate chordates, have kidneys with segmentally arranged excretory tubules; so, the excretory structures of vertebrate ancestors may have been segmented.

Structure of the Mammalian Excretory System

As a prelude to exploring kidney function, let's take a closer look at the routes that fluids follow in the mammalian excretory system. The excretory system of mammals centers on a pair of kidneys. In humans, each kidney is about 10 cm long and is supplied with blood by a **renal artery** and drained by a **renal vein** (Figure 44.14a). Blood flow through the kidneys is voluminous. The kidneys account for less than 1% of human body mass but receive roughly 25% of the blood exiting the heart. Urine exits each kidney through a duct called the **ureter**, and both ureters drain into a common **urinary bladder**. During urination, urine is expelled from the bladder through a tube called the **urethra**, which empties to the outside near the vagina in females and through the penis in males. Urination is regulated by sphincter muscles close to the junction of the urethra and the bladder.

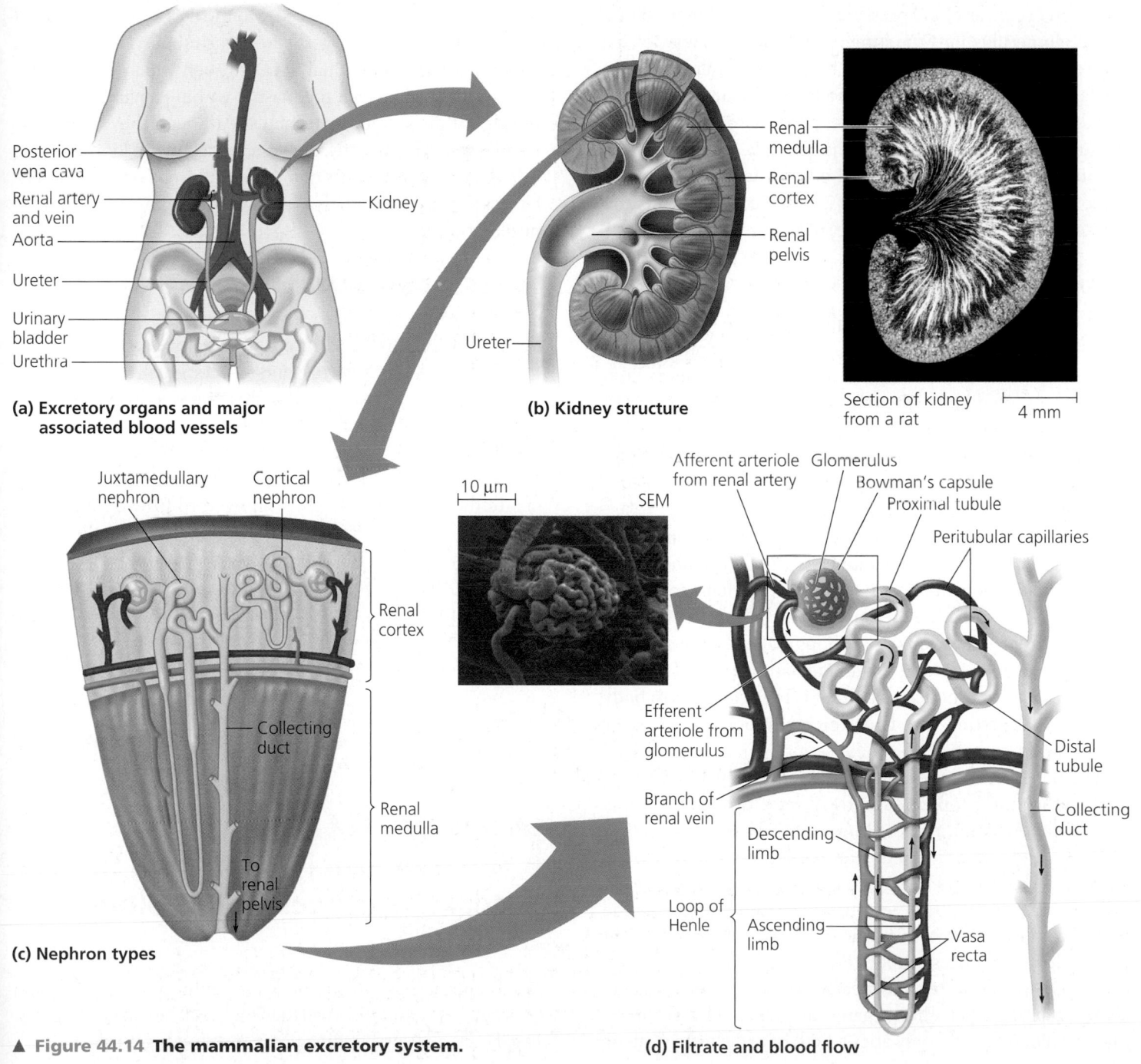

(a) **Excretory organs and major associated blood vessels**

(b) **Kidney structure**

Section of kidney from a rat
4 mm

(c) **Nephron types**

(d) **Filtrate and blood flow**

▲ Figure 44.14 **The mammalian excretory system.**

The mammalian kidney has an outer **renal cortex** and an inner **renal medulla (Figure 44.14b)**. Microscopic excretory tubules and their associated blood vessels pack both regions. Weaving back and forth across the cortex and medulla is the **nephron**, the functional unit of the vertebrate kidney. A nephron consists of a single long tubule as well as a ball of capillaries called the **glomerulus (Figure 44.14c** and **d)**. The blind end of the tubule forms a cup-shaped swelling, called **Bowman's capsule**, which surrounds the glomerulus. Each human kidney contains about a million nephrons, with a total tubule length of 80 km.

Filtration of the Blood

Filtration occurs as blood pressure forces fluid from the blood in the glomerulus into the lumen of Bowman's capsule (see Figure 44.14d). The porous capillaries and specialized cells of the capsule are permeable to water and small solutes, but not to blood cells or large molecules such as plasma proteins. Thus, the filtrate in Bowman's capsule contains salts, glucose, amino acids, vitamins, nitrogenous wastes, and other small molecules. Because filtration of small molecules is nonselective, the mixture mirrors the concentrations of these substances in blood plasma.

Pathway of the Filtrate

From Bowman's capsule, the filtrate passes into the **proximal tubule**, the first of three major regions of the nephron. Next is the **loop of Henle**, a hairpin turn with a descending limb and an ascending limb. The **distal tubule**, the last region of the nephron, empties into a **collecting duct**, which receives processed filtrate from many nephrons. This filtrate flows from all of the collecting ducts of the kidney into the **renal pelvis**, which is drained by the ureter.

Among the vertebrates, only mammals and some birds have loops of Henle. In the human kidney, 85% of the nephrons are **cortical nephrons**, which have short loops of Henle and are almost entirely confined to the renal cortex. The other 15%, the **juxtamedullary nephrons**, have loops that extend deeply into the renal medulla. It is the juxtamedullary nephrons that enable mammals to produce urine that is hyperosmotic to body fluids, an adaptation that is extremely important for water conservation.

The nephron and the collecting duct are lined by a transport epithelium that processes the filtrate, forming the urine. One of this epithelium's most important tasks is reabsorption of solutes and water. Under normal conditions, approximately 1,600 L of blood flows through a pair of human kidneys each day, a volume about 300 times the total volume of blood in the body. From this enormous traffic of blood, the nephrons and collecting ducts process about 180 L of initial filtrate. Of this, about 99% of the water and nearly all of the sugars, amino acids, vitamins, and other organic nutrients are reabsorbed into the blood, leaving only about 1.5 L of urine to be voided.

Blood Vessels Associated with the Nephrons

Each nephron is supplied with blood by an **afferent arteriole**, an offshoot of the renal artery that branches to form the capillaries of the glomerulus (see Figure 44.14d). The capillaries converge as they leave the glomerulus, forming an **efferent arteriole**. Branches of this vessel form the **peritubular capillaries**, which surround the proximal and distal tubules. A third set of capillaries extend downward and form the **vasa recta**, hairpin-shaped capillaries that serve the long loop of Henle of juxtamedullary nephrons.

The direction of blood flow within the capillaries of the vasa recta is opposite that of the filtrate in the neighboring loop of Henle (see Figure 44.14d). Said another way, each ascending portion of the vasa recta lies next to the descending portion of a loop of Henle, and vice versa. Both the tubules and capillaries are immersed in interstitial fluid, through which various substances diffuse between the plasma within capillaries and the filtrate within the nephron tubule. Although they do not exchange materials directly, the vasa recta and the loop of Henle function together as part of a countercurrent system that enhances nephron efficiency, a topic we will explore further in the next section.

CONCEPT 44.4

The nephron is organized for stepwise processing of blood filtrate

We'll continue our exploration of the nephron with a discussion of filtrate processing. We will then focus further on how tubules, capillaries, and surrounding tissue function together.

From Blood Filtrate to Urine: *A Closer Look*

In this section, we will follow filtrate along its path in the nephron and collecting duct, examining how each region contributes to the stepwise processing of filtrate into urine. The circled numbers correspond to the numbers in **Figure 44.15**.

1 Proximal tubule. Reabsorption in the proximal tubule is critical for the recapture of ions, water, and valuable nutrients from the huge initial filtrate volume. NaCl (salt) in the filtrate diffuses into the cells of the transport epithelium, where Na^+ is actively transported into the interstitial fluid. This transfer of positive charge out of the tubule drives the passive transport of Cl^-. As salt moves from the filtrate to the interstitial fluid, water follows by osmosis. The salt and water then diffuse from the interstitial fluid into the peritubular capillaries. Glucose, amino acids, potassium ions (K^+), and other essential substances are also actively or passively transported from the filtrate to the interstitial fluid and then into the peritubular capillaries.

Processing of filtrate in the proximal tubule helps maintain a relatively constant pH in body fluids. Cells of the transport epithelium secrete H^+ but also synthesize and secrete ammonia, which acts as a buffer to trap H^+ in the form of ammonium ions (NH_4^+). The more acidic the filtrate, the more ammonia the cells produce and secrete, and a mammal's urine usually contains some ammonia from this source (even though most nitrogenous waste is excreted as urea). The proximal tubules also reabsorb about 90% of the buffer bicarbonate (HCO_3^-) from the filtrate, contributing further to pH balance in body fluids.

As the filtrate passes through the proximal tubule, materials to be excreted become concentrated. Many wastes leave the body fluids during the nonselective filtration process and remain in the filtrate while water and salts are reabsorbed. Urea, for example, is reabsorbed at a much lower rate than are salt and water. Some other toxic materials are actively secreted into filtrate from surrounding tissues. For example, drugs and toxins that have been processed in the liver pass from the peritubular capillaries into the interstitial fluid. These molecules then enter the proximal tubule, where they are actively secreted from the transport epithelium into the lumen.

2 Descending limb of the loop of Henle. Reabsorption of water continues as the filtrate moves into the descending limb of the loop of Henle. Here numerous water channels formed by **aquaporin** proteins make the transport epithelium freely permeable to water. In contrast, there is a near absence of channels for

Filtrate

H_2O
Salts (NaCl and others)
HCO_3^-
H^+
Urea
Glucose; amino acids
Some drugs

Key

→ Active transport
→ Passive transport

▲ **Figure 44.15 The nephron and collecting duct: regional functions of the transport epithelium.** The numbered regions in this diagram are keyed to the circled numbers in the text discussion of kidney function.

? *Some cells lining tubules in the kidney synthesize organic solutes to maintain normal cell volume. Where in the kidney would you find these cells? Explain.*

salt and other small solutes, resulting in a very low permeability for these substances.

For water to move out of the tubule by osmosis, the interstitial fluid bathing the tubule must be hyperosmotic to the filtrate. This condition is met along the entire length of the descending limb, because the osmolarity of the interstitial fluid increases progressively from the outer cortex to the inner medulla of the kidney. As a result, the filtrate undergoes a loss of water and an accompanying increase in solute concentration at every point in its downward journey along the descending limb.

❸ Ascending limb of the loop of Henle. The filtrate reaches the tip of the loop and then travels within the ascending limb as it returns to the cortex. Unlike the descending limb, the ascending limb has a transport epithelium that contains ion channels, but not water channels. Indeed, this membrane is impermeable to water. Lack of permeability to water is very rare among biological membranes and is critical to the function of the ascending limb.

The ascending limb has two specialized regions: a thin segment near the loop tip and a thick segment adjacent to the distal tubule. As filtrate ascends in the thin segment, NaCl, which became concentrated in the descending limb, diffuses out of the permeable tubule into the interstitial fluid. This movement of NaCl out of the tubule helps maintain the osmolarity of the interstitial fluid in the medulla. The movement of NaCl out of the filtrate continues in the thick segment of the ascending limb. Here, however, the epithelium actively transports NaCl into the interstitial fluid. As a result of losing salt but not water, the filtrate becomes progressively more dilute as it moves up to the cortex in the ascending limb of the loop.

❹ Distal tubule. The distal tubule plays a key role in regulating the K^+ and NaCl concentration of body fluids. This regulation involves variation in the amount of the K^+ that is secreted into the filtrate, as well as the amount of NaCl reabsorbed from the filtrate. Like the proximal tubule, the distal tubule contributes to pH regulation by the controlled secretion of H^+ and reabsorption of HCO_3^-.

❺ Collecting duct. The collecting duct carries the filtrate through the medulla to the renal pelvis. As filtrate passes along the transport epithelium of the collecting duct, hormonal control of permeability and transport determines the extent to which the urine becomes concentrated.

When the kidneys are conserving water, aquaporin channels in the collecting duct allow water molecules to cross the epithelium. At the same time, the epithelium remains impermeable to salt and, in the renal cortex, to urea. As the collecting duct traverses the gradient of osmolarity in the kidney, the filtrate becomes increasingly concentrated, losing more and more water by osmosis to the hyperosmotic interstitial fluid. In the inner medulla, the duct becomes permeable to urea. Be-cause of the high urea concentration in the filtrate at this point, some urea diffuses out of the duct and into the interstitial fluid. Along with NaCl, this urea contributes to the high osmolarity of the interstitial fluid in the medulla. The net result is urine that is hyperosmotic to the general body fluids.

In producing dilute rather than concentrated urine, the kidney actively reabsorbs salts without allowing water to follow by osmosis. At these times, the epithelium lacks water channels, and NaCl is actively transported out of filtrate. As we will see shortly, the state of the collecting duct epithelium is controlled by hormones that together maintain homeostasis for osmolarity, blood pressure, and blood volume.

Solute Gradients and Water Conservation

The mammalian kidney's ability to conserve water is a key terrestrial adaptation. In humans, the osmolarity of blood is about 300 mOsm/L, but the kidney can excrete urine up to four times as concentrated—about 1,200 mOsm/L. Some mammals can do even better: Australian hopping mice, which live in dry desert regions, can produce urine with an osmolarity of 9,300 mOsm/L, 25 times as concentrated as the animal's blood.

In a mammalian kidney, the production of hyperosmotic urine is possible only because considerable energy is expended for the active transport of solutes against concentration gradients. The nephrons—particularly the loops of Henle—can be thought of as energy-consuming machines that produce an osmolarity gradient suitable for extracting water from the filtrate in the collecting duct. The two primary solutes affecting osmolarity are NaCl, which is deposited in the renal medulla by the loop of Henle, and urea, which passes across the epithelium of the collecting duct in the inner medulla (see Figure 44.15).

The Two-Solute Model

To better understand the physiology of the mammalian kidney as a water-conserving organ, let's retrace the flow of filtrate through the excretory tubule. This time, let's focus on how the juxtamedullary nephrons maintain an osmolarity gradient in the tissues that surround the loop of Henle and how they use that gradient to excrete a hyperosmotic urine **(Figure 44.16)**. Filtrate passing from Bowman's capsule to the proximal tubule has an osmolarity of about 300 mOsm/L, the same as blood. A large amount of water *and* salt is reabsorbed from the filtrate as it flows through the proximal tubule in the renal cortex. As a result, the filtrate's volume decreases substantially, but its osmolarity remains about the same.

As the filtrate flows from cortex to medulla in the descending limb of the loop of Henle, water leaves the tubule by osmosis. Solutes, including NaCl, become more concentrated, increasing the osmolarity of the filtrate. The highest osmolarity (about 1,200 mOsm/L) occurs at the elbow of the loop of

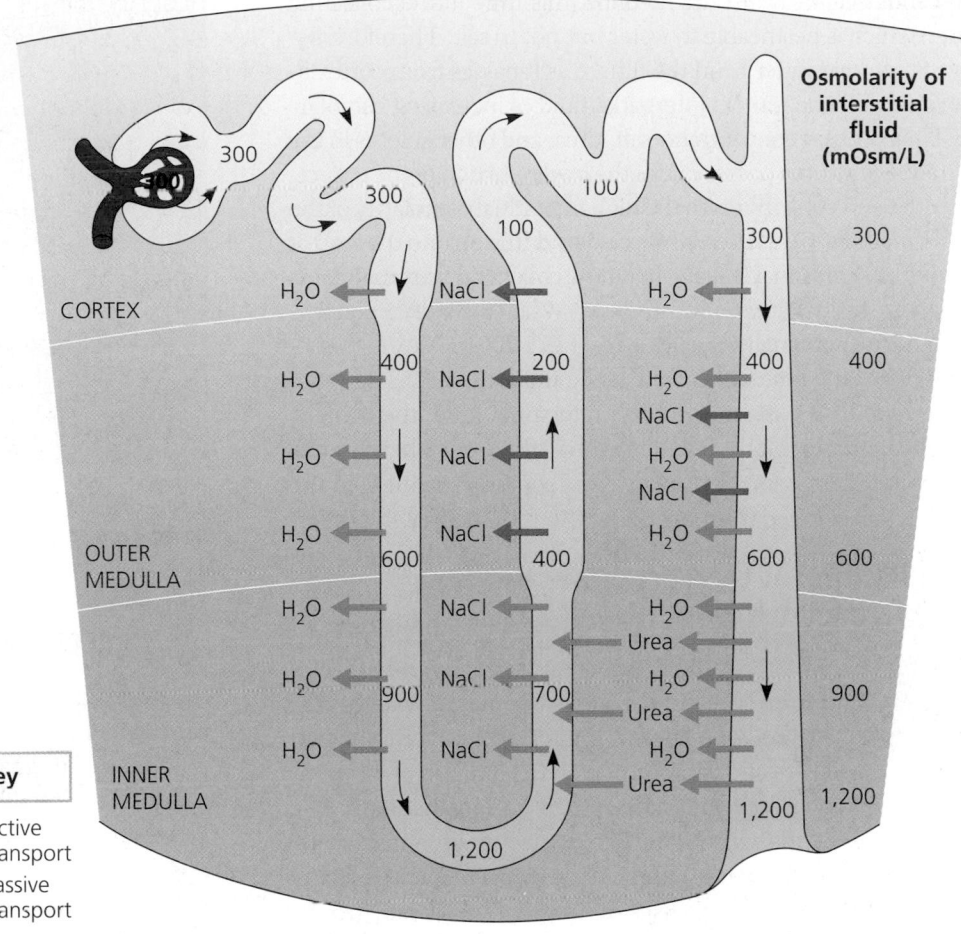

► **Figure 44.16 How the human kidney concentrates urine: the two-solute model.** Two solutes contribute to the osmolarity of the interstitial fluid: NaCl and urea. The loop of Henle maintains the interstitial gradient of NaCl, which increases in the descending limb and decreases in the ascending limb. Urea diffuses into the interstitial fluid of the medulla from the collecting duct (most of the urea in the filtrate remains in the collecting duct and is excreted). The filtrate makes three trips between the cortex and medulla: first down, then up, and then down again in the collecting duct. As the filtrate flows in the collecting duct past interstitial fluid of increasing osmolarity, more water moves out of the duct by osmosis, thereby concentrating the solutes, including urea, that are left behind in the filtrate.

WHAT IF? *The drug furosemide blocks the cotransporters for Na⁺ and Cl⁻ in the ascending limb of the loop of Henle. What effect would you expect this drug to have on urine volume?*

Key

→ Active transport
→ Passive transport

Henle. This maximizes the diffusion of salt out of the tubule as the filtrate rounds the curve and enters the ascending limb, which is permeable to salt but not to water. NaCl diffusing from the ascending limb helps maintain a high osmolarity in the interstitial fluid of the renal medulla.

Notice that the loop of Henle has several qualities of a countercurrent system, such as those mechanisms that maximize oxygen absorption by fish gills (see Figure 42.22) or reduce heat loss in endotherms (see Figure 40.12). In those cases, the countercurrent mechanisms involve passive movement along either an oxygen concentration gradient or a heat gradient. In contrast, the countercurrent system involving the loop of Henle expends energy to actively transport NaCl from the filtrate in the upper part of the ascending limb of the loop. Such countercurrent systems, which expend energy to create concentration gradients, are called **countercurrent multiplier systems**. The countercurrent multiplier system involving the loop of Henle maintains a high salt concentration in the interior of the kidney, enabling the kidney to form concentrated urine.

What prevents the capillaries of the vasa recta from dissipating the gradient by carrying away the high concentration of NaCl in the medulla's interstitial fluid? As we noted earlier (see Figure 44.14d), the descending and ascending vessels of the vasa recta carry blood in opposite directions through the kidney's osmolarity gradient. As the descending vessel conveys blood toward the inner medulla, water is lost from the blood and NaCl is gained by diffusion. These fluxes are reversed as blood flows back toward the cortex in the ascending vessel, with water reentering the blood and salt diffusing out. Thus, the vasa recta can supply the kidney with nutrients and other important substances carried by the blood without interfering with the osmolarity gradient that makes it possible for the kidney to excrete hyperosmotic urine.

The countercurrent-like characteristics of the loop of Henle and the vasa recta help to generate the steep osmotic gradient between the medulla and cortex. However, diffusion will eventually eliminate any osmotic gradient within animal tissue unless gradient formation is supported by an expenditure of energy. In the kidney, this expenditure largely occurs in the thick segment of the ascending limb of the loop of Henle, where NaCl is actively transported out of the tubule. Even with the benefits of countercurrent exchange, this process—along with other renal active transport systems—consumes considerable ATP. Thus, for its size, the kidney has one of the highest metabolic rates of any organ.

As a result of active transport of NaCl out of the thick segment of the ascending limb, the filtrate is actually hypoosmotic to body fluids by the time it reaches the distal tubule. Now the filtrate descends again toward the medulla, this time in the collecting duct, which is permeable to water but not to salt. Therefore, osmosis extracts water from the filtrate as it passes from cortex to medulla and encounters interstitial fluid of increasing osmolarity. This process concentrates salt, urea, and other solutes in the filtrate. Some urea passes out of the lower portion of the collecting duct and contributes to the high interstitial osmolarity of the inner medulla. (This urea is recycled by diffusion into the loop of Henle, but continual leakage from the collecting duct maintains a high interstitial urea concentration.) When the kidney concentrates urine maximally, the urine reaches 1,200 mOsm/L, the osmolarity of the interstitial fluid in the inner medulla. Although *isoosmotic* to the inner medulla's interstitial fluid, the urine is *hyperosmotic* to blood and interstitial fluid elsewhere in the body. This high osmolarity allows the solutes remaining in the urine to be excreted from the body with minimal water loss.

Adaptations of the Vertebrate Kidney to Diverse Environments

Vertebrate animals occupy habitats ranging from rain forests to deserts and from some of the saltiest bodies of water to the nearly pure waters of high mountain lakes. Variations in nephron structure and function equip the kidneys of different vertebrates for osmoregulation in their various habitats. The adaptations of the vertebrate kidney are made apparent by comparing species that inhabit a wide range of environments or by comparing the responses of different vertebrate groups to similar environmental conditions.

Mammals

The juxtamedullary nephron, with its urine-concentrating features, is a key adaptation to terrestrial life, enabling mammals to get rid of salts and nitrogenous wastes without squandering water. As we have seen, the remarkable ability of the mammalian kidney to produce hyperosmotic urine depends on the precise arrangement of the tubules and collecting ducts in the renal cortex and medulla. In this respect, the kidney is one of the clearest examples of how the function of an organ is inseparably linked to its structure.

Mammals that excrete the most hyperosmotic urine, such as Australian hopping mice, North American kangaroo rats, and other desert mammals, have loops of Henle that extend deep into the medulla. Long loops maintain steep osmotic gradients in the kidney, resulting in urine becoming very concentrated as it passes from cortex to medulla in the collecting ducts.

In contrast, beavers, muskrats, and other aquatic mammals that spend much of their time in fresh water and rarely face problems of dehydration have nephrons with relatively short loops, resulting in a much lower ability to concentrate urine. Terrestrial mammals living in moist conditions have loops of Henle of intermediate length and the capacity to produce urine intermediate in concentration to that produced by freshwater and desert mammals.

▲ **Figure 44.17 The roadrunner (*Geococcyx californianus*), an animal well adapted for conserving water.**

Birds and Other Reptiles

Most birds, including the albatross (see Figure 44.1) and the roadrunner **(Figure 44.17)**, live in environments that are dehydrating. Like mammals, birds have kidneys with juxtamedullary nephrons that specialize in conserving water. However, the nephrons of birds have loops of Henle that extend less far into the medulla than those of mammals. Thus, bird kidneys cannot concentrate urine to the high osmolarities achieved by mammalian kidneys. Although birds can produce hyperosmotic urine, their main water conservation adaptation is having uric acid as the nitrogen waste molecule. Since uric acid can be excreted as a paste, it reduces urine volume.

The kidneys of other reptiles, having only cortical nephrons, produce urine that is isoosmotic or hypoosmotic to body fluids. However, the epithelium of the chamber called the cloaca helps conserve fluid by reabsorbing some of the water present in urine and feces. Also like birds, most other reptiles excrete their nitrogenous wastes as uric acid.

Freshwater Fishes and Amphibians

Freshwater fishes are hyperosmotic to their surroundings, so they must excrete excess water continuously. In contrast to mammals and birds, freshwater fishes produce large volumes of very dilute urine. Their kidneys, which contain many nephrons, produce filtrate at a high rate. Freshwater fishes conserve salts by reabsorbing ions from the filtrate in their distal tubules, leaving water behind.

Amphibian kidneys function much like those of freshwater fishes. When in fresh water, the kidneys of frogs excrete dilute urine while the skin accumulates certain salts from the water by active transport. On land, where dehydration is the most pressing problem of osmoregulation, frogs conserve body fluid by reabsorbing water across the epithelium of the urinary bladder.

Marine Bony Fishes

The tissues of marine bony fishes gain excess salts from their surroundings and lose water. These environmental challenges are opposite to those faced by their freshwater relatives. Compared with freshwater fishes, marine fishes have fewer and smaller nephrons, and their nephrons lack a distal tubule. In addition, their kidneys have small glomeruli, and some lack glomeruli entirely. In keeping with these features, filtration rates are low and very little urine is excreted.

The main function of kidneys in marine bony fishes is to get rid of divalent ions (those with a charge of 2+ or 2−) such as calcium (Ca^{2+}), magnesium (Mg^{2+}), and sulfate (SO_4^{2-}). Marine fishes take in divalent ions by incessantly drinking seawater. They rid themselves of these ions by secreting them into the proximal tubules of the nephrons and excreting them in urine. Secretion by the gills maintains proper levels of monovalent ions (charge of 1+ or 1−) such as Na^+ and Cl^-.

▲ **Figure 44.18 A vampire bat (*Desmodus rotundas*), a mammal with a unique excretory situation.**

CONCEPT CHECK 44.4

1. What do the number and length of nephrons indicate about the habitat of fishes? How do these features correlate with rates of urine production?
2. Many medications make the epithelium of the collecting duct less permeable to water. How would taking such a drug affect kidney output?
3. **WHAT IF?** If blood pressure in the afferent arteriole leading to a glomerulus decreased, how would the rate of blood filtration within Bowman's capsule be affected? Explain.

For suggested answers, see Appendix A.

CONCEPT 44.5
Hormonal circuits link kidney function, water balance, and blood pressure

In mammals, both the volume and osmolarity of urine are adjusted according to an animal's water and salt balance and its rate of urea production. In situations of high salt intake and low water availability, a mammal can excrete urea and salt in small volumes of hyperosmotic urine with minimal water loss. If salt is scarce and fluid intake is high, the kidney can instead get rid of the excess water with little salt loss by producing large volumes of hypoosmotic urine. At such times, the urine can be as dilute as 70 mOsm/L, compared with an osmolarity of 300 mOsm/L for human blood.

The South American vampire bat shown in **Figure 44.18** illustrates the versatility of the mammalian kidney. Bats of this species feed at night on the blood of large birds and mammals. The bats use their sharp teeth to make a small incision in the prey's skin and then lap up blood from the wound (the prey animal is typically not seriously harmed). Anticoagulants in the bat's saliva prevent the blood from clotting. Because vampire bats often search for hours and fly long distances to locate a suitable victim, they benefit from consuming as much blood as possible when they do find prey—so much that after feeding, a bat could be too heavy to fly. However, the bat's kidneys offload much of the water absorbed from a blood meal by excreting large volumes of dilute urine as it feeds, up to 24% of body mass per hour. Having lost enough weight to take off, the bat can fly back to its roost in a cave or hollow tree, where it spends the day.

In the roost, the bat faces a different regulatory problem. Most of the nutrition it derives from blood comes in the form of protein. Digesting proteins generates large quantities of urea, but roosting bats lack access to the drinking water necessary to dilute it. Instead, their kidneys shift to producing small quantities of highly concentrated urine (up to 4,600 mOsm/L), an adjustment that disposes of the urea load while conserving as much water as possible. The vampire bat's ability to alternate rapidly between producing large amounts of dilute urine and small amounts of very hyperosmotic urine is an essential part of its adaptation to an unusual food source.

Antidiuretic Hormone

A combination of nervous and hormonal controls manages the osmoregulatory function of the mammalian kidney. One key hormone in this regulatory circuitry is **antidiuretic hormone (ADH)**, also called *vasopressin*. ADH is produced in the hypothalamus of the brain and stored in the posterior pituitary gland, located just below the hypothalamus. Osmoreceptor cells in the hypothalamus monitor the osmolarity of blood and regulate release of ADH from the posterior pituitary.

To understand the role of ADH, let's consider what occurs when blood osmolarity rises, such as after ingesting salty food or losing water through sweating. In response to an increase in osmolarity above the set point of 300 mOsm/L, more ADH is released into the bloodstream **(Figure 44.19a)**. When ADH reaches the kidney, its main targets are the distal tubules and collecting ducts. There, ADH brings about changes that make the epithelium more permeable to water. The resulting increase in water reabsorption concentrates urine, reduces urine volume, and lowers blood osmolarity back toward the set point. (Only the gain of additional water in food and drink can bring osmolarity all the way back to 300 mOsm/L.) As the osmolarity of the blood subsides, a negative-feedback mechanism reduces the activity of osmoreceptor cells in the hypothalamus, and ADH secretion is reduced.

A reduction in blood osmolarity below the set point has the opposite set of effects. For example, intake of a large volume of water leads to a decrease in ADH secretion to a very low level. The resulting decrease in permeability of the distal tubules and collecting ducts reduces water reabsorption, resulting in discharge of large volumes of dilute urine. (Diuresis refers to increased urination, and ADH is called *anti*diuretic hormone because it opposes this state.)

ADH influences water uptake in the kidney by regulating the water-selective channels formed by aquaporins. Binding of ADH to receptor molecules leads to a temporary increase in the number of aquaporin molecules in the membranes of col-

lecting duct cells **(Figure 44.19b)**. Additional channels recapture more water, reducing urine volume.

Mutations that prevent ADH production or that inactivate the ADH receptor gene block the increase in channel number and thus the ADH response. The resulting disorder can cause severe dehydration and solute imbalance due to production of urine that is abnormally large in volume and very dilute. These symptoms give the condition its name: *diabetes insipidus* (from the Greek for "to pass through" and "having no flavor").

Dutch researcher Bernard van Oost and his colleagues wondered whether mutations in an aquaporin gene itself might also cause diabetes insipidus. Having found aquaporin gene mutations in a patient, they set out to determine whether the alterations led to nonfunctional water channels **(Figure 44.20)**.

Taken together with previous studies, the experiments of the Dutch researchers demonstrate that a wide variety of genetic defects can disrupt ADH regulation of water balance in the body. Even in the absence of such genetic changes, certain substances can alter the regulation of osmolarity. For example, alcohol can disturb water balance by inhibiting ADH release, leading to excessive urinary water loss and dehydration (which may cause some of the symptoms of a hangover). Normally, blood osmo-

(a) The hypothalamus contributes to homeostasis for blood osmolarity by triggering thirst and ADH release.

(b) ADH acts on the collecting duct of the kidney to promote increased reabsorption of water.

▲ **Figure 44.19 Regulation of fluid retention by antidiuretic hormone (ADH).**

Can aquaporin mutations cause diabetes insipidus?

EXPERIMENT Bernard van Oost and colleagues at the University of Nijmegen, in the Netherlands, were studying a patient who had diabetes insipidus, but whose ADH receptor gene was normal. Sequencing of the patient's DNA revealed two different mutations, one in each copy of an aquaporin gene. To determine whether each mutation blocked channel formation, they studied the mutant proteins in a cell that could be manipulated and studied outside the body. The cell they chose was the frog oocyte, which can be collected in large numbers from an adult female and will express foreign genes. The researchers synthesized messenger RNA from clones of the wild-type and mutant aquaporin genes and injected the synthetic RNA into oocytes. Within the oocytes, the cellular machinery translated the RNA into aquaporin proteins. To determine if the mutant aquaporin proteins made functional water channels, the investigators transferred the oocytes from a 200-mOsm to a 10-mOsm solution. They then measured swelling by light microscopy and calculated the permeability of the oocytes to water.

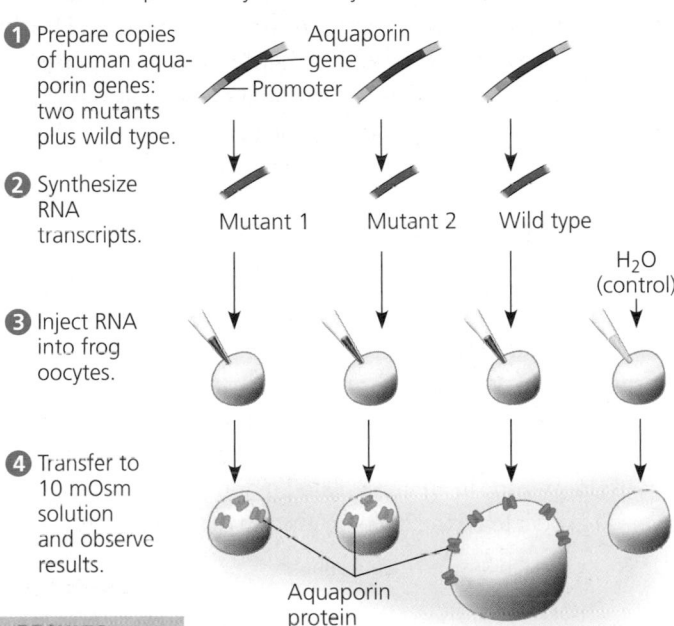

1 Prepare copies of human aquaporin genes: two mutants plus wild type.

2 Synthesize RNA transcripts.

Mutant 1   Mutant 2   Wild type

H_2O (control)

3 Inject RNA into frog oocytes.

4 Transfer to 10 mOsm solution and observe results.

Aquaporin protein

RESULTS

Injected RNA	Permeability (μm/s)
Wild-type aquaporin	196
None	20
Aquaporin mutant 1	17
Aquaporin mutant 2	18

CONCLUSION Because each mutation inactivates aquaporin as a water channel, the patient's disorder can be attributed to these mutations.

SOURCE P. M. T. Deen et al., Requirement of human renal water channel aquaporin-2 for vasopressin-dependent concentration of urine, *Science* 264:92–95 (1994).

WHAT IF? If you measured ADH levels in patients with ADH receptor mutations and in patients with aquaporin mutations, what would you expect to find, compared with wild-type subjects?

---

larity, ADH release, and water reabsorption in the kidney are all linked in a feedback loop that contributes to homeostasis.

The Renin-Angiotensin-Aldosterone System

A second regulatory mechanism that helps to maintain homeostasis is the **renin-angiotensin-aldosterone system (RAAS)**. The RAAS involves a specialized tissue called the **juxtaglomerular apparatus (JGA)**, located near the afferent arteriole that supplies blood to the glomerulus **(Figure 44.21)**. When blood pressure or blood volume in the afferent arteriole drops (for instance, as a result of blood loss or reduced intake of salt), the JGA releases the enzyme renin. Renin initiates chemical reactions that cleave a plasma protein called angiotensinogen, yielding a peptide called **angiotensin II**.

Functioning as a hormone, angiotensin II raises blood pressure by constricting arterioles, which decreases blood flow to many capillaries, including those of the kidney. Angiotensin II also stimulates the adrenal glands to release a hormone called **aldosterone**. This hormone acts on the nephrons' distal

Liver

Angiotensinogen

Distal tubule

JGA releases renin

Renin

Angiotensin I

ACE

Angiotensin II

Juxtaglomerular apparatus (JGA)

Adrenal gland

Aldosterone

Increased Na^+ and H_2O reabsorption in distal tubules

Arteriole constriction

STIMULUS: Low blood volume or blood pressure (for example, due to dehydration or blood loss)

Homeostasis: Blood pressure, volume

▲ Figure 44.21 **Regulation of blood volume and pressure by the renin-angiotensin-aldosterone system (RAAS).**

tubules, making them reabsorb more sodium (Na^+) and water and increasing blood volume and pressure.

Because angiotensin II acts in several ways that increase blood pressure, drugs that block angiotensin II production are widely used to treat hypertension (chronic high blood pressure). Many of these drugs are specific inhibitors of angiotensin converting enzyme (ACE), which catalyzes the second step in the production of an angiotensin II. As shown in Figure 44.21, renin released from the JGA acts on a circulating substrate, angiotensinogen, forming angiotensin I. ACE in vascular endothelium, particularly in the lungs, then splits off two amino acids from angiotensin I, forming active angiotensin II. Blocking ACE activity with drugs prevents angiotensin II production and thereby often lowers blood pressure into the normal range.

Homeostatic Regulation of the Kidney

The renin-angiotensin-aldosterone system operates as part of a complex feedback circuit that results in homeostasis. A drop in blood pressure and blood volume triggers renin release from the JGA. In turn, the rise in blood pressure and volume resulting from the various actions of angiotensin II and aldosterone reduces the release of renin.

The functions of ADH and the RAAS may seem to be redundant, but this is not the case. Both increase water reabsorption, but they counter different osmoregulatory problems. The release of ADH is a response to an increase in blood osmolarity, as when the body is dehydrated from excessive water loss or inadequate water intake. However, a situation that causes an excessive loss of both salt and body fluids—a major wound, for example, or severe diarrhea—will reduce blood volume *without* increasing osmolarity. This will not affect ADH release, but the RAAS will respond to the drop in blood volume and pressure by increasing water and Na^+ reabsorption. Thus, ADH and the

RAAS are partners in homeostasis. ADH alone would lower blood Na^+ concentration by stimulating water reabsorption in the kidney, but the RAAS helps maintain the osmolarity of body fluids at the set point by stimulating Na^+ reabsorption.

Another hormone, **atrial natriuretic peptide (ANP)**, opposes the RAAS. The walls of the atria of the heart release ANP in response to an increase in blood volume and pressure. ANP inhibits the release of renin from the JGA, inhibits NaCl reabsorption by the collecting ducts, and reduces aldosterone release from the adrenal glands. These actions lower blood volume and pressure. Thus, ADH, the RAAS, and ANP provide an elaborate system of checks and balances that regulate the kidney's ability to control the osmolarity, salt concentration, volume, and pressure of blood. The precise regulatory role of ANP is an area of active research.

In all animals, certain of the intricate physiological machines we call organs work continuously in maintaining solute and water balance and excreting nitrogenous wastes. The details that we have reviewed in this chapter only hint at the great complexity of the neural and hormonal mechanisms involved in regulating these homeostatic processes.

CONCEPT CHECK 44.5

1. How does alcohol affect regulation of water balance in the body?
2. Why could it be dangerous to drink a very large amount of water in a short period of time?
3. **WHAT IF?** Conn's syndrome is a condition caused by tumors of the adrenal cortex that secrete high amounts of aldosterone in an unregulated manner. What would you expect to be the major symptom of this disorder?

For suggested answers, see Appendix A.

Chapter 44 Review

MEDIA Go to www.campbellbiology.com for BioFlix 3-D Animations, MP3 Tutors, Videos, Practice Tests, an eBook, and more.

SUMMARY OF KEY CONCEPTS

CONCEPT 44.1

Osmoregulation balances the uptake and loss of water and solutes (pp. 954–959)

▶ Osmoregulation is based largely on the controlled movement of solutes between internal fluids and the external environment, as well as the movement of water, which follows by osmosis.

▶ **Osmosis and Osmolarity** Cells require a balance between osmotic gain and loss of water. Water uptake and loss are balanced by various mechanisms of osmoregulation in different environments.

▶ **Osmotic Challenges** Osmoconformers, all of which are marine animals, are isoosmotic with their surroundings and do not regulate their osmolarity. Among marine animals, most invertebrates are osmoconformers.

▶ **Energetics of Osmoregulation** Osmoregulators expend energy to control water uptake and loss in a hypoosmotic or hyperosmotic environment, respectively. Sharks have an osmolarity slightly higher than seawater because they retain urea. Terrestrial animals combat desiccation through behavioral adaptations, water-conserving excretory organs, and drinking and eating food with high water content. Animals in temporary waters may be anhydrobiotic.

Animal	Inflow/Outflow	Urine
Freshwater fish. Lives in water less concentrated than body fluids; fish tends to gain water, lose salt	Does not drink water Salt in H_2O in (active transport by gills) Salt out	▶ Large volume of urine ▶ Urine is less concentrated than body fluids
Marine bony fish. Lives in water more concentrated than body fluids; fish tends to lose water, gain salt	Drinks water Salt in H_2O out Salt out (active transport by gills)	▶ Small volume of urine ▶ Urine is slightly less concentrated than body fluids
Terrestrial vertebrate. Terrestrial environment; tends to lose body water to air	Drinks water Salt in (by mouth) H_2O and salt out	▶ Moderate volume of urine ▶ Urine is more concentrated than body fluids

▶ **Transport Epithelia in Osmoregulation** Water balance and waste disposal depend on transport epithelia, layers of specialized epithelial cells that regulate the solute movements required for waste disposal and for tempering changes in body fluids.

CONCEPT **44.2**

An animal's nitrogenous wastes reflect its phylogeny and habitat (pp. 959–960)

▶ **Forms of Nitrogenous Waste** Protein and nucleic acid metabolism generates ammonia, a toxic waste product. Most aquatic animals excrete ammonia across the body surface or gill epithelia into the surrounding water. The liver of mammals and most adult amphibians converts ammonia to the less toxic urea, which is carried to the kidneys, concentrated, and excreted with a minimal loss of water. Uric acid is a slightly soluble nitrogenous waste excreted in the paste-like urine of land snails, insects, and many reptiles, including birds.

▶ **The Influence of Evolution and Environment on Nitrogenous Wastes** The kind of nitrogenous waste excreted depends on an animal's evolutionary history and habitat. The amount of nitrogenous waste produced is coupled to the animal's energy budget and amount of dietary protein.

CONCEPT **44.3**

Diverse excretory systems are variations on a tubular theme (pp. 960–964)

▶ **Excretory Processes** Most excretory systems produce urine by refining a filtrate derived from body fluids. Key functions of most excretory systems are filtration (pressure filtering of body fluids, producing a filtrate); production of urine from the filtrate by selective reabsorption (reclaiming valuable solutes from the filtrate); and secretion (addition of toxins and other solutes from the body fluids to the filtrate).

▶ **Survey of Excretory Systems** Extracellular fluid is filtered into the protonephridia of the flame bulb system in flatworms; these tubules excrete a dilute fluid and may also function in osmoregulation. Each segment of an earthworm has a pair of open-ended metanephridia that collect coelomic fluid and produce dilute urine. In insects, Malpighian tubules function in osmoregulation and removal of nitrogenous wastes from the hemolymph. Insects produce a relatively dry waste matter, an important adaptation to terrestrial life. Kidneys, the excretory organs of vertebrates, function in both excretion and osmoregulation.

▶ **Structure of the Mammalian Excretory System** Excretory tubules (consisting of nephrons and collecting ducts) and associated blood vessels pack the kidney. Filtration occurs as blood pressure forces fluid from the blood in the glomerulus into the lumen of Bowman's capsule. Filtration of small molecules is nonselective, and the filtrate initially contains a mixture of small molecules that mirrors the concentrations of these substances in blood plasma. Fluid from several nephrons flows into a collecting duct. The ureter conveys urine from the renal pelvis to the urinary bladder.

MEDIA

Activity Structure of the Human Excretory System

CONCEPT **44.4**

The nephron is organized for stepwise processing of blood filtrate (pp. 964–969)

▶ **From Blood Filtrate to Urine:** *A Closer Look* Nephrons control the composition of the blood by filtration, secretion, and reabsorption. Secretion and reabsorption in the proximal tubule substantially alter the volume and composition of filtrate. The descending limb of the loop of Henle is permeable to water but not to salt; water moves by osmosis into the hyperosmotic interstitial fluid. The ascending limb is permeable to salt, but not to water, with salt leaving as the filtrate ascends first by diffusion and then by active transport. The distal tubule and collecting duct play key roles in regulating the K^+ and NaCl concentration of body fluids. The collecting duct carries the filtrate through the medulla to the renal pelvis and can respond to hormonal signals to reabsorb water.

▶ **Solute Gradients and Water Conservation** In a mammalian kidney, the cooperative action of the loops of Henle and the collecting ducts is largely responsible for the osmotic gradient that concentrates the urine. A countercurrent multiplier system involving the loop of Henle maintains the gradient of salt concentration in the interior of the kidney, which enables the kidney to form concentrated urine. The urine can be further concentrated by water exiting the filtrate by osmosis in the collecting duct. Urea, which diffuses out of the collecting duct as it traverses the inner medulla, contributes to the osmotic gradient of the kidney.

▶ **Adaptations of the Vertebrate Kidney to Diverse Environments** The form and function of nephrons in various vertebrates are related primarily to the requirements for osmoregulation in the animal's habitat. Desert mammals, which excrete the most hyperosmotic urine, have loops of Henle that extend deep into the kidney medulla, whereas mammals living in moist or aquatic habitats have shorter loops and excrete less concentrated urine. Although birds can produce a hyperosmotic urine, the main water conservation adaptation of birds is removal of nitrogen as uric acid, which can be excreted as a paste. Most other terrestrial reptiles excrete uric acid. Freshwater fishes and amphibians produce large volumes of very dilute urine. The kidneys of marine bony fishes have low filtration rates and excrete very little urine.

MEDIA

Activity Nephron Function

CONCEPT 44.5

Hormonal circuits link kidney function, water balance, and blood pressure (pp. 969–972)

▶ **Antidiuretic Hormone** ADH is released from the posterior pituitary gland when the osmolarity of blood rises above a set point. ADH increases epithelial permeability to water in the distal tubules and collecting ducts of the kidney. The permeability increase in the collecting duct results from an increase in the number of water channels in the membrane.

▶ **The Renin-Angiotensin-Aldosterone System** When blood pressure or blood volume in the afferent arteriole drops, renin released from the juxtaglomerular apparatus (JGA) initiates conversion of angiotensinogen to angiotensin II. Functioning as a hormone, angiotensin II raises blood pressure by constricting arterioles and triggering release of the hormone aldosterone. The rise in blood pressure and volume in turn reduces the release of renin.

▶ **Homeostatic Regulation of the Kidney** ADH and the RAAS have overlapping but distinct functions. Atrial natriuretic peptide (ANP) opposes the action of the RAAS.

MEDIA

Activity Control of Water Reabsorption
Investigation What Affects Urine Production?

TESTING YOUR KNOWLEDGE

SELF-QUIZ

1. *Unlike* an earthworm's metanephridia, a mammalian nephron
   a. is intimately associated with a capillary network.
   b. forms urine by changing fluid composition inside a tubule.
   c. functions in both osmoregulation and excretion.
   d. receives filtrate from blood instead of coelomic fluid.
   e. has a transport epithelium.

2. Which of the following is *not* a normal response to increased blood osmolarity in humans?
   a. increased permeability of the collecting duct to water
   b. production of more dilute urine
   c. release of ADH by the pituitary gland
   d. increased thirst
   e. reduced urine production

3. The high osmolarity of the renal medulla is maintained by all of the following *except*
   a. diffusion of salt from the thin segment of the ascending limb of the loop of Henle.
   b. active transport of salt from the upper region of the ascending limb.
   c. the spatial arrangement of juxtamedullary nephrons.
   d. diffusion of urea from the collecting duct.
   e. diffusion of salt from the descending limb of the loop of Henle.

4. Natural selection should favor the highest proportion of juxtamedullary nephrons in which of the following species?
   a. a river otter
   b. a mouse species living in a tropical rain forest
   c. a mouse species living in a temperate broadleaf forest
   d. a mouse species living in a desert
   e. a beaver

5. Which process in the nephron is *least* selective?
   a. filtration   d. secretion
   b. reabsorption   e. salt pumping by the loop of Henle
   c. active transport

6. Which of the following animals generally has the lowest volume of urine production?
   a. a marine shark
   b. a salmon in freshwater
   c. a marine bony fish
   d. a freshwater bony fish
   e. a shark inhabiting freshwater Lake Nicaragua

7. African lungfish, which are often found in small stagnant pools of fresh water, produce urea as a nitrogenous waste. What is the advantage of this adaptation?
   a. Urea takes less energy to synthesize than ammonia.
   b. Small stagnant pools do not provide enough water to dilute the toxic ammonia.
   c. The highly toxic urea makes the pool uninhabitable to potential competitors.
   d. Urea forms an insoluble precipitate.
   e. Urea makes lungfish tissue hypoosmotic to the pool.

8. **DRAW IT** Using Figure 44.4 as an example, sketch the exchange of salt (NaCl) and water between a shark and its marine environment.

For Self-Quiz answers, see Appendix A.

MEDIA Visit **www.campbellbiology.com** for a Practice Test.

EVOLUTION CONNECTION

9. Merriam's kangaroo rats (*Dipodomys merriami*) live in North American habitats ranging from moist, cool woodlands to hot deserts. Assuming that natural selection has resulted in differences in water conservation between *D. merriami* populations, propose a hypothesis concerning the relative rates of evaporative water loss by populations that live in moist versus dry environments. Using a humidity sensor to detect evaporative water loss by kangaroo rats, how could you test your hypothesis?

SCIENTIFIC INQUIRY

10. You are exploring kidney function in kangaroo rats. You measure urine volume and osmolarity, as well as the amount of chloride (Cl^-) and urea in the urine. If the water source provided to the animals were switched from tap water to a 2% NaCl solution, what change in urine osmolarity would you expect? How would you determine if this change was more likely due to a change in the excretion of Cl^- or urea?

Hormones and the Endocrine System

KEY CONCEPTS

45.1 Hormones and other signaling molecules bind to target receptors, triggering specific response pathways

45.2 Negative feedback and antagonistic hormone pairs are common features of the endocrine system

45.3 The endocrine and nervous systems act individually and together in regulating animal physiology

45.4 Endocrine glands respond to diverse stimuli in regulating metabolism, homeostasis, development, and behavior

OVERVIEW

The Body's Long-Distance Regulators

In becoming an adult, a butterfly like the anise swallowtail (*Papilio zelicaon*) in **Figure 45.1** is dramatically transformed. The plump, crawling caterpillar that encases itself in a cocoon bears little resemblance to the delicate free-flying butterfly that emerges days later. Within the cocoon, specialized groups of cells assemble into the adult tissues and organs while most other tissues of the caterpillar break down.

A caterpillar's complete change of body form, called *metamorphosis*, is one of many biological processes controlled by hormones. In animals, a **hormone** (from the Greek *horman*, to excite) is a molecule that is secreted into the extracellular fluid, circulates in the blood or hemolymph, and communicates regulatory messages throughout the body. In the case of the caterpillar, communication by hormones regulates the timing of metamorphosis and ensures that different parts of the insect's adult body develop in unison.

Although the circulatory system allows a hormone to reach all cells of the body, only its target cells have the receptors that enable a response. A hormone elicits a specific response—such as a change in metabolism—from its target cells, whereas cells lacking a receptor for that particular hormone are unaffected.

▲ Figure 45.1 **What role do hormones play in transforming a caterpillar (below) into a butterfly?**

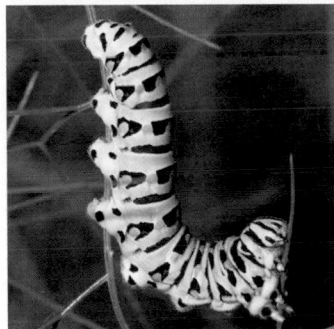

Chemical signaling by hormones is the function of the **endocrine system**, one of the two basic systems for communication and regulation throughout the body. Hormones secreted by endocrine cells regulate reproduction, development, energy metabolism, growth, and behavior. The other major communication and control system is the **nervous system**, a network of specialized cells—neurons—that transmit signals along dedicated pathways. These signals in turn regulate other cells, including neurons, muscle cells, and endocrine cells. Because signaling by neurons can regulate the release of hormones, the nervous and endocrine systems often overlap in function.

In this chapter, we'll begin with an overview of the different types of chemical signaling in animals. We will then explore how hormones regulate target cells, how hormone secretion is regulated, and how hormones help maintain homeostasis. We will also look at how the activities of the endocrine and nervous systems are coordinated. We'll conclude by examining the role of hormones in regulating growth, development, and reproduction, topics we'll return to in Chapters 46 and 47.

CONCEPT 45.1

Hormones and other signaling molecules bind to target receptors, triggering specific response pathways

Hormones, the focus of this chapter, are one of several types of secreted chemicals that transmit information between animal cells. Let's consider the similarities and differences in the functions of these signaling molecules.

Types of Secreted Signaling Molecules

Hormones and other signaling molecules trigger responses by binding to specific receptor proteins in or on target cells. Only cells that have receptors for a particular secreted molecule are target cells; other cells are unresponsive to that molecule. Molecules used in signaling are often classified by the type of secreting cell and the route taken by the signal in reaching its target.

Hormones

As illustrated in **Figure 45.2a**, hormones secreted into extracellular fluids by endocrine cells reach target cells via the bloodstream (or hemolymph). Some endocrine system cells are found in organs that are part of other organ systems. For example, within the digestive and excretory systems, the stomach and kidney both contain endocrine cells. Other endocrine cells are grouped in ductless organs called **endocrine glands**.

Like isolated endocrine cells, endocrine glands secrete hormones directly into the surrounding fluid. Endocrine glands thus contrast with *exocrine glands*, such as salivary glands, which have ducts that carry secreted substances onto body surfaces or into body cavities. This distinction is reflected in their names: The Greek *endo* (within) and *exo* (out of) reflect secretion into or out of body fluids, while *crine* (from the Greek for "separate") reflects movement away from the secreting cell.

Hormones serve a range of functions in the body. They maintain homeostasis; mediate responses to environmental stimuli; and regulate growth, development, and reproduction. For example, hormones coordinate the body's responses to stress, dehydration, or low blood glucose. They also control the appearance of characteristics that distinguish a juvenile animal from an adult.

Local Regulators

Many types of cells produce **local regulators**, secreted molecules that act over short distances and reach their target cells solely by diffusion. In Chapter 43, we saw how immune cells communicate with each other by local regulators called cytokines (see Figures 43.17 and 43.19). As we will discuss shortly, local regulators play roles in many other processes, including blood pressure regulation, nervous system function, and reproduction.

Local regulators function in paracrine and autocrine signaling. In **paracrine** signaling (from the Greek *para*, to one side of), target cells lie near the secreting cell **(Figure 45.2b)**. In **autocrine** signaling (from the Greek *auto*, self), the secreted molecules act on the secreting cell itself **(Figure 45.2c)**. Some secreted molecules have both paracrine and autocrine activity. Although the definition of hormones can be broadened to include local regulators, in this chapter we use *hormone* to refer to chemicals that reach target cells through the bloodstream.

Neurotransmitters and Neurohormones

Secreted molecules also have a critical role in the transmission of information by neurons. Neurons communicate with target cells, such as other neurons and muscle cells, at specialized junctions known as synapses. At many synapses, neurons secrete molecules called **neurotransmitters** that diffuse a very short distance to bind receptors on the target cells **(Figure 45.2d)**. Neurotransmitters are central to sensation, memory, cognition, and movement, as we will explore in Chapters 48–50.

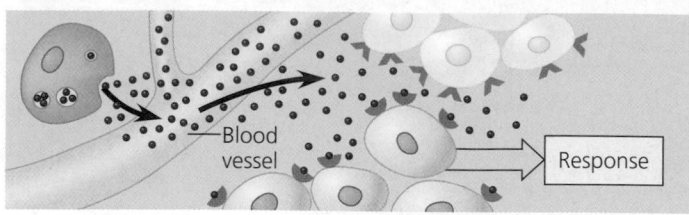

(a) In **endocrine signaling**, secreted molecules diffuse into the bloodstream and trigger responses in target cells anywhere in the body.

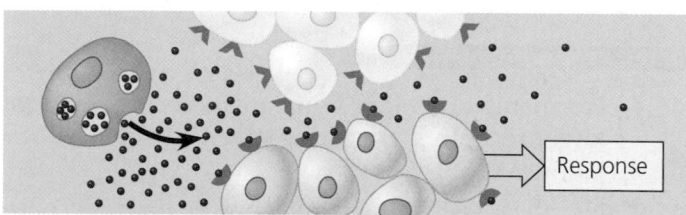

(b) In **paracrine signaling**, secreted molecules diffuse locally and trigger a response in neighboring cells.

(c) In **autocrine signaling**, secreted molecules diffuse locally and trigger a response in the cells that secrete them.

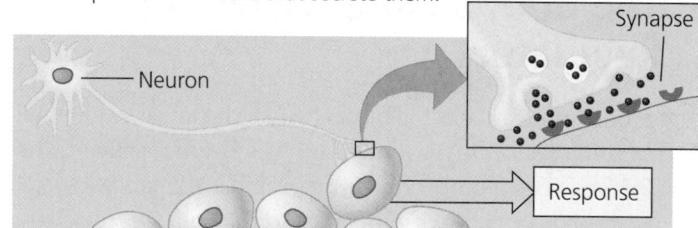

(d) In **synaptic signaling**, neurotransmitters diffuse across synapses and trigger responses in cells of target tissues (neurons, muscles, or glands).

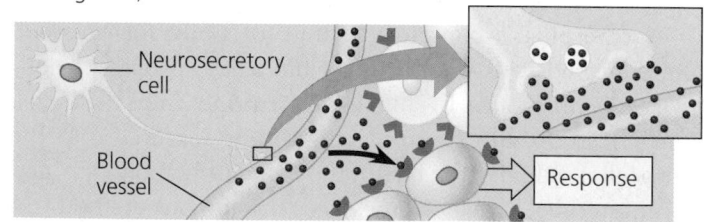

(e) In **neuroendocrine signaling**, neurohormones diffuse into the bloodstream and trigger responses in target cells anywhere in the body.

▲ **Figure 45.2 Intercellular communication by secreted molecules.** In each type of signaling, secreted molecules bind to a specific receptor protein expressed by target cells. Receptors are sometimes located inside cells, but for simplicity all are drawn here on the cell surface.

In neuroendocrine signaling, *neurosecretory cells*, specialized neurons typically found in the brain, secrete molecules that diffuse from nerve cell endings into the bloodstream (Figure 45.2e). These molecules, which travel through the bloodstream to reach target cells, are a class of hormones called **neurohormones**. One example is ADH (vasopressin), a hormone critical to kidney function and water balance (see Chapter 44).

Pheromones

Not all secreted signaling molecules act within the body. Members of the same animal species sometimes communicate with **pheromones**, chemicals that are released into the external environment. Pheromones serve many functions, including marking trails leading to food, defining territories, warning of predators, and attracting potential mates.

Chemical Classes of Hormones

Having distinguished hormones from other secreted signaling molecules based on the type and location of cells involved, we turn now to the chemical composition of hormones. Based on their structure and pathway for synthesis, hormones are often divided into three groups: polypeptides (proteins and peptides), amines, and steroids.

Figure 45.3 displays examples of each major hormone class. The polypeptide hormone insulin is made up of two polypeptide chains. Like most hormones in this group, insulin is formed by cleavage of a longer protein chain. Epinephrine and thyroxine are amine hormones, which are synthesized from a single amino acid, either tyrosine or tryptophan. Steroid hormones, such as cortisol, are lipids that contain four fused carbon rings. All are derived from the steroid cholesterol (see Figure 5.15).

As Figure 45.3 also indicates, hormones vary in their solubility in aqueous and lipid-rich environments. Polypeptides and many amine hormones are water-soluble. Being insoluble in lipids, these hormones cannot pass through the plasma membranes of cells. In contrast, steroid hormones, as well as other largely nonpolar hormones, such as thyroxine, are lipid-soluble and can pass through cell membranes readily. As we will discuss next, whether or not a hormone is able to cross cell membranes correlates with a difference in the location of receptors in target cells.

Hormone Receptor Location:
Scientific Inquiry

In studying hormone receptors, biologists needed to find out where they are located and where they functionally interact with hormones. To learn how they answered these questions, let's review some of the critical experiments.

Evidence that receptors for steroid hormones are located inside target cells came from studying the vertebrate hormone estradiol, a form of estrogen. For most mammals, including humans, estrogens are necessary for the normal development and function of the female reproductive system. In experiments conducted in the early 1960s, female rats were treated with radioactive forms of estradiol. When the researchers examined cells from the rats' reproductive systems, they found that the hormone had accumulated within the nuclei. In contrast, estradiol failed to accumulate in the cells of tissues that are not responsive to estrogens.

When scientists later identified the receptors for estrogens, they confirmed that the receptor molecules were located inside cells. Other steroid hormones and lipid-soluble hormones such as thyroxine also had intracellular receptors. But what about water-soluble hormones? Because these hormones cannot diffuse across a lipid bilayer, researchers hypothesized that their receptors would be located on the cell surface. Studies demonstrating that radioactive hormones bind to isolated cell membranes supported this model. Nevertheless, some biologists wondered whether water-soluble hormones could also initiate signaling from within cells.

In the 1970s, John Horowitz and colleagues at the University of California, Davis, investigated whether receptors for a water-soluble hormone are exclusively on the cell surface. In frogs, melanocyte-stimulating hormone (MSH) controls the location of pigment granules in skin cells. To determine where the hormone is active, the investigators used microinjection, a

Water-soluble	Lipid-soluble

Polypeptide: Insulin   0.8 nm

Steroid: Cortisol

Amine: Epinephrine

Amine: Thyroxine

▲ **Figure 45.3 Hormones differ in form and solubility.**
Structures of insulin, a polypeptide hormone; epinephrine and thyroxine, amine hormones; and cortisol, a steroid hormone. Insulin and epinephrine are water-soluble; thyroxine and cortisol are lipid-soluble.

Where in the cell is the receptor for melanocyte-stimulating hormone?

EXPERIMENT John Horowitz and colleagues at the University of California, Davis, were studying how melanocyte-stimulating hormone (MSH), a peptide hormone, triggers changes in the skin color of frogs. Skin cells called melanocytes contain the dark brown pigment melanin in cytoplasmic organelles called melanosomes. The skin appears light when melanosomes cluster tightly around the melanocyte nuclei. When a frog encounters a dark environment, increased production of MSH causes melanosomes to disperse throughout the cytoplasm, darkening the skin and making the frog less visible to predators. To identify the location of the receptors that control melanosome clustering, the researchers microinjected MSH into the melanocytes or into the surrounding interstitial fluid.

RESULTS Microinjecting MSH into individual melanocytes did not induce melanosome dispersion. However, microinjection into the interstitial fluid (blue) surrounding the melanocytes caused the melanosomes to disperse.

MSH injected into melanocyte

Melanocyte with melanosomes (black dots)

Melanosomes do not disperse

Nucleus

Melanosomes disperse

MSH injected into interstitial fluid (blue)

CONCLUSION These results provided evidence that MSH interacts with a receptor on the outside surface of the cell to induce a response.

SOURCE J. Horowitz et al., The response of single melanophores to extracellular and intracellular iontophoretic injection of melanocyte-stimulating hormone, *Endocrinology* 106:770–777 (1980).

WHAT IF? What result would you expect if you carried out the same experiments with a lipid-soluble hormone that had a receptor in the nucleus? Explain.

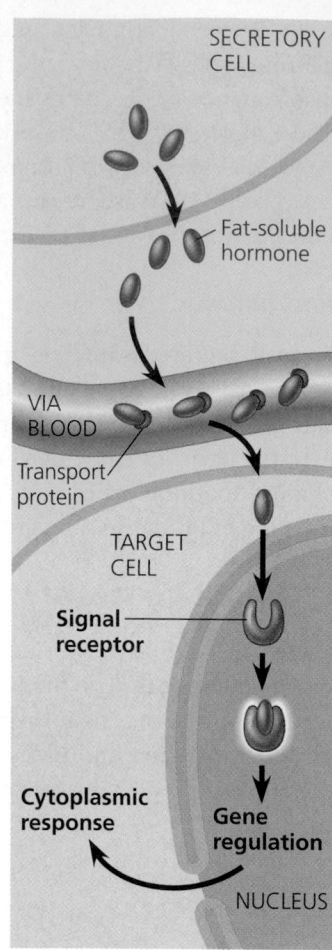

(a) Receptor in plasma membrane

(b) Receptor in cell nucleus

▲ **Figure 45.5 Receptor location varies with hormone type. (a)** A water-soluble hormone binds to a signal receptor protein on the surface of a target cell. This interaction triggers events that lead to either a change in cytoplasmic function or a change in gene transcription in the nucleus. **(b)** A lipid-soluble hormone penetrates the target cell's plasma membrane and binds to an intracellular signal receptor, either in the cytoplasm or in the nucleus (shown here). The hormone-receptor complex acts as a transcription factor, typically activating gene expression.

? *Suppose you were studying a cell's response to a particular hormone, and you observed that the cell continued to respond to the hormone even when treated with a chemical that blocks transcription. What could you surmise about the hormone and its receptor?*

technique that can introduce tiny amounts of a substance into a cell or surrounding fluid **(Figure 45.4)**. Their experiments revealed that MSH triggered a response only if it was injected into the interstitial fluid, allowing it to bind to cell-surface receptors.

Cellular Response Pathways

Receptor location is one of several differences between the response pathways for water-soluble and lipid-soluble hormones **(Figure 45.5)**. Water-soluble hormones are secreted by exocytosis, travel freely in the bloodstream, and bind to cell-surface signal receptors. Binding of such hormones to receptors induces changes in cytoplasmic molecules and sometimes alters gene transcription (synthesis of messenger RNA molecules). In contrast, lipid-soluble hormones diffuse out

across the membranes of endocrine cells and travel in the bloodstream bound to transport proteins. Upon diffusing into target cells, they bind to intracellular signal receptors and trigger changes in gene transcription.

To understand the distinct cellular responses to water-soluble and lipid-soluble hormones, we'll examine each further.

Pathway for Water-Soluble Hormones

The binding of a water-soluble hormone to a signal receptor protein triggers events at the plasma membrane that result in a cellular response. The response may be the activation of an enzyme, a change in the uptake or secretion of specific molecules, or a rearrangement of the cytoskeleton. In addition,

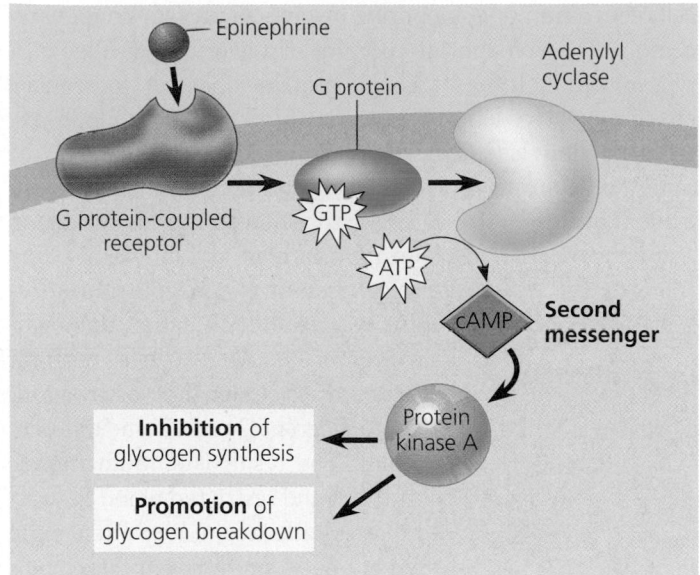

▲ Figure 45.6 **Cell-surface hormone receptors trigger signal transduction.**

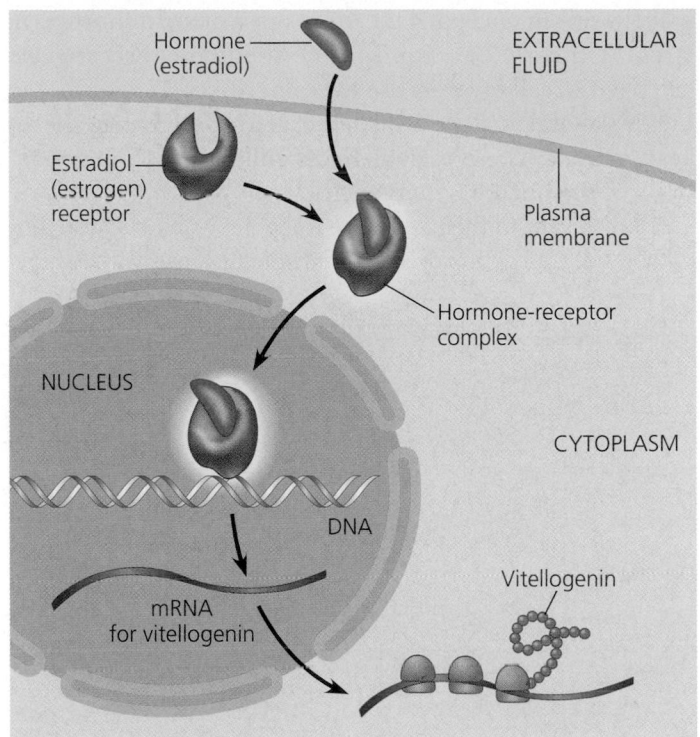

▲ Figure 45.7 **Steroid hormone receptors directly regulate gene expression.**

some cell-surface receptors cause proteins in the cytoplasm to move into the nucleus and alter transcription of specific genes.

The series of changes in cellular proteins that converts the extracellular chemical signal to a specific intracellular response is called **signal transduction**. As described in Chapter 11, a signal transduction pathway typically involves multiple steps, each involving specific molecular interactions.

To explore how signal transduction contributes to hormone signaling, let's consider one response to short-term stress. When you find yourself in a stressful situation, perhaps running to catch a bus, your adrenal glands secrete **epinephrine**. When epinephrine reaches liver cells, it binds to a G protein-coupled receptor in the plasma membrane, as discussed in Chapter 11 and reviewed in **Figure 45.6**. The binding of hormone to receptor triggers a cascade of events involving synthesis of cyclic AMP (cAMP) as a short-lived *second messenger*. Activation of protein kinase A by cAMP leads to activation of an enzyme required for glycogen breakdown and inactivation of an enzyme necessary for glycogen synthesis. The net result is that the liver releases glucose into the bloodstream, providing the fuel you need to chase the departing bus.

Pathway for Lipid-Soluble Hormones

Intracellular receptors usually perform the entire task of transducing a signal within a target cell. The hormone activates the receptor, which then directly triggers the cell's response. In most cases, the response to a lipid-soluble hormone is a change in gene expression.

Steroid hormone receptors are located in the cytosol prior to binding to a hormone. When a steroid hormone binds to its cytosolic receptor, a hormone-receptor complex forms, which moves into the nucleus. There, the receptor portion of the complex interacts with DNA or with a DNA-binding protein, stimulating transcription of specific genes. For example, estradiol has a specific receptor in the liver cells of female birds and frogs. Binding of estradiol to this receptor activates transcription of the gene for the protein vitellogenin **(Figure 45.7)**. Following translation of the messenger RNA, vitellogenin is secreted and transported in the blood to the reproductive system, where it is used to produce egg yolk.

Thyroxine, vitamin D, and other lipid-soluble hormones that are not steroid hormones have receptors that are typically located in the nucleus. These receptors bind hormone molecules that diffuse from the bloodstream across both the plasma membrane and nuclear envelope. Once bound by a hormone, the receptor binds to specific sites in the cell's DNA and stimulates the transcription of specific genes.

Recent experiments indicate that lipid-soluble hormones can sometimes trigger responses at the cell surface without first entering the nucleus. How and when these responses arise are currently the subjects of active investigation.

Multiple Effects of Hormones

Many hormones elicit more than one type of response in the body. The effects brought about by a particular hormone can vary if target cells differ in the molecules that receive or produce the response to that hormone. Consider the effects of epinephrine in mediating the body's response to short-term stress **(Figure 45.8)**. Epinephrine simultaneously triggers glycogen breakdown in the liver, increased blood flow to major skeletal muscles, and decreased blood flow to the digestive tract. These varied effects enhance the rapid reactions of the body in emergencies.

Tissues vary in their response to epinephrine because they vary in their receptors or signal transduction pathways. Target cell recognition of epinephrine involves G protein-coupled receptors. The epinephrine receptor of a liver cell is called a β-type receptor. It acts through protein kinase A to regulate enzymes in glycogen metabolism **(Figure 45.8a)**. In blood vessels supplying skeletal muscle, the same kinase activated by the same epinephrine receptor inactivates a muscle-specific enzyme **(Figure 45.8b)**. The result is smooth muscle relaxation and hence increased blood flow. In contrast, intestinal blood vessels express an α-type epinephrine receptor **(Figure 45.8c)**. Rather than activate protein kinase A, the α receptor triggers a distinct signaling pathway involving a different G protein and different enzymes. The result is smooth muscle contraction and restricted blood flow.

Lipid-soluble hormones often exert different effects on different target cells as well. For example, the estrogen that stimulates a bird's liver to synthesize the yolk protein vitellogenin also stimulates its reproductive system to synthesize proteins that form the egg white.

In some cases, a given hormone has different effects in different *species*. For instance, thyroxine produced by the thyroid gland regulates metabolism in frogs, humans, and other vertebrates. However, thyroxine has an additional and distinct effect in frogs, stimulating resorption of the tadpole's tail in its metamorphosis into an adult **(Figure 45.9)**.

▲ **Figure 45.8 One hormone, different effects.** Epinephrine, the primary "fight-or-flight" hormone, produces different responses in different target cells. Target cells with the same receptor exhibit different responses if they have different signal transduction pathways and/or effector proteins [compare (a) with (b)]. Responses of target cells may also differ if they have different receptors for the hormone [compare (b) with (c)].

▲ **Figure 45.9 Specialized role of a hormone in frog metamorphosis.** The hormone thyroxine is responsible for the resorption of the tadpole's tail (a) as the frog develops into its adult form (b).

Signaling by Local Regulators

Recall that local regulators are secreted molecules that link neighboring cells (paracrine signaling) or that provide feedback to the secreting cell (autocrine signaling). Once secreted, local regulators act on their target cells within seconds or even milliseconds, eliciting responses more quickly than do hormones. Nevertheless, the pathways by which local regulators trigger responses are the same as those activated by hormones.

Several types of chemical compounds function as local regulators. Polypeptide local regulators include **cytokines**, which play a role in immune responses (see Chapter 43), and most **growth factors**, which stimulate cell proliferation and differentiation. Many types of cells grow, divide, and develop normally only when growth factors are present in their extracellular environment.

The gas **nitric oxide (NO)**, which consists of nitrogen double-bonded to oxygen, serves in the body as both a neurotransmitter and a local regulator. When the level of oxygen (O_2) in the blood falls, endothelial cells in blood vessel walls synthesize and release NO. Nitric oxide activates an enzyme that relaxes the neighboring smooth muscle cells, resulting in vasodilation, which improves blood flow to tissues. In human males, the ability of NO to promote vasodilation enables sexual function by increasing blood flow into the penis, producing an erection. Highly reactive and potentially toxic, NO usually triggers changes in a target cell within a few seconds of contact and then breaks down. The drug Viagra (sildenafil citrate), a treatment for male erectile dysfunction, sustains an erection by interfering with this breakdown of NO.

A group of local regulators called **prostaglandins** are modified fatty acids. They are so named because they were first discovered in prostate gland secretions that contribute to semen. Prostaglandins are produced by many cell types and have varied activities. In semen that reaches the reproductive tract of a female, prostaglandins stimulate the smooth muscles of the female's uterine wall to contract, helping sperm reach an egg. At the onset of childbirth, prostaglandin-secreting cells of the placenta cause the nearby muscles of the uterus to become more excitable, helping to induce labor (see Figure 46.18).

In the immune system, prostaglandins promote fever and inflammation and also intensify the sensation of pain. The anti-inflammatory and pain-relieving effects of aspirin and ibuprofen are due to the inhibition of prostaglandin synthesis by these drugs. Prostaglandins also help regulate the aggregation of platelets, one step in the formation of blood clots. Because blood clots can cause a heart attack by blocking blood flow in vessels that supply the heart (see Chapter 42), some physicians recommend that people at risk for a heart attack take aspirin on a regular basis. However, because prostaglandins also help maintain a protective lining in the stomach, long-term aspirin therapy can cause debilitating stomach irritation.

CONCEPT CHECK 45.1

1. How do the mechanisms that induce responses in target cells differ for water-soluble hormones and lipid-soluble hormones?
2. In what way does one activity described for prostaglandins resemble that of a pheromone?
3. **WHAT IF?** Which explanation of the distinct effects of epinephrine in different tissues might best account for the distinct effects of hormones in different species? Explain your answer.

For suggested answers, see Appendix A.

Negative feedback and antagonistic hormone pairs are common features of the endocrine system

So far, we have explored the chemical nature of hormones and other signaling molecules and gained a basic understanding of their activities in cells. We turn now to considering how regulatory pathways that control hormone secretion are organized. For these and later examples taken from the human endocrine system, **Figure 45.10** provides a useful point of reference for locating endocrine glands and tissues.

Simple Hormone Pathways

In response to an internal or environmental stimulus, endocrine cells secrete a particular hormone. The hormone travels in the bloodstream to target cells, where it interacts with its specific receptors. Signal transduction within target cells brings about a physiological response. Finally, the response leads to a reduction in the stimulus and the pathway shuts off.

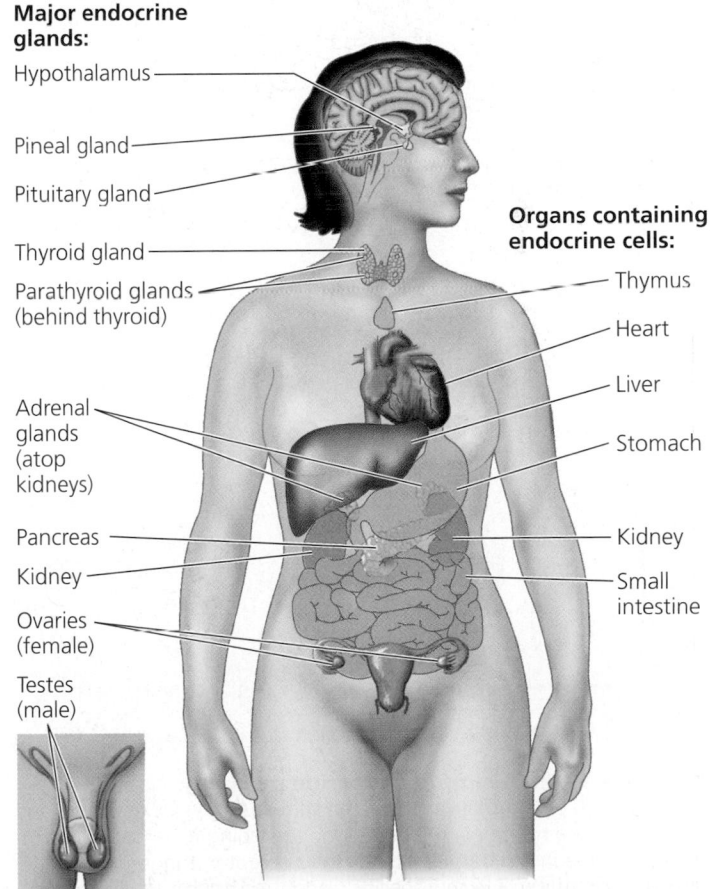

Major endocrine glands:
- Hypothalamus
- Pineal gland
- Pituitary gland
- Thyroid gland
- Parathyroid glands (behind thyroid)
- Adrenal glands (atop kidneys)
- Pancreas
- Kidney
- Ovaries (female)
- Testes (male)

Organs containing endocrine cells:
- Thymus
- Heart
- Liver
- Stomach
- Kidney
- Small intestine

▲ Figure 45.10 **Major human endocrine glands.**

In the example shown in **Figure 45.11**, acidic stomach contents released into the duodenum (the first part of the small intestine) serve as the stimulus. Low pH in the small intestine stimulates certain endocrine cells of the duodenum, called S cells, to secrete the hormone *secretin*. Secretin enters the bloodstream and reaches target cells in the **pancreas**, a gland located behind the stomach (see Figure 45.10), causing them to release bicarbonate, which raises the pH in the duodenum. The pathway is self-limiting because the response to secretin (bicarbonate release) reduces the stimulus (low pH).

A feedback loop connecting the response to the initial stimulus is characteristic of control pathways. For secretin and many other hormones, the response pathway involves **negative feedback**, a loop in which the response reduces the initial stimulus. By decreasing or abolishing hormone signaling, negative-feedback regulation prevents excessive pathway activity. Negative-feedback loops are an essential part of many hormone pathways, especially those involved in maintaining homeostasis.

Simple hormone pathways are widespread among animals. Some homeostatic control systems rely on sets of simple hormone pathways with coordinated activities. One common arrangement is a pair of pathways, each counterbalancing the other. To see how such control systems operate, we'll consider the regulation of blood glucose levels.

▲ **Figure 45.11 A simple endocrine pathway.** A change in some internal or external variable—the stimulus—causes the endocrine cell to secrete a hormone (red dots). Upon reaching its target cell via the bloodstream, the hormone binds to its receptor, triggering signal transduction that results in a specific response. Secretin signaling is an example of a simple endocrine pathway.

Insulin and Glucagon: Control of Blood Glucose

In humans, metabolic balance depends on a blood glucose concentration at or very near 90 mg/100 mL. Because glucose is a major fuel for cellular respiration and a key source of carbon skeletons for biosynthesis, maintaining blood glucose concentrations near this set point is a critical bioenergetic and homeostatic function.

Two antagonistic hormones, insulin and glucagon, regulate the concentration of glucose in the blood **(Figure 45.12)**. Each hormone operates in a simple endocrine pathway regulated by negative feedback. When blood glucose rises above the set point, release of **insulin** triggers uptake of glucose from the blood, decreasing the blood glucose concentration. When blood glucose drops below the set point, the release of **glucagon** promotes the release of glucose into the blood, increasing the blood glucose concentration. Because insulin and glucagon have opposing effects, the combined activity of these two hormones tightly controls the concentration of glucose in the blood.

Glucagon and insulin are produced in the pancreas. Scattered throughout the pancreas are clusters of endocrine cells known as the **islets of Langerhans**. Each islet has *alpha cells*, which make glucagon, and *beta cells*, which make insulin. Like all hormones, insulin and glucagon are secreted into the interstitial fluid and enter the circulatory system.

Overall, hormone-secreting cells make up only 1–2% of the mass of the pancreas. Other cells in the pancreas produce and secrete bicarbonate ions and digestive enzymes. These secretions are released into small ducts that empty into the pancreatic duct, which leads to the small intestine (see Figure 41.14). Thus, the pancreas is both an endocrine gland and an exocrine gland with functions in the endocrine and digestive systems.

Target Tissues for Insulin and Glucagon

Insulin lowers blood glucose levels by stimulating nearly all body cells outside the brain to take up glucose from the blood. (Brain cells can take up glucose without insulin, so the brain almost always has access to circulating fuel.) Insulin also decreases blood glucose by slowing glycogen breakdown in the liver and inhibiting the conversion of amino acids and glycerol (from fats) to glucose.

Glucagon influences blood glucose levels through its effects on target cells in the liver. The liver, skeletal muscles, and adipose tissues store large amounts of fuel. The liver and muscles store sugar as glycogen, whereas cells in adipose tissue convert sugars to fats. Of these tissues, only those in the liver are sensitive to glucagon. When the blood glucose level decreases to or below the set point (approximately 90 mg/100 mL), glucagon signals the liver cells to increase glycogen hydrolysis, convert amino acids and glycerol to glucose, and release glucose into

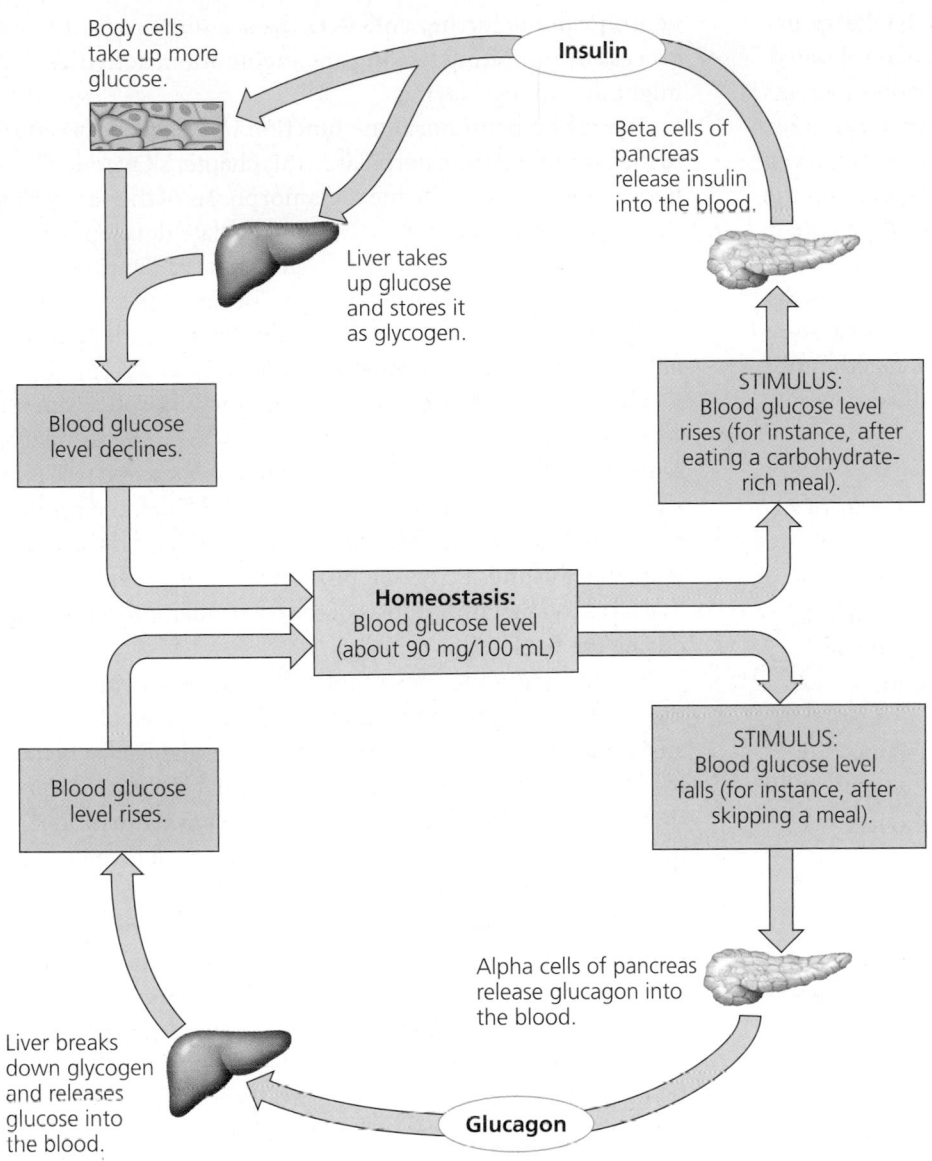

Body cells take up more glucose.

Insulin

Beta cells of pancreas release insulin into the blood.

Liver takes up glucose and stores it as glycogen.

Blood glucose level declines.

STIMULUS:
Blood glucose level rises (for instance, after eating a carbohydrate-rich meal).

Homeostasis:
Blood glucose level (about 90 mg/100 mL)

Blood glucose level rises.

STIMULUS:
Blood glucose level falls (for instance, after skipping a meal).

Alpha cells of pancreas release glucagon into the blood.

Liver breaks down glycogen and releases glucose into the blood.

Glucagon

▲ **Figure 45.12 Maintenance of glucose homeostasis by insulin and glucagon.** The antagonistic effects of insulin and glucagon help maintain the blood glucose level near its set point.

the bloodstream. The net effect is to restore the blood glucose level to the set point.

The antagonistic effects of glucagon and insulin are vital to managing fuel storage and consumption by body cells. For both hormones, the liver is a critical target. As discussed in Chapter 41, nutrients absorbed by blood vessels of the small intestine are transported directly to the liver by the hepatic portal vein. Within the liver, glucagon and insulin regulate nutrient processing in ways that support glucose homeostasis. However, glucose homeostasis also relies on responses to glucagon and insulin elsewhere in the body as well as responses to other hormones—growth hormone and glucocorticoids—discussed later in this chapter.

Diabetes Mellitus

A disruption in glucose homeostasis can be quite serious, affecting the heart, blood vessels, eyes, and kidneys. One such disorder, **diabetes mellitus**, is caused by a deficiency of insulin or a decreased response to insulin in target tissues. Blood glucose levels rise, but cells are unable to take up enough glucose to meet metabolic needs. Instead, fat becomes the main substrate for cellular respiration. In severe cases, acidic metabolites formed during fat breakdown accumulate in the blood, threatening life by lowering blood pH and depleting sodium and potassium ions from the body.

In people with diabetes mellitus, the high level of glucose in blood exceeds the capacity of the kidneys to reabsorb this nutrient. Glucose that remains in the filtrate is excreted. For this reason, the presence of sugar in urine is one test for this disorder. As glucose is concentrated in the urine, more water is excreted along with it, resulting in excessive volumes of urine. *Diabetes* (from the Greek *diabainein*, to pass through) refers to this copious urination; and *mellitus* (from the Greek *meli*, honey) refers to the presence of sugar in urine. (*Diabetes insipidus*, discussed in Chapter 44, is a rare disorder of kidney function that results in large volumes of dilute urine but no major disruption in glucose metabolism.)

There are two main types of diabetes mellitus. Each is marked by high blood glucose, but with very different causes. *Type 1 diabetes*, or insulin-dependent diabetes, is an autoimmune disorder in which the immune system destroys the beta cells of the pancreas. Type 1 diabetes, which usually appears during childhood, destroys the person's ability to produce insulin. Treatment consists of insulin, typically injected several times daily. In the past, insulin was extracted from animal pancreases, but now human insulin can be obtained from genetically engineered bacteria, a relatively inexpensive source (see Figure 20.2). Stem cell research may someday provide a cure for type 1 diabetes by generating replacement beta cells that restore insulin production by the pancreas.

Type 2 diabetes, or non-insulin-dependent diabetes, is characterized by a failure of target cells to respond normally to insulin. Insulin is produced, but target cells fail to take up glucose from the blood, and blood glucose levels remain elevated. Although heredity can play a role in type 2 diabetes, excess body weight and lack of exercise significantly increase the risk. This form of diabetes generally appears after age 40, but even children who are overweight and sedentary can develop the disease. More than 90% of people with diabetes have type 2. Many can control their blood glucose levels with regular exercise and a healthy diet; some require medications. Nevertheless, type 2 diabetes is the seventh most common cause of death in the United States and a growing public health problem worldwide.

CONCEPT CHECK 45.2

1. In a glucose tolerance test, periodic measurements of blood glucose level are taken after a person drinks a glucose-rich solution. In a healthy individual, blood glucose rises moderately at first but falls to near normal within 2–3 hours. Predict the results of this test in a person with diabetes mellitus. Explain your answer.

2. What property of a stimulus might make negative feedback less important for a hormone pathway?

3. **WHAT IF?** Consider a diabetes patient who has a family history of type 2 diabetes but is active and not obese. To identify genes that might be defective in the patient, which genes would you examine first?

For suggested answers, see Appendix A.

CONCEPT 45.3

The endocrine and nervous systems act individually and together in regulating animal physiology

Our discussion to this point has focused on the structure of hormones and the organization of hormone pathways. We'll now consider how signals from the nervous system initiate and regulate endocrine signaling. We will begin with examples from invertebrates and then turn to the vertebrate brain and endocrine system.

Coordination of Endocrine and Nervous Systems in Invertebrates

In all animals but the simplest invertebrates, the endocrine and nervous systems are integrated in the control of reproduction and development. In the sea slug *Aplysia*, for instance, specialized nerve cells secrete egg-laying hormone, which stimulates the animal to lay thousands of eggs. This neurohormone further enhances the sea slug's reproductive success by inhibiting feeding and locomotion, activities that might disrupt egg-laying.

To explore neurohormone function in insects, let's return to the example of the caterpillar in this chapter's Overview. Before hormones stimulate the metamorphosis of the caterpillar, a larva, into the adult butterfly, they regulate development of a newly hatched egg into the fully grown larva. During its development, the larva grows in stages. Because its exoskeleton cannot stretch, the larva must periodically molt, shedding the old exoskeleton and secreting a new one.

The signals that direct molting and metamorphosis in insects originate in the brain (**Figure 45.13**). There, neurosecretory cells produce *prothoracicotropic hormone* (PTTH), a peptide neurohormone. In response to PTTH, the prothoracic glands, a pair of endocrine glands just behind the brain, release **ecdysone**. Ecdysone promotes each successive molt, as well as the metamorphosis of the caterpillar into a butterfly during the final molt.

Because ecdysone causes both molting and metamorphosis, what determines when metamorphosis takes place? The answer is found in a pair of small endocrine glands just behind the brain. Called the corpora allata (singular, *corpus allatum*), they secrete a third signaling molecule, **juvenile hormone**. As its name suggests, one of the many functions of juvenile hormone is to maintain larval (juvenile) characteristics.

Juvenile hormone influences development indirectly by modulating the activity of ecdysone. In the presence of high levels of juvenile hormone, ecdysone stimulates molting that results in a larger larva. At the end of the larval stage, the level of juvenile hormone wanes. When the juvenile hormone level is low, ecdysone-induced molting produces the cocoon, or pupal form, within which metamorphosis occurs.

Knowledge of insect neurohormone and hormone signaling has important agricultural applications. For example, synthetic versions of juvenile hormone are used as a biological pest control method to prevent insects from maturing into reproducing adults.

Coordination of Endocrine and Nervous Systems in Vertebrates

In vertebrates, the **hypothalamus** plays a central role in integrating the endocrine and nervous systems. One of several endocrine glands located in the brain (**Figure 45.14**), the hypothalamus receives information from nerves throughout the body and from other parts of the brain. In response, it initiates endocrine signaling appropriate to environmental conditions. In many vertebrates, for example, nerve signals from the brain pass sensory information to the hypothalamus about seasonal changes and the availability of a mate. The hypothalamus, in turn, regulates the release of reproductive hormones required for breeding.

① Neurosecretory cells in the brain produce prothoracicotropic hormone (PTTH), which is stored in the corpora cardiaca (singular, *corpus cardiacum*) until release.

Brain

Neurosecretory cells

Corpus cardiacum

Corpus allatum

PTTH

Prothoracic gland

Low JH

④ Juvenile hormone (JH), secreted by the corpora allata, determines the result of the molt. At relatively high concentrations of JH, ecdysone-stimulated molting produces another larval stage because JH suppresses metamorphosis. But when levels of JH fall below a certain concentration, a pupa forms at the next ecdysone-induced molt. The adult insect emerges from the pupa.

② PTTH signals its main target organ, the prothoracic gland, to produce the hormone ecdysone.

Ecdysone

Juvenile hormone (JH)

③ Ecdysone secretion from the prothoracic gland is episodic, with each release stimulating a molt.

EARLY LARVA

LATER LARVA

PUPA

ADULT

▲ **Figure 45.13 Hormonal regulation of insect development.** Most insects go through a series of larval stages, with each molt (shedding of the old exoskeleton) leading to a larger larva. Molting of the final larval stage gives rise to a pupa, in which metamorphosis produces the adult form of the insect. Hormones control the progression of stages, as shown here.

Signals from the hypothalamus travel to the **pituitary gland**, a gland located at its base. Roughly the size and shape of a lima bean, the pituitary has discrete posterior and anterior parts (lobes), which are actually two glands, the posterior pituitary and the anterior pituitary (see Figure 45.14). These glands initially develop in separate regions of the embryo. Although they fuse together later in development, their functions are distinct.

The **posterior pituitary**, or *neurohypophysis*, is an extension of the hypothalamus that grows downward toward the mouth during embryonic development. The posterior pituitary stores and secretes two hormones made by the hypothalamus.

The **anterior pituitary**, or *adenohypophysis*, develops from a fold of tissue at the roof of the embryonic mouth; this tissue grows upward toward the brain and eventually loses its connection to the mouth. Hormones released by the hypothalamus regulate secretion of hormones by the anterior pituitary.

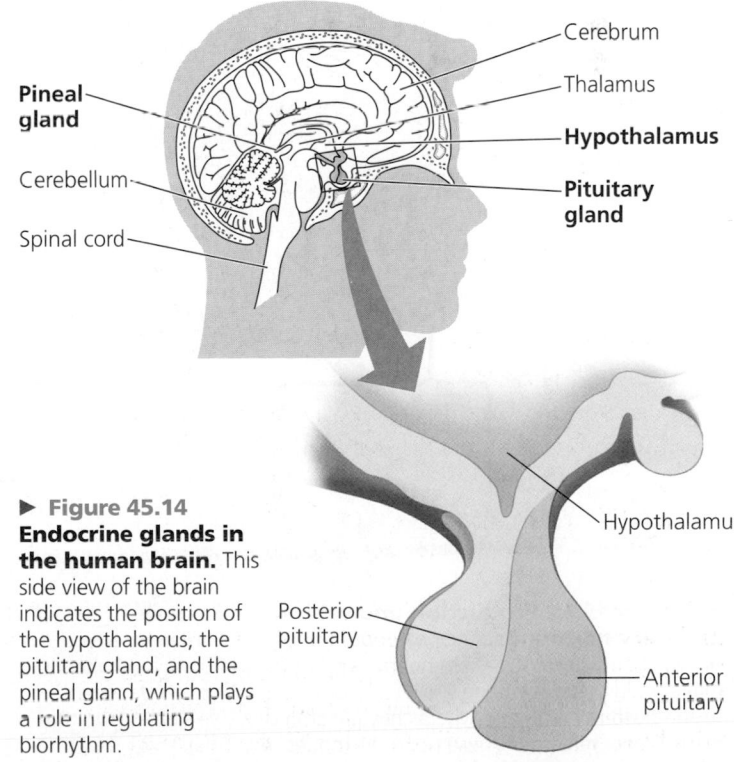

Cerebrum

Thalamus

Pineal gland

Hypothalamus

Cerebellum

Pituitary gland

Spinal cord

▶ **Figure 45.14 Endocrine glands in the human brain.** This side view of the brain indicates the position of the hypothalamus, the pituitary gland, and the pineal gland, which plays a role in regulating biorhythm.

Hypothalamus

Posterior pituitary

Anterior pituitary

Under the control of the hypothalamus, the anterior pituitary and posterior pituitary produce a set of hormones central to endocrine signaling throughout the body, as evident in **Table 45.1**. (This table will also be a useful reference later.) We'll consider the posterior pituitary, which releases just two hormones, first.

Posterior Pituitary Hormones

The posterior pituitary releases two neurohormones, oxytocin and antidiuretic hormone (ADH). Synthesized in the hypothalamus, these hormones travel along the long axons of neurosecretory cells to the posterior pituitary (**Figure 45.15**). There they are stored, to be released as needed.

One function of **oxytocin** in mammals is to regulate milk release during nursing; this function is mediated by a simple neurohormone pathway (**Figure 45.16**). In such pathways, a stimulus received by a sensory neuron stimulates a neurosecretory cell. The neurosecretory cell then secretes a neurohormone, which diffuses into the bloodstream and travels to target cells. In the case of the oxytocin pathway, the initial stimulus is the infant's suckling. Stimulation of sensory nerve cells in the nipples generates signals in the nervous system that reach the hypothalamus. A nerve impulse from the hypothalamus then triggers the release of oxytocin from the posterior pituitary gland. In response to circulating oxytocin, the mammary glands secrete milk.

The oxytocin pathway regulating the mammary gland provides an example of a positive-feedback mechanism. Unlike negative feedback, which dampens a stimulus, **positive feedback** reinforces a stimulus, leading to an even greater response. Thus, oxytocin stimulates milk release, which leads to more suckling and therefore more stimulation. Activation of the pathway is sustained until the baby stops suckling.

Oxytocin has several additional roles related to reproduction. When mammals give birth, it induces target cells in the uterine muscles to contract. This pathway, too, is characterized by positive-feedback regulation, such that it drives the birth process to completion. Oxytocin also functions in regulating mood and sexual arousal in both males and females.

The second hormone released by the posterior pituitary, **antidiuretic hormone (ADH)**, or *vasopressin*, helps regulate blood osmolarity. As you read in Chapter 44, ADH is one of several hormones that regulate kidney function. In particular, ADH increases water retention in the kidneys, thus decreasing urine volume.

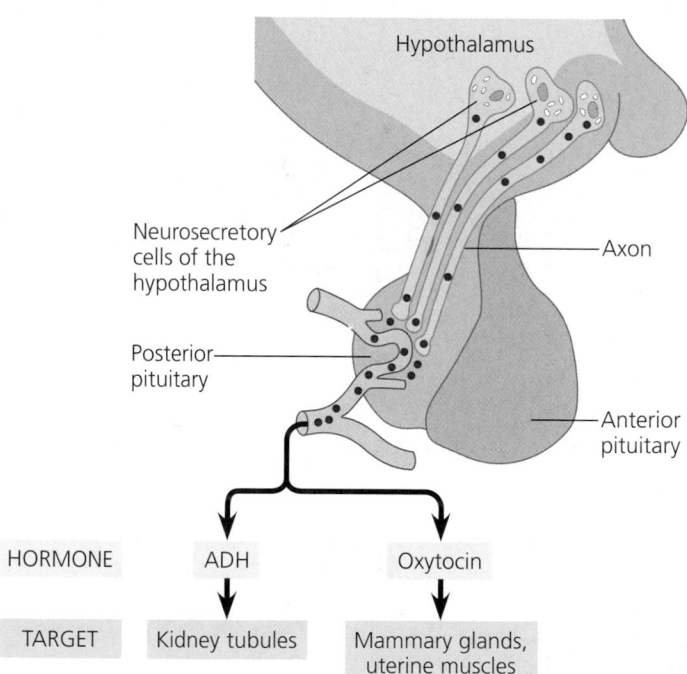

▲ **Figure 45.15 Production and release of posterior pituitary hormones.** The posterior pituitary gland is an extension of the hypothalamus. Certain neurosecretory cells in the hypothalamus make antidiuretic hormone (ADH) and oxytocin, which are transported to the posterior pituitary, where they are stored. Nerve signals from the brain trigger release of these neurohormones (red dots).

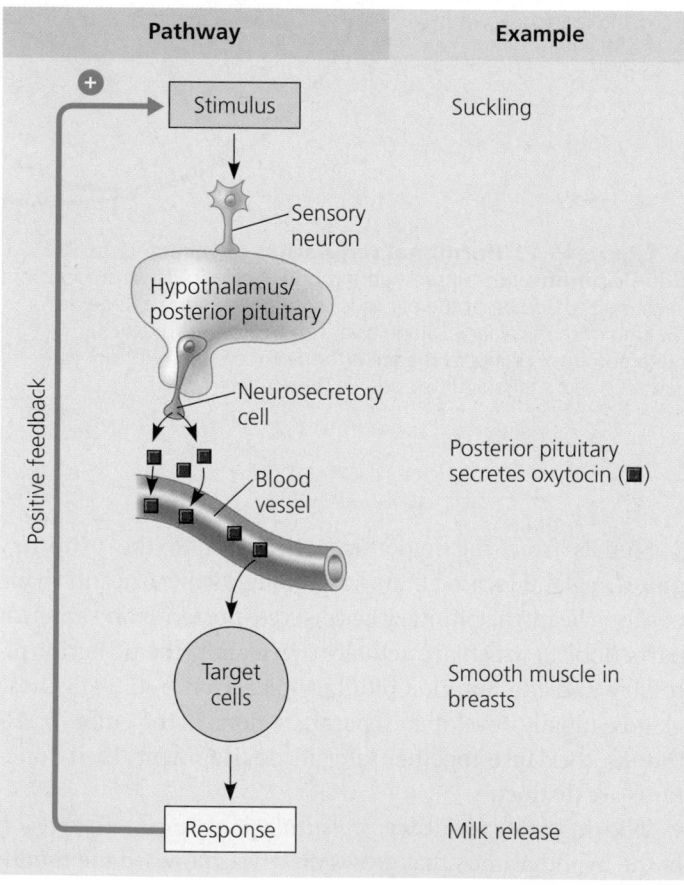

▲ **Figure 45.16 A simple neurohormone pathway.** In this example, the stimulus causes the hypothalamus to send a nerve impulse to the posterior pituitary, which responds by secreting a neurohormone (red squares). Upon reaching its target cell via the bloodstream, the neurohormone binds to its receptor, triggering signal transduction that results in a specific response. In the neurohormone pathway for oxytocin signaling, the response increases the stimulus, forming a positive-feedback loop that amplifies signaling in the pathway.

Table 45.1 Major Human Endocrine Glands and Some of Their Hormones

Gland	Hormone	Chemical Class	Representative Actions	Regulated By
Hypothalamus	Hormones released from the posterior pituitary and hormones that regulate the anterior pituitary (see below)			
Posterior pituitary gland (releases neurohormones made in hypothalamus)	Oxytocin	Peptide	Stimulates contraction of uterus and mammary gland cells	Nervous system
	Antidiuretic hormone (ADH)	Peptide	Promotes retention of water by kidneys	Water/salt balance
Anterior pituitary gland	Growth hormone (GH)	Protein	Stimulates growth (especially bones) and metabolic functions	Hypothalamic hormones
	Prolactin (PRL)	Protein	Stimulates milk production and secretion	Hypothalamic hormones
	Follicle-stimulating hormone (FSH)	Glycoprotein	Stimulates production of ova and sperm	Hypothalamic hormones
	Luteinizing hormone (LH)	Glycoprotein	Stimulates ovaries and testes	Hypothalamic hormones
	Thyroid-stimulating hormone (TSH)	Glycoprotein	Stimulates thyroid gland	Hypothalamic hormones
	Adrenocorticotropic hormone (ACTH)	Peptide	Stimulates adrenal cortex to secrete glucocorticoids	Hypothalamic hormones
Thyroid gland	Triiodothyronine (T_3) and thyroxine (T_4)	Amine	Stimulate and maintain metabolic processes	TSH
	Calcitonin	Peptide	Lowers blood calcium level	Calcium in blood
Parathyroid glands	Parathyroid hormone (PTH)	Peptide	Raises blood calcium level	Calcium in blood
Pancreas	Insulin	Protein	Lowers blood glucose level	Glucose in blood
	Glucagon	Protein	Raises blood glucose level	Glucose in blood
Adrenal glands Adrenal medulla	Epinephrine and norepinephrine	Amines	Raise blood glucose level; increase metabolic activities; constrict certain blood vessels	Nervous system
Adrenal cortex	Glucocorticoids	Steroid	Raise blood glucose level	ACTH
	Mineralocorticoids	Steroid	Promote reabsorption of Na^+ and excretion of K^+ in kidneys	K^+ in blood; angiotensin II
Gonads Testes	Androgens	Steroid	Support sperm formation; promote development and maintenance of male secondary sex characteristics	FSH and LH
Ovaries	Estrogens	Steroid	Stimulate uterine lining growth; promote development and maintenance of female secondary sex characteristics	FSH and LH
	Progestins	Steroid	Promote uterine lining growth	FSH and LH
Pineal gland	Melatonin	Amine	Involved in biological rhythms	Light/dark cycles

Tropic effects only:
FSH (follicle-stimulating hormone)
LH (luteinizing hormone)
TSH (thyroid-stimulating hormone)
ACTH (adrenocorticotropic hormone)

Nontropic effects only:
Prolactin
MSH (melanocyte-stimulating hormone)

Nontropic and tropic effects:
GH (growth hormone)

Neurosecretory cells
of the hypothalamus

Hypothalamic
releasing and
inhibiting
hormones
(red dots)

Portal vessels

Posterior pituitary

Endocrine cells of
the anterior pituitary

Pituitary hormones
(blue dots)

◄ **Figure 45.17**
Production and release of anterior pituitary hormones. The release of hormones synthesized in the anterior pituitary gland is controlled by hypothalamic releasing and inhibiting hormones. The hypothalamic hormones are secreted by neurosecretory cells and enter a capillary network within the hypothalamus. These capillaries drain into portal vessels that connect with a second capillary network in the anterior pituitary.

HORMONE	FSH and LH	TSH	ACTH	Prolactin	MSH	GH
TARGET	Testes or ovaries	Thyroid	Adrenal cortex	Mammary glands	Melanocytes	Liver, bones, other tissues

Anterior Pituitary Hormones

The anterior pituitary synthesizes and secretes many different hormones and is itself regulated by hormones secreted by the hypothalamus **(Figure 45.17)**. Each hypothalamic hormone is either a *releasing hormone* or an *inhibiting hormone*, reflecting its role in promoting or inhibiting release of one or more specific hormones by the anterior pituitary. *Thyrotropin-releasing hormone (TRH)*, for example, is a product of the hypothalamus that stimulates the anterior pituitary to secrete thyrotropin, also known as *thyroid-stimulating hormone (TSH)*. Every anterior pituitary hormone is controlled by at least one releasing hormone. Some have both a releasing hormone and an inhibiting hormone.

The hypothalamic releasing and inhibiting hormones are secreted near capillaries at the base of the hypothalamus. The capillaries drain into short blood vessels, called portal vessels, which subdivide into a second capillary bed within the anterior pituitary. In this way, the releasing and inhibiting hormones have direct access to the gland they control.

Hormone Cascade Pathways

Sets of hormones from the hypothalamus, the anterior pituitary, and a target endocrine gland are often organized into a hormone cascade pathway **(Figure 45.18)**. Signals to the brain stimulate the hypothalamus to secrete a hormone that in turn either stimulates or inhibits release of a particular anterior pituitary hormone. The anterior pituitary hormone acts on a target endocrine tissue, stimulating secretion of yet another hormone that exerts systemic metabolic or developmental effects.

To learn how a hormone cascade pathway works, let's consider activation of the thyroid gland when an infant is exposed to cold (see Figure 45.18). When a young child's body temperature drops, the hypothalamus secretes TRH. TRH targets the anterior pituitary, which responds by secreting TSH. TSH acts on the thyroid gland to stimulate release of *thyroid hormone*. As it accumulates, thyroid hormone increases metabolic rate, releasing thermal energy that raises body temperature.

Like simple hormone pathways, hormone cascade pathways typically involve negative feedback. In the case of the thyroid hormone pathway, thyroid hormone itself carries out negative feedback. Because thyroid hormone blocks TSH release from the anterior pituitary and TRH release from the hypothalamus, the negative-feedback loop prevents overproduction of thyroid hormone. Overall, the hormone cascade pathway brings about a self-limiting response to the original stimulus in the target cells.

Tropic Hormones

TSH is an example of a **tropic hormone**—a hormone that regulates the function of endocrine cells or glands. Three other anterior pituitary hormones act primarily or exclusively as tropic hormones: **follicle-stimulating hormone (FSH)**, **luteinizing hormone (LH)**, and **adrenocorticotropic hormone (ACTH)**.

Pathway	Example

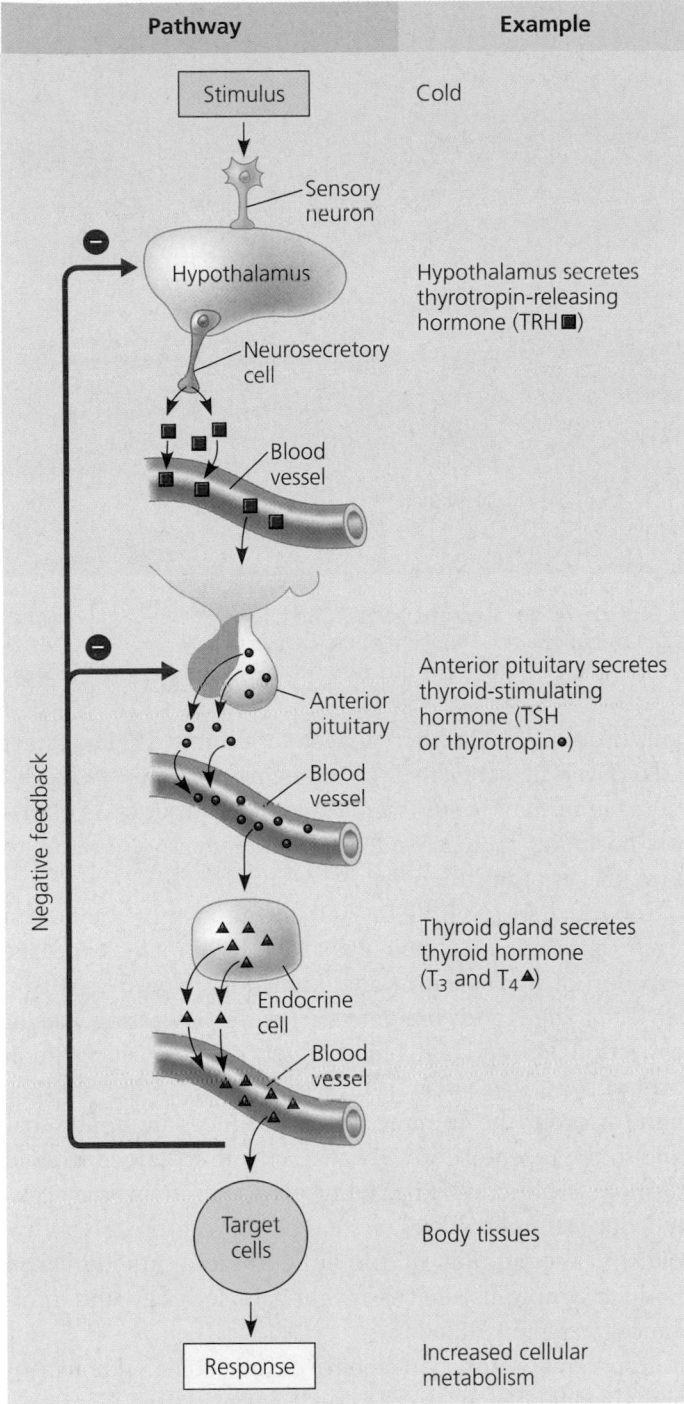

Stimulus — Cold

Hypothalamus — Hypothalamus secretes thyrotropin-releasing hormone (TRH ■)

Anterior pituitary — Anterior pituitary secretes thyroid-stimulating hormone (TSH or thyrotropin ●)

Thyroid gland secretes thyroid hormone (T_3 and T_4 ▲)

Target cells — Body tissues

Response — Increased cellular metabolism

▲ **Figure 45.18 A hormone cascade pathway.** In response to the stimulus, the hypothalamus secretes a releasing hormone (red squares) that targets the anterior pituitary. The anterior pituitary responds by secreting a second tropic hormone (red dots), which travels through the bloodstream to an endocrine gland. In response to this tropic hormone, the endocrine gland secretes a hormone (red triangles) that travels to target cells, where it induces a response. In the example of thyroid hormone regulation, thyroid hormone exerts negative feedback on the hypothalamus and anterior pituitary. This feedback inhibits release of TRH and TSH, preventing overreaction to the stimulus (such as low temperature in the case of a human infant).

? *Suppose a lab test of two patients, each diagnosed with excessive thyroid hormone production, revealed elevated levels of TSH in one but not the other. Was the diagnosis of one patient necessarily incorrect? Explain.*

FSH and LH stimulate the activities of the male and female gonads, the testes and ovaries, respectively. For this reason, FSH and LH are also known as *gonadotropins*. In Chapter 46, we will discuss how these hormones regulate reproductive functions.

ACTH stimulates the production and secretion of steroid hormones by the adrenal cortex. We will take a closer look at the hormone pathway involving ACTH later in this chapter.

Nontropic Hormones

Two major hormones of the anterior pituitary target nonendocrine tissues and are thus nontropic. They are prolactin and melanocyte-stimulating hormone (MSH).

Prolactin (PRL) is remarkable for the diversity of its effects among vertebrate species. For example, prolactin stimulates mammary gland growth and milk synthesis in mammals, regulates fat metabolism and reproduction in birds, delays metamorphosis in amphibians, and regulates salt and water balance in freshwater fishes. These varied roles suggest that prolactin is an ancient hormone with functions that have diversified during the evolution of vertebrate groups.

As you saw in Figure 45.4, **melanocyte-stimulating hormone (MSH)** regulates the activity of pigment-containing cells in the skin of some amphibians (as well as fishes and reptiles). In mammals, MSH appears to act on neurons in the brain, inhibiting hunger.

Growth Hormone

Growth hormone (GH), which is secreted by the anterior pituitary, stimulates growth through tropic and nontropic effects. A major target, the liver, responds to GH by releasing *insulin-like growth factors* (*IGFs*), which circulate in the blood and directly stimulate bone and cartilage growth. (IGFs also appear to play a key role in aging in many animal species.) In the absence of GH, the skeleton of an immature animal stops growing. GH also exerts diverse metabolic effects that tend to raise blood glucose levels, thus opposing the effects of insulin.

Abnormal production of GH in humans can result in several disorders, depending on when the problem occurs and whether it involves hypersecretion (too much) or hyposecretion (too little). Hypersecretion of GH during childhood can lead to gigantism, in which the person grows unusually tall—as tall as 2.4 m (8 feet)—though body proportions remain relatively normal. Excessive GH production in adulthood stimulates bony growth in the few tissues that are still responsive to the hormone. Because remaining target cells are predominantly in the face, hands, and feet, the result is an overgrowth of the extremities called acromegaly (from the Greek *acros*, extreme, and *mega*, large).

Hyposecretion of GH in childhood retards long-bone growth and can lead to pituitary dwarfism. Individuals with this disorder are for the most part properly proportioned but generally reach a height of only about 1.2 m (4 feet). If diagnosed before puberty, pituitary dwarfism can be treated successfully with human GH.

Since the mid-1980s, scientists have produced human GH from bacteria programmed with DNA encoding the hormone (see Chapter 20). Treatment with this genetically engineered GH is now fairly routine for children with pituitary dwarfism.

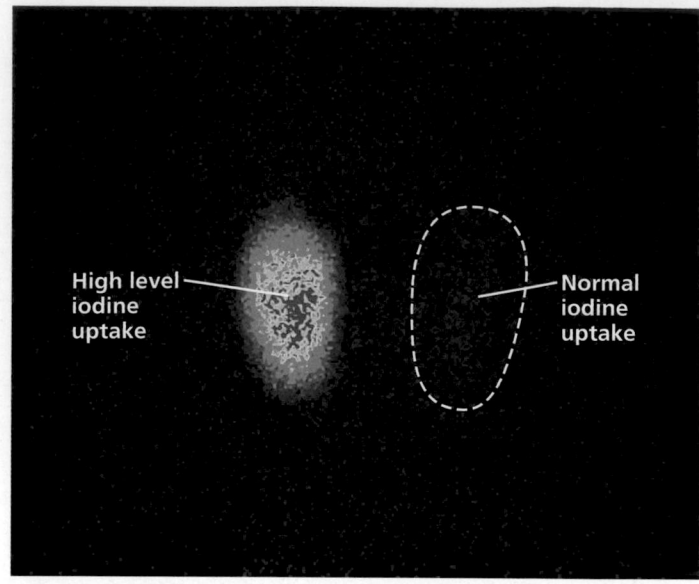

▲ **Figure 45.19 Thyroid scan.** A tumor in one lobe of the thyroid gland caused the accumulation of radioactive iodine.

CONCEPT 45.4
Endocrine glands respond to diverse stimuli in regulating metabolism, homeostasis, development, and behavior

Having seen how endocrine glands in the brain initiate hormone cascade pathways, we return here to the broader question of how endocrine signaling regulates animal physiology. We'll focus on metabolism, homeostasis, development, and behavior, leaving the topic of reproduction largely for later chapters. We will discuss more examples of hormone regulation by metabolic stimuli, by nervous system input, and by hormones of the anterior pituitary. To begin, let's explore a pathway introduced in Figure 45.18, the hormone cascade leading to thyroid hormone production.

Thyroid Hormone: Control of Metabolism and Development

Among the vertebrates, thyroid hormone, secreted by the thyroid gland, regulates both homeostasis and development. In humans and other mammals, thyroid hormone regulates bioenergetics; helps maintain normal blood pressure, heart rate, and muscle tone; and regulates digestive and reproductive functions. In these animals, the **thyroid gland** consists of two lobes on the ventral surface of the trachea (see Figure 42.24). In many other vertebrates, the two halves of the gland are separately located on the two sides of the pharynx.

The term *thyroid hormone* actually refers to a pair of very similar hormones derived from the amino acid tyrosine. **Triiodothyronine (T_3)** contains three iodine atoms, whereas tetraiodothyronine, or **thyroxine (T_4)**, contains four iodine atoms (see Figure 45.3). In mammals, the same receptor binds both hormones. The thyroid secretes mainly T_4, but target cells convert most of it to T_3 by removing one iodine atom. Because iodine in the body is dedicated to the production of thyroid hormone, radioactive forms of iodine are often used to form images of the thyroid gland (**Figure 45.19**).

Too much or too little thyroid hormone in the blood can result in serious metabolic disorders. In humans, excessive secretion of thyroid hormone, known as hyperthyroidism, can lead to high body temperature, profuse sweating, weight loss, irritability, and high blood pressure. The most common form of hyperthyroidism is Graves' disease. In this autoimmune disorder, the immune system produces antibodies that bind to the receptor for TSH and activate sustained thyroid hormone production. Protruding eyes, caused by fluid accumulation behind the eyes, are a typical symptom. Hypothyroidism, a condition of too little thyroid function, can produce symptoms such as weight gain, lethargy, and intolerance to cold in adults.

Proper thyroid function requires dietary iodine. Although iodine is readily obtained from seafood or from iodized salt, people in many parts of the world suffer from inadequate iodine in their diet. Without sufficient iodine, the thyroid gland cannot synthesize adequate amounts of T_3 and T_4, and the resulting low blood levels of T_3 and T_4 cannot exert the usual negative feedback on the hypothalamus and anterior pituitary (see Figure 45.18). As a consequence, the pituitary continues to secrete TSH. Elevated TSH levels cause an enlargement of the thyroid that results in goiter, a characteristic swelling of the neck (see Figure 2.4).

Among the vertebrates, thyroid hormones have a variety of roles in development and maturation. A striking example is the thyroid control of the metamorphosis of a tadpole into a frog, which involves massive reorganization of many different tissues (see Figure 45.9). All vertebrates require thyroid hormones for the normal functioning of bone-forming cells and the branching of nerve cells during embryonic development of the brain. In humans, congenital hypothyroidism, an inherited condition of thyroid deficiency, results in markedly retarded skeletal growth and poor mental development. These defects can often be prevented, at least partially, if treatment with thyroid hormones begins early in life. Iodine deficiency in childhood causes the same defects, but it is fully preventable if iodized salt is used in food preparation.

Parathyroid Hormone and Vitamin D: Control of Blood Calcium

Because calcium ions (Ca^{2+}) are essential to the normal functioning of all cells, homeostatic control of blood calcium level is critical. If the blood Ca^{2+} level falls substantially, skeletal muscles begin to contract convulsively, a potentially fatal condition called tetany. If the blood Ca^{2+} level rises substantially, precipitates of calcium phosphate can form in body tissues, leading to widespread organ damage.

In mammals, the **parathyroid glands**, a set of four small structures embedded in the posterior surface of the thyroid (see Figure 45.10), play a major role in blood Ca^{2+} regulation. When blood Ca^{2+} falls below a set point of about 10 mg/100 mL, these glands release **parathyroid hormone (PTH)**.

PTH raises the level of blood Ca^{2+} by direct and indirect effects **(Figure 45.20)**. In bone, PTH causes the mineralized matrix to decompose and release Ca^{2+} into the blood. In the kidneys, PTH directly stimulates reabsorption of Ca^{2+} through the renal tubules. PTH also has an indirect effect on the kidneys, promoting the conversion of vitamin D to an active hormone. An inactive form of vitamin D, a steroid-derived molecule, is obtained from food or synthesized in the skin when exposed to sunlight. Vitamin D activation begins in the liver and is completed in the kidneys, the process stimulated by PTH. The active form of vitamin D acts directly on the intestines, stimulating the uptake of Ca^{2+} from food and thus augmenting the effect of PTH. As blood Ca^{2+} rises, a negative-feedback loop inhibits further release of PTH from the parathyroid glands (not shown in figure).

The thyroid gland can also contribute to calcium homeostasis. If blood Ca^{2+} rises above the set point, the thyroid gland releases **calcitonin**, a hormone that inhibits bone resorption and enhances Ca^{2+} release by the kidney. In fishes, rodents, and some other animals, calcitonin is required for Ca^{2+} homeostasis. In humans, however, it is apparently needed only during the extensive bone growth of childhood.

Adrenal Hormones: Response to Stress

The **adrenal glands** of vertebrates are in each case associated with the kidneys (the *renal* organs). In mammals, each adrenal gland is actually made up of two glands with different cell types, functions, and embryonic origins: the *adrenal cortex*, the outer portion, and the *adrenal medulla*, the central portion. The adrenal cortex consists of true endocrine cells, whereas the secretory cells of the adrenal medulla derive from neural tissue during embryonic development. Thus, like the pituitary gland, each adrenal gland is a fused endocrine and neuroendocrine gland.

Catecholamines from the Adrenal Medulla

Imagine that while walking in the woods at night you hear a growling noise nearby. "A bear?" you wonder. Your heart beats faster, your breath quickens, your muscles tense, and your thoughts speed up. These and other rapid responses to perceived danger comprise the "fight-or-flight" response. This coordinated set of physiological changes is triggered by two hormones of the adrenal medulla, epinephrine (also known as adrenaline) and **norepinephrine** (noradrenaline). Both are **catecholamines**, a class of amine hormones synthesized from the amino acid tyrosine.

The adrenal medulla secretes epinephrine and norepinephrine in response to stress—whether extreme pleasure or life-

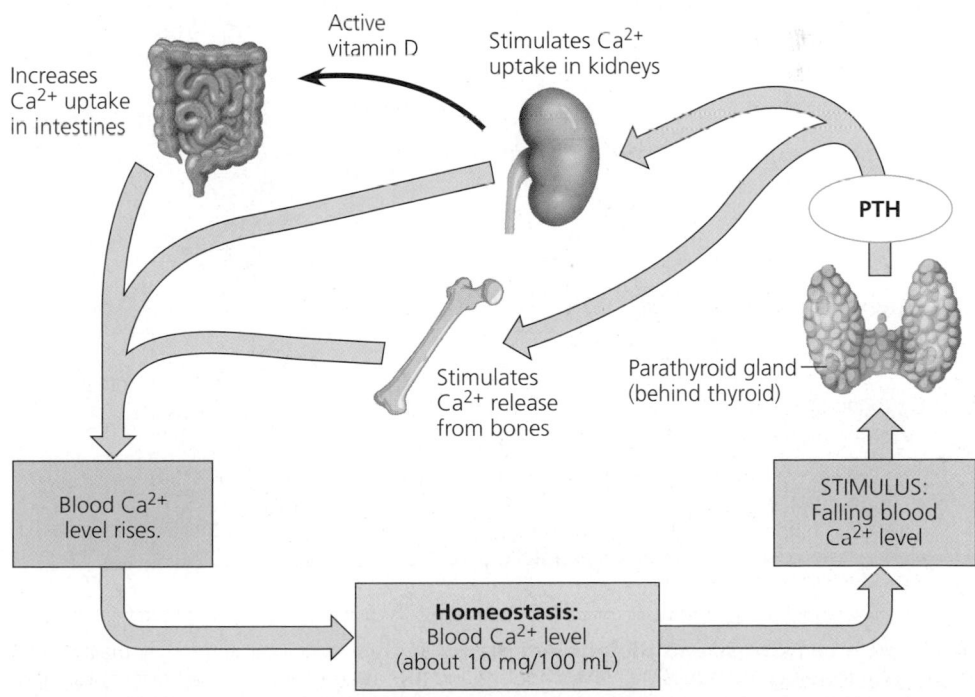

▲ Figure 45.20 **The roles of parathyroid hormone (PTH) in regulating blood calcium levels in mammals.**

threatening danger. A major activity of these hormones is to increase the amount of chemical energy available for immediate use. Both epinephrine and norepinephrine increase the rate of glycogen breakdown in the liver and skeletal muscles, promote glucose release by liver cells, and stimulate the release of fatty acids from fat cells. The released glucose and fatty acids circulate in the blood and can be used by body cells as fuel.

In addition to increasing the availability of energy sources, epinephrine and norepinephrine exert profound effects on the cardiovascular and respiratory systems. For example, they increase both the heart rate and stroke volume and dilate the bronchioles in the lungs, actions that raise the rate of oxygen delivery to body cells. For this reason, doctors may prescribe epinephrine as a heart stimulant or to open the airways during an asthma attack. The catecholamines also alter blood flow, causing constriction of some blood vessels and dilation of others (see Figure 45.8). The overall effect is to shunt blood away from the skin, digestive organs, and kidneys, while increasing the blood supply to the heart, brain, and skeletal muscles. Epinephrine generally has a stronger effect on heart and metabolic rates, while the primary role of norepinephrine is in modulating blood pressure.

Nerve signals carried from the brain via involuntary (autonomic) neurons regulate secretion by the adrenal medulla. In response to a stressful stimulus, nerve impulses travel to the adrenal medulla, where they trigger the release of catecholamines **(Figure 45.21a)**. Acting on target tissues, epinephrine and norepinephrine each function in a simple neurohormone pathway. As we will see in Chapter 48, epinephrine and norepinephrine also function as neurotransmitters.

Steroid Hormones from the Adrenal Cortex

Hormones from the adrenal cortex also function in the body's response to stress. But in contrast to the adrenal medulla, which reacts to nervous input, the adrenal cortex responds to endocrine signals. Stressful stimuli cause the hypothalamus to secrete a releasing hormone that stimulates the anterior pituitary to release the tropic hormone ACTH. When ACTH reaches the adrenal cortex via the bloodstream, it stimulates

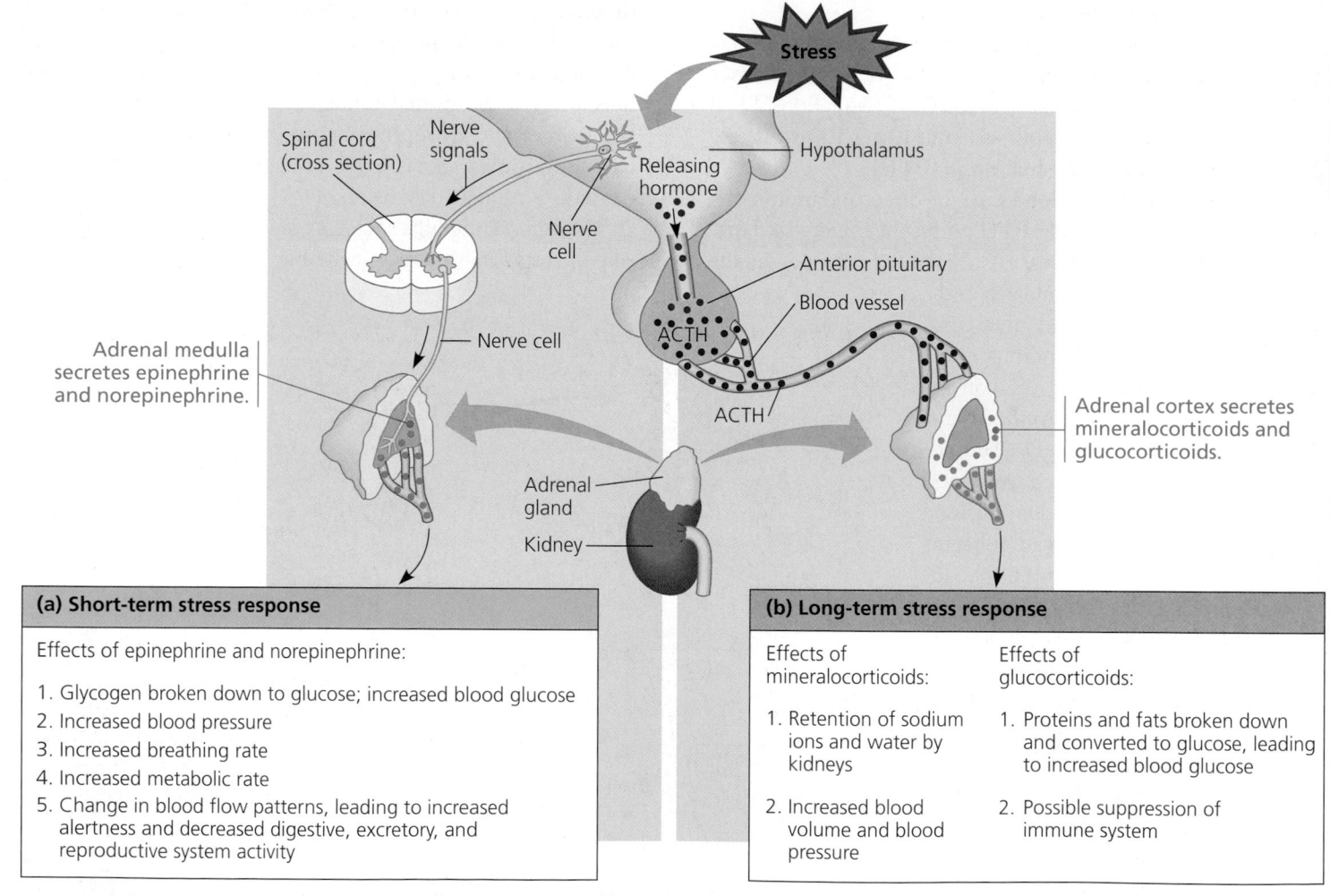

(a) Short-term stress response

Effects of epinephrine and norepinephrine:

1. Glycogen broken down to glucose; increased blood glucose
2. Increased blood pressure
3. Increased breathing rate
4. Increased metabolic rate
5. Change in blood flow patterns, leading to increased alertness and decreased digestive, excretory, and reproductive system activity

(b) Long-term stress response

Effects of mineralocorticoids:

1. Retention of sodium ions and water by kidneys
2. Increased blood volume and blood pressure

Effects of glucocorticoids:

1. Proteins and fats broken down and converted to glucose, leading to increased blood glucose
2. Possible suppression of immune system

▲ **Figure 45.21 Stress and the adrenal gland.** Stressful stimuli cause the hypothalamus to activate **(a)** the adrenal medulla via nerve impulses and **(b)** the adrenal cortex via hormonal signals. The adrenal medulla mediates short-term responses to stress by secreting the catecholamine hormones epinephrine and norepinephrine. The adrenal cortex controls more prolonged responses by secreting corticosteroids.

the endocrine cells to synthesize and secrete a family of steroids called **corticosteroids (Figure 45.21b)**. The two main types of corticosteroids in humans are *glucocorticoids* and *mineralocorticoids.*

As reflected in their name, **glucocorticoids** have a primary effect on glucose metabolism. Augmenting the fuel-mobilizing effects of glucagon from the pancreas, glucocorticoids promote glucose synthesis from noncarbohydrate sources, such as proteins, making more glucose available as fuel. Glucocorticoids, such as cortisol (see Figure 45.3), act on skeletal muscle, causing the breakdown of muscle proteins. The resulting amino acids are transported to the liver and kidneys, where they are converted to glucose and released into the blood. The synthesis of glucose from muscle proteins provides circulating fuel when the body requires more glucose than the liver can mobilize from its glycogen stores.

When glucocorticoids are introduced into the body at levels above those normally present, they suppress certain components of the body's immune system. Because of this anti-inflammatory effect, glucocorticoids are sometimes used to treat inflammatory diseases such as arthritis. However, long-term use can have serious side effects, reflecting the potent activity of glucocorticoids on metabolism. For these reasons, nonsteroidal anti-inflammatory drugs (NSAIDs), such as aspirin or ibuprofen, generally are preferred for treating chronic inflammatory conditions.

Mineralocorticoids, named for their effects on mineral metabolism, act principally in maintaining salt and water balance. For example, the mineralocorticoid *aldosterone* functions in ion and water homeostasis of the blood. Low blood volume or pressure leads to production of angiotensin II, which stimulates the secretion of aldosterone (see Figure 44.21). Aldosterone, in turn, stimulates cells in the kidneys to reabsorb sodium ions and water from filtrate, raising blood pressure and volume. Aldosterone also functions in the body's response to severe stress. In these circumstances, a rise in blood ACTH levels increases the rate at which the adrenal cortex secretes aldosterone as well as glucocorticoids.

The corticosteroid products of the adrenal cortex include small amounts of steroid hormones that function as sex hormones. All steroid hormones are synthesized from cholesterol, and their structures differ in only minor ways (see Figure 4.9). However, these small structural differences are associated with major differences in effects. The sex hormones produced by the adrenal cortex are mainly "male" hormones (androgens), with small amounts of "female" hormones (estrogens and progestins). There is evidence that adrenal androgens account for the sex drive in adult females, but otherwise the physiological roles of the adrenal sex hormones are not well understood.

Gonadal Sex Hormones

Sex hormones affect growth, development, reproductive cycles, and sexual behavior. Whereas the adrenal glands secrete small quantities of these hormones, the testes of males and ovaries of females are their principal sources. The gonads produce and secrete three major categories of steroid hormones: androgens, estrogens, and progestins. All three types are found in both males and females but in significantly different proportions.

The testes primarily synthesize **androgens**, the main one being **testosterone**. Testosterone first functions before birth, as shown in the 1940s by French researcher Alfred Jost. He was interested in how hormones determine whether an individual develops as a male or female. Working with rabbits, Jost carried out a surgical study that provided a simple and unexpected answer **(Figure 45.22)**. His studies established that for mammals (but not all animals), female development is the default process in embryos.

Androgens have a major role again at human puberty, when they are responsible for the development of human male secondary sex characteristics. High concentrations of androgen lead to a low voice and male patterns of hair growth, as well as increases in muscle and bone mass. The muscle-building, or anabolic, action of testosterone and related steroids has enticed

▼ **Figure 45.22** **Inquiry**

What role do hormones play in making a mammal male or female?

EXPERIMENT Alfred Jost, at the College de France in Paris, wondered whether gonadal hormones instruct an embryo to develop as male or female in accord with its chromosome set. Working with rabbit embryos still in the mother's uterus, at a stage before sex differences are observable, he surgically removed the portion of each embryo that would form the ovaries or testes. When the baby rabbits were born, Jost made note of both chromosomal sex and the sexual differentiation of the genital structures.

RESULTS

	Appearance of Genitals	
Chromosome Set	No surgery	Embryonic gonad removed
XY (male)	Male	Female
XX (female)	Female	Female

CONCLUSION In rabbits, male development requires a hormonal signal from the male gonad. In the absence of this signal, all embryos develop as female. Jost later demonstrated that embryos developed male genitals if the surgically removed gonad was replaced with a crystal of testosterone. In fact, the process of sex determination occurs in a highly similar manner in all mammals, including humans.

SOURCE A. Jost, Recherches sur la differenciation sexuelle de l'embryon de lapin (Studies on the sexual differentiation of the rabbit embryo), *Archives d'Anatomie Microscopique et de Morphologie Expérimentale* 36:271–316 (1947).

WHAT IF? What result would Jost have obtained if female development also required a signal from the gonad?

some athletes to take them as supplements, despite prohibitions against their use in nearly all sports. Use of anabolic steroids, while effective in increasing muscle mass, can cause severe acne outbreaks and liver damage. In addition, anabolic steroids have a negative-feedback effect on testosterone production, causing significant decreases in sperm count and testicular size.

Estrogens, of which the most important is **estradiol**, are responsible for the maintenance of the female reproductive system and the development of female secondary sex characteristics. In mammals, **progestins**, which include **progesterone**, are primarily involved in preparing and maintaining tissues of the uterus required to support the growth and development of an embryo.

Androgens, estrogens, and progestins are components of hormone cascade pathways. Synthesis of these hormones is controlled by gonadotropins (FSH and LH) from the anterior pituitary gland (see Figure 45.17). FSH and LH secretion is in turn controlled by a releasing hormone from the hypothalamus, GnRH (gonadotropin-releasing hormone). We will examine the feedback relationships that regulate gonadal steroid secretion in detail in Chapter 46.

Melatonin and Biorhythms

We conclude our discussion of the vertebrate endocrine system with the **pineal gland**, a small mass of tissue near the center of the mammalian brain (see Figure 45.14). The pineal gland synthesizes and secretes the hormone **melatonin**, a modified amino acid. Depending on the species, the pineal gland contains light-sensitive cells or has nervous connections from the eyes that control its secretory activity.

Melatonin regulates functions related to light and to seasons marked by changes in day length. Although melatonin affects skin pigmentation in many vertebrates, its primary functions relate to biological rhythms associated with reproduction. Melatonin is secreted at night, and the amount released depends on the length of the night. In winter, for example, when days are short and nights are long, more melatonin is secreted. Recent evidence suggests that the main target of melatonin is a group of neurons in the hypothalamus called the suprachiasmatic nucleus (SCN), which functions as a biological clock. Melatonin seems to decrease the activity of the SCN, and this effect may be related to its role in mediating rhythms. We will consider biological rhythms further in Chapter 49, where we will analyze experiments on SCN function.

In the next chapter, we will look at reproduction in both vertebrates and invertebrates. There we will see that the endocrine system is central not only to the survival of the individual, but also to the propagation of the species.

CONCEPT CHECK 45.4

1. How does the fact that two adrenal hormones act as neurotransmitters relate to the developmental origin of the adrenal gland?
2. How would a decrease in the number of corticosteroid receptors in the hypothalamus affect levels of corticosteroids in the blood?
3. **WHAT IF?** Suppose you receive an injection of cortisone, a glucocorticoid, in an inflamed joint. What aspects of glucocorticoid activity would you be exploiting? If a glucocorticoid pill were also effective at treating the inflammation, why would it still be preferable to introduce the drug locally?

For suggested answers, see Appendix A.

Chapter 45 Review

SUMMARY OF KEY CONCEPTS

CONCEPT 45.1

Hormones and other signaling molecules bind to target receptors, triggering specific response pathways (pp. 975–981)

▶ **Types of Secreted Signaling Molecules** Hormones are secreted into extracellular fluids by endocrine cells or ductless glands and reach target cells via the bloodstream. Local regulators act on neighboring cells in paracrine signaling, and on the secreting cell itself in autocrine signaling. Neurotransmitters also act locally, but some nerve cells secrete neurohormones that can act throughout the body. Signaling molecules called pheromones are released into the environment for communication between animals of the same species.

▶ **Chemical Classes of Hormones** Hormones can be polypeptides, amines, or steroids and can be water-soluble or lipid-soluble.

▶ **Hormone Receptor Location:** *Scientific Inquiry* Peptide/protein hormones and most hormones derived from amino acids bind to receptors embedded in the plasma membrane. Steroid hormones and thyroid hormones enter target cells and bind to specific protein receptors in the cytosol or nucleus.

▶ **Cellular Response Pathways** Binding of water-soluble hormones to cell-surface receptors triggers intracellular signal transduction, leading to specific responses in the cytoplasm or changes in gene expression. Complexes of a lipid-soluble hormone and its receptor act in the nucleus to regulate transcription of specific genes.

- ▶ **Multiple Effects of Hormones** The same hormone may have different effects on target cells that have different receptors for the hormone or different signal transduction pathways.

- ▶ **Signaling by Local Regulators** Local regulators include cytokines and growth factors (proteins/peptides), nitric oxide (a gas), and prostaglandins (modified fatty acids).

MEDIA

Activity Overview of Cell Signaling
Activity Peptide Hormone Action
Activity Steroid Hormone Action

CONCEPT 45.2

Negative feedback and antagonistic hormone pairs are common features of the endocrine system (pp. 981–984)

- ▶ **Simple Hormone Pathways**

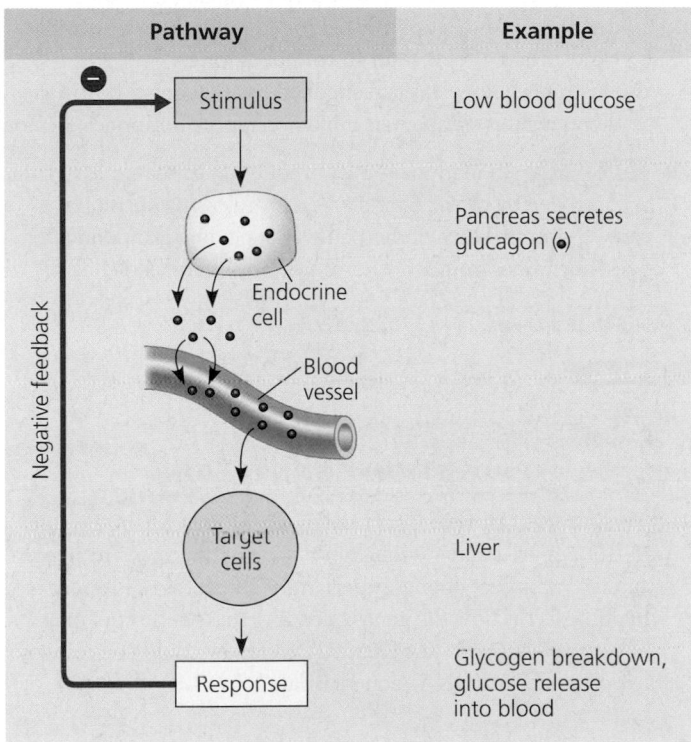

Pathway	Example
Stimulus	Low blood glucose
Endocrine cell (Pancreas)	Pancreas secretes glucagon (●)
Blood vessel	
Target cells	Liver
Response	Glycogen breakdown, glucose release into blood

Negative feedback

- ▶ **Insulin and Glucagon: Control of Blood Glucose** Insulin (from beta cells of the pancreas) reduces blood glucose levels by promoting cellular uptake of glucose, glycogen formation in the liver, protein synthesis, and fat storage. Glucagon (from alpha cells of the pancreas) increases blood glucose levels by stimulating conversion of glycogen to glucose in the liver and breakdown of fat and protein to glucose. Diabetes mellitus, which is marked by elevated blood glucose levels, results from inadequate production of insulin (type 1) or loss of responsiveness of target cells to insulin (type 2).

CONCEPT 45.3

The endocrine and nervous systems act individually and together in regulating animal physiology (pp. 984–990)

- ▶ The endocrine and nervous systems often function together in maintaining homeostasis, development, and reproduction.

- ▶ **Coordination of Endocrine and Nervous Systems in Invertebrates** Diverse hormones regulate different aspects of homeostasis in invertebrates. In insects, molting and development are controlled by prothoracicotropic hormone (PTTH), a tropic neurohormone; ecdysone, whose release is triggered by PTTH; and juvenile hormone.

- ▶ **Coordination of Endocrine and Nervous Systems in Vertebrates** The hypothalamus, on the underside of the brain, contains sets of neurosecretory cells. Some produce direct-acting hormones that are stored in and released from the posterior pituitary. Other hypothalamic cells produce hormones that are transported by portal blood vessels to the anterior pituitary. These hormones either promote or inhibit the release of hormones from the anterior pituitary.

- ▶ **Posterior Pituitary Hormones** The two hormones released from the posterior pituitary act directly on nonendocrine tissues. Oxytocin induces uterine contractions and release of milk from mammary glands, and antidiuretic hormone (ADH) enhances water reabsorption in the kidneys.

- ▶ **Anterior Pituitary Hormones** Hormones from the hypothalamus act as releasing or inhibiting hormones for hormone secretion by the anterior pituitary. Most anterior pituitary hormones are tropic, acting on endocrine tissues or glands to regulate hormone secretion. Often, anterior pituitary hormones act in a cascade. In the case of thyrotropin, or thyroid-stimulating hormone (TSH), TSH secretion is regulated by thyrotropin-releasing hormone (TRH), and TSH in turn regulates secretion of thyroid hormone. Like TSH, follicle-stimulating hormone (FSH), luteinizing hormone (LH), and adrenocorticotropic hormone (ACTH) are tropic. Prolactin and melanocyte-stimulating hormone (MSH) are nontropic anterior pituitary hormones. Prolactin stimulates milk production in mammals but has diverse effects in different vertebrates. MSH influences skin pigmentation in some vertebrates and fat metabolism in mammals. Growth hormone (GH) promotes growth directly and has diverse metabolic effects; it also stimulates the production of growth factors by other tissues.

CONCEPT 45.4

Endocrine glands respond to diverse stimuli in regulating metabolism, homeostasis, development, and behavior (pp. 990–994)

- ▶ **Thyroid Hormone: Control of Metabolism and Development** The thyroid gland produces iodine-containing hormones (T_3 and T_4) that stimulate metabolism and influence development and maturation. Secretion of T_3 and T_4 is controlled by the hypothalamus and pituitary in a hormone cascade pathway.

- ▶ **Parathyroid Hormone and Vitamin D: Control of Blood Calcium** Parathyroid hormone (PTH), secreted by the parathyroid glands, causes bone to release Ca^{2+} into the blood and stimulates reabsorption of Ca^{2+} in the kidneys. PTH also stimulates the kidneys to activate vitamin D, which promotes intestinal uptake of Ca^{2+} from food. Calcitonin, secreted by the thyroid, has the opposite effects in bones and kidneys as PTH. Calcitonin is important for calcium homeostasis in adults of some vertebrates, but not humans.

- ▶ **Adrenal Hormones: Response to Stress** Neurosecretory cells in the adrenal medulla release epinephrine and norepinephrine in response to stress-activated impulses from the nervous system. These hormones mediate various fight-or-flight responses. The adrenal cortex releases three functional classes of steroid hormones. Glucocorticoids, such as cortisol, influence glucose metabolism and the immune system; mineralocorticoids, primarily aldosterone, help regulate salt and water balance. The adrenal cortex also produces small amounts of sex hormones.

▶ **Gonadal Sex Hormones** The gonads—testes and ovaries—produce most of the body's sex hormones: androgens, estrogens, and progestins. All three types are produced in males and females but in different proportions.

▶ **Melatonin and Biorhythms** The pineal gland, located within the brain, secretes melatonin. Release of melatonin is controlled by light/dark cycles. Its primary functions appear to be related to biological rhythms associated with reproduction.

MEDIA

Activity Human Endocrine Glands and Hormones
Investigation How Do Thyroxine and TSH Affect Metabolism?

TESTING YOUR KNOWLEDGE

SELF-QUIZ

1. Which of the following is *not* an accurate statement?
   a. Hormones are chemical messengers that travel to target cells through the circulatory system.
   b. Hormones often regulate homeostasis through antagonistic functions.
   c. Hormones of the same chemical class usually have the same function.
   d. Hormones are secreted by specialized cells usually located in endocrine glands.
   e. Hormones are often regulated through feedback loops.

2. A distinctive feature of the mechanism of action of thyroid hormones and steroid hormones is that
   a. these hormones are regulated by feedback loops.
   b. target cells react more rapidly to these hormones than to local regulators.
   c. these hormones bind with specific receptor proteins on the plasma membrane of target cells.
   d. these hormones bind to receptors inside cells.
   e. these hormones affect metabolism.

3. Growth factors are local regulators that
   a. are produced by the anterior pituitary.
   b. are modified fatty acids that stimulate bone and cartilage growth.
   c. are found on the surface of cancer cells and stimulate abnormal cell division.
   d. are proteins that bind to cell-surface receptors and stimulate growth and development of target cells.
   e. convey messages between nerve cells.

4. Which hormone is *incorrectly* paired with its action?
   a. oxytocin—stimulates uterine contractions during childbirth
   b. thyroxine—stimulates metabolic processes
   c. insulin—stimulates glycogen breakdown in the liver
   d. ACTH—stimulates the release of glucocorticoids by the adrenal cortex
   e. melatonin—affects biological rhythms, seasonal reproduction

5. An example of antagonistic hormones controlling homeostasis is
   a. thyroxine and parathyroid hormone in calcium balance.
   b. insulin and glucagon in glucose metabolism.
   c. progestins and estrogens in sexual differentiation.
   d. epinephrine and norepinephrine in fight-or-flight responses.
   e. oxytocin and prolactin in milk production.

6. Which of the following is the most likely explanation for hypothyroidism in a patient whose iodine level is normal?
   a. a disproportionate production of T_3 to T_4
   b. hyposecretion of TSH
   c. hypersecretion of TSH
   d. hypersecretion of MSH
   e. a decrease in the thyroid secretion of calcitonin

7. The main target organs for tropic hormones are
   a. muscles.   d. kidneys.
   b. blood vessels.   e. nerves.
   c. endocrine glands.

8. The relationship between the insect hormones ecdysone and PTTH
   a. is an example of the interaction between the endocrine and nervous systems.
   b. illustrates homeostasis achieved by positive feedback.
   c. demonstrates that peptide-derived hormones have more widespread effects than steroid hormones.
   d. illustrates homeostasis maintained by antagonistic hormones.
   e. demonstrates competitive inhibition for the hormone receptor.

9. **DRAW IT** In mammals, milk production by mammary glands is controlled by prolactin and prolactin-releasing hormone. Draw a simple sketch of this pathway, including glands and tissues, hormones, routes for hormone movement, and effects.

For Self-Quiz answers, see Appendix A.

MEDIA Visit **www.campbellbiology.com** for a Practice Test.

EVOLUTION CONNECTION

10. The intracellular receptors used by all the steroid and thyroid hormones are similar enough in structure that they are all considered members of one "superfamily" of proteins. Propose a hypothesis for how the genes encoding these receptors may have evolved. (*Hint:* See Figure 21.13.) How could you test your hypothesis using DNA sequence data?

SCIENTIFIC INQUIRY

11. Chronically high levels of glucocorticoids, called Cushing's syndrome, can result in obesity, muscle weakness, and depression. Excessive activity of either the pituitary or the adrenal gland can be the cause. To determine which gland has abnormal activity in a particular patient, doctors use the drug dexamethasone, a synthetic glucocorticoid that blocks ACTH release. Based on the graph, which gland is affected in patient X?

Animal Reproduction

▲ **Figure 46.1 How can each of these earthworms be both male and female?**

OVERVIEW

Pairing Up for Sexual Reproduction

The two earthworms (genus *Lumbricus*) in **Figure 46.1** are mating. If not disturbed, they will remain above ground and joined like this for several hours. Sperm will be transferred, and fertilized eggs will be produced. A few weeks later, sexual reproduction will be complete. New worms will hatch, but which parent will be the mother? The answer is simple yet probably unexpected: Both will.

As humans, we tend to think of reproduction in terms of the mating of males and females and the fusion of sperm and eggs. Animal reproduction, however, takes many forms. In some species, individuals change their sex during their lifetime, while in others, such as earthworms, an individual is both male and female at the same time. There are animals that can fertilize their own eggs, as well as others that can reproduce without any form of sex. For certain species, such as honeybees, reproduction is limited to a few individuals within a large population.

The many aspects of animal form and function we have studied in earlier chapters can be viewed, in the broadest context, as adaptations contributing to reproductive success. Individuals are transient. A population transcends the finite life spans of its members only by reproduction, the generation of new individuals from existing ones. In this chapter, we will compare the diverse reproductive mechanisms that have evolved in the animal kingdom. We will then examine details of mammalian reproduction, particularly that of humans. Deferring the cellular and molecular details of embryonic development until the next chapter, we will focus here on the physiology of reproduction, mostly from the perspective of the parents.

CONCEPT 46.1

Both asexual and sexual reproduction occur in the animal kingdom

There are two principal modes of animal reproduction. In **sexual reproduction**, the fusion of haploid gametes forms a diploid cell, the **zygote**. The animal that develops from a zygote can in turn give rise to gametes by meiosis (see Figure 13.8). The female gamete, the **egg**, is a large, nonmotile cell. The male gamete, the **sperm**, is generally a much smaller, motile cell. **Asexual reproduction** is the generation of new individuals without the fusion of egg and sperm. In most asexual animals, reproduction relies entirely on mitotic cell division.

Mechanisms of Asexual Reproduction

A number of distinct forms of asexual reproduction are found among the invertebrates. Many invertebrates can reproduce asexually by **fission**, the separation of a parent organism into

▲ **Figure 46.2 Asexual reproduction of a sea anemone (*Anthopleura elegantissima*).** The individual in the center of this photograph is undergoing fission, a type of asexual reproduction. Two smaller individuals will form as the parent divides approximately in half. Each offspring will be a genetic copy of the parent.

two individuals of approximately equal size (**Figure 46.2**). Also common among invertebrates is **budding**, in which new individuals arise from outgrowths of existing ones. For example, in certain species of coral and hydra, new individuals grow out from the parent's body (see Figure 13.2). Stony corals, which can grow to be more than 1 m across, are cnidarian colonies of several thousand connected individuals. In another form of asexual reproduction, some invertebrates, including certain sponges, release specialized groups of cells that can grow into new individuals.

A two-step process of asexual reproduction involves *fragmentation*, the breaking of the body into several pieces, followed by *regeneration*, the regrowth of lost body parts. If more than one piece grows and develops into a complete animal, the net effect is reproduction: In sea stars (starfish) of the genus *Linckia*, an arm that is broken off the body can regenerate an entire sea star. (Many other species of sea star can grow a new arm to replace a lost one, but do not create new individuals by regeneration.) Numerous sponges, cnidarians, bristle worms, and sea squirts reproduce by fragmentation and regeneration.

Parthenogenesis is a form of asexual reproduction in which an egg develops without being fertilized. The progeny of parthenogenesis can be either haploid or diploid. If haploid, the offspring develop into adults that produce eggs or sperm without meiosis. Reproduction by parthenogenesis occurs in certain species of bees, wasps, and ants. In the case of honeybees, males (drones) are fertile hap-

loid adults that arise by parthenogenesis. In contrast, female honeybees, including both the sterile workers and the fertile queens, are diploid adults that develop from fertilized eggs. Among vertebrates, parthenogenesis is observed in roughly one in every thousand species. Recently discovered examples include the Komodo dragon and a species of hammerhead shark. In both cases, zookeepers were surprised to find offspring that had been parthenogenetically produced when females were kept apart from males of their species.

Sexual Reproduction: An Evolutionary Enigma

The vast majority of eukaryotic species reproduce sexually. Sex must enhance reproductive success or survival, because it would otherwise rapidly disappear. To see why, consider an animal population in which half the females reproduce sexually and half reproduce asexually (**Figure 46.3**). We'll assume that the number of offspring per female is a constant, two in this case. The two offspring of an asexual female would both be daughters that are each able to give birth to more reproductive daughters. In contrast, half of a sexual female's offspring will be male. The number of offspring will remain the same at each generation, because both a male and a female are required to reproduce. Thus, the asexual condition will increase in frequency at each generation. Yet despite this "twofold cost," sex is maintained even in animal species that can also reproduce asexually.

What advantage does sex provide? The answer remains elusive. Most hypotheses focus on the unique combinations of parental genes formed during meiotic recombination and fertilization. By producing offspring of varied phenotypes, sexual reproduction may enhance the reproductive success of parents when environmental factors, such as pathogens, change relatively rapidly. In contrast, asexual reproduction is expected to be most advantageous in stable, favorable environments because it perpetuates successful genotypes faithfully and precisely.

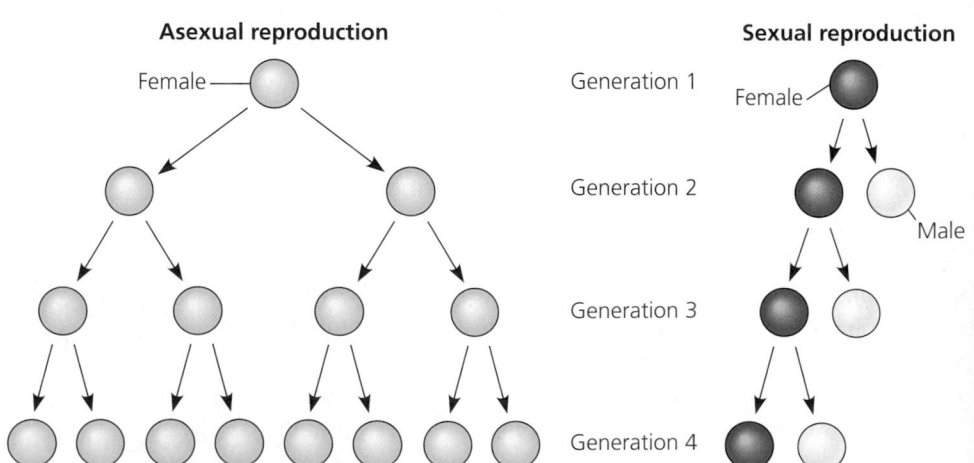

▲ **Figure 46.3 The "reproductive handicap" of sex.** These diagrams contrast the reproductive output of females (blue circles) over four generations for asexual versus sexual reproduction, assuming two surviving offspring per female. The asexual population rapidly outgrows the sexual one.

There are a number of reasons why the unique gene combinations formed during sexual reproduction might be advantageous. One is that beneficial gene combinations arising through recombination might speed up adaptation. Although this idea appears straightforward, the theoretical advantage is significant only when the rate of beneficial mutations is high and population size is small. Another idea is that the shuffling of genes during sexual reproduction might allow a population to rid itself of sets of harmful genes more readily. Experiments to test these and other hypotheses are ongoing in many laboratories.

Reproductive Cycles and Patterns

Most animals exhibit cycles in reproductive activity, often related to changing seasons. In this way, animals conserve resources, reproducing only when sufficient energy sources or stores are available and when environmental conditions favor the survival of offspring. For example, ewes (female sheep) have a reproductive cycle lasting 15–17 days. **Ovulation**, the release of mature eggs, occurs at the midpoint of each cycle. A ewe's cycles generally occur only during fall and early winter, and the length of any resulting pregnancy is five months. Thus, most lambs are born in the early spring, the time when their chances of survival are optimal. Even in such relatively unvarying habitats as the tropics or the ocean, animals generally reproduce only at certain times of the year. Reproductive cycles are controlled by hormones, which in turn are regulated by environmental cues. Common environmental cues are changes in day length, seasonal temperature, rainfall, and lunar cycles.

Animals may reproduce exclusively asexually or sexually, or they may alternate between the two modes. In aphids, rotifers, and water fleas (genus *Daphnia*), a female can produce eggs of two types. One type of egg requires fertilization to develop, but the other type does not and develops instead by parthenogenesis. In the case of *Daphnia*, the switch between sexual and asexual reproduction is often related to season. Asexual reproduction occurs when conditions are favorable, whereas sexual reproduction occurs during times of environmental stress.

Several genera of fishes, amphibians, and reptiles reproduce exclusively by a complex form of parthenogenesis that involves the doubling of chromosomes after meiosis, producing diploid offspring. For example, about 15 species of whiptail lizards in the genus *Aspidoscelis* reproduce exclusively by parthenogenesis. There are no males in these species, but the lizards carry out courtship and mating behaviors typical of sexual species of the same genus. During the breeding season, one female of each mating pair mimics a male (**Figure 46.4a**). Each member of the pair alternates roles two or three times during the season (**Figure 46.4b**). An individual adopts female behavior prior to ovulation, when the level of the female sex hormone estradiol is high, then switches to male-like behavior after ovulation, when the level of progesterone is highest. Ovulation is more likely to occur if the individual is

mounted during the critical time of the hormone cycle; isolated lizards lay fewer eggs than those that go through the motions of sex. Apparently, these parthenogenetic lizards evolved from species having two sexes and still require certain sexual stimuli for maximum reproductive success.

Sexual reproduction that involves encounters between members of the opposite sex presents a problem for sessile (stationary) animals, such as barnacles; burrowing animals, such as clams; and some parasites, including tapeworms. One evolutionary solution to this problem is **hermaphroditism**, in which each individual has both male and female reproductive systems (the term *hermaphrodite* is derived from the names Hermes and

(a) Both lizards in this photograph are *A. uniparens* females. The one on top is playing the role of a male. Every two or three weeks during the breeding season, individuals switch sex roles.

(b) The sexual behavior of *A. uniparens* is correlated with the cycle of ovulation mediated by sex hormones. As the blood level of estradiol rises, the ovaries grow, and the lizard behaves as a female. After ovulation, the estradiol level drops abruptly, and the progesterone level rises; these hormone levels correlate with male-like behavior.

▲ **Figure 46.4 Sexual behavior in parthenogenetic lizards.** The desert-grassland whiptail lizard (*Aspidoscelis uniparens*) is an all-female species. These reptiles reproduce by parthenogenesis, the development of an unfertilized egg. Nevertheless, ovulation is stimulated by mating behavior.

Aphrodite, a Greek god and goddess). Because each hermaphrodite reproduces as both a male and a female, any two individuals can mate. Each animal donates and receives sperm during mating, as the earthworms in Figure 46.1 are doing. In some species, hermaphrodites are also capable of self-fertilization.

Another reproductive pattern involves sex reversal, in which an individual changes its sex during its lifetime. The bluehead wrasse (*Thalassoma bifasciatum*), a coral reef fish, provides a well-studied example. These wrasses live in harems consisting of a single male and several females. When the male dies, the largest (and usually oldest) female in the harem becomes the new male. Within a week, the transformed individual is producing sperm instead of eggs. Because the male defends the harem against intruders, a larger size may be more important for males than females in ensuring successful reproduction.

Certain oyster species provide an example of sex reversal from male to female. By reproducing as males and then later reversing sex, these oysters become female when their size is greatest. Since the number of gametes produced generally increases with size much more for females than for males, sex reversal in this direction maximizes gamete production. The result is enhanced reproductive success: Because oysters are sedentary animals and simply release their gametes into the surrounding water, more gametes result in more offspring.

CONCEPT 46.2
Fertilization depends on mechanisms that bring together sperm and eggs of the same species

Fertilization—the union of sperm and egg—can be either external or internal. In species with **external fertilization**, the female releases eggs into the environment, where the male then fertilizes them. Other species have **internal fertilization**: Sperm are deposited in or near the female reproductive tract, and fertilization occurs within the tract. (We'll discuss the cellular and molecular details of fertilization in Chapter 47.)

A moist habitat is almost always required for external fertilization, both to prevent the gametes from drying out and to allow the sperm to swim to the eggs. Many aquatic invertebrates simply shed their eggs and sperm into the surroundings, and fertilization occurs without the parents making physical contact. However, timing is crucial to ensure that mature sperm and eggs encounter one another.

Among some species with external fertilization, individuals clustered in the same area release their gametes into the water at the same time, a process known as *spawning*. In some cases, chemical signals that one individual generates in releasing gametes trigger others to release gametes. In other cases, environmental cues, such as temperature or day length, cause a whole population to release gametes at one time. For example, the palolo worm, native to coral reefs of the South Pacific, times its spawn to both the season and the lunar cycle. In October or November, when the moon is in its last quarter, palolo worms break in half, releasing tail segments engorged with sperm or eggs. These packets rise to the ocean surface and burst in such vast numbers that the sea surface turns milky with gametes. The sperm quickly fertilize the floating eggs, and within hours, the palolo's once-a-year reproductive frenzy is complete.

When external fertilization is not synchronous across a population, individuals may exhibit specific mating behaviors leading to the fertilization of the eggs of one female by one male **(Figure 46.5)**. Such "courtship" behavior has two important benefits: It allows mate selection (see Chapter 23) and, by triggering the release of both sperm and eggs, increases the probability of successful fertilization.

Internal fertilization is an adaptation that enables sperm to reach an egg efficiently, even when the environment is dry. It typically requires cooperative behavior that leads to copulation,

▲ **Figure 46.5 External fertilization.** Many amphibians reproduce by external fertilization. In most species, behavioral adaptations ensure that a male is present when the female releases eggs. Here, a female frog (on bottom) has released a mass of eggs in response to being clasped by a male. The male released sperm (not visible) at the same time, and external fertilization has already occurred in the water.

as well as sophisticated and compatible reproductive systems. Male copulatory organs deliver sperm, and the female reproductive tract often has receptacles for storage and delivery of sperm to mature eggs.

No matter how fertilization occurs, the mating animals may make use of *pheromones*, chemicals released by one organism that can influence the physiology and behavior of other individuals of the same species (see Chapter 45). Pheromones are small, volatile or water-soluble molecules that disperse into the environment and, like hormones, are active in tiny amounts. Many pheromones function as mate attractants, enabling some female insects to be detected by males from as far as a mile away. (We will discuss mating behavior and pheromones further in Chapter 51.)

Ensuring the Survival of Offspring

All species generally produce more offspring than can survive to reproduce. Species with external fertilization tend to produce very large numbers of gametes, but the fraction of zygotes that survive is often quite small. Internal fertilization usually produces fewer zygotes, and is also often associated with a variety of mechanisms that provide greater protection of the embryos and parental care of the young. For example, the internally fertilized eggs of many species of terrestrial animals exhibit adaptations that protect against water loss and physical damage during their external development. In the case of birds and other reptiles, as well as monotremes (egg-laying mammals), the zygotes consist of eggs with calcium- and protein-containing shells and a series of internal membranes (see Chapter 34). In contrast, the fertilized eggs of fishes and amphibians have only a gelatinous coat and lack membranes within them.

Rather than secreting a protective eggshell, some animals retain the embryo for some portion of its development within the female's reproductive tract. Embryos of marsupial mammals, such as kangaroos and opossums, spend only a short period in the uterus; the embryos then crawl out and complete fetal development attached to a mammary gland in the mother's pouch. However, the embryos of eutherian (placental) mammals, such as humans, remain in the uterus throughout fetal development. There they are nourished by the mother's blood supply through a specialized temporary organ, the placenta. The embryos of some fishes and sharks also complete development internally, although typically the embryo and mother in such species lack any connection dedicated to nutrient exchange.

When a baby eagle hatches out of an egg or when a human is born, the newborn is not yet capable of independent existence. Instead, adult birds feed their young and mammals nurse their offspring. Parental care is in fact much more widespread than you might suspect. For example, there are many invertebrates that provide parental care **(Figure 46.6)**. Among vertebrates, the gastric brooding frogs (genus *Rheobatrachus*) of Australia provided a particularly unusual example prior to their

▲ **Figure 46.6 Parental care in an invertebrate.** Compared with many other insects, giant water bugs of the genus *Belostoma* produce relatively few offspring, but offer much greater parental protection. Following internal fertilization, the female glues her fertilized eggs to the back of the male (shown here). The male carries them for days, frequently fanning water over them to keep the eggs moist, aerated, and free of parasites.

extinction in the 1980s. During reproduction, the female frog would carry the tadpoles in her stomach until they underwent metamorphosis and hopped out of her mouth as young frogs.

Gamete Production and Delivery

Sexual reproduction in animals relies on sets of cells that serve as precursors for ova and sperm. A group of cells dedicated to this purpose is often established very early in embryogenesis and remains in an inactive state while the overall body plan develops. Cycles of growth and mitosis then increase, or *amplify*, the number of cells available for making eggs or sperm.

In producing gametes from the amplified precursor cells and making them available for fertilization, animals employ a variety of reproductive systems. The simplest systems do not even include discrete **gonads**, the organs that produce gametes in most animals. The palolo and most other polychaete worms (phylum Annelida) have separate sexes but do not have distinct gonads; rather, the eggs and sperm develop from undifferentiated cells lining the coelom (body cavity). As the gametes mature, they are released from the body wall and fill the coelom. Depending on the species, mature gametes may be shed through the excretory opening, or the swelling mass of eggs may split a portion of the body open, spilling the eggs into the environment.

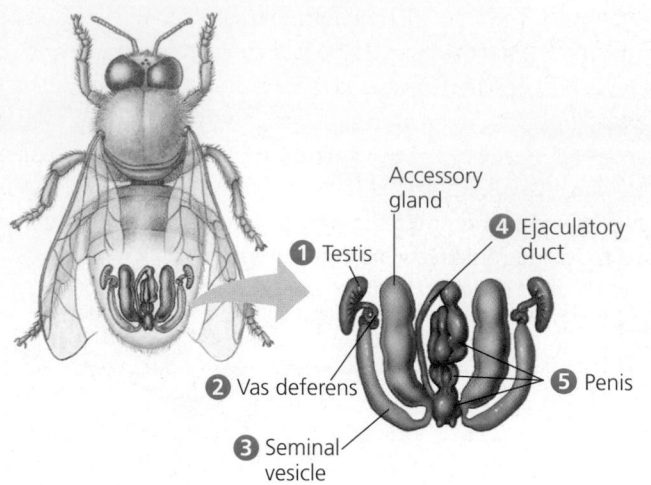

(a) **Male honeybee (drone).** Sperm form in the testes, pass through the sperm ducts (vas deferens), and are stored in the seminal vesicles. The male ejaculates sperm along with fluid from the accessory glands. (Males of some species of insects and other arthropods have appendages called claspers that grasp the female during copulation.)

▲ **Figure 46.7 Insect reproductive anatomy.**
Circled numbers indicate sequences of sperm and egg movement.

More elaborate reproductive systems include sets of accessory tubes and glands that carry, nourish, and protect the gametes and sometimes the developing embryos. Most insects, for example, have separate sexes with complex reproductive systems **(Figure 46.7)**. In the male, sperm develop in a pair of testes and are passed along a coiled duct to two seminal vesicles for storage. During mating, sperm are ejaculated into the female reproductive system. There, eggs develop in a pair of ovaries and are conveyed through ducts to the vagina, where fertilization occurs. In many insect species, the female reproductive system includes a **spermatheca**, a sac in which sperm may be stored for extended periods, a year or more in some species. Because the female releases male gametes from the spermatheca only in response to the appropriate stimuli, fertilization occurs under conditions likely to be well suited to embryonic development. Even more complex reproductive systems can be found in some animals whose body plans are otherwise fairly simple, such as parasitic flatworms **(Figure 46.8)**.

The basic plans of all vertebrate reproductive systems are quite similar, but there are some important variations. In many nonmammalian vertebrates, the digestive, excretory, and reproductive systems have a common opening to the outside, the **cloaca**, a structure that was probably also present in the ancestors of all vertebrates. In contrast, mammals generally lack a cloaca and have a separate opening for the digestive tract. In addition, most female mammals have separate openings for the excretory and reproductive systems. Among most vertebrates, the uterus is partly or completely divided into two chambers. However, in humans and other mammals that produce only one or a few young at a time, as well as in birds and many snakes, the uterus is a single structure. Male reproduc-

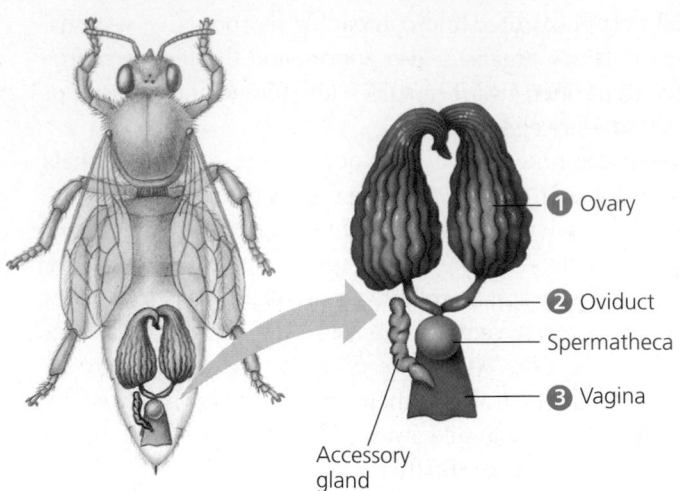

(b) **Female honeybee (queen).** Eggs develop in the ovaries and then pass through the oviducts and into the vagina. A pair of accessory glands (only one is shown) add protective secretions to the eggs in the vagina. After mating, sperm are stored in the spermatheca, a sac connected to the vagina by a short duct.

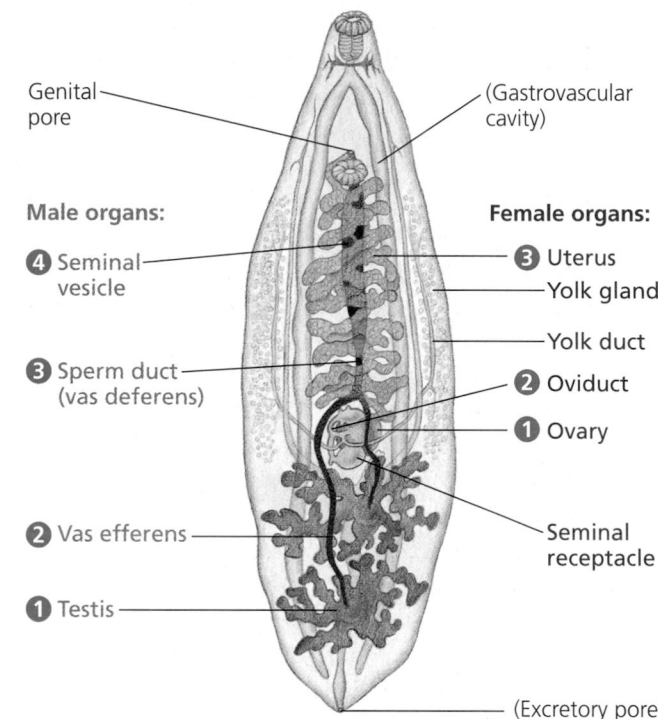

▲ **Figure 46.8 Reproductive anatomy of a hermaphrodite.**
Most flatworms (phylum Platyhelminthes) are hermaphrodites. In this parasitic liver fluke, both male and female reproductive systems open to the outside via the genital pore. Sperm, made in the testis, travel as shown by the numbered sequence to the seminal vesicle, which stores them. During copulation, sperm are ejaculated into the female system (usually of another individual) and then move through the uterus to the seminal receptacle. Eggs from the ovary pass into the oviduct, where they are fertilized by sperm from the seminal receptacle and coated with yolk and shell material secreted by the yolk glands. From the oviduct, the fertilized eggs pass into the uterus and then out of the body.

tive systems differ mainly in the copulatory organs. Many nonmammalian vertebrates lack a well-developed penis and instead ejaculate sperm by turning the cloaca inside out.

▼ Figure 46.9 **Inquiry**

Why is sperm usage biased when female fruit flies mate twice?

EXPERIMENT When a female fruit fly mates with two different males, 80% of the offspring result from the second mating. Some scientists had postulated that ejaculate from the second male displaces stored sperm from the first mating. To test this hypothesis, Rhonda Snook, at the University of Sheffield, and David Hosken, at the University of Zurich, took advantage of mutations that alter the male reproductive system. "No-ejaculate" males mate, but do not transfer any sperm or fluid to females. "No-sperm" males mate and ejaculate, but make no sperm. The researchers allowed females to mate twice, first with wild-type males and then with either wild-type males, no-sperm males, or no-ejaculate males. As a control, some females were mated only once. The scientists then dissected each female under a microscope and recorded whether sperm were absent from the spermatheca, the sperm storage organ.

RESULTS

CONCLUSION Because mating reduces sperm storage when no sperm or fluids are transferred, the hypothesis that ejaculate from a second mating displaces stored sperm is incorrect. Instead, it appears that females sometimes get rid of stored sperm in response to mating. This might represent a way for females to replace stored sperm, possibly of diminished fitness, with fresh sperm.

SOURCE R. R. Snook and D. J. Hosken, Sperm death and dumping in *Drosophila*, *Nature* 428:939–941 (2004).

WHAT IF? Suppose the males in the first mating had a mutant allele for the dominant trait of reduced eye size. Predict what fraction, if any, of the females would produce some offspring with smaller eyes.

Although fertilization involves the union of a single egg and sperm, animals often mate with more than one member of the other sex. Indeed, monogamy, the sustained sexual partnership of two individuals, is relatively rare among animals, including most mammals other than humans. Mechanisms have evolved, however, that enhance the reproductive success of a male with a particular female and diminish the chance of that female mating successfully with another partner. For example, some male insects transfer secretions that make a female less receptive to courtship, reducing the likelihood of her mating again. Can females also influence the relative reproductive success of their mates? This question intrigued Rhonda Snook and David Hosken, collaborators

working in the United Kingdom and Switzerland, respectively. Studying female fruit flies that copulated with one male and then another, the researchers traced the fate of sperm transferred in the first mating. As shown in **Figure 46.9**, they found that female fruit flies play a major role in determining the reproductive outcome of multiple matings. Nevertheless, the processes by which gametes and individuals compete during reproduction are only partly understood and remain a vibrant research area.

CONCEPT CHECK 46.2

1. How does internal fertilization facilitate life on land?
2. What mechanisms have evolved in animals with (a) external fertilization and (b) internal fertilization that help ensure that offspring survive to adulthood?
3. **WHAT IF?** Suppose you were analyzing chemicals found in the ejaculate of male fruit flies and discovered a peptide that kills microbes. What hypotheses might you formulate as to the function of this peptide?

For suggested answers, see Appendix A.

CONCEPT 46.3

Reproductive organs produce and transport gametes

Having surveyed some of the general features of animal reproduction, we will focus the rest of the chapter on humans, beginning with the anatomy of the reproductive system in each sex.

Female Reproductive Anatomy

The female's external reproductive structures are the clitoris and two sets of labia, which surround the clitoris and vaginal opening. The internal organs are the gonads, which produce both eggs and reproductive hormones, and a system of ducts and chambers, which receive and carry gametes and house the embryo and fetus (**Figure 46.10** on the next page).

Ovaries

The female gonads are a pair of ovaries that flank the uterus and are held in place in the abdominal cavity by ligaments. The outer layer of each ovary is packed with **follicles**, each consisting of an **oocyte**, a partially developed egg, surrounded by a group of support cells. The surrounding cells nourish and protect the oocyte during much of **oogenesis**, the formation and development of an ovum. Although at birth the ovaries together contain about 1–2 million follicles, only about 500 follicles fully mature between puberty and menopause. During a typical 4-week menstrual cycle, one follicle matures and expels its egg, a process called ovulation. Prior to ovulation, cells of the follicle produce the primary female sex hormone, estradiol (a type of

▼ **Figure 46.10 Reproductive anatomy of the human female.** Some nonreproductive structures are labeled in parentheses for orientation purposes.

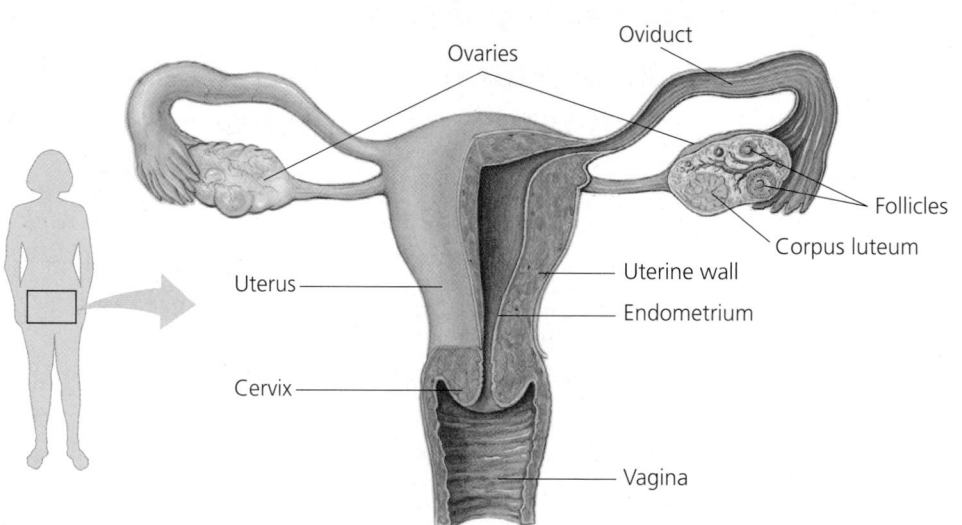

epithelial lining of the duct help collect the egg by drawing fluid from the body cavity into the oviduct. Together with wavelike contractions of the oviduct, the cilia convey the egg down the duct to the **uterus**, also known as the womb. The uterus is a thick, muscular organ that can expand during pregnancy to accommodate a 4-kg fetus. The inner lining of the uterus, the **endometrium**, is richly supplied with blood vessels. The neck of the uterus is the **cervix**, which opens into the vagina.

Vagina and Vulva

The **vagina** is a muscular but elastic chamber that is the site for insertion of the penis and deposition of sperm during copulation. The vagina, which also serves as the birth canal through which a baby is born, opens to the outside at the **vulva**, the collective term for the external female genitals.

A pair of thick, fatty ridges, the **labia majora**, encloses and protects the rest of the vulva. The vaginal opening and the separate opening of the urethra are located within a cavity bordered by a pair of slender skin folds, the **labia minora**. A thin piece of tissue called the **hymen** partly covers the vaginal opening in humans at birth, and usually until sexual intercourse or vigorous physical activity ruptures it. Located at the upper intersection of the labia minora, the **clitoris** consists of a short shaft supporting a rounded **glans**, or head, covered by a small hood of skin, the **prepuce**. During sexual arousal, the clitoris, vagina, and labia minora all engorge with blood and enlarge; in fact, the clitoris consists largely of erectile tissue. Richly supplied with nerve endings, it is one of the most sensitive points of sexual stimulation. Sexual arousal also induces glands located near the vaginal opening to secrete lubricating mucus, thereby facilitating intercourse.

Mammary Glands

Mammary glands are present in both sexes but normally produce milk only in females. Though not part of the reproductive system, the female mammary glands are important to reproduction. Within the glands, small sacs of epithelial tissue secrete milk, which drains into a series of ducts opening at the nipple. The breasts contain connective and fatty (adipose) tissue in addition to the mammary glands. Because the low level

estrogen). After ovulation, the residual follicular tissue grows within the ovary, forming a mass called the **corpus luteum** ("yellow body"). The corpus luteum secretes additional estradiol, as well as progesterone, a hormone that helps maintain the uterine lining during pregnancy. If the egg cell is not fertilized, the corpus luteum degenerates, and a new follicle matures during the next cycle.

Oviducts and Uterus

An **oviduct**, or fallopian tube, extends from the uterus toward each ovary. The dimensions of this tube vary along its length, with the inside diameter near the uterus being as narrow as a human hair. At ovulation, the egg is released into the abdominal cavity near the funnel-like opening of the oviduct. Cilia on the of estradiol in males limits the development of the fat deposits, male breasts usually remain small.

Male Reproductive Anatomy

The human male's external reproductive organs are the scrotum and penis. The internal reproductive organs consist of gonads that produce both sperm and reproductive hormones, accessory glands that secrete products essential to sperm movement, and ducts that carry the sperm and glandular secretions **(Figure 46.11)**.

Testes

The male gonads, or **testes** (singular, *testis*), consist of many highly coiled tubes surrounded by several layers of connective tissue. These tubes are the **seminiferous tubules**, where sperm form. The **Leydig cells**, scattered between the seminiferous tubules, produce testosterone and other androgens (see Chapter 45).

For most mammals, sperm production occurs properly only when the testes are cooler than normal body temperature. In humans and many other mammals, the **scrotum**, a fold of the body wall, maintains testis temperature about 2°C below that in the abdominal cavity. The testes develop high in the abdominal cavity and descend into the scrotum just before birth; a testis within a scrotum is often termed a *testicle*. In many rodents, the testes are drawn back into the abdominal cavity between breeding seasons, interrupting sperm maturation. Some mammals whose body temperature is low enough to allow sperm maturation—such as monotremes, whales, and elephants—retain the testes within the abdominal cavity at all times.

Ducts

From the seminiferous tubules of a testis, the sperm pass into the coiled tubules of the **epididymis**. In humans, it takes 3 weeks for sperm to pass through the 6-m-long tubules of each epididymis.

During this passage, the sperm complete their maturation and become motile, although they acquire the ability to fertilize an egg only when exposed to the chemical environment of the female reproductive system. During **ejaculation**, the sperm are propelled from each epididymis through a muscular duct, the **vas deferens**. Each vas deferens (one from each epididymis) extends around and behind the urinary bladder, where it joins a duct from the seminal vesicle, forming a short **ejaculatory duct**. The ejaculatory ducts open into the **urethra**, the outlet tube for both the excretory system and the reproductive system. The urethra runs through the penis and opens to the outside at the tip of the penis.

Accessory Glands

Three sets of accessory glands—the seminal vesicles, the prostate gland, and the bulbourethral

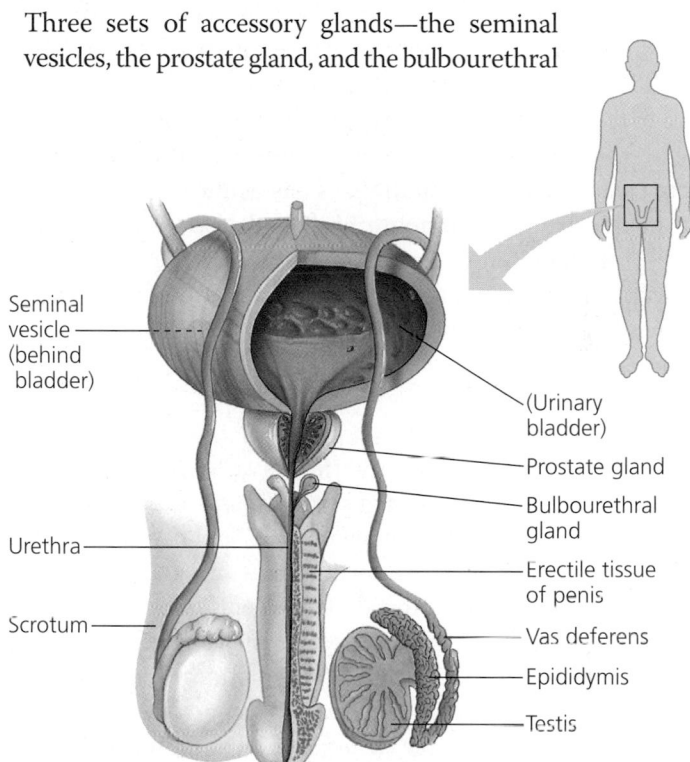

Seminal vesicle (behind bladder)

Urethra

Scrotum

(Urinary bladder)

Prostate gland

Bulbourethral gland

Erectile tissue of penis

Vas deferens

Epididymis

Testis

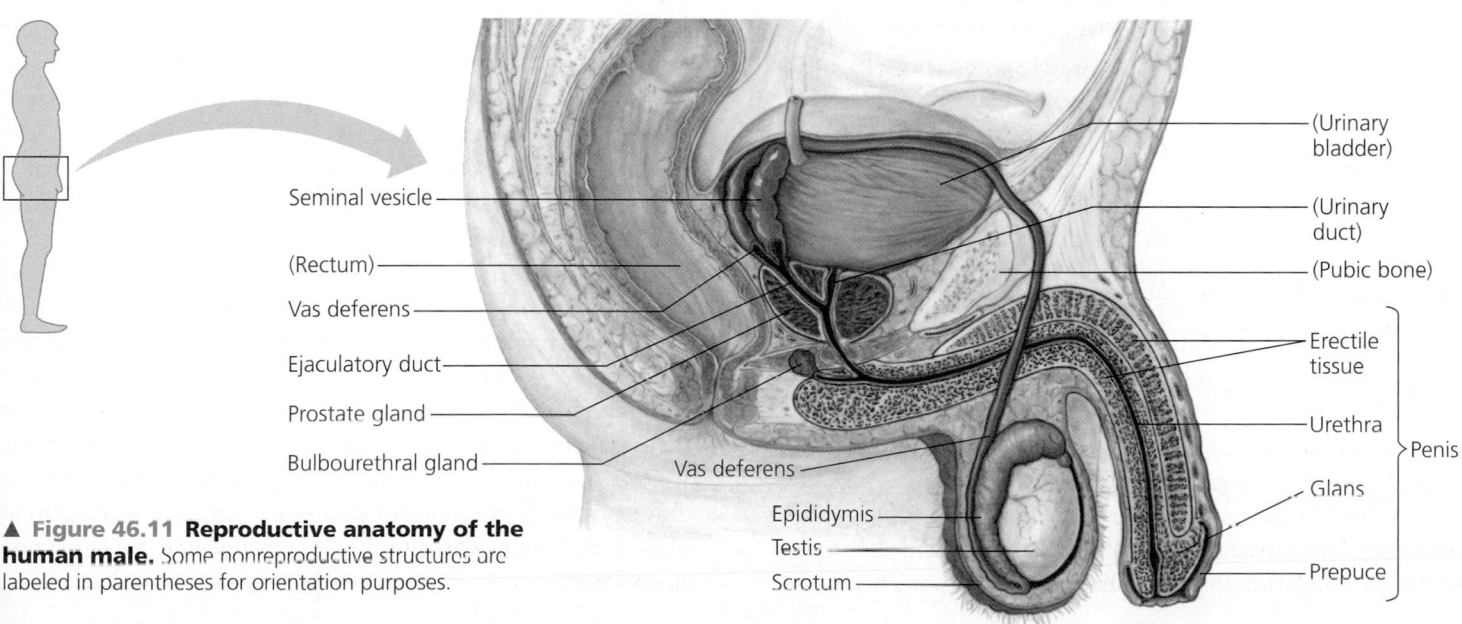

Seminal vesicle

(Rectum)

Vas deferens

Ejaculatory duct

Prostate gland

Bulbourethral gland

Vas deferens

Epididymis

Testis

Scrotum

(Urinary bladder)

(Urinary duct)

(Pubic bone)

Erectile tissue

Urethra

Glans

Prepuce

Penis

▲ **Figure 46.11 Reproductive anatomy of the human male.** Some nonreproductive structures are labeled in parentheses for orientation purposes.

glands—produce secretions that combine with sperm to form **semen**, the fluid that is ejaculated. Two **seminal vesicles** contribute about 60% of the volume of semen. The fluid from the seminal vesicles is thick, yellowish, and alkaline. It contains mucus, the sugar fructose (which provides most of the sperm's energy), a coagulating enzyme, ascorbic acid, and local regulators called prostaglandins (see Chapter 45).

The **prostate gland** secretes its products directly into the urethra through several small ducts. This fluid is thin and milky; it contains anticoagulant enzymes and citrate (a sperm nutrient). The prostate gland is the source of some of the most common medical problems of men over age 40. Benign (noncancerous) enlargement of the prostate occurs in more than half of all men in this age-group and in almost all men over 70. In addition, prostate cancer, which most often afflicts men 65 and older, is one of the most common human cancers.

The *bulbourethral glands* are a pair of small glands along the urethra below the prostate. Before ejaculation, they secrete clear mucus that neutralizes any acidic urine remaining in the urethra. Bulbourethral fluid also carries some sperm released before ejaculation, which is one reason for the high failure rate of the withdrawal method of birth control (coitus interruptus).

Penis

The human **penis** contains the urethra, as well as three cylinders of spongy erectile tissue. During sexual arousal, the erectile tissue, which is derived from modified veins and capillaries, fills with blood from the arteries. As this tissue fills, the increasing pressure seals off the veins that drain the penis, causing it to engorge with blood. The resulting erection enables the penis to be inserted into the vagina. Alcohol consumption, certain drugs, emotional issues, and aging all can cause a temporary inability to achieve an erection (erectile dysfunction). For individuals with long-term erectile dysfunction, drugs such as Viagra promote the vasodilating action of the local regulator nitric oxide (NO; see Chapter 45); the resulting relaxation of smooth muscles in the blood vessels of the penis enhances blood flow into the erectile tissues. Although all mammals rely on penile erection for mating, the penis of rodents, raccoons, walruses, whales, and several other mammals also contains a bone, the baculum, which probably further stiffens the penis for mating.

The main shaft of the penis is covered by relatively thick skin. The head, or glans, of the penis has a much thinner covering and is consequently more sensitive to stimulation. The human glans is covered by a fold of skin called the prepuce, or foreskin, which may be removed by circumcision.

Human Sexual Response

As mentioned earlier, many animals exhibit elaborate mating behavior. The arousal of sexual interest in humans is particularly complex, involving a variety of psychological as well as physical factors. Reproductive structures in the male and female that are quite different in appearance often serve similar functions, reflecting their shared developmental origin. For example, the same embryonic tissues give rise to the glans of the penis and the clitoris, the scrotum and the labia majora, and the skin on the penis and the labia minora.

The general pattern of human sexual response is similar in males and females. Two types of physiological reactions predominate in both sexes: **vasocongestion**, the filling of a tissue with blood, and **myotonia**, increased muscle tension. Both skeletal and smooth muscle may show sustained or rhythmic contractions, including those associated with orgasm.

The sexual response cycle can be divided into four phases: excitement, plateau, orgasm, and resolution. An important function of the excitement phase is to prepare the vagina and penis for **coitus** (sexual intercourse). During this phase, vasocongestion is particularly evident in erection of the penis and clitoris; enlargement of the testicles, labia, and breasts; and vaginal lubrication. Myotonia may occur, resulting in nipple erection or tension of the arms and legs.

In the plateau phase, these responses continue as a result of direct stimulation of the genitals. In females, the outer third of the vagina becomes vasocongested, while the inner two-thirds slightly expands. This change, coupled with the elevation of the uterus, forms a depression for receiving sperm at the back of the vagina. Breathing increases and heart rate rises, sometimes to 150 beats per minute—not only in response to the physical effort of sexual activity, but also as an involuntary response to stimulation of the autonomic nervous system (see Figure 49.8).

Orgasm is characterized by rhythmic, involuntary contractions of the reproductive structures in both sexes. Male orgasm has two stages. The first, emission, occurs when the glands and ducts of the reproductive tract contract, forcing semen into the urethra. Expulsion, or ejaculation, occurs when the urethra contracts and the semen is expelled. During female orgasm, the uterus and outer vagina contract, but the inner two-thirds of the vagina does not. Orgasm is the shortest phase of the sexual response cycle, usually lasting only a few seconds. In both sexes, contractions occur at about 0.8-second intervals and may also involve the anal sphincter and several abdominal muscles.

The resolution phase completes the cycle and reverses the responses of the earlier stages. Vasocongested organs return to their normal size and color, and muscles relax. Most of the changes of resolution are completed within 5 minutes, but some may take as long as an hour. Following orgasm, the male typically enters a refractory period, lasting anywhere from a few minutes to hours, during which erection and orgasm cannot be achieved. Females do not have a refractory period, making possible multiple orgasms within a short period of time.

CONCEPT 46.4
The timing and pattern of meiosis in mammals differ for males and females

Reproduction in mammals involves two distinct types of gametes. Sperm are small and motile. In contrast, eggs, which provide the initial food stores for the embryo, are typically much larger. For embryonic development to be successful, eggs must mature in synchrony with the tissues of the female reproductive system that support the fertilized embryo. Reflecting these differences, egg and sperm development involve distinct patterns of meiotic division. We will highlight these distinctions, as well as several basic similarities, as we explore **gametogenesis**, the production of gametes.

Spermatogenesis, the formation and development of sperm, is continuous and prolific in adult males. To produce hundreds of millions of sperm each day, cell division and maturation occur throughout the seminiferous tubules coiled within the two testes. On page 1008, **Figure 46.12** details the steps and organization of spermatogenesis in humans. For a single sperm, the process takes about seven weeks from start to finish.

Oogenesis, the development of mature oocytes (eggs), is a prolonged process in the human female. Immature eggs form in the ovary of the female embryo but do not complete their development until years, and often decades, later. Page 1009 describes oogenesis in the human ovary. Be sure to study Figure 46.12 before proceeding.

Spermatogenesis differs from oogenesis in three significant ways. First, only in spermatogenesis do all four products of meiosis develop into mature gametes. In oogenesis, cytokinesis during meiosis is unequal, with almost all the cytoplasm segregated to a single daughter cell, the secondary oocyte. This large cell is destined to become the egg; the other products of meiosis, smaller cells called polar bodies, degenerate. Second, spermatogenesis, including the mitotic divisions of stem cells and differentiated spermatogonia, occurs throughout adolescence and adulthood. During oogenesis in human females, mitotic divisions are thought to be complete before birth, and the production of mature gametes ceases at about age 50. Third, spermatogenesis produces mature sperm from precursor cells in a continuous sequence, whereas oogenesis has long interruptions.

CONCEPT 46.5
The interplay of tropic and sex hormones regulates mammalian reproduction

In both males and females, the coordinated actions of hormones from the hypothalamus, anterior pituitary, and gonads govern human reproduction. The hypothalamus secretes gonadotropin-releasing hormone (GnRH), which directs the anterior pituitary to secrete the gonadotropins, follicle-stimulating hormone (FSH) and luteinizing hormone (LH) (see Figure 45.17). These two hormones regulate gametogenesis directly, through target tissues in the gonads, as well as indirectly, by regulating sex hormone production. The principal sex hormones are steroid hormones: in males, androgens, especially testosterone; in females, estrogens, especially estradiol, and progesterone. Like the gonadotropins, the sex hormones regulate gametogenesis directly and indirectly.

Sex hormones serve many functions in addition to promoting gamete production. In many vertebrates, androgens are responsible for male vocalizations, such as the territorial songs of birds and the mating calls of frogs. During human embryogenesis, androgens promote the development of the primary sex characteristics of males, the structures directly involved in reproduction. These include the seminal vesicles and other ducts, as well as external reproductive anatomy. At puberty, sex hormones in both males and females induce formation of secondary sex characteristics, the physical and behavioral features that are not directly related to the reproductive system. In males, androgens cause the voice to deepen, facial and pubic

Exploring Human Gametogenesis

Spermatogenesis

These drawings correlate the mitotic and meiotic divisions in sperm development with the microscopic structure of seminiferous tubules. The initial or *primordial* germ cells of the embryonic testes divide and differentiate into stem cells that divide mitotically to form **spermatogonia**, which in turn generate spermatocytes, also by mitosis. Each spermatocyte gives rise to four spermatids through meiotic cell divisions that reduce the chromosome number from diploid ($2n = 46$ in humans) to haploid ($n = 23$). Spermatids undergo extensive changes in cell shape and organization to differentiate into sperm.

Within the seminiferous tubules, there is a concentric organization of the steps of spermatogenesis. Stem cells are situated near the outer edge of the tubules. As spermatogenesis proceeds, cells move steadily inward as they pass through the spermatocyte and spermatid stages. In the last step, mature sperm are released into the lumen of the tubule. The sperm pass from the lumen into the epididymis, where they become motile.

The structure of a sperm cell fits its function. In humans, as in most species, a head containing the haploid nucleus is tipped with a special vesicle, the **acrosome**, which contains enzymes that help the sperm penetrate the egg. Behind the head, the sperm cell contains large numbers of mitochondria (or a single large mitochondrion in some species) that provide ATP for movement of the tail, which is a flagellum.

Epididymis

Seminiferous tubule

Testis

Cross section of seminiferous tubule

Sertoli cell nucleus

Lumen of seminiferous tubule

Neck

Tail

Midpiece   Head

Plasma membrane

Mitochondria

Nucleus

Acrosome

Primary spermatocyte

Spermatids (at two stages of differentiation)

Sperm cell

Primordial germ cell in embryo

Mitotic divisions

Spermatogonial stem cell — $2n$

Mitotic divisions

Spermatogonium — $2n$

Mitotic divisions

Primary spermatocyte — $2n$

Meiosis I

Secondary spermatocyte — n n

Meiosis II

Early spermatid — n n n n

Differentiation (Sertoli cells provide nutrients)

Sperm cell — n n n n

Oogenesis

Oogenesis begins in the female embryo with the production of **oogonia** from primordial germ cells. The oogonia divide mitotically to form cells that begin meiosis, but stop the process at prophase I. Contained within small follicles (cavities lined with protective cells), these **primary oocytes** arrest development before birth. Beginning at puberty, follicle-stimulating hormone (FSH) periodically stimulates a small group of follicles to resume growth and development. Typically, only one follicle fully matures each month, with its primary oocyte completing meiosis I. The second meiotic division begins, but stops at metaphase. Thus arrested in meiosis II, the **secondary oocyte** is released at ovulation, when its follicle breaks open. Only if a sperm penetrates the oocyte does meiosis II resume. (In other animal species, the sperm may enter the oocyte at the same stage, earlier, or later.) Each of the two meiotic divisions involves unequal cytokinesis, with the smaller cells becoming polar bodies that eventually degenerate (the first polar body may or may not divide again). Thus, the functional product of complete oogenesis is a single mature egg already containing a sperm head; fertilization is defined strictly as the fusion of the haploid nuclei of the sperm and secondary oocyte, although we often use it loosely to mean the entry of the sperm head into the egg.

The ruptured follicle left behind after ovulation develops into the corpus luteum. If the released oocyte is not fertilized and does not complete oogenesis, the corpus luteum degenerates.

It was long thought that women and most other female mammals are born with all the primary oocytes they will ever have. In 2004, however, researchers reported that multiplying oogonia exist in the ovaries of adult mice and can develop into oocytes. Scientists are now looking for similar cells in human ovaries. It is possible that the marked decline in fertility that occurs as women age results from a depletion of oogonia in addition to the degeneration of aging oocytes.

Ovary

In embryo

Primordial germ cell

Mitotic divisions

$2n$ — **Oogonium**

Mitotic divisions

$2n$ — **Primary oocyte** (present at birth), arrested in prophase of meiosis I

First polar body n

Completion of meiosis I and onset of meiosis II

n — **Secondary oocyte,** arrested at metaphase of meiosis II

Ovulation, sperm entry

Second polar body n

Completion of meiosis II

n — **Fertilized egg**

Primary oocyte within follicle

Growing follicle

Mature follicle

Ruptured follicle

Ovulated secondary oocyte

Corpus luteum

Degenerating corpus luteum

hair to develop, and muscles to grow (by stimulating protein synthesis). Androgens also promote specific sexual behaviors and sex drive, as well as an increase in general aggressiveness. Estrogens similarly have multiple effects in females. At puberty, estradiol stimulates breast and pubic hair development. Estradiol also influences female sexual behavior, induces fat deposition in the breasts and hips, increases water retention, and alters calcium metabolism.

Gametogenesis involves the same basic set of hormonal controls in males and females. In examining these hormonal circuits, we will begin with the simpler system found in males.

Hormonal Control of the Male Reproductive System

In males, the FSH and LH secreted in response to GnRH are both required for normal spermatogenesis. Each acts on a distinct type of cell in the testis **(Figure 46.13)**. FSH promotes the activity of Sertoli cells. Within the seminiferous tubules, these cells nourish developing sperm (see Figure 46.12). LH regulates Leydig cells, cells located in the interstitial space between the seminiferous tubules. In response to LH, Leydig cells secrete testosterone and other androgens, which promote spermatogenesis in the tubules. Both androgen secretion and spermatogenesis occur continuously from puberty onward.

Two negative-feedback mechanisms control sex hormone production in males (see Figure 46.13). Testosterone regulates blood levels of GnRH, FSH, and LH through inhibitory effects

▲ **Figure 46.13 Hormonal control of the testes.** Gonadotropin-releasing hormone (GnRH) from the hypothalamus stimulates the anterior pituitary to secrete two gonadotropins, follicle-stimulating hormone (FSH) and luteinizing hormone (LH). FSH acts on Sertoli cells, which nourish developing sperm. LH acts on Leydig cells, which produce androgens, chiefly testosterone. Negative feedback by testosterone on the hypothalamus and anterior pituitary regulates blood levels of GnRH, LH, and FSH. FSH secretion is also subject to negative feedback by inhibin secreted by Sertoli cells.

on the hypothalamus and anterior pituitary. In addition, **inhibin**, a hormone that in males is produced by Sertoli cells, acts on the anterior pituitary gland to reduce FSH secretion. Together, these negative-feedback circuits maintain androgen production at optimal levels.

The Reproductive Cycles of Females

Upon reaching sexual maturity, human males carry out gametogenesis continuously, whereas human females produce gametes in cycles. Ovulation occurs only after the endometrium (lining of the uterus) has started to thicken and develop a rich blood supply, preparing the uterus for the possible implantation of an embryo. If pregnancy does not occur, the uterine lining is sloughed off, and another cycle begins. The cyclic shedding of the endometrium from the uterus, which occurs in a flow through the cervix and vagina, is called **menstruation**.

There are two closely linked reproductive cycles in human females. The changes in the uterus define the **menstrual cycle**, also called the **uterine cycle**. Menstrual cycles average 28 days in length (although cycles vary, ranging from about 20 to 40 days). The cyclic events that occur in the ovaries define the **ovarian cycle**. Hormone activity links the two cycles, synchronizing ovarian follicle growth and ovulation with the establishment of a uterine lining that can support embryonic development.

Let's examine the reproductive cycle of the human female in more detail **(Figure 46.14)**. Although the ovaries produce inhibin, we will omit this hormone from our discussion, since its function in females is unclear. We'll begin with the series of events that occur before the egg is fertilized.

The Ovarian Cycle

The reproductive cycle begins ❶ with the release from the hypothalamus of GnRH, which ❷ stimulates the anterior pituitary to secrete small amounts of FSH and LH. ❸ Follicle-stimulating hormone (as its name implies) stimulates follicle growth, aided by LH, and ❹ the cells of the growing follicles start to make estradiol. Notice that there is a slow rise in the amount of estradiol secreted during most of the **follicular phase**, the part of the ovarian cycle during which follicles grow and oocytes mature. (Several follicles begin to grow with each cycle, but usually only one matures; the others disintegrate.) The low levels of estradiol inhibit secretion of the pituitary hormones, keeping the levels of FSH and LH relatively low. During this portion of the cycle, regulation of the hormones controlling reproduction closely parallels the regulation observed in males (see Figure 46.13).

❺ When estradiol secretion by the growing follicle begins to rise steeply, ❻ the FSH and LH levels increase markedly. Whereas a low level of estradiol inhibits the secretion of pituitary gonadotropins, a high concentration has the opposite effect: It stimulates gonadotropin secretion by acting on the hypothalamus to increase its output of GnRH. The effect is greater for LH because the high concentration of estradiol increases the GnRH sensitivity of LH-releasing cells in the pituitary. In addition, follicles respond more strongly to LH at this stage because more of their cells have receptors for this hormone.

The increase in LH concentration caused by increased estradiol secretion from the growing follicle is an example of positive feedback. The result is final maturation of the follicle. **7** The maturing follicle, which contains an internal fluid-filled cavity, grows very large, forming a bulge near the surface of the ovary. The follicular phase ends at ovulation, about a day after the LH surge. In response to the peak in LH levels, the follicle and adjacent wall of the ovary rupture, releasing the secondary oocyte. There is sometimes a distinctive pain in the lower abdomen at or near the time of ovulation; this pain localizes to the left or right side, corresponding to whichever ovary has matured a follicle during that cycle.

The **luteal phase** of the ovarian cycle follows ovulation. **8** LH stimulates the follicular tissue left behind in the ovary to transform into the corpus luteum, a glandular structure. Under continued stimulation by LH, the corpus luteum secretes progesterone and estradiol. As progesterone and estradiol levels rise, the combination of these steroid hormones exerts negative feedback on the hypothalamus and pituitary, reducing the secretion of LH and FSH to very low levels. Near the end of the luteal phase, low gonadotropin levels cause the corpus luteum to disintegrate, triggering a sharp decline in estradiol and progesterone concentrations. The decreasing levels of ovarian steroid hormones liberate the hypothalamus and pituitary from the negative-feedback effect of these hormones. The pituitary can then begin to secrete enough FSH to stimulate the growth of new follicles in the ovary, initiating the next ovarian cycle.

The Uterine (Menstrual) Cycle

Prior to ovulation, ovarian steroid hormones stimulate the uterus to prepare for support of an embryo. Estradiol se-

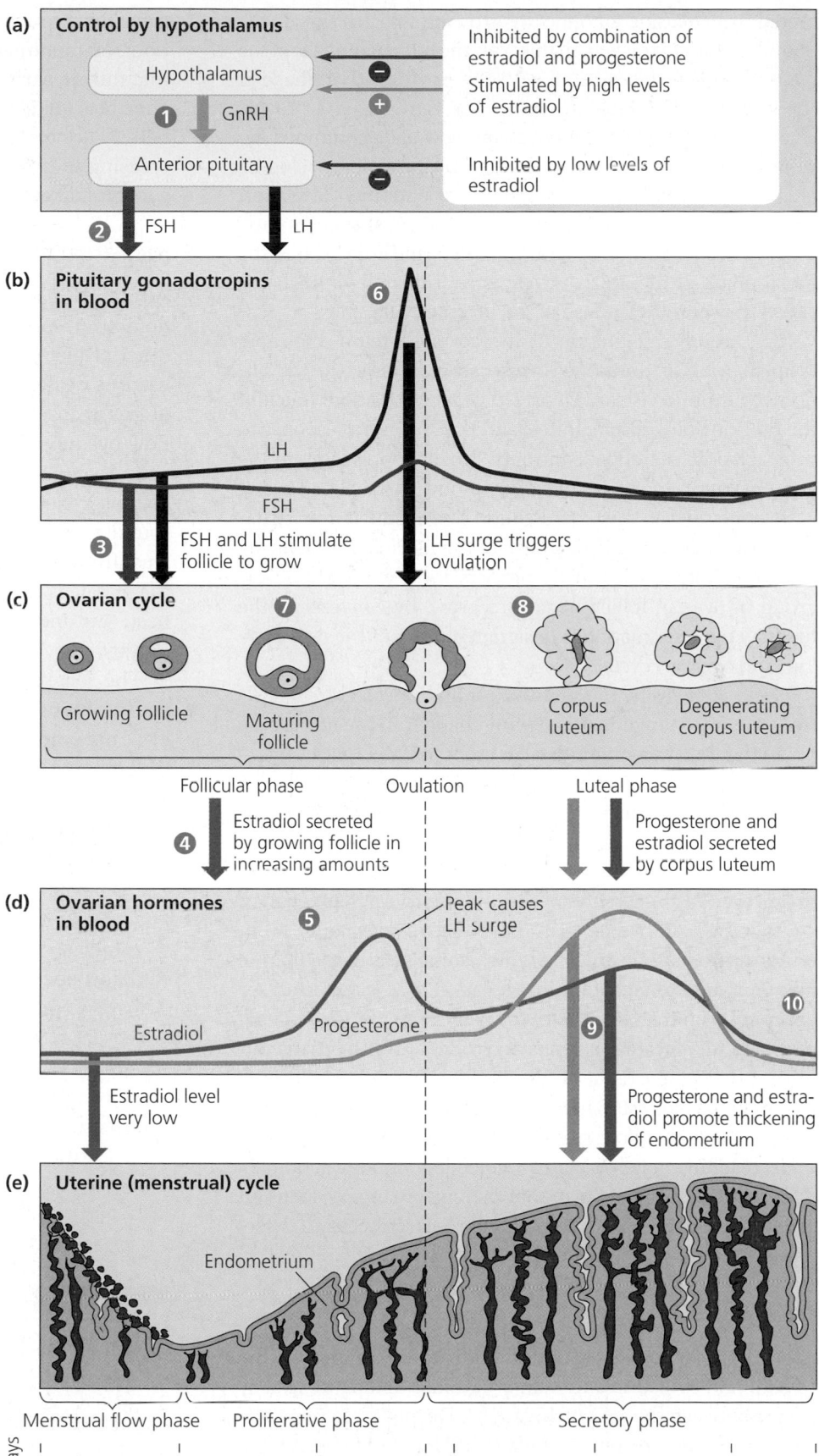

▲ **Figure 46.14 The reproductive cycle of the human female.** This figure shows how (c) the ovarian cycle and (e) the uterine (menstrual) cycle are regulated by changing hormone levels in the blood, depicted in parts (a), (b), and (d). The time scale at the bottom of the figure applies to parts (b)–(e).

creted in increasing amounts by growing follicles signals the endometrium to thicken. In this way, the follicular phase of the ovarian cycle is coordinated with the **proliferative phase** of the uterine cycle. After ovulation, ❾ estradiol and progesterone secreted by the corpus luteum stimulate continued development and maintenance of the uterine lining, including enlargement of arteries and growth of endometrial glands. These glands secrete a nutrient fluid that can sustain an early embryo even before it implants in the uterine lining. Thus, the luteal phase of the ovarian cycle is coordinated with what is called the **secretory phase** of the uterine cycle.

❿ Upon disintegration of the corpus luteum, the rapid drop in ovarian hormone levels causes arteries in the endometrium to constrict. Deprived of its circulation, much of the uterine lining disintegrates, and the uterus, in response to prostaglandin secretion, contracts. Small blood vessels in the endometrium constrict, releasing blood that is shed along with endometrial tissue and fluid. The result is menstruation—the **menstrual flow phase** of the uterine cycle. During menstruation, which usually persists for a few days, a new group of ovarian follicles begin to grow. By convention, the first day of menstruation is designated day 1 of the new uterine (and ovarian) cycle.

Cycle after cycle, the maturation and release of egg cells from the ovary are integrated with changes in the uterus, the organ that must accommodate an embryo if the egg cell is fertilized. If an embryo has not implanted in the endometrium by the end of the secretory phase of the uterine cycle, a new menstrual flow commences, marking the start of the next cycle. Later in the chapter, you will learn about override mechanisms that prevent disintegration of the endometrium in pregnancy.

About 7% of women of reproductive age suffer from **endometriosis**, a disorder in which some cells of the uterine lining migrate to an abdominal location that is abnormal, or **ectopic** (from the Greek *ektopos*, away from a place). Having migrated to a location such as an oviduct, ovary, or large intestine, the ectopic tissue still responds to stimulation by hormones in the bloodstream. Like the uterine endometrium, the ectopic tissue therefore swells and breaks down each ovarian cycle, resulting in pelvic pain and bleeding into the abdomen. Treatments, involving hormonal therapy or surgery, focus on lessening discomfort, while ongoing research seeks to determine why endometriosis occurs.

Menopause

After about 500 cycles, a woman undergoes **menopause**, the cessation of ovulation and menstruation. Menopause usually occurs between the ages of 46 and 54. During these years, the ovaries lose their responsiveness to FSH and LH, resulting in a decline in estradiol production by the ovary.

Menopause is an unusual phenomenon; in most other species, both females and males retain their reproductive capacity throughout life. Is there an evolutionary explanation for menopause? One intriguing hypothesis proposes that during early human evolution, undergoing menopause after bearing several children allowed a mother to provide better care for her children and grandchildren, thereby increasing the survival of individuals who share much of her genetic makeup.

Menstrual Versus Estrous Cycles

All female mammals undergo a thickening of the endometrium prior to ovulation, but only humans and certain other primates have menstrual cycles. Other mammals have **estrous cycles**, in which in the absence of a pregnancy, the uterus reabsorbs the endometrium and no extensive fluid flow occurs. Whereas human females may engage in sexual activity at any point in their menstrual cycle, mammals with estrous cycles typically copulate only during the period surrounding ovulation. This period of sexual activity, called estrus (from the Latin *oestrus*, frenzy, passion), is the only time the female is receptive to mating. Estrus is sometimes called heat, and indeed, the female's body temperature increases slightly.

The length and frequency of reproductive cycles vary widely among mammals. Bears and wolves have one estrous cycle per year; elephants have several. Rats have estrous cycles throughout the year, each lasting only 5 days.

CONCEPT CHECK 46.5

1. FSH and LH get their names from events of the female reproductive cycle, but they also function in males. How are their functions in females and males similar?
2. How does an estrous cycle differ from a menstrual cycle, and in what animals are the two types of cycles found?
3. **WHAT IF?** If a human female begins taking estradiol and progesterone immediately after the start of a new menstrual cycle, what effect on ovulation should she expect? Explain.

For suggested answers, see Appendix A.

CONCEPT 46.6

In placental mammals, an embryo develops fully within the mother's uterus

Having surveyed the ovarian and uterine cycles of human females, we turn now to reproduction itself, beginning with the events that transform an egg into a developing embryo.

Conception, Embryonic Development, and Birth

During human copulation, 2–5 mL of semen is transferred, with 70–130 million sperm in each milliliter. The alkalinity of the semen helps neutralize the acidic environment of the vagina, protecting the sperm and increasing their motility. When first ejaculated, the semen coagulates, which may serve to keep the ejaculate in place until sperm reach the cervix. Soon after, anticoagulants liquefy the semen, and the sperm begin swimming through the uterus and oviducts.

Fertilization—also called **conception** in humans—occurs when a sperm fuses with an egg (mature oocyte) in the oviduct **(Figure 46.15a)**. About 24 hours later, the resulting zygote begins dividing, a process called **cleavage**. After another 2–3 days, the embryo typically arrives at the uterus as a ball of 16 cells. By about 1 week after fertilization, cleavage has produced an embryonic stage called the **blastocyst**, a sphere of cells surrounding a central cavity.

Several days after blastocyst formation, the embryo implants into the endometrium **(Figure 46.15b)**. Only after implantation can an embryo develop into a fetus. The implanted embryo secretes hormones that signal its presence and regulate the mother's reproductive system. One embryonic hormone, **human chorionic gonadotropin (hCG)**, acts like pituitary LH in maintaining secretion of progesterone and estrogens by the corpus luteum through the first few months of pregnancy. In the absence of this hormonal override during pregnancy, the corpus luteum would deteriorate and progesterone levels would drop, resulting in menstruation and loss of the embryo. Levels of hCG in the maternal blood are so high that some is excreted in the urine, where its presence is the basis of a common early pregnancy test.

The condition of carrying one or more embryos in the uterus is called **pregnancy**, or **gestation**. Human pregnancy averages 266 days (38 weeks) from fertilization of the egg, or 40 weeks from the start of the last menstrual cycle. Duration of pregnancy in other placental mammals correlates with body size and the maturity of the young at birth. Many rodents have gestation periods of about 21 days, whereas those of dogs are closer to 60 days. In cows, gestation averages 270 days (almost the same as in humans), while in elephants it lasts more than 600 days.

❸ Cleavage (cell division) begins in the oviduct as the embryo is moved toward the uterus by peristalsis and the movements of cilia.

❷ Fertilization occurs. A sperm enters the oocyte; meiosis of the oocyte is completed; and the nuclei of the oocyte and the sperm fuse, producing a zygote.

❶ Ovulation releases a secondary oocyte, which enters the oviduct.

Ovary

Uterus

Endometrium

❹ Cleavage continues. By the time the embryo reaches the uterus, it is a ball of cells. It floats in the uterus for several days, nourished by endometrial secretions. It becomes a blastocyst.

❺ The blastocyst implants in the endometrium about 7 days after conception.

(a) From ovulation to implantation

Endometrium | Inner cell mass

Cavity

Blastocyst

Trophoblast

(b) Implantation of blastocyst

▲ Figure 46.15 **Formation of the zygote and early post-fertilization events.**

Not all fertilized eggs are capable of completing development. Many pregnancies terminate spontaneously as a result of chromosomal or developmental abnormalities. Much less often, a fertilized egg lodges in the oviduct (fallopian tube), resulting in a tubal, or ectopic, pregnancy. Such pregnancies cannot be sustained and may rupture the oviduct, resulting in serious internal bleeding. A number of conditions, including endometriosis, increase the likelihood of tubal pregnancy. Bacterial infections arising during childbirth, from medical procedures, or as a sexually transmitted disease can also scar the oviduct, making ectopic pregnancy more likely.

First Trimester

Human gestation can be divided for convenience into three **trimesters** of about three months each. The first trimester is the time of most radical change for both the mother and the embryo. Let's take up our story where we left off, at implantation. The endometrium responds to implantation by growing over the blastocyst. The embryo's body structures now begin to differentiate. (You will learn much more about embryonic development in Chapter 47.)

During its first 2–4 weeks of development, the embryo obtains nutrients directly from the endometrium. Meanwhile, the outer layer of the blastocyst, called the **trophoblast**, grows outward and mingles with the endometrium, eventually helping form the **placenta**. This disk-shaped organ, containing both embryonic and maternal blood vessels, can weigh close to 1 kg. Material diffusing between the maternal and embryonic circulatory systems supplies nutrients, provides immune protection, exchanges respiratory gases, and disposes of metabolic wastes for the embryo. Blood from the embryo travels to the placenta through the arteries of the umbilical cord and returns via the umbilical vein **(Figure 46.16)**.

Splitting of the embryo during the first month of development can result in identical, or *monozygotic* (one-egg), twins. Fraternal, or *dizygotic*, twins arise in a very different way: Two follicles mature in a single cycle, followed by independent fertilization and implantation of two genetically distinct embryos.

The first trimester is the main period of **organogenesis**, the development of the body organs **(Figure 46.17)**. It is during organogenesis that the embryo is most susceptible to damage, such as from radiation or drugs, that can lead to birth defects. At 8 weeks, all the major structures of the adult are present in rudimentary form, and the embryo is called a **fetus**. The heart begins beating by the 4th week; a heartbeat can be detected at 8–10 weeks. At the end of the first trimester, the fetus, although well differentiated, is only 5 cm long.

▲ **Figure 46.16 Placental circulation.**
From the 4th week of development until birth, the placenta, a combination of maternal and embryonic tissues, transports nutrients, respiratory gases, and wastes between the embryo or fetus and the mother. Maternal blood enters the placenta in arteries, flows through blood pools in the endometrium, and leaves via veins. Embryonic or fetal blood, which remains in vessels, enters the placenta through arteries and passes through capillaries in fingerlike chorionic villi, where oxygen and nutrients are acquired. As indicated in the drawing, the fetal (or embryonic) capillaries and villi project into the maternal portion of the placenta. Fetal blood leaves the placenta through veins leading back to the fetus. Materials are exchanged by diffusion, active transport, and selective absorption between the fetal capillary bed and the maternal blood pools.

? *In a very rare genetic disorder, the absence of a particular enzyme leads to increased testosterone production. When the fetus has this disorder, the mother develops a male-like pattern of body hair during the pregnancy. Explain.*

(a) 5 weeks. Limb buds, eyes, the heart, the liver, and rudiments of all other organs have started to develop in the embryo, which is only about 1 cm long.

(b) 14 weeks. Growth and development of the offspring, now called a fetus, continue during the second trimester. This fetus is about 6 cm long.

(c) 20 weeks. Growth to nearly 20 cm in length requires adoption of the fetal position (head at knees) due to the limited space available.

▲ Figure 46.17 **Human fetal development.**

Meanwhile, the mother is also undergoing rapid changes. High levels of progesterone initiate changes in her reproductive system: increased mucus in the cervix forms a plug to protect against infection, the maternal part of the placenta grows, the uterus gets larger, and (by negative feedback on the hypothalamus and pituitary) ovulation and menstrual cycling stop. The breasts also enlarge rapidly and are often quite tender. About three-fourths of all pregnant women experience nausea, misleadingly called "morning sickness," during the first trimester.

Second Trimester

During the second trimester, the uterus grows enough for the pregnancy to become obvious. The fetus itself grows to about 30 cm in length and is very active. The mother may feel fetal movements as early as one month into the second trimester; fetal activity is typically visible through the abdominal wall one to two months later. Hormone levels stabilize as hCG declines; the corpus luteum deteriorates; and the placenta completely takes over the production of progesterone, the hormone that maintains the pregnancy.

Third Trimester

During the final trimester, the fetus grows to about 3–4 kg in weight and 50 cm in length. Fetal activity may decrease as the fetus fills the available space. As the fetus grows and the uterus expands around it, the mother's abdominal organs become compressed and displaced, leading to frequent urination, digestive blockages, and strain in the back muscles.

A complex interplay of local regulators (prostaglandins) and hormones (chiefly estradiol and oxytocin) induces and regulates **labor**, the process by which childbirth occurs **(Figure 46.18)**. A series of strong, rhythmic uterine contrac-

▲ Figure 46.18 **A model for the induction of labor.**
? *What would happen if a pregnant woman were given a single dose of oxytocin at the end of 39 weeks gestation?*

tions during the three stages of labor bring about birth, or *parturition*. The first stage is the opening up and thinning of the cervix, ending with complete dilation. The second stage is expulsion, or delivery, of the baby. Continuous strong contractions force the fetus out of the uterus and through the vagina. The final stage of labor is delivery of the placenta. **Figure 46.19** on the next page summarizes these three stages.

Lactation is an aspect of postnatal care unique to mammals. In response to suckling by the newborn, as well as changes in estradiol levels after birth, the hypothalamus signals the anterior pituitary to secrete prolactin, which stimulates the mammary glands to produce milk. Suckling also stimulates the

1 Dilation of the cervix

Placenta
Umbilical cord
Uterus
Cervix

2 Expulsion: delivery of the infant

Uterus
Placenta (detaching)
Umbilical cord

3 Delivery of the placenta

▲ **Figure 46.19 The three stages of labor.**

secretion of a posterior pituitary hormone, oxytocin, which triggers release of milk from the mammary glands (see Figure 45.15).

Maternal Immune Tolerance of the Embryo and Fetus

Pregnancy is an immunological puzzle. Half of the embryo's genes are inherited from the father; thus, many of the chemical markers present on the surface of the embryo are foreign to the mother. Why, then, does the mother not reject the embryo as a foreign body, as she would a tissue or organ graft from another

person? One intriguing clue comes from the relationship between certain autoimmune disorders and pregnancy. It is known, for example, that the symptoms of rheumatoid arthritis, an autoimmune disease of the joints, become less severe during pregnancy. Thus, the overall regulation of the immune system appears to be altered by the reproductive process. Sorting out these changes and how they might protect the developing fetus is an active area of research for immunologists.

Contraception and Abortion

Contraception, the deliberate prevention of pregnancy, can be achieved in a number of ways. Some contraceptive methods prevent gamete development or release from female or male gonads; others prevent fertilization by keeping sperm and egg apart; and still others prevent implantation of an embryo **(Figure 46.20)**. The following brief introduction to the biology of the most often used methods makes no pretense of being a contraception manual. For more complete information, you should consult a health-care provider.

Fertilization can be prevented by abstinence from sexual intercourse or by any of several barriers that keep live sperm from contacting the egg. Temporary abstinence, often called the **rhythm method** of birth control or **natural family planning**, depends on refraining from intercourse when conception is most likely. Because the egg can survive in the oviduct for 24–48 hours and sperm for up to 5 days, a couple practicing temporary abstinence should not engage in intercourse for a number of days prior and subsequent to ovulation. The most effective methods for timing ovulation combine several indicators, including changes in cervical mucus and body temperature during the menstrual cycle. Thus, natural family planning requires that the couple be knowledgeable about these physiological signs. A pregnancy rate of 10–20% is typically reported for couples practicing natural family planning. (Pregnancy rate is the average number of women who become pregnant during a year for every 100 women using a particular pregnancy prevention method, expressed as a percentage.) Some couples use ovulation-timing methods to *increase* the probability of conception.

As a method of preventing fertilization, *coitus interruptus*, or withdrawal (removal of the penis from the vagina before ejaculation), is unreliable. Sperm from a previous ejaculate may be transferred in secretions that precede ejaculation. Furthermore, a split-second lapse in timing or willpower can result in tens of millions of sperm being transferred before withdrawal.

The several **barrier methods** of contraception that block the sperm from meeting the egg have pregnancy rates of less than 10%. The **condom** is a thin, latex rubber or natural membrane sheath that fits over the penis to collect the semen. For sexually active individuals, latex condoms are the only contraceptives that are highly effective in preventing the spread of sexually transmitted diseases, including AIDS. (This protection is, however, not absolute.) Another common barrier

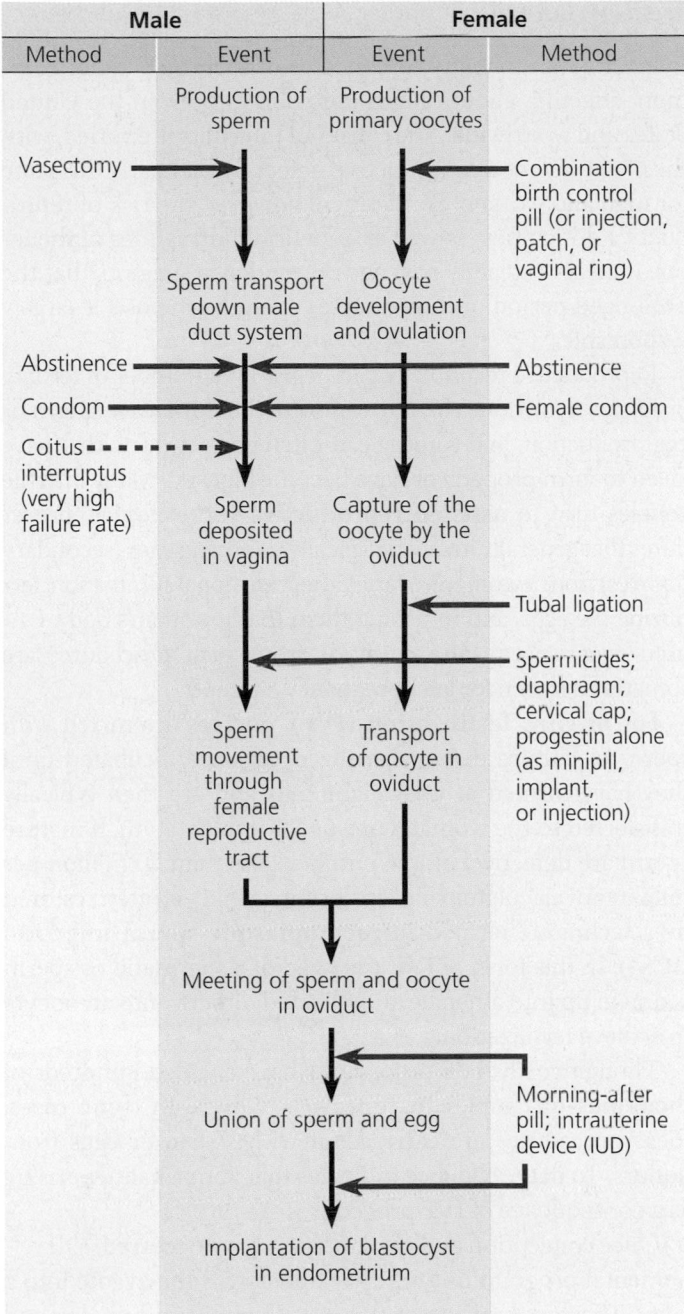

Male		Female	
Method	Event	Event	Method

Production of sperm → Sperm transport down male duct system

Production of primary oocytes → Oocyte development and ovulation

Vasectomy →

Combination birth control pill (or injection, patch, or vaginal ring) →

Abstinence → ← Abstinence

Condom → ← Female condom

Coitus interruptus (very high failure rate) ‑ ‑ ‑ ‑>

Sperm deposited in vagina

Capture of the oocyte by the oviduct

← Tubal ligation

← Spermicides; diaphragm; cervical cap; progestin alone (as minipill, implant, or injection)

Sperm movement through female reproductive tract

Transport of oocyte in oviduct

Meeting of sperm and oocyte in oviduct

Union of sperm and egg ← Morning-after pill; intrauterine device (IUD)

Implantation of blastocyst in endometrium

▲ **Figure 46.20 Mechanisms of several contraceptive methods.** Red arrows indicate where these methods, devices, or products interfere with events from the production of sperm and primary oocytes to an implanted, developing embryo.

device is the **diaphragm**, a dome-shaped rubber cap inserted into the upper portion of the vagina before intercourse. Both of these devices have lower pregnancy rates when used in conjunction with a spermicidal (sperm-killing) foam or jelly. Other barrier devices include the cervical cap, which fits tightly around the opening of the cervix and is held in place by suction, and the vaginal pouch, or "female condom."

Except for complete abstinence from sexual intercourse, the most effective means of birth control are sterilization, intrauterine devices (IUDs), and hormonal contraceptives. Steril-

ization (discussed later) is almost 100% effective. The IUD has a pregnancy rate of 1% or less and is the most commonly used reversible method of birth control outside the United States. Placed in the uterus by a doctor, the IUD interferes with fertilization and implantation. Hormonal contraceptives, most often in the form of **birth control pills**, also have pregnancy rates of 1% or less.

The most commonly prescribed birth control pills are a combination of a synthetic estrogen and a synthetic progestin (progesterone-like hormone). This combination mimics negative feedback in the ovarian cycle, stopping the release of GnRH by the hypothalamus and thus of FSH and LH by the pituitary. The prevention of LH release blocks ovulation. In addition, the inhibition of FSH secretion by the low dose of estrogens in the pills prevents follicles from developing. A similar combination of hormones is also available as an injection, in a ring inserted into the vagina, and as a skin patch. Combination birth control pills can also be used in high doses as "morning-after" pills. Taken within 3 days after unprotected intercourse, they prevent fertilization or implantation with an effectiveness of about 75%.

A different type of hormone-based contraceptive contains only progestin. Progestin causes thickening of a woman's cervical mucus so that it blocks sperm from entering the uterus. Progestin also decreases the frequency of ovulation and causes changes in the endometrium that may interfere with implantation if fertilization occurs. Progestin can be administered in several ways: time-release, match-sized capsules that are implanted under the skin and last for five years, injections that last for three months, and tablet (minipill) form taken daily. Pregnancy rates for progestin treatment are very low.

Hormone-based contraceptives have both beneficial and harmful side effects. For women taking a combination pill, cardiovascular problems are the most serious concern. Women who smoke cigarettes regularly face a three to ten times greater risk of dying from cardiovascular disease if they also use oral contraceptives. Among nonsmokers, birth control pills slightly raise a woman's risk of abnormal blood clotting, high blood pressure, heart attack, and stroke. Although oral contraceptives increase the risk for these cardiovascular disorders, they eliminate the dangers of pregnancy; women on birth control pills have mortality rates about one-half those of pregnant women. Also, the pill decreases the risk of ovarian and endometrial cancers.

One elusive research goal has been a reversible chemical contraceptive for men. Recent strategies have focused on hormone combinations that suppress gonadotropin release and thereby block spermatogenesis. Testosterone included in such combinations has two desirable effects: inhibiting reproductive functions of the hypothalamus and pituitary and maintaining secondary sex characteristics. Although there have been some promising results, hormonal male contraceptives are still in the testing stage.

Sterilization is the permanent prevention of gamete release. **Tubal ligation** in women usually involves cauterizing or tying off (ligating) a section of each oviduct to prevent eggs from traveling into the uterus. Similarly, **vasectomy** in men is the tying off or excision of a small section of each vas deferens to prevent sperm from entering the urethra. Both male and female sterilization procedures are relatively safe and free from harmful effects. Sex hormone secretion and sexual function are unaffected by both procedures, with no change in menstrual cycles in females or ejaculate volume in males. However, the procedures are difficult to reverse, so each should be considered permanent.

Abortion is the termination of a pregnancy in progress. Spontaneous abortion, or miscarriage, is very common; it occurs in as many as one-third of all pregnancies, often before the woman is even aware she is pregnant. In addition, each year about 850,000 women in the United States choose to have an abortion performed by a physician.

A drug called mifepristone, or RU486, enables a woman to terminate pregnancy nonsurgically within the first 7 weeks. RU486 blocks progesterone receptors in the uterus, thus preventing progesterone from maintaining pregnancy. It is taken with a small amount of prostaglandin to induce uterine contractions.

Modern Reproductive Technologies

Recent scientific and technological advances have made it possible to address many reproductive problems, including genetic diseases and infertility.

Detecting Disorders During Pregnancy

Many genetic diseases and developmental problems can now be diagnosed while the fetus is in the uterus. Ultrasound imaging, which generates images using sound frequencies above the normal hearing range, is commonly used to analyze the fetus's size and condition. Amniocentesis and chorionic villus sampling are techniques in which a needle is used to obtain fetal cells from fluid or tissue surrounding the embryo; these cells then provide the basis for genetic analysis (see Figure 14.18). An alternative technique for obtaining fetal tissue relies on the fact that a few fetal blood cells leak across the placenta into the mother's bloodstream. A blood sample from the mother yields fetal cells that can be identified with specific antibodies (which bind to proteins on the surface of fetal cells) and then tested for genetic disorders.

Diagnosing genetic diseases in a fetus poses ethical questions. To date, almost all detectable disorders remain untreatable in the uterus, and many cannot be corrected even after birth. Parents may be faced with difficult decisions about whether to terminate a pregnancy or to raise a child who may have profound defects and a short life expectancy. These are complex issues that demand careful, informed thought and competent genetic counseling.

Treating Infertility

Infertility—an inability to conceive offspring—is quite common, affecting about one in ten couples both in the United States and worldwide. The causes of infertility are varied, with the likelihood of a reproductive defect being nearly the same for men and women. For women, however, the risk of reproductive difficulties, as well as genetic abnormalities of the fetus, increases steadily past age 35; evidence suggests that the prolonged period of time oocytes spend in meiosis is largely responsible.

Reproductive technology can help with a number of fertility problems. Hormone therapy can sometimes increase sperm or egg production, and surgery can often correct ducts that have failed to form properly or have become blocked. Many infertile couples turn to **assisted reproductive technologies**, procedures that generally involve surgically removing eggs (secondary oocytes) from a woman's ovaries after hormonal stimulation, fertilizing the eggs, and returning them to the woman's body. Unused eggs, sperm, and embryos from such procedures are sometimes frozen for later pregnancy attempts.

For *in vitro* fertilization (**IVF**), oocytes are mixed with sperm in culture dishes. Fertilized eggs are incubated until they have formed at least eight cells and are then typically transferred to the woman's uterus for implantation. If mature sperm are defective, of low number (less than 20 million per milliliter of ejaculate), or even absent, fertility is often restored by a technique termed **intracytoplasmic sperm injection (ICSI)**. In this form of IVF, the head of a spermatid or sperm is drawn up into a needle and injected directly into an oocyte to achieve fertilization.

Though costly, IVF procedures have enabled hundreds of thousands of couples to conceive children. In some cases, these procedures are carried out with sperm or eggs from donors. To date, evidence indicates that abnormalities arising as a consequence of IVF procedures are rare.

Once conception and implantation have occurred, a developmental program unfolds that transforms the zygote into a baby. The mechanisms of this development in humans and other animals are the subject of Chapter 47.

CONCEPT CHECK 46.6

1. Why does testing for hCG (human chorionic gonadotropin) work as a pregnancy test early in pregnancy but not late in pregnancy? What is the function of hCG in pregnancy?
2. In what ways are tubal ligation and vasectomy similar?
3. **WHAT IF?** If a spermatid nucleus were used for ICSI, what normal steps of gametogenesis and conception would be bypassed?

For suggested answers, see Appendix A.

SUMMARY OF KEY CONCEPTS

CONCEPT 46.1

Both asexual and sexual reproduction occur in the animal kingdom (pp. 997–1000)

▶ Sexual reproduction requires the fusion of male and female gametes, forming a diploid zygote. Asexual reproduction is the production of offspring without gamete fusion.

▶ **Mechanisms of Asexual Reproduction** Fission, budding, fragmentation with regeneration, and parthenogenesis are mechanisms of asexual reproduction in various invertebrates.

▶ **Sexual Reproduction: An Evolutionary Enigma** Facilitating selection for or against sets of genes may explain why sexual reproduction is widespread among animal species.

▶ **Reproductive Cycles and Patterns** Most animals reproduce exclusively sexually or asexually; but some alternate between the two. Variations on these two modes are made possible through parthenogenesis, hermaphroditism, and sex reversal. Hormones and environmental cues control reproductive cycles.

CONCEPT 46.2

Fertilization depends on mechanisms that bring together sperm and eggs of the same species (pp. 1000–1003)

▶ In external fertilization, sperm fertilize eggs shed into the external environment. In internal fertilization, egg and sperm unite within the female's body. In either case, fertilization requires coordinated timing, which may be mediated by environmental cues, pheromones, or courtship behavior. Internal fertilization requires behavioral interactions between males and females, as well as compatible copulatory organs.

▶ **Ensuring the Survival of Offspring** The production of relatively few offspring by internal fertilization is often associated with greater protection of embryos and parental care.

▶ **Gamete Production and Delivery** Reproductive systems range from undifferentiated cells in the body cavity that produce gametes to complex assemblages of male and female gonads with accessory tubes and glands that carry and protect gametes and developing embryos. Although sexual reproduction involves a partnership, it also provides an opportunity for competition between individuals and between gametes.

CONCEPT 46.3

Reproductive organs produce and transport gametes (pp. 1003–1007)

▶ **Female Reproductive Anatomy** Externally, the human female has the labia majora, labia minora, and clitoris, which form the vulva surrounding the openings of the vagina and urethra. Internally, the vagina is connected to the uterus, which connects to two oviducts. Two ovaries (female gonads) are stocked with follicles containing oocytes. After ovulation, the remnant of the follicle forms a corpus luteum, which secretes hormones for a variable duration, depending on whether pregnancy occurs. Although separate from the reproductive system, the mammary glands evolved in association with parental care.

▶ **Male Reproductive Anatomy** External reproductive structures of the human male are the scrotum and penis. The male gonads, or testes, are held in the scrotum, where they are kept at the lower temperature necessary for mammalian spermatogenesis. The testes possess hormone-producing cells and sperm-forming seminiferous tubules that successively lead into the epididymis, vas deferens, ejaculatory duct, and urethra, which exits at the tip of the penis.

▶ **Human Sexual Response** Both males and females experience the erection of certain body tissues due to vasocongestion and myotonia, culminating in orgasm.

CONCEPT 46.4

The timing and pattern of meiosis in mammals differ for males and females (p. 1007)

▶ Gametogenesis, or gamete production, consists of oogenesis in females and spermatogenesis in males. Sperm develop continuously, whereas oocyte maturation is discontinuous and cyclic. Meiosis generates one large egg in oogenesis, but four sperm in spermatogenesis.

Gametogenesis

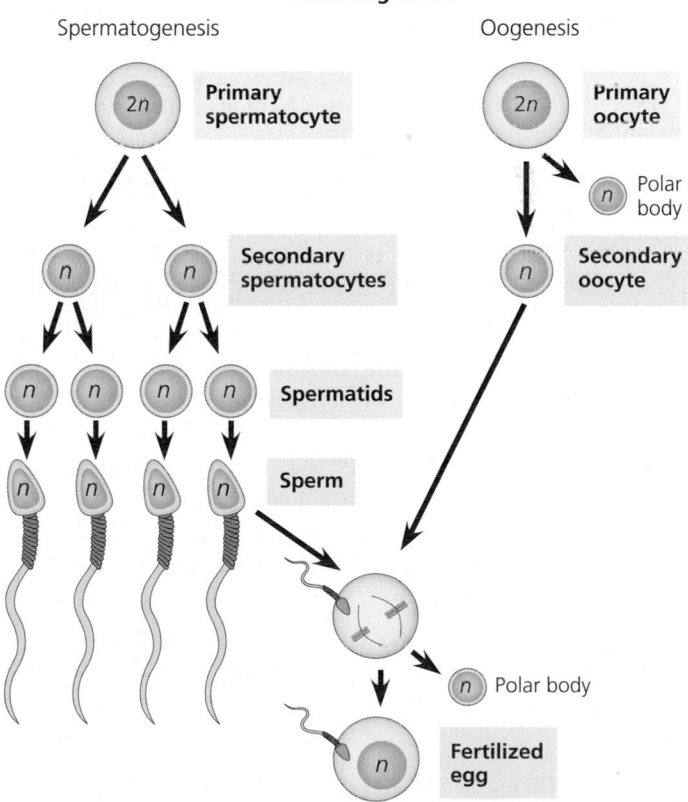

The interplay of tropic and sex hormones regulates mammalian reproduction (pp. 1007–1012)

▶ **Hormonal Control of the Male Reproductive System** Androgens (chiefly testosterone) from the testes cause the development of primary and secondary sex characteristics in the male. Androgen secretion and sperm production are both controlled by hypothalamic and pituitary hormones.

▶ **The Reproductive Cycles of Females** Cyclic secretion of GnRH from the hypothalamus and of FSH and LH from the anterior pituitary orchestrate the female reproductive cycle. FSH and LH bring about changes in the ovary and uterus via estrogens, primarily estradiol, and progesterone. The developing follicle produces estradiol, and the corpus luteum secretes progesterone and estradiol. Positive and negative feedback regulate hormone levels and coordinate the cycle.

Estrous cycles differ from menstrual cycles in that the endometrial lining is reabsorbed rather than shed and in the limitation of sexual receptivity to a heat period.

CONCEPT **46.6**

In placental mammals, an embryo develops fully within the mother's uterus (pp. 1012–1018)

▶ **Conception, Embryonic Development, and Birth** After fertilization and the completion of meiosis in the oviduct, the zygote undergoes cleavage and develops into a blastocyst before implantation in the endometrium. Human pregnancy can be divided into three trimesters. All major organs start developing by 8 weeks. Positive feedback involving prostaglandins and the hormones estradiol and oxytocin regulates labor.

▶ **Maternal Immune Tolerance of the Embryo and Fetus** A pregnant woman's acceptance of her "foreign" offspring likely reflects partial suppression of the maternal immune response.

▶ **Contraception and Abortion** Contraceptive methods may prevent release of mature gametes from the gonads, fertilization, or implantation of the embryo.

▶ **Modern Reproductive Technologies** Available technologies can help detect problems before birth and assist infertile couples by hormonal methods or *in vitro* fertilization.

TESTING YOUR KNOWLEDGE

SELF-QUIZ

1. Which of the following characterizes parthenogenesis?
   a. An individual may change its sex during its lifetime.
   b. Specialized groups of cells grow into new individuals.
   c. An organism is first a male and then a female.
   d. An egg develops without being fertilized.
   e. Both mates have male and female reproductive organs.

2. In male mammals, excretory and reproductive systems share
   a. the testes.   d. the vas deferens.
   b. the urethra.   e. the prostate.
   c. the seminal vesicle.

3. Which of the following is *not* properly paired?
   a. seminiferous tubule—cervix   d. labia majora—scrotum
   b. Sertoli cells—follicle cells   e. vas deferens—oviduct
   c. testosterone—estradiol

4. Which of the following is a true statement?
   a. All mammals have menstrual cycles.

   b. The endometrial lining is shed in menstrual cycles but reabsorbed in estrous cycles.
   c. Estrous cycles occur more often than menstrual cycles.
   d. Estrous cycles are not controlled by hormones.
   e. Ovulation occurs before the endometrium thickens in estrous cycles.

5. Peaks of LH and FSH production occur during
   a. the menstrual flow phase of the uterine cycle.
   b. the beginning of the follicular phase of the ovarian cycle.
   c. the period just before ovulation.
   d. the end of the luteal phase of the ovarian cycle.
   e. the secretory phase of the menstrual cycle.

6. For which of the following is the number the same in spermatogenesis and oogenesis?
   a. interruptions in meiotic divisions
   b. functional gametes produced by meiosis
   c. meiotic divisions required to produce each gamete
   d. gametes produced in a given time period
   e. different cell types produced by meiosis

7. During human gestation, rudiments of all organs develop
   a. in the first trimester.
   b. in the second trimester.
   c. in the third trimester.
   d. while the embryo is in the oviduct.
   e. during the blastocyst stage.

8. Which statement about human reproduction is false?
   a. Fertilization occurs in the oviduct.
   b. Effective hormonal contraceptives are currently available only for females.
   c. An oocyte completes meiosis after a sperm penetrates it.
   d. The earliest stages of spermatogenesis occur closest to the lumen of the seminiferous tubules.
   e. Spermatogenesis and oogenesis require different temperatures.

9. **DRAW IT** In human spermatogenesis, mitosis of a stem cell gives rise to one cell that remains a stem cell and one cell that becomes a spermatogonium. (a) Draw four rounds of mitosis for a stem cell, and label the daughter cells. (b) For one spermatogonium, draw the cells it would produce from one round of mitosis followed by meiosis. Label the cells, and label mitosis and meiosis. (c) What would happen if stem cells divided like spermatogonia?

For Self-Quiz answers, see Appendix A.

MEDIA Visit **www.campbellbiology.com** for a Practice Test.

EVOLUTION CONNECTION

10. Hermaphroditism is often found in animals that are fixed to a surface. Motile species are less often hermaphroditic. Why?

SCIENTIFIC INQUIRY

11. You discover a new egg-laying worm species. You dissect four adults and find both oocytes and sperm in each. Cells outside the gonad contain five chromosome pairs. Lacking genetic variants, how would you determine whether the worms can self-fertilize?

Animal Development 47

▲ Figure 47.1 **How did this complex embryo form from a single cell?**

KEY CONCEPTS

47.1 After fertilization, embryonic development proceeds through cleavage, gastrulation, and organogenesis

47.2 Morphogenesis in animals involves specific changes in cell shape, position, and adhesion

47.3 The developmental fate of cells depends on their history and on inductive signals

OVERVIEW

A Body-Building Plan

The 7-week-old human embryo in **Figure 47.1** has already achieved an astounding number of milestones in its development. Many of its organs are in place: Its digestive tract traverses the length of its body, and its heart (the red spot in the center) is pulsating. Its brain is forming at the upper left, and the blocks of tissue that will construct the vertebrae are lined up along its back. How did this intricately detailed embryo develop from a single-celled zygote no bigger than the period at the end of the previous sentence?

The question of how a zygote becomes an animal has intrigued scientists for centuries. In the 1700s, the prevailing notion was *preformation*: the idea that the egg or sperm contains an embryo—a preformed, miniature infant, or "homunculus"— that simply becomes larger during development (**Figure 47.2**). The competing explanation of embryonic development was *epigenesis*: the idea that the form of an animal emerges gradually from a relatively formless egg. Epigenesis was originally proposed 2,000 years earlier by Aristotle, who had snipped open a window in the shell of a chicken egg and observed the developing embryo daily during its three-week incubation. As microscopy improved during the 1800s, biologists following in Aristotle's

▲ Figure 47.2 **A "homunculus" inside the head of a human sperm.** This engraving was made in 1694.

footsteps could see that embryos took shape in a series of progressive stages, and epigenesis displaced preformation as the favored explanation among embryologists.

An organism's development is orchestrated by a genetic program involving not only the genome of the zygote but also molecules placed into the egg by the mother. These molecules, which include proteins and RNAs, are called **cytoplasmic determinants**. As the zygote divides, differences arise between early embryonic cells due to the uneven distribution of cytoplasmic determinants and to signals from neighboring cells. These differences set the stage for distinct programs of gene expression to be carried out in each cell and its descendants. As cell division continues during embryonic development, the specific pattern of gene expression in particular cells sends them down unique paths toward their ultimate fates in the fully formed organism. This process of cell specialization in structure and function is called **cell differentiation**. Along with cell division and differentiation, development involves **morphogenesis**, the process by which an organism takes shape and the differentiated cells occupy their appropriate locations.

By combining molecular genetics with classical approaches to embryology, developmental biologists have learned a great deal about the transformation of a fertilized egg into an animal with multiple tissues and organs. Because animals display a wide variety of body plans, it is not surprising that embryonic development occurs by different schemes. Studies of numerous species, however, have revealed that animals share many basic mechanisms of development and use a common genetic toolkit.

In Chapter 18, we described the development of the fruit fly (*Drosophila melanogaster*). *Drosophila* is well suited to genetic analysis because mutants are easy to obtain in this species, so its genetic program is probably the best understood of any animal. *Drosophila* is a good example of a **model organism**, a species that lends itself to the study of a particular question, is representative of a larger group, and is easy to grow in the lab. In this chapter, we will concentrate mainly on model organisms that have been the subject of classical embryological studies as well as more recent molecular analyses: the sea urchin, the frog, the chick, and the nematode *Caenorhabditis elegans*. We will also explore some aspects of human embryonic development; even though humans are not model organisms, we are, of course, intensely interested in our own species.

We will begin with a description of the basic stages of embryonic development common to most animals. Then we will look at the cellular and molecular mechanisms that result in generation of the body form. Finally, we will consider the process by which embryonic cells travel down differentiation pathways that enable them to play their roles in a fully functional animal.

CONCEPT **47.1**

After fertilization, embryonic development proceeds through cleavage, gastrulation, and organogenesis

Important processes regulating development occur during fertilization and the three stages that begin to build the body of most animals. During the first stage, called *cleavage*, cell division creates a hollow ball of cells, the blastula, from the zygote. The second stage, *gastrulation*, rearranges the blastula into a three-layered embryo, the gastrula. During the third stage, *organogenesis*, interactions and movements of the three layers generate rudimentary organs from which adult structures grow.

In our discussion, we will focus on a few species that have been used to investigate each of these processes. For each stage of development, we first consider the species about which the most is known and then compare the same process in other species. We begin by looking at the fertilization of an egg by a sperm.

Fertilization

A complex series of developmental events in the gonads of the parents produces sperm and eggs (gametes), the highly specialized cell types that unite during fertilization (see Figure 46.12). The main function of fertilization is the combining of haploid sets of chromosomes from two individuals into a single diploid cell, the zygote. Contact of the sperm with the egg's surface also initiates metabolic reactions within the egg that trigger the onset of embryonic development, thus "activating" the egg.

Fertilization has been studied most extensively in sea urchins. Their gametes can simply be combined in seawater in the lab-oratory, and subsequent events are easily observed. Although sea urchins (members of phylum Echinodermata) are not vertebrates or even chordates, they share with those two groups the characteristic of deuterostome development (see Figure 32.9). Despite differences in the details, fertilization and early development in sea urchins provide good general models for similar events in vertebrates.

The Acrosomal Reaction

The eggs of sea urchins are fertilized externally after the animals release their gametes into the surrounding seawater. The jelly coat that surrounds the egg exudes soluble molecules that attract the sperm, which swim toward the egg.

When the head of a sea urchin sperm contacts the jelly coat of a sea urchin egg, molecules in the egg's coat trigger the **acrosomal reaction** in the sperm (**Figure 47.3**). This reaction begins when a specialized vesicle at the tip of the sperm, called the **acrosome**, discharges hydrolytic enzymes. These enzymes digest the jelly coat, enabling a sperm structure called the *acrosomal process* to elongate, penetrating the coat. Molecules of a protein on the tip of the acrosomal process then adhere to specific sperm receptor proteins that extend from the egg plasma membrane through the surrounding meshwork of extracellular matrix, called the *vitelline layer*. In sea urchins and many other animals, this "lock-and-key" recognition of molecules ensures that eggs will be fertilized only by sperm of the same species. Such specificity is especially important when fertilization occurs externally in water, which may be teeming with gametes of other species.

Contact of the tip of the acrosomal process with the egg membrane leads to the fusion of sperm and egg plasma membranes. The sperm nucleus then enters the egg cytoplasm. Contact and fusion of the membranes causes ion channels to open in the egg's plasma membrane, allowing sodium ions to flow into the egg and change the membrane potential (see Chapter 7). This change in membrane potential, called depolarization, is a common feature of fertilization in animals. Occurring within about 1–3 seconds after a sperm binds to an egg, depolarization prevents additional sperm from fusing with the egg's plasma membrane. Without this **fast block to polyspermy**, multiple sperm could fertilize the egg, resulting in an aberrant number of chromosomes in the zygote.

The Cortical Reaction

The membrane depolarization lasts for only a minute or so, thus blocking polyspermy only in the short term. However, fusion of the egg and sperm plasma membranes also triggers a series of changes in the egg that cause a longer-lasting block.

Key players in the longer-lasting block are numerous vesicles lying just beneath the egg plasma membrane, in the rim of cytoplasm known as the *cortex*. Within seconds after a sperm binds to the egg, these vesicles, called **cortical granules**, fuse

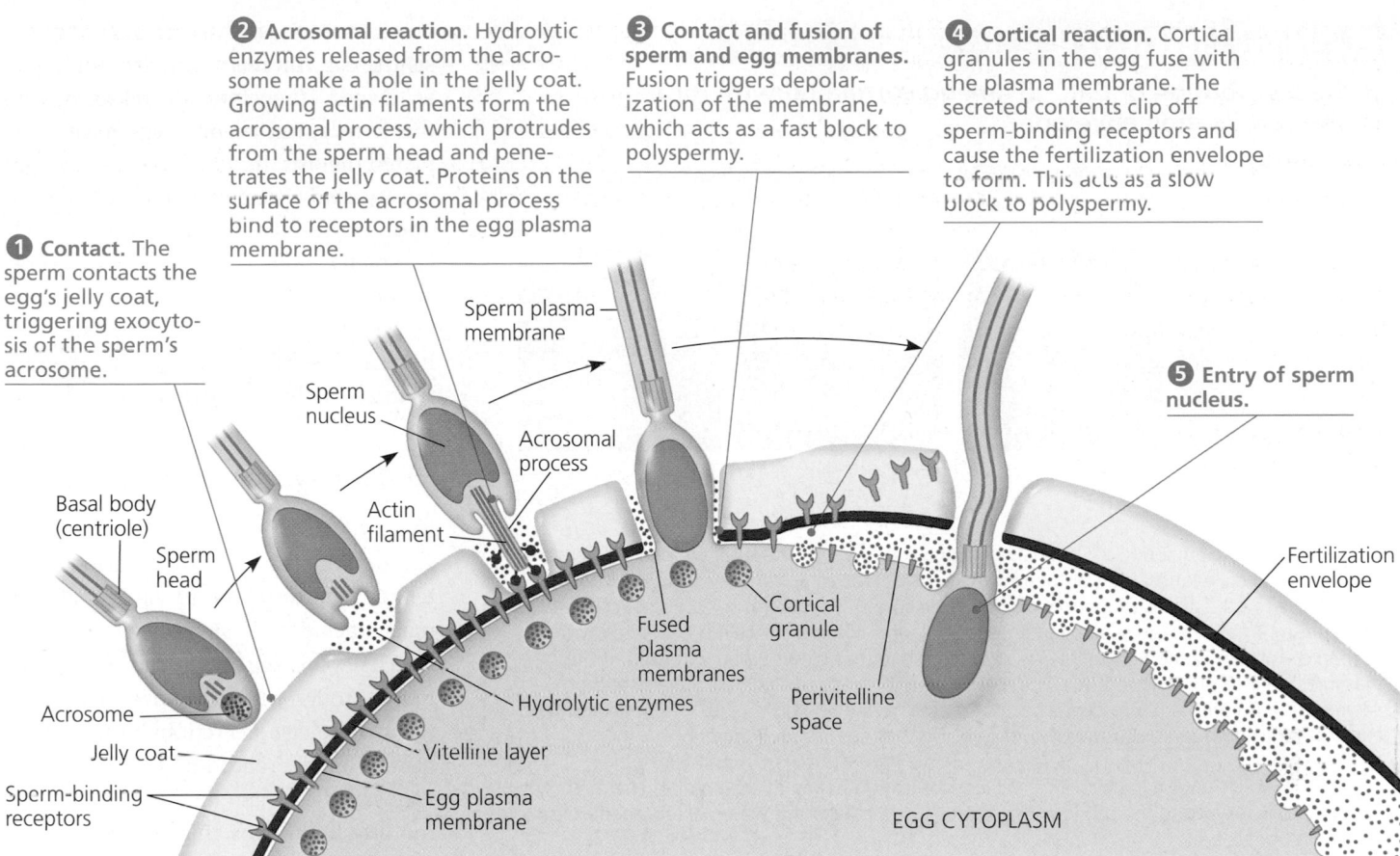

② Acrosomal reaction. Hydrolytic enzymes released from the acrosome make a hole in the jelly coat. Growing actin filaments form the acrosomal process, which protrudes from the sperm head and penetrates the jelly coat. Proteins on the surface of the acrosomal process bind to receptors in the egg plasma membrane.

③ Contact and fusion of sperm and egg membranes. Fusion triggers depolarization of the membrane, which acts as a fast block to polyspermy.

④ Cortical reaction. Cortical granules in the egg fuse with the plasma membrane. The secreted contents clip off sperm-binding receptors and cause the fertilization envelope to form. This acts as a slow block to polyspermy.

① Contact. The sperm contacts the egg's jelly coat, triggering exocytosis of the sperm's acrosome.

⑤ Entry of sperm nucleus.

Sperm plasma membrane

Sperm nucleus

Acrosomal process

Basal body (centriole)

Actin filament

Sperm head

Fertilization envelope

Acrosome

Cortical granule

Jelly coat

Fused plasma membranes

Perivitelline space

Sperm-binding receptors

Hydrolytic enzymes

Vitelline layer

Egg plasma membrane

EGG CYTOPLASM

▲ **Figure 47.3 The acrosomal and cortical reactions during sea urchin fertilization.** The events following contact of a single sperm and egg ensure that the nucleus of only one sperm enters the egg cytoplasm. The icon at left is a simplified drawing of an adult sea urchin. Throughout the chapter, this and other icons of an adult frog, chicken, and human indicate the animals whose embryos are featured in certain figures.

with the egg plasma membrane, initiating the **cortical reaction** (see Figure 47.3, step 4). Cortical granules contain a treasure trove of molecules that are now secreted into the *perivitelline space*, which lies between the plasma membrane and the vitelline layer. The secreted enzymes and other macromolecules together push the vitelline layer away from the egg and harden the layer, forming a protective **fertilization envelope** that resists the entry of additional sperm nuclei. Another enzyme clips off and releases the external portions of the remaining receptor proteins, along with any attached sperm. The fertilization envelope and other changes in the egg's surface function together as a longer-term **slow block to polyspermy**.

Experimental evidence, including the results described in **Figure 47.4** on the next page, indicates that a high concentration of calcium ions (Ca^{2+}) in the egg is essential for the cortical reaction to occur. Sperm binding activates a signal transduction pathway that causes Ca^{2+} to be released from the egg's endoplasmic reticulum into the cytosol (see Figure 11.12). The elevated Ca^{2+} levels then cause cortical granules to fuse with the plasma membrane. Although understood in greatest detail in sea urchins, the cortical reaction triggered by Ca^{2+} also occurs in vertebrates such as fishes and mammals.

Activation of the Egg

Another outcome of the sharp rise in Ca^{2+} concentration in the egg's cytosol is a substantial increase in the rates of cellular respiration and protein synthesis by the egg, known as *egg activation*. Although egg activation is normally triggered by the binding and fusion of sperm, the unfertilized eggs of many species can be artificially activated by the injection of Ca^{2+} or by various mildly injurious treatments, such as temperature shock. Artificial activation switches on the metabolic responses of the egg and causes it to begin developing by parthenogenesis (without fertilization by a sperm; see Chapter 46). It is even possible to artificially activate an egg that has had its own nucleus removed. This finding shows that proteins and mRNAs present in the cytoplasm of the unfertilized egg are sufficient for egg activation.

About 20 minutes after it enters the egg, the sperm nucleus merges with the egg nucleus, creating the diploid nucleus of the zygote. DNA synthesis begins, and the first cell division occurs after about 90 minutes in the case of sea urchins and some frogs, marking the end of the fertilization stage.

Fertilization in other species shares many features with the process in sea urchins. However, the timing of events differs

Inquiry

Is the distribution of Ca²⁺ in an egg correlated with formation of the fertilization envelope?

EXPERIMENT During fertilization, fusion of cortical granules with the egg plasma membrane causes the fertilization envelope to rise and spread around the egg from the point of sperm binding.

10 sec after fertilization   25 sec   35 sec   1 min   500 μm

Knowing that calcium ion (Ca²⁺) signaling is involved in exocytosis, Rick Steinhardt, Gerald Schatten, and colleagues, then at the University of California at Berkeley, hypothesized that an increase in Ca²⁺ levels triggers cortical granule fusion. To test this hypothesis, they tracked the release of free Ca²⁺ in sea urchin eggs after sperm binding to see if it correlated with formation of the fertilization envelope. A fluorescent dye that glows when it binds free Ca²⁺ was injected into unfertilized eggs. The researchers then added sea urchin sperm and observed the eggs with a fluorescence microscope. Schatten and colleagues later repeated the experiment using a more sensitive dye, producing the results shown here.

RESULTS A rise in cytosolic Ca²⁺ concentration began at the point of sperm entry and spread in a wave to the other side of the egg. Soon after the wave passed, the fertilization envelope rose.

1 sec before fertilization   10 sec after fertilization   20 sec   30 sec   500 μm

CONCLUSION The researchers concluded that Ca²⁺ release is correlated with cortical granule exocytosis and formation of the fertilization envelope, supporting their hypothesis that an increase in Ca²⁺ levels triggers cortical granule fusion.

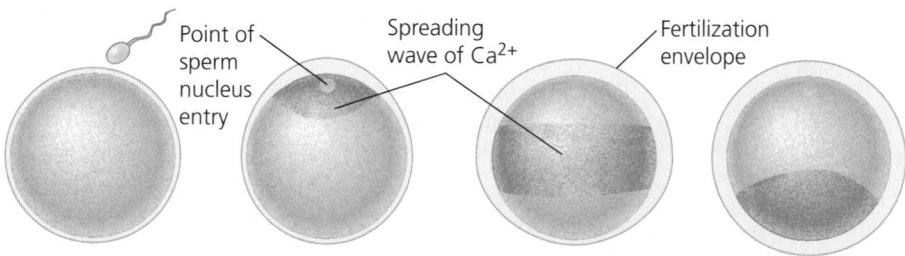

Point of sperm nucleus entry   Spreading wave of Ca²⁺   Fertilization envelope

SOURCES R. Steinhardt et al., Intracellular calcium release at fertilization in the sea urchin egg, *Developmental Biology* 58:185–197 (1977). M. Hafner et al., Wave of free calcium at fertilization in the sea urchin egg visualized with Fura-2, *Cell Motility and the Cytoskeleton* 9:271–277 (1988).

WHAT IF? Suppose you were given a chemical compound that could enter the egg and bind to Ca²⁺, blocking its function. How would you use this compound to further test the hypothesis that a rise in Ca²⁺ levels triggers exocytosis?

among species, as does the stage of meiosis the egg has reached by the time it is fertilized. When they are released from the female, sea urchin eggs have completed meiosis. In other species, the eggs are arrested at a specific stage of meiosis; upon fertilization, meiosis is quickly completed along with many of the events already described. Human eggs, for example, are arrested at metaphase of meiosis II (see Figure 46.12) until they are fertilized in the female reproductive tract.

Fertilization in Mammals

In contrast to the external fertilization of sea urchins and most other marine invertebrates, fertilization in terrestrial animals, including mammals, is generally internal. This ensures a moist environment through which the sperm can move toward the egg. Secretions in the mammalian female reproductive tract are responsible for an increase in sperm motility. In humans, this enhancement of sperm function requires about 6 hours of exposure to the female reproductive tract.

The mammalian egg is cloaked by follicle cells released along with the egg during ovulation. A sperm must travel through this layer of follicle cells before it reaches the **zona pellucida**, the extracellular matrix of the egg. One component of the zona pellucida functions as a sperm receptor. Binding of a sperm to this receptor induces an acrosomal reaction similar to that of sea urchin sperm, facilitating sperm passage through the zona pellucida to the egg and exposing a protein on the sperm that binds with the egg plasma membrane. At this point, the two cells fuse **(Figure 47.5)**.

As in sea urchin fertilization, the binding of a sperm to the egg triggers changes within the egg that lead to a cortical reaction, the release of enzymes from cortical granules to the outside of the cell via exocytosis. The released enzymes catalyze changes in the zona pellucida, which then functions as the slow block to polyspermy. (No fast block to polyspermy is known to exist in mammals.)

After the egg and sperm membranes fuse, the whole sperm, tail and all, is taken into the egg. The centriole that acted as the basal body of the sperm's flagellum ultimately generates the mitotic spindle for the first cell division. The haploid nuclei of the mammalian sperm and egg do not fuse immediately as they do in sea urchin fertilization. Instead, the envelopes of both nuclei disperse, and the two sets of chromosomes (one set from each gamete) share a common spindle apparatus during the first mitotic division of the zygote. Thus, only after this first division do the chromosomes from the two parents coex-ist in a true diploid nucleus with a nuclear membrane. Fertilization is much slower in mammals than in sea urchins: The first cell division occurs 12–36 hours after sperm binding in mammals, compared with about 90 minutes in sea urchins. This cell division marks the beginning of the next stage, cleavage.

Cleavage

Once fertilization is completed, a succession of rapid cell divisions ensues in many species. During this period, called **cleavage**, the cells carry out the S (DNA synthesis) and M (mitosis) phases of the cell cycle; however, they often virtually skip the G_1 and G_2 (gap) phases, and little or no protein synthesis occurs (see Figure 12.5 for a review of the cell cycle). As a result, the embryo does not enlarge significantly during this period of development. Cleavage simply partitions the cytoplasm of one large cell, the zygote, into many smaller cells called **blastomeres**, each with its own nucleus, as depicted for an echinoderm embryo in **Figure 47.6**.

The first five to seven divisions produce a cluster of cells, within which a fluid-filled cavity called the **blastocoel** begins to form. The blastocoel is fully formed in the **blastula** (plural, *blastulae*), which is thus a hollow ball of cells. During cleavage, different regions of cytoplasm present in the original undivided egg end up in separate blastomeres. Because the regions may contain different cytoplasmic determinants, such as specific mRNAs and proteins, in many species this partitioning sets the stage for subsequent developmental events.

The eggs and zygotes of sea urchins and other animals, with the possible exception of mammals, have a definite polarity, established as the egg developed within the mother during oogenesis. During cleavage in such organisms, the planes of division

![Fertilization in mammals illustration with labels: Zona pellucida, Follicle cell, Sperm basal body, Sperm nucleus, Cortical granules]

▲ **Figure 47.5 Fertilization in mammals.** The sperm shown here has traveled through the follicle cells and zona pellucida and has fused with the egg. The cortical reaction has begun, initiating events that ensure that only one sperm nucleus enters the cytoplasm of the egg.

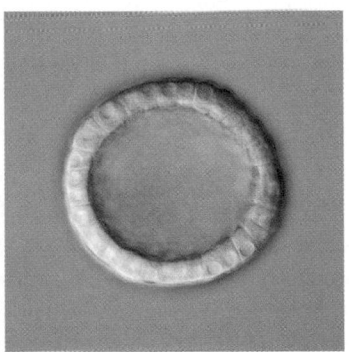

(a) Fertilized egg. Shown here is the zygote shortly before the first cleavage division, surrounded by the fertilization envelope.

(b) Four-cell stage. Remnants of the mitotic spindle can be seen between the two pairs of cells that have just completed the second cleavage division.

(c) Early blastula. After further cleavage divisions, the embryo is a multicellular ball that is still surrounded by the fertilization envelope. The blastocoel has begun to form in the center.

(d) Later blastula. A single layer of cells surrounds a large blastocoel. Although not visible here, the fertilization envelope is still present; the embryo will soon hatch from it and begin swimming.

▲ **Figure 47.6 Cleavage in an echinoderm embryo.** Cleavage is a series of mitotic cell divisions that transform the zygote into a blastula, a hollow ball composed of cells called blastomeres. These light micrographs show the embryonic stages of a sand dollar, which are virtually identical to those of a sea urchin.

follow a specific pattern relative to the poles of the zygote. The polarity is defined by the uneven distribution of substances in the cytoplasm, including not only cytoplasmic determinants but also **yolk** (stored nutrients). In frogs and many other animals, the distribution of yolk is a key factor influencing the pattern of cleavage. Yolk is often concentrated toward one pole of the egg, called the **vegetal pole**; the yolk concentration decreases significantly toward the opposite pole, the **animal pole**. The animal pole is also the site where the polar bodies of oogenesis bud from the cell (see Figure 46.12).

Establishment of the three body axes occurs early in development **(Figure 47.7a)**. This process has been well studied in particular frog species where the animal and vegetal hemispheres of the zygote, named for their respective poles, can be distinguished by color. The animal hemisphere is a deep gray because dark-colored melanin granules are embedded in the cortex in this region. The lack of melanin granules in the vegetal hemisphere allows the yellow color of the yolk to be visible.

The animal-vegetal axis of the egg determines the anterior-posterior (head-tail) axis of the embryo, so we can consider the anterior-posterior axis to be already in place in the egg. (Note, however, that these two axes are not equivalent: The head does not form where the animal pole is.) Following fusion of the egg and the sperm, rearrangement of the amphibian egg cytoplasm establishes the dorsal-ventral (back-belly) axis **(Figure 47.7b)**. The plasma membrane and associated cortex rotate with respect to the inner cytoplasm, a movement called *cortical rotation*. The animal hemisphere cortex moves toward the vegetal inner cytoplasm on the side where the sperm nucleus entered, which is always in the animal hemisphere. The vegetal hemisphere cortex across from the side of sperm nucleus entry moves toward the inner cytoplasm of the animal hemisphere.

Cortical rotation allows molecules in the unpigmented vegetal cortex on the side opposite sperm nucleus entry, placed there during oogenesis, to interact with molecules in the inner cytoplasm of the animal hemisphere. These interactions activate previously inactive proteins of the vegetal cortex. This in turn leads to the formation of cytoplasmic determinants that will later affect gene expression in the cells that inherit them, initiating development of dorsal structures. In this way, cortical rotation establishes the dorsal-ventral axis of the zygote. In some species, this rotation also exposes a light gray region of cytoplasm, the **gray crescent**, that had previously been covered by the pigmented animal cortex near the equator of the egg (see Figure 47.7b). Located on the side opposite sperm nucleus entry, the gray crescent serves as a marker for the future dorsal side of the embryo. The lighter pigment of the gray crescent can persist through many rounds of cell division.

Figure 47.8 shows the cleavage planes during the initial cell divisions in frogs. The first two divisions in frogs are merid-

(a) The three axes of the fully developed embryo.

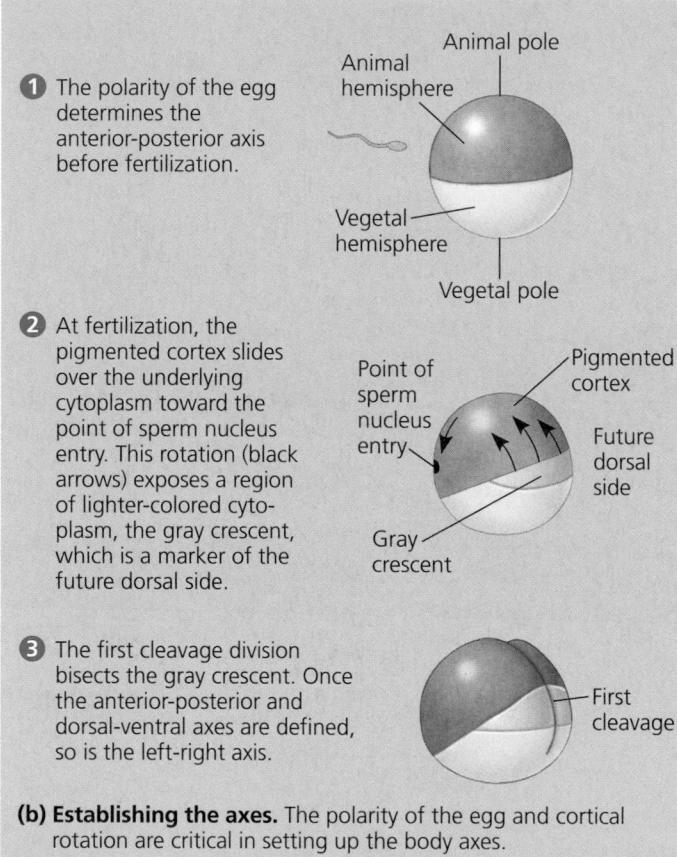

❶ The polarity of the egg determines the anterior-posterior axis before fertilization.

Animal pole

Animal hemisphere

Vegetal hemisphere

Vegetal pole

❷ At fertilization, the pigmented cortex slides over the underlying cytoplasm toward the point of sperm nucleus entry. This rotation (black arrows) exposes a region of lighter-colored cytoplasm, the gray crescent, which is a marker of the future dorsal side.

Point of sperm nucleus entry

Pigmented cortex

Future dorsal side

Gray crescent

❸ The first cleavage division bisects the gray crescent. Once the anterior-posterior and dorsal-ventral axes are defined, so is the left-right axis.

First cleavage

(b) Establishing the axes. The polarity of the egg and cortical rotation are critical in setting up the body axes.

▲ **Figure 47.7 The body axes and their establishment in an amphibian.** All three axes are established before the zygote begins to undergo cleavage.

? *To study axis establishment, researchers can block cortical rotation or force it to occur in a specific direction. One such study resulted in a two-headed embryo because the "back" developed on both sides. What do you think the researchers did to obtain such an embryo?*

ional (vertical), resulting in four blastomeres of equal size, each extending from the animal pole to the vegetal pole. The third division is equatorial (horizontal), producing an eight-celled embryo. However, the highly uneven distribution of yolk in the frog zygote displaces the mitotic apparatus and eventual cytokinesis toward the animal end of the dividing cells in equatorial divisions. As a result, the four blastomeres in the animal hemisphere are smaller than those in the vegetal

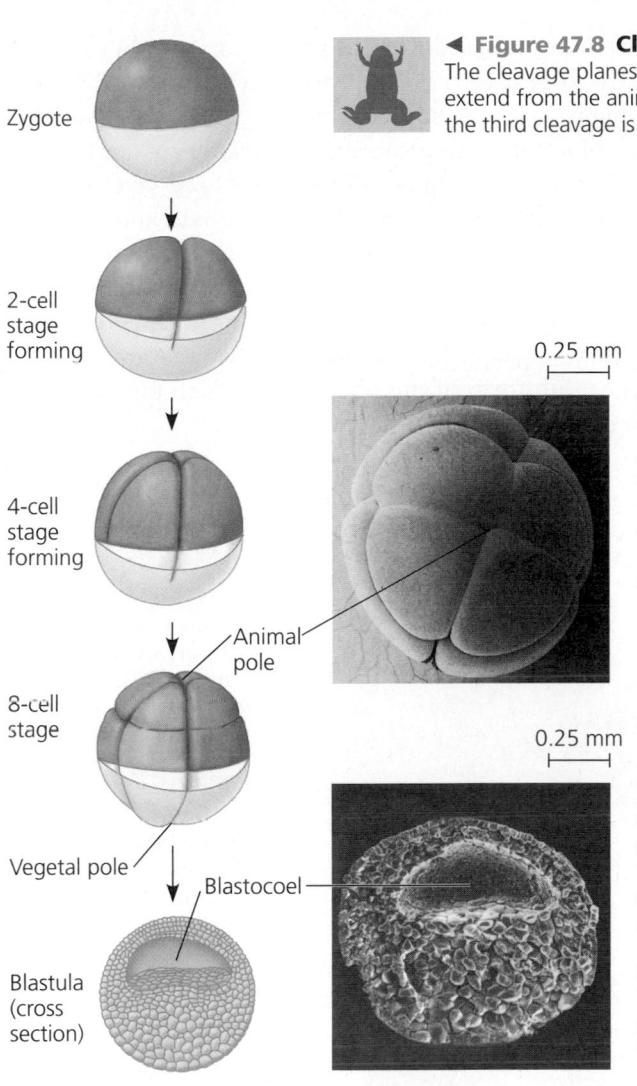

Zygote

2-cell stage forming

4-cell stage forming

8-cell stage

Animal pole

Vegetal pole

Blastocoel

Blastula (cross section)

▶ **Figure 47.8 Cleavage in a frog embryo.** The cleavage planes in the first and second divisions extend from the animal pole to the vegetal pole, but the third cleavage is perpendicular to the polar axis.

0.25 mm

8-cell stage (viewed from the animal pole). The large amount of yolk displaces the third cleavage toward the animal pole, forming two tiers of cells. The four cells near the animal pole (closer, in this view) are smaller than the other four cells (SEM).

0.25 mm

Blastula (at least 128 cells). As cleavage continues, a fluid-filled cavity, the blastocoel, forms within the embryo. Because of unequal cell division due to the large amount of yolk in the vegetal hemisphere, the blastocoel is located in the animal hemisphere. Both the drawing and the SEM show cross sections of a blastula with about 4,000 cells.

hemisphere at the eight-cell stage. The displacing effect of the yolk persists in subsequent divisions, which produce a blastula. In frogs, this unequal cell division causes the blastocoel to be located in the animal hemisphere.

Although the eggs of sea urchins and some other animals have less yolk than frog eggs, they still have an animal-vegetal axis, owing to uneven distribution of other substances. Without the restraint imposed by yolk, however, the blastomeres formed during cleavage are more likely to be of similar size, particularly during the first few divisions (see Figure 47.6). Nonetheless, the general cleavage pattern in frogs is seen in sea urchins and other echinoderms, in most chordates, and indeed in most deuterostomes. In animals whose eggs contain relatively little yolk, the blastocoel is centrally located, and the cleavage furrow passes all the way through the cells, a pattern called **holoblastic cleavage**.

Yolk is most plentiful and has its most pronounced effect on cleavage in the eggs of birds, other reptiles, many fishes, and insects. In these species, the volume of yolk is so great that cleavage furrows cannot pass through it, and only the region of the egg lacking yolk undergoes cleavage. This incomplete division of a yolk-rich egg is known as **meroblastic cleavage**.

In birds, for example, the part of the egg we commonly call the yolk is actually the entire egg cell, swollen with yolk nutrients. If you crack open a chicken egg and observe the yolk, you may see a small whitish area, which is a pool of cytoplasm located at the animal pole. Cleavage of the fertilized egg is restricted to this yolk-free cytoplasm; the dense yolk remains uncleaved. Early cleavage divisions in a bird embryo produce a cap of cells that rest on the undivided yolk and sort into upper and lower layers. The cavity between these two layers is the avian version of the blastocoel, and this embryonic stage is the avian equivalent of the blastula, although its form is different from the hollow ball of an early sea urchin or frog embryo.

In insects such as *Drosophila*, the zygote's nucleus is situated *within* a mass of yolk. Cleavage begins with the nucleus undergoing mitotic divisions that are not accompanied by cytokinesis. In other words, no cell membranes form around the early nuclei. The first several hundred nuclei are spread throughout the yolk and later migrate to the outer edge of the embryo. After several more rounds of mitosis, a plasma membrane forms around each nucleus, and the embryo, now the equivalent of a blastula, consists of a single layer of about 6,000 cells surrounding a mass of yolk.

Gastrulation

After cleavage, the rate of cell division slows dramatically. Groups of cells then undergo the morphogenetic process called **gastrulation**, taking up new locations that will allow the later formation of tissues and organs. During this process, the embryo is called a **gastrula** (plural, *gastrulae*). For organisms with a two-layered body plan, such as the cnidarian *Hydra*, this rearrangement can be fairly simple. For most animals, however, gastrulation is a dramatic rearrangement of the cells of the blastula that produces a three-layered embryo with a primitive digestive tube. Although gastrulation differs in detail from one animal group to another, the process is driven by the same general mechanisms in all species: changes in cell motility, changes in cell shape, and changes in cellular adhesion to other cells and to molecules of the extracellular matrix. The result of gastrulation is that some cells at or near the surface of the blastula move to an interior location, and three cell layers are established. The positioning of the three cell layers in the fully developed gastrula allows cells to interact with each other in new ways, leading to the generation of the body's organs.

The three layers produced by gastrulation are embryonic tissues collectively called the embryonic **germ layers**. In the late gastrula, the **ectoderm** forms the outer layer, the **endoderm** lines the embryonic digestive tract, and the **mesoderm** partly fills the space between the ectoderm and the endoderm. Eventually, these three cell layers develop into all the tissues and organs of the adult animal. Here we examine the events that occur during gastrulation in the sea urchin, frog, and chick.

Figure 47.9 outlines gastrulation in a sea urchin embryo. The sea urchin blastula consists of a single layer of cells enclosing the central blastocoel. Gastrulation begins at the vegetal pole, where individual cells detach from the blastocoel wall and enter the blastocoel as migratory cells called *mesenchyme cells*. The remaining cells near the vegetal pole flatten slightly and form a *vegetal plate* that buckles inward as a result of cell shape changes we will discuss later. This process is called **invagination**. The buckled vegetal plate then undergoes extensive rearrangement of its cells, transforming the shallow invagination into a deeper, narrower, blind-ended tube called the **archenteron**. The open end of the archenteron, which will become the anus, is called the **blastopore**. A second opening, which will become the mouth, forms when the opposite end of the archenteron touches the inside of the ectoderm and the two layers fuse, producing a rudimentary digestive tube. As you learned in Chapter 32, the developmental mode of animals can be categorized in part by whether the mouth is the first opening formed (protostome development) or the second (deuterostome development). Sea urchins and other echinoderms have deuterostome development, as do chordates like ourselves and other vertebrates.

Gastrulation in sea urchins produces an embryo with a primitive digestive tube and three germ layers, which developmental biologists commonly color-code in diagrams: blue for ectoderm, red for mesoderm, and yellow for endoderm (see Figure 47.9). This three-layered body plan is characteristic of most animal phyla and is established very early in development. In the sea urchin, the gastrula develops into a ciliated larva that drifts in ocean surface waters as zooplankton, feeding on bacteria and unicellular algae. Eventually, the larva metamorphoses into the adult form of the sea urchin, which takes up residence on the ocean floor.

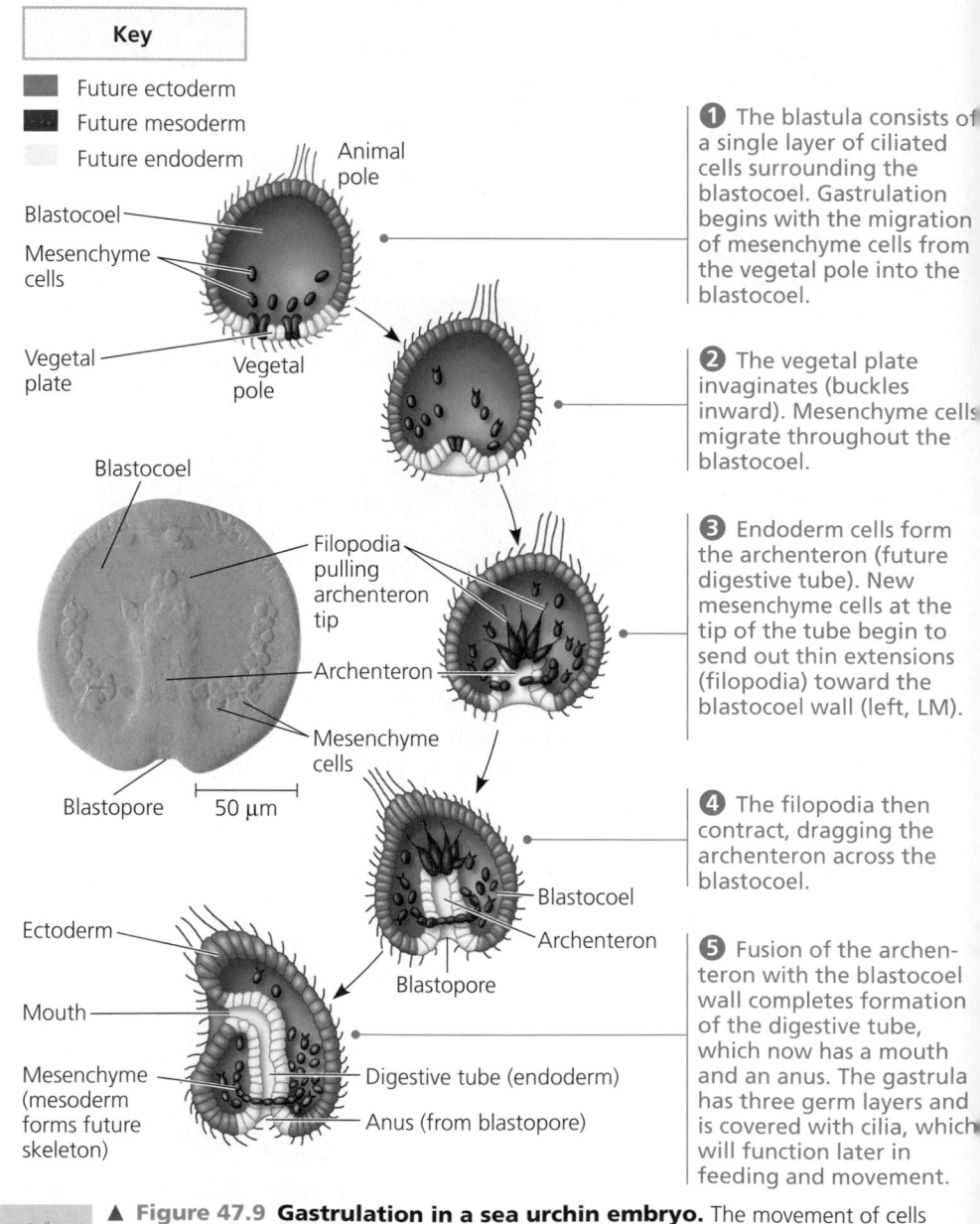

Key

Future ectoderm
Future mesoderm
Future endoderm

Animal pole

Blastocoel

Mesenchyme cells

Vegetal plate

Vegetal pole

Blastocoel

Filopodia pulling archenteron tip

Archenteron

Mesenchyme cells

Blastopore   50 μm

Ectoderm

Mouth

Mesenchyme (mesoderm forms future skeleton)

Blastocoel

Archenteron

Blastopore

Digestive tube (endoderm)

Anus (from blastopore)

❶ The blastula consists of a single layer of ciliated cells surrounding the blastocoel. Gastrulation begins with the migration of mesenchyme cells from the vegetal pole into the blastocoel.

❷ The vegetal plate invaginates (buckles inward). Mesenchyme cells migrate throughout the blastocoel.

❸ Endoderm cells form the archenteron (future digestive tube). New mesenchyme cells at the tip of the tube begin to send out thin extensions (filopodia) toward the blastocoel wall (left, LM).

❹ The filopodia then contract, dragging the archenteron across the blastocoel.

❺ Fusion of the archenteron with the blastocoel wall completes formation of the digestive tube, which now has a mouth and an anus. The gastrula has three germ layers and is covered with cilia, which will function later in feeding and movement.

▲ **Figure 47.9 Gastrulation in a sea urchin embryo.** The movement of cells during gastrulation forms an embryo with a primitive digestive tube and three germ layers. Some of the mesodermal mesenchyme cells that migrate inward (step ❶) will eventually secrete calcium carbonate and form a simple internal skeleton. Embryos in steps ❶–❸ are viewed from the front, those in ❹ and ❺ from the side.

In the frog, gastrulation also produces a three-layered embryo with an archenteron. The mechanics of gastrulation are more complicated in a frog, however, because of the large, yolk-laden cells of the vegetal hemisphere and because the wall of the blastula is more than one cell thick in most species. Gastrulation begins on the dorsal side of the blastula when a group of cells begins to invaginate—change shape and push inward—forming a crease along the region where the gray crescent formed in the zygote (see Figure 47.7). It may help to

think of this crease as the site where two thin lips are pressed together. The part above this crease becomes the dorsal side of the blastopore, called the **dorsal lip** (Figure 47.10). Like a slowly widening frown, the blastopore extends at each end of the crease as new cells push inward. Finally, the two ends of the blastopore meet on the ventral side. The blastopore is now a complete circle.

As the blastopore is forming, future endoderm and mesoderm cell layers on the surface of the embryo roll over the edge

❶ Gastrulation begins when a small indented crease, the blastopore, appears on the dorsal side of the late blastula. The crease is formed by cells changing shape and pushing inward from the surface (invagination). Sheets of outer cells then roll inward over the dorsal lip (involution) and move into the interior (shown by the dashed arrow), where they will form endoderm and mesoderm. Meanwhile, cells at the animal pole, the future ectoderm, change shape and begin spreading over the outer surface.

❷ The blastopore extends around both sides of the embryo (red arrows), as more cells invaginate. When the ends finally meet on the other side, the blastopore forms a circle that becomes smaller as ectoderm spreads downward over the surface. Internally, continued involution expands the endoderm and mesoderm, and the archenteron begins to form; as a result, the blastocoel becomes smaller.

❸ Late in gastrulation, the endoderm-lined archenteron has completely replaced the blastocoel and the three germ layers are in place. The circular blastopore surrounds a plug of yolk-filled cells.

Key	
■	Future ectoderm
■	Future mesoderm
□	Future endoderm

▲ **Figure 47.10 Gastrulation in a frog embryo.**
In the frog blastula, the blastocoel is displaced toward the animal pole and is surrounded by a wall several cells thick. The cell movements that begin gastrulation occur on the dorsal side of the blastula, where the gray crescent was located in the zygote (see Figure 47.7b). Although still visible as gastrulation begins, the gray crescent is not shown here.

of the lip into the interior of the embryo, a process called **involution**. Once inside the embryo, these cells move away from the blastopore toward the animal pole and become organized into layers of endoderm and mesoderm, with the endoderm on the inside. The blastocoel collapses during this process, displaced by the archenteron that is formed by the tube of endoderm. As gastrulation is completed, the circular lip of the blastopore encircles a **yolk plug** consisting of the outer nutrient-laden cells; these protruding cells will move inward as expansion of the ectoderm causes the blastopore to shrink further. At this point, the cells remaining on the surface make up the ectoderm, the tube of endoderm is the innermost layer, and the mesoderm lies between them. As in the sea urchin, the frog's anus develops from the blastopore, and the mouth eventually breaks through at the opposite end of the archenteron after it extends to the ventral side near the animal pole.

Gastrulation in the chick is similar to frog gastrulation in that it involves cells moving from the surface of the embryo to an interior location. In birds, however, the inward movement of cells during gastrulation is affected by the large mass of yolk pressing against the bottom of the embryo. Recall that cleav-

age in the chick results in a stage equivalent to the blastula. This stage, called the *blastoderm*, consists of upper and lower layers—the *epiblast* and *hypoblast*—lying atop the yolk mass. All the cells that will form the embryo come from the epiblast. During gastrulation, some epiblast cells move toward the midline of the blastoderm and then detach and move inward toward the yolk **(Figure 47.11)**. The pileup of cells moving inward at the blastoderm's midline produces a thickening called the **primitive streak**, which runs along the embryo's anterior-posterior axis. The primitive streak is functionally equivalent to the blastopore in the frog, but the two structures are oriented differently in the two embryos. Some of the inward-moving epiblast cells displace hypoblast cells and form the endoderm; other epiblast cells move laterally once they are midway into the blastocoel, forming the mesoderm. The epiblast cells that remain on the surface give rise to the ectoderm. Although the hypoblast contributes no cells to the embryo, it seems to help direct the formation of the primitive streak before the onset of gastrulation and is required for normal development. The hypoblast cells later segregate from the endoderm and eventually form portions of a sac that surrounds the yolk and a stalk that connects the yolk mass to the embryo.

Despite variations in how the three germ layers form in different species, once they are in place, gastrulation is complete. Now is the time when the embryo's organs begin to form.

Organogenesis

Various regions of the three embryonic germ layers develop into the rudiments of organs during the process of **organogenesis**. Whereas gastrulation involves mass movements of cells, organogenesis involves more localized shape changes in both tissues and individual cells. The first evidence of organ building is the appearance of tissue folds and splits and dense clustering (condensation) of cells.

Figure 47.12 shows some events during early organogenesis in a frog. The organs that begin to take shape first in the embryos of frogs and other chordates are the neural tube and the **notochord**, the skeletal rod characteristic of all chordate embryos. The notochord is formed from dorsal mesoderm that condenses when cells associate tightly as a group just above the archenteron (Figure 47.12a). The ectoderm above the notochord becomes the *neural plate* in response to a number of signaling molecules secreted by mesodermal and other tissues. Changes in cell shape then cause the neural plate to curve inward, rolling itself into the **neural tube**, which runs along the anterior-posterior axis of the embryo (Figure 47.12b). The neural tube will become the animal's central nervous system—the brain in the head and the spinal cord down the rest of the body. The signaling received by the ectoderm is a good example of a process seen often during organogenesis: One germ layer sends molecular signals to

▲ **Figure 47.11 Gastrulation in a chick embryo.** The chick blastula consists of an upper layer of cells, the epiblast, and a lower layer, the hypoblast, with a space (the blastocoel) lying between them. This is a cross section at a right angle to the primitive streak, looking toward the anterior end of a gastrulating embryo. During gastrulation, some cells of the epiblast migrate (arrows) into the interior of the embryo through the primitive streak. Some of these cells move downward and form endoderm, pushing aside the hypoblast cells, while others migrate laterally and form mesoderm. The cells left behind on the surface of the embryo at the end of gastrulation will become ectoderm.

(a) Neural plate formation. By this stage, the notochord has developed from dorsal mesoderm, and the dorsal ectoderm has thickened, forming the neural plate, in response to signals from other embryonic tissues. The neural folds are the two ridges that form the lateral edges of the neural plate. These folds are visible in the LM of a whole embryo.

(b) Neural tube formation. Infolding and pinching off of the neural plate generates the neural tube. Note the neural crest cells, which will migrate and give rise to numerous structures. (See also Figure 34.7.)

(c) Somites. The SEM is a side view of the whole embryo at the tail-bud stage. Part of the ectoderm has been removed to reveal the somites, blocks of tissue that will give rise to segmental structures such as vertebrae. The drawing shows a similar-stage embryo after formation of the neural tube, as if the embryo in the SEM were cut and viewed in cross section. By this time, the lateral mesoderm has begun to separate into two tissue layers that line the coelom, or body cavity. The somites, formed from mesoderm, flank the notochord.

 ▲ **Figure 47.12 Early organogenesis in a frog embryo.**

another, thereby affecting gene expression and determining the fate of the second.

In vertebrate embryos, a band of cells called the *neural crest* develops along the borders where the neural tube pinches off from the ectoderm. **Neural crest cells** subsequently migrate to various parts of the embryo, forming peripheral nerves, parts of teeth, skull bones, and so many other different cell types that some developmental biologists have suggested that the neural crest could be considered a fourth germ layer.

Other condensations of cells occur in strips of mesoderm lateral to the notochord, which separate into blocks called **somites** (Figure 47.12c). The somites are arranged serially on both sides along the length of the notochord. Parts of the somites dissociate into mesenchyme cells, which migrate individually to new locations. Note that these cells are both mesodermal and mesenchymal (migratory). (Be careful not to confuse the two terms.) Some mesenchyme cells gather around the notochord and form the vertebrae. Parts of the notochord between the vertebrae persist as the inner portions of the vertebral disks in adults. (These are the disks that can "slip," causing back pain.) Somite cells that become mesenchymal later also form the muscles associated with the vertebral column and the ribs. Note that serially repeating structures of the embryo (somites) form repeated structures in the adult. The serial origin of the vertebral column, ribs, and their muscles reinforces the idea that chordates are basically segmented animals, although the segmentation becomes less obvious later in development. Lateral to the somites, the mesoderm splits into two layers that form the lining of the body cavity, or coelom (see Figure 32.8).

► **Figure 47.13**
Organogenesis in a chick embryo.

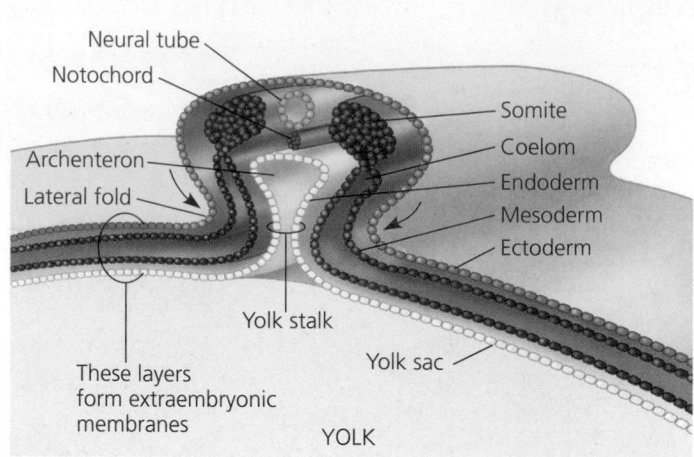

Neural tube
Notochord
Archenteron
Lateral fold
Yolk stalk
These layers form extraembryonic membranes
YOLK
Somite
Coelom
Endoderm
Mesoderm
Ectoderm
Yolk sac

(a) Early organogenesis. The archenteron forms when lateral folds pinch the embryo away from the yolk. The embryo remains open to the yolk, attached by the yolk stalk, about midway along its length, as shown in this cross section. The notochord, neural tube, and somites subsequently develop much as they do in the frog. The germ layers lateral to the embryo itself form extraembryonic membranes (to be discussed later).

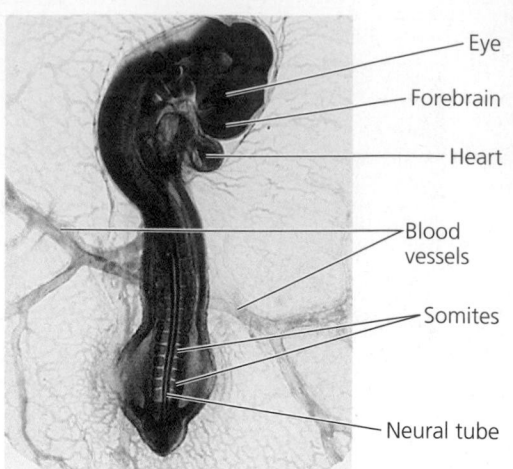

Eye
Forebrain
Heart
Blood vessels
Somites
Neural tube

(b) Late organogenesis. Rudiments of most major organs have already formed in this chick embryo, which is about 56 hours old and about 2–3 mm long. The extraembryonic membranes eventually are supplied by blood vessels extending from the embryo; several major blood vessels are seen here (LM).

As organogenesis progresses, morphogenesis and cell differentiation continue to refine the organs that arise from the three embryonic germ layers; many of the internal organs are derived from two of the three layers. Embryonic development of the frog leads to a larval stage, the tadpole, which hatches from the jelly coat that originally protected the egg and developing embryo. Later, metamorphosis transforms the frog from the aquatic, herbivorous tadpole to the terrestrial, carnivorous adult.

Organogenesis in the chick is quite similar to that in the frog. After the three germ layers are formed, the borders of the blastoderm fold downward and come together, pinching the embryo into a three-layered tube joined under the middle of the body to the yolk **(Figure 47.13a)**. Neural tube formation, development of the notochord and somites, and other events in organogenesis occur much as in the frog embryo. The rudiments of the major organs are evident in a 2- to 3-day-old chick embryo **(Figure 47.13b)**.

In invertebrates, organogenesis is somewhat different, which makes sense, given that their body plans diverge significantly from those of vertebrates. The underlying mechanisms, however, involve many of the same cellular activities: cell migration, cell condensations, cell signaling between different tissues, and cell shape changes generating new organs. For example, in flies and other insects, tissues of the nervous system form when ectoderm along the anterior-posterior axis rolls into a tube inside the embryo, like the vertebrate neural tube. Interestingly, however, the tube is on the ventral side of the fly embryo rather than the dorsal side, where it is in vertebrates. In spite of the different locations, the molecular signaling pathways that bring about the events in the two groups are very similar, underscoring their ancient shared evolutionary history.

Specifying the location of the three germ layers in a gastrula is quite straightforward, but during organogenesis, as you can see, the layers move and change shape, defying generalization. **Figure 47.14** summarizes organogenesis by listing the germ

► **Figure 47.14 Adult derivatives of the three embryonic germ layers in vertebrates.**

? *Given what you know about the three germ layers and morphogenesis, propose an explanation for how the epithelial linings of the mouth and anus are formed.*

ECTODERM	MESODERM	ENDODERM
• Epidermis of skin and its derivatives (including sweat glands, hair follicles) • Epithelial lining of mouth and anus • Cornea and lens of eye • Nervous system • Sensory receptors in epidermis • Adrenal medulla • Tooth enamel • Epithelium of pineal and pituitary glands	• Notochord • Skeletal system • Muscular system • Muscular layer of stomach and intestine • Excretory system • Circulatory and lymphatic systems • Reproductive system (except germ cells) • Dermis of skin • Lining of body cavity • Adrenal cortex	• Epithelial lining of digestive tract • Epithelial lining of respiratory system • Lining of urethra, urinary bladder, and reproductive system • Liver • Pancreas • Thymus • Thyroid and parathyroid glands

layers that produce the major organs and tissues in frogs, chicks, and other vertebrates.

Developmental Adaptations of Amniotes

All vertebrate embryos require an aqueous environment for development. In the case of fishes and amphibians, the egg is usually laid in the surrounding sea or pond and needs no special water-filled enclosure. The movement of vertebrates onto land could occur only after the evolution of structures that would allow reproduction in dry environments. Two such structures exist today: (1) the shelled egg of birds and other reptiles, as well as a few mammals (monotremes), and (2) the uterus of marsupial and eutherian mammals. Inside the shell or uterus, the embryos of these animals are surrounded by fluid within a sac formed by a membrane called the amnion. Reptiles (including birds) and mammals are therefore called **amniotes** (see Chapter 34).

Amnion. The amnion protects the embryo in a fluid-filled cavity that prevents dehydration and cushions mechanical shock.

Allantois. The allantois functions as a disposal sac for certain metabolic wastes produced by the embryo. The membrane of the allantois also functions with the chorion as a respiratory organ.

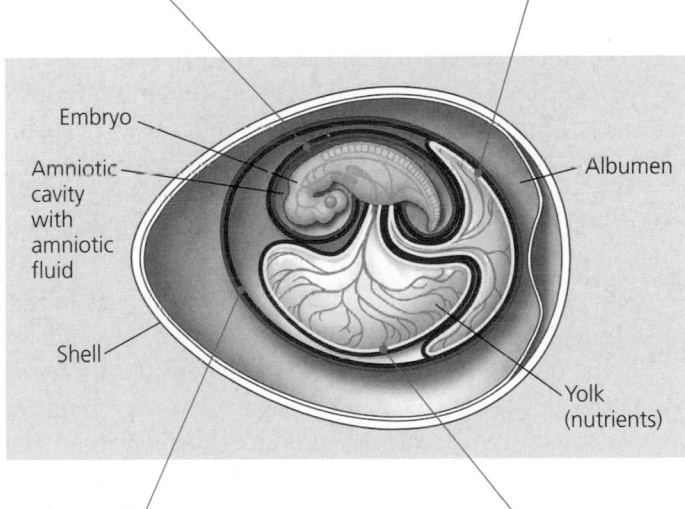

Embryo

Amniotic cavity with amniotic fluid

Shell

Albumen

Yolk (nutrients)

Chorion. The chorion and the membrane of the allantois exchange gases between the embryo and the surrounding air. Oxygen and carbon dioxide diffuse freely across the egg's shell.

Yolk sac. The yolk sac surrounds the yolk, a stockpile of nutrients stored in the egg. Blood vessels in the yolk sac membrane transport nutrients from the yolk into the embryo. Other nutrients are stored in the albumen (the "egg white").

▲ **Figure 47.15 Extraembryonic membranes in birds and other reptiles.** There are four extraembryonic membranes: the amnion, the allantois, the chorion, and the yolk sac. Each membrane is a sheet of cells that develops from portions of two germ layers that are outside the embryo (see Figure 47.13a).

You have already seen that embryonic development of the chick, an amniote, is very similar to that of the frog, a vertebrate that lacks an amnion. However, in the chick, development also includes the formation of **extraembryonic membranes**, membranes located outside the embryo. Notice in Figure 47.13a that only part of each germ layer contributes to the embryo itself. The parts of the germ layers located outside the embryo proper develop into four extraembryonic membranes, each a sheet of cells derived from two germ layers **(Figure 47.15)**. The **chorion**, which completely surrounds the embryo and the other extraembryonic membranes, functions in gas exchange. The **amnion** eventually encloses the embryo in a protective, fluid-filled amniotic cavity. Below the developing embryo proper, the **yolk sac** encloses the yolk, which provides nutrients until the time of hatching. The **allantois** disposes of waste products and contributes to gas exchange. These four extraembryonic membranes provide a "life-support system" for further embryonic development within the shelled egg or the uterus of an amniote.

We will discuss mammalian extraembryonic membranes next as we describe early development in mammalian embryos. Formation of the placenta, a structure found only in marsupial and eutherian mammals, is an important part of this process.

Mammalian Development

In contrast with the large, yolky eggs of birds, other reptiles, and monotremes, mammalian eggs are typically quite small, storing little in the way of food reserves. In most mammalian species, fertilization takes place in the oviduct, and the earliest stages of development occur while the embryo completes its journey down the oviduct to the uterus (see Figure 46.15). As already mentioned, the mammalian egg and zygote have not yet been shown to exhibit polarity with respect to cytoplasmic contents, and cleavage of the zygote, which lacks yolk, is holoblastic. Despite the lack of yolk, however, mammalian gastrulation and early organogenesis follow a pattern similar to that of birds and other reptiles.

Because ethical concerns preclude experimentation on human embryos, knowledge about human development has been based partly on what we can extrapolate from other mammals, such as the mouse, and partly on observation of very early human development following *in vitro* fertilization. In humans, the first division is complete about 36 hours after fertilization, the second division at about 60 hours, and the third division at about 72 hours. The blastomeres are equal in size. At the eight-cell stage, the blastomeres become tightly adhered to one another, causing the outer surface of the embryo to take on a smooth appearance. **Figure 47.16**, on the next page, depicts development of the human embryo starting about 6 days after fertilization. Our description in the text follows the numbers in the figure.

Endometrial epithelium (uterine lining)

Inner cell mass

Trophoblast

Blastocoel

❶ Blastocyst reaches uterus.

Maternal blood vessel

Expanding region of trophoblast

Epiblast

Hypoblast

Trophoblast

❷ Blastocyst implants (7 days after fertilization).

Expanding region of trophoblast

Amniotic cavity

Epiblast

Hypoblast

Yolk sac (from hypoblast)

Extraembryonic mesoderm cells (from epiblast)

Chorion (from trophoblast)

❸ Extraembryonic membranes start to form (10–11 days), and gastrulation begins (13 days).

Amnion

Chorion

Ectoderm

Mesoderm

Endoderm

Yolk sac

Extraembryonic mesoderm

Allantois

❹ Gastrulation has produced a three-layered embryo with four extraembryonic membranes.

▲ **Figure 47.16 Four stages in early embryonic development of a human.** The epiblast gives rise to the three germ layers, which form the embryo proper. See the text for a description of each stage.

❶ At the completion of cleavage, the embryo has more than 100 cells arranged around a central cavity and has traveled down the oviduct to the uterus. This embryonic stage, the **blastocyst**, is the mammalian version of a blastula. Clustered at one end of the blastocyst cavity is a group of cells called the **inner cell mass**, which will subsequently develop into the embryo proper and form or contribute to all the extraembryonic membranes. It is the cells of the very early blastocyst stage that are the source of embryonic stem cell lines.

❷ The **trophoblast**, the outer epithelium of the blastocyst, does not contribute to the embryo itself but instead provides support services. First, it initiates implantation by secreting enzymes that break down molecules of the endometrium, the lining of the uterus. This allows the blastocyst to invade the endometrium. Then, as the trophoblast thickens through cell division, it extends fingerlike projections into the surrounding maternal tissue, which is rich in blood vessels. Invasion by the trophoblast leads to erosion of capillaries in the endometrium, causing blood to spill out and bathe trophoblast tissues. Around the time of implantation, the inner cell mass of the blastocyst forms a flat disk with an upper layer of cells, the *epiblast*, and a lower layer, the *hypoblast*, which are homologous to the epiblast and hypoblast of birds. As in birds, the human embryo develops almost entirely from epiblast cells.

❸ As implantation is completed, gastrulation begins. Cells move inward from the epiblast through a primitive streak and form mesoderm and endoderm, just as in the chick (see Figure 47.11). At the same time, extraembryonic membranes begin to form. The trophoblast continues to expand into the endometrium. The invading trophoblast, mesodermal cells derived from the epiblast, and adjacent endometrial tissue all contribute to formation of the placenta (see Figure 46.16). The placenta is a vital organ that mediates exchange of nutrients, gases, and nitrogenous wastes between the embryo and the mother. The placenta also produces hormones and protects the embryo from a maternal immune response.

❹ By the end of gastrulation, the embryonic germ layers have formed. The three-layered embryo is now surrounded by proliferating extraembryonic mesoderm and the four extraembryonic membranes.

The extraembryonic membranes in mammals are homologous to those of birds and other reptiles (see Figure 47.15) and develop in a similar way. Gas exchange occurs across the chorion, and the amnion cushions the developing embryo. The fluid from the amniotic cavity is the "water" expelled from the mother's vagina when the amnion breaks just prior to childbirth. Below the developing mammalian embryo, the yolk sac encloses more fluid. Although this cavity contains no yolk, the membrane that surrounds it is given the same name as the homologous membrane in birds and other reptiles. The yolk sac membrane of mammals is a site of early formation of blood cells, which later migrate into the embryo proper. The allantois in mammals is incorporated into the umbilical cord. Here it forms blood vessels that transport oxygen and nutrients from the placenta to the embryo and rid the embryo of carbon dioxide and nitrogenous wastes. Thus, the extraembryonic membranes of shelled eggs, where embryos are nourished with yolk, were conserved in mammals as they diverged from reptiles in the course of evolution, but with modifications adapted to development within the reproductive tract of the mother.

As you learned in Chapter 46, identical (monozygotic) twins can arise when embryonic cells become separated. The timing of the separation determines the nature of the twins' arrangement in the uterus with regard to their extraembryonic membranes. If the separation occurs quite early, before the trophoblast and inner cell mass become differentiated, then two embryos will grow, each with its own chorion and amnion. This is the case in about a third of twin births. In most of the remainder, the separation occurs a little later, after the chorion forms but before the amnion forms. The two embryos that develop therefore share a chorion but have separate amnions. In very rare cases, two groups of cells become separated even later, and the two embryos share a common chorion and amnion.

In this section, you have learned about the main events of embryonic development in animals. Next, we will address the cellular and molecular mechanisms by which these events occur.

CONCEPT CHECK **47.1**

1. How does the fertilization envelope form in sea urchins? What is its function?
2. A frog zygote and frog blastula are nearly the same size. Explain this observation.
3. Contrast the effects of cleavage and gastrulation on development of the embryo.
4. Explain how the neural tube forms and how neural crest cells arise.
5. **WHAT IF?** Predict what would happen if you injected Ca^{2+} into an unfertilized sea urchin egg.
6. **WHAT IF?** How many chorions and amnions are present in the case of conjoined ("Siamese") twins? (These twins are always monozygotic.)

For suggested answers, see Appendix A.

CONCEPT **47.2**

Morphogenesis in animals involves specific changes in cell shape, position, and adhesion

Although biologists are far from fully understanding cellular and molecular developmental mechanisms, several key princi-

ples have emerged as being fundamental to the development of all animals. Morphogenesis is a major aspect of development in both animals and plants, but only in animals does it involve the *movement* of cells. The rigid cell wall that surrounds plant cells prevents complex movements like those occurring during gastrulation. In animals, movement of parts of a cell can bring about changes in cell shape or enable a cell to migrate from one place to another within the embryo. Changes in both cell shape and cell position are involved in cleavage, gastrulation, and organogenesis. Here we consider some of the cellular components and behaviors that contribute to these events.

The Cytoskeleton, Cell Motility, and Convergent Extension

Changes in the shape of a cell usually involve reorganization of the cytoskeleton (see Table 6.1). Consider, for example, how the cells of the neural plate form the neural tube **(Figure 47.17)**. First, microtubules oriented parallel to the dorsal-ventral axis of the embryo apparently help lengthen the cells in that direction. At the dorsal end of each cell is a parallel array of microfilaments (actin filaments) oriented crosswise. These microfilaments contract, giving the cells a wedge shape that forces the ectoderm layer to

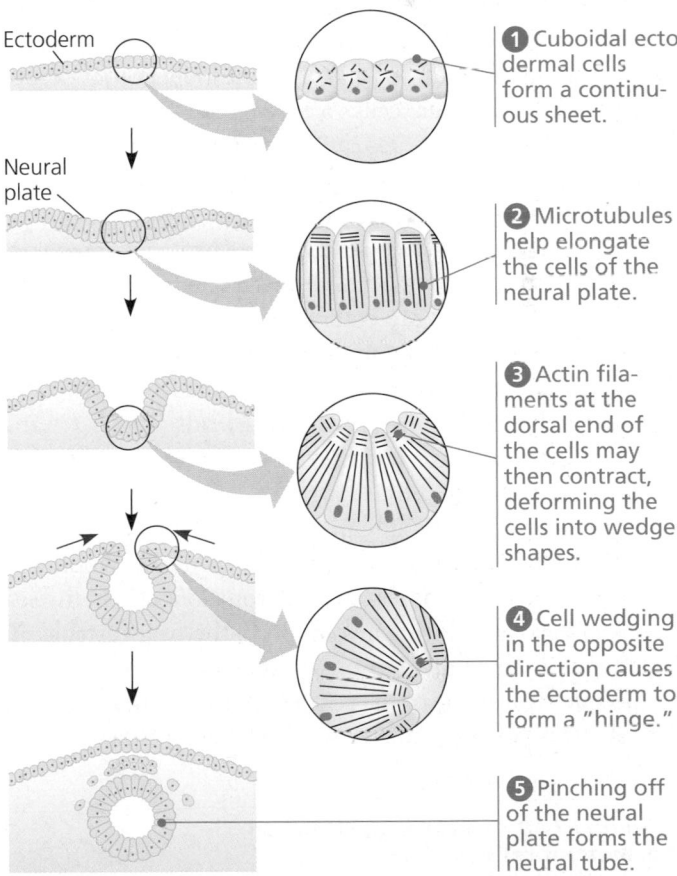

Ectoderm

Neural plate

1 Cuboidal ectodermal cells form a continuous sheet.

2 Microtubules help elongate the cells of the neural plate.

3 Actin filaments at the dorsal end of the cells may then contract, deforming the cells into wedge shapes.

4 Cell wedging in the opposite direction causes the ectoderm to form a "hinge."

5 Pinching off of the neural plate forms the neural tube.

▲ **Figure 47.17 Change in cell shape during morphogenesis.** Reorganization of the cytoskeleton is associated with morphogenetic changes in embryonic tissues, as shown here for the formation of the neural tube in vertebrates.

bend inward. Similar changes in cell shape occur throughout development in other places, such as the hinge regions where the neural tube is pinching off from the ectoderm and sites where evaginations (outpocketings) of tissue layers form.

The cytoskeleton also drives cell migration, the active movement of cells from one place to another in developing animals. Cells "crawl" within the embryo by using cytoskeletal fibers to extend and retract cellular protrusions. This type of motility is akin to the amoeboid movement described in Figure 6.27b; but in contrast with the thick pseudopodia of some amoeboid cells, the cellular protrusions of migrating embryonic cells are usually flat sheets (lamellipodia) or spikes (filopodia).

During gastrulation in some organisms, invagination begins when cuboidal cells on the surface of the blastula become wedge-shaped. However, the movement of cells deeper into the embryo involves the extension of filopodia by cells at the leading edge of the migrating tissue. The cells that first move through the blastopore and up along the inside of the blastocoel wall drag others behind them, thus helping direct movement of the entire sheet of cells from the embryo's surface into appropriate locations in the blastocoel. The involuted sheet then forms the endoderm and mesoderm of the embryo (see Figure 47.10). There are also many situations in which cells migrate individually, as when the cells of a somite or the neural crest disperse to various parts of the embryo. In fact, during gastrulation in many species, the mesoderm moves into the embryo as individual cells. We have seen two such examples thus far, in the sea urchin and the chick.

Cell crawling is also involved in **convergent extension**, a type of morphogenetic movement in which the cells of a tissue layer rearrange themselves so that the sheet becomes narrower (converges) while it becomes longer (extends). It's as if a crowd of people waiting to enter a theater for a concert were told that the doors would not open until they formed a single-file line; the line would become much longer as it narrowed. In the embryo, the cells elongate, with their ends pointing in the direction they will move, and they wedge between each other into fewer columns of cells **(Figure 47.18)**. When many cells converge this way, the tissue can extend dramatically. Convergent extension is important in early embryonic development. It occurs, for example, as the archenteron elongates in the sea urchin embryo and during involution in the frog gastrula. In the latter case, convergent extension is responsible for changing the spherical shape of the gastrula to the rounded rectangular shape of the frog embryo seen in Figure 47.12c.

Role of Cell Adhesion Molecules and the Extracellular Matrix

Scientists are refining their understanding of the signaling pathways that trigger and guide cell movement and cell interactions during morphogenesis. A key group of proteins that contribute to cell migration and stable tissue structure are glycoproteins called **cell adhesion molecules (CAMs)**, transmembrane cell-surface proteins that bind to CAMs on other cells. CAMs vary in amount, chemical identity, or both from one type of cell to another. These differences help regulate morphogenetic movements and tissue building.

One important class of CAMs is the **cadherins**, which require calcium ions outside the cell for proper function. There are many different cadherins, and the gene for each cadherin is expressed in specific locations at specific times during embryonic development. Janet Heasman, Chris Wylie, and colleagues have vividly demonstrated the importance of one particular cadherin in the formation of the frog blastula **(Figure 47.19)**. Cadherins are also involved in the tight adhesion of cells in the mammalian embryo that first occurs at the eight-cell stage, when cadherin production begins.

The processes of cell migration and tissue organization also involve the extracellular matrix (ECM), the meshwork of secreted glycoproteins and other macromolecules lying outside the plasma membranes of cells (see Figure 6.30). The ECM helps to guide cells in many types of morphogenetic movements, such as migration of individual cells or shape changes of cell sheets. On the cells that undergo movement, membrane proteins act as receptors that bind specific ECM molecules. An organized array of ECM fibers may function as tracks, directing migrating cells along particular routes. Other substances in the ECM keep cells on the correct paths by *inhibiting* migration off the path. Thus, nonmigratory cells along migration pathways may promote or inhibit movement of other cells, depending on the specific molecules they secrete into the ECM.

Several kinds of extracellular glycoproteins, such as fibronectin, promote cell migration by providing specific molecular anchorage for moving cells. For example, fibronectin plays such a role at the leading edge of the involuting tissue during frog gastrulation. Fibronectin fibers line the roof of the blastocoel, and as the future mesoderm moves into the interior of the embryo, the cells at the free edge of the involuting sheet migrate along the fibers (see Figure 47.10). Researchers can prevent the attachment of cells to fibronectin by injecting embryos with antibodies against either fibronectin or the

▶ **Figure 47.18 Convergent extension of a sheet of cells.** In this simplified diagram, the cells elongate in a particular direction and crawl between each other (convergence), as the sheet becomes longer and narrower (extension).

Is cadherin required for development of the blastula?

EXPERIMENT In 1994, Janet Heasman, Chris Wylie, and colleagues, then at the Wellcome/CRC Institute in Cambridge, England, injected frog eggs with nucleic acid complementary to the mRNA encoding a cadherin known as EP cadherin. This "antisense" nucleic acid leads to destruction of EP cadherin mRNA, so no EP cadherin protein is produced. Frog sperm were then added to experimental (injected) eggs and to control (noninjected) eggs. The embryos that developed were observed with a scanning electron microscope.

RESULTS As shown in these SEMs of cut-open embryos, fertilized control eggs developed into normal blastulae, but fertilized experimental eggs did not. In the absence of EP cadherin, the blastocoel did not form properly, and the cells were arranged in a disorganized fashion.

0.25 mm   0.25 mm

Control embryo   Embryo without EP cadherin

CONCLUSION During embryonic development in the frog, the cell adhesion molecule EP cadherin is required for proper cell organization in the blastula.

SOURCE J. Heasman et al., A functional test for maternally inherited cadherin in *Xenopus* shows its importance in cell adhesion at the blastula stage, *Development* 120:49–57 (1994).

WHAT IF? What do you predict would be the effect on embryos if you placed frog blastulae in water from which all the calcium had been removed?

receptors that bind fibronectin at the cell surface. Either treatment prevents the crawling of mesoderm.

A wealth of evidence supports the conclusion that moving cells engage in an ongoing dialogue with the ECM and other cells in the vicinity. As migrating cells move along specific paths, a variety of receptor proteins on their surfaces pick up directional cues from the immediate environment. Such signaling molecules, which may be ECM molecules or small soluble factors (see Chapter 11), can initiate intracellular signaling pathways that direct the orientation of cytoskeletal elements so that the cell moves in the proper direction. Such signaling may also affect the expression or function of other proteins involved in the migration.

Based on previous studies, Mungo Marsden and Doug DeSimone were intrigued by the possibility that cell-ECM and cell-cell binding systems might affect each other during convergent extension. **Figure 47.20** describes their initial experi-

Is an organized fibronectin matrix required for convergent extension?

EXPERIMENT Mungo Marsden and Doug DeSimone, at the University of Virginia, wondered whether an organized fibronectin matrix was essential for convergent extension. Into the blastocoels of frog blastulae, they injected molecules that would block the interaction of fibronectin with its receptor protein on cell surfaces, knowing from previous work that this would block organization of the fibronectin matrix. As a control, they injected a very similar molecule that did not block matrix assembly. They compared convergent extension in matrix-blocked and control embryos in a series of experiments, two of which are shown here.

Experiment 1: In whole embryos, a probe was used to detect the presence of an mRNA that marks tissues normally undergoing convergent extension.

Experiment 2: Certain tissues that normally undergo convergent extension were removed from embryos, placed between glass cover slips, allowed to develop, and observed through a microscope.

RESULTS

Experiment 1: The marked tissue in the matrix-blocked whole embryo was shorter and wider than that in the control embryo.

Control   Matrix blocked

Experiment 2: Cells (nuclei marked by yellow arrowheads) were tightly packed in a column in the control tissues but not in the matrix-blocked tissues. (Red arrows indicate column widths.)

Control   Matrix blocked

CONCLUSION Fibronectin matrix assembly is crucial for the cell behaviors underlying convergent extension.

SOURCE M. Marsden and D. W. DeSimone, Integrin-ECM interactions regulate cadherin-dependent cell adhesion and are required for convergent extension in *Xenopus*, *Current Biology* 13.1182–1191 (2003).

WHAT IF? Suppose you wanted to determine if convergent extension can occur on a *preexisting* fibronectin matrix or if it requires a matrix formed *during* convergent extension. If you could make an artificial fibronectin matrix on glass cover slips, how would you design an experiment to ask this question?

ments to investigate this possibility. The results of their full study support a model in which fibronectin binding to its receptor provides a molecular signal to the cell that ultimately affects the function of cadherins. ECM molecules and cadherins thus appear to be linked in a single pathway driving convergent extension.

As you have seen, cell behavior and the molecular mechanisms underlying it are crucial to the morphogenesis of the embryo. In the next section, you'll learn that the same basic cellular and genetic processes ensure that the various types of cells end up in the right places in each embryo.

CONCEPT 47.3

The developmental fate of cells depends on their history and on inductive signals

Coupled with the morphogenetic changes that give an animal and its parts their characteristic shapes, development also requires the timely differentiation of many kinds of cells in specific locations. In Chapter 20, you learned about the principle of genomic equivalence: Virtually every cell in an organism has the same genome. However, different cell types make different sets of proteins because they end up expressing different sets of genes. Therefore, during differentiation, some mechanism must send cells down different pathways of gene expression. Two general principles integrate our current knowledge of the genetic and cellular mechanisms that underlie differentiation during embryonic development.

First, *during early cleavage divisions, embryonic cells must somehow become different from one another.* In many animal species, initial differences between cells result from the uneven distribution of cytoplasmic determinants in the unfertilized egg. By partitioning the heterogeneous cytoplasm of a polarized egg, cleavage parcels out different mRNAs, proteins, and other molecules to blastomeres in a type of asymmetrical cell division (see Figure 18.15a). These cytoplasmic determinants are in many cases transcription factors, DNA-binding proteins that activate one set of genes rather than another.

Thus, the resulting differences in the cells' cytoplasmic composition help specify the body axes and influence the expression of genes that affect the cells' developmental fate. In amniotes, local environmental differences play the principal role in establishing early differences between embryonic cells. For example, cells of the inner cell mass are located internally in the early human embryo, whereas trophoblast cells are located on the outside surface of the blastocyst. The different environments of these two groups of cells appear to determine their very different fates.

Second, *once initial cell asymmetries are set up, subsequent interactions among the embryonic cells influence their fate, usually by causing changes in gene expression.* This mechanism, called **induction**, eventually brings about the differentiation of the many specialized cell types making up an animal. Induction may be mediated by diffusible signaling molecules or, if the cells are in contact, by cell-surface interactions.

It will help to keep these two principles in mind as we delve into the molecular and cellular mechanisms of differentiation and morphogenesis during embryonic development of the species we're focusing on in this chapter. But to ask questions about *how* the fate of an early embryonic cell is determined, we need to know what that fate is. So let's first look at some historic experiments that provided early researchers with information about cell fates.

Fate Mapping

Biologists have studied the early development of many species, carefully scrutinizing each cell division, in an attempt to follow the fate and trace the ancestry of each embryonic cell. These labor-intensive studies have produced extremely useful territorial diagrams of embryonic development, called **fate maps**.

In classic studies performed in the 1920s, German embryologist Walther Vogt charted fate maps for the different regions of early amphibian embryos. Vogt's results were among the earliest indications that the lineages of cells making up the three germ layers created by gastrulation are traceable to cells in the blastula, before gastrulation has begun **(Figure 47.21a)**. Later researchers developed techniques that allowed them to mark an individual blastomere during cleavage and then follow the marker as it was distributed to all the mitotic descendants of that cell **(Figure 47.21b)**.

Perhaps the ultimate approach to fate mapping has been carried out on the soil-dwelling nematode *Caenorhabditis elegans*. This worm is easily raised in the laboratory in petri dishes. It is about 1 mm long, has a simple transparent body with only a few types of cells, and grows from zygote to mature adult in only 3½ days. Most individuals are hermaphrodites, producing both eggs and sperm, which has advantages for genetic studies.

The attributes of *C. elegans* allowed Sydney Brenner, Robert Horvitz, and Jonathan Sulston to determine the complete

(a) Fate map of a frog embryo. The fates of groups of cells in a frog blastula (left) were determined in part by marking different regions of the blastula surface with nontoxic dyes of various colors. The embryos were sectioned at later stages of development, such as the neural tube stage shown on the right, and the locations of the dyed cells determined. The two embryonic stages shown here represent the result of numerous such experiments.

(b) Cell lineage analysis in a tunicate. In lineage analysis, an individual blastomere is injected with a dye during cleavage, as indicated in the drawings of 64-cell embryos of a tunicate, an invertebrate chordate (top). The dark regions in the light micrographs of larvae (bottom) correspond to the cells that developed from the two different blastomeres indicated in the drawings.

▲ **Figure 47.21 Fate mapping for two chordates.**

cell lineage of this organism, using a multipronged approach. Every adult hermaphrodite of the species has exactly 959 somatic cells, which arise from the zygote in virtually the same way for every individual. Careful microscopic observations during the entire period of development, coupled with experiments in which particular cells or groups of cells were destroyed by a laser beam or through mutations, resulted in the cell lineage diagram shown in **Figure 47.22**. In 2002, these researchers shared a Nobel Prize for their accomplishment, which led to *C. elegans* becoming the model organism of choice for many developmental biologists.

Developmental biologists have combined fate-mapping studies with experimental manipulation of parts of embryos to ascertain whether a cell's fate can be changed. Starting with the normal embryo's fate map, researchers can examine how the differentiation of cells is altered in experimental situations or in mutant embryos. Two important conclusions have emerged. First, in most animals, specific tissues of the older embryo are the products of certain early "founder cells" that contain unique factors as the result of asymmetrical cell divisions. Second, as development proceeds, a cell's *developmental potential*—the range of

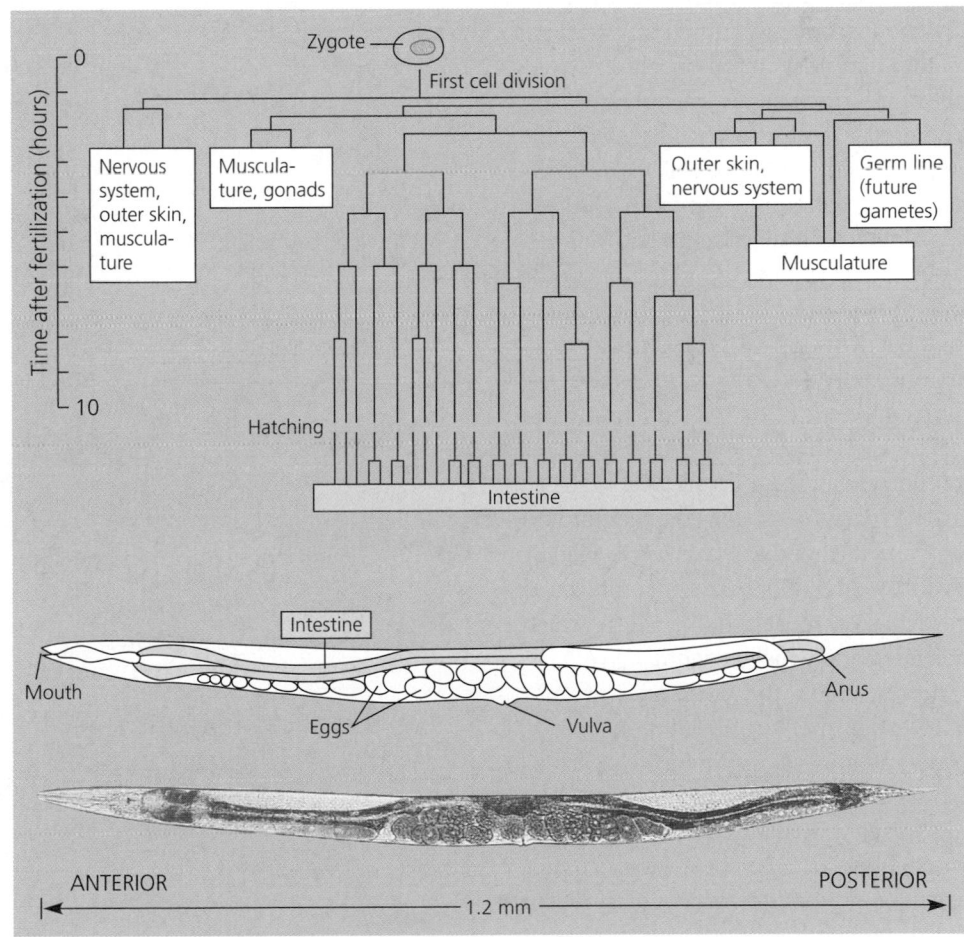

▲ **Figure 47.22 Cell lineage in *Caenorhabditis elegans*.** The *C. elegans* embryo is transparent, making it possible for researchers to trace the lineage of every cell, from the zygote to the adult worm (LM). The diagram shows a detailed lineage only for the intestine, which is derived exclusively from one of the first four cells formed from the zygote. The eggs will be fertilized internally and released through the vulva.

structures that it can give rise to—becomes restricted. Let's look more closely at these two aspects by which cell fates are determined. (For review of cell fate determination, see Chapter 18.)

Establishing Cellular Asymmetries

To understand at the molecular level how embryonic cells acquire their fates, it is helpful to think first about how the basic axes of the embryo are established. This can often be traced to a specific event in early development that sets up a particular cellular asymmetry, thus beginning to lay out the body plan.

The Axes of the Basic Body Plan

As you have learned, a bilaterally symmetrical animal has an anterior-posterior axis, a dorsal-ventral axis, and left and right sides (see Figure 47.7a). Establishing this basic body plan is the first step in morphogenesis and a prerequisite for the development of tissues and organs.

In nonamniote vertebrates, basic instructions for forming the body axes are established early, during oogenesis or fertilization. For example, in many frogs, including the species we've discussed, the locations of melanin and yolk in the unfertilized egg define the animal and vegetal hemispheres, respectively. The animal-vegetal axis indirectly determines the anterior-posterior body axis. Fertilization then triggers cortical rotation, which establishes the dorsal-ventral axis and at the same time leads to the appearance of the gray crescent, whose position marks the dorsal side (see Figure 47.7b). Once any two axes are established, the third (in this case, the left-right) axis is specified by default. (Of course, specific molecular mechanisms must then establish which side is left and which is right.)

In amniotes, the body axes are not fully established until later. In chicks, gravity is apparently involved in establishing the anterior-posterior axis as the egg travels down the hen's oviduct before being laid. Later, pH differences between the two sides of the blastoderm cells establish the dorsal-ventral axis. If the pH is artificially reversed above and below the blastoderm, the part facing the egg white will turn into the belly (ventral side) and the side facing the yolk will turn into the back (dorsal side), op-

posite to their normal fates. In mammals, no polarity is obvious until after cleavage. However, the results of recent experiments suggest that the orientation of the egg and sperm nuclei before they fuse influences the location of the first cleavage plane and thus may play a role in establishing the embryonic axes.

Restriction of the Developmental Potential of Cells

In many species that have cytoplasmic determinants, only the zygote is **totipotent**—that is, capable of developing into all the different cell types of that species. In these organisms, the first cleavage is asymmetrical, with the two blastomeres

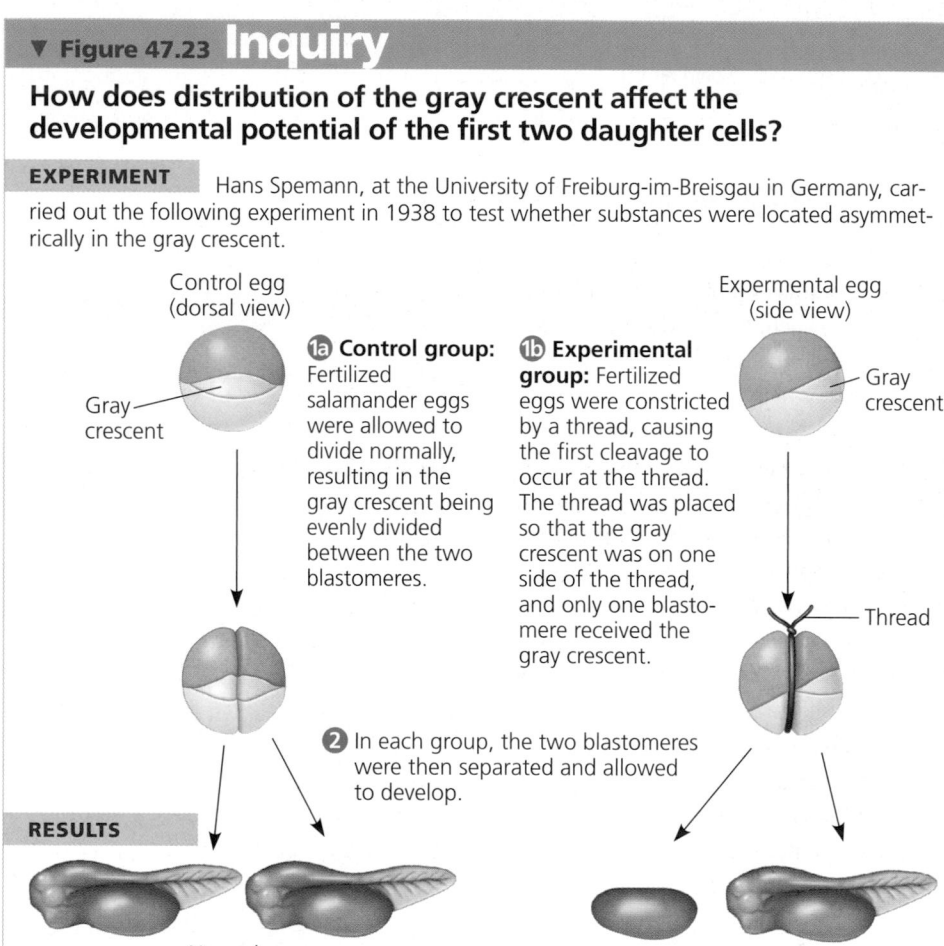

▼ **Figure 47.23** **Inquiry**

How does distribution of the gray crescent affect the developmental potential of the first two daughter cells?

EXPERIMENT Hans Spemann, at the University of Freiburg-im-Breisgau in Germany, carried out the following experiment in 1938 to test whether substances were located asymmetrically in the gray crescent.

Control egg (dorsal view)

Gray crescent

1a Control group: Fertilized salamander eggs were allowed to divide normally, resulting in the gray crescent being evenly divided between the two blastomeres.

1b Experimental group: Fertilized eggs were constricted by a thread, causing the first cleavage to occur at the thread. The thread was placed so that the gray crescent was on one side of the thread, and only one blastomere received the gray crescent.

Experimental egg (side view)

Gray crescent

Thread

2 In each group, the two blastomeres were then separated and allowed to develop.

RESULTS

Normal

Belly piece

Normal

Blastomeres that received half or all of the material in the gray crescent developed into normal embryos, but a blastomere that received none of the gray crescent gave rise to an abnormal embryo without dorsal structures. Spemann called it a "belly piece."

CONCLUSION The developmental potential of the two blastomeres normally formed during the first cleavage division depends on their acquisition of cytoplasmic determinants localized in the gray crescent.

SOURCE H. Spemann, *Embryonic Development and Induction*, Yale University Press, New Haven (1938).

WHAT IF? In a similar experiment 40 years earlier, embryologist Hans Roux allowed the first cleavage to occur and then used a needle to kill just one blastomere. The embryo that developed from the remaining blastomere (plus remnants of the dead cell) was abnormal, resembling a half-embryo. Propose a hypothesis to explain why Roux's result differed from the control result in Spemann's experiment.

receiving different cytoplasmic determinants. However, even in species that have cytoplasmic determinants, the first cleavage may occur along an axis that produces two identical blastomeres, which then have equal developmental potential. This occurs in amphibians, for instance, as demonstrated in 1938 in an experiment by German zoologist Hans Spemann (Figure 47.23). Thus, the fates of embryonic cells can be affected not only by the distribution of cytoplasmic determinants but also by how this distribution relates to the zygote's characteristic pattern of cleavage.

In contrast with the embryonic cells of many other animals, the cells of mammalian embryos remain totipotent until the 16-cell stage, when their location determines whether they will give rise to cells of the trophoblast or of the inner cell mass of the blastocyst, thus establishing their ultimate fates. Through the 8-cell stage, the blastomeres of a mammalian embryo all look alike, and each can form a complete embryo if isolated. Researchers have taken this as evidence that the early blastomeres of mammals probably receive equivalent amounts of cytoplasmic components from the egg. Recent work, however, suggests that the very early cells (even the first two) are not actually equivalent in a normal embryo, and their ability to form a complete embryo if isolated shows that they may be able to regulate their fate, depending on their environment. The jury is still out on this matter, which is an area of great interest to researchers.

Regardless of how similar or different early embryonic cells are in a particular species, the progressive restriction of developmental potential is a general feature of development in all animals. In some species, the cells of the early gastrula retain the capacity to give rise to more than one kind of cell, though they have lost their totipotency. If left alone, the dorsal ectoderm of an early amphibian gastrula will develop into a neural plate above the notochord. And if the dorsal ectoderm is experimentally replaced with ectoderm from some other location in the same gastrula, the transplanted tissue will form a neural plate. But if the same experiment is performed on a late-stage gastrula, the transplanted ectoderm will not respond to its new environment and will not form a neural plate. In general, the tissue-specific fates of cells in a late gastrula are fixed. Even when they are manipulated experimentally, these cells usually give rise to the same types of cells as in the normal embryo, indicating that their fate is already determined.

Cell Fate Determination and Pattern Formation by Inductive Signals

Once embryonic cell division creates cells that differ from each other, the cells begin to influence each other's fates by induction. At the molecular level, the response to an inductive signal is usually to switch on a set of genes that make the receiving cells differentiate into a specific tissue. Here we examine two examples of induction, an essential process in the development of many tissues in most animals.

The "Organizer" of Spemann and Mangold

The importance of induction during development of amphibians was dramatically demonstrated in transplantation experiments performed by Hans Spemann and his student Hilde Mangold in the 1920s. Based on the results of their most famous experiment, summarized in Figure 47.24, they concluded that

▼ **Figure 47.24 Inquiry**

Can the dorsal lip of the blastopore induce cells in another part of the amphibian embryo to change their developmental fate?

EXPERIMENT In 1924, Hans Spemann and Hilde Mangold, at the University of Freiburg-im-Breisgau in Germany, transplanted a piece of the dorsal lip from a pigmented newt gastrula to the ventral side of a nonpigmented newt gastrula to investigate the inductive ability of the dorsal lip. Cross sections of the gastrulae are shown here.

Dorsal lip of blastopore

Pigmented gastrula (donor embryo)

Nonpigmented gastrula (recipient embryo)

RESULTS The recipient embryo formed a second notochord and neural tube in the region of the transplant, and eventually most of a second embryo developed. Examination of the interior of the double embryo revealed that the secondary structures were formed partly, but not wholly, from recipient tissue.

Primary embryo

Secondary (induced) embryo

Primary structures:
Neural tube
Notochord

Secondary structures:
Notochord (pigmented cells)
Neural tube (mostly nonpigmented cells)

CONCLUSION The transplanted dorsal lip was able to induce cells in a different region of the recipient to form structures different from their normal fate. In effect, the transplanted dorsal lip "organized" the later development of an entire extra embryo.

SOURCE H. Spemann and H. Mangold, Induction of embryonic primordia by implantation of organizers from a different species, Trans. V. Hamburger (1924). Reprinted in *International Journal of Developmental Biology* 45:13–38 (2001).

WHAT IF? Because the transplanted dorsal lip caused the recipient tissue to become something it would not otherwise have become, a signal of some sort must have passed from the dorsal lip. If you identified a protein candidate for the signaling molecule, how could you test whether it actually functions in signaling?

the dorsal lip of the blastopore in the early gastrula functions as an "organizer" of the embryo's body plan by initiating a chain of inductions that results in the formation of the notochord, the neural tube, and other organs.

Developmental biologists are still working intensively to identify the molecular basis of induction by *Spemann's organizer* (also called the *gastrula organizer* or simply the *organizer*). An important clue has come from studies of a growth factor called bone morphogenetic protein 4 (BMP-4). (Bone morphogenetic proteins, a family of related proteins with a variety of developmental roles, derive their name from members of the family that are important in bone formation.) In amphibians, a high concentration of BMP-4 signals cells on the ventral side of the gastrula to travel down the pathway toward formation of ventral structures. One major function of the cells of the organizer seems to be to *inactivate* BMP-4 on the dorsal side of the embryo by producing proteins that bind to BMP-4, rendering it unable to signal. This inactivation, along with signaling by other molecules not yet identified, promotes formation of dorsal structures such as the notochord and neural tube. In tissues between the dorsal and ventral sides, a lower concentration of BMP-4 results in lateral structures appropriate for the specific location along the dorsal-ventral axis. The varying concentration of BMP-4 along this axis is an example of a morphogen gradient (see Chapter 18). Proteins related to BMP-4 and its inhibitors are also found in other animals, including invertebrates such as the fruit fly, where they also regulate the dorsal-ventral axis. The ubiquity of these molecules suggests that they evolved long ago and may participate in the development of many different organisms.

The induction by BMP-4 of ventral and lateral structures is only one example of many cell-cell interactions that transform the three germ layers into organ systems. Many inductions seem to involve a sequence of inductive steps from different surrounding tissues that progressively determine the fate of cells. In the eye, for example, lens formation by ectodermal cells involves precisely timed inductive signals from ectodermal, mesodermal, and endodermal cells.

Formation of the Vertebrate Limb

The action of the gastrula organizer is a classic example of induction, and we can see that the organizer induces cells to take on their fates in appropriate locations relative to each other. Thus, inductive signals play a major role in **pattern formation**—the development of an animal's spatial organization, the arrangement of organs and tissues in their characteristic places in three-dimensional space. The molecular cues that control pattern formation, called **positional information**, tell a cell where it is with respect to the animal's body axes and help to determine how the cell and its descendants will respond to molecular signaling.

(a) Organizer regions. Vertebrate limbs develop from protrusions called limb buds, each consisting of mesoderm cells covered by a layer of ectoderm. Two regions in each limb bud, the apical ectodermal ridge (AER, shown in this SEM) and the zone of polarizing activity (ZPA), play key roles as organizers in limb pattern formation.

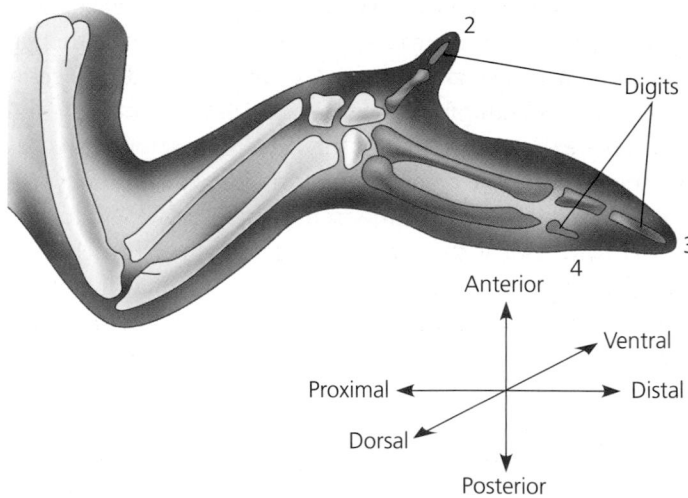

(b) Wing of chick embryo. As the bud develops into a limb, a specific pattern of tissues emerges. In the chick wing, for example, the digits are always present in the arrangement shown here. Pattern formation requires each embryonic cell to receive some kind of positional information indicating location along the three axes of the limb. The AER and ZPA secrete molecules that help provide this information. (Numbers are assigned to the digits based on a convention established for vertebrate limbs. The chicken wing has only four digits; the first digit points backward and is not shown in the diagram.)

▲ **Figure 47.25 Vertebrate limb development.**

In Chapter 18, we discussed pattern formation in the development of *Drosophila*. For the study of pattern formation in vertebrates, a classic model system has been limb development in the chick. The wings and legs of chicks, like all vertebrate limbs, begin as limb buds, bumps of mesodermal tissue covered by a layer of ectoderm (Figure 47.25a). Each component of a chick limb, such as a specific bone or muscle, develops with a precise location and orientation relative to three axes: the proximal-distal axis (the "shoulder-to-fingertip" axis), the anterior-posterior axis (the "thumb-to-little finger" axis), and the dorsal-ventral axis (the "knuckle-to-palm" axis). The embryonic cells within a limb bud respond to positional information indicating location along these three axes (Figure 47.25b).

Two critical organizer regions in a limb bud have profound effects on the limb's development. These regions are present in all vertebrate limb buds, including those that will develop into forelimbs (such as wings or arms) and those destined to become hind limbs. The cells of these regions secrete proteins that provide key positional information to the other cells of the bud.

One limb-bud organizer region is the **apical ectodermal ridge (AER)**, a thickened area of ectoderm at the tip of the bud (see Figure 47.25a). Removing the AER blocks outgrowth of the limb along the proximal-distal axis. The cells of the AER secrete several protein signals in the fibroblast growth factor (FGF) family that promote limb-bud outgrowth. If the AER is surgically removed and beads soaked with FGF are put in its place, a nearly normal limb will develop. In 2006, researchers identified an FGF-secreting AER that appears to be responsible for building a shark's unpaired (median) fins. This finding suggests that the AER may have predated the appearance of paired limbs in the vertebrate lineage, giving the AER a longer evolutionary history than previously thought.

The second major limb-bud organizer region is the **zone of polarizing activity (ZPA)**, a block of mesodermal tissue located underneath the ectoderm where the posterior side of the bud is attached to the body (see Figure 47.25a). The ZPA is necessary for proper pattern formation along the anterior-posterior axis of the limb. Cells nearest the ZPA give rise to the posterior structures, such as the most posterior of the chick's three digits (positioned like our little finger); cells farthest from the ZPA form anterior structures, including the most anterior digit (like our thumb).

The tissue transplantation experiment outlined in **Figure 47.26** supports the hypothesis that the ZPA produces an inductive signal that conveys positional information indicating "posterior." Indeed, researchers have discovered that the cells of the ZPA secrete an important protein growth factor called Sonic hedgehog.* These cells set up a gradient of Sonic hedgehog and other growth factors that Sonic hedgehog causes to be expressed. If cells genetically engineered to produce large amounts of Sonic hedgehog are implanted in the anterior region of a normal limb bud, a mirror-image limb results—just as if a

---

▼ Figure 47.26 **Inquiry**

What role does the zone of polarizing activity (ZPA) play in limb pattern formation in vertebrates?

EXPERIMENT In 1985, Dennis Summerbell and Lawrence Honig, then at the National Institute for Medical Research in Mill Hill, near London, were eager to investigate the nature of the zone of polarizing activity. They transplanted ZPA tissue from a donor chick embryo under the ectoderm in the anterior margin of a limb bud in another chick (the host).

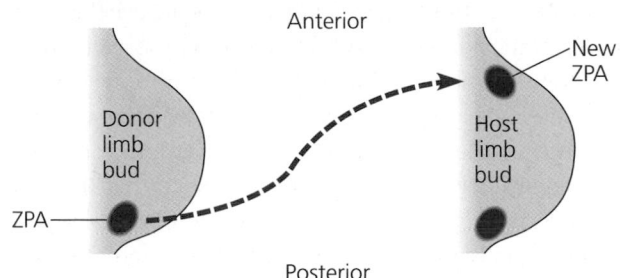

RESULTS The host limb bud developed extra digits from host tissue in a mirror-image arrangement to the normal digits, which also formed (compare with Figure 47.25b, which shows a normal chick wing).

CONCLUSION The mirror-image duplication observed in this experiment suggests that ZPA cells secrete a signal that diffuses from its source and conveys positional information indicating "posterior." As the distance from the ZPA increases, the signal concentration decreases, and hence more anterior digits develop.

SOURCE L. S. Honig and D. Summerbell, Maps of strength of positional signaling activity in the developing chick wing bud, *Journal of Embryology and Experimental Morphology* 87:163–174 (1985).

WHAT IF? Suppose you learned that the ZPA forms after the AER, leading you to develop the hypothesis that the AER is necessary for formation of the ZPA. Given what you know about molecules expressed in the AER and ZPA (see the text), how could you test your hypothesis?

ZPA had been grafted there. Studies of the mouse version of Sonic hedgehog suggest that extra toes in mice—and perhaps also in humans—can result when the wrong amounts of this protein are produced in part of the limb bud.

---

* Sonic hedgehog gets its name from two sources: its similarity to a *Drosophila* protein called Hedgehog, which is involved in segmentation of the fly embryo, and a video game character.

The *Hox* genes that you learned about in Chapter 21 also seem to play various roles at several distinct points during limb pattern formation. The importance of these genes in humans is illustrated by a condition called polysyndactyly ("many digits joined together"), which is caused by a specific mutation in a *Hox* gene named *HoxD13* (**Figure 47.27**).

Such observations, along with experiments like those previously described, support the notion that pattern formation requires cells to receive and interpret environmental cues that vary from one location to another. These cues, acting together along three axes, often in gradients, tell cells where they are in the three-dimensional realm of a developing organ. For instance, we now know that in vertebrate limb development, specific proteins serve as some of these cues and that organizer regions such as the AER and the ZPA function as signaling centers. Researchers have recently established that these two regions also interact with each other by way of signaling molecules and signaling pathways that influence each other's developmental fates. Such mutual signaling interactions between mesoderm and ectoderm also occur during formation of the neural tube and many other tissues and organs.

What determines whether a limb bud develops into a forelimb or a hind limb? The cells receiving the signals from the AER and ZPA respond according to their developmental histories. Before the AER or ZPA issues its signals, earlier developmental signaling has set up patterns of *Hox* gene expression that distinguish the future forelimbs from the future hind limbs and the different regions within a limb from each other. These differences cause cells of the forelimb and hind limb buds—and cells in different parts of each limb bud—to react differently to the same positional cues.

Thus, constructing the fully formed animal involves a sequence of events that include many steps of signaling and differentiation. Initial cell asymmetries allow different types of cells to influence each other, resulting in the expression of specific sets of genes. The products of these genes then direct cells to differentiate into specific types. Coordinated with morphogenesis, various pathways of pattern formation occur in all the different parts of the developing embryo. These processes ultimately produce a complex arrangement of multiple tissues and organs, each functioning in its appropriate location and each coordinated with the other tissues and organs of the whole organism.

▲ **Figure 47.27 Human polysyndactyly in a baby's foot due to a homozygous mutation in a *Hox* gene.**

CONCEPT CHECK 47.3

1. Although there are three body axes, only two must be determined during development. Why?
2. **WHAT IF?** If the ventral cells of an early frog gastrula are experimentally induced to express large amounts of a protein that inhibits BMP-4, could a second embryo develop? Explain.
3. **WHAT IF?** If you removed the ZPA from a limb bud and then placed a bead soaked in Sonic hedgehog in the middle of the limb bud, what would be the most likely result?

For suggested answers, see Appendix A.

Chapter 47 Review

SUMMARY OF KEY CONCEPTS

CONCEPT 47.1

After fertilization, embryonic development proceeds through cleavage, gastrulation, and organogenesis (pp. 1022–1035)

▶ **Fertilization** Fertilization brings together the nuclei of sperm and egg, forming a diploid zygote, and activates the egg, initiating embryonic development. The acrosomal reaction, which is triggered when the sperm meets the egg,

releases hydrolytic enzymes that digest material surrounding the egg. Gamete contact and/or fusion depolarizes the egg cell membrane and sets up a fast block to polyspermy in many animals. Sperm-egg fusion also initiates the cortical reaction:

Sperm-egg fusion and depolarization of egg membrane (fast block to polyspermy)

Cortical granule release (cortical reaction)

Formation of fertilization envelope (slow block to polyspermy)

In mammalian fertilization, the cortical reaction modifies the zona pellucida as a slow block to polyspermy.

▶ **Cleavage** Fertilization is followed by cleavage, a period of rapid cell division without growth, which results in the production of a large number of cells called blastomeres. Cleavage planes usually follow a specific pattern relative to the animal and vegetal poles of the zygote. In many species, cleavage creates a multicellular ball called the blastula, which contains a fluid-filled cavity, the blastocoel.

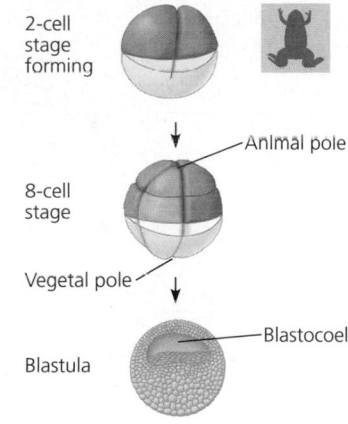

Holoblastic cleavage (division of the entire egg) occurs in species whose eggs have little or moderate amounts of yolk (as in sea urchins, frogs, and mammals). Meroblastic cleavage (incomplete division of the egg) occurs in species with yolk-rich eggs (as in birds and other reptiles).

▶ **Gastrulation** Gastrulation transforms the blastula into a gastrula, which has a primitive digestive cavity (the archenteron) and three embryonic germ layers: the ectoderm (blue), mesoderm (red), and endoderm (yellow).

▶ **Organogenesis** The organs of the animal body develop from specific portions of the three embryonic germ layers. Early events in organogenesis in vertebrates include formation of the notochord by condensation of dorsal mesoderm, formation of the coelom from splitting of lateral mesoderm, and development of the neural tube from infolding of the ectodermal neural plate:

 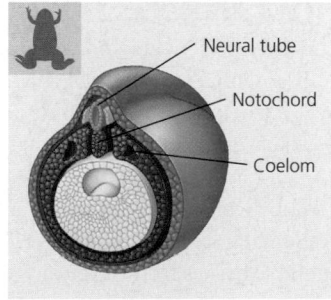

▶ **Developmental Adaptations of Amniotes** The embryos of birds, other reptiles, and mammals develop within a fluid-filled sac that is contained within a shell or the uterus. In these organisms, the three germ layers give rise not only to embryonic tissue but also to the four extraembryonic membranes: the amnion, chorion, yolk sac, and allantois.

▶ **Mammalian Development** The eggs of marsupial and eutherian mammals are small and store few nutrients. They exhibit holoblastic cleavage and show no obvious polarity. Gastrulation and organogenesis, however, resemble the processes in birds and other reptiles. After fertilization and early cleavage in the oviduct, the blastocyst implants in the uterus. The trophoblast initiates formation of the fetal portion of the placenta, and the embryo proper develops from a single layer of cells, the epiblast, within the blastocyst. Extraembryonic membranes homologous to those of birds and other reptiles function in intrauterine development.

MEDIA

Activity Sea Urchin Development
Investigation What Determines Cell Differentiation in the Sea Urchin?
Activity Frog Development

CONCEPT 47.2

Morphogenesis in animals involves specific changes in cell shape, position, and adhesion (pp. 1035–1038)

▶ **The Cytoskeleton, Cell Motility, and Convergent Extension** Cytoskeletal rearrangements are responsible for changes in both the shape and position of cells. Both kinds of changes are involved in tissue invaginations, as occurs in gastrulation, for example. In convergent extension, cell movements cause a sheet of cells to become narrower and longer.

▶ **Role of Cell Adhesion Molecules and the Extracellular Matrix** Cell adhesion molecules such as cadherins help hold cells together in tissues. Fibers of the extracellular matrix provide anchorage for cells and also help guide migrating cells toward their destinations. Fibronectin and other glycoproteins located on cell surfaces are important for cell migration and appear to affect cadherin function.

CONCEPT 47.3

The developmental fate of cells depends on their history and on inductive signals (pp. 1038–1044)

▶ **Fate Mapping** Experimentally derived fate maps of embryos have shown that specific regions of the zygote or blastula develop into specific parts of older embryos. The complete cell lineage has been worked out for *C. elegans*.

▶ **Establishing Cellular Asymmetries** In nonamniotes, unevenly distributed cytoplasmic determinants in the egg are important in establishing the body axes and in setting up differences between the blastomeres resulting from cleavage of the zygote. Cells that receive different cytoplasmic determinants undergo different fates. In amniotes, local environmental differences play the major role in establishing initial differences between cells and later the body axes. As embryonic development proceeds, the developmental potential of cells becomes progressively more limited in all species.

▶ **Cell Fate Determination and Pattern Formation by Inductive Signals** Cells in a developing embryo receive and respond to positional information that varies with location. This information is often in the form of signaling molecules secreted by cells in special "organizer" regions of the embryo, such as the dorsal lip of the blastopore in the amphibian gastrula and the AER and ZPA of the vertebrate limb bud. The signaling molecules influence gene expression in the cells that receive them, leading to differentiation and the development of particular structures.

SELF-QUIZ

1. The cortical reaction of sea urchin eggs functions directly in
   a. the formation of a fertilization envelope.
   b. the production of a fast block to polyspermy.
   c. the release of hydrolytic enzymes from the sperm.
   d. the generation of an electrical impulse by the egg.
   e. the fusion of egg and sperm nuclei.

2. Which of the following is common to the development of both birds and mammals?
   a. holoblastic cleavage   d. yolk plug
   b. epiblast and hypoblast   e. gray crescent
   c. trophoblast

3. The archenteron develops into
   a. the mesoderm.   d. the placenta.
   b. the blastocoel.   e. the lumen of the digestive tract.
   c. the endoderm.

4. In a frog embryo, the blastocoel is
   a. completely obliterated by yolk.
   b. lined with endoderm during gastrulation.
   c. located in the animal hemisphere.
   d. the cavity that becomes the coelom.
   e. the cavity that later forms the archenteron.

5. What structural adaptation in chickens allows them to lay their eggs in arid environments, rather than in water?
   a. extraembryonic membranes
   b. yolk
   c. cleavage
   d. gastrulation
   e. development of the brain from ectoderm

6. In an amphibian embryo, a group of cells called neural crest cells
   a. rolls up and forms the neural tube.
   b. develops into the main sections of the brain.
   c. produces cells that migrate to form teeth, skull bones, and other structures in the embryo.
   d. has been shown by experiments to be the organizer region of the developing embryo.
   e. induces the formation of the notochord.

7. In the early development of an amphibian embryo, Spemann's "organizer" is located in the
   a. neural tube.
   b. notochord.
   c. archenteron roof.
   d. dorsal ectoderm.
   e. dorsal lip of the blastopore.

8. **DRAW IT** Fill in the blanks in the figure below, and draw arrows showing the movement of ectoderm, mesoderm, and endoderm.

Species: _____

Stage: _____

For Self-Quiz answers, see Appendix A.

MEDIA Visit www.campbellbiology.com for a Practice Test.

EVOLUTION CONNECTION

9. Evolution in insects and vertebrates has involved the repeated duplication of body segments, followed by fusion of some segments and specialization of their structure and function. What parts of vertebrate anatomy reflect the vertebrate segmentation pattern?

SCIENTIFIC INQUIRY

10. The "snout" of a frog tadpole bears a sucker. A salamander tadpole has a mustache-shaped structure called a balancer in the same area. Suppose that you perform an experiment in which you transplant ectoderm from the side of a young salamander embryo to the snout of a frog embryo. The tadpole that develops has a balancer. When you transplant ectoderm from the side of a slightly older salamander embryo to the snout of a frog embryo, the frog tadpole ends up with a patch of salamander skin on its snout. Suggest a hypothesis to explain these results in terms of developmental mechanisms. How might you test your hypothesis?

SCIENCE, TECHNOLOGY, AND SOCIETY

11. Many scientists think that fetal tissue transplants offer great potential for treating Parkinson's disease, epilepsy, diabetes, Alzheimer's disease, and spinal cord injuries. Why might tissues from a fetus be particularly useful for replacing diseased or damaged cells in patients with such conditions? Some people would allow only tissues from miscarriages to be used in fetal transplant research. However, most researchers prefer to use tissues from surgically aborted fetuses. Why? Explain your position on this controversial issue.

48 Neurons, Synapses, and Signaling

▲ Figure 48.1 **What makes this snail such a deadly predator?**

KEY CONCEPTS

48.1 Neuron organization and structure reflect function in information transfer

48.2 Ion pumps and ion channels maintain the resting potential of a neuron

48.3 Action potentials are the signals conducted by axons

48.4 Neurons communicate with other cells at synapses

OVERVIEW

Lines of Communication

The tropical cone snail (*Conus geographus*) in **Figure 48.1** is both beautiful and dangerous. A carnivore, this marine snail hunts, kills, and dines on fish. Injecting venom with a hollow, harpoon-like part of its mouth, the cone snail paralyzes its free-swimming prey in seconds. The cone snail's venom is so potent that a single injection has killed scuba divers unaware of the danger within its intricately patterned shell. What makes cone snail venom so fast acting and lethal? The answer is a mixture of molecules that disable **neurons**, the nerve cells that transfer information within the body. Because the venom almost instantaneously disrupts neuronal control of vital functions, such as locomotion and respiration, an animal attacked by the cone snail can neither defend itself nor escape.

Communication by neurons largely consists of two distinct types of signals: long-distance electrical signals and short-distance chemical signals. The specialized structure of neurons allows them to use pulses of electrical current to receive, transmit, and regulate the flow of information over long distances within the body. In transferring information from one cell to another, neurons often rely on chemical signals that act over very short distances. The cone snail's venom is particu-

larly potent because it interferes with both electrical and chemical signaling by neurons.

Neurons transfer many different types of information. They transmit sensory information, control heart rate, coordinate hand and eye movement, record memories, generate dreams, and much more. All of this information is transmitted within neurons as an electrical current, consisting of the movement of ions. The connections made by a neuron specify what information is transmitted. Interpreting signals in the nervous system therefore involves sorting a complex set of neuronal paths and connections. In more complex animals, this higher-order processing is carried out largely in groups of neurons organized into a **brain** or into simpler clusters called **ganglia**.

In this chapter, we examine the structure of a neuron and explore the molecules and physical principles that govern signaling by neurons. In Chapter 49, we will look at the organization of nervous systems and at higher-order information processing in vertebrates. In Chapter 50, we will investigate systems that detect environmental stimuli and systems that carry out the body's responses to those stimuli. Finally, in Chapter 51, we will consider how these nervous system functions are integrated into the activities and interactions that make up animal behavior.

CONCEPT 48.1

Neuron organization and structure reflect function in information transfer

Before delving into the activity of an individual neuron, let's take an overall look at how neurons function in the flow of information through the animal body. We'll use as our example the squid, an organism that has some extraordinarily large nerve cells that are well suited for physiological studies.

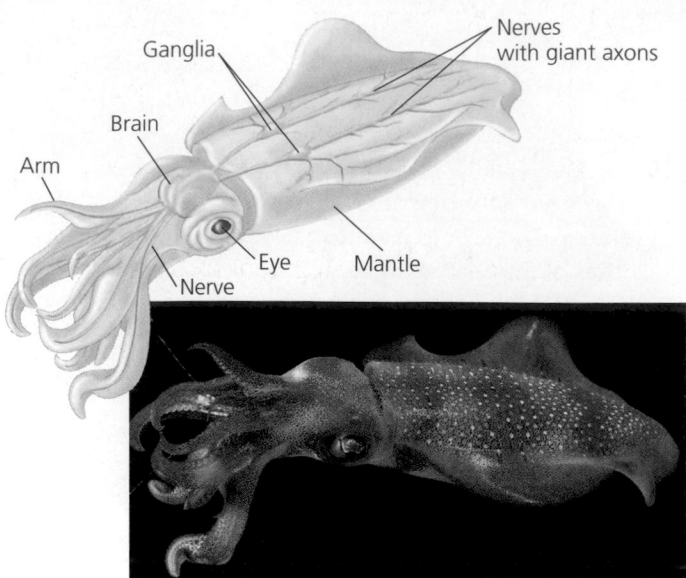

▲ **Figure 48.2 Overview of the squid nervous system.**
Signals travel from the brain to the muscular mantle along *giant axons*, nerve cell extensions of unusually large diameter.

▲ **Figure 48.3 Summary of information processing.**

Introduction to Information Processing

Like the cone snail in Figure 48.1, the squid in **Figure 48.2** is an active predator. Using its brain to process information captured by its image-forming eyes, the squid surveys its environment. When the squid spots prey, signals traveling from its brain to neurons in its mantle cause muscle contractions that propel the squid forward.

The squid's hunting activity illustrates the three stages in information processing: sensory input, integration, and motor output. In all but the simplest animals, specialized populations of neurons handle each stage. **Sensory neurons** transmit information from eyes and other sensors that detect external stimuli (light, sound, touch, heat, smell, and taste) or internal conditions (such as blood pressure, blood carbon dioxide level, and muscle tension). This information is sent to processing centers in the brain or in ganglia. Neurons in the brain or ganglia integrate (analyze and interpret) the sensory input, taking into account the immediate context and the animal's experience. The vast majority of neurons in the brain are **interneurons**, which make only local connections. Motor output relies on neurons that extend out of the processing centers in bundles called *nerves* and generate output by triggering muscle or gland activity. For example, **motor neurons** transmit signals to muscle cells, causing them to contract.

In many animals, the neurons that carry out integration are organized in a **central nervous system (CNS)**, which includes the brain and a longitudinal nerve cord. The neurons that carry information into and out of the CNS constitute the **peripheral nervous system (PNS)**. **Figure 48.3** summarizes CNS and PNS function in information flow within the nervous system. In exploring how this transmission of information occurs, we'll begin with the unique structure of neurons.

Neuron Structure and Function

The ability of a neuron to receive and transmit information is based on a highly specialized cellular organization **(Figure 48.4)**. Most of a neuron's organelles, including its nucleus, are located in the **cell body**. A typical neuron has numerous **dendrites** (from the Greek *dendron*, tree), highly branched extensions that *receive* signals from other neurons. A neuron also has a single **axon**, an extension that *transmits* signals to other cells. Axons are often much longer than dendrites, and some, such as those that reach from the spinal cord of a giraffe to the muscle cells in its feet, are over a meter long. The cone-shaped region of an axon where it joins the cell body is called the **axon hillock**; as we will see, this is typically the region where the signals that travel down the axon are generated. Near its other end, the axon usually divides into several branches.

Each branched end of an axon transmits information to another cell at a junction called a **synapse** (see Figure 48.4). The part of each axon branch that forms this specialized junction is a **synaptic terminal**. At most synapses, chemical messengers called **neurotransmitters** pass information from the transmitting neuron to the receiving cell. In describing a synapse, we refer to the transmitting neuron as the **presynaptic cell** and the neuron, muscle, or gland cell that receives the signal as the **postsynaptic cell**. Depending on the number of synapses a neuron has with other cells, its shape can vary from simple to quite complex **(Figure 48.5)**. Some interneurons have highly branched dendrites that take part in about 100,000 synapses. In contrast, neurons with simpler dendrites have far fewer synapses.

To function normally, the neurons of vertebrates and most invertebrates require supporting cells called glial cells, or **glia** (from a Greek word meaning "glue"). Depending on the type, glia may nourish neurons, insulate the axons of neurons, or regulate the extracellular fluid surrounding neurons. Overall, glia outnumber neurons in the mammalian brain 10- to 50-fold. We will examine functions of specific glia later in this chapter and in Chapter 49.

Figure 48.4 Neuron structure and organization.

Dendrites

Stimulus

Nucleus

Axon hillock

Cell body

Presynaptic cell

Axon

Signal direction

Synapse

Synaptic terminals

Neurotransmitter

Postsynaptic cell

Synaptic terminals

CONCEPT CHECK 48.1

1. Describe the basic pathway of information flow through neurons that cause you to turn your head when someone calls your name.
2. One cone snail species is nicknamed the cigarette snail because the victim is said to have just enough time to smoke one cigarette before dying. What properties of the nervous system account for the rapid action of cone snail venom?
3. **WHAT IF?** How would severing an axon affect the flow of information in a neuron? Explain.

For suggested answers, see Appendix A.

Dendrites

Axon

Cell body

Portion of axon

80 μm

Cell bodies of overlapping neurons with moderate branching (fluorescently labeled laser confocal image)

Sensory neuron

Interneurons

Motor neuron

Figure 48.5 Structural diversity of neurons.
In the drawings, cell bodies and dendrites are black and axons are red. The sensory neuron, unlike the other neurons here, has a cell body located partway along the axon that conveys signals from the dendrites to the axon's terminal branches. The micrograph shows tissue from a rat brain, with interneurons labeled green, glia red, and DNA blue (revealing locations of cell nuclei). These interneurons are the same type as those in the bottom drawing.

Ion pumps and ion channels maintain the resting potential of a neuron

As you read in Chapter 7, all cells have a **membrane potential**, a voltage (difference in electrical charge) across their plasma membrane. In neurons, inputs from other neurons or specific stimuli cause changes in this membrane potential that act as signals, transmitting and processing information. Rapid changes in membrane potential are what enable us to see a flower, read a book, or climb a tree. Thus, to understand how neurons function, we first need to examine how membrane potentials are formed, maintained, and altered.

The membrane potential of a resting neuron—one that is not sending signals—is its **resting potential** and is typically between −60 and −80 mV (millivolts). The minus sign indicates that the inside of a neuron at rest is negative relative to the outside.

Formation of the Resting Potential

Potassium ions (K^+) and sodium ions (Na^+) play critical roles in the formation of the resting potential. For each, there is a concentration gradient across the plasma membrane of a neuron. In the case of mammalian neurons, the concentration of K^+ is 140 millimolar (mM) inside the cell, but only 5 mM outside. The Na^+ concentration gradient is nearly the opposite: 150 mM outside and only 15 mM inside (**Figure 48.6a**). These Na^+ and K^+ gradients are maintained by *sodium-potassium pumps* in the plasma membrane. As discussed in Chapter 7, these ion pumps use the energy of ATP hydrolysis to actively transport Na^+ out of the cell and K^+ into the cell (**Figure 48.6b**). (There are also concentration gradients for chloride ions (Cl^-) and other anions, but we will ignore these for the moment.)

The concentration gradients of K^+ and Na^+ across the plasma membrane represent a chemical form of potential energy. Converting this chemical potential to an electrical potential involves **ion channels**, pores formed by clusters of specialized proteins that span the membrane. Ion channels allow ions to diffuse back and forth across the membrane. As ions diffuse through channels, they carry with them units of electrical charge. Any resulting *net* movement of positive or negative charge will generate a voltage, or potential, across the membrane.

The ion channels that establish the membrane potential have *selective permeability*, meaning that they allow only certain ions to pass. For example, a potassium channel allows K^+ to diffuse freely across the membrane, but not other ions, such as Na^+. As shown in Figure 48.6b, a resting neuron has many open potassium channels, but very few open sodium channels.

(a) The values shown represent the approximate concentrations in millimoles per liter (mM) for ions in the fluids within and surrounding a mammalian neuron: [K^+] = potassium concentration; [Na^+] = sodium concentration; [Cl^-] = chloride concentration; and [A^-] = other anions.

(b) The sodium-potassium pump generates and maintains the ionic gradients of Na^+ and K^+ shown in (a). The pump uses ATP to actively transport Na^+ out of the cell and K^+ into the cell. Although there is a substantial concentration gradient of sodium across the membrane, very little net diffusion of Na^+ occurs because there are very few open sodium channels. In contrast, the large number of open potassium channels allow a significant net outflow of K^+. Because the membrane is only weakly permeable to chloride and other anions, this outflow of K^+ results in a net negative charge inside the cell.

▲ **Figure 48.6 The basis of the membrane potential.**

The diffusion of K^+ through open potassium channels is critical for formation of the resting potential. In the resting mammalian neuron, these channels allow K^+ to pass in either direction across the membrane. Because the concentration of K^+ is much higher inside the cell, the chemical concentration gradient favors a net outflow of K^+. However, since the potassium channels allow only K^+ to pass, Cl^- and other anions inside the cell cannot accompany the K^+ across the membrane. As a result, the outflow of K^+ leads to an excess of negative charge inside the cell. This buildup of negative charge within the neuron is the source of the membrane potential.

What prevents the buildup of negative charge from increasing indefinitely? The answer lies in the electrical potential itself. The excess negative charges inside the cell exert an attractive force that opposes the flow of additional positively charged potassium ions out of the cell. The separation of charge (voltage) thus results in an electrical gradient that counterbalances the chemical concentration gradient of K^+.

Modeling of the Resting Potential

The net flow of K^+ out of a neuron proceeds until the chemical and electrical forces are in balance. How well do just these two forces account for the resting potential in a mammalian neuron? To answer this question, let's consider a simple model consisting of two chambers separated by an artificial membrane (Figure 48.7a). To begin, imagine that the membrane contains many open ion channels, all of which allow only K^+ to diffuse across. To produce a concentration gradient for K^+ like that of a mammalian neuron, we place a solution of 140 mM potassium chloride (KCl) in the inner chamber and 5 mM KCl in the outer chamber. The potassium ions (K^+) will diffuse down their concentration gradient into the outer chamber. But because the chloride ions (Cl^-) lack a means of crossing

the membrane, there will be an excess of negative charge in the inner chamber.

When our model neuron reaches equilibrium, the electrical gradient will exactly balance the chemical gradient, such that no further net diffusion of K^+ occurs across the membrane. The magnitude of the membrane voltage at equilibrium for a particular ion is called that ion's **equilibrium potential** (E_{ion}). For a membrane permeable to a single type of ion, E_{ion} can be calculated using a formula called the Nernst equation. At human body temperature (37°C) and for an ion with a net charge of 1+, such as K^+ or Na^+, the Nernst equation is

$$E_{ion} = 62 \text{ mV} \left(\log \frac{[\text{ion}]_{\text{outside}}}{[\text{ion}]_{\text{inside}}} \right)$$

Plugging the K^+ concentrations into the Nernst equation reveals that the equilibrium potential for K^+ (E_K) is −90 mV (see Figure 48.7a). The minus sign indicates that K^+ is at equilibrium when the inside of the membrane is 90 mV more negative than the outside.

Although the equilibrium potential for K^+ is −90 mV, the resting potential of a mammalian neuron is somewhat less negative. This difference reflects the small but steady movement of Na^+ across the few open sodium channels in a resting neuron. Because the concentration gradient of Na^+ has a direction opposite to that of K^+, Na^+ diffuses into the cell and thus makes the inside of the cell less negative. If we model a membrane in which the only open channels are selectively permeable to Na^+, we find that a tenfold higher concentration of Na^+ in the outer chamber results in an equilibrium potential (E_{Na}) of +62 mV (Figure 48.7b). The resting potential of an actual neuron is −60 to −80 mV. The resting potential is much closer to E_K than to E_{Na} in a neuron because there are many open potassium channels but only a small number of open sodium channels.

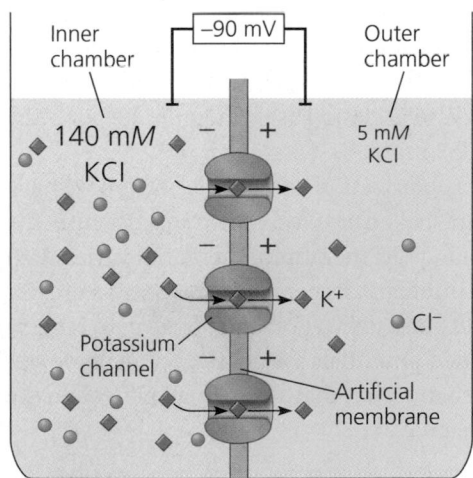

(a) **Membrane selectively permeable to K+**

Nernst equation for K+ equilibrium potential at 37°C:

$$E_K = 62 \text{ mV} \left(\log \frac{5 \text{ m}M}{140 \text{ m}M} \right) = -90 \text{ mV}$$

(b) **Membrane selectively permeable to Na+**

Nernst equation for Na+ equilibrium potential at 37°C:

$$E_{Na} = 62 \text{ mV} \left(\log \frac{150 \text{ m}M}{15 \text{ m}M} \right) = +62 \text{ mV}$$

◀ **Figure 48.7 Modeling a mammalian neuron.** Each container is divided into two chambers by an artificial membrane. Ion channels allow free diffusion for particular ions, resulting in the net ion flow represented by arrows. **(a)** The presence of open potassium channels makes the membrane selectively permeable to K^+, and the inner chamber contains a 28-fold higher concentration of K^+ than the outer chamber; at equilibrium, the inside of the membrane is −90 mV relative to the outside. **(b)** The membrane is selectively permeable to Na^+, and the inner chamber contains a tenfold lower concentration of Na^+ than the outer chamber; at equilibrium, the inside of the membrane is +62 mV relative to the outside.

WHAT IF? *Adding channels specific for one type of ion to the membrane in (b) would alter the membrane potential. Which ion passes through these channels, and in what direction would the membrane potential change?*

Because neither K^+ nor Na^+ is at equilibrium in a resting neuron, each ion has a net flow (a current) across the membrane. The resting potential remains steady, which means that the K^+ and Na^+ currents are equal and opposite. Ion concentrations on either side of the membrane also remain steady because the charge separation needed to generate the resting potential is extremely small (about 10^{-12} mole/cm^2 of membrane). This represents the movement of far fewer ions than would be required to alter the chemical concentration gradient.

Under conditions that allow Na^+ to cross the membrane more readily, the membrane potential will move toward E_{Na} and away from E_K. As we will see in the next section, this is precisely what happens during the transmission of a nerve impulse along an axon.

Action potentials are the signals conducted by axons

We saw in the previous section that the resting potential results from the fact that the plasma membrane of a resting neuron contains many open potassium channels but only a few open sodium channels. However, when neurons are active, membrane permeability and membrane potential change. The changes occur because neurons contain **gated ion channels**, ion channels that open or close in response to stimuli. This gating of ion channels forms the basis of nearly all electrical signaling in the nervous system. The opening or closing of ion channels alters the membrane's permeability to particular ions, which in turn alters the membrane potential. How have scientists studied these changes? The technique of intracellular recording provides a readout of the state of a single neuron in real time **(Figure 48.8)**.

To begin exploring gated channels, let's consider what happens when gated potassium channels that are closed in a resting neuron open. Opening more potassium channels increases the

▼ Figure 48.8 Research Method

Intracellular Recording

APPLICATION Electrophysiologists use intracellular recording to measure the membrane potential of neurons and other cells.

TECHNIQUE A microelectrode is made from a glass capillary tube filled with an electrically conductive salt solution. One end of the tube tapers to an extremely fine tip (diameter <1 μm). While looking through a microscope, the experimenter uses a micropositioner to insert the tip of the microelectrode into a cell. A voltage recorder (usually an oscilloscope or a computer-based system) measures the voltage between the microelectrode tip inside the cell and a reference electrode placed in the solution outside the cell.

Microelectrode

Voltage recorder

Reference electrode

membrane's permeability to K^+, increasing the net diffusion of K^+ out of the neuron. In other words, the inside of the membrane becomes more negative **(Figure 48.9a)**. As the membrane potential approaches E_K (−90 mV at 37°C), the separation of charge, or polarity, increases. Thus, the increase in the magnitude of the membrane potential is called a **hyperpolarization**. In general, hyperpolarization results from any stimulus that increases either the outflow of positive ions or the inflow of negative ions.

Although opening potassium channels causes hyperpolarization, opening some other types of ion channels has an opposite effect, making the inside of the membrane less negative **(Figure 48.9b)**. This reduction in the magnitude of the membrane potential is called a **depolarization**. Depolarization in neurons often involves gated sodium channels. If the gated sodium channels open, the membrane's permeability to Na^+ increases, causing a depolarization as the membrane potential shifts toward E_{Na} (+62 mV at 37°C).

The types of hyperpolarization and depolarization we have considered so far are called *graded potentials* because the magnitude of the change in membrane potential varies with the strength of the stimulus. A larger stimulus causes a greater change in permeability and thus a greater change in the membrane potential. Graded potentials are not the actual nerve signals that travel along axons, but they have a major effect on the generation of nerve signals.

Production of Action Potentials

Many of the gated ion channels in neurons are **voltage-gated ion channels**; that is, they open or close in response to a

(a) Graded hyperpolarizations produced by two stimuli that increase membrane permeability to K⁺. The larger stimulus produces a larger hyperpolarization.

(b) Graded depolarizations produced by two stimuli that increase membrane permeability to Na⁺. The larger stimulus produces a larger depolarization.

(c) Action potential triggered by a depolarization that reaches the threshold.

▲ **Figure 48.9 Graded potentials and an action potential in a neuron.**

change in the membrane potential. If a depolarization opens voltage-gated sodium channels, the resulting flow of Na⁺ into the neuron results in further depolarization. Because the sodium channels are voltage gated, an increased depolarization in turn causes more sodium channels to open, leading to an even greater flow of current. The result is a very rapid opening of all the voltage-gated sodium channels. Such a series of events triggers a massive change in membrane voltage called an **action potential (Figure 48.9c)**.

Action potentials are the nerve impulses, or signals, that carry information along an axon. Before we can discuss how these signals move, or propagate, along an axon, we must first understand more about the changes in membrane voltage that accompany an action potential.

Action potentials occur whenever a depolarization increases the membrane voltage to a particular value, called the **threshold**. For mammalian neurons, the threshold is a membrane potential of about −55 mV. Once initiated, the action potential has a magnitude that is independent of the strength of the triggering stimulus. Because action potentials occur fully or not at all, they represent an *all-or-none* response to stimuli. This all-or-none property reflects the fact that depolarization opens voltage-gated sodium channels, and the opening of sodium channels causes further depolarization. This positive-feedback loop of depolarization and channel opening triggers an action potential whenever the membrane potential reaches the threshold.

Generation of Action Potentials: *A Closer Look*

In most neurons, an action potential lasts only 1–2 milliseconds (msec). Because action potentials are so brief, a neuron can produce hundreds of them per second. Furthermore, the frequency with which a neuron generates action potentials can vary in response to input. Such differences in action potential frequency convey information about signal strength. In hearing, for example, louder sounds are reflected by more frequent action potentials in neurons connecting the ear to the brain.

The characteristic shape of the graph of an action potential (see Figure 48.9c) reflects the large change in membrane potential resulting from ion movement through voltage-gated sodium and potassium channels. Membrane depolarization opens both types of channels, but they respond independently and sequentially. Sodium channels open first, initiating the action potential. As the action potential proceeds, the sodium channels become inactivated: A loop of the channel protein moves, blocking ion flow through the opening. Sodium channels remain inactivated until after the membrane returns to the resting potential and the channels close. Potassium channels open more slowly than sodium channels, but remain open and functional throughout the action potential.

To understand further how voltage-gated channels shape the action potential, we'll consider the process as a series of stages (Figure 48.10). ❶ At the resting potential, most voltage-gated sodium channels are closed. Some potassium channels are open, but most voltage-gated potassium channels are closed. ❷ When a stimulus depolarizes the membrane, some gated sodium channels open, allowing more Na^+ to diffuse into the cell. The Na^+ inflow causes further depolarization, which opens still more gated sodium channels, allowing even more Na^+ to diffuse into the cell. ❸ Once the threshold is crossed, this positive-feedback cycle rapidly brings the membrane potential close to E_{Na}. This stage is called the *rising phase*. ❹ However, two events prevent the membrane potential from actually reaching E_{Na}: Voltage-gated sodium chan-

nels inactivate soon after opening, halting Na^+ inflow; and most voltage-gated potassium channels open, causing a rapid outflow of K^+. Both events quickly bring the membrane potential back toward E_K. This stage is called the *falling phase*. ❺ In the final phase of an action potential, called the *undershoot*, the membrane's permeability to K^+ is higher than at rest, so the membrane potential is closer to E_K than it is at the resting potential. The gated potassium channels eventually close, and the membrane potential returns to the resting potential.

The sodium channels remain inactivated during the falling phase and the early part of the undershoot. As a result, if a

Key
○ Na^+
◆ K^+

❸ **Rising phase of the action potential**
Depolarization opens most sodium channels, while the potassium channels remain closed. Na^+ influx makes the inside of the membrane positive with respect to the outside.

❷ **Depolarization** A stimulus opens some sodium channels. Na^+ inflow through those channels depolarizes the membrane. If the depolarization reaches the threshold, it triggers an action potential.

❹ **Falling phase of the action potential**
Most sodium channels become inactivated, blocking Na^+ inflow. Most potassium channels open, permitting K^+ outflow, which makes the inside of the cell negative again.

❺ **Undershoot** The sodium channels close, but some potassium channels are still open. As these potassium channels close and the sodium channels become unblocked, the membrane returns to its resting state.

❶ **Resting state** The gated Na^+ and K^+ channels are closed. Ungated channels (not shown) maintain the resting potential.

▲ **Figure 48.10 The role of voltage-gated ion channels in the generation of an action potential.** The circled numbers on the graph in the center and the colors of the action potential phases correspond to the five diagrams showing voltage-gated sodium and potassium channels in a neuron's plasma membrane. (Ungated ion channels are not illustrated.)

MEDIA **BioFlix** Visit www.campbellbiology.com for the BioFlix 3-D Animation on How Neurons Work.

second depolarizing stimulus occurs during this period, it will be unable to trigger an action potential. The "downtime" following an action potential when a second action potential cannot be initiated is called the **refractory period**. This interval sets a limit on the maximum frequency at which action potentials can be generated. As we will discuss shortly, the refractory period also ensures that all signals in an axon travel in one direction, from the cell body to the axon terminals.

Note that the refractory period is due to the inactivation of sodium channels, not to a change in the ion gradients across the plasma membrane. The flow of charged particles during an action potential involves far too few ions to change the concentration on either side of the plasma membrane.

Conduction of Action Potentials

An action potential functions as a long-distance signal by regenerating itself as it travels from the cell body to the synaptic terminals, much like a flame traveling along a lit fuse. At the site where an action potential is initiated (usually the axon hillock), Na$^+$ inflow during the rising phase creates an electrical current that depolarizes the neighboring region of the axon membrane **(Figure 48.11)**. The depolarization in the neighboring region is large enough to reach the threshold, causing the action potential to be reinitiated there. This process is repeated over and over again as the action potential travels the length of the axon. At each position along the axon, the process is identical, such that the shape and magnitude of the action potential remain constant.

Immediately behind the traveling zone of depolarization due to Na$^+$ inflow is a zone of repolarization due to K$^+$ outflow. In the repolarized zone, the sodium channels remain inactivated. Consequently, the inward current that depolarizes the axon membrane *ahead* of the action potential cannot produce another action potential *behind* it. This prevents action potentials from traveling back toward the cell body. Thus, an action potential that starts at the axon hillock moves in only one direction—toward the synaptic terminals.

Conduction Speed

Several factors affect the speed at which action potentials are conducted. One is axon diameter: Wider axons conduct action potentials more rapidly than narrow ones because resistance to electrical current flow is inversely proportional to the cross-sectional area of a conductor (such as a wire or an axon). Just as a wide hose offers less resistance to the flow of water than a narrow hose does, a wide axon provides less resistance to the current associated with an action potential than a narrow axon does. Therefore, the resulting depolarization can spread farther along the interior of a wide axon, bringing more distant regions of the membrane to the threshold sooner. In invertebrates, conduction speed varies from several centimeters per second in very narrow axons to about 30 m/sec in the giant axons of some

1 An action potential is generated as Na$^+$ flows inward across the membrane at one location.

2 The depolarization of the action potential spreads to the neighboring region of the membrane, reinitiating the action potential there. To the left of this region, the membrane is repolarizing as K$^+$ flows outward.

3 The depolarization-repolarization process is repeated in the next region of the membrane. In this way, local currents of ions *across* the plasma membrane cause the action potential to be propagated *along* the length of the axon.

▲ **Figure 48.11 Conduction of an action potential.** The three parts of this figure show events that occur in an axon at three successive times as an action potential passes from left to right. At each point along the axon, voltage-gated ion channels go through the sequence of changes described in Figure 48.10. The colors of membrane regions shown here correspond to the action potential phases in Figure 48.10.

arthropods and molluscs (see Figure 48.2). These giant axons (up to 1 mm wide) function in rapid behavioral responses, such as the muscle contraction that propels a squid toward its prey.

Vertebrate axons have narrow diameters but can still conduct action potentials at high speed. How is this possible? The adaptation that enables fast conduction in narrow axons is a **myelin sheath**, a layer of electrical insulation that surrounds

▲ **Figure 48.12 Schwann cells and the myelin sheath.** In the PNS, glia called Schwann cells wrap themselves around axons, forming layers of myelin. Gaps between adjacent Schwann cells are called nodes of Ranvier. The TEM shows a cross section through a myelinated axon.

0.1 μm

▶ **Figure 48.13 Saltatory conduction.** In a myelinated axon, the depolarizing current during an action potential at one node of Ranvier spreads along the interior of the axon to the next node (blue arrows), where it will reinitiate itself. Thus, the action potential jumps from node to node as it travels along the axon (red arrows).

vertebrate axons **(Figure 48.12)**. Myelin sheaths are produced by two types of glia—**oligodendrocytes** in the CNS and **Schwann cells** in the PNS. During development, these specialized glia wrap axons in many layers of membrane. The membranes forming these layers are mostly lipid, which is a poor conductor of electrical current. Thus, the myelin sheath provides electrical insulation for the axon, analogous to the plastic insulation that covers many electrical wires.

The insulation provided by the myelin sheath has the same effect as increasing the axon's diameter: It causes the depolarizing current associated with an action potential to spread farther along the interior of the axon, bringing more distant regions of the membrane to the threshold sooner. The great advantage of myelination is its space efficiency. A myelinated axon 20 μm in diameter has a conduction speed faster than that of a squid giant axon that has a diameter 40 times greater. Furthermore, more than 2,000 of those myelinated axons can be packed into the space occupied by just one giant axon.

In a myelinated axon, voltage-gated sodium channels are restricted to gaps in the myelin sheath called **nodes of Ranvier** (see Figure 48.12). The extracellular fluid is in contact with the axon membrane only at the nodes. As a result, action potentials are not generated in the regions between the nodes. Rather, the inward current produced during the rising phase of the action potential at a node travels all the way to the next node, where it depolarizes the membrane and regenerates the action potential **(Figure 48.13)**. This mechanism is called **saltatory conduction**

(from the Latin *saltare*, to leap) because the action potential appears to jump along the axon from node to node.

CONCEPT CHECK 48.3

1. How does an action potential differ from a graded potential?

2. In the disease multiple sclerosis (from the Greek *skleros*, hard), myelin sheaths gradually harden and deteriorate. How would this affect nervous system function?

3. **WHAT IF?** Suppose that a mutation caused gated sodium channels to remain inactivated for a longer time following an action potential. How would such a mutation affect the maximum frequency at which action potentials could be generated? Explain.

For suggested answers, see Appendix A.

CONCEPT **48.4**

Neurons communicate with other cells at synapses

In most cases, action potentials are not transmitted from neurons to other cells. However, information is transmitted, and this transmission occurs at the synapses. Some synapses, called *electrical synapses*, contain gap junctions (see Figure 6.32), which *do* allow electrical current to flow directly from one neuron to another. In both vertebrates and invertebrates, electrical synapses synchronize the activity of neurons responsible for certain rapid, unvarying behaviors. For example, electrical synapses associated with the giant axons of squids and lobsters facilitate the swift execution of escape responses. There are also many electrical synapses in the vertebrate brain.

The majority of synapses are *chemical synapses*, which involve the release of a chemical neurotransmitter by the presynaptic neuron. The cell body and dendrites of one postsynaptic neuron may receive inputs from chemical synapses with hundreds or even thousands of synaptic terminals **(Figure 48.14)**. At each terminal, the presynaptic neuron synthesizes the neurotransmitter and packages it in multiple membrane-bounded compartments called **synaptic vesicles**. The arrival of an action potential at a synaptic terminal depolarizes the plasma membrane, opening voltage-gated channels that allow Ca^{2+} to diffuse into the terminal **(Figure 48.15)**. The resulting rise in Ca^{2+} concentration in the terminal causes some of the synaptic vesicles to fuse with the terminal membrane, releasing the neurotransmitter. The neuro-

transmitter then diffuses across the **synaptic cleft**, the narrow gap that separates the presynaptic neuron from the postsynaptic cell.

Information transfer is much more readily modified at chemical synapses than at electrical synapses. A variety of factors can affect the amount of neurotransmitter that is released or the responsiveness of the postsynaptic cell. Such modifications underlie an animal's ability to alter its behavior in response to change and form the basis for learning and memory, as you will learn in Chapter 49.

Postsynaptic neuron

Synaptic terminals of pre-synaptic neurons

5 µm

▲ **Figure 48.14 Synaptic terminals on the cell body of a postsynaptic neuron** (colorized SEM).

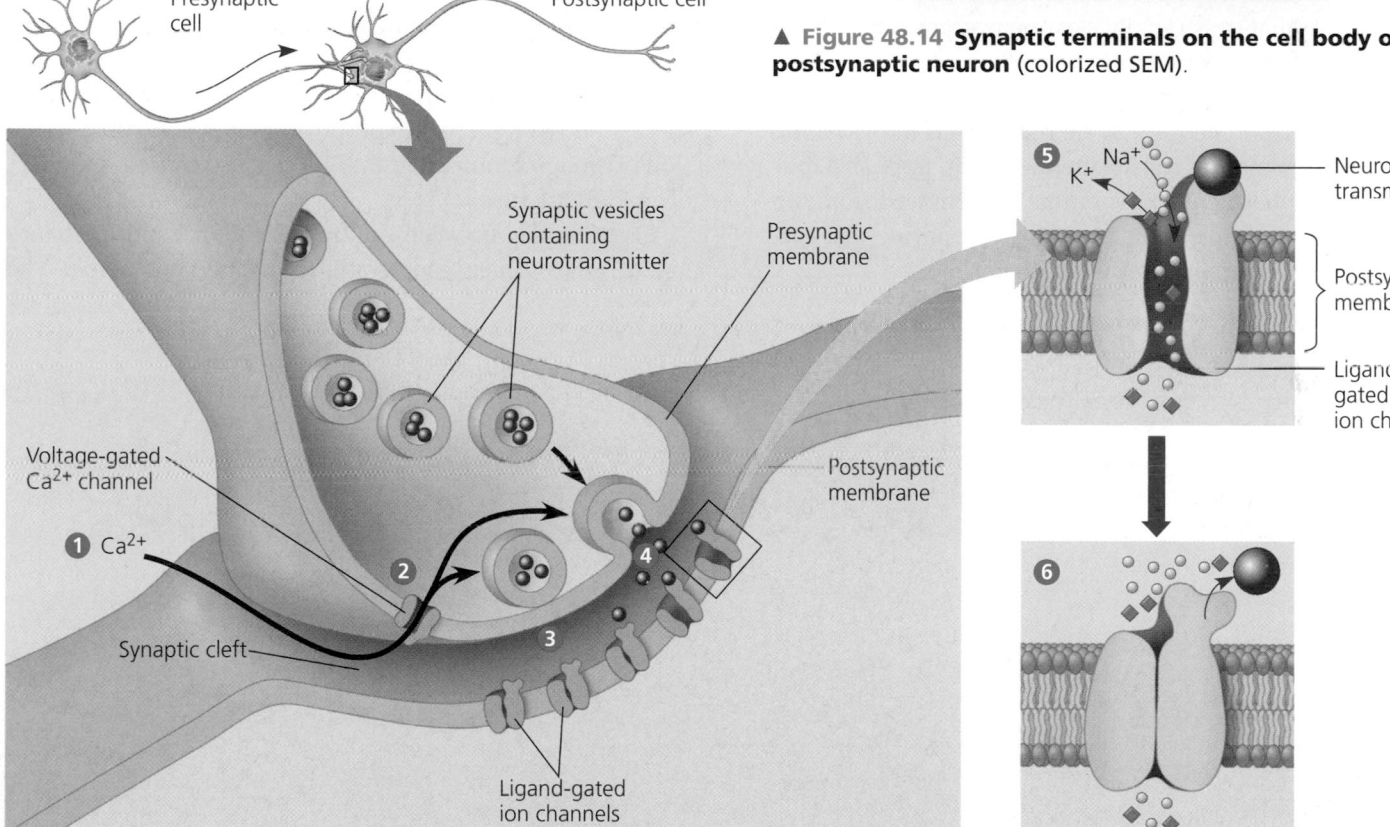

Presynaptic cell

Postsynaptic cell

Synaptic vesicles containing neurotransmitter

Presynaptic membrane

Voltage-gated Ca^{2+} channel

1 Ca^{2+}

2

3

4

Synaptic cleft

Postsynaptic membrane

Ligand-gated ion channels

5 Na^+ K^+

Neuro-transmitter

Postsynaptic membrane

Ligand-gated ion channel

6

▲ **Figure 48.15 A chemical synapse.**
1 When an action potential depolarizes the plasma membrane of the synaptic terminal, it **2** opens voltage-gated calcium channels in the membrane, triggering an influx of Ca^{2+}. **3** The elevated Ca^{2+} concentration in the terminal causes synaptic vesicles to fuse with the presynaptic membrane. **4** The vesicles release neurotransmitter into the synaptic cleft. **5** The neurotransmitter binds to the receptor portion of ligand-gated ion channels in the postsynaptic membrane, opening the channels. In the synapse illustrated here, both Na^+ and K^+ can diffuse through the channels. **6** The neurotransmitter is released from the receptors, and the channels close. Synaptic transmission ends when the neurotransmitter diffuses out of the synaptic cleft, is taken up by the synaptic terminal or by another cell, or is degraded by an enzyme.

WHAT IF? *If all the Ca^{2+} in the fluid surrounding a neuron were removed, how would this affect the transmission of information within and between neurons?*

Generation of Postsynaptic Potentials

At many chemical synapses, as in Figure 48.15, *ligand-gated* ion channels capable of binding to the neurotransmitter are clustered in the membrane of the postsynaptic cell, directly opposite the synaptic terminal. Binding of the neurotransmitter to a particular part of the channel opens the channel and allows specific ions to diffuse across the postsynaptic membrane. The result is generally a *postsynaptic potential*, a change in the membrane potential of the postsynaptic cell. At synapses like the one in the figure, the neurotransmitter binds to a type of channel through which both K^+ and Na^+ can diffuse. When those channels open, the postsynaptic membrane depolarizes as the membrane potential approaches a value roughly midway between E_K and E_{Na}. Because these depolarizations bring the membrane potential toward threshold, they are called **excitatory postsynaptic potentials (EPSPs)**. At other synapses, a different neurotransmitter binds to channels that are selectively permeable for only K^+ or Cl^-. When those channels open, the postsynaptic membrane hyperpolarizes. Hyperpolarizations produced in this manner are called **inhibitory postsynaptic potentials (IPSPs)** because they move the membrane potential farther from threshold.

Various mechanisms rapidly clear neurotransmitters from the synaptic cleft, terminating their effect on postsynaptic cells. Certain neurotransmitters may be actively transported into the presynaptic neuron, to be repackaged into synaptic vesicles, or they may be transported into glia, to be metabolized as fuel. Other neurotransmitters are removed from the synaptic cleft by simple diffusion or by an enzyme that catalyzes hydrolysis of the neurotransmitter.

Summation of Postsynaptic Potentials

Unlike action potentials, which are all-or-none events, postsynaptic potentials are graded; their magnitude varies with a number of factors, including the amount of neurotransmitter released by the presynaptic neuron. Furthermore, postsynaptic potentials usually do *not* regenerate as they spread along the membrane of a cell; they become smaller with distance from the synapse. Recall that most synapses on a neuron are located on its dendrites or cell body, whereas action potentials are generally initiated at the axon hillock. Therefore, a single EPSP is usually too small to trigger an action potential in a postsynaptic neuron **(Figure 48.16a)**.

On some occasions, two EPSPs occur at a single synapse in such rapid succession that the postsynaptic neuron's membrane potential has not returned to the resting potential before the arrival of the second EPSP. When that happens, the EPSPs add together, an effect called **temporal summation (Figure 48.16b)**. Moreover, EPSPs produced nearly simultaneously by *different* synapses on the same postsynaptic neuron can also add together, an effect called **spatial summation (Figure 48.16c)**. Through spatial and temporal summation, several EPSPs can depolarize the membrane at the axon hillock to the threshold, causing the postsynaptic neuron to produce an action potential. Summation applies as well to IPSPs: Two or more IPSPs occurring nearly simultaneously or in rapid succession have a larger hyperpolarizing effect than a single IPSP. Through summation, an IPSP can also counter the effect of an EPSP **(Figure 48.16d)**.

The interplay between multiple excitatory and inhibitory inputs is the essence of integration in the nervous system. The

▲ **Figure 48.16 Summation of postsynaptic potentials.** These graphs trace changes in the membrane potential at a postsynaptic neuron's axon hillock. The arrows indicate times when postsynaptic potentials occur at two excitatory synapses (E₁ and E₂, green in the diagrams above the graphs) and at one inhibitory synapse (I, red). Like most EPSPs, those produced at E₁ or E₂ do not reach the threshold at the axon hillock without summation.

axon hillock is the neuron's integrating center, the region where the membrane potential at any instant represents the summed effect of all EPSPs and IPSPs. Whenever the membrane potential at the axon hillock reaches the threshold, an action potential is generated and travels along the axon to its synaptic terminals. After the refractory period, the neuron may produce another action potential, provided the membrane potential at the axon hillock once again reaches the threshold.

Modulated Synaptic Transmission

So far, we have focused on synapses containing ligand-gated ion channels, in which a neurotransmitter binds directly to an ion channel, causing the channel to open. However, there are also synapses in which the receptor for the neurotransmitter is *not* part of an ion channel. Instead, binding of the neurotransmitter to its receptor in the postsynaptic cell activates a signal transduction pathway involving a second messenger (see Chapter 11). Compared with the postsynaptic potentials produced by ligand-gated channels, the effects of these second-messenger systems have a slower onset but last longer (minutes or even hours). Second messengers modulate the responsiveness of postsynaptic neurons to inputs in diverse ways, such as by altering the number of open potassium channels.

A variety of signal transduction pathways play a role in modulating synaptic transmission. One of the best-studied pathways involves cyclic AMP (cAMP) as a second messenger. For example, when the neurotransmitter norepinephrine binds to its receptor, the neurotransmitter-receptor complex activates a G protein, which in turn activates adenylyl cyclase, the enzyme that converts ATP to cAMP (see Figure 11.11). Cyclic AMP activates protein kinase A, which phosphorylates specific channel proteins in the postsynaptic membrane, causing them to open or close. Because of the amplifying effect of the signal transduction pathway, the binding of a neurotransmitter molecule to a single receptor can open or close many channels.

Neurotransmitters

There are more than 100 known neurotransmitters. However, nearly all of these fall into one of a few groups based on chemical structure. As shown in **Table 48.1**, the major classes of

Table 48.1 Major Neurotransmitters

Neurotransmitter	Structure	Functional Class	Secretion Sites
Acetylcholine		Excitatory to vertebrate skeletal muscles; excitatory or inhibitory at other sites	CNS; PNS; vertebrate neuromuscular junction
Biogenic Amines			
Norepinephrine		Excitatory or inhibitory	CNS; PNS
Dopamine		Generally excitatory; may be inhibitory at some sites	CNS; PNS
Serotonin		Generally inhibitory	CNS
Amino Acids			
GABA (gamma-aminobutyric acid)	$H_2N—CH_2—CH_2—CH_2—COOH$	Inhibitory	CNS; invertebrate neuromuscular junction
Glutamate	$H_2N—CH—CH_2—CH_2—COOH$ with COOH	Excitatory	CNS; invertebrate neuromuscular junction
Glycine	$H_2N—CH_2—COOH$	Inhibitory	CNS
Neuropeptides (a very diverse group, only two of which are shown)			
Substance P	Arg—Pro—Lys—Pro—Gln—Gln—Phe—Phe—Gly—Leu—Met	Excitatory	CNS; PNS
Met-enkephalin (an endorphin)	Tyr—Gly—Gly—Phe—Met	Generally inhibitory	CNS
Gases			
Nitric oxide	N≡O	Excitatory or inhibitory	PNS

neurotransmitters are acetylcholine, biogenic amines, amino acids, neuropeptides, and gases.

A single neurotransmitter may have more than a dozen different receptors. Furthermore, the receptors for a specific neurotransmitter can vary significantly in their effects on postsynaptic cells. For this reason, many drugs used to treat nervous system diseases or affect brain function are targeted to specific receptors rather than particular neurotransmitters.

Acetylcholine

One of the most common neurotransmitters in both invertebrates and vertebrates is **acetylcholine**. Except in the heart, vertebrate neurons that form a synapse with muscle cells release acetylcholine as an excitatory transmitter. Acetylcholine binds to receptors on ligand-gated channels in the muscle cell, producing an EPSP. Nicotine, a chemical found in tobacco and tobacco smoke, binds to the same receptors, which are also found elsewhere in the PNS and in the CNS. Nicotine's effects as a physiological and psychological stimulant result from its affinity for this type of acetylcholine receptor. Acetylcholine activity is terminated by *acetylcholinesterase*, an enzyme in the synaptic cleft that hydrolyzes the neurotransmitter.

Certain bacteria produce a toxin that specifically inhibits presynaptic release of acetylcholine. This toxin is the cause of a rare but severe form of food poisoning called botulism. Untreated botulism is typically fatal because muscles required for breathing fail to contract when acetylcholine release is blocked. Recently, the same botulinum toxin has become a controversial tool in a cosmetic procedure. Injections of the toxin, known by the trade name Botox, minimize wrinkles around the eyes or mouth by blocking transmission at synapses that control particular facial muscles.

In regulating vertebrate cardiac (heart) muscle, acetylcholine has inhibitory rather than excitatory effects. In the heart, acetylcholine released by neurons activates a signal transduction pathway. The G proteins in the pathway inhibit adenylyl cyclase and open potassium channels in the muscle cell membrane. Both effects reduce the rate at which cardiac muscle cells contract.

Biogenic Amines

Biogenic amines are neurotransmitters derived from amino acids. The biogenic amine **serotonin** is synthesized from tryptophan. Several other biogenic amines, the catecholamines, are derived from tyrosine. One catecholamine, **dopamine**, acts only as a neurotransmitter. Two others—**epinephrine** and **norepinephrine**—act both as neurotransmitters and as hormones (see Chapter 45).

In the PNS of vertebrates, norepinephrine is one of two major neurotransmitters, the other being acetylcholine. Acting through a G protein-coupled receptor (see Chapter 11), nor-

epinephrine generates EPSPs in the autonomic nervous system, a branch of the PNS discussed in Chapter 49.

In the CNS, the biogenic amines are often involved in modulating synaptic transmission. Dopamine and serotonin are released at many sites in the brain and affect sleep, mood, attention, and learning. Some psychoactive drugs, including LSD and mescaline, apparently produce their hallucinatory effects by binding to brain receptors for serotonin and dopamine.

Biogenic amines have a central role in a number of nervous system disorders and treatments (see Chapter 49). The degenerative illness Parkinson's disease is associated with a lack of dopamine in the brain. In addition, depression is often treated with drugs that increase the brain concentrations of biogenic amines. Prozac, for instance, enhances the effect of serotonin by inhibiting its reuptake after release.

Amino Acids

Two amino acids serve as the major neurotransmitters in the vertebrate CNS: **gamma-aminobutyric acid (GABA)** and **glutamate**. GABA, which appears to be the neurotransmitter at most inhibitory synapses in the brain, produces IPSPs by increasing the permeability of the postsynaptic membrane to Cl^-. In contrast, glutamate, the most common neurotransmitter in the brain, is always excitatory. A third amino acid, glycine, acts at inhibitory synapses in parts of the CNS that lie outside of the brain.

Neuropeptides

Several **neuropeptides**, relatively short chains of amino acids, serve as neurotransmitters that operate via signal transduction pathways. Such peptides are typically produced by cleavage of much larger protein precursors. The neuropeptide **substance P** is a key excitatory neurotransmitter that mediates our perception of pain, while other neuropeptides, called **endorphins**, function as natural analgesics, decreasing pain perception.

In the 1970s, Candace Pert, then a graduate student at Johns Hopkins University, and her research supervisor, Solomon Snyder, discovered endorphins as an outcome of their research on the biochemistry of behavior. Previous studies had indicated that the brain contains specific receptors for opiates, painkilling drugs such as morphine and heroin. To find these receptors, Pert and Snyder had the insight to apply existing knowledge about the activity of different drugs in the brain **(Figure 48.17)**. In a single, straightforward experiment, they provided the first demonstration that opiate receptors exist. Setting out to identify molecules normally present in the brain that could also activate these receptors, they discovered endorphins.

Endorphins are produced in the brain during times of physical or emotional stress, such as childbirth. In addition to relieving

Does the brain have a specific protein receptor for opiates?

EXPERIMENT In 1973, Candace Pert and Solomon Snyder, of Johns Hopkins University, were searching for an opiate receptor in the mammalian brain. It was known that the drug naloxone antagonizes (opposes) the narcotic effect of opiates. Pert and Snyder reasoned that naloxone acts as an opiate antagonist by binding tightly to the opiate receptor without activating the receptor. They first prepared radioactive naloxone and then incubated it with a protein mixture prepared from rodent brains. If proteins that could bind naloxone were present, the radioactivity would become stably associated with the protein mixture. Furthermore, the researchers could determine whether a specific receptor was present by examining the ability of different drug molecules to interfere with the binding activity.

RESULTS

Drug	Opiate	Concentration That Blocked Naloxone Binding
Morphine	Yes	$6 \times 10^{-9}\ M$
Methadone	Yes	$2 \times 10^{-8}\ M$
Levorphanol	Yes	$2 \times 10^{-9}\ M$
Phenobarbital	No	No effect at $10^{-4}\ M$
Atropine	No	No effect at $10^{-4}\ M$
Serotonin	No	No effect at $10^{-4}\ M$

CONCLUSION Because opiates interfere with naloxone binding, but unrelated drugs do not, the binding activity had the specificity expected of the opiate receptor. Pert and Snyder also found that the binding activity was present in tissue from regions of the brain involved in the sensation of pain, but not in tissue from the cerebellum, a brain region that coordinates motor activity.

SOURCE C. B. Pert and S. H. Snyder, Opiate receptor: demonstration in nervous tissue, *Science* 179:1011–1014 (1973).

WHAT IF? How would the results have been affected if the researchers had used a radioactive opiate rather than a radioactive opiate antagonist?

pain, they decrease urine output, depress respiration, and produce euphoria, as well as other emotional effects. Because opiates bind to the same receptor proteins as endorphins, opiates mimic endorphins and produce many of the same physiological effects (see Figure 2.18).

Gases

In common with many other types of cells, some neurons in vertebrates release dissolved gases, notably nitric oxide (NO; see Chapter 45), that act as local regulators. For example, during sexual arousal, certain neurons in human males release NO into the erectile tissue of the penis. In response, smooth muscle cells in the blood vessel walls of the erectile tissue relax, which causes the blood vessels to dilate and fill the spongy erectile tissue with blood, producing an erection. As you read in Chapter 45, the erectile dysfunction drug Viagra increases the ability to achieve and maintain an erection by inhibiting an enzyme that terminates the action of NO.

Unlike most neurotransmitters, NO is not stored in cytoplasmic vesicles but is instead synthesized on demand. NO diffuses into neighboring target cells, produces a change, and is broken down—all within a few seconds. In many of its targets, including smooth muscle cells, NO works like many hormones, stimulating an enzyme to synthesize a second messenger that directly affects cellular metabolism.

Although inhaling air containing the gas carbon monoxide (CO) can be deadly, the vertebrate body produces small amounts of CO, some of which acts as a neurotransmitter. Carbon monoxide is generated by the enzyme heme oxygenase, one form of which is found in certain populations of neurons in the brain and PNS. In the brain, CO regulates the release of hypothalamic hormones. In the PNS, it acts as an inhibitory neurotransmitter that hyperpolarizes intestinal smooth muscle cells.

In the next chapter, we will consider how the cellular and biochemical mechanisms we have discussed contribute to nervous system function on the system level.

CONCEPT CHECK 48.4

1. How is it possible for a particular neurotransmitter to produce opposite effects in different tissues?
2. Organophosphate pesticides work by inhibiting acetylcholinesterase, the enzyme that breaks down the neurotransmitter acetylcholine. Explain how these toxins would affect EPSPs produced by acetylcholine.
3. **WHAT IF?** If a drug mimicked the activity of GABA in the CNS, what general effect on behavior might you expect? Explain.

For suggested answers, see Appendix A.

Chapter 48 Review

MEDIA   Go to **www.campbellbiology.com** for BioFlix 3-D Animations, MP3 Tutors, Videos, Practice Tests, an eBook, and more.

SUMMARY OF KEY CONCEPTS

CONCEPT 48.1

Neuron organization and structure reflect function in information transfer (pp. 1047–1049)

▶ **Introduction to Information Processing** Nervous systems process information in three stages: sensory input, integration, and motor output to effector cells. Nervous systems are often divided into a central nervous system (CNS) that includes the brain and nerve cord and a peripheral nervous system (PNS).

▶ **Neuron Structure and Function** Most neurons have highly branched dendrites that receive signals from other neurons. They also typically have a single axon that transmits signals to other cells at synapses. Neurons have a wide variety of shapes that reflect their input and output interactions and depend on glia for supporting functions.

MEDIA
Activity Neuron Structure

CONCEPT 48.2

Ion pumps and ion channels maintain the resting potential of a neuron (pp. 1050–1052)

▶ **Formation of the Resting Potential** Every living cell has a voltage across its plasma membrane called a membrane potential. The inside of the cell is negative relative to the outside.

▶ **Modeling of the Resting Potential** The membrane potential depends on ionic gradients across the plasma membrane: The concentration of Na^+ is higher in the extracellular fluid than in the cytosol, while the reverse is true for K^+. A neuron that is not transmitting signals contains many open potassium channels and few open sodium channels in its plasma membrane. The diffusion of K^+ and Na^+ through these channels leads to the separation of charges across the membrane, producing the resting potential.

CONCEPT 48.3

Action potentials are the signals conducted by axons (pp. 1052–1056)

▶ Neurons have gated ion channels that open or close in response to stimuli, leading to changes in membrane potential. A change in the membrane potential toward a more negative value is a hyperpolarization; a change toward a more positive value is a depolarization. Changes in membrane potential that vary with the strength of a stimulus are known as graded potentials.

▶ **Production of Action Potentials** An action potential is a brief, all-or-none depolarization of a neuron's plasma membrane. When a graded depolarization brings the membrane potential to the threshold, many voltage-gated Na^+ channels open, triggering an inflow of Na^+ that rapidly brings the membrane potential to a positive value. The membrane potential is restored to its normal resting value by the inactivation of sodium channels and by the opening of many voltage-gated potassium channels, which increases K^+ outflow.

MEDIA
BioFlix 3-D Animation How Neurons Work
Activity Nerve Signals: Action Potentials
Investigation What Triggers Nerve Impulses?

▶ **Generation of Action Potentials: *A Closer Look*** A refractory period follows the action potential, corresponding to the interval when the sodium channels are inactivated.

▶ **Conduction of Action Potentials** An action potential travels from the axon hillock to the synaptic terminals by regenerating itself along the axon. The speed of conduction of an action potential increases with the diameter of the axon and, in many vertebrate axons, with myelination. Action potentials in myelinated axons jump between the nodes of Ranvier, a process called saltatory conduction.

CONCEPT 48.4

Neurons communicate with other cells at synapses (pp. 1056–1061)

▶ In an electrical synapse, electrical current flows directly from one cell to another via gap junctions. In a chemical synapse, depolarization of the synaptic terminal causes synaptic vesicles to fuse with the terminal membrane and release neurotransmitter into the synaptic cleft.

▶ **Generation of Postsynaptic Potentials** At many synapses, the neurotransmitter binds to ligand-gated ion channels in the postsynaptic membrane, producing an excitatory or inhibitory postsynaptic potential (EPSP or IPSP). After release, the neurotransmitter diffuses out of the synaptic cleft, is taken up by surrounding cells, or is degraded by enzymes.

▶ **Summation of Postsynaptic Potentials** A single neuron has many synapses on its dendrites and cell body. Whether it generates an action potential depends on the temporal and spatial summation of EPSPs and IPSPs at the axon hillock.

► **Modulated Synaptic Transmission** The binding of neurotransmitter to some receptors activates signal transduction pathways, which produce slowly developing but long-lasting effects in the postsynaptic cell.

► **Neurotransmitters** The same neurotransmitter can produce different effects on different types of cells, depending on the receptor type. Major known neurotransmitters include acetylcholine, biogenic amines (serotonin, dopamine, epinephrine, and norepinephrine); the amino acids GABA, glutamate, and glycine; neuropeptides; and gases such as nitric oxide.

MEDIA

Activity Signal Transmission at a Chemical Synapse

TESTING YOUR KNOWLEDGE

SELF-QUIZ

1. What happens when a neuron's membrane depolarizes?
   a. There is a net diffusion of Na^+ out of the cell.
   b. The equilibrium potential for K^+ (E_K) becomes more positive.
   c. The neuron's membrane voltage becomes more positive.
   d. The neuron becomes less likely to generate an action potential.
   e. The inside of the cell becomes more negative relative to the outside.

2. Why are action potentials usually conducted in only one direction along an axon?
   a. The nodes of Ranvier can conduct potentials in only one direction.
   b. The brief refractory period prevents reopening of voltage-gated Na^+ channels.
   c. The axon hillock has a higher membrane potential than the terminals of the axon.
   d. Ions can flow along the axon in only one direction.
   e. Voltage-gated channels for both Na^+ and K^+ open in only one direction.

3. A common feature of action potentials is that they
   a. cause the membrane to hyperpolarize and then depolarize.
   b. can undergo temporal and spatial summation.
   c. are triggered by a depolarization that reaches the threshold.
   d. move at the same speed along all axons.
   e. result from the diffusion of Na^+ and K^+ through ligand-gated channels.

4. Which of the following is a *direct* result of depolarizing the presynaptic membrane of an axon terminal?
   a. Voltage-gated calcium channels in the membrane open.
   b. Synaptic vesicles fuse with the membrane.
   c. The postsynaptic cell produces an action potential.
   d. Ligand-gated channels open, allowing neurotransmitters to enter the synaptic cleft.
   e. An EPSP or IPSP is generated in the postsynaptic cell.

5. Where are neurotransmitter receptors located?
   a. on the nuclear membrane
   b. at nodes of Ranvier
   c. on the postsynaptic membrane
   d. on the membranes of synaptic vesicles
   e. in the myelin sheath

6. Temporal summation always involves
   a. both inhibitory and excitatory inputs.
   b. synapses at more than one site.
   c. myelinated axons.
   d. electrical synapses.
   e. inputs that are not simultaneous.

For Self-Quiz answers, see Appendix A.

MEDIA Visit **www.campbellbiology.com** for a Practice Test.

7. **DRAW IT** Suppose a researcher inserts a pair of electrodes at two different positions along the middle of an axon dissected out of a squid. By applying a depolarizing stimulus, the researcher brings the plasma membrane at both positions to threshold. Using the drawing below as a starting point, create one or more drawings that illustrate where each action potential would terminate.

EVOLUTION CONNECTION

8. An action potential is an all-or-none event. This on/off signaling is an evolutionary adaptation of animals that must sense and act in a complex environment. It is possible to imagine a nervous system in which the action potentials are graded, with the amplitude depending on the size of the stimulus. What advantage might on/off signaling have over a graded (continuously variable) kind of signaling?

SCIENTIFIC INQUIRY

9. From what you know about action potentials and synapses, propose two or three hypotheses for how various anesthetics might prevent pain.

SCIENCE, TECHNOLOGY, AND SOCIETY

10. Nervous system damage from accidents or disease can cause pain that is sensed as a constant burning, an electrical shock, or shooting pain. Researchers are conducting studies to determine whether cone snail toxins can be used to treat these types of pain. How would you envision these toxins being used? What risks might there be for the patient? Could such toxins pose a risk for large-scale bioterrorist attacks?

Nervous Systems 49

▲ Figure 49.1 **How do scientists map activity within the human brain?**

KEY CONCEPTS

49.1 Nervous systems consist of circuits of neurons and supporting cells

49.2 The vertebrate brain is regionally specialized

49.3 The cerebral cortex controls voluntary movement and cognitive functions

49.4 Changes in synaptic connections underlie memory and learning

49.5 Nervous system disorders can be explained in molecular terms

OVERVIEW

Command and Control Center

What happens in your brain when you picture something with your "mind's eye"? Until quite recently, scientists had little hope of answering that question. The human brain contains an estimated 10^{11} (100 billion) neurons. The circuits that interconnect these brain cells are more complex than those of even the most powerful supercomputers. Yet except for rare glimpses, such as during brain surgery, even the large-scale circuitry of the living human brain has been hidden from view. That's no longer the case, thanks in part to recent technologies that can record brain activity from outside a person's skull (Figure 49.1).

The image in Figure 49.1 was produced by functional magnetic resonance imaging (fMRI). During an fMRI, the subject lies with his or her head in the center of a large, doughnut-shaped magnet. When the brain is scanned with electromagnetic waves, changes in blood oxygen where the brain is active generate a signal that can be recorded. A computer then uses the data to construct a three-dimensional map of the subject's brain activity, like the one shown in Figure 49.1. These recordings can be made while the subject is doing various tasks, such as speaking, moving a hand, looking at pictures, or forming a mental image of a person's face. Scientists can then look for a correlation between a particular task and activity in specific regions of the brain.

The ability to sense and react originated billions of years ago with prokaryotes that could detect changes in their environment and respond in ways that enhanced their survival and reproductive success. For example, bacteria keep moving in a particular direction as long as they encounter increasing concentrations of a food source. Later, modification of simple recognition and response processes provided multicellular organisms with a mechanism for communication between cells of the body. By the time of the Cambrian explosion more than 500 million years ago (see Chapter 32), systems of neurons allowing animals to sense and move rapidly were present in essentially their current forms.

In this chapter, we will discuss the organization and evolution of animal nervous systems, exploring how groups of neurons function in specialized circuits dedicated to specific tasks. First we'll focus on specialization in regions of the vertebrate brain. We will then turn to the ways in which brain activity makes information storage and organization possible. Finally, we'll consider several disorders of the nervous system that are the subject of intense research today.

CONCEPT 49.1

Nervous systems consist of circuits of neurons and supporting cells

In most animals with nervous systems, clusters of neurons perform specialized functions. However, such clustering is absent in the cnidarians, the simplest animals with nervous systems. Hydras, jellies, and other cnidarians have radially symmetrical bodies organized around a gastrovascular cavity (see Figure 33.5). In most cnidarians, a series of interconnected nerve cells form a diffuse **nerve net** (**Figure 49.2a**), which controls the contraction and expansion of the gastrovascular cavity.

In more complex animals, the axons of multiple nerve cells are often bundled together, forming **nerves**. These fibrous structures channel and organize information flow along specific routes through the nervous system. For example, sea stars have a set of radial nerves connecting to a central nerve ring (**Figure 49.2b**). Within each arm, the radial nerve is linked to a nerve net from which it receives input and to which it sends signals controlling motor activity. Such an arrangement is better suited to controlling elaborate movements than a single diffuse nerve net.

Animals with elongated, bilaterally symmetrical bodies have even more specialized nervous systems. Such animals exhibit cephalization, an evolutionary trend toward a clustering of sensory neurons and interneurons at the anterior (front) end. One or more nerve cords extending toward the posterior (back) end connect these structures with nerves elsewhere in the body. In nonsegmented worms, such as the planarian shown in **Figure 49.2c**, a small brain and longitudinal nerve cords constitute the simplest clearly defined *central nervous system (CNS)*. In some such animals, the entire nervous system is constructed from only a small number of cells, as shown by studies of another nonsegmented worm, the nematode *C. elegans*. In this species, an adult worm has exactly 302 neu-

rons, no more and no fewer. More complex invertebrates, such as segmented worms (annelids; **Figure 49.2d**) and arthropods (**Figure 49.2e**), have many more neurons. The behavior of such animals is regulated by more complicated brains and by ventral nerve cords containing ganglia, segmentally arranged clusters of neurons.

Within an animal group, nervous system organization often correlates with lifestyle. For example, the sessile and slow-moving molluscs, such as clams and chitons, have relatively simple sense organs and little or no cephalization (**Figure 49.2f**). In contrast, active predatory molluscs, such as octopuses and squids (**Figure 49.2g**), have the most sophisticated nervous systems of any invertebrates, rivaling even those of some vertebrates. With large image-forming eyes and a brain containing millions of neurons, octopuses can learn to discriminate between visual patterns and to perform complex tasks.

In vertebrates (**Figure 49.2h**), the brain and the spinal cord form the CNS; nerves and ganglia comprise the *peripheral nervous system (PNS)*. Regional specialization is a hallmark of both systems, as we will examine further in the remainder of this chapter.

Organization of the Vertebrate Nervous System

The brain and spinal cord of the vertebrate CNS are tightly coordinated. The brain provides the integrative power that

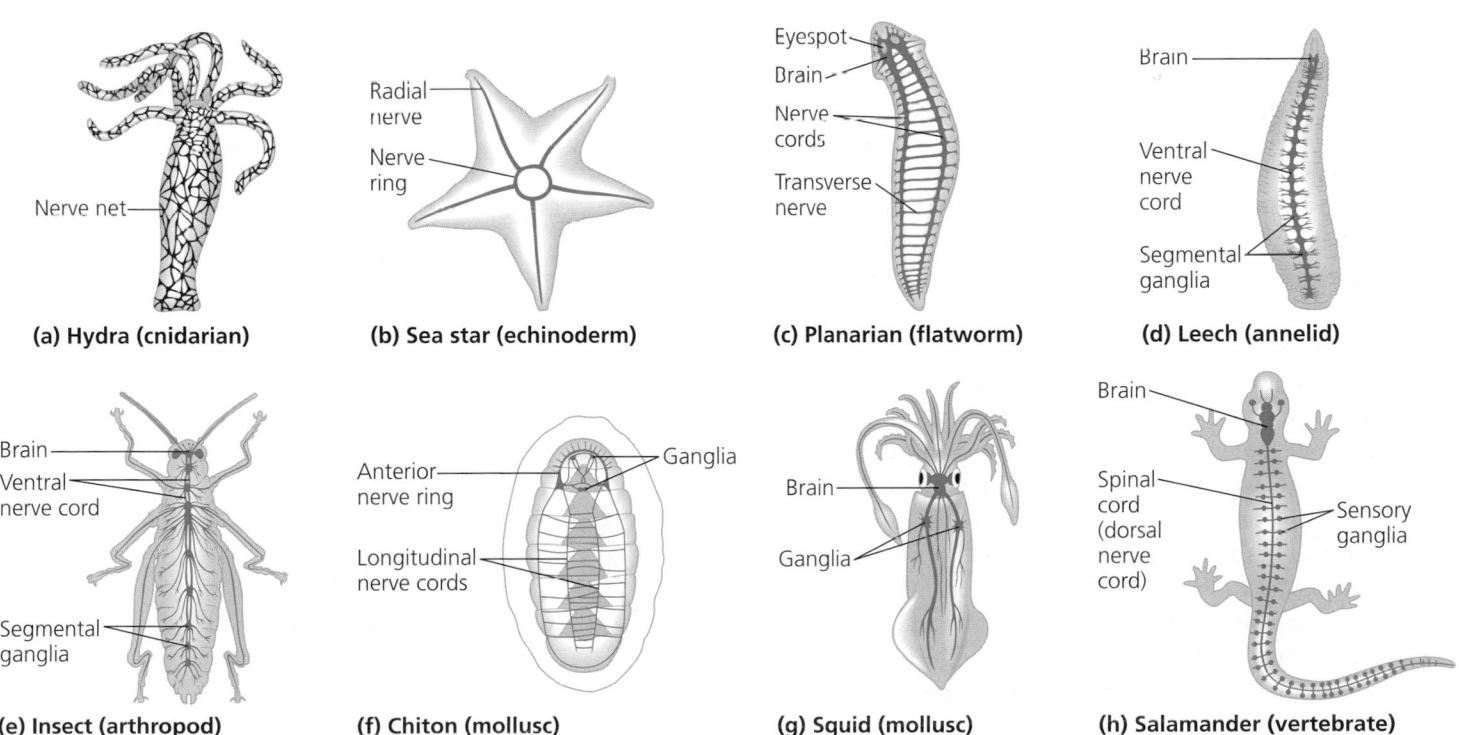

(a) Hydra (cnidarian)   (b) Sea star (echinoderm)   (c) Planarian (flatworm)   (d) Leech (annelid)

(e) Insect (arthropod)   (f) Chiton (mollusc)   (g) Squid (mollusc)   (h) Salamander (vertebrate)

▲ **Figure 49.2 Nervous system organization. (a)** A hydra contains individual neurons (purple) organized in a diffuse nerve net. **(b–h)** Animals with more sophisticated nervous systems contain groups of neurons (blue) organized into nerves and often ganglia and a brain.

2 Sensors detect a sudden stretch in the quadriceps.

3 **Sensory neurons** convey the information to the spinal cord.

4 In response to signals from the sensory neurons, **motor neurons** convey signals to the quadriceps, causing it to contract and jerking the lower leg forward.

Cell body of sensory neuron in dorsal root ganglion

Gray matter

Quadriceps muscle

1 The reflex is initiated artificially by tapping the tendon connected to the quadriceps muscle.

White matter

5 Sensory neurons also communicate with **interneurons** in the spinal cord.

Hamstring muscle

6 The interneurons inhibit motor neurons that lead to the hamstring muscle. This inhibition prevents contraction of the hamstring, which would resist the action of the quadriceps.

Spinal cord (cross section)

— Sensory neuron
— Motor neuron
— Interneuron

▲ **Figure 49.3 The knee-jerk reflex.** Many neurons are involved in the reflex, but for simplicity, only a few neurons are shown.

underlies the complex behavior of vertebrates. The spinal cord, which runs lengthwise inside the vertebral column (spine), conveys information to and from the brain and generates basic patterns of locomotion. The spinal cord also acts independently of the brain as part of the simple nerve circuits that produce **reflexes**, the body's automatic responses to certain stimuli.

A reflex protects the body by triggering a rapid, involuntary response to a particular stimulus. For example, if you put your hand on a hot burner, a reflex begins to pull your hand back well before the sensation of pain has been processed in your brain. Similarly, if your knees buckle when you pick up a heavy object, the tension across your knees triggers a reflex that contracts the thigh muscles, helping you stay upright and support the load. During a physical exam, your doctor may trigger this knee-jerk reflex with a mallet to help assess nervous system function **(Figure 49.3)**.

Unlike the ventral nerve cord of many invertebrates, the spinal cord of vertebrates runs along the dorsal side of the body **(Figure 49.4)**. Although the vertebrate spinal cord does not contain segmental ganglia, such ganglia are present just outside the spinal cord. Furthermore, an underlying segmental organization is apparent in the arrangement of neurons within the spinal cord.

The brain and spinal cord of vertebrates are derived from the dorsal embryonic nerve cord, which is hollow—a hallmark of chordates (see Chapter 34). During development, the

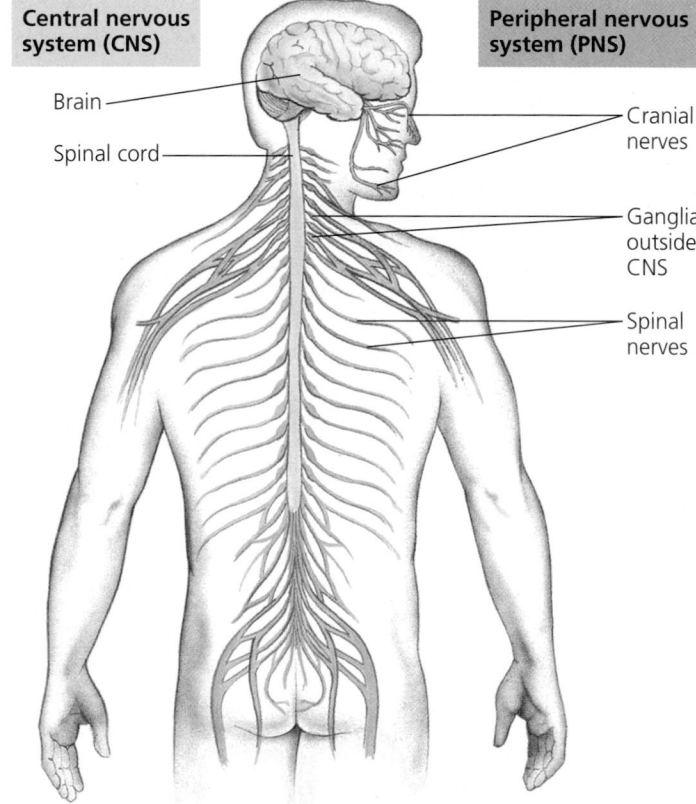

Central nervous system (CNS)

Brain

Spinal cord

Peripheral nervous system (PNS)

Cranial nerves

Ganglia outside CNS

Spinal nerves

▲ **Figure 49.4 The vertebrate nervous system.** The central nervous system consists of the brain and spinal cord (yellow). Cranial nerves, spinal nerves, and ganglia outside the central nervous system make up the peripheral nervous system (dark gold).

hollow cavity of the embryonic nerve cord is transformed into the narrow **central canal** of the spinal cord and the **ventricles** of the brain **(Figure 49.5)**. Both the central canal and the four ventricles are filled with **cerebrospinal fluid**, which is formed by filtration of arterial blood in the brain. The cerebrospinal fluid circulates slowly through the central canal and ventricles and then drains into the veins, supplying different parts of the brain with nutrients and hormones and carrying away wastes. In mammals, the cerebrospinal fluid

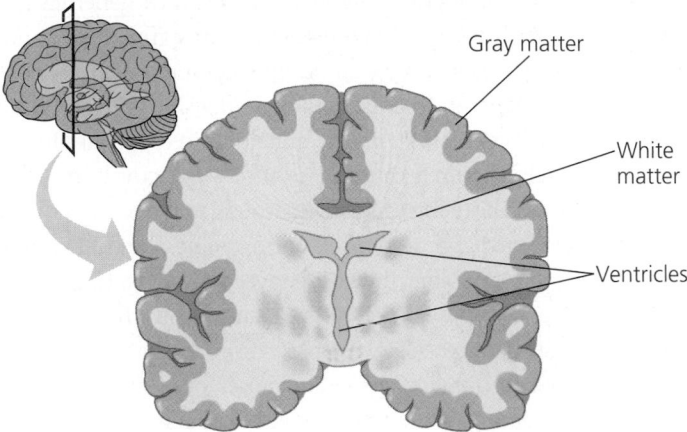

▲ **Figure 49.5 Ventricles, gray matter, and white matter.**
Ventricles deep in the brain's interior contain cerebrospinal fluid. Most of the gray matter is on the surface of the brain, surrounding the white matter.

also cushions the brain and spinal cord by circulating between layers of connective tissue that surround the CNS.

In addition to these fluid-filled spaces, the brain and the spinal cord contain gray matter and white matter. **Gray matter** consists mainly of neuron cell bodies, dendrites, and unmyelinated axons. In contrast, **white matter** consists of bundled axons that have myelin sheaths, which give the axons a whitish appearance. White matter in the spinal cord lies on the outside, consistent with its function in linking the CNS to sensory and motor neurons of the PNS. As shown in Figure 49.5, white matter in the brain is instead predominantly on the inside, reflecting the role of signaling between neurons of the brain in learning, feeling emotions, processing sensory information, and generating commands.

Glia in the CNS

The glia present throughout the vertebrate brain and spinal cord fall into a number of different categories, many of which are illustrated in **Figure 49.6**. Ependymal cells line the ventricles and have cilia that promote circulation of the cerebrospinal fluid. Microglia protect the nervous system from invading microorganisms. Oligodendrocytes function in axon myelination, a critical activity in the vertebrate nervous system (see Chapter 48). (Schwann cells perform this function in the PNS.)

Among the different types of glia, **astrocytes** appear to have the most diverse set of functions. They provide structural support for neurons and regulate the extracellular concentrations of ions and neurotransmitters. Astrocytes can respond to activity in neighboring neurons by facilitating information transfer at synapses and in some instances releasing neurotransmitters. Astrocytes adjacent to active neurons cause nearby blood vessels to dilate, increasing blood flow to the area and enabling the neurons to obtain oxygen and glucose more quickly. During development, astrocytes induce cells that line the capillaries in the CNS to form tight junctions (see Figure 6.32). The result is the **blood-brain barrier**, which restricts the passage of most substances into the CNS. The existence of this barrier permits tight control of the extracellular chemical environment of the brain and spinal cord.

Radial glia (not shown) play a critical role in development of the nervous system. In an embryo, radial glia form tracks along which newly formed neurons

(a) The glia in vertebrates include ependymal cells, astrocytes, microglia, oligodendrocytes, and Schwann cells.

(b) In this section through a mammalian cerebral cortex, the green cells are astrocytes labeled with a fluorescent antibody. The blue dots are the nuclei of astrocytes and other cells labeled with a DNA-binding dye. The term *astrocyte* refers to the starlike shape of the cells (LM).

50 μm

▲ **Figure 49.6 Glia in the vertebrate nervous system.**

migrate from the neural tube, the structure that gives rise to the CNS (see Figures 47.12 and 47.13). Both radial glia and astrocytes can also act as stem cells, generating neurons and additional glia. Researchers view these multipotent precursors as a potential way to replace neurons and glia that are lost to injury or disease, a topic we'll explore further in Concept 49.5.

The Peripheral Nervous System

The PNS transmits information to and from the CNS and plays a large role in regulating an animal's movement and internal environment (Figure 49.7). Sensory information reaches the CNS along PNS neurons designated as *afferent* (from the Latin, meaning "to bring toward"). Following information processing within the CNS, instructions then travel to muscles, glands, and endocrine cells along PNS neurons designated as *efferent* (from the Latin, meaning "to carry off").

Structurally, the vertebrate PNS consists of left-right pairs of cranial and spinal nerves and their associated ganglia (see Figure 49.4). The **cranial nerves** connect the brain with locations mostly in organs of the head and upper body. The **spinal nerves** run between the spinal cord and parts of the body below the head. Most of the cranial nerves and all of the spinal nerves contain both afferent and efferent neurons. A few cranial nerves are afferent only. For example, the olfactory nerve, which extends between the nose and the brain, is dedicated to conveying sensory information for *olfaction*, the sense of smell.

As shown in Figure 49.7, the efferent branch of the PNS consists of two functional components: the motor system and the autonomic nervous system. The **motor system** consists of neurons that carry signals to skeletal muscles, mainly in response to *external* stimuli. Although the motor system is often considered voluntary because it is subject to conscious control, much skeletal muscle activity is actually controlled by the brainstem or by reflexes mediated by the spinal cord. The **autonomic nervous system** regulates the *internal* environment by controlling smooth and cardiac muscles and the organs of the digestive, cardiovascular, excretory, and endocrine systems. This control is generally involuntary. Three divisions—sympathetic, parasympathetic, and enteric—together make up the autonomic nervous system.

The sympathetic and parasympathetic divisions of the autonomic nervous system have largely antagonistic (opposite) functions in regulating organ function (Figure 49.8). Activation of the **sympathetic division** corresponds to arousal and energy generation (the "fight-or-flight" response). For example, the heart beats faster, digestion is inhibited, the liver converts glycogen to glucose, and secretion of epinephrine (adrenaline) from the adrenal medulla is stimulated (see Chapter 45). Activation of the **parasympathetic division** generally causes opposite responses that promote calming and a return to self-maintenance functions ("rest and digest"). For example, increased activity in the parasympathetic division lowers heart rate, enhances digestion, and increases glycogen production. In regulating reproductive activity, however, the parasympathetic division complements rather than antagonizes the sympathetic division (see Figure 49.8). The overall functions of the sympathetic and parasympathetic divisions are reflected in the location of neurons in each division and the neurotransmitters that these neurons release (Table 49.1).

The **enteric division** of the PNS consists of networks of neurons in the digestive tract, pancreas, and gallbladder. Within these organs, neurons of the enteric division control secretion, and they also control the smooth muscles that produce peristalsis (see Chapter 41). Although the enteric division can function independently, it is normally regulated by the sympathetic and parasympathetic divisions.

The motor and autonomic nervous systems often cooperate in maintaining homeostasis. In response to a drop in body temperature, for example, the hypothalamus signals the autonomic nervous system to constrict surface blood vessels, reducing heat loss. At the same time, the hypothalamus signals the motor system to cause shivering, which increases heat production.

▲ **Figure 49.7 Functional hierarchy of the vertebrate peripheral nervous system.** Representative organs and activities are illustrated for each branch.

Parasympathetic division

Action on target organs:

Constricts pupil of eye

Stimulates salivary gland secretion

Constricts bronchi in lungs

Slows heart

Stimulates activity of stomach and intestines

Stimulates activity of pancreas

Stimulates gallbladder

Promotes emptying of bladder

Promotes erection of genitals

Synapse

Cervical

Thoracic

Lumbar

Sacral

Sympathetic ganglia

Sympathetic division

Action on target organs:

Dilates pupil of eye

Inhibits salivary gland secretion

Relaxes bronchi in lungs

Accelerates heart

Inhibits activity of stomach and intestines

Inhibits activity of pancreas

Stimulates glucose release from liver; inhibits gallbladder

Stimulates adrenal medulla

Inhibits emptying of bladder

Promotes ejaculation and vaginal contractions

◄ **Figure 49.8 The parasympathetic and sympathetic divisions of the autonomic nervous system.** Most pathways in each division consist of preganglionic neurons (having cell bodies in the CNS) and postganglionic neurons (having cell bodies in ganglia in the PNS).

? *Most tissues regulated by the autonomic nervous system receive both sympathetic and parasympathetic input from postganglionic neurons. Responses are typically local. In contrast, the adrenal medulla receives input only from the sympathetic division and only from preganglionic neurons, yet responses are observed throughout the body. Explain.*

Table 49.1 Properties of Parasympathetic and Sympathetic Neurons

	Parasympathetic Division	Sympathetic Division
Preganglionic Neurons		
Location	Brainstem, sacral segments of spinal cord	Thoracic and lumbar segments of spinal cord
Neurotransmitter released	Acetylcholine	Acetylcholine
Postganglionic Neurons		
Location	Ganglia close to or within target organs	Ganglia close to target organs or chain of ganglia near spinal cord
Neurotransmitter released	Acetylcholine	Norepinephrine

CONCEPT CHECK 49.1

1. Which division of your autonomic nervous system would likely be activated if you learned that an exam you had forgotten about would start in 5 minutes? Explain your answer.

2. The parasympathetic and sympathetic divisions of the PNS (see Figure 49.8 and Table 49.1) use the same neurotransmitters at the axon terminals of preganglionic neurons, but different transmitters at the axon terminals of postganglionic neurons. How does this difference correlate with the function of the axons bringing signals into and out of the ganglia in the two divisions?

3. **WHAT IF?** Suppose you had an accident that severed a small nerve required to move some of the fingers of your right hand. Would you also expect an effect on sensation from those fingers?

For suggested answers, see Appendix A.

CONCEPT 49.2
The vertebrate brain is regionally specialized

Having considered the organization of the spinal cord and PNS, we turn now to the brain. In discussing brain organization, biologists often refer to subdivisions that are apparent at particular stages of embryonic development. In all vertebrates, three anterior bulges of the neural tube—the **forebrain**, **midbrain**, and **hindbrain**—become evident as the embryo develops (**Figure 49.9a**). By the 5th week of embryonic development in humans, there are five brain regions (**Figure 49.9b**). Three of these regions—those derived from the midbrain and hindbrain—give rise to the brainstem, a set of structures that form the lower part of the brain (**Figure 49.9c**). The hindbrain also gives rise to a major brain center, the cerebellum, that is not part of the brainstem.

As embryogenesis proceeds, the most profound changes in the human brain occur in the *telencephalon*, the region of the forebrain that gives rise to the adult **cerebrum**. Rapid, expansive growth of the telencephalon during the 2nd and 3rd months causes the outer portion of the cerebrum, called the cerebral cortex, to extend over and around much of the rest of the brain. Major centers that develop from the *diencephalon* are the thalamus, hypothalamus, and epithalamus.

As we survey the function of the structures in the adult brain, we'll periodically refer to Figure 49.9 and to the embryonic history of a particular region.

The Brainstem

The **brainstem** functions in homeostasis, coordination of movement, and conduction of information to and from higher brain centers. Sometimes called the "lower brain," it forms a stalk with cap-like swellings at the anterior end of the spinal cord. The adult brainstem consists of the midbrain, the **pons**, and the **medulla oblongata** (commonly called the **medulla**).

The transfer of information between the PNS and the midbrain and forebrain is one of the most important functions of the medulla and pons. All axons carrying sensory information to and motor instructions from higher brain regions pass

---

Embryonic brain regions | **Brain structures present in adult**

Forebrain
— Telencephalon — Cerebrum (includes cerebral cortex, white matter, basal nuclei)
— Diencephalon — Diencephalon (thalamus, hypothalamus, epithalamus)

Midbrain
— Mesencephalon — Midbrain (part of brainstem)

Hindbrain
— Metencephalon — Pons (part of brainstem), cerebellum
— Myelencephalon — Medulla oblongata (part of brainstem)

(a) Embryo at 1 month
Midbrain
Hindbrain
Forebrain

(b) Embryo at 5 weeks
Mesencephalon
Metencephalon
Diencephalon
Myelencephalon
Spinal cord
Telencephalon

(c) Adult
Cerebrum
Diencephalon:
Hypothalamus
Thalamus
Pineal gland (part of epithalamus)
Brainstem:
Midbrain
Pons
Medulla oblongata
Pituitary gland
Spinal cord
Cerebellum
Central canal

▲ **Figure 49.9 Development of the human brain.**

through the brainstem. The medulla and pons also help coordinate large-scale body movements, such as running and climbing. In carrying instructions about these movements from cell bodies in the midbrain and forebrain to synapses in the spinal cord, most axons cross in the medulla from one side of the CNS to the other. As a result, the right side of the brain controls much of the movement of the left side of the body, and vice versa.

The midbrain contains centers for receiving and integrating several types of sensory information. It also sends coded sensory information along neurons to specific regions of the forebrain. All sensory axons involved in hearing either terminate in the midbrain or pass through it on their way to the cerebrum. In nonmammalian vertebrates, portions of the midbrain form prominent optic lobes that in some cases are the animal's only visual centers. In mammals, vision is integrated in the cerebrum, not the midbrain. The midbrain instead coordinates visual reflexes, such as the peripheral vision reflex: The head turns toward an object approaching from the side without the brain having formed an image of the object.

Signals from the brainstem affect attention, alertness, appetite, and motivation. The medulla contains centers that control several automatic, homeostatic functions, including breathing, heart and blood vessel activity, swallowing, vomiting, and digestion. The pons also participates in some of these activities; for example, it regulates the breathing centers in the medulla (see Figure 42.27). These activities of the brainstem rely on axons that reach many areas of the cerebral cortex and cerebellum, releasing neurotransmitters such as norepinephrine, dopamine, serotonin, and acetylcholine.

Arousal and Sleep

As anyone who has drifted off to sleep listening to a lecture (or reading a book) knows, attentiveness and mental alertness can change rapidly. Such transitions are regulated by the brainstem and cerebrum, which control both arousal and sleep. Arousal is a state of awareness of the external world. Sleep is a state in which external stimuli are received but not consciously perceived.

The brainstem contains several centers for controlling arousal and sleep. One such regulator is the **reticular formation**, a diffuse network of neurons in the core of the brainstem (Figure 49.10). Acting as a sensory filter, the reticular formation determines which incoming information reaches the cerebral cortex. The more information the cortex receives, the more alert and aware a person is, although the brain often ignores certain stimuli while actively processing other inputs. Sleep and wakefulness are also regulated by specific parts of the brainstem: The pons and medulla contain centers that cause sleep when stimulated, and the midbrain has a center that causes arousal.

All birds and mammals show characteristic sleep/wake cycles. Melatonin, a hormone produced by the pineal gland, appears to play an important role in these cycles. As you read in Chapter 45, peak melatonin secretion occurs at night. Mela-

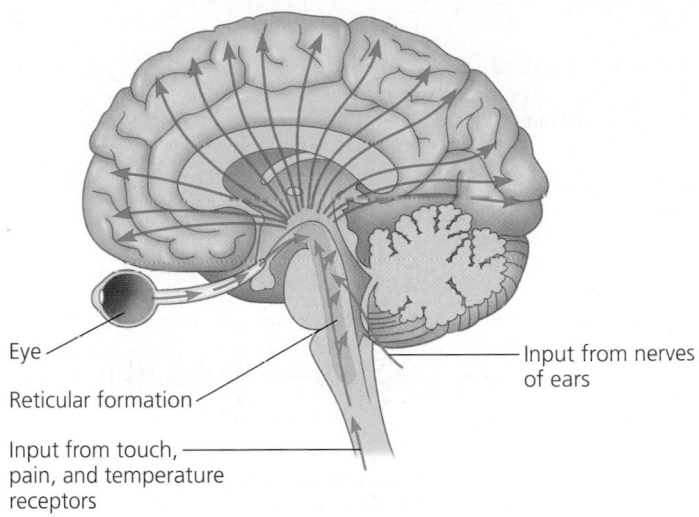

▲ Figure 49.10 The reticular formation. This system of neurons distributed throughout the core of the brainstem filters sensory input (blue arrows), blocking familiar and repetitive information that constantly enters the nervous system. It sends the filtered input to the cerebral cortex (green arrows).

tonin has been promoted as a dietary supplement to treat sleep disturbances, such as those associated with jet lag, insomnia, seasonal affective disorder, and depression. Melatonin is synthesized from serotonin, which itself may be the neurotransmitter of the sleep-producing centers. Serotonin in turn is synthesized from the amino acid tryptophan. Although the protein in milk contains relatively high levels of tryptophan, it remains uncertain whether drinking milk at bedtime increases production of serotonin and melatonin, thus aiding sleep.

Although we know very little about the function of sleep, it is clear that sleep is essential for survival. Contrary to appearances, sleep is an active state, at least for the brain. By placing electrodes at multiple sites on the scalp, we can record patterns of electrical activity called brain waves in an electroencephalogram (EEG). These recordings reveal that brain wave frequencies change as the brain progresses through distinct stages of sleep. One hypothesis is that sleep and dreams are involved in consolidating learning and memory: Experiments show that regions of the brain activated during a learning task can become active again during sleep.

Some animals display evolutionary adaptations that allow for substantial activity during sleep. Bottlenose dolphins, for example, swim while sleeping, rising to the surface to breathe air on a regular basis. How do they manage this feat? A critical clue came from American physiologist John Lilly, who in 1964 observed that dolphins sleep with one eye open and one closed. As in humans and other mammals, the forebrain of dolphins is physically and functionally divided into two halves, the right and left hemispheres. Lilly suggested that a dolphin sleeping with one eye closed could mean that just one side of the brain was asleep. In 1977, Russian scientist Lev Mukhametov set out to test Lilly's hypothesis by collecting EEG recordings from each

Location	Time: 0 hours	Time: 1 hour
Left hemisphere	ⱲⱲⱲⱲ	ⱲⱲⱲ
Right hemisphere	ⱲⱲⱲ	ⱲⱲⱲⱲ

▲ **Figure 49.11 Dolphins can be asleep and awake at the same time.** EEG recordings were made separately for the two sides of a dolphin's brain. Low-frequency activity was recorded in one hemisphere while higher-frequency activity typical of being awake was recorded in the other hemisphere.

hemisphere of sleeping dolphins **(Figure 49.11)**. Mukhametov's findings demonstrate that dolphins do in fact sleep with one brain hemisphere at a time.

The Cerebellum

The **cerebellum**, which develops from part of the hindbrain (see Figure 49.9), coordinates movements and balance. The cerebellum receives sensory information about the position of the joints and the length of the muscles, as well as input from the auditory (hearing) and visual systems. It also monitors motor commands issued by the cerebrum. Information from the cerebrum passes first to the pons and from there to the cerebellum. The cerebellum integrates this information as it carries out coordination and error checking during motor and perceptual functions. Hand-eye coordination is an example of cerebellar control; if the cerebellum is damaged, the eyes can follow a moving object, but they will not stop at the same place as the object. Hand movement toward the object will also be erratic. The cerebellum also helps in learning and remembering motor skills.

The Diencephalon

The embryonic diencephalon— the forebrain division that evolved earliest in vertebrate history—develops into three adult brain regions: the thalamus, hypothalamus, and epithalamus (see Figure 49.9). The thalamus and hypothalamus are major integrating centers that act as relay stations for information flow in the body. The *epithalamus* includes the pineal gland, the source of melatonin. It also contains one of several clusters of capillaries that generate cerebrospinal fluid from blood.

The **thalamus** is the main input center for sensory information going to the cerebrum. Incoming information from all the senses is sorted in the thalamus and sent to the appropriate cerebral centers for further processing. The thalamus also receives input from the cerebrum and other parts of the brain that regulate emotion and arousal. The thalamus is formed by two masses, each roughly the size and shape of a walnut.

Much smaller even than the thalamus, the **hypothalamus** is one of the most important brain regions for the control of homeostasis. As discussed in Chapters 40 and 45, the hypothalamus contains the body's thermostat, as well as centers for regulating hunger, thirst, and many other basic survival mechanisms. The hypothalamus is the source of posterior pituitary hormones and of releasing hormones that act on the anterior pituitary (see Figures 45.15 and 45.17). In addition, hypothalamic centers play a role in sexual and mating behaviors, the fight-or-flight response, and pleasure.

Biological Clock Regulation by the Hypothalamus

Specialized nerve cells in the hypothalamus regulate circadian rhythms, daily cycles of biological activity. Such cycles occur in organisms ranging from bacteria to fungi, plants, insects, birds, and humans (see Chapters 39 and 51). In mammals, the cycles controlled by the hypothalamus influence a number of physiological processes, including sleep, body temperature, hunger, and hormone release. As in other organisms, circadian rhythms in mammals rely on a **biological clock**, a molecular mechanism that directs periodic gene expression and cellular activity. Although biological clocks are typically synchronized to the cycles of light and dark in the environment, they can maintain a roughly 24-hour cycle even in the absence of environmental cues. For example, humans kept in a constant environment exhibit a cycle length of 24.2 hours, with very little variation among individuals.

In mammals, circadian rhythms are coordinated by a group of neurons in the hypothalamus called the **suprachiasmatic nucleus**, or **SCN**. (Certain clusters of neurons in the CNS are referred to as "nuclei.") In response to transmission of sensory information by the eyes, the SCN acts as a pacemaker, synchronizing the biological clock in cells throughout the body to the natural cycles of day length. By surgically removing the SCN from laboratory animals, scientists demonstrated that the SCN is required for circadian rhythms: Animals without an SCN lack rhythmicity in behaviors and in electrical activity of the brain. These experiments did not, however, reveal whether rhythms originate in the SCN or elsewhere. In 1990, Michael Menaker and colleagues at the University of Virginia answered this question with the aid of a mutation that changes the circadian rhythm of hamsters (**Figure 49.12**). By transplanting brain tissue between normal and mutant hamsters, these scientists were able to show that the SCN determines the circadian rhythm of the whole animal.

▼ Figure 49.12 **Inquiry**

Which cells control the circadian rhythm in mammals?

EXPERIMENT   The τ (tau) mutation alters the period of the circadian rhythm in hamsters. Whereas wild-type hamsters have a cycle lasting 24 hours in the absence of external cues, hamsters homozygous for the τ mutation have a circadian cycle lasting only about 20 hours. To determine if the SCN controls circadian rhythm, Michael Menaker and colleagues surgically removed the SCN from wild-type and τ hamsters. Several weeks later, each of these hamsters received an SCN transplanted from a hamster of the opposite genotype.

RESULTS   In 80% of the hamsters in which the SCN had been destroyed, an SCN transplant restored rhythmic activity. For hamsters in which rhythm was restored, the net effect of the two procedures (SCN destruction and replacement) on circadian rhythm is graphed below. Each of the eight lines represents the change in the observed circadian cycle for an individual hamster.

- ● Wild-type hamster
- ▲ Wild-type hamster with SCN from τ hamster
- ● τ hamster
- ▲ τ hamster with SCN from wild-type hamster

CONCLUSION   Cells associated with the suprachiasmatic nucleus determine the period of circadian rhythm.

SOURCE   M. R. Ralph, M. Menaker, et al., Transplanted suprachiasmatic nucleus determines circadian period, *Science* 247: 975–978 (1990).

WHAT IF?   Suppose you identified a hamster mutant that lacked rhythmic activity. How might you use this mutant in transplant experiments with wild-type or τ mutant hamsters to demonstrate that the mutation affected the pacemaker function of the SCN?

The Cerebrum

In mammals, information processing is largely centered in the cerebrum. The cerebrum develops from the embryonic telencephalon, an outgrowth of the forebrain that arose early in vertebrate evolution as a region supporting olfactory reception as well as auditory and visual processing. The cerebrum is divided into right and left **cerebral hemispheres**. Each hemisphere consists of an outer covering of gray matter, the cerebral cortex; internal white matter; and groups of neurons collectively called *basal nuclei* that are located deep within the white matter (**Figure 49.13**). The basal nuclei are important centers for planning and learning movement sequences. Damage in this brain region during fetal development can result in cerebral palsy, a defect disrupting how motor commands are issued to the muscles.

The cerebral cortex is particularly extensive in mammals, where it is vital for perception, voluntary movement, and learning. In humans, it accounts for about 80% of total brain mass and is highly convoluted (see Figure 49.13). The convolutions allow the cerebral cortex to have a large surface area and still fit inside the skull: Less than 5 mm thick, it has a surface area of approximately 1,000 cm^2.

Like the rest of the cerebrum, the cerebral cortex is divided into right and left sides, each of which is responsible for the opposite half of the body. The left side of the cortex receives information from, and controls the movement of, the right side of the body, and vice versa. A thick band of axons known as the **corpus callosum** enables the right and left cerebral cortices to communicate (see Figure 49.13).

If damage occurs to the cerebrum early in development, the normal functions of the damaged area are frequently redirected elsewhere. A dramatic example of this phenomenon results from a treatment for the most extreme cases of epilepsy, a

▲ **Figure 49.13 The human brain viewed from the rear.** The corpus callosum and basal nuclei are not visible from the surface because they are completely covered by the left and right cerebral hemispheres. The lighter blue structure is the cerebellum.

◀ **Figure 49.14 Comparison of regions for higher cognition in avian and human brains.** Although structurally different, the pallium of the avian brain (left cross section) and the cerebral cortex of the human brain (right cross section) have similar roles in higher cognitive activities and make many similar connections with other brain structures.

condition causing episodes of electrical disturbance, or seizures, in the brain. In those rare infants who are severely affected and do not respond to medication, an entire cerebral hemisphere is sometimes surgically removed. Amazingly, recovery is nearly complete. The remaining hemisphere eventually assumes most of the functions normally provided by the entire cerebrum, although one side of the body is much weaker than the other. Even in adults, damage to a portion of the cerebral cortex can trigger the development or use of new brain circuits, leading in some cases to recovery of function.

Evolution of Cognition in Vertebrates

In humans, the outermost part of the cerebral cortex forms the *neocortex*, six parallel layers of neurons arranged tangential to the brain surface. It was long thought that a large, highly convoluted neocortex was required for advanced *cognition*, the perception and reasoning that constitute knowledge. Both primates and cetaceans (whales, dolphins, and porpoises) possess an extensively convoluted neocortex. Because birds lack such a structure, they were thought to have substantially lower intellectual capacity. In recent years, however, this viewpoint has been shown to be wrong: There are now abundant examples of sophisticated information processing by birds. Western scrub jays (*Aphelocoma californica*) can remember the relative period of time that has passed since they stored and hid specific food items. New Caledonian crows (*Corvus moneduloides*) are highly skilled at making and using tools, an ability otherwise well documented only for humans and some other apes. African gray parrots (*Psittacus erithacus*) understand relational concepts that are numerical or abstract, distinguishing between "same" and "different" and grasping the concept of "none."

The sophisticated cognitive ability of birds is based on an evolutionary variation on the architecture of the *pallium*, the top or outer portion of the brain. Whereas the human pallium—the cerebral cortex—contains flat sheets of cells in six layers, the avian pallium contains neurons clustered into nuclei. It is likely that the common ancestor of birds and mammals had a pallium in which neurons were organized into nuclei, as is still found in birds. Early in mammalian evolution, this nuclear organization was transformed into a layered one. Connectivity was maintained during this transformation such that, for example, the pallium of both mammals and birds receives sensory input—sights, sounds, and touch—from the thalamus. The result was two different arrangements, each of which supports complex and flexible brain function **(Figure 49.14)**.

Although scientists are just starting to investigate the avian pallium, the cerebral cortex of mammals has been studied extensively for many decades. We'll consider the current state of knowledge about this remarkable structure in the next section.

CONCEPT CHECK 49.2

1. When you wave your right hand, what part of your brain initiates the action?

2. When a police officer stops a driver for driving erratically and suspects that the person is intoxicated, the officer may ask the driver to close his or her eyes and touch his or her nose. What can you deduce from this test about alcohol's effect on a particular part of the brain?

3. **WHAT IF?** Suppose you examine individuals with damage to the CNS that has resulted in either coma (a prolonged state of unconsciousness) or general paralysis (a loss of muscle function throughout the body). Relative to the position of the reticular formation, where would you predict the site of injury to lie in each group of patients? Explain.

For suggested answers, see Appendix A.

The cerebral cortex controls voluntary movement and cognitive functions

Each side of the cerebral cortex is customarily described as having four lobes, called the frontal, temporal, occipital, and parietal lobes (each lobe is named for a bone of the skull). Researchers have identified a number of functional areas within each lobe (Figure 49.15). These include *primary sensory areas*, each of which receives and processes a specific type of sensory information, and *association areas*, which integrate the information from various parts of the brain.

During mammalian evolution, most of the increase in size of the cerebral cortex was due to an expansion of the association areas. Whereas a rat's cerebral cortex contains mainly primary sensory areas, the human cerebral cortex consists largely of association areas responsible for more complex behavior and learning.

Information Processing in the Cerebral Cortex

As you will learn further in Chapter 50, the cerebral cortex receives sensory input from two types of sources. Some input is received from dedicated sensory organs, such as the eyes and nose. Other sensory input relies on receptors in the hands, scalp, and elsewhere. These *somatosensory* receptors (from the Greek *soma*, body) provide information about touch, pain, pressure, temperature, and the position of muscles and limbs.

Most sensory information coming into the cortex is directed via the thalamus to primary sensory areas within the brain lobes. The thalamus directs different types of input to distinct locations: visual information to the occipital lobe; auditory input to the temporal lobe; and somatosensory information to the parietal lobe (see Figure 49.15). Information about taste also goes to the parietal lobe, but to a region separate from that for somatosensory input. Olfactory information is sent first to regions of the cortex that are similar in mammals and reptiles and then via the thalamus to an interior part of the frontal lobe.

Information received at the primary sensory areas is passed along to nearby association areas, which process particular features in the sensory input. In the occipital lobe, for example, some groups of neurons in the primary visual area are specifically sensitive to rays of light oriented in a particular direction. In the visual association area, information related to such features is combined in a region dedicated to recognizing complex images, such as faces.

Integrated sensory information passes to the frontal association area, which helps plan actions and movement. The cerebral cortex may then generate motor commands that cause particular behaviors—moving a limb or saying hello, for example. These commands consist of action potentials produced by neurons in the motor cortex, which lies at the rear of the frontal lobe (see Figure 49.15). The action potentials travel along axons to the brainstem and spinal cord, where they excite motor neurons, which in turn excite skeletal muscle cells.

In both the somatosensory cortex and the motor cortex, neurons are distributed in an orderly fashion according to the part of the body that generates the sensory input or receives the

◄ Figure 49.15 **The human cerebral cortex.** Each side of the cerebral cortex is divided into four lobes, and each lobe has specialized functions. Some of the association areas on the left side of the brain (shown here) have different functions from those on the right side (not shown).

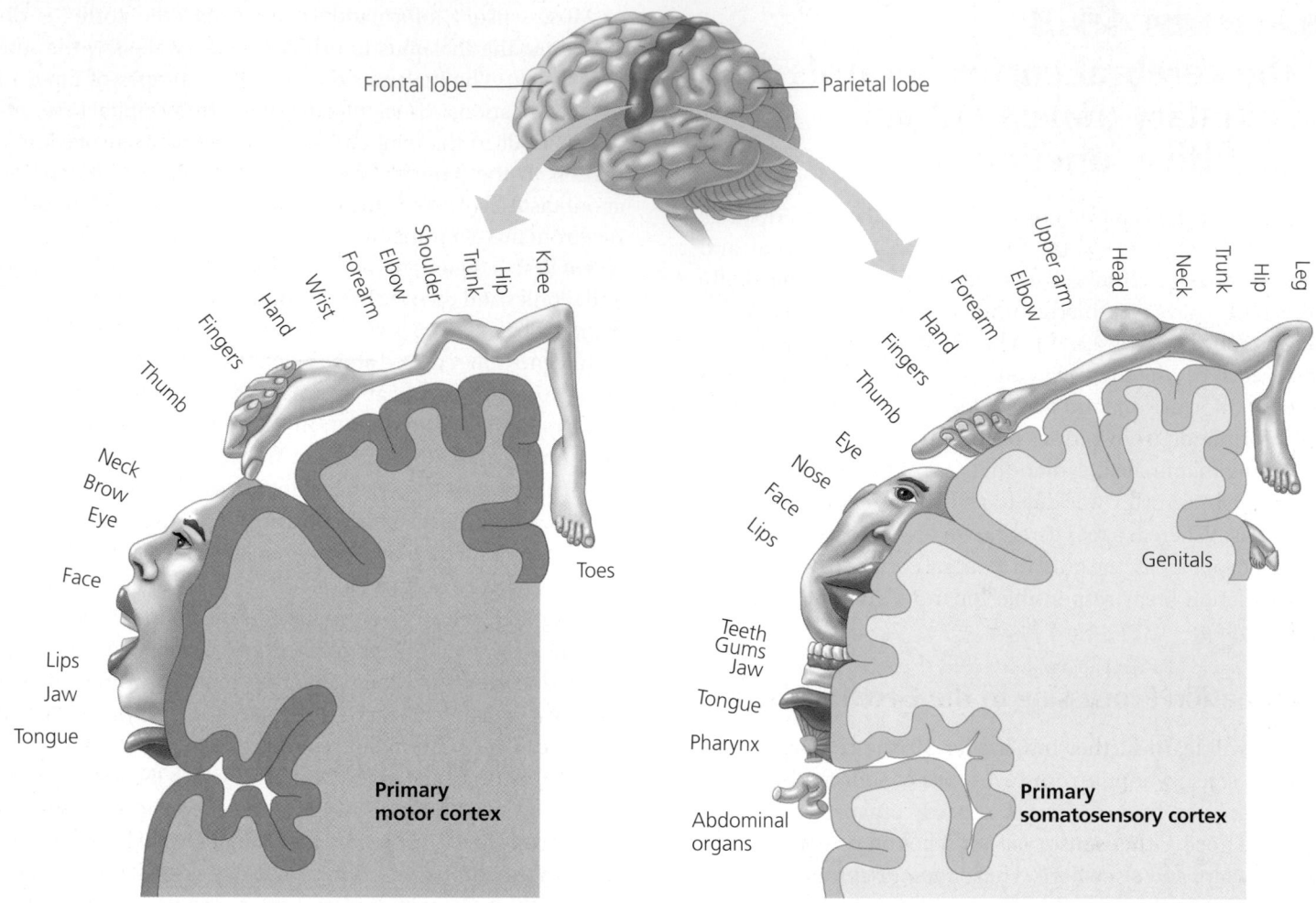

▲ **Figure 49.16 Body part representation in the primary motor and primary somatosensory cortices.** In these cross-sectional maps of the cortices, the cortical surface area devoted to each body part is represented by the relative size of that part in the cartoons.

motor commands **(Figure 49.16)**. For example, neurons that process sensory information from the legs and feet are located in the region of the somatosensory cortex that lies closest to the midline. Neurons that control muscles in the legs and feet are located in the corresponding region of the motor cortex. Notice in Figure 49.16 that the cortical surface area devoted to each body part is not proportional to the size of the part. Instead, surface area correlates with the extent of neuronal control needed for muscles in a particular body part (for the motor cortex) or with the number of sensory neurons that extend axons to that part (for the somatosensory cortex). Thus, the surface area of the motor cortex devoted to the face is much larger than that devoted to the trunk, reflecting in large part how extensively facial muscles are involved in communication.

Language and Speech

The mapping of higher cognitive functions to specific brain areas began in the 1800s when physicians learned that damage to particular regions of the cortex by injuries, strokes, or tumors can produce distinctive changes in a person's behavior. The French physician Pierre Broca conducted postmortem (after death) examinations of patients who had been able to understand language but unable to speak. He discovered that many of these patients had defects in a small region of the left frontal lobe. That region, now known as *Broca's area*, is located in front of the part of the primary motor cortex that controls muscles in the face. The German physician Karl Wernicke also conducted examinations and found that damage to a posterior portion of the left temporal lobe, now called *Wernicke's area*, abolished the ability to comprehend speech but not the ability to speak. Over a century later, studies of brain activity using fMRI and positron-emission tomography (PET; see Chapter 2) have confirmed that Broca's area is active during speech generation **(Figure 49.17**, lower left image) and Wernicke's area is active when speech is heard (Figure 49.17, upper left image).

Broca's area and Wernicke's area are part of a much larger network of brain regions involved in language. Reading a printed word without speaking activates the visual cortex (Figure 49.17, upper right image), whereas reading a printed word out loud activates both the visual cortex and Broca's area.

▲ **Figure 49.17 Mapping language areas in the cerebral cortex.** These PET images show regions with different activity levels in one person's brain during four activities, all related to speech.

Frontal and temporal areas become active when meaning must be attached to words, such as when a person generates verbs to go with nouns or groups related words or concepts (Figure 49.17, lower right image).

Lateralization of Cortical Function

Although each cerebral hemisphere in humans has sensory and motor connections to the opposite side of the body, the two hemispheres do not have identical functions. For example, the left side of the cerebrum has a dominant role with regard to language, as reflected in the location of both Broca's area and Wernicke's area in the left hemisphere. There are also subtler distinctions in the functions of the two hemispheres. For example, the left hemisphere is more adept at math and logical operations. In contrast, the right hemisphere appears to be dominant in the recognition of faces and patterns, spatial relations, and nonverbal thinking. The establishment of these differences in hemisphere function in humans is called **lateralization**.

At least some lateralization relates to handedness, the preference for using one hand for certain motor activities. Across human populations, roughly 90% of individuals are more skilled with their right hand than with their left hand. Studies using fMRI have revealed how language processing differs in relation to handedness. When subjects thought of words without speaking out loud, brain activity was localized to the left hemisphere in 96% of right-handed subjects but in only 76% of left-handed subjects.

The two hemispheres normally work together harmoniously, trading information back and forth through the fibers of the corpus callosum. The importance of this exchange is revealed in patients whose corpus callosum has been surgically severed. As with removal of a cerebral hemisphere, this procedure is a treatment of last resort for the most extreme forms of epilepsy. Individuals with a severed corpus callosum exhibit a "split-brain" effect. When they see a familiar word in their left field of vision, they cannot read the word: The sensory information that travels from the left field of vision to the right hemisphere cannot reach the language centers in the left hemisphere. Each hemisphere in such patients functions independently of the other.

Emotions

The generation and experience of emotions involve many regions of the brain. One such region, shown in **Figure 49.18**, contains the *limbic system* (from the Latin *limbus*, border), a group of structures surrounding the brainstem in mammals. The limbic system, which includes the amygdala, the hippocampus, and parts of the thalamus, is not dedicated to a single function. Instead, structures within the limbic system have diverse functions, including emotion, motivation, olfaction, behavior, and memory. Furthermore, parts of the brain outside the limbic system also participate in generating and experiencing emotion. For example, emotions that manifest themselves in behaviors such as laughing and crying involve an interaction of parts of the limbic system with sensory areas of the cerebrum. Structures in the forebrain also attach emotional "feelings" to basic, survival-related functions controlled by the brainstem, including aggression, feeding, and sexuality.

Emotional experiences are often stored as memories that can be recalled by similar circumstances. In the case of fear, emotional memory is stored separately from the memory system that supports explicit recall of events. The focus of emotional

▲ **Figure 49.18 The limbic system.**

memory is the **amygdala**, which is located in the temporal lobe (see Figure 49.18). To study the function of the human amygdala, researchers sometimes present adult subjects with an image, followed by an unpleasant experience, such as a mild electrical shock. After several trials, study participants experience autonomic arousal—as measured by increased heart rate or sweating—if they see the image again. People with brain damage confined to the amygdala can recall the image, because their explicit memory is intact, but do not exhibit autonomic arousal.

The prefrontal cortex, a part of the frontal lobes critical for emotional experience, is also important in temperament and decision making. This combination of functions was discovered in 1848 from the remarkable medical case of Phineas Gage. Gage was working on a railroad construction site when an explosion drove a meter-long iron rod through his head. The rod, which was more than 3 cm in diameter at one end, entered his skull just below his left eye and exited through the top of his head, damaging large portions of his frontal lobe. Astonishingly, Gage recovered, but his personality changed dramatically. He became emotionally detached, impatient, and erratic in his behavior.

Tumors that develop in the frontal lobe sometimes cause the same combination of symptoms that Gage experienced. Intellect and memory seem intact, but decision making is flawed and emotional responses are diminished. In the 20th century, the same problems were also observed as a consequence of frontal lobotomy, a surgical procedure that severs the connection between the prefrontal cortex and the limbic system. Once a common treatment for severe behavioral disorders, frontal lobotomy later was abandoned as a medical practice. Behavioral disorders are now typically treated with medications, as discussed later in this chapter.

Consciousness

The study of human consciousness was long considered outside the province of science, more appropriate as a subject for philosophy or religion. One reason for this view is that consciousness is both broad—encompassing our awareness of ourselves and our experiences—and subjective. Over the past few decades, however, neuroscientists have begun studying consciousness using brain-imaging techniques such as fMRI and PET scans (see Figures 49.1 and 49.17). It is now possible to compare activity in the human brain during different states of consciousness—for example, before and after a person is aware of seeing an object. These imaging techniques can also be used to compare the conscious and unconscious processing of sensory information. Such studies do not pinpoint a "consciousness center" in the brain; rather, they offer an increasingly detailed picture of how neuronal activity correlates with conscious experiences.

Support is growing for the hypothesis that consciousness is an emergent property (see Chapter 1) of the brain, and that it

recruits activities in many areas of the cerebral cortex. Several models postulate the existence of a sort of "scanning mechanism" that repetitively sweeps across the brain, integrating widespread activity into a unified, conscious moment. Still, a well-supported theory of consciousness may have to wait until brain-imaging technology becomes more sophisticated.

CONCEPT CHECK 49.3

1. How is the study of individuals with damage to a particular part of the brain used to provide insight into the normal function of that region?
2. Two brain areas important in the generation or perception of speech are Broca's area and Wernicke's area. How is the function of each area related to the activity of the surrounding portion of the cerebral cortex?
3. **WHAT IF?** If a woman with a severed corpus callosum viewed a photograph of a familiar face, first in the left field of vision and then in the right field, why would it be difficult for her to put a name to the face in either field?

For suggested answers, see Appendix A.

CONCEPT **49.4**
Changes in synaptic connections underlie memory and learning

During embryonic development, regulated gene expression and signal transduction establish the overall structure of the nervous system (see Chapter 47). Two processes then dominate the remaining development of the nervous system. The first is a competition among neurons for survival. Neurons compete for growth-supporting factors, which are produced in limited quantities by tissues that direct neuron growth. Cells that don't reach the proper locations fail to receive such factors and undergo programmed cell death. The competition is so severe that half of the neurons formed in the embryo are eliminated. The net effect is the preferential survival of neurons that are located properly within the nervous system.

Synapse elimination is the second major process that shapes nervous system development in the embryo. A developing neuron forms numerous synapses, more than are required for its proper function. The activity of that neuron then stabilizes some synapses and destabilizes others. By the end of embryogenesis, neurons on average have lost more than half of their initial synapses, leaving behind the connections that survive into adulthood.

Together, neuron and synapse elimination set up the network of cells and connections within the nervous system required throughout life.

Neural Plasticity

Although the basic architecture of the CNS is established during embryonic development, it can change after birth. This capacity for the nervous system to be remodeled, especially in response to its own activity, is called **neural plasticity**.

Much of the reshaping of the nervous system occurs at synapses. When activity at a synapse correlates with that of other synapses, changes may occur that reinforce that synaptic connection. Conversely, when the activity of a synapse fails to correlate with that of other synapses, the synaptic connection sometimes becomes weaker. **Figure 49.19a** illustrates how these processes can result in either the addition or loss of a synapse. If you think of signals in the nervous system as traffic on a highway, such changes are comparable to adding or removing an entrance ramp. The net effect is to increase signaling between particular pairs of neurons and decrease signaling at other sites. As shown in **Figure 49.19b**, changes can also strengthen or weaken signaling at a synapse. In our traffic analogy, this would be equivalent to widening or narrowing an entrance ramp.

Remodeling and refining of the nervous system occur in many contexts. For example, these processes are necessary steps in how we develop the ability to sense our surroundings, a topic covered in Chapter 50. They are also critical to the nervous system's limited ability to recover from injury or disease. Remodeling and refinement also underlie memory and learning, our next topic.

Memory and Learning

Though we may not be aware of it, we are constantly checking what is happening against what just happened a few moments ago. We hold information for a time in **short-term memory** locations and then release it if it becomes irrelevant. If we wish to retain knowledge of a name, phone number, or other fact, the mechanisms of **long-term memory** are activated. If we later need to recall the name or number, we fetch it from long-term memory and return it to short-term memory.

Scientists have long wondered where in the brain short-term and long-term memories are located. We now know that both types of memory involve the storage of information in the cerebral cortex. In short-term memory, this information is accessed via temporary links or associations formed in the hippocampus. When memories are made long-term, the links in the hippocampus are replaced by more permanent connections within the cerebral cortex itself. The hippocampus is thus essential for acquiring new long-term memories, but not for maintaining them. For this reason, people who suffer damage to the hippocampus are to some extent trapped in the past: They cannot form any new lasting memories but can freely recall events from before their injury.

What evolutionary advantage might be offered by organizing short-term and long-term memories differently? Current thinking is that the delay in forming connections in the cerebral cortex allows long-term memories to be integrated gradually into the existing store of knowledge and experience, providing a basis for more meaningful associations. Consistent with this idea, the transfer of information from short-term to long-term memory is enhanced by the association of new data with data previously learned and stored in long-term memory. For example, it's easier to learn a new card game if you already have "card sense" from playing other card games.

Motor skills, such as walking, tying your shoes, or writing, are usually learned by repetition. You can perform these skills without consciously recalling the individual steps required to do these tasks correctly. Learning skills and procedures, such as those required to ride a bicycle, appears to involve cellular mechanisms very similar to those responsible for brain growth and development. In such cases, neurons actually make new connections. In contrast, memorizing phone numbers, facts, and places—which can be very rapid and may require only one exposure to the relevant item—may rely mainly on changes in the strength of existing neuronal connections. Next we will consider one way that such changes in strength can take place.

(a) Synapses are strengthened or weakened in response to activity. High-level activity at the synapse of the postsynaptic neuron with presynaptic neuron N_1 leads to recruitment of additional axon terminals from that neuron. Lack of activity at the synapse with presynaptic neuron N_2 leads to loss of functional connections with that neuron.

(b) If two synapses on the same postsynaptic cell are often active at the same time, the strength of the postsynaptic response may increase at both synapses.

▲ **Figure 49.19 Neural plasticity.** Synaptic connections can change over time, depending on the activity level at the synapse.

(a) Synapse prior to long-term potentiation (LTP). The NMDA glutamate receptors open in response to glutamate, but are blocked by Mg^{2+}.

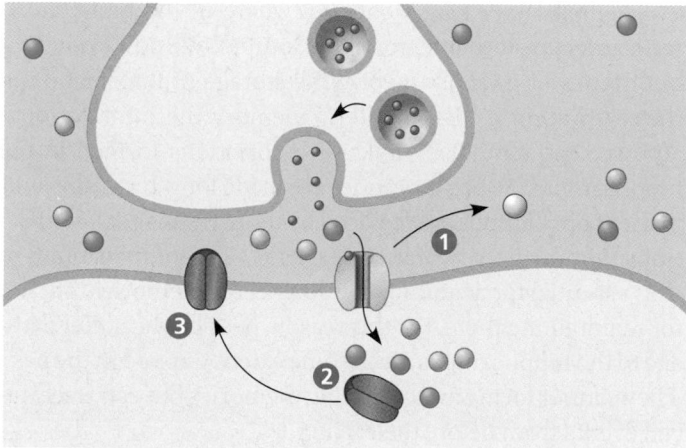

(b) Establishing LTP. Activity at nearby synapses depolarizes the postsynaptic membrane, causing Mg^{2+} release from NMDA receptors. The unblocked receptors respond to glutamate by allowing an influx of Na^+ and Ca^{2+}. The Ca^{2+} influx triggers insertion of stored AMPA glutamate receptors into the postsynaptic membrane.

(c) Synapse exhibiting LTP. Glutamate release activates AMPA receptors that trigger depolarization, unblocking NMDA receptors. Together, the AMPA and NMDA receptors trigger postsynaptic potentials strong enough to initiate action potentials without input from other synapses. Additional mechanisms (not shown) contribute to LTP, including receptor modification by protein kinases.

▲ **Figure 49.20 Long-term potentiation in the brain.**

Long-Term Potentiation

Researchers have identified several processes that can alter a synaptic connection, making the flow of communication either more efficient or less efficient. We will focus here on **long-term potentiation (LTP)**, a lasting increase in the strength of synaptic transmission. LTP, which was first characterized in tissue slices from the hippocampus, involves a presynaptic neuron that releases the excitatory neurotransmitter glutamate. For LTP to occur, there must be a brief high-frequency series of action potentials in this presynaptic neuron. In addition, these action potentials must arrive at the synaptic terminal at the same time that the postsynaptic cell receives a depolarizing stimulus.

LTP involves two types of glutamate receptors, each named for a molecule—NMDA or AMPA—that artificially activates that particular receptor. As shown in **Figure 49.20**, the set of receptors present on the postsynaptic membranes changes in response to an active synapse and a depolarizing stimulus. The result is LTP—a stable increase in the size of the postsynaptic potentials at the synapse. Because LTP can last for days or weeks in dissected tissue, it is thought to represent one of the fundamental processes by which memories are stored and learning takes place.

CONCEPT CHECK 49.4

1. Outline two mechanisms by which the flow of information between two neurons in adults is increased.
2. Individuals with localized brain damage have been very useful in the study of many brain functions. Why is this unlikely to be true for consciousness?
3. **WHAT IF?** Suppose that a person with damage to the hippocampus is unable to acquire new long-term memories. Why might the acquisition of short-term memories also be impaired?

For suggested answers, see Appendix A.

CONCEPT 49.5
Nervous system disorders can be explained in molecular terms

Disorders of the nervous system, including schizophrenia, depression, drug addiction, Alzheimer's disease, and Parkinson's disease, are a major public health problem. Together, they result in more hospitalizations in the United States than do heart disease or cancer. Until recently, hospitalization was typically the only available treatment, and many affected individuals were institutionalized for the rest of their lives. Today, many disorders that alter mood or behavior can be treated with medications, reducing average hospital stays for these disorders to only a few weeks. At the same time, societal attitudes are changing as awareness grows that nervous system disorders often result from chemical or anatomical changes in the brain.

Many challenges remain, however, especially for Alzheimer's and other diseases that lead to nervous system degeneration.

Major research efforts are under way to identify genes that cause or contribute to disorders of the nervous system. Identifying such genes offers hope for identifying causes, predicting outcomes, and developing effective treatments. For most nervous system disorders, however, genetic contributions only partially account for which individuals are affected. The other significant contribution to disease comes from environmental factors. Unfortunately, environmental contributions are typically very difficult to identify.

To distinguish between genetic and environmental variables, scientists often carry out family studies. In such studies, researchers track how family members are related genetically, which individuals are affected, and which family members grew up in the same household. These studies are especially informative when one of the affected individuals has a genetically identical twin or an adopted sibling who is genetically unrelated. The results of family studies indicate that certain nervous system disorders, such as schizophrenia, have a very strong genetic component **(Figure 49.21)**.

Schizophrenia

About 1% of the world's population suffer from **schizophrenia**, a severe mental disturbance characterized by psychotic episodes

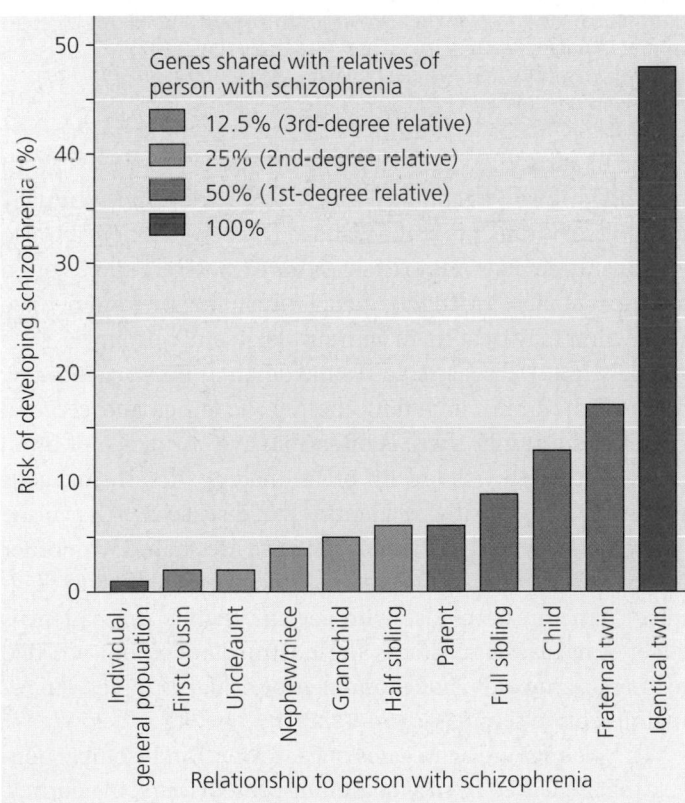

▲ **Figure 49.21 Genetic contribution to schizophrenia.** First cousins, uncles, and aunts of a person with schizophrenia have twice the risk of unrelated members of the population of developing the disease. The risks for closer relatives are many times greater.

in which patients have a distorted perception of reality. People with schizophrenia typically suffer from hallucinations (such as "voices" that only they can hear) and delusions (for example, the idea that others are plotting to harm them). Despite the commonly held notion, schizophrenia does not necessarily result in multiple personalities. Rather, the name schizophrenia (from the Greek *schizo*, split, and *phren*, mind) refers to the fragmentation of what are normally integrated brain functions.

Two lines of evidence suggest that schizophrenia affects neuronal pathways that use dopamine as a neurotransmitter. First, the drug amphetamine ("speed"), which stimulates dopamine release, can produce the same set of symptoms as schizophrenia. Second, many of the drugs that alleviate the symptoms of schizophrenia block dopamine receptors. Schizophrenia may also alter glutamate signaling, since the street drug "angel dust," or PCP, blocks glutamate receptors and induces strong schizophrenia-like symptoms.

Fortunately, medications frequently can alleviate the major symptoms of schizophrenia. Although the first treatments developed often had substantial negative side effects, newer medications are equally effective and much safer to use. Ongoing research aimed at identifying the genetic mutations responsible for schizophrenia may yield new insights about the causes of the disease and lead to even more effective therapies.

Depression

Depression is a disorder characterized by depressed mood, as well as abnormalities in sleep, appetite, and energy level. Two broad forms of depressive illness are known: major depressive disorder and bipolar disorder. Individuals affected by **major depressive disorder** undergo periods—often lasting many months—during which once enjoyable activities provide no pleasure and provoke no interest. One of the most common nervous system disorders, major depression affects about one in every seven adults at some point, and twice as many women as men. **Bipolar disorder**, or manic-depressive disorder, involves swings of mood from high to low and affects about 1% of the world's population. Like schizophrenia, bipolar disorder and major depression have genetic and environmental components.

In bipolar disorder, the manic phase is characterized by high self-esteem, increased energy, a flow of ideas, overtalkativeness, and increased risk taking. In its milder forms, this phase is sometimes associated with great creativity, and some well-known artists, musicians, and literary figures (including Vincent Van Gogh, Robert Schumann, Virginia Woolf, and Ernest Hemingway, to name a few) have had very productive periods during manic phases. The depressive phase comes with lowered ability to feel pleasure, loss of motivation, sleep disturbances, and feelings of worthlessness. These symptoms can be so severe that affected individuals attempt suicide. Nevertheless, some patients prefer to endure the depressive phase rather than take medication and risk losing the enhanced creative output of their manic phase.

Major depressive and bipolar disorders are among the nervous system disorders for which available therapies are most effective. Many drugs used to treat depressive illness, including fluoxetine (Prozac), increase the activity of biogenic amines in the brain. Depressive disorders are also sometimes treated with anticonvulsant drugs or lithium.

Drug Addiction and the Brain Reward System

Drug addiction is a disorder characterized by compulsive consumption of a drug and loss of control in limiting intake. Any of a number of drugs that vary considerably in their effects on the CNS can be addictive. For example, cocaine and amphetamine act as stimulants, whereas heroin is a pain-relieving sedative. However, all of these drugs, as well as alcohol and nicotine, are addictive for the same reason: Each increases activity of the brain's reward system, neural circuitry that normally functions in pleasure, motivation, and learning. In the absence of drug addiction, the reward system provides motivation for activities that enhance survival and reproduction, such as eating in response to hunger, drinking when thirsty, and engaging in sexual activity when aroused. In addicted individuals, "wanting" is instead directed toward further drug consumption.

Scientists have made enormous progress in learning how the brain's reward system works and how particular drugs affect its function. Laboratory animals have proved especially useful. Rats, for example, will provide themselves with cocaine, heroin, or amphetamine when given a dispensing system linked to a lever in their cage. Furthermore, they exhibit addictive behavior in such circumstances, continuing to self-administer the drug rather than seek food, even to the point of starvation. These and other studies have led to the identification of both the organization of the reward system and its key neurotransmitter, dopamine.

Inputs to the reward system are received by neurons in a region near the base of the brain called the *ventral tegmental area (VTA)*. When activated, these neurons direct action potentials along axons that synapse with neurons in specific regions of the cerebrum. There, the axon terminals release dopamine.

Addictive drugs affect the reward system in several ways. First, each drug has an immediate effect that enhances the activity of the dopamine pathway **(Figure 49.22)**. As addiction develops, there are also long-lasting changes in the reward circuitry. The result is a craving for the drug that is present independent of any pleasure associated with consumption. As scientists continue to expand their knowledge about both the reward system and addiction, there is hope that the insights will lead to more effective prevention measures and treatments.

Alzheimer's Disease

Alzheimer's disease is a mental deterioration, or dementia, characterized by confusion, memory loss, and a variety of other symptoms. Its incidence is age related, rising from about 10% at

▲ Figure 49.22 Effects of addictive drugs on the reward pathway of the mammalian brain. Addictive drugs alter the transmission of signals in the pathway formed by neurons of the ventral tegmental area (VTA).

? *If you depolarized the cell bodies in the ventral tegmental area, what effect would you expect?*

age 65 to about 35% at age 85. The disease is progressive, with patients gradually becoming less able to function and eventually needing to be dressed, bathed, and fed by others. There are also personality changes, almost always for the worse. Patients often lose their ability to recognize people, including their immediate family, and may treat them with suspicion and hostility.

Alzheimer's disease leads to the death of neurons in many areas of the brain, including the hippocampus and cerebral cortex. As a result, there is often massive shrinkage of brain tissue. Although visible with brain imaging, this shrinkage is not enough to positively identify the disease. Furthermore, many symptoms of Alzheimer's disease are shared with other forms of dementia. It is therefore difficult for doctors to diagnose Alzheimer's disease with certainty while the patient is alive. What is diagnostic is the postmortem finding of two features—amyloid plaques and neurofibrillary tangles—in remaining brain tissue **(Figure 49.23)**.

The plaques are aggregates of β-amyloid, an insoluble peptide that is cleaved from a membrane protein found in neurons. Membrane enzymes, called secretases, catalyze the cleavage, causing β-amyloid to accumulate in plaques outside the neurons. It is these plaques that appear to trigger the death of surrounding neurons.

Amyloid plaque   Neurofibrillary tangle   20 μm

▲ **Figure 49.23 Microscopic signs of Alzheimer's disease.**
A hallmark of Alzheimer's disease is the presence in brain tissue of
neurofibrillary tangles surrounding plaques made of β-amyloid (LM).

The neurofibrillary tangles observed in Alzheimer's disease
are primarily made up of the tau protein. (This protein is unrelated to the τ (tau) mutation that affects circadian rhythm in hamsters; see Figure 49.12.) The normal function of tau in neurons is
to help regulate the movement of nutrients along microtubules.
In Alzheimer's disease, tau undergoes changes that cause it to
bind to itself, resulting in neurofibrillary tangles. There is evidence that changes in tau are associated with the appearance of
Alzheimer's disease in relatively young individuals.

An enormous effort has led to the recent development of
drugs that are partially effective in relieving the symptoms of
Alzheimer's disease, but there is currently no cure.

Parkinson's Disease

A motor disorder, **Parkinson's disease** is characterized by difficulty in initiating movements, slowness of movement, and rigidity. Patients often have muscle tremors, poor balance, a flexed
posture, and a shuffling gait. Their facial muscles become rigid,
making them less able to vary their expressions. Like Alzheimer's
disease, Parkinson's disease is a progressive brain illness and is
more common with advancing age. The incidence of Parkinson's
disease is about 1% at age 65 and about 5% at age 85. In the U.S.
population, approximately 1 million people are afflicted.

The symptoms of Parkinson's disease result from the death
of neurons in the midbrain that normally release dopamine at
synapses in the basal nuclei. As with Alzheimer's disease, protein aggregates accumulate. Most cases of Parkinson's disease
lack an identifiable cause; however, a rare form of the disease
that appears in relatively young adults has a clear genetic basis. Molecular studies of mutations linked to this early-onset
Parkinson's disease reveal disruption of genes required for certain mitochondrial functions. Researches are investigating
whether mitochondrial defects also contribute to the more
frequent form of the disease in older patients.

At present there is no cure for Parkinson's disease. Approaches used to manage the symptoms include brain surgery,
deep-brain stimulation, and drugs such as L-dopa, a molecule
that can cross the blood-brain barrier and be converted to
dopamine in the CNS. One potential cure is to implant
dopamine-secreting neurons, either in the midbrain or in the
basal nuclei. Laboratory studies of this strategy show promise:
In rats with an experimentally induced condition that mimics
Parkinson's disease, implanting dopamine-secreting neurons
can lead to a recovery of motor control. Whether this regener-
ative approach can also work in humans is one of many important questions in modern brain research.

Stem Cell-Based Therapy

A major current research effort is directed at finding ways to replace brain tissue that has ceased to function properly. Unlike the
PNS, the mammalian CNS cannot fully repair itself when damaged or diseased. Surviving neurons in the brain can make new
connections and sometimes compensate for damage, as in the
remarkable recoveries of some stroke victims. Generally speaking, however, brain and spinal cord injuries, strokes, and disorders that destroy CNS neurons, such as Alzheimer's disease and
Parkinson's disease, have devastating and irreversible effects.

The possibility of repairing a damaged or diseased brain with
new nerve cells became much more plausible after a groundbreaking 1998 report that the adult human brain produces new
neurons. This finding, which overturned a widely held idea, resulted from research carried out by Fred Gage at the Salk Institute
in California and Peter Ericksson at the Sahlgrenska University
Hospital in Sweden. The evidence that new neurons form in the
brains of adults came from a group of terminally ill cancer patients who had agreed to donate their brains for research upon
their death. To monitor their tumor growth, the patients were
given bromodeoxyuridine (BrdU), an altered nucleotide that is
incorporated into DNA during replication. DNA containing
BrdU can be readily detected and thus marks cells that grow and
divide after BrdU enters the body. Gage and Ericksson reasoned
that BrdU would mark not only the growing tumor but also any
cells in the brain that had recently divided. When the patients
were examined postmortem, there was evidence of newly divided
neurons in the hippocampus of each brain (**Figure 49.24**).

The discovery of dividing neurons in the adult brain indicated the presence of stem cells. Recall from Chapters 20 and 46

◀ **Figure 49.24 A
newly born neuron in
the hippocampus of a
human adult.** All the red
cells in this LM are neurons.
The cell that is both red
and green is a neuron that
has incorporated BrdU,
indicating that it resulted
from a recent cell division.

10 μm

that stem cells retain the ability to divide indefinitely. While some of their progeny remain undifferentiated, others differentiate into specialized cells. In the brain, the stem cells are called neural progenitor cells and are committed to becoming either neurons or glia. One goal of researchers is to find a way to induce the body's own neural progenitor cells to differentiate into specific types of neurons or glia when and where they are needed. Another quest is to restore function in a damaged CNS by transplantation of cultured neural progenitor cells.

Having surveyed CNS organization and function, we will examine in the next chapter how sensory systems gather the signals processed by the CNS and how the responses initiated by the CNS lead to muscle contraction and locomotion.

Chapter 49 Review

SUMMARY OF KEY CONCEPTS

CONCEPT 49.1

Nervous systems consist of circuits of neurons and supporting cells (pp. 1064–1069)

▶ Invertebrate nervous systems range in complexity from simple nerve nets to highly centralized nervous systems having complicated brains and ventral nerve cords. In vertebrates, the central nervous system (CNS) consists of the brain and the spinal cord, which is located dorsally. The CNS integrates information, while the nerves of the peripheral nervous system (PNS) transmit sensory and motor signals between the CNS and the rest of the body.

▶ **Organization of the Vertebrate Nervous System** The simplest circuits in the vertebrate nervous system are found in reflex responses in which sensory input is linked to motor output without involvement of the brain. Neurons in vertebrates are supported by several types of glia, including astrocytes, oligodendrocytes, Schwann cells, ependymal cells, and radial glia.

▶ **The Peripheral Nervous System** The PNS consists of paired cranial and spinal nerves and associated ganglia. Signals reach the CNS along afferent neurons and leave the CNS via efferent neurons. The efferent neurons function in either the motor system, which carries signals to skeletal muscles, or the autonomic nervous system, which regulates the primarily automatic, visceral functions of smooth and cardiac muscles. The autonomic nervous system has three divisions: the sympathetic and parasympathetic divisions, which usually have antagonistic effects on target organs, and the enteric division, which controls the activity of the digestive tract, pancreas, and gallbladder.

MEDIA

Activity Neuron Structure

CONCEPT 49.2

The vertebrate brain is regionally specialized (pp. 1070–1074)

▶ **The Brainstem** The pons and medulla serve as relay stations for information traveling between the PNS and the higher brain. The reticular formation, a network of neurons within the brainstem, regulates sleep and arousal.

▶ **The Cerebellum** The cerebellum helps coordinate motor, perceptual, and cognitive functions. It also is involved in learning and remembering motor skills.

▶ **The Diencephalon** The thalamus is the main center through which sensory and motor information passes to the cerebrum. The hypothalamus regulates homeostasis and basic survival behaviors. In addition, the suprachiasmatic nucleus (SCN) in the hypothalamus acts as the pacemaker for circadian rhythms.

▶ **The Cerebrum** The cerebrum has two hemispheres, each of which consists of cortical gray matter overlying white matter and basal nuclei, which are important in planning and learning movements. In mammals, the convoluted cerebral cortex is also called the neocortex. A thick band of axons, the corpus callosum, provides communication between the right and left cerebral cortices.

▶ **Evolution of Cognition in Vertebrates** The region of the avian brain called the pallium contains clustered nuclei that carry out functions similar to those performed by the mammalian cerebral cortex.

CONCEPT **49.3**

The cerebral cortex controls voluntary movement and cognitive functions (pp. 1075–1078)

▶ Each side of the cerebral cortex has four lobes—frontal, temporal, occipital, and parietal—that contain primary sensory areas and association areas.

▶ **Information Processing in the Cerebral Cortex** Specific types of sensory input enter the primary sensory areas. Adjacent association areas process particular features in the sensory input and integrate information from different sensory areas. In the somatosensory cortex and the motor cortex, neurons are distributed according to the part of the body that generates sensory input or receives motor commands.

▶ **Language and Speech** Portions of the frontal and temporal lobes, including Broca's area and Wernicke's area, are essential for generating and understanding language.

▶ **Lateralization of Cortical Function** The left cerebral hemisphere has a dominant role with regard to language and is often the focus of math and logic operations. The right hemisphere appears to be stronger at pattern recognition and nonverbal thinking. At least some of this lateralization of functions relates to handedness.

▶ **Emotions** The generation and experience of emotions involve many regions of the brain, with the amygdala playing a key role in recognizing and recalling a number of emotions.

▶ **Consciousness** Modern brain-imaging techniques suggest that consciousness may be an emergent property of the brain based on activity in many areas of the cortex.

CONCEPT **49.4**

Changes in synaptic connections underlie memory and learning (pp. 1078–1080)

▶ During development, more neurons and synapses form than are needed. The programmed death of neurons and elimination of synapses in embryos establish the basic structure of the nervous system.

▶ **Neural Plasticity** Reshaping of the adult nervous system often occurs at synapses. Changes can involve the loss or addition of a synapse or the strengthening or weakening of signaling at a synapse.

▶ **Memory and Learning** Short-term memory relies on temporary associations in the hippocampus. In long-term memory, these temporary links are replaced by connections within the cerebral cortex. This transfer of information from short-term to long-term memory is enhanced by the association of new data with that already in long-term memory.

▶ **Long-Term Potentiation** LTP is a lasting increase in the strength of synaptic transmission and appears to be an important process in memory storage and learning.

MEDIA

Activity Signal Transmission at a Chemical Synapse

CONCEPT **49.5**

Nervous system disorders can be explained in molecular terms (pp. 1080–1084)

▶ **Schizophrenia** Schizophrenia, which is characterized by hallucinations, delusions, and other symptoms, affects neuronal pathways that use dopamine as a neurotransmitter.

▶ **Depression** Bipolar disorder, characterized by manic (high-mood) and depressive (low-mood) phases, and major depression, in which patients have a persistent low mood, are often treated with drugs that increase the activity of biogenic amines in the brain.

▶ **Drug Addiction and the Brain Reward System** The compulsive drug use that characterizes addiction reflects altered activity of the brain's reward system, which normally provides motivation for actions, such as eating, that enhance survival or reproduction.

▶ **Alzheimer's Disease** Alzheimer's disease is an age-related dementia in which neurofibrillary tangles and amyloid plaques form in the brain.

▶ **Parkinson's Disease** Parkinson's disease is a motor disorder caused by the death of dopamine-secreting neurons and associated with the presence of protein aggregates.

▶ **Stem Cell-Based Therapy** The adult human brain contains stem cells that can differentiate into mature neurons. The induction of stem cell differentiation and the transplantation of cultured stem cells are potential methods for replacing neurons lost to trauma or disease.

TESTING YOUR KNOWLEDGE

SELF-QUIZ

1. Wakefulness is regulated by the reticular formation, which is present in the
   a. basal nuclei.
   b. cerebral cortex.
   c. brainstem.
   d. limbic system.
   e. spinal cord.

2. Which of the following structures or regions is *incorrectly* paired with its function?
   a. limbic system—motor control of speech
   b. medulla oblongata—homeostatic control
   c. cerebellum—coordination of movement and balance
   d. corpus callosum—communication between the left and right cerebral cortices
   e. hypothalamus—regulation of temperature, hunger, and thirst

3. What is the neocortex?
   a. a primitive brain region that is common to reptiles and mammals
   b. a region deep in the cortex that is associated with the formation of emotional memories
   c. a central part of the cortex that receives olfactory information

d. an additional outer layer of neurons in the cerebral cortex that is unique to mammals

e. an association area of the frontal lobe that is involved in higher cognitive functions

4. Patients with damage to Wernicke's area have difficulty
   a. coordinating limb movement.
   b. generating speech.
   c. recognizing faces.
   d. understanding language.
   e. experiencing emotion.

5. The sympathetic division of the autonomic portion of the PNS does all of the following *except*
   a. relaxing bronchi in lungs.
   b. inhibiting bladder emptying.
   c. stimulating glucose release.
   d. accelerating heart rate.
   e. stimulating the salivary glands.

6. The cerebral cortex plays a major role in all of the following *except*
   a. short-term memory.
   b. long-term memory.
   c. circadian rhythm.
   d. foot-tapping rhythm.
   e. breath holding.

7. **DRAW IT** Draw a simple circuit for the pain withdrawal reflex that pulls your hand away when you prick your finger on a sharp object. (a) Using a circle to represent the spinal cord, label the types of neurons, the direction of information flow in each, and the locations of synapses. (b) Draw a simple diagram of the brain indicating where pain would eventually be perceived.

For Self-Quiz answers, see Appendix A.

MEDIA Visit www.campbellbiology.com for a Practice Test.

EVOLUTION CONNECTION

8. Scientists often use measures of "higher-order thinking" to assess intelligence in other animals. For example, birds are judged to have sophisticated thought processes because they can use tools and make use of abstract concepts. What problems do you see in defining intelligence in these ways?

SCIENTIFIC INQUIRY

9. Consider an individual who had been fluent in American Sign Language before suffering damage to the left cerebral hemisphere. After the injury, this person could still understand signs, but could not readily generate signs that represented his thoughts. What two hypotheses might explain this finding, and how might you distinguish between them?

SCIENCE, TECHNOLOGY, AND SOCIETY

10. With increasingly sophisticated methods for scanning brain activity, scientists are rapidly developing the ability to detect an individual's particular emotions and thought processes from outside the body. What benefits and problems do you envision when such technology becomes readily available?

50
Sensory and Motor Mechanisms

▲ Figure 50.1 **Can a moth evade a bat in the dark?**

OVERVIEW

Sensing and Acting

A flash of light reveals an instant in a nighttime confrontation (**Figure 50.1**). A bat, patrolling the summer air in search of food, is on the verge of catching a moth. Startled from its flight, the moth has only a fraction of a second to escape death. What will happen?

Both predator and prey rely on sensation and response. The bat produces pulses of sound and uses the returning echoes to direct its flight toward the moth. At the same time, the bat's ultrasonic chirps activate vibration sensors in the abdomen of the moth. The moth most likely detects the bat at 30 m, a distance ten times that at which the bat could sense the moth. Altering the motor output to its wing muscles, the moth begins an evasive maneuver. The bat, however, flies much faster than the moth. In this encounter, the insect is unlikely to survive.

The detection and processing of sensory information and the generation of motor output provide the physiological basis for all animal activity. Although it is customary to think of behavior as a linear sequence of sensing, analyzing, and acting, this is not the case. When animals are in motion, they are constantly probing the environment, sensing changes and using the information to generate the next action. This is a continuous cycle rather than a linear sequence, with sensation directing output and action altering sensory input.

In this chapter, we will explore the processes of sensing and acting in both invertebrates and vertebrates. We will start with sensory processes that convey information about the external and internal environment to the brain. We will then consider the structure and function of muscles and skeletons that carry out movements as instructed by the brain. Finally, we will investigate various mechanisms of animal movement.

CONCEPT 50.1

Sensory receptors transduce stimulus energy and transmit signals to the central nervous system

All stimuli represent forms of energy. Sensation involves converting this energy to a change in the membrane potential of sensory receptor cells and thereby regulating the output of action potentials to the central nervous system (CNS).

Sensory Pathways

We'll begin our consideration of sensory systems with the sensory pathway controlled by the stretch receptor of a crayfish

1 Reception
Bending of crayfish activates stretch receptor in muscle.

2 Transduction
Stretch receptor converts muscle deflection to a change in membrane potential in the cell body (receptor potential).

3 Transmission
Receptor potential triggers action potentials that travel along the axon of the stretch receptor.

4 Perception
Processing of action potentials that reach the brain via the axon of the stretch receptor produces perception of body bending.

▲ **Figure 50.2 A simple sensory pathway: Response of a crayfish stretch receptor to bending.**

(Figure 50.2). This and other sensory pathways have in common four basic functions: sensory reception, transduction, transmission, and perception.

Sensory Reception and Transduction

A sensory pathway begins with **sensory reception**, the detection of a stimulus by sensory cells. Most sensory cells are specialized neurons or epithelial cells. Some exist singly; others are found collected in sensory organs, such as eyes and ears. Sensory cells and organs, as well as the structures within sensory cells that respond to specific stimuli, are called **sensory receptors**. Many sensory receptors detect stimuli from outside the body, such as heat, light, pressure, and chemicals, but there are also receptors for stimuli from within the body, such as blood pressure and body position.

In the case of the crayfish, bending of body muscle stimulates stretch-sensitive dendrites in the stretch receptor cell to open ion channels (see Figure 50.2). In other sensory receptors, channels open or close when substances outside the cell bind to proteins on the membrane or when pigments in the sensory receptor absorb light. The resulting flow of ions across the plasma membrane changes the membrane potential.

The conversion of a physical or chemical stimulus to a change in the membrane potential of a sensory receptor is called **sensory transduction**, and the change in membrane potential itself is known as a **receptor potential**. Receptor potentials are graded potentials; their magnitude varies with the strength of the stimulus (see Figure 50.2).

One remarkable feature of many sensory receptors is their extreme sensitivity: They can detect the smallest possible physical unit of stimulus. For example, most light receptors can detect a single quantum (photon) of light, and chemical receptors can detect a single molecule.

Transmission

Sensory information is transmitted through the nervous system in the form of nerve impulses, or action potentials. For many sensory receptors, transducing the energy in a stimulus into a receptor potential initiates **transmission** of action potentials to the CNS. Some sensory receptor cells, such as the crayfish stretch receptor, are neurons that produce action potentials; they have an axon that extends into the CNS (see Figure 50.2). As we will see shortly, other sensory receptor cells release neurotransmitters at synapses with sensory (afferent) neurons. At almost all such synapses, the receptor releases an excitatory neurotransmitter. (One exception is in the vertebrate visual system, discussed in Concept 50.4.)

The magnitude of a receptor potential controls the rate at which action potentials are produced by a sensory receptor. If the receptor is a sensory neuron, a larger receptor potential results in more frequent action potentials (see Figure 50.2). If the receptor is not a sensory neuron, a larger receptor potential causes more neurotransmitter to be released, which usually increases the production of action potentials by the postsynaptic neuron.

Many sensory neurons spontaneously generate action potentials at a low rate. In these neurons, a stimulus does not switch the production of action potentials on or off, but it does change how often an action potential is produced. In this manner, such neurons are also able to alert the CNS to changes in stimulus intensity.

Processing of sensory information can occur before, during, and after transmission of action potentials to the CNS. In many cases, the *integration* of sensory information begins as soon as the information is received. Receptor potentials produced by stimuli delivered to different parts of a sensory receptor cell are integrated through summation, as are postsynaptic potentials in sensory neurons that synapse with multiple receptors (see Figure 48.16). As we will discuss shortly, sensory structures such as eyes also provide higher levels of integration, and the brain further processes all incoming signals.

Perception

When action potentials reach the brain via sensory neurons, circuits of neurons process this input, generating the **perception** of the stimuli. Perceptions—such as colors, smells, sounds, and tastes—are constructions formed in the brain and do not exist outside it. If a tree falls and no animal is present to hear it, is there a sound? The fall certainly produces pressure waves in the air, but if sound is defined as a perception, then there is none unless an animal senses the waves and its brain perceives them.

Action potentials are all-or-none events (see Figure 48.9c). An action potential triggered by light striking the eye has the same properties as an action potential triggered by air vibrating in the ear. How, then, do we distinguish sights, sounds, and other stimuli? The answer lies in the connections that link sensory receptors to the brain. Action potentials from sensory receptors travel along neurons that are dedicated to a particular stimulus; these dedicated neurons synapse with particular neurons in the brain or spinal cord. As a result, the brain distinguishes sensory stimuli such as sight or sound solely by along which paths to the brain the action potentials arrive.

Amplification and Adaptation

The transduction of stimuli by sensory receptors is subject to two types of modification—amplification and adaptation. **Amplification** refers to the strengthening of stimulus energy during transduction. The effect can be considerable. For example, an action potential conducted from the eye to the human brain has about 100,000 times as much energy as the few photons of light that triggered it. Amplification that occurs in

sensory receptor cells often requires signal transduction pathways involving second messengers. Because these pathways include enzyme-catalyzed reactions, they amplify signal strength through the formation of many product molecules by a single enzyme molecule. Amplification may also take place in accessory structures of a complex sense organ, as when sound waves are enhanced by a factor of more than 20 before reaching receptors in the innermost part of the ear.

Upon continued stimulation, many receptors undergo a decrease in responsiveness termed **sensory adaptation** (not to be confused with the evolutionary term *adaptation*). Without sensory adaptation, you would be constantly aware of feeling every beat of your heart and every bit of clothing on your body. Adaptation also enables you to see, hear, and smell changes in environments that vary widely in stimulus intensity.

Types of Sensory Receptors

A sensory cell typically has a single type of receptor specific for a particular stimulus, such as light or cold. Often, distinct cells and receptors are responsible for particular qualities of a sensation, such as distinguishing red from blue. Before exploring these specializations, let's consider sensory receptor function at a more basic level. We can classify sensory receptors into five categories based on the nature of the stimuli they transduce: mechanoreceptors, chemoreceptors, electromagnetic receptors, thermoreceptors, and pain receptors.

Mechanoreceptors

Mechanoreceptors sense physical deformation caused by forms of mechanical energy such as pressure, touch, stretch, motion, and sound. Mechanoreceptors typically consist of ion channels that are linked to structures that extend outside the cell, such as "hairs" (cilia), as well as internal cell structures, such as the cytoskeleton. Bending or stretching of the external structure generates tension that alters the permeability of the ion channels. This change in ion permeability alters the membrane potential, resulting in a depolarization or hyperpolarization (see Chapter 48).

The vertebrate stretch receptor, like that of the crayfish (see Figure 50.2), is a mechanoreceptor that detects muscle movement. The mechanoreceptors in this case are dendrites of sensory neurons that spiral around the middle of small skeletal muscle fibers. Groups of about 2 to 12 of these fibers, formed into a spindle shape and surrounded by connective tissue, are distributed throughout the muscle, parallel to other muscle fibers. When the muscle is stretched, the spindle fibers are stretched, depolarizing sensory neurons and triggering action potentials that are transmitted to the spinal cord. The familiar knee-jerk reflex (see Figure 49.3) relies on just this type of interaction between spindle fibers and stretch receptors.

The mammalian sense of touch also relies on mechanoreceptors that are the dendrites of sensory neurons. Touch receptors

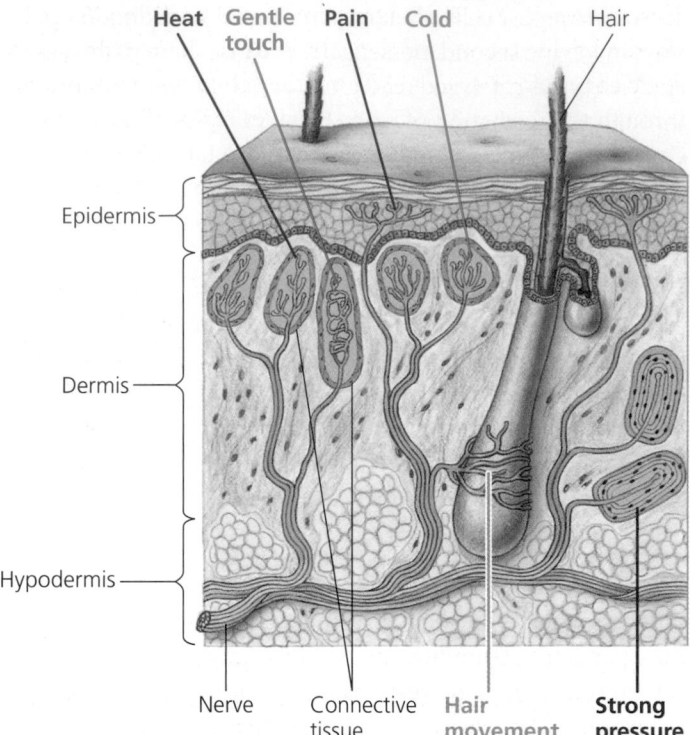

▲ Figure 50.3 **Sensory receptors in human skin.** Most receptors in the dermis are encapsulated by connective tissue. Receptors in the epidermis are naked dendrites, as are hair movement receptors that wind around the base of hairs in the dermis.

▲ Figure 50.4 **Chemoreceptors in an insect.** The antennae of the male silkworm moth *Bombyx mori* are covered with sensory hairs, visible in the SEM enlargement. The hairs have chemoreceptors that are highly sensitive to the sex pheromone released by the female.

are often embedded in layers of connective tissue. The structure of the connective tissue and the location of the receptors dramatically affect the type of mechanical energy (light touch, vibration, or strong pressure) that best stimulates them **(Figure 50.3)**. Receptors that detect a light touch or vibration are close to the surface of the skin; they transduce very slight inputs of mechanical energy into receptor potentials. Receptors that respond to stronger pressure and vibrations are in deep skin layers. Other receptors sense movement of hairs. For example, cats and many rodents have extremely sensitive mechanoreceptors at the base of their whiskers. Because deflection of different whiskers triggers action potentials that reach different cells in the brain, an animal's whiskers provide detailed information about nearby objects.

Chemoreceptors

Chemoreceptors include both general receptors—those that transmit information about total solute concentration—and specific receptors—those that respond to individual kinds of molecules. Osmoreceptors in the mammalian brain, for example, are general receptors that detect changes in the total solute concentration of the blood and stimulate thirst when osmolarity increases (see Figure 44.19). Most animals also have receptors for specific molecules, including glucose, oxygen, carbon dioxide, and amino acids. Two of the most sensitive and specific chemoreceptors known are found in the antennae of the male

silkworm moth **(Figure 50.4)**; they detect the two chemical components of the female moth sex pheromone. In all these examples, the stimulus molecule binds to the specific chemoreceptor on the membrane of the sensory cell and initiates changes in ion permeability.

Electromagnetic Receptors

Electromagnetic receptors detect various forms of electromagnetic energy, such as visible light, electricity, and magnetism. Photoreceptors, electromagnetic receptors that detect energy in the form of light, are often organized into eyes. Some snakes have very sensitive infrared receptors that detect the body heat of prey **(Figure 50.5a)**. Some fishes generate electrical currents and use electroreceptors to locate objects, such as prey, that disturb those currents. The platypus, a monotreme mammal, has electroreceptors on its bill that probably detect electric fields generated by the muscles of crustaceans, frogs, small fish, and other prey. Many animals appear to use Earth's magnetic field lines to orient themselves as they migrate **(Figure 50.5b)**. The iron-containing mineral magnetite is found in the skulls of many vertebrates (including salmon, pigeons, sea turtles, and humans), in the abdomen of bees, in the teeth of some molluscs, and in certain protists and prokaryotes that orient to Earth's magnetic field. Once collected by sailors to make compasses for navigation, magnetite may be part of an orienting mechanism in many animals (see Chapter 51).

(a) This rattlesnake and other pit vipers have a pair of infrared receptors, one anterior to and just below each eye. These organs are sensitive enough to detect the infrared radiation emitted by a warm mouse a meter away. The snake moves its head from side to side until the radiation is detected equally by the two receptors, indicating that the mouse is straight ahead.

(b) Some migrating animals, such as these beluga whales, apparently sense Earth's magnetic field and use the information, along with other cues, for orientation.

▲ **Figure 50.5 Specialized electromagnetic receptors.**

Thermoreceptors

Thermoreceptors detect heat and cold. Located in the skin and in the anterior hypothalamus, thermoreceptor cells send information to the body's thermostat, located in the posterior hypothalamus. The key to understanding how sensory cells detect temperature initially came from the dinner table, not the laboratory. Jalapeno and cayenne peppers taste "hot" because they contain a natural product called capsaicin. It turns out that exposing sensory neurons to capsaicin triggers an influx of calcium ions. When scientists identified the receptor protein that opens a calcium channel upon binding capsaicin, they made a fascinating discovery: The receptor responds not only to the chemical capsaicin, but also to high temperatures (42°C or higher). In essence, we describe spicy foods as "hot" because they activate the same sensory receptors as do hot soup and coffee.

Mammals have a number of kinds of thermoreceptors, each specific for a particular temperature range. The capsaicin receptor and at least five other types of thermoreceptors be-

long to the TRP (transient receptor potential) family of ion channel proteins. Remarkably, the TRP-type receptor specific for temperatures below 28°C can be activated by menthol, a plant product that we perceive to have a "cool" flavor.

Pain Receptors

Extreme pressure or temperature, as well as certain chemicals, can damage animal tissues. To detect stimuli that reflect such noxious (or harmful) conditions, animals rely on **nociceptors** (from the Latin *nocere*, to hurt), also called **pain receptors**. By triggering defensive reactions, such as withdrawal from danger, the perception of pain serves an important function. Rare individuals who are born without the ability to perceive pain may die from conditions such as a ruptured appendix because they cannot feel the associated pain and are unaware of the danger.

In humans, certain naked dendrites detect noxious thermal, mechanical, or chemical stimuli (see Figure 50.3). The capsaicin receptor, which acts as a thermoreceptor, is thus also a nociceptor. Although nociceptor density is highest in skin, some pain receptors are associated with other organs.

Chemicals produced in an animal's body sometimes enhance the perception of pain. For example, damaged tissues produce prostaglandins, which act as local regulators of inflammation (see Chapter 45). Prostaglandins worsen pain by increasing nociceptor sensitivity to noxious stimuli. Aspirin and ibuprofen reduce pain by inhibiting the synthesis of prostaglandins.

CONCEPT CHECK 50.1

1. Which one of the five categories of sensory receptors is primarily dedicated to external stimuli?
2. Why does eating food containing "hot" peppers sometimes cause you to sweat?
3. **WHAT IF?** If you stimulated a sensory neuron electrically, how would that stimulation be perceived?

For suggested answers, see Appendix A.

CONCEPT 50.2

The mechanoreceptors responsible for hearing and equilibrium detect moving fluid or settling particles

Hearing and the perception of body equilibrium, or balance, are related in most animals. For both senses, mechanoreceptor cells produce receptor potentials when settling particles or moving fluid cause deflection of cell surface structures.

Sensing of Gravity and Sound in Invertebrates

To sense gravity and maintain equilibrium, most invertebrates rely on sensory organs called **statocysts** (Figure 50.6). A common type of statocyst consists of a layer of ciliated receptor cells surrounding a chamber that contains one or more **statoliths**, which are grains of sand or other dense granules. Gravity causes the statoliths to settle to the low point in the chamber, stimulating mechanoreceptors in that location. Such statocysts can be found at the fringe of jellies and at the base of antennules in lobsters and crayfish. In experiments in which statoliths were replaced with metal shavings, researchers "tricked" crayfish into swimming upside down by using magnets to pull the shavings to the upper end of the statocysts.

Many (perhaps most) insects have body hairs that vibrate in response to sound waves. Hairs of different stiffnesses and lengths vibrate at different frequencies. Often, hairs are tuned to frequencies of sounds produced by other organisms. For example, some caterpillars have vibrating body hairs that can detect the buzzing wings of predatory wasps, warning the caterpillars of the danger. Similarly, fine hairs on the antennae of a male mosquito vibrate in a specific way in response to the hum produced by the beating wings of flying females. In this way, the male mosquito can locate a potential mate. The importance of this sensory system for mosquitoes in mate attraction can be demonstrated very simply: A tuning fork vibrating at the same frequency as a that of a female's wings will by itself attract males.

Many insects also detect sound by means of "ears" consisting of a tympanic membrane (eardrum) stretched over an internal air chamber (Figure 50.7). Sound waves vibrate the tympanic membrane, stimulating receptor cells attached to the

▲ **Figure 50.7 An insect's "ear"—on its leg.** The tympanic membrane, visible in this SEM of a cricket's front leg, vibrates in response to sound waves. The vibrations stimulate mechanoreceptors attached to the inside of the tympanic membrane.

inside of the membrane and resulting in nerve impulses that are transmitted to the brain. As discussed at the beginning of the chapter, this sensory system allows some moths to perceive the high-pitched sounds produced by bats, potentially helping the moth to escape. Similarly, a cockroach's ability to detect vibrations caused by a descending human foot often provides enough warning for the insect to avoid being crushed.

Hearing and Equilibrium in Mammals

In mammals, as in most other terrestrial vertebrates, the sensory organs for hearing and equilibrium are closely associated. **Figure 50.8** explores the structure and function of these organs in the human ear.

Hearing

Vibrating objects, such as a plucked guitar string or the vocal cords of your instructor, create pressure waves in the surrounding air. In *hearing*, the ear converts the energy of these waves to nerve impulses that the brain perceives as sound. To hear music, speech, or noise in our environment, we rely on sensory receptors that are hair cells, a type of mechanoreceptor. Before the vibration waves reach the hair cells, however, they are amplified and transformed by several accessory structures.

The first steps in hearing involve structures in the ear that convert the vibrations of moving air to pressure waves in fluid. Upon reaching the outer ear, moving air causes the tympanic membrane to vibrate. The three bones of the middle ear transmit the vibrations to the oval window, a membrane on the cochlea's surface. When one of those bones, the stapes, vibrates against the oval window, it creates pressure waves in the fluid inside the cochlea.

Upon entering the vestibular canal, the fluid pressure waves push down on the cochlear duct and basilar membrane. In response, the basilar membrane and attached hair cells vibrate up and down. The hairs projecting from the moving hair cells are

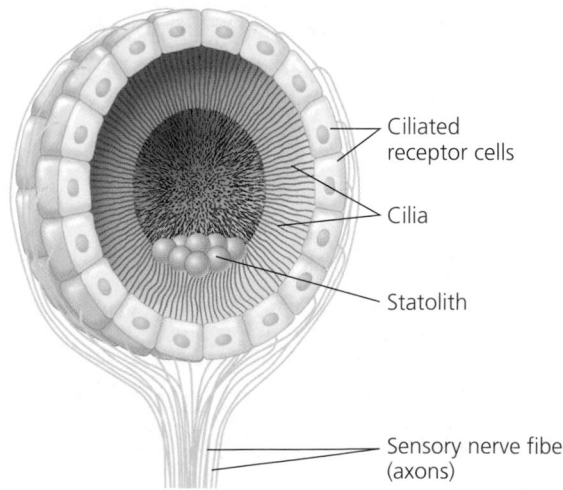

Ciliated
receptor cells

Cilia

Statolith

Sensory nerve fibers
(axons)

▲ **Figure 50.6 The statocyst of an invertebrate.** The settling of statoliths to the low point in the chamber bends cilia on receptor cells in that location, providing the brain with information about the orientation of the body with respect to gravity.

▼ Figure 50.8

Exploring The Structure of the Human Ear

1 Overview of Ear Structure The **outer ear** consists of the external pinna and the auditory canal, which collect sound waves and channel them to the **tympanic membrane** (eardrum), separating the outer and middle ear. In the **middle ear**, three small bones—the malleus (hammer), incus (anvil), and stapes (stirrup) transmit vibrations to the **oval window**, which is a membrane beneath the stapes. The middle ear also opens into the **Eustachian tube**, which connects to the pharynx and equalizes pressure between the middle ear and the atmosphere. The **inner ear** consists of fluid-filled chambers, including the **semicircular canals**, which function in equilibrium, and the coiled **cochlea** (Latin, "snail"), which is involved in hearing.

2 The Cochlea The cochlea has two large canals—an upper vestibular canal and a lower tympanic canal—separated by a smaller cochlear duct. The vestibular and tympanic canals contain a fluid called perilymph, and the cochlear duct is filled with a fluid called endolymph.

Hair cell bundle from a bullfrog; the longest cilia shown are about 8 μm (SEM).

4 Hair Cells Projecting from each hair cell is a bundle of rod-shaped "hairs," each containing a core of actin filaments. Vibration of the basilar membrane in response to sound raises and lowers the hair cells, bending the hairs against the surrounding fluid and the tectorial membrane. Displacement of the hairs within the bundle activates mechanoreceptors, changing the hair cell membrane potential.

3 The Organ of Corti The floor of the cochlear duct, the basilar membrane, bears the **organ of Corti**, which contains the mechanoreceptors of the ear, hair cells with hairs projecting into the cochlear duct. Many of the hairs are attached to the tectorial membrane, which hangs over the organ of Corti like an awning. Sound waves make the basilar membrane vibrate, which results in bending of the hairs and depolarization of the hair cells.

CHAPTER FIFTY Sensory and Motor Mechanisms **1093**

deflected by the tectorial membrane that lies in a fixed position immediately above (see Figure 50.8). With each vibration, the hairs projecting above the hair cells bend first in one direction and then the other. Mechanoreceptors in the hair cells respond to the bending by opening or closing ion channels in the plasma membrane. As shown in **Figure 50.9**, bending in one direction depolarizes hair cells, increasing neurotransmitter release and the frequency of action potentials directed to the brain along the auditory nerve. Bending the hairs in the other direction hyperpolarizes the hair cells, reducing neurotransmitter release and the frequency of auditory nerve sensations.

What prevents pressure waves from reverberating within the ear and causing prolonged sensation? Once pressure waves travel through the vestibular canal, they pass around the apex (tip) of the cochlea. The waves then continue through the tympanic canal, dissipating as they strike the **round window (Figure 50.10a)**. This damping of sound waves resets the apparatus for the next vibrations that arrive.

The ear conveys information to the brain about two important sound variables: volume and pitch. *Volume* (loudness) is determined by the amplitude, or height, of the sound wave. A large-amplitude sound wave causes more vigorous vibration of the basilar membrane, greater bending of the hairs on hair cells, and more action potentials in the sensory neurons. *Pitch* is a function of a sound wave's frequency, the number of vibrations per unit time. High-frequency waves produce high-pitched sounds, whereas low-frequency waves produce low-pitched sounds. Pitch is commonly expressed in cycles per second, or hertz (Hz). Healthy young humans can hear in the range of 20–20,000 Hz; dogs can hear sounds as high as 40,000 Hz; and bats can emit and hear clicking sounds at frequencies above 100,000 Hz, using this ability to locate objects.

The cochlea can distinguish pitch because the basilar membrane is not uniform along its length: It is relatively narrow and stiff at the base of the cochlea near the oval window and wider and more flexible at the apex. Each region of the basilar membrane is tuned to a particular vibration frequency **(Figure 50.10b)**. At any instant, the region of the membrane vibrating most vigorously triggers the highest frequency of action potentials in the neuronal pathway leading to the brain. There, within the cerebral cortex, the actual perception of pitch occurs. Axons in the auditory nerve project into auditory areas of the cerebral cortex according to the region of the basilar membrane in which the signal originated. When a particular site in our cortex is stimulated, we perceive the sound of a particular pitch.

Equilibrium

Several organs in the inner ear of humans and most other mammals detect body movement, position, and balance. Situated in a vestibule behind the oval window, the **utricle** and **saccule** allow us to perceive position with respect to gravity or linear movement **(Figure 50.11)**. Each of these chambers contains a sheet of hair cells that project into a gelatinous material. Embedded in this gel

(a) No bending of hairs

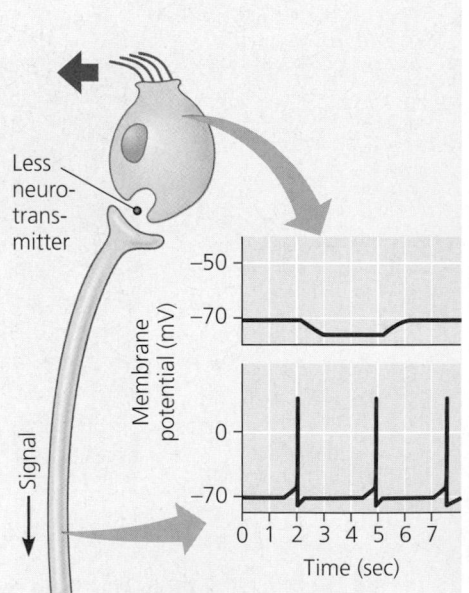

(b) Bending of hairs in one direction   **(c) Bending of hairs in other direction**

▲ **Figure 50.9 Sensory reception by hair cells.** Vertebrate hair cells required for hearing and balance have "hairs" formed into a bundle that bends when surrounding fluid moves. Each hair cell releases an excitatory neurotransmitter at a synapse with a sensory neuron, which conducts action potentials to the CNS. Bending of the bundle in one direction depolarizes the hair cell, causing it to release more neurotransmitter and increasing the frequency of action potentials in the sensory neuron. Bending in the other direction has the opposite effect.

(a) For purposes of illustration, the cochlea is shown partially uncoiled. Vibrations of the stapes against the oval window produce pressure waves in the fluid (perilymph) of the cochlea. The waves (black arrows) travel to the apex of the cochlea through the vestibular canal and back toward the base through the tympanic canal. The energy in the waves causes the basilar membrane (pink) to vibrate, stimulating hair cells.

(b) Variation in the stiffness of the basilar membrane (pink) along its length "tunes" specific regions to specific frequencies. As a result, different frequencies of pressure waves in the cochlea cause different portions of the basilar membrane to vibrate, stimulating particular hair cells and sensory neurons. The selective stimulation of hair cells is perceived in the brain as sound of a certain pitch.

▲ **Figure 50.10 Transduction in the cochlea.**

? *A musical chord consists of several notes, each formed by a sound wave of different frequency. When you hear a chord, where in your body are these notes combined?*

The semicircular canals, arranged in three spatial planes, detect angular movements of the head. Each canal has at its base a swelling containing a cluster of hair cells.

The hairs of the hair cells project into a gelatinous cap called the cupula. When the head starts or stops rotating, fluid in the semicircular canals presses against the cupula, bending the hairs.

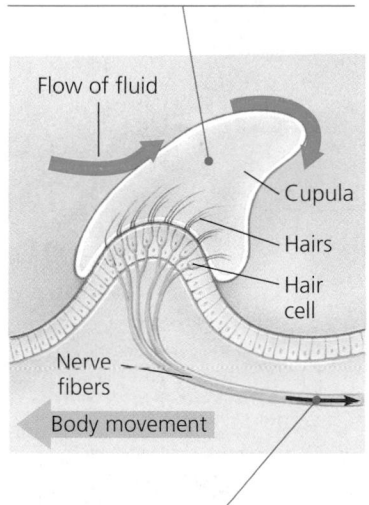

The utricle and saccule tell the brain which way is up and inform it of the body's position or linear acceleration.

Bending of the hairs increases the frequency of action potentials in sensory neurons in direct proportion to the amount of rotational acceleration.

▲ **Figure 50.11 Organs of equilibrium in the inner ear.**

are many small calcium carbonate particles called otoliths ("ear stones"). When you tilt your head, the otoliths press on the hairs protruding into the gel. Through the hair cell receptors, this deflection of the hairs is transformed into a change in the output of sensory neurons, signaling the brain that your head is at an angle. The otoliths are also responsible for your ability to perceive acceleration, as, for example, when a stationary car in which you are sitting pulls forward. Because the utricle is oriented horizontally and the saccule is positioned vertically, you can detect motion in either the forward-and-back or up-and-down direction.

Three semicircular canals connected to the utricle detect turning of the head and other forms of angular acceleration (see Figure 50.11). Within each canal the hair cells form a single cluster, with the hairs projecting into a gelatinous cap called the cupula. Because the three canals are arranged in the three spatial planes, they can detect angular motion of the head in any direction. For example, if you turn your head from left to right, the fluid within the horizontal canal pushes against the cupula, deflecting the hairs. The brain interprets the resulting changes in impulse production by the sensory neurons as turning of the head. If you spin in place, the fluid and canal eventually come to equilibrium and remain in that state until you stop. At that point the moving fluid encounters a stationary cupula, triggering the false sensation of angular motion that we call dizziness.

Hearing and Equilibrium in Other Vertebrates

Unlike the mammalian hearing apparatus, the ear of a fish does not open to the outside of the body and has no eardrum or cochlea. The vibrations of the water caused by sound waves are conducted through the skeleton of the head to a pair of inner ears, setting otoliths in motion and stimulating hair cells. The fish's air-filled swim bladder (see Figure 34.16) also vibrates in response to sound. Some fishes, including catfishes and minnows, have a series of bones that conduct vibrations from the swim bladder to the inner ear.

As discussed in Chapter 34, most fishes and aquatic amphibians also have a **lateral line system** along both sides of their body **(Figure 50.12)**. The system contains mechanoreceptors

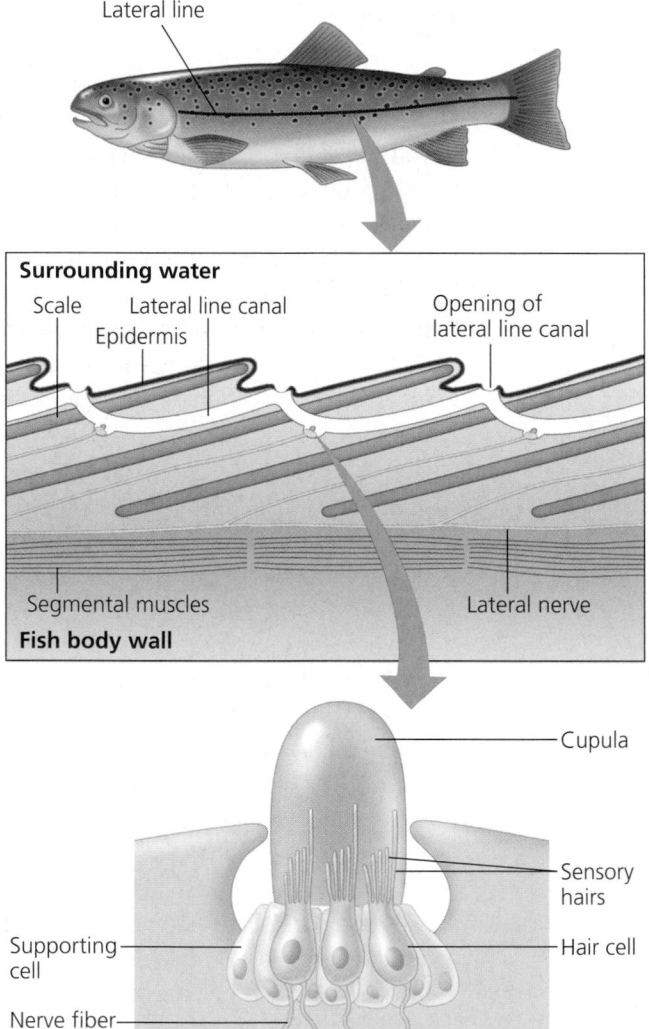

▲ **Figure 50.12 The lateral line system in a fish.** Water flowing through the system bends hair cells. The hair cells transduce the energy into receptor potentials, triggering action potentials that are conveyed to the brain. The lateral line system enables a fish to monitor water currents, pressure waves produced by moving objects, and low-frequency sounds conducted through the water.

that detect low-frequency waves by a mechanism similar to that of the mammalian inner ear. Water from the animal's surroundings enters the lateral line system through numerous pores and flows along a tube past the mechanoreceptors. As in our semicircular canals, receptors are formed from a cluster of hair cells whose hairs are embedded in a gelatinous cap, the cupula. Water movement bends the cupula, depolarizing the hair cells and leading to action potentials that are transmitted along the axons of sensory neurons to the brain. In this way, the fish perceives its movement through water or the direction and velocity of water currents flowing over its body. The lateral line system also detects water movements or vibrations generated by prey, predators, and other moving objects.

In terrestrial vertebrates, the inner ear has evolved as the main organ of hearing and equilibrium. Some amphibians have a lateral line system as tadpoles, but not as adults living on land. In the ear of a terrestrial frog or toad, sound vibrations in the air are conducted to the inner ear by a tympanic membrane on the body surface and a single middle ear bone. Birds, like mammals, have a cochlea. However, as in amphibians, sound is conducted from the tympanic membrane to the inner ear by a single bone.

CONCEPT CHECK 50.2

1. How are statocysts adaptive for animals that burrow underground or live deep in the ocean?
2. **WHAT IF?** Suppose a series of pressure waves in your cochlea causes a vibration of the basilar membrane that moves gradually from the apex toward the base. How would your brain interpret this stimulus?
3. **WHAT IF?** If the stapes became fused to the other middle ear bones or to the oval window, how would this condition affect hearing? Explain.

For suggested answers, see Appendix A.

CONCEPT 50.3

The senses of taste and smell rely on similar sets of sensory receptors

Many animals use their chemical senses to find mates (as when male silk moths respond to pheromones emitted by females), to recognize territory that has been marked by some chemical substance (as when dogs and cats sniff boundaries that have been staked out by their spraying neighbors), and to help navigate during migration (as when salmon use the unique scent of their streams of origin to return for breeding). Animals such as ants and bees that live in large social groups rely extensively on chemical "conversation." In all animals, chemical senses are important in feeding behavior. For example, a hydra retracts its tentacles toward its mouth when it detects the compound glutathione, which is released from prey captured by the tentacles.

The perceptions of **gustation** (taste) and **olfaction** (smell) both depend on chemoreceptors that detect specific chemicals in the environment. In the case of terrestrial animals, taste is the detection of chemicals called **tastants** that are present in a solution, and smell is the detection of **odorants** that are carried through the air. There is no distinction between taste and smell in aquatic animals.

The taste receptors of insects are located within sensory hairs called sensilla, which are located on the feet and in mouthparts. These animals use their sense of taste to select food. A tasting hair contains several chemoreceptors, each especially responsive to a particular class of tastant, such as sugar or salt. Insects are also capable of smelling airborne odorants using olfactory hairs, usually located on the antennae (see Figure 50.4).

Taste in Mammals

The receptor cells for taste in mammals are modified epithelial cells organized into **taste buds**, which are scattered in several areas of the tongue and mouth (**Figure 50.13**). Most taste buds on the tongue are associated with nipple-shaped projections called papillae. The receptors in taste buds are responsible for recognizing five types of tastants. Four represent the familiar taste perceptions—sweet, sour, salty, and bitter. The fifth, called umami (Japanese for "delicious"), is elicited by the amino acid glutamate. Often used as a flavor enhancer, monosodium glutamate (MSG) occurs naturally in foods such as meat and aged cheese, imparting a quality sometimes described as savory. Any region of the tongue with taste buds can detect any of the five types of taste. (The frequently reproduced taste maps of the tongue are thus incorrect.)

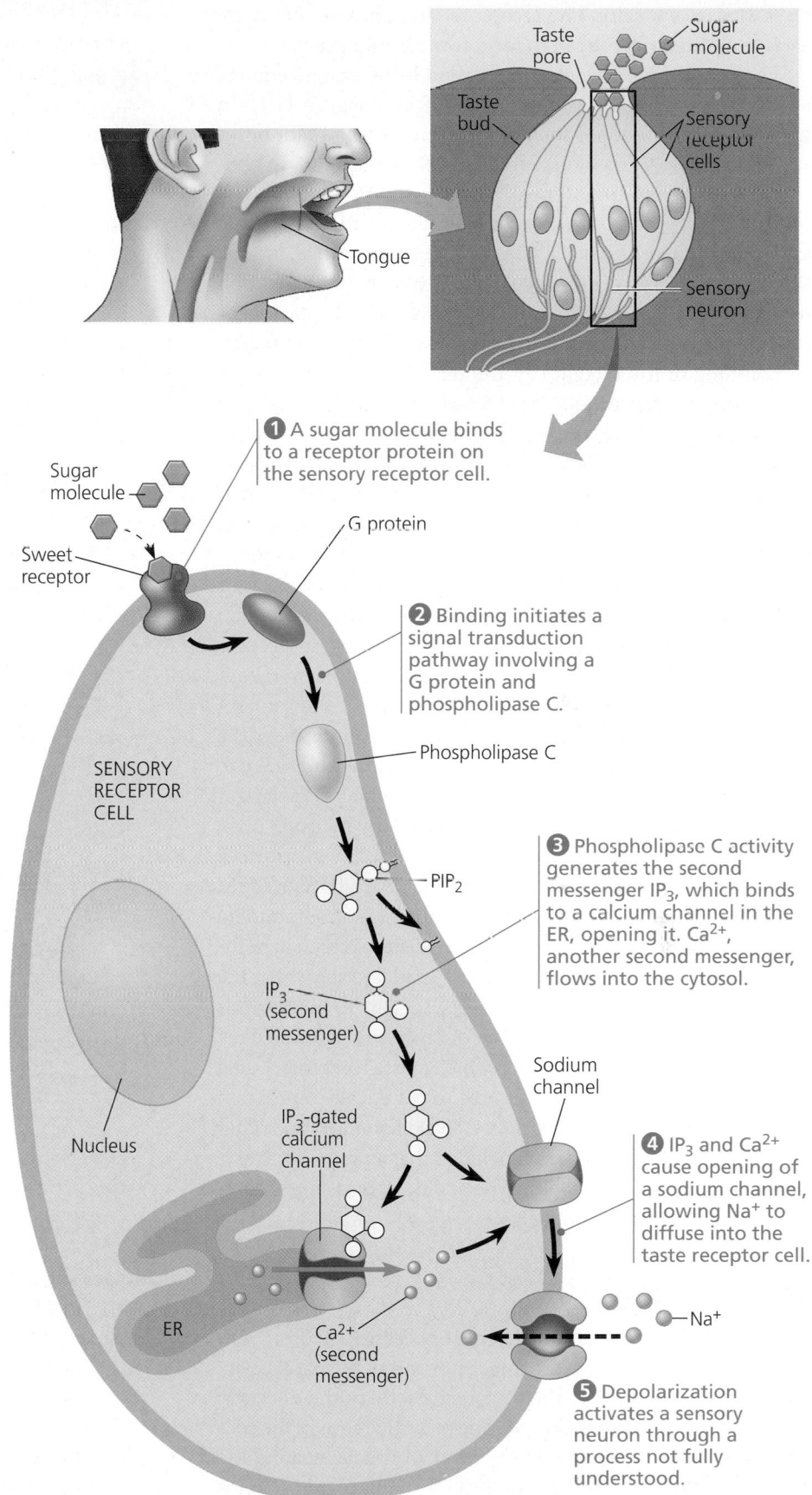

1 A sugar molecule binds to a receptor protein on the sensory receptor cell.

2 Binding initiates a signal transduction pathway involving a G protein and phospholipase C.

3 Phospholipase C activity generates the second messenger IP_3, which binds to a calcium channel in the ER, opening it. Ca^{2+}, another second messenger, flows into the cytosol.

4 IP_3 and Ca^{2+} cause opening of a sodium channel, allowing Na^+ to diffuse into the taste receptor cell.

5 Depolarization activates a sensory neuron through a process not fully understood.

▲ Figure 50.13 **Sensory transduction by a sweet receptor.**

Researchers have identified the receptor proteins for all of the tastes except salty. The receptors fall into two categories, each evolutionarily related to receptors for other senses.

The sensation of sweet, umami, and bitter tastes requires a G protein-coupled receptor, or GPCR (see Figure 11.7). In humans, there are more than 30 different receptors for bitter taste, each able to recognize multiple bitter tastants. In contrast, humans have one type of sweet receptor and one type of umami receptor, each assembled from a different pair of GPCR proteins. Other GPCR proteins are critical for the sense of smell, as we will discuss shortly. Signal transduction to sensory neurons occurs similarly for all GPCR-type receptors; Figure 50.13 illustrates this process for the sweet receptor. Binding of the receptor to the tastant molecule—in this case, a sugar—triggers a signal transduction pathway involving a G protein, the enzyme phospholipase C and the second messengers IP_3 and Ca^{2+}. These second messengers cause opening of an ion channel, allowing an influx of Na^+ that depolarizes the membrane. Scientists are currently exploring how this depolarization leads to sensory neuron activation.

Unlike the other identified taste receptors, the receptor for sour tastants belongs to the TRP (transient receptor potential) family. Formed from a pair of TRP proteins, the sour receptor is similar to the capsaicin receptor and other thermoreceptor proteins. In taste buds, the TRP proteins of the sour receptor assemble into a channel in the plasma membrane of the taste cell. Binding of an acid or other sour-tasting substance to the receptor triggers a change in the ion channel. Depolarization occurs, resulting in activation of a sensory neuron.

For decades, many researchers assumed that a taste cell could have more than one type of receptor. An alternative idea is that each taste cell has a single receptor type, programming the cell to recognize only one of the five tastes. Which hypothesis is correct? In 2005, Ken Mueller, a graduate student at the University of California at San Diego, set out to answer this question. Working in the laboratory of Professor Charles Zuker, Mueller had identified the family of bitter taste receptors. Using a cloned bitter receptor, he was able to genetically reprogram gustation in a mouse (**Figure 50.14**). Based on these and other experiments, the researchers concluded that an individual taste cell expresses a single receptor type and detects tastants representing only one of the five tastes.

Smell in Humans

In olfaction, unlike gustation, the sensory cells are neurons. Olfactory receptor cells line the upper portion of the nasal cavity and send impulses along their axons directly to the olfactory bulb of the brain (**Figure 50.15**). The receptive ends of the cells contain cilia that extend into the layer of mucus coating the nasal cavity. When an odorant diffuses into this region, it binds to a specific GPCR protein called an odorant receptor (OR) on the plasma membrane of the olfactory cilia. These events

▼ **Figure 50.14** **Inquiry**

How do mammals detect different tastes?

EXPERIMENT   To investigate the basis of mammalian taste perception, Ken Mueller, Nick Ryba, and Charles Zuker used a chemical called phenyl-β-D-glucopyranoside (PBDG). Humans find the taste of PBDG extremely bitter. Mice, however, appear to lack a receptor for PBDG. Whereas mice avoid drinking water containing other bitter tastants, they show no aversion to water that contains PBDG.

Using a molecular cloning strategy, Mueller generated mice that made the human PBDG receptor in cells that normally make either a sweet receptor or a bitter receptor. The mice were given a choice of two bottles, one filled with pure water and one filled with water containing PBDG at varying concentrations. The researchers then observed whether the mice had an attraction or an aversion to PBDG.

RESULTS

Relative consumption = (Fluid intake from bottle containing PBDG ÷ Total fluid intake) × 100%

CONCLUSION   The researchers found that the presence of a bitter receptor in sweet taste cells is sufficient to cause mice to be attracted to a bitter chemical. They concluded that the mammalian brain must therefore perceive sweet or bitter taste solely on the basis of which sensory neurons are activated.

SOURCE   K. L. Mueller et al., The receptors and coding logic for bitter taste, *Nature* 434:225–229 (2005).

WHAT IF?   Suppose instead of the PBDG receptor the researchers had used a receptor specific for a sweetener that humans crave but mice ignore. How would the results of the experiment have differed?

trigger signal transduction leading to the production of cyclic AMP. In olfactory cells, cyclic AMP opens channels in the plasma membrane that are permeable to both Na^+ and Ca^{2+}. The flow of these ions into the receptor cell leads to depolarization of the membrane, generating action potentials.

Humans can distinguish thousands of different odors, each caused by a structurally distinct odorant. This level of sensory discrimination requires many different ORs. In 1991, Richard Axel and Linda Buck, working at Columbia University, discovered a family of more than 1,000 OR genes—about 3% of all human

▲ **Figure 50.15 Smell in humans.** Odorant molecules bind to specific receptor proteins in the plasma membrane of olfactory receptor cells, triggering action potentials.

WHAT IF? *If you spray an "air freshener" in a musty room, would you be affecting detection, transmission, or perception of the odorants responsible for the musty smell?*

genes. Each olfactory receptor cell appears to express one OR gene. Cells with different odorant selectivities are interspersed in the nasal cavity. Those cells that express the same OR gene transmit action potentials to the same small region of the olfactory bulb. In 2004, Axel and Buck shared a Nobel Prize for their studies of the gene family and receptors that function in olfaction.

Although the receptors and brain pathways for taste and smell are independent, the two senses do interact. Indeed, much of the complex flavor we experience when eating is due to our sense of smell. If the olfactory system is blocked, as by a head cold, the perception of taste is sharply reduced.

CONCEPT CHECK 50.3

1. Explain why some taste receptor cells and all olfactory receptor cells use G protein-coupled receptors, yet only olfactory receptor cells produce action potentials.
2. Pathways involving G proteins provide an opportunity for an increase in signal strength in the course of signal transduction, a change referred to as amplification. How might this be beneficial in olfaction?
3. **WHAT IF?** If you discovered a mutation in mice that disrupted the ability to taste sweet, bitter, and umami, but not sour or salty, what might you predict about where this mutation acts in the signaling pathways used by these receptors?

For suggested answers, see Appendix A.

CONCEPT 50.4

Similar mechanisms underlie vision throughout the animal kingdom

Many types of light detectors have evolved in the animal kingdom, from simple clusters of cells that detect only the direction and intensity of light to complex organs that form images.

Vision in Invertebrates

Most invertebrates have some kind of light-detecting organ. One of the simplest is the ocellus (plural, *ocelli*) of planarians **(Figure 50.16)**. A pair of ocelli, which are sometimes called eyespots or eyecups, are located in the head region. The ocelli are surrounded on three sides by a layer of darkly pigmented cells that block light. Light shining on the planarian stimulates light-sensitive cells called **photoreceptors** in each ocellus only through the opening where there are no pigmented cells. Because the opening of one ocellus faces left and slightly forward and that of the other ocellus faces right and forward, light shining from one side of the planarian stimulates only the ocellus on that side. The planarian brain compares the rate of action potentials coming from the two ocelli and directs turning movements that minimize the stimulation of both ocelli. The result is that the planarian moves away from the light source

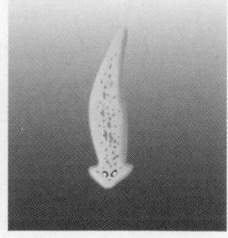

(a) The planarian's brain directs the body to turn until the sensations from the two ocelli are equal and minimal, causing the animal to move away from light.

Ocellus

Light

Photoreceptor

Visual pigment

Ocellus

Nerve to brain

Screening pigment

(b) Whereas light striking the front of an ocellus excites the photoreceptors, light striking the back is blocked by the screening pigment. In this way, the ocelli indicate the direction of a light source, triggering the light avoidance behavior.

▲ **Figure 50.16 Ocelli and orientation behavior of a planarian.**

until it reaches a shaded location, where a rock or other object is likely to hide the animal from predators.

Two major types of image-forming eyes have evolved in invertebrates: the compound eye and the single-lens eye. **Compound eyes** are found in insects and crustaceans (phylum Arthropoda) and in some polychaete worms (phylum Annelida). A compound eye consists of up to several thousand light detectors called **ommatidia** (the "facets" of the eye), each with its own light-focusing lens **(Figure 50.17)**. Each ommatidium detects light from a tiny portion of the visual field. A compound eye is very effective at detecting movement, an important adaptation for flying insects and small animals constantly threatened with predation. Whereas the human eye can distinguish only about 50 flashes of light per second, the compound eyes of some insects can detect flickering at six times that rate. (If they slipped into a movie theater, these insects could easily resolve each frame of the film being projected as a separate still image). Insects also have excellent color vision, and some (including bees) can see into the ultraviolet (UV) range of the electromagnetic spectrum. Because UV light is invisible to us, we miss seeing differences in the environment that bees and other insects detect. In studying animal behavior, we cannot extrapolate our sensory world to other species; different animals have different sensitivities and different brain organizations.

(a) The faceted eyes on the head of a fly, photographed with a stereomicroscope.

2 mm

Cornea

Crystalline cone

Lens

Rhabdom

Photoreceptor

Axons

Ommatidium

(b) The cornea and crystalline cone of each ommatidium together function as a lens that focuses light on the rhabdom, a stack of pigmented plates of microvilli extending inward from a circle of photoreceptors. The rhabdom traps light, serving as the photosensitive part of the ommatidium. Information gathered from different intensities of light entering the many ommatidia from different angles is used to form a visual image.

▲ **Figure 50.17 Compound eyes.**

Among invertebrates, **single-lens eyes** are found in some jellies and polychaetes, as well as spiders and many molluscs. A single-lens eye works on a camera-like principle. The eye of an octopus or squid, for example, has a small opening, the **pupil**, through which light enters. Like a camera's adjustable aperture, the **iris** contracts or expands, changing the diameter of the pupil to let in more or less light. Behind the pupil, a single lens focuses light on a layer of photoreceptors. Similar to a camera's focusing action, muscles in an invertebrate's single-lens eye move the lens forward or backward, focusing on objects at different distances.

The Vertebrate Visual System

We turn next to the eyes of vertebrates, which differ from the single-lens eyes of invertebrates in several respects. Although the eye is the first stage in vision, remember that it is actually the brain that "sees." Thus, to understand vision, we must examine how action potentials arise in the vertebrate eye and then follow these signals to the visual centers of the brain, where images are perceived.

Structure of the Eye

The globe of the vertebrate eye, or eyeball, consists of the **sclera**, a tough white outer layer of connective tissue, and a thin, pigmented inner layer called the **choroid (Figure 50.18)**. At the front of the eye, the sclera becomes the transparent **cornea**, which lets light into the eye and acts as a fixed lens. Also at the front of the eye, the choroid forms the doughnut-shaped iris, which gives the eye its color. By changing size, the iris regulates the amount of light entering the pupil, the hole in the center of the iris. Just inside the choroid, the **retina** forms the innermost layer of the eyeball and contains layers of neu-

rons and photoreceptors. Information from the photoreceptors leaves the eye at the optic disk, a spot on the lower outside of the retina where the optic nerve attaches to the eye. Because there are no photoreceptors in the optic disk, it forms a "blind spot": Light focused onto that part of the retina is not detected.

The **lens** and **ciliary body** divide the eye into two cavities, an anterior cavity between the cornea and the lens and a much larger posterior cavity behind the lens. The ciliary body constantly produces the clear, watery **aqueous humor** that fills the anterior cavity. Blockage of the ducts that drain the aqueous humor can produce glaucoma, a condition in which increased pressure in the eye damages the optic nerve, causing vision loss and sometimes blindness. The posterior cavity, filled with the jellylike **vitreous humor**, constitutes most of the volume of the eye. The lens itself is a transparent disk of protein. Many fishes focus by moving the lens forward or backward, as do squids and octopuses. Humans and other mammals, however, focus by changing the shape of the lens **(Figure 50.19)**. When focusing on a close object, the lens becomes almost spherical. When viewing a distant object, the lens is flattened.

The human retina contains **rods** and **cones**, two types of photoreceptors that differ in shape and in function. Rods are more sensitive to light but do not distinguish colors; they enable us to see at night, but only in black and white. Cones provide color vision, but, being less sensitive, contribute very little to night vision. There are three types of cones. Each has a different sensitivity across the visible spectrum, providing an optimal response to red, green, or blue light.

The relative numbers of rod and cones in the retina varies among different animals, correlating to some degree with the extent to which an animal is active at night. Most fishes, amphibians, and reptiles, including birds, have strong color vision. Humans and other primates also see color well, but are among the minority of mammals with this ability. Many mammals are nocturnal, and having a high proportion of rods in the retina is an adaptation that gives these animals keen night vision. Cats, for instance, are usually most active at night; they have limited color vision and probably see a pastel world during the day.

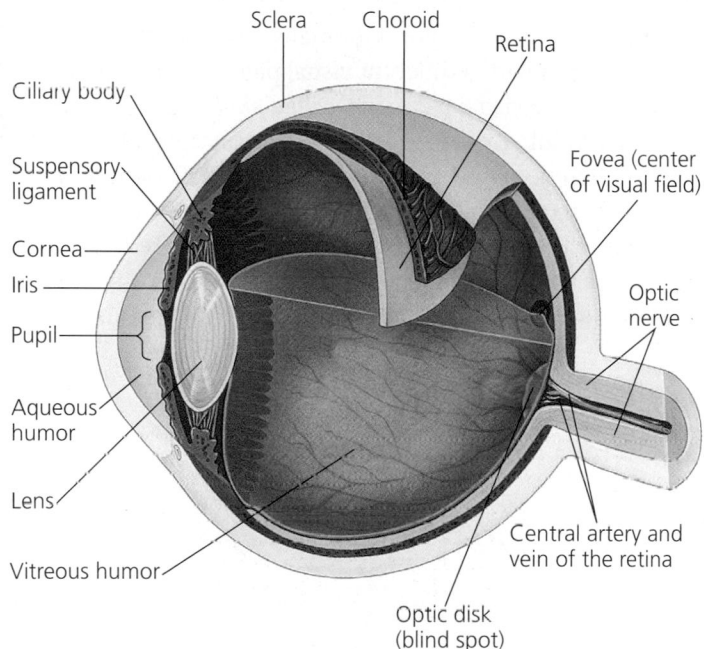

▲ **Figure 50.18 Structure of the vertebrate eye.** In this longitudinal section of the eye, the jellylike vitreous humor is illustrated only in the lower half of the eyeball. The conjunctiva, a mucous membrane that surrounds the sclera, is not shown.

(a) Near vision (accommodation)

(b) Distance vision

◀ **Figure 50.19 Focusing in the mammalian eye.** Ciliary muscles control the shape of the lens, which bends light and focuses it on the retina. The thicker the lens, the more sharply the light is bent.

The distribution of rods and cones varies across the human retina. Overall, the human retina contains about 125 million rods and about 6 million cones. The **fovea**, the center of the visual field, has no rods but has a very high density of cones—about 150,000 cones per square millimeter. The ratio of rods to cones increases with distance from the fovea, with the peripheral regions having only rods. In daylight, you achieve your sharpest vision by looking directly at an object, such that light shines on the tightly packed cones in your fovea. At night, looking directly at a dimly lit object is ineffective, since the rods—the more sensitive light receptors—are found outside the fovea. Thus, for example, you see a dim star best by focusing on a point just to one side of it.

Sensory Transduction in the Eye

Each rod or cone in the vertebrate retina contains visual pigments that consist of a light-absorbing molecule called **retinal** (a derivative of vitamin A) bound to a membrane protein called an **opsin**. The opsin present in rods, when combined with retinal, makes up the visual pigment **rhodopsin (Figure 50.20)**. Absorption of light by rhodopsin shifts one bond in retinal from a *cis* to a *trans* arrangement, converting the molecule from an angled shape to a straight shape (see Chapter 4). This change in configuration destabilizes and activates rhodopsin. Because it changes the color of rhodopsin from purple to yellow, light activation of rhodopsin is called "bleaching."

Following light absorption, signal transduction in photoreceptor cells closes sodium channels. In the dark, the binding of cyclic GMP to these sodium channels causes them to remain open. Breakdown of cyclic GMP in response to light allows sodium channels to close, hyperpolarizing the photoreceptor cell. **Figure 50.21** illustrates the pathway linking light to cyclic GMP breakdown in a rod: Activated rhodopsin activates a G protein, which in turn activates the enzyme that hydrolyzes cyclic GMP.

Rhodopsin returns to its inactive state when enzymes convert retinal back to the *cis* form. In very bright light, however, rhodopsin remains bleached, and the response in the rods becomes saturated. If the amount of light entering the eyes decreases abruptly, the bleached rods do not regain full responsiveness for several minutes. This is why you are temporarily blinded if you pass quickly from the bright sunshine into a movie theater or other dark environment.

The perception of color in humans is based on three types of cones, each with a different visual pigment—red, green, or blue. The three visual pigments, called *photopsins*, are formed from the binding of retinal to three distinct opsin proteins. Slight differences in the opsin proteins are sufficient for each photopsin to absorb light optimally at a different wavelength. Although the visual pigments are designated as red, green, or blue, their absorption spectra in fact overlap. For this reason, the brain's perception of intermediate hues depends on the

(a) Rods contain the visual pigment rhodopsin, which is embedded in a stack of membranous disks in the rod's outer segment. Rhodopsin consists of the light-absorbing molecule retinal bonded to opsin, an integral membrane protein. Opsin has seven α helices that span the disk membrane.

(b) Retinal exists as two isomers. Absorption of light converts the *cis* isomer to the *trans* isomer, which causes opsin to change its conformation (shape). After a few minutes, retinal detaches from opsin. In the dark, enzymes convert retinal back to its *cis* form, which recombines with opsin, forming rhodopsin.

▲ **Figure 50.20 Activation of rhodopsin by light.**

▲ Figure 50.21 Receptor potential production in a rod cell. Note that in rods (and cones) the receptor potential is a hyperpolarization, not a depolarization.

① Light isomerizes retinal, activating rhodopsin.

② Active rhodopsin in turn activates a G protein called transducin.

③ Transducin activates the enzyme phosphodiesterase.

④ Activated phosphodiesterase detaches cGMP from Na⁺ channels in the plasma membrane by hydrolyzing cGMP to GMP.

⑤ The Na⁺ channels close when cGMP detaches. The membrane's permeability to Na⁺ decreases, and the rod hyperpolarizes.

differential stimulation of two or more classes of cones. For example, when both red and green cones are stimulated, we may see yellow or orange, depending on which class is more strongly stimulated.

Abnormal color vision typically results from alterations in the genes for one or more photopsin proteins. Because the genes for the red and green pigments are located on the X chromosome, a single defective copy of either gene can disrupt color vision in males (see Figure 15.7 to review the genetics of sex-linked traits). For this reason, color blindness is more common in males than females and nearly always affects perception of red or green (the blue pigment gene is on human chromosome 7).

Processing of Visual Information

The processing of visual information begins in the retina itself, where both rods and cones form synapses with neurons called **bipolar cells (Figure 50.22)**. In the dark, rods and cones are depolarized and continually release the neurotransmitter glutamate (see Table 48.1) at these synapses. Some bipolar cells depolarize in response to glutamate, whereas others hyperpolarize. Which of the two responses a bipolar cell exhibits depends on the type of glutamate receptor present on its surface at the synapse. When light strikes the rods and cones, they hyperpolarize, shutting off their release of glutamate. In response, the bipolar cells that are depolarized by glutamate hyperpolarize, and those that are hyperpolarized by glutamate depolarize.

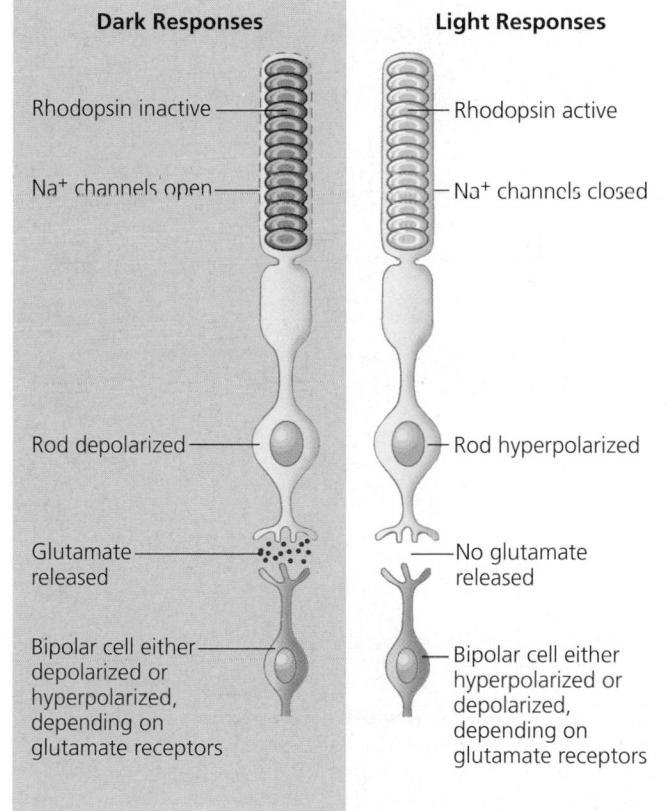

▲ Figure 50.22 Synaptic activity of rod cells in light and dark.

? *Like rods, cone cells are depolarized when rhodopsin is inactive. In the case of a cone, why might it be misleading to call this a dark response?*

In addition to bipolar cells, information processing in the retina requires three other types of neurons—ganglion, horizontal, and amacrine cells **(Figure 50.23)**. **Ganglion cells** synapse with bipolar cells and transmit action potentials to the brain via axons in the optic nerve. **Horizontal cells** and **amacrine cells** function in neural pathways that integrate visual information before it is sent to the brain. For all of the photoreceptors and neurons in the retina, the patterns of functional organization are reflected in an ordered and layered

Retina

Optic nerve

Light

To brain

Retina — Choroid

Photoreceptors

Neurons

Cone Rod

Light

Amacrine cell

Horizontal cell

Optic nerve fibers

Ganglion cell

Bipolar cell

Pigmented epithelium

▲ **Figure 50.23 Cellular organization of the vertebrate retina.** Light must pass through several relatively transparent layers of cells before reaching the rods and cones. These photoreceptors communicate via bipolar cells with ganglion cells, which have axons that transmit visual sensations (action potentials) to the brain. Each bipolar cell receives information from several rods or cones, and each ganglion cell from several bipolar cells. Horizontal and amacrine cells integrate information across the retina. Red arrows indicate the pathway of visual information from the photoreceptors to the optic nerve.

arrangement of cell bodies and synapses (see Figure 50.23). Because of this physical arrangement, light must pass through several layers of neurons to reach the photoreceptors. Light intensity is not significantly diminished, however, since the neurons in the retina are relatively transparent.

Signals from rods and cones can follow several different pathways in the retina. Some information passes directly from photoreceptors to bipolar cells to ganglion cells. In other cases, horizontal cells carry signals from one rod or cone to other photoreceptors and to several bipolar cells. When an illuminated rod or cone stimulates a horizontal cell, the horizontal cell inhibits more distant photoreceptors and bipolar cells that are not illuminated. The result is that the light spot appears lighter and the dark surroundings even darker. This form of integration, called **lateral inhibition**, sharpens edges and enhances contrast in the image. Amacrine cells distribute some information from one bipolar cell to several ganglion cells. Lateral inhibition is repeated by the interactions of the amacrine cells with the ganglion cells and occurs at all levels of visual processing in the brain.

A single ganglion cell receives information from an array of rods and cones, each of which responds to light coming from a particular location. Together, the rods or cones that feed information to one ganglion cell define a *receptive field*—the part of the visual field to which the ganglion can respond. The fewer rods or cones that supply a single ganglion cell, the smaller the receptive field. A smaller receptive field results in a sharper image, because the information as to where light struck the retina is more precise. The ganglion cells of the fovea have very small receptive fields, so visual acuity (sharpness) in the fovea is high.

Axons of ganglion cells form the optic nerves that transmit sensations from the eyes to the brain **(Figure 50.24)**. The two optic nerves meet at the **optic chiasm** near the center of the base of the cerebral cortex. Axons in the optic nerves are routed at the optic chiasm such that sensations from the left visual field of both eyes are transmitted to the right side of the brain, and sensations from the right visual field are transmitted to the left side of the brain. (Note that each visual field, whether right or left, involves input from both eyes.)

Within the brain, most ganglion cell axons lead to the **lateral geniculate nuclei**, which have axons that reach the **primary visual cortex** in the cerebrum (see Figure 50.24). Additional neurons carry the information to higher-order visual processing and integrating centers elsewhere in the cortex.

Point-by-point information in the visual field is projected along neurons onto the visual cortex. How does the cortex convert a complex set of action potentials representing two-dimensional images focused on the retina to three-dimensional perceptions of our surroundings? Researchers estimate that at least 30% of the cerebral cortex, comprising hundreds of millions of neurons in perhaps dozens of integrating centers, takes part in formulating

Left visual field

Right visual field

Left eye

Right eye

Optic nerve

Optic chiasm

Lateral geniculate nucleus

Primary visual cortex

▲ **Figure 50.24 Neural pathways for vision.** Each optic nerve contains about a million axons that synapse with interneurons in the lateral geniculate nuclei. The nuclei relay sensations to the primary visual cortex, one of many brain centers that cooperate in constructing our visual perceptions.

what we actually "see." Determining how these centers integrate such components of our vision as color, motion, depth, shape, and detail is the focus of much exciting research.

Evolution of Visual Perception

Despite their diversity, all photoreceptors contain similar pigment molecules that absorb light. Furthermore, animals as diverse as flatworms, annelids, arthropods, and vertebrates share genes associated with the embryonic development of photoreceptors. Thus, the genetic underpinnings of all photoreceptors likely evolved in the earliest bilateral animals.

Recent research indicates that there are other photoreceptors in the vertebrate retina in addition to rods and cones. In particular, a visual pigment called melanopsin is found in retinal ganglion cells. Inactivating the melanopsin gene in mice alters their ability to reset their circadian rhythm in response to light. The effect of melanopsin on circadian rhythms and light responses in humans is a subject of active investigation.

CONCEPT CHECK 50.4

1. Contrast the light-detecting organs of planarians and flies. How is each organ adaptive for the lifestyle of the animal?
2. In a condition called presbyopia, the eyes' lenses lose much of their elasticity and maintain a flat shape. Explain how this condition affects a person's vision.
3. **WHAT IF?** If you perceive an object floating across your field of view, how might you determine whether the image represents a real object or a disturbance in your eye or a neural circuit of your brain?

For suggested answers, see Appendix A.

CONCEPT 50.5
The physical interaction of protein filaments is required for muscle function

Throughout our discussions of sensory mechanisms, we have seen how sensory inputs to the nervous system result in specific behaviors: the escape maneuver of a moth that detects a bat's sonar, the upside-down swimming of a crayfish with manipulated statocysts, the feeding movements of a hydra when it tastes glutathione, and the movement of planarians away from light. Underlying the diverse forms of behavior in animals are common fundamental mechanisms. Flying, swimming, eating, and crawling all require muscle activity in response to nervous system input.

Muscle cell function relies on microfilaments, which are the actin components of the cytoskeleton. Recall from Chapter 6 that microfilaments, like microtubules, function in cell motility. In muscles, microfilament movement powered by chemical energy brings about contraction; muscle extension occurs only passively. To understand how microfilaments contribute to muscle contraction, we must analyze the structure of muscles and muscle fibers. We will begin by examining vertebrate skeletal muscle and then turn our attention to other types of muscle.

Vertebrate Skeletal Muscle

Vertebrate **skeletal muscle**, which is attached to the bones and is responsible for their movement, is characterized by a hierarchy of smaller and smaller units (**Figure 50.25**). Most skeletal muscles consist of a bundle of long fibers running parallel to the length of the muscle. Each fiber is a single cell with multiple nuclei, reflecting its formation by the fusion of many embryonic cells. A muscle fiber contains a bundle of smaller **myofibrils** arranged longitudinally. The myofibrils, in turn, are composed of thin filaments and thick filaments. **Thin filaments** consist of two strands of actin and two strands of a regulatory protein (not shown here) coiled around one another. **Thick filaments** are staggered arrays of myosin molecules.

Skeletal muscle is also called **striated muscle** because the regular arrangement of the filaments creates a pattern of light and dark bands. Each repeating unit is a **sarcomere**, the basic contractile unit of the muscle. The borders of the sarcomere are lined up in adjacent myofibrils and contribute to the striations visible with a light microscope. Thin filaments are attached at the Z lines and project toward the center of the sarcomere, while thick filaments are attached at the M lines centered in the sarcomere. In a muscle fiber at rest, thick and thin filaments only partially overlap. Near the edge of the sarcomere are only thin filaments, whereas the zone in the center contains only thick filaments. This arrangement is the key to how the sarcomere, and hence the whole muscle, contracts.

The Sliding-Filament Model of Muscle Contraction

We can explain much of what happens during contraction of a whole muscle by focusing on a single sarcomere (**Figure 50.26**). According to the **sliding-filament model** of muscle contraction, neither the thin filaments nor the thick filaments change in length when the sarcomere shortens; rather, the filaments slide past each other longitudinally, increasing the overlap of the thin and thick filaments.

The sliding of the filaments is based on the interaction between the myosin and actin molecules that make up the thick and thin filaments. Each myosin molecule consists of a long "tail" region and a globular "head" region extending to the side. The tail adheres to the tails of other myosin molecules that form the thick filament. The head is the center of bioenergetic reactions that power muscle contractions. It can bind ATP and hydrolyze it into ADP and inorganic phosphate. As shown in **Figure 50.27**, hydrolysis of ATP converts myosin to a high-energy form that can bind to actin, form a cross-bridge, and pull the thin filament toward the center of the sarcomere. The cross-bridge is broken when a new molecule of ATP binds to the myosin head. In a repeating cycle, the free head cleaves the new ATP and attaches to a new binding site on another actin molecule farther along the thin filament. Each of the approximately 350 heads of a thick filament forms and reforms about five cross-bridges per second, driving filaments past each other.

A typical muscle fiber at rest contains only enough ATP for a few contractions. The energy needed for repetitive contractions is stored in two other compounds: creatine phosphate and glycogen. Creatine phosphate can transfer a phosphate group to ADP to synthesize additional ATP. The resting supply of creatine phosphate is sufficient to sustain contractions for about 15 seconds. Glycogen is broken down to glucose, which can be used to generate ATP by either aerobic respiration or glycolysis (and lactic acid fermentation; see Chapter 9). Using the glucose

▲ **Figure 50.25 The structure of skeletal muscle.**

► **Figure 50.26 The sliding-filament model of muscle contraction.** The drawings on the left show that the lengths of the thick (myosin) filaments (purple) and thin (actin) filaments (orange) remain the same as a muscle fiber contracts.

Relaxed muscle

Contracting muscle

Fully contracted muscle

Sarcomere

Contracted Sarcomere

0.5 µm

Thick filament

Thin filaments

1 Starting here, the myosin head is bound to ATP and is in its low-energy configuration.

Thin filament

ATP

Myosin head (low-energy configuration)

Thick filament

5 Binding of a new molecule of ATP releases the myosin head from actin, and a new cycle begins.

ATP

2 The myosin head hydrolyzes ATP to ADP and inorganic phosphate (P_i) and is in its high-energy configuration.

Actin

Myosin binding sites

ADP

P_i

Myosin head (high-energy configuration)

Thin filament moves toward center of sarcomere.

Myosin head (low-energy configuration)

$ADP + P_i$

ADP

P_i

Cross-bridge

3 The myosin head binds to actin, forming a cross-bridge.

4 Releasing ADP and P_i, myosin returns to its low-energy configuration, sliding the thin filament.

MEDIA

BioFlix Visit www.campbellbiology.com for the BioFlix 3-D Animation on Muscle Contraction.

▲ **Figure 50.27 Myosin-actin interactions underlying muscle fiber contraction.**
? *When ATP binds, what prevents the filaments from sliding back into their original positions?*

from a typical muscle fiber's glycogen store, glycolysis can support about 1 minute of sustained contraction, whereas aerobic respiration can power contractions for nearly an hour.

The Role of Calcium and Regulatory Proteins

Calcium ions (Ca^{2+}) and proteins bound to actin play a critical role in muscle cell contraction and relaxation. **Tropomyosin**, a regulatory protein, and the **troponin complex**, a set of additional regulatory proteins, are bound to the actin strands of thin filaments. In a muscle fiber at rest, tropomyosin covers the myosin-binding sites along the thin filament, preventing actin and myosin from interacting (**Figure 50.28a**). When Ca^{2+} accumulates in the cytosol, it binds to the troponin complex, causing the proteins bound along the actin strands to shift position and expose the myosin-binding sites on the thin filament (**Figure 50.28b**). Thus, when the Ca^{2+} concentration rises in the cytosol, the thin and thick filaments slide past each other, and the muscle fiber contracts. When the Ca^{2+} concentration falls, the binding sites are covered, and contraction stops.

Motor neurons cause muscle contraction by triggering release of Ca^{2+} into the cytosol of muscle cells with which they form synapses. This regulation of Ca^{2+} concentration is a multistep process involving a network of membranes and compartments within the muscle cell. As you read the following description, refer to the overview and diagram in **Figure 50.29**.

The arrival of an action potential at the synaptic terminal of a motor neuron causes release of the neurotransmitter acetyl-choline. Binding of acetylcholine to receptors on the muscle fiber leads to a depolarization, triggering an action potential. Within the muscle fiber, the action potential spreads deep into the interior, following infoldings of the plasma membrane called **transverse (T) tubules**. The T tubules make close contact with the **sarcoplasmic reticulum (SR)**, a specialized endoplasmic reticulum. Spread of the action potential along the T tubules triggers changes in the SR, opening Ca^{2+} channels. Calcium ions stored in the interior of the SR flow through these open channels into the cytosol and bind to the troponin complex, initiating contraction of the muscle fiber.

When motor neuron input stops, the muscle cell relaxes. As it relaxes, the filaments slide back to their starting position. During this phase, proteins in the cell reset the muscle for the next cycle of contraction. Relaxation begins as transport proteins in the SR pump Ca^{2+} out of the cytosol. When the Ca^{2+} concentration in the cytosol is low, the regulatory proteins bound to the thin filament shift back to their starting position, once again blocking the myosin-binding sites. At the same time, the Ca^{2+} pumped from the cytosol accumulates in the SR, providing the stores needed to respond to the next action potential.

Several diseases cause paralysis by interfering with the excitation of skeletal muscle fibers by motor neurons. In amyotrophic lateral sclerosis (ALS), also called Lou Gehrig's disease, motor neurons in the spinal cord and brainstem degenerate, and the muscle fibers with which they synapse atrophy. ALS is progressive and usually fatal within five years after symptoms appear; currently there is no cure or treatment. Myasthenia gravis is an autoimmune disease in which a person produces antibodies to the acetylcholine receptors on skeletal muscle fibers. As the number of these receptors decreases, synaptic transmission between motor neurons and muscle fibers declines. Fortunately, effective treatments are available for this disease.

Nervous Control of Muscle Tension

Whereas contraction of a single skeletal muscle fiber is a brief all-or-none twitch, contraction of a whole muscle, such as the biceps in your upper arm, is graded; you can voluntarily alter the extent and strength of its contraction. There are two basic mechanisms by which the nervous system produces graded contractions of whole muscles: (1) by varying the number of muscle fibers that contract and (2) by varying the rate at which muscle fibers are stimulated. Let's consider each mechanism in turn.

In a vertebrate skeletal muscle, each muscle fiber is controlled by only one motor neuron, but each branched motor neuron may form synapses with many muscle fibers. There may be hundreds of motor neurons controlling a muscle, each with its own pool of muscle fibers scattered throughout the muscle. A **motor unit** consists of a single motor neuron and all the muscle fibers it controls. When a motor neuron produces an action potential,

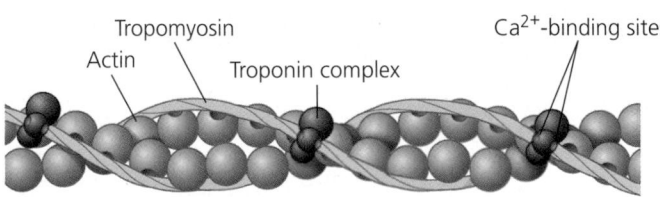

Tropomyosin
Actin
Troponin complex
Ca^{2+}-binding sites

(a) Myosin-binding sites blocked

Ca^{2+}

Myosin-binding site

(b) Myosin-binding sites exposed

▲ **Figure 50.28 The role of regulatory proteins and calcium in muscle fiber contraction.** Each thin filament consists of two strands of actin, tropomyosin, and the troponin complex.

▼ Figure 50.29

Exploring The Regulation of Skeletal Muscle Contraction

The electrical, chemical, and molecular events regulating skeletal muscle contraction are shown in a cutaway view of a muscle cell and in the enlarged diagram below. Action potentials (red arrows) triggered by the motor neuron sweep across the muscle fiber and into it along the transverse (T) tubules, initiating the movements of calcium (green dots) that regulate muscle activity.

Synaptic terminal — Motor neuron axon — T tubule — Sarcoplasmic reticulum — Myofibril — Plasma membrane of muscle fiber — Sarcomere — Mitochondrion — Ca^{2+} released from sarcoplasmic reticulum

Synaptic terminal of motor neuron

1 Acetylcholine (ACh) released at synaptic terminal diffuses across synaptic cleft and binds to receptor proteins on muscle fiber's plasma membrane, triggering an action potential in muscle fiber.

Synaptic cleft — T Tubule — Plasma membrane

ACh

2 Action potential is propagated along plasma membrane and down T tubules.

SR

3 Action potential triggers Ca^{2+} release from sarcoplasmic reticulum (SR).

Ca^{2+} ATPase pump

Ca^{2+}

ATP

CYTOSOL

7 Tropomyosin blockage of myosin-binding sites is restored; contraction ends, and muscle fiber relaxes.

ADP
P_i

6 Cytosolic Ca^{2+} is removed by active transport into SR after action potential ends.

4 Calcium ions bind to troponin in thin filament; myosin-binding sites exposed.

Ca^{2+}

5 Myosin cross-bridges alternately attach to actin and detach, pulling thin filament toward center of sarcomere; ATP powers sliding of filaments.

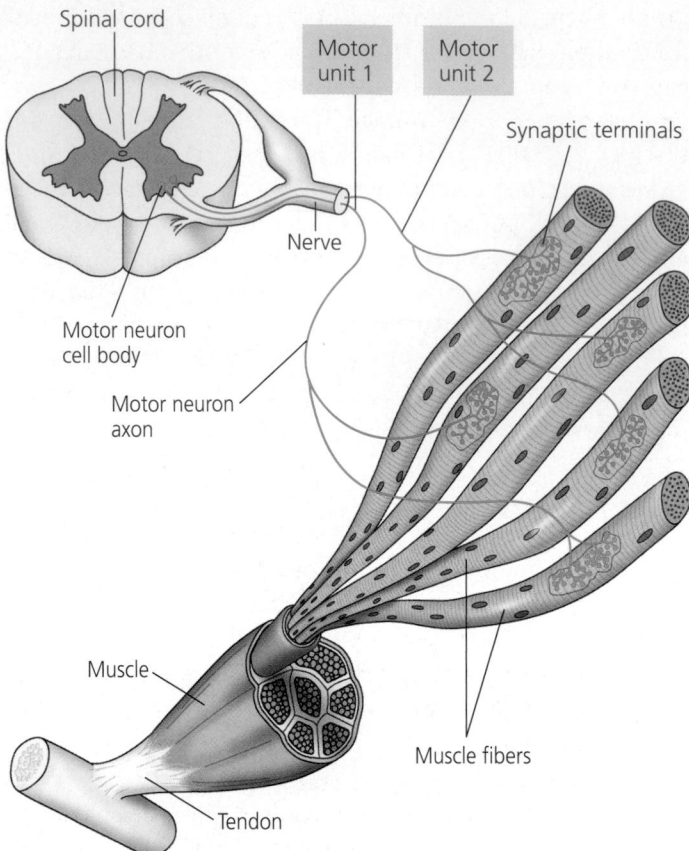

▲ **Figure 50.30 Motor units in a vertebrate skeletal muscle.** Each muscle fiber (cell) has a single synapse with one motor neuron, but each motor neuron typically synapses with many muscle fibers. A motor neuron and all the muscle fibers it controls constitute a motor unit.

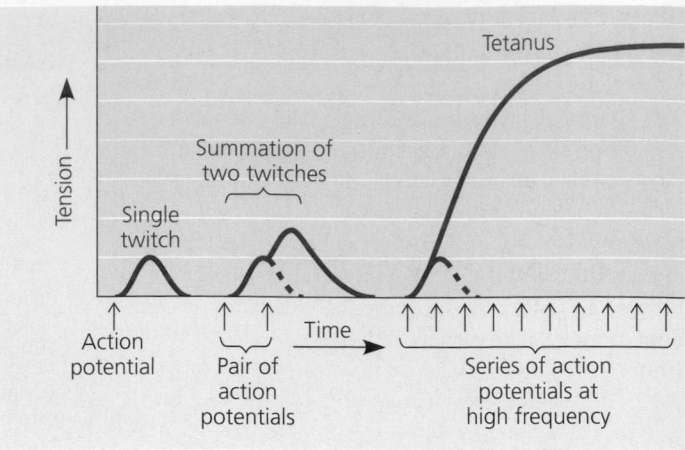

▲ **Figure 50.31 Summation of twitches.** This graph compares the tension developed in a muscle fiber in response to a single action potential in a motor neuron, a pair of action potentials, and a series of action potentials. The dashed lines show the tension that would have developed if only the first action potential had occurred.

all the muscle fibers in its motor unit contract as a group **(Figure 50.30)**. The strength of the resulting contraction depends on how many muscle fibers the motor neuron controls. In most muscles, the number of muscle fibers in different motor units ranges from a few to hundreds. The nervous system can thus regulate the strength of contraction in a muscle by determining how many motor units are activated at a given instant and by selecting large or small motor units to activate. The force (tension) developed by a muscle progressively increases as more and more of the motor neurons controlling the muscle are activated, a process called **recruitment** of motor neurons. Depending on the number of motor neurons your brain recruits and the size of their motor units, you can lift a fork or something much heavier, like your biology textbook.

Some muscles, especially those that hold up the body and maintain posture, are almost always partially contracted. In such muscles, the nervous system may alternate activation among the motor units, reducing the length of time any one set of fibers is contracted. Prolonged contraction can result in muscle fatigue due to the depletion of ATP and dissipation of ion gradients required for normal electrical signaling. Although accumulation of lactate (see Figure 9.18) may also con-

tribute to muscle fatigue, recent research actually points to a beneficial effect of lactate on muscle function.

The second mechanism by which the nervous system produces graded whole-muscle contractions is by varying the rate of muscle fiber stimulation. A single action potential produces a twitch lasting about 100 msec or less. If a second action potential arrives before the muscle fiber has completely relaxed, the two twitches add together, resulting in greater tension **(Figure 50.31)**. Further summation occurs as the rate of stimulation increases. When the rate is high enough that the muscle fiber cannot relax at all between stimuli, the twitches fuse into one smooth, sustained contraction called **tetanus** (not to be confused with the disease of the same name). Motor neurons usually deliver their action potentials in rapid-fire volleys, and the resulting summation of tension results in the smooth contraction typical of tetanus rather than the jerky actions of individual twitches.

The increase in tension during summation and tetanus occurs because muscle fibers are connected to bones via tendons and connective tissues. When a muscle fiber contracts, it stretches these elastic structures, which then transmit tension to the bones. In a single twitch, the muscle fiber begins to relax before the elastic structures are fully stretched. During summation, however, the high-frequency action potentials maintain an elevated concentration of Ca^{2+} in the muscle fiber's cytosol, prolonging cross-bridge cycling and causing greater stretching of the elastic structures. During tetanus, the elastic structures are fully stretched, and all of the tension generated by the muscle fiber is transmitted to the bones.

Types of Skeletal Muscle Fibers

Our discussion to this point has focused on the general properties of vertebrate skeletal muscles. There are, however, several distinct types of skeletal muscle fibers, each of which is adapted to a particular set of functions. Scientists typically classify these varied fiber types either by the source of ATP used to power muscle activity or by the speed of muscle contraction. We'll consider each of the two classification schemes.

Oxidative and Glycolytic Fibers Fibers that rely mostly on aerobic respiration are called oxidative fibers. Such fibers are specialized in ways that enable them to make use of a steady energy supply: They have many mitochondria, a rich blood supply, and a large amount of an oxygen-storing protein called **myoglobin**. Myoglobin, a brownish red pigment, binds oxygen more tightly than does hemoglobin, so it can effectively extract oxygen from the blood. A second class of fibers use glycolysis as their primary source of ATP and are called glycolytic fibers. Having a larger diameter and less myoglobin than oxidative fibers, glycolytic fibers fatigue much more readily. The two fiber types are readily apparent in the muscle of poultry and fish: The light meat is composed of glycolytic fibers, and the dark meat is made up of oxidative fibers rich in myoglobin.

Fast-Twitch and Slow-Twitch Fibers Muscle fibers vary in the speed with which they contract, with **fast-twitch fibers** developing tension two to three times faster than **slow-twitch fibers**. Fast fibers are used for brief, rapid, powerful contractions. Slow fibers, often found in muscles that maintain posture, can sustain long contractions. A slow fiber has less sarcoplasmic reticulum and pumps Ca^{2+} more slowly than a fast fiber. Because Ca^{2+} remains in the cytosol longer, a muscle twitch in a slow fiber lasts about five times as long as one in a fast fiber.

The difference in contraction speed between slow-twitch and fast-twitch fibers mainly reflects the rate at which their myosin heads hydrolyze ATP. However, there isn't a one-to-one relationship between contraction speed and ATP source. Whereas all slow-twitch fibers are oxidative, fast-twitch fibers can be either glycolytic or oxidative.

Most human skeletal muscles contain both fast- and slow-twitch fibers, although the muscles of the eye and hand are exclusively fast twitch. In a muscle that has a mixture of fast and slow fibers, the relative proportions of each are genetically determined. However, if such a muscle is used repeatedly for activities requiring high endurance, some fast glycolytic fibers can develop into fast oxidative fibers. Because fast oxidative fibers fatigue more slowly than fast glycolytic fibers, the result will be a muscle that is more resistant to fatigue.

Some vertebrates have skeletal muscle fibers that twitch at rates far faster than any human muscle. For example, both the rattlesnake's rattle and the dove's coo are produced by superfast muscles that can contract and relax every 10 msec.

Other Types of Muscle

Although all muscles share the same fundamental mechanism of contraction—actin and myosin filaments sliding past each other—there are many different types of muscle. Vertebrates, for example, have cardiac muscle and smooth muscle in addition to skeletal muscle (see Figure 40.5).

Vertebrate **cardiac muscle** is found in only one place—the heart. Like skeletal muscle, cardiac muscle is striated. However, structural differences between skeletal and cardiac muscle fibers result in differences in their electrical and membrane properties. Whereas skeletal muscle fibers do not produce action potentials unless stimulated by a motor neuron, cardiac muscle cells have ion channels in their plasma membrane that cause rhythmic depolarizations, triggering action potentials without input from the nervous system. Action potentials of cardiac muscle cells last up to 20 times longer than those of the skeletal muscle fibers. Plasma membranes of adjacent cardiac muscle cells interlock at specialized regions called **intercalated disks**, where gap junctions (see Figure 6.32) provide direct electrical coupling between the cells. Thus, the action potential generated by specialized cells in one part of the heart spreads to all other cardiac muscle cells, causing the whole heart to contract. A long refractory period prevents summation and tetanus.

Smooth muscle in vertebrates is found mainly in the walls of hollow organs, such as blood vessels and organs of the digestive tract. Smooth muscle cells lack striations because their actin and myosin filaments are not regularly arrayed along the length of the cell. Instead, the thick filaments are scattered throughout the cytoplasm, and the thin filaments are attached to structures called dense bodies, some of which are tethered to the plasma membrane. There is less myosin than in striated muscle fibers, and the myosin is not associated with specific actin strands. Some smooth muscle cells contract only when stimulated by neurons of the autonomic nervous system. Others can generate action potentials without input from neurons—they are electrically coupled to one another. Smooth muscles contract and relax more slowly than striated muscles.

Although smooth muscle contraction is regulated by Ca^{2+}, the mechanism for regulation is different from that in skeletal and cardiac muscle. Smooth muscle cells have no troponin complex or T tubules, and their sarcoplasmic reticulum is not well developed. During an action potential, Ca^{2+} enters the cytosol mainly through the plasma membrane. Calcium ions cause contraction by binding to the protein calmodulin, which activates an enzyme that phosphorylates the myosin head, enabling cross-bridge activity.

Invertebrates have muscle cells similar to vertebrate skeletal and smooth muscle cells, and arthropod skeletal muscles are nearly identical to those of vertebrates. However, the flight muscles of insects are capable of independent, rhythmic contraction, so the wings of some insects can actually beat faster than action potentials can arrive from the central nervous system. Another interesting evolutionary adaptation has been discovered in the muscles that hold a clam's shell closed. The thick filaments in these muscles contain a protein called paramyosin that enables the muscles to remain contracted for as long as a month with only a low rate of energy consumption.

CONCEPT **50.6**

Skeletal systems transform muscle contraction into locomotion

So far we have focused on muscles as effectors for nervous system output. To move an animal in part or in whole, muscles must work in concert with the skeleton. Unlike the softer tissues in an animal body, the skeleton provides a rigid structure to which muscles can attach. Because muscles exert force only during contraction, moving a body part back and forth typically requires two muscles attached to the same section of the skeleton. We can see such an arrangement of muscles in the upper portion of a human arm or grasshopper leg (Figure 50.32). Although we call such muscles an antagonistic pair, their function is actually cooperative, coordinated by the nervous system. For example, when you extend your arm, motor neurons trigger your triceps muscle to contract while the absence of neuronal input allows your biceps to relax.

Skeletons function in support and protection as well as movement. Most land animals would sag from their own weight if they had no skeleton to support them. Even an animal living in water would be a formless mass without a framework to

maintain its shape. In many animals, a hard skeleton also protects soft tissues. For example, the vertebrate skull protects the brain, and the ribs of terrestrial vertebrates form a cage around the heart, lungs, and other internal organs.

Types of Skeletal Systems

Although we tend to think of skeletons only as interconnected sets of bones, skeletons come in many different forms. Hardened support structures can be external (as in exoskeletons), internal (as in endoskeletons), or even absent (as in fluid-based or hydrostatic skeletons).

Hydrostatic Skeletons

A **hydrostatic skeleton** consists of fluid held under pressure in a closed body compartment. This is the main type of skeleton in most cnidarians, flatworms, nematodes, and annelids (see Chapter 33). These animals control their form and movement by using muscles to change the shape of fluid-filled compartments. Among the cnidarians, for example, a hydra elongates by closing its mouth and using contractile cells in its body wall to constrict its central gastrovascular cavity.

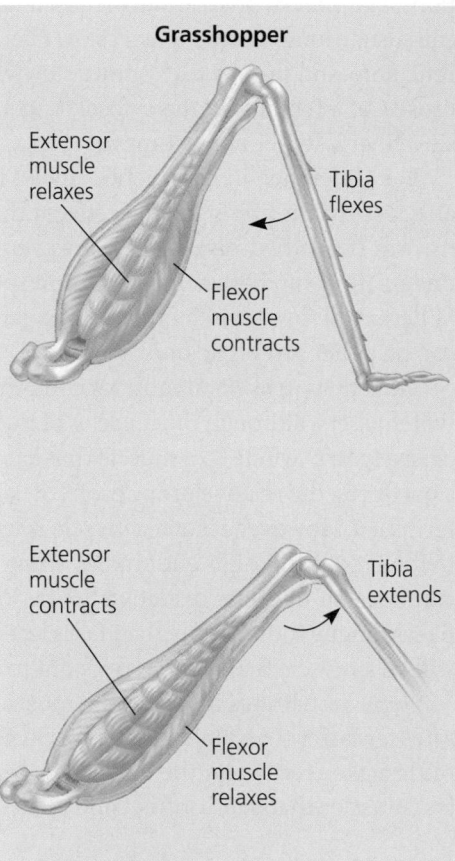

▲ **Figure 50.32 The interaction of muscles and skeletons in movement.** Back-and-forth movement of a body part is generally accomplished by antagonistic muscles. This arrangement works with either an internal skeleton, as in mammals, or an external skeleton, as in insects.

Because water cannot be compressed very much, decreasing the diameter of the cavity forces the cavity to become longer.

Worms use hydrostatic skeletons in diverse ways to move through their environment. In planarians and other flatworms, the interstitial fluid is kept under pressure and functions as the main hydrostatic skeleton. Planarian movement results mainly from muscles in the body wall exerting localized forces against the hydrostatic skeleton. Nematodes (roundworms) hold fluid in their body cavity, which is a pseudocoelom (see Figure 32.8b). Contractions of longitudinal muscles move the animal forward by undulations, or wavelike motions, of the body. In earthworms and other annelids, the coelomic fluid functions as a hydrostatic skeleton. The coelomic cavity in many annelids is divided by septa between the segments, allowing the animal to change the shape of each segment individually, using both circular and longitudinal muscles. Such annelids use their hydrostatic skeleton for **peristalsis**, a type of movement produced by rhythmic waves of muscle contractions passing from front to back **(Figure 50.33)**.

Hydrostatic skeletons are well suited for life in aquatic environments. They may also cushion internal organs from shocks and provide support for crawling and burrowing in terrestrial animals. However, a hydrostatic skeleton cannot support terrestrial activities in which an animal's body is held off the ground, such as walking or running.

Exoskeletons

An **exoskeleton** is a hard encasement deposited on an animal's surface. For example, most molluscs are enclosed in a calcium carbonate shell secreted by the mantle, a sheetlike extension of the body wall (see Figure 33.15). As the animal grows, it enlarges its shell by adding to the outer edge. Clams and other bivalves close their hinged shell using muscles attached to the inside of this exoskeleton.

The jointed exoskeleton of arthropods is a cuticle, a non-living coat secreted by the epidermis. Muscles are attached to knobs and plates of the cuticle that extend into the interior of the body. About 30–50% of the arthropod cuticle consists of **chitin**, a polysaccharide similar to cellulose (see Figure 5.10). Fibrils of chitin are embedded in a protein matrix, forming a composite material that combines strength and flexibility. Where protection is most important, the cuticle is hardened with organic compounds that cross-link the proteins of the exoskeleton. Some crustaceans, such as lobsters, harden portions of their exoskeleton even more by adding calcium salts. In contrast, there is little cross-linking of proteins or inorganic salt deposition in places where the cuticle must be thin and flexible, such as leg joints. With each growth spurt, an arthropod must shed its exoskeleton (molt) and produce a larger one.

Endoskeletons

An **endoskeleton** consists of hard supporting elements, such as bones, buried within the soft tissues of an animal. Sponges are reinforced by hard needlelike structures of inorganic material (see Figure 33.4) or by softer fibers made of protein. Echinoderms have an endoskeleton of hard plates called ossicles beneath their skin. The ossicles are composed of magnesium carbonate and calcium carbonate crystals and are usually bound together by protein fibers. Whereas the ossicles of sea urchins are tightly bound, the ossicles of sea stars are more loosely linked, allowing a sea star to change the shape of its arms.

Chordates have an endoskeleton consisting of cartilage, bone, or some combination of these materials (see Figure 40.5). The mammalian skeleton is built from more than 200 bones,

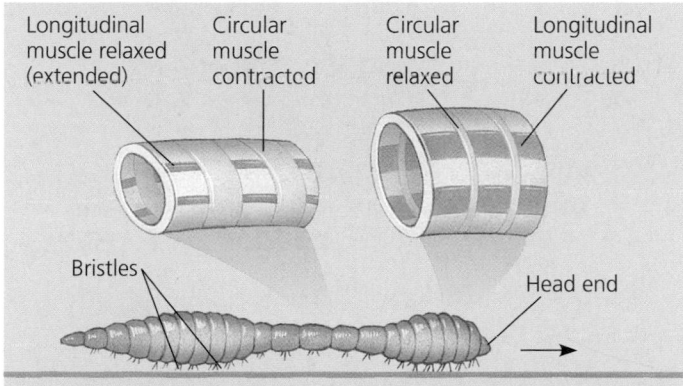

Longitudinal muscle relaxed (extended)   Circular muscle contracted   Circular muscle relaxed   Longitudinal muscle contracted

Bristles   Head end

(a) At the moment depicted, body segments at the earthworm's head end and just in front of the rear end are short and thick (longitudinal muscles contracted; circular muscles relaxed) and are anchored to the ground by bristles. The other segments are thin and elongated (circular muscles contracted; longitudinal muscles relaxed).

Head end

(b) The head has moved forward because circular muscles in the head segments have contracted. Segments behind the head and at the rear are now thick and anchored, thus preventing the worm from slipping backward.

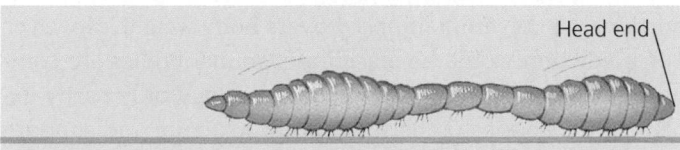

Head end

(c) The head segments are thick again and anchored in their new positions. The rear segments have released their hold on the ground and have been pulled forward.

▲ **Figure 50.33 Crawling by peristalsis.** Contraction of the longitudinal muscles thickens and shortens the earthworm; contraction of the circular muscles constricts and elongates it.

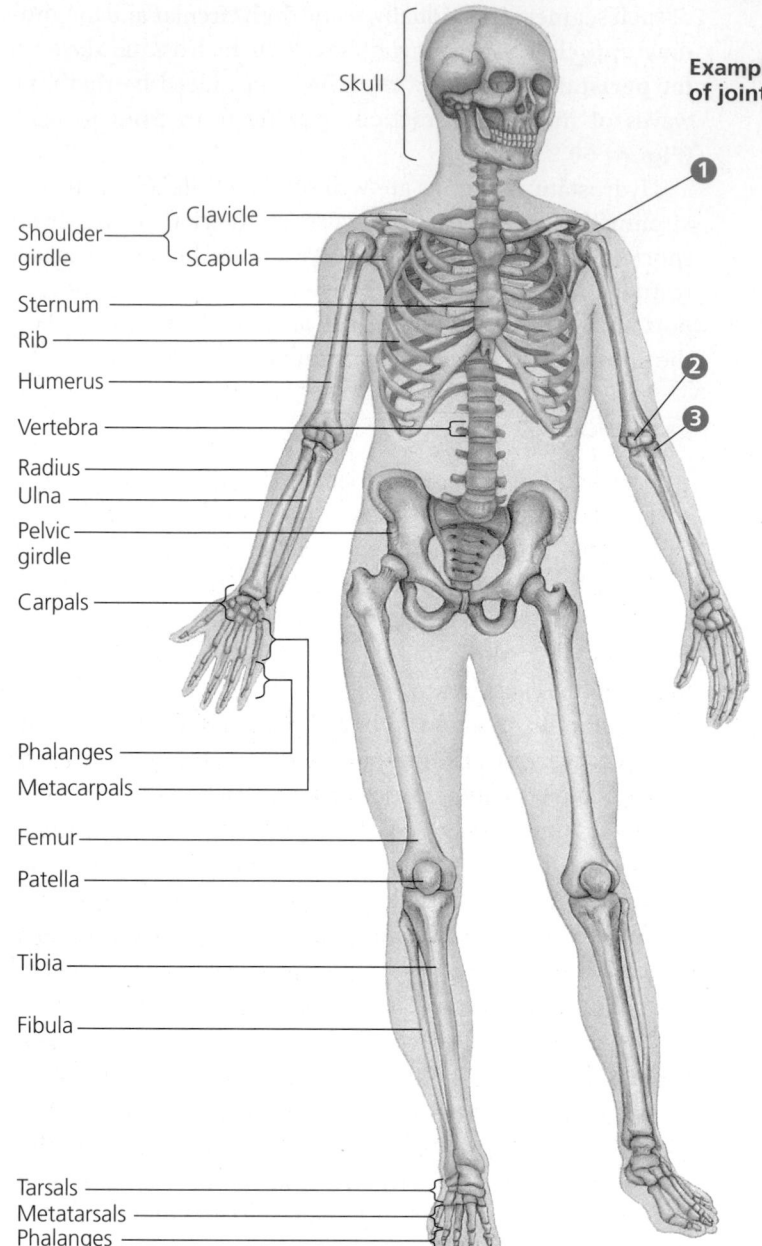

Skull

Examples
of joints

Shoulder
girdle { Clavicle

Scapula

Sternum

Rib

Humerus

Vertebra

Radius

Ulna

Pelvic
girdle

Carpals

Phalanges

Metacarpals

Femur

Patella

Tibia

Fibula

Tarsals
Metatarsals
Phalanges

1 **Ball-and-socket joints**, where the humerus contacts the shoulder girdle and where the femur contacts the pelvic girdle, enable us to rotate our arms and legs and move them in several planes.

Head of
humerus

Scapula

Humerus

Ulna

2 **Hinge joints**, such as between the humerus and the head of the ulna, restrict movement to a single plane.

Ulna

Radius

3 **Pivot joints** allow us to rotate our forearm at the elbow and to move our head from side to side.

▲ **Figure 50.34 Bones and joints of the human skeleton.**

some fused together and others connected at joints by ligaments that allow freedom of movement (**Figure 50.34**).

Size and Scale of Skeletons

In analyzing the structure and function of any animal skeleton, it is useful to consider the effects of size and scale as they might apply for an engineer designing a bridge or building. For example, the strength of a building support depends on its cross-sectional area, which increases with the square of its diameter. In contrast, the strain on that support depends on the building's weight, which increases with the cube of its height or other linear dimension. In common with the structure of a bridge or building, an animal's body structure must support its size. Consequently, a large animal has very different body pro-

portions than a small animal. If a mouse were scaled up to an elephant's size, its slender legs would buckle under its weight.

In simply applying the building analogy, we might predict that the size of an animal's leg bones should be directly proportional to the strain imposed by its body weight. However, our prediction would be inaccurate; animal bodies are complex and nonrigid, and the building analogy only partly explains the relationship between body structure and support. An animal's leg size relative to its body size is only part of the story. It turns out that body posture—the position of the legs relative to the main body—is more important in supporting body weight, at least in mammals and birds. Muscles and tendons (connective tissue that joins muscle to bone), which hold the legs of large mammals relatively straight and positioned under the body, bear most of the load.

Types of Locomotion

Movement is a hallmark of animals. Even sessile animals move their body parts: Sponges use beating flagella to generate water currents that draw and trap small food particles, and sessile cnidarians wave tentacles that capture prey (see Chapter 33). Most animals, however, are mobile and spend a considerable portion of their time and energy actively searching for food, as well as escaping from danger and looking for mates. Our focus here is **locomotion**, or active travel from place to place.

Animals have diverse modes of locomotion. Most animal phyla include species that swim. On land and in the sediments on the floor of the sea and lakes, animals crawl, walk, run, or hop. Active flight (in contrast to gliding downward from a tree or elevated ground) has evolved in only a few animal groups: insects, reptiles (including birds), and, among the mammals, bats. A group of large flying reptiles died out millions of years ago, leaving birds and bats as the only flying vertebrates.

In all its modes, locomotion requires that an animal expend energy to overcome two forces that tend to keep it stationary: friction and gravity. Exerting force requires energy-consuming cellular work.

Swimming

Because most animals are reasonably buoyant in water, overcoming gravity is less of a problem for swimming animals than for species that move on land or through the air. On the other hand, water is a much denser and more viscous medium than air, and thus drag (friction) is a major problem for aquatic animals. A sleek, fusiform (torpedo-like) shape is a common adaptation of fast swimmers (see Figure 40.2).

Animals swim in diverse ways. For instance, many insects and four-legged vertebrates use their legs as oars to push against the water. Squids, scallops, and some cnidarians are jet-propelled, taking in water and squirting it out in bursts. Sharks and bony fishes swim by moving their body and tail from side to side, while whales and dolphins move by undulating their body and tail up and down.

Locomotion on Land

In general, the problems of locomotion on land are the opposite of those in water. On land, a walking, running, hopping, or crawling animal must be able to support itself and move against gravity, but air poses relatively little resistance, at least at moderate speeds. When a land animal walks, runs, or hops, its leg muscles expend energy both to propel it and to keep it from falling down. With each step, the animal's leg muscles must overcome inertia by accelerating a leg from a standing start. For moving on land, powerful muscles and strong skeletal support are more important than a streamlined shape.

Diverse adaptations for traveling on land have evolved in various vertebrates. For example, kangaroos have large, powerful muscles in their hind legs, suitable for locomotion by hopping

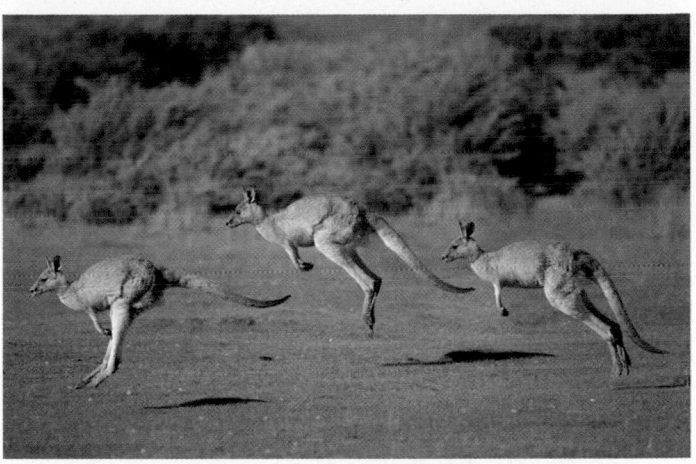

▲ **Figure 50.35 Energy-efficient locomotion on land.** Members of the kangaroo family travel from place to place mainly by leaping on their large hind legs. Kinetic energy momentarily stored in tendons after each leap provides a boost for the next leap. In fact, a large kangaroo hopping at 30 km/hr uses no more energy per minute than it does at 6 km/hr. The large tail helps balance the kangaroo when it leaps as well as when it sits.

(Figure 50.35). As a kangaroo lands after each leap, tendons in its hind legs momentarily store energy. The farther the animal hops, the more energy the tendons store. Analogous to the energy in a compressed spring, the energy stored in the tendons is available for the next jump and reduces the total amount of energy the animal must expend to travel. The legs of an insect, a dog, or a human also retain some energy during walking or running, although a considerably smaller share than do those of a kangaroo.

Maintaining balance is another prerequisite for walking, running, or hopping. A kangaroo's large tail helps balance its body during leaps and also forms a stable tripod with its hind legs when the animal sits or moves slowly. Illustrating the same principle, a walking cat, dog, or horse keeps three feet on the ground. Bipedal animals, such as humans and birds, keep part of at least one foot on the ground when walking. When an animal runs, all four feet (or both feet for bipeds) may be off the ground briefly, but at running speeds it is momentum more than foot contact that keeps the body upright.

Crawling poses a very different situation. Because much of its body is in contact with the ground, a crawling animal must exert considerable effort to overcome friction. You have read how earthworms crawl by peristalsis. Many snakes crawl by undulating their entire body from side to side. Assisted by large, movable scales on its underside, a snake's body pushes against the ground, propelling the animal forward. Boa constrictors and pythons creep straight forward, driven by muscles that lift belly scales off the ground, tilt the scales forward, and then push them backward against the ground.

Flying

Gravity poses a major problem for a flying animal because its wings must develop enough lift to overcome gravity's downward force. The key to flight is wing shape. All types of wings are airfoils—structures whose shape alters air currents in a way that helps animals or airplanes stay aloft. As for the body to which the wings attach, a fusiform shape helps reduce drag in air as it does in water.

Flying animals are relatively light, with body masses ranging from less than a gram for some insects to about 20 kg for the largest flying birds. Many flying animals have structural adaptations that contribute to low body mass. Birds, for example, have no urinary bladder or teeth and have relatively large bones with air-filled regions that help lessen the bird's weight (see Chapter 34).

Energy Costs of Locomotion

During the 1960s, three scientists at Duke University—Dick Taylor, Vance Tucker, and Knut Schmidt-Nielsen—became interested in the bioenergetics of locomotion. Physiologists typically determine an animal's rate of energy use during locomotion by measuring oxygen consumption or carbon dioxide production (see Chapter 40). To apply such a strategy to flight, Tucker trained parakeets to fly in a wind tunnel while wearing a face mask (Figure 50.36). By connecting the mask to a tube that collected the air the bird exhaled as it flew, Tucker could measure rates of gas exchange and calculate energy expenditure. In the meantime, Taylor and Schmidt-Nielsen measured energy consumption at rest and during locomotion for animals of widely varying body sizes.

In 1971, Schmidt-Nielsen was invited to give a lecture at a scientific meeting in Germany. In preparation for his speech, he set out to compare the energy cost of different forms of locomotion. He decided to express energy cost as the amount of fuel it takes to transport a given amount of body weight over a set distance. By converting data from many studies of animal locomotion to this common framework, Schmidt-Nielsen drew important conclusions about energy expenditure and locomotion (Figure 50.37).

Schmidt-Nielsen's calculations demonstrated that the energy cost of locomotion depends on the mode of locomotion and the environment. Running animals generally expend more energy per meter traveled than equivalently sized swimming animals,

▲ **Figure 50.36 Measuring energy usage during flight.** The tube connected to the plastic face mask collects the gases this parakeet exhales during flight in a wind tunnel.

partly because running and walking require energy to overcome gravity. Swimming is the most energy-efficient mode of locomotion (assuming that an animal is specialized for swimming). And if we compare the energy consumption per minute rather than per meter, we find that flying animals use more energy than swimming or running animals with the same body mass.

The studies described in Figure 50.37 also provide insight into the relationship of size to energy expenditure during locomotion. The downward slope of each line on the graph shows that a larger animal travels more efficiently than a smaller animal specialized for the same mode of transport. For example, a 450-kg horse expends less energy *per kilogram of body mass* than a 4-kg cat running the same distance. Of course, the total amount of energy expended in locomotion is greater for the larger animal.

▼ **Figure 50.37** **Inquiry**

What are the energy costs of locomotion?

EXPERIMENT   Knut Schmidt-Nielsen wondered whether there were general principles governing the energy costs of different types of locomotion among diverse animal species. To answer this question, he drew on his own studies as well as the scientific literature for measurements made when animals swam in water flumes, ran on treadmills, or flew in wind tunnels. He converted all of these data to a common set of units and graphed the results.

RESULTS

This graph plots the energy cost, in calories per kilogram of body mass per meter traveled, against body weight for animals specialized for running, flying, and swimming. Note that both axes are plotted on logarithmic scales.

CONCLUSION   For most animals of a given body mass, swimming is the most energy-efficient and running the least energy-efficient mode of locomotion. In addition, a small animal typically expends more energy per kilogram of body mass than a large animal, regardless of the type of locomotion used.

SOURCE   K. Schmidt-Nielsen, Locomotion: Energy cost of swimming, flying, and running, *Science* 177:222–228 (1972).

WHAT IF?   If you plotted the efficiency of a duck as a swimmer on this graph, where might you expect it to fall, and why?

Energy from food that is used for locomotion is unavailable for other activities, such as growth and reproduction. Therefore, structural and behavioral adaptations that maximize the efficiency of locomotion increase the evolutionary fitness of an organism.

Although we have discussed sensory receptors and muscles separately in this chapter, they are part of a single integrated system linking together brain, body, and the external world. An animal's behavior is the product of this system. In Chapter 51, we'll discuss behavior in the context of animal form and function and also link it to ecology, the study of interactions between organisms and their environment.

CONCEPT CHECK 50.6

1. In what way are septa an important feature of the earthworm skeleton?
2. Contrast swimming and flying in terms of the main problems they pose and the adaptations that allow animals to overcome those problems.
3. **WHAT IF?** Suppose you wanted to extend your arm from the elbow by controlling your biceps muscle rather than your triceps. How could you manage this feat?

For suggested answers, see Appendix A.

Chapter 50 Review

SUMMARY OF KEY CONCEPTS

CONCEPT 50.1

Sensory receptors transduce stimulus energy and transmit signals to the central nervous system (pp. 1087–1091)

▶ **Sensory Pathways** Sensory receptors are usually specialized neurons or epithelial cells that detect external or internal stimuli. Sensory reception, the detection of a stimulus by sensory cells, precedes transduction, the conversion of stimulus energy to a change in the membrane potential of a sensory receptor. The resulting receptor potential controls transmission of action potentials to the CNS, where sensory information is integrated to generate perceptions. Signal transduction pathways in receptor cells often amplify the signal, which causes the receptor cell either to produce action potentials or to release neurotransmitter at a synapse with a sensory neuron.

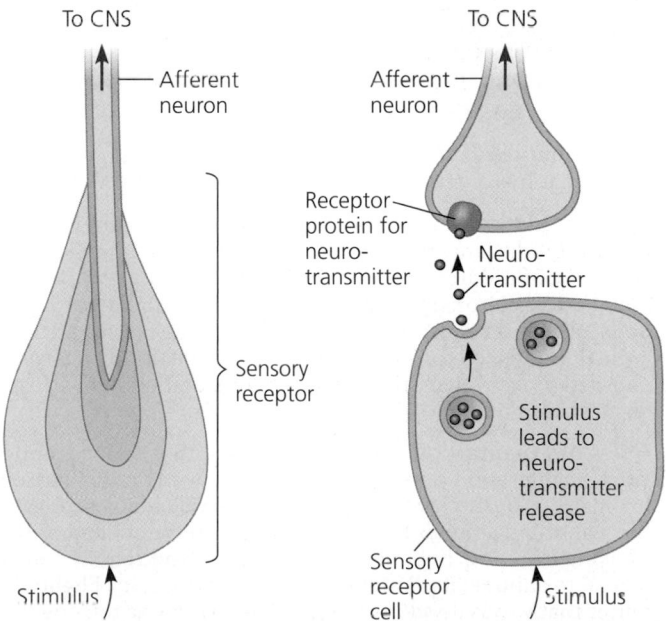

(a) Receptor *is* afferent neuron. **(b)** Receptor *regulates* afferent neuron.

▶ **Types of Sensory Receptors** Mechanoreceptors respond to stimuli such as pressure, touch, stretch, motion, and sound. Chemoreceptors detect either total solute concentrations or specific molecules. Electromagnetic receptors detect different forms of electromagnetic radiation. Various types of thermoreceptors signal surface and core temperatures of the body. Pain is detected by a group of diverse receptors that respond to excess heat, pressure, or specific classes of chemicals.

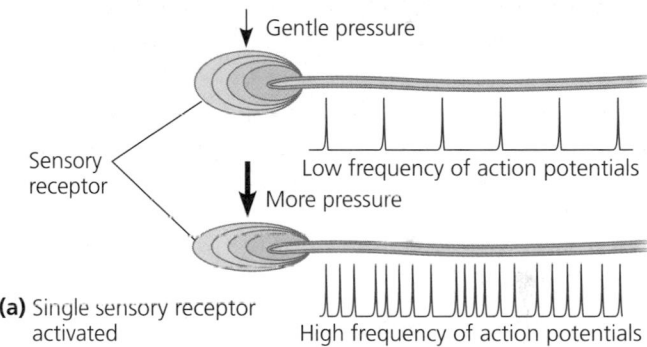

(a) Single sensory receptor activated

(b) Multiple receptors activated

CONCEPT 50.2

The mechanoreceptors responsible for hearing and equilibrium detect moving fluid or settling particles (pp. 1091–1096)

▶ **Sensing of Gravity and Sound in Invertebrates** Most invertebrates sense their orientation with respect to gravity by means of statocysts. Many arthropods sense sounds with body hairs that vibrate and with localized "ears," consisting of a tympanic membrane and receptor cells.

▶ **Hearing and Equilibrium in Mammals** The tympanic membrane (eardrum) transmits sound waves to three small bones of the middle ear, which transmit the waves through the oval window to the fluid in the coiled cochlea of the inner ear. Pressure waves in the fluid vibrate the basilar membrane, depolarizing hair cells and triggering action potentials that travel via the auditory nerve to the brain. Each region of the basilar membrane vibrates most vigorously at a particular frequency and leads to excitation of a specific auditory area of the cerebral cortex. Receptors in the saccule, utricle, and three semicircular canals of the inner ear function in balance and equilibrium.

▶ **Hearing and Equilibrium in Other Vertebrates** The detection of water movement in fishes and aquatic amphibians is accomplished by a lateral line system containing clustered hair cells.

CONCEPT 50.3

The senses of taste and smell rely on similar sets of sensory receptors (pp. 1096–1099)

▶ **Taste in Mammals** Both taste and smell depend on the stimulation of chemoreceptors by small dissolved molecules that bind to proteins on the plasma membrane. In humans, taste receptors are organized into taste buds on the tongue and in the mouth. Sensory cells within taste buds express a single receptor type specific for one of the five taste perceptions—sweet, sour, salty, bitter, and umami (elicited by glutamate).

▶ **Smell in Humans** Olfactory receptor cells line the upper part of the nasal cavity. Their axons extend to the olfactory bulb of the brain. More than 1,000 genes code for membrane proteins that bind to specific classes of odorants, and each receptor cell appears to express only one of those genes.

CONCEPT 50.4

Similar mechanisms underlie vision throughout the animal kingdom (pp. 1099–1105)

▶ **Vision in Invertebrates** The light detectors of invertebrates include the simple light-sensitive eyespots of planarians; the image-forming compound eyes of insects, crustaceans, and some polychaetes; and the single-lens eyes of some jellies, polychaetes, spiders, and many molluscs.

▶ **The Vertebrate Visual System** The main parts of the vertebrate eye are the sclera, which includes the cornea; the choroid, which includes the iris; the retina, which contains the photoreceptors; and the lens, which focuses light on the retina. Photoreceptors (rods and cones) contain a pigment, retinal, bonded to a protein (opsin). Absorption of light by retinal triggers a signal transduction pathway that hyperpolarizes the photoreceptors, causing them to release less neurotransmitter. Synapses transmit information from photoreceptors to bipolar cells and then to ganglion cells, whose axons in the optic nerve convey action potentials to the brain. Other neurons in the retina integrate information before it is sent to the brain. Most axons in the optic nerves go to the lateral geniculate nuclei, which relay information to the primary visual cortex.

MEDIA

Activity Structure and Function of the Eye

CONCEPT 50.5

The physical interaction of protein filaments is required for muscle function (pp. 1105–1112)

▶ **Vertebrate Skeletal Muscle** Vertebrate skeletal muscle consists of a bundle of muscle cells (fibers), each of which contains myofibrils composed of thin filaments of (mostly) actin and thick filaments of myosin. Myosin heads, energized by the hydrolysis of ATP, bind to the thin filaments, forming cross-bridges. Bending of the myosin heads exerts force on the thin filaments. When ATP binds to the myosin heads, they release, ready to start a new cycle. Repeated cycles cause the thick and thin filaments to slide past each other, shortening the sarcomere and contracting the muscle fiber.

A motor neuron initiates contraction by releasing acetylcholine, which depolarizes the muscle fiber. Action potentials travel to the interior of the muscle fiber along the T tubules, stimulating the release of Ca^{2+} from the sarcoplasmic reticulum. The Ca^{2+} repositions the tropomyosin-troponin complex on the thin filaments, exposing the myosin-binding sites on actin and allowing the cross-bridge cycle to proceed. A motor unit consists of a motor neuron and the muscle fibers it controls. Recruiting multiple motor units results in stronger contractions. A twitch results from a single action potential in a motor neuron. More rapidly delivered action potentials produce a graded contraction by summation. Tetanus is a state of smooth and sustained contraction produced when motor neurons deliver a volley of action potentials. Skeletal muscle fibers can be slow-twitch oxidative, fast-twitch oxidative, or fast-twitch glycolytic.

▶ **Other Types of Muscle** Cardiac muscle, found only in the heart, consists of striated cells that are electrically connected by intercalated disks and that can generate action potentials without input from neurons. In smooth muscles, contractions are slow and may be initiated by the muscles themselves or by stimulation from neurons in the autonomic nervous system.

MEDIA

BioFlix 3-D Animation Muscle Contraction
Activity Skeletal Muscle Structure
Activity Muscle Contraction
Investigation How Do Electrical Stimuli Affect Muscle Contraction?

CONCEPT 50.6

Skeletal systems transform muscle contraction into locomotion (pp. 1112–1117)

▶ Skeletal muscles, often present in antagonistic pairs, provide movement by contracting and pulling against the skeleton.

▶ **Types of Skeletal Systems** A hydrostatic skeleton, found in most cnidarians, flatworms, nematodes, and annelids, consists of fluid under pressure in a closed body compartment. Exoskeletons, found in most molluscs and arthropods, are hard coverings deposited on the surface of an animal. Endoskeletons, found in sponges, echinoderms, and chordates, are rigid supporting elements embedded within an animal's body.

▶ **Types of Locomotion** Swimming, locomotion on land, and flying each present particular challenges. Overcoming friction is a major problem for swimmers. Gravity is less of a problem for swimming animals than for those that move on land or fly. Walking, running, hopping, or crawling on land requires an animal to support itself and to move against gravity. Flight requires that wings develop enough lift to overcome the downward force of gravity.

► **Energy Costs of Locomotion** Animals that are specialized for swimming expend less energy per meter traveled than equivalently sized animals specialized for flying or running. In addition, larger animals are more efficient than smaller animals specialized for the same mode of locomotion.

MEDIA

Activity Human Skeleton

TESTING YOUR KNOWLEDGE

SELF-QUIZ

1. Which of the following sensory receptors is *incorrectly* paired with its category?
   a. hair cell—mechanoreceptor
   b. muscle spindle—mechanoreceptor
   c. taste receptor—chemoreceptor
   d. rod—electromagnetic receptor
   e. olfactory receptor—electromagnetic receptor

2. Some sharks close their eyes just before they bite. Although they cannot see their prey, their bites are on target. Researchers have noted that sharks often misdirect their bites at metal objects and that sharks can find batteries buried under the sand of an aquarium. This evidence suggests that sharks keep track of their prey during the split second before they bite in the same way that
   a. a rattlesnake finds a mouse in its burrow.
   b. a male silkworm moth locates a mate.
   c. a bat finds moths in the dark.
   d. a platypus locates its prey in a muddy river.
   e. a flatworm avoids light places.

3. The transduction of sound waves into action potentials takes place
   a. within the tectorial membrane as it is stimulated by the hair cells.
   b. when hair cells are bent against the tectorial membrane, causing them to depolarize and release neurotransmitter that stimulates sensory neurons.
   c. as the basilar membrane becomes more permeable to sodium ions and depolarizes, initiating an action potential in a sensory neuron.
   d. as the basilar membrane vibrates at different frequencies in response to the varying volume of sounds.
   e. within the middle ear as the vibrations are amplified by the malleus, incus, and stapes.

4. Which of the following is an *incorrect* statement about the vertebrate eye?
   a. The vitreous humor regulates the amount of light entering the pupil.
   b. The transparent cornea is an extension of the sclera.
   c. The fovea is the center of the visual field and contains only cones.
   d. The ciliary muscle functions in accommodation.
   e. The retina lies just inside the choroid and contains the photoreceptor cells.

5. When light strikes the rhodopsin in a rod, retinal isomerizes, initiating a signal transduction pathway that
   a. depolarizes the neighboring bipolar cells and initiates an action potential in a ganglion cell.
   b. depolarizes the rod, causing it to release the neurotransmitter glutamate, which excites bipolar cells.
   c. hyperpolarizes the rod, reducing its release of glutamate, which excites some bipolar cells and inhibits others.
   d. hyperpolarizes the rod, increasing its release of glutamate, which excites amacrine cells but inhibits horizontal cells.
   e. converts cGMP to GMP, opening sodium channels and hyperpolarizing the membrane, causing the rhodopsin to become bleached.

6. During the contraction of a vertebrate skeletal muscle fiber, calcium ions
   a. break cross-bridges by acting as a cofactor in the hydrolysis of ATP.
   b. bind with troponin, changing its shape so that the myosin-binding sites on actin are exposed.
   c. transmit action potentials from the motor neuron to the muscle fiber.
   d. spread action potentials through the T tubules.
   e. reestablish the polarization of the plasma membrane following an action potential.

7. **DRAW IT** Based on the information in the text, fill in the following graph. Use one line for rods and another line for cones.

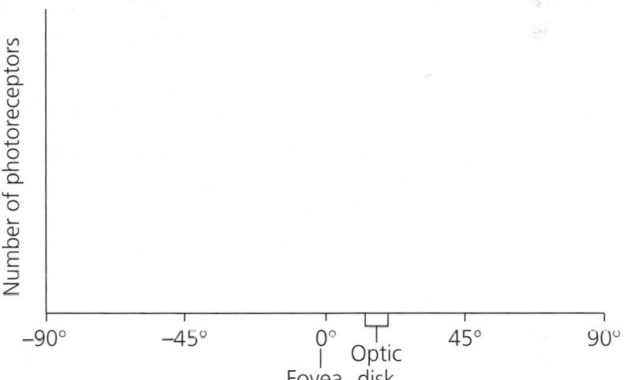

For Self-Quiz answers, see Appendix A.

MEDIA Visit **www.campbellbiology.com** for a Practice Test.

EVOLUTION CONNECTION

8. In general, locomotion on land requires more energy than locomotion in water. By integrating what you have learned throughout these chapters on animal functions, discuss some of the evolutionary adaptations of mammals that support the high energy requirements for moving on land.

SCIENTIFIC INQUIRY

9. Although skeletal muscles generally fatigue fairly rapidly, clam shell muscles have a protein called paramyosin that allows them to sustain contraction for up to a month. From your knowledge of the cellular mechanism of contraction, propose a hypothesis to explain how paramyosin might work. How would you test your hypothesis experimentally?

Animal Behavior

▲ **Figure 51.1 Why do cranes dance?**

OVERVIEW

Shall We Dance?

Red-crowned cranes (*Grus japonensis*), at one and a half meters in height, tower over the marshes and bogs of East Asia. Using their sharp eyesight, they pinpoint a variety of prey, including insects, fish, amphibians, and small rodents. Often, when the cranes gather in pairs or groups, they also prance, stretch, bow, and leap: In short, they dance (**Figure 51.1**). How do cranes decide that it is time to dance? Moreover, why do they dance at all?

Animal behavior, be it solitary or social, fixed or variable, is based on physiological systems and processes. An individual **behavior** is an action carried out by muscles or glands under control of the nervous system in response to a stimulus. Examples of behavior include an animal using muscles in its chest and throat to produce a song, or releasing a particular scent to mark its territory. Behavior is an essential part of acquiring nutrients for digestion and of finding a partner for sexual reproduction. Behavior also contributes to homeostasis, as in honeybees huddling to produce and conserve heat (see Chapter 40). In short, all of animal physiology contributes to behavior, and animal behavior influences all of physiology.

Being essential for survival and reproduction, behavior is subject to substantial natural selection over time. Selection that acts on behavior also affects anatomy because body form and appearance contribute directly to the recognition and communication that underlie many behaviors. For example, the dance of the red-crowned crane enables males and females to form lifelong mating pairs. The birds' distinctive body shape, striking coloration, and characteristic pattern of vocalizations are adaptations that enable potential mates to recognize and communicate with each other during courtship.

In this chapter, we'll examine how behavior is controlled, how it develops during an animal's life, and how it is influenced by both genes and the environment. We'll also explore the ways in which behavior evolves over many generations. In moving from our study of an animal's inner workings to its interactions with the outside world, we also provide a transition to the broader study of ecology, the focus of Unit Eight.

CONCEPT 51.1
Discrete sensory inputs can stimulate both simple and complex behaviors

Collectively, an animal's behavior is the sum of its responses to external and internal stimuli. Consider, for example, the male silky anole lizard (*Norops sericeus*) shown in **Figure 51.2**: He is extending his dewlap, a brightly colored skin flap beneath the throat. At various times, male anoles appear to use dewlaps to facilitate recognition by members of their own species, to establish territories, and to attract mates. Given the variety of stimuli and functions potentially associated with this and other animal behaviors, how can biologists determine how animal behaviors arose and exactly what functions they serve?

▲ Figure 51.2 **A male silky anole with dewlap extended.**

To address this question, pioneering behavioral biologists in the mid-1900s developed **ethology**, the scientific study of how animals behave, particularly in their natural environments. One early ethologist, Niko Tinbergen, of the Netherlands, suggested that understanding any behavior requires answering four questions, which can be summarized as follows:

1. What stimulus elicits the behavior, and what physiological mechanisms mediate the response?
2. How does the animal's experience during growth and development influence the response?
3. How does the behavior aid survival and reproduction?
4. What is the behavior's evolutionary history?

The first two questions ask about **proximate causation**: "how" a behavior occurs or is modified. The last two ask about **ultimate causation**: "why" a behavior occurs in the context of natural selection.

To understand the distinction between proximate and ultimate causation, let's return to the red-crowned cranes in Figure 51.1. Having formed a mating pair, the cranes breed in spring and early summer. A question about proximate causation is to ask *how* seasonal changes influence when red-crowned cranes mate. This question might lead us to examine the effect of day length on the crane's production of and responses to particular hormones. In contrast, asking *why* red-crowned cranes reproduce in spring and summer relates to ultimate causation. One hypothesis is that in those seasons parents are more likely to find food for rapidly growing offspring, which would increase reproductive success relative to breeding in other seasons.

Today, the ideas of proximate and ultimate causation underlie **behavioral ecology**, the study of the ecological and evolutionary basis for animal behavior. As we'll see shortly, Tinbergen, along with Austrian ethologists Karl von Frisch and Konrad Lorenz, not only provided a conceptual foundation for studying animal behavior but also applied these ideas to the study of specific behaviors. In recognition of their achievements, the three shared a Nobel Prize in 1973.

Let's begin by exploring behavioral responses to well-defined stimuli, starting with an example from Tinbergen's work.

Fixed Action Patterns

A type of behavior directly linked to a simple stimulus is the **fixed action pattern**, a sequence of unlearned acts that is essentially unchangeable and, once initiated, usually carried to completion. The trigger is an external cue known as a **sign stimulus**. Tinbergen studied what has become a classic example of a sign stimulus and fixed action pattern in the male three-spined stickleback fish (*Gasterosteus aculeatus*). Male sticklebacks, which have red bellies, attack other males that invade their nesting territories. Tinbergen noticed that his sticklebacks also behaved aggressively when a red truck passed in front of their tank. Inspired by this chance observation, he carried out experiments showing that the red color of an intruder's underside normally triggers the attack behavior. A male stickleback will not attack a fish lacking red coloration (note that female sticklebacks never have red bellies), but will attack even unrealistic models if they contain areas of red color **(Figure 51.3)**.

(a) A male stickleback fish attacks other male sticklebacks that invade its nesting territory. The red belly of the intruding male (left) acts as the sign stimulus that releases the aggressive behavior.

(b) The realistic model at the top, without a red underside, produces no aggressive response in a male three-spined stickleback. The other models, with red undersides, produce strong responses.

▲ Figure 51.3 **Sign stimuli in a classic fixed action pattern.**
? *Suggest an explanation for why this behavior evolved (ultimate causation).*

Oriented Movement

Environmental cues not only trigger some simple behaviors but also provide stimuli that animals use to change or orient both simple and complex movements in a particular direction.

Kinesis and Taxis

In changing locations, some animals rely on **kinesis**, a change in activity or turning rate in response to a stimulus. For example, sow bugs (genus *Oniscus*) exhibit a kinesis in response to variation in humidity. These terrestrial crustaceans become more active in dry areas and less active in humid areas. They do not move toward or away from specific conditions, but their increased movement under dry conditions makes it more likely that they will leave a dry area and encounter a moist area, where they survive better **(Figure 51.4)**.

In contrast to a kinesis, a **taxis** is an oriented movement toward (positive taxis) or away from (negative taxis) some stimulus. For example, trout and many other river fishes automatically swim or orient themselves in an upstream direction (toward the current). This taxis keeps the fish from being swept away and keeps it facing the direction from which food will come.

Migration

Migration—a regular, long-distance change in location—is observed in a wide variety of birds, fishes, and other animals **(Figure 51.5)**. In migrating, many animals pass through environments they have not previously encountered. How, then, do they find their way? Some migrating animals track their position relative to the sun, but there are problems with this approach. For one, the sun's position relative to Earth changes throughout the day. Numerous studies have demonstrated that animals adjust for these changes by means of a *circadian clock*, an internal mechanism that maintains a 24-hour activity rhythm or cycle (see Chapter 49). For example, experiments with controlled cycles of light and dark reveal that birds orient differently relative to the sun at distinct times of the day. Nocturnal animals can instead use the North Star, which has a constant position in the night sky. But there remains a second problem: Clouds can obscure both sun and stars. A simple experiment with homing pigeons demonstrates how animals can overcome this obstacle. On an overcast day, placing a small magnet on the head of a homing pigeon prevents it from returning efficiently to its roost. By sensing their position relative to Earth's magnetic field, pigeons and other animals can navigate without solar or celestial cues.

There are two competing hypotheses as to how animals detect Earth's magnetic field in navigating long-distance movements. One idea is based on the discovery of bits of magnetite, a magnetic iron mineral, in the heads of migrating fishes and birds. Some scientists hypothesize that Earth's pull on magnetite-containing structures triggers transmission of nerve impulses to the

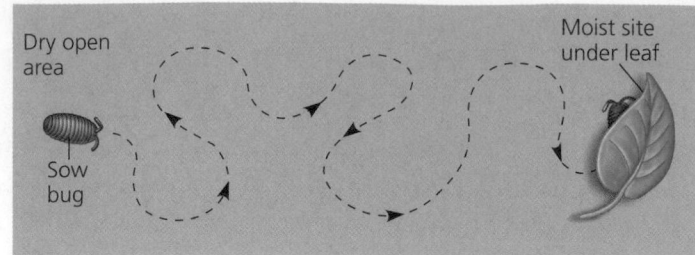

▲ **Figure 51.4 A kinesis.** Movements that vary with humidity may increase the chance that a sow bug will encounter and stay in a moist environment.

▲ **Figure 51.5 Migration.** Each spring, western sandpipers (*Calidris mauri*) migrate from their wintering grounds, which may be as far south as Peru, to their breeding grounds in Alaska. In the autumn, they return to their wintering grounds.

brain. The second hypothesis proposes that animals are guided by the effects of Earth's magnetic field on photoreceptors in the visual system. The idea that animals "see" the magnetic field is supported by experiments showing that birds require light of particular wavelengths in their daytime or nighttime environment to orient themselves in a magnetic field.

Behavioral Rhythms

Although the circadian clock plays a small but significant role in navigation by some migrating species, it has a major role in the daily activity of all animals. As discussed in Chapter 49, the output of the clock is a circadian rhythm, a daily cycle of rest and activity with far-reaching effects on behavioral physiology. The clock is normally synchronized with the light and dark cycles of the environment but can maintain rhythmic activity under constant environmental conditions, such as during hibernation. Having unraveled the basic molecular mechanism underlying this biological clock, scientists are now turning their attention to how signals from the clock regulate and coordinate daily behaviors.

Some behaviors, such as migration and reproduction, reflect biological rhythms with a longer cycle, or period, than the circadian rhythm. Behavioral rhythms linked to the yearly cycle of seasons are called *circannual rhythms*. Although migration and reproduction typically correlate with food availability, these behaviors are not a direct response to changes in food intake. Instead, circannual rhythms, like circadian rhythms, are influenced by the periods of daylight and darkness in the environment. For example, studies with several bird species have shown that an artificial environment with extended daylight can induce out-of-season migratory behavior.

Not all biological rhythms are linked to the light and dark cycles in the environment. Consider, for instance, the fiddler crab (genus *Uca*). Male fiddler crabs have a distinctive asymmetry: One claw grows to giant proportions, half the mass of the entire body **(Figure 51.6)**. (The name *fiddler* comes from the crab's appearance during feeding, when the smaller front claw moves to and from the mouth in front of the enlarged claw.) The adult male crabs live in burrows in mudflats or sand that are covered and uncovered by the tides. During courtship, a male positions himself at the entrance to his burrow, waving his enlarged claw to attract a potential mate. Once he lures a female to his burrow, he seals her in with mud or sand in preparation for mating. This courtship behavior is linked not to day length but to the timing of the new and full moon: Timing behavior to the lunar cycle links the crab's reproduction to the times of greatest tidal movement. The tides disperse larvae to deeper waters, where they complete early development in relative safety before returning to the tidal flats.

Animal Signals and Communication

Claw waving by fiddler crabs during courtship is an example of one animal (the male crab) generating the stimulus that guides the behavior of another animal (the female crab). A stimulus transmitted from one animal to another is called a **signal**. The transmission and reception of signals constitute animal **communication**, an essential element of interactions between individuals.

As an introduction to the common modes of animal communication, let's consider the courtship behavior of the fruit

▲ **Figure 51.6 Male fiddler crab beckoning to potential mates.** The behavioral cycles of the fiddler crab are linked to the tides that cover and uncover its burrow.

fly (*Drosophila melanogaster*). Courtship in these flies constitutes a *stimulus-response chain*, in which the response to each stimulus is itself the stimulus for the next behavior.

Fruit fly courtship begins with a male identifying and orienting toward a female of the same species **(Figure 51.7a)**. When the male sees the female, he relies on *visual communication*, the flow of information to the visual system. In addition, the male's sense of smell, or olfactory system, detects chemicals released into the air by the female. This is an example of *chemical communication*, the transmission and reception of signals in the form of specific molecules. Having recognized the female, the male approaches and taps the female with a foreleg **(Figure 51.7b)**. This touching, or

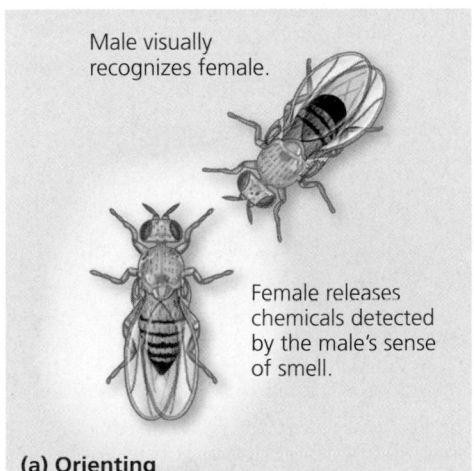

Male visually recognizes female.

Female releases chemicals detected by the male's sense of smell.

(a) Orienting

Male taps female's abdomen with a foreleg.

(b) Tapping

Male extends and vibrates wing, producing a courtship song.

(c) "Singing"

▲ **Figure 51.7 Courtship behavior of the fruit fly.** Fruit fly courtship involves a fixed set of behaviors that follow one another in fixed order.

tactile communication, alerts the female to the male's presence. In the process, chemicals on her abdomen are transferred to the male, providing further chemical confirmation of her species identity. In the third stage of courtship, the male extends and vibrates his wing, producing a specific courtship song (Figure 51.7c). This singing, an example of *auditory communication*, informs the female that the male is of the same species. Only if all of these forms of communication are successful will a receptive female allow the male to attempt copulation.

The form of communication used to transmit information is closely related to an animal's lifestyle and environment. For example, most terrestrial mammals are nocturnal, which makes visual displays relatively ineffective. Instead, these species use olfactory and auditory signals, which work as well in the dark as in the light. In contrast, most birds are diurnal (active mainly in daytime) and communicate primarily by visual and auditory signals. Unlike most mammals, humans are diurnal and, like birds, use primarily visual and auditory communication. We can thus detect and appreciate the songs and bright colors used by birds to communicate but miss many chemical cues on which other mammals base their behavior.

The information content of animal communication varies considerably. One remarkable example is the symbolic language by which honeybees share information about the location of food sources. The language was discovered in the 1940s by Karl von Frisch, who watched individual European honeybees (*Apis mellifera*) as they returned to hives modified for observation. A returning bee quickly becomes the center of attention for other bees, called followers (Figure 51.8a). If the food source is close to the hive (less than 50 m away), the returning bee moves in tight circles while waggling its abdomen from side to side (Figure 51.8b). This behavior, called the "round dance," motivates the follower bees to leave the hive and search for nearby food.

When the source of food is farther from the nest, the returning bee instead performs a "waggle dance." This dance, consisting of a half-circle swing in one direction, a straight run during which the bee waggles its abdomen, and a half-circle swing in the other direction, com-municates to the follower bees both the direction and distance of the food source from the hive (Figure 51.8c). The angle of the straight run relative to the hive's vertical surface is the same as the horizontal angle of the food in relation to the sun. For example, if the returning bee runs at a 30° angle to the right of vertical, the follower bees leaving the hive fly 30° to the right of the horizontal direction of the sun. A dance with a longer straight run, and therefore more abdominal waggles per run, indicates a greater distance to the food source. As follower bees exit the hive, they fly almost directly to the area indicated by the waggle dance. By using flower odor and other clues, they locate the food source within this area.

(a) Worker bees cluster around a bee that recently returned from a foraging trip.

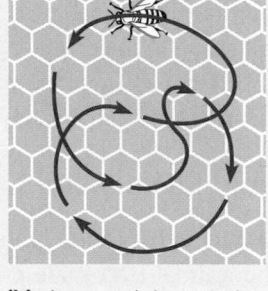

(b) The round dance indicates that food is near.

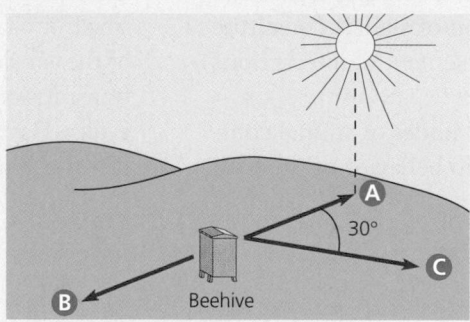

(c) The waggle dance, performed when food is distant, resembles a figure eight (below). Distance is indicated by the number of abdominal waggles performed in the straight-run part of the dance. Direction is indicated by the angle (in relation to the vertical surface of the hive) of the straight run.

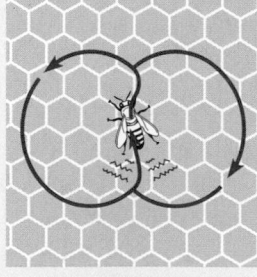

Location **A**: Food source is in same direction as sun.

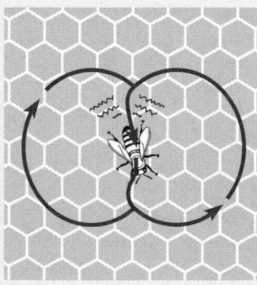

Location **B**: Food source is in direction opposite sun.

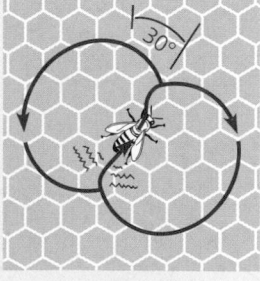

Location **C**: Food source is 30° to right of sun.

▲ **Figure 51.8 Honeybee dance language.** Honeybees returning to the hive communicate the location of food sources through the symbolic language of a dance.

Pheromones

Many animals that communicate through odors emit chemical substances called **pheromones**. Pheromones are especially common among mammals and insects and often relate to reproductive behavior. For example, pheromones are the basis for the chemical communication in fruit fly courtship (see Figure 51.7). Pheromones are not limited to short-distance signaling, however. Researchers have shown that the pheromones from a female moth can attract a mate from several kilometers away. Once the moths are together, pheromones also trigger specific courtship behaviors.

The context of a pheromone can be as important as the chemical itself. In a honeybee colony, pheromones produced by the queen and her daughters, the workers, maintain the hive's complex social order. When male honeybees (drones) are outside the hive, where they can mate with a queen, they are attracted to her pheromone; when drones are inside the hive, they are unaffected by the queen's pheromone.

Pheromones also function in nonreproductive behavior. For example, when a minnow or catfish is injured, an alarm substance released from the fish's skin disperses in the water, inducing a fright response in other fish. These nearby fish become more vigilant and form tightly packed schools, often near the bottom, where they are safer from attack (Figure 51.9). Pheromones can be very effective at remarkably low concentrations. For instance, just 1 cm^2 of skin from a fathead minnow contains sufficient alarm substance to induce a reaction in 58,000 L of water.

(a) Minnows are widely dispersed in an aquarium before an alarm substance is introduced.

(b) Within seconds of the alarm substance being introduced, minnows aggregate near the bottom of the aquarium and reduce their movement.

▲ Figure 51.9 **Minnows responding to the presence of an alarm substance.**

CONCEPT **51.2**

Learning establishes specific links between experience and behavior

For many behaviors we have discussed—such as fixed action patterns, taxis, and pheromone signaling—nearly all individuals in a population exhibit virtually the same behavior, despite internal and environmental differences during development and throughout life. Behavior that is developmentally fixed in this way is called **innate behavior**. In other cases, behavior is variable, depending on experience. One of the most powerful ways that environmental conditions can influence behavior is through **learning**, the modification of behavior based on specific experiences.

Habituation

One of the simplest forms of learning is **habituation**, a loss of responsiveness to stimuli that convey little or no new information. For example, many mammals and birds recognize alarm calls of members of their species, but eventually stop responding if these calls are not followed by an actual attack (the "cry-wolf" effect). Habituation allows an animal's nervous system to focus on stimuli that signal the presence of food, a mate, or real danger, rather than waste time or energy on stimuli that are irrelevant to the animal's survival and reproduction. In this way, habituation may increase an individual's fitness—its contribution to the gene pool of the next generation (see Chapter 23).

Imprinting

A type of behavior that includes both learned and innate components is **imprinting**, the formation at a specific stage in life of a long-lasting behavioral response to a particular individual or object. Imprinting is distinguished from other types of learning by having a **sensitive period**, also called a critical period, a limited developmental phase when certain behaviors can be learned. During the sensitive period, the young imprint on their parent and learn the basic behaviors of their species, while the parent learns to recognize its offspring. Among gulls, for instance, the sensitive period for a parent to bond with its young lasts one to two days. If bonding does not occur, the parent will not care for the infant, leading to death for the offspring and a decrease in reproductive success for the parent.

But how do the young know on whom—or what—to imprint? For example, how do young birds know that they should follow their mother? The tendency to respond is innate in the birds; the outside world provides the *imprinting stimulus*, something to which the response will be directed. Experiments with many species of waterfowl indicate that they have no innate recognition of "mother." They respond to and identify with the first object they encounter that has certain key characteristics. In classic experiments done in the 1930s, Konrad Lorenz showed that the principal imprinting stimulus in greylag geese (*Anser anser*) is a nearby object that is moving away from the young. When incubator-hatched goslings spent their first few hours with Lorenz rather than with a goose, they imprinted on him and steadfastly followed him from then on **(Figure 51.10a)**. Furthermore, they showed no recognition of their biological mother or other adults of their own species.

Cranes also imprint as hatchlings, creating both problems and opportunities in efforts to save endangered crane species. For instance, in an experiment, a group of 77 whooping cranes (*Grus americana*), which are endangered, were hatched and raised by sandhill cranes (*Grus canadensis*). Because the whooping cranes imprinted on their foster parents, none formed a mating pair-bond with another whooping crane. Therefore, captive breeding programs now isolate young cranes and expose them to the sights and sounds of members of their own species. To aid crane conservation further, young whooping cranes have been imprinted on humans in "crane suits" and taught to follow these "parents" flying ultralight aircraft along new migration routes **(Figure 51.10b)**. Importantly, these cranes still form mating pair-bonds with other whooping cranes, indicating that the crane costumes had the features required to direct "normal" imprinting.

Spatial Learning

Every natural environment shows some spatial variation, such as in the locations of nest sites, hazards, food, and prospective mates. Consequently, an organism's fitness may be enhanced by the capacity for **spatial learning**, the establishment of a memory that reflects the environment's spatial structure.

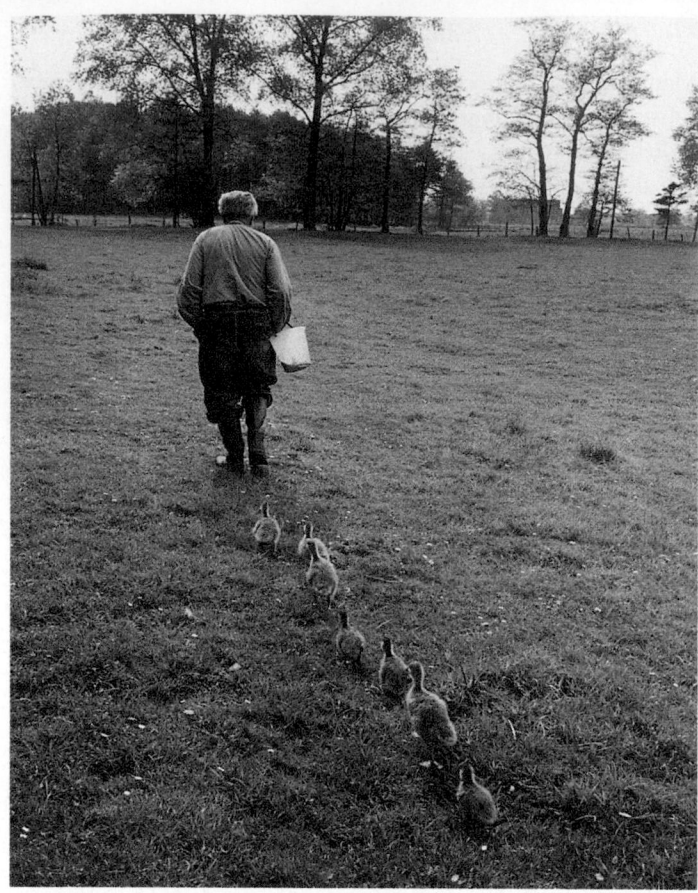

(a) These young greylag geese imprinted on ethologist Konrad Lorenz.

(b) A pilot wearing a crane suit and flying an ultralight plane acts as a surrogate parent to direct the migration of whooping cranes.

▲ **Figure 51.10 Imprinting.** Imprinting can be altered to (a) investigate animal behavior or (b) direct animal behavior.

WHAT IF? *Suppose the geese following Lorenz were bred to each other. How might their imprinting on Lorenz affect their offspring? Explain.*

Ethologist Niko Tinbergen studied spatial learning while a graduate student in 1932 in the Netherlands. Tinbergen was intrigued by the behavior of the female digger wasp (*Philanthus triangulum*), which nests in small burrows dug into sand dunes. He noticed that when a wasp left her nest to go hunting, she covered the entrance with sand. Upon her return, she flew directly to her hidden nest, despite the presence of hundreds of other burrows in the area. Tinbergen hypothesized that a wasp locates her nest by learning its position relative to visible **landmarks**, or location indicators. To test this hypothesis, Tinbergen carried out an experiment in the natural habitat of the wasps (**Figure 51.11**). By manipulating objects around nest entrances, Tinbergen demonstrated that digger wasps engage in visual learning. This experiment was so simple and informative that it could be summarized very concisely. In fact, at 32 pages, Tinbergen's Ph.D. thesis is still the shortest ever approved at Leiden University.

Cognitive Maps

Some animals guide their activity by a **cognitive map**, a representation in the nervous system of the spatial relationships between objects in an animal's surroundings. Rather than relying solely on moving from landmark to landmark, animals using cognitive maps can navigate more flexibly and efficiently by relating landmark positions to one another.

One striking example of cognitive mapping is found in the Clark's nutcracker (*Nucifraga columbiana*). Nutcrackers are corvids, the bird family that also includes ravens, crows, and jays. In the fall, a single nutcracker stores as many as 30,000 pine seeds in thousands of hiding places called caches, distributed over an area as large as 35 km^2. During the winter, the birds relocate many of their caches. By experimentally varying the distance between landmarks, researchers demonstrated that birds can identify the halfway point between landmarks. Such behavior suggests that nutcrackers employ an abstract geometric rule, which we can approximate as "Seed caches are found halfway between particular landmarks." Such rules, a fundamental property of cognitive maps, reduce the amount of detail required to remember an object's location. As we discussed in Chapter 49, corvids also display other forms of higher nervous system function.

Associative Learning

Learning also involves making associations between experiences. Consider, for example, a white-footed mouse that bites into the brightly colored caterpillar of a monarch butterfly, only to get a mouthful of distasteful fluid. Following this experience, the mouse may avoid attacking insects of similar appearance. The ability to associate one environmental feature (such as a color) with another (such as a foul taste) is called **associative learning**.

Associative learning can be divided into two types: classical conditioning and operant conditioning. In **classical conditioning,** an arbitrary stimulus becomes associated with a particular outcome. Russian physiologist Ivan Pavlov carried out early experiments in classical conditioning, demonstrating that if he always rang a bell just before feeding a dog, the dog would eventually salivate at the bell's sound alone, in anticipation of food. In **operant conditioning,** also called trial-and-error learning, an

▼ Figure 51.11 **Inquiry**

Does a digger wasp use landmarks to find her nest?

EXPERIMENT A female digger wasp covers the entrance to her nest while foraging for food, but finds the correct wasp nest reliably upon her return 30 minutes or more later. To test the hypothesis that a wasp learns visual landmarks that mark her nest before she leaves on hunting trips, Niko Tinbergen marked one nest with a ring of pinecones while the wasp was in the burrow. He returned two days later, shifted the ring of pinecones away from the nest, and waited to observe the wasp's behavior.

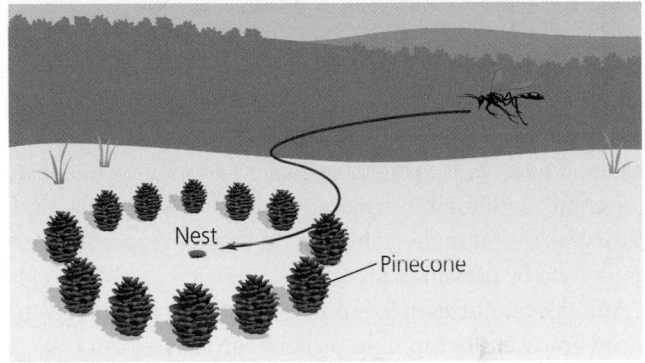

RESULTS When the wasp returned, she flew to the center of the pinecone circle instead of to the nearby nest. Repeating the experiment with many wasps, Tinbergen obtained the same results.

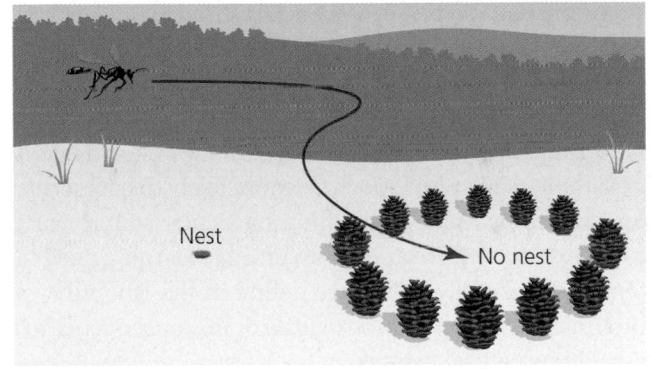

CONCLUSION The experiment supported the hypothesis that digger wasps use visual landmarks to keep track of their nests.

SOURCE N. Tinbergen, *The Study of Instinct*, Clarendon Press, Oxford (1951).

WHAT IF? Suppose the digger wasp had returned to her original nest site, despite the pinecones having been moved. What alternative hypotheses might you propose regarding how the wasp finds her nest and why the pinecones didn't misdirect the wasp?

animal learns to associate one of its own behaviors with a reward or punishment and then tends to repeat or avoid that behavior. For instance, a predator may learn to avoid certain kinds of potential prey if they are associated with painful experiences

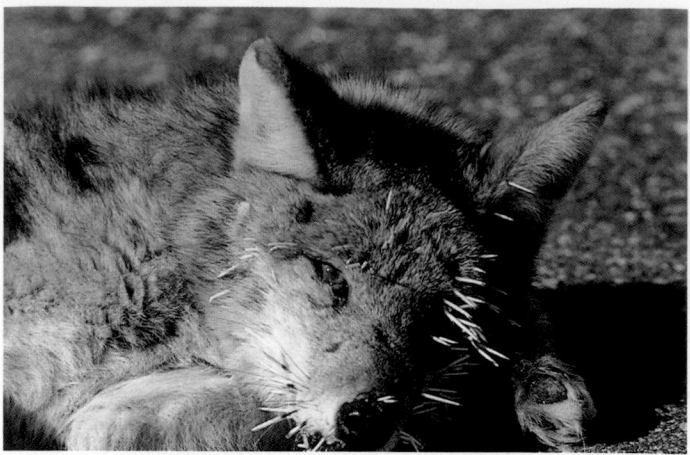

▲ **Figure 51.12 Operant conditioning.** Having received a face full of quills, a young coyote has probably learned to avoid porcupines.

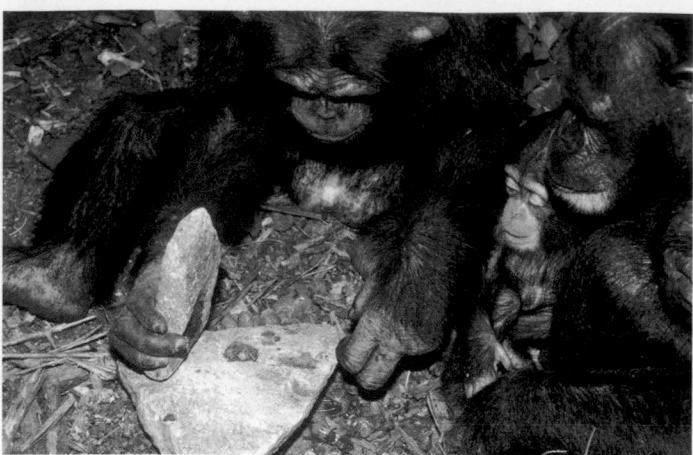

▲ **Figure 51.13 A young chimpanzee learning to crack oil palm nuts by observing an experienced elder.**

(Figure 51.12). B. F. Skinner, an American pioneer in the study of operant conditioning, explored this type of learning in the laboratory by, for example, training a rat through repeated trials to obtain food by pressing a lever.

Animals cannot learn to link just any stimulus with a given behavior, however. For example, pigeons can learn to associate danger with a particular sound but not with a particular color. The pigeons' inability to associate a color with danger does not reflect an inability to distinguish visual clues because pigeons *can* learn to associate a color with food. Rather, the development and organization of the pigeon nervous system apparently restrict the associations that can be formed. Such restrictions are not limited to birds. Rats, for example, can learn to avoid illness-inducing food on the basis of smells but not sights or sounds.

The associations readily formed by an animal often reflect relationships likely to occur in nature. In the case of a rat's diet, for example, a harmful food is far more likely to have a certain odor than to be associated with a particular sound. For this reason, experiments regarding associative learning need to be interpreted carefully: What we define in the laboratory as a limitation in learning may be of little or no consequence to the animal in its natural habitat.

Cognition and Problem Solving

The most complex forms of learning involve **cognition**—the process of knowing represented by awareness, reasoning, recollection, and judgment. In addition to primates, many groups of animals, including insects, appear to exhibit cognition in controlled laboratory studies. In one experiment, honeybees were shown a color and then presented with a Y-shaped maze in which one arm was the same color. If the bees flew into that arm of the maze, they were rewarded. They were then shown a black-and-white sample with either vertical or horizontal bars and tested in a maze that had vertical bars in one arm and horizontal bars in the other. They most often chose the arm with bars oriented in the same way as the sample. Another set of bees trained in the color mazes were re-

warded for flying into the arm that had a *different* color than the sample. When these bees were tested in mazes with the bars, they chose the arm that differed from the sample. Honeybees thus can apparently distinguish on the basis of "same" and "different."

The information-processing ability of a nervous system can also be revealed in **problem solving**, the cognitive activity of devising a method to proceed from one state to another in the face of real or apparent obstacles. For example, if a chimpanzee is placed in a room with several boxes on the floor and a banana hung high out of reach, the chimp can "size up" the situation and stack the boxes, enabling it to reach the food. Such problem-solving behavior is highly developed in some mammals, especially primates and dolphins. Notable examples have also been observed in some bird species, especially ravens, crows, and jays. In one study, ravens were confronted with food hanging from a branch by a string. After failing to grab the food in flight, one raven flew to the branch and alternately pulled up and stepped on the string until the food was within reach. A number of other ravens eventually arrived at similar solutions. Nevertheless, some ravens failed to solve the problem, indicating that problem-solving success in this species, as in others, varies with individual experience and abilities.

Many animals learn to solve problems by observing the behavior of other individuals. Young wild chimpanzees, for example, learn how to crack oil palm nuts with two stones by copying experienced chimpanzees **(Figure 51.13)**.

Development of Learned Behaviors

Most of the acquired behaviors we have discussed involve learning that takes place over a relatively short time. Development of some other behaviors, such as singing in some bird species, occurs in distinct stages. The first stage of song learning for white-crowned sparrows takes place early in life. If a fledgling sparrow is prevented from hearing real sparrows or recordings of sparrow songs during the first 50 days of life, it fails to develop the adult song of its species. Although the young bird does not sing during the sensitive period, it memorizes the song of its species by listening to other white-crowned sparrows sing. During the sensitive period, fledglings chirp more in response to songs of their own species than to songs of other species. Thus, although young white-crowned sparrows learn the songs they will sing as adults, learning appears to be bounded by genetically controlled preferences.

The sensitive period when a white-crowned sparrow memorizes its species' song is followed by a second learning phase when the juvenile bird sings tentative notes called a subsong. The juvenile bird hears its own singing and compares it with the song memorized during the sensitive period. Once a sparrow's own song matches the one it memorized, the song "crystallizes" as the final song, and the bird sings only this adult song for the rest of its life.

There are important exceptions to the song-learning scenario seen in white-crowned sparrows. Canaries, for example, do not have a single sensitive period for song learning. A young canary begins with a subsong, but the full song the canary develops is not crystallized in the same way as it is in white-crowned sparrows. Between breeding seasons, the song becomes flexible again, and an adult male may learn new song "syllables" each year, adding to the song it already sings.

These examples of song learning illustrate how experience and genetics influence development of a behavior. We'll examine this subject more extensively in the next section, exploring how variation in environment and genetic makeup influence animal behavior.

CONCEPT CHECK 51.2

1. How might associative learning explain why unrelated distasteful or stinging insects have similar colors?
2. Clark's nutcrackers hide tens of thousands of seeds each fall, some of which they never retrieve. Why might there be an evolutionary advantage for the species if individuals forget the location of some caches?
3. **WHAT IF?** Suppose you designed a laboratory environment using just a few objects as landmarks. How might you position and manipulate the objects to determine whether an animal could use a cognitive map to remember the location of a food source?

For suggested answers, see Appendix A.

CONCEPT 51.3
Both genetic makeup and environment contribute to the development of behaviors

Animal behavior, like anatomy and physiology, is governed by complex interactions between genetic and environmental factors. Although the DNA sequence of the genome provides instructions for the development of behavior, many factors—including the environment of the fertilized egg and the animal's diet, social interactions, and surroundings—modify how these instructions are carried out. This fact contrasts sharply with the popular conception that behavior is due *either* to genes (nature) *or* to environment (nurture). In this section, we'll explore how scientists determine to what extent differences in genetic makeup and environment underlie differences in animal behavior.

Experience and Behavior

One informative approach to identifying environmental contributions to behavior is a **cross-fostering study**, in which the young of one species are placed in the care of adults from another species. The extent to which the offspring's behavior changes in such a situation is one measure of how the social and physical environment influences behavior.

The males of certain mouse species have behavioral differences that are well suited for cross-fostering experiments. Male California mice (*Peromyscus californicus*) are highly aggressive toward other mice and provide extensive parental care. In contrast, male white-footed mice (*Peromyscus leucopus*) are less aggressive and engage in little parental care. When the pups of each species were placed in the nests of the other species, the cross-fostering altered the behavior of both species (**Table 51.1**). For instance, male California mice raised by white-footed mice were less aggressive toward intruders. Experience during development thus can have a strong influence on aggressive behavior in these rodents. However, the cross-fostering affected a wider range of behaviors for California mice than for white-footed mice.

The mouse cross-fostering experiments reveal that the influence of experience on behavior need not be confined to a single generation. When the cross-fostered California mice became parents, they spent less time retrieving their offspring than California mice raised by their own species. Thus, experience during development can modify physiology in a way

Table 51.1 Influence of Cross-Fostering on Male Mice*

Species	Aggression Toward an Intruder	Aggression in Neutral Situation	Paternal Behavior
California mice fostered by white-footed mice	Reduced	No difference	Reduced
White-footed mice fostered by California mice	No difference	Increased	No difference

*Comparisons are with mice raised by parents of their own species.

that alters parental behavior, extending the influence of environment to a subsequent generation.

For humans, the influence of genetics and environment on behavior can be explored by a **twin study**, in which researchers compare the behavior of identical twins raised apart with those raised in the same household. As discussed in Chapter 49, twin studies have been instrumental in studying human behavioral disorders, such as schizophrenia, anxiety disorders, and alcoholism. These investigations have revealed that the degree of susceptibility governed by genetic differences between individuals varies among mental disorders but is almost always greater than 20% and less than 80%. Both environment and genetics therefore contribute significantly to the behaviors that characterize these disorders in humans.

Regulatory Genes and Behavior

So far, we have talked about how experience can influence the genetic regulation of behavior. But how do genes direct behavior? As a field of research, behavioral genetics is still in its infancy. Nevertheless, we already know a great deal about some behaviors, such as courtship in certain insects.

The courtship behavior of the male fruit fly shown in Figure 51.7 involves a complex series of actions in response to multiple sensory stimuli. Nevertheless, recent evidence indicates that a single gene called *fru* controls the entire male courtship ritual. Males lacking a functional *fru* gene fail to court and mate with females. (The name *fru* is short for *fruitless*, reflecting the absence of offspring from the mutant males.) Normal male and female flies express distinct forms of the *fru* gene. When females are genetically manipulated to express the male form of *fru*, they court other females, performing the role normally played by the male. How can a single gene control so many behaviors and actions? The explanation lies in the fact that *fru* is a master regulatory gene that directs the expression and activity of many genes with narrower functions. Together, genes that are controlled by the *fru* gene bring about sex-specific development of the fly nervous system. In effect, *fru* programs the fly for male courtship behavior by overseeing a male-specific wiring of the central nervous system.

Further evidence of genetic influence on insect courtship comes from studies of the courtship song of the green lacewing. Found throughout central to northern Eurasia and North America, these insects include at least 15 species, identical in appearance but having different courtship songs. For the last three decades, Charles Henry, at the University of Connecticut, has explored the genetic basis for these differences. First, he showed that lacewings reared in isolation in the laboratory performed the song specific to their species. Thus, the courtship song must be genetically controlled. Henry then crossed different green lacewing species in the laboratory and analyzed the songs

produced by the hybrid offspring (**Figure 51.14**). These experiments demonstrated that each component or property of the courtship song is governed by a different gene. Furthermore, the

▼ Figure 51.14 **Inquiry**

Are the songs of green lacewing species under the control of multiple genes?

EXPERIMENT   Charles Henry, Lucía Martínez, and Kent Holsinger crossed males and females of *Chrysoperla plorabunda* and *Chrysoperla johnsoni*, two morphologically identical species of lacewings that sing different courtship songs.

SOUND RECORDINGS

Chrysoperla plorabunda parent:

Volley period
Standard repeating unit
Vibration volleys

crossed with

Chrysoperla johnsoni parent:

Volley period

Standard repeating unit

The researchers compared the songs of the male and female parents with those of the hybrid offspring that had been raised in isolation from other lacewings.

RESULTS   The F_1 hybrid offspring sing a song in which the length of the standard repeating unit is similar to that sung by the *Chrysoperla plorabunda* parent, but the volley period—the interval between vibration volleys—is more similar to that of the *Chrysoperla johnsoni* parent.

F_1 hybrids, typical phenotype:

Volley period

Standard repeating unit

CONCLUSION   Since the song of the hybrid offspring has features of the songs of both parents, the results indicate that the songs sung by *Chrysoperla plorabunda* and *Chrysoperla johnsoni* are under the control of more than one gene.

SOURCE   C. S. Henry et al., The inheritance of mating songs in two cryptic, sibling lacewing species, *Genetica* 116:269–289 (2002).

WHAT IF?   Suppose the hybrids generated in this experiment were fertile. Would the appearance of the hybrid song shown in the figure be likely to lead to the formation of a new species? Explain your answer.

distinct courtship song of each green lacewing species reflects genetic differences at multiple, independent loci.

Genetically Based Behavioral Variation in Natural Populations

Behavioral differences between closely related species, such as green lacewings, are common. Though often less obvious, significant differences in behavior can also be found *within* a species. When behavioral variation between populations of a species corresponds to variation in environmental conditions, it may be evidence of past evolution.

Case Study: *Variation in Migratory Patterns*

One species well suited to the study of behavioral variation is the blackcap (*Sylvia atricapilla*), a small migratory warbler. Blackcaps that breed in Germany generally migrate southwest to Spain and then south to Africa for the winter. In the 1950s, a few blackcaps began to spend their winters in Britain, and over time the population of blackcaps wintering in Britain grew to many thousands. Leg bands show that some of these birds had migrated westward from central Germany. Why were there now two patterns of migration from Germany? To answer this question, Peter Berthold, at the Max Planck Research Center in Radolfzell, Germany, devised a strategy to study migratory orientation in the laboratory (Figure 51.15). The results demonstrated that the two patterns of migration reflect genetic differences between the two populations.

Berthold's study indicates that the change in migratory behavior in western European blackcaps occurred both recently and rapidly. Before 1950, there were no known westward-migrating blackcaps in Germany. By the 1990s, westward migrants made up 7–11% of the blackcap populations of Germany. Once westward migration began, it persisted and increased in frequency, perhaps due to the widespread use of winter bird feeders in Britain, as well as shorter migration distances.

Case Study: *Variation in Prey Selection*

Another well-known example of genetically based behavioral variation within a species involves prey selection by the western garter snake (*Thamnophis elegans*). The natural diet of this species differs widely across its range in California. Coastal populations feed on salamanders, frogs, and toads, but predominantly on banana slugs (*Ariolimus californicus*). Inland populations feed on frogs, leeches, and fish, but not on banana slugs. In fact, banana slugs are rare or absent in the inland habitats.

When researchers offered banana slugs to snakes from each wild population, most coastal snakes readily ate them, whereas inland snakes tended to refuse. To what extent do experience and genetics contribute to a snake's fondness for banana slugs?

▼ Figure 51.15 **Inquiry**

Are differences in migratory orientation within a species genetically determined?

EXPERIMENT Peter Berthold and colleagues in southern Germany raised two sets of young birds for their study. One group consisted of the offspring of blackcaps captured while wintering in Britain and then bred in Germany in an outdoor cage. The other group consisted of young birds collected from nests near the laboratory and then raised in cages. In the autumn, Berthold's team placed the blackcaps captured in Britain and the young birds raised in cages in large, glass-covered funnel cages lined with carbon-coated paper for 1.5–2 hours. When the funnels were placed outside at night, the birds moved around, making marks on the paper that indicated the direction in which they were trying to "migrate."

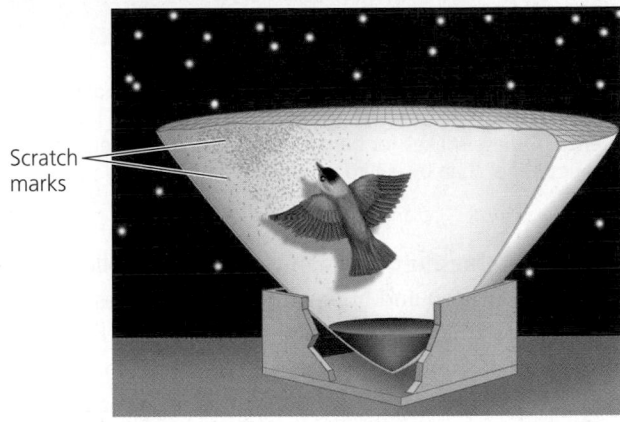

Scratch marks

RESULTS The wintering adult birds captured in Britain and their laboratory-raised offspring both attempted to migrate to the west. In contrast, the young birds collected from nests in southern Germany attempted to migrate to the southwest.

Adults from Britain and offspring of British adults

Young from SW Germany

CONCLUSION The young of the British blackcaps and the young birds from Germany (the control group) were raised under similar conditions but showed very different migratory orientations, indicating that migratory orientation has a genetic basis.

SOURCE P. Berthold et al., Rapid microevolution of migratory behavior in a wild bird species, *Nature* 360:668–690 (1992).

WHAT IF? Suppose the birds had not shown a difference in orientation in these experiments. Could you conclude that the behavior was not genetically based? Explain.

▲ **Figure 51.16 Western garter snake from a coastal habitat eating a banana slug.** Experiments indicate that the preference of these snakes for banana slugs may be influenced mainly by genetics rather than by environment.

To answer this question, pregnant snakes were collected from each wild population and housed in separate cages in the laboratory. While still very young, the offspring were offered a small piece of banana slug on each of ten days. More than 60% of the young snakes from coastal mothers ate banana slugs on eight or more of the ten days. In contrast, fewer than 20% of the young snakes from inland mothers ate a piece of banana slug even once. Perhaps not surprisingly, banana slugs thus appear to be a genetically acquired taste **(Figure 51.16)**.

How did a genetically determined difference in feeding preference come to match the snakes' habitats so well? It turns out that the coastal and inland populations also vary with respect to their ability to recognize and respond to odor molecules produced by banana slugs. Researchers hypothesize that when inland snakes colonized coastal habitats more than 10,000 years ago, some of them could recognize banana slugs by scent. Because these snakes took advantage of this food source, they had higher fitness than snakes in the population that ignored the slugs. Over hundreds or thousands of generations, the capacity to recognize the slugs as prey increased in frequency in the coastal population. The marked variation in behavior observed today between the coastal and inland populations may be evidence of this past evolutionary change.

Influence of Single-Locus Variation

Many scientists think that in most cases behavior is shaped by a large number of genes that individually have small effects. This does not imply, however, that variation at a single gene locus cannot have observable effects. In some cases, differences at a single locus can cause dramatic differences in behavior, even if the behavior requires the activity of many other genes. One striking example is the behavior of two closely related

◀ **Figure 51.17 A pair of prairie voles (*Microtus ochrogaster*) huddling.** Male North American prairie voles associate closely with their mates, as shown here, and contribute substantially to the care of young.

species of voles, which are small, mouse-like rodents. Male meadow voles (*Microtus pennsylvanicus*) are solitary and do not form lasting relationships with mates. Following mating, they pay little attention to their pups. In contrast, male prairie voles (*Microtus ochrogaster*) form a strong attachment, or *pair-bond*, with a single female after they mate **(Figure 51.17)**. Male prairie voles hover over their young pups, licking them and carrying them, while acting aggressively toward intruders.

Research suggested that a neurotransmitter released during mating is critical for the partnering and parental behavior of male voles. Known as vasopressin or ADH (see Chapter 44), this peptide binds to a specific receptor in the central nervous system. When male prairie voles are treated with a drug that inhibits the brain receptor for vasopressin, they fail to form pair-bonds after mating. Scientists have also observed that the vasopressin receptor gene of prairie voles is highly expressed in the brain, whereas that of meadow voles is not.

To test whether the amount of the vasopressin receptor present in the brain regulates the postmating behavior of voles, researchers inserted the vasopressin receptor gene from prairie voles into male meadow voles. The meadow voles carrying this gene not only developed brains with higher levels of the vasopressin receptor but also showed many of the same mating behaviors as male prairie voles, such as pair-bonding. Thus, although many genes influence pair-bond formation and parenting among voles, the level of the vasopressin receptor alone determines which behavioral pattern develops. When such strong single-locus effects occur, they provide an excellent opportunity to investigate behavioral evolution, as we'll see in the next section.

CONCEPT CHECK 51.3

1. Explain why geographic variation in garter snake prey choice might indicate that the behavior evolved by natural selection.

2. Why is it easier to identify mutations affecting courtship than those affecting other essential behaviors?

3. **WHAT IF?** Suppose that a pair of identical twins reared apart behave identically 80% of the time when performing a particular activity. What additional information would you need to draw a conclusion about the genetic basis of the behavior?

For suggested answers, see Appendix A.

▲ **Figure 51.18 Evolution of foraging behavior by laboratory populations of *Drosophila melanogaster*.** After 74 generations of living at low population density, *D. melanogaster* larvae (populations R1–R3) followed foraging paths significantly shorter than those of *D. melanogaster* larvae that had lived at high density (populations K1–K3).

CONCEPT 51.4

Selection for individual survival and reproductive success can explain most behaviors

The genetic components of behavior, like all other aspects of phenotype, evolve through natural selection for traits that enhance survival and reproductive success in a population. Two behaviors that can affect fitness most directly are foraging and mate choice.

Foraging Behavior

Because adequate nutrition is essential to an animal's survival and reproductive success, we should expect natural selection to refine behaviors that enhance the efficiency of feeding. Food-obtaining behavior, or **foraging**, includes not only eating but also any activities an animal uses to search for, recognize, and capture food items.

Evolution of Foraging Behavior

The fruit fly (*Drosophila melanogaster*) has provided scientists with an opportunity to examine how genetic variation might contribute to the evolution of foraging behavior. Variation in a gene called *forager* (*for*) dictates the food search behavior of fruit fly larvae. On average, larvae carrying the *for^R* ("Rover") allele travel nearly twice as far while feeding as larvae with the *for^s* ("sitter") allele. Experiments revealed that the enzyme encoded by the *forager* locus is more active in *for^R* than in *for^s* larvae. Because this type of enzyme typically is involved in signal transduction pathways (see Chapter 45), these results indicate that changes in processing of environmental information can substantially alter behavior.

Both the *for^R* and *for^s* alleles are present in natural populations. What circumstances might favor one or the other allele? The answer became apparent in experiments when flies were kept for many generations at either low or high population

densities. The larvae from the two samples clearly diverged in behavior, as measured by differences in average length of their foraging path (**Figure 51.18**). Larvae maintained for many generations at a low density foraged over shorter distances than those kept at high density. Furthermore, genetic tests indicated that the *for^s* allele had increased in frequency in the low-density populations, whereas the *for^R* allele had increased in frequency in the high-density group. These changes make sense. At low population density, short-distance foraging yields sufficient food, while long-distance foraging would result in unnecessary energy expenditure. Under crowded conditions, however, long-distance foraging could enable larvae to move beyond areas of food depletion. In summary, there was an observable and interpretable evolutionary change in behavior in the laboratory populations.

Optimal Foraging Model

To study the proximate and ultimate causation of diverse foraging strategies, behavioral ecologists sometimes apply a type of cost-benefit analysis used in economics. This idea proposes that foraging behavior is a compromise between the benefits of nutrition and the costs of obtaining food. These costs might include the energy expenditure of foraging as well as the risk of being eaten while foraging. According to this **optimal foraging model**, natural selection should favor a foraging behavior that minimizes the costs of foraging and maximizes the benefits.

As an example of how the optimal foraging model can be applied, let's consider the feeding behavior of the Northwestern crow (*Corvus caurinus*). On islands off British Columbia, these crows search rocky tide pools for gastropod molluscs called whelks. After spotting a whelk, the crow picks the whelk up in its beak, flies upward, and drops the whelk onto the rocks. If the drop is successful, the shell breaks and the crow can dine on the whelk's soft parts. If not, the crow flies up and drops the whelk again and again until the shell breaks. What determines how high the crow flies? The higher the crow flies, the greater the force with which the whelk strikes the rocks, increasing the chance the shell will break. Flying higher, however, means consuming more energy.

If energetic considerations dominated selection for the crow's foraging behavior, the average drop height might reflect a trade-off between the cost of flying higher and the benefit of more frequent success. To test this idea, researchers dropped whelks from different heights and noted the number of drops required to break a shell. For each height, they calculated the average number of drops and the average *total flight height*, the drop height times the average number of drops **(Figure 51.19)**. A drop height of about 5 m turned out to be optimal, breaking the shells with the lowest total flight height—in other words, with the least work. The actual average flight height for crows in their whelk-eating behavior is 5.23 m, very close to the prediction based on an optimal trade-off between energy gained (food) versus energy expended.

The close agreement between the predicted and actual flight heights suggests that the foraging model reflects the selective forces shaping the evolution of this behavior. However, other models could explain the findings equally well. For example, the average flight height could minimize the average *time* necessary to break open a whelk. Further experiments are needed to evaluate these possibilities.

▲ **Figure 51.19 Energy costs and benefits in foraging behavior.** Experimental results indicate that dropping shells from a height of 5 m results in breakage with the least amount of work. The actual drop height preferred by crows corresponds almost exactly to the height that minimizes total flight height.

Balancing Risk and Reward

One of the most significant potential costs to a forager is risk of predation. Maximizing energy gain and minimizing energy costs are of little benefit if the behavior makes the forager a likely meal for a predator. It seems logical, therefore, that predation risk would influence foraging behavior. Such appears to be the case for the mule deer (*Odocoileus hemionus*), which lives in the mountains of western North America. Researchers found that the food available for mule deer was fairly uniform across the potential foraging areas, although somewhat lower in open, nonforested areas. In contrast, the risk of predation differed greatly; mountain lions (*Puma concolor*), the major predator, killed large numbers of mule deer at forest edges and only a small number in open areas and forest interiors.

How does mule deer foraging behavior reflect the differences in predation risk in particular areas? Mule deer feed predominantly in open areas. Thus, it appears that mule deer foraging behavior reflects the large variation in predation risk and not the smaller variation in food availability. This result underscores that behavior often reflects a compromise between competing selective pressures.

Mating Behavior and Mate Choice

Mating behavior, which includes seeking or attracting mates, choosing among potential mates, and competing for mates, is the product of a form of natural selection called sexual selection (see Chapter 23). How mating behavior enhances reproductive success varies, depending on the species' mating system.

Mating Systems and Parental Care

As we saw for voles, the mating relationship between males and females varies a great deal from species to species. In many species, mating is **promiscuous**, with no strong pair-bonds or lasting relationships. In species in which the mates remain together for a longer period, the relationship may be **monogamous** (one male mating with one female) or **polygamous** (an individual of one sex mating with several of the other). Polygamous relationships most often involve a single male and many females, a system called **polygyny**, though some species exhibit **polyandry**, in which a single female mates with several males. Among monogamous species, males and females are often so much alike morphologically that they may be difficult or impossible to distinguish based on external characteristics **(Figure 51.20a)**. Polygynous species are generally dimorphic, with males being showier and often larger than females **(Figure 51.20b)**. Polyandrous species are also dimorphic, but in this case, females are generally more ornamented and larger than males **(Figure 51.20c)**.

The needs of the young are an important factor constraining the evolution of mating systems. Most newly hatched birds, for instance, cannot care for themselves. Rather, they require a large, continuous food supply, a need that is difficult for a single

(a) In monogamous species, such as these trumpeter swans, males and females are difficult to distinguish using external characteristics only.

(b) Among polygynous species, such as elk, the male (left) is often highly ornamented.

(c) In polyandrous species, such as these Wilson's phalaropes, females (top) are generally more ornamented than males.

▲ **Figure 51.20 Relationship between mating system and male and female forms.**

parent to meet. In such cases, a male that stays with and helps a single mate may ultimately have more viable offspring than it would by going off to seek additional mates. This may explain why most birds are monogamous. In contrast, for birds with young that can feed and care for themselves almost immediately after hatching, the males derive less benefit from staying with their partner. Males of these species, such as pheasants and quail, can maximize their reproductive success by seeking other mates, and polygyny is relatively common in such birds. In the case of mammals, the lactating female is often the only food source for the young; males usually play no role in raising the young. In mammalian species where males protect the females and young, such as lions, a male or small group of males typically takes care of many females at once in a harem.

Another factor influencing mating behavior and parental care is certainty of paternity. Young born to or eggs laid by a female definitely contain that female's genes. However, even within a normally monogamous relationship, a male other than the female's usual mate may have fathered that female's offspring. The certainty of paternity is relatively low in most species with internal fertilization because the acts of mating and birth (or mating and egg laying) are separated over time. This could explain why exclusively male parental care has evolved in very few species of birds and mammals. However, the males of many species with internal fertilization engage in behaviors that appear to increase their certainty of paternity. These behaviors include guarding females, removing any sperm from the female reproductive tract before copulation, and introducing large quantities of sperm to displace the sperm of other males. Certainty of paternity is much higher when egg laying and mating occur together, as in external fertilization. This may explain why parental care in aquatic invertebrates, fishes, and amphibians, when it occurs at all, is at least as likely to be by males as by females (**Figure 51.21**; see

Eggs

▲ **Figure 51.21 Paternal care by a male jawfish.** The male jawfish, which lives in tropical marine environments, holds the eggs it has fertilized in its mouth, keeping them aerated and protecting them from egg predators until the young hatch.

also Figure 46.6). Male parental care occurs in only 7% of fish and amphibian families with internal fertilization, but in 69% of families with external fertilization.

It is important to point out that *certainty of paternity* does not mean that animals are aware of those factors when they behave a certain way. Parental behavior correlated with certainty of paternity exists because it has been reinforced over generations by natural selection. Nevertheless, the relationship between certainty of paternity and male parental care remains an area of active research, enlivened by controversy.

Sexual Selection and Mate Choice

As you read in Chapter 23, the degree of sexual dimorphism within a species results from sexual selection, a form of natural selection in which differences in reproductive success among individuals are a consequence of differences in mating success. Recall from that chapter that sexual selection can take the form of *intersexual selection*, in which members of one sex choose mates on the basis of particular characteristics of the other sex, such as courtship songs, or *intrasexual selection*, which involves competition between members of one sex for mates. Let's look next at some experimental evidence for sexual selection.

Mate Choice by Females   Mate preferences by females may play a central role in the evolution of male behavior and anatomy through intersexual selection. As an example, let's consider the courtship behavior of stalk-eyed flies. The eyes of these insects are at the tips of stalks, which are longer in males than in females **(Figure 51.22)**. During courtship, a male presents himself to a female, front end on. Researchers have shown that females are more likely to mate with males that have relatively long eyestalks. Why would females favor this seemingly arbitrary trait? As discussed in Chapter 23, ornaments such as long eyestalks in these flies and bright coloration in male birds correlate in general with the male's health and vitality. A female

▲ **Figure 51.22 Male stalk-eyed flies.** Male eye span plays a role in ritualized contests between males, as shown here, and in mate selection by females.

▲ **Figure 51.23 Appearance of zebra finches in nature.** The male zebra finch (left) is more patterned and colorful than the female zebra finch.

that chooses a healthy male is likely to produce more offspring that survive to reproduce.

Experiments carried out with zebra finches reveal that imprinting can also contribute to mate choice. Both male and female zebra finches normally lack any feather crest on their head **(Figure 51.23)**. To explore whether parental appearance affects mate preference in offspring independent of any genetic influence, researchers provided zebra finches with artificial ornamentation. A 2.5-cm-long red feather was taped to the forehead feathers of either or both zebra finch parents when their chicks were 8 days old, approximately 2 days before they opened their eyes. A control group of zebra finches were raised by unadorned parents. When the chicks matured, they were presented with prospective mates that were either artificially ornamented with a red feather or non-ornamented **(Figure 51.24)**. Males showed no preference for either ornamented or non-ornamented mating partners. Females raised by non-ornamented parents or by parents in which only the female was ornamented also showed no preference. However, females raised by parents that were both ornamented or by a pair in which the male was ornamented preferred ornamented males as their own mates. Thus, female finches apparently take cues from their fathers in choosing mates.

Male Competition for Mates   The previous examples show how female choice can select for one best type of male in a given situation, resulting in low variation among males. Male competition for mates is a source of sexual selection that also can reduce variation among males. Such competition may involve **agonistic behavior**, an often ritualized contest that determines which competitor gains access to a resource, such as food or mates **(Figure 51.25)**. The outcome of such contests may be determined by strength, size, or the effective use of horns, teeth, and so forth, but the consequences may be psychological rather than physical (see Figure 51.22).

Experimental Groups of Parental Pairs

Both parents ornamented | Males ornamented | Females ornamented | **Control Group** Parents not ornamented

♂ ♀ | ♂ ♀ | ♂ ♀ | ♂ ♀

Offspring | | Offspring

Mate preference of female offspring: ornamented male | Mate preference of female offspring: none

♂ | ♂ ♂

▲ **Figure 51.24 Sexual selection influenced by imprinting.** Experiments demonstrated that female zebra finch chicks that had imprinted on artificially ornamented fathers preferred ornamented males as adult mates. For all experimental groups, male offspring showed no preference for either ornamented or non-ornamented female mates.

▲ **Figure 51.25 Agonistic interaction.** Male eastern grey kangaroos (*Macropus giganteus*) often "box" in contests that determine which male is most likely to mate with an available female. Typically, one male snorts loudly before striking the other around the head and throat with his forelimbs. Further snorting and cuffing, as well as grappling, often follow. If the male under attack does not retreat, the fight may escalate, with each male balancing on his tail while attempting to kick his rival with the sharp toenails of a hind leg.

Despite the potential for male competition to select for reduced variation, behavioral and morphological variation in males is extremely high in some vertebrate species, including species of fish and deer, as well as in a wide variety of invertebrates. In some species, sexual selection has led to the evolution of alternative male mating behavior and morphology. How do scientists analyze situations where more than one mating behavior can result in successful reproduction? One approach relies on the rules that govern games.

Applying Game Theory

Often, the fitness of a particular behavioral phenotype is influenced by other behavioral phenotypes in the population. In studying such situations, behavioral ecologists use a range of tools, including game theory. Developed by American mathematician John Nash and others to model human economic behavior, **game theory** evaluates alternative strategies in situations where the outcome depends on the strategies of all the individuals involved.

As an example of applying game theory to mating behavior, let's consider the side-blotched lizard (*Uta stansburiana*) of California. Males can have orange, blue, or yellow throats (**Figure 51.26**). Each throat color is associated with a different pattern of behavior. Orange-throat males are the most aggressive and defend large territories that contain many females. Blue-throat males are also territorial but defend smaller territories and fewer females. Yellow-throats are nonterritorial males that mimic females and use "sneaky" tactics to gain the chance to mate. Within a population, the fraction of males belonging to each genetically determined type varies over time. In one study population, the most frequent throat coloration changed over a

▲ **Figure 51.26 Male polymorphism in the side-blotched lizard (*Uta stansburiana*).** An orange-throat male, left; a blue-throat male, center; a yellow-throat male, right.

period of several years from blue to orange to yellow and back to blue. Evidence indicates that the mating success of each male type is influenced by the relative abundance of the other types in the population, an example of frequency-dependent selection.

By comparing the competition between side-blotched lizard males to the children's game of rock-paper-scissors, scientists devised an explanation for the cycles of variation in the lizard population. In the game, paper defeats rock, rock defeats scissors, and scissors defeats paper. Each hand symbol thus wins one matchup but loses the other. Similarly, each type of male lizard has an advantage over one other type, but not the other. When blue-throats are abundant, they can defend the few females in their territories from the advances of the sneaky yellow-throat males. However, blue-throats cannot defend their territories against the hyperaggressive orange-throats. Once the orange-throats become the most abundant, the larger number of females in each territory provides the opportunity for the yellow-throats to have greater mating success. The yellow-throats become more frequent, but then give way to the blue-throats, whose tactic of guarding small territories once again allows them the most success.

Game theory provides a way to think about complex evolutionary problems in which relative performance, not absolute performance, is the key to understanding the evolution of behavior. This makes game theory an important tool because the relative performance of one phenotype compared with others is a measure of Darwinian fitness.

CONCEPT CHECK 51.4

1. Why does the mode of fertilization correlate to a large degree with the presence or absence of male parental care?
2. Why was it important that the starting population for the fly-foraging experiments had both for^R and for^s alleles?
3. **WHAT IF?** Suppose a virus that infected a side-blotched lizard population killed many more males than females. How would the infection immediately affect the competition among the males for reproductive success?

For suggested answers, see Appendix A.

CONCEPT 51.5
Inclusive fitness can account for the evolution of altruistic social behavior

Many social behaviors are selfish; that is, they benefit the individual at the expense of others, especially competitors. Even in species in which individuals do not engage in agonistic behavior, most adaptations that benefit one individual will indirectly harm others. For example, superior foraging ability by one individual may leave less food for others. It is easy to understand the pervasive nature of selfishness if natural selection shapes behavior. Behavior that maximizes an individual's survival and reproductive success is favored by selection, regardless of how much damage such behavior does to another individual, a local population, or even an entire species. How, then, can we explain observed examples of what appears to be "unselfish" behavior?

Altruism

On occasion, some animals behave in ways that reduce their individual fitness but increase the fitness of other individuals in the population; this is our functional definition of **altruism**, or selflessness. Consider the Belding's ground squirrel, which lives in some mountainous regions of the western United States and is vulnerable to predators such as coyotes and hawks. A squirrel that sees a predator approach often gives a high-pitched alarm call that alerts unaware individuals to retreat to their burrows. Note that for the squirrel that warns others, the conspicuous alarm behavior increases the risk of being killed because it brings attention to the caller's location.

Another example of altruistic behavior occurs in honeybee societies, in which the workers are sterile. The workers themselves never reproduce, but they labor on behalf of a single fertile queen. Furthermore, the workers sting intruders, a behavior that helps defend the hive but results in the death of those workers.

Altruism is also observed in naked mole rats (*Heterocephalus glaber*), highly social rodents that live in underground chambers and tunnels in southern and northeastern Africa. The naked mole rat, which is almost hairless and nearly blind, lives in colonies of 75 to 250 or more individuals (**Figure 51.27**). Each colony has only one reproducing female, the queen, who mates with one to three males, called kings. The rest of the colony consists of nonreproductive females and males who forage for underground

▲ **Figure 51.27 Naked mole rats, a species of colonial mammal that exhibits altruistic behavior.** Pictured here is a queen nursing offspring while surrounded by other members of the colony.

roots and tubers and care for the queen, the kings, and new offspring. The nonreproductive individuals may sacrifice their own lives in trying to protect the queen or kings from snakes or other predators that invade the colony.

Inclusive Fitness

How can a Belding's ground squirrel, a worker honeybee, or a naked mole rat enhance its fitness by aiding members of the population that may be its closest competitors? How can altruistic behavior be maintained by evolution if it does not enhance the survival and reproductive success of the self-sacrificing individuals?

The selection for altruistic behavior is most readily apparent in the act of parents sacrificing for their offspring. When parents sacrifice their own well-being to produce and aid offspring, this actually increases the fitness of the parents because it maximizes their genetic representation in the population. However, individuals sometimes help others who are not their offspring.

Biologist William Hamilton proposed that an animal could increase its genetic representation in the next generation by "altruistically" helping close relatives other than its own offspring. Like parents and offspring, full siblings have half their genes in common. Therefore, selection might also favor helping siblings or helping one's parents produce more siblings. This idea led to Hamilton's idea of **inclusive fitness**, the total effect an individual has on proliferating its genes by producing its own offspring *and* by providing aid that enables other close relatives, who share many of those genes, to produce offspring.

Hamilton's Rule and Kin Selection

According to Hamilton, the three key variables in an act of altruism are the benefit to the recipient, the cost to the altruist, and the coefficient of relatedness. The benefit, B, is the average number of *extra* offspring that the beneficiary of an altruistic act produces. The cost, C, is how many *fewer* offspring the altruist produces. The **coefficient of relatedness**, r, equals the fraction of genes that, on average, are shared. Natural selection favors altruism when the benefit to the recipient multiplied by the coefficient of relatedness exceeds the cost to the altruist—in other words, when $rB > C$. This inequality is called **Hamilton's rule**.

To better understand Hamilton's rule, let's apply it to a human population in which the average individual has two children. We'll imagine that a young man is close to drowning in heavy surf, and his brother risks his life to swim out and pull his sibling to safety. Had the young man drowned, his reproductive output would have been zero; but now, if we use the average, he can father two children. The benefit to the recipient of this altruistic act is thus two offspring ($B = 2$). Let's say that in this kind of surf an average swimmer has a 25% chance

of drowning. We can then calculate the cost of the altruistic act as 0.25 times 2, the number of offspring expected if the altruist had stayed on shore: $C = 0.25 \times 2 = 0.5$. Finally, we note that full siblings who are not identical twins share half their genes on average ($r = 0.5$). One way to see this is in terms of the segregation of homologous chromosomes that occurs during meiosis of gametes (**Figure 51.28**; see also Chapter 13).

We can now use values of B, C, and r to evaluate whether natural selection would favor the altruistic act in our imaginary scenario. For our swimming brothers, $rB = 0.5 \times 2 = 1$ and $C = 0.5$. This satisfies Hamilton's rule; thus, natural selection would favor this altruistic act of one brother saving another. Averaging over many individuals and generations, any particular gene in the altruist will be passed on to more offspring if he risks the rescue than if he does not. Furthermore, among those genes propagated in this way may be some that contribute to altruistic behavior. The natural selection that favors altruistic behavior by enhancing reproductive success of relatives is called **kin selection**.

Kin selection weakens with hereditary distance. Siblings have an r of 0.5, but between an aunt and her niece, $r = 0.25$ (¼), and between first cousins, $r = 0.125$ (⅛). Notice that as the degree of relatedness decreases, the rB term in the Hamilton inequality also decreases. Would natural selection favor rescuing a cousin? Not unless the surf were less treacherous. For the original conditions, $rB = 0.125 \times 2 = 0.25$, which is only

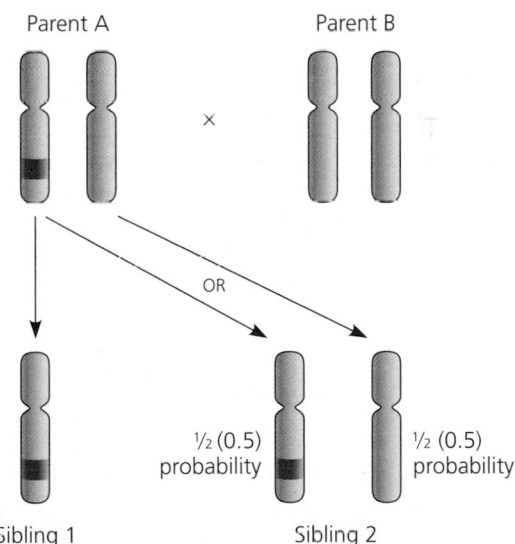

▲ **Figure 51.28 The coefficient of relatedness between siblings.** The red band indicates a particular allele (version of a gene) present on one chromosome, but not its homolog, in parent A. Sibling 1 has inherited the allele from parent A. There is a probability of ½ that sibling 2 will also inherit this allele from parent A. Any allele present on one chromosome of either parent will behave similarly. The coefficient of relatedness between the two siblings is thus ½, or 0.5.

WHAT IF? *The coefficient of relatedness of an individual to a full (nontwin) sibling or to either parent is the same, 0.5. Does this value also hold true in the cases of polyandry and polygyny?*

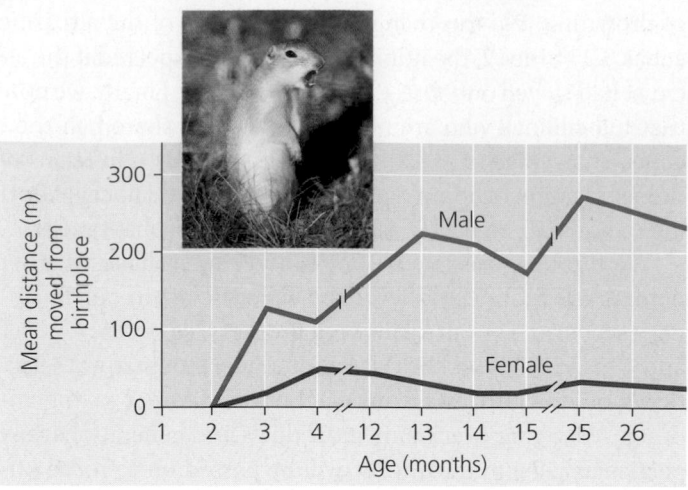

▲ Figure 51.29 Kin selection and altruism in Belding's ground squirrels. This graph helps explain the male-female difference in altruistic behavior of ground squirrels. Once weaned (pups are nursed for about one month), females are more likely than males to live near close relatives. Alarm calls that warn these relatives increase the inclusive fitness of the female altruist.

half the value of *C* (0.5). British geneticist J. B. S. Haldane appears to have anticipated these ideas when he jokingly stated that he would not lay down his life for one brother, but would do so for two brothers or eight cousins.

If kin selection explains altruism, then the examples of unselfish behavior we observe among diverse animal species should involve close relatives. This is in fact the case, but often in complex ways. Like most mammals, female Belding's ground squirrels settle close to their site of birth, whereas males settle at distant sites **(Figure 51.29)**. Since nearly all alarm calls are given by females, they are most likely aiding close relatives. In the case of worker bees, who are all sterile, anything they do to help the entire hive benefits the only permanent member who is reproductively active—the queen, who is their mother.

In the case of naked mole rats, DNA analyses have shown that all the individuals in a colony are closely related. Genetically, the queen appears to be a sibling, daughter, or mother of the kings, and the nonreproductive mole rats are the queen's direct descendants or her siblings. Therefore, when a nonreproductive individual enhances a queen's or king's chances of reproducing, the altruist increases the chance that some genes identical to its own will be passed to the next generation.

Reciprocal Altruism

Some animals occasionally behave altruistically toward others who are not relatives. A baboon may help an unrelated companion in a fight, or a wolf may offer food to another wolf even though they share no kinship. Such behavior can be adaptive if the aided individual returns the favor in the future. This sort of exchange of aid, called **reciprocal altruism**, is commonly invoked to explain altruism that occurs between unrelated humans. Reciprocal altruism is rare in other animals; it is limited largely to species (such as chimpanzees) with social groups stable enough that individuals have many chances to exchange aid. It is generally thought to occur when individuals are likely to meet again and when there would be negative consequences associated with not returning favors to individuals who had been helpful in the past, a pattern of behavior that behavioral ecologists refer to as "cheating."

Since cheating may benefit the cheater substantially, how could reciprocal altruism evolve? Game theory provides a possible answer in the form of a behavioral strategy called *tit for tat*. In the tit-for-tat strategy, an individual treats another in the same way it was treated the last time they met. Individuals adopting this behavior are always altruistic, or cooperative, on the first encounter with another individual and will remain so as long as their altruism is reciprocated. When their cooperation is not reciprocated, however, individuals employing tit for tat will retaliate immediately but return to cooperative behavior as soon as the other individual becomes cooperative. The tit-for-tat strategy has been used to explain the few apparently reciprocal altruistic interactions observed in animals—ranging from blood sharing between nonrelated vampire bats to social grooming in primates.

Social Learning

Earlier in the chapter, you read that some young chimpanzees learn to crack palm nuts by copying the behavior of more experienced individuals (see Figure 51.13). This type of learning through observing others is called **social learning**. Social learning forms the roots of **culture**, which can be defined as a system of information transfer through social learning or teaching that influences the behavior of individuals in a population. Cultural transfer of information can alter behavioral phenotypes and thereby influence the fitness of individuals. Culturally based changes in phenotype occur on a much shorter time scale than changes resulting from natural selection. Because we recognize social learning most easily in humans, we may take the process for granted or assume that social learning occurs only in humans. However, it can be seen in animal lineages that diverged from ours very long ago, some of which we describe next.

Case Study: *Mate-Choice Copying*

Mate-choice copying, a behavior in which individuals in a population copy the mate choice of others, has been studied in the guppy *Poecilia reticulata*. When a female guppy chooses between males with no other females present, the female almost always chooses the male with more orange coloration. To explore if the behavior of other females could influence this preference, an experiment was set up using both living females and

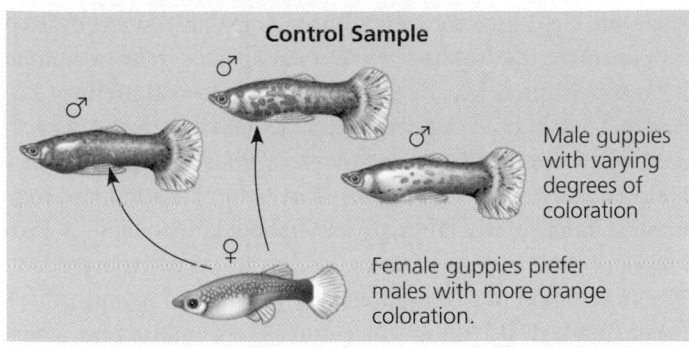

Control Sample

Male guppies with varying degrees of coloration

Female guppies prefer males with more orange coloration.

Experimental Sample

Female model in mock courtship with less orange male

Female guppies prefer males that are associated with another female.

▲ **Figure 51.30 Mate choice copying by female guppies (*Poecilia reticulata*).** Female guppies generally choose the males with more orange coloration. But when males were matched for orange or differed in amount of orange by 12% or 24%, females in the experimental group chose the *less* orange male that was presented with a model female. Females ignored the apparent choice of the model female only where the alternative male had 40% more orange coloration.

artificial model females **(Figure 51.30)**. If a female guppy observed the model "courting" a male with less extensive orange markings, she often copied the preference of the model female. That is, the female chose the male that had been presented in association with a model female rather than a more orange alternative. The exceptions were also informative. Mate-choice behavior typically did not change when the difference in coloration was particularly large. Mate-choice copying can thus mask genetically controlled female preference below a certain threshold of difference, in this case for male color.

Mate-choice copying, a form of social learning, has also been observed in several other fish and bird species. What is the selective pressure for such a mechanism? One possibility is that a female that mates with males that are attractive to other females increases the probability that her male offspring will also be attractive and have high reproductive success.

Case Study: *Social Learning of Alarm Calls*

Studies of the vervet monkeys (*Cercopithecus aethiops*) in Amboseli National Park, Kenya, demonstrated that a behavior could be modified through social learning. Vervet monkeys, which are about the size of a domestic cat, produce a complex set of alarm calls. Amboseli vervets give distinct alarm calls when they see leopards, eagles, or snakes, all of which prey on vervets. When a vervet sees a leopard, it gives a loud barking sound; when it sees an eagle, it gives a short double syllabled cough; and the snake alarm call is a "chutter." Upon hearing a particular alarm call, other vervets in the group behave in an appropriate way: They run up a tree on hearing the alarm for a leopard (vervets are nimbler than leopards in the trees); look up on hearing the alarm for an eagle; and look down on hearing the alarm for a snake **(Figure 51.31)**.

Infant vervet monkeys give alarm calls, but in a relatively undiscriminating way. For example, they give the "eagle" alarm on seeing any bird, including harmless birds such as bee-eaters. With age, the monkeys improve their accuracy. In fact, adult vervet monkeys give the eagle alarm only on seeing an eagle belonging to either of the two species that eat vervets. Infants probably learn how to give the right call by observing other members of the group and receiving social confirmation. For instance, if the infant gives the call on the right occasion—for instance, an eagle alarm when there is an eagle overhead—another member of the group will also give the eagle call. But if the infant gives the call when a bee-eater flies by, the adults in the group are silent. Thus, vervet monkeys have an initial, unlearned tendency to give calls on seeing potentially threatening objects in the environment. Learning fine-tunes the call so that by adulthood, vervets give calls only in response to genuine danger and are prepared to fine-tune the alarm calls of the next generation. However, neither vervets nor any other nonhuman

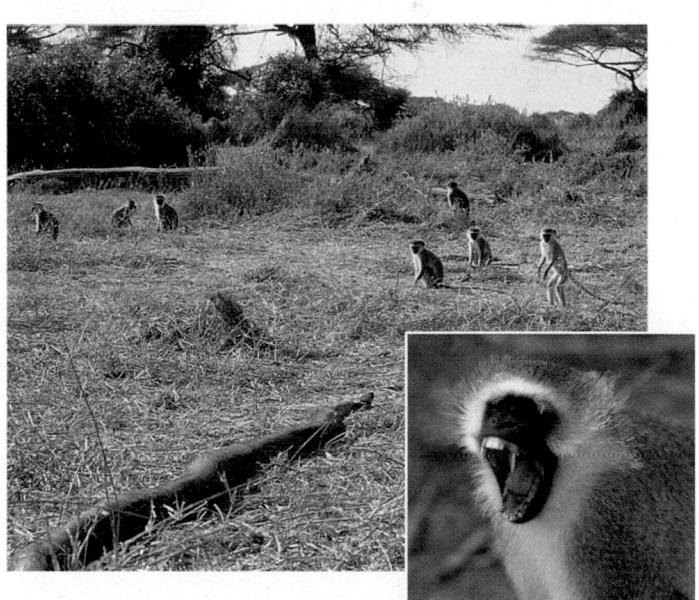

▲ **Figure 51.31 Vervet monkeys learning correct use of alarm calls.** On seeing a python (foreground), vervet monkeys give a distinct "snake" alarm call (inset), and the members of the group stand upright and look down.

► **Figure 51.32**
Both genes and culture build human nature. Teaching of a younger generation by an older generation is one of the basic ways in which all cultures are transmitted.

species comes close to matching the social learning and cultural transmission that occurs among humans **(Figure 51.32)**.

Evolution and Human Culture

Human culture is related to evolutionary theory in the discipline of **sociobiology**. The main premise of sociobiology is that certain behavioral characteristics exist because they are expressions of genes that have been perpetuated by natural selection. In his seminal 1975 book *Sociobiology: The New Synthesis*, E. O. Wilson speculated about the evolutionary basis of certain kinds of social behavior. By including a few examples from human culture, he sparked a debate that remains heated today.

The spectrum of human social behaviors may be influenced by our genetic makeup, but this is very different from saying that

genes are rigid determinants of behavior. This distinction is at the core of the debate about evolutionary perspectives on human behavior. Skeptics fear that evolutionary interpretations of human behavior could be used to justify the status quo in human society, thus rationalizing current social injustices. Evolutionary biologists argue that this is a gross oversimplification and misunderstanding of what the data tell us about human biology. Evolutionary explanations of human behavior do not reduce us to robots stamped out of rigid genetic molds. Just as individuals vary extensively in anatomical features, we should expect inherent variations in behavior as well. Environment intervenes in the pathway from genotype to phenotype for physical traits and even more so for behavioral traits. And because of our capacity for learning and our versatility, human behavior is probably more plastic than that of any other animal. Over our recent evolutionary history, we have built up a diversity of structured societies with governments, laws, cultural values, and religions that define what is acceptable behavior and what is not, even when unacceptable behavior might enhance an individual's Darwinian fitness. Perhaps it is our social and cultural institutions that make us distinct and that provide those qualities in which there is the least continuum between humans and other animals.

CONCEPT CHECK **51.5**

1. What is a possible explanation for cooperative behavior among nonrelated animals?
2. **WHAT IF?** If an animal were unable to distinguish close from distant relatives, would the concept of inclusive fitness still be applicable? Explain.
3. **WHAT IF?** Suppose you applied Hamilton's logic to a situation in which one individual was past reproductive age. Could there still be a selection for an altruistic act?

For suggested answers, see Appendix A.

Chapter **51** Review

SUMMARY OF KEY CONCEPTS

CONCEPT **51.1**

Discrete sensory inputs can stimulate both simple and complex behaviors (pp. 1120–1125)

► Behavior is the sum of responses to external and internal stimuli and includes muscular as well as nonmuscular activity. Ethology is the scientific study of animal behavior, particularly

in natural environments. The mid-20th-century ethologists developed a conceptual framework defined by a set of questions that highlight the complementary nature of two perspectives. Proximate, or "how," questions focus on the environmental stimuli, if any, that trigger a behavior, as well as the genetic, physiological, and anatomical mechanisms underlying a behavioral act. Ultimate, or "why," questions address the evolutionary significance of a behavior.

► **Fixed Action Patterns** Fixed action patterns are largely invariant behaviors triggered by simple cues known as sign stimuli.

► **Oriented Movement** Animal movements in response to external stimuli include kinesis, a behavior involving a change in activity or turning rate, and taxis, an oriented movement toward or away from some stimulus. Migratory movements involve navigation, which can be based on orientation relative to the sun, the stars, or Earth's magnetic field.

▶ **Behavioral Rhythms** Animal behavior is sometimes synchronized to the daily, or circadian, cycle of light and dark in the environment or to the annual changes in that cycle over the seasons.

▶ **Animal Signals and Communication** The transmission and reception of signals constitute animal communication. Animals use visual, auditory, chemical (usually olfactory), and tactile signals. Chemical substances called pheromones are sometimes used to transmit species-specific information through the environment.

> **MEDIA**
>
> **Activity** Honeybee Waggle Dance Video
> **Investigation** How Can Pillbug Responses to Environments Be Tested?

CONCEPT **51.2**

Learning establishes specific links between experience and behavior (pp. 1125–1129)

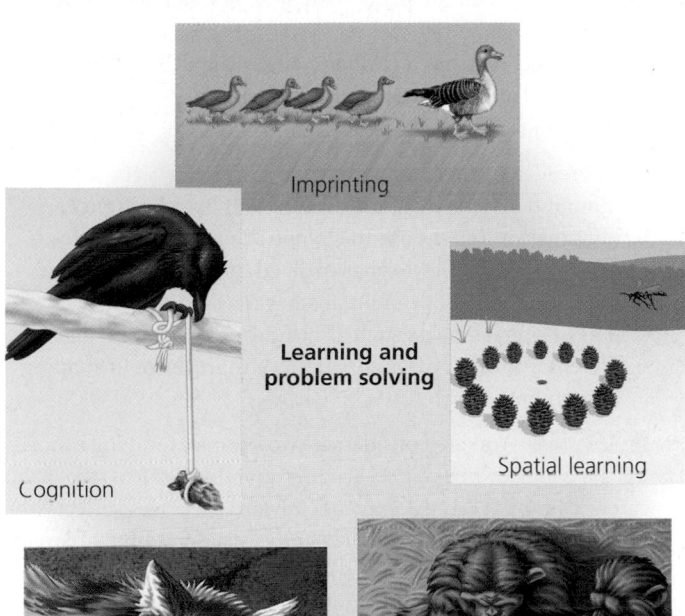

Imprinting

Cognition

Learning and problem solving

Spatial learning

Associative learning

Social learning

CONCEPT **51.3**

Both genetic makeup and environment contribute to the development of behaviors (pp. 1129–1133)

▶ Biologists study the ways both genes and the environment influence the development of behavioral phenotypes.

▶ **Experience and Behavior** The cross-fostering studies of California mice and white-footed mice have uncovered an influence of social environment on the aggressive and parental behaviors of these mice.

▶ **Regulatory Genes and Behavior** Genetic studies in insects have revealed the existence of master regulatory genes that control complex behaviors. Within the underlying hierarchy, multiple genes influence specific behaviors.

▶ **Genetically Based Behavioral Variation in Natural Populations** When behavioral variation within a species corresponds to variation in environmental conditions, it may be evidence of past evolution. Field and laboratory studies have documented the genetic basis for a change in migratory behavior in migratory birds over a period of a few decades. Studies with garter snakes reveal behavioral differences that correlate with geographic variation in prey availability.

▶ **Influence of Single-Locus Variation** Research has revealed that variation in a single gene underlies the differences in mating and parental behavior between two species of voles.

CONCEPT **51.4**

Selection for individual survival and reproductive success can explain most behaviors (pp. 1133–1138)

▶ **Foraging Behavior** Laboratory studies of *Drosophila* populations raised in high- and low-density conditions show a clear divergence in behavior linked to specific genes. An optimal foraging model is based on the idea that natural selection should favor foraging behavior that minimizes the costs of foraging and maximizes the benefits.

▶ **Mating Behavior and Mate Choice** How mate choice enhances reproductive success varies, depending on the species' mating system. The mating relationship between males and females, which includes monogamous, polygynous, and polyandrous mating systems, varies a great deal from species to species. Certainty of paternity has a significant influence on mating behavior and parental care. Mate preferences by females may play a central role in the evolution of male behavior and anatomy. Male competition for mates is a source of selection that also can reduce variation among males. Sexual selection can lead to the evolution of alternative male mating behavior and morphology. Game theory provides a way of thinking about evolution in situations where the fitness of a particular behavioral phenotype is influenced by other behavioral phenotypes in the population.

CONCEPT **51.5**

Inclusive fitness can account for the evolution of altruistic social behavior (pp. 1138–1142)

▶ **Altruism** On occasion, animals behave in altruistic ways that reduce their individual fitness but increase the fitness of the recipient of the behavior.

▶ **Inclusive Fitness** Altruistic behavior can be explained by the concept of inclusive fitness, the total effect an individual has on proliferating its genes by producing its own offspring *and* by providing aid that enables close relatives to produce offspring. Kin selection favors altruistic behavior by enhancing the reproductive success of relatives. Altruistic behavior toward unrelated individuals can be adaptive if the aided individual returns the favor in the future, an exchange of aid called reciprocal altruism.

▶ **Social Learning** Social learning forms the roots of culture, which can be defined as a system of information transfer through observation or teaching that influences the behavior of individuals in a population.

▶ **Evolution and Human Culture** Human behavior, like that of other species, is the result of interactions between genes and environment.

SELF-QUIZ

1. Which of the following is true of innate behaviors?
   a. Genes have very little influence on the expression of innate behaviors.
   b. Innate behaviors tend to vary considerably among members of a population.
   c. Innate behaviors are limited to invertebrate animals.
   d. Innate behaviors are expressed in most individuals in a population across a wide range of environmental conditions.
   e. Innate behaviors occur in invertebrates and some vertebrates but not in mammals.

2. Researchers have found that a region of the canary forebrain shrinks during the nonbreeding season and enlarges when breeding season begins. This annual enlargement of brain tissue is probably associated with the annual
   a. addition of new syllables to a canary's song repertoire.
   b. crystallization of subsong into adult songs.
   c. sensitive period in which canary parents imprint on new offspring.
   d. renewal of mating and nest-building behaviors.
   e. elimination of the memorized template for songs sung the previous year.

3. Although many chimpanzee populations live in environments containing oil palm nuts, members of only a few populations use stones to crack open the nuts. The most likely explanation for this behavioral difference between populations is that
   a. the behavioral difference is caused by genetic differences between populations.
   b. members of different populations have different nutritional requirements.
   c. the cultural tradition of using stones to crack nuts has arisen in only some populations.
   d. members of different populations differ in learning ability.
   e. members of different populations differ in manual dexterity.

4. Which of the following is *not* required for a behavioral trait to evolve by natural selection?
   a. In each individual, the form of the behavior is determined entirely by genes.
   b. The behavior varies among individuals.
   c. An individual's reproductive success depends in part on how the behavior is performed.
   d. Some component of the behavior is genetically inherited.
   e. An individual's genotype influences its behavioral phenotype.

5. Female spotted sandpipers aggressively court males and, after mating, leave the clutch of young for the male to incubate. This sequence may be repeated several times with different males until no available males remain, forcing the female to incubate her last clutch. Which of the following terms best describes this behavior?
   a. monogamy
   b. polygyny
   c. polyandry
   d. promiscuity
   e. certainty of paternity

6. According to Hamilton's rule,
   a. natural selection does not favor altruistic behavior that causes the death of the altruist.
   b. natural selection favors altruistic acts when the resulting benefit to the beneficiary, corrected for relatedness, exceeds the cost to the altruist.
   c. natural selection is more likely to favor altruistic behavior that benefits an offspring than altruistic behavior that benefits a sibling.
   d. the effects of kin selection are larger than the effects of direct natural selection on individuals.
   e. altruism is always reciprocal.

7. The core idea of sociobiology is that
   a. human behavior is rigidly determined by inheritance.
   b. humans cannot choose to change their social behavior.
   c. much human behavior has evolved by natural selection.
   d. the social behavior of humans has many similarities to that of social insects such as honeybees.
   e. the environment plays a larger role than genes in shaping human behavior.

8. **DRAW IT** You are considering two optimal foraging models for the behavior of a mussel-feeding shorebird, the oystercatcher. In model A, the energetic reward increases solely with mussel size. In model B, you take into consideration that larger mussels are more difficult to open. Draw a graph of reward (energy benefit on a scale of 0–10) versus mussel length (scale of 0–70 mm) for each model. Assume that mussels under 10 mm provide no benefit and are ignored by the birds. Also assume that mussels start becoming difficult to open when they reach 40 mm in length and impossible to open when 70 mm long. Considering the graphs you have drawn, how could you distinguish between the models by observation and measurement in the oystercatcher's habitat?

For Self-Quiz answers, see Appendix A.

MEDIA Visit **www.campbellbiology.com** for a Practice Test.

EVOLUTION CONNECTION

9. We often explain our behavior in terms of subjective feelings, motives, or reasons, but evolutionary explanations are based on reproductive fitness. What is the relationship between the two kinds of explanation? For instance, is a human explanation for behavior, such as "falling in love," incompatible with an evolutionary explanation? Does falling in love become more meaningful or less meaningful (or neither) if it has an evolutionary basis?

SCIENTIFIC INQUIRY

10. Scientists studying scrub jays found that "helpers" often assist mated pairs of birds in raising their young. The helpers lack territories and mates of their own. Instead, they help the territory owner gather food for their offspring. Propose a hypothesis to explain what advantage there might be for the helpers to engage in this behavior instead of seeking their own territories and mates. How would you test your hypothesis? If it is correct, what results would you expect your tests to yield?

Biological Inquiry: A Workbook of Investigative Cases Explore the behavior of a large gull population in a marina, and human attempts to control the population, in the case "Back to the Bay."

SCIENCE, TECHNOLOGY, AND SOCIETY

11. Researchers are very interested in studying identical twins separated at birth and raised apart. So far, the data suggest that such twins are much more alike than researchers predicted; they frequently have similar personalities, mannerisms, habits, and interests. What general question do you think researchers hope to answer by studying such twins? Why do identical twins make good subjects for this research? What are the potential pitfalls of this research? What abuses might occur if the studies are not evaluated critically and if the results are carelessly cited to support a social agenda?

UNIT 8

Ecology

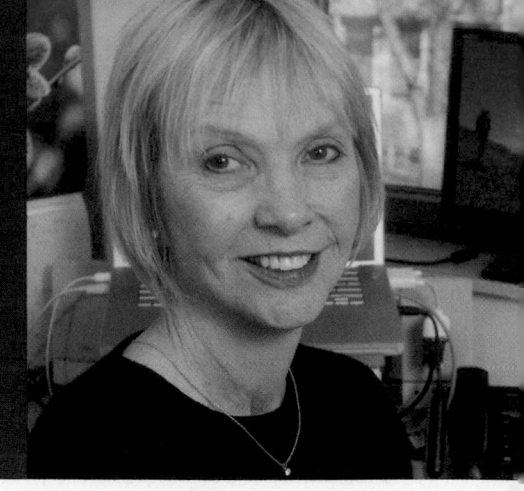

AN INTERVIEW WITH
Diana H. Wall

As a past president of the Ecological Society of America and the American Institute of Biological Sciences, and in many other national and international roles, Diana Wall has made major contributions to science and the public interest. She has also distinguished herself as a researcher on carbon cycling and other ecosystem processes, focusing on the tiny roundworms called nematodes. Dr. Wall has B.A. and Ph.D. degrees from the University of Kentucky. She was a professor at the University of California, Riverside before coming to Colorado State University, where she is a professor of biology and senior research scientist at the Natural Resource Ecology Laboratory. She does much of her fieldwork in Antarctica.

How did you get started in ecology?

In graduate school, where I studied plant pathology, I focused on the interactions between two species of nematodes and the plant roots they parasitize. Later, as a post-doc at UC Riverside, I participated in the International Biological Program (IBP). My job was to go to deserts in the western U.S. and try to find out how soil nematodes contributed to the energy balance in those ecosystems.

What was the International Biological Program?

The IBP was the first truly global research project in ecology. The overall goal was to understand Earth's productivity by taking comparable measurements across different ecosystems. (Productivity is the amount of new material—biomass—that's produced in an ecosystem.) Grassland researchers from all around the world were measuring the same things, desert researchers were measuring the same things, and so forth, enabling us to combine all the data and make global comparisons. It was a jump for me from studying the interactions between two species to be asking how such interactions fit into the global scheme of things.

Why are nematodes of interest to ecologists?

Although many people know nematodes as harmful parasites of animals or plants, most nematodes are good guys, especially the free-living ones in soil. As part of my work in the desert, I got interested in free-living soil nematodes, which feed on fungi or bacteria, or sometimes on smaller animals. The "good" nematodes accelerate the turnover of organic matter by feeding on soil microbes and then releasing compounds of carbon and nitrogen to the soil. Experiments have shown that soils without nematodes have slower rates of decomposition.

Nematodes are everywhere: in soils, in streams, in ocean sediments, and in many animals and plants. It's been estimated that four out of five animals on Earth are nematodes! The geographic distribution of different species of nematodes is something we're studying. We're doing a global-scale "latitudinal gradient" experiment, where we take soil samples at different latitudes—for example, from Sweden to South Africa. We're going into places that are hotspots of biodiversity above ground—and "coldspots" as well—and looking at what's below ground. We're classifying the nematodes to see how many species there are in the soil and how species distribution differs with latitude.

What impact have modern molecular methods had on this kind of study?

They've been great for research on the diversity of all kinds of microscopic organisms. We can now go beyond asking general questions about what such organisms do in the soil and ask exactly what they are. With soil invertebrates such as nematodes and mites, it can be very difficult to tell species apart morphologically. Now we can look at DNA sequences and say, whoa, this one is really different from that one, or, hey, this one is endemic to Antarctica but it's got a really close relative hanging out in Argentina.

Why is soil biodiversity important?

From a practical perspective, soil biodiversity—the number and abundance of different species living in soils—is probably critically important for soil fertility, and soil fertility is crucial for feeding and clothing the world's people. There's still much to be learned about the role of soil biodiversity in soil fertility. Simply how soils differ over the range from a forest to a desert is still a big question. Based on climate, geologic history, and biology, there are about 13,000 kinds of soil (called "series") in the United States alone. Each is a distinct habitat where microscopic soil creatures have evolved, and so not every species is widespread. Where the species are different, can you scale up from a difference between two farms, say, or between a farm and a nearby forest, and generalize about the connections between soil biodiversity and soil fertility? How do species that are just about everywhere contribute to soil fertility? Those questions are wide open for more research.

Another important question is whether there's a correlation between biodiversity above ground and below ground. Can we predict that an area of great biodiversity above ground will have a great diversity of mites, nematodes, and so forth below ground? And will their functions in the ecosystem be predictable, too? Because I don't want to go around digging up all the soils in the world! Once we understand something about that issue, we can start to think about the relationship between diversity and soil fertility. My big push now is to persuade people that you can't think of soil biodiversity as being unrelated to what's above ground. We used to think of the ocean as a dark garbage can, and we still tend to think of the soil that way. But we found out there are a lot of organisms in the ocean that carry out processes that benefit us, even if we don't have names for all of them. I think the same is true for soils.

How did you begin doing research in Antarctica? And what do you study there?

After the IBP, I continued working in hot deserts. They're a simpler system than a forest, for example, and therefore are more suitable for working out the factors that determine different food webs in the soil. To tease out the contribution of organisms other than plants, we would compare areas with and without plants. But that's hard to do, because plant roots seem to go everywhere, even in the desert. I wanted to find an even simpler system, with fewer variables—soils where there are no plant roots. I wrote to a colleague who was in Antarctica, and he sent me some soil for analysis. It certainly didn't have plant roots, and it did have nematodes.

But when I searched the scientific literature, I read that the soils of the Antarctic Dry Valleys, where my sample had come from, were sterile, with no organisms at all, not even prokaryotes! Only in melt streams had some life been found. Researchers had looked for bacteria in the soil, but only by trying to culture them, and nothing had shown up. This was before molecular methods had been developed for identifying microorganisms from DNA alone.

We went down to Antarctica for the first time in 1989. Only 2% of Antarctica is actually soil; the rest is rock and ice. And the Dry Valleys area has no visible vegetation; when you fly in, it looks like Mars. We had enough financial support for only one field season—so only two months to find out what lived in the soil there. We adapted our hot-desert methods for this cold desert, which has precipitation the equivalent of less than 3 cm of rain per year. And as we'd hoped, we soon saw that there was an abundance of life in the soil, as much as in the Chihuahuan Desert in New Mexico. We could not believe that other people had missed it.

Our method was simple: We would take a handful of soil, about 100 g, stir it up with a sugar solution, and centrifuge it. The nematodes float in the solution, and the rock particles sink. After rinsing off the nematodes, we count them and determine their species. It was amazing to me to see these animals, knowing that they spend nine months of the year in a hard, frozen, and dark environment. It turned out that they live in water films around soil pores, and use survival mechanisms similar to those of hot-desert nematodes. When they

receive certain environmental cues, such as dryness, they shrink their long bodies and curl up in a spiral, losing 99% of their water. When they're that small, they can disperse in wind. So this is a mechanism for spreading, as well as for surviving in a particular location.

These nematodes participate in very, very simple food chains, with only one to three tiers. For example, we have one chain with only two species of nematode: The one at the bottom eats bacteria, and the one above it may eat the bacteria-eater. It's remarkably simple compared with what is found in the soils up here.

In the last two years, we've been looking more closely at the different habitats. We've found that one species is almost everywhere in the valleys, *Scottnema lindsayae*; it's really tough, our "Rambo." But if there's too much salt in the soil or too much water, it's not present. We now have a model enabling us to predict where this species will be found around the valleys. In Antarctica, unlike elsewhere, I can look at individual nematode species and see that they have different niches; there's little overlap.

How is climate change affecting Antarctica?
Antarctica is the only continent that hasn't *on average* shown warming yet. The Antarctic Peninsula is warming rapidly, but the Dry Valleys are cooling, at least partly an indirect effect of ocean currents. Some people have made a big fuss about this cooling in attempts to disprove global warming. What we emphasize is that, while the continent as a whole is not warming, various regions are undergoing major changes, and there is warming and cooling occurring in different regions. In the Dry Valleys, we're seeing changes in every component of the ecosystem. For instance, we're seeing a decline in the abundance of the widespread *S. lindsayae*.

To look at this decline over a period of time, we've set up experiments in each valley basin.

We've made the soil wetter in places—because if an unusual amount of melting occurs when climate warms in this region, that's going to be the biggest driver of change. We want to see what that does to the *S. lindsayae* population and to the turnover of carbon in the soil. Because it's the only nematode species in many Dry Valley areas, we can easily use a carbon-isotope tracer to see how much carbon that one species is assimilating. The nematode population has very low biomass compared to what you see in the grassland here in Colorado, but it assimilates a greater percentage of organic carbon from the soil than do all the species here together. So it's a very important player in the ecosystem.

In places where we've manipulated the environment in the past, we're looking at how long it takes the soils to return to their original states. We're also looking at the effects of human trampling because the numbers of scientists and tourists are increasing tremendously. What we see is that human movement along a path disturbs the soil enough to cause a significant decline in nematodes. Furthermore, new, potentially invasive organisms are coming in on people's shoes and and clothing.

Antarctica is not isolated from the rest of the planet. The continents are all connected by ocean and atmosphere, and there is much more movement than we once thought. So future changes are something to worry about.

What is it like doing ecological research?
It's fun. You have an idea, you come up with a hypothesis, and then you get to test it in the lab or field. But as you test the hypothesis, you learn new things, and there are unexpected challenges. You have to try to fit everything you learn into a bigger picture. The process is like gathering all the blocks in a playpen and building a structure—without having the whole thing fall over.

Fieldwork has other kinds of pleasures. When you're in the field, you get to focus on one question that really interests you—during the Antarctic summer, there's a temptation to work 24 hours a day! At the same time, you usually have colleagues with different specialties there, and it's a great opportunity for freewheeling discussion and new insights. There's a great feeling of camaraderie.

Of course, there are frustrations, too. Collecting your data may be uncomfortable or boring. And you can spend a lot of time in the field that's not very productive or even a total failure. But the result of analyzing the data from a successful field trip can be a satisfying contribution to what we know about the world.

. . . the Dry Valleys area has no visible vegetation; when you fly in, it looks like Mars.

Inquiry in Action
Learn about an experiment by Diana Wall and a colleague in Inquiry Figure 54.19 on page 1210.

Left to right: Diana Wall, Jane Reece, Rob Jackson

An Introduction to Ecology and the Biosphere

52

52.1 Ecology integrates all areas of biological research and informs environmental decision making

52.2 Interactions between organisms and the environment limit the distribution of species

52.3 Aquatic biomes are diverse and dynamic systems that cover most of Earth

52.4 The structure and distribution of terrestrial biomes are controlled by climate and disturbance

OVERVIEW

The Scope of Ecology

High in the sky, a series of satellites circle Earth. These satellites aren't relaying the chatter of cell phones. Instead, they are transmitting data on the annual migration of gray whales **(Figure 52.1)**. Leaving their calving grounds near Baja California, adult and newborn gray whales (*Eschrichtius robustus*) swim side by side on a remarkable 8,000-km journey. They are headed to the Arctic Ocean to feed on the crustaceans, tube worms, and other creatures that thrive there in summer. The satellites also help biologists track a second journey, the recovery of the gray whales from the brink of extinction. A century ago, whaling had reduced the population to only a few hundred individuals. Today, after 70 years of protection from whaling, more than 20,000 travel to the Arctic each year.

What environmental factors determine the geographic distribution of gray whales? How do variations in their food supply affect the size of the gray whale population? Questions such as these are the subject of **ecology** (from the Greek *oikos*, home, and *logos*, to study), the scientific study of the interactions between organisms and the en-

▲ Figure 52.1 **Why do gray whales migrate?**

vironment. These interactions occur at a hierarchy of scales that ecologists study, from organismal to global **(Figure 52.2)**.

In addition to providing a conceptual framework for understanding the field of ecology, Figure 52.2 provides the organizational framework for our final unit. This chapter begins the unit by describing the breadth of ecology and some of the factors, both living and nonliving, that influence the distribution and abundance of organisms. The next three chapters examine population, community, and ecosystem ecology in detail. In the final chapter, we'll explore both landscape ecology and global ecology as we consider how ecologists apply biological knowledge to predict the global consequences of human activities, to conserve Earth's biodiversity, and to restore our planet's ecosystems.

CONCEPT 52.1

Ecology integrates all areas of biological research and informs environmental decision making

Ecology's roots are in discovery science (see Chapter 1). Naturalists, including Aristotle and Darwin, have long observed organisms in nature and systematically recorded their observations. Because extraordinary insight can be gained through this descriptive approach, called *natural history*, it remains a fundamental part of the science of ecology. Present-day ecologists still observe the natural world, albeit with genes-to-globe tools that would astound Aristotle and Darwin.

Modern ecology has become a rigorous experimental science as well. Ecologists generate hypotheses, manipulate the environment, and observe the outcome. Scientists interested in the effects of climate change on tree survival, for instance, might create drought and wet conditions in experimental plots instead

Exploring The Scope of Ecological Research

Ecologists work at different levels of the biological hierarchy, from individual organisms to the planet. Here we present a sample research question for each level in the biological hierarchy.

1 Organismal Ecology

Organismal ecology, which includes the subdisciplines of physiological, evolutionary, and behavioral ecology, is concerned with how an organism's structure, physiology, and (for animals) behavior meet the challenges posed by its environment.

◀ *How do hammerhead sharks select a mate?*

2 Population Ecology

A **population** is a group of individuals of the same species living in an area. **Population ecology** analyzes factors that affect population size and how and why it changes through time.

◀ *What environmental factors affect the reproductive rate of deer mice?*

3 Community Ecology

A **community** is a group of populations of different species in an area. **Community ecology** examines how interactions between species, such as predation and competition, affect community structure and organization.

◀ *What factors influence the diversity of species that make up a forest?*

4 Ecosystem Ecology

An **ecosystem** is the community of organisms in an area and the physical factors with which those organisms interact. **Ecosystem ecology** emphasizes energy flow and chemical cycling between organisms and the environment.

◀ *What factors control photosynthetic productivity in a temperate grassland ecosystem?*

5 Landscape Ecology

A **landscape** (or seascape) is a mosaic of connected ecosystems. Research in **landscape ecology** focuses on the factors controlling exchanges of energy, materials, and organisms across multiple ecosystems.

◀ *To what extent do the trees lining a river serve as corridors of dispersal for animals?*

6 Global Ecology

The **biosphere** is the global ecosystem—the sum of all the planet's ecosystems and landscapes. **Global ecology** examines how the regional exchange of energy and materials influences the functioning and distribution of organisms across the biosphere.

◀ *How does ocean circulation affect the global distribution of crustaceans?*

Trough

Pipe

"Dry" | "Wet" | "Ambient"

Troughs collect one-third of precipitation that falls on "dry" plot.

Pipes carry water from "dry" plot to "wet" plot.

"Ambient" plot receives natural amounts of rainfall.

▲ **Figure 52.3 Studying how a forest responds to altered precipitation.** At the Walker Branch Watershed in Tennessee, researchers used a system of troughs and pipes to create artificial "dry" and "wet" conditions within parts of a forest.

of waiting decades for the dry or wet years that could be representative of future rainfall. Paul Hanson and colleagues, at Oak Ridge National Laboratory in Tennessee, used just such an experimental approach in a Herculean study that lasted more than ten years. In one large plot of native forest, they collected one-third of the incoming precipitation and moved it to a second plot, while leaving a third plot unchanged as a control **(Figure 52.3)**. By comparing the growth and survival of trees in each plot, the researchers found that flowering dogwoods (*Cornus florida*) were more likely to die in drought conditions than were members of any other woody species examined.

Throughout this unit, you will encounter many more examples of ecological field experiments, whose complex challenges have made ecologists innovators in the areas of experimental design and statistical inference. As these examples also demonstrate, the interpretation of ecological experiments often depends on a broad knowledge of biology.

Linking Ecology and Evolutionary Biology

As we discussed in Chapter 23, organisms adapt to their environment over many generations through the process of natural selection; this adaptation occurs over many generations—the time frame of *evolutionary time*. The differential survival and reproduction of individuals that leads to evolution occurs in *ecological time*, the minute-to-minute time frame of interactions between organisms and the environment. One example of how events in ecological time have led to evolution was the selection for beak size in Galápagos finches (see Figure 23.1). Finches with bigger beaks were better able to eat the large, hard seeds available during the drought. Smaller-beaked birds, which required smaller, softer seeds that were in short supply, were less likely to survive.

We can see the link between ecology and evolution all around us. Suppose a farmer applies a new fungicide to protect a wheat crop from a fungus. The fungicide works well at first,

reducing the population size of the fungus—an ecological effect—and allowing the farmer to obtain higher yields from the crop. After a few years, however, the farmer has to apply higher and higher doses of the fungicide to obtain the same protection. The fungicide has altered the gene pool of the fungus—an evolutionary effect—by selecting for individuals that are resistant to the chemical. Eventually, the fungicide works so poorly that the farmer must find a different, more potent chemical to control the fungus.

Ecology and Environmental Issues

Ecology and evolutionary biology help us understand the emergence of pesticide-resistant organisms and many other environmental problems. Ecology also provides the scientific understanding needed to help us conserve and sustain life on Earth. Because of ecology's usefulness in conservation and environmental efforts, many people associate ecology with *environmentalism* (advocating the protection of nature).

Ecologists make an important distinction between science and advocacy. Many ecologists feel a responsibility to educate legislators and the public about environmental issues. How society uses ecological knowledge, however, depends on much more than science alone. If we know that phosphate promotes the growth of algae in lakes, for instance, policymakers may weigh the environmental benefits of limiting the use of phosphate-rich fertilizers against the costs of doing so. This distinction between knowledge and advocacy is clear in the guiding principles of the Ecological Society of America, a scientific organization that strives to "ensure the appropriate use of ecological science in environmental decision making."

An important milestone in applying ecological data to environmental problems was the publication of Rachel Carson's *Silent Spring* in 1962 **(Figure 52.4)**. In her book, which

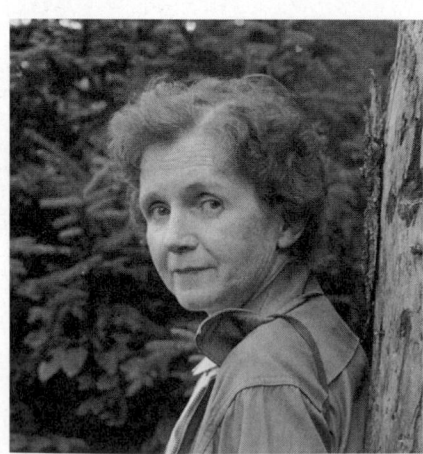

◀ **Figure 52.4 Rachel Carson.**

was seminal to the modern environmental movement, Carson (1907–1964) had a broad message: "The 'control of nature' is a phrase conceived in arrogance, born of the Neanderthal age of biology and philosophy, when it was supposed that nature exists for the convenience of man." Recognizing the network of connections among species, Carson warned that the widespread use of pesticides such as DDT was causing population declines in many more organisms than the insects targeted for control. She applied ecological principles to recommend a less wasteful, safer use of pesticides. Through her writing and her testimony before the U.S. Congress, Carson helped promote a new environmental ethic to lawmakers and the public. Her efforts led to a ban on DDT use in the United States and more stringent controls on the use of other chemicals.

CONCEPT CHECK 52.1

1. Contrast the terms *ecology* and *environmentalism*. How does ecology relate to environmentalism?

2. How can an event that occurs on the ecological time scale affect events that occur on an evolutionary time scale?

3. **WHAT IF?** A wheat farmer tests four fungicides on small plots and finds that the wheat yield is slightly higher when all four fungicides are used together than when any one fungicide is used alone. From an evolutionary perspective, what would be the likely long-term consequence of applying all four fungicides together?

For suggested answers, see Appendix A.

CONCEPT 52.2

Interactions between organisms and the environment limit the distribution of species

Earlier we introduced the range of scales at which ecologists work and explained how ecology can be used to understand, and make decisions about, our environment. In this section, we will examine how ecologists determine what controls the distribution of species, such as the gray whale in Figure 52.1.

In Chapter 22, we explored *biogeography*, the study of the past and present distribution of species, in the context of evolutionary theory. Ecologists have long recognized global and regional patterns in the distribution of organisms. Kangaroos, for instance, are found in Australia but nowhere else on Earth. Ecologists ask not only *where* species occur, but also *why* species occur where they do: What factors determine their distribution? In seeking to answer this question, ecologists focus on two kinds of factors: **biotic**, or living, factors—all the organisms that are part of the individual's environment—and **abiotic**, or nonliving, factors—all the chemical and physical factors, such as temperature, light, water, and nutrients, that influence the distribution and abundance of organisms.

Figure 52.5 presents an example of how both kinds of factors might affect the distribution of a species, in this case the red kangaroo (*Macropus rufus*). As the figure shows, red kangaroos are most abundant in a few areas in the interior of Australia, where precipitation is relatively sparse and variable. They are not found around most of the periphery of the continent, where

Kangaroos/km²
- 0–0.1
- 0.1–1
- 1–5
- 5–10
- 10–20
- > 20
- – – Limits of distribution

Climate in northern Australia is hot and wet, with seasonal drought.

Red kangaroos occur in most semi-arid and arid regions of the interior, where precipitation is relatively low and variable from year to year.

Southern Australia has cool, moist winters and warm, dry summers.

Southeastern Australia has a wet, cool climate.

▲ **Figure 52.5 Distribution and abundance of the red kangaroo in Australia, based on aerial surveys.**

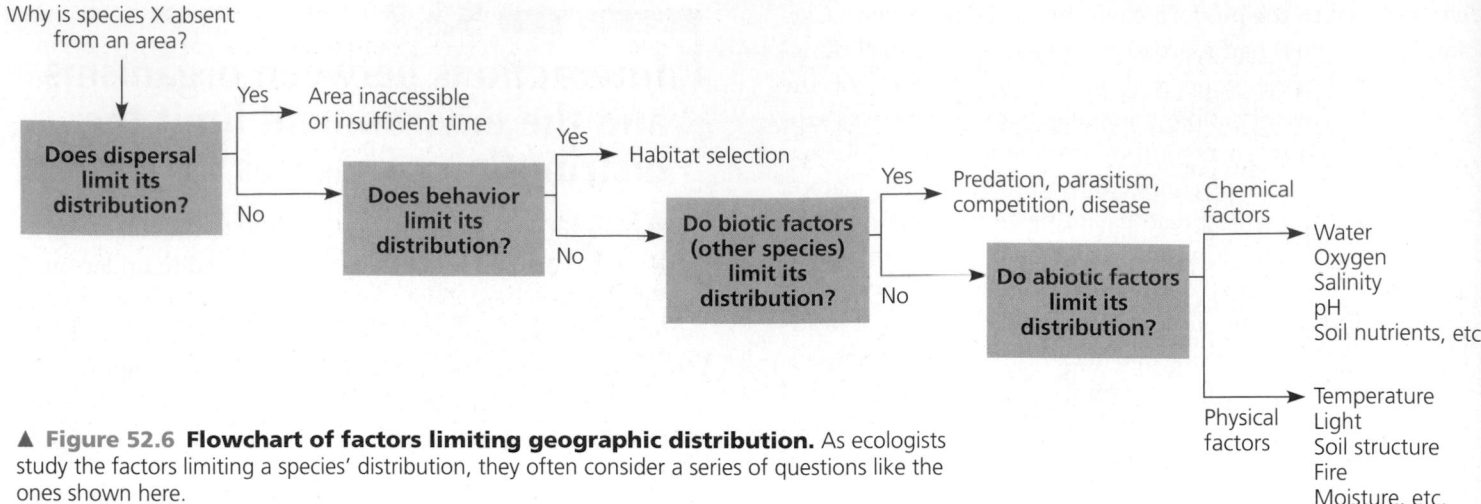

▲ **Figure 52.6 Flowchart of factors limiting geographic distribution.** As ecologists study the factors limiting a species' distribution, they often consider a series of questions like the ones shown here.

? *How might the importance of various abiotic factors differ for aquatic and terrestrial ecosystems?*

the climate ranges from moist to wet. At first glance, this distribution might suggest that an abiotic factor—the amount and variability of precipitation—directly determines where red kangaroos live. However, it is also possible that climate influences red kangaroo populations indirectly through biotic factors, such as pathogens, parasites, predators, competitors, and food availability. Ecologists generally need to consider multiple factors and alternative hypotheses when attempting to explain the distribution of species.

To see how ecologists might arrive at such an explanation, let's work our way through the series of questions in the flowchart in **Figure 52.6.**

Dispersal and Distribution

The movement of individuals away from their area of origin or from centers of high population density, called **dispersal**, contributes to the global distribution of organisms. A biogeographer might consider dispersal in hypothesizing why there are no kangaroos in North America: Kangaroos could not get there because a barrier to their dispersal existed. While land-bound kangaroos have not reached North America under their own power, other organisms that disperse more readily, such as some birds, have. The dispersal of organisms is critical to understanding both geographic isolation in evolution (see Chapter 24) and the broad patterns of current geographic distributions of species.

Natural Range Expansions

The importance of dispersal is most evident when organisms reach an area where they did not exist previously. For instance, 200 years ago, the cattle egret was found only in Africa and southwestern Europe. But in the late 1800s, some of these strong-flying birds managed to cross the Atlantic Ocean and colonize northeastern South America. From there, cattle egrets gradually spread southward and also northward through Central America and into North America, reaching

Florida by 1960 (**Figure 52.7**). Today they have breeding populations as far west as the Pacific coast of the United States and as far north as southern Canada.

Natural range expansions clearly show the influence of dispersal on distribution, but opportunities to observe such dispersal directly are rare. As a consequence, ecologists often turn to experimental methods to better understand the role of dispersal in limiting the distribution of species.

▲ **Figure 52.7 Dispersal of the cattle egret in the Americas.** Native to Africa, cattle egrets were first reported in South America in 1877.

Species Transplants

To determine if dispersal is a key factor limiting the distribution of a species, ecologists may observe the results of intentional or accidental transplants of the species to areas where it was previously absent. For a transplant to be considered successful, some of the organisms must not only survive in the new area but also reproduce there. If a transplant is successful, then we can conclude that the *potential* range of the species is larger than its *actual* range; in other words, the species *could* live in certain areas where it currently does not.

Species introduced to new geographic locations often disrupt the communities and ecosystems to which they have been introduced and spread far beyond the area of intended introduction (see Chapter 56). Consequently, ecologists rarely conduct transplant experiments across geographic regions. Instead, they document the outcome when a species has been transplanted for other purposes, such as to introduce game animals or predators of pest species, or when a species has been accidentally transplanted.

Behavior and Habitat Selection

As transplant experiments show, some organisms do not occupy all of their potential range, even though they may be physically able to disperse into the unoccupied areas. To follow our line of questioning from Figure 52.6, does behavior play a role in limiting distribution in such cases? When individuals seem to avoid certain habitats, even when the habitats are suitable, the organism's distribution may be limited by habitat selection behavior.

Although habitat selection is one of the least understood of all ecological processes, some instances in insects have been closely studied. Female insects often deposit eggs only in response to a very narrow set of stimuli, which may restrict distribution of the insects to certain host plants. Larvae of the European corn borer, for example, can feed on a wide variety of plants but are found almost exclusively on corn (maize) because egg-laying females are attracted by odors produced by the plant. Habitat selection behavior clearly restricts the plant species on which the corn borer is found.

Biotic Factors

If behavior does not limit the distribution of a species, our next question is whether biotic factors—that is, other species—are responsible (see Figure 52.6). In many cases, a species cannot complete its full life cycle if transplanted to a new area. This inability to survive and reproduce may be due to negative interactions with other organisms in the form of predation, parasitism, or competition. Alternatively, survival and reproduction may be limited by the absence of other species on which the transplanted species depends, such as pollinators for many flowering plants. Predators (organisms that kill their prey) and herbivores (organisms that eat plants or algae) are common examples of biotic factors that limit the distribution of species. Simply put, organisms that eat can limit the distribution of organisms that get eaten.

Let's examine one specific case of an herbivore limiting the distribution of a food species **(Figure 52.8)**. In certain marine ecosystems, there is often an inverse relationship between the abundance of sea urchins and seaweeds (large marine algae, such as kelp). Where sea urchins that graze on

---

▼ **Figure 52.8** **Inquiry**

Does feeding by sea urchins limit seaweed distribution?

EXPERIMENT   W. J. Fletcher, of the University of Sydney, Australia, reasoned that if sea urchins are a limiting biotic factor, then more seaweeds should invade an area from which sea urchins have been removed. To isolate the effect of sea urchins from that of another seaweed-eating animal, the limpet, he removed only urchins, only limpets, or both from study areas adjacent to a control site.

RESULTS   Fletcher observed a large difference in seaweed growth between areas with and without sea urchins.

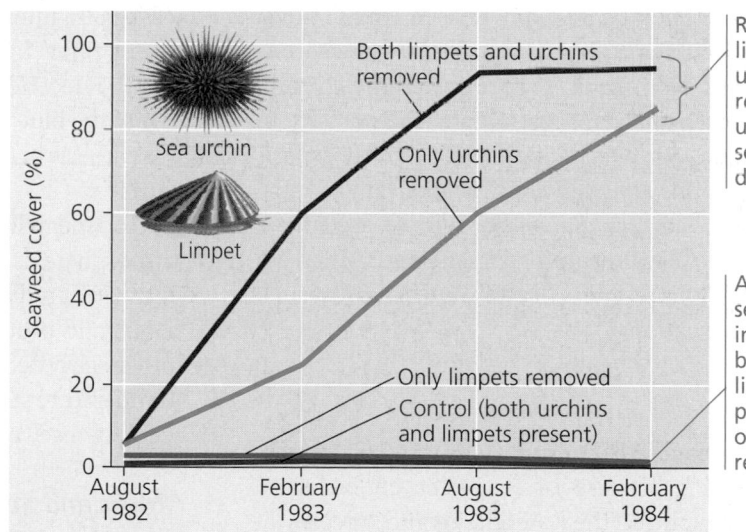

Removing both limpets and urchins or removing only urchins increased seaweed cover dramatically.

Almost no seaweed grew in areas where both urchins and limpets were present, or where only limpets were removed.

CONCLUSION   Removing both limpets and urchins resulted in the greatest increase in seaweed cover, indicating that both species have some influence on seaweed distribution. But since removing only urchins greatly increased seaweed growth while removing only limpets had little effect, Fletcher concluded that sea urchins have a much greater effect than limpets in limiting seaweed distribution.

SOURCE   W. J. Fletcher, Interactions among subtidal Australian sea urchins, gastropods, and algae: effects of experimental removals, *Ecological Monographs* 57:89–109 (1989).

WHAT IF?   Seaweed cover increased the most when both urchins *and* limpets were removed. How might you explain this result?

seaweeds and other algae are common, large stands of seaweeds do not become established. Thus, sea urchins appear to limit the local distribution of seaweeds. This kind of interaction can be tested by "removal and addition" experiments. In studies near Sydney, Australia, W. J. Fletcher tested the hypothesis that sea urchins are a biotic factor limiting seaweed distribution. Because there are often other herbivores in the habitats where seaweeds may grow, Fletcher performed a series of manipulative field experiments to isolate the influence of sea urchins on seaweeds in his study area (see Figure 52.8). By removing sea urchins from certain plots and observing the dramatic increase in seaweed cover, he showed that urchins limited the distribution of seaweeds.

In addition to predation and herbivory, the presence or absence of food resources, parasites, pathogens, and competing organisms can act as biotic limitations on species distribution. Some of the most striking cases of limitation occur when humans accidentally or intentionally introduce exotic predators or pathogens into new areas and wipe out native species. You will encounter examples of these impacts in Chapter 56, which discusses conservation ecology.

Abiotic Factors

The last question in the flowchart in Figure 52.6 considers whether abiotic factors, such as temperature, water, salinity, sunlight, or soil, might be limiting a species' distribution. If the physical conditions at a site do not allow a species to survive and reproduce, then the species will not be found there. Throughout this discussion, keep in mind that the environment is characterized by both *spatial heterogeneity* and *temporal heterogeneity*; that is, most abiotic factors vary in space and time. Although two regions of Earth may experience different conditions at any given time, daily and annual fluctuations of abiotic factors may either blur or accentuate regional distinctions. Furthermore, organisms can avoid some stressful conditions temporarily through behaviors such as dormancy or hibernation.

Temperature

Environmental temperature is an important factor in the distribution of organisms because of its effect on biological processes. Cells may rupture if the water they contain freezes (at temperatures below 0°C), and the proteins of most organisms denature at temperatures above 45°C. In addition, few organisms can maintain an active metabolism at very low or very high temperatures, though extraordinary adaptations enable some organisms, such as thermophilic prokaryotes (see Chapter 27), to live outside the temperature range habitable by other life. Most organisms function best within a specific range of environmental temperature. Temperatures outside that range may force some animals to expend energy regulating their internal temperature, as mammals and birds do (see Chapter 40).

Water

The dramatic variation in water availability among habitats is another important factor in species distribution. Species living at the seashore or in tidal wetlands can desiccate (dry out) as the tide recedes. Terrestrial organisms face a nearly constant threat of desiccation, and the distribution of terrestrial species reflects their ability to obtain and conserve water. Desert organisms, for example, exhibit a variety of adaptations for acquiring and conserving water in dry environments, as described in Chapter 44.

Salinity

As you learned in Chapter 7, the salt concentration of water in the environment affects the water balance of organisms through osmosis. Most aquatic organisms are restricted to either freshwater or saltwater habitats by their limited ability to osmoregulate (see Chapter 44). Although many terrestrial organisms can excrete excess salts from specialized glands or in feces, salt flats and other high-salinity habitats typically have few species of plants or animals.

Sunlight

Sunlight absorbed by photosynthetic organisms provides the energy that drives most ecosystems, and too little sunlight can limit the distribution of photosynthetic species. In forests, shading by leaves in the treetops makes competition for light especially intense, particularly for seedlings growing on the forest floor. In aquatic environments, every meter of water depth selectively absorbs about 45% of the red light and about 2% of the blue light passing through it. As a result, most photosynthesis in aquatic environments occurs relatively near the surface.

Too much light can also limit the survival of organisms. The atmosphere is thinner at higher elevations, absorbing less ultraviolet radiation, so the sun's rays are more likely to damage DNA and proteins in alpine environments (Figure 52.9). In other ecosystems, such as deserts, high light levels can increase temperature stress if animals are unable to avoid the light or to cool themselves through evaporation (see Chapter 40).

Rocks and Soil

The pH, mineral composition, and physical structure of rocks and soil limit the distribution of plants and thus of the animals that feed on them, contributing to the patchiness of terrestrial ecosystems. The pH of soil and water can limit the distribution of organisms directly, through extreme acidic or basic conditions, or indirectly, through the solubility of nutrients and toxins. In streams and rivers, the composition of the substrate (bottom surface) can affect water chemistry, which in turn influences the resident organisms. In freshwater and marine environments, the

▲ **Figure 52.9 Alpine tree.** Organisms living at high elevations are exposed to high levels of ultraviolet radiation. They face other challenges as well, including freezing temperatures and strong winds, which increase water loss and inhibit the growth of limbs on the windward side of trees.

structure of the substrate determines the organisms that can attach to it or burrow into it.

Now that we have surveyed some of the abiotic factors that affect the distribution of organisms, let's focus on how those factors vary with climate, as we consider the major role that climate plays in determining species distribution.

Climate

Four abiotic factors—temperature, precipitation, sunlight, and wind—are the major components of **climate**, the long-term, prevailing weather conditions in a particular area. Climatic factors, particularly temperature and water availability, have a major influence on the distribution of terrestrial organisms. We can describe climate patterns on two scales: **macroclimate**, patterns on the global, regional, and local level; and **microclimate**, very fine patterns, such as those encountered by the community of organisms that live beneath a fallen log. First let's consider Earth's macroclimate.

Global Climate Patterns

Earth's global climate patterns are determined largely by the input of solar energy and the planet's movement in space.

The sun's warming effect on the atmosphere, land, and water establishes the temperature variations, cycles of air movement, and evaporation of water that are responsible for dramatic latitudinal variations in climate. **Figure 52.10**, on the next two pages, summarizes Earth's climate patterns and how they are formed.

Regional, Local, and Seasonal Effects on Climate

Proximity to bodies of water and topographic features such as mountain ranges create regional climatic variations, and smaller features of the landscape contribute to local climatic variation. Seasonal variation is another influence on climate.

Bodies of Water   Ocean currents influence climate along the coasts of continents by heating or cooling overlying air masses, which may then pass across the land. Coastal regions are also generally moister than inland areas at the same latitude. The cool, misty climate produced by the cold California current that flows southward along the western United States supports a coniferous rain forest ecosystem in the Pacific Northwest and large redwood groves farther south. Similarly, the west coast of northern Europe has a mild climate because the Gulf Stream carries warm water from the equator to the North Atlantic, driven in part by the "great ocean conveyor belt" **(Figure 52.11)**. As a result, northwest Europe is warmer during winter than New England, which is farther south but is cooled by the Labrador Current flowing south from the coast of Greenland.

Because of the high specific heat of water (see Chapter 3), oceans and large lakes tend to moderate the climate of nearby land. During a hot day, when the land is warmer than the nearby body of water, air over the land heats up and

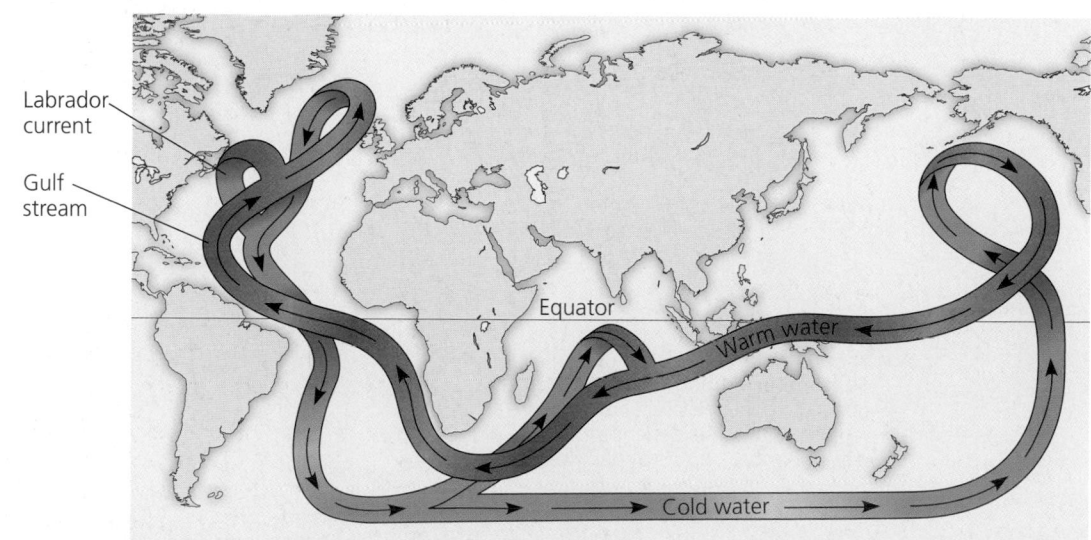

▲ **Figure 52.11 The great ocean conveyor belt.** Water is warmed at the equator and flows along the ocean surface to the North Atlantic, where it cools, becomes denser, and sinks thousands of meters. The deep, cold water may not return to the ocean surface for as long as 1,000 years.

Exploring Global Climate Patterns

Latitudinal Variation in Sunlight Intensity

Earth's curved shape causes latitudinal variation in the intensity of sunlight. Because sunlight strikes the **tropics** (those regions that lie between 23.5° north latitude and 23.5° south latitude) most directly, more heat and light per unit of surface area are delivered there. At higher latitudes, sunlight strikes Earth at an oblique angle, and thus the light energy is more diffuse on Earth's surface.

Low angle of incoming sunlight

Sun directly overhead at equinoxes

Low angle of incoming sunlight

90°N (North Pole)
60°N
30°N
23.5°N (Tropic of Cancer)
0° (equator)
23.5°S (Tropic of Capricorn)
30°S
60°S
90°S (South Pole)
Atmosphere

Seasonal Variation in Sunlight Intensity

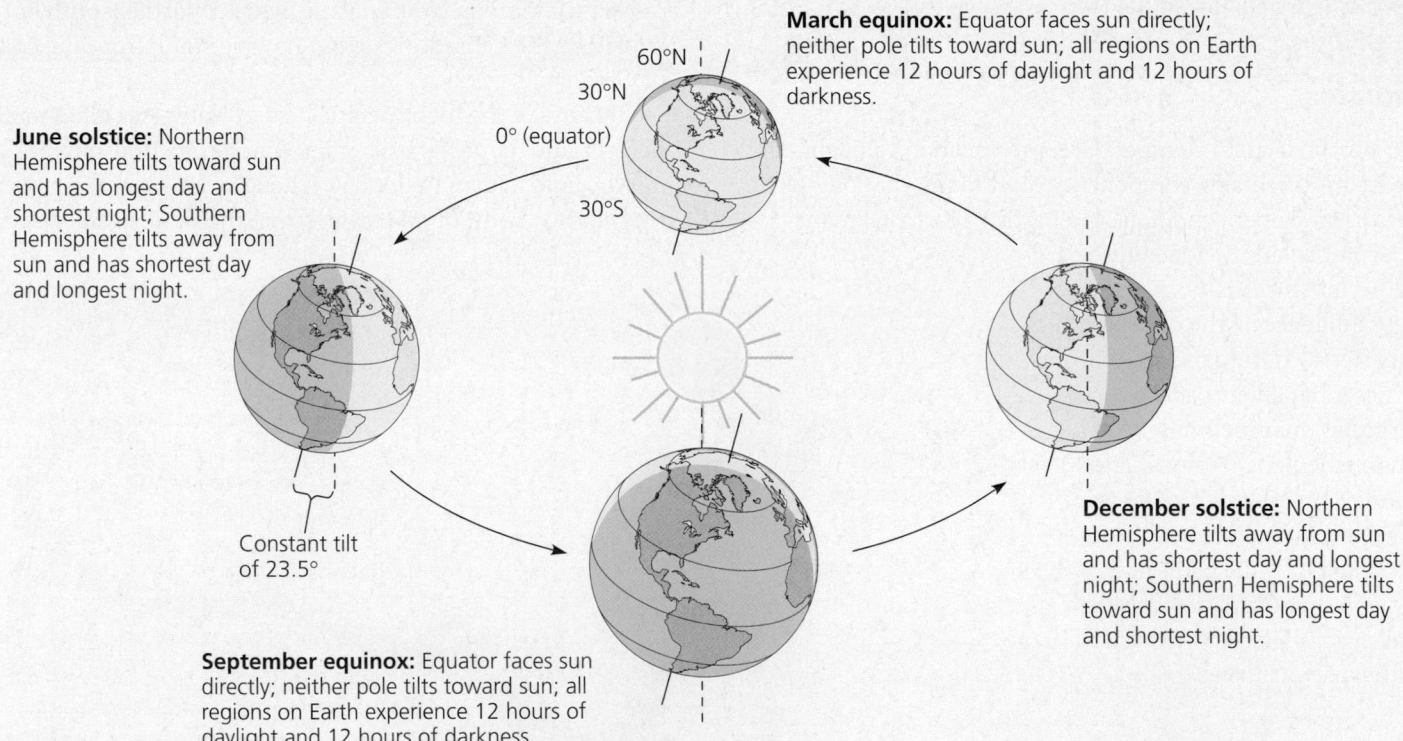

March equinox: Equator faces sun directly; neither pole tilts toward sun; all regions on Earth experience 12 hours of daylight and 12 hours of darkness.

June solstice: Northern Hemisphere tilts toward sun and has longest day and shortest night; Southern Hemisphere tilts away from sun and has shortest day and longest night.

60°N
30°N
0° (equator)
30°S

Constant tilt of 23.5°

September equinox: Equator faces sun directly; neither pole tilts toward sun; all regions on Earth experience 12 hours of daylight and 12 hours of darkness.

December solstice: Northern Hemisphere tilts away from sun and has shortest day and longest night; Southern Hemisphere tilts toward sun and has longest day and shortest night.

Earth's tilt causes seasonal variation in the intensity of solar radiation. Because the planet is tilted on its axis by 23.5° relative to its plane of orbit around the sun, the tropics experience the greatest annual input of solar radiation and the least seasonal variation. The seasonal variations of light and temperature increase toward the poles.

Global Air Circulation and Precipitation Patterns

Intense solar radiation near the equator initiates a global pattern of air circulation and precipitation. High temperatures in the tropics evaporate water from Earth's surface and cause warm, wet air masses to rise (blue arrows) and flow toward the poles. The rising air masses release much of their water content, creating abundant precipitation in tropical regions. The high-altitude air masses, now dry, descend (brown arrows) toward Earth, absorbing moisture from the land and creating an arid climate conducive to the development of the deserts that are common at latitudes around 30° north and south. Some of the descending air then flows toward the poles. At latitudes around 60° north and south, the air masses again rise and release abundant precipitation (though less than in the tropics). Some of the cold, dry rising air then flows to the poles, where it descends and flows back toward the equator, absorbing moisture and creating the comparatively rainless and bitterly cold climates of the polar regions.

Global Wind Patterns

Air flowing close to Earth's surface creates predictable global wind patterns. As Earth rotates on its axis, land near the equator moves faster than that at the poles, deflecting the winds from the vertical paths shown above and creating more easterly and westerly flows. Cooling trade winds blow from east to west in the tropics; prevailing westerlies blow from west to east in the temperate zones, defined as the regions between the Tropic of Cancer and the Arctic Circle and between the Tropic of Capricorn and the Antarctic Circle.

③ Cooler air sinks over water.

② Air cools at high elevation.

① Warm air over land rises.

④ Cool air over water moves inland, replacing rising warm air over land.

▲ Figure 52.12 **Moderating effects of a large body of water on climate.** This figure illustrates what happens on a hot summer day.

rises, drawing a cool breeze from the water across the land (Figure 52.12). At night, air over the now warmer water rises, drawing cooler air from the land back out over the water, replacing it with warmer air from offshore. The moderation of climate may be limited to the coast itself, however. In certain regions, such as southern California, cool, dry ocean breezes in summer are warmed when they contact the land, absorbing moisture and creating a hot, arid climate just a few kilometers inland (see Figure 3.5). This climate pattern also occurs around the Mediterranean Sea, which gives it the name *Mediterranean climate.*

Mountains   Mountains affect the amount of sunlight reaching an area and consequently the local temperature and rainfall. South-facing slopes in the Northern Hemisphere receive more sunlight than nearby north-facing slopes and are therefore warmer and drier. These abiotic differences influence species distribution; for example, in many mountains of western North America, spruce and other conifers occupy the cooler north-facing slopes, whereas shrubby, drought-resistant plants inhabit the south-facing slopes. In addition, every 1,000-m increase in elevation produces a temperature drop of approximately 6°C, equivalent to that produced by an 880-km increase in latitude. This is one reason the biological communities of mountains are similar to those at lower elevations but farther from the equator.

When warm, moist air approaches a mountain, the air rises and cools, releasing moisture on the windward side of the peak (Figure 52.13). On the leeward side, cooler, dry air descends, absorbing moisture and producing a "rain shadow." Deserts commonly occur on the leeward side of mountain ranges, a phenomenon evident in the Great Basin and the Mojave Desert of western North America, the Gobi Desert of Asia, and the small deserts found in the southwest corners of some Caribbean islands.

Seasonality   As described earlier, Earth's tilted axis of rotation and its annual passage around the sun cause strong seasonal cycles in middle to high latitudes (see Figure 52.10). In addition to these global changes in day length, solar radiation, and temperature, the changing angle of the sun over the course of the year affects local environments. For example, the belts of wet and dry air on either side of the equator move slightly northward and southward with the changing angle of the sun, producing marked wet and dry seasons around 20° north and 20° south latitude, where many tropical deciduous forests grow. In addition, seasonal changes in wind patterns produce variations in ocean currents, sometimes causing the upwelling of cold water from deep ocean layers. This nutrient-rich water stimulates the growth of surface-dwelling phytoplankton and the organisms that feed on them.

Microclimate

Many features in the environment influence microclimates by casting shade, affecting evaporation from soil, or changing wind patterns. For example, forest trees frequently moderate the microclimate below them. Consequently, cleared areas generally experience greater temperature extremes than the

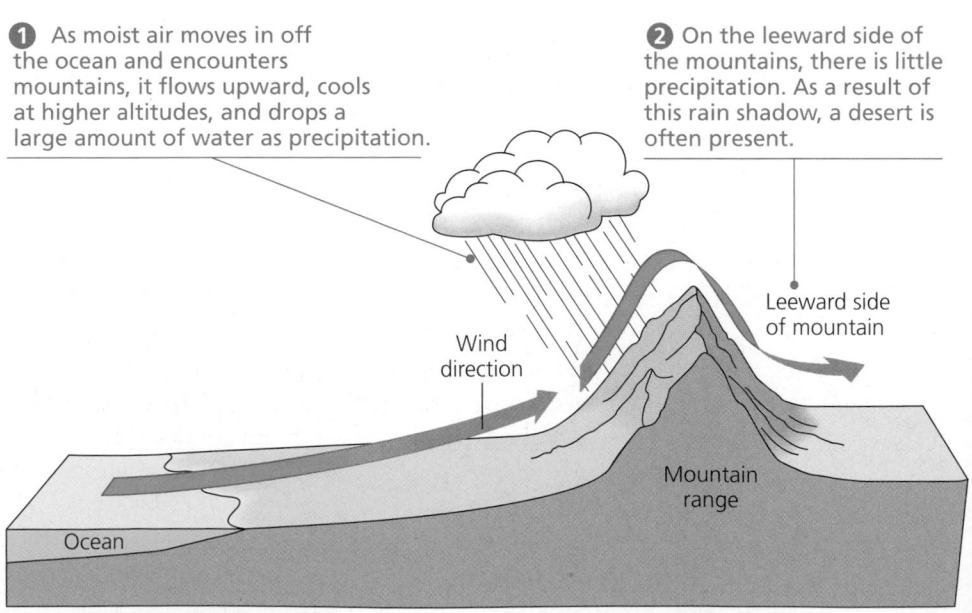

① As moist air moves in off the ocean and encounters mountains, it flows upward, cools at higher altitudes, and drops a large amount of water as precipitation.

② On the leeward side of the mountains, there is little precipitation. As a result of this rain shadow, a desert is often present.

Leeward side of mountain

Wind direction

Mountain range

Ocean

▲ Figure 52.13 **How mountains affect rainfall.**

forest interior because of greater solar radiation and wind currents that are established by the rapid heating and cooling of open land. Within a forest, low-lying ground is usually wetter than high ground and tends to be occupied by different species of trees. A log or large stone can shelter organisms such as salamanders, worms, and insects, buffering them from the extremes of temperature and moisture. Every environment on Earth is similarly characterized by a mosaic of small-scale differences in the abiotic factors that influence the local distributions of organisms.

Long-Term Climate Change

If temperature and moisture are the most important factors limiting the geographic ranges of plants and animals, then the global climate change currently under way will profoundly affect the biosphere (see Chapter 55). One way to predict the possible effects of climate change is to look back at the changes that have occurred in temperate regions since the last ice age ended.

Until about 16,000 years ago, continental glaciers covered much of North America and Eurasia. As the climate warmed and the glaciers retreated, tree distributions expanded northward. A detailed record of these migrations is captured in fossil pollen deposited in lakes and ponds. (It may seem odd to think of trees "migrating," but recall from Chapter 38 that wind and animals can disperse seeds, sometimes over great distances.) If researchers can determine the climatic limits of current geographic distributions for organisms, they can make predictions about how distributions will change with climatic warming. A major question when applying this approach to plants is whether seed dispersal is rapid enough to sustain the migration of each species as climate changes. For example, fossils suggest that the eastern hemlock was delayed nearly 2,500 years in its movement north at the end of the last ice age. This delay in seed dispersal was partly attributable to the lack of "wings" on the seeds, causing the seeds to fall close to their parent tree.

Let's look at a specific case of how the fossil record of past tree migrations can inform predictions about the biological impact of the current global warming trend. **Figure 52.14** shows the current and predicted geographic ranges of the American beech (*Fagus grandifolia*) under two different climate-change models. These models predict that the northern limit of the beech's range will move 700–900 km northward in the next century, and its southern range limit will move northward an even greater distance. If these predictions are even approximately correct, the beech must move 7–9 km per year northward to keep pace with the warming climate. However, since the end of the last ice age, the beech has migrated into its present range at a rate of only 0.2 km per year. Without human as-

(a) 4.5°C warming over next century

(b) 6.5°C warming over next century

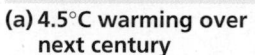

▲ **Figure 52.14 Current range and predicted range for the American beech (*Fagus grandifolia*) under two scenarios of climate change.**

? *The predicted range in each scenario is based on climate factors alone. What other factors might alter the distribution of this species?*

sistance in moving into new ranges where they can survive as the climate warms, species such as the American beech may have much smaller ranges and may even become extinct.

CONCEPT CHECK 52.2

1. Give examples of human actions that could expand a species' distribution by changing its (a) dispersal or (b) biotic interactions.
2. Explain how the sun's unequal heating of Earth's surface influences global climate patterns.
3. **WHAT IF?** You suspect that deer are restricting the distribution of a tree species by preferentially eating the seedlings of the tree. How might you test that hypothesis?

For suggested answers, see Appendix A.

CONCEPT 52.3

Aquatic biomes are diverse and dynamic systems that cover most of Earth

We have seen how both biotic and abiotic factors influence the distribution of organisms on Earth. Combinations of these factors determine the nature of Earth's many **biomes**, major terrestrial or aquatic life zones, characterized by vegetation type in terrestrial biomes or the physical environment in aquatic biomes. We'll begin by examining Earth's aquatic biomes.

Aquatic biomes account for the largest part of the biosphere in terms of area, and all types are found around the globe **(Figure 52.15)**. Ecologists distinguish between freshwater biomes and marine biomes on the basis of physical and chemical differences. For example, marine biomes generally have salt concentrations that average 3%, whereas freshwater biomes are usually characterized by a salt concentration of less than 0.1%.

The oceans make up the largest marine biome, covering about 75% of Earth's surface. Because of their vast size, they have an enormous impact on the biosphere. The evaporation of water from the oceans provides most of the planet's rainfall, and ocean temperatures have a major effect on world climate and wind patterns. In addition, marine algae and

▲ **Figure 52.15 The distribution of major aquatic biomes.**

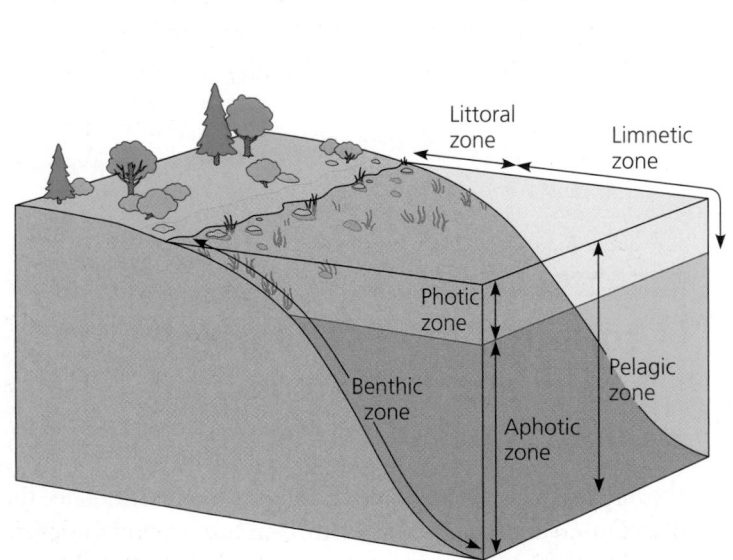

(a) Zonation in a lake. The lake environment is generally classified on the basis of three physical criteria: light penetration (photic and aphotic zones), distance from shore and water depth (littoral and limnetic zones), and whether it is open water (pelagic zone) or bottom (benthic zone).

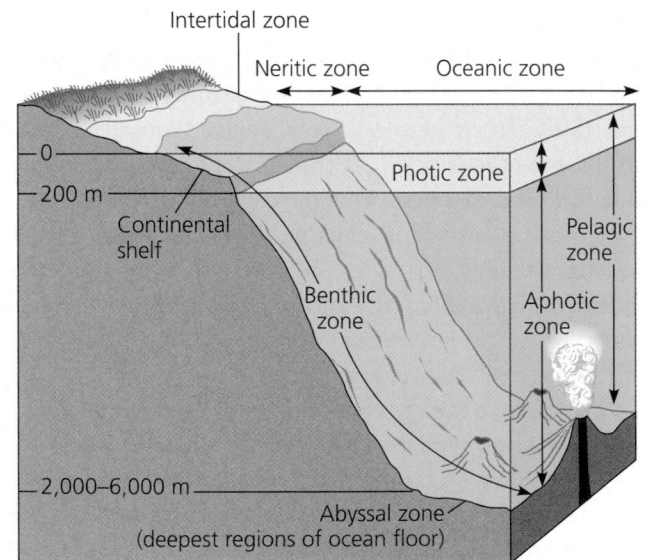

(b) Marine zonation. Like lakes, the marine environment is generally classified on the basis of light penetration (photic and aphotic zones), distance from shore and water depth (intertidal, neritic, and oceanic zones), and whether it is open water (pelagic zone) or bottom (benthic and abyssal zones).

▲ **Figure 52.16 Zonation in aquatic environments.**

photosynthetic bacteria supply a substantial portion of the world's oxygen and consume large amounts of atmospheric carbon dioxide.

Freshwater biomes are closely linked to the soils and biotic components of the terrestrial biomes through which they pass or in which they are situated. The particular characteristics of a freshwater biome are also influenced by the patterns and speed of water flow and the climate to which the biome is exposed.

Stratification of Aquatic Biomes

Many aquatic biomes are physically and chemically stratified (layered), as illustrated for both a lake and a marine environment in **Figure 52.16**, on the facing page. Light is absorbed by both the water itself and the photosynthetic organisms in it, so its intensity decreases rapidly with depth, as mentioned earlier. Ecologists distinguish between the upper **photic zone**, where there is sufficient light for photosynthesis, and the lower **aphotic zone**, where little light penetrates. At the bottom of all aquatic biomes, the substrate is called the **benthic zone**. Made up of sand and organic and inorganic sediments, the benthic zone is occupied by communities of organisms collectively called the **benthos**. A major source of food for many benthic species is dead organic matter called **detritus**, which "rains" down from the productive surface waters of the photic zone. In the ocean, the part of the benthic zone that lies between 2,000 and 6,000 m below the surface is known as the **abyssal zone**.

Thermal energy from sunlight warms surface waters to whatever depth the sunlight penetrates, but the deeper waters remain quite cold. In the ocean and in most lakes, a narrow layer of abrupt temperature change called a **thermocline** separates the more uniformly warm upper layer from more uniformly cold deeper waters. Lakes tend to be particularly layered with respect to temperature, especially during summer and winter, but many temperate lakes undergo a semiannual mixing of their waters as a result of changing temperature profiles **(Figure 52.17)**. This **turnover**, as it is called, brings oxygenated water from a lake's surface to the bottom and nutrient-rich water from the bottom to the surface in both spring and autumn. These cyclic changes in the abiotic properties of lakes are essential for the survival and growth of organisms at all levels within this ecosystem.

In both freshwater and marine environments, communities are distributed according to water depth, degree of light penetration, distance from shore, and whether they are found in open water or near the bottom. Marine communities, in particular, illustrate the limitations on species distribution that result from these abiotic factors. Plankton and many fish species occur in the relatively shallow photic zone (see Figure 52.16b). Because water absorbs light so well and the

1 In winter, the coldest water in the lake (0°C) lies just below the surface ice; water is progressively warmer at deeper levels of the lake, typically 4°C at the bottom.

2 In spring, as the sun melts the ice, the surface water warms to 4°C and sinks below the cooler layers immediately below, eliminating the thermal stratification. Spring winds mix the water to great depth, bringing oxygen to the bottom waters and nutrients to the surface.

3 In summer, the lake regains a distinctive thermal profile, with warm surface water separated from cold bottom water by a narrow vertical zone of abrupt temperature change, called a thermocline.

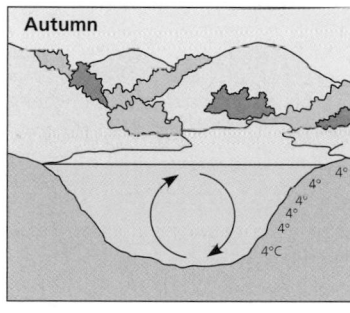

4 In autumn, as surface water cools rapidly, it sinks below the underlying layers, remixing the water until the surface begins to freeze and the winter temperature profile is reestablished.

▲ **Figure 52.17 Seasonal turnover in lakes with winter ice cover.** Because of the seasonal turnover shown here, lake waters are well oxygenated at all depths in spring and autumn; in winter and summer, when the lake is stratified by temperature, oxygen concentrations are lower in deeper waters and higher near the surface of the lake.

ocean is so deep, most of the ocean volume is virtually devoid of light (the aphotic zone) and harbors relatively little life, except for microorganisms and relatively sparse populations of fishes and invertebrates. Similar factors limit species distribution in deep lakes as well.

Figure 52.18, on the next four pages, surveys the major aquatic biomes.

Exploring Aquatic Biomes

Lakes

Physical Environment Standing bodies of water range from ponds a few square meters in area to lakes covering thousands of square kilometers. Light decreases with depth, creating stratification (see Figure 52.16a). Temperate lakes may have a seasonal thermocline (see Figure 52.17); tropical lowland lakes have a thermocline year-round.

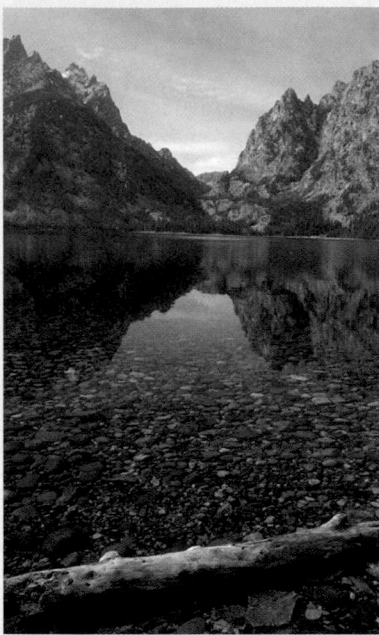

An oligotrophic lake in Grand Teton National Park, Wyoming

A eutrophic lake in the Okavango Delta, Botswana

Chemical Environment The salinity, oxygen concentration, and nutrient content differ greatly among lakes and can vary with season. **Oligotrophic lakes** are nutrient-poor and generally oxygen-rich; **eutrophic lakes** are nutrient-rich and often depleted of oxygen in the deepest zone in summer and if ice covered in winter. The amount of decomposable organic matter in bottom sediments is low in oligotrophic lakes and high in eutrophic lakes; high rates of decomposition in deeper layers of eutrophic lakes cause periodic oxygen depletion.

Geologic Features Oligotrophic lakes may become more eutrophic over time as runoff adds sediments and nutrients. They tend to have less surface area relative to their depth than eutrophic lakes have.

Photosynthetic Organisms Rooted and floating aquatic plants live in the **littoral zone**, the shallow, well-lighted waters close to shore. Farther from shore, where water is too deep to support rooted aquatic plants, the **limnetic zone** is inhabited by a variety of phytoplankton and cyanobacteria.

Heterotrophs In the limnetic zone, small drifting heterotrophs, or zooplankton, graze on the phytoplankton. The benthic zone is inhabited by assorted invertebrates whose species composition depends partly on oxygen levels. Fishes live in all zones with sufficient oxygen.

Human Impact Runoff from fertilized land and dumping of wastes lead to nutrient enrichment, which can produce algal blooms, oxygen depletion, and fish kills.

Wetlands

Physical Environment A **wetland** is a habitat that is inundated by water at least some of the time and that supports plants adapted to water-saturated soil. Some wetlands are inundated at all times, whereas others flood infrequently.

Chemical Environment Because of high organic production by plants and decomposition by microbes and other organisms, both the water and the soils are periodically low in dissolved oxygen. Wetlands have a high capacity to filter dissolved nutrients and chemical pollutants.

Geologic Features *Basin wetlands* develop in shallow basins, ranging from upland depressions to filled-in lakes and ponds. *Riverine wetlands* develop along shallow and periodically flooded banks of rivers and streams. *Fringe wetlands* occur along the coasts of large lakes and seas, where water flows back and forth because of rising lake levels or tidal action. Thus, fringe wetlands include both freshwater and marine biomes.

Photosynthetic Organisms Wetlands are among the most productive biomes on Earth. Their water-saturated soils favor the growth of plants such as floating pond lilies and emergent cattails, many sedges, tamarack, and black spruce, which have adaptations enabling them to grow in water or in soil that is periodically anaerobic owing to the presence of unaerated water. Woody plants dominate the vegetation of swamps, while bogs are dominated by sphagnum mosses.

Heterotrophs Wetlands are home to a diverse community of invertebrates, which in turn support a wide variety of birds. Herbivores,

Okefenokee National Wetland Reserve in Georgia

from crustaceans and aquatic insect larvae to muskrats, consume algae, detritus, and plants. Carnivores are also varied and may include dragonflies, otters, alligators, and owls.

Human Impact Draining and filling have destroyed up to 90% of wetlands, which help purify water and reduce peak flooding.

Streams and Rivers

Physical Environment   The most prominent physical characteristic of streams and rivers is their current. Headwater streams are generally cold, clear, turbulent, and swift. Farther downstream, where numerous tributaries may have joined, forming a river, the water is generally warmer and more turbid because of suspended sediment. Streams and rivers are stratified into vertical zones.

Chemical Environment   The salt and nutrient content of streams and rivers increases from the headwaters to the mouth. Headwaters are generally rich in oxygen. Downstream water may also contain substantial oxygen, except where there has been organic enrichment. A large fraction of the organic matter in rivers consists of dissolved or highly fragmented material that is carried by the current from forested streams.

Geologic Features   Headwater stream channels are often narrow, have a rocky bottom, and alternate between shallow sections and deeper pools. The downstream stretches of rivers are generally wide and meandering. River bottoms are often silty from sediments deposited over long periods of time.

Photosynthetic Organisms   Headwater streams that flow through grasslands or deserts may be rich in phytoplankton or rooted aquatic plants.

Heterotrophs   A great diversity of fishes and invertebrates inhabit unpolluted rivers and streams, distributed according to, and throughout, the vertical zones. In streams flowing through temperate or tropical forests, organic matter from terrestrial vegetation is the primary source of food for aquatic consumers.

Human Impact   Municipal, agricultural, and industrial pollution degrade water quality and kill aquatic organisms. Damming and flood control impair the natural functioning of stream and river ecosystems and threaten migratory species such as salmon.

A headwater stream in the Great Smoky Mountains

The Mississippi River far from its headwaters

Estuaries

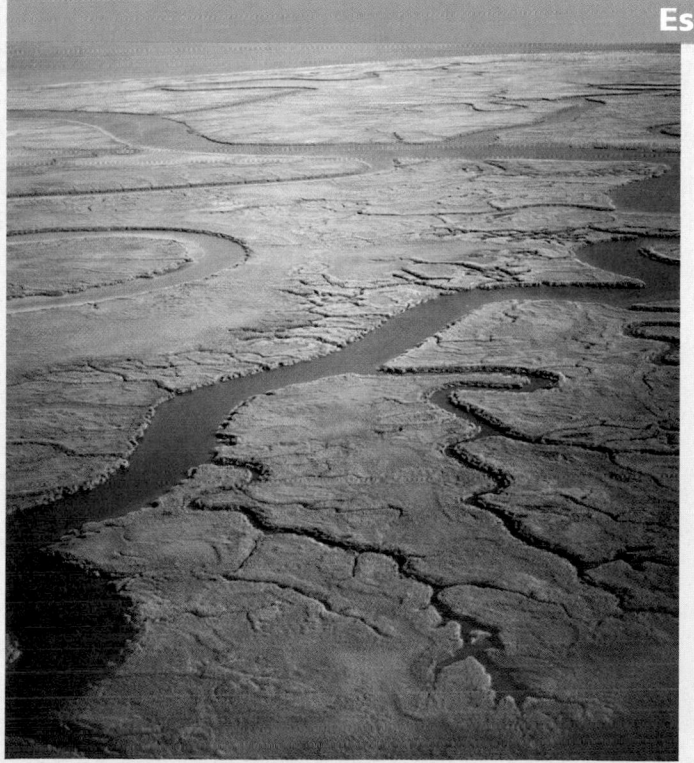

Physical Environment   An **estuary** is a transition area between river and sea. Seawater flows up the estuary channel during a rising tide and flows back down during the falling tide. Often, higher-density seawater occupies the bottom of the channel and mixes little with the lower-density river water at the surface.

Chemical Environment   Salinity varies spatially within estuaries, from nearly that of fresh water to that of seawater. Salinity also varies with the rise and fall of the tides. Nutrients from the river make estuaries, like wetlands, among the most productive biomes.

Geologic Features   Estuarine flow patterns combined with the sediments carried by river and tidal waters create a complex network of tidal channels, islands, natural levees, and mudflats.

Photosynthetic Organisms   Saltmarsh grasses and algae, including phytoplankton, are the major producers in estuaries.

Heterotrophs   Estuaries support an abundance of worms, oysters, crabs, and many fish species that humans consume. Many marine invertebrates and fishes use estuaries as a breeding ground or migrate through them to freshwater habitats upstream. Estuaries are also crucial feeding areas for waterfowl and some marine mammals.

Human Impact   Pollution from upstream, and also filling and dredging, have disrupted estuaries worldwide.

An estuary in a low coastal plain of Georgia

Continued on next page

Exploring **Aquatic Biomes**

Intertidal Zones

Rocky intertidal zone on the Oregon coast

Physical Environment   An **intertidal zone** is periodically submerged and exposed by the tides, twice daily on most marine shores. Upper zones experience longer exposures to air and greater variations in temperature and salinity. Changes in physical conditions from the upper to the lower intertidal zones limit the distributions of many organisms to particular strata, as shown in the photograph.

Chemical Environment   Oxygen and nutrient levels are generally high and are renewed with each turn of the tides.

Geologic Features   The substrates of intertidal zones, which are generally either rocky or sandy, select for particular behavior and anatomy among intertidal organisms. The configuration of bays or coastlines influences the magnitude of tides and the relative exposure of intertidal organisms to wave action.

Photosynthetic Organisms   A high diversity and biomass of attached marine algae inhabit rocky intertidal zones, especially in the lower zone. Sandy intertidal zones exposed to vigorous wave action generally lack attached plants or algae, while sandy intertidal zones in protected bays or lagoons often support rich beds of sea grass and algae.

Heterotrophs   Many of the animals in rocky intertidal environments have structural adaptations that enable them to attach to the hard substrate. The composition, density, and diversity of animals change markedly from the upper to the lower intertidal zones. Many of the animals in sandy or muddy intertidal zones, such as worms, clams, and predatory crustaceans, bury themselves and feed as the tides bring sources of food. Other common animals are sponges, sea anemones, echinoderms, and small fishes.

Human Impact   Oil pollution has disrupted many intertidal areas.

Oceanic Pelagic Zone

Physical Environment   The **oceanic pelagic zone** is a vast realm of open blue water, constantly mixed by wind-driven oceanic currents. Because of higher water clarity, the photic zone extends to greater depths than in coastal marine waters.

Chemical Environment   Oxygen levels are generally high. Nutrient concentrations are generally lower than in coastal waters. Because they are thermally stratified year-round, some tropical areas of the oceanic pelagic zone have lower nutrient concentrations than temperate oceans. Turnover between fall and spring renews nutrients in the photic zones of temperate and high-latitude ocean areas.

Geologic Features   This biome covers approximately 70% of Earth's surface and has an average depth of nearly 4,000 m. The deepest point in the ocean is more than 10,000 m beneath the surface.

Photosynthetic Organisms   The dominant photosynthetic organisms are phytoplankton, including photosynthetic bacteria, that drift with the oceanic currents. Spring turnover and renewal of nutrients in temperate oceans produces a surge of phytoplankton growth. Because of the large extent of this biome, photosynthetic plankton account for about half of the photosynthetic activity on Earth.

Heterotrophs   The most abundant heterotrophs in this biome are zooplankton. These protists, worms, copepods, shrimp-like krill, jellies, and the small larvae of invertebrates and fishes graze on photosynthetic plankton. The oceanic pelagic zone also includes free-swimming animals, such as large squids, fishes, sea turtles, and marine mammals.

Human Impact   Overfishing has depleted fish stocks in all Earth's oceans, which have also been polluted by waste dumping.

Open ocean off the island of Hawaii

Coral Reefs

Physical Environment   **Coral reefs** are formed largely from the calcium carbonate skeletons of corals. Shallow reef-building corals live in the photic zone of relatively stable tropical marine environments with high water clarity, primarily on islands and along the edge of some continents. They are sensitive to temperatures below about 18–20°C and above 30°C. Deep-sea coral reefs, found between 200 and 1,500 m deep, are less known than their shallow counterparts but harbor as much diversity as many shallow reefs do.

Chemical Environment   Corals require high oxygen levels and are excluded by high inputs of fresh water and nutrients.

Geologic Features   Corals require a solid substrate for attachment. A typical coral reef begins as a *fringing reef* on a young, high island, forming an offshore *barrier reef* later in the history of the island and becoming a *coral atoll* as the older island submerges.

Photosynthetic Organisms   Unicellular algae live within the tissues of the corals, forming a mutualistic relationship that provides the corals with organic molecules. Diverse multicellular red and green algae growing on the reef also contribute substantial amounts of photosynthesis.

Heterotrophs   Corals, a diverse group of cnidarians (see Chapter 33), are themselves the predominant animals on coral reefs. However, fish and invertebrate diversity is exceptionally high. Overall animal diversity on coral reefs rivals that of tropical forests.

A coral reef in the Red Sea

Human Impact   Collecting of coral skeletons and overfishing have reduced populations of corals and reef fishes. Global warming and pollution may be contributing to large-scale coral death. Development of coastal mangroves for aquaculture has also reduced spawning grounds for many species of reef fishes.

Marine Benthic Zone

Physical Environment   The **marine benthic zone** consists of the seafloor below the surface waters of the coastal, or **neritic**, zone and the offshore, pelagic zone (see Figure 52.16b). Except for shallow, near-coastal areas, the marine benthic zone receives no sunlight. Water temperature declines with depth, while pressure increases. As a result, organisms in the very deep benthic, or **abyssal**, zone are adapted to continuous cold (about 3°C) and very high water pressure.

Chemical Environment   Except in some areas of organic enrichment, oxygen is present at sufficient concentrations to support a diversity of animals.

Geologic Features   Soft sediments cover most of the benthic zone. However, there are areas of rocky substrate on reefs, submarine mountains, and new oceanic crust.

Autotrophs   Photosynthetic organisms, mainly seaweeds and filamentous algae, are limited to shallow benthic areas with sufficient light to support them. Unique assemblages of organisms, such as those shown in the photo, are found near **deep-sea hydrothermal vents** on mid-ocean ridges. In these dark, hot environments, the food producers are chemoautotrophic prokaryotes (see Chapter 27) that obtain energy by oxidizing H_2S formed by a reaction of the hot water with dissolved sulfate (SO_4^{2-}).

Heterotrophs   Neritic benthic communities include numerous invertebrates and fishes. Beyond the photic zone, most consumers depend entirely on organic matter raining down from above. Among the animals of the deep-sea hydrothermal vent communities are giant tube worms (pictured at left), some more than 1 m long. They are nourished by chemoautotrophic prokaryotes that live as symbionts within their bodies. Many other invertebrates, including arthropods and echinoderms, are also abundant around the hydrothermal vents.

Human Impact   Overfishing has decimated important benthic fish populations, such as the cod of the Grand Banks off Newfoundland. Dumping of organic wastes has created oxygen-deprived benthic areas.

A deep-sea hydrothermal vent community

The first two questions refer to Figure 52.18.

1. Many organisms living in estuaries experience fresh- and saltwater conditions each day with the rising and falling of tides. What challenge does this pose for the physiology of the organisms?

2. Why are phytoplankton, and not benthic algae or rooted aquatic plants, the dominant photosynthetic organisms of the oceanic pelagic zone?

3. **WHAT IF?** Water leaving a reservoir behind a dam is often taken from deep layers of the reservoir. Would you expect fish found in a river below a dam in summer to be species that prefer colder or warmer water than fish found in an undammed river? Explain.

For suggested answers, see Appendix A.

CONCEPT 52.4

The structure and distribution of terrestrial biomes are controlled by climate and disturbance

All the abiotic factors discussed in this chapter, but especially climate, are important in determining why a particular terrestrial biome is found in a certain area. Because there are latitudinal patterns of climate over Earth's surface (see Figure 52.10), there are also latitudinal patterns of biome distribution (Figure 52.19). These biome patterns in turn are modified by **disturbance**, an event (such as a storm, fire, or human activ-

ity) that changes a community, removing organisms from it and altering resource availability. Frequent fires, for instance, can kill woody plants and keep a savanna from becoming the woodland that climate alone would otherwise support.

Climate and Terrestrial Biomes

We can see the great impact of climate on the distribution of organisms by constructing a **climograph**, a plot of the temperature and precipitation in a particular region. **Figure 52.20** is a climograph of annual mean temperature and precipitation for some of the biomes found in North America. Notice that the range of precipitation in northern coniferous forests is similar to that in temperate forests, but the temperature ranges are different. Grasslands are generally drier than either kind of forest, and deserts are drier still.

Factors other than mean temperature and precipitation also play a role in determining where biomes exist. For example, certain areas in North America with a particular combination of temperature and precipitation support a temperate broadleaf forest, but other areas with similar values for these variables support a coniferous forest. How do we explain this variation? First, remember that the climograph is based on annual *averages*. Often, however, the *pattern* of climatic variation is as important as the average climate. Some areas may receive regular precipitation throughout the year, whereas other areas with the same annual precipitation have distinct wet and dry seasons. A similar phenomenon may occur with respect to temperature. Other environmental characteristics, such as the type of bedrock in an area, may greatly affect mineral nutrient availability and soil structure, which in turn affect the kind of vegetation that can grow.

▲ **Figure 52.19 The distribution of major terrestrial biomes.** Although biomes are mapped here with sharp boundaries, biomes actually grade into one another, sometimes over large areas.

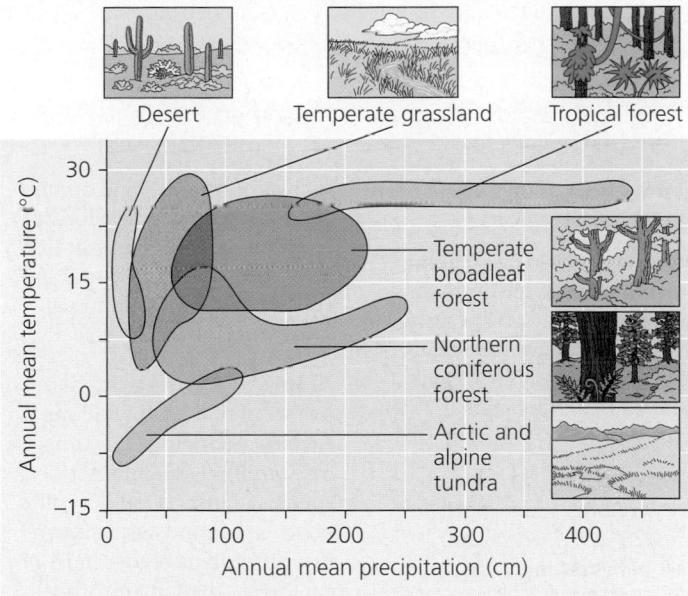

▲ **Figure 52.20 A climograph for some major types of biomes in North America.** The areas plotted here encompass the range of annual mean temperature and precipitation in the biomes.

General Features of Terrestrial Biomes and the Role of Disturbance

Most terrestrial biomes are named for major physical or climatic features and for their predominant vegetation. Temperate grasslands, for instance, are generally found in middle latitudes, where the climate is more moderate than in the tropics or polar regions, and are dominated by various grass species (see Figure 52.19). Each biome is also characterized by microorganisms, fungi, and animals adapted to that particular environment. For example, temperate grasslands are more likely than forests to be populated by large grazing mammals.

Although Figure 52.19 shows distinct boundaries between the biomes, in actuality, terrestrial biomes usually grade into each other without sharp boundaries. The area of intergradation, called an **ecotone**, may be wide or narrow.

Vertical layering is an important feature of terrestrial biomes, and the shapes and sizes of plants largely define that layering. In many forests, for example, the layers from top to bottom consist of the upper **canopy**, the low-tree layer, the shrub understory, the ground layer of herbaceous plants, the forest floor (litter layer), and the root layer. Nonforest biomes have similar, though usually less pronounced, layers. Grasslands have an herbaceous layer of grasses and forbs (small broadleaf plants), a litter layer, and a root layer. Layering of vegetation provides many different habitats for animals, which often occupy well-defined feeding groups, from the insectivorous birds and bats that feed above canopies to the small mammals, numerous worms, and arthropods that search for food in the litter and root layers.

The species composition of each kind of biome varies from one location to another. For instance, in the northern conifer-

ous forest (taiga) of North America, red spruce is common in the east but does not occur in most other areas, where black spruce and white spruce are abundant. In an example of convergent evolution (see Figure 26.7), cacti living in North American deserts appear very similar to plants called euphorbs found in African deserts, although cacti and euphorbs belong to different evolutionary lineages.

Biomes are dynamic, and disturbance rather than stability tends to be the rule. For example, hurricanes create openings for new species in tropical and temperate forests. In northern coniferous forests, gaps are produced when old trees die and fall over or when snowfall breaks branches. These gaps allow deciduous species, such as aspen and birch, to grow. As a result, biomes usually exhibit extensive patchiness, with several different communities represented in any particular area.

In many biomes, the dominant plants depend on periodic disturbance. For example, natural wildfires are an integral component of grasslands, savannas, chaparral, and many coniferous forests. However, fires are no longer common across much of the Great Plains because tallgrass prairie ecosystems have been converted to agricultural fields that rarely burn. Before agricultural and urban development, much of the southeastern United States was dominated by a single conifer species, the longleaf pine. Without periodic burning, broadleaf trees tended to replace the pines. Forest managers now use fire as a tool to help maintain many coniferous forests.

Figure 52.21, on the next four pages, summarizes the major features of terrestrial biomes. As you read about the characteristics of each biome, remember that humans have altered much of Earth's surface, replacing original biomes with urban and agricultural ones. Most of the eastern United States, for example, is classified as temperate broadleaf forest, but little of that original forest remains.

Throughout this chapter, you have seen how the distributions of organisms and biomes depend on both abiotic and biotic factors. In the next chapter, we will begin to work our way down the hierarchy outlined in Figure 52.2, focusing on how abiotic and biotic factors influence the ecology of populations.

CONCEPT CHECK 52.4

1. Based on the climograph in Figure 52.20, what mainly differentiates dry tundra and deserts?
2. Identify the natural biome in which you live and summarize its abiotic and biotic characteristics. Do these reflect your actual surroundings? Explain.
3. **WHAT IF?** If global warming increases average temperatures on Earth by 4°C in this century, predict which biome is most likely to replace tundra in some locations as a result. Explain your answer.

For suggested answers, see Appendix A.

Exploring Terrestrial Biomes

Tropical Forest

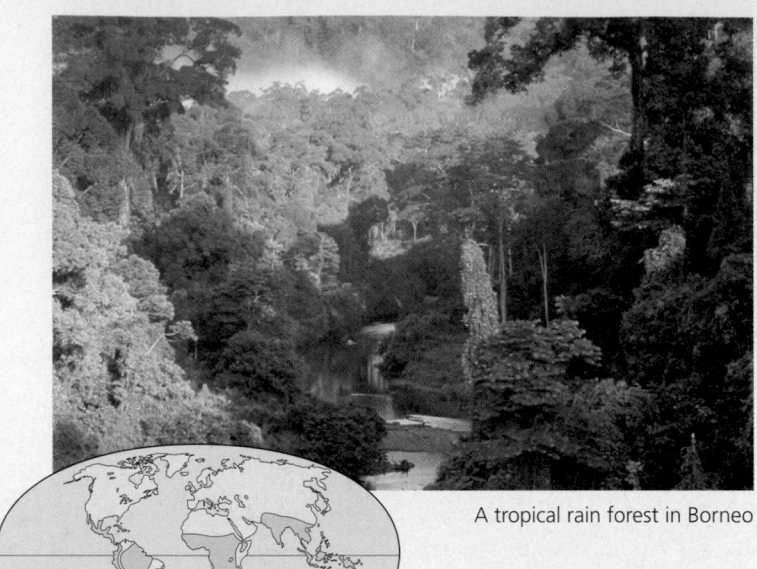

A tropical rain forest in Borneo

Distribution Equatorial and subequatorial regions.

Precipitation In **tropical rain forests**, rainfall is relatively constant, about 200–400 cm annually. In **tropical dry forests**, precipitation is highly seasonal, about 150–200 cm annually, with a six- to seven-month dry season.

Temperature Air temperatures are high year-round, averaging 25–29°C with little seasonal variation.

Plants Tropical forests are vertically layered, and competition for light is intense. Layers in rain forests include emergent trees that grow above a closed canopy, the canopy trees, one or two layers of subcanopy trees, and shrub and herb layers. There are generally fewer layers in tropical dry forests. Broadleaf evergreen trees are dominant in tropical rain forests, whereas tropical dry forest trees drop their leaves during the dry season. Epiphytes such as bromeliads and orchids generally cover tropical forest trees but are less abundant in dry forests. Thorny shrubs and succulent plants are common in some tropical dry forests.

Animals Earth's tropical forests are home to millions of species, including an estimated 5–30 million still undescribed species of insects, spiders, and other arthropods. In fact, animal diversity is higher in tropical forests than in any other terrestrial biome. The animals, including amphibians, birds and other reptiles, mammals, and arthropods, are adapted to the vertically layered environment and are often inconspicuous.

Human Impact Humans long ago established thriving communities in tropical forests. Rapid population growth leading to agriculture and development is now destroying some tropical forests.

Desert

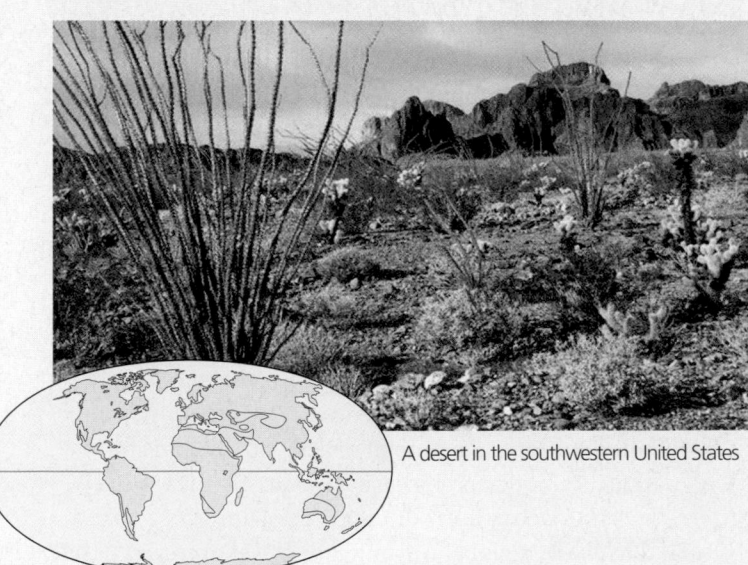

A desert in the southwestern United States

Distribution **Deserts** occur in bands near 30° north and south latitude or at other latitudes in the interior of continents (for instance, the Gobi Desert of north central Asia).

Precipitation Precipitation is low and highly variable, generally less than 30 cm per year.

Temperature Temperature is variable seasonally and daily. Maximum air temperature in hot deserts may exceed 50°C; in cold deserts air temperature may fall below −30°C.

Plants Desert landscapes are dominated by low, widely scattered vegetation; the proportion of bare ground is high compared with other terrestrial biomes. The plants include succulents such as cacti, deeply rooted shrubs, and herbs that grow during the infrequent moist periods. Desert plant adaptations include heat and desiccation tolerance, water storage, and reduced leaf surface area. Physical defenses, such as spines, and chemical defenses, such as toxins in the leaves of shrubs, are common. Many of the plants exhibit C_4 or CAM photosynthesis (see Chapter 10).

Animals Common desert animals include many kinds of snakes and lizards, scorpions, ants, beetles, migratory and resident birds, and seed-eating rodents. Many species are nocturnal. Water conservation is a common adaptation, with some species surviving on water from metabolic breakdown of carbohydrates in seeds.

Human Impact Long-distance transport of water and deep groundwater wells have allowed humans to maintain substantial populations in deserts. Conversion to irrigated agriculture and urbanization have reduced the natural biodiversity of some deserts.

Savanna

Distribution Equatorial and subequatorial regions.

Precipitation Rainfall, which is seasonal, averages 30–50 cm per year. The dry season can last up to eight or nine months.

Temperature The **savanna** is warm year-round, averaging 24–29°C, but with somewhat more seasonal variation than in tropical forests.

Plants The scattered trees found at different densities in the savanna often are thorny and have small leaves, an apparent adaptation to the relatively dry conditions. Fires are common in the dry season, and the dominant plant species are fire-adapted and tolerant of seasonal drought. Grasses and forbs, which make up most of the ground cover, grow rapidly in response to seasonal rains and are tolerant of grazing by large mammals and other herbivores.

Animals Large plant-eating mammals, such as wildebeests and bison, and predators, including lions and hyenas, are common inhabitants. However, the dominant herbivores are actually insects, especially termites. During seasonal droughts, grazing mammals often migrate to parts of the savanna with more forage and scattered watering holes.

Human Impact There is evidence that the earliest humans lived in savannas. Fires set by humans may help maintain this biome. Cattle ranching and overhunting have led to declines in large-mammal populations.

A savanna in Kenya

Chaparral

Distribution This biome occurs in midlatitude coastal regions on several continents, and its many names reflect its far-flung distribution: **chaparral** in North America, *matorral* in Spain and Chile, *garigue* and *maquis* in southern France, and *fynbos* in South Africa.

Precipitation Precipitation is highly seasonal, with rainy winters and long, dry summers. Annual precipitation generally falls within the range of 30–50 cm.

Temperature Fall, winter, and spring are cool, with average temperatures in the range of 10–12°C. Average summer temperature can reach 30°C, and daytime maximum temperature can exceed 40°C.

Plants Chaparral is dominated by shrubs and small trees, along with a many kinds of grasses and herbs. Plant diversity is high, with many species confined to a specific, relatively small geographic area. Adaptations to drought include the tough evergreen leaves of woody plants, which reduce water loss. Adaptations to fire are also prominent. Some of the shrubs produce seeds that will germinate only after a hot fire; food reserves stored in their fire-resistant roots enable them to resprout quickly and use nutrients released by the fire.

Animals Native mammals include browsers, such as deer and goats, that feed on twigs and buds of woody vegetation, and a high diversity of small mammals. Chaparral areas also support many species of amphibians, birds and other reptiles, and insects.

Human Impact Chaparral areas have been heavily settled and reduced through conversion to agriculture and urbanization. Humans contribute to the fires that sweep across the chaparral.

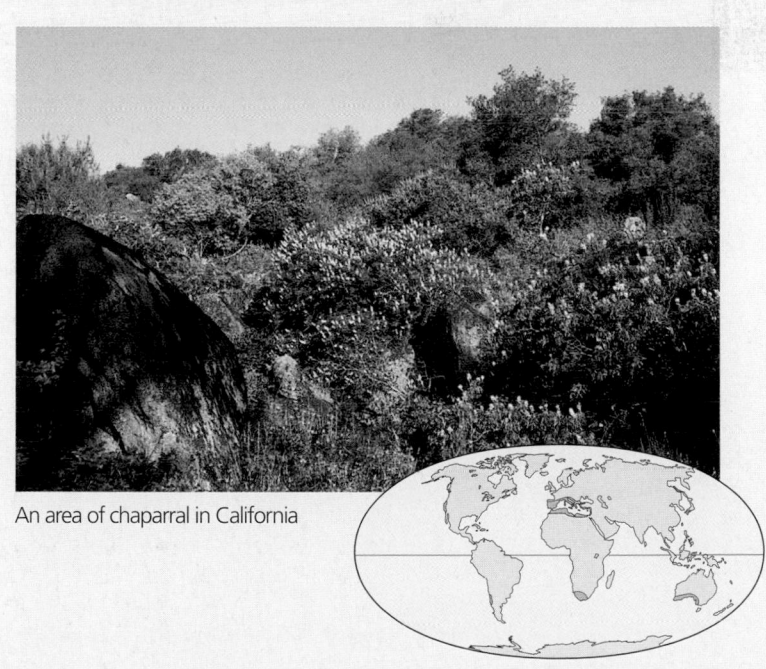

An area of chaparral in California

Continued on next page

Exploring Terrestrial Biomes

Temperate Grassland

Sheyenne National Grassland in North Dakota

Distribution The veldts of South Africa, the *puszta* of Hungary, the pampas of Argentina and Uruguay, the steppes of Russia, and the plains and prairies of central North America are all **temperate grasslands**.

Precipitation Precipitation is often highly seasonal, with relatively dry winters and wet summers. Annual precipitation generally averages between 30 and 100 cm. Periodic drought is common.

Temperature Winters are generally cold, with average temperatures frequently falling well below −10°C. Summers, with average temperatures often approaching 30°C, are hot.

Plants The dominant plants are grasses and forbs, which vary in height from a few centimeters to 2 m in tallgrass prairie. Many have adaptations that help them survive periodic, protracted droughts and fire: For example, grasses can sprout quickly following fire. Grazing by large mammals helps prevent establishment of woody shrubs and trees.

Animals Native mammals include large grazers such as bison and wild horses. Temperate grasslands are also inhabited by a wide variety of burrowing mammals, such as prairie dogs in North America.

Human Impact Deep, fertile soils make temperate grasslands ideal places for agriculture, especially for growing grains. As a consequence, most grassland in North America and much of Eurasia has been converted to farmland. In some drier grasslands, cattle and other grazers have helped change parts of the biome into desert.

Northern Coniferous Forest

Rocky Mountain National Park in Colorado

Distribution Extending in a broad band across northern North America and Eurasia to the edge of the arctic tundra, the **northern coniferous forest**, or *taiga*, is the largest terrestrial biome on Earth.

Precipitation Annual precipitation generally ranges from 30 to 70 cm, and periodic droughts are common. However, some coastal coniferous forests of the U.S. Pacific Northwest are temperate rain forests that may receive over 300 cm of annual precipitation.

Temperature Winters are usually cold and long; summers may be hot. Some areas of coniferous forest in Siberia typically range in temperature from −50°C in winter to over 20°C in summer.

Plants Cone-bearing trees, such as pine, spruce, fir, and hemlock, dominate northern coniferous forests. The conical shape of many conifers prevents too much snow from accumulating and breaking their branches. The diversity of plants in the shrub and herb layers of these forests is lower than in temperate broadleaf forests.

Animals While many migratory birds nest in northern coniferous forests, other species reside there year-round. The mammals of this biome, which include moose, brown bears, and Siberian tigers, are diverse. Periodic outbreaks of insects that feed on the dominant trees can kill vast tracts of trees.

Human Impact Although they have not been heavily settled by human populations, northern coniferous forests are being logged at an alarming rate, and the old-growth stands of these trees may soon disappear.

Temperate Broadleaf Forest

Distribution Found mainly at midlatitudes in the Northern Hemisphere, with smaller areas in New Zealand and Australia.

Precipitation Precipitation can average from about 70 to over 200 cm annually. Significant amounts fall during all seasons, including summer rain and, in some forests, winter snow.

Temperature Winter temperatures average around 0°C. Summers, with maximum temperatures near 35°C, are hot and humid.

Plants A mature **temperate broadleaf forest** has distinct vertical layers, including a closed canopy, one or two strata of understory trees, a shrub layer, and an herbaceous stratum. There are few epiphytes. The dominant plants in the Northern Hemisphere are deciduous trees, which drop their leaves before winter, when low temperatures would reduce photosynthesis and make water uptake from frozen soil difficult. In Australia, evergreen eucalyptus dominate these forests.

Animals In the Northern Hemisphere, many mammals hibernate in winter, while many bird species migrate to warmer climates. The mammals, birds, and insects make use of all vertical layers of the forest.

Human Impact Temperate broadleaf forest has been heavily settled on all continents. Logging and land clearing for agriculture and urban development destroyed virtually all the original deciduous forests in North America. However, owing to their capacity for recovery, these forests are returning over much of their former range.

Great Smoky Mountains National Park in North Carolina

Tundra

Distribution **Tundra** covers expansive areas of the Arctic, amounting to 20% of Earth's land surface. High winds and low temperatures create similar plant communities, called *alpine tundra*, on very high mountaintops at all latitudes, including the tropics.

Precipitation Precipitation averages from 20 to 60 cm annually in arctic tundra but may exceed 100 cm in alpine tundra.

Temperature Winters are long and cold, with averages in some areas below −30°C. Summers are short with low temperatures, generally averaging less than 10°C.

Plants The vegetation of tundra is mostly herbaceous, consisting of a mixture of mosses, grasses, and forbs, along with some dwarf shrubs and trees and lichens. A permanently frozen layer of soil called **permafrost** restricts the growth of plant roots.

Animals Large grazing musk oxen are resident, while caribou and reindeer are migratory. Predators include bears, wolves, and foxes. Many bird species migrate to the tundra for summer nesting.

Human Impact Tundra is sparsely settled but has become the focus of significant mineral and oil extraction in recent years.

Denali National Park, Alaska, in autumn

Chapter 52 Review

SUMMARY OF KEY CONCEPTS

CONCEPT 52.1

Ecology integrates all areas of biological research and informs environmental decision making (pp. 1148–1151)

▶ **Linking Ecology and Evolutionary Biology** Events that occur in ecological time affect life in evolutionary time.

▶ **Ecology and Environmental Issues** Ecologists distinguish between the science of ecology and environmental advocacy. Ecology provides a scientific basis for solving environmental problems, but policymakers must also balance social, economic, and political factors in reaching their decisions.

MEDIA Activity Science, Technology, and Society: DDT

CONCEPT 52.2

Interactions between organisms and the environment limit the distribution of species (pp. 1151–1159)

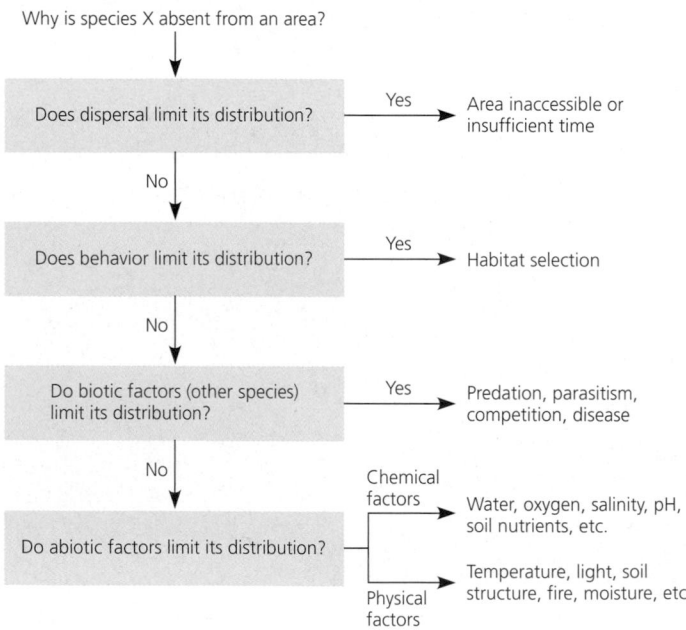

▶ **Climate** Global climate patterns are largely determined by the input of solar energy and Earth's revolution around the sun. Bodies of water, mountains, and the changing angle of the sun over the year exert regional, local, and seasonal effects on climate. Fine-scale differences in abiotic factors determine microclimates.

MEDIA Activity Adaptations to Biotic and Abiotic Factors
Investigation How Do Abiotic Factors Affect Distribution of Organisms?

CONCEPT 52.3

Aquatic biomes are diverse and dynamic systems that cover most of Earth (pp. 1159–1166)

▶ **Stratification of Aquatic Biomes** Aquatic biomes account for the largest part of the biosphere in terms of area and are generally stratified (layered) with regard to light penetration, temperature, and community structure. Marine biomes have a higher salt concentration than freshwater biomes.

MEDIA Activity Aquatic Biomes

CONCEPT 52.4

The structure and distribution of terrestrial biomes are controlled by climate and disturbance (pp. 1166–1171)

▶ **Climate and Terrestrial Biomes** Climographs show that temperature and precipitation are correlated with biomes, but because biomes overlap, other abiotic factors play a role in biome location.

▶ **General Features of Terrestrial Biomes and the Role of Disturbance** Terrestrial biomes are often named for major physical or climatic factors and for their predominant vegetation. Vertical layering is an important feature of terrestrial biomes. Disturbance, both natural and human induced, influences the type of vegetation found in biomes.

MEDIA Activity Terrestrial Biomes

TESTING YOUR KNOWLEDGE

SELF-QUIZ

1. Which of the following areas of study focuses on the exchange of energy, organisms, and materials between ecosystems?
   a. population ecology
   b. organismal ecology
   c. landscape ecology
   d. ecosystem ecology
   e. community ecology

2. **WHAT IF?** If Earth's axis of rotation suddenly became perpendicular to the plane of its orbit, the most predictable effect would be
   a. no more night and day.
   b. a big change in the length of the year.
   c. a cooling of the equator.
   d. a loss of seasonal variation at high latitudes.
   e. the elimination of ocean currents.

3. When climbing a mountain, we can observe transitions in biological communities that are analogous to the changes
   a. in biomes at different latitudes.
   b. at different depths in the ocean.
   c. in a community through different seasons.
   d. in an ecosystem as it evolves over time.
   e. across the United States from east to west.

4. The oceans affect the biosphere in all of the following ways *except*
   a. producing a substantial amount of the biosphere's oxygen.
   b. removing carbon dioxide from the atmosphere.
   c. moderating the climate of terrestrial biomes.
   d. regulating the pH of freshwater biomes and terrestrial groundwater.
   e. being the source of most of Earth's rainfall.

5. Which lake zone would be absent in a very shallow lake?
   a. benthic zone
   b. aphotic zone
   c. pelagic zone
   d. littoral zone
   e. limnetic zone

6. Which of the following is true with respect to oligotrophic lakes and eutrophic lakes?
   a. Oligotrophic lakes are more subject to oxygen depletion.
   b. Rates of photosynthesis are lower in eutrophic lakes.
   c. Eutrophic lake water contains lower concentrations of nutrients.
   d. Eutrophic lakes are richer in nutrients.
   e. Sediments in oligotrophic lakes contain larger amounts of decomposable organic matter.

7. Which of the following is characteristic of most terrestrial biomes?
   a. annual average rainfall in excess of 250 cm
   b. a distribution predicted almost entirely by rock and soil patterns
   c. clear boundaries between adjacent biomes
   d. vegetation demonstrating stratification
   e. cold winter months

8. Which of the following biomes is correctly paired with the description of its climate?
   a. savanna—low temperature, precipitation uniform during the year
   b. tundra—long summers, mild winters
   c. temperate broadleaf forest—relatively short growing season, mild winters
   d. temperate grasslands—relatively warm winters, most rainfall in summer
   e. tropical forests—nearly constant day length and temperature

9. Suppose that the number of bird species is determined mainly by the number of vertical strata found in the environment. If so, in which of the following biomes would you find the greatest number of bird species?
   a. tropical rain forest
   b. savanna
   c. desert
   d. temperate broadleaf forest
   e. temperate grassland

10. **DRAW IT** After reading the experiment of W. J. Fletcher described in Figure 52.8, you decide to study feeding relationships among sea otters, sea urchins, and kelp on your own. You know that sea otters prey on sea urchins and that urchins eat kelp. At four coastal sites, you measure kelp abundance. Then you spend one day at each site and mark whether otters are present or absent every 5 minutes during daylight hours. Make a graph that shows how otter density depends on kelp abundance, using the data shown below. Then formulate a hypothesis to explain the pattern you observed.

Site	Kelp Abundance (% cover)	Otter Density (# sightings per day)
1	75	98
2	15	18
3	60	85
4	25	36

For Self-Quiz answers, see Appendix A.

MEDIA Visit **www.campbellbiology.com** for a Practice Test.

EVOLUTION CONNECTION

11. Discuss how the concept of time applies to ecological situations and evolutionary changes. Do ecological time and evolutionary time ever overlap? If so, what are some examples?

SCIENTIFIC INQUIRY

12. Jens Clausen and colleagues, at the Carnegie Institution of Washington, studied how the size of yarrow plants (*Achillea lanulosa*) growing on the slopes of the Sierra Nevada varied with elevation. They found that plants from low elevations were generally taller than plants from high elevations, as shown below:

Source: J. Clausen et al., Experimental studies on the nature of species. III. Environmental responses of climatic races of *Achillea*, Carnegie Institution of Washington Publication No. 581 (1948).

Clausen and colleagues proposed two hypotheses to explain this variation within a species: (1) There are genetic differences between populations of plants found at different elevations. (2) The species has developmental flexibility and can assume tall or short growth forms, depending on local abiotic factors. If you had seeds from yarrow plants found at low and high elevations, what experiments would you perform to test these hypotheses?

Population Ecology

53

OVERVIEW

Counting Sheep

On the rugged Scottish island of Hirta, ecologists have been studying a population of sheep for more than 50 years **(Figure 53.1)**. What makes these animals worth studying for such a long time? Soay sheep are a rare and ancient breed, the closest living relative of the domesticated sheep that lived in Europe thousands of years ago. To help preserve the breed, in 1932 conservationists captured sheep on Soay Island, at the time the animals' only home, and released them on nearby Hirta. There, the sheep became valuable for a second reason: They provided an ideal opportunity to study how an isolated population of animals changes in size when food is plentiful and predators are absent. Surprisingly, ecologists found that the number of sheep on Hirta swung dramatically under these conditions, sometimes changing by more than 50% from one year to the next.

Why do populations of some species fluctuate greatly while populations of other species do not? To answer this question, we turn to the field of **population ecology**, the study of populations in relation to their environment. Population ecology

▲ Figure 53.1 **What causes a sheep population to fluctuate in size?**

explores how biotic and abiotic factors influence the density, distribution, size, and age structure of populations.

Our earlier study of populations in Chapter 23 emphasized the relationship between population genetics—the structure and dynamics of gene pools—and evolution. Evolution remains a central theme as we now view populations in the context of ecology. In this chapter, we will first examine some of the structural and dynamic aspects of populations. We will then explore the tools and models ecologists use to analyze populations and the factors that regulate the abundance of organisms. Finally, we will apply these basic concepts as we examine recent trends in the size and makeup of the human population.

CONCEPT 53.1

Dynamic biological processes influence population density, dispersion, and demographics

A **population** is a group of individuals of a single species living in the same general area. Members of a population rely on the same resources, are influenced by similar environmental factors, and are likely to interact and breed with one another. Populations can evolve as natural selection acts on heritable variations among individuals and changes the frequencies of various traits over time (see Chapter 23).

Three fundamental characteristics of a population are its density, dispersion, and demographics.

Density and Dispersion

At any given moment, a population has specific boundaries and a specific size (the number of individuals living within those boundaries). Ecologists usually begin investigating a population by defining boundaries appropriate to the organism under study and to the questions being asked. A population's boundaries may be natural ones, as in the case of the sheep on Hirta Island, or they may be arbitrarily defined by an investigator—for example, the oak trees within a specific county in Minnesota. Once defined, the population can be described in terms of its density and dispersion. **Density** is the number of individuals per unit area or volume: the number of oak trees per square kilometer in the Minnesota county or the number of *Escherichia coli* bacteria per milliliter in a test tube. **Dispersion** is the pattern of spacing among individuals within the boundaries of the population.

Density: A Dynamic Perspective

In rare cases, population size and density can be determined by counting all individuals within the boundaries of the population. We could count all the Soay sheep on Hirta Island or all the sea stars in a tide pool, for example. Large mammals that live in herds, such as buffalo or elephants, can sometimes be counted accurately from airplanes. In most cases, however, it is impractical or impossible to count all individuals in a population. Instead, ecologists use a variety of sampling techniques to estimate densities and total population sizes. For example, they might count the number of oak trees in several randomly located 100 × 100 m plots (samples), calculate the average density in the samples, and then extrapolate to estimate the population size in the entire area. Such estimates are most accurate when there are many sample plots and when the habitat is fairly homogeneous. In other cases, instead of counting individual organisms, population ecologists estimate density from an index of population size, such as the number of nests, burrows, tracks, calls, or fecal droppings. Ecologists also use the **mark-recapture method** to estimate the size of wildlife populations (**Figure 53.2**).

Density is not a static property but changes as individuals are added to or removed from a population (**Figure 53.3**).

▼ **Figure 53.2** **Research Method**

Determining Population Size Using the Mark-Recapture Method

APPLICATION   Ecologists cannot count all the individuals in a population if the organisms move too quickly or are hidden from view. In such cases, researchers often use the mark-recapture method to estimate population size. Andrew Gormley and colleagues at the University of Otago applied this method to a population of endangered Hector's dolphins (*Cephalorhynchus hectori*) near Banks Peninsula, in New Zealand.

Hector's dolphins

TECHNIQUE   Scientists typically begin by capturing a random sample of individuals in a population. They tag, or "mark," each individual and then release it. With some species, researchers can identify individuals without physically capturing them. For example, Gormley and colleagues identified 180 Hector's dolphins by photographing their distinctive dorsal fins from boats.

After waiting for the marked or otherwise identified individuals to mix back into the population, usually a few days or weeks, scientists capture or sample a second set of individuals. At Banks Peninsula, Gormley's team encountered 44 dolphins in their second sampling, 7 of which they had photographed before. The number of marked animals recaptured in the second sampling (x) divided by the total number of individuals captured in the second sampling (n) should equal the number of individuals marked and released in the first sampling (m) divided by the estimated population size (N):

$$\frac{x}{n} = \frac{m}{N} \qquad \text{or, solving for population size,} \qquad N = \frac{\overline{mn}}{x}$$

The method assumes that marked and unmarked individuals have the same probability of being captured or sampled, that the marked organisms have mixed completely back into the population, and that no individuals are born, die, immigrate, or emigrate during the resampling interval.

RESULTS   Based on these initial data, the estimated population size of Hector's dolphins at Banks Peninsula would be 180 × 44/7 = 1,131 individuals. Repeated sampling by Gormley and colleagues suggested a true population size closer to 1,100.

SOURCE   A. M. Gormley et al., Capture-recapture estimates of Hector's dolphin abundance at Banks Peninsula, New Zealand, *Marine Mammal Science* 21:204–216 (2005).

Births

Births and immigration add individuals to a population.

Immigration

Deaths

Deaths and emigration remove individuals from a population.

Emigration

▲ **Figure 53.3** **Population dynamics.**

Additions occur through birth (which we will define in this context to include all forms of reproduction) and **immigration**, the influx of new individuals from other areas. The factors that remove individuals from a population are death (mortality) and **emigration**, the movement of individuals out of a population.

While birth and death rates influence the density of all populations, immigration and emigration also alter the density of many populations. For example, long-term studies of Belding's ground squirrels (*Spermophilus beldingi*) in the vicinity of Tioga Pass, in the Sierra Nevada of California, show that some of the squirrels move nearly 2 km from where they are born, making them immigrants to other populations. Paul Sherman and Martin Morton, then at Cornell University and Occidental College, respectively, estimated that immigrants made up 1–8% of the males and 0.7–6% of the females in the study population. Although these immigrant percentages may seem small, they represent biologically significant exchanges between populations over time.

Patterns of Dispersion

Within a population's geographic range, local densities may vary substantially. Variations in local density are among the most important characteristics for a population ecologist to study, since they provide insight into the environmental associations and social interactions of individuals in the population. Environmental differences—even at a local level—contribute to variation in population density; some habitat patches are simply more suitable for a species than are others. Social interactions between members of the population, which may maintain patterns of spacing between individuals, can also contribute to variation in population density.

The most common pattern of dispersion is *clumped*, with the individuals aggregated in patches. Plants and fungi are often clumped where soil conditions and other environmental factors favor germination and growth. Mushrooms, for instance, may be clumped within and on top of a rotting log. Insects and salamanders may be clumped under the same log because of the higher humidity there. Clumping of animals may also be associated with mating behavior. Mayflies, which survive only a day or two as mating adults, often swarm in great numbers, a behavior that increases their chance of mating. Sea stars group together in tide pools, where food is readily available and where they can breed successfully **(Figure 53.4a)**. Forming groups may also increase the effectiveness of certain predators; for example, a wolf pack is more likely than a single wolf to subdue a moose or other large prey animal.

A *uniform*, or evenly spaced, pattern of dispersion may result from direct interactions between individuals in the population. For example, some plants secrete chemicals that inhibit the germination and growth of nearby individuals that could compete for resources. Animals often exhibit uniform dispersion as a result of antagonistic social interactions, such as **territoriality**— the defense of a bounded physical space against encroachment

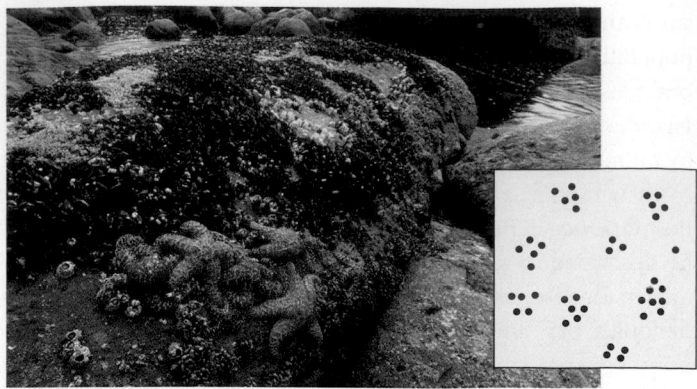

(a) Clumped. Many animals, such as these sea stars, group together where food is abundant.

(b) Uniform. Birds nesting on small islands, such as these king penguins on South Georgia Island in the South Atlantic Ocean, often exhibit uniform spacing, maintained by aggressive interactions between neighbors.

(c) Random. Many plants, such as these dandelions, grow from windblown seeds that land at random and later germinate.

▲ **Figure 53.4 Patterns of dispersion within a population's geographic range.**
WHAT IF? *Patterns of dispersion sometimes depend on the scale of the observation. How might the dispersion of the penguins look to you if you were flying in an airplane over the ocean?*

by other individuals **(Figure 53.4b)**. Uniform patterns are not as common in populations as clumped patterns are.

In *random* dispersion (unpredictable spacing), the position of each individual is independent of other individuals. This pattern occurs in the absence of strong attractions or repulsions among individuals of a population or where key physical or chemical factors are relatively homogeneous across the study area. For example, plants established by windblown seeds, such as dandelions, may be randomly distributed in a fairly consistent habitat (Figure 53.4c). Random patterns are not as common in nature as one might expect; most populations show at least a tendency toward a clumped distribution.

Demographics

The factors that influence population density and dispersion patterns—ecological needs of a species, structure of the environment, and interactions between individuals within the population—also influence other characteristics of populations. **Demography** is the study of the vital statistics of populations and how they change over time. Of particular interest to demographers are birth rates and how they vary among individuals (specifically among females, as you'll read shortly) and death rates. A useful way of summarizing some of the vital statistics of a population is with a life table.

Life Tables

About a century ago, when life insurance first became available, insurance companies began to estimate how long, on average, individuals of a given age could be expected to live. To do this, demographers developed **life tables**, age-specific summaries of the survival pattern of a population. Population ecologists adapted this approach to the study of nonhuman populations.

The best way to construct a life table is to follow the fate of a **cohort**, a group of individuals of the same age, from birth until all are dead. To build the life table, we need to determine the number of individuals that die in each age-group and calculate the proportion of the cohort surviving from one age to the next. Sherman and Morton's studies of the Belding's ground squirrels near Tioga Pass produced the life table in **Table 53.1**. The table reveals many things about the population. For instance, the third and eighth columns list, respectively, the proportions of females and males in the cohort that are still alive at each age. A comparison of the fifth and tenth columns reveals that males have higher death rates than females.

Survivorship Curves

A graphic method of representing the data in a life table is a **survivorship curve**, a plot of the proportion or numbers in a cohort still alive at each age. As an example, let's use the data for Belding's ground squirrels in Table 53.1 to construct a survivorship curve for this population. Generally, a survivorship curve is constructed beginning with a cohort of a specified size—say, 1,000 individuals. We can do this for the Belding's ground squirrel population by multiplying the proportion

Table 53.1 Life Table for Belding's Ground Squirrels (*Spermophilus beldingi*) at Tioga Pass, in the Sierra Nevada of California*

	FEMALES					MALES				
Age (years)	Number Alive at Start of Year	Proportion Alive at Start of Year	Number of Deaths During Year	Death Rate[†]	Average Additional Life Expectancy (years)	Number Alive at Start of Year	Proportion Alive at Start of Year	Number of Deaths During Year	Death Rate[†]	Average Additional Life Expectancy (years)
0–1	337	1.000	207	0.61	1.33	349	1.000	227	0.65	1.07
1–2	252[††]	0.386	125	0.50	1.56	248[††]	0.350	140	0.56	1.12
2–3	127	0.197	60	0.47	1.60	108	0.152	74	0.69	0.93
3–4	67	0.106	32	0.48	1.59	34	0.048	23	0.68	0.89
4–5	35	0.054	16	0.46	1.59	11	0.015	9	0.82	0.68
5–6	19	0.029	10	0.53	1.50	2	0.003	0	1.00	0.50
6–7	9	0.014	4	0.44	1.61	0				
7–8	5	0.008	1	0.20	1.50					
8–9	4	0.006	3	0.75	0.75					
9–10	1	0.002	1	1.00	0.50					

*Females and males have different mortality schedules, so they are tallied separately.
[†]The death rate is the proportion of individuals dying during the specific time interval.
[††]Includes 122 females and 126 males first captured as 1-year-olds and therefore not included in the count of squirrels age 0–1.
Source: P. W. Sherman and M. L. Morton, Demography of Belding's ground squirrel, *Ecology* 65:1617–1628 (1984).

▲ **Figure 53.5 Survivorship curves for male and female Belding's ground squirrels.** The logarithmic scale on the *y*-axis allows the number of survivors to be visible across the entire range (2–1,000 individuals) on the graph.

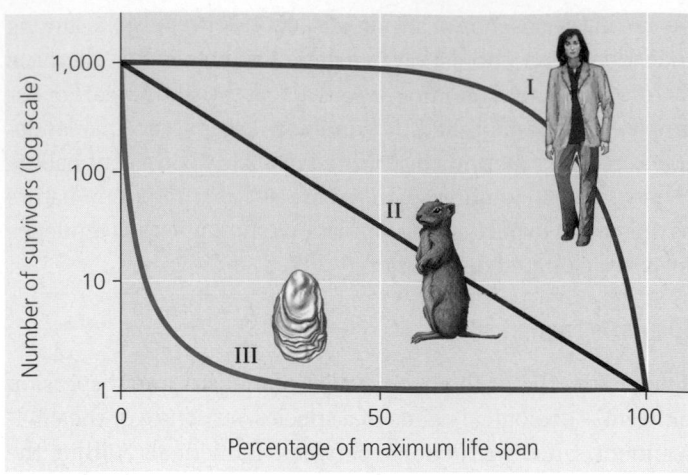

▲ **Figure 53.6 Idealized survivorship curves: Types I, II, and III.** The *y*-axis is logarithmic and the *x*-axis is on a relative scale, so that species with widely varying life spans can be presented together on the same graph.

alive at the start of each year (the third and eighth columns of Table 53.1) by 1,000 (the hypothetical beginning cohort). The result is the number alive at the start of each year. Plotting these numbers versus age for female and male Belding's ground squirrels yields **Figure 53.5.** The relatively straight lines of the plots indicate relatively constant rates of death; however, male Belding's ground squirrels have a lower survival rate overall than females have.

Figure 53.5 represents just one of many patterns of survivorship exhibited by natural populations. Though diverse, survivorship curves can be classified into three general types **(Figure 53.6).** A Type I curve is flat at the start, reflecting low death rates during early and middle life, and then drops steeply as death rates increase among older age-groups. Many large mammals, including humans, that produce few offspring but provide them with good care exhibit this kind of curve. In contrast, a Type III curve drops sharply at the start, reflecting very high death rates for the young, but flattens out as death rates decline for those few individuals that survive the early period of die-off. This type of curve is usually associated with organisms that produce very large numbers of offspring but provide little or no care, such as long-lived plants, many fishes, and most marine invertebrates. An oyster, for example, may release millions of eggs, but most offspring die in the larval stage from predation or other causes. Those few that survive long enough to attach to a suitable substrate and begin growing a hard shell tend to survive for a relatively long time. Type II curves are intermediate, with a constant death rate over the organism's life span. This kind of survivorship occurs in Belding's ground squirrels (see Figure 53.5) and some other rodents, various invertebrates, some lizards, and some annual plants.

Many species fall somewhere between these basic types of survivorship or show more complex patterns. In birds, for example, mortality is often high among the youngest individuals (as in a Type III curve) but fairly constant among adults (as in a Type II curve). Some invertebrates, such as crabs, may show a "stair-stepped" curve, with brief periods of increased mortality during molts, followed by periods of lower mortality when their protective exoskeleton is hard.

In populations not experiencing immigration or emigration, survivorship is one of the two key factors determining changes in population size. The other key factor determining population trends in such populations is reproductive rate.

Reproductive Rates

Demographers who study sexually reproducing species generally ignore the males and concentrate on the females in a population because only females produce offspring. Therefore, demographers view populations in terms of females giving rise to new females. The simplest way to describe the reproductive pattern of a population is to ask how reproductive output varies with the ages of females.

A **reproductive table,** or fertility schedule, is an age-specific summary of the reproductive rates in a population. It is constructed by measuring the reproductive output of a cohort from birth until death. For a sexual species, the reproductive table tallies the number of female offspring produced by each age-group. **Table 53.2** illustrates a reproductive table for Belding's ground squirrels. Reproductive output for sexual organisms such as birds and mammals is the product of the proportion of females of a given age that are breeding and the number of female offspring of those breeding females. Multiplying these numbers gives the average number of female offspring for each female in a given age-group (the last column in Table 53.2). For Belding's ground squirrels, which begin to reproduce at age 1 year, reproductive output rises to a peak at 4 years of age and then falls off in older females.

Table 53.2 Reproductive Table for Belding's Ground Squirrels at Tioga Pass				
Age (years)	Proportion of Females Weaning a Litter	Mean Size of Litters (Males + Females)	Mean Number of Females in a Litter	Average Number of Female Offspring*
0–1	0.00	0.00	0.00	0.00
1–2	0.65	3.30	1.65	1.07
2–3	0.92	4.05	2.03	1.87
3–4	0.90	4.90	2.45	2.21
4–5	0.95	5.45	2.73	2.59
5–6	1.00	4.15	2.08	2.08
6–7	1.00	3.40	1.70	1.70
7–8	1.00	3.85	1.93	1.93
8–9	1.00	3.85	1.93	1.93
9–10	1.00	3.15	1.58	1.58

*The average number of female offspring is the proportion weaning a litter multiplied by the mean number of females in a litter.

Source: P. W. Sherman and M. L. Morton, Demography of Belding's ground squirrel, *Ecology* 65:1617–1628 (1984).

Reproductive tables vary greatly, depending on the species. Squirrels have a litter of two to six young once a year for less than a decade, whereas oak trees drop thousands of acorns each year for tens or hundreds of years. Mussels and other invertebrates may release hundreds of thousands of eggs in a spawning cycle. Why a particular type of reproductive pattern evolves in a particular population—one of many questions at the interface of population ecology and evolutionary biology—is the subject of life history studies, the topic of the next section.

CONCEPT CHECK 53.1

1. One species of forest bird is highly territorial, while a second lives in flocks. Predict each species' likely pattern of dispersion, and explain.

2. **DRAW IT** Each female of a particular fish species produces millions of eggs per year. Draw and label the most likely survivorship curve for this species, and explain your choice.

3. **WHAT IF?** As noted in Figure 53.2, an important assumption of the mark-recapture method is that marked individuals have the same probability of being recaptured as unmarked individuals. Describe a situation where this assumption might not be valid, and explain how the estimate of population size would be affected.

For suggested answers, see Appendix A.

CONCEPT 53.2

Life history traits are products of natural selection

Natural selection favors traits that improve an organism's chances of survival and reproductive success. In every species, there are trade-offs between survival and traits such as frequency of reproduction, number of offspring produced (number of seeds produced by plants; litter or clutch size for animals), and investment in parental care. The traits that affect an organism's schedule of reproduction and survival (from birth through reproduction to death) make up its **life history**. A life history entails three basic variables: when reproduction begins (the age at first reproduction or age at maturity), how often the organism reproduces, and how many offspring are produced during each reproductive episode.

With the important exception of humans, which we will consider later in the chapter, organisms do not choose consciously when to reproduce or how many offspring to have. Rather, organisms' life history traits are evolutionary outcomes reflected in their development, physiology, and behavior.

Evolution and Life History Diversity

The fundamental idea that evolution accounts for the diversity of life is manifest in a broad range of life histories found in nature. Pacific salmon, for example, hatch in the headwaters of a stream and then migrate to the open ocean, where they require one to four years to mature. The salmon eventually return to the freshwater stream to spawn, producing thousands of eggs in a single reproductive opportunity before they die. This "one-shot" pattern of **big-bang reproduction**, or **semelparity** (from the Latin *semel*, once, and *parere*, to beget), also occurs in some plants, such as the agave, or "century plant" **(Figure 53.7)**.

▶ Figure 53.7 **An agave (*Agave americana*), an example of big-bang reproduction.** The leaves of the plant are visible at the base of the giant flowering stalk, which is produced only at the end of the agave's life.

Agaves generally grow in arid climates with unpredictable rainfall and poor soils. An agave grows for years, accumulating nutrients in its tissues, until there is an unusually wet year. It then sends up a large flowering stalk, produces seeds, and dies. This life history is an adaptation to the agave's harsh desert environment.

In contrast to semelparity is **iteroparity** (from the Latin *iterare*, to repeat), or **repeated reproduction**. Some lizards, for example, produce a few large eggs during their second year of life and then reproduce annually for several years.

What factors contribute to the evolution of semelparity versus iteroparity? A current hypothesis suggests that there are two critical factors: the survival rate of the offspring and the likelihood that the adult will survive to reproduce again. Where the survival rate of offspring is low, typically in highly variable or unpredictable environments, the prediction is that big-bang reproduction (semelparity) will be favored. Adults are also less likely to survive in such environments, so producing large numbers of offspring should increase the probability that at least some of those offspring will survive. Repeated reproduction (iteroparity) may be favored in more dependable environments where adults are more likely to survive to breed again and where competition for resources may be intense. In such cases, a few relatively large, well-provisioned offspring should have a better chance of surviving until they are capable of reproducing.

Nature abounds with life histories that are intermediate between the two extremes of semelparity and iteroparity. Oak trees and sea urchins are examples of organisms that can live a long time but repeatedly produce relatively large numbers of offspring.

"Trade-offs" and Life Histories

Natural selection cannot maximize all reproductive variables simultaneously. We might imagine an organism that could produce as many offspring as a semelparous species, provision them well like an iteroparous species, and do so repeatedly, but such organisms do not exist. Time, energy, and nutrients limit the reproductive capabilities of all organisms. In the broadest sense, there is a trade-off between reproduction and survival. A study of red deer in Scotland showed that females that reproduced in a given summer were more likely to die during the next winter than females that did not reproduce. A study of European kestrels also demonstrated the survival cost to parents of caring for young (**Figure 53.8**).

Selective pressures influence the trade-off between the number and size of offspring. Plants and animals whose young are subject to high mortality rates often produce large numbers of relatively small offspring. Plants that colonize disturbed environments, for example, usually produce many small seeds, only a few of which may reach a suitable habitat. Small size may also increase the chance of seedling establish-

▼ **Figure 53.8** Inquiry

How does caring for offspring affect parental survival in kestrels?

EXPERIMENT Cor Dijkstra and colleagues in the Netherlands studied the effects of parental caregiving in European kestrels over five years. The researchers transferred chicks among nests to produce reduced broods (three or four chicks), normal broods (five or six), and enlarged broods (seven or eight). They then measured the percentage of male and female parent birds that survived the following winter. (Both males and females provide care for chicks.)

RESULTS

CONCLUSION The lower survival rates of kestrels with larger broods indicate that caring for more offspring negatively affects survival of the parents.

SOURCE C. Dijkstra et al., Brood size manipulations in the kestrel (*Falco tinnunculus*): effects on offspring and parent survival, *Journal of Animal Ecology* 59:269–285 (1990).

WHAT IF? The males of many bird species provide no parental care. If this were true for the European kestrel, how would the experimental results differ from those shown above?

ment by enabling the seeds to be carried longer distances to a broader range of habitats (**Figure 53.9a**). Animals that suffer high predation rates, such as quail, sardines, and mice, also tend to produce large numbers of offspring.

In other organisms, extra investment on the part of the parent greatly increases the offspring's chances of survival. Walnut trees and coconut palms both provision large seeds with energy and nutrients that help the seedlings become established (**Figure 53.9b**). In animals, parental investment in offspring does not always end after incubation or gestation. For instance, primates generally bear only one or two offspring at a time. Parental care and an extended period of learning in the first several years of life are very important to offspring fitness in these species.

(a) Most weedy plants, such as this dandelion, grow quickly and produce a large number of seeds, ensuring that at least some will grow into plants and eventually produce seeds themselves.

(b) Some plants, such as this coconut palm, produce a moderate number of very large seeds. Each seed's large endosperm provides nutrients for the embryo, an adaptation that helps ensure the success of a relatively large fraction of offspring.

▲ **Figure 53.9 Variation in the size of seed crops in plants.**

CONCEPT CHECK **53.2**

1. Consider two rivers: One is spring fed and has a constant water volume and temperature year-round; the other drains a desert landscape and floods and dries out at unpredictable intervals. Which river would you predict is more likely to support many species of iteroparous animals? Why?
2. In the fish called the peacock wrasse (*Symphodus tinca*), females disperse some of their eggs widely and lay other eggs in a nest. Only the latter receive parental care. Explain the trade-offs in reproduction that this behavior illustrates.
3. **WHAT IF?** Mice that cannot find enough food or that experience other forms of stress will sometimes abandon their young. Explain how this behavior might have evolved in the context of reproductive trade-offs and life history.

For suggested answers, see Appendix A.

CONCEPT 53.3

The exponential model describes population growth in an idealized, unlimited environment

Populations of all species, regardless of their life histories, have the potential to expand greatly when resources are abundant. To appreciate the potential for population increase, consider a bacterium that can reproduce by fission every 20 minutes under ideal laboratory conditions. There would be 2 bacteria after 20 minutes, 4 after 40 minutes, and 8 after 60 minutes. If reproduction continued at this rate, with no mortality, for only a day and a half, there would be enough bacteria to form a layer a foot deep over the entire globe. At the other life history extreme, an elephant may produce only 6 offspring in a 100-year life span. Still, Charles Darwin once estimated that the descendants of a single pair of mating elephants would number 19 million within only 750 years. Darwin's estimate may not have been precisely correct, but such analyses led him to recognize the tremendous capacity for growth in all populations. Although unlimited growth does not occur for long in nature, studying population growth in an idealized, unlimited environment reveals the capacity of species for increase and the conditions under which that capacity may be expressed.

Per Capita Rate of Increase

Imagine a population consisting of a few individuals living in an ideal, unlimited environment. Under these conditions, there are no restrictions on the abilities of individuals to harvest energy, grow, and reproduce, aside from the inherent biological limitations of their life history traits. The population will increase in size with every birth and with the immigration of individuals from other populations, and it will decrease in size with every death and with the emigration of individuals out of the population. We can thus define a change in population size during a fixed time interval with the following verbal equation:

$$\begin{pmatrix}\text{Change in}\\\text{population}\\\text{size during}\\\text{time}\\\text{interval}\end{pmatrix} = \begin{pmatrix}\text{Births}\\\text{during}\\\text{time}\\\text{interval} + \begin{matrix}\text{Immigrants}\\\text{entering}\\\text{population}\\\text{during time}\\\text{interval}\end{matrix}\end{pmatrix} - \begin{pmatrix}\text{Deaths}\\\text{during}\\\text{time}\\\text{interval} + \begin{matrix}\text{Emigrants}\\\text{leaving}\\\text{population}\\\text{during time}\\\text{interval}\end{matrix}\end{pmatrix}$$

For simplicity here, we will ignore the effects of immigration and emigration, although a more complex formulation would certainly include these factors. We can also use mathematical notation to express this simplified relationship more concisely. If N represents population size and t represents time, then ΔN is the change in population size and Δt is the time interval (appropriate to the life span or generation time of the species) over which we are evaluating population growth. (The Greek letter delta, Δ, indicates change, such as change in time.) We can now rewrite the verbal equation as

$$\frac{\Delta N}{\Delta t} = B - D$$

where B is the number of births in the population during the time interval and D is the number of deaths.

Next, we can convert this simple model into one in which births and deaths are expressed as the average number of births and deaths per individual (per capita) during the specified time interval. The *per capita birth rate* is the number of offspring produced per unit time by an average member of the population. If, for example, there are 34 births per year in a population of 1,000 individuals, the annual per capita birth rate is 34/1,000, or 0.034. If we know the annual per capita birth rate (symbolized by b), we can use the formula $B = bN$ to calculate the expected number of births per year in a population of any size. For example, if the annual per capita birth rate is 0.034 and the population size is 500,

$$B = bN$$
$$B = 0.034 \times 500$$
$$B = 17 \text{ per year}$$

Similarly, the *per capita death rate* (symbolized by d) allows us to calculate the expected number of deaths per unit time in a population of any size, using the formula $D = dN$. If $d = 0.016$ per year, we would expect 16 deaths per year in a population of 1,000 individuals. For natural populations or those in the laboratory, the per capita birth and death rates can be calculated from estimates of population size and data in life tables and reproductive tables (for example, Tables 53.1 and 53.2).

Now we can revise the population growth equation again, this time using per capita birth and death rates rather than the numbers of births and deaths:

$$\frac{\Delta N}{\Delta t} = bN - dN$$

One final simplification is in order. Population ecologists are most interested in the *difference* between the per capita birth rate and per capita death rate. This difference is the *per capita rate of increase*, or r:

$$r = b - d$$

The value of r indicates whether a given population is growing ($r > 0$) or declining ($r < 0$). **Zero population growth (ZPG)** occurs when the per capita birth and death rates are equal ($r = 0$). Births and deaths still occur in such a population, of course, but they balance each other exactly.

Using the per capita rate of increase, we can now rewrite the equation for change in population size as

$$\frac{\Delta N}{\Delta t} = rN$$

Remember that this equation is for a discrete, or fixed, time interval (often one year, as in the previous example) and does not include immigration or emigration. Most ecologists prefer to use differential calculus to express population growth *instantaneously*, as growth rate at a particular instant in time:

$$\frac{dN}{dt} = r_{inst} N$$

In this case r_{inst} is simply the instantaneous per capita rate of increase. If you have not yet studied calculus, don't be intimidated by the form of the last equation; it is similar to the previous one, except that the time intervals Δt are very short and are expressed in the equation as dt. In fact, as Δt becomes shorter, the discrete r approaches the instantaneous r_{inst} in value.

Exponential Growth

Earlier we described a population whose members all have access to abundant food and are free to reproduce at their physiological capacity. Population increase under these ideal conditions is called **exponential population growth**, also known as geometric population growth. Under these conditions, the per capita rate of increase may assume the maximum rate for the species, denoted as r_{max}. The equation for exponential population growth is

$$\frac{dN}{dt} = r_{max} N$$

The size of a population that is growing exponentially increases at a constant rate, resulting eventually in a J-shaped growth curve when population size is plotted over time **(Figure 53.10)**. Although the maximum *rate* of increase is constant, the population accumulates more new individuals per unit of time when it is large than when it is small; thus, the

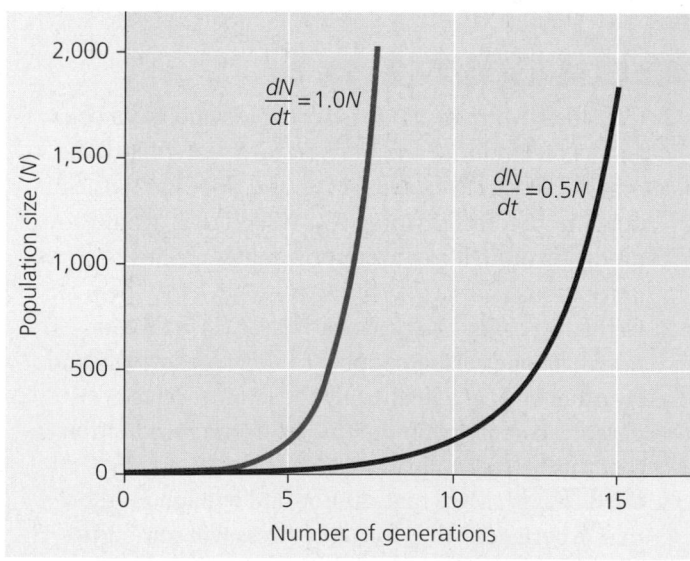

▲ **Figure 53.10 Population growth predicted by the exponential model.** This graph compares growth in two populations with different values of r_{max}. Increasing the value from 0.5 to 1.0 increases the rate of rise in population size over time, as reflected by the relative slopes of the curves at any given population size.

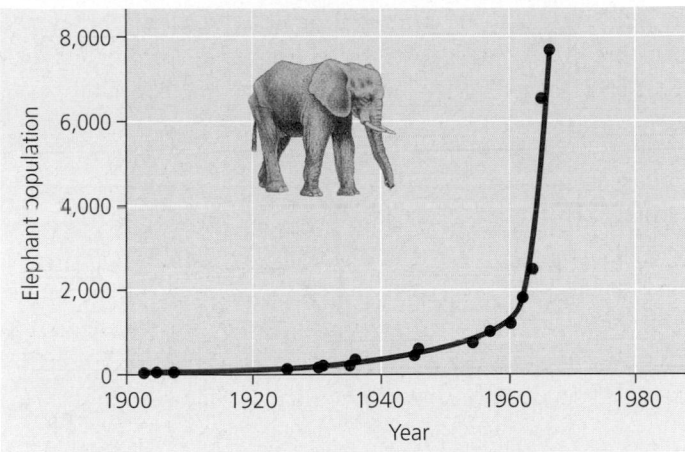

▲ **Figure 53.11 Exponential growth in the African elephant population of Kruger National Park, South Africa.**

curves in Figure 53.10 get progressively steeper over time. This occurs because population growth depends on N as well as r_{max}, and larger populations experience more births (and deaths) than small ones growing at the same per capita rate. It is also clear from Figure 53.10 that a population with a higher maximum rate of increase ($dN/dt = 1.0N$) will grow faster than one with a lower rate of increase ($dN/dt = 0.5N$).

The J-shaped curve of exponential growth is characteristic of some populations that are introduced into a new environment or whose numbers have been drastically reduced by a catastrophic event and are rebounding. For example, the population of elephants in Kruger National Park, South Africa, grew exponentially for approximately 60 years after they were first protected from hunting **(Figure 53.11)**. The increasingly large number of elephants eventually caused enough damage to vegetation in the park that a collapse in their food supply was likely. To protect other species and the park ecosystem before that happened, park managers began limiting the elephant population by using birth control and exporting elephants to other countries.

CONCEPT CHECK 53.3

1. Explain why a constant rate of increase (r_{max}) for a population produces a growth graph that is J-shaped rather than a straight line.

2. Where is exponential growth by a plant population more likely—on a newly formed volcanic island or in a mature, undisturbed rain forest? Why?

3. **WHAT IF?** In 2006, the United States had a population of about 300 million people. If there were 14 births and 8 deaths per 1,000 people, what was the country's net population growth that year (ignoring immigration and emigration, which are substantial)? Do you think the United States is currently experiencing exponential population growth? Explain.

For suggested answers, see Appendix A.

The logistic model describes how a population grows more slowly as it nears its carrying capacity

The exponential growth model assumes that resources are unlimited, which is rarely the case in the real world. As population density increases, each individual has access to fewer resources. Ultimately, there is a limit to the number of individuals that can occupy a habitat. Ecologists define **carrying capacity**, symbolized as K, as the maximum population size that a particular environment can sustain. Carrying capacity varies over space and time with the abundance of limiting resources. Energy, shelter, refuge from predators, nutrient availability, water, and suitable nesting sites can all be limiting factors. For example, the carrying capacity for bats may be high in a habitat with abundant flying insects and roosting sites, but lower where there is abundant food but fewer suitable shelters.

Crowding and resource limitation can have a profound effect on population growth rate. If individuals cannot obtain sufficient resources to reproduce, the per capita birth rate (b) will decline. If they cannot consume enough energy to maintain themselves, or if disease or parasitism increases with density, the per capita death rate (d) may increase. A decrease in b or an increase in d results in a lower per capita rate of increase (r).

The Logistic Growth Model

We can modify our mathematical model to incorporate changes in growth rate as the population size nears the carrying capacity. In the **logistic population growth** model, the per capita rate of increase approaches zero as the carrying capacity is reached.

To construct the logistic model, we start with the exponential population growth model and add an expression that reduces the per capita rate of increase as N increases. If the maximum sustainable population size (carrying capacity) is K, then K − N is the number of additional individuals the environment can support, and $(K - N)/K$ is the fraction of K that is still available for population growth. By multiplying the exponential rate of increase $r_{max}N$ by $(K - N)/K$, we modify the change in population size as N increases:

$$\frac{dN}{dt} = r_{max}N\ \frac{(K - N)}{K}$$

When N is small compared to K, the term $(K - N)/K$ is large, and the per capita rate of increase, $r_{max}(K - N)/K$, is close to the maximum rate of increase. But when N is large and resources are limiting, then $(K - N)/K$ is small, and so is the per capita rate of increase. When N equals K, the population stops

Table 53.3 Logistic Growth of a Hypothetical Population ($K = 1,500$)

Population Size (N)	Intrinsic Rate of Increase (r_{max})	$\dfrac{K-N}{K}$	Per Capita Rate of Increase: $r_{max}\left(\dfrac{K-N}{K}\right)$	Population Growth Rate:* $r_{max}N\left(\dfrac{K-N}{K}\right)$
25	1.0	0.98	0.98	+25
100	1.0	0.93	0.93	+93
250	1.0	0.83	0.83	+208
500	1.0	0.67	0.67	+333
750	1.0	0.50	0.50	+375
1,000	1.0	0.33	0.33	+333
1,500	1.0	0.00	0.00	0

*Rounded to the nearest whole number.

▲ **Figure 53.12 Population growth predicted by the logistic model.** The rate of population growth slows as population size (N) approaches the carrying capacity (K) of the environment. The red line shows logistic growth in a population where $r_{max} = 1.0$ and $K = 1,500$ individuals. For comparison, the blue line illustrates a population continuing to grow exponentially with the same r_{max}.

growing. **Table 53.3** shows calculations of population growth rate for a hypothetical population growing according to the logistic model, with $r_{max} = 1.0$ per individual per year. Notice that the overall population growth rate is highest, +375 individuals per year, when the population size is 750, or half the carrying capacity. At a population size of 750, the per capita rate of increase remains relatively high (one-half the maximum rate), but there are more reproducing individuals (N) in the population than at lower population sizes.

The logistic model of population growth produces a sigmoid (S-shaped) growth curve when N is plotted over time (the red line in **Figure 53.12**). New individuals are added to the population most rapidly at intermediate population sizes, when there is not only a breeding population of substantial size, but also lots of available space and other resources in the environment. The population growth rate slows dramatically as N approaches K.

Note that we haven't said anything yet about *why* the population growth rate slows as N approaches K. For a population's growth rate to decrease, either the birth rate *b* must decrease, the death rate *d* must increase, or both. Later in the chapter, we will consider some of the factors affecting these rates.

The Logistic Model and Real Populations

The growth of laboratory populations of some small animals, such as beetles and crustaceans, and of some microorganisms, such as paramecia, yeasts, and bacteria, fits an S-shaped curve fairly well under conditions of limited resources **(Figure 53.13a)**. These populations are grown in a constant environment lacking predators and competing species that may reduce growth of the populations, conditions that rarely occur in nature.

Some of the basic assumptions built into the logistic model clearly do not apply to all populations. The logistic model assumes that populations adjust instantaneously to growth and approach carrying capacity smoothly. In reality, there is often a lag time before the negative effects of an increasing population are realized. If food becomes limiting for a population, for instance, reproduction will decline eventually, but females may use their energy reserves to continue reproducing for a short time. This may cause the population to overshoot its carrying capacity temporarily, as shown for the water fleas in **Figure 53.13b**. If the population then drops below carrying capacity, there will be a delay in population growth until the increased number of offspring are actually born. Still other populations fluctuate greatly, making it difficult even to define carrying capacity. We will examine some possible reasons for such fluctuations later in the chapter.

The logistic model also incorporates the idea that regardless of population density, each individual added to a population has the same negative effect on population growth rate. However, some populations show an *Allee effect* (named after W. C. Allee, of the University of Chicago, who first described it), in which individuals may have a more difficult time surviving or reproducing if the population size is too small. For example, a single plant may be damaged by excessive wind if it is standing alone, but it would be protected in a clump of individuals.

The logistic model is a useful starting point for thinking about how populations grow and for constructing more complex models. The model is also important in conservation

(a) A *Paramecium* population in the lab. The growth of *Paramecium aurelia* in small cultures (black dots) closely approximates logistic growth (red curve) if the researcher maintains a constant environment.

(b) A *Daphnia* population in the lab. The growth of a population of water fleas (*Daphnia*) in a small laboratory culture (black dots) does not correspond well to the logistic model (red curve). This population overshoots the carrying capacity of its artificial environment before it settles down to an approximately stable population size.

biology for predicting how rapidly a particular population might increase in numbers after it has been reduced to a small size and for estimating sustainable harvest rates for fish and wildlife populations. Conservation biologists can use the model to estimate the critical size below which populations of certain organisms, such as the northern subspecies of the white rhinoceros (*Ceratotherium simum*), may become extinct **(Figure 53.14)**. Like any good starting hypothesis, the logistic model has stimulated research that has led to a better understanding of the factors affecting population growth.

The Logistic Model and Life Histories

The logistic model predicts different per capita growth rates for populations of low or high density relative to the carrying

▲ **Figure 53.14 White rhinoceros mother and calf.** The two animals pictured here are members of the southern subspecies, which has a population of more than 10,000 individuals. The northern subspecies is critically endangered, with a population of fewer than 25 individuals.

capacity of the environment. At high densities, each individual has few resources available, and the population grows slowly. At low densities, per capita resources are relatively abundant, and the population grows rapidly. Different life history features are favored under each condition. At high population density, selection favors adaptations that enable organisms to survive and reproduce with few resources. Competitive ability and efficient use of resources should be favored in populations that are at or near their carrying capacity. (Note that these are the traits we associated earlier with iteroparity.) At low population density, adaptations that promote rapid reproduction, such as the production of numerous, small offspring, should be favored.

Ecologists have attempted to connect these differences in favored traits at different population densities with the logistic growth model. Selection for life history traits that are sensitive to population density is known as ***K*-selection**, or density-dependent selection. In contrast, selection for life history traits that maximize reproductive success in uncrowded environments (low densities) is called ***r*-selection**, or density-independent selection. These names follow from the variables of the logistic equation. *K*-selection is said to operate in populations living at a density near the limit imposed by their resources (the carrying capacity, *K*), where competition among individuals is relatively strong. Mature trees growing in an old-growth forest are an example of *K*-selected organisms. In contrast, *r*-selection is said to maximize *r*, the per capita rate of increase, and occurs in environments in which population densities are well below carrying capacity or individuals face little competition. Such conditions are often found in disturbed habitats.

Like the concepts of semelparity and iteroparity, the concepts of *K*- and *r*-selection represent two extremes in a range of actual life histories. The framework of *K*- and *r*-selection, grounded in the idea of carrying capacity, has helped ecologists to propose alternative hypotheses of life history evolution. These alternative hypotheses, in turn, have stimulated more thorough study of how factors such as disturbance, stress, and the frequency of opportunities for successful reproduction affect the evolution of life histories. They have also forced ecologists to address the important question we alluded to earlier: Why does population growth rate decrease as population size approaches carrying capacity? Answering this question is the focus of the next section.

CONCEPT **53.5**

Many factors that regulate population growth are density dependent

In this section, we will apply biology's unifying theme of *feedback regulation* (see Chapter 1) to populations. What environmental factors keep populations from growing indefinitely? Why are some populations fairly stable in size, while others, such as the Soay sheep on Hirta Island, are not (see Figure 53.1)?

Population regulation is an area of ecology that has many practical applications. In agriculture, a farmer may want to reduce the abundance of insect pests or stop the growth of an invasive weed that is spreading rapidly. Conservation ecologists need to know what environmental factors create favorable feeding or breeding habitats for endangered species, such as the white rhinoceros and the whooping crane. Management programs based on population-regulating factors have helped prevent the extinction of many endangered species.

Population Change and Population Density

To understand why a population stops growing, it is helpful to study how the rates of birth, death, immigration, and emigration change as population density rises. If immigration and emigration offset each other, then a population grows when the birth rate exceeds the death rate and declines when the death rate exceeds the birth rate.

A birth rate or death rate that does *not* change with population density is said to be **density independent**. In a classic study of population regulation, Andrew Watkinson and John Harper, of the University of Wales, found that the mortality of dune fescue grass (*Vulpia membranacea*) is mainly due to physical factors that kill similar proportions of a local population, regardless of its density. For example, drought stress that arises when the roots of the grass are uncovered by shifting sands is a density-independent factor. In contrast, a death rate that rises as population density rises is said to be **density dependent**, as is a birth rate that falls with rising density. Watkinson and Harper found that reproduction by dune fescue declines as population density increases, in part because water or nutrients become more scarce. Thus, in this grass population, the key factors regulating birth rate are density dependent, while death rate is largely regulated by density-independent factors. **Figure 53.15** models how a population may stop increasing and reach equilibrium as a result of various combinations of density-dependent and density-independent regulation.

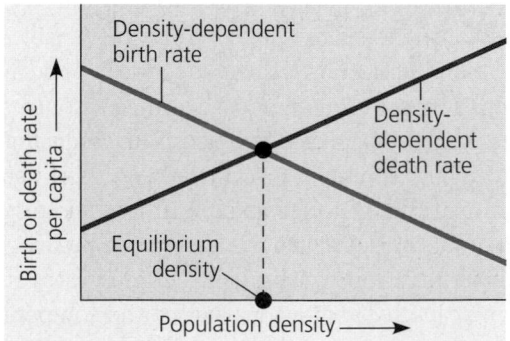

(a) Both birth rate and death rate change with population density.

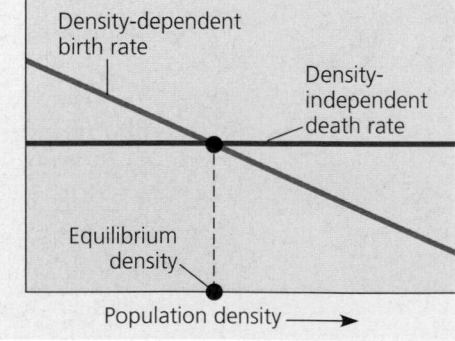

(b) Birth rate changes with population density while death rate is constant.

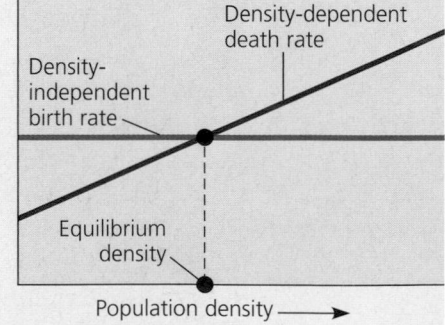

(c) Death rate changes with population density while birth rate is constant.

▲ **Figure 53.15 Determining equilibrium for population density.** This simple model considers only birth and death rates (immigration and emigration rates are assumed to be either zero or equal).

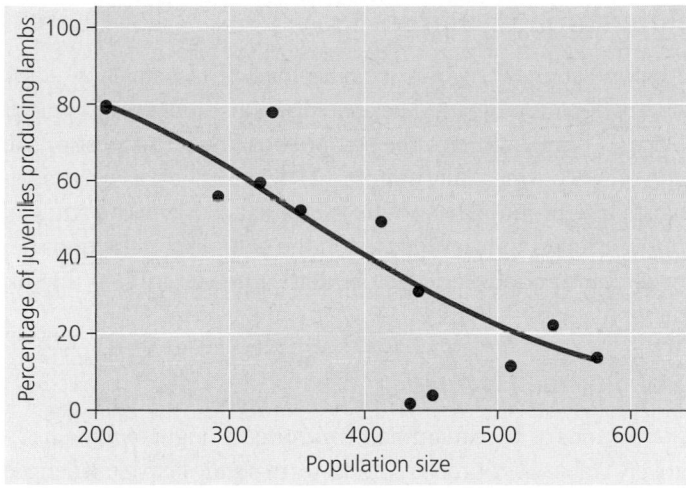

▲ **Figure 53.16 Decreased reproduction at high population densities.** Reproduction by juvenile Soay sheep on Hirta Island drops dramatically as population size increases.

Density-Dependent Population Regulation

Without some type of negative feedback between population density and the vital rates of birth and death, a population would never stop growing. Density-dependent regulation provides that feedback, operating through mechanisms that help to reduce birth rates and increase death rates, halting population growth.

Competition for Resources

In a crowded population, increasing population density intensifies competition for declining nutrients and other resources, resulting in a lower birth rate. Crowding can reduce reproduction by plants, as discussed earlier for dune fescue. Many animal populations also experience internal competition for food and other resources. On Hirta Island, ecologists have closely monitored the relationship between Soay sheep density and reproduction for many years. Their results show that the effects of increasing density on birth rate are strongest for the youngest sheep that reproduce, typically 1-year-old juveniles **(Figure 53.16)**.

Territoriality

In many vertebrates and some invertebrates, territoriality can limit population density. In this case, territory space becomes the resource for which individuals compete. Cheetahs, for example, are highly territorial, using chemical communication to warn other cheetahs of their territorial boundaries **(Figure 53.17a)**. Maintaining a territory increases the likelihood that a cheetah will capture enough food to reproduce. Oceanic birds, such as gannets, often nest on rocky islands to avoid predators **(Figure 53.17b)**. Up to a certain population density, most gannets can find a suitable

(a) Cheetahs stake out their territories with a chemical marker in urine.

(b) Gannets nest virtually a peck apart and defend their territories by calling and pecking at one another.

▲ **Figure 53.17 Territoriality.** In some animals, defense of territories provides negative feedback on population density.

nest site, but beyond that threshold, few additional birds breed successfully. Birds that cannot obtain a nesting spot do not reproduce. The presence of surplus, or nonbreeding, individuals is a good indication that territoriality is restricting population growth, as it does in many bird populations.

Disease

Population density can also influence the health and thus the survival of organisms. If the transmission rate of a particular disease depends on a certain level of crowding in a population, the disease's impact may be density dependent. Among plants, the severity of infection by fungal pathogens is often greater in locations where the density of the host plant population is higher. Animals, too, can experience an increased rate of infection by pathogens at high population densities. Steven Kohler and Wade Hoiland, of the Illinois Natural History Survey, showed that in caddis flies (*Brachycentrus americanus*, a stream-dwelling insect), peaks in disease-related mortality followed years of high insect abundance, leading to cyclic fluctuations in the density of the caddis fly population. In humans, the lung disease tuberculosis, which is caused by bacteria that spread through the air when an infected person sneezes or coughs, strikes a greater percentage of people living in densely populated cities than those in rural areas.

Predation

Predation may be an important cause of density-dependent mortality if a predator encounters and captures more food as the population density of the prey increases. As a prey population builds up, predators may feed preferentially on that species, consuming a higher percentage of individuals. For example, trout may concentrate for a few days on a particular species of insect that is emerging from its aquatic larval stage and then switch to eating another insect species as it becomes more abundant.

Toxic Wastes

The accumulation of toxic wastes can contribute to density-dependent regulation of population size. In laboratory cultures of microorganisms, metabolic by-products accumulate as the populations grow, poisoning the organisms within this limited, artificial environment. For example, ethanol accumulates as a by-product of yeast fermentation. The alcohol content of wine is usually less than 13% because that is the maximum concentration of ethanol that most wine-producing yeast cells can tolerate.

Intrinsic Factors

For some animal species, intrinsic (physiological) factors, rather than the extrinsic (environmental) factors we've just discussed, appear to regulate population size. For instance, white-footed mice in a small field enclosure will multiply, but eventually their reproductive rate will decline until the population ceases to grow. This drop in reproduction is associated with aggressive interactions that increase with population density, and it occurs even when food and shelter are provided in abundance. High population densities in mice can induce a stress syndrome in which hormonal changes delay sexual maturation, cause reproductive organs to shrink, and depress the immune system. In this case, high densities cause an increase in mortality and a decrease in birth rates. Similar effects of crowding occur in other wild rodent populations.

These various examples of population regulation by negative feedback show how increased densities cause population growth rates to decline by affecting reproduction, growth, and survivorship. But although negative feedback helps explain why populations stop growing, it does not address why some populations fluctuate dramatically while others remain relatively stable. This is the topic we address next.

Population Dynamics

All populations for which we have long-term data show some fluctuation in numbers. These fluctuations from year to year or place to place influence the seasonal or annual harvest of fish and other commercially important species. They also give ecologists insight into what controls population size. The study of **population dynamics** focuses on the complex interactions between biotic and abiotic factors that cause variation in the size of populations.

Stability and Fluctuation

Populations of large mammals were once thought to remain relatively stable over time, but long-term studies have challenged that idea. The numbers of Soay sheep on Hirta Island fluctuate greatly, rising or falling by more than half from one year to the next **(Figure 53.18)**. What causes the size of this population to change so dramatically? The most important factor appears to be the weather. Harsh weather, particularly cold, wet winters, weakens the sheep and decreases food availability, leading to a decrease in the size of the population. When sheep numbers are high, other factors, such as an increase in the density of parasites, also cause the population to shrink. Conversely, when sheep numbers are low and the weather is mild, food is readily available and the population grows quickly.

Like the Soay sheep population on Hirta, the moose population on Isle Royale in Lake Superior also fluctuates over time. In the case of the moose, predation is an additional factor that regulates the population. Moose from the mainland colonized the island around 1900 by walking across the frozen lake. Wolves, which rely on moose for most of their food, followed around 1950. Because the lake has not frozen over in recent years, both populations have been isolated from immigration and emigration. Despite this isolation, the moose population

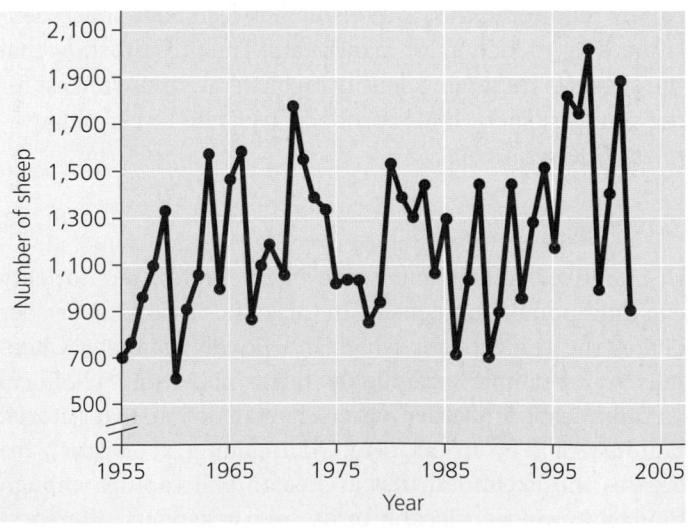

▲ Figure 53.18 **Variation in size of the Soay sheep population on Hirta Island, 1955–2002.**

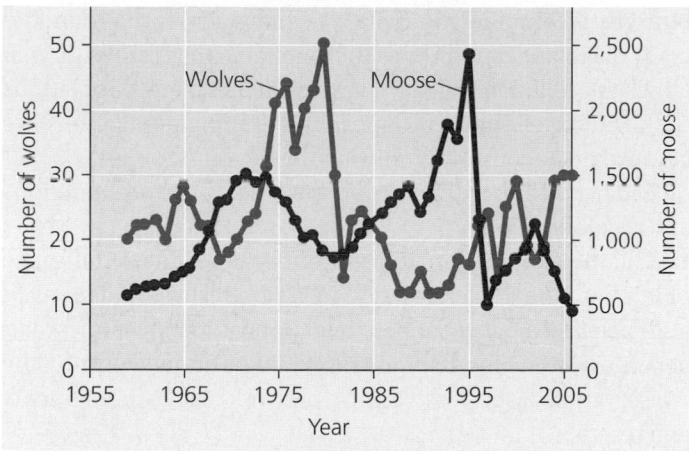

▲ Figure 53.19 Fluctuations in moose and wolf populations on Isle Royale, 1959–2006.

? *The first several moose reached Isle Royale in the early 1900s, and by 1925 the population on the island had grown to 2,000. Why do you think it was able to grow so quickly? What growth model best describes this initial growth?*

▲ Figure 53.20 Population cycles in the snowshoe hare and lynx. Population counts are based on the number of pelts sold by trappers to the Hudson Bay Company.

? *What do you observe about the relative timing of the peaks in lynx numbers and hare numbers? What might explain this observation?*

experienced two major increases and collapses during the last 45 years **(Figure 53.19).** The first collapse coincided with a peak in the numbers of wolves from 1975 to 1980. The second collapse, around 1995, coincided with harsh winter weather, which increased the energy needs of the animals and made it harder for the moose to find food under the deep snow.

Population Cycles: Scientific Inquiry

While many populations fluctuate at unpredictable intervals, others undergo regular boom-and-bust cycles. Some small herbivorous mammals, such as voles and lemmings, tend to have 3- to 4-year cycles, and some birds, such as ruffed grouse and ptarmigans, have 9- to 11-year cycles.

One striking example of population cycles is the 10-year cycling of snowshoe hares (*Lepus americanus*) and lynx (*Lynx canadensis*) in the far northern forests of Canada and Alaska. Lynx are predators that specialize in preying on snowshoe hares, so it is not surprising that lynx numbers rise and fall with the numbers of hares **(Figure 53.20).** But why do hare numbers rise and fall in 10-year cycles? Three main hypotheses have been proposed. First, the cycles may be caused by food shortage during winter. Hares eat the terminal twigs of small shrubs such as willow and birch in winter, although why this food supply might cycle in 10-year intervals is uncertain. Second, the cycles may be due to predator-prey interactions. Many predators other than lynx eat hares, and they may overexploit their prey. Third, the size of the hare population may vary with sunspot activity, which also undergoes cyclic changes. When sunspot activity is low, slightly less atmospheric ozone is produced, and slightly more UV radiation reaches Earth's surface. In response, plants produce more UV-blocking chemicals and fewer chemicals that deter herbivores, increasing the quality of the hares' food.

Let's consider the evidence for the hypotheses. If hare cycles are due to winter food shortage, then they should stop if extra food is provided to a field population. Researchers have conducted such experiments in the Yukon for 20 years—over two hare cycles. They have found that hare populations in the areas with extra food have increased about threefold in density but have continued to cycle in the same way as the unfed control populations. Thus, food supplies alone do not cause the hare cycle shown in Figure 53.20, so we can reject the first hypothesis.

Using radio collars, ecologists have tracked individual hares to determine why they died. Predators killed almost 90% of the hares in such studies, and none of the hares appeared to have died of starvation. These data support the second hypothesis. When ecologists excluded predators from one area with electric fences and excluded predators *and* provided food in another area, they found that the hare cycle is driven largely by excessive predation but that food availability also plays an important role, particularly in the winter. Perhaps better-fed hares are more likely to escape from predators.

To test the third hypothesis, ecologists compared the timing of hare cycles and sunspot activity. As predicted, periods of low sunspot activity were followed by peaks in the hare population. The results of all of these experiments suggest that both predation and sunspot activity may regulate the cycling of hare numbers and that food availability plays a less important role.

The availability of prey is the major factor influencing population changes for predators such as lynx, great-horned owls, and weasels, each of which depends heavily on a single prey species. When prey become scarce, predators often turn on one another. Coyotes kill both foxes and lynx, and great-horned owls kill smaller birds of prey as well as weasels, accelerating the collapse of the predator populations. Long-term experimental studies help to unravel the causes of such population cycles.

Immigration, Emigration, and Metapopulations

So far our discussion of population dynamics has focused mainly on the contributions of births and deaths. However, immigration and emigration also influence populations, particularly when a number of local populations are linked, forming a **metapopulation**. For example, immigration and emigration link the Belding's ground squirrel population we discussed earlier to other populations of the species, all of which make up a metapopulation.

Local populations in a metapopulation can be thought of as occupying discrete patches of suitable habitat in a sea of unsuitable habitat. The patches vary in size, quality, and isolation from other patches, factors that influence how many individuals move among the populations. Patches with many individuals, for instance, can supply more emigrants to other patches. If one population becomes extinct, the patch it occupied can be recolonized by immigrants from another population.

The Glanville fritillary (*Melitaea cinxia*) illustrates the movement of individuals between populations (**Figure 53.21**). This

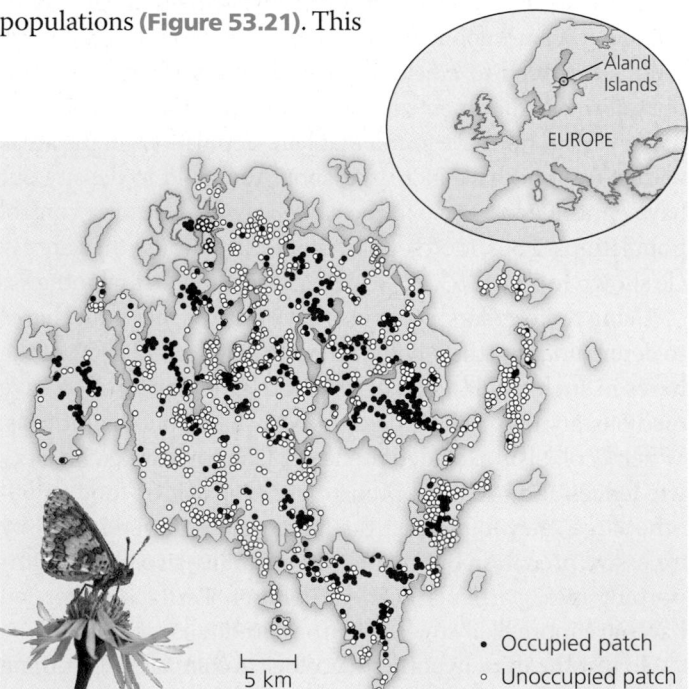

▲ **Figure 53.21 The Glanville fritillary: a metapopulation.** On the Åland Islands, local populations of this butterfly (filled circles) are found in only a fraction of the suitable habitat patches (open circles) at any given time. Individuals can move between local populations and colonize unoccupied patches.

• Occupied patch
○ Unoccupied patch

5 km

butterfly is found in about 500 meadows across the Åland Islands of Finland, but its potential habitat in the islands is much larger, approximately 4,000 suitable patches. New populations of the butterfly regularly appear and existing populations become extinct, constantly shifting the locations of the 500 colonized patches. The species persists in a balance of extinctions and recolonizations.

The metapopulation concept underscores the significance of immigration and emigration in the butterfly populations. It also helps ecologists understand population dynamics and gene flow in patchy habitats, providing a framework for the conservation of species living in a network of habitat fragments and reserves.

CONCEPT CHECK 53.5

1. Identify three density-dependent factors that limit population size, and explain how each exerts negative feedback.
2. Describe three attributes of habitat patches that could affect population density and rates of immigration and emigration.
3. **WHAT IF?** If you were studying an endangered species that, like the snowshoe hare, has a 10-year population cycle, how long would you need to study the species to determine if its population size is declining? Explain.

For suggested answers, see Appendix A.

CONCEPT 53.6

The human population is no longer growing exponentially but is still increasing rapidly

In the last few centuries, the human population has grown at an unprecedented rate, more like the elephant population in Kruger National Park (see Figure 53.11) than the fluctuating populations we considered in Concept 53.5. No population can grow indefinitely, however, and humans are no exception. In this last section of the chapter, we'll apply the concepts of population dynamics to the specific case of the human population.

The Global Human Population

The exponential growth model in Figure 53.10 approximates the human population explosion since 1650. Ours is a singular case; it is unlikely that any other population of large animals has ever sustained so much growth for so long (**Figure 53.22**). The human population increased relatively slowly until about 1650, at which time approximately 500 million people inhabited Earth. Our population doubled to 1 billion within the next two centuries, doubled again to 2 billion between 1850 and 1930, and

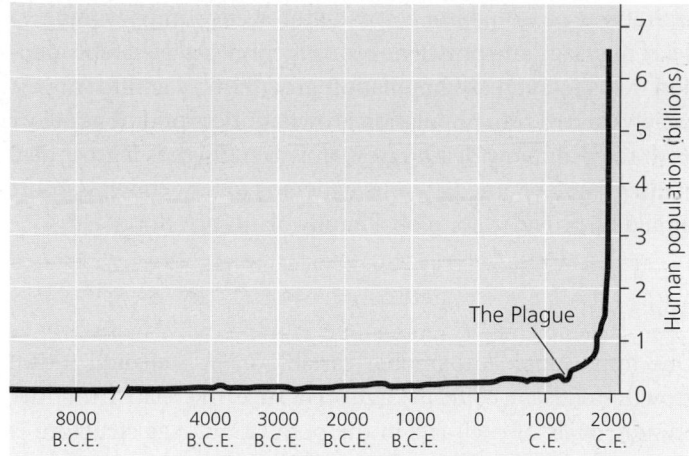

▲ **Figure 53.22 Human population growth (data as of 2006).** The global human population has grown almost continuously throughout history, but it skyrocketed after the Industrial Revolution. Though it is not apparent at this scale, the rate of population growth has slowed in recent decades, mainly as a result of decreased birth rates throughout the world.

doubled still again by 1975 to more than 4 billion. The global population is now more than 6.6 billion people and is increasing by about 75 million each year. The population grows by approximately 200,000 people each day, the equivalent of adding a city the size of Amarillo, Texas, or Madison, Wisconsin. It takes only about four years for world population growth to add the equivalent of another United States. Population ecologists predict a population of 7.8–10.8 billion people on Earth by the year 2050.

Though the global population is still growing, the *rate* of growth began to slow during the 1960s **(Figure 53.23)**. The annual rate of increase in the global population peaked at 2.2% in 1962; by 2005, it had declined to 1.15%. Current models project a continued decline in the annual growth rate to just over 0.4% by 2050, a rate that would still add 36 million more people per year if the population climbs to a projected 9 billion. The reduction in growth rate over the past four decades shows that the human population has departed from true exponential growth, which assumes a constant rate. This departure is the result of fundamental changes in population dynamics due to diseases, including AIDS, and to voluntary population control.

Regional Patterns of Population Change

So far we have described changes in the global population, but population dynamics vary widely from region to region. In a stable regional human population, birth rate equals death rate (disregarding the effects of immigration and emigration). Two possible configurations for a stable population are

Zero population growth = High birth rate − High death rate

or

Zero population growth = Low birth rate − Low death rate

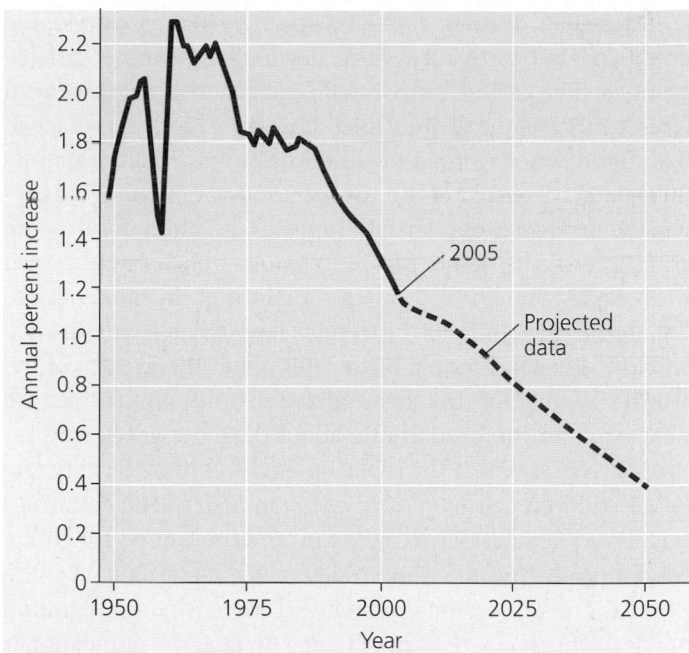

▲ **Figure 53.23 Annual percent increase in the global human population (data as of 2005).** The sharp dip in the 1960s is due mainly to a famine in China in which about 60 million people died.

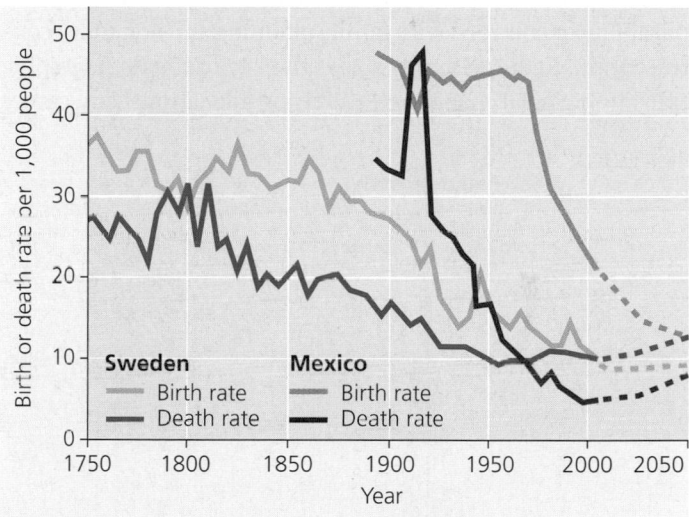

▲ **Figure 53.24 Demographic transition in Sweden and Mexico, 1750–2050 (data as of 2005).**

The movement toward the second configuration is called the **demographic transition**. **Figure 53.24** compares the demographic transition in one of the most industrialized countries, Sweden, and in a less industrialized country, Mexico. The demographic transition in Sweden took about 150 years, from 1810 to 1960, when birth rates finally approached death rates; in Mexico, the changes are projected to continue until sometime after 2050, almost the same length of time as they took in Sweden. Demographic transition is associated with an increase in the quality of health care and sanitation as well as improved access to education, especially for women.

After 1950, death rates declined rapidly in most developing countries, but birth rates have declined in a more variable manner. The fall in birth rate has been most dramatic in China. In 1970, the Chinese birth rate predicted an average of 5.9 children per woman per lifetime (total fertility rate); by 2004, largely because of the government's strict one-child policy, the expected total fertility rate was 1.7 children. In some countries of Africa, the transition to lower birth rates has also been rapid, though birth rates remain high in most of sub-Saharan Africa. In India, birth rates have fallen more slowly.

How do such variable birth rates affect the growth of the world's population? In industrialized nations, populations are near equilibrium (growth rate about 0.1% per year), with reproductive rates near the replacement level (total fertility rate = 2.1 children per female). In many industrialized countries, including Canada, Germany, Japan, and the United Kingdom, total reproductive rates are in fact *below* replacement. These populations will eventually decline if there is no immigration and if the birth rate does not change. In fact, the population is already declining in many eastern and central European countries. Most of the current global population growth (1.15% per year) is concentrated in less industrialized countries, where about 80% of the world's people now live.

A unique feature of human population growth is our potential ability to control it with family planning and voluntary contraception. Reduced family size is the key to the demographic transition. Social change and the rising educational and career aspirations of women in many cultures encourage women to delay marriage and postpone reproduction. Delayed reproduction helps to decrease population growth rates and to move a society toward zero population growth under conditions of low birth rates and low death rates. However, there is a great deal of disagreement among world leaders as to how much support should be provided for global family planning efforts.

Age Structure

One important demographic variable in present and future growth trends is a country's **age structure**, the relative number of individuals of each age in the population. Age structure is commonly graphed as "pyramids" like those in **Figure 53.25**. For Afghanistan, the pyramid is bottom-heavy, skewed toward young individuals who will grow up and may sustain the explosive growth with their own reproduction. The age structure for the United States is relatively even until the older, post-reproductive ages, except for a bulge that corresponds to the "baby boom" that lasted for about two decades after the end of World War II. Even though couples born during those years have had an average of fewer than two children, the nation's overall birth rate still exceeds the death rate because so many "boomers" and their offspring are still of reproductive age. Moreover, although the current total reproductive rate in the United States is 2.1 children per woman—approximately replacement rate—the population is projected to grow slowly

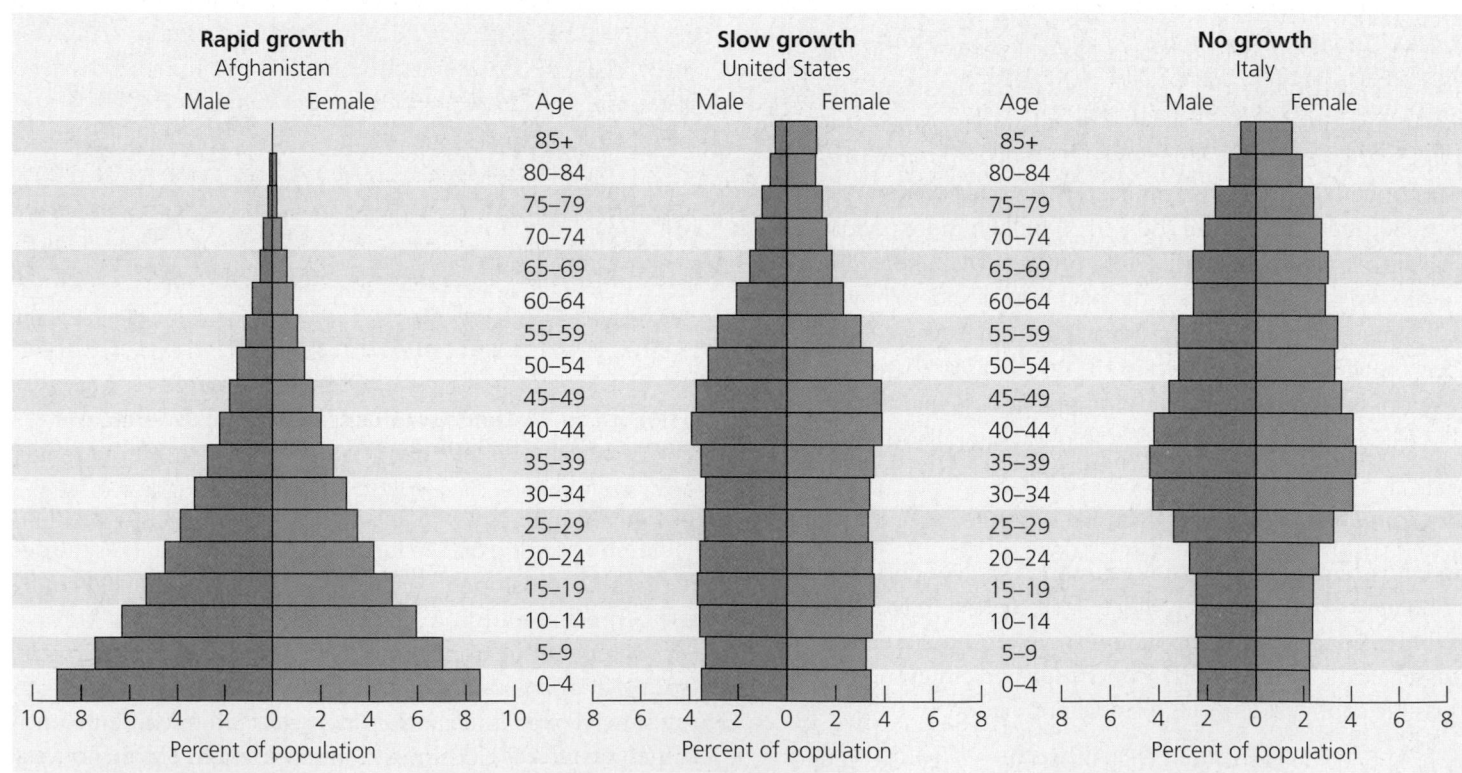

▲ **Figure 53.25 Age-structure pyramids for the human population of three countries (data as of 2005).** As of 2007, the annual rate of population growth was approximately 2.6% in Afghanistan, 0.9% in the United States, and 0.0% in Italy.

through 2050 as a result of immigration. For Italy, the pyramid has a small base, indicating that individuals younger than reproductive age are relatively underrepresented in the population. This situation contributes to the projection of a population decrease in Italy.

Age-structure diagrams not only predict a population's growth trends but can also illuminate social conditions. Based on the diagrams in Figure 53.25, we can predict, for instance, that employment and education opportunities will continue to be a significant problem for Afghanistan in the foreseeable future. The large number of young entering the Afghan population could also be a source of continuing social and political unrest, particularly if their needs and aspirations are not met. In Italy and the United States, a decreasing proportion of younger working-age people will soon be supporting an increasing population of retired "boomers." In the United States, this demographic feature has made the future of Social Security and Medicare a major political issue. Understanding age structures can help us plan for the future.

Infant Mortality and Life Expectancy

Infant mortality, the number of infant deaths per 1,000 live births, and *life expectancy at birth*, the predicted average length of life at birth, vary widely among different human populations. These differences reflect the quality of life faced by children at birth and influence the reproductive choices parents make. If infant mortality is high, then parents are likely to have more children to ensure that some of them reach adulthood. **Figure 53.26** contrasts average infant mortality and life expectancy in the industrialized and less industrialized countries of the world in 2005. While these averages are markedly different, they do not capture the broad range of the human condition. In 2005, for example, the infant mortality rate was 163 (16.3%) in Afghanistan

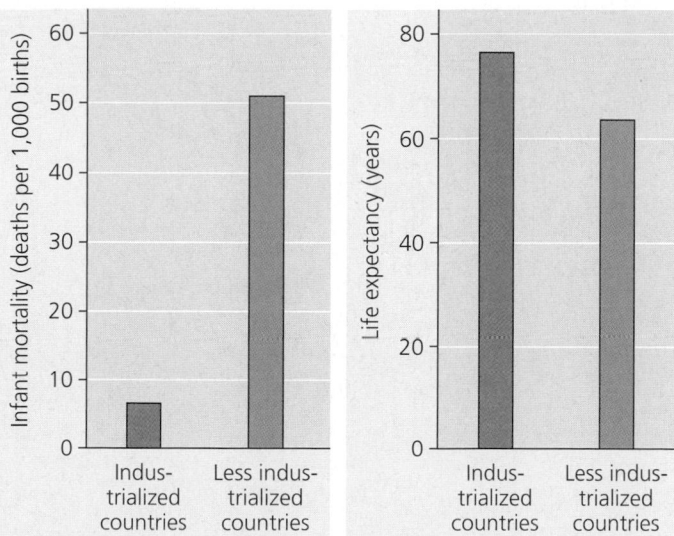

▲ **Figure 53.26 Infant mortality and life expectancy at birth in industrialized and less industrialized countries (data as of 2005).**

but only 3 (0.3%) in Japan, while life expectancy at birth was 43 years in Afghanistan and 81 years in Japan. Although global life expectancy has been increasing since about 1950, more recently it has dropped in a number of regions, including countries of the former Soviet Union and in sub-Saharan Africa. In these regions, the combination of social upheaval, decaying infrastructure, and infectious diseases such as AIDS and tuberculosis is reducing life expectancy. In the South African country of Angola, for instance, life expectancy in 2005 was approximately 39 years, about half that in Japan, Sweden, Italy, and Spain.

Global Carrying Capacity

No ecological question is more important than the future size of the human population. The projected worldwide population size depends on assumptions about future changes in birth and death rates. As we noted earlier, population ecologists project a global population of approximately 7.8–10.8 billion people in 2050. In other words, without some catastrophe, an estimated 1–4 billion people will be added to the population in the next four decades because of the momentum of population growth. But just how many humans can the biosphere support? Will the world be overpopulated in 2050? Is it *already* overpopulated?

Estimates of Carrying Capacity

For over three centuries, scientists have attempted to estimate the human carrying capacity of Earth. The first known estimate, 13.4 billion, was made in 1679 by Anton van Leeuwenhoek, the discoverer of protists (see Chapter 28). Since then, estimates have varied from less than 1 billion to more than 1,000 billion (1 trillion), with an average of 10–15 billion.

Carrying capacity is difficult to estimate, and the scientists who provide these estimates use different methods to get their answers. Some current researchers use curves like that produced by the logistic equation (see Figure 53.12) to predict the future maximum of the human population. Others generalize from existing "maximum" population density and multiply this number by the area of habitable land. Still others base their estimates on a single limiting factor, such as food, and consider many variables, including the amount of available farmland, the average yield of crops, the prevalent diet—vegetarian or meat-based— and the number of calories needed per person per day.

Limits on Human Population Size

A more comprehensive approach to estimating the carrying capacity of Earth is to recognize that humans have multiple constraints: We need food, water, fuel, building materials, and other resources, such as clothing and transportation. The **ecological footprint** concept summarizes the aggregate land and water area required by each person, city, or nation to produce all the resources it consumes and to absorb all the waste it generates.

One way to estimate the ecological footprint of the entire human population is to add up all the ecologically productive land on the planet and divide by the population. This calculation yields approximately 2 hectares (ha) per person (1 ha = 2.47 acres). Reserving some land for parks and conservation means reducing this allotment to 1.7 ha per person—the benchmark for comparing actual ecological footprints. Anyone who consumes resources that require more than 1.7 ha to produce is said to be using an unsustainable share of Earth's resources. A typical ecological footprint for a person in the United States is about 10 ha.

Ecologists sometimes calculate ecological footprints using other currencies besides land area. For instance, the amount of photosynthesis that occurs on Earth is finite, constrained by the amount of land and sea area and by the sun's radiation. Scientists recently studied the extent to which people around the world consume seven types of photosynthetic products: plant foods, wood for building and fuel, paper, fiber, meat, milk, and eggs (the last three based on estimates of how much plant material goes into their production). **Figure 53.27** shows that areas with high population densities, such as China and India, have high consumption rates. However, areas of much lower population density but higher *per capita* consumption, such as parts of the United States and Europe, have equally high rates, as much as 400 times the rate at which photosynthetic products are produced locally. The combination of population density *and* resource use per person determines our global ecological footprint.

We can only speculate about Earth's ultimate carrying capacity for the human population or about what factors will eventually limit our growth. Perhaps food will be the main fac-

tor. Malnutrition and famine are common in some regions, but they result mainly from unequal distribution of food rather than inadequate production. So far, technological improvements in agriculture have allowed food supplies to keep up with global population growth. However, the principles of energy flow through ecosystems (explained in Chapter 55) tell us that environments can support a larger number of herbivores than carnivores. If everyone ate as much meat as the wealthiest people in the world, less than half of the present world population could be fed by current food harvests.

Perhaps we humans will eventually be limited by suitable space, like the gannets on oceanic islands. Certainly, as our population grows, the conflict over how space is utilized will intensify, and agricultural land will be developed for housing. There seem to be few limits, however, on how closely humans can be crowded together, as long as adequate food and water are provided to them and space is available to dispose of their waste.

Humans could also run out of nonrenewable resources, such as certain metals and fossil fuels. The demands of many populations have already far exceeded the local and even regional supplies of one renewable resource—fresh water. More than 1 billion people do not have access to sufficient water to meet their basic sanitation needs. It is also possible that the human population will eventually be limited by the capacity of the environment to absorb its wastes. In such cases, Earth's current human occupants could lower the planet's long-term carrying capacity for future generations.

Some optimists have suggested that because of our ability to develop technology, human population growth has no practical limits. Technology has undoubtedly increased Earth's

Log (g carbon/year)

13.4

9.8

5.8

Not analyzed

▲ **Figure 53.27 The amount of photosynthetic products that humans use around the world.** The unit of measurement is the logarithm of the number of grams of photosynthetic products consumed each year. The greatest usage is in places where population density is high or where people consume the most resources individually (high per capita consumption).

carrying capacity for humans, but as we have emphasized, no population can continue to grow indefinitely. After reading this chapter, you should realize that there is no single carrying capacity for the human population on Earth. How many people our planet can sustain depends on the quality of life each of us enjoys and the distribution of wealth across people and nations, topics of great concern and political debate. Unlike other organisms, we can decide whether zero population growth will be attained through social changes based on human choices or through increased mortality due to resource limitation, plagues, war, and environmental degradation.

Chapter 53 Review

SUMMARY OF KEY CONCEPTS

CONCEPT 53.1

Dynamic biological processes influence population density, dispersion, and demographics (pp. 1174–1179)

▶ **Density and Dispersion** Population density—the number of individuals per unit area or volume—results from the interplay of births, deaths, immigration, and emigration. Environmental and social factors influence the dispersion of individuals.

Patterns of dispersion

Clumped

Uniform

Random

▶ **Demographics** Populations increase from births and immigration and decrease from deaths and emigration. Life tables, survivorship curves, and reproductive tables summarize specific demographic trends.

MEDIA
Activity Techniques for Estimating Population Density and Size
Activity Investigating Survivorship Curves

CONCEPT 53.2

Life history traits are products of natural selection (pp. 1179–1181)

▶ Life history traits are evolutionary outcomes reflected in the development, physiology, and behavior of an organism.

▶ **Evolution and Life History Diversity** Big-bang, or semelparous, organisms reproduce once and die. Iteroparous organisms produce offspring repeatedly.

▶ **"Trade-offs" and Life Histories** Life history traits such as brood size, age at maturity, and parental caregiving represent trade-offs between conflicting demands for time, energy, and nutrients.

CONCEPT 53.3

The exponential model describes population growth in an idealized, unlimited environment (pp. 1181–1183)

▶ **Per Capita Rate of Increase** If immigration and emigration are ignored, a population's growth rate (the per capita rate of increase) equals birth rate minus death rate.

▶ **Exponential Growth** The exponential growth equation $dN/dt = r_{max}N$ represents a population's potential growth in an unlimited environment, where r_{max} is the maximum per capita, or intrinsic, rate of increase and N is the number of individuals in the population.

$$\frac{dN}{dt} = r_{max}N$$

Population size (N)

Number of generations

CONCEPT 53.4

The logistic model describes how a population grows more slowly as it nears its carrying capacity (pp. 1183–1186)

▶ Exponential growth cannot be sustained for long in any population. A more realistic population model limits growth by incorporating carrying capacity (K), the maximum population size the environment can support.

▶ **The Logistic Growth Model** According to the logistic equation $dN/dt = r_{max}N(K - N)/K$, growth levels off as population size approaches the carrying capacity.

K = carrying capacity

Population size (N)

$$\frac{dN}{dt} = r_{max} N \left(\frac{K - N}{K}\right)$$

Number of generations

▶ **The Logistic Model and Real Populations** The logistic model fits few real populations perfectly, but it is useful for estimating possible growth.

▶ **The Logistic Model and Life Histories** Two hypothetical but controversial life history patterns are *K*-selection, or density-dependent selection, and *r*-selection, or density-independent selection.

CONCEPT 53.5

Many factors that regulate population growth are density dependent (pp. 1186–1190)

▶ **Population Change and Population Density** In density-dependent population regulation, death rates rise and birth rates fall with increasing density. In density-independent population regulation, birth and death rates do not change with increasing density.

▶ **Density-Dependent Population Regulation** Density-dependent changes in birth and death rates curb population increase through negative feedback and can eventually stabilize a population near its carrying capacity. Density-dependent limiting factors include intraspecific competition for limited food or space, increased predation, disease, stress due to crowding, and buildup of toxic substances.

▶ **Population Dynamics** Because changing environmental conditions periodically disrupt them, all populations exhibit some size fluctuations. Many populations undergo regular boom-and-bust cycles that are influenced by complex interactions between biotic and abiotic factors. A metapopulation is a group of populations linked by immigration and emigration.

MEDIA

Biology Labs On-Line PopulationEcologyLab

CONCEPT 53.6

The human population is no longer growing exponentially but is still increasing rapidly (pp. 1190–1195)

▶ **The Global Human Population** Since about 1650, the global human population has grown exponentially, but within the last 40 years, the rate of growth has fallen by nearly 50%. Differences in age structure show that while some nations' populations are growing rapidly, those of others are stable or declining in size. Infant mortality rates and life expectancy at birth differ markedly between industrialized and less industrialized countries.

▶ **Global Carrying Capacity** The carrying capacity of Earth for humans is uncertain. Ecological footprint is the aggregate land and water area needed to produce all the resources a person or group of people consume and to absorb all of their waste. It is one measure of how close we are to the carrying capacity of Earth. With a world population of more than 6.6 billion people, we are already using many resources in an unsustainable manner.

MEDIA

Activity Human Population Growth
Activity Analyzing Age-Structure Pyramids
GraphIt! Age Pyramids and Population Growth
Biology Labs On-Line DemographyLab

TESTING YOUR KNOWLEDGE

SELF-QUIZ

1. The observation that members of a population are uniformly distributed suggests that
   a. the size of the area occupied by the population is increasing.
   b. resources are distributed unevenly.
   c. the members of the population are competing for access to a resource.
   d. the members of the population are neither attracted to nor repelled by one another.
   e. the density of the population is low.

2. Population ecologists follow the fate of same-age cohorts to
   a. determine a population's carrying capacity.
   b. determine if a population is regulated by density-dependent processes.
   c. determine the birth rate and death rate of each group in a population.
   d. determine the factors that regulate the size of a population.
   e. determine if a population's growth is cyclic.

3. According to the logistic growth equation

$$\frac{dN}{dt} = r_{max}N \frac{(K - N)}{K}$$

   a. the number of individuals added per unit time is greatest when *N* is close to zero.
   b. the per capita growth rate (*r*) increases as *N* approaches *K*.
   c. population growth is zero when *N* equals *K*.
   d. the population grows exponentially when *K* is small.
   e. the birth rate (*b*) approaches zero as *N* approaches *K*.

4. A population's carrying capacity
   a. can be accurately calculated using the logistic growth model.
   b. generally remains constant over time.
   c. increases as the per capita growth rate (*r*) decreases.
   d. may change as environmental conditions change.
   e. can never be exceeded.

5. Which pair of terms most accurately describes life history traits for a stable population of wolves?
   a. semelparous; *r*-selected
   b. semelparous; *K*-selected
   c. iteroparous; *r*-selected
   d. iteroparous; *K*-selected
   e. iteroparous; *N*-selected

6. During exponential growth, a population always
   a. grows by thousands of individuals.
   b. grows at its maximum per capita rate.
   c. quickly reaches its carrying capacity.
   d. cycles through time.
   e. loses some individuals to emigration.

7. Scientific study of the population cycles of the snowshoe hare and its predator, the lynx, has revealed that
   a. the prey population is controlled by predators alone.
   b. hares and lynx are so mutually dependent that each species cannot survive without the other.
   c. multiple biotic and abiotic factors contribute to the cycling of the hare and lynx populations.
   d. both hare and lynx populations are regulated mainly by abiotic factors.
   e. the hare population is *r*-selected and the lynx population is *K*-selected.

8. Based on current growth rates, Earth's human population in 2010 will be closest to
   a. 2 million.   d. 7 billion.
   b. 3 billion.   e. 10 billion.
   c. 4 billion.

9. Which of the following statements about human population in industrialized countries is *incorrect*?
   a. Average family size is relatively small.
   b. The population has undergone the demographic transition.
   c. Life history is *r*-selected.
   d. The survivorship curve is Type I.
   e. Age distribution is relatively uniform.

10. A recent study of ecological footprints concluded that
    a. Earth's carrying capacity for humans is about 10 billion.
    b. Earth's carrying capacity would increase if per capita meat consumption increased.
    c. current demand by industrialized countries for resources is much smaller than the ecological footprint of those countries.
    d. the ecological footprint of the United States is large because per capita resource use is high.
    e. it is not possible for technological improvements to increase Earth's carrying capacity for humans.

11. **DRAW IT** To estimate which age cohort in a population of females produces the most female offspring, you need information about the number of offspring produced per capita within that cohort and the number of individuals alive in the cohort. Make this estimate for Belding's ground squirrels by multiplying the number of females alive at the start of the year (column 2 in Table 53.1) by the average number of female offspring produced per female (column 5 in Table 53.2). Draw a bar graph with female age in years on the *x*-axis (0–1, 1–2, and so on) and total number of female offspring produced for each age cohort on the *y*-axis. Which cohort of female Belding's ground squirrels produces the most female young?

For Self-Quiz answers, see Appendix A.

MEDIA Visit **www.campbellbiology.com** for a Practice Test.

EVOLUTION CONNECTION

12. Write a paragraph contrasting the conditions that favor the evolution of semelparous (one-time) reproduction versus iteroparous (repeated) reproduction.

SCIENTIFIC INQUIRY

13. You are testing the hypothesis that the population density of a particular plant species influences the rate at which a pathogenic fungus infects the plant. Because the fungus causes visible scars on the leaves, you can easily determine whether a plant is infected. Design an experiment to test your hypothesis. Include your experimental treatments and control, the data you will collect, and the results expected if your hypothesis is correct.

SCIENCE, TECHNOLOGY, AND SOCIETY

14. Many people regard the rapid population growth of less industrialized countries as our most serious environmental problem. Others think that the population growth in industrialized countries, though smaller, is actually a greater environmental threat. What problems result from population growth in (a) less industrialized countries and (b) industrialized nations? Which do you think is a greater threat, and why?

Community Ecology

54

▲ Figure 54.1 **How many interactions between species are occurring in this scene?**

KEY CONCEPTS

54.1 Community interactions are classified by whether they help, harm, or have no effect on the species involved

54.2 Dominant and keystone species exert strong controls on community structure

54.3 Disturbance influences species diversity and composition

54.4 Biogeographic factors affect community biodiversity

54.5 Community ecology is useful for understanding pathogen life cycles and controlling human disease

OVERVIEW

A Sense of Community

On your next walk through a park or in the woods, or even across campus, look for evidence of interactions between different species. You may observe birds using trees as nesting sites, bees pollinating flowers, spiders trapping insects in their webs, or ferns growing in shade provided by trees—a tiny sample of the many interactions between species that exist in any ecological theater.

Some ecological interactions are more obvious than others. At first glance, **Figure 54.1** depicts a simple interaction between an herbivore, a hornworm caterpillar, and its preferred food, a tomato plant. But the white objects on the caterpillar's back are telltale signs of an interaction between the caterpillar and a third species, a parasitic wasp. The wasp lays its eggs inside the caterpillar, and the larvae that emerge from the eggs feed on the caterpillar's tissues. The larvae then develop into adult wasps inside the white cocoons on their host's back. This interaction will eventually kill the caterpillar.

In Chapter 53, you learned how individuals within a population can affect other individuals of the same species. This chapter will examine ecological interactions between populations of different species. A group of populations of different species living close enough to interact is called a biological **community**. Ecologists define the boundaries of a particular community to fit their research questions: They might study the community of decomposers and other organisms living on a rotting log, the benthic community in Lake Superior, or the community of trees and shrubs in Shenandoah National Park.

We begin this chapter by exploring the kinds of interactions that occur between species in a community. We then consider several of the factors that are most significant in structuring a community—in determining how many species there are, which particular species are present, and the relative abundance of these species. Finally, we will apply some of the principles of community ecology to the study of human disease.

CONCEPT 54.1

Community interactions are classified by whether they help, harm, or have no effect on the species involved

Some key relationships in the life of an organism are its interactions with individuals of other species in the community. These **interspecific interactions** include competition, predation, herbivory, and symbiosis (including parasitism, mutualism, and commensalism). In this section, we will define and describe each of these interactions, recognizing that ecologists do not always agree on the precise boundaries of each type of interaction.

We will use the symbols + and − to indicate how each interspecific interaction affects the survival and reproduction of the two species engaged in the interaction. For example, predation is a $+/-$ interaction, with a positive effect on the survival and reproduction of the predator population and a negative effect on that of the prey population. Mutualism is a $+/+$ interaction because the survival and reproduction of each species is increased in the presence of the other. A 0 indicates that a population is not affected by the interaction in any known way.

Historically, most ecological research has focused on interactions that have a negative effect on at least one species, such as competition and predation. However, positive interactions are ubiquitous, and their contributions to community structure are the subject of considerable study today.

Competition

Interspecific competition is a $-/-$ interaction that occurs when individuals of different species compete for a resource that limits their growth and survival. For instance, weeds growing in a garden compete with garden plants for soil nutrients and water. Grasshoppers and bison in the Great Plains compete for the grass they both eat. Lynx and foxes in the northern forests of Alaska and Canada compete for prey such as snowshoe hares. In contrast, some resources, such as oxygen, are rarely in short supply; thus, although most species use this resource, they do not usually compete for it.

Competitive Exclusion

What happens in a community over time when two species directly compete for limited resources? In 1934, the Russian ecologist G. F. Gause studied this question in laboratory experiments with two closely related species of ciliated protists, *Paramecium aurelia* and *Paramecium caudatum*. He cultured the species under stable conditions, adding a constant amount of food every day. When Gause grew the two species in separate cultures, each population grew rapidly and then leveled off at what was apparently the carrying capacity of the culture (see Figure 53.13a for an illustration of the logistic growth of *P. aurelia*). But when Gause cultured the two species together, *P. caudatum* was driven to extinction in the culture. Gause inferred that *P. aurelia* had a competitive edge in obtaining food, and he concluded that two species competing for the same limiting resources cannot coexist in the same place. In the absence of disturbance, one species will use the resources more efficiently and thus reproduce more rapidly than the other. Even a slight reproductive advantage will eventually lead to local elimination of the inferior competitor, an outcome called **competitive exclusion**.

Ecological Niches

The sum of a species' use of the biotic and abiotic resources in its environment is called the species' **ecological niche**. American ecologist Eugene Odum used the following analogy to explain the niche concept: If an organism's habitat is its "address," the niche is the organism's "profession." Put another way, an organism's niche is its ecological role—how it "fits into" an ecosystem. For example, the niche of a tropical tree lizard consists of, among many components, the temperature range it tolerates, the size of branches on which it perches, the time of day when it is active, and the sizes and kinds of insects it eats.

We can use the niche concept to restate the principle of competitive exclusion: Two species cannot coexist permanently in a community if their niches are identical. However, ecologically similar species *can* coexist in a community if there are one or more significant differences in their niches. When competition between species with identical niches does not lead to local extinction of either species, it is generally because one species' niche becomes modified. In other words, evolution by natural selection can result in one of the species using a different set of resources. The differentiation of niches that enables similar species to coexist in a community is called **resource partitioning (Figure 54.2)**. You can think of resource partitioning in a community as "the ghost of competition past"—the indirect evidence of earlier interspecific competition resolved by the evolution of niche differentiation.

As a result of competition, a species' *fundamental niche*, which is the niche potentially occupied by that species, is often different from its *realized niche*, the portion of its fundamental niche that it actually occupies in a particular environment.

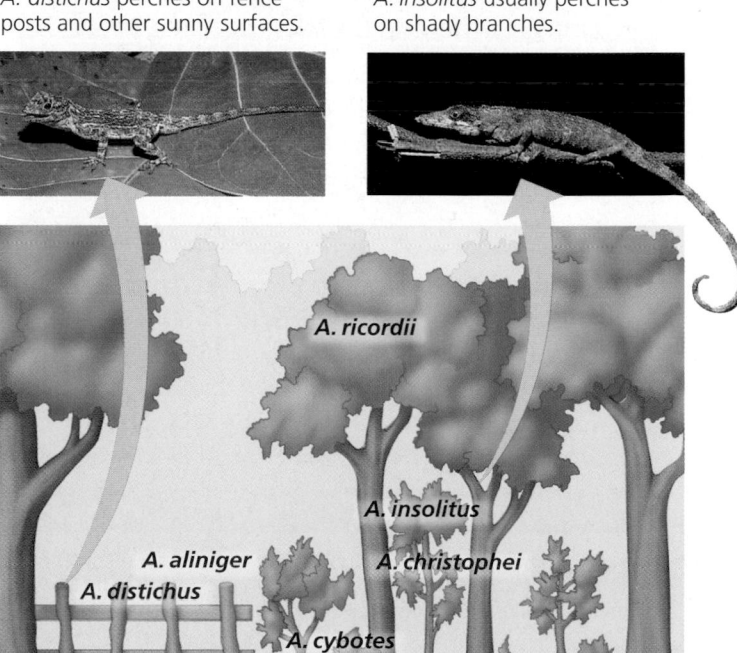

A. distichus perches on fence posts and other sunny surfaces.

A. insolitus usually perches on shady branches.

A. ricordii

A. insolitus

A. aliniger

A. christophei

A. distichus

A. cybotes

A. etheridgei

▲ **Figure 54.2 Resource partitioning among Dominican Republic lizards.** Seven species of *Anolis* lizards live in close proximity, and all feed on insects and other small arthropods. However, competition for food is reduced because each lizard species has a different preferred perch, thus occupying a distinct niche.

Ecologists can identify the fundamental niche of a species by testing the range of conditions in which it grows and reproduces in the absence of competitors. They can also test whether a potential competitor limits a species' realized niche by removing the competitor and seeing if the first species expands into the newly available space (**Figure 54.3**). The classic

experiment depicted in the figure clearly showed that competition from one barnacle species kept a second barnacle species from occupying part of its fundamental niche.

Character Displacement

Closely related species whose populations are sometimes allopatric (geographically separate; see Chapter 24) and sometimes sympatric (geographically overlapping) provide more evidence for the importance of competition in structuring communities. In some cases, the allopatric populations of such species are morphologically similar and use similar resources. By contrast, sympatric populations, which would potentially compete for resources, show differences in body structures and in the resources they use. This tendency for characteristics to diverge more in sympatric populations of two species than in allopatric populations of the same two species is called **character displacement**. An example of character displacement is the variation in beak size between different populations of the Galápagos finches *Geospiza fuliginosa* and *Geospiza fortis* (**Figure 54.4**).

▼ Figure 54.3 Inquiry

Can a species' niche be influenced by interspecific competition?

EXPERIMENT Ecologist Joseph Connell studied two barnacle species— *Chthamalus stellatus* and *Balanus balanoides*—that have a stratified distribution on rocks along the coast of Scotland. *Chthamalus* is usually found higher on the rocks than *Balanus*. To determine whether the distribution of *Chthamalus* is the result of interspecific competition with *Balanus*, Connell removed *Balanus* from the rocks at several sites.

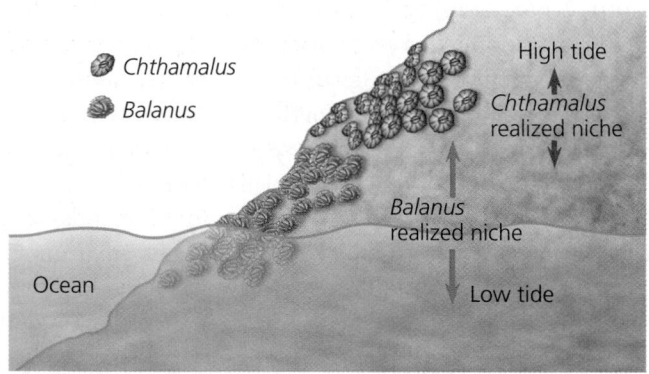

RESULTS *Chthamalus* spread into the region formerly occupied by *Balanus*.

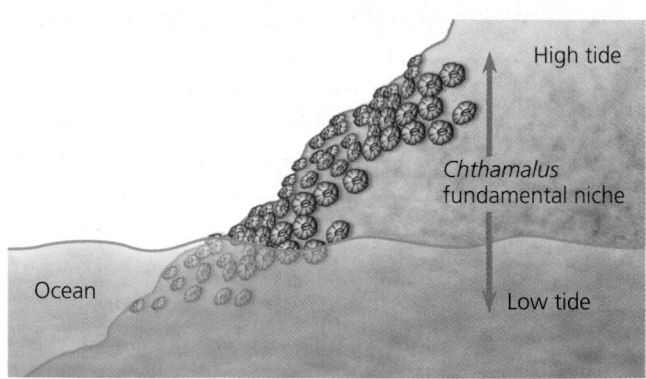

CONCLUSION Interspecific competition makes the realized niche of *Chthamalus* much smaller than its fundamental niche.

SOURCE J. H. Connell, The influence of interspecific competition and other factors on the distribution of the barnacle *Chthamalus stellatus*, *Ecology* 42:710–723 (1961).

WHAT IF? Other observations showed that *Balanus* cannot survive high on the rocks because it dries out during low tides. How would *Balanus*'s realized niche compare with its fundamental niche?

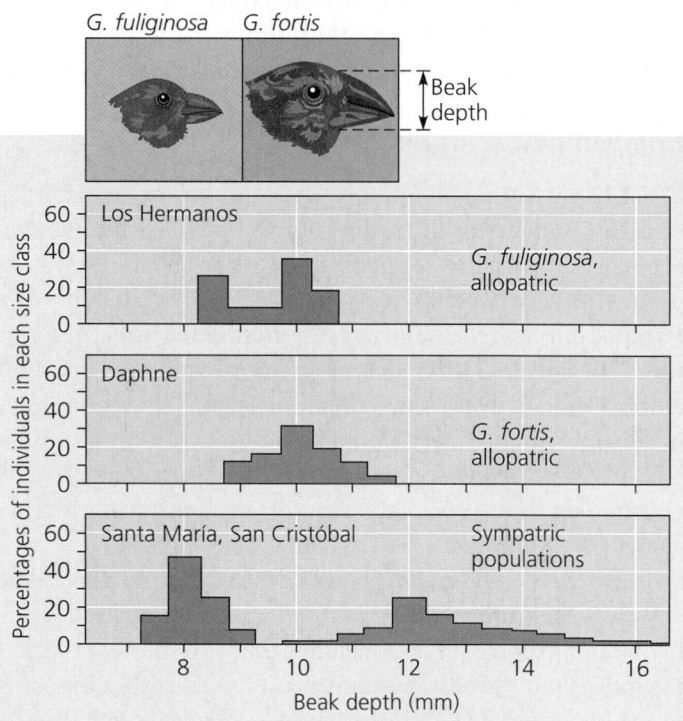

▲ **Figure 54.4 Character displacement: indirect evidence of past competition.** Allopatric populations of *Geospiza fuliginosa* and *Geospiza fortis* on Los Hermanos and Daphne Islands have similar beak morphologies (top two graphs) and presumably eat similarly sized seeds. However, where the two species are sympatric on Santa María and San Cristóbal, *G. fuliginosa* has a shallower, smaller beak and *G. fortis* a deeper, larger one (bottom graph), adaptations that favor eating different sizes of seeds.

? *Suppose that the sympatric populations of both finch species colonized a new island that contained seeds of only one size. What would you expect to happen to the differences in beak size over time? Explain your reasoning.*

Predation

Predation refers to a $+/-$ interaction between species in which one species, the predator, kills and eats the other, the prey. Though the term *predation* generally elicits such images as a lion attacking and eating an antelope, it applies to a wide range of interactions. An animal that kills a plant by eating the plant's tissues can also be considered a predator. Because eating and avoiding being eaten are prerequisite to reproductive success, the adaptations of both predators and prey tend to be refined through natural selection.

Many important feeding adaptations of predators are both obvious and familiar. Most predators have acute senses that enable them to locate and identify potential prey. In addition, many predators have adaptations such as claws, teeth, fangs, stingers, or poison that help them catch and subdue the or-

ganisms on which they feed. Rattlesnakes and other pit vipers, for example, find their prey with a pair of heat-sensing organs located between their eyes and nostrils (see Figure 50.5a), and they kill small birds and mammals by injecting them with toxins through their fangs. Predators that pursue their prey are generally fast and agile, whereas those that lie in ambush are often disguised in their environments.

Just as predators possess adaptations for capturing prey, prey animals have adaptations that help them avoid being eaten. Some common behavioral defenses are hiding, fleeing, and forming herds or schools. Active self-defense is less common, though some large grazing mammals vigorously defend their young from predators such as lions. Other behavioral defenses include alarm calls that summon many individuals of the prey species, which then mob the predator.

Animals also display a variety of morphological and physiological defensive adaptations. For example, **cryptic coloration**, or camouflage, makes prey difficult to spot **(Figure 54.5a)**. Other animals have mechanical or chemical defenses. For example, most predators are strongly discouraged by the familiar defenses of porcupines and skunks. Some animals, such as the European fire salamander, can synthesize toxins, whereas others passively acquire a chemical defense by accumulating toxins from the plants they eat. Animals with effective chemical defenses often exhibit bright **aposematic coloration**, or warning coloration, such as that of the poison dart frog **(Figure 54.5b)**. Aposematic coloration seems to be adaptive: There is evidence that predators are particularly cautious in dealing with potential prey having bright color patterns (see Chapter 1).

Some prey species gain significant protection by mimicking the appearance of other species. In **Batesian mimicry**, a palatable or harmless species mimics an unpalatable or harmful model. For example, the larva of the hawkmoth *Hemeroplanes ornatus* puffs up its head and thorax when disturbed, looking like the head of a small poisonous snake **(Figure 54.5c)**. In this case, the mimicry even involves behavior; the larva weaves its head back and forth and hisses like a snake. In **Müllerian mimicry**, two or more unpalatable species, such as the cuckoo bee and yellow jacket, resemble each other **(Figure 54.5d)**. Presumably, each species gains an additional

▼ Figure 54.5 **Examples of defensive coloration in animals.**

(a) Cryptic coloration

▶ Canyon tree frog

(b) Aposematic coloration

▶ Poison dart frog

(c) Batesian mimicry: A harmless species mimics a harmful one.

◀ Hawkmoth larva

▼ Green parrot snake

(d) Müllerian mimicry: Two unpalatable species mimic each other.

◀ Cuckoo bee

▼ Yellow jacket

advantage because the more unpalatable prey there are, the more quickly and effectively predators adapt, avoiding any prey with that particular appearance. The shared appearance thus becomes a kind of aposematic coloration. In an example of convergent evolution, unpalatable animals in several different taxa have similar patterns of coloration: Black and yellow or red stripes characterize unpalatable animals as diverse as yellow jackets and coral snakes (see Figure 1.25).

Predators also use mimicry. For example, some snapping turtles have tongues that resemble a wriggling worm, thus luring small fish. Any fish that tries to eat the "bait" is itself quickly consumed as the turtle's strong jaws snap closed. Anglerfish also lure prey with their own bait, in this case a modified bone of the dorsal fin that luminesces in some species.

Herbivory

Ecologists use the term **herbivory** to refer to a $+/-$ interaction in which an organism eats parts of a plant or alga. While large mammalian herbivores such as cattle, sheep, and water buffalo may be most familiar, most herbivores are actually invertebrates, such as grasshoppers and beetles. In the ocean, herbivores include snails, sea urchins, some tropical fishes, and certain mammals, such as the manatee **(Figure 54.6)**.

Like predators, herbivores have many specialized adaptations. Many herbivorous insects have chemical sensors on their feet that enable them to distinguish between toxic and nontoxic plants as well as between more nutritious and less nutritious plants. Some mammalian herbivores, such as goats, use their sense of smell to examine plants, rejecting some and eating others. They may also eat just a specific part of a plant, such as the flowers. Many herbivores also have specialized teeth or digestive systems adapted for processing vegetation (see Chapter 41).

Unlike prey animals, plants cannot run away to avoid being eaten. Instead, a plant's arsenal against herbivores may feature chemical toxins or structures such as spines and thorns.

▲ **Figure 54.6 A West Indies manatee (*Trichechus manatus*) in Florida.** The animal in this photo is feeding on water hyacinth, an introduced species.

Among the plant compounds that serve as chemical weapons are the poison strychnine, produced by the tropical vine *Strychnos toxifera*; nicotine, from the tobacco plant; and tannins, from a variety of plant species. Plants in the genus *Astragalus* accumulate selenium toxins; they are known as "locoweeds" because the cattle and sheep that eat them wander aimlessly in circles and may even die. Compounds that are not toxic to humans but may be distasteful to many herbivores are responsible for the familiar flavors of cinnamon, cloves, and peppermint. Certain plants produce chemicals that cause abnormal development in some insects that eat them.

Symbiosis

When individuals of two or more species live in direct and intimate contact with one another, their relationship is called **symbiosis**. This text adopts a general definition of symbiosis that includes all such interactions, whether harmful, helpful, or neutral. Some biologists define symbiosis more narrowly as a synonym for mutualism, in which both species benefit.

Parasitism

Parasitism is a $+/-$ symbiotic interaction in which one organism, the **parasite**, derives its nourishment from another organism, its **host**, which is harmed in the process. Parasites that live within the body of their host, such as tapeworms, are called **endoparasites**; parasites that feed on the external surface of a host, such as ticks and lice, are called **ectoparasites**. In one particular type of parasitism, parasitoid insects—usually small wasps—lay eggs on or in living hosts (see Figure 54.1). The larvae then feed on the body of the host, eventually killing it. Some ecologists have estimated that at least one-third of all species on Earth are parasites.

Many parasites have complex life cycles involving multiple hosts. The life cycle of the blood fluke, which currently infects approximately 200 million people around the world, involves two hosts: humans and freshwater snails (see Figure 33.11). Some parasites change the behavior of their hosts in a way that increases the probability of the parasite being transferred from one host to another. For instance, the presence of parasitic acanthocephalan (spiny-headed) worms leads their crustacean hosts to engage in a variety of atypical behaviors, including leaving protective cover and moving into the open. As a result of their modified behavior, the crustaceans have a greater chance of being eaten by the birds that are the second host in the parasitic worm's life cycle.

Parasites can significantly affect the survival, reproduction, and density of their host population, either directly or indirectly. For example, ticks that live as ectoparasites on moose weaken their hosts by withdrawing blood and causing hair breakage and loss, increasing the chance that the moose will die from cold stress or predation by wolves. Some of the declines of the moose population on Isle Royale, Michigan, have been attributed to tick outbreaks (see Figure 53.19).

Mutualism

Mutualistic symbiosis, or **mutualism**, is an interspecific interaction that benefits both species (+/+). We have described many examples of mutualism in previous chapters: nitrogen fixation by bacteria in the root nodules of legumes; the digestion of cellulose by microorganisms in the digestive systems of termites and ruminant mammals; the exchange of nutrients in mycorrhizae, associations of fungi and the roots of plants; and photosynthesis by unicellular algae in corals. The interaction between termites and the microorganisms in their digestive system is an example of *obligate mutualism*, in which at least one species has lost the ability to survive without its partner. In *facultative mutualism*, as in the acacia-ant example shown in **Figure 54.7**, both species can survive alone.

Mutualistic relationships sometimes involve the evolution of related adaptations in both species, with changes in either species likely to affect the survival and reproduction of the other. For example, most flowering plants have adaptations such as nectar or fruit that attract animals that function in pollination or seed dispersal (see Chapter 38). In turn, many animals have adaptations that help them find and consume nectar.

Commensalism

An interaction between species that benefits one of the species but neither harms nor helps the other (+/0) is called **commensalism**. Commensal interactions are difficult to document in nature because any close association between species likely affects both species, even if only slightly. For instance, "hitchhiking" species, such as algae that live on the shells of aquatic turtles or barnacles that attach to whales, are sometimes considered commensal. The hitchhikers gain a place to grow while having seemingly little effect on their ride. However, the hitchhikers may in fact slightly decrease the reproductive success of their hosts by reducing the hosts' efficiency of movement in searching for food or escaping from predators. Conversely, the hitchhikers may provide a benefit in the form of camouflage.

Some associations that are possibly commensal involve one species obtaining food that is inadvertently exposed by another. For instance, cowbirds and cattle egrets feed on insects flushed out of the grass by grazing bison, cattle, horses, and other herbivores. Because the birds increase their feeding rates when following the herbivores, they clearly benefit from the association. Much of the time, the herbivores may be unaffected by the relationship (**Figure 54.8**). However, they, too, may sometimes derive some benefit; the birds tend to be opportunistic feeders that occasionally remove and eat ticks and other ectoparasites from the herbivores. They may also give warning to the herbivores of a predator's approach.

All four types of interactions that we have discussed so far—competition, predation, herbivory, and symbiosis—strongly influence the structure of communities. You will see other examples of these interactions throughout this chapter.

(a) Certain species of acacia trees in Central and South America have hollow thorns that house stinging ants of the genus *Pseudomyrmex*. The ants feed on nectar produced by the tree and on protein-rich swellings (orange in the photograph) at the tips of leaflets.

(b) The acacia benefits because the pugnacious ants, which attack anything that touches the tree, remove fungal spores, small herbivores, and debris, and clip vegetation that grows close to the acacia.

▲ **Figure 54.7 Mutualism between acacia trees and ants.**

▲ Figure 54.8 **A possible example of commensalism between cattle egrets and water buffalo.**

1. Explain how interspecific competition, predation, and mutualism differ in their effects on the interacting populations of two species.
2. According to the principle of competitive exclusion, what outcome is expected when two species with identical niches compete for a resource? Why?
3. **WHAT IF?** Suppose you live in an agricultural area. What examples of the four types of community interactions (competition, predation, herbivory, and symbiosis) might you see in the growing or use of food?

For suggested answers, see Appendix A.

CONCEPT 54.2
Dominant and keystone species exert strong controls on community structure

Although the interactions of many species influence biological communities, sometimes a few species exert strong control on a community's structure, particularly on the composition, relative abundance, and diversity of its species. Before examining the effects of these particularly influential species, we first need to consider two fundamental features of community structure: species diversity and feeding relationships.

Species Diversity

The **species diversity** of a community—the variety of different kinds of organisms that make up the community—has two components. One is **species richness**, the number of different species in the community. The other is the **relative abundance** of the different species, the proportion each species represents of all individuals in the community. For example, imagine two small forest communities, each with 100 individuals distributed among four tree species (A, B, C, and D) as follows:

Community 1: 25A, 25B, 25C, 25D
Community 2: 80A, 5B, 5C, 10D

The species richness is the same for both communities because they both contain four species of trees, but the relative abundance is very different **(Figure 54.9)**. You would easily notice the four types of trees in community 1, but without looking carefully, you might see only the abundant species A in the second forest. Most observers would intuitively describe community 1 as the more diverse of the two communities.

Ecologists use many tools to quantitatively compare the diversity of different communities across time and space. They often calculate an index of diversity based on species richness

Community 1
A: 25% B: 25% C: 25% D: 25%

Community 2
A: 80% B: 5% C: 5% D: 10%

▲ **Figure 54.9 Which forest is more diverse?** Ecologists would say that community 1 has greater species diversity, a measure that includes both species richness and relative abundance.

and relative abundance. One widely used index is the **Shannon diversity** (H):

$$H = -[(p_A \ln p_A) + (p_B \ln p_B) + (p_C \ln p_C) + \ldots]$$

where A, B, C . . . are the species in the community, p is the relative abundance of each species, and ln is the natural logarithm. Let's use this equation to calculate the Shannon diversity of the two communities in Figure 54.9. For community 1, $p = 0.25$ for each community, so $H = -4 \times (0.25 \ln 0.25) = 1.39$. For community 2, $H = -[(0.8 \ln 0.8) + (0.05 \ln 0.05) + (0.05 \ln 0.05) + (0.1 \ln 0.1)] = 0.71$. These calculations confirm our intuitive description of community 1 as more diverse.

Determining the number and relative abundance of species in a community is easier said than done. Many sampling techniques can be used, but since most species in a community are relatively rare, it may be hard to obtain a sample size large enough to be representative. It is also difficult to census the highly mobile or less visible members of communities, such as mites, nematodes, and microorganisms. The small size of microorganisms makes them particularly difficult to sample, so ecologists now use molecular tools to help determine microbial diversity **(Figure 54.10)**. Although measuring species diversity is often challenging, it is essential not only for understanding community structure but for conserving biodiversity, as you will read in Chapter 56.

▼ Figure 54.10 **Research Method**

Determining Microbial Diversity Using Molecular Tools

APPLICATION Ecologists are increasingly using molecular techniques, such as the analysis of restriction fragment length polymorphisms (RFLPs), to determine microbial diversity and richness in environmental samples. As used in this application, RFLP analysis produces a DNA fingerprint for microbial taxa based on sequence variations in the DNA that encodes the small subunit of ribosomal RNA. Noah Fierer and Rob Jackson, of Duke University, used this method to compare the diversity of soil bacteria in 98 habitats across North and South America to help identify environmental variables associated with high bacterial diversity.

TECHNIQUE Researchers first extract and purify DNA from the microbial community in each sample. They use the polymerase chain reaction (PCR) to amplify the ribosomal DNA and label the DNA with a fluorescent dye (see Chapter 20). Restriction enzymes then cut the amplified, labeled DNA into fragments of different lengths, which are separated by gel electrophoresis. The number and abundance of these fragments characterize the DNA fingerprint of the sample.

Based on their RFLP analysis, Fierer and Jackson calculated the Shannon diversity (H) of each sample. They then looked for a correlation between H and several environmental variables, including vegetation type, mean annual temperature and rainfall, and acidity and quality of the soil at each site.

RESULTS The diversity of bacterial communities in soils across North and South America was related almost exclusively to soil pH, with the Shannon diversity being highest in neutral soils and lowest in acidic soils. Amazonian rain forests, which have extremely high plant and animal diversity, had the most acidic soils and the lowest bacterial diversity of the samples tested.

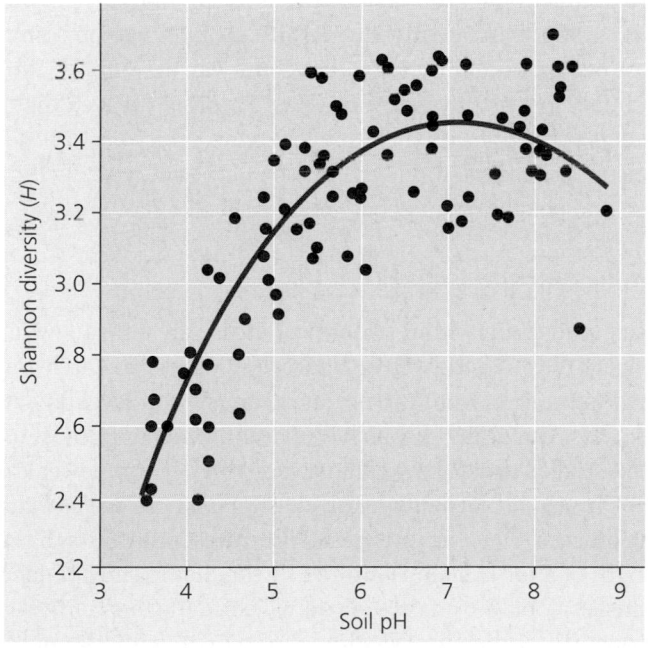

SOURCE N. Fierer and R. B. Jackson, The diversity and biogeography of soil bacterial communities, *Proceedings of the National Academy of Sciences USA* 103:626–631 (2006).

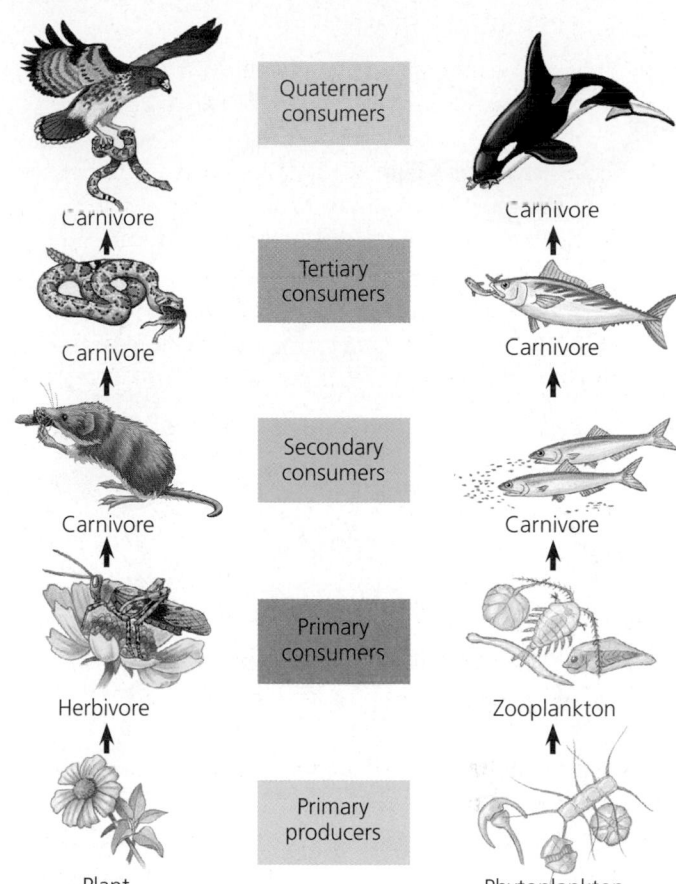

A terrestrial food chain   **A marine food chain**

▲ **Figure 54.11 Examples of terrestrial and marine food chains.** The arrows trace energy and nutrients that pass through the trophic levels of a community when organisms feed on one another. Decomposers, which "feed" on organisms from all trophic levels, are not shown here.

Trophic Structure

The structure and dynamics of a community depend to a large extent on the feeding relationships between organisms—the **trophic structure** of the community. The transfer of food energy up the trophic levels from its source in plants and other autotrophic organisms (primary producers) through herbivores (primary consumers) to carnivores (secondary, tertiary, and quaternary consumers) and eventually to decomposers is referred to as a **food chain (Figure 54.11)**.

Food Webs

In the 1920s, Oxford University biologist Charles Elton recognized that food chains are not isolated units but are linked together in **food webs**. An ecologist can summarize the trophic relationships of a community by diagramming a food web with arrows linking species according to who eats whom. In an antarctic pelagic community, for example, the primary producers are phytoplankton, which serve as food for the dominant

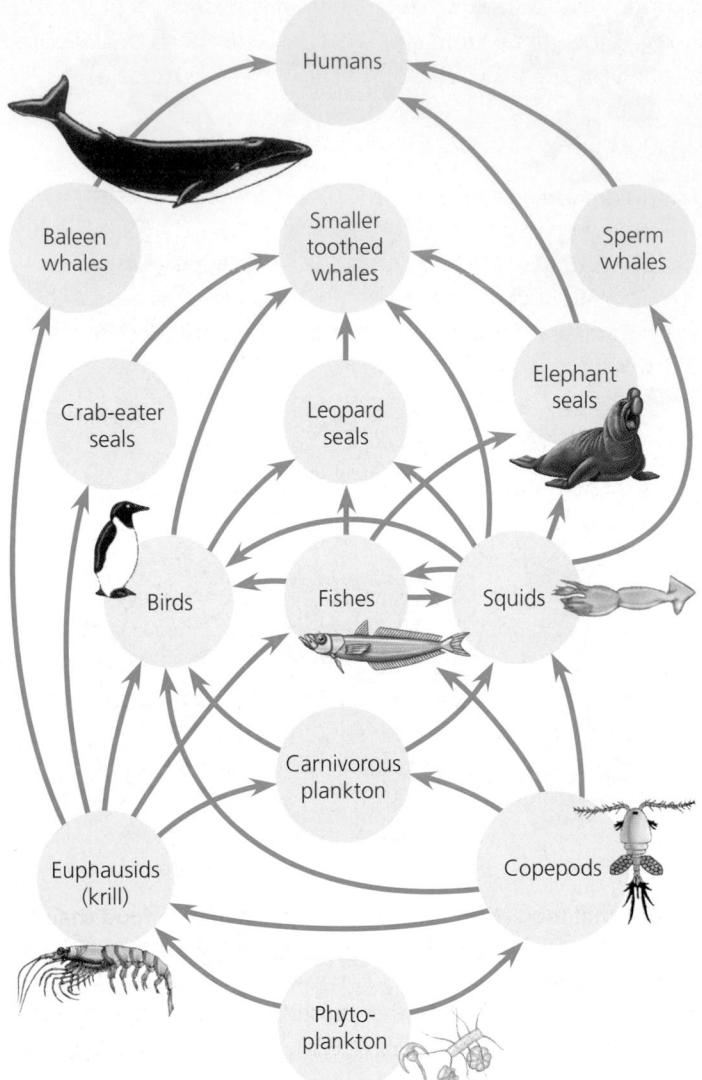

▲ **Figure 54.12 An antarctic marine food web.** Arrows follow the transfer of food from the producers (phytoplankton) up through the trophic levels. For simplicity, this diagram omits decomposers.

▲ **Figure 54.13 Partial food web for the Chesapeake Bay estuary on the U.S. Atlantic coast.** The sea nettle (*Chrysaora quinquecirrha*) and juvenile striped bass (*Morone saxatilis*) are the main predators of fish larvae (bay anchovy and several other species). Note that sea nettles are secondary consumers (black arrows) when they eat zooplankton, but tertiary consumers (red arrows) when they eat fish larvae, which are themselves secondary consumers of zooplankton.

grazing zooplankton, especially euphausids (krill) and copepods, both of which are crustaceans **(Figure 54.12)**. These zooplankton species are in turn eaten by various carnivores, including other plankton, penguins, seals, fishes, and baleen whales. Squids, which are carnivores that feed on fishes as well as zooplankton, are another important link in these food webs, as they are in turn eaten by seals and toothed whales. During the time when whales were commonly hunted for food, humans became the top predator in this food web. Having hunted many whale species to low numbers, humans are now harvesting at lower trophic levels, catching krill as well as fishes for food.

How are food chains linked into food webs? First, a given species may weave into the web at more than one trophic level. In the food web shown in Figure 54.12, euphausids feed on phytoplankton as well as on other grazing zooplankton, such as copepods. Such "nonexclusive" consumers are also found in terrestrial communities. For instance, foxes are omnivores whose

diet includes berries and other plant materials, herbivores such as mice, and other predators, such as weasels. Humans are among the most versatile of omnivores.

Food webs can be very complicated, but we can simplify them for easier study in two ways. First, we can group species with similar trophic relationships in a given community into broad functional groups. For example, in Figure 54.12, more than 100 phytoplankton species are grouped as the primary producers in the food web. A second way to simplify a food web for closer study is to isolate a portion of the web that interacts very little with the rest of the community. **Figure 54.13** illustrates a partial food web for sea nettles (a type of cnidarian) and juvenile striped bass in Chesapeake Bay.

Limits on Food Chain Length

Each food chain within a food web is usually only a few links long. In the antarctic web of Figure 54.12, there are rarely more than seven links from the producers to any top-level predator, and most chains in this web have fewer links. In fact, most food webs studied to date have chains consisting of five or fewer links.

Why are food chains relatively short? There are two main hypotheses. One, the **energetic hypothesis**, suggests that the length of a food chain is limited by the inefficiency of energy transfer along the chain. As you will read in Chapter 55, only about 10% of the energy stored in the organic matter of each trophic level is converted to organic matter at the next trophic level. Thus, a producer level consisting of 100 kg of plant material can support about 10 kg of herbivore **biomass** (the total mass of all individuals in a population) and 1 kg of carnivore biomass. The energetic hypothesis predicts that food chains should be relatively longer in habitats of higher photosynthetic production, since the starting amount of energy is greater than in habitats with lower photosynthetic production.

A second hypothesis, the **dynamic stability hypothesis**, proposes that long food chains are less stable than short chains. Population fluctuations at lower trophic levels are magnified at higher levels, potentially causing the local extinction of top predators. In a variable environment, top predators must be able to recover from environmental shocks (such as extreme winters) that can reduce the food supply all the way up the food chain. The longer a food chain is, the more slowly top predators can recover from environmental setbacks. This hypothesis predicts that food chains should be shorter in unpredictable environments.

Most of the data available support the energetic hypothesis. For example, ecologists have used tree-hole communities in tropical forests as experimental models to test the energetic hypothesis. Many trees have small branch scars that rot, forming holes in the tree trunk. The tree holes hold water and provide a habitat for tiny communities consisting of microorganisms and insects that feed on leaf litter, as well as predatory insects. **Figure 54.14** shows the results of experiments in which researchers manipulated productivity (leaf litter falling into the tree holes). As predicted by the energetic hypothesis, holes with the most leaf litter, and hence the greatest total food supply at the producer level, supported the longest food chains.

Another factor that may limit food chain length is that carnivores in a food chain tend to be larger at successive trophic levels. The size of a carnivore and its feeding mechanism put some upper limit on the size of food it can take into its mouth. And except in a few cases, large carnivores cannot live on very small food items because they cannot procure enough food in a given time to meet their metabolic needs. Among the exceptions are baleen whales, huge suspension feeders with adaptations that enable them to consume enormous quantities of krill and other small organisms (see Figure 41.6).

Species with a Large Impact

Certain species have an especially large impact on the structure of entire communities either because they are highly abundant or because they play a pivotal role in community dynamics. The impact of these species can occur either through their trophic interactions or through their influences on the physical environment.

Dominant Species

Dominant species are those species in a community that are the most abundant or that collectively have the highest biomass. As a result, dominant species exert a powerful control over the occurrence and distribution of other species. For example, the abundance of sugar maples, the dominant plant species in many eastern North American forest communities, has a major impact on abiotic factors such as shading and soil, which in turn affect which other species live there.

There is no single explanation for why a species becomes dominant in a community. One hypothesis suggests that dominant species are competitively superior in exploiting limited resources such as water or nutrients. Another explanation is that dominant species are most successful at avoiding predation or the impact of disease. This latter idea could explain the high biomass attained in some environments by **invasive species**, organisms (typically introduced by humans) that take hold outside their native range. Such species may not face the natural predators and agents of disease that would otherwise hold their populations in check.

One way to discover the impact of a dominant species is to remove it from the community. This type of experiment has been carried out many times by accident. The American chestnut was a dominant tree in deciduous forests of eastern North America before 1910, making up more than 40% of mature trees. Then humans accidentally introduced the fungal disease chestnut blight to New York City via nursery stock imported from Asia. Between 1910 and 1950, this fungus killed all the chestnut trees in eastern North America. In this case, removing the dominant species had a relatively small impact on some species but severe effects on others. Oaks, hickories, beeches, and red maples that were already present in the forest increased in abundance and replaced the chestnuts. No mammals or birds seemed to have been harmed by the loss of the chestnut, but seven species of moths and butterflies that fed on the tree became extinct.

The American chestnut story is only one example of a community response to the loss of a dominant species. More research is needed before we can generalize about the overall effects of such losses.

▲ **Figure 54.14 Test of the energetic hypothesis for the restriction of food chain length.** Researchers manipulated the productivity of tree-hole communities in Queensland, Australia, by providing leaf litter input at three levels. Reducing energy input reduced food chain length, a result consistent with the energetic hypothesis.

? *According to the dynamic stability hypothesis, which productivity treatment should have the most stable food chain? Explain.*

▼ Figure 54.15 Inquiry

Is *Pisaster ochraceus* a keystone predator?

EXPERIMENT In rocky intertidal communities of western North America, the relatively uncommon sea star *Pisaster ochraceus* preys on mussels such as *Mytilus californianus*, a dominant species and strong competitor for space. Robert Paine, of the University of Washington, removed *Pisaster* from an area in the intertidal zone and examined the effect on species richness.

RESULTS In the absence of *Pisaster*, species richness declined as mussels monopolized the rock face and eliminated most other invertebrates and algae. In a control area where *Pisaster* was not removed, species richness changed very little.

CONCLUSION *Pisaster* acts as a keystone species, exerting an influence on the community that is not reflected in its abundance.

SOURCE R. T. Paine, Food web complexity and species diversity, *American Naturalist* 100:65–75 (1966).

WHAT IF? Suppose that an invasive fungus killed most individuals of *Mytilus* at these sites. What do you think would happen to species richness if *Pisaster* were then removed?

Keystone Species

In contrast to dominant species, **keystone species** are not necessarily abundant in a community. They exert strong control on community structure not by numerical might but by their pivotal ecological roles, or niches. One way to identify keystone species is by removal experiments like the one described in **Figure 54.15**, which highlights the importance of a

(a) Sea otter abundance

(b) Sea urchin biomass

(c) Total kelp density

▲ **Figure 54.16 Sea otters as keystone predators in the North Pacific.** The graphs correlate changes over time in sea otter abundance **(a)** with changes in sea urchin biomass **(b)** and changes in kelp density **(c)** in kelp forests at Adak Island (part of the Aleutian Island chain). The vertical diagram on the right represents the food chain after orcas (top) entered the chain.

keystone species in maintaining the diversity of an intertidal community.

The sea otter, a keystone predator in the North Pacific, offers another example **(Figure 54.16)**. Sea otters feed on sea urchins, and sea urchins feed mainly on kelp. In areas where sea otters are abundant, sea urchins are rare and kelp forests are well developed. Where sea otters are rare, sea urchins are common and kelp is almost absent. Over the last 20 years, orcas have been preying on sea otters as the whales' usual prey has declined. As a result, sea otter populations have declined precipitously in large areas off the coast of western Alaska, sometimes at rates as high as 25% per year. The loss of this keystone species has allowed sea urchin populations to increase, resulting in the loss of kelp forests.

Foundation Species (Ecosystem "Engineers")

Some organisms exert their influence on a community not through their trophic interactions but by causing physical changes in the environment. Such organisms may alter the environment through their behavior or their large collective biomass.

Species that dramatically alter their physical environment on a large scale are called ecosystem "engineers" or, to avoid implying conscious intent, "foundation species." A familiar foundation species is the beaver (Figure 54.17), which, through tree felling and dam building, can transform landscapes. The effects of foundation species on other species can be positive or negative, depending on the needs of the other species.

By altering the structure or dynamics of the environment, foundation species sometimes act as **facilitators**: They have positive effects on the survival and reproduction of other species in the community. For example, by modifying soils, the black rush *Juncus gerardi* increases the species richness in some zones of New England salt marshes. *Juncus* helps prevent salt buildup in the soil by shading the soil surface, which reduces evaporation (Figure 54.18a). *Juncus* also prevents the salt marsh soils from becoming oxygen depleted as it transports oxygen to its belowground tissues. Sally Hacker and Mark Bertness, of Brown University, uncovered some of *Juncus*'s facilitation effects by removing *Juncus* from study plots. Their experiment suggested that without *Juncus*, the up-

▲ **Figure 54.17 Beavers as ecosystem "engineers."** By felling trees, building dams, and creating ponds, beavers can transform large areas of forest into flooded wetlands.

(a) Salt marsh with *Juncus* (foreground)

(b)

▲ **Figure 54.18 Facilitation by black rush (*Juncus gerardi*) in New England salt marshes.** Black rush facilitates the occupation of the middle upper zone of the marsh, which increases local plant species richness.

per middle intertidal zone would support 50% fewer plant species (Figure 54.18b).

Bottom-Up and Top-Down Controls

Simplified models based on relationships between adjacent trophic levels are useful for discussing community organization. For example, let's consider the three possible relationships between plants (*V* for vegetation) and herbivores (*H*):

$$V \rightarrow H \qquad V \leftarrow H \qquad V \leftrightarrow H$$

The arrows indicate that a change in the biomass of one trophic level causes a change in the other trophic level. $V \rightarrow H$ means that an increase in vegetation will increase the numbers or biomass of herbivores, but not vice versa. In this situation, herbivores are limited by vegetation, but vegetation is not limited by herbivory. In contrast, $V \leftarrow H$ means that an increase in herbivore biomass will decrease the abundance of vegetation, but not vice versa. A double-headed arrow indicates that feedback flows in both directions, with each trophic level sensitive to changes in the biomass of the other.

Two models of community organization are common: the bottom-up model and the top-down model. The $V \rightarrow H$ linkage suggests a **bottom-up model**, which postulates a unidirectional influence from lower to higher trophic levels. In this case, the presence or absence of mineral nutrients (*N*) controls plant (*V*) numbers, which control herbivore (*H*) numbers, which in turn control predator (*P*) numbers. The simplified bottom-up model is thus $N \rightarrow V \rightarrow H \rightarrow P$. To change the community structure of a bottom-up community, you need to alter biomass at the lower trophic levels, allowing those changes to propagate up through the food web. For example, if you add mineral nutrients to stimulate growth of vegetation, then the higher trophic levels should also increase in biomass. If you add predators to or remove predators from a bottom-up community, however, the effect should not extend down to the lower trophic levels.

In contrast, the **top-down model** postulates the opposite: Predation mainly controls community organization because predators limit herbivores, herbivores limit plants, and plants limit nutrient levels through their uptake of nutrients during growth and reproduction. The simplified top-down model, $N \leftarrow V \leftarrow H \leftarrow P$, is also called the *trophic cascade model*. For example, in a lake community with four trophic levels, the model predicts that removing the top carnivores will increase the abundance of primary carnivores, in turn decreasing the number of herbivores, increasing phytoplankton abundance, and decreasing concentrations of mineral nutrients. If there were only three trophic levels in a lake, removing primary carnivores would increase the number of herbivores and decrease phytoplankton abundance, causing nutrient levels to rise. The effects of any manipulation thus move down the trophic structure as alternating $+/-$ effects.

Diana Wall (see interview on pages 1146–1147) and Ross Virginia investigated whether bottom-up or top-down factors are more important in a community of soil nematodes in the deserts of Antarctica. They chose this extreme environment because its nematode community contains only two or three species and is therefore easier to manipulate and study than other more species-rich communities. Their experiment, described in **Figure 54.19**, showed that top-down factors appear to control the organization of this simple community.

The top-down model has practical applications. For example, ecologists have applied the top-down model to improve water quality in polluted lakes. This approach, called **biomanipulation**, attempts to prevent algal blooms and eutrophication by altering the density of higher-level consumers in lakes instead of using chemical treatments. In lakes with three trophic levels, for example, removing fish should improve water quality by increasing zooplankton and thereby decreasing algal populations. In lakes with four trophic levels, adding top predators should have the same effect. We can summarize this scenario with the following diagram:

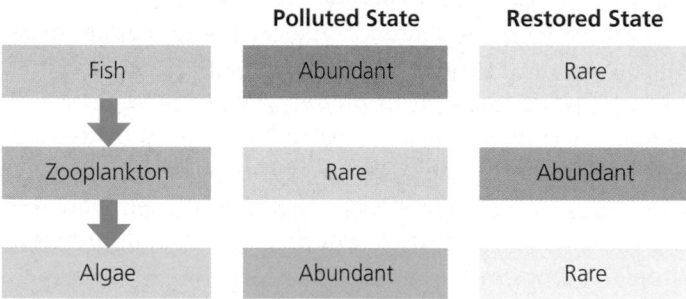

	Polluted State	Restored State
Fish	Abundant	Rare
Zooplankton	Rare	Abundant
Algae	Abundant	Rare

Ecologists used biomanipulation on a large scale in Lake Vesijärvi in southern Finland. Lake Vesijärvi is a large (110 km²), shallow lake that was polluted with city sewage and industrial wastewater until 1976. After pollution controls reduced these inputs, the water quality of the lake began to improve. By 1986, however, massive blooms of cyanobacteria started to occur in the lake. These blooms coincided with a dense population of roach, a fish that had benefited from the mineral nutrients that the pollution provided over many years. Roach eat zooplankton, which otherwise keep the cyanobacteria and algae in check. To reverse these changes, ecologists removed nearly a million kilograms of fish from Lake Vesijärvi between 1989 and 1993, reducing roach to about 20% of their former abundance. At the same time, the ecologists stocked the lake with pike perch, a predatory fish that eats roach. This added a fourth trophic level to the lake, which kept down the population of roach. Biomanipulation was a success in Lake Vesijärvi. The water became clear, and the last cyanobacterial bloom was in 1989. The lake remains clear even though roach removal ended in 1993.

As these examples show, communities vary in their degree of bottom-up and top-down control. To manage agricultural landscapes, parks, reservoirs, and fisheries, we need to understand each particular community's dynamics.

▼ **Figure 54.19** **Inquiry**

Are soil nematode communities in Antarctica controlled by bottom-up or top-down factors?

EXPERIMENT　Previous research in the deserts of Antarctica had shown that the predatory nematode *Eudorylaimus antarcticus* becomes less abundant in drier soils, but its prey species, the nematode *Scottnema lindsayae*, does not. To determine whether bottom-up or top-down factors control interactions in these communities, Diana Wall and Ross Virginia, then both of Colorado State University, decreased the abundance of *E. antarcticus* in selected plots by warming and drying the soil. They placed clear plastic chambers over the ground for a year to trap the heat from sunlight and warm the soil by 5°C.

RESULTS　The density of *E. antarcticus* in the warmed plots dropped to one-quarter of the density in control plots. In contrast, the density of *S. lindsayae* increased by one-sixth.

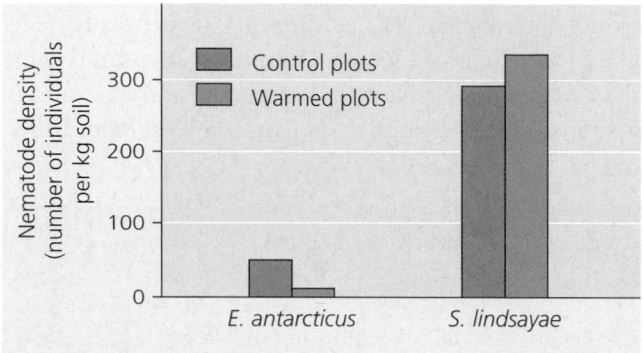

CONCLUSION　The prey species' increase in density as the predator density declined suggests that this soil nematode community is controlled by top-down factors.

SOURCE　D. Wall-Freckman and R. A. Virginia, Low-diversity Antarctic soil nematode communities: distribution and response to disturbance, *Ecology* 78:363–369 (1997).

WHAT IF?　Suppose a second predatory species existed in this community and that its abundance was unaffected by soil warming. How would you expect the density of *S. lindsayae* to change if the experiment were repeated under these conditions? Explain.

CONCEPT CHECK **54.2**

1. What two components contribute to species diversity? Explain how two communities that contain the same number of species can differ in species diversity.
2. Describe two hypotheses that explain why food chains are usually short, and state a key prediction of each hypothesis.
3. **WHAT IF?**　Consider a grassland with five trophic levels: plants, grasshoppers, snakes, raccoons, and bobcats. If you released additional bobcats into the grassland, how would plant biomass change if the bottom-up model applied? If the top-down model applied?

For suggested answers, see Appendix A.

Disturbance influences species diversity and composition

Decades ago, most ecologists favored the traditional view that biological communities are in a state of equilibrium, a more or less stable balance, unless seriously disturbed by human activities. The "balance of nature" view focused on interspecific competition as a key factor determining community composition and maintaining stability in communities. *Stability* in this context refers to a community's tendency to reach and maintain a relatively constant composition of species.

One of the earliest proponents of this view, F. E. Clements, of the Carnegie Institution of Washington, argued in the early 1900s that the community of plants at a site had only one state of equilibrium, controlled solely by climate. According to Clements, biotic interactions caused the species in this *climax community* to function as an integrated unit—in effect, as a superorganism. His argument was based on the observation that certain species of plants are consistently found together, such as the oaks, maples, birches, and beeches in deciduous forests of the northeastern United States.

Other ecologists questioned whether most communities were at equilibrium or functioned as integrated units. A. G. Tansley, of Oxford University, challenged the concept of a climax community, arguing that differences in soils, topography, and other factors created many potential communities that were stable within a region. H. A. Gleason, of the University of Chicago, saw communities not as superorganisms but more as chance assemblages of species found in the same area simply because they happen to have similar abiotic requirements—for example, for temperature, rainfall, and soil type. Gleason and other ecologists also realized that disturbance keeps many communities from reaching a state of equilibrium in species diversity or composition. A **disturbance** is an event, such as a storm, fire, flood, drought, overgrazing, or human activity, that changes a community by removing organisms from it or altering resource availability.

This recent emphasis on change has produced the **nonequilibrium model**, which describes most communities as constantly changing after being affected by disturbances. Even where relatively stable communities do exist, they can be rapidly transformed into nonequilibrium communities. Let's now take a look at the ways disturbances influence community structure and composition.

Characterizing Disturbance

The types of disturbances and their frequency and severity vary from community to community. Storms disturb almost all communities, even those in the oceans, through the action of waves. Fire is a significant disturbance in most terrestrial communities; in fact, chaparral and some grassland biomes require regular burning to maintain their structure and species composition. Freezing is a frequent occurrence in many rivers, lakes, and ponds, and many streams and ponds are disturbed by spring flooding and seasonal drying. A high level of disturbance is generally the result of a high intensity *and* high frequency of disturbance, while low disturbance levels can result from either a low intensity or low frequency of disturbance.

The **intermediate disturbance hypothesis** states that moderate levels of disturbance can create conditions that foster greater species diversity than low or high levels of disturbance. High levels of disturbance reduce species diversity by creating environmental stresses that exceed the tolerances of many species or by subjecting the community to such a high frequency of disturbance that slow-growing or slow-colonizing species are excluded. At the other extreme, low levels of disturbance can reduce species diversity by allowing competitively dominant species to exclude less competitive species. Meanwhile, intermediate levels of disturbance can foster greater species diversity by opening up habitats for occupation by less competitive species. Such intermediate disturbance levels rarely create conditions so severe that they exceed the environmental tolerances of or rate of recovery by potential community members.

The intermediate disturbance hypothesis is supported by many terrestrial and aquatic studies. In one such study, ecologists in New Zealand compared the richness of invertebrate taxa living in the beds of streams exposed to different frequencies and intensities of flooding (**Figure 54.20**). When floods occurred either very frequently or rarely, invertebrate richness was low. Frequent floods made it difficult for some species to become established in the streambed, while rare floods resulted in species being displaced by superior competitors. Invertebrate richness peaked in streams that had an intermediate frequency or intensity of flooding, as predicted by the intermediate disturbance hypothesis.

▲ **Figure 54.20 Testing the intermediate disturbance hypothesis.** Researchers identified the taxa (species or genera) of invertebrates at two locations in each of 27 New Zealand streams. They assessed the intensity of flooding at each location using an index of streambed disturbance. The number of invertebrate taxa peaked when the intensity of flooding was at intermediate levels.

Although moderate levels of disturbance appear to maximize species diversity, small and large disturbances can have important effects on community structure. Small-scale disturbances can create patches of different habitats across a landscape, which can be a key to maintaining diversity in a community. Large-scale disturbances are also a natural part of many communities. Much of Yellowstone National Park, for example, is dominated by lodgepole pine, a tree that requires the rejuvenating influence of periodic fires. Lodgepole cones remain closed until exposed to intense heat. When a forest fire burns the trees, the cones open and the seeds are released. The new generation of lodgepole pines can then thrive on nutrients released from the burned trees and in the sunlight that is no longer blocked by taller trees.

In the summer of 1988, extensive areas of Yellowstone burned during a severe drought. By 1989, burned areas in the park were largely covered with new vegetation, suggesting that the species in this community are adapted to rapid recovery after fire (Figure 54.21). In fact, large-scale fires have periodically swept through the lodgepole pine forests of Yellowstone and other northern areas for thousands of years. In contrast, more southerly pine forests were historically affected by frequent but low-intensity fires. In these forests, a century of human intervention to suppress small fires has allowed an unnatural buildup of fuels and elevated the risk of large, severe fires to which the species are not adapted.

Studies of the Yellowstone forest community and many others indicate that they are nonequilibrium communities, changing continually because of natural disturbances and the internal processes of growth and reproduction. Mounting evidence suggests that nonequilibrium conditions resulting from disturbance are in fact the norm for most communities.

Ecological Succession

Changes in the composition and structure of terrestrial communities are most apparent after some severe disturbance, such as a volcanic eruption or a glacier, strips away all the existing vegetation. The disturbed area may be colonized by a variety of species, which are gradually replaced by other species, which are in turn replaced by still other species—a process called **ecological succession**.

When this process begins in a virtually lifeless area where soil has not yet formed, such as on a new volcanic island or on the rubble (moraine) left by a retreating glacier, it is called **primary succession**. Often the only life-forms initially present are autotrophic prokaryotes and heterotrophic prokaryotes and protists. Lichens and mosses, which grow from windblown spores, are commonly the first macroscopic photosynthesizers to colonize such areas. Soil develops gradually as rocks weather and organic matter accumulates from the decomposed remains of the early colonizers. Once soil is present, the lichens and mosses are usually overgrown by grasses, shrubs, and trees that sprout from seeds blown in from nearby areas or carried in by animals. Eventually, an area is colonized by plants that become the community's prevalent form of vegetation. Producing such a community through primary succession may take hundreds or thousands of years.

Secondary succession occurs when an existing community has been cleared by some disturbance that leaves the soil intact, as in Yellowstone following the 1988 fires (see Figure 54.21). Sometimes the area begins to return to something like its original state. For instance, in a forested area that has been cleared for farming and later abandoned, the earliest plants to recolonize are often herbaceous species that grow from windblown or animal-borne seeds. If the area has not been burned or

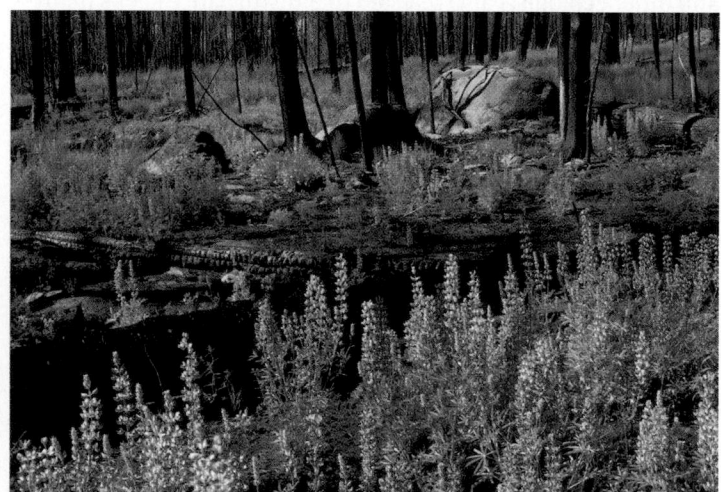

(a) Soon after fire. The burn left a patchy landscape. Note the unburned trees in the far distance.

(b) One year after fire. The community has begun to recover. A variety of herbaceous plants, different from those in the former forest, cover the ground.

▲ **Figure 54.21 Recovery following a large-scale disturbance.** The 1988 Yellowstone National Park fires burned large areas of forests dominated by lodgepole pines.

heavily grazed, woody shrubs may in time replace most of the herbaceous species, and forest trees may eventually replace most of the shrubs.

Early arrivals and later-arriving species may be linked in one of three key processes. The early arrivals may *facilitate* the appearance of the later species by making the environment more favorable—for example, by increasing the fertility of the soil. Alternatively, the early species may *inhibit* establishment of the later species, so that successful colonization by later species occurs in spite of, rather than because of, the activities of the early species. Finally, the early species may be completely independent of the later species, which *tolerate* conditions created early in succession but are neither helped nor hindered by early species.

Let's look at how these various processes contribute to primary succession on glacial moraines. Ecologists have conducted the most extensive research on moraine succession at Glacier Bay in southeastern Alaska, where glaciers have retreated more than 100 km since 1760 (Figure 54.22). By studying the communities on moraines at different distances from the mouth of the bay, ecologists can examine different stages in succession. ❶ The exposed moraine is colonized first by pioneering species that include liverworts, mosses, fireweed, scat-

tered *Dryas* (a mat-forming shrub), willows, and cottonwood. ❷ After about three decades, *Dryas* dominates the plant community. ❸ A few decades later, the area is invaded by alder, which forms dense thickets up to 9 m tall. In the next two centuries, these alder stands are overgrown first by Sitka spruce ❹ and later by a combination of western hemlock and mountain hemlock. In areas of poor drainage, the forest floor of this spruce-hemlock forest is invaded by sphagnum moss, which holds large amounts of water and acidifies the soil, eventually killing the trees. Thus, by about 300 years after glacial retreat, the vegetation consists of sphagnum bogs on the poorly drained flat areas and spruce-hemlock forest on the well-drained slopes.

How is succession on glacial moraines related to the environmental changes caused by transitions in the vegetation? The bare soil exposed as the glacier retreats is quite basic, with a pH of 8.0–8.4 due to the carbonate compounds in the parent rocks. The soil pH falls rapidly as vegetation develops. Decomposition of acidic spruce needles in particular reduces the pH of the soil from 7.0 to approximately 4.0. The soil concentrations of mineral nutrients also change with time. Because the bare soil after glacial retreat is low in nitrogen content, almost all the pioneer plant species begin succession with poor

❶ Pioneer stage, with fireweed dominant

❷ *Dryas* stage

❹ Spruce stage

❸ Alder stage

▲ Figure 54.22 **Glacial retreat and primary succession at Glacier Bay, Alaska.** The different shades of blue on the map show retreat of the glacier since 1760, based on historical descriptions.

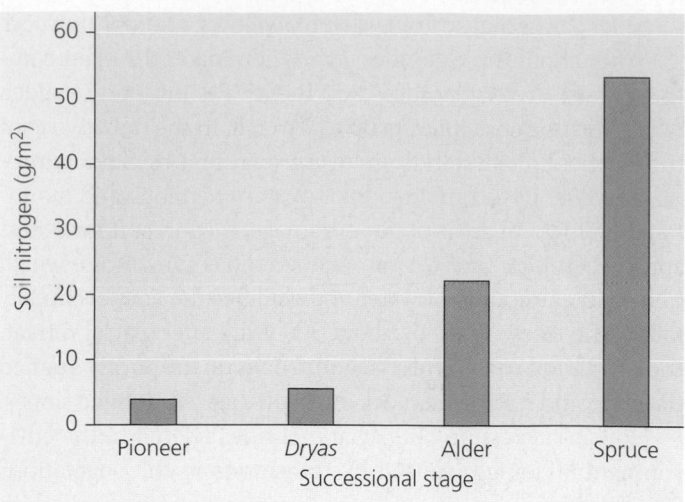

▲ **Figure 54.23 Changes in soil nitrogen content during succession at Glacier Bay.**

▲ Figure 54.24 **Disturbance of the ocean floor by trawling.** These photos show the seafloor off northwestern Australia before (top) and after (bottom) deep-sea trawlers have passed.

growth and yellow leaves due to inadequate nitrogen supply. The exceptions are *Dryas* and, particularly, alder; these species have symbiotic bacteria that fix atmospheric nitrogen (see Chapter 37). Soil nitrogen content increases rapidly during the alder stage of succession and continues to increase during the spruce stage **(Figure 54.23)**. By altering soil properties, pioneer plant species permit new plant species to grow, and the new plants in turn alter the environment in different ways, contributing to succession.

Human Disturbance

Ecological succession is a response to disturbance of the environment, and one of the strongest agents of disturbance today is human activity. Of all animals, humans have the greatest impact on biological communities worldwide. Agricultural development has disrupted what were once the vast grasslands of the North American prairie. Logging and clearing for urban development, mining, and farming have reduced large tracts of forests to small patches of disconnected woodlots in many parts of the United States and throughout Europe. After forests are clear-cut, weedy and shrubby vegetation often colonizes the area and dominates it for many years. This type of vegetation is also found in agricultural fields that are no longer under cultivation and in vacant lots and construction sites.

Human disturbance of communities is by no means limited to the United States and Europe; nor is it a recent problem. Tropical rain forests are quickly disappearing as a result of clear-cutting for lumber, cattle grazing, and farmland. Centuries of overgrazing and agricultural disturbance have contributed to famine in parts of Africa by turning seasonal grasslands into vast barren areas.

Humans disturb marine ecosystems just as extensively as terrestrial ones. The effects of ocean trawling, where boats drag weighted nets across the seafloor, are similar to those of clear-cutting a forest or plowing a field **(Figure 54.24)**. The trawls scrape and scour corals and other life on the seafloor and in its sediments. In a typical year, ships trawl 15 million km^2 of ocean floor, an area about the size of South America and 150 times larger than the area of forests that are clear-cut annually.

Because human disturbance is often severe, it reduces species diversity in many communities. In Chapter 56, we will take a closer look at how community disturbance by human activities is affecting the diversity of life.

CONCEPT 54.4

Biogeographic factors affect community biodiversity

So far we have examined relatively small-scale or local factors that influence the diversity of communities, including the effects of species interactions, dominant species, and many types of disturbances. Ecologists also recognize that large-scale biogeographic factors contribute to the tremendous range of diversity observed in biological communities. The contributions of two biogeographic factors in particular—the latitude of a community and the area it occupies—have been investigated for more than a century.

Latitudinal Gradients

In the 1850s, both Charles Darwin and Alfred Wallace pointed out that plant and animal life was generally more abundant and diverse in the tropics than in other parts of the globe. Since that time, many researchers around the world have confirmed this observation. For example, one study found that a 6.6-hectare (1 ha = 10,000 m²) plot in tropical Malaysia contained 711 tree species, while a 2-ha plot of deciduous forest in Michigan typically contains just 10 to 15 tree species. Moreover, in all of western Europe north of the Alps there are only 50 tree species. Many groups of animals show similar latitudinal gradients. For instance, there are more than 200 species of ants in Brazil but only 7 in Alaska.

The two key factors in latitudinal gradients of species richness are probably evolutionary history and climate. Over the course of evolutionary time, species diversity may increase in a community as more speciation events occur. Tropical communities are generally older than temperate or polar communities. This age difference stems partly from the fact that the growing season is about five times as long in tropical forests as in the tundra communities of high latitudes. In effect, biological time, and hence intervals between speciation events, run about five times as fast in the tropics as near the poles. And many polar and temperate communities have repeatedly "started over" as a result of major disturbances in the form of glaciations.

Climate is likely the primary cause of the latitudinal gradient in biodiversity. In terrestrial communities, the two main climatic factors correlated with biodiversity are solar energy input and water availability, both of which are relatively high in the tropics. These factors can be considered together by measuring a community's rate of **evapotranspiration**, the evaporation of water from soil plus the transpiration of water from plants. Evapotranspiration, a function of solar radiation, temperature, and water availability, is much higher in hot areas with abundant rainfall than in areas with low temperatures or low precipitation. *Potential evapotranspiration*, a measure of potential water loss that assumes that water is readily available, is determined by the amount of solar radiation and temperature and is highest in regions where both are plentiful. The species richness of plants and animals correlates with both measures of evapotranspiration **(Figure 54.25)**.

Area Effects

In 1807, naturalist and explorer Alexander von Humboldt described one of the first patterns of biodiversity to be recognized,

(a) Trees

(b) Vertebrates

▲ **Figure 54.25 Energy, water, and species richness. (a)** Species richness of North American trees increases most predictably with actual evapotranspiration, while **(b)** vertebrate species richness in North America increases most predictably with potential evapotranspiration. Evapotranspiration values are expressed as rainfall equivalents.

the **species-area curve**: All other factors being equal, the larger the geographic area of a community, the more species it has. The likely explanation for this pattern is that larger areas offer a greater diversity of habitats and microhabitats than smaller areas. In conservation biology, developing species-area curves for the key taxa in a community helps ecologists predict how the potential loss of a certain area of habitat is likely to affect the community's biodiversity.

▲ **Figure 54.26 Species-area curve for North American breeding birds.** Both area and number of species are plotted on a logarithmic scale. The data points range from a 0.2-ha plot with 3 species in Pennsylvania to the whole United States and Canada (1.9 billion ha) with 625 species.

Figure 54.26 is a species-area curve for North American breeding birds (birds with breeding populations in the mapped area, as opposed to migrant populations). The slope indicates the extent to which species richness increases with community area. While the slopes of different species-area curves vary, the basic concept of diversity increasing with increasing area applies in a variety of situations, from surveys of ant diversity in New Guinea to the number of plant species on islands of different sizes. In fact, island biogeography provides some of the best examples of species-area curves, as we will discuss next.

Island Equilibrium Model

Because of their isolation and limited size, islands provide excellent opportunities for studying the biogeographic factors that affect the species diversity of communities. By "islands," we mean not only oceanic islands, but also habitat islands on land, such as lakes, mountain peaks separated by lowlands, or natural woodland fragments surrounded by areas disturbed by humans—in other words, any patch surrounded by an environment not suitable for the "island" species. In the 1960s, American ecologists Robert MacArthur and E. O. Wilson developed a general model of island biogeography identifying the key determinants of species diversity on an island with a given set of physical characteristics **(Figure 54.27)**.

Consider a newly formed oceanic island that receives colonizing species from a distant mainland. Two factors that determine the number of species on the island are the rate at which new species immigrate to the island and the rate at which species become extinct on the island. At any given time, an island's immigration and extinction rates are affected by the number of species already present. As the number of species on the island increases, the immigration rate of new species decreases, because any individual reaching the island is less likely to represent a species that is not already present. At the same time, as more species inhabit an island, extinction rates on the island increase because of the greater likelihood of competitive exclusion.

Two physical features of the island further affect immigration and extinction rates: its size and its distance from the mainland. Small islands generally have lower immigration rates because potential colonizers are less likely to reach a small island. For instance, birds blown out to sea by a storm

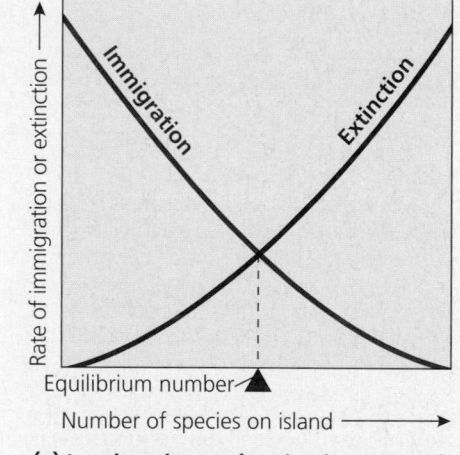

(a) Immigration and extinction rates. The equilibrium number of species on an island represents a balance between the immigration of new species and the extinction of species already there.

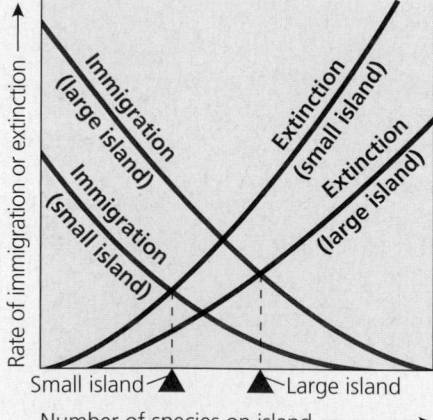

(b) Effect of island size. Large islands may ultimately have a larger equilibrium number of species than small islands because immigration rates tend to be higher and extinction rates lower on large islands.

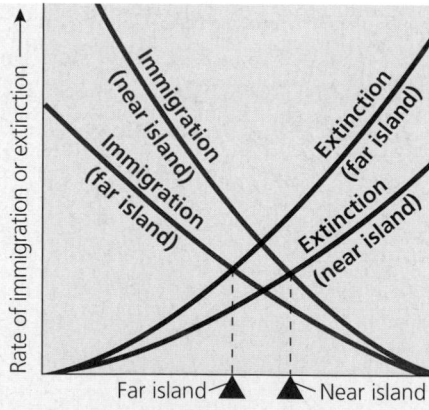

(c) Effect of distance from mainland. Near islands tend to have larger equilibrium numbers of species than far islands because immigration rates to near islands are higher and extinction rates lower.

▲ **Figure 54.27 The equilibrium model of island biogeography.** Black triangles represent equilibrium numbers of species.

are more likely to land by chance on a larger island than on a small one. Small islands also have higher extinction rates, as they generally contain fewer resources and less diverse habitats for colonizing species to partition. Distance from the mainland is also important; for two islands of equal size, a closer island generally has a higher immigration rate than one farther away. Because of their higher immigration rates, closer islands also have lower extinction rates, as arriving colonists help sustain the presence of a species on a near island and prevent its extinction.

These relationships make up MacArthur and Wilson's model of island biogeography (see Figure 54.27). Immigration and extinction rates are plotted as a function of the number of species present on the island. This model is called the *island equilibrium model* because an equilibrium will eventually be reached where the rate of species immigration equals the rate of species extinction. The number of species at this equilibrium point is correlated with the island's size and distance from the mainland. Like any ecological equilibrium, this species equilibrium is dynamic; immigration and extinction continue, and the exact species composition may change over time.

MacArthur and Wilson's studies of the diversity of plants and animals on many island chains, including the Galápagos Islands, support the prediction that species richness increases with island size, in keeping with the island equilibrium model (**Figure 54.28**). Species counts also fit the prediction that the number of species decreases with increasing remoteness of the island.

The island equilibrium model's predictions of equilibria in the species composition of communities may apply in only a limited number of cases and over relatively short periods, where colonization is the main process affecting species composition. Over longer periods, abiotic disturbances such as storms, adaptive evolutionary changes, and speciation generally alter the species composition and community structure on islands. Nonetheless, the model is widely applied in conservation biology, particularly for the design of habitat reserves and for providing a starting point for predicting the effects of habitat loss on species diversity.

▼ **Figure 54.28** **Inquiry**

How does species richness relate to area?

FIELD STUDY Ecologists Robert MacArthur and E. O. Wilson studied the number of plant species on the Galápagos Islands, which vary greatly in size, in relation to the area of each island.

RESULTS

CONCLUSION Plant species richness increases with island size, supporting the island equilibrium model.

SOURCE R. H. MacArthur and E. O. Wilson, *The Theory of Island Biogeography*, Princeton University Press, Princeton, NJ (1967).

WHAT IF? Four islands in this study ranging in area from about 40 to 10,000 ha all contained about 50 plant species. What does such variation tell you about the simple assumptions of the island equilibrium model?

CONCEPT **54.5**

Community ecology is useful for understanding pathogen life cycles and controlling human disease

Now that we have examined several important factors that structure ecological communities, let's finish the chapter by examining community interactions involving **pathogens**—disease-causing microorganisms, viruses, viroids, or prions (viroids and prions are infectious RNA molecules and proteins, respectively; see Chapter 19). Scientists have recently come to appreciate how universal the effects of pathogens are in ecological communities. Pathogens can alter community structure quickly and extensively, as you saw in the discussion of chestnut blight and the fungus that causes it (see Concept 54.2). Ecologists are also applying ecological knowledge to help track and control the pathogens that cause human diseases.

Pathogens and Community Structure

In spite of the potential of pathogens to limit populations, pathogens have until recently been the subject of relatively few ecological studies. This imbalance is now being addressed as dramatic events highlight the ecological importance of disease.

Coral reef communities are increasingly susceptible to the influence of newly discovered pathogens. White-band disease, caused by an unknown pathogen, has resulted in dramatic changes in the structure and composition of Caribbean reefs. The disease kills corals by causing their tissue to slough off in a band from the base to the tip of the branches (Figure 54.29). Because of the disease, staghorn coral (*Acropora cervicornis*) has virtually disappeared from the Caribbean since the 1980s. In the same region, populations of elkhorn coral (*Acropora palmata*) have also been decimated. Such corals provide key habitat for lobsters as well as snappers and other fish species. When the corals die, they are quickly overgrown by algae. Surgeonfish and other herbivores that feed on algae come to dominate the fish community. Eventually, the corals topple because of damage from storms and other disturbances. The complex, three-dimensional structure of the reef disappears, and diversity plummets.

Pathogens also influence community structure in terrestrial ecosystems. In the forests and savannas of California, trees of several species are dying from sudden oak death (SOD). This recently discovered disease is caused by the fungus-like protist *Phytophthora ramorum* (see Chapter 28). SOD was first described in California in 1995 when hikers noticed trees dying around San Francisco Bay. By 2007, it had spread more than 650 km. During that time, it killed more than a million oaks and other trees from the central California coast to southern Oregon. The loss of these oaks led to a decrease in the abundance of at least five bird species, including the acorn woodpecker and the oak titmouse, that rely on the oaks for food and habitat. Although there is currently no cure for SOD, scientists

▲ Figure 54.29 **White-band disease visible on a coral.**

recently sequenced the genome of *P. ramorum* in hopes of finding a way to fight the pathogen.

One reason ecologists now study pathogens is that human activities are transporting pathogens around the world at unprecedented rates. Genetic analyses using simple sequence DNA (see Chapter 21) suggest that the fungus that causes SOD likely came from Europe through the horticulture trade. Similarly, the pathogens that cause human diseases are spread by our global economy. A person traveling by airplane can quickly introduce a pathogen to a new location; this mechanism may have been how the West Nile virus arrived in North America in 1999. Many diseases are becoming more common, and community ecology is needed to help study and combat them.

Community Ecology and Zoonotic Diseases

Three-quarters of today's emerging human diseases, including hantavirus and mad cow disease (see Chapter 19), and many historically important ones, such as malaria (see Chapter 28), are caused by **zoonotic pathogens**. Zoonotic pathogens are defined as those that are transferred from other animals to humans, either through direct contact with an infected animal or by means of an intermediate species, called a **vector**. The vectors that spread zoonotic diseases are often parasites, including ticks, lice, and mosquitoes. Community ecologists can help prevent zoonotic diseases by identifying key species interactions involving pathogens and their vectors and by tracking pathogen spread.

Understanding parasite life cycles enables scientists to devise ways to control zoonotic diseases. The disease river blindness, for instance, is caused by a nematode transmitted by blackflies. When the World Health Organization began a global fight against river blindness, doctors had no medical treatments for the disease. Scientists focused instead on controlling the blackflies that spread the pathogenic nematodes. They used airplanes to spray biodegradable insecticides (which were monitored to minimize harm to aquatic communities). Ivermectin, a drug that kills the nematodes, was developed in 1987, and since then the combination of vector control and ivermectin use has saved the sight of an estimated 300,000 people. However, research published in 2007 suggests that the nematodes are developing resistance to ivermectin, so blackfly control remains a key part of the program to fight the disease.

Ecologists also use their knowledge of community interactions to track the spread of zoonotic diseases. A timely example is ecological research on the spread of avian flu. Avian flu is caused by highly contagious viruses transmitted through the saliva and feces of birds (see Chapter 19). Most of these viruses affect wild birds mildly, but they often cause stronger symptoms in domesticated birds, the most common source of human infections. Since 2003, one particular viral strain, called H5N1, has killed hundreds of millions of poultry and more than 150 people. Millions more people are at risk of infection.

the Americas. The most likely place for infected wild birds to enter the Americas is Alaska, the entry point for ducks, geese, and shorebirds that migrate across the Bering Sea from Asia each year. Ecologists are studying the potential spread of the virus by trapping and testing migrating and resident birds in Alaska **(Figure 54.30)**. These ecological detectives are trying to catch the first wave of the disease entering North America.

Community ecology provides the foundation for understanding the life cycles of pathogens and their interactions with hosts. Pathogen interactions are also greatly influenced by changes in the environment. To control pathogens and the diseases they cause, scientists need an ecosystem perspective—an intimate knowledge of how the pathogens interact with other species and with their environment. Ecosystems are the subject of Chapter 55.

▲ **Figure 54.30 Tracking avian flu.** Graduate student Travis Booms, of the University of Alaska, Fairbanks, bands a young gyrfalcon (*Falco rusticolus*) as part of a project to monitor the spread of the disease.

Control programs that quarantine domestic birds or monitor their transport may be ineffective if avian flu spreads naturally through the movements of wild birds. From 2003 to 2006, the H5N1 strain spread rapidly from southeast Asia into Europe and Africa, but by late 2007 it had not appeared in Australia or

---

CONCEPT CHECK 54.5

1. What are pathogens?
2. Some parasites require contact with at least two host species to complete their life cycle. Why might this characteristic be important for the spread of certain zoonotic diseases?
3. **WHAT IF?** Suppose a new zoonotic disease emerges from a tropical rain forest. Doctors have no way yet to treat the disease, so preventing infections is particularly important. As a community ecologist, how might you help prevent the spread of the disease?

For suggested answers, see Appendix A.

Chapter 54 Review

SUMMARY OF KEY CONCEPTS

CONCEPT 54.1

Community interactions are classified by whether they help, harm, or have no effect on the species involved (pp. 1198–1204)

▶ Populations are linked by interspecific interactions that affect the survival and reproduction of the species that engage in them. These interactions include competition, predation, herbivory, and symbiosis. Parasitism, mutualism, and commensalism are types of symbiotic interactions.

MEDIA

Activity Interspecific Interactions
Biology Labs On-Line PopulationEcologyLab

Interspecific Interaction	Description
Competition (−/−)	Two or more species compete for a resource that is in short supply. The competitive exclusion principle states that two species cannot coexist in the same community if their niches (ecological roles) are identical.
Predation (+/−)	One species, the predator, kills and eats the other, the prey. Predation has led to diverse adaptations, including mimicry.
Herbivory (+/−)	An herbivore eats part of a plant or alga. Plants have various chemical and mechanical defenses against herbivory, and herbivores have specialized adaptations for feeding.
Symbiosis	Individuals of two or more species live in close contact with one another. Symbiosis includes parasitism, mutualism, and commensalism.
Parasitism (+/−)	The parasite derives its nourishment from a second organism, its host, which is harmed.
Mutualism (+/+)	Both species benefit from the interaction.
Commensalism (+/0)	One species benefits from the interaction, while the other is unaffected by it.

Dominant and keystone species exert strong controls on community structure (pp. 1204–1210)

▶ **Species Diversity** Species diversity measures the number of species in a community—its species richness—and their relative abundance. A community with similar abundances of species is more diverse than one in which one or two species are abundant and the remainder are rare.

▶ **Trophic Structure** Trophic structure is a key factor in community dynamics. Food chains link the trophic levels from producers to top carnivores. Branching food chains and complex trophic interactions form food webs. The energetic hypothesis suggests that the length of a food chain is limited by the inefficiency of energy transfer along the chain. The dynamic stability hypothesis proposes that long food chains are less stable than short chains.

▶ **Species with a Large Impact** Dominant species and keystone species exert strong controls on community structure. Dominant species are the most abundant species in a community, and their dominance is achieved by having high competitive ability. Keystone species are usually less abundant species that exert a disproportionate influence on community structure because of their ecological niche. Ecosystem "engineers," also called foundation species, exert influence on community structure through their effects on the physical environment.

▶ **Bottom-Up and Top-Down Controls** The bottom-up model proposes a unidirectional influence from lower to higher trophic levels, in which nutrients and other abiotic factors are the main determinants of community structure, including the abundance of primary producers. The top-down model proposes that control of each trophic level comes from the trophic level above, with the result that predators control herbivores, which in turn control primary producers.

MEDIA

Investigation How Are Impacts on Community Diversity Measured?
Activity Food Webs

Disturbance influences species diversity and composition (pp. 1211–1214)

▶ **Characterizing Disturbance** More and more evidence suggests that disturbance and lack of equilibrium, rather than stability and equilibrium, are the norm for most communities. According to the intermediate disturbance hypothesis, moderate levels of disturbance can foster higher species diversity than can low or high levels of disturbance.

▶ **Ecological Succession** Ecological succession is the sequence of community and ecosystem changes after a disturbance. Primary succession occurs where no soil exists when succession begins; secondary succession begins in an area where soil remains after a disturbance. Mechanisms that produce community change during succession include facilitation and inhibition.

▶ **Human Disturbance** Humans are the most widespread agents of disturbance, and their effects on communities often reduce species diversity. Humans also prevent some naturally occurring disturbances, such as fire, which can be important to community structure.

MEDIA

Activity Primary Succession

Biogeographic factors affect community biodiversity (pp. 1214–1217)

▶ **Latitudinal Gradients** Species richness generally declines along a latitudinal gradient from the tropics to the poles. The greater age of tropical environments may account for the greater species richness of the tropics. Climate also influences the biodiversity gradient through energy (heat and light) and water.

▶ **Area Effects** Species richness is directly related to a community's geographic size, a principle formalized in the species-area curve.

▶ **Island Equilibrium Model** Species richness on islands depends on island size and distance from the mainland. The island equilibrium model maintains that species richness on an ecological island reaches an equilibrium where new immigrations are balanced by extinctions. This model may not apply over long periods, during which abiotic disturbances, evolutionary changes, and speciation may alter community structure.

MEDIA

Activity Exploring Island Biogeography
GraphIt! Species-Area Effect and Island Biogeography

Community ecology is useful for understanding pathogen life cycles and controlling human disease (pp. 1217–1219)

▶ **Pathogens and Community Structure** Recent work has highlighted the role that pathogens play in structuring terrestrial and marine communities.

▶ **Community Ecology and Zoonotic Diseases** Zoonotic diseases, caused by pathogens transferred from other animals to humans, are the largest class of emerging human diseases. Community ecology provides the framework for understanding the species interactions associated with such pathogens and for our ability to track and control their spread.

TESTING YOUR KNOWLEDGE

SELF-QUIZ

1. The feeding relationships among the species in a community determine the community's
   a. secondary succession.
   b. ecological niche.
   c. trophic structure.
   d. species-area curve.
   e. species richness.

2. The principle of competitive exclusion states that
   a. two species cannot coexist in the same habitat.
   b. competition between two species always causes extinction or emigration of one species.
   c. competition in a population promotes survival of the best-adapted individuals.
   d. two species that have exactly the same niche cannot coexist in a community.
   e. two species will stop reproducing until one species leaves the habitat.

3. Keystone predators can maintain species diversity in a community if they
   a. competitively exclude other predators.
   b. prey on the community's dominant species.
   c. allow immigration of other predators.
   d. reduce the number of disruptions in the community.
   e. prey only on the least abundant species in the community.

4. Food chains are sometimes short because
   a. only a single species of herbivore feeds on each plant species.
   b. local extinction of a species causes extinction of the other species in its food chain.
   c. most of the energy in a trophic level is lost as it passes to the next higher level.
   d. predator species tend to be less diverse and less abundant than prey species.
   e. most producers are inedible.

5. Based on the intermediate disturbance hypothesis, a community's species diversity is
   a. increased by frequent massive disturbance.
   b. increased by stable conditions with no disturbance.
   c. increased by moderate levels of disturbance.
   d. increased when humans intervene to eliminate disturbance.
   e. increased by intensive disturbance by humans.

6. Which of the following could qualify as a top-down control on a grassland community?
   a. limitation of plant biomass by rainfall amount
   b. influence of temperature on competition among plants
   c. influence of soil nutrients on the abundance of grasses versus wildflowers
   d. effect of grazing intensity by bison on plant species diversity
   e. effect of humidity on plant growth rates

7. The most plausible hypothesis to explain why species richness is higher in tropical than in temperate regions is that
   a. tropical communities are younger.
   b. tropical regions generally have more available water and higher levels of solar radiation.
   c. higher temperatures cause more rapid speciation.
   d. biodiversity increases as evapotranspiration decreases.
   e. tropical regions have very high rates of immigration and very low rates of extinction.

8. According to the equilibrium model of island biogeography, species richness would be greatest on an island that is
   a. small and remote.
   b. large and remote.
   c. large and close to a mainland.
   d. small and close to a mainland.
   e. environmentally homogeneous.

9. Community 1 contains 100 individuals distributed among four species (A, B, C, and D). Community 2 contains 100 individuals distributed among three species (A, B, and C).
   Community 1: 5A, 5B, 85C, 5D
   Community 2: 30A, 40B, 30C
   Calculate the Shannon diversity (H) for each community. Which community is more diverse?

10. **DRAW IT** Figure 54.13 presents a partial food web for the Chesapeake Bay estuary. Another important species in Chesapeake Bay is the blue crab (*Callinectes sapidus*). It is an omnivore, eating eelgrass and other primary producers as well as clams. Blue crabs are also cannibals. In turn, the crabs are a preferred food source for the endangered Kemp's Ridley sea turtle and, of course, for people. Based on this information, draw a food web that includes the blue crab. Assuming that the top-down model holds for this system, what would happen to the abundance of eelgrass if people were banned from catching crabs?

For Self-Quiz answers, see Appendix A.

MEDIA Visit www.campbellbiology.com for a Practice Test.

EVOLUTION CONNECTION

11. Explain why adaptations of particular organisms to interspecific competition may not necessarily represent instances of character displacement. What would a researcher have to demonstrate about two competing species to make a convincing case for character displacement?

SCIENTIFIC INQUIRY

12. An ecologist studying plants in the desert performed the following experiment. She staked out two identical plots, each of which included a few sagebrush plants and numerous small annual wildflowers. She found the same five wildflower species in roughly equal numbers on both plots. She then enclosed one of the plots with a fence to keep out kangaroo rats, the most common grain-eaters of the area. After two years, four of the wildflower species were no longer present in the fenced plot, but one species had increased drastically. The control plot had not changed in species diversity. Using the principles of community ecology, propose a hypothesis to explain her results. What additional evidence would support your hypothesis?

SCIENCE, TECHNOLOGY, AND SOCIETY

13. By 1935, hunting and trapping had eliminated wolves from the United States except for Alaska. Because wolves have since been protected as an endangered species, they have moved south from Canada and have become reestablished in the Rocky Mountains and northern Great Lakes region. Conservationists who would like to speed up wolf recovery have reintroduced wolves into Yellowstone National Park. Local ranchers are opposed to bringing back the wolves because they fear predation on their cattle and sheep. What are some reasons for reestablishing wolves in Yellowstone National Park? What effects might the reintroduction of wolves have on the ecological communities in the region? What might be done to mitigate the conflicts between ranchers and wolves?

Ecosystems

▲ Figure 55.1 **What makes this ecosystem dynamic?**

KEY CONCEPTS

55.1 Physical laws govern energy flow and chemical cycling in ecosystems

55.2 Energy and other limiting factors control primary production in ecosystems

55.3 Energy transfer between trophic levels is typically only 10% efficient

55.4 Biological and geochemical processes cycle nutrients between organic and inorganic parts of an ecosystem

55.5 Human activities now dominate most chemical cycles on Earth

OVERVIEW

Observing Ecosystems

Sitting beside a mountain lake, you watch the last rays of the sun reflected on its surface (**Figure 55.1**). While enjoying the tranquil scene, you begin to sense that the lake is much more dynamic than you first thought. Small rings form where fish snatch insects that have fallen to the lake's surface. A stream flows into the lake, delivering a bounty of mineral nutrients and organic matter. A slight breeze carries the lake's scent, shaped by microorganisms whose activities affect the composition of Earth's atmosphere. More than just a body of water, the lake is an **ecosystem**, the sum of all the organisms living within its boundaries and all the abiotic factors with which they interact.

An ecosystem can encompass a vast area, such as a forest, or a microcosm, such as the space under a fallen log or a small pool (**Figure 55.2**). As with populations and communities, the boundaries of ecosystems sometimes are not discrete. Many ecologists view the entire biosphere as a global ecosystem, a composite of all the local ecosystems on Earth.

Regardless of an ecosystem's size, its dynamics involve two processes that cannot be fully described by population or community phenomena: energy flow and chemical cycling. Energy enters most ecosystems as sunlight. It is converted to chemical energy by autotrophs, passed to heterotrophs in the organic compounds of food, and dissipated as heat. Chemical elements, such as carbon and nitrogen, are cycled among abiotic and biotic components of the ecosystem. Photosynthetic organisms assimilate these elements in inorganic form from the air, soil, and water and incorporate them into their biomass, some of which is consumed by animals. The elements are returned in inorganic form to the environment by the metabolism of plants and animals and by other organisms, such as bacteria and fungi, that break down organic wastes and dead organisms.

Both energy and matter are transformed in ecosystems through photosynthesis and feeding relationships. Unlike matter, however, energy cannot be recycled. Therefore, an ecosystem must be powered by a continuous influx of energy from an external source—in most cases, the sun. Energy flows through ecosystems, whereas matter cycles within and through them.

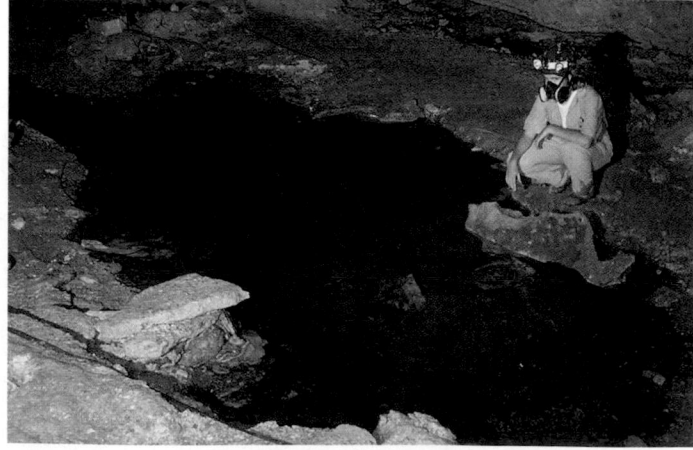

▲ Figure 55.2 **A cave pool.** This small ecosystem is home to a complex microbial community.

Resources critical to human survival and welfare, ranging from the food we eat to the oxygen we breathe, are products of ecosystem processes. In this chapter, we will explore the dynamics of energy flow and chemical cycling, emphasizing the results of ecosystem experiments. One way to study ecosystem processes is to alter environmental factors, such as temperature or the abundance of nutrients, and study how ecosystems respond. We will also consider some of the impacts of human activities on energy flow and chemical cycling. Those impacts are evident not just in human-dominated ecosystems, such as cities and farms, but in the most remote ecosystems on Earth.

CONCEPT **55.1**

Physical laws govern energy flow and chemical cycling in ecosystems

In Unit Two, we saw how cells transform energy and matter, subject to the laws of thermodynamics. Like cell biologists, ecosystem ecologists study the transformations of energy and matter within a system and measure the amounts of both that cross the system's boundaries. By grouping the species in a community into trophic levels of feeding relationships (see Chapter 54), we can follow the transformations of energy in an ecosystem and map the movements of chemical elements.

Conservation of Energy

Because ecosystem ecologists study the interactions of organisms with the physical environment, many ecosystem approaches are based on well-established laws of physics and chemistry. The first law of thermodynamics, which you studied in Chapter 8, states that energy cannot be created or destroyed but only transferred or transformed. Thus, we can potentially account for the transfer of energy through an ecosystem from its input as solar radiation to its release as heat from organisms. Plants and other photosynthetic organisms convert solar energy to chemical energy, but the total amount of energy does not change: The total amount of energy stored in organic molecules plus the amounts reflected and dissipated as heat must equal the total solar energy intercepted by the plant. One area of ecosystem ecology involves computing such energy budgets and tracing energy flow through ecosystems in order to understand the factors that control these energy transfers. Such transfers help determine how many organisms a habitat can support and the amount of food humans can harvest from a given site.

One implication of the second law of thermodynamics, which states that every exchange of energy increases the entropy of the universe, is that energy conversions cannot be completely efficient; some energy is always lost as heat (see Chapter 8). This idea suggests that we can measure the efficiency of ecological energy conversions in the same way we measure the efficiency of light bulbs and car engines. Energy flowing through ecosystems is ultimately dissipated into space as heat, so if the sun were not continuously providing energy to Earth, most ecosystems would vanish.

Conservation of Mass

Matter, like energy, cannot be created or destroyed. This **law of conservation of mass** is as important to ecosystem ecologists as the laws of thermodynamics are. Because mass is conserved, we can determine how much of a chemical element cycles within an ecosystem or is gained or lost by that ecosystem over time.

Unlike energy, chemical elements are continually recycled within ecosystems. A carbon atom in CO_2 is released from the soil by a decomposer, taken up by a grass through photosynthesis, consumed by a bison or other grazer, and returned to the soil in the bison's waste. The measurement and analysis of such chemical cycling within ecosystems and in the biosphere as a whole are an important aspect of ecosystem ecology.

Although elements are not lost on a global scale, they move between ecosystems as inputs and outputs. In a forest ecosystem, for example, most mineral nutrients—the essential elements that plants obtain from soil—enter as dust or as solutes dissolved in rainwater or leached from rocks in the ground. Nitrogen is also supplied through the biological process of nitrogen fixation (see Figure 37.9). On the output side, gases return elements to the atmosphere, and water carries materials away. Like organisms, ecosystems are open systems, absorbing energy and mass and releasing heat and waste products.

Most inputs and outputs are small compared to the amounts recycled within ecosystems. Still, the balance between inputs and outputs determines whether an ecosystem is a source or a sink for a given element. If a mineral nutrient's outputs exceed its inputs, it will eventually limit production in that system. Human activities often change the balance of inputs and outputs considerably, as we will see later in this chapter.

Energy, Mass, and Trophic Levels

As you read in Chapter 54, ecologists assign species to trophic levels on the basis of their main source of nutrition and energy. The trophic level that ultimately supports all others consists of autotrophs, also called the **primary producers** of the ecosystem. Most autotrophs are photosynthetic organisms that use light energy to synthesize sugars and other organic compounds, which they then use as fuel for cellular respiration and as building material for growth. Plants, algae, and photosynthetic prokaryotes are the biosphere's main autotrophs, although chemosynthetic prokaryotes are the primary producers in certain ecosystems, such as deep-sea hydrothermal vents (see Figure 52.18) and some spring-fed pools in caves (see Figure 55.2).

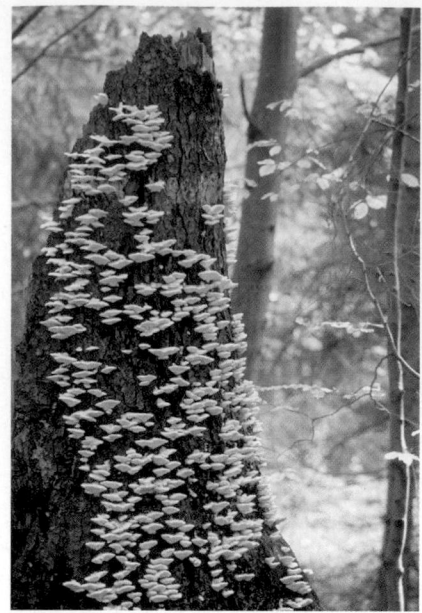

▲ **Figure 55.3 Fungi decomposing a dead tree.**

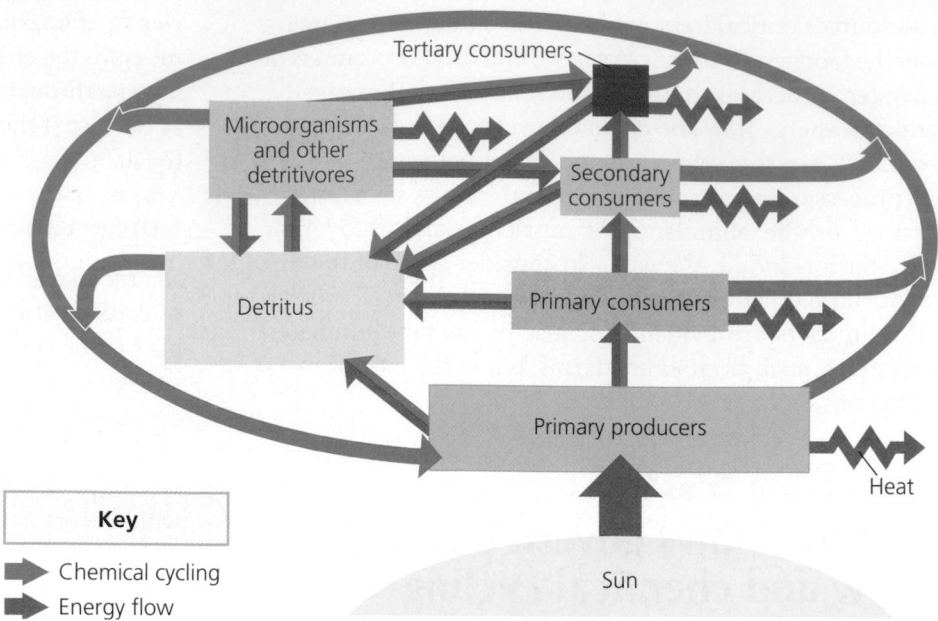

Key

➡ Chemical cycling
➡ Energy flow

▲ Figure 55.4 **An overview of energy and nutrient dynamics in an ecosystem.** Energy enters, flows through, and exits an ecosystem, whereas chemical nutrients cycle primarily within it. In this generalized scheme, energy (dark orange arrows) enters from the sun as radiation, moves as chemical energy transfers through the food web, and exits as heat radiated into space. Most transfers of nutrients (blue arrows) through the trophic levels lead eventually to detritus; the nutrients then cycle back to the primary producers.

Organisms in trophic levels above the primary producers are heterotrophs, which directly or indirectly depend on the biosynthetic output of primary producers. Herbivores, which eat plants and other primary producers, are **primary consumers**. Carnivores that eat herbivores are **secondary consumers**, and carnivores that eat other carnivores are **tertiary consumers**.

Another important group of heterotrophs consists of the detritivores. **Detritivores**, or **decomposers**, are consumers that get their energy from **detritus**, which is nonliving organic material, such as the remains of dead organisms, feces, fallen leaves, and wood. Many detritivores are in turn eaten by secondary and tertiary consumers. Two important groups of detritivores are prokaryotes and fungi **(Figure 55.3)**. These organisms secrete enzymes that digest organic material; they then absorb the breakdown products, linking the consumers and primary producers in an ecosystem. In a forest, for example, birds eat earthworms that have been feeding on leaf litter and its associated prokaryotes and fungi.

Even more important than this channeling of resources from producers to consumers is the role that detritivores play in recycling chemical elements back to primary producers. Detritivores convert organic materials from all trophic levels to inorganic compounds usable by primary producers, closing the loop of an ecosystem's chemical cycling. Producers can then recycle these elements into organic compounds. If decomposition stopped, all life on Earth would cease as detritus piled up and the supply of chemical ingredients for the syn-

thesis of new organic matter was exhausted. **Figure 55.4** summarizes the trophic relationships in an ecosystem.

CONCEPT 55.2

Energy and other limiting factors control primary production in ecosystems

The amount of light energy converted to chemical energy (organic compounds) by autotrophs during a given time period is an ecosystem's **primary production**. This photosynthetic product is the starting point for studies of ecosystem metabolism and energy flow.

Ecosystem Energy Budgets

Most primary producers use light energy to synthesize energy-rich organic molecules, which are subsequently broken down to generate ATP (see Chapter 10). Consumers acquire their organic fuels secondhand (or even third- or fourthhand) through food webs such as those in Figures 54.12 and 54.13. Therefore, the amount of all photosynthetic production sets the spending limit for the entire ecosystem's energy budget.

The Global Energy Budget

Every day, Earth's atmosphere is bombarded by about 10^{22} joules of solar radiation (1 J = 0.239 cal). This is enough energy to supply the demands of the entire human population for approximately 25 years at 2006 consumption levels. As described in Chapter 52, the intensity of the solar energy striking Earth varies with latitude, with the tropics receiving the greatest input. Most incoming solar radiation is absorbed, scattered, or reflected by clouds and dust in the atmosphere. The amount of solar radiation that ultimately reaches Earth's surface limits the possible photosynthetic output of ecosystems.

Furthermore, only a small fraction of the solar radiation that makes it to Earth's surface is used in photosynthesis. Much of the radiation strikes materials that don't photosynthesize, such as ice and soil. Of the radiation that does reach photosynthetic organisms, only certain wavelengths are absorbed by photosynthetic pigments; the rest is transmitted, reflected, or lost as heat. As a result, only about 1% of the visible light that strikes photosynthetic organisms is converted to chemical energy by photosynthesis. Nevertheless, Earth's primary producers collectively create about 150 billion metric tons (150×10^{12} kg) of organic material each year.

Gross and Net Primary Production

Total primary production in an ecosystem is known as that ecosystem's **gross primary production (GPP)**—the amount of light energy that is converted to chemical energy by photosynthesis per unit time. Not all of this production is stored as organic material in the primary producers because they use some of the molecules as fuel in their own cellular respiration. **Net primary production (NPP)** is equal to gross primary production minus the energy used by the primary producers for respiration (R):

$$NPP = GPP - R$$

In many ecosystems, NPP is about one-half of GPP. To ecologists, net primary production is the key measurement because it represents the storage of chemical energy that will be available to consumers in the ecosystem.

Net primary production can be expressed as energy per unit area per unit time ($J/m^2 \cdot yr$) or as biomass (mass of vegetation) added to the ecosystem per unit area per unit time ($g/m^2 \cdot yr$). (Note that biomass is usually expressed in terms of the dry mass of organic material.) An ecosystem's net primary production should not be confused with the *total* biomass of photosynthetic autotrophs present at a given time, a measure called the *standing crop*. Net primary production is the amount of *new* biomass added in a given period of time. Although a forest has a very large standing crop, its net primary production may actually be less than that of some grasslands, which do not accumulate much vegetation because animals consume the plants rapidly and because grasses and herbs decompose more quickly than trees do.

Satellites provide a powerful tool for studying global patterns of primary production (**Figure 55.5**). Images produced from satellite data show that different ecosystems vary considerably in

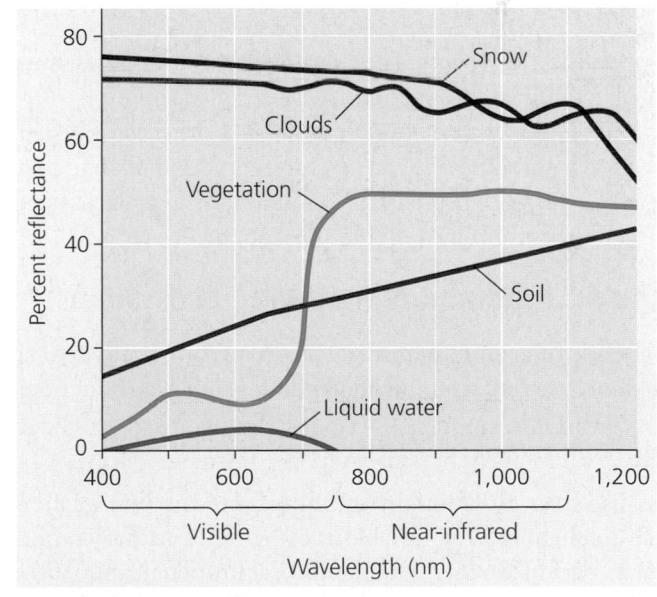

▼ Figure 55.5 **Research Method**

Determining Primary Production with Satellites

APPLICATION Because chlorophyll captures visible light (see Figure 10.9), photosynthetic organisms absorb more visible wavelengths (about 380–750 nm) than near-infrared wavelengths (750–1,100 nm). Scientists use this difference in absorption to estimate the rate of photosynthesis in different regions of the globe using satellites.

TECHNIQUE Most satellites determine what they "see" by comparing the ratios of wavelengths reflected back to them. Vegetation reflects much more near-infrared radiation than visible radiation, producing a reflectance pattern very different from that of snow, clouds, soil, and liquid water.

RESULTS Scientists use the satellite data to help produce maps of primary production like that in Figure 55.6.

Net primary production (kg carbon/m²·yr)

| 0 | 1 | 2 | 3 |

▲ **Figure 55.6 Global net primary production in 2002.** The map is based on data, such as chlorophyll activity, collected by satellites. Note that tropical areas on land have the highest rates of production (yellow and red on the map).

? *Does this global map accurately reflect the importance of some highly productive habitats, such as wetlands, coral reefs, and coastal zones? Explain.*

their net primary production **(Figure 55.6)**. Tropical rain forests are among the most productive terrestrial ecosystems and contribute a large portion of the planet's overall net primary production. Estuaries and coral reefs also have very high net primary production, but their contribution to the global total is relatively small because these ecosystems cover only about one-tenth the area covered by tropical rain forests. One striking aspect of Figure 55.6 is how unproductive the oceans are per unit area compared to tropical forests and some other ecosystems. Because of their vast size, however, the oceans altogether contribute as much global net primary production as terrestrial systems do.

What limits primary production in ecosystems? To ask this question another way, what factors could we change to increase or decrease primary production for a given ecosystem? We'll address this question first for aquatic ecosystems.

Primary Production in Aquatic Ecosystems

In aquatic (marine and freshwater) ecosystems, both light and nutrients are important in controlling primary production.

Light Limitation

Because solar radiation drives photosynthesis, you might expect that light is a key variable in controlling primary production in oceans. Indeed, the depth of light penetration affects primary production throughout the photic zone of an ocean or lake (see Figure 52.16). About half of the solar radiation is absorbed in the first 15 m of water. Even in "clear" water, only 5–10% of the radiation may reach a depth of 75 m.

If light were the main variable limiting primary production in the ocean, we would expect production to increase along a gradient from the poles toward the equator, which receives the greatest intensity of light. However, you can see in Figure 55.6 that there is no such gradient. Another factor must influence primary production in the ocean.

Nutrient Limitation

More than light, nutrients limit primary production in different geographic regions of the ocean and in lakes. A **limiting nutrient** is the element that must be added for production to increase. The nutrient most often limiting marine production is either nitrogen or phosphorus. Concentrations of these nutrients are very low in the photic zone because they are rapidly taken up by phytoplankton and because detritus tends to sink.

As detailed in **Figure 55.7**, nutrient enrichment experiments confirmed that nitrogen was limiting phytoplankton growth off the south shore of Long Island, New York. Practical applications of this work include preventing algal "blooms" caused by nitrogen pollution that fertilizes the phytoplankton. Eliminating phosphates from sewage, once thought to be the cause of the problem, will not help prevent algal blooms unless nitrogen pollution is also controlled.

Several large areas of the ocean, however, have low phytoplankton densities in spite of relatively high nitrogen concentrations. For example, the Sargasso Sea, a subtropical region of the Atlantic Ocean, has some of the clearest water in the world because of its very low density of phytoplankton. A series of nutrient enrichment experiments revealed that the availability of the micronutrient iron can limit primary production there **(Table 55.1)**. Windblown dust from the land is the main input of iron to the ocean, but relatively little windblown dust reaches the center of oceans.

The finding that iron limits production in some oceanic ecosystems encouraged marine ecologists to carry out recent large-scale experiments in the Pacific Ocean. In one study, researchers spread low concentrations of dissolved iron over 72 km² of ocean and then measured the change in phytoplankton density over a seven-day period. A massive phytoplankton bloom occurred, as indicated by increased chlorophyll concentration in the water. Adding iron stimulates growth of cyanobacteria that fix atmospheric nitrogen (see Chapter 27), and the extra nitrogen stimulates proliferation of phytoplankton.

Areas of upwelling, where nutrient-rich deep waters circulate to the ocean surface, have exceptionally high primary production, which supports the hypothesis that nutrient availability

Which nutrient limits phytoplankton production along the coast of Long Island?

EXPERIMENT   Pollution from duck farms concentrated near Moriches Bay adds both nitrogen and phosphorus to the coastal water off Long Island, New York. To determine which nutrient limits phytoplankton growth in this area, John Ryther and William Dunstan, of the Woods Hole Oceanographic Institution, cultured the phytoplankton *Nannochloris atomus* with water collected from several sites (labeled A–G on the map below). They added either ammonium (NH_4^+) or phosphate (PO_4^{3-}) to some of the cultures.

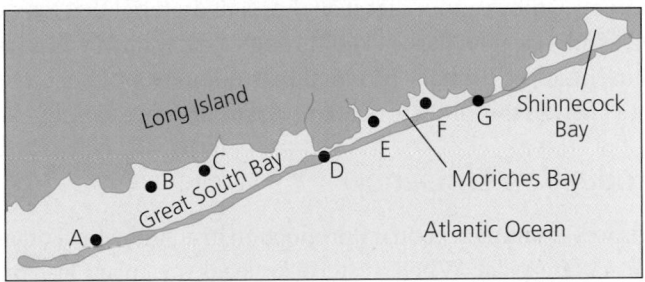

RESULTS   The addition of ammonium caused heavy phytoplankton growth in the cultures, but the addition of phosphate did not.

CONCLUSION   Since adding phosphorus, which was already in rich supply, had no effect on *Nannochloris* growth, whereas adding nitrogen increased phytoplankton density dramatically, the researchers concluded that nitrogen is the nutrient that limits phytoplankton growth in this ecosystem.

SOURCE   J. H. Ryther and W. M. Dunstan, Nitrogen, phosphorus, and eutrophication in the coastal marine environment, *Science* 171:1008–1013 (1971).

WHAT IF?   How would you expect the results of this experiment to change if new duck farms substantially increased the amount of pollution in the water? Explain your reasoning.

Table 55.1 Nutrient Enrichment Experiment for Sargasso Sea Samples

Nutrients Added to Experimental Culture	Relative Uptake of ^{14}C by Cultures*
None (controls)	1.00
Nitrogen (N) + phosphorus (P) only	1.10
N + P + metals (excluding iron)	1.08
N + P + metals (including iron)	12.90
N + P + iron	12.00

*^{14}C uptake by cultures measures primary production.

Source: D. W. Menzel and J. H. Ryther, Nutrients limiting the production of phytoplankton in the Sargasso Sea, with special reference to iron, *Deep Sea Research* 7:276–281 (1961).

---

determines marine primary production. Because the steady supply of nutrients stimulates growth of the phytoplankton populations that form the base of marine food webs, upwelling areas are prime fishing locations. The largest areas of upwelling occur in the Southern Ocean (also called the Antarctic Ocean) and the coastal waters off Peru, California, and parts of western Africa.

Nutrient limitation is also common in freshwater lakes. During the 1970s, scientists showed that sewage and fertilizer runoff from farms and yards added large amounts of nutrients to lakes. Cyanobacteria and algae grow rapidly in response to these added nutrients, ultimately reducing the oxygen concentration and clarity of the water. This process, known as **eutrophication** (from the Greek *eutrophos*, well nourished), has many ecological impacts, including the eventual loss of all but the most tolerant fish species from the lakes (see Figure 52.18). Controlling eutrophication requires knowing which polluting nutrient is responsible; nitrogen is rarely the limiting factor for primary production in lakes. A series of whole-lake experiments conducted by ecologists showed that phosphorus availability limited cyanobacterial growth. This and other research led to the use of phosphate-free detergents and other important water quality reforms.

Primary Production in Terrestrial Ecosystems

On a large geographic scale, temperature and moisture are the main factors controlling primary production in terrestrial ecosystems. Note again in Figure 55.6 that tropical rain forests, with their warm, wet conditions that promote plant growth, are the most productive of all terrestrial ecosystems. In contrast, low-productivity terrestrial ecosystems are generally dry—for example, deserts—or cold and dry—for example, the arctic tundra. Between these extremes lie the temperate forest and grassland ecosystems, which have moderate climates and intermediate productivity. These contrasts in climate can be represented by a measure called **actual evapotranspiration**,

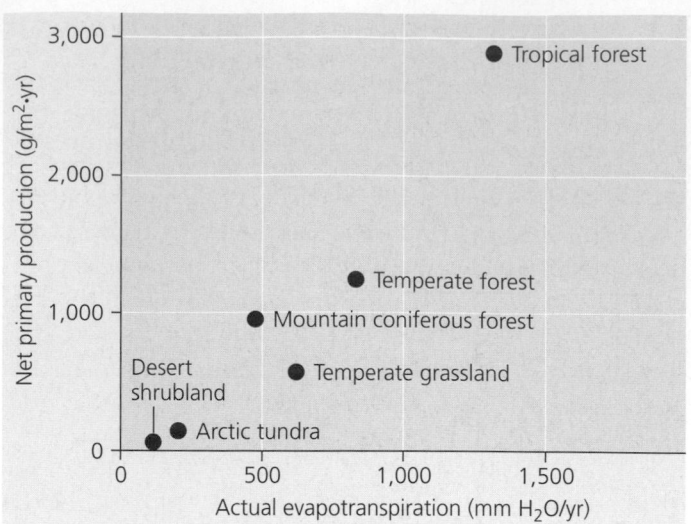

▲ **Figure 55.8 Relationship between net primary production and actual evapotranspiration in six terrestrial ecosystems.**

which is the annual amount of water transpired by plants and evaporated from a landscape, usually measured in millimeters. Actual evapotranspiration increases with the amount of precipitation in a region and the amount of solar energy available to drive evaporation and transpiration. **Figure 55.8** shows the positive relationship between net primary production and actual evapotranspiration in selected ecosystems.

On a more local scale, mineral nutrients in the soil can limit primary production in terrestrial ecosystems. As in aquatic ecosystems, nitrogen and phosphorus are most often the nutrients limiting terrestrial production. Adding a nonlimiting nutrient, even one that is scarce, will not stimulate production. Conversely, adding more of the limiting nutrient will increase production until some other nutrient becomes limiting.

Studies relating nutrients to terrestrial primary production have practical applications in agriculture. Farmers maximize their crop yields by using fertilizers with the right balance of nutrients for the local soil and the type of crop.

CONCEPT CHECK **55.2**

1. Why is only a small portion of the solar energy that strikes Earth's atmosphere stored by primary producers?
2. How can ecologists experimentally determine the factor that limits primary production in an ecosystem?
3. **WHAT IF?** As part of a science project, a student is trying to estimate total primary production of plants in a prairie ecosystem for a year. Once each quarter, the student cuts a plot of grass with a lawnmower and then collects and weighs the cuttings to estimate plant production. What components of plant primary production is the student missing with this approach?

For suggested answers, see Appendix A.

Energy transfer between trophic levels is typically only 10% efficient

The amount of chemical energy in consumers' food that is converted to their own new biomass during a given time period is called the **secondary production** of the ecosystem. Consider the transfer of organic matter from primary producers to herbivores, the primary consumers. In most ecosystems, herbivores eat only a small fraction of plant material produced. Moreover, they cannot digest all the plant material that they *do* eat, as anyone who has walked through a dairy farm will attest. Thus, much of primary production is not used by consumers. Let's analyze this process of energy transfer more closely.

Production Efficiency

First let's examine secondary production in an individual organism—a caterpillar. When a caterpillar feeds on a plant leaf, only about 33 J out of 200 J (48 cal), or one-sixth of the energy in the leaf, is used for secondary production, or growth **(Figure 55.9)**. The caterpillar uses some of the remaining energy for cellular respiration and passes the rest in its feces. The energy contained in the feces remains in the ecosystem temporarily, but most of it is lost as heat after the feces are consumed by detritivores. The energy used for the caterpillar's respiration is also lost from the ecosystem as heat. This is why energy is said to flow through, not cycle within, ecosystems. Only the chemical energy stored by

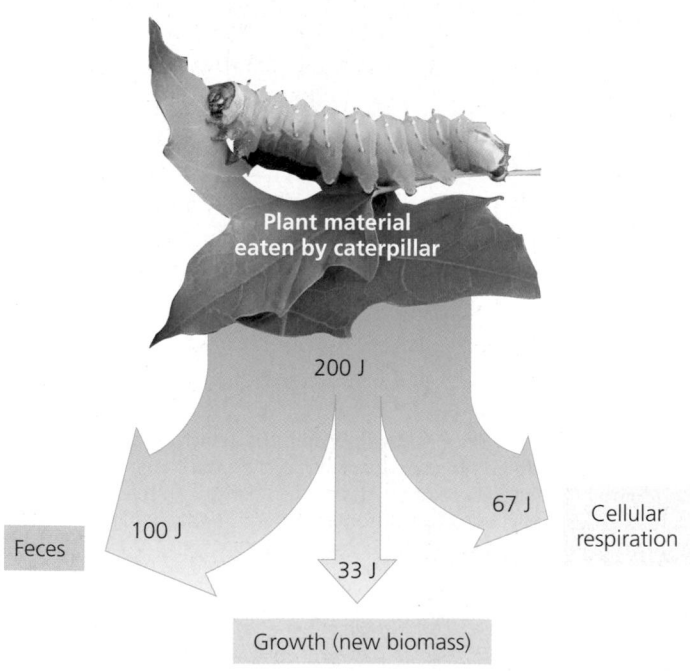

▲ **Figure 55.9 Energy partitioning within a link of the food chain.** Less than 17% of the caterpillar's food is actually used for secondary production (growth).

herbivores as biomass (through growth or the production of off-spring) is available as food to secondary consumers.

We can measure the efficiency of animals as energy transformers using the following equation:

$$\text{Production efficiency} = \frac{\text{Net secondary production} \times 100\%}{\text{Assimilation of primary production}}$$

Net secondary production is the energy stored in biomass represented by growth and reproduction. Assimilation consists of the total energy taken in and used for growth, reproduction, and respiration. **Production efficiency**, therefore, is the percentage of energy stored in assimilated food that is *not* used for respiration. For the caterpillar in Figure 55.9, production efficiency is 33%; 67 J of the 100 J of assimilated energy is used for respiration. (Note that the energy lost as undigested material in feces does not count toward assimilation.) Birds and mammals typically have low production efficiencies, in the range of 1–3%, because they use so much energy in maintaining a constant, high body temperature. Fishes, which are ectotherms (see Chapter 40), have production efficiencies around 10%. Insects and microorganisms are even more efficient, with production efficiencies averaging 40% or more.

Trophic Efficiency and Ecological Pyramids

Let's scale up now from the production efficiencies of individual consumers to the flow of energy through trophic levels.

Trophic efficiency is the percentage of production transferred from one trophic level to the next. Trophic efficiencies must always be less than production efficiencies because they take into account not only the energy lost through respiration and contained in feces, but also the energy in organic material in a lower trophic level that is not consumed by the next trophic level. Trophic efficiencies are generally about 10% and range from approximately 5% to 20%, depending on the type of ecosystem. In other words, 90% of the energy available at one trophic level typically is *not* transferred to the next. This loss is multiplied over the length of a food chain. For example, if 10% of available energy is transferred from primary producers to primary consumers, and 10% of that energy is transferred to secondary consumers, then only 1% of net primary production is available to secondary consumers (10% of 10%).

The progressive loss of energy along a food chain severely limits the abundance of top-level carnivores that an ecosystem can support. Only about 0.1% of the chemical energy fixed by photosynthesis can flow all the way through a food web to a tertiary consumer, such as a snake or a shark. This explains why most food webs include only about four or five trophic levels (see Chapter 54).

The loss of energy with each transfer in a food chain can be represented by a *pyramid of net production*, in which the trophic levels are arranged in tiers (**Figure 55.10**). The width of each tier is proportional to the net production, expressed in joules, of each trophic level. The highest level, which represents top-level pred-

ators, contains relatively few individuals. Because populations of top predators are typically small and the animals may be widely spaced within their habitats, many predator species are highly susceptible to extinction (as well as to the evolutionary consequences of small population size, discussed in Chapter 23).

One important ecological consequence of low trophic efficiencies is represented in a *biomass pyramid*, in which each tier represents the standing crop (the total dry mass of all organisms) in one trophic level. Most biomass pyramids narrow sharply from primary producers at the base to top-level carnivores at the apex because energy transfers between trophic levels are so inefficient (**Figure 55.11a**). Certain aquatic ecosystems, however,

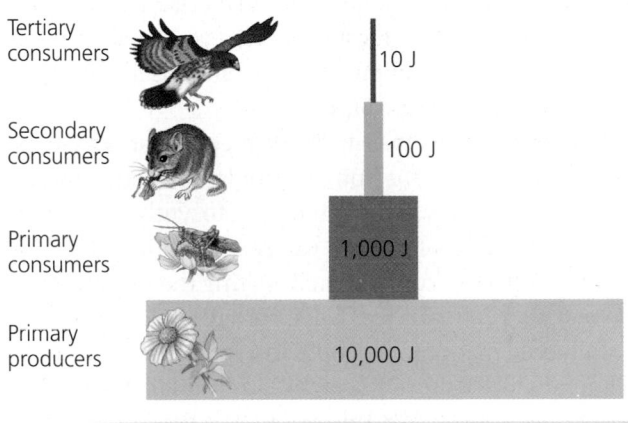

▲ **Figure 55.10 An idealized pyramid of net production.** This example assumes a trophic efficiency of 10% for each link in the food chain. Notice that primary producers convert only about 1% of the energy available to them to net primary production.

Trophic level	Dry mass (g/m²)
Tertiary consumers	1.5
Secondary consumers	11
Primary consumers	37
Primary producers	809

(a) Most biomass pyramids show a sharp decrease in biomass at successively higher trophic levels, as illustrated by data from a Florida bog.

Trophic level	Dry mass (g/m²)
Primary consumers (zooplankton)	21
Primary producers (phytoplankton)	4

(b) In some aquatic ecosystems, such as the English Channel, a small standing crop of primary producers (phytoplankton) supports a larger standing crop of primary consumers (zooplankton).

▲ **Figure 55.11 Pyramids of biomass (standing crop).** Numbers denote the dry mass of all organisms at each trophic level.

have inverted biomass pyramids: Primary consumers outweigh the producers (Figure 55.11b). Such inverted biomass pyramids occur because the producers—phytoplankton—grow, reproduce, and are consumed so quickly by the zooplankton that they never develop a large population size, or standing crop. In other words, the phytoplankton have a short **turnover time**, which means they have a small standing crop compared to their production:

$$\text{Turnover time} = \frac{\text{Standing crop (g/m}^2\text{)}}{\text{Production (g/m}^2\text{·day)}}$$

Because the phytoplankton continually replace their biomass at such a rapid rate, they can support a biomass of zooplankton bigger than their own biomass. Nevertheless, because phytoplankton have much higher production than zooplankton, the pyramid of *production* for this ecosystem is still bottom-heavy, like the one in Figure 55.10.

The dynamics of energy flow through ecosystems have important implications for the human population. Eating meat is a relatively inefficient way of tapping photosynthetic production. A person obtains far more calories by eating grains directly as a primary consumer than by eating the same amount of grain fed to an animal. Worldwide agriculture could, in fact, successfully feed many more people and require less cultivated land if humans all fed more efficiently—as primary consumers, eating only plant material. Consequently, estimates of Earth's human carrying capacity (see Chapter 53) depend greatly on our diet and on the amount of resources each of us consumes.

The Green World Hypothesis

Earlier in this book, you learned why the world is green: Plants reflect more green light than red or blue light (see Figure 10.9). Land plants store approximately 70×10^{10} metric tons of carbon, and global terrestrial primary production is about 6×10^{10} metric tons per year. However, herbivores annually consume less than one-sixth the global NPP by plants (Figure 55.12).

Most of the rest is eventually consumed by detritivores. Thus, despite occasional outbreaks of pests, herbivores are generally only a minor nuisance to plants.

Why do herbivores consume such a small fraction of plants' net primary production? According to the **green world hypothesis**, terrestrial herbivores are held in check by a variety of factors. Plant defenses, such as spines or noxious chemicals (see Chapter 39), limit the success of herbivores. Low nutrient concentrations in plant tissues mean that large quantities of biomass are needed to support each herbivore. Other factors also limit the number of herbivores, including abiotic pressures, such as temperature and moisture extremes; intraspecific competition, including territorial behavior; and interspecific competition, particularly from predators, parasites, and pathogens (as in the top-down model of community structure, which you learned about in Chapter 54).

In the next section, we will look at how the transfer of nutrients along with energy through food webs is part of a larger picture of chemical cycling in ecosystems.

CONCEPT CHECK 55.3

1. If an insect that eats plant seeds containing 100 J of energy uses 30 J of that energy for respiration and excretes 50 J in its feces, what is the insect's net secondary production? What is its production efficiency?
2. Tobacco leaves contain nicotine, a poisonous compound that is energetically expensive for the plant to make. What advantage might the plant gain by using some of its resources to produce nicotine?
3. **WHAT IF?** As part of a new reality show on television, a group of overweight people are trying to safely lose in one month as much weight as possible. In addition to eating less, what could they do to decrease their production efficiency for the food they eat?

For suggested answers, see Appendix A.

► **Figure 55.12 A green ecosystem.** Most terrestrial ecosystems have large standing crops of vegetation despite the large number of resident herbivores. The green world hypothesis offers possible explanations for this observation.

Biological and geochemical processes cycle nutrients between organic and inorganic parts of an ecosystem

Although most ecosystems receive an abundant supply of solar energy, chemical elements are available only in limited amounts. (The meteorites that occasionally strike Earth are the only extraterrestrial source of new matter.) Life on Earth therefore depends on the recycling of essential chemical elements. While an organism is alive, much of its chemical stock is replaced continuously as nutrients are assimilated and waste products released. When the organism dies, the atoms in its complex molecules are returned in simpler compounds to the atmosphere, water, or soil by the action of decomposers. Decomposition replenishes the pools of inorganic nutrients that plants and other autotrophs use to build new organic matter. Because nutrient cycles involve both biotic and abiotic components, they are called **biogeochemical cycles**.

Biogeochemical Cycles

An element's specific route through a biogeochemical cycle depends on the element and the trophic structure of the ecosystem. We can, however, recognize two general categories of biogeochemical cycles: global and local. Gaseous forms of carbon, oxygen, sulfur, and nitrogen occur in the atmosphere, and cycles of these elements are essentially global. For example, some of the carbon and oxygen atoms a plant acquires from the air as CO_2 may have been released into the atmosphere by the respiration of an organism in a distant locale. Other elements, including phosphorus, potassium, and calcium, are too heavy to occur as gases at Earth's surface. In terrestrial ecosystems, these elements cycle more locally, absorbed from the soil by plant roots and eventually returned to the soil by decomposers. In aquatic systems, however, they cycle more broadly as dissolved forms carried in currents.

Before examining the details of individual cycles, let's look at a general model of nutrient cycling that includes the main reservoirs of elements and the processes that transfer elements between reservoirs **(Figure 55.13)**. Each reservoir is defined by two characteristics: whether it contains organic or inorganic materials and whether or not the materials are directly available for use by organisms.

The nutrients in living organisms themselves and in detritus (reservoir A in Figure 55.13) are available to other organisms when consumers feed and when detritivores consume nonliving organic matter. Some material moved from the living organic reservoir to the fossilized organic reservoir (reservoir B) long ago, when dead organisms were converted to coal, oil, or peat (fossil fuels). Nutrients in these deposits generally cannot be assimilated directly.

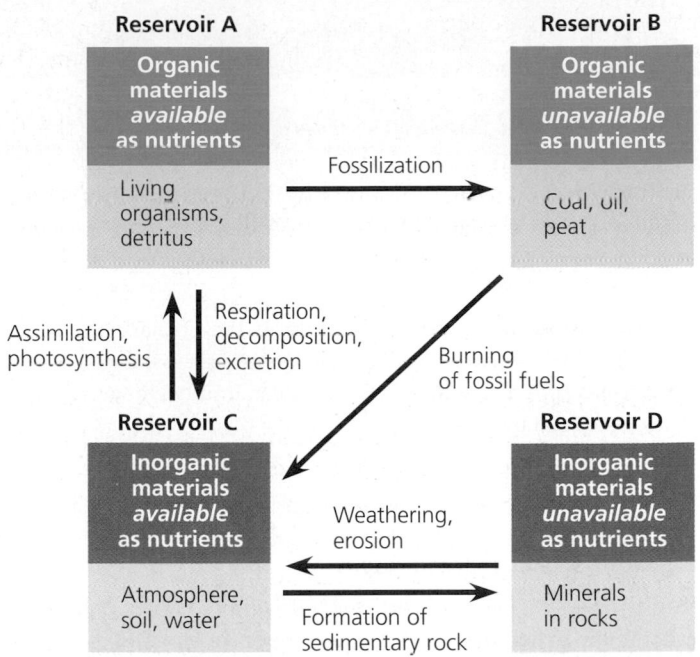

▲ **Figure 55.13 A general model of nutrient cycling.** Arrows indicate the processes that move nutrients between reservoirs.

? *Recent evidence suggests that mycorrhizal fungi can release acids that dissolve some minerals, including calcium phosphate. Where does this fungal activity fit into the model?*

Inorganic materials (elements and compounds) that are dissolved in water or present in soil or air (reservoir C) are available for use. Organisms assimilate materials from this reservoir directly and return chemicals to it through the relatively rapid processes of cellular respiration, excretion, and decomposition. Although most organisms cannot directly tap into the inorganic elements tied up in rocks (reservoir D), these nutrients may slowly become available through weathering and erosion. Similarly, unavailable organic materials move into the available reservoir of inorganic nutrients when fossil fuels are burned, releasing exhaust into the atmosphere.

How have ecologists worked out the details of chemical cycling in various ecosystems? Two common methods use isotopes—either by adding tiny amounts of radioactive isotopes of specific elements and tracking their progress or by following the movement of naturally occurring, nonradioactive isotopes through the biotic and abiotic components of an ecosystem. For example, scientists have been able to trace the flow into ecosystems of radioactive carbon (^{14}C) released into the atmosphere during atom bomb testing in the 1950s and early 1960s. This "spike" of ^{14}C can be used to date the age of bones and teeth, to measure the turnover rate of soil organic matter, and to follow changes in many other carbon pools in the environment.

Figure 55.14, on the next two pages, provides a detailed look at the cycling of water, carbon, nitrogen, and phosphorus. Examine these four biogeochemical cycles closely, considering the major reservoirs of each chemical and the processes that drive the movement of each chemical through its cycle.

Exploring Nutrient Cycles

The Water Cycle

Biological importance Water is essential to all organisms (see Chapter 3), and its availability influences the rates of ecosystem processes, particularly primary production and decomposition in terrestrial ecosystems.

Forms available to life Liquid water is the primary physical phase in which water is used, though some organisms can harvest water vapor. Freezing of soil water can limit water availability to terrestrial plants.

Reservoirs The oceans contain 97% of the water in the biosphere. Approximately 2% is bound in glaciers and polar ice caps, and the remaining 1% is in lakes, rivers, and groundwater, with a negligible amount in the atmosphere.

Key processes The main processes driving the water cycle are evaporation of liquid water by solar energy, condensation of water vapor into clouds, and precipitation. Transpiration by terrestrial plants also moves significant volumes of water into the atmosphere. Surface and groundwater flow can return water to the oceans, completing the water cycle. The widths of the arrows in the diagram reflect the relative contribution of each process to the movement of water in the biosphere.

The Carbon Cycle

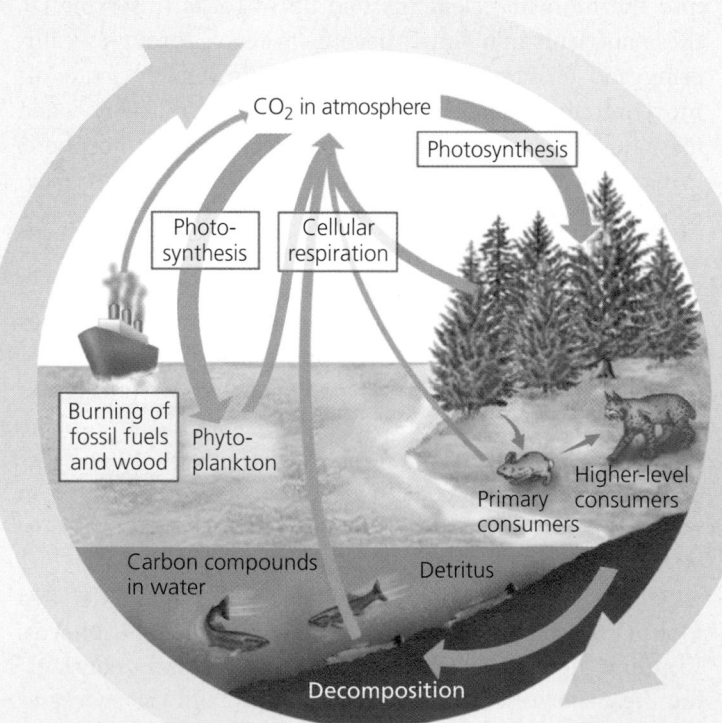

Biological importance Carbon forms the framework of the organic molecules essential to all organisms.

Forms available to life Photosynthetic organisms utilize CO_2 during photosynthesis and convert the carbon to organic forms that are used by consumers, including animals, fungi, and heterotrophic protists and prokaryotes.

Reservoirs The major reservoirs of carbon include fossil fuels, soils, the sediments of aquatic ecosystems, the oceans (dissolved carbon compounds), plant and animal biomass, and the atmosphere (CO_2). The largest reservoir is sedimentary rocks such as limestone; however, this pool turns over very slowly.

Key processes Photosynthesis by plants and phytoplankton removes substantial amounts of atmospheric CO_2 each year. This quantity is approximately equaled by CO_2 added to the atmosphere through cellular respiration by producers and consumers. Over geologic time, volcanoes are also a substantial source of CO_2. The burning of fossil fuels is adding significant amounts of additional CO_2 to the atmosphere. The widths of the arrows reflect the relative contribution of each process.

The Terrestrial Nitrogen Cycle

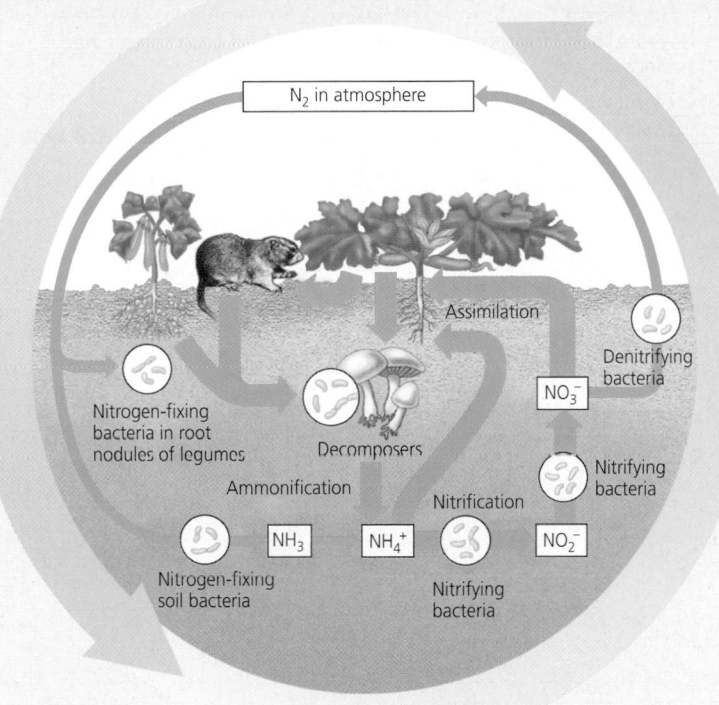

N₂ in atmosphere

Assimilation

Nitrogen-fixing bacteria in root nodules of legumes

Decomposers

Denitrifying bacteria

NO₃⁻

Ammonification

Nitrification

Nitrifying bacteria

Nitrogen-fixing soil bacteria

NH₃   NH₄⁺   NO₂⁻

Nitrifying bacteria

Biological importance Nitrogen is part of amino acids, proteins, and nucleic acids and is often a limiting plant nutrient.

Forms available to life Plants can use two inorganic forms of nitrogen—ammonium (NH_4^+) and nitrate (NO_3^-)—and some organic forms, such as amino acids. Various bacteria can use all of these forms as well as nitrite (NO_2^-). Animals can use only organic forms of nitrogen.

Reservoirs The main reservoir of nitrogen is the atmosphere, which is 80% nitrogen gas (N_2). The other reservoirs are soils and the sediments of lakes, rivers, and oceans (bound nitrogen); surface water and groundwater (dissolved nitrogen); and the biomass of living organisms.

Key processes The major pathway for nitrogen to enter an ecosystem is via *nitrogen fixation*, the conversion of N_2 by bacteria to forms that can be used to synthesize nitrogenous organic compounds (see Chapter 37). Some nitrogen is also fixed by lightning. Nitrogen fertilizer, precipitation, and blowing dust can also provide substantial inputs of NH_4^+ and NO_3^- to ecosystems. *Ammonification* decomposes organic nitrogen to NH_4^+. In *nitrification*, NH_4^+ is converted to NO_3^- by nitrifying bacteria. Under anaerobic conditions, denitrifying bacteria use NO_3^- in their metabolism instead of O_2, releasing N_2 in a process known as *denitrification*. The widths of the arrows reflect the relative contribution of each process.

The Phosphorus Cycle

Biological importance Organisms require phosphorus as a major constituent of nucleic acids, phospholipids, and ATP and other energy-storing molecules and as a mineral constituent of bones and teeth.

Forms available to life The most biologically important inorganic form of phosphorus is phosphate (PO_4^{3-}), which plants absorb and use in the synthesis of organic compounds.

Reservoirs The largest accumulations of phosphorus are in sedimentary rocks of marine origin. There are also large quantities of phosphorus in soils, in the oceans (in dissolved form), and in organisms. Because humus and soil particles bind phosphate, the recycling of phosphorus tends to be quite localized in ecosystems.

Key processes Weathering of rocks gradually adds PO_4^{3-} to soil; some leaches into groundwater and surface water and may eventually reach the sea. Phosphate taken up by producers and incorporated into biological molecules may be eaten by consumers and distributed through the food web. Phosphate is returned to soil or water through either decomposition of biomass or excretion by consumers. Because there are no significant phosphorus-containing gases, only relatively small amounts of phosphorus move through the atmosphere, usually in the forms of dust and sea spray. The widths of the arrows reflect the relative contribution of each process.

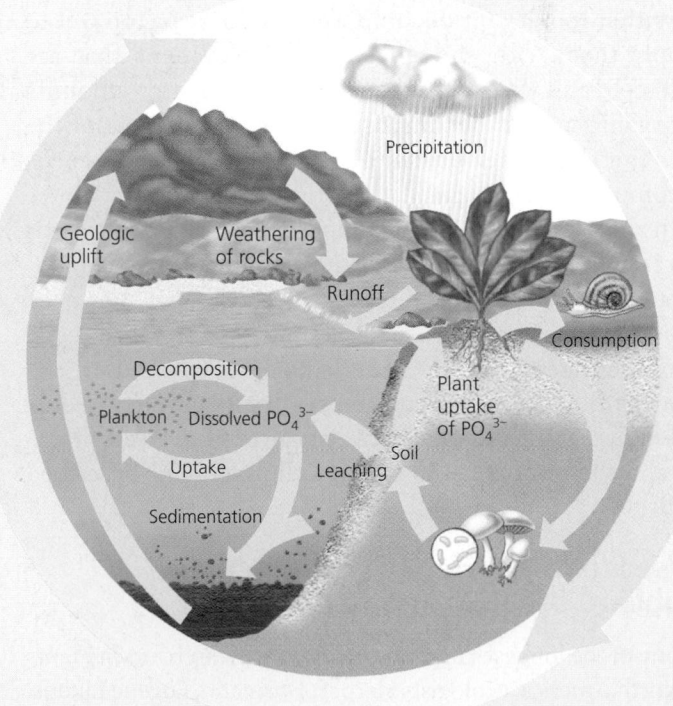

Precipitation

Geologic uplift

Weathering of rocks

Runoff

Consumption

Decomposition

Plankton   Dissolved PO₄³⁻

Plant uptake of PO₄³⁻

Uptake   Leaching   Soil

Sedimentation

Decomposition and Nutrient Cycling Rates

The diagrams in Figure 55.14 illustrate the essential role that decomposers (detritivores) play in recycling carbon, nitrogen, and phosphorus. The rates at which these nutrients cycle in different ecosystems are extremely variable, mostly as a result of differences in rates of decomposition.

Decomposition is controlled by the same factors that limit primary production in aquatic and terrestrial ecosystems (see Concept 55.2). Those factors include temperature, moisture, and nutrient availability. Decomposers usually grow faster and decompose material more quickly in warmer ecosystems (Figure 55.15). In tropical rain forests, for instance, most organic material decomposes in a few months to a few years, while in temperate forests, decomposition takes four to six years, on average. The difference is largely the result of the higher temperatures and more abundant precipitation in tropical rain forests.

Because decomposition in a tropical rain forest is rapid, relatively little organic material accumulates as leaf litter on the forest floor; about 75% of the nutrients in the ecosystem is present in the woody trunks of trees, and about 10% is contained in the soil. Thus, the relatively low concentrations of some nutrients in the soil of tropical rain forests result from a short cycling time, not from a lack of these elements in the ecosystem. In temperate forests, where decomposition is much slower, the soil may contain as much as 50% of all the organic material in the ecosystem. The nutrients that are present in temperate forest detritus and soil may remain there for fairly long periods before plants assimilate them.

Decomposition on land is also slower when conditions are either too dry for decomposers to thrive or too wet to supply them with enough oxygen. Ecosystems that are both cold and wet, such as peatlands, store large amounts of organic matter; decomposers grow poorly most of the year there, and net primary production greatly exceeds decomposition.

In aquatic ecosystems, decomposition in anaerobic muds can take 50 years or more. Bottom sediments are comparable to the detritus layer in terrestrial ecosystems; however, algae and aquatic plants usually assimilate nutrients directly from the water. Thus, the sediments often constitute a nutrient sink, and aquatic ecosystems are very productive only when there is interchange between the bottom layers of water and the surface (as in the upwelling regions described earlier).

Case Study: Nutrient Cycling in the Hubbard Brook Experimental Forest

In one of the longest-running ecological research experiments in North America, ecologists Herbert Bormann, Eugene Likens, and their colleagues have been studying nutrient cycling in a

▼ Figure 55.15 **Inquiry**

How does temperature affect litter decomposition in an ecosystem?

EXPERIMENT   Researchers with the Canadian Forest Service placed identical samples of organic material on the ground in 21 sites across Canada (marked by letters on the map below). Three years later, they returned to see how much of each sample had decomposed.

RESULTS   Litter mass decreased four times faster in warmer ecosystems than in colder ones.

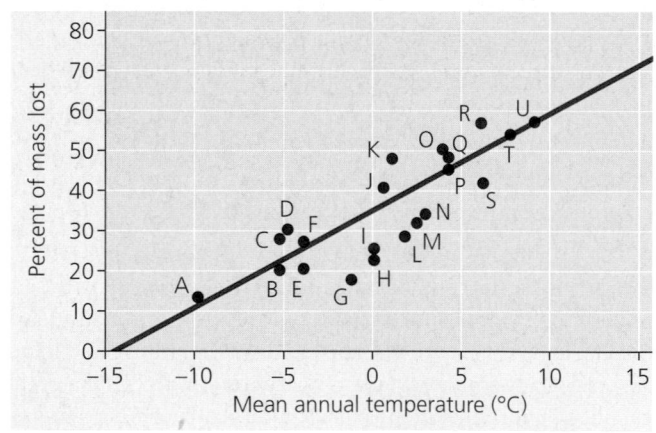

CONCLUSION   Decomposition increases with temperature across much of Canada.

SOURCE   T. R. Moore et al., Litter decomposition rates in Canadian forests, *Global Change Biology* 5:75–82 (1999).

WHAT IF?   What factors other than temperature might also have varied across these 21 sites? How might this variation have affected the interpretation of the results?

forest ecosystem since 1963. Their study site, the Hubbard Brook Experimental Forest in the White Mountains of New Hampshire, is a deciduous forest with several valleys, each drained by a small creek that is a tributary of Hubbard Brook. Bedrock impenetrable to water is close to the surface of the soil, and each valley constitutes a watershed that can drain only through its creek.

The research team first determined the mineral budget for each of six valleys by measuring the input and outflow of several key nutrients. They collected rainfall at several sites to measure the amount of water and dissolved minerals added to the ecosystem. To monitor the loss of water and minerals, they constructed a small concrete dam with a V-shaped spillway across the creek at the bottom of each valley (Figure 55.16a). About 60% of the water added to the ecosystem as rainfall and snow exits through the stream, and the remaining 40% is lost by evapotranspiration.

Preliminary studies confirmed that internal cycling within a terrestrial ecosystem conserves most of the mineral nutrients. For example, only about 0.3% more calcium (Ca^{2+}) left a valley via its creek than was added by rainwater, and this small net loss was probably replaced by chemical decomposition of the bedrock. During most years, the forest actually registered small net gains of a few mineral nutrients, including nitrogen.

In one experiment, the trees in one valley were cut down and then the valley was sprayed with herbicides for three years to prevent regrowth of plants (Figure 55.16b). All the original plant material was left in place to decompose. The inflow and outflow of water and minerals in this experimentally altered watershed were compared with those in a control watershed. Over the three years, water runoff from the altered watershed increased by 30–40%, apparently because there were no plants to absorb and transpire water from the soil. Net losses of minerals from the altered watershed were huge. The concentration of Ca^{2+} in the creek increased 4-fold, for example, and the concentration of K^+ increased by a factor of 15. Most remarkable was the loss of nitrate, whose concentration in the creek increased 60-fold, reaching levels considered unsafe for drinking water (Figure 55.16c).

This study demonstrated that the amount of nutrients leaving an intact forest ecosystem is controlled mainly by the plants. The effects of deforestation occur within a few months and continue as long as living plants are absent.

The 45 years of data from Hubbard Brook reveal some other trends. For instance, in the last half century, acid rain and snow have dissolved most of the Ca^{2+} in the forest soil, and the streams have carried it away. By the 1990s, the forest biomass at Hubbard Brook had stopped increasing, apparently because of a lack of Ca^{2+}. To test this idea, ecologists at Hubbard Brook began a massive experiment in 1998. They first established a control and an experimental watershed, which they monitored over two years before using a helicopter to add Ca^{2+} to the experimental watershed. By 2006, sugar maple trees growing in the Ca^{2+}-enriched location had higher Ca^{2+} concentrations in their foliage, healthier crowns, and

(a) Concrete dams and weirs built across streams at the bottom of watersheds enabled researchers to monitor the outflow of water and nutrients from the ecosystem.

(b) One watershed was clear-cut to study the effects of the loss of vegetation on drainage and nutrient cycling.

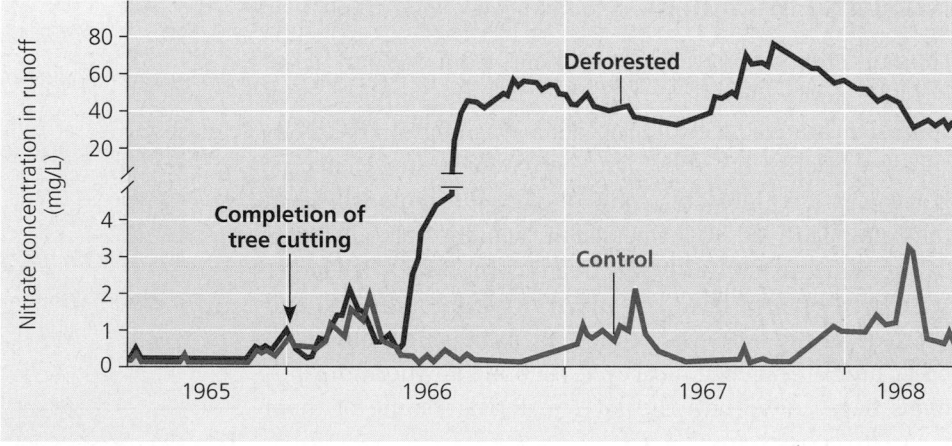

(c) The concentration of nitrate in runoff from the deforested watershed was 60 times greater than in a control (unlogged) watershed.

▲ Figure 55.16 **Nutrient cycling in the Hubbard Brook Experimental Forest: an example of long-term ecological research.**

greater seedling establishment than those growing in the control watershed. These data suggest that sugar maple declines in the northeastern United States and southern Canada are attributable at least in part to the consequences of soil acidification.

The Hubbard Brook studies, as well as many other long-term ecological research projects funded by the National Science Foundation, assess natural ecosystem processes and provide important insight into the mechanisms by which human activities affect these processes.

CONCEPT 55.5
Human activities now dominate most chemical cycles on Earth

As the human population has grown rapidly in size (see Concept 53.6), our activities and technological capabilities have disrupted the trophic structure, energy flow, and chemical cycling of ecosystems. In fact, most chemical cycles are now influenced more by human activities than by natural processes.

Nutrient Enrichment

Human activity often removes nutrients from one part of the biosphere and adds them to another. On the simplest level, someone eating a piece of broccoli in Washington, DC, consumes nutrients that only days before were in the soil in California; a short time later, some of these nutrients will be in the Potomac River, having passed through the person's digestive system and a local sewage treatment facility. On a larger scale, nutrients in farm soil may run off into streams and lakes, depleting nutrients in one area, increasing them in another, and altering chemical cycles in both. Furthermore, humans have added entirely novel materials—some of them toxic—to ecosystems.

Humans have altered nutrient cycles so much that we can no longer understand any cycle without taking these effects into account. Let's examine a few specific examples of how humans are impacting the biosphere's chemical dynamics.

Agriculture and Nitrogen Cycling

After natural vegetation is cleared from an area, the existing reserve of nutrients in the soil is sufficient to grow crops for some time. In agricultural ecosystems, however, a substantial fraction of these nutrients is exported from the area in crop biomass. The "free" period for crop production—when there is no need to add nutrients to the soil—varies greatly. When some of the early North American prairie lands were first tilled, good crops could be produced for decades because the large store of organic materials in the soil continued to decompose and provide nutrients. By contrast, some cleared land in the tropics can be farmed for only one or two years because so little of the ecosystems' nutrient load is contained in the soil. Despite such variations, in any area under intensive agriculture, the natural store of nutrients eventually becomes exhausted.

Nitrogen is the main nutrient lost through agriculture; thus, agriculture has a great impact on the nitrogen cycle. Plowing mixes the soil and speeds up decomposition of organic matter, releasing nitrogen that is then removed when crops are harvested. Applied fertilizers make up for the loss of usable nitrogen from agricultural ecosystems **(Figure 55.17)**. In addition, as we saw in the case of Hubbard Brook, without plants to take up nitrates from the soil, the nitrates are likely to be leached from the ecosystem.

Recent studies indicate that human activities have more than doubled Earth's supply of fixed nitrogen available to primary producers. Industrial fertilizers provide the largest additional nitrogen source. Fossil fuel combustion also releases nitrogen oxides, which enter the atmosphere and dissolve in rainwater; the nitrogen ultimately enters ecosystems as nitrate. Increased cultivation of legumes, with their nitrogen-fixing symbionts, is a third way in which humans increase the amount of fixed nitrogen in the soil.

▲ **Figure 55.17 Fertilization of a corn (maize) crop.** To replace the nutrients removed in crops, farmers must apply fertilizers—either organic, such as manure or mulch, or synthetic, as shown here.

Winter   Summer

◀ **Figure 55.18 The dead zone arising from nitrogen pollution in the Mississippi basin.** In these satellite images from 2004, red and orange represent high concentrations of phytoplankton and river sediment in the Gulf of Mexico. This dead zone extends much farther from land in summer than in winter.

Contamination of Aquatic Ecosystems

The key problem with excess nutrients is the **critical load**, the amount of added nutrient, usually nitrogen or phosphorus, that can be absorbed by plants without damaging ecosystem integrity. For example, nitrogenous minerals in the soil that exceed the critical load eventually leach into groundwater or run off into freshwater and marine ecosystems, contaminating water supplies and killing fish. Nitrate concentrations in groundwater are increasing in most agricultural regions, sometimes exceeding safe levels for drinking.

Many rivers contaminated with nitrates and ammonium from agricultural runoff and sewage drain into the Atlantic Ocean, with the highest inputs coming from northern Europe and the central United States. The Mississippi River carries nitrogen pollution to the Gulf of Mexico, fueling a phytoplankton bloom each summer. When the phytoplankton die, their decomposition creates an extensive "dead zone" of low oxygen availability along the coast (**Figure 55.18**). Fish, shrimp, and other marine animals disappear from some of the most economically important waters in the country. To reduce the size of the dead zone, farmers have begun using fertilizers more efficiently, and managers are restoring wetlands in the Mississippi watershed, two changes stimulated by the results of ecosystem experiments.

Nutrient runoff can also lead to the eutrophication of lakes, as you learned in Concept 55.2. The bloom and subsequent die-off of algae and cyanobacteria and the ensuing depletion of oxygen are similar to what occurs in a marine dead zone. Such conditions threaten the survival of organisms. For example, eutrophication of Lake Erie coupled with overfishing wiped out commercially important fishes such as blue pike, whitefish, and lake trout by the 1960s. Since then, tighter regulations on waste dumping into the lake have enabled some fish populations to rebound, but many native species of fishes and invertebrates have not recovered.

Acid Precipitation

The burning of wood and of fossil fuels, including coal and oil, releases oxides of sulfur and nitrogen that react with water in the atmosphere, forming sulfuric and nitric acid, respectively.

The acids eventually fall to Earth's surface as acid precipitation—rain, snow, sleet, or fog that has a pH less than 5.2. Acid precipitation lowers the pH of streams and lakes and affects soil chemistry and nutrient availability. Although acid precipitation has been occurring since the Industrial Revolution, the emissions that cause it have increased during the past century, mainly from ore smelters and electrical generating plants.

Acid precipitation is a regional problem arising from local emissions. Smelters and generating plants are built with exhaust stacks more than 300 m high that reduce pollution at ground level but export it far downwind. Sulfur and nitrogen pollutants may drift hundreds of kilometers before falling as acid precipitation.

In the 1960s, ecologists determined that lake-dwelling organisms in eastern Canada were dying because of air pollution from factories in the midwestern United States. Lakes and streams in southern Norway and Sweden were losing fish because of acid rain from pollutants generated in Great Britain and central Europe. By 1980, the pH of precipitation in large areas of North America and Europe averaged 4.0–4.5 and occasionally dropped as low as 3.0.

In terrestrial ecosystems, such as the deciduous forests of New England, the change in soil pH due to acid precipitation causes calcium and other nutrients to leach from the soil (see the Hubbard Brook studies in Concept 55.4). The nutrient deficiencies affect the health of plants and limit their growth. Acid precipitation can also damage plants directly, mainly by leaching nutrients from leaves.

Freshwater ecosystems are particularly sensitive to acid precipitation. The lakes in North America and northern Europe that are most readily damaged by acid precipitation are those that have a low concentration of bicarbonate, an important buffer (see Chapter 3). Fish populations have declined in thousands of such lakes in Norway and Sweden, where the pH of the water has dropped below 5.0. In Canada, newly hatched lake trout, a keystone predator, die when the pH drops below 5.4. When the trout are replaced by acid-tolerant fish, the dynamics of food webs change dramatically.

Several large ecosystem experiments have been carried out to test the feasibility of reversing the effects of acid precipitation. One is the Ca^{2+} addition experiment at Hubbard Brook discussed earlier in this chapter. Another is a 17-year experiment

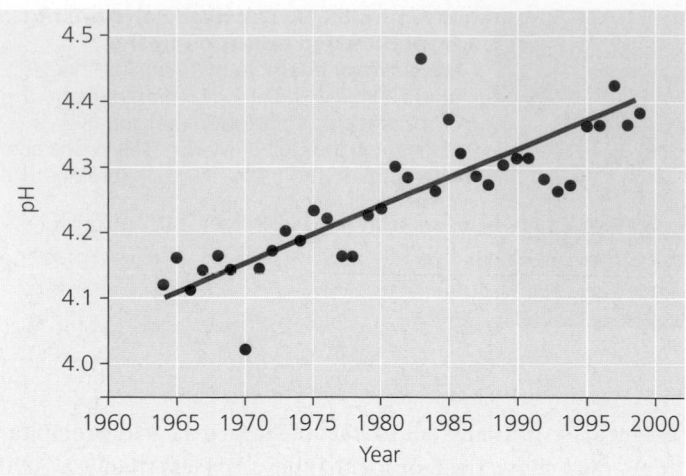

▲ **Figure 55.19 Changes in the pH of precipitation at Hubbard Brook.** Although still very acidic, the precipitation in this northeastern U.S. forest has been increasing in pH for more than three decades.

in Norway in which scientists built a glass roof over a forest and then showered the forest with precipitation from which acids had been removed. This "clean" precipitation quickly increased the pH and decreased the nitrate, ammonium, and sulfate concentrations in stream water in the forest. Results from this and other experiments helped convince leaders of more than 40 European nations to sign a treaty to reduce air pollution.

Environmental regulations and new industrial technologies have enabled many developed countries to reduce sulfur dioxide emissions during the past 40 years. In the United States, for example, sulfur dioxide emissions decreased 31% between 1993 and 2002. As a result, precipitation in the northeastern United States is gradually becoming less acidic (**Figure 55.19**). However, ecologists estimate that it will take decades for aquatic ecosystems in this region to recover, even if sulfur dioxide emissions continue to decrease. Meanwhile, emissions of nitrogen oxides are increasing in the United States, and emissions of sulfur dioxide and acid precipitation continue to damage forests in central and eastern Europe.

Toxins in the Environment

Humans release an immense variety of toxic chemicals, including thousands of synthetic compounds previously unknown in nature, with little regard for the ecological consequences. Organisms acquire toxic substances from the environment along with nutrients and water. Some of the poisons are metabolized and excreted, but others accumulate in specific tissues, especially fat. One of the reasons accumulated toxins are particularly harmful is that they become more concentrated in successive trophic levels of a food web, a process called **biological magnification**. Magnification occurs because the biomass at any given trophic level is produced from a much larger biomass ingested from the level

below (see Concept 55.3). Thus, top-level carnivores tend to be the organisms most severely affected by toxic compounds in the environment.

One class of industrially synthesized compounds that have demonstrated biological magnification are the chlorinated hydrocarbons, which include the industrial chemicals called PCBs (polychlorinated biphenyls) and many pesticides, such as DDT. Current research implicates many of these compounds in endocrine system disruption in a large number of animal species, including humans. Biological magnification of PCBs has been found in the food web of the Great Lakes, where the concentration of PCBs in herring gull eggs, at the top of the food web, is nearly 5,000 times that in phytoplankton, at the base of the food web (**Figure 55.20**).

An infamous case of biological magnification that harmed top-level carnivores involved DDT, a chemical used to control insects such as mosquitoes and agricultural pests. In the decade after World War II, the use of DDT grew rapidly; its ecological consequences were not yet fully understood. By the 1950s, scientists were learning that DDT persists in the environment and is transported by water to areas far from where it is applied. One of the first signs that DDT was a serious en-

Herring gull eggs 124 ppm

Lake trout 4.83 ppm

Smelt 1.04 ppm

Concentration of PCBs

Zooplankton 0.123 ppm

Phytoplankton 0.025 ppm

▲ **Figure 55.20 Biological magnification of PCBs in a Great Lakes food web.**

vironmental problem was a decline in the populations of pelicans, ospreys, and eagles, birds that feed at the top of food webs. The accumulation of DDT (and DDE, a product of its breakdown) in the tissues of these birds interfered with the deposition of calcium in their eggshells. When the birds tried to incubate their eggs, the weight of the parents broke the shells of affected eggs, resulting in catastrophic declines in the birds' reproduction rates. Rachel Carson's book *Silent Spring* helped bring the problem to public attention in the 1960s (see Chapter 52), and DDT was banned in the United States in 1971. A dramatic recovery in populations of the affected bird species followed.

In much of the tropics, DDT is still used to control the mosquitoes that spread malaria and other diseases. Societies there face a trade-off between saving human lives and protecting other species. The best approach seems to be to apply DDT sparingly and to couple its use with mosquito netting and other low-technology solutions. The complicated history of DDT illustrates the importance of understanding the ecological connections between diseases and communities (see Concept 54.5).

Many toxins cannot be degraded by microorganisms and persist in the environment for years or even decades. In other cases, chemicals released into the environment may be relatively harmless but are converted to more toxic products by reaction with other substances, by exposure to light, or by the metabolism of microorganisms. For example, mercury, a by-product of plastic production and coal-fired power generation, has been routinely expelled into rivers and the sea in an insoluble form. Bacteria in the bottom mud convert the waste to methylmercury (CH_3Hg^+), an extremely toxic soluble compound that accumulates in the tissues of organisms, including humans who consume fish from the contaminated waters.

Greenhouse Gases and Global Warming

Human activities release a variety of gaseous waste products. People once thought that the vast atmosphere could absorb these materials indefinitely, but we now know that such additions can cause fundamental changes to the atmosphere and to its interactions with the rest of the biosphere. In this section, we will examine how increasing atmospheric carbon dioxide concentration and global warming af-

fect ecosystems. Although global warming will likely bring some benefits to people, it will also bring enormous costs to humans and to many other species on Earth.

Rising Atmospheric CO₂ Levels

Since the Industrial Revolution, the concentration of CO_2 in the atmosphere has been increasing as a result of the burning of fossil fuels and deforestation. Scientists estimate that the average CO_2 concentration in the atmosphere before 1850 was about 274 ppm. In 1958, a monitoring station began taking very accurate measurements on Hawaii's Mauna Loa peak, a location far from cities and high enough for the atmosphere to be well mixed. At that time, the CO_2 concentration was 316 ppm **(Figure 55.21)**. Today, it exceeds 380 ppm, an increase of about 40% since the mid-19th century. If CO_2 emissions continue to increase at the present rate, by the year 2075 the atmospheric concentration of this gas will be more than double what it was at the start of the Industrial Revolution.

Increased productivity by plants is one predictable consequence of increasing CO_2 levels. In fact, when CO_2 concentrations are raised in experimental chambers such as greenhouses, most plants grow faster. Because C_3 plants are more limited than C_4 plants by CO_2 availability (see Chapter 10), one effect of

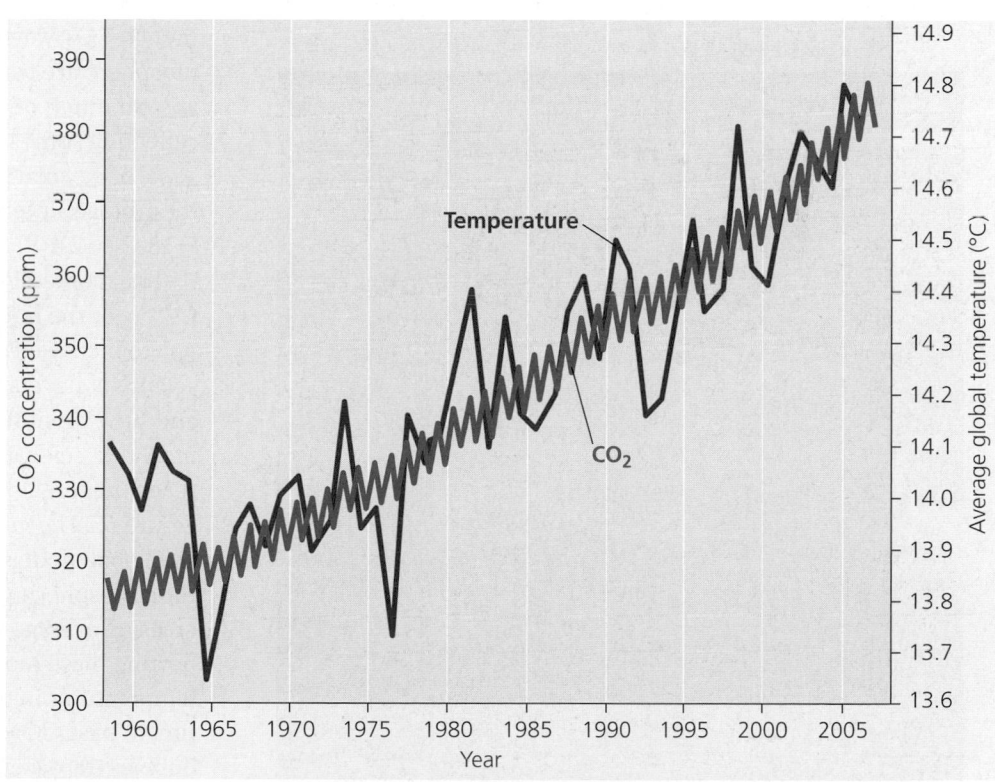

▲ **Figure 55.21 Increase in atmospheric carbon dioxide concentration at Mauna Loa, Hawaii, and average global temperatures.** Aside from normal seasonal fluctuations, the CO_2 concentration (blue curve) has increased steadily from 1958 to 2007. Though average global temperatures (red curve) fluctuated a great deal over the same period, there is a clear warming trend.

increasing global CO_2 concentration may be the spread of C_3 species into terrestrial habitats that currently favor C_4 plants. Such changes could influence whether corn (maize), a C_4 plant and the most important grain crop in the United States, will be replaced by wheat and soybeans, C_3 crops that could outproduce corn in a CO_2-enriched environment. To predict the gradual and complex effects of rising CO_2 levels on productivity and species composition, scientists are turning to long-term field experiments.

How Elevated CO_2 Levels Affect Forest Ecology: The FACTS-I Experiment

To assess how the increasing atmospheric concentration of CO_2 might affect temperate forests, scientists at Duke University began the Forest-Atmosphere Carbon Transfer and Storage (FACTS-I) experiment in 1995. The researchers are manipulating the concentration of CO_2 to which trees are exposed. The FACTS-I experiment includes six plots in an 80-hectare (200-acre) tract of loblolly pine within the university's experimental forest. Each plot consists of a circular area, approximately 30 m in diameter, ringed by 16 towers (Figure 55.22). In three of the six plots, the towers produce air containing about 1½ times present-day CO_2 concentrations. Instruments on a tall tower in the center of each plot measure the direction and speed of the wind, adjusting the distribution of CO_2 to maintain a stable CO_2 concentration. All other factors, such as temperature, precipitation, and wind speed and direction, vary normally for both experimental plots and adjacent control plots exposed to atmospheric CO_2.

The FACTS-I study is testing how elevated CO_2 levels influence tree growth, carbon concentration in soils, insect populations, soil moisture, the growth of plants in the forest understory, and other factors. After ten years, trees in the experimental plots produced about 15% more wood each year than those in the control plots. This increased growth is important for timber production and carbon storage but is far lower than predicted from the results of greenhouse experiments. The availability of nitrogen and other nutrients apparently limits the ability of the trees to use the extra CO_2. Researchers at FACTS-I began removing this limitation in 2005 by fertilizing half of each plot with ammonium nitrate.

In most of the world's ecosystems, nutrients limit ecosystem productivity and fertilizers are unavailable. The results of FACTS-I and other experiments suggest that increased atmospheric CO_2 levels will increase plant production somewhat, but far less than scientists predicted even a decade ago.

The Greenhouse Effect and Climate

Rising concentrations of long-lived greenhouse gases such as CO_2 are also changing Earth's heat budget. Much of the solar radiation that strikes the planet is reflected back into space. Although CO_2, water vapor, and other greenhouse gases in the atmosphere are transparent to visible light, they intercept and absorb much of the infrared radiation the Earth emits, re-reflecting some of it back toward Earth. This process retains some of the solar heat. If it were not for this **greenhouse effect**, the average air temperature at Earth's surface would be a frigid $-18°C$ ($-2.4°F$), and most life as we know it could not exist.

The marked increase in the concentration of atmospheric CO_2 over the last 150 years concerns scientists because of its link to increased global temperature. For more than a century, scientists have studied how greenhouse gases warm Earth and how fossil fuel burning could contribute to the warming. Most scientists are convinced that such warming has already begun and will increase rapidly this century (see Figure 55.21).

Global models predict that by the end of the 21st century, the atmospheric CO_2 concentration will more than double, increasing average global temperature by about 3°C (5°F). Supporting these models is a correlation between CO_2 levels and temperatures in prehistoric times. One way climatologists estimate past CO_2 concentrations is to measure CO_2 levels in bubbles trapped in glacial ice, some of which are half a million years old. Prehistoric temperatures are inferred by several methods, including analysis of past vegetation based on fossils and the chemical isotopes in sediments and corals. An increase of only 1.3°C would make the world warmer than at any time in the past 100,000 years.

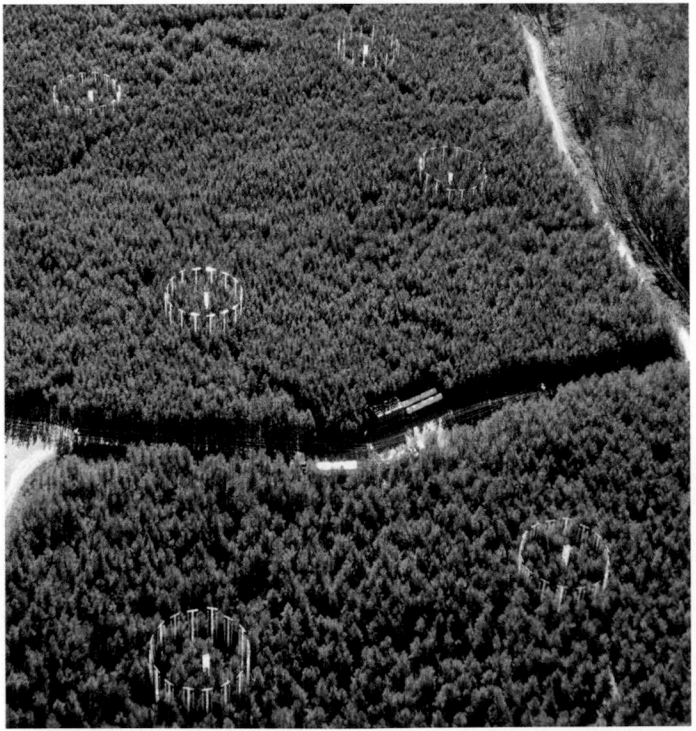

▲ **Figure 55.22 Large-scale experiment on the effects of elevated CO_2 concentration.** Rings of towers in the Duke University Experimental Forest emit enough carbon dioxide to raise and maintain CO_2 levels 200 ppm above present-day concentrations in half of the experimental plots.

The ecosystems where the largest warming has *already* occurred are those in the far north, particularly northern coniferous forests and tundra. As snow and ice melt and uncover darker, more absorptive surfaces, these systems reflect less radiation back to the atmosphere and warm further. Arctic sea ice in the summer of 2007 covered the smallest area on record. Climate models suggest that there may be no summer ice there by the end of this century, decreasing habitat for polar bears, seals, and seabirds. Higher temperatures also increase the likelihood of fires. In boreal forests of western North America and Russia, fires have burned twice the usual area in recent decades.

A warming trend would also alter the geographic distribution of precipitation, making major agricultural areas of the central United States much drier, for example. However, the various mathematical models disagree about the details of how climate in each region will be affected. By studying how past periods of global warming and cooling affected plant communities, ecologists are trying to predict the consequences of future temperature changes. Analysis of fossilized pollen indicates that plant communities change dramatically with changes in temperature. Past climate changes occurred gradually, though, and plant and animal populations had time to migrate into areas where abiotic conditions allowed them to survive. Many organisms, especially plants that cannot disperse rapidly over long distances, may not be able to survive the high rates of climate change projected to result from global warming. Furthermore, many habitats today are much more fragmented than they were in the past (see Chapter 56), further limiting the ability of many organisms to migrate.

We will need many tools to slow global warming. Quick progress can be made in using energy more efficiently and in replacing fossil fuels with renewable solar and wind power and, more controversially, with nuclear power. Today, coal, gasoline, wood, and other organic fuels remain central to industrialized societies and cannot be burned without releasing CO_2. Stabilizing CO_2 emissions will require concerted international effort and the acceptance of changes in both personal lifestyles and industrial processes. Many ecologists think that effort suffered a major setback in 2001, when the United States pulled out of the Kyoto Protocol, a 1997 pledge by industrialized nations to reduce their CO_2 output by about 5%. Such a reduction would be a first step in the journey to stabilize atmospheric CO_2 concentrations.

Depletion of Atmospheric Ozone

Life on Earth is protected from the damaging effects of ultraviolet (UV) radiation by a layer of ozone molecules (O_3) located in the stratosphere 17–25 km above Earth's surface. However, satellite studies of the atmosphere show that the ozone layer has been gradually thinning since the mid-1970s **(Figure 55.23)**. The destruction of atmospheric ozone results mainly

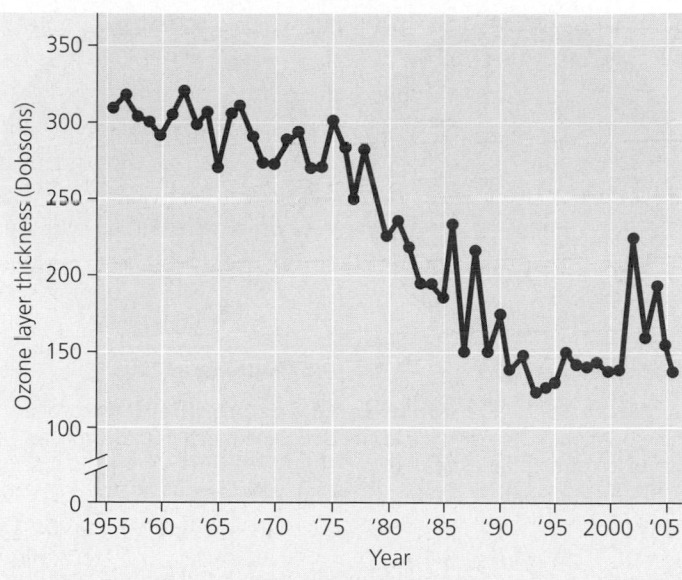

▲ **Figure 55.23 Thickness of the ozone layer over Antarctica in units called Dobsons.**

1 Chlorine from CFCs interacts with ozone (O_3), forming chlorine monoxide (ClO) and oxygen (O_2).

2 Two ClO molecules react, forming chlorine peroxide (Cl_2O_2).

3 Sunlight causes Cl_2O_2 to break down into O_2 and free chlorine atoms. The chlorine atoms can begin the cycle again.

▲ **Figure 55.24 How free chlorine in the atmosphere destroys ozone.**

from the accumulation of chlorofluorocarbons (CFCs), chemicals used in refrigeration and in manufacturing. When the breakdown products from these chemicals rise to the stratosphere, the chlorine they contain reacts with ozone, reducing it to molecular O_2 **(Figure 55.24)**. Subsequent chemical reactions liberate the chlorine, allowing it to react with other ozone molecules in a catalytic chain reaction.

The thinning of the ozone layer is most apparent over Antarctica in spring, where cold, stable air allows the chain reaction to continue. The magnitude of ozone depletion and the size of the ozone hole have generally increased in recent years, and the hole sometimes extends as far as the southernmost portions of Australia, New Zealand, and South America

(a) September 1979　　　**(b) September 2006**

▲ **Figure 55.25 Erosion of Earth's ozone shield.** The ozone hole over Antarctica is visible as the dark blue patch in these images based on atmospheric data.

(Figure 55.25). At the more heavily populated middle latitudes, ozone levels have decreased 2–10% during the past 20 years.

Decreased ozone levels in the stratosphere increase the intensity of UV rays reaching Earth's surface. The consequences of ozone depletion for life on Earth may be severe for plants, animals, and microorganisms. Some scientists expect increases in both lethal and nonlethal forms of skin cancer and in cataracts among humans, as well as unpredictable effects on crops and natural communities, especially the phytoplankton that are responsible for a large proportion of Earth's primary production.

To study the consequences of ozone depletion, ecologists have conducted field experiments in which they use filters to decrease or block the UV radiation in sunlight. One such experiment, performed on a scrub ecosystem near the tip of South America, showed that when the ozone hole passed over the area, the amount of UV radiation reaching the ground increased sharply, causing more DNA damage in plants that were not protected by filters. Scientists have shown similar DNA damage and a reduction in phytoplank-

ton growth when the ozone hole opens over the Southern Ocean each year.

The good news about the ozone hole is how quickly many countries have responded to it. Since 1987, approximately 190 nations, including the United States, have signed the Montreal Protocol, a treaty that regulates the use of ozone-depleting chemicals. Many nations, again including the United States, have ended the production of CFCs. As a consequence of these actions, chlorine concentrations in the stratosphere have stabilized and ozone depletion is slowing. Even if all CFCs were globally banned today, however, chlorine molecules that are already in the atmosphere would continue to influence stratospheric ozone levels for at least 50 years.

The partial destruction of Earth's ozone shield is one more example of how much humans have been able to disrupt the dynamics of ecosystems and the biosphere. It also highlights our ability to solve environmental problems when we set our minds to it. In this book's final chapter, we will explore how scientists in the fields of conservation biology and restoration ecology are studying the effects of human activities on Earth's biodiversity and are using ecological knowledge to reduce those effects.

CONCEPT CHECK　55.5

1. How can the addition of excess nutrients to a lake threaten its fish population?
2. In the face of biological magnification of toxins, is it healthier to feed at a lower or higher trophic level? Explain.
3. **WHAT IF?**　There are vast stores of organic matter in the soils of northern coniferous forests and tundra around the world. Based on what you learned about decomposition from Figure 55.15, suggest an explanation for why scientists who study global warming are closely monitoring these stores.

For suggested answers, see Appendix A.

Chapter 55 Review

MEDIA　Go to **www.campbellbiology.com** for BioFlix 3-D Animations, MP3 Tutors, Videos, Practice Tests, an eBook, and more.

SUMMARY OF KEY CONCEPTS

CONCEPT 55.1

Physical laws govern energy flow and chemical cycling in ecosystems (pp. 1223–1224)

▶ **Conservation of Energy** An ecosystem consists of all the organisms in a community and all the abiotic factors with which

they interact. The laws of physics and chemistry apply to ecosystems, particularly in regard to the flow of energy. Energy is conserved but degraded to heat during ecosystem processes.

▶ **Conservation of Mass** Ecologists study how much of a chemical element enters and leaves an ecosystem and cycles within it. Inputs and outputs are generally small compared to recycled amounts, but their balance determines whether the ecosystem gains or loses an element over time.

► Energy, Mass, and Trophic Levels

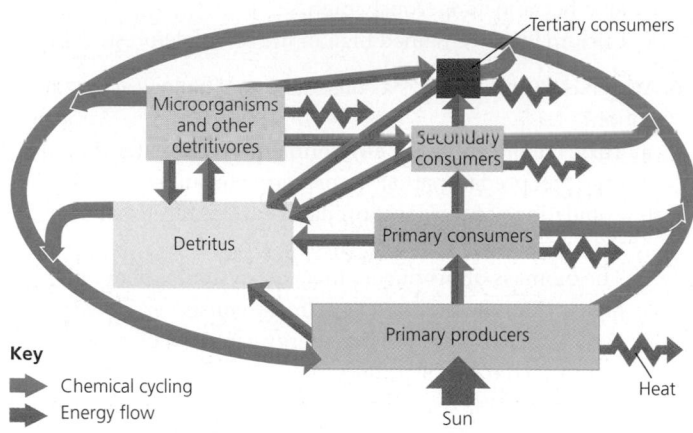

Key
- ➤ Chemical cycling
- ➤ Energy flow

CONCEPT **55.2**

Energy and other limiting factors control primary production in ecosystems (pp. 1224–1228)

► **Ecosystem Energy Budgets** Primary production sets the spending limit for the global energy budget. Gross primary production is the total energy assimilated by an ecosystem in a given period. Net primary production, the energy accumulated in autotroph biomass, equals gross primary production minus the energy used by the primary producers for respiration. Only net primary production is available to consumers.

► **Primary Production in Aquatic Ecosystems** In marine and freshwater ecosystems, light and nutrients limit primary production. Within the photic zone, the factor that most often limits primary production is a nutrient such as nitrogen, phosphorus, or iron.

► **Primary Production in Terrestrial Ecosystems** In terrestrial ecosystems, climatic factors such as temperature and moisture affect primary production on a large geographic scale. More locally, a soil nutrient is often the limiting factor in primary production.

MEDIA

Investigation How Do Temperature and Light Affect Primary Production?

CONCEPT **55.3**

Energy transfer between trophic levels is typically only 10% efficient (pp. 1228–1230)

► **Production Efficiency** The amount of energy available to each trophic level is determined by the net primary production and the efficiency with which food energy is converted to biomass at each link in the food chain. The percentage of energy transferred from one trophic level to the next, called trophic efficiency, is generally 5–20%, with 10% being the typical value. Pyramids of net production and biomass reflect low trophic efficiency.

► **The Green World Hypothesis** According to the green world hypothesis, herbivores consume only a small percentage of vegetation because predators, pathogens, competition, nutrient limitations, and other factors keep their populations in check.

MEDIA

Activity Pyramids of Production
GraphIt! Animal Food Production Efficiency and Food Policy
MP3 Tutor Energy Flow in Ecosystems

CONCEPT **55.4**

Biological and geochemical processes cycle nutrients between organic and inorganic parts of an ecosystem (pp. 1231–1236)

► **Biogeochemical Cycles**

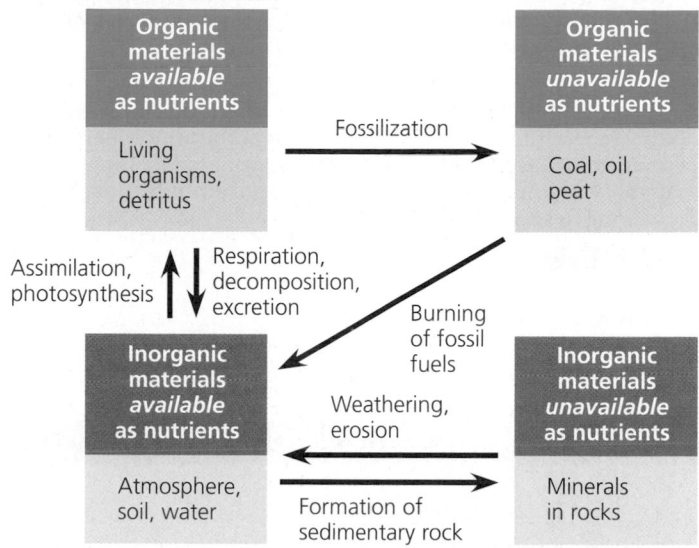

Water moves in a global cycle driven by solar energy. The carbon cycle primarily reflects the reciprocal processes of photosynthesis and cellular respiration. Nitrogen enters ecosystems through atmospheric deposition and nitrogen fixation by prokaryotes, but most of the nitrogen cycling in natural ecosystems involves local cycles between organisms and soil or water. The phosphorus cycle is relatively localized.

► **Decomposition and Nutrient Cycling Rates** The proportion of a nutrient in a particular form and its cycling time in that form vary among ecosystems, largely because of differences in the rate of decomposition.

► *Case Study*: **Nutrient Cycling in the Hubbard Brook Experimental Forest** Nutrient cycling is strongly regulated by vegetation. The Hubbard Brook study showed that logging increases water runoff and can cause large losses of minerals. It also demonstrated the importance of long-term ecological measurements in documenting the occurrence of and recovery from environmental problems.

MEDIA

Activity Energy Flow and Chemical Cycling
Activity The Carbon Cycle
Activity The Nitrogen Cycle

CONCEPT **55.5**

Human activities now dominate most chemical cycles on Earth (pp. 1236–1242)

► **Nutrient Enrichment** Agriculture removes nutrients from ecosystems, so large supplements are usually required. The nutrients in fertilizer can pollute groundwater and surface-water aquatic ecosystems, where they can stimulate excess algal growth (eutrophication).

► **Acid Precipitation** Burning of fossil fuels is the main cause of acid precipitation. North American and European ecosystems downwind from industrial regions have been damaged by rain and snow containing nitric acid and sulfuric acid.

► **Toxins in the Environment** Toxins can become concentrated in successive trophic levels of food webs. The release of toxic wastes has polluted the environment with harmful substances that often persist for long periods and become concentrated along the food chain by biological magnification.

► **Greenhouse Gases and Global Warming** Because of the burning of wood and fossil fuels and other human activities, the atmospheric concentration of CO_2 has been steadily increasing. The ultimate effects include significant global warming and other climate changes.

► **Depletion of Atmospheric Ozone** The ozone layer reduces the penetration of UV radiation through the atmosphere. Human activities, including release of chlorine-containing pollutants, are eroding the ozone layer, but government policies are helping to solve the problem.

MEDIA

Activity Water Pollution from Nitrates
Activity The Greenhouse Effect
GraphIt! Atmospheric CO_2 and Temperature Changes
MP3 Tutor Global Warming

TESTING YOUR KNOWLEDGE

SELF-QUIZ

1. Which of the following organisms is *incorrectly* paired with its trophic level?
   a. cyanobacterium—primary producer
   b. grasshopper—primary consumer
   c. zooplankton—primary producer
   d. eagle—tertiary consumer
   e. fungus—detritivore

2. Which of these ecosystems has the *lowest* net primary production per square meter?
   a. a salt marsh   d. a grassland
   b. an open ocean   e. a tropical rain forest
   c. a coral reef

3. Nitrifying bacteria participate in the nitrogen cycle mainly by
   a. converting nitrogen gas to ammonia.
   b. releasing ammonium from organic compounds, thus returning it to the soil.
   c. converting ammonia to nitrogen gas, which returns to the atmosphere.
   d. converting ammonium to nitrate, which plants absorb.
   e. incorporating nitrogen into amino acids and organic compounds.

4. Which of the following has the greatest effect on the rate of chemical cycling in an ecosystem?
   a. the ecosystem's rate of primary production
   b. the production efficiency of the ecosystem's consumers
   c. the rate of decomposition in the ecosystem
   d. the trophic efficiency of the ecosystem
   e. the location of the nutrient reservoirs in the ecosystem

5. The Hubbard Brook watershed deforestation experiment yielded all of the following results *except* that
   a. most minerals were recycled within a forest ecosystem.
   b. the flow of minerals out of a natural watershed was offset by minerals flowing in.

   c. deforestation increased water runoff.
   d. the nitrate concentration in waters draining the deforested area became dangerously high.
   e. calcium levels remained high in the soil of deforested areas.

6. Which of the following is a consequence of biological magnification?
   a. Toxic chemicals in the environment pose greater risk to top-level predators than to primary consumers.
   b. Populations of top-level predators are generally smaller than populations of primary consumers.
   c. The biomass of producers in an ecosystem is generally higher than the biomass of primary consumers.
   d. Only a small portion of the energy captured by producers is transferred to consumers.
   e. The amount of biomass in the producer level of an ecosystem decreases if the producer turnover time increases.

7. The main cause of the increase in the amount of CO_2 in Earth's atmosphere over the past 150 years is
   a. increased worldwide primary production.
   b. increased worldwide standing crop.
   c. an increase in the amount of infrared radiation absorbed by the atmosphere.
   d. the burning of larger amounts of wood and fossil fuels.
   e. additional respiration by the rapidly growing human population.

8. **DRAW IT** Using Figure 55.21 as a starting point, extend the *x*-axis to the year 2100. Then extend the CO_2 curve, assuming that the CO_2 concentration continues to rise as fast as it did from 1974 to 2007. What will be the approximate CO_2 concentration in 2100? What ecological factors and human decisions will influence the actual rise in CO_2 concentration? How might additional scientific data help societies predict this value?

For Self-Quiz answers, see Appendix A.

MEDIA Visit **www.campbellbiology.com** for a Practice Test.

EVOLUTION CONNECTION

9. Some biologists have suggested that ecosystems are emergent, "living" systems capable of evolving. One manifestation of this idea is environmentalist James Lovelock's Gaia hypothesis, which views Earth itself as a living, homeostatic entity—a kind of superorganism. Use the principles of evolution you have learned in this book to critique the idea that ecosystems and the biosphere can evolve. If ecosystems are capable of evolving, is this a form of Darwinian evolution? Why or why not?

SCIENTIFIC INQUIRY

10. Using two neighboring ponds in a forest as your study site, design a controlled experiment to measure the effect of falling leaves on net primary production in a pond.

Biological Inquiry: A Workbook of Investigative Cases Explore how changes to the Chesapeake affect shellfishing with the case "Back to the Bay."

Conservation Biology and Restoration Ecology

KEY CONCEPTS

56.1 Human activities threaten Earth's biodiversity

56.2 Population conservation focuses on population size, genetic diversity, and critical habitat

56.3 Landscape and regional conservation aim to sustain entire biotas

56.4 Restoration ecology attempts to restore degraded ecosystems to a more natural state

56.5 Sustainable development seeks to improve the human condition while conserving biodiversity

OVERVIEW

Striking Gold

Tucking its wings, a bird lands on a branch deep inside a tropical jungle. Sensing the motion, a conservation biologist scans the branch through binoculars, a glimpse of golden orange stopping her short. Staring back is a smoky honeyeater, a species that had never been described before **(Figure 56.1)**. In 2005, a team of American, Indonesian, and Australian biologists experienced many moments like this as they spent a month cataloging the living riches hidden in a remote mountain range in Indonesia. In addition to the honeyeater, they discovered dozens of new frog, butterfly, and plant species, including five new palms.

To date, scientists have described and formally named about 1.8 million species of organisms. Some biologists think that about 10 million more species currently exist; others estimate the number to be as high as 100 million. Some of the greatest concentrations of species are found in the tropics. Unfortunately, tropical forests are being cleared at an alarming rate to make room for and support a burgeoning human population. Rates of deforestation in Indonesia are among the highest in the world **(Figure 56.2)**. What will become of the smoky honeyeater and other newly discovered species in Indonesia if such deforestation continues unchecked?

▲ Figure 56.1 **What will be the fate of this newly described bird species?**

Throughout the biosphere, human activities are altering trophic structures, energy flow, chemical cycling, and natural disturbance—ecosystem processes on which we and all other species depend (see Chapter 55). We have physically altered nearly half of Earth's land surface, and we use over half of all accessible surface fresh water. In the oceans, stocks of most major fisheries are shrinking because of overharvesting. By some estimates, we are pushing more species toward extinction than the large asteroid or comet that triggered the mass extinctions at the close of the Cretaceous period 65.5 million years ago (see Figure 25.16).

Biology is the science of life. Thus, it is fitting that our final chapter focuses on two disciplines that seek to preserve life. **Conservation biology** integrates ecology, physiology, molecular biology, genetics, and evolutionary biology to conserve biological diversity at all levels. Efforts to sustain ecosystem processes and stem the loss of biodiversity also connect the life sciences with the social sciences, economics, and humanities.

▲ Figure 56.2 **Tropical deforestation in West Kalimantan, an Indonesian province.**

Restoration ecology applies ecological principles to return ecosystems that have been disturbed by human activity to a condition as similar as possible to their natural state.

In this chapter, we will take a closer look at the biodiversity crisis and examine some of the conservation and restoration strategies being adopted to slow the rate of species loss.

CONCEPT 56.1
Human activities threaten Earth's biodiversity

Extinction is a natural phenomenon that has been occurring since life first evolved; it is the *rate* of extinction that is responsible for today's biodiversity crisis (see Chapter 25). Because we can only estimate the number of species currently existing, we cannot determine the exact rate of species loss. However, we do know for certain that the extinction rate is high and that human activities threaten Earth's biodiversity at all levels.

Three Levels of Biodiversity

Biodiversity—short for biological diversity—can be considered at three main levels: genetic diversity, species diversity, and ecosystem diversity (Figure 56.3).

Genetic Diversity

Genetic diversity comprises not only the individual genetic variation *within* a population, but also the genetic variation *between* populations that is often associated with adaptations to local conditions (see Chapter 23). If one population becomes extinct, then a species may have lost some of the genetic diversity that makes microevolution possible. This erosion of genetic diversity in turn reduces the adaptive prospects of the species.

The loss of genetic diversity throughout the biosphere also affects human welfare. If we lose wild populations of plants closely related to agricultural species, we lose genetic resources that could be used to improve crop qualities, such as disease resistance, through plant breeding. For example, plant breeders responded to devastating outbreaks of the grassy stunt virus in rice (*Oryza sativa*) by screening 7,000 populations of this species and its close relatives for resistance to the virus. One population of a single relative, Indian rice (*Oryza nivara*), demonstrated resistance to the virus, and scientists succeeded in breeding the resistant trait into commercial rice varieties. Today, the original disease-resistant population has apparently become extinct in the wild.

Species Diversity

Public awareness of the biodiversity crisis centers on species diversity—the variety of species in an ecosystem or throughout the biosphere (see Chapter 54). As more species are lost to extinction, species diversity decreases. The U.S. Endangered

Genetic diversity in a vole population

Species diversity in a coastal redwood ecosystem

Community and ecosystem diversity across the landscape of an entire region

▲ **Figure 56.3 Three levels of biodiversity.** The oversized chromosomes in the top diagram symbolize the genetic variation within the population.

Species Act (ESA) defines an **endangered species** as one that is "in danger of extinction throughout all or a significant portion of its range." Also defined for protection by the ESA, **threatened species** are those that are considered likely to become endangered in the foreseeable future. The following are just a few statistics that illustrate the problem of species loss:

▶ According to the International Union for Conservation of Nature and Natural Resources (IUCN), 12% of the nearly 10,000 known species of birds and at least 20% of the nearly 5,000 known species of mammals are threatened.

▶ A survey by the Center for Plant Conservation showed that of the nearly 20,000 known plant species in the United States, 200 have become extinct since such records have been kept, and 730 are endangered or threatened.

- About 20% of the known species of freshwater fishes in the world have either become extinct during historical times or are seriously threatened. In North America, 123 freshwater animal species have become extinct since 1900, and hundreds more species are threatened. The extinction rate for North American freshwater fauna is about five times as high as that for terrestrial animals.
- According to a 2004 report in the journal *Science* that was based on a global assessment of amphibians by more than 500 scientists, 32% of all known amphibian species are either very near extinction or endangered.

Extinction of species may be local; for example, a species may be lost in one river system but survive in an adjacent one. Global extinction of a species means that it is lost from *all* the ecosystems in which it lived, leaving them permanently impoverished (**Figure 56.4**).

(a) Philippine eagle

(b) Yangtze River dolphin

(c) Javan rhinoceros

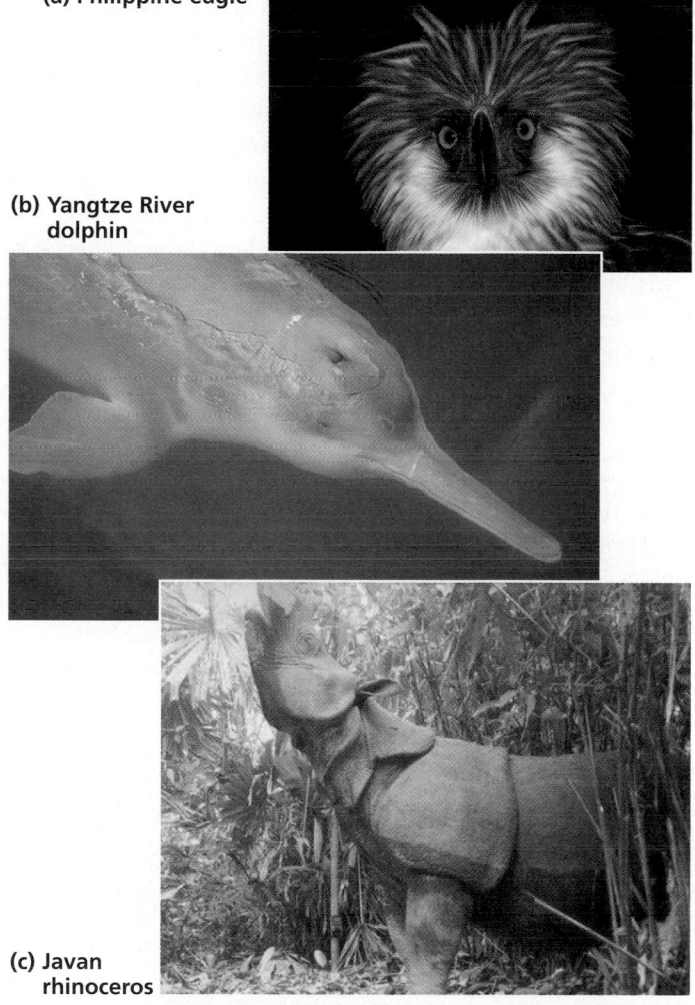

▲ **Figure 56.4 A hundred heartbeats from extinction.** These are just three members of what E. O. Wilson calls the Hundred Heartbeat Club, species with fewer than 100 individuals remaining on Earth. The Yangtze River dolphin was even thought to be extinct, but a few individuals were reportedly sighted in 2007.

? *To document that a species has actually become extinct, what spatial and temporal factors would you need to consider?*

Ecosystem Diversity

The variety of the biosphere's ecosystems is a third level of biological diversity. Because of the network of community interactions among populations of different species within an ecosystem, the local extinction of one species can have a negative impact on the overall species richness of the community (see Figure 54.15). For instance, bats called "flying foxes" are important pollinators and seed dispersers in the Pacific Islands, where they have been subject to increasing pressure from hunters, who sell them as luxury foods (**Figure 56.5**). Conservation biologists fear that the extinction of flying foxes would also harm the native plants of the Samoan islands, where more than 79% of the trees depend on flying foxes for pollination or seed dispersal.

Some ecosystems have already been heavily impacted by humans, and others are being altered at a rapid pace. For example, since European colonization, more than 50% of wetlands in the contiguous United States have been drained and converted to other ecosystems, primarily agricultural ones. In California, Arizona, and New Mexico, approximately 90% of native riparian communities have been affected by overgrazing, flood control, water diversions, lowering of water tables, and invasion by non-native plants.

Biodiversity and Human Welfare

Why should we care about the loss of biodiversity? Perhaps the purest reason is what E. O. Wilson calls *biophilia*, our sense of connection to nature and other forms of life. The belief that other species are entitled to life is a pervasive theme of many religions and the basis of a moral argument that we should protect biodiversity. There is also a concern for future human generations: Is it fair to deprive them of Earth's species richness? Paraphrasing an old proverb, G. H. Brundtland, a former prime minister of Norway, said: "We must consider our planet to be on

▲ **Figure 56.5 The endangered Marianas "flying fox" bat (*Pteropus mariannus*), an important pollinator.**

loan from our children, rather than being a gift from our ancestors." In addition to such philosophical and moral justifications, species and genetic diversity bring us many practical benefits.

Benefits of Species and Genetic Diversity

Many species that are threatened could potentially provide crops, fibers, and medicines for human use, making biodiversity a crucial natural resource. In the United States, about 25% of the prescriptions dispensed from pharmacies contain substances originally derived from plants. In the 1970s, researchers discovered that the rosy periwinkle, which grows on the island of Madagascar, off the coast of Africa, contains alkaloids that inhibit cancer cell growth (**Figure 56.6**). This discovery led to treatments for two deadly forms of cancer, Hodgkin's disease and a form of childhood leukemia, resulting in remission in most cases. Madagascar is also home to five other species of periwinkles, one of which is approaching extinction. The loss of these species would mean the loss of any possible medicinal benefits they might offer.

Each loss of a species means the loss of unique genes, some of which may code for enormously useful proteins. Consider the example of Taq polymerase, a DNA polymerase first extracted from the bacterium *Thermus aquaticus* in hot springs at Yellowstone National Park. This enzyme is an essential part of the polymerase chain reaction (PCR) because it is stable at the high temperatures required for PCR (see Figure 20.8). DNA from many other species of prokaryotes in a variety of environments is used in the mass production of proteins for new medicines, foods, petroleum substitutes, industrial chemicals, and other products. However, because millions of species may become extinct before we even know about them, we stand to lose irretrievably the valuable genetic potential held in their unique libraries of genes.

Ecosystem Services

The benefits that individual species provide to humans are often substantial, but saving individual species is only part of the rationale for saving ecosystems. Humans evolved in Earth's ecosystems, and we rely on these systems and their inhabitants for our survival. **Ecosystem services** encompass all the processes through which natural ecosystems help sustain human life on Earth. Ecosystems purify our air and water. They detoxify and decompose our wastes and reduce the impacts of extreme weather and flooding. The organisms in ecosystems pollinate our crops, control pests, and create and preserve our soils. Moreover, ecosystems provide all these services and countless others for free.

Perhaps because we don't attach a monetary value to the services of natural ecosystems, we generally undervalue them. In a controversial 1997 article, ecologist Robert Costanza and his colleagues estimated the value of Earth's ecosystem services at $33 trillion per year, nearly twice the gross national product of all the countries on Earth at that time ($18 trillion). It may be more realistic, and more meaningful, to do the accounting on a smaller scale. In 1996, New York City invested more than $1 billion to buy land and restore habitat in the Catskill Mountains, the source of much of the city's fresh water. This investment was spurred by increasing pollution of the water by sewage, pesticides, and fertilizers. By harnessing ecosystem services to purify its water naturally, the city saved $8 billion it would have otherwise spent to build a new filtration plant and $300 million a year to run the plant.

There is growing evidence that the functioning of ecosystems, and hence their capacity to perform services, is linked to biodiversity. As human activities reduce biodiversity, we are reducing the capacity of the planet's ecosystems to perform processes critical to our own survival.

Three Threats to Biodiversity

Many different human activities threaten biodiversity on local, regional, and global scales. The threats posed by these activities are of three major types: habitat loss, introduced species, and overexploitation.

Habitat Loss

Human alteration of habitat is the single greatest threat to biodiversity throughout the biosphere. Habitat loss has been brought about by agriculture, urban development, forestry, mining, and pollution. Global warming is already altering habitats today and will have an even larger effect later this century (see Chapter 55). When no alternative habitat is available or a species is unable to move, habitat loss may mean extinction. The IUCN implicates destruction of physical habitat for 73% of the species that have become extinct, endangered, vulnerable, or rare in the last few hundred years.

Habitat loss and fragmentation may occur over immense regions. For instance, approximately 98% of the tropical dry forests of Central America and Mexico have been cleared (cut down). Clearing of tropical rain forest in the state of Veracruz,

▶ **Figure 56.6**
The rosy periwinkle (*Catharanthus roseus*), a plant that saves lives.

▲ **Figure 56.7 Habitat fragmentation in the foothills of Los Angeles.** Development in the valleys may confine the organisms that inhabit the narrow strips of hillside.

Mexico, mostly for cattle ranching, has resulted in the loss of approximately 91% of the original forest, leaving a fragmented archipelago of small forest islands. Other natural habitats have also been fragmented by human activities (**Figure 56.7**).

In almost all cases, habitat fragmentation leads to species loss, since the smaller populations in habitat fragments have a higher probability of local extinction. The prairies of North America are an example: Prairie covered about 800,000 hectares of southern Wisconsin when Europeans first arrived, but now occupies less than 0.1% of its original area. Plant diversity surveys of 54 Wisconsin prairie remnants were conducted in 1948–1954 and then repeated in 1987–1988. During the three decades between the surveys, the various prairie fragments lost between 8% and 60% of their plant species.

Though most studies have focused on terrestrial ecosystems, habitat loss is also a major threat to aquatic biodiversity, especially along continental coasts and around coral reefs. About 93% of coral reefs, among Earth's most species-rich aquatic communities, have been damaged by human activities. At the current rate of destruction, 40–50% of the reefs, home to one-third of marine fish species, could disappear in the next 30 to 40 years. Freshwater habitats are also being lost, often as a result of the dams, reservoirs, channel modification, and flow regulation now affecting most of the world's rivers. For example, the more than 30 dams and locks built along the Mobile River basin, in the southeastern United States, changed river depth and flow and thereby helped drive more than 40 species of endemic mussels and snails to extinction.

Introduced Species

Introduced species, also called non-native or exotic species, are those that humans move, either intentionally or accidentally, from the species' native locations to new geographic regions. Rapid human travel by ship and airplane has accelerated the transplant of species. Free from the predators, parasites, and pathogens that limit their populations in their native habitats, such transplanted species may spread very rapidly through a new region.

Some introduced species that gain a foothold disrupt their adopted community, often by preying on native organisms or outcompeting them for resources. The brown tree snake was accidentally introduced to the island of Guam as a "stowaway" in military cargo after World War II (**Figure 56.8a**). Since then, 12 species of birds and 6 species of lizards on which the snakes prey have become extinct on Guam. The devastating zebra mussel was introduced into the Great Lakes of North America in 1988, most likely in the ballast water of ships arriving from Europe. Efficient suspension-feeding molluscs that form dense colonies, zebra mussels have extensively disrupted freshwater ecosystems, threatening native aquatic species. Zebra mussels have also clogged water intake structures, disrupting domestic and industrial water supplies and causing billions of dollars in damage.

Humans have deliberately introduced many species with good intentions but disastrous effects. For example, an Asian plant called kudzu, which the U.S. Department of Agriculture once introduced in the southern United States to help control erosion, has taken over large areas of the landscape there (**Figure 56.8b**). The European starling, brought intentionally into New York's Central Park in 1890 by a citizens' group intent on introducing all the plants and animals mentioned in Shakespeare's plays, quickly spread across North America, increasing to a population of more than 100 million and displacing many native songbirds.

Introduced species are a worldwide problem, contributing to approximately 40% of the extinctions recorded since 1750

(a) Brown tree snake, introduced to Guam in cargo

(b) Introduced kudzu thriving in South Carolina

▲ **Figure 56.8 Two introduced species.**

and costing billions of dollars annually in damage and control efforts. There are more than 50,000 introduced species in the United States alone.

Overexploitation

The term *overexploitation* refers generally to the human harvesting of wild organisms at rates exceeding the ability of populations of those species to rebound. Species with restricted habitats, such as small islands, are particularly vulnerable to overexploitation. One such species was the great auk, a large, flightless seabird found on islands in the North Atlantic Ocean. By the 1840s, humans had hunted the great auk to extinction to satisfy demand for its feathers, eggs, and meat.

Also susceptible to overexploitation are large organisms with low intrinsic reproductive rates, such as elephants, whales, and rhinoceroses. The decline of Earth's largest extant terrestrial animals, the African elephants, is a classic example of the impact of overhunting. Largely because of the trade in ivory, elephant populations have been declining in most of Africa during the last 50 years. An international ban on the sale of new ivory resulted in increased poaching (illegal hunting), so the ban had little effect in much of central and eastern Africa. Only in South Africa, where once-decimated herds have been well protected for nearly a century, have elephant populations been stable or increasing (see Chapter 53).

Conservation biologists increasingly use the tools of molecular genetics to track the origins of tissues harvested from threatened and endangered species. For instance, Samuel Wasser and colleagues, at the University of Washington, created a DNA reference map for the African elephant using DNA isolated from elephant dung. By comparing this reference map with DNA isolated from a small sample of ivory harvested either legally or by poachers, they can determine where the elephant was killed to within a few hundred kilometers. Similarly, biologists using phylogenetic analyses of mitochondrial DNA (mtDNA) showed that some whale meat sold in Japanese fish markets came from illegally harvested species, including fin and humpback whales, which are endangered (see Figure 26.6).

Many populations of commercially important marine fishes, once thought to be inexhaustible, have been dramatically reduced by overfishing. The exploding human population's increasing demand for protein, coupled with new harvesting technologies, such as long-line fishing and modern trawlers, have reduced these fish populations to levels that cannot sustain further exploitation. The fate of the North Atlantic bluefin tuna is just one example. Until the past few decades, this big tuna was considered a sport fish of little commercial value—just a few cents per pound for cat food. Then, in the 1980s, wholesalers began airfreighting fresh, iced bluefin to Japan for sushi and sashimi. In that market, the fish now brings up to $100 per pound (Figure 56.9). With the in-

▲ **Figure 56.9 Overexploitation.** North Atlantic bluefin tuna are auctioned in a Japanese fish market.

creased harvesting spurred by such high prices, it took just ten years to reduce the western North Atlantic bluefin population to less than 20% of its 1980 size. The collapse of the northern cod fishery off Newfoundland in the 1990s is a more recent example of how it is possible to overharvest what was formerly a very common species.

CONCEPT CHECK 56.1

1. Explain why it is too narrow to define the biodiversity crisis as simply a loss of species.
2. Identify the three main threats to biodiversity and explain how each damages diversity.
3. **WHAT IF?** Imagine two populations of a fish species, one in the Mediterranean Sea and one in the Caribbean Sea. Now imagine two scenarios: (1) The populations breed separately, and (2) adults of both populations migrate to the North Atlantic to interbreed. Which scenario would result in a greater loss of genetic diversity if the Mediterranean population were harvested to extinction? Explain your answer.

For suggested answers, see Appendix A.

CONCEPT 56.2
Population conservation focuses on population size, genetic diversity, and critical habitat

Biologists focusing on conservation at the population and species levels follow two main approaches: the small-population approach and the declining-population approach.

Small-Population Approach

A species is designated as endangered when its populations are very small. Small populations are particularly vulnerable to overexploitation, habitat loss, and the other threats to biodiversity that you read about in Concept 56.1. After such factors have taken their toll on population size, a population's smallness itself can drive it to extinction. Conservation biologists who adopt the small-population approach study the processes that cause extinctions once population sizes have been severely reduced.

The Extinction Vortex

A small population is prone to positive-feedback loops of inbreeding and genetic drift that draw the population down an **extinction vortex** toward smaller and smaller population size until no individuals exist (**Figure 56.10**). One key factor driving the extinction vortex is the loss of the genetic variation necessary to enable evolutionary responses to environmental change, such as the appearance of new strains of pathogens. Both inbreeding and genetic drift can cause a loss of genetic variation (see Chapter 23), and the effects of both processes become more significant as a population shrinks. Inbreeding often reduces fitness because offspring are more likely to be homozygous for harmful recessive traits.

Not all small populations are doomed by low genetic diversity, and low genetic variability does not automatically lead to permanently small populations. For instance, over-

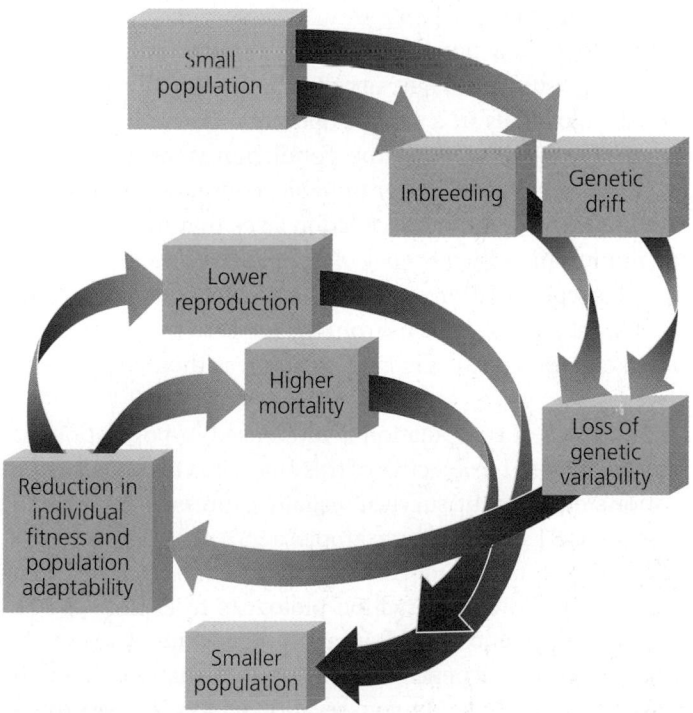

▲ **Figure 56.10 Processes culminating in an extinction vortex.**

hunting of northern elephant seals in the 1890s reduced the species to only 20 individuals—clearly a bottleneck with reduced genetic variation. Since that time, however, the northern elephant seal populations have rebounded to about 150,000 individuals today, though their genetic variation remains relatively low. Furthermore, a number of plant species seem to have inherently low genetic variability. For example, many populations of cord grass (*Spartina anglica*), which thrives in salt marshes, are genetically uniform at many loci. *S. anglica* arose from a few parent plants only about a century ago by hybridization and allopolyploidy (see Figure 24.11). Having spread by cloning, this species now dominates large areas of tidal mudflats in Europe and Asia. Thus, in rare cases, low genetic diversity has not impeded population growth.

Case Study: *The Greater Prairie Chicken and the Extinction Vortex*

When Europeans arrived in North America, the greater prairie chicken (*Tympanuchus cupido*) was common from New England to Virginia and all across the western prairies of the continent. As you read in Chapter 23, land cultivation for agriculture fragmented the populations of this species, and its abundance decreased drastically. In Illinois, there were millions of greater prairie chickens in the 19th century, but fewer than 50 were left by 1993. Researchers found that the decline in the Illinois population was associated with a decrease in fertility. As a test of the extinction vortex hypothesis, the scientists imported genetic variation by transplanting 271 birds from larger populations elsewhere (**Figure 56.11**, on the next page). The Illinois population rebounded, confirming that it had been on its way down the extinction vortex until rescued by the transfusion of genetic variation.

Minimum Viable Population Size

How small does a population have to be before it starts down an extinction vortex? The answer depends on the type of organism and other factors. For example, large predators that feed high on the food chain usually require very large individual ranges, resulting in very low population densities. Therefore, not all rare species concern conservation biologists. All populations, however, require some minimum size in order to remain viable.

The minimal population size at which a species is able to sustain its numbers and survive is known as the **minimum viable population (MVP)**. MVP is usually estimated for a given species using computer models that integrate many factors. The calculation may include, for example, an estimate of how many individuals in a small population are likely to be killed by some natural catastrophe such as a storm. Once in the extinction vortex, two or three years in a row of bad weather could finish off a population that is already below MVP.

What caused the drastic decline of the Illinois greater prairie chicken population?

EXPERIMENT Researchers had observed that the population collapse of the greater prairie chicken was mirrored in a reduction in fertility, as measured by the hatching rate of eggs. Comparison of DNA samples from the Jasper County, Illinois, population with DNA from feathers in museum specimens showed that genetic variation had declined in the study population (see Figure 23.10). In 1992, Ronald Westemeier, Jeffrey Brawn, and colleagues began transplanting prairie chickens from Minnesota, Kansas, and Nebraska in an attempt to increase genetic variation.

RESULTS After translocation (blue arrow), the viability of eggs rapidly increased, and the population rebounded.

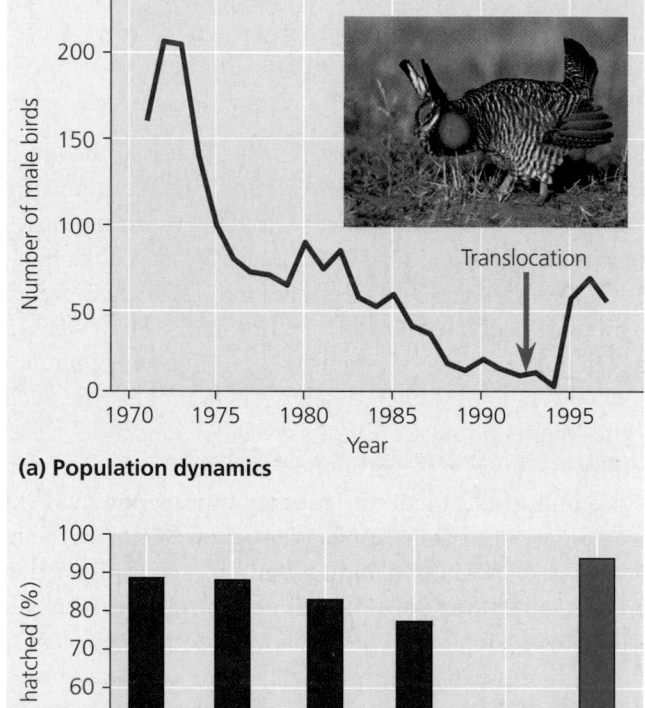

(a) Population dynamics

(b) Hatching rate

CONCLUSION Reduced genetic variation had started the Jasper County population of prairie chickens down the extinction vortex.

SOURCE R. L. Westemeier et al., Tracking the long-term decline and recovery of an isolated population, *Science* 282:1695–1698 (1998).

Inquiry in Action Read and analyze the original paper in *Inquiry in Action: Interpreting Scientific Papers.*

WHAT IF? Given the success of using transplanted birds as a tool for increasing the percentage of hatched eggs in Illinois, why wouldn't you transplant *additional* birds immediately to Illinois?

Effective Population Size

Genetic variation is the key issue in the small-population approach. The *total* size of a population may be misleading because only certain members of the population breed successfully and pass their alleles on to offspring. Therefore, a meaningful estimate of MVP requires the researcher to determine the **effective population size**, which is based on the breeding potential of the population.

The following formula incorporates the sex ratio of breeding individuals into the estimate of effective population size, abbreviated N_e:

$$N_e = \frac{4N_fN_m}{N_f + N_m}$$

where N_f and N_m are, respectively, the number of females and the number of males that successfully breed. If we apply this formula to an idealized population whose total size is 1,000 individuals, N_e will also be 1,000 if every individual breeds and the sex ratio is 500 females to 500 males. In this case, $N_e = (4 \times 500 \times 500)/(500 + 500) = 1,000$. Any deviation from these conditions (not all individuals breed or there is not a 1:1 sex ratio) reduces N_e. For instance, if the total population size is 1,000 but only 400 females and 400 males breed, then $N_e = (4 \times 400 \times 400)/(400 + 400) = 800$, or 80% of the total population size. Numerous life history traits can influence N_e, and alternative formulas for estimating N_e take into account family size, age at maturation, genetic relatedness among population members, the effects of gene flow between geographically separated populations, and population fluctuations.

In actual study populations, N_e is always some fraction of the total population. Thus, simply determining the total number of individuals in a small population does not provide a good measure of whether the population is large enough to avoid extinction. Whenever possible, conservation programs attempt to sustain total population sizes that include at least the minimum viable number of *reproductively active* individuals. The conservation goal of sustaining effective population size (N_e) above MVP stems from the concern that populations retain enough genetic diversity to adapt as their environment changes.

The MVP of a population is often used in population viability analysis. The objective of this analysis is to predict a population's chances for survival, usually expressed as a specific probability of survival (for example, a 95% chance) over a particular time interval (for instance, 100 years). Such modeling approaches allow conservation biologists to explore the potential consequences of alternative management plans. Because modeling depends on reliable information about the populations under study, conservation biology is most robust when theoretical modeling is combined with field studies of the managed populations.

Case Study: *Analysis of Grizzly Bear Populations*

One of the first population viability analyses was conducted in 1978 by Mark Shaffer, of Duke University, as part of a long-term study of grizzly bears in Yellowstone National Park and its surrounding areas (Figure 56.12). A threatened species in the United States, the grizzly bear (*Ursus arctos horribilis*) is currently found in only 4 of the 48 contiguous states. Its populations in those states have been drastically reduced and fragmented: In 1800, an estimated 100,000 grizzlies ranged over about 500 million hectares of mostly continuous habitat, while today only about 1,000 individuals in six relatively isolated populations range over less than 5 million hectares.

Shaffer attempted to determine viable sizes for the Yellowstone grizzly populations. Using life history data obtained for individual Yellowstone bears over a 12-year period, he simulated the effects of environmental factors on survival and reproduction. His models predicted that, given a suitable habitat, a Yellowstone grizzly bear population of 70 to 90 individuals would have about a 95% chance of surviving for 100 years, whereas a population of 100 bears would have a 95% chance of surviving for twice as long, about 200 years.

How does the actual size of the Yellowstone grizzly population compare with Shaffer's estimates of MVP? A current estimate puts the total grizzly bear population in the greater Yellowstone ecosystem at about 400 individuals. The relationship of this estimate to the effective population size, N_e, depends on several factors. Usually, only a few dominant males breed, and it may be difficult for them to locate females, since individuals inhabit such extensive areas. Moreover, females may reproduce only when there is abundant food. As a result, N_e is only about 25% of the total population size, or about 100 bears.

Because small populations tend to lose genetic variation over time, a number of research teams have analyzed proteins, mtDNA, and short tandem repeats (see Chapter 21) to assess genetic variability in the Yellowstone grizzly bear population. All results to date indicate that the Yellowstone population has less genetic variability than other grizzly bear populations in North America. However, the isolation and decline in genetic variability in the Yellowstone grizzly bear population were gradual during the 20th century and not as severe as feared: Museum specimens collected in the early 1900s demonstrate that genetic variability among the Yellowstone grizzly bears was low even then.

How might conservation biologists increase the effective size and genetic variation of the Yellowstone grizzly bear population? Migration between isolated populations of grizzlies could increase both effective and total population sizes. Computer models predict that introducing only two unrelated bears each decade into a population of 100 individuals would reduce the loss of genetic variation by about half. For the grizzly bear, and probably for many other species whose populations are very small, finding ways to promote dispersal among populations may be one of the most urgent conservation needs.

This case study and that of the greater prairie chicken bridge small-population models to practical applications in conservation. Next, we look at an alternative approach to understanding the biology of extinction.

Declining-Population Approach

The declining-population approach focuses on threatened and endangered populations that show a downward trend, even if the population is far above MVP. The distinction between a declining population (which is not always small) and a small population (which is not always declining) is less important than the different priorities of the two basic conservation approaches. The small-population approach emphasizes smallness itself as an ultimate cause of a population's extinction, especially through loss of genetic diversity. In contrast, the declining-population approach emphasizes the environmental factors that caused a population decline in the first place. If, for example, an area is deforested, then species that depend on trees will decline in number and become locally extinct, whether or not they retain genetic variation.

Steps for Analysis and Intervention

The declining-population approach requires that population declines be evaluated on a case-by-case basis, with researchers carefully dissecting the causes of a decline before taking steps to correct it. If, for example, the biological magnification of a toxic pollutant is harming some top-level consumer such as a predatory bird (see Chapter 55), then managers need to reduce or eliminate the pollutant in the environment to restore vulnerable populations of the bird. Although most situations are

▲ **Figure 56.12 Long-term monitoring of a grizzly bear population.** The ecologist is fitting this tranquilized bear with a radio collar so that the bear's movements can be compared with those of other individuals in the Yellowstone National Park population.

more complex, we can use the following steps for analyzing declining populations:

1. Confirm, using population data, that the species is presently in decline or that it was formerly more widely distributed or more abundant.
2. Study the natural history of this and related species, including reviewing the research literature, to determine the species' environmental requirements.
3. Develop hypotheses for all possible causes of the decline, including human activities and natural events, and list the predictions of each hypothesis.
4. Because many factors may be correlated with the decline, test the most likely hypothesis first. For example, remove the suspected agent of decline to see if the experimental population rebounds compared to a control population.
5. Apply the results of the diagnosis to manage the threatened species and monitor recovery.

The following case study is an example of how the declining-population approach has been applied in recent years to one endangered species.

Case Study: *Decline of the Red-Cockaded Woodpecker*

The red-cockaded woodpecker (*Picoides borealis*) is an endangered species endemic to the southeastern United States. This species requires mature pine forests, preferably ones dominated by the longleaf pine, for its habitat. Most woodpeckers nest in dead trees, but the red-cockaded woodpecker drills its nest holes in mature, living pine trees. Red-cockaded woodpeckers also drill small holes around the entrance to their nest cavity, which causes resin from the tree to ooze down the trunk. The resin seems to repel certain predators, such as corn snakes, that eat bird eggs and nestlings.

Another critical habitat factor for this woodpecker species is that the understory of plants around the pine trunks must be low (**Figure 56.13a**). Breeding birds tend to abandon nests when vegetation among the pines is thick and higher than about 4.5 m (**Figure 56.13b**). Apparently, the birds require a clear flight path between their home trees and the neighboring feeding grounds. Periodic fires have historically swept through longleaf pine forests, keeping the undergrowth low.

One factor leading to decline of the red-cockaded woodpecker is the destruction or fragmentation of suitable habitats by logging and agriculture. By recognizing key habitat factors, protecting some longleaf pine forests, and using controlled fires to reduce forest undergrowth, conservation managers have helped restore habitat that can support viable populations. However, designing a recovery program was complicated by the birds' social organization. Red-cockaded woodpeckers live in groups of one breeding pair and up to four "helpers," mostly males (an example of altruism; see Chapter 51). Helpers are offspring that do not disperse and breed but remain behind to help incubate eggs and feed nestlings. They may eventually attain breeding status within the flock when older birds die, but the wait may take years, and even then, helpers must compete to breed. Young birds that do disperse as members of new groups also have a tough path to reproductive success. New groups usually occupy abandoned territories or start at a new site and excavate nesting cavities, which

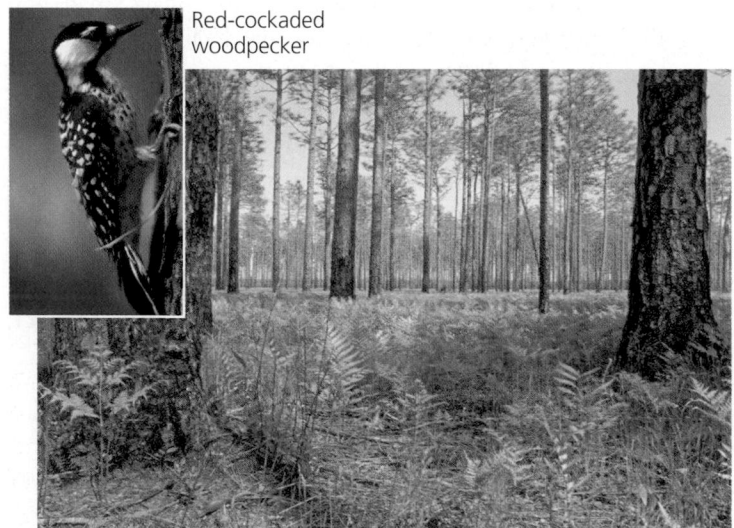

Red-cockaded woodpecker

(a) Forests that can sustain red-cockaded woodpeckers have low undergrowth.

(b) Forests that cannot sustain red-cockaded woodpeckers have high, dense undergrowth that impacts the woodpeckers' access to feeding grounds.

▲ **Figure 56.13 Habitat requirements of the red-cockaded woodpecker.**

? *How is habitat disturbance absolutely necessary for the long-term survival of the woodpecker?*

can take several years. Individuals generally have a better chance of reproducing by remaining behind than by dispersing and expending the effort to excavate homes in new territories.

To test the hypothesis that this social behavior contributes to the decline of the red-cockaded woodpecker, Carole Copeyon, Jeffrey Walters, and Jay Carter, of North Carolina State University, constructed cavities in pine trees at 20 sites. The results were dramatic: Cavities in 18 of the 20 sites were colonized by red-cockaded woodpeckers, and new breeding groups formed only in these sites. The experiment supported the hypothesis that this woodpecker species had been leaving much suitable habitat unoccupied because of a lack of breeding cavities. Based on this experiment, conservationists initiated a habitat maintenance program that included controlled burning and excavation of new breeding cavities, enabling this endangered species to begin to recover.

Weighing Conflicting Demands

Determining population numbers and habitat needs is only part of the effort to save species. Scientists also need to weigh a species' biological and ecological needs against other conflicting demands. Conservation biology often highlights the relationship between science, technology, and society. For example, an ongoing, sometimes bitter debate in the U.S. Pacific Northwest pits habitat preservation for northern spotted owl, timber wolf, grizzly bear, and bull trout populations against job opportunities in the timber, mining, and other resource extraction industries. Programs to restock wolves in Yellowstone National Park were opposed by some recreationists concerned for human safety and by many ranchers concerned with potential loss of livestock.

Large, high-profile vertebrates are not always the focal point in such conflicts, but habitat use is almost always the issue. Should work proceed on a new highway bridge if it destroys the only remaining habitat of a species of freshwater mussel? If you were the owner of a coffee plantation growing varieties that thrive in bright sunlight, would you be willing to change to shade-tolerant varieties that produce less coffee per area but can grow beneath trees that support large numbers of songbirds?

Another important consideration is the ecological role of a species. Because we will not be able to save every endangered species, we must determine which species are most important for conserving biodiversity as a whole. Identifying keystone species and finding ways to sustain their populations can be central to maintaining communities and ecosystems.

Management aimed at conserving a single species carries with it the possibility of negatively affecting populations of other species. For example, management of open pine forests for the red-cockaded woodpecker might impact migratory birds that use later-successional broadleaf forests. To test for such impacts, ecologists compared bird communities near clusters of nest cavities in managed pine forests with communities in forests not managed for the woodpeckers. Contrary to expectations, the managed sites supported higher numbers and a higher diversity of other birds than the control forests. In this case, managing for one bird species increased the diversity of an entire community of birds. In most situations, conservation must look beyond single species and consider the whole community and ecosystem as an important unit of biodiversity.

CONCEPT 56.3
Landscape and regional conservation aim to sustain entire biotas

Preservation efforts historically focused on saving individual species, but efforts today often aim to sustain the biodiversity of entire communities, ecosystems, and landscapes. Such a broad view requires understanding and applying the principles of community, ecosystem, and landscape ecology as well as the principles of human population dynamics and economics. The goals of landscape ecology (see Chapter 52), of which ecosystem management is a part, include understanding past, present, and future patterns of landscape use and making biodiversity conservation part of land-use planning.

Landscape Structure and Biodiversity

The biodiversity of a given landscape is in large part a function of the structure of the landscape. Understanding landscape structure is critically important in conservation because many species use more than one kind of ecosystem, and many live on the borders between ecosystems.

Fragmentation and Edges

The boundaries, or *edges*, between ecosystems—such as between a lake and the surrounding forest or between cropland and suburban housing tracts—are defining features of landscapes (Figure 56.14). An edge has its own set of physical conditions, which differ from those on either side of it. The soil surface of an edge between a forest patch and a burned area receives more sunlight and is usually hotter and drier than the forest interior, but it is cooler and wetter than the soil surface in the burned area.

Some organisms thrive in edge communities because they gain resources from both adjacent areas. The ruffed grouse (*Bonasa umbellatus*) is a bird that needs forest habitat for nesting, winter food, and shelter, but it also needs forest openings with dense shrubs and herbs for summer food. White-tailed deer also thrive in edge habitats, where they can browse on woody shrubs; deer populations often expand when forests are logged and more edges are exposed.

The proliferation of edge species can have positive or negative effects on biodiversity. A 1997 study in Cameroon comparing edge and interior populations of the little greenbul (a tropical rain forest bird) suggested that forest edges may be important sites of speciation. On the other hand, communities in which edges arise from human alterations often have reduced biodiversity because the relatively large percentage of edge habitat leads to a preponderance of edge-adapted species. For example, the brown-headed cowbird (*Molothrus ater*) is an edge-adapted species that lays its eggs in the nests of other birds, particularly migratory songbirds. Cowbirds need forests, where they can parasitize the nests of other birds, and also open fields, where they forage on insects. Thus, their populations are growing where forests are being cut and fragmented, creating more edge habitat and open land. Increasing cowbird parasitism and loss of habitat are correlated with declining populations of several of the cowbird's host species.

The influence of fragmentation on the structure of communities has been explored since 1979 in the long-term Biological Dynamics of Forest Fragments Project. Located in the heart of the Amazon River basin, the study area consists of isolated fragments of forest separated from surrounding continuous tropical rain forest by distances of 80–1,000 m (Figure 56.15). Researchers from all over the world have clearly documented

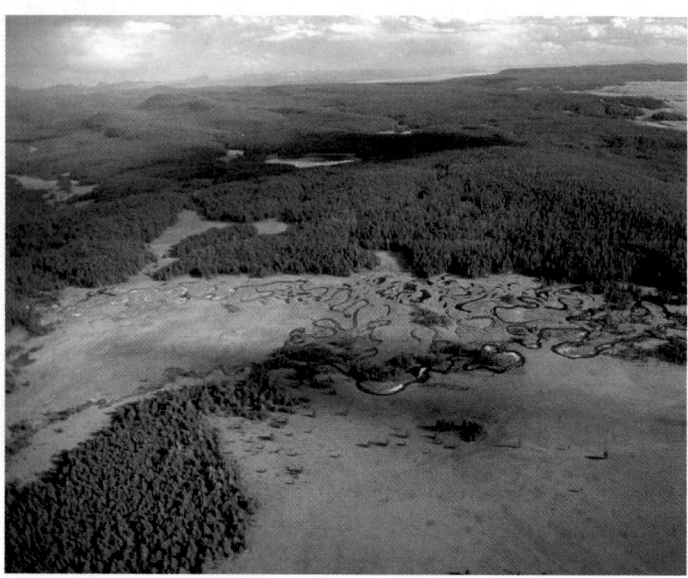

(a) Natural edges. Grasslands give way to forest ecosystems in Yellowstone National Park.

(b) Edges created by human activity. Pronounced edges (roads) surround clear-cuts in this photograph of a heavily logged rain forest in Malaysia.

▲ **Figure 56.14 Edges between ecosystems.**

▲ Figure 56.15 **Amazon rain forest fragments created as part of the Biological Dynamics of Forest Fragments Project.**

the physical and biological effects of this fragmentation in organisms ranging from bryophytes to beetles to birds. They have consistently found that species adapted to forest interiors show the greatest declines in the smallest fragments, suggesting that landscapes dominated by small fragments will support fewer species, mainly due to loss of interior-adapted species.

Corridors That Connect Habitat Fragments

In fragmented habitats, the presence of a **movement corridor**, a narrow strip or series of small clumps of habitat connecting otherwise isolated patches, can be extremely important for conserving biodiversity. Streamside habitats often serve as corridors, and in some nations, government policy prohibits altering these riparian areas. In areas of heavy human use, artificial corridors are sometimes constructed. Bridges or tunnels, for instance, can reduce the number of animals killed trying to cross highways (Figure 56.16).

Movement corridors also can promote dispersal and reduce inbreeding in declining populations. Corridors have been shown to increase the exchange of individuals in many organisms, including butterflies, voles, and aquatic plants. Corridors are especially important to species that migrate between different habitats seasonally. However, a corridor can also be harmful—as, for example, in the spread of disease. In a 2003 study, Agustin Estrada-Peña, of the University of Zaragoza, Spain, showed that habitat corridors facilitate the movement of disease-carrying ticks among forest patches in northern Spain. All the effects of corridors are not yet understood, and their impact is an area of active research in conservation biology and restoration ecology.

Establishing Protected Areas

Conservation biologists are applying their understanding of community, ecosystem, and landscape dynamics in establishing protected areas to slow biodiversity loss. Currently, governments have set aside about 7% of the world's land in various forms of reserves. Choosing where to place and how to design nature reserves poses many challenges. Should the reserve be managed to minimize the risks of fire and predation to a threatened species? Or should the reserve be left as natural as possible, with such processes as fires ignited by lightning allowed to play out on their own? This is just one of the debates that arise among people who share an interest in the health of national parks and other protected areas. In deciding which areas are of highest conservation priority, biologists often focus on hot spots of biological diversity.

Finding Biodiversity Hot Spots

A **biodiversity hot spot** is a relatively small area with an exceptional concentration of endemic species and a large number of endangered and threatened species (Figure 56.17). Nearly 30% of all bird species are confined to only about 2% of Earth's land area. Approximately 50,000 plant species, or about one-sixth of all known plant species, inhabit just 18 hot

▲ **Figure 56.16 An artificial corridor.** This bridge in Banff National Park, Canada, helps animals cross a human-created barrier.

■ Terrestrial biodiversity hot spots

▲ Marine biodiversity hot spots

◀ **Figure 56.17 Earth's terrestrial and marine biodiversity hot spots.**

Equator

spots covering 0.5% of the global land surface. Together, the "hottest" of the terrestrial biodiversity hot spots total less than 1.5% of Earth's land but are home to more than a third of all species of plants, amphibians, reptiles (including birds), and mammals. Hot spots also include aquatic ecosystems, such as coral reefs and certain river systems.

Biodiversity hot spots are obviously good choices for nature reserves, but identifying them is not always simple. One problem is that a hot spot for one taxonomic group, such as butterflies, may not be a hot spot for some other taxonomic group, such as birds. Designating an area as a biodiversity hot spot is often biased toward saving vertebrates and plants, with less attention paid to invertebrates and microorganisms. Some biologists are also concerned that the hot-spot strategy places too much emphasis on such a small fraction of Earth's surface.

Philosophy of Nature Reserves

Nature reserves are biodiversity islands in a sea of habitat degraded to varying degrees by human activity. Protected "islands" are not isolated from their surroundings, however, and the nonequilibrium model we described in Chapter 54 applies to nature reserves as well as to the larger landscapes in which they are embedded.

An earlier policy—that protected areas should be set aside to remain unchanged forever—was based on the concept that ecosystems are balanced, self-regulating units. As we saw in Chapter 54, however, disturbance is a functional component of all ecosystems, and management policies that ignore natural disturbances or attempt to prevent them have generally failed. For instance, setting aside an area of a fire-dependent community, such as a portion of a tallgrass prairie, chaparral, or dry pine forest, with the intention of saving it is unrealistic if periodic burning is excluded. Without the dominant disturbance, the fire-adapted species are usually outcompeted and biodiversity is reduced.

Because human disturbance and fragmentation are increasingly common landscape features, the dynamics of disturbances, populations, edges, and corridors are all important for designing and managing protected areas. An important conservation question is whether to create fewer large reserves or more numerous small reserves. One argument for extensive reserves is that large, far-ranging animals with low-density populations, such as the grizzly bear, require extensive habitats. More extensive areas also have proportionately smaller perimeters than smaller areas and are therefore less affected by edges. As conservation biologists learn more about the requirements for achieving minimum viable populations for endangered species, they realize that most national parks and other reserves are far too small. For example, the area needed for the long-term survival of the Yellowstone grizzly bear population is more than ten times the combined area of Yellowstone and Grand Teton National Parks (Figure 56.18). Given

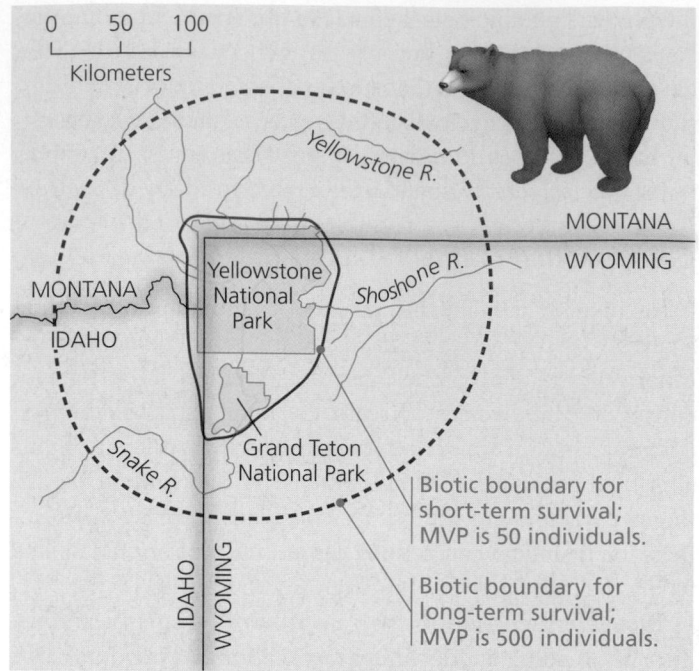

▲ **Figure 56.18 Biotic boundaries for grizzly bears in Yellowstone and Grand Teton National Parks.** The biotic boundaries (solid and dashed red lines) surround the areas needed to support minimum viable populations of 50 and 500 bears. Even the smaller of these areas is larger than the two parks.

political and economic realities, many existing parks will not be enlarged, and most newly created reserves will also be too small. Areas of private and public land surrounding reserves will likely have to contribute to biodiversity conservation. On the other side of the argument, smaller, unconnected reserves may slow the spread of disease throughout a population.

In practical terms, land use by humans may outweigh all other considerations and ultimately dictate the size and shape of protected areas. Much of the land left for conservation efforts is useless for exploitation by agriculture or forestry. But in some cases, as when reserve land is surrounded by commercially viable property, the use of land for agriculture or forestry must be integrated into conservation strategies.

Zoned Reserves

Several nations have adopted a zoned reserve approach to landscape management. A **zoned reserve** is an extensive region that includes areas relatively undisturbed by humans surrounded by areas that have been changed by human activity and are used for economic gain. The key challenge of the zoned reserve approach is to develop a social and economic climate in the surrounding lands that is compatible with the long-term viability of the protected core. These surrounding areas continue to be used to support the human population, but with regulations that prevent the types of extensive alterations likely to impact the protected area. As a result, the surrounding habitats serve as buffer zones against further intrusion into the undisturbed area.

The small Central American nation of Costa Rica has become a world leader in establishing zoned reserves (Figure 56.19). An agreement initiated in 1987 reduced Costa Rica's international debt in return for land preservation there. The agreement resulted in eight zoned reserves, called "conservation areas," that contain designated national park land. Costa Rica is making progress toward managing its zoned reserves, and the buffer zones provide a steady, lasting supply of forest products, water, and hydroelectric power and also support sustainable agriculture and tourism. An important goal is providing a stable economic base for people living there. As University of Pennsylvania ecologist Daniel Janzen, a leader in tropical conservation, has said, "The likelihood of long-term survival of a conserved wildland area is directly proportional to the economic health and stability of the society in which that wildland is embedded."

Destructive practices that are not compatible with long-term ecosystem conservation and from which there is often little local profit, such as massive logging, large-scale single-crop agriculture, and extensive mining, are ideally confined to the outermost fringes of the buffer zones and are gradually being discouraged.

Costa Rica relies on its zoned reserve system to maintain at least 80% of its native species, but the system is not without problems. A 2003 analysis of land cover change between 1960 and 1997 showed negligible deforestation within Costa Rica's national parks and a gain in forest cover in the 1-km buffer around the parks. However, significant losses in forest cover were discovered in the 10-km buffer zones around all national parks, which threaten to turn the parks into isolated habitat islands.

Although marine ecosystems have also been heavily impacted by human exploitation, reserves in the ocean are far less common than reserves on land. Many fish populations around the world have collapsed as increasingly sophisticated equipment puts nearly all potential fishing grounds within human reach. In response, Fiona Gell and Callum Roberts, of the University of York, England, have proposed establishing marine reserves around the world that would be off limits to fishing. Gell and Roberts present strong evidence that a patchwork of marine reserves can serve as a means of both increasing fish populations within the reserves and improving fishing success in nearby areas. Their proposed system is a modern application of a centuries-old practice in the Fiji Islands in which some areas have historically remained closed to fishing—a traditional example of the zoned reserve concept.

The United States adopted such a system in establishing the Florida Keys National Marine Sanctuary in 1990 (Figure 56.20). Populations of marine organisms, including fishes and lobsters, recovered quickly after harvests were banned in the 9,500-km^2 reserve. Larger and more abundant fish now produce larvae that

(a) Boundaries of the zoned reserves are indicated by black outlines.

(b) Local schoolchildren marvel at the diversity of life in one of Costa Rica's reserves.

▲ **Figure 56.19 Zoned reserves in Costa Rica.**

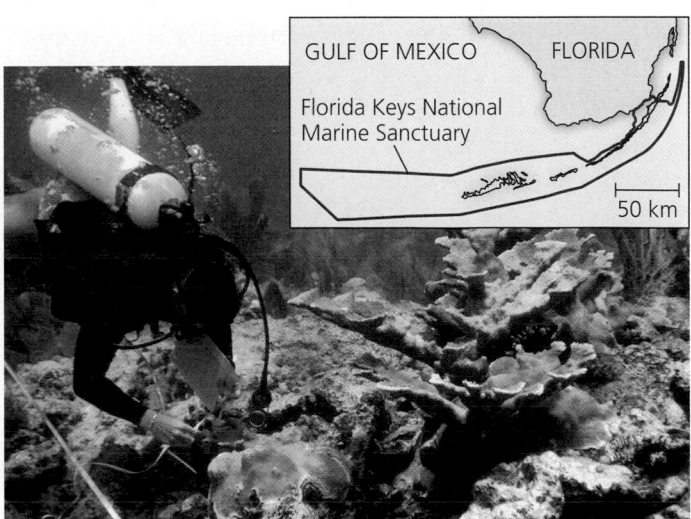

▲ **Figure 56.20 A diver measuring coral in the Florida Keys National Marine Sanctuary.**

help repopulate reefs and improve fishing outside the sanctuary. The increased marine life within the sanctuary also makes it a favorite for recreational divers, increasing the economic value of this zoned reserve.

CONCEPT CHECK   56.3

1. What is a biodiversity hot spot?
2. How do zoned reserves provide economic incentives for long-term conservation of protected areas?
3. **WHAT IF?** Suppose a developer proposes to clear-cut a forest that serves as a corridor between two parks. To compensate, the developer also proposes to add the same area of forest to one of the parks. As a professional ecologist, how might you argue for retaining the corridor?

For suggested answers, see Appendix A.

CONCEPT 56.4

Restoration ecology attempts to restore degraded ecosystems to a more natural state

Given enough time, biological communities can recover naturally from most disturbances through the stages of ecological succession that we discussed in Chapter 54. Sometimes that recovery takes centuries, though, particularly when humans degrade the environment. Degraded habitats are increasing in area because the natural rate of recovery by successional processes is often slower than the rate of degradation by human activities. The soils of many tropical areas quickly become unproductive and are soon abandoned after being cleared for farming. Mining activities may last for several decades, but the lands are then abandoned in a degraded state. Many ecosystems are also damaged inadvertently by the dumping of toxic chemicals or such mishaps as oil spills.

Restoration ecology seeks to initiate or speed up the recovery of degraded ecosystems. One of its basic assumptions is that environmental damage is at least partly reversible. This optimistic view must be balanced by a second assumption—that ecosystems are not infinitely resilient. Restoration ecologists therefore work to identify and manipulate the processes that most limit the speed of recovery of ecosystems from disturbances. Where disturbance is so severe that restoring all of a habitat is impractical, ecologists try to reclaim as much of a habitat or ecological process as possible, within the limits of the time and money available to them.

In extreme cases, the structure of a site may first need to be restored before biological restoration can occur. If a stream was straightened to channel water quickly through a suburb, restoration ecologists may reconstruct a meandering channel to slow down the flow of water eroding the stream bank. To restore an open-pit mine, engineers may first grade the site with heavy equipment to reestablish a gentle slope, spreading topsoil when the slope is in place (Figure 56.21). Once such physical reconstruction is complete—or when it is not needed—biological restoration is the next step.

Two key strategies in restoration ecology are bioremediation and biological augmentation.

Bioremediation

The use of organisms, usually prokaryotes, fungi, or plants, to detoxify polluted ecosystems is known as **bioremediation** (see Chapter 27). Some plants adapted to soils containing heavy metals can accumulate high concentrations of potentially toxic metals such as zinc, nickel, lead, and cadmium in

(a) In 1991, before restoration

(b) In 2000, near the completion of restoration

▲ Figure 56.21 **A gravel and clay mine site in New Jersey before and after restoration.**

(a) Wastes containing uranium were dumped in these four unlined pits for more than 30 years, contaminating soils and groundwater.

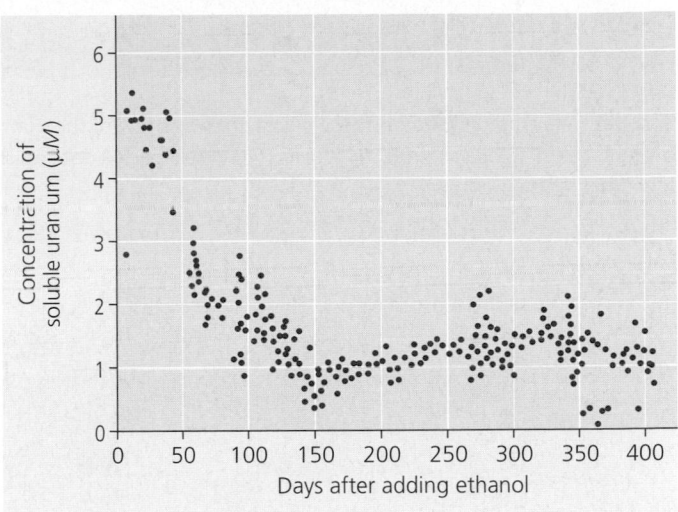

(b) After ethanol was added, microbial activity decreased the concentration of soluble uranium in groundwater near the pits.

▲ **Figure 56.22 Bioremediation of groundwater contaminated with uranium at Oak Ridge National Laboratory, Tennessee.**

their tissues. Restoration ecologists can use such plants to revegetate sites polluted by mining and other human activities and then harvest the plants to remove the metals from the ecosystem. Researchers in the United Kingdom discovered a lichen species that grows on soil polluted with uranium dust left over from mining. The lichen concentrates uranium in a dark pigment, making it useful as a biological monitor and potentially as a remediator.

Ecologists are examining the abilities of many prokaryotes to carry out bioremediation of soils and water. Scientists have sequenced the genomes of at least seven prokaryotic species specifically for their bioremediation potential. One of the species, the bacterium *Shewanella oneidensis*, appears particularly promising. It can metabolize more than ten elements under aerobic and anaerobic conditions to generate its energy. For instance, it converts soluble uranium, chromium, and nitrogen to insoluble forms that are less likely to leach into streams or groundwater. Wei-Min Wu and colleagues, at Oak Ridge National Laboratory, in Tennessee, stimulated the growth of *Shewanella* and other uranium-reducing bacteria by adding ethanol to groundwater contaminated with uranium; over five months, the concentration of soluble uranium dropped by 80% **(Figure 56.22)**. In the future, genetic engineering may become increasingly useful as a tool for improving the performance of prokaryotes and other organisms as bioremediators.

Biological Augmentation

In contrast to bioremediation, which is a strategy for removing harmful substances, **biological augmentation** uses organisms to add essential materials to a degraded ecosystem. Augmenting ecosystem processes requires determining what factors, such as chemical nutrients, have been removed from an area and thus limit its rate of recovery. Encouraging the growth of plants that thrive in nutrient-poor soils often speeds up the rate of successional changes that can lead to recovery of damaged sites. In alpine ecosystems of the western United States, nitrogen-fixing herbs such as lupines are often planted to bolster nitrogen concentrations in soils disturbed by mining and other uses. Once these nitrogen-fixing plants become established, other native species are better able to obtain enough nitrogen from the soil to survive. In other systems where the soil has been severely disturbed or where topsoil is missing entirely, plant roots may lack the mycorrhizal symbionts that help them meet their nutritional needs (see Chapter 31). Ecologists restoring a tallgrass prairie in Minnesota recognized this limitation and significantly accelerated the recovery of native species by adding mycorrhizal symbionts to the soil they seeded.

Exploring Restoration

Because restoration ecology is a relatively new discipline and because ecosystems are complex, restoration ecologists generally learn as they go. Many restoration ecologists advocate adaptive management: experimenting with several promising types of management to learn what works best.

The long-term objective of restoration is to speed the reestablishment of an ecosystem as similar as possible to the predisturbance ecosystem. **Figure 56.23**, on the next two pages, identifies several ambitious and successful restoration projects around the world. The great number of such projects, the dedication of the people engaged in them, and the successes that have been achieved suggest that restoration ecology will continue to grow as a discipline for many years.

Exploring Restoration Ecology Worldwide

The examples highlighted on these pages are just a few of the many restoration ecology projects taking place around the world. The color-coded dots on the map indicate the locations of the projects.

Truckee River, Nevada. Damming and water diversions during the 20th century reduced flow in the Truckee River, Nevada, leading to declines in riparian forests. Restoration ecologists worked with water managers to ensure that sufficient water would be released during the short season of seed release by the native cottonwood and willow trees for seedlings to become established. Nine years of controlled-flow release led to the result shown here: a dramatic recovery of cottonwood-willow riparian forest.

Kissimmee River, Florida. The Kissimmee River was converted from a meandering river to a 90-km canal, threatening many fish and wetland bird populations. Kissimmee River restoration has filled 12 km of drainage canal and reestablished 24 km of the original 167 km of natural river channel. Pictured here is a section of the Kissimmee canal that has been plugged (wide, light strip on the right side of the photo), diverting flow into remnant river channels in the center of the photo. The project will also restore the natural flow regime, which will foster self-sustaining populations of wetland birds and fishes.

Tropical dry forest, Costa Rica. Clearing for agriculture, mainly for livestock grazing, eliminated approximately 98% of tropical dry forest in Central America and Mexico. Reversing this trend, tropical dry forest restoration in Costa Rica has used domestic livestock to disperse the seeds of native trees into open grasslands. The photo shows one of the first trees (right center), dispersed as seed by livestock, to colonize former pastureland. This project is a model for joining restoration ecology with the local economy and educational institutions.

Rhine River, Europe. Centuries of dredging and channeling for navigation (see the barges in the wide, main channel on the right side of the photo) have straightened the once-meandering Rhine River and disconnected it from its floodplain and associated wetlands. The countries along the Rhine, particularly France, Germany, Luxembourg, the Netherlands, and Switzerland, are cooperating to reconnect the river to side channels, such as the one shown on the left side of the photo. Such side channels increase the diversity of habitats available to aquatic biota, improve water quality, and provide flood protection.

Coastal Japan. Seaweed and seagrass beds are important nursery grounds for a wide variety of fishes and shellfish. Once extensive but now reduced by development, these beds are being restored in the coastal areas of Japan. Techniques include constructing suitable seafloor habitat, transplanting from natural beds using artificial substrates, and hand seeding (shown in this photograph).

Succulent Karoo, South Africa. In this desert region of southern Africa, as in many arid regions, overgrazing by livestock has damaged vast areas. Reversing this trend, private landowners and government agencies in South Africa are restoring large areas of this unique region, revegetating the land and employing more sustainable resource management. The photo shows a small sample of the exceptional plant diversity of the Succulent Karoo; its 5,000 plant species include the highest diversity of succulent plants in the world.

Maungatautari, New Zealand. Weasels, rats, pigs, and other introduced species pose a serious threat to New Zealand's native plants and animals, including the kiwi, a flightless, ground-dwelling bird. The goal of the Maungatautari restoration project is to exclude all exotic mammals from a 3,400-ha reserve located on a forested volcanic cone. A specialized fence around the reserve eliminates the need to continue setting traps and using poisons that can harm native wildlife. In 2006, a pair of critically endangered takahe (a species of flightless rail) were released into the reserve in hopes of reestablishing a breeding population of this colorful bird on New Zealand's north island.

CONCEPT CHECK 56.4

1. Identify the main goal of restoration ecology.

2. How do bioremediation and biological augmentation differ?

3. **WHAT IF?** In what way is the Kissimmee River project a more complete ecological restoration than the Maungatautari project (see Figure 56.23)?

For suggested answers, see Appendix A.

CONCEPT **56.5**

Sustainable development seeks to improve the human condition while conserving biodiversity

With the increasing loss and fragmentation of habitats, we face difficult trade-offs in how to manage Earth's resources. Preserving all habitat patches isn't feasible, so biologists must help societies set conservation priorities by identifying which habitat patches are most crucial. Ideally, implementing these priorities should also improve the quality of life for local people. Ecologists use the concept of *sustainability* as a tool to establish long-term conservation priorities.

Sustainable Biosphere Initiative

We must understand the complex interconnections of the biosphere to protect species from extinction and to improve the quality of human life. To this end, many nations, scientific societies, and other groups have embraced the concept of **sustainable development**, development that meets the needs of people today without limiting the ability of future generations to meet their needs. The forward-looking Ecological Society of America, the world's largest organization of professional ecologists, endorses a research agenda called the Sustainable Biosphere Initiative. The goal of this initiative is to define and acquire the basic ecological information needed to develop, manage, and conserve Earth's resources as responsibly as possible. The research agenda includes studies of global change, including interactions between climate and ecological processes; biological diversity and its role in maintaining ecological processes; and the ways in which the productivity of natural and artificial ecosystems can be sustained. This initiative requires a strong commitment of human and economic resources.

Achieving sustainable development is an ambitious goal. To sustain ecosystem processes and stem the loss of biodiversity, we must connect life science with the social sciences, economics, and humanities. We must also reassess our personal values. Those of us living in wealthier nations have a larger ecological footprint than do people living in developing na-

tions (see Chapter 53). By reducing our orientation toward short-term gain, we can learn to value the natural processes that sustain us. The following case study illustrates how the combination of scientific and personal efforts can make a significant difference in creating a truly sustainable world.

Case Study: Sustainable Development in Costa Rica

The success of conservation in Costa Rica that we discussed in Concept 56.3 has involved an essential partnership between the national government, nongovernment organizations (NGOs), and private citizens. Many nature reserves established by individuals have been recognized by the government as national wildlife reserves and given significant tax benefits. However, conservation and restoration of biodiversity make up only one facet of sustainable development; the other key facet is improving the human condition.

How have the living conditions of the Costa Rican people changed as the country has pursued its conservation goals? As we discussed in Chapter 53, two of the most fundamental indicators of living conditions are infant mortality rate and life expectancy. From 1930 to 2007, the infant mortality rate in Costa Rica declined from 170 to 9 per 1,000 live births; over the same period, life expectancy increased from about 43 years to 77 years **(Figure 56.24)**. Another indicator of living conditions is literacy rate. The 2004 literacy rate in Costa Rica was 96%, compared to 97% in the United States. Such statistics show that living conditions in Costa Rica have improved greatly over the period in which the country has dedicated itself to conservation and restoration. While this result does not prove that conservation *causes* an increase in human welfare, we can say with certainty that development in Costa Rica has attended to both nature *and* people.

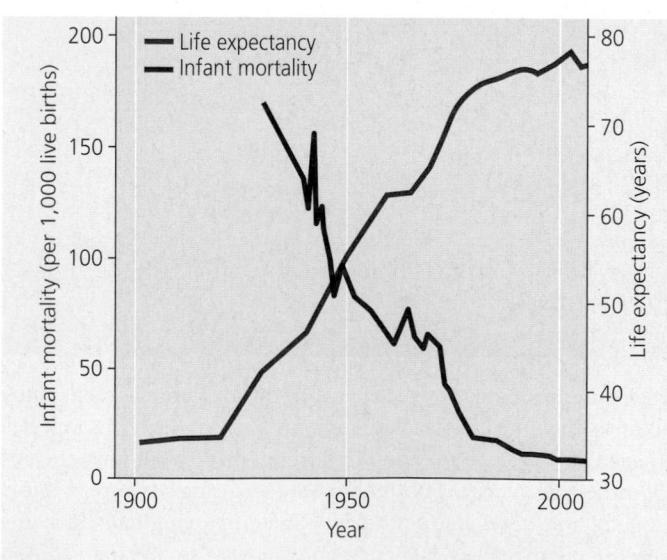

▲ Figure 56.24 **Infant mortality and life expectancy at birth in Costa Rica.**

Despite the successes in Costa Rica, many problems remain. One of the challenges that the country faces is maintaining its commitment to conservation while its population grows. Costa Rica is in the middle of a rapid demographic transition (see Chapter 53), and even though birth rates are dropping rapidly, its population is growing at about 1.5% annually (compared to 0.9% growth in the United States). Costa Rica's population, which is currently about 4 million, is predicted to continue to grow until the middle of this century, when it is projected to level off at approximately 6 million. If recent success is any guide, the people of Costa Rica will overcome the challenge of population growth in their quest for sustainable development.

The Future of the Biosphere

Our modern lives are very different from those of early humans, who hunted and gathered to survive. Their reverence for the natural world is evident in the early murals of wildlife they painted on cave walls **(Figure 56.25a)** and in the stylized visions of life they sculpted from bone and ivory **(Figure 56.25b)**.

Our lives reflect remnants of our ancestral attachment to nature and the diversity of life—the concept of *biophilia* that we introduced early in this chapter. We evolved in natural environments rich in biodiversity, and we still have an affinity for such settings **(Figure 56.25c)**. E. O. Wilson makes the case that our biophilia is innate, an evolutionary product of natural selection acting on a brainy species whose survival depended on a close connection to the environment and a practical appreciation of plants and animals.

Our appreciation of life guides the field of biology today. We celebrate life by deciphering the genetic code that makes each species unique. We embrace life by using fossils and DNA to chronicle the march of evolution through time. We preserve life through our efforts to classify and protect the millions of species on Earth. We respect life by using nature responsibly and reverently to improve human welfare.

Biology is the scientific expression of our desire to know nature. We are most likely to protect what we appreciate, and we are most likely to appreciate what we understand. By learning about the processes and diversity of life, we also become more aware of ourselves and our place in the biosphere. We hope this book serves you well in this lifelong adventure.

(a) Detail of animals in a 36,000-year-old cave painting, Lascaux, France

---

CONCEPT CHECK **56.5**

1. What is meant by the term *sustainable development*?
2. How might biophilia influence us to conserve species and restore ecosystems?
3. **WHAT IF?** Suppose a new fishery is discovered, and you are put in charge of developing it sustainably. What ecological data might you want on the fish population? What criteria would you apply for the fishery's development?

For suggested answers, see Appendix A.

(b) A 30,000-year-old ivory carving of a water bird, found in Germany

(c) Biologist Carlos Rivera Gonzales examining a tiny tree frog in Peru

▲ **Figure 56.25 Biophilia, past and present.**

SUMMARY OF KEY CONCEPTS

CONCEPT 56.1

Human activities threaten Earth's biodiversity (pp. 1246–1250)

▶ **Three Levels of Biodiversity**

Genetic diversity: source of variations that enable populations to adapt to environmental changes

Species diversity: important in maintaining structure of communities and food webs

Ecosystem diversity: provides life-sustaining services such as nutrient cycling and waste decomposition

▶ **Biodiversity and Human Welfare** Our biophilia enables us to recognize the value of biodiversity for its own sake. Other species also provide humans with food, fiber, medicines, and ecosystem services.

▶ **Three Threats to Biodiversity** Three major threats to biodiversity are habitat loss, introduced species, and overexploitation.

CONCEPT 56.2

Population conservation focuses on population size, genetic diversity, and critical habitat (pp. 1250–1255)

▶ **Small-Population Approach** When a population drops below a minimum viable population (MVP) size, its loss of genetic variation due to nonrandom mating and genetic drift can trap it in an extinction vortex.

▶ **Declining-Population Approach** The declining-population approach focuses on the environmental factors that cause decline, regardless of absolute population size. It follows a step-by-step proactive conservation strategy.

▶ **Weighing Conflicting Demands** Conserving species often requires resolving conflicts between the habitat needs of endangered species and human demands.

CONCEPT 56.3

Landscape and regional conservation aim to sustain entire biotas (pp. 1255–1260)

▶ **Landscape Structure and Biodiversity** The structure of a landscape can strongly influence biodiversity. As habitat fragmentation increases and edges become more extensive, biodiversity tends to decrease. Movement corridors can promote dispersal and help sustain populations.

▶ **Establishing Protected Areas** Biodiversity hot spots are also hot spots of extinction and thus prime candidates for protection. Sustaining biodiversity in parks and reserves requires management to ensure that human activities in the surrounding landscape do not harm the protected habitats. The zoned reserve model recognizes that conservation efforts often involve working in landscapes that are greatly affected by human activity.

CONCEPT 56.4

Restoration ecology attempts to restore degraded ecosystems to a more natural state (pp. 1260–1264)

▶ **Bioremediation** Restoration ecologists harness organisms to detoxify polluted ecosystems.

▶ **Biological Augmentation** Ecologists also use organisms to add essential materials to ecosystems.

▶ **Exploring Restoration** The newness and complexity of restoration ecology require scientists to consider alternative solutions and adjust approaches based on experience.

CONCEPT 56.5

Sustainable development seeks to improve the human condition while conserving biodiversity (pp. 1264–1265)

▶ **Sustainable Biosphere Initiative** The goal of the Sustainable Biosphere Initiative is to acquire the ecological information needed for the development, management, and conservation of Earth's resources.

▶ *Case Study:* **Sustainable Development in Costa Rica** Costa Rica's success in conserving tropical biodiversity has involved partnerships between the government, other organizations, and private citizens. Human living conditions in Costa Rica have improved along with ecological conservation.

▶ **The Future of the Biosphere** By learning about biological processes and the diversity of life, we become more aware of our close connection to the environment and the value of other organisms in it.

TESTING YOUR KNOWLEDGE

SELF-QUIZ

1. Ecologists conclude there is a biodiversity crisis because
   a. biophilia causes humans to feel ethically responsible for protecting other species.
   b. scientists have at last discovered and counted most of Earth's species and can now accurately calculate the current extinction rate.
   c. current extinction rates are very high and many species are threatened or endangered.
   d. many potential life-saving medicines are being lost as species evolve.
   e. there are too few biodiversity hot spots.

2. Which of the following would be considered an example of bioremediation?
   a. adding nitrogen-fixing microorganisms to a degraded ecosystem to increase nitrogen availability
   b. using a bulldozer to regrade a strip mine
   c. identifying a new biodiversity hot spot
   d. reconfiguring the channel of a river
   e. adding seeds of a chromium-accumulating plant to soil contaminated by chromium

3. What is the effective population size (N_e) of a population of 50 strictly monogamous swans (40 males and 10 females) if every female breeds successfully?
   a. 50   b. 40   c. 30   d. 20   e. 10

4. One characteristic that distinguishes a population in an extinction vortex from most other populations is that
   a. its habitat is fragmented.
   b. it is a rare, top-level predator.
   c. its effective population size is much lower than its total population size.
   d. its genetic diversity is very low.
   e. it is not well adapted to edge conditions.

5. The discipline that applies ecological principles to returning degraded ecosystems to more natural states is known as
   a. population viability analysis.
   b. landscape ecology.
   c. conservation ecology.
   d. restoration ecology.
   e. resource conservation.

6. What is the single greatest threat to biodiversity?
   a. overexploitation of commercially important species
   b. introduced species that compete with or prey on native species
   c. pollution of Earth's air, water, and soil
   d. disruption of trophic relationships as more and more prey species become extinct
   e. habitat alteration, fragmentation, and destruction

7. Which of the following strategies would most rapidly increase the genetic diversity of a population in an extinction vortex?
   a. Capture all remaining individuals in the population for captive breeding followed by reintroduction to the wild.
   b. Establish a reserve that protects the population's habitat.
   c. Introduce new individuals transported from other populations of the same species.
   d. Sterilize the least fit individuals in the population.
   e. Control populations of the endangered population's predators and competitors.

8. Of the following statements about protected areas that have been established to preserve biodiversity, which one is *not* correct?
   a. About 25% of Earth's land area is now protected.
   b. National parks are one of many types of protected areas.
   c. Most protected areas are too small to protect species.
   d. Management of a protected area should be coordinated with management of the land surrounding the area.
   e. It is especially important to protect biodiversity hot spots.

For Self-Quiz answers, see Appendix A.

EVOLUTION CONNECTION

9. One factor favoring rapid population growth by an introduced species is the absence of the predators, parasites, and pathogens that controlled its population in the region where it evolved. Over the long term, how should evolution by natural selection influence the rate at which the native predators, parasites, and pathogens in a region of introduction attack an introduced species?

SCIENTIFIC INQUIRY

10. **DRAW IT** Suppose that you are in charge of planning a forest reserve, and one of your goals is to help sustain local populations of woodland birds suffering from parasitism by the brown-headed cowbird. Reading research reports, you note that female cowbirds are usually reluctant to penetrate more than about 100 m into a forest and that nest parasitism is reduced for woodland birds nesting in denser, more central forest regions. The forested area you have to work with extends about 6,000 m from east to west and 1,000 m from north to south. Intact forest surrounds the reserve everywhere but on the west side, where the reserve borders deforested pastureland, and in the southwest corner, where it borders an agricultural field for 500 m. Your plan must include space for a small maintenance building, which you estimate to take up about 100 m². It will also be necessary to build a road, 10 m by 1,000 m, from the north to the south side of the reserve. Draw a map of the reserve, showing where you would construct the road and the building to minimize cowbird intrusion along edges. Explain your reasoning.

CHAPTER 1

Figure Questions
Figure 1.3 Of the properties shown in this figure, the lawn mower shows only order, regulation, and energy processing. **Figure 1.6** The arrangement of fingers and opposable thumb in the human hand, combined with fingernails and a complex system of nerves and muscles, allows the hand to grasp and manipulate objects with great dexterity. **Figure 1.13** Substance B would be made continuously and would accumulate in large amounts. Neither C nor D would be made. **Figure 1.27** The percentage of brown artificial snakes attacked would probably be higher than the percentage of artificial kingsnakes attacked in all areas (whether or not inhabited by coral snakes). **Figure 1.28** The hole would allow some mixing of blood between the two ventricles. As a result, some of the blood pumped from the left ventricle to the body would not have received oxygen in the lungs, and some of the blood pumped to the lungs would already carry oxygen.

Concept Check 1.1
1. Examples: A molecule consists of *atoms* bonded together. Each organelle has an orderly arrangement of *molecules*. Photosynthetic plant cells contain *organelles* called chloroplasts. A tissue consists of a group of similar *cells*. Organs such as the heart are constructed from several *tissues*. A complex multicellular organism, such as a plant, has several types of *organs*, such as leaves and roots. A population is a set of *organisms* of the same species. A community consists of *populations* of the various species inhabiting a specific area. An ecosystem consists of a biological *community* along with the nonliving factors important to life, such as air, soil, and water. The biosphere is made up of all of Earth's *ecosystems*. **2.** (a) Structure and function are correlated. (b) Cells are an organism's basic units, *and* the continuity of life is based on heritable information in the form of DNA. (c) Organisms interact with their environments, exchanging matter and energy. **3.** Some possible answers: *Evolution:* All plants have chloroplasts, indicating their descent from a common ancestor. *Emergent properties:* The ability of a human heart to pump blood requires an intact heart; it is not a capability of any of the heart's tissues or cells working alone. *Exchange of matter and energy with the environment:* A mouse eats food, then uses the nutrients for growth and the generation of energy for its activities; some of the food material is expelled in urine and feces, and some of the energy returns to the environment as heat. *Structure and function:* The strong, sharp teeth of a wolf are well suited to grasping and dismembering its prey. *Cells:* The digestion of food is made possible by chemicals (chiefly enzymes) made by cells of the digestive tract. *DNA:* Human eye color is determined by the combination of genes inherited from the two parents. *Feedback regulation:* When your stomach is full, it signals your brain to decrease your appetite.

Concept Check 1.2
1. An address pinpoints a location by tracking from broader to narrower categories—a state, city, zip, street, and building number. This is analogous to the groups-subordinate-to-groups structure of biological taxonomy. **2.** Natural selection starts with the naturally occurring heritable variation in a population and then "edits" the population as individuals with heritable traits better suited to the environment survive and reproduce more successfully than others. **3.**

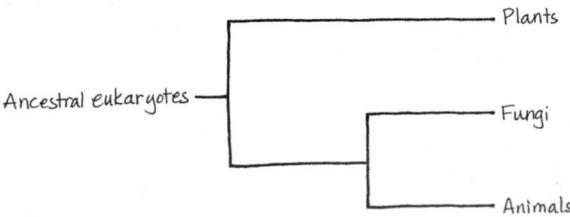

Concept Check 1.3
1. Inductive reasoning derives generalizations from specific cases; deductive reasoning predicts specific outcomes from general premises. **2.** Compared to a hypothesis, a scientific theory is usually more general and substantiated by a much greater amount of evidence. Natural selection is an explanatory idea that applies to all kinds of organisms and is supported by vast amounts of evidence of various kinds. **3.** Based on the results shown in Figure 1.27, you might predict that the colorful artificial snakes would be attacked more often than the brown ones, simply because they are easier to see. This prediction assumes that the area in Virginia where you are working has predators that attack snakes but no poisonous snakes that resemble the colorful artificial snakes.

Self-Quiz
1. b **2.** d **3.** a **4.** c **5.** c **6.** c **7.** c **8.** d **9.** b **10.** c
11. Your figure should show: (1) For the biosphere, the Earth with an arrow coming out of a tropical ocean; (2) for the ecosystem, a distant view of a coral reef; (3) for the community, a collection of reef animals and algae, with corals, fish, some seaweed, and any other organisms you can think of; (4) for the population, a group of fish of the same species; (5) for the organism, one fish from your population; (6) for the organ, the fish's stomach, and for the organ system, the whole digestive tract (see Chapter 41 for help); (7) for a tissue, a group of similar cells from the stomach; (8) for a cell, one cell from the tissue, showing its nucleus and a few other organelles; (9) for an organelle, the nucleus, where most of the cell's DNA is located; and (10) for a molecule, a DNA double helix. Your sketches can be very rough!

CHAPTER 2

Figure Questions
Figure 2.2 The most significant difference in the results would be that the two *Cedrela* saplings inside each garden would show similar amounts of dying leaf tissue because a poisonous chemical released from the *Duroia* trees would presumably reach the saplings via the air or soil and would not be blocked by the insect barrier. The *Cedrela* saplings planted outside the gardens would not show damage unless *Duroia* trees were nearby. Also, any ants present on the unprotected *Cedrela* saplings inside the gardens would probably not be observed making injections into the leaves. However, formic acid would likely still be found in the ants' glands, as for most species of ants.
Figure 2.9 Atomic number = 12; 12 protons, 12 electrons; three electron shells; 2 electrons in the valence shell
Figure 2.16

Figure 2.19 The plant is submerged in water (H_2O), in which the CO_2 is dissolved. The sun's energy is used to make sugar, which is found in the plant and can act as food for the plant itself, as well as for animals that eat the plant. The oxygen (O_2) is present in the bubbles.

Concept Check 2.1
1. Table salt is made up of sodium and chlorine. We are able to eat the compound, showing that it has different properties from those of a metal and a poisonous gas. **2.** Yes, because an organism requires trace elements, even though

only in small amounts. **3.** A person with an iron deficiency will probably show effects of low oxygen in the blood, such as fatigue. (The condition is called anemia and can also result from too few red blood cells or abnormal hemoglobin.)

Concept Check 2.2

1. 7 **2.** $^{15}_{7}N$ **3.** 9 electrons; two electron shells; $1s$, $2s$, $2p$ (three orbitals); 1 electron is needed to fill the valence shell. **4.** The elements in a row all have the same number of electron shells. In a column, all the elements have the same number of electrons in their valence shells.

Concept Check 2.3

1. Each carbon atom has only three covalent bonds instead of the required four. **2.** The attractions between oppositely charged ions form ionic bonds. **3.** If researchers can synthesize molecules that mimic these shapes, they may be able to treat diseases or conditions caused by the inability of affected individuals to synthesize such molecules.

Concept Check 2.4

1.

$$H:H + \ddot{O}::\ddot{O} \rightarrow \begin{array}{c} :\ddot{O}:H \\ H \\ :\ddot{O}:H \\ H \end{array}$$

$$2H_2 \qquad O_2 \qquad 2H_2O$$

2. At equilibrium, the forward and reverse reactions occur at the same rate. **3.** $C_6H_{12}O_6 + 6\,O_2 \rightarrow 6\,CO_2 + 6\,H_2O$ + Energy. Glucose and oxygen react to form carbon dioxide, water, and energy. We breathe in oxygen because we need it for this reaction to occur, and we breathe out carbon dioxide because it is a by-product of this reaction. By the way, this reaction is called cellular respiration, and you will learn more about it in Chapter 9.

Self-Quiz

1. a **2.** b **3.** b **4.** c **5.** b **6.** a **7.** b **8.** b

9.

a. $\ddot{O}::\overset{A}{C}:H$ This structure doesn't make sense because the valence shell of carbon is incomplete; carbon can form 4 bonds.

b. $H:\ddot{O}:\overset{H}{\underset{H}{C}}:\ddot{C}::\ddot{O}$ This structure makes sense because all valence shells are complete, and all bonds have the correct number of electrons.

c. $H:\overset{H}{\underset{H}{C}}:H.\overset{H}{C}::\ddot{O}$ This structure doesn't make sense because H has only 1 electron to share, so it cannot form bonds with 2 atoms.

d. This structure doesn't make sense for several reasons: The valence shell of oxygen is incomplete; oxygen can form 2 bonds. $:\ddot{O}:$ $H:N..H$ H has only 1 electron to share, so it cannot form a double bond. Nitrogen usually makes only 3 bonds. It does not have enough electrons to make 2 single bonds, make a double bond, and complete its valence shell.

CHAPTER 3

Figure Questions

Figure 3.6 Without hydrogen bonds, water would behave like other small molecules, and the solid phase (ice) would be denser than liquid water. The ice would sink to the bottom, and because it would no longer insulate the whole body of water, it could freeze. Freezing would take a longer time because the Antarctic is an ocean (the Southern Ocean), not a pond or lake, but the average annual temperature at the South Pole is $-50°C$, so eventually it

would freeze. The krill could not survive. **Figure 3.7** Heating the solution would cause the water to evaporate faster than it is evaporating at room temperature. At a certain point, there wouldn't be enough water molecules to solubilize the salt ions. The salt would start coming out of solution and re-forming crystals. Eventually, all the water would evaporate, leaving behind a pile of salt like the original pile. **Figure 3.11** Given that Ca^{2+} and CO_3^{2-} must interact to form $CaCO_3$, you would predict that $[Ca^{2+}]$ would also have an effect on the calcification rate, and this result is observed in the current study. Under natural conditions in the oceans, the $[Ca^{2+}]$ remains relatively constant, so the $[CO_3^{2-}]$ has a much more important effect on calcification rate.

Concept Check 3.1

1. Electronegativity is the attraction of an atom for the electrons of a covalent bond. Because oxygen is more electronegative than hydrogen, the oxygen atom in H_2O pulls electrons toward itself, resulting in a partial negative charge on the oxygen atom and partial positive charges on the hydrogen atoms. Oppositely charged ends of water molecules are attracted to each other, forming a hydrogen bond. **2.** The hydrogen atoms of one molecule, with their partial positive charges, would repel the hydrogen atoms of the adjacent molecule. **3.** Water molecules would not be polar, and they would not form hydrogen bonds with each other.

Concept Check 3.2

1. Hydrogen bonds hold neighboring water molecules together. This cohesion helps the molecules resist gravity. Adhesion between water molecules and the walls of water-conducting cells also counters gravity. As water evaporates from leaves, the chain of water molecules in water-conducting cells moves upward. **2.** High humidity hampers cooling by suppressing the evaporation of sweat. **3.** As water freezes, it expands because water molecules move farther apart in forming ice crystals. When there is water in a crevice of a boulder, expansion due to freezing may crack the rock. **4.** The molecular mass of NaCl is 58.5 daltons. A mole would have a mass of 58.5 g, so you would measure out 0.5 mol, or 29.3 g, of NaCl and gradually add water, stirring until it is dissolved. You would add water to bring the final volume to 1 L. **5.** The hydrophobic substance repels water, perhaps helping to keep the ends of the legs from becoming coated with water and breaking through the surface. If the legs were coated with a hydrophilic substance, water would be drawn up them, possibly making it more difficult for the water strider to walk on water.

Concept Check 3.3

1. 10^5, or 100,000 **2.** $[H^+] = 0.01\ M = 10^{-2}\ M$, so pH = 2 **3.** $CH_3COOH \rightleftharpoons CH_3COO^- + H^+$. CH_3COOH is the acid (the H^+ donor) and CH_3COO^- is the base (the H^+ acceptor). **4.** The pH of the water should go from 7 to about 2; the pH of the acetic acid solution will only decrease a small amount, because the reaction shown for question 3 will shift to the left, with CH_3COO^- accepting the influx of H^+ and becoming CH_3COOH molecules.

Self-Quiz

1. d **2.** c **3.** b **4.** c **5.** c **6.** d **7.** c **8.** c

9.

CHAPTER 4

Figure Questions

Figure 4.2 Because the concentration of the reactants influences the equilibrium (as discussed in Chapter 2), there might be more HCN relative to CH_2O, since there would be a higher concentration of the reactant gas that contains nitrogen.

Figure 4.4

$$Na\cdot \qquad \cdot\ddot{P}\cdot \qquad \cdot\ddot{\ddot{S}}: \qquad \cdot\ddot{\ddot{Cl}}:$$

Figure 4.7

H–C–H (structure diagram)

Figure 4.10 Molecule b, because there are not only the two electronegative oxygens of the carboxyl group, but also an oxygen on the next (carbonyl) carbon. All of these oxygens help make the bond between the O and H of the —OH group more polar, thus making the dissociation of H$^+$ more likely.

Concept Check 4.1

1. Amino acids are essential molecules for living organisms. Their synthesis from gases of the primitive atmosphere on Earth demonstrated that life's molecules could initially have been synthesized from nonliving molecules.   **2.** The spark provides energy needed for the inorganic molecules in the atmosphere to react with each other. (You'll learn more about energy and chemical reactions in Chapter 8.)

Concept Check 4.2

1. (structure diagram: C=C with H's)

2. The forms of C_4H_{10} in (b) are structural isomers, as are the butenes in (c). **3.** Both consist largely of hydrocarbon chains.   **4.** No. There is not enough diversity in the atoms. It can't form structural isomers because there is only one way for three carbons to attach to each other (in a line). There are no double bonds, so geometric isomers are not possible. Each carbon has at least two hydrogens attached to it, so the molecule is symmetrical and cannot have enantiomeric isomers.

Concept Check 4.3

1. It has both an amino group (—NH$_2$), which makes it an amine, and a carboxyl group (—COOH), which makes it a carboxylic acid.   **2.** The ATP molecule loses a phosphate, becoming ADP.

3. (structure diagram)   A chemical group that can act as a base has been replaced with a group that can act as an acid, increasing the acidic properties of the molecule. The shape of the molecule would also change, likely changing the molecules with which it can interact.

Self-Quiz

1. b   **2.** d   **3.** a   **4.** b   **5.** b   **6.** a   **7.** d

8. (·Si· diagram)   Si has four valence electrons, the same number as carbon. Therefore, silicon would be able to form long chains, including branches, that could act as skeletons for organic molecules. It would clearly do this much better than neon (with no valence electrons) or aluminum (with three valence electrons).

CHAPTER 5

Figure Questions
Figure 5.4

Linear form → Ring forming → Ring form (structure diagrams)

Four carbons are in the fructose ring, and two are not. (The latter two carbons are hanging off carbons 2 and 5, which are in the ring.) This form differs from glucose, which has five carbons in the ring and one that is not. (Note that the orientation of this fructose molecule is flipped relative to the one in Figure 5.5b.)

Figure 5.18

Figure 5.25 The green spiral is an α helix.

Concept Check 5.1

1. Proteins, carbohydrates, lipids, and nucleic acids   **2.** Nine, with one water required to hydrolyze each connected pair of monomers   **3.** The amino acids in the green bean protein are released in hydrolysis reactions and incorporated into other proteins in dehydration reactions.

Concept Check 5.2

1. $C_3H_6O_3$ **2.** $C_{12}H_{22}O_{11}$ **3.** The absence of these prokaryotes would hamper the cow's ability to obtain energy from food and could lead to weight loss and possibly death.

Concept Check 5.3

1. Both have a glycerol molecule attached to fatty acids. The glycerol of a fat has three fatty acids attached, whereas the glycerol of a phospholipid is attached to two fatty acids and one phosphate group.   **2.** Human sex hormones are steroids, a type of hydrophobic compound.   **3.** The oil droplet membrane could consist of a single layer of phospholipids rather than a bilayer, because an arrangement in which the hydrophobic tails of the membrane phospholipids were in contact with the hydrocarbon regions of the oil molecules would be more stable.

Concept Check 5.4

1. The function of a protein is a consequence of its specific shape, which is lost when a protein becomes denatured.   **2.** Secondary structure involves hydrogen bonds between atoms of the polypeptide backbone. Tertiary structure involves bonding between atoms of the R groups of the amino acid subunits.   **3.** Primary structure, the amino acid sequence, affects the secondary structure, which affects the tertiary structure, which affects the quaternary structure (if any). In short, the amino acid sequence affects the shape of the protein. Because the function of a protein depends on its shape, a change in primary structure can destroy a protein's function.

Concept Check 5.5

1.   5′ end

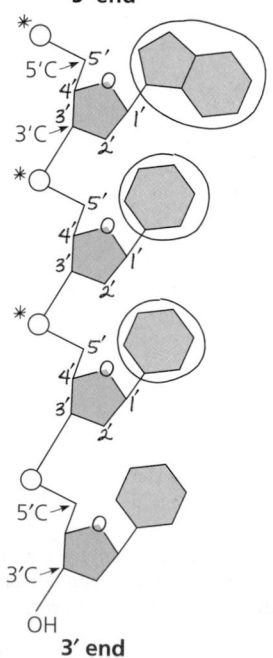

3′ end

2. 5′-TAGGCCT-3′
3′-ATCCGGA-5′

3. (a)

Mismatch

5′-T A A G C C T-3′
3′-A T C C G G A-5′

(b)

3′-A T T C G G A-5′

Self-Quiz

1. d **2.** c **3.** a **4.** b **5.** a **6.** d **7.** b
8.

	Monomers or Components	Polymer or larger molecule	Type of linkage
Sugars	Monosaccharides	Polysaccharides	Glycosidic linkages
Lipids	Fatty acids	Triacylglycerols	Ester linkages
Proteins	Amino acids	Polypeptides	Peptide bonds
Nucleic acids	Nucleotides	Polynucleotides	Phosphodiester linkages

9.

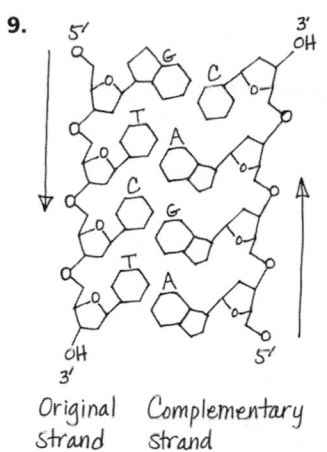

Original strand   Complementary strand

CHAPTER 6

Figure Questions

Figure 6.7 A phospholipid is a lipid, consisting of a glycerol molecule joined to two fatty acids and one phosphate group. Together, the glycerol and phosphate end of the phospholipid form is the "head," which is hydrophilic, while the hydrocarbon chains on the fatty acids form hydrophobic "tails." The presence in a single molecule of both a hydrophilic and a hydrophobic region makes the molecule ideal as the main building block of a membrane.

Figure 6.22 Each centriole has 9 sets of 3 microtubules, so the entire centrosome has 54. Each microtubule consists of a helical array of tubulin dimers (as shown in Table 6.1).

1 microtubule

Figure 6.29 The microtubules would reorient, and based on the earlier results, the cellulose synthase proteins would also change their path, orienting along the repositioned microtubules. (This is, in fact, what was observed.)

Concept Check 6.1

1. Stains used for light microscopy are colored molecules that bind to cell components, affecting the light passing through, while stains used for electron microscopy involve heavy metals that affect the beams of electrons passing through. **2.** (a) Light microscope, (b) scanning electron microscope, (c) transmission electron microscope

Concept Check 6.2

1. See Figure 6.9.
2.

This cell would have the same volume as the cells in columns 2 and 3 but proportionally more surface area than that in column 2 and less than that in column 3. Thus, the surface-to-volume ratio should be greater than 1.2 but less than 6. To obtain the surface area, you'd have to add the area of the six sides (the top, bottom, sides, and ends): 125 + 125 + 125 + 125 + 1 + 1 = 502. The surface-to-volume ratio equals 502 divided by a volume of 125, or 4.0.

Concept Check 6.3

1. Ribosomes in the cytoplasm translate the genetic message, carried from the DNA in the nucleus by mRNA, into a polypeptide chain. **2.** Nucleoli consist of DNA and the ribosomal RNA (rRNA) made according to its instructions, as well as proteins imported from the cytoplasm. Together, the rRNA and proteins are assembled into large and small ribosomal subunits. (These are exported through nuclear pores to the cytoplasm, where they will participate in polypeptide synthesis.) **3.** The information in a gene (on a chromosome in the nucleus) is used to synthesize an mRNA that is then transported through a nuclear pore to the cytoplasm. There it is translated into protein, which is transported back through a nuclear pore into the nucleus, where it joins other proteins and DNA, forming chromatin.

Concept Check 6.4

1. The primary distinction between rough and smooth ER is the presence of bound ribosomes on the rough ER. While both types of ER make phospholipids, membrane proteins and secretory proteins are all produced on the ribosomes of the rough ER. The smooth ER also functions in detoxification, carbohydrate metabolism, and storage of calcium ions. **2.** Transport vesicles move membranes and substances they enclose between other components of the endomembrane system. **3.** The mRNA is synthesized in the nucleus and then passes out through a nuclear pore to be translated on a bound ribosome, attached to the rough ER. The protein is synthesized into the lumen of the ER and perhaps modified there. A transport vesicle carries the protein to the Golgi apparatus. After further modification in the Golgi, another transport vesicle carries it back to the ER, where it will perform its cellular function.

Concept Check 6.5

1. Both organelles are involved in energy transformation, mitochondria in cellular respiration and chloroplasts in photosynthesis. They both have multiple membranes that separate their interiors into compartments. In both organelles, the innermost membranes—cristae, or infoldings of the inner membrane, in mitochondria, and the thylakoid membranes in chloroplasts—have large surface areas with embedded enzymes that carry out their main functions. **2.** Mitochondria, chloroplasts, and peroxisomes are not derived from the ER, nor are they connected physically or via transport vesicles to organelles of the endomembrane system. Mitochondria and chloroplasts are structurally quite different from vesicles derived from the ER, which are bounded by a single membrane.

Concept Check 6.6

1. Both systems of movement involve long filaments that are moved in relation to each other by motor proteins that grip, release, and grip again adjacent polymers. **2.** Dynein arms, powered by ATP, move neighboring doublets of microtubules relative to one another. Because they are anchored within the organelle and with respect to each other, the doublets bend instead of sliding past one another. **3.** Such individuals have defects in the microtubule-based movement of cilia and flagella. Thus, the sperm can't move because of malfunctioning flagella; the airways are compromised; and signaling events during embryogenesis do not occur correctly due to malfunctioning cilia.

Concept Check 6.7

1. The most obvious difference is the presence of direct cytoplasmic connections between cells of plants (plasmodesmata) and animals (gap junctions). These connections result in the cytoplasm being continuous between adjacent cells. **2.** The cell would not be able to function properly and would probably soon die, as the cell wall or ECM must be permeable to allow the exchange of matter between the cell and its external environment. Molecules involved with energy production and use must be allowed entry, as well as those that provide information about the cell's environment. Other molecules, such as products synthesized by the cell for export and the by-products of cellular respiration, must be allowed to exit.

Self-Quiz

1. c **2.** b **3.** d **4.** d **5.** b **6.** c **7.** e **8.** a
9. See Figure 6.9.

CHAPTER 7

Figure Questions

Figure 7.6 You couldn't rule out movement of proteins within the cell membrane of the same species. You might speculate that the membrane lipids and proteins from one species weren't able to mingle with those from the other species because of some incompatibility. **Figure 7.9** A transmembrane protein like the integrin dimer in (f) might change its shape upon binding to a particular ECM molecule. The new shape might enable the interior portion of the protein to bind to a second, cytoplasmic protein that would relay the message to the inside of the cell, as shown in (c). **Figure 7.12** The orange solute would be evenly distributed throughout the solution on both sides of the membrane. The solution levels would not be affected because the orange solute can diffuse through the membrane and equalize its concentration. Thus, no additional osmosis of water would take place in either direction.

Concept Check 7.1

1. They are on the inner side of the transport vesicle membrane. **2.** Plants adapted to cold environments would be expected to have more unsaturated fatty acids in their membranes because those remain fluid at lower temperatures. Plants adapted to hot environments would be expected to have more saturated fatty acids, which would allow the fatty acids to "stack" more closely, making the membranes less fluid and therefore helping them to stay intact at higher temperatures.

Concept Check 7.2

1. O_2 and CO_2 are both small nonpolar molecules that can easily pass through the hydrophobic core of a membrane. **2.** Water is a polar molecule, so it cannot pass very rapidly through the hydrophobic region in the middle of a phospholipid bilayer. **3.** The hydronium ion is charged, while glycerol is not. Charge is probably more significant than size as a basis for exclusion by the aquaporin channel.

Concept Check 7.3

1. CO_2 is a small nonpolar molecule that can diffuse through the plasma membrane. As long as it diffuses away so the concentration remains low outside the cell, it will continue to exit the cell in this way. (This is the opposite of the case for O_2, described in this section.) **2.** The water is hypotonic to the plant cells, so they take up water and the cells of the vegetable remain turgid, rather than plasmolyzing. The vegetable (for example, lettuce or spinach) remains crisp and not wilted. **3.** The activity of the *Paramecium's* contractile vacuole will decrease. The vacuole pumps out excess water that flows into the cell; this flow occurs only in a hypotonic environment.

Concept Check 7.4

1. The pump uses ATP. To establish a voltage, ions have to be pumped against their gradients, which requires energy. **2.** Each ion is being transported against its electrochemical gradient. If either ion were flowing down its electrochemical gradient, this *would* be considered cotransport. **3.** Even if proton pumps were still using ATP and moving protons, no proton gradient would become established. This would have serious consequences for the cells, because processes like the cotransport of sucrose (as well as synthesis of ATP) depend on establishment of a proton gradient.

Concept Check 7.5

1. Exocytosis. When a transport vesicle fuses with the plasma membrane, the vesicle membrane becomes part of the plasma membrane. **2.** Receptor-mediated endocytosis. In this case, one specific kind of molecule needs to be taken up at a particular time; pinocytosis takes up substances in a nonspecific manner.

Self-Quiz

1. b **2.** c **3.** a **4.** d **5.** b
6. a.

b. The solution outside is hypotonic. It has less sucrose, which is a nonpenetrating solute.
c. See answer for (a).
d. The artificial cell will become more turgid.
e. Eventually, the two solutions will have the same solute concentrations. Even though sucrose can't move through the membrane, water flow (osmosis) will lead to isotonic conditions.

CHAPTER 8

Figure Questions

Figure 8.14   **Figure 8.18**

Figure 8.21 Because the affinity of the caspase for the inhibitor is very low (as is expected of an allosterically inhibited enzyme), the inhibitor is likely to diffuse away. Because no additional source of the inhibitory compound is present (the concentration of inhibitor is very low), the inhibitor is unlikely to bind again to the enzyme once the covalent linkage is broken. Thus, normal activity of the enzyme would most likely not be affected. (This test was performed by the researchers, and enzyme activity was observed to be normal upon release of the inhibitor.)

Concept Check 8.1

1. The second law is the trend toward randomness. Equal concentrations of a substance on both sides of a membrane is a more random distribution than unequal concentrations. Diffusion of a substance to a region where it is initially less concentrated increases entropy, as described by the second law. **2.** The apple has potential energy in its position hanging on the tree, and the sugars and other nutrients it contains have chemical energy. The apple has kinetic energy as it falls from the tree to the ground. Finally, when the apple is digested and its molecules broken down, some of the chemical energy is used to do work, and the rest is lost as thermal energy. **3.** The sugar crystals become less ordered (entropy increases) as they dissolve and become randomly spread out in the water. Over time, the water evaporates, and the crystals form again because the water volume is insufficient to keep them in solution. While the reappearance of sugar crystals may represent a "spontaneous" increase in order (decrease in entropy), it is balanced by the decrease in order (increase in entropy) of the water molecules, which changed from a relatively compact arrangement in liquid water to a much more dispersed and disordered form in water vapor.

Concept Check 8.2

1. Cellular respiration is a spontaneous and exergonic process. The energy released from glucose is used to do work in the cell or is lost as heat. **2.** Hydrogen ions can perform work only if their concentrations on each side of a membrane differ. When the H^+ concentrations are the same, the system is at equilibrium and can do no work. **3.** The reaction is exergonic because it releases energy—in this case, in the form of light. (This is a chemical version of the bioluminescence seen in Figure 8.1.)

Concept Check 8.3

1. ATP transfers energy to endergonic processes by phosphorylating (adding phosphate groups to) other molecules. (Exergonic processes phosphorylate ADP to regenerate ATP.) **2.** A set of coupled reactions can transform the first combination into the second. Since, overall, this is an exergonic process, ΔG is negative and the first group must have more free energy. (See Figure 8.10.)

Concept Check 8.4

1. A spontaneous reaction is a reaction that is exergonic. However, if it has a high activation energy that is rarely attained, the rate of the reaction may be low. **2.** Only the specific substrate(s) will fit properly into the active site of an enzyme, the part of the enzyme that carries out catalysis. **3.** Increase the concentration of the normal substrate (succinate) and see whether the rate of reaction increases. If it does, malonate is a competitive inhibitor.

Concept Check 8.5

1. The activator binds in such a way that it stabilizes the active form of an enzyme, whereas the inhibitor stabilizes the inactive form. **2.** You might choose to screen chemical compounds that bind allosterically to the enzyme, because allosteric regulatory sites are less likely to share similarity between different enzymes.

Self-Quiz

1. b **2.** c **3.** b **4.** a **5.** c **6.** c **7.** c

Scientific Inquiry

9.

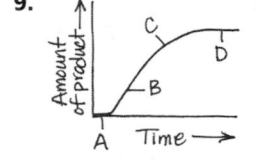

A: The substrate molecules are entering the cells, so no product is made yet.
B: There is sufficient substrate, so the reaction is proceeding at a maximum rate.
C: As the substrate is used up, the rate falls.
D: The line is flat because no new substrate remains and thus no new product appears.

CHAPTER 9

Figure Questions

Figure 9.7 Because an enzyme is catalyzing this reaction and there is no external source of energy, it must be exergonic, and the reactants must be at a higher energy level than the products. **Figure 9.9** It would probably stop glycolysis, or at least slow it down, since this would tend to push the equilibrium for this step toward the left. If less (or no) glyceraldehyde-3-phosphate were made, step 6 would slow down (or be unable to occur). **Figure 9.15** Rotation in the opposite direction (blue bars) would be expected to hydrolyze some of the ATP present, lowering ATP concentration below the background level. Thus, the blue bars would be expected to be lower than the gray bars, which is not what the researchers observed. (A possible explanation: In the article, the researchers explained that when they enclosed ATP synthases in a chamber for this assay, a number of the complexes adhered to the chamber ceiling instead of the nickel plate. The enzymes adhering to the chamber ceiling would be expected to spin in an opposite direction to those on the nickel plate on the floor. When the floor-based enzymes produce ATP during a particular spin (yellow bars), those on the ceiling would be expected to consume ATP, which would make the yellow bars lower than they would have been if all enzymes were floor-based. The opposite is also true: When the floor-based enzymes hydrolyze ATP (blue bars), the ceiling-based enzymes would be synthesizing ATP, which would make the blue bars higher than if all enzymes were floor-based. Evidence of this phenomenon is shown in the graph: The spins expected to hydrolyze ATP (blue bars) result in higher ATP levels than those with no rotation (gray bars), suggesting that there are probably some "upside-down" ceiling-based complexes generating ATP while the rest are floor-based and are hydrolyzing ATP.) **Figure 9.16** At first, some ATP could be made, since electron transport could proceed as far as complex III, and a small H^+ gradient could be built up. Soon, however, no more electrons could be passed to complex III because it could not be reoxidized by passing its electrons to complex IV.

Concept Check 9.1

1. Both processes include glycolysis, the citric acid cycle, and oxidative phosphorylation. In aerobic respiration, the final electron acceptor is molecular oxygen (O_2), whereas in anaerobic respiration, the final electron acceptor is a different substance. **2.** $C_4H_6O_5$ would be oxidized and NAD^+ would be reduced.

Concept Check 9.2

1. NAD^+ acts as the oxidizing agent in step 6, accepting electrons from glyceraldehyde-3-phosphate, which thus acts as the reducing agent. **2.** Since the overall process of glycolysis results in net production of ATP, it would make sense for the process to slow down when ATP levels have increased substantially. Thus we would expect ATP to allosterically inhibit phosphofructokinase.

Concept Check 9.3

1. NADH and $FADH_2$; they will donate electrons to the electron transport chain. **2.** CO_2 is released from the pyruvate that is formed during glycolysis, and CO_2 is also released during the citric acid cycle. **3.** In both cases, the precursor molecule loses a CO_2 molecule and then donates electrons to an electron carrier in an oxidation step. Also, the product has been activated due to the attachment of a CoA group.

Concept Check 9.4

1. Oxidative phosphorylation would stop entirely, resulting in no ATP production by this process. Without oxygen to "pull" electrons down the electron transport chain, H^+ would not be pumped into the mitochondrion's intermembrane space and chemiosmosis would not occur. **2.** Decreasing the pH is the addition of H^+. It would establish a proton gradient even without the function of the electron transport chain, and we would expect ATP synthase to function and synthesize ATP. (In fact, it was experiments like this that provided support for chemiosmosis as an energy-coupling mechanism.)

Concept Check 9.5

1. A derivative of pyruvate—such as acetaldehyde during alcohol fermentation—or pyruvate itself during lactic acid fermentation; oxygen. **2.** The cell would need to consume glucose at a rate about 19 times the consumption rate in the aerobic environment (2 ATP are generated by fermentation versus up to 38 ATP by cellular respiration).

Concept Check 9.6

1. The fat is much more reduced; it has many —CH_2— units, and in all these bonds the electrons are equally shared. The electrons present in a carbohydrate molecule are already somewhat oxidized (shared unequally in bonds), as quite a few of them are bound to oxygen. **2.** When we consume more food than necessary for metabolic processes, our body synthesizes fat as a way of storing energy for later use. **3.** AMP will accumulate, stimulating phosphofructokinase, which increases the rate of glycolysis. Since oxygen is not present, the cell will convert pyruvate to lactate in lactic acid fermentation, providing a supply of ATP.

Self-Quiz

1. b **2.** d **3.** c **4.** c **5.** a **6.** a **7.** d **8.** b **9.** b
10.

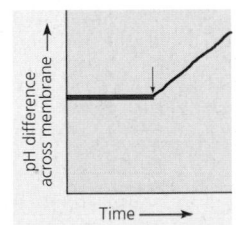

CHAPTER 10

Figure Questions

Figure 10.9 Red, but not violet-blue, wavelengths would pass through the filter, so the bacteria would not congregate where the violet-blue light normally comes through. Therefore, the left "peak" of bacteria would not be present, but the right peak would be observed because the red wavelengths passing through the filter would be used for photosynthesis. **Figure 10.11** In the leaf, most of the chlorophyll electrons excited by photon absorption are used to power the reactions of photosynthesis.

Figure 10.18

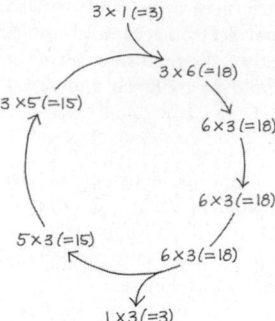

Three carbon atoms enter the cycle, one by one, as individual CO_2 molecules, and leave the cycle in one three-carbon molecule (G3P) per three turns of the cycle.

Concept Check 10.1

1. CO_2 enters leaves via stomata, and water enters via roots and is carried to leaves through veins. **2.** Using ^{18}O, a heavy isotope of oxygen, as a label, van Niel was able to show that the oxygen produced during photosynthesis originates in water, not in carbon dioxide. **3.** The light reactions could *not* keep producing NADPH and ATP without the $NADP^+$, ADP, and $\textcircled{P}_i$ that the Calvin cycle generates. The two cycles are interdependent.

Concept Check 10.2

1. Green, because green light is mostly transmitted and reflected—not absorbed—by photosynthetic pigments **2.** In chloroplasts, light-excited electrons are trapped by a primary electron acceptor, which prevents them from dropping back to the ground state. In isolated chlorophyll, there is no electron acceptor, so the photoexcited electrons immediately drop back down to the ground state, with the emission of light and heat. **3.** Water (H_2O) is the initial electron donor; $NADP^+$ accepts electrons at the end of the electron transport chain, becoming reduced to NADPH. **4.** In this experiment, the rate of ATP synthesis would slow and eventually stop. Because the added compound would not allow a proton gradient to build up across the membrane, ATP synthase could not catalyze ATP production.

Concept Check 10.3

1. 6, 18, 12 **2.** The more potential energy a molecule stores, the more energy and reducing power is required for the formation of that molecule. Glucose is a valuable energy source because it is highly reduced, storing lots of potential energy in its electrons. To reduce CO_2 to glucose, much energy and reducing power are required in the form of large numbers of ATP and NADPH molecules, respectively. **3.** The light reactions require ADP and $NADP^+$, which would not be formed in sufficient quantities from ATP and NADPH if the Calvin cycle stopped.

Concept Check 10.4

1. Photorespiration decreases photosynthetic output by adding oxygen, instead of carbon dioxide, to the Calvin cycle. As a result, no sugar is generated (no carbon is fixed), and O_2 is used rather than generated. **2.** Without PS II, no O_2 is generated in bundle-sheath cells. This avoids the problem of O_2 competing with CO_2 for binding to rubisco in these cells. **3.** C_4 and CAM species would replace many of the C_3 species.

Self-Quiz

1. d **2.** b **3.** b **4.** c **5.** d **6.** d **7.** c

Scientific Inquiry

9.

The ATP would end up outside the thylakoid. The chloroplasts were able to make ATP in the dark because the researchers set up an artificial proton concentration gradient across the thylakoid membrane; thus, the light reactions were not necessary to establish the H^+ gradient required for ATP synthesis by ATP synthase.

CHAPTER 11

Figure Questions

Figure 11.6 Epinephrine is a signaling molecule; presumably it binds to a cell-surface receptor protein. **Figure 11.8** The testosterone molecule is hydrophobic and can therefore pass directly through the lipid bilayer of the plasma membrane into the cell. (Hydrophilic molecules cannot do this.) **Figure 11.9** The active form of protein kinase 2 **Figure 11.10** The signaling molecule (cAMP) would remain in its active form and would continue to signal. **Figure 11.16** In the model, the directionality of growth is determined by the association of Fus3 with the membrane near the site of receptor activation. Thus, the development of shmoos would be severely compromised, and the affected cell would likely resemble the ΔFus3 and Δformin cells.

Concept Check 11.1

1. The two cells of opposite mating type (**a** and **α**) each secrete a certain signaling molecule, which can only be bound by receptors carried on cells of the opposite mating type. Thus, the **a** mating factor cannot bind to another **a** cell and cause it to grow toward the first **a** cell. Only an **α** cell can "receive" the signaling molecule and respond by directed growth (see Figure 11.16 for more information). **2.** The secretion of neurotransmitter molecules at a synapse is an example of local signaling. The electrical signal that travels along a very long nerve cell and is passed to the next nerve cell can be considered an example of long-distance signaling. (Note, however, that local signaling at the synapse between two cells is necessary for the signal to pass from one cell to the next.) **3.** Glucose-1-phosphate is not generated, because the activation of the enzyme requires an intact cell, with an intact receptor in the membrane and an intact signal transduction pathway. The enzyme cannot be activated directly by interaction with the signaling molecule in the test tube. **4.** Glycogen phosphorylase acts in the third stage, the response to epinephrine signaling.

Concept Check 11.2

1. The water-soluble NGF molecule cannot pass through the lipid membrane to reach intracellular receptors, as steroid hormones can. Therefore, you'd expect the NGF receptor to be in the plasma membrane—which is, in fact, the case. **2.** The cell with the faulty receptor would not be able to respond appropriately to the signaling molecule when it was present. This would most likely have dire consequences for the cell, since regulation of the cell's activities by this receptor would not occur appropriately.

Concept Check 11.3

1. A protein kinase is an enzyme that transfers a phosphate group from ATP to a protein, usually activating that protein (often a second type of protein kinase). Many signal transduction pathways include a series of such interactions, in which each phosphorylated protein kinase in turn phosphorylates the next protein kinase in the series. Such phosphorylation cascades carry a signal from outside the cell to the cellular protein(s) that will carry out the response. **2.** Protein phosphatases reverse the effects of the kinases. **3.** Information is transduced by way of sequential protein-protein interactions that change protein shapes, causing them to function in a way that passes the signal along. **4.** The IP_3-gated channel opens, allowing calcium ions to flow out of the ER, which raises the cytosolic Ca^{2+} concentration.

Concept Check 11.4

1. At each step in a cascade of sequential activations, one molecule or ion may activate numerous molecules functioning in the next step. **2.** Scaffolding proteins hold molecular components of signaling pathways in a complex with each other. Different scaffolding proteins would assemble different collections of proteins, leading to different cellular responses in the two cells.

Concept Check 11.5

1. In formation of the hand or paw in mammals, cells in the regions between the digits are programmed to undergo apoptosis. This serves to shape the digits of the hand or paw so that they are not webbed. **2.** If a receptor protein for a death-signaling molecule was defective so that it was activated for signaling even in the absence of the death signal, this would lead to apoptosis when it wouldn't normally occur. Similar defects in any of the proteins in the signaling pathway, which would activate these relay or response proteins in the absence of interaction with the previous protein or second messenger in the pathway, would have the same effect. Conversely, if any protein in the pathway were defective in its ability to respond to an interaction with an early protein or other molecule or ion, apoptosis would not occur when it normally should. For example, a receptor protein for a death-signaling ligand might not be able to be activated, even when ligand was bound. This would stop the signal from being transduced into the cell.

Self-Quiz
1. c **2.** d **3.** a **4.** c **5.** c **6.** b **7.** a **8.** d
9. This is one possible drawing of the pathway. (Similar drawings would also be correct.)

CHAPTER 12

Figure Questions
Figure 12.4

Circling the other chromatid instead would also be correct. The chromosome has four arms. **Figure 12.6** 12; 2; 2; 1
Figure 12.7

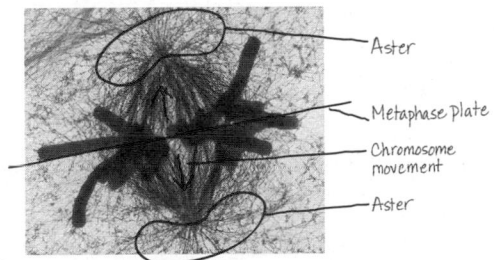

Figure 12.8 The mark would have moved toward the nearer pole. The lengths of fluorescent microtubules between that pole and the mark would have decreased, while the lengths between the chromosomes and the mark would have remained the same. **Figure 12.13** In both cases, the G_1 nucleus would have remained in G_1 until the time it normally would have entered the S phase. Chromosome condensation and spindle formation would not have occurred until the S and G_2 phases had been completed. **Figure 12.15** The cell would divide under conditions where it was inappropriate to do so. If the daughter cells and their descendants also ignored the checkpoint and divided, there would soon be an abnormal mass of cells. (This type of inappropriate cell division can contribute to the development of cancer.) **Figure 12.16** Given that control experiments showed that the *cdc2* protein kinase was the primary source of kinase activity detected in this experiment, there would be virtually no kinase activity. The percentage of cells dividing would be zero because the cells would be unable to undergo mitosis without the *cdc2* kinase. **Figure 12.18** The cells in the vessel with PDGF would not be able to respond to the growth factor signal and thus would not divide. The culture would resemble that without the added PDGF.

Concept Check 12.1
1. 32 cells **2.** 2 **3.** 39; 39; 78

Concept Check 12.2
1. 6; 12 **2.** Cytokinesis results in two genetically identical daughter cells in both plant cells and animal cells, but the mechanism of dividing the cytoplasm is different in animals and plants. In an animal cell, cytokinesis occurs by cleavage, which divides the parent cell in two with a contractile ring of actin filaments. In a plant cell, a cell plate forms in the middle of the cell and grows until its membrane fuses with the plasma membrane of the parent cell. A new cell wall grows inside the cell plate. **3.** They elongate the cell during anaphase. **4.** Sample answer: Each type of chromosome consists of a single molecule of DNA with attached proteins. If stretched out, the molecules of DNA would be many times longer than the cells in which they reside. During cell division, the two copies of each type of chromosome actively move apart, and one copy ends up in each of the two daughter cells. Chromosome movement in both types of cells may involve similar cytoskeletal proteins. **5.** During eukaryotic cell division, tubulin is involved in spindle formation and chromosome movement, while actin functions during cytokinesis. In bacterial binary fission, it's the opposite: Tubulin-like molecules are thought to act in daughter cell separation, and actin-like molecules are thought to move the daughter bacterial chromosomes to opposite ends of the cell. **6.** From the end of S phase in interphase through the end of metaphase in mitosis

Concept Check 12.3
1. The nucleus on the right was originally in the G_1 phase; therefore, it had not yet duplicated its chromosome. The nucleus on the left was in the M phase, so it had already duplicated its chromosome. **2.** A sufficient amount of MPF has to build up for a cell to pass the G_2 checkpoint. **3.** Most body cells are in a nondividing state called G_0. **4.** Both types of tumors consist of abnormal cells. A benign tumor stays at the original site and can usually be surgically removed. Cancer cells from a malignant tumor spread from the original site by metastasis and may impair the functions of one or more organs. **5.** The cells might divide even in the absence of PDGF, in which case they would not stop when the surface of the culture vessel was covered; they would continue to divide, piling on top of one another.

Self-Quiz
1. b **2.** a **3.** a **4.** c **5.** c **6.** e **7.** a **8.** b
9. See Figure 12.6 for a description of major events.

10.

Interphase · Prophase

Microtubules

Prometaphase · Metaphase · Anaphase

Nuclear envelope forming

Telophase and cytokinesis

CHAPTER 13

Figure Questions

Figure 13.4 The haploid number, *n*, is 3. A set is always haploid.   **Figure 13.7** A short strand of DNA is shown here for simplicity, but each chromosome or chromatid contains a very long coiled and folded DNA molecule.

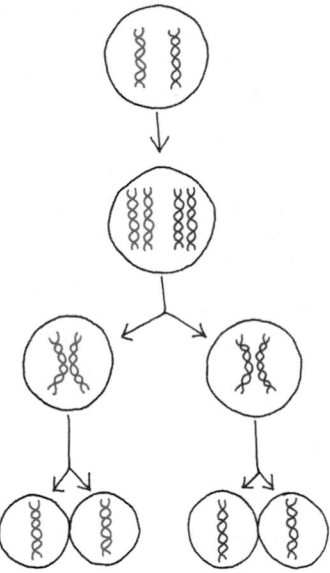

Figure 13.9 Yes. Each of the chromosomes shown in telophase I has one nonrecombinant chromatid and one recombinant chromatid. Therefore, eight possible sets of chromosomes can be generated for the cell on the left and eight for the cell on the right.   **Figure 13.10** The chromosomes arising from chromatids of the unlabeled chromosome would be expected to behave exactly like those of the labeled chromosome. Therefore, the graph would look identical to the one shown in the figure.

Concept Check 13.1

1. Parents pass genes to their offspring; the genes program cells to make specific enzymes and other proteins, whose cumulative action produces an individual's inherited traits.   **2.** Such organisms reproduce by mitosis, which generates offspring whose genomes are exact copies of the parent's

genome (in the absence of mutation).   **3.** She should clone it. Breeding it would generate offspring that have additional variation, which she no longer desires now that she has obtained her ideal orchid.

Concept Check 13.2

1. A female has two X chromosomes; a male has an X and a Y.   **2.** In meiosis, the chromosome count is reduced from diploid to haploid; the union of two haploid gametes in fertilization restores the diploid chromosome count.   **3.** The haploid number (*n*) is 7; the diploid number (2*n*) is 14.   **4.** This organism has the life cycle shown in Figure 13.6c. Therefore, it must be a fungus or a protist, perhaps an alga.

Concept Check 13.3

1. The chromosomes are similar in that each is composed of two sister chromatids, and the individual chromosomes are positioned similarly on the metaphase plate. The chromosomes differ in that in a mitotically dividing cell, sister chromatids of each chromosome are genetically identical, but in a meiotically dividing cell, sister chromatids are genetically distinct because of crossing over in meiosis I. Moreover, the chromosomes in metaphase of mitosis can be a diploid set or a haploid set, but the chromosomes in metaphase of meiosis II always consist of a haploid set.   **2.** If crossing over did not occur, the two homologs would not be associated in any way. This might result in incorrect arrangement of homologs during metaphase I and ultimately in formation of gametes with an abnormal number of chromosomes.

Concept Check 13.4

1. Mutations in a gene lead to the different versions (alleles) of that gene. **2.** Without crossing over, independent assortment of chromosomes during meiosis I theoretically can generate 2^n possible haploid gametes, and random fertilization can produce $2^n \times 2^n$ possible diploid zygotes. Because the haploid number (*n*) of grasshoppers is 23 and that of fruit flies is 4, two grasshoppers would be expected to produce a greater variety of zygotes than would two fruit flies.   **3.** If the segments of the maternal and paternal chromatids that undergo crossing over are genetically identical and thus have the same two alleles for every gene, then the recombinant chromosomes will be genetically equivalent to the parental chromosomes. Crossing over contributes to genetic variation only when it involves the rearrangement of different alleles.

Self-Quiz

1. a **2.** d **3.** b **4.** a **5.** d **6.** c **7.** d **8.** This cell must be undergoing meiosis because homologous chromosomes are associated with each other; this does not occur in mitosis.   **9.** Metaphase I
10.

The chromosomes of one color make up a haploid set.
All red and blue chromosomes together make up a diploid set.

CHAPTER 14

Figure Questions

Figure 14.3 All offspring would have purple flowers. (The ratio would be one purple to zero white.) The P generation plants are true-breeding, so mating two purple-flowered plants produces the same result as self-pollination: All the offspring have the same trait.

Figure 14.8

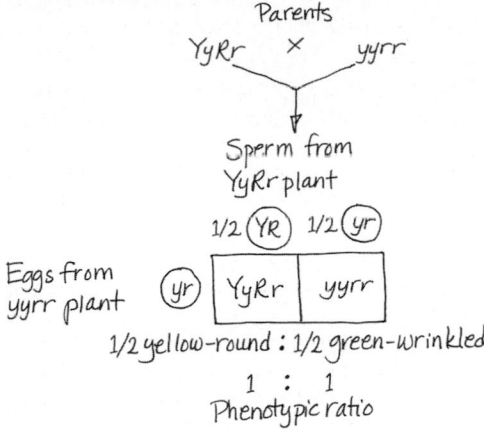

If dependent assortment:

Parents

YyRr × yyrr

Sperm from YyRr plant

1/2 (YR)   1/2 (yr)

Eggs from yyrr plant (yr) | YyRr | yyrr

1/2 yellow-round : 1/2 green-wrinkled

1 : 1

Phenotypic ratio

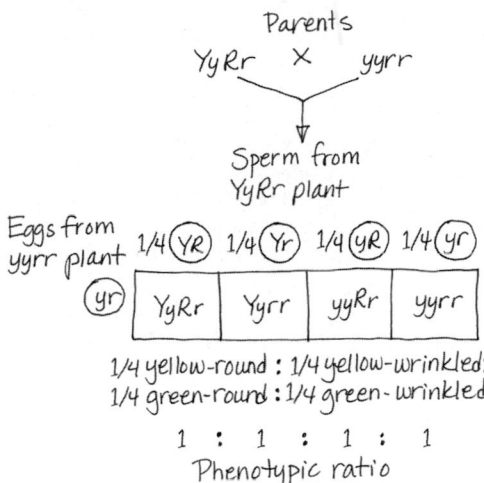

If independent assortment:

Parents

YyRr × yyrr

Sperm from YyRr plant

1/4 (YR)   1/4 (Yr)   1/4 (yR)   1/4 (yr)

Eggs from yyrr plant (yr) | YyRr | Yyrr | yyRr | yyrr

1/4 yellow-round : 1/4 yellow-wrinkled:
1/4 green-round : 1/4 green-wrinkled

1 : 1 : 1 : 1

Phenotypic ratio

Yes, this cross would also have allowed Mendel to make different predictions for the two hypotheses, thereby allowing him to distinguish the correct one. **Figure 14.10** Your classmate would probably point out that the F₁ generation hybrids show an intermediate phenotype between those of the homozygous parents, which supports the blending hypothesis. You could respond that crossing the F₁ hybrids results in the reappearance of the white phenotype, rather than identical pink offspring, which fails to support the idea of blending traits during inheritance. **Figure 14.11** Both the I^A and I^B alleles are dominant to the i allele, which results in no attached carbohydrate. The I^A and I^B alleles are codominant; both are expressed in the phenotype of $I^A I^B$ heterozygotes, who have type AB blood.

Figure 14.13

The majority of individuals have intermediate phenotypes (skin color in the middle range), while fewer individuals have phenotypes at either end (very dark or very light skin). (As you may know, this is called a "bell curve" and represents a "normal distribution.") **Figure 14.16** In the Punnett square, two of the three individuals with normal coloration are carriers, so the probability is ⅔.

Concept Check 14.1

1. A cross of $Ii \times ii$ would yield offspring with a genotypic ratio of 1 Ii : 1 ii (2:2 is an equivalent answer) and a phenotypic ratio of 1 inflated : 1 constricted (2:2 is equivalent).

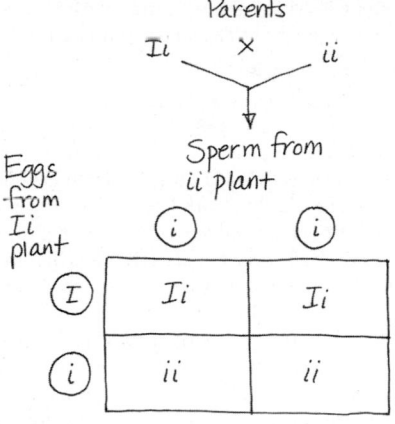

Parents

Ii × ii

Sperm from ii plant

(i)   (i)

Eggs from Ii plant (I) | Ii | Ii

(i) | ii | ii

Genotypic ratio 1 Ii : 1 ii
(2:2 is equivalent)

Phenotypic ratio 1 inflated : 1 constricted
(2:2 is equivalent)

2. According to the law of independent assortment, 25 plants (¹⁄₁₆ of the offspring) are predicted to be *aatt*, or recessive for both characters. The actual result is likely to differ slightly from this value.

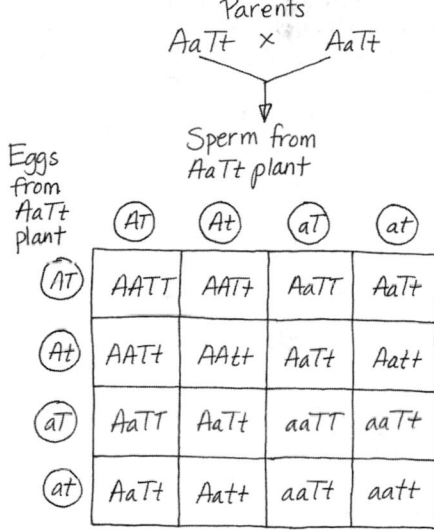

Parents

AaTt × AaTt

Sperm from AaTt plant

(AT)   (At)   (aT)   (at)

Eggs from AaTt plant

(AT) | AATT | AATt | AaTT | AaTt
(At) | AATt | AAtt | AaTt | Aatt
(aT) | AaTT | AaTt | aaTT | aaTt
(at) | AaTt | Aatt | aaTt | aatt

3. The plant could make eight different gametes (*YRI, YRi, YrI, Yri, yRI, yRi, yrI,* and *yri*). To fit all the possible gametes in a self-pollination, a Punnett square would need 8 rows and 8 columns. It would have spaces for the 64 possible unions of gametes in the offspring.

Concept Check 14.2

1. ½ homozygous dominant (*CC*), 0 homozygous recessive (*cc*), and ½ heterozygous (*Cc*)   **2.** ¼ *BBDD*; ¼ *BbDD*; ¼ *BBDd*; ¼ *BbDd*   **3.** The genotypes that fulfill this condition are *ppyyIi, ppYyii, Ppyyii, ppYYii,* and *ppyyii*. Use the multiplication rule to find the probability of getting each genotype, and then use the addition rule to find the overall probability of meeting the conditions of this problem:

ppyy Ii	½ (probability of pp) × ¼ (yy) × ½ (Ii)	= $\frac{1}{16}$
pp Yy ii	½ (pp) × ½ (Yy) × ½ (ii)	= $\frac{2}{16}$
Pp yy ii	½ (Pp) × ¼ (yy) × ½ (ii)	= $\frac{1}{16}$
pp YY ii	½ (pp) × ¼ (YY) × ½ (ii)	= $\frac{1}{16}$
pp yy ii	½ (pp) × ¼ (yy) × ½ (ii)	= $\frac{1}{16}$

Fraction predicted to have at least two recessive traits = $\frac{6}{16}$ or ³⁄₈

Concept Check 14.3

1. Incomplete dominance describes the relationship between two alleles of a single gene, whereas epistasis relates to the genetic relationship between two genes (and the respective alleles of each). **2.** Half of the children would be expected to have type A blood and half type B blood. **3.** The black and white alleles are incompletely dominant, with heterozygotes being gray in color. A cross between a gray rooster and a black hen should yield approximately equal numbers of gray and black offspring.

Concept Check 14.4

1. $\frac{1}{9}$ (Since cystic fibrosis is caused by a recessive allele, Beth and Tom's siblings who have CF must be homozygous recessive. Therefore, each parent must be a carrier of the recessive allele. Since neither Beth nor Tom has CF, this means they each have a $\frac{2}{3}$ chance of being a carrier. If they are both carriers, there is a $\frac{1}{4}$ chance that they will have a child with CF. $\frac{2}{3} \times \frac{2}{3} \times \frac{1}{4} = \frac{1}{9}$); 0 (Both Beth and Tom would have to be carriers to produce a child with the disease.) **2.** Joan's genotype is *Dd*. Because the allele for polydactyly (*D*) is dominant to the allele for five digits per appendage (*d*), the trait is expressed in people with either the *DD* or *Dd* genotype. But because Joan's father does not have polydactyly, his genotype must be *dd*, which means Joan inherited a *d* allele from him. Therefore Joan, who does have the trait, must be heterozygous. **3.** Since polydactyly is a dominant trait, one of the parents of an affected individual should show the trait. Therefore, this must be an extremely rare case of a mutation that occurred during formation of one of the gametes involved in the fertilization that created Peter.

Genetics Problems

1. Gene, l. Allele, e. Character, g. Trait, b. Dominant allele, j. Recessive allele, a. Genotype, k. Phenotype, h. Homozygous, c. Heterozygous, f. Testcross, i. Monohybrid cross, d.

2.

Parents

$GgIi \times GgIi$

Sperm

Eggs	GI	Gi	gI	gi
GI	$GGII$	$GGIi$	$GgII$	$GgIi$
Gi	$GGIi$	$GGii$	$GgIi$	$Ggii$
gI	$GgII$	$GgIi$	$ggII$	$ggIi$
gi	$GgIi$	$Ggii$	$ggIi$	$ggii$

9 green-inflated : 3 green-constricted :
3 yellow-inflated : 1 yellow-constricted

3. Parental cross is $AAC^R C^R \times aaC^W C^W$. F_1 genotype is $AaC^R C^W$, phenotype is all axial-pink. F_2 genotypes are $1 AAC^R C^R : 2 AAC^R C^W : 1 AAC^W C^W : 2 AaC^R C^R : 4 AaC^R C^W : 2 AaC^W C^W : 1 aaC^R C^R : 2 aaC^R C^W : 1 aaC^W C^W$. F_2 phenotypes are 3 axial-red : 6 axial-pink : 3 axial-white : 1 terminal-red : 2 terminal-pink : 1 terminal-white.

4. a. $\frac{1}{64}$
b. $\frac{1}{64}$
c. $\frac{1}{8}$
d. $\frac{1}{32}$

5. Albino (*b*) is a recessive trait; black (*B*) is dominant. First cross: parents $BB \times bb$; gametes *B* and *b*; offspring all *Bb* (black coat). Second cross: parents $Bb \times bb$; gametes $\frac{1}{2}$ *B* and $\frac{1}{2}$ *b* (heterozygous parent) and *b*; offspring $\frac{1}{2}$ *Bb* and $\frac{1}{2}$ *bb*.

6. a. $PPLl \times PPLl$, $PPLl \times PpLl$, or $PPLl \times ppLl$.
b. $ppLl \times ppLl$.
c. $PPLL \times$ any of the 9 possible genotypes or $PpLl \times ppLL$.
d. $PpLl \times Ppll$.
e. $PpLl \times PpLl$.

7. Man $I^A i$; woman $I^B i$; child *ii*. Other genotypes for children are $\frac{1}{4} I^A I^B$, $\frac{1}{4} I^A i$, $\frac{1}{4} I^B i$.

8. a. $\frac{3}{4} \times \frac{3}{4} \times \frac{3}{4} = \frac{27}{64}$
b. $1 - \frac{27}{64} = \frac{37}{64}$
c. $\frac{1}{4} \times \frac{1}{4} \times \frac{1}{4} = \frac{1}{64}$
d. $1 - \frac{1}{64} = \frac{63}{64}$

9. a. $\frac{1}{256}$
b. $\frac{1}{16}$
c. $\frac{1}{256}$
d. $\frac{1}{64}$
e. $\frac{1}{128}$

10. a. 1
b. $\frac{1}{32}$
c. $\frac{1}{8}$
d. $\frac{1}{2}$

11. $\frac{1}{9}$

12. Matings of the original mutant cat with true-breeding noncurl cats will produce both curl and noncurl F_1 offspring if the curl allele is dominant, but only noncurl offspring if the curl allele is recessive. You would obtain some true-breeding offspring homozygous for the curl allele from matings between the F_1 cats resulting from the original curl $\times$ noncurl crosses whether the curl trait is dominant or recessive. You know that cats are true-breeding when curl $\times$ curl matings produce only curl offspring. As it turns out, the allele that causes curled ears is dominant. **13.** $\frac{1}{16}$ **14.** 25% will be cross-eyed; all of the cross-eyed offspring will also be white. **15.** The dominant allele *I* is epistatic to the *P/p* locus, and thus the genotypic ratio for the F_1 generation will be 9 $I\_P\_$ (colorless) : 3 I_pp (colorless) : 3 $iiP\_$ (purple) : 1 $iipp$ (red). Overall, the phenotypic ratio is 12 colorless : 3 purple : 1 red. **16.** Recessive. All affected individuals (Arlene, Tom, Wilma, and Carla) are homozygous recessive *aa*. George is *Aa*, since some of his children with Arlene are affected. Sam, Ann, Daniel, and Alan are each *Aa*, since they are all unaffected children with one affected parent. Michael also is *Aa*, since he has an affected child (Carla) with his heterozygous wife Ann. Sandra, Tina, and Christopher can each have the *AA* or *Aa* genotype. **17.** $\frac{1}{2}$ **18.** $\frac{1}{6}$ **19.** $9 B\_A\_$ (agouti) : $3 B\_aa$ (black) : $3 bbA\_$ (white) : $1 bbaa$ (white). Overall, 9 agouti : 3 black : 4 white.

CHAPTER 15

Figure Questions

Figure 15.2 The ratio would be 1 yellow-round : 1 green-round : 1 yellow-wrinkled : 1 green-wrinkled. **Figure 15.4** About $\frac{3}{4}$ of the F_2 offspring would have red eyes and about $\frac{1}{4}$ would have white eyes. About half of the white-eyed flies would be female and half would be male; about half of the red-eyed flies would be female. **Figure 15.7** All the males would be color-blind, and all the females would be carriers. **Figure 15.9** The two largest classes would still be the parental-type offspring, but now they would be gray-vestigial and black-normal because those were the specific allele combinations in the P generation. **Figure 15.10** The two chromosomes below, left are like the two chromosomes inherited by the F_1 female, one from each P generation fly. They are passed by the F_1 female intact to the offspring and thus could be called "parental" chromosomes. The other two chromosomes result from crossing over during meiosis in the F_1 female. Because they have combinations of alleles not seen in either of the F_1 female's chromosomes, they can be called "recombinant" chromosomes.

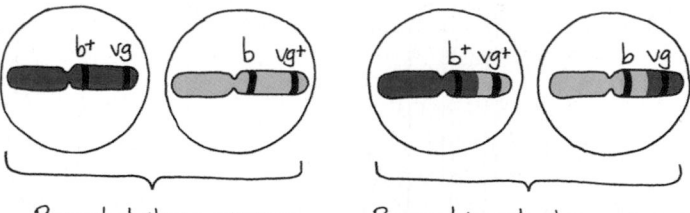

Concept Check 15.1

1. The law of segregation relates to the inheritance of alleles for a single character. The law of independent assortment of alleles relates to the inheritance of alleles for two characters. **2.** The physical basis for the law of segregation is the separation of homologs in anaphase I. The physical basis for the law of independent assortment is the alternative arrangements of homologous chromosome pairs in metaphase I. **3.** To show the mutant phenotype, a male needs to possess only one mutant allele. If this gene had been on a pair of autosomes, *two* mutant alleles would have had to be present for an individual to show the mutant phenotype, a much less probable situation.

Concept Check 15.2

1. Because the gene for this eye-color character is located on the X chromosome, all female offspring will be red-eyed and heterozygous ($X^{w+}X^{w}$); all male offspring will inherit a Y chromosome from the father and be white-eyed ($X^{w}Y$). **2.** ¼; ½ chance that the child will inherit a Y chromosome from the father and be male × ½ chance that he will inherit the X carrying the disease allele from his mother. If the child is a boy, there is a ½ chance he will have the disease; a female would have zero chance (but ½ chance of being a carrier). **3.** The cells in the eye responsible for color vision must come from multiple cells in the early embryo. The descendants of half of those cells express the allele for normal color vision and half the allele for color blindness. Having half the number of mature eye cells expressing the normal allele must be sufficient for normal color vision.

Concept Check 15.3

1. Crossing over during meiosis I in the heterozygous parent produces some gametes with recombinant genotypes for the two genes. Offspring with a recombinant phenotype arise from fertilization of the recombinant gametes by homozygous recessive gametes from the double-mutant parent. **2.** In each case, the alleles contributed by the female parent determine the phenotype of the offspring because the male contributes only recessive alleles in this cross. **3.** No. The order could be *A-C-B* or *C-A-B*. To determine which possibility is correct, you need to know the recombination frequency between *B* and *C*.

Concept Check 15.4

1. At some point during development, one of the embryo's cells may have failed to carry out mitosis after duplicating its chromosomes. Subsequent normal cell cycles would produce genetic copies of this tetraploid cell. **2.** In meiosis, a combined 14-21 chromosome will behave as one chromosome. If a gamete receives the combined 14-21 chromosome and a normal copy of chromosome 21, trisomy 21 will result when this gamete combines with a normal gamete during fertilization. **3.** No. The child can be either $I^{A}I^{A}i$ or $I^{A}ii$. A sperm of genotype $I^{A}I^{A}$ could result from nondisjunction in the father during meiosis II, while an egg with the genotype *ii* could result from nondisjunction in the mother during either meiosis I or meiosis II.

Concept Check 15.5

1. Inactivation of an X chromosome in females and genomic imprinting. Because of X inactivation, the effective dose of genes on the X chromosome is the same in males and females. As a result of genomic imprinting, only one allele of certain genes is phenotypically expressed. **2.** The genes for leaf coloration are located in plastids within the cytoplasm. Normally, only the maternal parent transmits plastid genes to offspring. Since variegated offspring are produced only when the female parent is of the B variety, we can conclude that variety B contains both the wild-type and mutant alleles of pigment genes, producing variegated leaves. **3.** The situation is similar to that for chloroplasts. Each cell contains numerous mitochondria, and in affected individuals, most cells contain a variable mixture of normal and mutant mitochondria. The normal mitochondria carry out enough cellular respiration for survival.

Genetics Problems

1. 0; ½, ¹⁄₁₆ **2.** Recessive; if the disorder were dominant, it would affect at least one parent of a child born with the disorder. The disorder's inheritance is sex-linked because it is seen only in boys. For a girl to have the disorder, she would have to inherit recessive alleles from *both* parents. This would be very rare, since males with the recessive allele on their X chromosome die in their early teens. **3.** ¼ for each daughter (½ chance that child will be female × ½ chance of a homozygous recessive genotype); ½ for first son. **4.** 17% **5.** 6%. Wild type (heterozygous for normal wings and red eyes) × recessive homozygote with vestigial wings and purple eyes

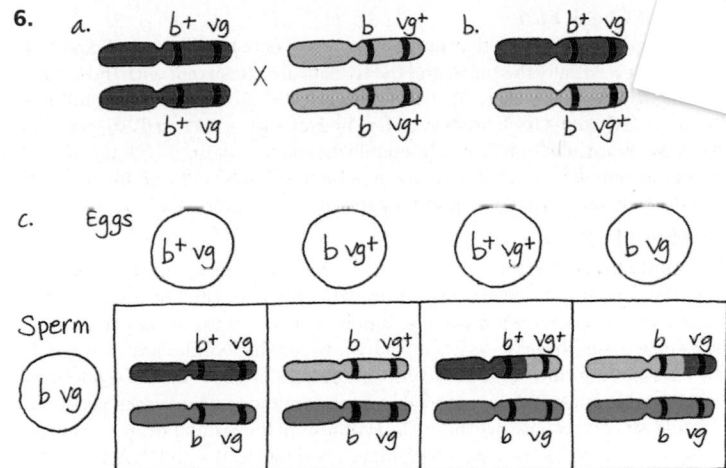

6.

d. 41.5% gray body, vestigial wings
41.5% black body, normal wings
8.5% gray body, normal wings
8.5% black body, vestigial wings

7. The disorder would always be inherited from the mother. **8.** The inactivation of two X chromosomes in XXX women would leave them with one genetically active X, as in women with the normal number of chromosomes. Microscopy should reveal two Barr bodies in XXX women. **9.** *D–A–B–C* **10.** Fifty percent of the offspring would show phenotypes that resulted from crossovers. These results would be the same as those from a cross where *A* and *B* were not linked. Further crosses involving other genes on the same chromosome would reveal the linkage and map distances. **11.** Between *T* and *A*, 12%; between *A* and *S*, 5% **12.** Between *T* and *S*, 18%; sequence of genes is *T-A-S* **13.** 450 each of blue-oval and white-round (parentals) and 50 each of blue-round and white-oval (recombinants) **14.** About one-third of the distance from the vestigial-wing locus to the brown-eye locus **15.** Because bananas are triploid, homologous pairs cannot line up during meiosis. Therefore, it is not possible to generate gametes that can fuse to produce a zygote with the triploid number of chromosomes.

CHAPTER 16

Figure Questions

Figure 16.2 The living S cells found in the blood sample were able to reproduce to yield more S cells, indicating that the S trait is a permanent, heritable change, rather than just a one-time use of the dead S cells' capsules. **Figure 16.4** The radioactivity would have been found in the pellet when proteins were labeled (batch 1) because proteins would have had to enter the bacterial cells to program them with genetic instructions. It's hard for us to imagine now, but the DNA might have played a structural role that allowed some of the proteins to be injected while it remained outside the bacterial cell (thus no radioactivity in the pellet in batch 2). **Figure 16.11** The tube from the first replication would look the same, with a middle band of hybrid ^{15}N-^{14}N DNA, but the second tube would not have the upper band of two light blue strands. Instead it would have a bottom band of two dark blue strands, like the bottom band in the result predicted after one replication in the conservative model. **Figure 16.12** In the bubble at the top in (b), arrows should be drawn pointing left and right to indicate the two replication forks. **Figure 16.14** Looking at any of the DNA strands, we see that one end is called the 5′ end and the other the 3′ end. If we proceed from the 5′ end to the 3′ end on the left-most strand, for example, we list the components in this order: phosphate group → 5′ C of the sugar → 3′ C → phosphate → 5′ C → 3′ C. Going in the opposite direction on the same strand, the components proceed in the reverse order: 3′ C → 5′ C → phosphate. Thus, the two directions are distinguishable, which is what we mean when we say that the strands have directionality. (Review Figure 16.5 if necessary.) **Figure 16.22** The cells in the mutant would probably have the same defects in meiosis that were seen in this experiment, such as the failure of condensin to be concentrated in a small region in the nucleus. The defect in the two mutants is essentially the same: In the mutant described in the experiment, the kinase doesn't function properly; in the newly discovered mutant, the kinase could not phosphorylate the correct amino acid because that amino acid is missing.

Concept Check 16.1

1. Chargaff's rules state that in DNA, the percentages of A and T and of G and C are essentially the same, and the fly data are consistent with those rules. (Slight variations are most likely due to limitations of analytical technique.) **2.** In the Watson-Crick model, each A hydrogen-bonds to a T, so in a DNA double helix, their numbers are equal; the same is true for G and C. **3.** The mouse injected with the mixture of heat-killed S cells and living R cells would have survived, since neither type of cell alone could have killed the mouse.

Concept Check 16.2

1. Complementary base pairing ensures that the two daughter molecules are exact copies of the parent molecule. When the two strands of the parent molecule separate, each serves as a template on which nucleotides are arranged, by the base-pairing rules, into new complementary strands. **2.** DNA pol III covalently adds nucleotides to new DNA strands and proofreads each added nucleotide for correct base pairing. **3.** Synthesis of the leading strand is initiated by an RNA primer, which must be removed and replaced with DNA, a task that could not be performed if the cell's DNA pol I were nonfunctional. In the overview box in Figure 16.17, just to the left of the top origin of replication, a functional DNA pol I would replace the RNA primer of the leading strand (shown in red) with DNA nucleotides (blue).

Concept Check 16.3

1. A nucleosome is made up of eight histone proteins, two each of four different types, around which DNA is wound. Linker DNA runs from one nucleosome to the next. **2.** Euchromatin is chromatin that becomes less compacted during interphase and is accessible to the cellular machinery responsible for gene activity. Heterochromatin, on the other hand, remains quite condensed during interphase and contains genes that are largely inaccessible to this machinery. **3.** Like histones, the *E. coli* proteins would be expected to contain many basic (positively charged) amino acids, such as lysine and arginine, which can form weak bonds with the negatively charged phosphate groups on the sugar-phosphate backbone of the DNA molecule.

Self-Quiz

1. c **2.** d **3.** b **4.** c **5.** b **6.** d **7.** a **8.** c
10.

New DNA strand (olive)
Parental DNA strand (purple)
Sliding clamp
DNA pol III
Single-strand binding protein
Direction of replication

CHAPTER 17

Figure Questions

Figure 17.2 The previously presumed pathway would have been wrong. The new results would support this pathway: precursor → citrulline → ornithine → arginine. They would also indicate that class I mutants have a defect in the second step and class II mutants have a defect in the first step. **Figure 17.8** The RNA polymerase would bind directly to the promoter, rather than depending on the previous binding of other factors. **Figure 17.24** The mRNA on the right (the longest one) started transcription first. The ribosome at the top, closest to the DNA, started translating first and thus has the longest polypeptide.

Concept Check 17.1

1. A polypeptide made up of 10 Gly (glycine) amino acids

2. Template sequence
(from problem): 3′-TTCAGTCGT-5′

Nontemplate sequence: 5′-AAGTCAGCA-3′

mRNA sequence: 5′-AAGUCAGCA-3′

The nontemplate and mRNA base sequences are the same, except there is T in the nontemplate strand of DNA wherever there is U in the mRNA.

3. "Template sequence" (from nontemplate sequence in problem, written 3′ → 5′): 3′-ACGACTGAA-5′

mRNA sequence: 5′-UGCUGACUU-3′

Translated: Cys-STOP-Leu

(Remember that the mRNA is antiparallel to the DNA strand.) A protein translated from the nontemplate sequence would have a completely different amino acid sequence and would surely be nonfunctional. (It would also be shorter because of the stop signal shown in the mRNA sequence above—and possibly others earlier in the mRNA sequence.)

Concept Check 17.2

1. Both assemble nucleic acid chains from monomer nucleotides whose order is determined by complementary base pairing to a template strand. Both synthesize in the 5′ → 3′ direction, antiparallel to the template. DNA polymerase requires a primer, but RNA polymerase can start a nucleotide chain from scratch. DNA polymerase uses nucleotides with the sugar deoxyribose and the base T, whereas RNA polymerase uses nucleotides with the sugar ribose and the base U. **2.** The promoter is the region of DNA to which RNA polymerase binds to begin transcription, and it is at the upstream end of the gene (transcription unit). **3.** In a bacterial cell, RNA polymerase recognizes the gene's promoter and binds to it. In a eukaryotic cell, transcription factors mediate the binding of RNA polymerase to the promoter. **4.** The transcription factor that recognizes the TATA sequence would be unable to bind, so RNA polymerase could not bind and transcription of that gene probably would not occur.

Concept Check 17.3

1. The 5′ cap and poly-A tail facilitate mRNA export from the nucleus, prevent the mRNA from being degraded by hydrolytic enzymes, and facilitate ribosome attachment. **2.** In editing a video, segments are cut out and discarded (like introns), and the remaining segments are joined together (like exons) so that the regions of joining ("splicing") are not noticeable. **3.** Six different forms could be made because alternative splicing could generate six different mRNAs (two possibilities for exon 4 × three possibilities for exon 7).

Concept Check 17.4

1. First, each aminoacyl-tRNA synthetase specifically recognizes a single amino acid and attaches it only to an appropriate tRNA. Second, a tRNA charged with its specific amino acid binds only to an mRNA codon for that amino acid. **2.** Polyribosomes enable the cell to produce multiple copies of a polypeptide very quickly. **3.** A signal peptide on the leading end of the polypeptide being synthesized is recognized by a signal-recognition particle that brings the ribosome to the ER membrane. There the ribosome attaches and continues to synthesize the polypeptide, depositing it in the ER lumen. **4.** The structure and function of the ribosome seem to depend more on the rRNAs than on the ribosomal proteins. Because it is single-stranded, an RNA molecule can hydrogen-bond with itself and with other RNA molecules. RNA molecules make up the interface between the two ribosomal subunits, so presumably RNA-RNA binding helps hold the ribosome together. The binding site for mRNA in the ribosome could include rRNA that can bind the mRNA. (In fact, this turns out to be the case.) Also, complementary bonding within an RNA molecule allows it to assume a particular three-dimensional shape, and, along with the RNA's functional groups, presumably enables rRNA to catalyze peptide bond formation during translation.

Concept Check 17.5

1. In the mRNA, the reading frame downstream from the deletion is shifted, leading to a long string of incorrect amino acids in the polypeptide and, in most cases, a stop codon will arise, leading to premature termination. The polypeptide will most likely be nonfunctional.

2.

Normal DNA sequence
(template strand is on top): 3′-TACTTGTCCGATATC-5′
5′-ATGAACAGGCTATAG-3′

mRNA sequence: 5′-AUGAACAGGCUAUAG-3′

Amino acid sequence: Met-Asn-Arg-Leu-STOP

Mutated DNA sequence
(template strand is on top): 3′-TACTTGTCCAATATC-5′
5′-ATGAACAGGTTATAG-3′

mRNA sequence: 5′-AUGAACAGGUUAUAG-3′

Amino acid sequence: Met-Asn-Arg-Leu-STOP

The amino acid sequence is Met-Asn-Arg-Leu both before and after the mutation because the mRNA codons 5′-CUA-3′ and 5′-UUA-3′ both code for Leu. (The fifth codon is a stop codon.)

Concept Check 17.6

1. No, transcription and translation are separated in space and time in a eukaryotic cell, a result of the eukaryotic cell's nuclear compartment. **2.** When one ribosome terminates translation and dissociates, the two subunits would be very close to the cap. This could facilitate their rebinding and initiating synthesis of a new polypeptide, thus increasing the efficiency of translation.

Self-Quiz

1. b **2.** d **3.** a **4.** a **5.** d **6.** e **7.** b

8.

Type of RNA	Functions
Messenger RNA (mRNA)	Carries information specifying amino acid sequences of proteins from DNA to ribosomes.
Transfer RNA (tRNA)	Serves as adapter molecule in protein synthesis; translates mRNA codons into amino acids.
Ribosomal RNA (rRNA)	Plays catalytic (ribozyme) roles and structural roles in ribosomes.
Primary transcript	Is a precursor to mRNA, rRNA, or tRNA, before being processed. Some intron RNA acts as a ribozyme, catalyzing its own splicing.
Small nuclear RNA (snRNA)	Plays structural and catalytic roles in spliceosomes, the complexes of protein and RNA that splice pre-mRNA.

CHAPTER 18

Figure Questions

Figure 18.3 As the concentration of tryptophan in the cell falls, eventually there will be none bound to repressor molecules. These will then take on their inactive shapes and dissociate from the operator, allowing transcription of the operon to resume. The enzymes for tryptophan synthesis will be made, and they will begin to synthesize tryptophan again in the cell. **Figure 18.10** The albumin gene enhancer has the three control elements colored yellow, gray, and red. The sequences in the two cells would be identical, since the cells are in the same organism. **Figure 18.16** Even if the mutant MyoD protein couldn't activate the *myoD* gene, it could still turn on genes for the other proteins in the pathway (other transcription factors, which would turn on the genes for muscle-specific proteins, for example). Therefore, some differentiation would occur. But unless there were other activators that could compensate for the loss of the MyoD protein's activation of the *myoD* gene, the cell would not be able to maintain its differentiated state. **Figure 18.19** Normal Bicoid protein would be made in the anterior end and compensate for the presence of mutant *bicoid* mRNA put into the egg by the mother. Development should be normal, with a head present. **Figure 18.21** The mutation is likely to be recessive because it is more likely to have an effect if both copies of the gene are mutated and code for nonfunctional proteins. If one normal copy of the gene is present, its product could inhibit the cell cycle. (However, there are also known cases of dominant *p53* mutations.)

Concept Check 18.1

1. Binding by the *trp* corepressor (tryptophan) activates the *trp* repressor, shutting off transcription of the *trp* operon; binding by the *lac* inducer (allolactose) inactivates the *lac* repressor, leading to transcription of the *lac* operon. **2.** The cell would continuously produce β-galactosidase and the two other enzymes for lactose utilization, even in the absence of lactose, thus wasting cell resources. **3.** With glucose scarce, cAMP would be bound to CAP and CAP would be bound to the promoter, favoring the binding of RNA polymerase. However, in the absence of lactose, the repressor would be bound to the operator, blocking RNA polymerase binding to the promoter. The operon genes would therefore not be transcribed. If another sugar were present and the genes encoding enzymes for its breakdown were in an operon regulated like the *lac* operon, we might expect to find active transcription of those genes.

Concept Check 18.2

1. Histone acetylation is generally associated with gene expression, while DNA methylation is generally associated with lack of expression. **2.** General transcription factors function in assembling the transcription initiation complex at the promoters for all genes. Specific transcription factors bind to control elements associated with a particular gene and, once bound, either increase (activators) or decrease (repressors) transcription of that gene. **3.** The three genes should have some similar or identical sequences in the control elements of their enhancers. Because of this similarity, the same specific transcription factors could bind to the enhancers of all three genes and stimulate their expression coordinately. **4.** Degradation of the mRNA, regulation of translation, activation of the protein (by chemical modification, for example), and protein degradation **5.** Expression of the gene encoding the yellow activator (YA) must be regulated at one of the steps shown in Figure 18.6. The YA gene might be transcribed only in liver cells because the necessary activators for the enhancer of the YA gene are found only in liver cells.

Concept Check 18.3

1. Both miRNAs and siRNAs are small, single-stranded RNAs that associate with a complex of proteins and then can base-pair with mRNAs that have a complementary sequence. This base pairing leads to either degradation of the mRNA or blockage of its translation. Some siRNAs, in association with other proteins, can bind back to the chromatin in a certain region, causing chromatin changes that affect transcription. Both miRNAs and siRNAs are processed from double-stranded RNA precursors by the enzyme Dicer. However, miRNAs are encoded by genes in the cell's genome, and the single transcript folds back on itself to form one or more double-stranded hairpins, each of which is processed into an miRNA. In contrast, siRNAs arise from a longer stretch of double-stranded RNA, which may be introduced into the cell by a virus or an experimenter. In some cases, a cellular gene codes for one RNA strand of the precursor molecule, and an enzyme then synthesizes the complementary strand. **2.** The mRNA would persist and be translated into the cell division–promoting protein, and the cell would probably divide. If the intact miRNA is necessary for inhibition of cell division, then division of this cell might be inappropriate. Uncontrolled cell division could lead to formation of a mass of cells (tumor) that prevents proper functioning of the organism.

Concept Check 18.4

1. Cells undergo differentiation during embryonic development, becoming different from each other; in the adult organism, there are many highly specialized cell types. **2.** By binding to a receptor on the receiving cell's surface and triggering a signal transduction pathway that affects gene expression **3.** Because their products, made and deposited into the egg by the mother, determine the head and tail ends, as well as the back and belly, of the embryo (and eventually the adult fly) **4.** The lower cell is synthesizing signaling molecules because the gene encoding them is activated, meaning that the appropriate specific transcription factors are binding to the gene's enhancer. The genes encoding these specific transcription factors are also being expressed in this cell because the transcriptional activators that can turn them on were expressed in the precursor to this cell. A similar explanation also applies to the cells expressing the receptor proteins. This scenario began with specific cytoplasmic determinants localized in specific regions of the egg. These cytoplasmic determinants were distributed unevenly to daughter cells, resulting in cells going down different developmental pathways.

Concept Check 18.5

1. The protein product of a proto-oncogene is usually involved in a pathway that stimulates cell division. The protein product of a tumor-suppressor gene is usually involved in a pathway that inhibits cell division. **2.** When an individual has inherited an oncogene or a mutant allele of a tumor-suppressor gene **3.** A cancer-causing mutation in a proto-oncogene usually makes the gene product overactive, whereas a cancer-causing mutation in a tumor-suppressor gene usually makes the gene product nonfunctional.

Self-Quiz

1. d **2.** a **3.** d **4.** a **5.** c **6.** e **7.** a **8.** c **9.** b **10.** b
11. a.

The purple, blue, and red activator proteins would be present.

b.

Only gene 4 would be transcribed.

c. In nerve cells, the orange, blue, green, and black activators would have to be present, thus activating transcription of genes 1, 2, and 4. In skin cells, the red, black, purple, and blue activators would have to be present, thus activating genes 3 and 5.

CHAPTER 19

Figure Questions

Figure 19.2 Beijerinck might have concluded that the agent was a toxin produced by the plant that was able to pass through a filter but that became more and more dilute. In this case, he would have concluded that the infectious agent could not reproduce. **Figure 19.4** Top vertical arrow: Infection. Left upper arrow: Replication. Right upper arrow: Transcription. Right middle arrow: Translation. Lower left and right arrows: Self-assembly. Bottom middle arrow: Exit. **Figure 19.7** Any class V virus, including the viruses that cause influenza (flu), measles, and mumps.

Concept Check 19.1

1. TMV consists of one molecule of RNA surrounded by a helical array of proteins. The influenza virus has eight molecules of RNA, each surrounded by a helical array of proteins, similar to the arrangement of the single RNA molecule in TMV. Another difference is that the influenza virus has an outer envelope. **2.** One of the arguments for regarding viruses as nonliving is that they cannot perform any activity characteristic of living organisms unless they are inside a host cell. This virus challenges that generalization because the virus can change its shape without having access to host cell proteins. (Further analysis suggested that the projections contain proteins related to intermediate filaments that may polymerize spontaneously under certain conditions.)

Concept Check 19.2

1. Lytic phages can only carry out lysis of the host cell, whereas lysogenic phages may either lyse the host cell or integrate into the host chromosome. In the latter case, the viral DNA (prophage) is simply replicated along with the host chromosome. Under certain conditions, a prophage may exit the host chromosome and initiate a lytic cycle. **2.** The genetic material of these viruses is RNA, which is replicated inside the infected cell by enzymes encoded by the virus. The viral genome (or a complementary copy of it) serves as mRNA for the synthesis of viral proteins. **3.** Because it synthesizes DNA from its RNA genome. This is the reverse ("retro") of the usual DNA → RNA information flow. **4.** There are many steps that could be interfered with: binding of the virus to the cell, reverse transcriptase function, integration into the host cell chromosome, genome synthesis (in this case, transcription of RNA from the integrated provirus), assembly of the virus inside the cell, and budding of the virus. (Many, if not all, of these are targets of actual medical strategies to block progress of the infection in HIV-infected people.)

Concept Check 19.3

1. Mutations can lead to a new strain of a virus that can no longer be effectively fought by the immune system, even if an animal had been exposed to the original strain; a virus can jump from one species to a new host; and a rare virus can spread if a host population becomes less isolated. **2.** In horizontal transmission, a plant is infected from an external source of virus, which could enter through a break in the plant's epidermis due to damage by herbivores. In vertical transmission, a plant inherits viruses from its parent either via infected seeds (sexual reproduction) or via an infected cutting (asexual reproduction). **3.** Humans are not within the host range of TMV, so they can't be infected by the virus. **4.** It is unlikely that human air travel could have spread the virus, since existing strains of the virus do not seem to be transmissible from human to human. It is conceivable but unlikely that an infected human traveling from Asia passed the virus to birds in Africa and Europe. It is possible that domestic birds carried the virus, perhaps in shipments of poultry. The likeliest scenario of all may be that migratory wild birds carried the virus during their migrations and passed it to domestic and wild birds in the new locations. To test these latter hypotheses, the timing of the outbreaks should be analyzed to see if they correlate with recent poultry shipments or known wild bird migrations. Any such migratory birds should be tested for the presence of the African or European strain of the virus, based on the nucleotide sequences of their genomes.

Self-Quiz

1. d **2.** b **3.** c **4.** d **5.** c
6. As shown below, the viral genome would be translated into capsid proteins and envelope glycoproteins directly, rather than after a complementary RNA copy was made. A complementary RNA strand would still be made, however, that could be used as a template for many new copies of the viral genome.

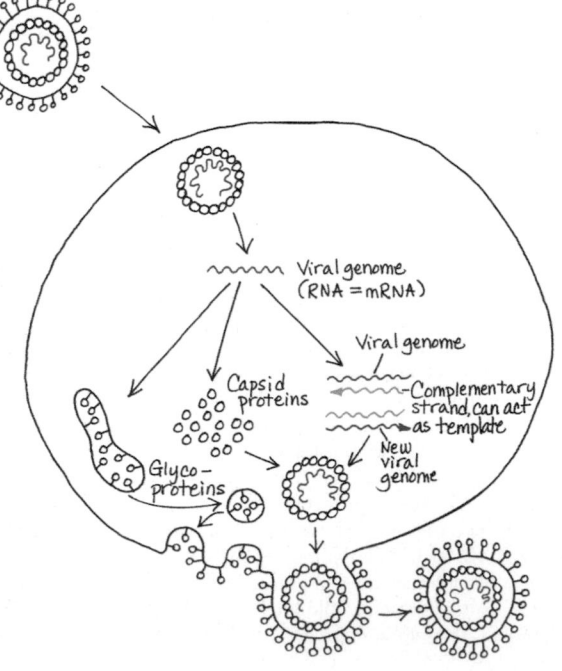

CHAPTER 20

Figure Questions
Figure 20.3

5′ A A G C T T 3′ $\xrightarrow{\text{Hind III}}$ 5′ A 3′ + 5′ A G C T T 3′
3′ T T C G A A 5′   3′ T T C G A 5′   3′ A 5′

Figure 20.4 Cells containing no plasmid at all would be able to grow; these colonies would be white because they would lack functional *lacZ* genes.
Figure 20.10 Grow each clone of cells in culture. Isolate the plasmids from each and cut them with the restriction enzyme originally used to make the clone (see Figure 20.4). Run each sample on an electrophoretic gel, and recover the DNA of the insert from the gel band. **Figure 20.16** The researchers might have concluded that differentiated cells are irreversibly changed so that they can make only one type of tissue in the plant. (This result would support the idea that cloning isn't possible.) **Figure 20.17** None of the eggs with the transplanted nuclei would have developed into a tadpole. Also, the result might include only some of the tissues of a tadpole which might differ depending on which nucleus was transplanted. (This assumes that there was some way to tell the four cells apart, as one can in some frog species.)

Concept Check 20.1
1. The covalent sugar-phosphate bonds of the DNA strands **2.** Yes, *PvuI* will cut the molecule

5′ C C T T G A C G A T C G T T A C C G 3′
3′ G G A A C T G C T A G C A A T G G C 5′

$\downarrow$ PvuI

5′ C C T T G A C G A T 3′   +   5′ C G T T A C C G 3′
3′ G G A A C T G C 5′   3′ T A G C A A T G G C 5′

3. Some human genes are too large to be incorporated into bacterial plasmids. Bacterial cells lack the means to process RNA transcripts into mRNA, and even if the need for RNA processing is avoided by using cDNA, bacteria lack enzymes to catalyze the post-translational processing that many human proteins require to function properly. **4.** 5′-CGGT-3′ and 5′-CCTT-3′

Concept Check 20.2
1. Any restriction enzyme will cut genomic DNA in many places, generating such a large number of fragments that they would appear as a smear rather than distinct bands when the gel is stained after electrophoresis. **2.** In Southern blotting, Northern blotting, and microarray analysis, the labeled probe binds only to the specific target sequence owing to complementary nucleic acid hybridization (DNA-DNA hybridization in Southern blotting and microarray analysis, DNA-RNA hybridization in Northern blotting). In DNA sequencing, primers base-pair to the template, allowing DNA synthesis to start. In RT-PCR, the primers must base-pair with their target sequences in the DNA mixture. **3.** If a spot is green, the gene represented on that spot is expressed only in normal tissue. If red, the gene is expressed only in cancerous tissue. If yellow, the gene is expressed in both. And if black, the gene is expressed in neither type of tissue. As a researcher interested in cancer development, you would want to study genes represented by spots that are green or red because these are genes for which the expression level differs between the two types of tissues. Some of these genes may be expressed differently as a result of cancer, but others might play a role in causing cancer.

Concept Check 20.3
1. No, primarily because of subtle (and perhaps not so subtle) differences in their environments **2.** The state of chromatin modification in the nucleus from the intestinal cell was undoubtedly less similar to that of a nucleus from a fertilized egg, explaining why many fewer of these nuclei were able to be reprogrammed. In contrast, the chromatin in a nucleus from a cell at the four-cell stage would have been much more like that of a nucleus in a fertilized egg and therefore much more easily programmed to direct development. **3.** A technique would have to be worked out for turning a human iPS cell into a pancre-

atic cell (probably by inducing expression of pancreas-specific regulatory genes in the cell).

Concept Check 20.4
1. Stem cells continue to reproduce themselves. **2.** Herbicide resistance, pest resistance, disease resistance, salinity resistance, delayed ripening, and improved nutritional value **3.** Because hepatitis A is an RNA virus, you could isolate RNA from the blood and try to detect copies of hepatitis A RNA by one of three methods. First, you could run the RNA on a gel and then do a Northern blot using probes complementary to hepatitis A genome sequences. A second approach would be to use reverse transcriptase to make cDNA from the RNA in the blood, run the cDNA on a gel, and do a Southern blot using the same probe. However, neither of these methods would be as sensitive as RT-PCR, in which you would reverse transcribe the blood RNA into cDNA and then use PCR to amplify the cDNA, using primers specific to hepatitis A sequences. If you then ran the products on an electrophoretic gel, the presence of a band would support your hypothesis.

Self-Quiz
1. b **2.** b **3.** c **4.** b **5.** a **6.** c **7.** c **8.** d
9.

10. A cDNA library, made using mRNA from human lens cells, which would be expected to contain many copies of crystallin mRNAs

CHAPTER 21

Figure Questions
Figure 21.3 The fragments in stage 2 of this figure are like those in stage 2 of Figure 21.2, but in this figure their order relative to each other is not known and will be determined later by computer. The order of the fragments in Figure 21.2 is completely known before sequencing begins. (Determining the order takes longer but makes the eventual sequence assembly much easier.) **Figure 21.9** The transposon would be cut out of the DNA at the original site rather than copied, so part (a) would show the original stretch of DNA without the transposon after the mobile transposon had been cut out. **Figure 21.10** The RNA transcripts extending from the DNA in each transcription unit are shorter on the left and longer on the right. This means that RNA polymerase must be starting on the left end of the unit and moving toward the right. **Figure 21.13** Pseudogenes are nonfunctional. They could have arisen by any mutations in the second copy that made the gene product unable to function. Examples would be base changes that introduce stop codons in the sequence, alter amino acids, or change a region of the gene promoter so that the gene can no longer be expressed. **Figure 21.14** Let's say a transposable element (TE) existed in the intron to the left of the indicated EGF exon in the *EGF* gene, and the same TE was present in the intron to the left of the indicated F exon

in the fibronectin gene. During meiotic recombination, these TEs could cause nonsister chromatids on the same chromosome to pair up incorrectly, as seen in Figure 21.12. One gene might end up with an F exon next to an EGF exon. Further mistakes in pairing over many generations might result in these two exons being separated from the rest of the gene and placed next to a single or duplicated K exon. In general, the presence of repeated sequences in introns and between genes facilitates these processes because it allows incorrect pairing of nonsister chromatids, leading to novel exon combinations.

Figure 21.16 Since you know that chimpanzees do not speak but humans do, you'd probably want to know how many amino acid differences there are between the human wild-type FOXP2 protein and that of the chimpanzee and whether these changes affect the function of the protein. (As we explain later in the text, there are two amino acid differences.) You know that humans with mutations in this gene have severe language impairment. You would want to learn more about the human mutations by checking whether they affect the same amino acids in the gene product that the chimpanzee sequence differences affect. If so, those amino acids might play an important role in the function of the protein in language. Going further, you could analyze the differences between the chimpanzee and mouse FOXP2 proteins. You might ask: Are they more similar than the chimpanzee and human proteins? (It turns out that the chimpanzee and mouse proteins have only one amino acid difference and thus are more similar than the chimpanzee and human proteins, which have two differences, and than the human and mouse proteins, which have three differences.)

Concept Check 21.1

1. In a linkage map, genes and other markers are ordered with respect to each other, but only the relative distances between them are known. In a physical map, the actual distances between markers, expressed in base pairs, are known. **2.** The three-stage approach employed in the Human Genome Project involves linkage mapping, physical mapping, and then sequencing of short, overlapping fragments that previously have been ordered relative to each other (see Figure 21.2). The whole-genome shotgun approach eliminates the linkage mapping and physical mapping stages; instead, short fragments generated by multiple restriction enzymes are sequenced and then ordered by computer programs that identify overlapping regions (see Figure 21.3). **3.** Because the two mouse species are very closely related, their genome sequences are expected to be very similar. This means that the field mouse genome fragments could be compared with the assembled lab mouse genome, providing valuable information to use in placing the field mouse genome fragments in the correct order. In a sense, the lab mouse genome could be used as a rough map for the field mouse genome, removing the necessity to carry out complete genetic and physical mapping for the field mouse.

Concept Check 21.2

1. The Internet allows centralization of databases such as GenBank and software resources such as BLAST, making them freely accessible. Having all the data in a central database, easily accessible on the Internet, minimizes the possibility of errors and of researchers working with different data. It streamlines the process of science, since all researchers are able to use the same software programs, rather than each having to obtain their own software. It speeds up dissemination of data and ensures as much as possible that errors are corrected in a timely fashion. These are just a few answers; you can probably think of more. **2.** Cancer is a disease caused by multiple factors. To focus on a single gene or a single defect would ignore other factors that may influence the cancer and even the behavior of the single gene being studied. The systems approach, because it takes into account many factors at the same time, is more likely to lead to an understanding of the causes and most useful treatments for cancer. **3.** The DNA would first be sequenced and analyzed for whether the mutation is in the coding region for a gene or in a promoter or enhancer, affecting the expression of a gene. In either case, the nature of the gene product could be explored by searching the protein database for similar proteins. If similar proteins have known functions, that would provide a clue about the function of your protein. Otherwise, biochemical and other methods could provide some ideas about possible function. Software could be used to compare what is known about your protein and similar proteins.

Concept Check 21.3

1. Alternative splicing of RNA transcripts from a gene and post-translational processing of polypeptides **2.** The total number of completed genomes is found by clicking on "Published Complete Genomes." Add the figures for bacterial, archaeal, and eukaryotic "ongoing genomes" to get the number "in progress." Finally, look at the top of the Published Complete Genomes page to get numbers of completed genomes for each domain. (*Note:* You can click on the "Size" column and the table will be re-sorted by genome size. Scroll down to get an idea of relative sizes of genomes in the three domains. Remember, though, that most of the sequenced genomes are bacterial.) **3.** Prokaryotes are generally smaller cells than eukaryotic cells, and they reproduce by binary fission. The evolutionary process involved is natural selection for more quickly reproducing cells: The faster they can replicate their DNA and divide, the more likely they will be able to dominate a population of prokaryotes. The less DNA they have to replicate, then, the faster they will reproduce.

Concept Check 21.4

1. The number of genes is higher in mammals, and the amount of noncoding DNA is greater. Also, the presence of introns in mammalian genes makes them longer, on average, than prokaryotic genes. **2.** Introns are interspersed within the coding sequences of genes. Many copies of each transposable element are scattered throughout the genome. Simple sequence DNA is concentrated at the centromeres and telomeres and is clustered in other locations. **3.** In the rRNA gene family, identical transcription units for the three different RNA products are present in long, tandemly repeated arrays. The large number of copies of the rRNA genes enable organisms to produce the rRNA for enough ribosomes to carry out active protein synthesis, and the single transcription unit ensures that the relative amounts of the different rRNA molecules produced are correct. Each globin gene family consists of a relatively small number of nonidentical genes. The differences in the globin proteins encoded by these genes result in production of hemoglobin molecules adapted to particular developmental stages of the organism. **4.** First, you could check the sequence by translating it into a predicted amino acid sequence and see if there are multiple stop codons. If there aren't, the next step would be to see whether the gene is expressed, probably by carrying out a Northern blot or *in situ* hybridization to look for the mRNA in the cells that express the gene.

Concept Check 21.5

1. If meiosis is faulty, two copies of the entire genome can end up in a single cell. Errors in crossing over during meiosis can lead to one segment being duplicated while another is deleted. During DNA replication, slippage backward along the template strand can result in a duplication. **2.** For either gene, a mistake in crossing over during meiosis could have occurred between the two copies of that gene, such that one ended up with a duplicated exon. This could have happened several times, resulting in the multiple copies of a particular exon in each gene. **3.** Homologous transposable elements scattered throughout the genome provide sites where recombination can occur between different chromosomes. Movement of these elements into coding or regulatory sequences may change expression of genes. Transposable elements also can carry genes with them, leading to dispersion of genes and in some cases different patterns of expression. Transport of an exon during transposition and its insertion into a gene may add a new functional domain to the originally encoded protein, a type of exon shuffling. **4.** Because more offspring are born to women who have this inversion, it must provide some advantage. It would be expected to persist and spread in the population. (In fact, evidence in the study allowed the researchers to conclude that it has been increasing in proportion in the population. You'll learn more about population genetics in the next unit.)

Concept Check 21.6

1. Because both humans and macaques are primates, their genomes are expected to be more similar than the macaque and mouse genomes are. The mouse lineage diverged from the primate lineage before the human and macaque lineages diverged. **2.** Homeotic genes differ in their *non*homeobox sequences, which determine the interactions of homeotic gene products with other transcription factors and hence which genes are regulated by the homeotic genes. These nonhomeobox sequences differ in the two organisms, as do the expression patterns of the homeobox genes. **3.** *Alu* elements must have undergone transposition more actively in the human genome for some reason. Their increased numbers may have then allowed more recombination errors in the human genome, resulting in more or different duplications. The divergence of the organization and content of the two genomes presumably accelerated divergence of the two species by making matings less and less likely to result in fertile offspring.

Self-Quiz
1. c **2.** e **3.** a **4.** e **5.** c **6.** a
7.
  1. ATETI...PKSSD...TSSTT...NARRD
  2. ATETI...PKSSE...TSSTT...NARRD
  3. ATETI...PKSSD...TSSTT...NARRD
  4. ATETI...PKSSD...TSSNT...SARRD
  5. ATETI...PKSSD...TSSTT...NARRD
  6. VTETI...PKSSD...TSSTT...NARRD

  a. Lines 1, 3, and 5 are the C, G, R species.
  b. Line 4 is the human sequence.
  c. Line 6 is the orangutan sequence.
  d. There is one amino acid difference between the mouse (line 2) and the C, G, R species; there are three amino acid differences between the mouse and the human.
  e. Because only one amino acid difference arose during the 60–100 million years since the mouse and C, G, R species diverged, it is somewhat surprising that two additional amino acid differences resulted during the 6 million years since chimpanzees and humans diverged. This indicates that the *FOXP2* gene has been evolving faster in the human lineage than in the lineages of other primates.

CHAPTER 22

Figure Questions
Figure 22.8 More than 5.5 million years ago. **Figure 22.13** The original pool of the transplanted guppy population contains pike-cichlids, a potent predator of adult guppies. Brightly colored adult males would be at a disadvantage in this pool. Thus, it is likely that color patterns in the guppy population would become more drab if they were returned to their original pool. **Figure 22.19** Based on this evolutionary tree, crocodiles are more closely related to birds than to lizards because they share a more recent common ancestor with birds (ancestor ⑤) than with lizards (ancestor ④).

Concept Check 22.1
1. Hutton and Lyell proposed that events in the past were caused by the same processes operating today. This principle suggested that Earth must be much older than a few thousand years, the age that was widely accepted at that time. Hutton and Lyell also thought that geologic change occurs gradually, stimulating Darwin to reason that the slow accumulation of small changes could ultimately produce the profound changes documented in the fossil record. In this context, the age of Earth was important to Darwin, because unless Earth was very old, he could not envision how there would have been enough time for evolution to occur. **2.** By these criteria, Cuvier's explanation of the fossil record and Lamarck's hypothesis of evolution are both scientific. Cuvier suggested that catastrophes and the resulting extinctions were usually confined to local regions, and that such regions were later repopulated by a different set of species that immigrated from other areas. These assertions can be tested against the fossil record (they have been found to be false). With respect to Lamarck, his principle of use and disuse can be used to make testable predictions for fossils of groups such as whale ancestors as they adapt to a new habitat. Lamarck's principle of the inheritance of acquired characteristics can be tested directly in living organisms (it has been found to be false).

Concept Check 22.2
1. Organisms share characteristics (the unity of life) because they share common ancestors; the great diversity of life occurs because new species have repeatedly formed when descendant organisms gradually adapted to different environments, becoming different from their ancestors. **2.** All species have the potential to produce more offspring (overreproduce) than can be supported by the environment. This ensures there will be what Darwin called a "struggle for existence" in which many of the offspring are eaten, starved, diseased, or unable to reproduce for a variety of other reasons. Members of a population exhibit a range of heritable variations, some of which make it likely that their bearers will leave more offspring than other individuals (for example, the bearer may escape predators more effectively or be more tolerant of the physical conditions of the environment). Over time, natural selection imposed by factors such as predators, lack of food, or the physical conditions of the environment can increase the proportion of individuals with favorable traits in a population (evolutionary adaptation). **3.** The fossil mammal species (or its ancestors) would most likely have colonized the Andes from within South America, whereas ancestors of mammals currently found in African mountains would most likely have colonized those mountains from other parts of Africa. As a result, the Andes fossil species would share a more recent common ancestor with South American mammals than with mammals in Africa. Thus, for many of its traits, the fossil mammal species would probably more closely resemble mammals that live in South American jungles than mammals that live on African mountains.

Concept Check 22.3
1. An environmental factor such as a drug does not create new traits such as drug resistance, but rather selects for traits among those that are already present in the population. **2.** (a) Despite their different functions, the forelimbs of different mammals are structurally similar because they all represent modifications of a structure found in the common ancestor. (b) Convergent evolution: The similarities between the sugar glider and flying squirrel indicate that similar environments selected for similar adaptations despite different ancestry.

3. At the time that dinosaurs originated, Earth's landmasses formed a single large continent, Pangaea. Because many dinosaurs were large and mobile, it is likely that early members of these groups lived on many different parts of Pangaea. When Pangaea broke apart, fossils of these organisms would have moved with the rocks in which they were deposited. As a result, we would predict that fossils of early dinosaurs would have a broad geographic distribution (this prediction has been upheld).

Self-Quiz
1. b **2.** c **3.** d **4.** d **5.** a **6.** d
8. (a)

(b) The rapid rise in the percentage of mosquitoes resistant to DDT was most likely caused by natural selection in which mosquitoes resistant to DDT could survive and reproduce while other mosquitoes could not. (c) In India—where DDT resistance first appeared—natural selection would have caused the frequency of resistant mosquitoes to increase over time. If resistant mosquitoes then migrated from India (for example, transported by wind or in planes, trains, or ships) to other parts of the world, the frequency of DDT resistance would increase there as well.

CHAPTER 23

Figure Questions
Figure 23.7 The predicted frequencies are 36% $C^R C^R$, 48% $C^R C^W$, and 16% $C^W C^W$. **Figure 23.12** Because such a shift in prevailing winds would increase the transfer of alleles (gene flow) from plants living on mine soils to plants living at the location marked by the arrow, the change would probably lead to an increase in the index of copper tolerance of plants at that location. **Figure 23.16** Crossing a single female's eggs with both an SC and an LC male's sperm allowed the researchers to directly compare the effects of the males' contribution to the next generation, since both batches of offspring had the same maternal contribution. This isolation of the male's impact enabled researchers to draw conclusions about differences in genetic "quality" between the SC and LC males. **Figure 23.18** The researchers measured

the percentages of successfully reproducing adults out of the breeding adult population that had each phenotype. This approach of determining which phenotype was favored by selection assumes that reproduction was a sufficient indicator of relative fitness (as opposed to counting the number of eggs laid or offspring hatched, for example) and that mouth phenotype was the driving factor determining the fishes' ability to reproduce.

Concept Check 23.1

1. (a) Within a population, genetic differences among individuals provide the raw material on which natural selection and other mechanisms can act. Without such differences, allele frequencies could not change over time—and hence the population could not evolve. (b) Genetic variation among populations can arise by natural selection if selection favors different alleles in different populations; this might occur, for example, if the different populations experienced different environmental conditions. Genetic variation among populations can also arise by genetic drift when the genetic differences between populations are selectively neutral.   **2.** Many mutations occur in somatic cells that do not produce gametes and so are lost when the organism dies. Of mutations that do occur in cell lines that produce gametes, many do not have a phenotypic effect on which natural selection can act. Others have a harmful effect and are thus unlikely to increase in frequency because they decrease the reproductive success of their bearers.   **3.** Its genetic variation (whether measured at the level of the gene or at the level of nucleotide sequences) would probably drop over time. During meiosis, crossing over and the independent assortment of chromosomes produce many new combinations of alleles. In addition, a population contains a vast number of possible mating combinations, and fertilization brings together the gametes of individuals with different genetic backgrounds. Thus, via crossing over, independent assortment of chromosomes, and fertilization, sexual reproduction reshuffles alleles into fresh combinations each generation. Without sexual reproduction, new sources of genetic variation would be reduced, causing the overall amount of genetic variation to drop.

Concept Check 23.2

1. 750. Half the loci (250) are fixed, meaning only one allele exists for each locus: $250 \times 1 = 250$. There are two alleles each for the other loci: $250 \times 2 = 500$. $250 + 500 = 750$.   **2.** $p^2 + 2pq$; p^2 represents homozygotes with two A alleles, and $2pq$ represents heterozygotes with one A allele.   **3.** There are 120 individuals in the population, so there are 240 alleles. Of these, there are 124 A alleles—32 from the 16 AA individuals and 92 from the 92 Aa individuals. Thus, the frequency of the A allele is $p = 124/240 = 0.52$; hence, the frequency of the a allele is $q = 0.48$. Based on the Hardy-Weinberg equation, if the population were not evolving, the frequency of genotype AA should be $p^2 = 0.52 \times 0.52 = 0.27$; the frequency of genotype Aa should be $2pq = 2 \times 0.52 \times 0.48 = 0.5$; and the frequency of genotype aa should be $q^2 = 0.48 \times 0.48 = 0.23$. In a population of 120 individuals, these expected genotype frequencies lead us to predict that there would be 32 AA individuals (0.27×120), 60 Aa individuals (0.5×120), and 28 aa individuals (0.23×120). The actual numbers for the population (16 AA, 92 Aa, 12 aa) deviate from these expectations (fewer homozygotes and more heterozygotes than expected). This suggests that the population is not in Hardy-Weinberg equilibrium and hence is evolving.

Concept Check 23.3

1. Natural selection is more "predictable" in that it alters allele frequencies in a nonrandom way: It tends to increase the frequency of alleles that increase the organism's reproductive success in its environment and decrease the frequency of alleles that decrease the organism's reproductive success. Alleles subject to genetic drift increase or decrease in frequency by chance alone, whether or not they are advantageous.   **2.** Genetic drift results from chance events that cause allele frequencies to fluctuate at random from generation to generation; within a population, this process tends to decrease genetic variation over time. Gene flow is the exchange of alleles between populations; a process that can introduce new alleles to a population and hence may increase its genetic variation (albeit slightly, since rates of gene flow are often low).   **3.** Selection is not important at this locus; furthermore, the populations are reasonably large, and hence the effects of genetic drift should not be pronounced. Gene flow is occurring via the movement of pollen and seeds. Thus, allele and genotype frequencies in these populations should become more similar over time as a result of gene flow.

Concept Check 23.4

1. Zero, because fitness includes reproductive contribution to the next generation, and a sterile mule cannot produce offspring.   **2.** Although both gene flow and genetic drift can increase the frequency of advantageous alleles in a population, they can also decrease the frequency of advantageous alleles or increase the frequency of harmful alleles. Only natural selection *consistently* results in an increase in the frequency of alleles that enhance survival or reproduction. Thus, natural selection is the only mechanism that consistently causes adaptive evolution.   **3.** The three modes of natural selection (directional, stabilizing, and disruptive) are defined in terms of the selective advantage of different *phenotypes*, not different genotypes. Thus, the type of selection represented by heterozygote advantage depends on the phenotype of the heterozygotes. In this question, because heterozygous individuals have a more extreme phenotype than either homozygote, heterozygote advantage represents directional selection.

Self-Quiz

1. d   **2.** a   **3.** e
4. b   **5.** b
7. The frequency of the lap^{94} allele forms a cline, decreasing as one moves from southwest to northeast across Long Island Sound.

A hypothesis that explains the cline and accounts for the observations stated in the question is that the cline is maintained by an interaction between selection and gene flow. Under this hypothesis, in the southwest portion of the Sound, salinity is relatively low, and selection against the lap^{94} allele is strong. Moving toward the northeast and into the open ocean, where salinity is relatively high, selection favors a high frequency of the lap^{94} allele. However, because mussel larvae disperse long distances, gene flow prevents the lap^{94} allele from becoming fixed in the open ocean or from declining to zero in the southwestern portion of Long Island Sound.

CHAPTER 24

Figure Questions

Figure 24.3 Allele 1 (found in some birds in Population B) is more closely related to alleles found in Population A than to other alleles found in Population B. This implies that the ancestral allele from which allele 1 descended existed in Population A. Hence, the direction of gene flow was from Population A to Population B.   **Figure 24.9** This change would have the effect of increasing gene flow between the populations, which would make the evolution of reproductive isolation more difficult.   **Figure 24.12** Such results would suggest that mate choice based on coloration does not provide a reproductive barrier between these two cichlid species.   **Figure 24.14** Because the populations had only just begun to diverge from one another at this point in the process, it is likely that any existing barriers to reproduction would weaken over time.   **Figure 24.20** The presence of *M. cardinalis* plants that carry the *M. lewisii yup* allele would make it more likely that bumblebees would transfer pollen between the two monkey flower species. As a result, we would expect the number of hybrid offspring to increase.

Concept Check 24.1
1. (a) All except the biological species concept can be applied to both asexual and sexual species because they define species on the basis of characteristics other than ability to reproduce. In contrast, the biological species concept can be applied only to sexual species. (b) The easiest species concept to apply in the field would be the morphological species concept because it is based only on the appearance of the organism. Additional information about its ecological habits, evolutionary history, and reproduction are not required. **2.** Because these birds live in fairly similar environments and can breed successfully in captivity, the reproductive barrier in nature is probably prezygotic; given the species differences in habitat preference, this barrier could result from habitat isolation.

Concept Check 24.2
1. In allopatric speciation, a new species forms while in geographic isolation from its parent species; in sympatric speciation, a new species forms in the absence of geographic isolation. Geographic isolation greatly reduces gene flow between populations, whereas ongoing gene flow is more likely in sympatry. As a result, sympatric speciation is less common than allopatric speciation. **2.** Gene flow between subsets of a population that live in the same area can be reduced in a variety of ways. In some species—especially plants—changes in chromosome number can block gene flow and establish reproductive isolation in a single generation. Gene flow can also be reduced in sympatric populations by habitat differentiation (as seen in the apple maggot fly, *Rhagoletis*) and sexual selection (as seen in Lake Victoria cichlids). **3.** Allopatric speciation would be less likely to occur on a nearby island than on an isolated island of the same size. The reason we expect this result is that continued gene flow between mainland populations and those on a nearby island reduces the chance that enough genetic divergence will take place for allopatric speciation to occur.

Concept Check 24.3
1. Hybrid zones are regions in which members of different species meet and mate, producing some offspring of mixed ancestry. Such regions are "natural laboratories" in which to study speciation because scientists can directly observe factors that cause (or fail to cause) reproductive isolation. **2.** (a) If hybrids consistently survive and reproduce poorly compared to the offspring of intraspecific matings, it is possible that reinforcement would occur. If it did, natural selection would cause prezygotic barriers to reproduction between the parent species to strengthen over time, decreasing the production of unfit hybrids and leading to a completion of the speciation process. (b) If hybrid offspring survive and reproduce as well as the offspring of intraspecific matings, indiscriminate mating between the parent species would lead to the production of large numbers of hybrid offspring. As these hybrids mated with each other and with members of both parent species, the gene pools of the parent species could fuse over time, reversing the speciation process.

Concept Check 24.4
1. The time between speciation events includes (1) the length of time that it takes for populations of a newly formed species to begin diverging reproductively from one another and (2) the time it takes for speciation to be complete once this divergence begins. Although speciation can occur rapidly once populations have begun to diverge from one another, it may take millions of years for that divergence to begin. **2.** Investigators transferred alleles at the *yup* locus (which influences flower color) from each parent species to the other. *M. lewisii* plants with an *M. cardinalis yup* allele received many more visits from hummingbirds than usual; hummingbirds usually pollinate *M. cardinalis* but avoid *M. lewisii*. Similarly, *M. cardinalis* plants with an *M. lewisii yup* allele received many more visits from bumblebees than usual; bumblebees usually pollinate *M. lewisii* and avoid *M. cardinalis*. Thus, alleles at the *yup* locus can influence pollinator choice, which in these species provides the primary barrier to interspecific mating. Nevertheless, the experiment does not prove that the *yup* locus alone controls barriers to reproduction between *M. lewisii* and *M. cardinalis*; other genes

might enhance the effect of the *yup* locus (by modifying flower color) or cause entirely different barriers to reproduction (for example, gametic isolation or a postzygotic barrier).

Self-Quiz
1. b **2.** a **3.** c **4.** e **5.** d **6.** c
8. One possible process is

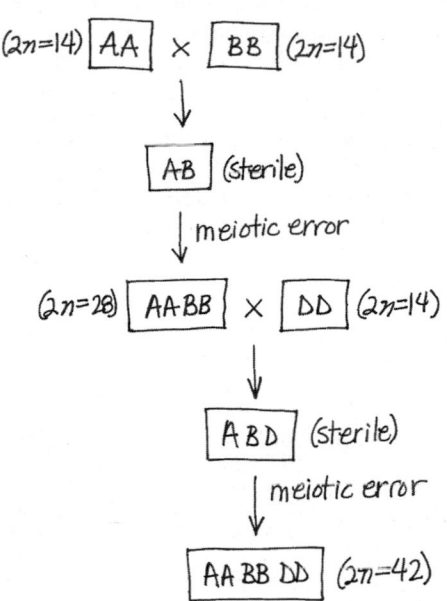

CHAPTER 25

Figure Questions
Figure 25.5 Because uranium-238 has a half-life of 4.5 billion years, the *x*-axis would be relabeled (in billions of years) as: 4.5, 9, 13.5, and 18. **Figure 25.23** The coding sequence of the *Pitx1* gene would differ between the marine and lake populations, but patterns of gene expression would not.

Concept Check 25.1
1. The hypothesis that conditions on early Earth could have permitted the synthesis of organic molecules from inorganic ingredients **2.** In contrast to random mingling of molecules in an open solution, segregation of molecular systems by membranes could concentrate organic molecules, assisting biochemical reactions. **3.** No. Such a result would only show that life *could* have begun as in the experiment.

Concept Check 25.2
1. 22,920 years (four half-lives: 5,730 × 4) **2.** The fossil record shows that different groups of organisms dominated life on Earth at different points in time and that many organisms once alive are now extinct; specific examples of these points can be found in Figure 25.4. The fossil record also indicates that new groups of organisms can arise via the gradual modification of previously existing organisms, as illustrated by fossils that document the origin of mammals from cynodont ancestors. **3.** The discovery of such a (hypothetical) fossil organism would indicate that aspects of our current understanding of the origin of mammals are not correct because mammals are thought to have originated much more recently (see Figure 25.6). For example, such a discovery could suggest that the dates of previous fossil discoveries are not correct or that the lineages shown in Figure 25.6 shared features with mammals but were not their direct ancestors. Such a discovery would also suggest that radical changes in multiple aspects of the skeletal structure of organisms could arise suddenly—an idea that is not supported by the known fossil record.

Concept Check 25.3
1. Free oxygen attacks chemical bonds and can inhibit enzymes and damage cells. **2.** All eukaryotes have mitochondria or remnants of these organelles, but not all eukaryotes have plastids. **3.** A fossil record of life today would include many organisms with hard body parts (such as vertebrates

and many marine invertebrates), but might not include some species we are very familiar with, such as those that have small geographic ranges and/or small population sizes (for example, all five rhinoceros species).

Concept Check 25.4
1. Continental drift alters the physical geography and climate of Earth, as well as the extent to which organisms are geographically isolated. Because these factors affect extinction and speciation rates, continental drift has a major impact on life on Earth. **2.** Mass extinctions; major evolutionary innovations; the diversification of another group of organisms (which can provide new sources of food); migration to new locations where few competitor species exist. **3.** Their fossils should be present right up to the time of the catastrophic event, then disappear. Reality is a bit more complicated because the fossil record is not perfect. So the most recent fossil for a species might be a million years before the mass extinction, even if the species did not become extinct until the mass extinction.

Concept Check 25.5
1. Heterochrony can cause a variety of morphological changes. For example, if the onset of sexual maturity changes, a retention of juvenile characteristics (paedomorphosis) may result. Paedomorphosis can be caused by small genetic changes that result in large changes in morphology, as seen in the axolotl salamander. **2.** In animal embryos, *Hox* genes influence the development of structures such as limbs or feeding appendages. As a result, changes in these genes—or in the regulation of these genes—are likely to have major effects on morphology. **3.** From genetics, we know that gene regulation is altered by how well transcription factors bind to noncoding DNA sequences called control elements. Thus, if changes in morphology are often caused by changes in gene regulation, portions of noncoding DNA that contain control elements are likely to be strongly affected by natural selection.

Concept Check 25.6
1. Complex structures do not evolve all at once, but in increments, with natural selection selecting for adaptive variants of the earlier versions. **2.** Although the myxoma virus is highly lethal, initially some of the rabbits are resistant (0.2% of infected rabbits are not killed). Thus, assuming resistance is an inherited trait, we would expect the rabbit population to show a trend for increased resistance to the virus. We would also expect the virus to show an evolutionary trend toward reduced lethality. We would expect this trend because a rabbit infected with a less lethal virus would be more likely to live long enough for a mosquito to bite it and hence potentially transmit the virus to another rabbit. (A virus that kills its rabbit host before a mosquito transmits it to another rabbit dies with its host.)

Self-Quiz
1. c **2.** a **3.** e **4.** b **5.** c **6.** d **7.** b
8.

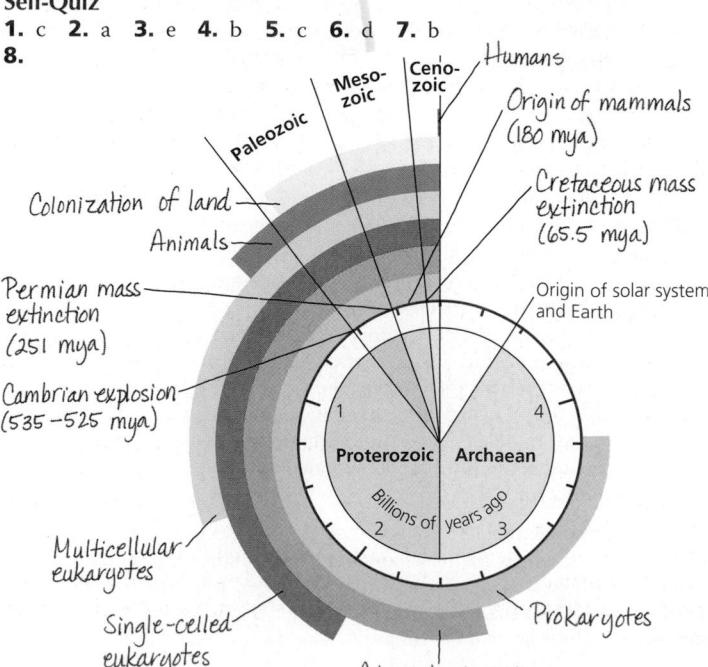

CHAPTER 26

Figure Questions
Figure 26.5 This new version does not alter any of the evolutionary relationships shown in Figure 26.5. For example, B and C remain sister taxa, taxon A is still as closely related to taxon B as it is to taxon C, and so on.

Figure 26.6 Mistakes can occur while performing the experiment (such as errors in DNA sequencing) and analyzing the results (such as misaligning the DNA sequences of different species). But an erroneous conclusion—such as concluding that a sample was from a humpback whale when in fact it came from a gray whale—could be reached even if no such errors were made. A particular humpback whale might, for example, happen to have a DNA sequence that was rare for its species, yet common for another species. To reduce the chance that such events could lead to an erroneous conclusion, gene trees could be constructed for multiple genes; if similar results emerged from all of these gene trees, there would be little reason to doubt the conclusions. **Figure 26.9** There are four possible bases (A, C, G, T) at each nucleotide position. If the base at each position depends on chance, not common descent, we would expect roughly one out of four (25%) of them to be the same. **Figure 26.12** The zebrafish lineage; of the five vertebrate lineages shown, its branch length is the longest. **Figure 26.19** The molecular clock indicates that the divergence time is roughly 45–50 million years. **Figure 26.21** Bacteria was the first to emerge. Archaea is the sister domain to Eukarya.

Concept Check 26.1
1. We are classified the same down to the class level; both the leopard and human are mammals. Leopards belong to order Carnivora, whereas humans do not. **2.** The branching pattern of the tree indicates that the badger and the wolf share a common ancestor that is more recent than the ancestor that these two animals share with the leopard. **3.** The tree in (c) shows a different pattern of evolutionary relationships. In (c), C and B are sister taxa, whereas C and D are sister taxa in (a) and (b).
4.

Concept Check 26.2
1. (a) Analogy, since porcupines and cacti are not closely related and since most other animals and plants do not have similar structures; (b) homology, since cats and humans are both mammals and have homologous forelimbs, of which the hand and paw are the lower part; (c) analogy, since owls and hornets are not closely related and since the structure of their wings is very different. **2.** Species 2 and 3 are more likely to be closely related. Small genetic changes (as between species 2 and 3) can produce divergent physical appearances, whereas if genes have diverged greatly (as in species 1 and 2), that suggests that the lineages have been separate for a long time.

Concept Check 26.3
1. No; hair is a shared ancestral character common to all mammals and thus is not helpful in distinguishing different mammalian subgroups. **2.** The principle of maximum parsimony states that the hypothesis about nature we investigate first should be the simplest explanation found to be consistent with the facts. Actual evolutionary relationships may differ from those inferred by

parsimony owing to complicating factors such as convergent evolution.
3. The traditional classification provides a poor match to evolutionary history, thus violating the basic principle of cladistics—that classification should be based on common descent. Both birds and mammals originated from groups traditionally designated as reptiles, making reptiles as traditionally delineated a paraphyletic group. These problems can be addressed by removing *Dimetrodon* and cynodonts from the reptiles, and by considering birds as a group of reptiles (specifically, as a group of dinosaurs).

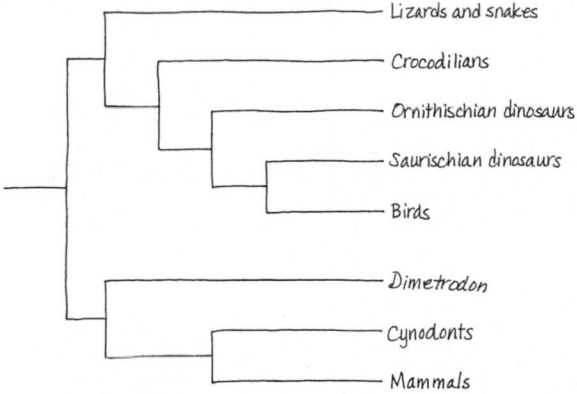

Concept Check 26.4

1. Proteins are gene products. Their amino acid sequences are determined by the nucleotide sequences of the DNA that codes for them. Thus, differences between comparable proteins in two species reflect underlying genetic differences. **2.** These observations suggest that the evolutionary lineages leading to species 1 and species 2 diverged from one another before a gene duplication event in species 1 produced gene B from gene A.

Concept Check 26.5

1. A molecular clock is a method of estimating the actual time of evolutionary events based on numbers of base changes in orthologous genes. It is based on the assumption that the regions of genomes being compared evolve at constant rates. **2.** There are many portions of the genome that do not code for genes; many base changes in these regions could accumulate through drift without affecting an organism's fitness. Even in coding regions of the genome, some mutations may not have a critical effect on genes or proteins. **3.** The gene (or genes) used for the molecular clock may have evolved more slowly in these two taxa than in the species used to calibrate the clock; as a result, the clock would underestimate the time at which the taxa diverged from one another.

Concept Check 26.6

1. The kingdom Monera included bacteria and archaea, but we now know that these organisms are in separate domains. Kingdoms are subsets of domains, so a single kingdom (like Monera) that includes taxa from different domains is not valid (it is polyphyletic). **2.** Because of horizontal gene transfer, some genes in eukaryotes are more closely related to bacteria, while others are more closely related to archaea; thus, depending on which genes are used, phylogenetic trees constructed from DNA data can yield conflicting results.
3.

Archaea	Bacteria	Eukarya
Bacteria	Archaea	Bacteria
Eukarya	Eukarya	Archaea

The third tree, in which the eukaryotic lineage diverged first, is not likely to receive support from genetic data because the fossil record shows that prokaryotes originated long before eukaryotes.

Self-Quiz

1. b **2.** d **3.** a **4.** d **5.** c **6.** d **7.** d

9.

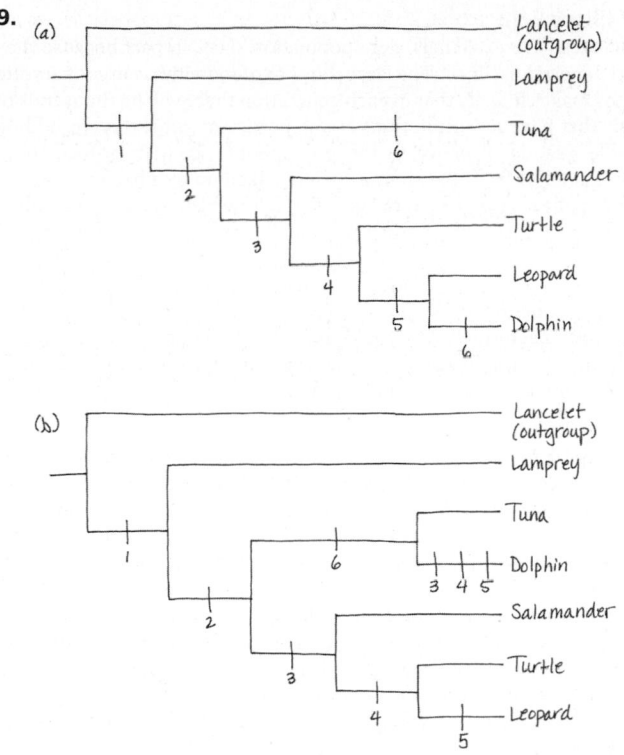

(c) The tree in (a) requires seven evolutionary changes, while the tree in (b) requires nine evolutionary changes. Thus, the tree in (a) is the most parsimonious, since it requires fewer evolutionary changes.

CHAPTER 27

Figure Questions

Figure 27.10 It is likely that the expression or sequence of genes that affect glucose metabolism may have changed; genes for metabolic processes no longer needed by the cell also may have changed. **Figure 27.12** The population that included individuals capable of conjugation would probably be more successful, since some of its members could form recombinant cells whose new gene combinations might be advantageous in a novel environment. **Figure 27.17** Thermophiles live in very hot environments, so it is likely that their enzymes can continue to function normally at much higher temperatures than do the enzymes of other organisms. At low temperatures, however, the enzymes of thermophiles may not function as well as the enzymes of other organisms. **Figure 27.19** From the graph, plant uptake can be estimated as 0.7, 0.6, and 0.95 (mg K) for strains 1, 2, and 3, respectively. These values average to 0.75 mg K. If bacteria had no effect, the average plant uptake of potassium for strains 1, 2, and 3 should be close to 0.5 mg K, the value observed for plants grown in bacteria-free soil.

Concept Check 27.1

1. Adaptations include the capsule (shields prokaryotes from host's immune system) and endospores (enable cells to survive harsh conditions and to revive when the environment becomes favorable). **2.** Prokaryotic cells generally lack the internal compartmentalization of eukaryotic cells. Prokaryotic genomes have much less DNA than eukaryotic genomes, and most of this DNA is contained in a single ring-shaped chromosome located in the nucleoid rather than within a true membrane-bounded nucleus. In addition, many prokaryotes also have plasmids, small ring-shaped DNA molecules containing a few genes. **3.** Because prokaryotic populations evolve rapidly in response to their environment, it is likely that bacteria from endospores that formed 40 years ago would already be adapted to the polluted conditions. Hence, at least initially, these bacteria would probably grow better than bacteria from endospores that formed 150 years ago, when the lake was not polluted.

Concept Check 27.2

1. Prokaryotes have extremely large population sizes, in part because they have short generation times. The large number of individuals in prokaryotic populations makes it likely that in each generation there will be thousands of individuals that have new mutations at any particular gene, thereby adding considerable genetic diversity to the population. **2.** In transformation, naked, foreign DNA from the environment is taken up by a bacterial cell. In transduction, phages carry bacterial genes from one bacterial cell to another. In conjugation, a bacterial cell directly transfers plasmid or chromosomal DNA to another cell via a mating bridge that temporarily connects the two cells. **3.** Yes. Genes for antibiotic resistance could be transferred (by transformation, transduction, or conjugation) from the nonpathogenic bacterium to a pathogenic bacterium; this could make the pathogen an even greater threat to human health. In general, transformation, transduction, and conjugation tend to increase the spread of resistance genes.

Concept Check 27.3

1. A phototroph derives its energy from light, while a chemotroph gets its energy from chemical sources. An autotroph derives its carbon from inorganic sources (often CO_2), while a heterotroph gets its carbon from organic sources. Thus, there are four nutritional modes: photoautotrophic, photoheterotrophic (unique to prokaryotes), chemoautotrophic (unique to prokaryotes), and chemoheterotrophic. **2.** Chemoheterotrophy; the bacterium must rely on chemical sources of energy, since it is not exposed to light, and it must be a heterotroph if it requires an organic source of carbon rather than CO_2 (or another inorganic source, like bicarbonate). **3.** If humans could fix nitrogen, we could build proteins using atmospheric N_2 and hence would not need to eat high-protein foods such as meat or fish. Our diet would, however, need to include a source of carbon, along with minerals and water. Thus, a typical meal might consist of carbohydrates as a carbon source, along with fruits and vegetables to provide essential minerals (and additional carbon).

Concept Check 27.4

1. Before molecular systematics, taxonomists classified prokaryotes according to phenotypic characters that did not clarify evolutionary relationships. Molecular comparisons—of DNA in particular—indicate key divergences in prokaryotic lineages. **2.** By not requiring that organisms be cultured in the laboratory, genetic prospecting has revealed an immense diversity of previously unknown prokaryotic species. Over time, the ongoing discovery of new species by genetic prospecting is likely to alter our understanding of prokaryotic phylogeny greatly. **3.** At present, all known methanogens are archaea in the clade Euryarchaeota; this suggests that this unique metabolic pathway arose in ancestral species within Euryarchaeota. Since Bacteria and Archaea have been separate evolutionary lineages for billions of years, the discovery of a methanogen from the domain Bacteria would suggest that adaptations that enabled the use of CO_2 to oxidize H_2 evolved at least twice—once in Archaea (within Euryarchaeota) and once in Bacteria.

Concept Check 27.5

1. Although prokaryotes are small, their large numbers and metabolic abilities enable them to play key roles in ecosystems by decomposing wastes, recycling chemicals, and affecting the concentrations of nutrients available to other organisms. **2.** *Bacteroides thetaiotaomicron*, which lives inside the human intestine, benefits by obtaining nutrients from the digestive system and by receiving protection from competing bacteria from host-produced antimicrobial compounds to which it is not sensitive. The human host benefits because the bacterium manufactures carbohydrates, vitamins, and other nutrients. **3.** Some of the many different species of prokaryotes that live in the human gut compete with one another for resources (in the food you eat). Because different prokaryotic species have different adaptations, a change in diet may alter which species can grow most rapidly, thus altering species abundance.

Concept Check 27.6

1. Sample answers: eating fermented foods such as yogurt, sourdough bread, or cheese; receiving clean water from sewage treatment; taking medicines produced by bacteria. **2.** No. If the poison is secreted as an exotoxin, live bacteria could be transmitted to another person. But the same is true if the poison is an endotoxin—only in this case, the live bacteria that are transmitted may be descendants of the (now-dead) bacteria that produced the poison. **3.** Strain K-12 may have lost genes by deletion mutations. A phylogenetic analysis would help distinguish between these hypotheses—if some of the genes found in O157:H7 but not in K-12 are present in the common ancestor of the two strains, that would suggest that strain K-12 lost these genes over the course of its evolution.

1. e **2.** a **3.** d **4.** d **5.** b **6.** a
8. (a)

(b) Some *Rhizobium* strains are much more effective at promoting plant growth than are other *Rhizobium* strains; the most ineffective strains have little positive effect (plant growth with these strains differs little from plant growth in the absence of *Rhizobium*). The ineffective strains may transfer relatively little nitrogen to their plant host, hence limiting plant growth.

CHAPTER 28

Figure Questions

Figure 28.10 Merozoites are produced by the asexual (mitotic) cell division of haploid sporozoites; similarly, gametocytes are produced by the asexual cell division of merozoites. Hence, it is likely that individuals in these three stages have the same complement of genes and that morphological differences between them result from changes in gene expression. **Figure 28.22** The following stage should be circled: step 6, where a mature cell undergoes mitosis and forms four or more daughter cells. In step 7, the zoospores eventually grow into mature haploid cells, but they do not produce new daughter cells. Likewise, in step 2, a mature cell develops into a gamete, but it does not produce new daughter cells. **Figure 28.23** If the assumption is correct, then their results indicate that the DHFR-TS gene fusion may be a derived trait shared by members of four supergroups of eukaryotes (Excavata, Chromalveolata, Rhizaria, and Archaeplastida). However, if the assumption is not correct, the presence or absence of the gene fusion may tell little about phylogenetic history. For example, if the genes fused multiple times, groups could share the trait because of convergent evolution rather than common descent. If the genes were secondarily split, a group with such a split could be placed (incorrectly) in Unikonta rather than its correct placement in one of the other four supergroups.

Concept Check 28.1

1. Sample response: Protists include unicellular, colonial, and multicellular organisms; photoautotrophs, heterotrophs, and mixotrophs; species that reproduce asexually, sexually, or both ways; and organisms with diverse physical forms and adaptations. **2.** Strong evidence shows that eukaryotes acquired mitochondria after an early eukaryote first engulfed and then formed an endosymbiotic association with an alpha proteobacterium. Similarly, chloroplasts in red and green algae appear to have descended from a photosynthetic cyanobacterium that was engulfed by an ancient heterotrophic eukaryote. Secondary endosymbiosis also played an important role: Various protist lineages acquired plastids by engulfing unicellular red or green algae. **3.** The modified tree would look as follows:

Concept Check 28.2

1. Their mitochondria do not have an electron transport chain and so cannot function in aerobic respiration. **2.** Since the unknown protist is more closely related to diplomonads than to euglenids, it must have evolved after the diplomonads and parabasalids diverged from the euglenozoans. In addition, since the unknown species has fully functional mitochondria—yet both diplomonads and parabasalids do not—it is likely that the unknown species evolved *before* the last common ancestor of the diplomonads and parabasalids.

Concept Check 28.3

1. Some DNA data indicate that Chromalveolata is a monophyletic group, but other DNA data fail to support this result. In support of monophyly, for many species in the group, the structure of their plastids and the sequence of their plastid DNA suggest that the group originated by a secondary endosymbiosis event (in which a red alga was engulfed). However, other species in the group lack plastids entirely, making the secondary endosymbiosis hypothesis difficult to test. **2.** Figure 13.6b. Algae and plants with alternation of generations have a multicellular haploid stage *and* a multicellular diploid stage. In the other two life cycles, either the haploid stage or the diploid stage is unicellular. **3.** The plastid DNA would likely be more similar to the chromosomal DNA of cyanobacteria based on the well-supported hypothesis that eukaryotic plastids (such as those found in the eukaryotic groups listed) originated by an endosymbiosis event in which a eukaryote engulfed a cyanobacterium. If the plastid is derived from the cyanobacterium, its DNA would be derived from the bacterial DNA.

Concept Check 28.4

1. Because foram tests are hardened with calcium carbonate, they form long-lasting fossils in marine sediments and sedimentary rocks. **2.** Convergent evolution. The different organisms have come to display similar morphological adaptations over time owing to their similar lifestyles.

Concept Check 28.5

1. Many red algae contain an accessory pigment called phycoerythrin, which gives them a reddish color and allows them to carry out photosynthesis in relatively deep coastal water. Also unlike brown algae, red algae have no flagellated stages in their life cycle and must depend on water currents to bring gametes together for fertilization. **2.** *Ulva*'s thallus contains many cells and is differentiated into leaflike blades and a rootlike holdfast. *Caulerpa*'s thallus is composed of multinucleate filaments without cross-walls, so it is essentially one large cell. **3.** Red algae have no flagellated stages in their life cycle and hence must depend on water currents to bring their gametes together. This feature of their biology might increase the difficulty of reproducing on land. In contrast, the gametes of green algae are flagellated, making it possible for them to swim in thin films of water. In addition, a variety of green algae contain compounds in their cytoplasm, cell wall, or zygote coat that protect against intense sunlight and other terrestrial conditions. Such compounds may have increased the chance that descendants of green algae could survive on land.

Concept Check 28.6

1. Amoebozoans have lobe-shaped pseudopodia, whereas forams have threadlike pseudopodia. **2.** Slime molds are fungus-like in that they produce fruiting bodies that aid in the dispersal of spores, and they are animal-like in that they are motile and ingest food. However, slime molds are more closely related to gymnamoebas and entamoebas than to fungi or animals. **3.** Support. Unikonts lack the unique cytoskeletal features shared by many excavates (see Concept 28.2). Thus, if the unikonts were the first group of eukaryotes to diverge from other eukaryotes (as shown in Figure 28.23), it would be unlikely that the eukaryote common ancestor had the cytoskeletal features found today in many excavates. Such a result would strengthen the case that many excavates share cytoskeletal features because they are members of a monophyletic group, the Excavata.

Concept Check 28.7

1. Because photosynthetic protists lie at the base of aquatic food webs, many aquatic organisms depend on them for food, either directly or indirectly. (In addition, a substantial percentage of the oxygen produced in photosynthesis on Earth is made by photosynthetic protists.) **2.** Protists form mutualistic and parasitic associations with other organisms. Examples include parabasalids that form a mutualistic symbiosis with termites, as well as the oomycete *Phytophthora ramorum*, a parasite of oak trees. **3.** Corals depend on their dinoflagellate symbionts for nourishment, so coral bleaching would be expected to cause the corals to die. As the corals die, less food will be available for fishes and other species that eat coral. As a result, populations of these species may decline, and that, in turn, might cause populations of their predators to decline.

Self-Quiz
1. d **2.** b **3.** c **4.** d **5.** e **6.** d
7.

Pathogens that share a relatively recent common ancestor with humans should also share metabolic and structural characteristics with humans. Because drugs target the pathogen's metabolism or structure, developing drugs that harm the pathogen but not the patient should be most difficult for pathogens with whom we share the most recent evolutionary history. Working backward in time, we can use the phylogenetic tree to determine the order in which humans shared a common ancestor with pathogens in different taxa. This process leads to the prediction that it should be hardest to develop drugs to combat animal pathogens, followed by choanoflagellate pathogens, fungal and nucleariid pathogens, amoebozoans, other protists, and finally prokaryotes.

CHAPTER 29

Figure Questions
Figure 29.7

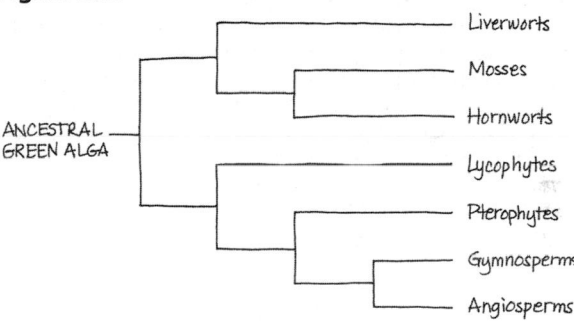

Figure 29.10 Because the moss reduces nitrogen loss from the ecosystem, species that typically colonize the soils after the moss probably experience higher soil nitrogen levels than they otherwise would—an effect that may benefit these species, since nitrogen is an essential nutrient that often is in short supply. **Figure 29.13** A fern that had wind-dispersed sperm would not require water for fertilization, thus removing a difficulty that ferns face when they live in arid environments. The fern would also be under strong selection to produce sperm above ground (as opposed to the current situation, where some fern gametophytes are located below ground).

Concept Check 29.1

1. Land plants share some key traits only with charophytes: rosette cellulose-synthesizing complexes, presence of peroxisome enzymes, similarity in sperm structure, and the formation of a phragmoplast in cell division. Comparisons of nuclear and chloroplast genes also point to a common ancestry. **2.** Spore walls toughened by sporopollenin (protects against harsh environmental conditions); multicellular, dependent embryos (provides nutrients and protection to the developing embryo); cuticle (reduces water loss). **3.** The multicellular diploid stage of the life cycle would not reproduce sexually. Instead, both males and females would produce haploid spores by meiosis. These spores would give rise to multicellular male and female haploid stages—a major change from the single-celled haploid stages (sperm and eggs) that we actually have. The multicellular haploid stages would produce gametes and reproduce sexually. An individual at the multicellular haploid stage of the human life cycle might look like us, or it might look completely different.

Concept Check 29.2

1. Bryophytes do not have an extensive vascular transport system, and their life cycle is dominated by gametophytes rather than sporophytes. **2.** Answers may include the following: Large surface area of protonema enhances absorption of water and minerals; the vase-shaped archegonia protect eggs during fertilization and transport nutrients to the embryos via placental transfer cells; the stalk-like seta conducts nutrients from the gametophyte to the capsule, where spores are produced; the peristome enables gradual spore discharge; stomata enable CO_2/O_2 exchange while minimizing water loss; lightweight spores are readily dispersed by wind.

3.

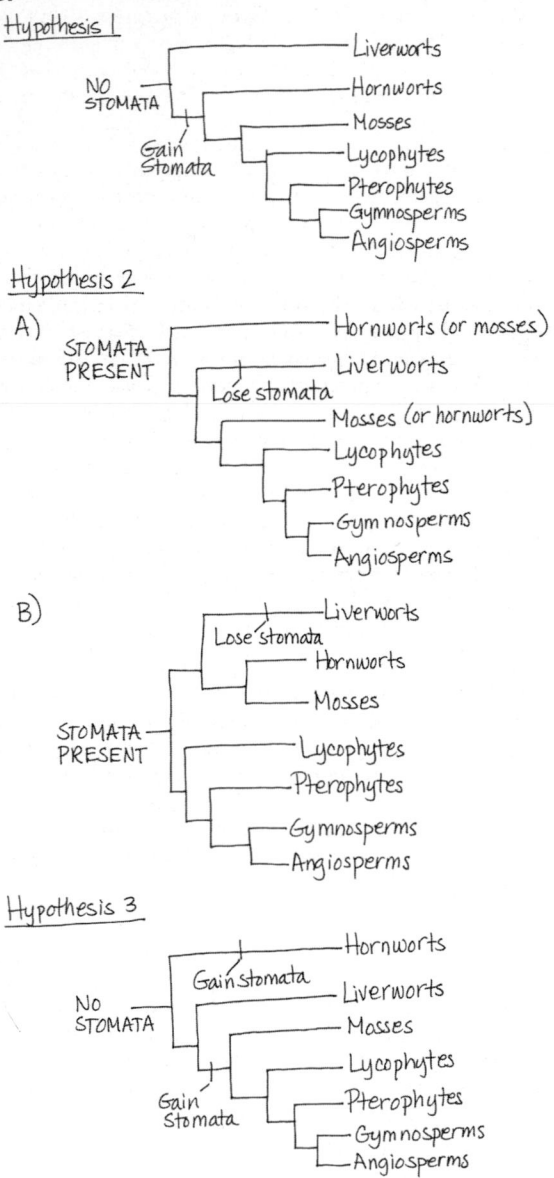

Concept Check 29.3

1. Lycophytes have microphylls, whereas seed plants and pterophytes (ferns and their relatives) have megaphylls. Pterophytes and seed plants also share other traits not found in lycophytes, such as overtopping growth and the initiation of new root branches at various points along the length of an existing root. **2.** Both seedless vascular plants and bryophytes have flagellated sperm that require moisture for fertilization; this shared similarity poses challenges for these species in arid regions. With respect to key differences, seedless vascular plants have lignified, well-developed vascular tissue, a trait that enables the sporophyte to grow tall and that has transformed life on Earth (via the formation of forests). Seedless vascular plants also have true leaves and roots, which, when compared to bryophytes, provides increased surface area for photosynthesis and improves their ability to extract nutrients from soil. **3.** If lycophytes and pterophytes formed a clade, the traits shared by pterophytes and seed plants might have been present in the common ancestor of all vascular plants, but lost in the lycophytes. Alternatively, the common ancestor of all vascular plants may have lacked the traits shared by pterophytes and seed plants; in this case, pterophytes and seed plants would share these traits as a result of convergent evolution.

Self-Quiz

1. b **2.** e **3.** a **4.** d **5.** c **6.** b **7.** c
8. a. diploid; b. haploid; c. haploid; d. diploid; e. haploid
9. Based on our current understanding of the evolution of major plant groups, the phylogeny has the four branch points shown here:

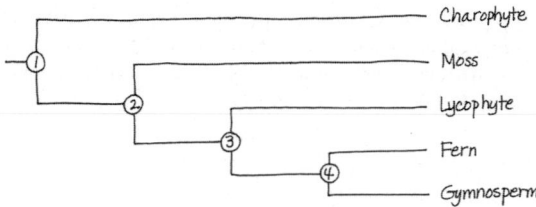

Derived characters unique to the charophyte and land plant clade (indicated by branch point 1) include rosette cellulose-synthesizing complexes, peroxisome enzymes, flagellated sperm structure, and a phragmoplast. Derived characters unique to the land plant clade (branch point 2) include apical meristems, alternation of generations, walled spores produced in sporangia, and multicellular gametangia. Derived characters unique to the vascular plant clade (branch point 3) include life cycles with dominant sporophytes, complex vascular systems (xylem and phloem), and well-developed roots and leaves. Derived characters unique to the pterophyte and seed plant clade (branch point 4) include megaphylls and overtopping growth.

CHAPTER 30

Figure Questions

Figure 30.3 Three: (1) the current sporophyte (cells of ploidy $2n$, found in the integument, or seed coat); (2) the female gametophyte (cells of ploidy n, found in the food supply); and (3) the sporophyte of the next generation (cells of ploidy $2n$, found in the embryo). **Figure 30.12** No. The branching order shown could still be correct if *Amborella* and other early angiosperms had originated prior to 150 million years ago but angiosperm fossils of that age had not yet been discovered. In such a situation, the 140-million-year-old date for the origin of the angiosperms shown on the phylogeny would be incorrect. **Figure 30.14** This study establishes a correlation between the type of floral symmetry and the rate of plant speciation—but it is possible that floral symmetry is correlated with another factor that was the actual cause of the observed results. Note, however, that floral symmetry was associated with increased speciation rates in a variety of different plant lineages. This suggests—but does not establish—that differences in floral symmetry cause differences in speciation rates. In general, strong evidence for causation can come from controlled, manipulative experiments, but such experiments are usually not possible for studies of past evolutionary events.

Concept Check 30.1

1. To have any chance of reaching the eggs, the flagellated sperm of seedless vascular plants must swim through a film of water, usually over a distance of no more than a few centimeters. In contrast, the sperm of seed plants do not require water because they are produced within pollen grains that can be transported long distances by wind or by animal pollinators. Although flagellated in some species, the sperm of seed plants do not require mobility because pollen tubes convey them from the point at which the pollen grain is deposited (near the ovules) directly to the eggs. **2.** The reduced gametophytes of seed plants are nurtured by sporophytes and protected from stress, such as drought conditions and UV radiation. Pollen grains have tough protective walls. Seeds have one or two layers of protective tissue, the seed coat, that improve survival by providing more protection from environmental stresses than do the walls of spores. Seeds also contain a stored supply of food, which enables seeds to live longer than spores and provides developing embryos with nourishment for growth. **3.** If seed plants were homosporous, only one type of spore would be produced—as opposed to the actual situation in which microspores give rise to sperm cells within pollen grains, and megaspores give rise to eggs within ovules. Thus, if structures like pollen grains and seeds were produced, they would arise in a very different way from how they now are formed.

Concept Check 30.2

1. Although gymnosperms are similar in not having their seeds enclosed in ovaries and fruits, their seed-bearing structures vary greatly. For instance, cycads have large cones, whereas some gymnosperms, such as *Ginkgo* and *Gnetum*, have small cones that look somewhat like berries, even though they are not fruits. Leaf shape also varies greatly, from the needles of many conifers to the palmlike leaves of cycads to *Gnetum* leaves that look like those of flowering plants. **2.** The life cycle illustrates heterospory, as ovulate cones produce megaspores and pollen cones produce microspores. The reduced gametophytes are evident in the form of the microscopic pollen grains and the microscopic female gametophyte within the megaspore. The egg is shown developing within an ovule, and a pollen tube is shown conveying the sperm. The figure also shows the protective and nutritive features of a seed. **3.** No. Fossil evidence indicates that gymnosperms originated at least 305 million years ago, but this does not mean that angiosperms are that old—only that the most recent common ancestor of gymnosperms and angiosperms must be that old.

Concept Check 30.3

1. In the oak's life cycle, the tree (the sporophyte) produces flowers, which contain gametophytes in pollen grains and ovules; the eggs in ovules are fertilized; the mature ovaries develop into dry fruits called acorns. We can view the oak's life cycle as starting when the acorn seeds germinate, resulting in embryos giving rise to seedlings and finally to mature trees, which produce flowers—and then more acorns. **2.** Pine cones and flowers both have sporophylls, modified leaves that produce spores. Pine trees have separate pollen cones (with pollen grains) and ovulate cones (with ovules inside cone scales). In flowers, pollen grains are produced by the anthers of stamens, and ovules are within the ovaries of carpels. Unlike pine cones, many flowers produce both pollen and ovules. **3.** Such a discovery would remove support for the idea, based on 125-million-year-old *Archaefructus sinensis* fossils, that the earliest angiosperms may have been herbaceous, aquatic plants.

Concept Check 30.4

1. Because extinction is irreversible, it decreases the total diversity of plants, many of which may have brought important benefits to humans. **2.** A detailed phylogeny of the seed plants would identify many different monophyletic groups of seed plants. Using this phylogeny, researchers could look for clades that contained species in which medicinally useful compounds had already been discovered. Identification of such clades would allow researchers to concentrate their search for new medicinal compounds among clade members—as opposed to searching for new compounds in species that were selected at random from the more than 250,000 existing species of seed plants.

Self-Quiz

1. d **2.** a **3.** b **4.** a **5.** d
6.

8. (a)

(b) The phylogeny indicates that basal angiosperms differed from other angiosperms in terms of the number of cells in female gametophytes and the ploidy of the endosperm. The ancestral state of the angiosperms cannot be determined from these data alone. It is possible that the common ancestor of angiosperms had seven-celled female gametophytes and triploid endosperm and hence that the eight-celled and four-celled conditions found in basal angiosperms represent derived traits for those lineages. Alternatively, either the eight-celled or four-celled condition may represent the ancestral state.

CHAPTER 31

Figure Questions

Figure 31.2 DNA from each of these mushrooms would be identical if each mushroom is part of a single hyphal network, as is likely. **Figure 31.16** One or both of the following would apply to each species: DNA analyses would reveal that it is a member of the ascomycetes clade, or aspects of its sexual life cycle would indicate that it is an ascomycete (for example, it would produce asci and ascospores). **Figure 31.21** Two possible controls would be E−P− and E+P−. Results from an E−P− control could be compared with results from the E−P+ experiment, and results from an E+P− control could be compared with results from the E+P+ experiment; together, these two comparisons would indicate whether the addition of the pathogen causes an increase in leaf mortality. Results from an E−P− experiment could also be compared with results from the second control (E+P−) to determine whether adding the endophytes has a negative effect on the plant.

Concept Check 31.1

1. Both a fungus and a human are heterotrophs. Many fungi digest their food externally by secreting enzymes into the food and then absorbing the small molecules that result from digestion. Other fungi absorb such small molecules directly from their environment. In contrast, humans (and most other animals) ingest relatively large pieces of food and digest the food within their bodies. **2.** The ancestors of such a mutualist most likely secreted powerful enzymes to digest the body of their insect host. Since such enzymes would harm a living host, it is likely that the mutualist would not produce such enzymes or would restrict their secretion and use.

Concept Check 31.2

1. The majority of the fungal life cycle is spent in the haploid stage, whereas the majority of the human life cycle is spent in the diploid stage. **2.** The two mushrooms might be reproductive structures of the same mycelium (the same organism). Or they might be parts of two separate organisms that have arisen from a single parent organism through asexual reproduction and thus carry the same genetic information.

Concept Check 31.3

1. DNA evidence indicates that fungi, animals, and their protistan relatives form a clade, the opisthokonts. Furthermore, an early-diverging fungal lineage, the chytrids, have posterior flagella, as do most other opisthokonts. This suggests that other fungal lineages lost their flagella after diverging from chytrids. **2.** This indicates that fungi had already established mutualistic relationships with plants by the date the fossils of the earliest vascular plants had formed. **3.** Fungi are heterotrophs. Prior to the colonization of land by plants, terrestrial fungi could have lived only where other organisms (or their remains) were present and provided a source of food. Thus, if fungi had colonized land before plants, they could have fed on any prokaryotes or protists that lived on land or by the water's edge—but not on the plants or animals on which many fungi feed today.

Concept Check 31.4

1. Flagellated spores **2.** Possible answers include the following: In zygomycetes, the sturdy, thick-walled zygosporangium can withstand harsh conditions and then undergo karyogamy and meiosis when the environment is favorable for reproduction. In glomeromycetes, the hyphae have a specialized morphology that enables the fungi to form arbuscular mycorrhizae with plant roots. In ascomycetes, the asexual spores (conidia) are often produced in chains or clusters at the tips of conidiophores, where they are easily dispersed by wind. The often cup-shaped ascocarps house the sexual spore-forming asci. In basidiomycetes, the basidiocarp supports and protects a large surface area of basidia, from which spores are dispersed. **3.** Such a change to the life cycle of an ascomycete would reduce the number and genetic diversity of ascospores that result from a mating event. Ascospore number would drop because a mating event would lead to the formation of only one ascus. Ascospore genetic diversity would also drop because in ascomycetes, one mating event leads to the formation of asci by many different dikaryotic cells. As a result, genetic recombination and meiosis occurs independently many different times—which could not happen if only a single ascus was formed. It is also likely that if such an ascomycete formed an ascocarp, the shape of the ascocarp would differ considerably from that found in its close relatives.

Concept Check 31.5

1. A suitable environment for growth, retention of water and minerals, protection from intense sunlight, and protection from being eaten **2.** A hardy spore stage enables dispersal to host organisms through a variety of mechanisms; their ability to grow rapidly in a favorable new environment enables them to capitalize on the host's resources. **3.** Many different outcomes might have occurred. Organisms that currently form mutualisms with fungi might have gained the ability to perform the tasks currently done by their fungal partners, or they might have formed similar mutualisms with other organisms (such as bacteria). Alternatively, organisms that currently form mutualisms with fungi might be less effective at living in their present environments. For example, the colonization of land by plants might have been more difficult. And if plants did eventually colonize land without fungal mutualists, natural selection might have favored plants that formed more highly divided and extensive root systems (in part replacing mycorrhizae).

Self-Quiz

1. b **2.** c **3.** d **4.** e **5.** b **6.** a
8.

As indicated by the raw data and bar graph, grass plants with endophytes (E+) produced more new shoots and had greater biomass than did grass plants that lacked endophytes (E−). These differences were especially pronounced at the highest soil temperature, where E− grass plants produced no new shoots and had a biomass of zero (indicating they were dead).

CHAPTER 32

Figure Questions

Figure 32.3 As described in ❶ and ❷, choanoflagellates and a broad range of animals have collar cells. Since collar cells have never been observed in plants, fungi, or non-choanoflagellate protists, this suggests that choanoflagellates may be more closely related to animals than to other eukaryotes. If choanoflagellates are more closely related to animals than is any other group of eukaryotes, choanoflagellates and animals should share other traits that are not found in other eukaryotes. The data described in ❸ are consistent with this prediction. **Figure 32.6** The sea anemone embryos could be infused with a protein that can bind to β-catenin's DNA-binding site, thereby limiting the extent to which β-catenin activates the transcription of genes necessary for gastrulation. Such an experiment would provide an independent check of the results shown in step 4. **Figure 32.10** Ctenophora is the sister phylum in this figure, while Cnidaria is the sister phylum in Figure 32.11.

Concept Check 32.1

1. In most animals, the zygote undergoes cleavage, which leads to the formation of a blastula. Next, in gastrulation, one end of the embryo folds inward, producing layers of embryonic tissue. As the cells of these layers differentiate, a wide variety of animal forms result. Despite the diversity of animal forms, animal development is controlled by a similar set of *Hox* genes across a broad range of taxa. **2.** The imaginary plant would require tissues composed of cells that were analogous to the muscle and nerve cells found in animals: "muscle" tissue would be necessary for the plant to chase prey, and "nerve" tissue would be required for the plant to coordinate its movements when chasing prey. To digest captured prey, the plant would need to either secrete enzymes into one or more digestive cavities (which could be modified leaves, as in a Venus' flytrap), or secrete enzymes outside of its body and feed by absorption. To extract nutrients from the soil—yet be able to chase prey—the plant would need something other than fixed roots, perhaps retractable "roots" or a way to ingest soil. To conduct photosynthesis, the plant would require chloroplasts. Overall, such an imaginary plant would be very similar to an animal that had chloroplasts and retractable roots.

Concept Check 32.2

1. c, b, a, d **2.** We cannot infer whether animals originated before or after fungi. If correct, the date provided for the most recent common ancestor of fungi and animals would indicate that animals originated some time within the last billion years. The fossil record indicates that animals originated at least 565 million years ago. Thus, we could conclude only that animals originated some time between 565 million years ago and 1 billion years ago.

Concept Check 32.3

1. Grade-level characteristics are those that multiple lineages share regardless of evolutionary history. Some grade-level characteristics may have evolved multiple times independently. Features that unite clades are derived characteristics that originated in a common ancestor and were passed on to the various descendants. **2.** A snail has a spiral and determinate cleavage pattern; a human has radial, indeterminate cleavage. In a snail, the coelomic cavity is formed by splitting of mesoderm masses; in a human, the coelom forms from folds of archenteron. In a snail, the mouth forms from the blastopore; in a human, the anus develops from the blastopore. **3.** Most coelomate triploblasts have two openings to their digestive tract, a mouth and an anus. As such, their bodies have a structure that is analogous to that of a doughnut: The digestive tract (the hole of the doughnut) runs from the mouth to the anus and is surrounded by various tissues (the solid part of the doughnut). The doughnut analogy is most obvious at early stages of development (see Figure 32.9c).

Concept Check 32.4

1. Cnidarians possess true tissues, while sponges do not. Also unlike sponges, cnidarians exhibit body symmetry, though it is radial and not bilateral as in other animal phyla. **2.** The morphology-based tree divides Bilateria into two major clades: Deuterostomia and Protostomia. The molecular-based tree recognizes three major clades: Deuterostomia, Ecdysozoa, and Lophotrochozoa. **3.** Both statements could be correct. Figure 32.11 shows that the lineage leading to Deuterostomia was the first to diverge from the other two main bilaterian lineages (those leading to Lophotrochozoa and Ecdysozoa). By itself, however, this information does not indicate whether the most recent common ancestor of the Deuterostomia lived before or after the first arthropods. For example, the ancestors of Deuterostomia could have diverged from the ancestors of Lophotrochozoa and Ecdysozoa 570 million years ago; it could have then taken 35 million years for the clade Deuterostomia to originate, but only 10 million years for first Ecdysozoa and then the arthropod clades to originate.

Self-Quiz

1. a **2.** d **3.** b **4.** e **5.** c **6.** e

8.

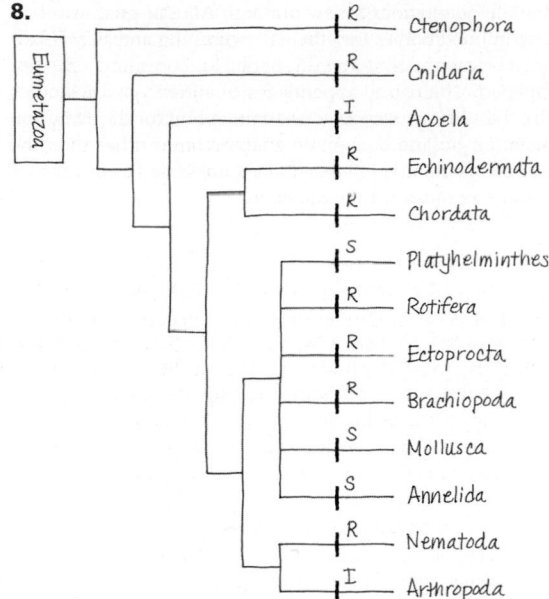

From the phylogeny, it appears that radial cleavage is the ancestral condition for eumetazoans. However, because relationships within Lophotrochozoa are not resolved, we cannot estimate the precise number of times that cleavage patterns have changed over the course of evolution. If, for example, Platyhelminthes, Mollusca, and Annelida form a clade, it would be reasonable to infer three cleavage pattern changes (one in Acoela, one in the ancestor of this hypothetical clade, and one in Arthropoda). Various other possible relationships among lophotrochozoans lead to other estimates.

CHAPTER 33

Figure Questions

Figure 33.8 Within a reproductive polyp, a cell that gives rise to a medusa would have to divide by meiosis. A resulting haploid cell would then divide repeatedly (by mitosis), forming a haploid medusa. Later, cells in the medusa's gonads would divide by mitosis, forming the haploid eggs and sperm. **Figure 33.11** Adding fertilizer to the water supply would probably increase the abundance of algae. This, in turn, might increase the abundance of both snails (which eat algae) and blood flukes (which require snails as an intermediate host). As a result, the occurrence of schistosomiasis might increase. **Figure 33.28** Such a result would be consistent with the *Ubx* and *abd-A Hox* genes having played a major role in the evolution of increased body segment diversity in arthropods. However, by itself, such a result would simply show that the presence of the *Ubx* and *abd-A Hox* genes was *correlated with* an increase in body segment diversity in arthropods; it would not provide direct experimental evidence that the acquisition of the *Ubx* and *adb-A* genes *caused* an increase in arthropod body segment diversity.

Concept Check 33.1

1. The flagella of choanocytes draw water through their collars, which trap food particles. The particles are engulfed by phagocytosis and digested, either by choanocytes or by amoebocytes. **2.** The collar cells of sponges (and other animals—see Chapter 32) bear a striking resemblance to a choanoflagellate cell. This suggests that the last common ancestor of animals and their protist sister group may have resembled a choanoflagellate. Nevertheless, mesomycetozoans could still be the sister group of animals. If this is the case, the lack of collar cells in mesomycetozoans would indicate that over time their structure evolved in ways that caused it to no longer resemble a choanoflagellate cell.

Concept Check 33.2

1. Both the polyp and the medusa are composed of an outer epidermis and an inner gastrodermis separated by a gelatinous layer, the mesoglea. The polyp is a cylindrical form that adheres to the substrate by its aboral end; the medusa is a flattened, mouth-down form that moves freely in the water. **2.** Cnidarian stinging cells (cnidocytes) function in defense and prey capture. They contain capsule-like organelles (cnidae), which in turn contain coiled threads. The threads either inject poison or stick to and entangle small prey. **3.** This

would suggest that the life cycle of basal cnidarians was probably dominated by the medusa stage. Over time, the polyp stage came to be increasingly important in some groups, such as Hydrozoa, which alternate between medusa and polyp stages, and Anthozoa, which lack the medusa stage entirely.

Concept Check 33.3

1. Tapeworms can absorb food from their environment and release ammonia into their environment through their body surface because their body is very flat, due in part to the lack of a coelom. **2.** The function of the foot reflects the locomotion required in each class. Gastropods use their foot as a holdfast or to move slowly on the substrate. In cephalopods, the foot functions as a siphon and tentacles. **3.** The inner tube is the alimentary canal, which runs the length of the body. The outer tube is the body wall. The two tubes are separated by the coelom. **4.** Many lophotrochozoans lack skeletons or other structures that could support their soft bodies against the force of gravity, making it difficult for them to live above the surface of the soil. Some species, such as ectoprocts (bryozoans), have a sturdy exoskeleton, but they are stationary and so would find it difficult to capture food on land. (Note that those lophotrochozoans that do live above the soil surface, such as slugs, have some form of hydrostatic skeleton.)

Concept Check 33.4

1. Nematodes lack body segments and a true coelom; annelids have both. **2.** Arthropod mouthparts are modified appendages, which are bilaterally paired. **3.** The arthropod exoskeleton, which had already evolved in the ocean, allowed terrestrial species to retain water and support their bodies on land. Wings allowed them to disperse quickly to new habitats and to find food and mates. The tracheal system allows for efficient gas exchange despite the presence of an exoskeleton. **4.** Yes. Under the traditional hypothesis, we would expect body segmentation to be controlled by similar *Hox* genes in annelids and arthropods. However, if annelids are in Lophotrochozoa and arthropods are in Ecdysozoa, body segmentation may have evolved independently in these two groups. In such a case, we might expect that different *Hox* genes would control the development of body segmentation in the two clades.

Concept Check 33.5

1. Each tube foot consists of an ampulla and a podium. When the ampulla squeezes, it forces water into the podium, which causes the podium to expand and contact the substrate. Adhesive chemicals are then secreted from the base of the podium, thereby attaching the podium to the substrate. **2.** These two organisms look very different from one another, but they share features found in all echinoderms, such as a water vascular system and tube feet. Hence, their shared characteristics probably result from homology, not analogy. **3.** Both insects and nematodes are members of Ecdysozoa, one of the three major clades of bilaterians. Therefore, a characteristic shared by *Drosophila* and *Caenorhabditis* may be informative for other members of their clade—but not necessarily for members of Deuterostomia. Instead, Figure 33.2 suggests that a species within Echinodermata or Chordata might be a more appropriate invertebrate model organism from which to draw inferences about humans and other vertebrates.

Self-Quiz

1. c **2.** a **3.** d **4.** e **5.** b **6.** e
7.

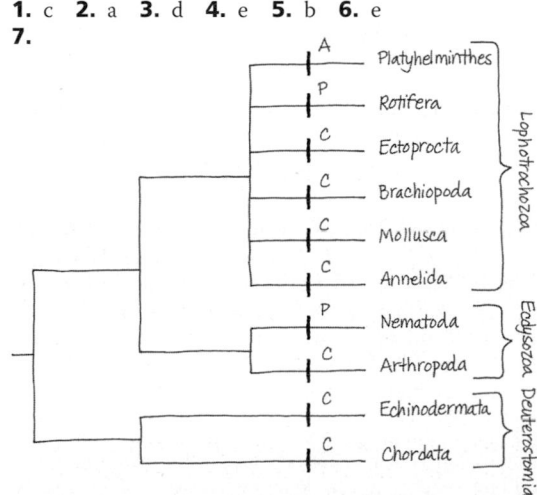

(a) Both phyla in Deuterostomia are coelomates, suggesting that their most recent common ancestor had a true coelom. Lophotrochozoa contains one phylum of acoelomates (Platyhelminthes), one phylum of pseudocoelomates (Rotifera), and four phyla of coelomates (Ectoprocta, Brachiopoda, Mollusca, Annelida); thus, we cannot from this information alone infer the condition of the most recent common ancestor shared by these phyla. Similarly, since Ecdysozoa contains one phylum of pseudocoelomates (Nematoda) and one phylum of coelomates (Arthropoda), we cannot infer whether their most recent common ancestor had a true coelom or not. (b) Depending on whether or not the last common ancestor of Bilateria had a true coelom, the presence of a true coelom has either been lost or gained multiple times during the evolutionary history of bilaterians. Thus, the presence of a true coelom appears to change over the course of evolution.

CHAPTER 34

Figure Questions

Figure 34.20 Amphibians must have originated some time between the date that the most recent common ancestor of *Hynerpeton* and later tetropods originated (380 mya) and the date of the earliest known fossils of amphibians (shown in the figure as 340 mya). **Figure 34.37** The phylogeny shows humans as the sister group to the genus *Pan*. This relationship is consistent with humans being placed in *Pan* along with its two living members, chimpanzees and bonobos. **Figure 34.43** It is not likely that these two sources of error significantly influenced the results. We can conclude this in part because the results were reproducible: similar sequences were found for mtDNA obtained from two different Neanderthal fossils and sequenced by two different research teams. In addition, the close relationship of the two Neanderthal mtDNA sequences to each other would not be expected if the fossil DNA had broken down considerably. Similarly, the fact that Europeans and other living humans formed a sister group to the Neanderthals, and that chimpanzees formed a sister group to the human/Neanderthal clade also would not be expected had the DNA broken down greatly—nor would these results be expected if the fossil DNA sequences were contaminated (for example, by DNA from microorganisms or from living humans).

Concept Check 34.1

1. As water passes through the slits, food particles are filtered from the water and transported to the digestive system. **2.** In humans, these characters are present only in the embryo. The notochord becomes disks between the vertebrae, the tail is almost completely lost, and the pharyngeal clefts develop into various adult structures. **3.** Not necessarily. It would be possible that the chordate common ancestor had this gene, which was then lost in the lancelet lineage and retained in other chordates. However, it would also be possible that the chordate common ancestor lacked this gene—this could occur if the gene originated after lancelets diverged from other chordates yet before tunicates diverged from other chordates.

Concept Check 34.2

1. Hagfishes have a head and skull made of cartilage, plus a small brain, sensory organs, and tooth-like structures. They have a neural crest, gill slits, and more extensive organ systems. In addition, hagfishes have slime glands that ward off predators and may repel competing scavengers. **2.** *Myllokunmingia*. Fossils of this organism provide evidence of ear capsules and eye capsules; these structures are part of the skull. Thus, *Myllokunmingia* is considered a craniate, as are humans. *Haikouella* did not have a skull. **3.** Such a finding suggests that early organisms with a head were favored by natural selection in several different evolutionary lineages. However, while a logical argument can be made that having a head was advantageous, fossils alone do not constitute proof.

Concept Check 34.3

1. Lampreys have a round, rasping mouth, which they use to attach to fish. Conodonts had two sets of mineralized dental elements, which may have been used to impale prey and cut it into smaller pieces. **2.** In armored jawless vertebrates, bone served as external armor that may have provided protection from predators. Some species also had mineralized mouthparts, which could be used for either predation or scavenging. Still others had mineralized fin rays, which may have enabled them to swim more rapidly and with greater steering control.

Concept Check 34.4

1. Both are gnathostomes and have jaws, four clusters of *Hox* genes, enlarged forebrains, and lateral line systems. Shark skeletons consist mainly of cartilage, whereas tuna have bony skeletons. Sharks also have a spiral valve. Tuna have an operculum and a swim bladder, as well as flexible rays supporting their fins. **2.** Aquatic gnathostomes have jaws (an adaptation for feeding)

and paired fins and a tail (adaptations for swimming). Aquatic gnathostomes also typically have streamlined bodies for efficient swimming and swim bladders or other mechanisms (such as oil storage in sharks) for buoyancy. **3.** Yes, that could have happened. The paired appendages of aquatic gnathostomes other than the lobe-fins could have served as a starting point for the evolution of limbs. The colonization of land by aquatic gnathostomes other than the lobe-fins might have been facilitated in lineages that possessed lungs, as that would have enabled those organisms to breathe air.

Concept Check 34.5

1. Tetrapods are thought to have originated about 360 million years ago when the fins of some lobe-fins evolved into the limbs of tetrapods. In addition to their four limbs—a key derived trait for which the group is named—other derived traits of tetrapods include a neck (consisting of vertebrae that separate the head from the rest of the body), a pelvic girdle that is fused to the backbone, and a lack of gill slits. **2.** Some fully aquatic species are paedomorphic, retaining larval features for life in water as adults. Species that live in dry environments may avoid dehydration by burrowing or living under moist leaves, and they protect their eggs with foam nests, viviparity, and other adaptations. **3.** Many amphibians spend part of their life cycle in aquatic environments and part on land. Thus, they may be exposed to a wide range of environmental problems, including water and air pollution and the loss or degradation of aquatic and/or terrestrial habitats. In addition, amphibians have highly permeable skin, providing relatively little protection from external conditions, and their eggs do not have a protective shell.

Concept Check 34.6

1. The amniotic egg provides protection to the embryo and allows the embryo to develop on land, eliminating the necessity of a watery environment for reproduction. Another key adaptation is rib cage ventilation, which improves the efficiency of air intake and may have allowed early amniotes to dispense with breathing through their skin. And not breathing through their skin allowed amniotes to develop relatively impermeable skin, thereby conserving water. **2.** Birds have weight-saving modifications, including the absence of teeth, a urinary bladder, and a second ovary in females. The wings and feathers are adaptations that facilitate flight, and so are efficient respiratory and circulatory systems that support a high metabolic rate. **3.**

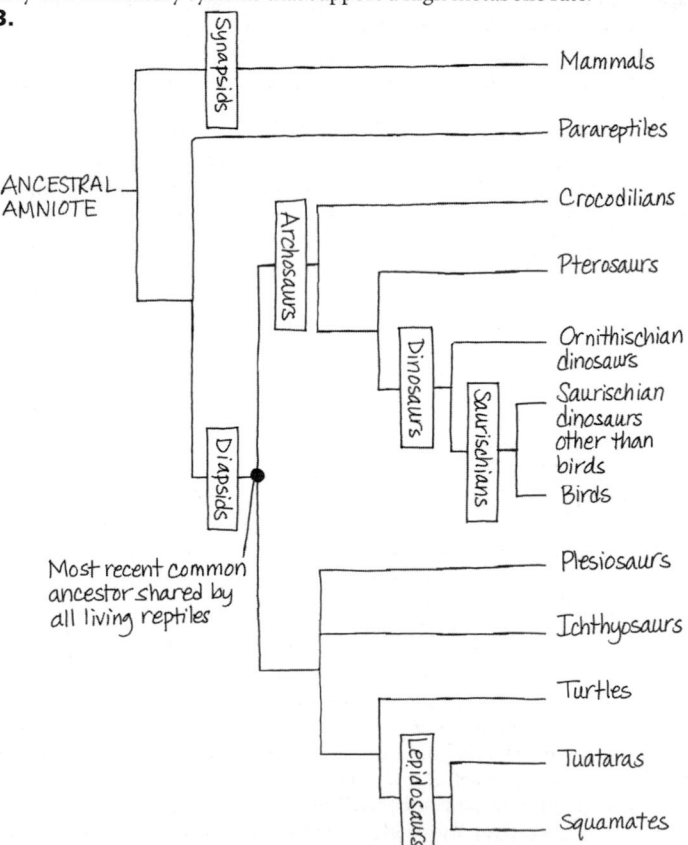

Under this convention, the reptiles would consist of all groups in Figure 34.24 except parareptiles and mammals.

Concept Check 34.7

1. Monotremes lay eggs. Marsupials give birth to very small live young that attach to a nipple in the mother's pouch, where they complete development. Eutherians give birth to more developed live young.   **2.** Hands and feet adapted for grasping, flat nails, large brain, forward-looking eyes on a flat face, parental care, moveable big toe and thumb.   **3.** Mammals are endothermic, enabling them to live in a wide range of habitats. Milk provides young with a balanced set of nutrients, and hair and a layer of fat under the skin help mammals retain heat. Mammals have differentiated teeth, enabling them to eat many different kinds of food. Mammals also have relatively large brains, and many species are capable learners. Following the mass extinction at the end of the Cretaceous period, the absence of large terrestrial dinosaurs may have opened many new ecological niches to mammals, promoting their adaptive radiation. Continental drift also isolated many groups of mammals from one another, promoting the formation of many new species.

Concept Check 34.8

1. Hominins are a clade within the ape clade that includes humans and all species more closely related to humans than other apes. The derived characters of hominins include bipedal locomotion and relatively larger brains.   **2.** In hominins, bipedal locomotion evolved long before large brain size. *Homo ergaster*, for example, was fully upright, bipedal, and as tall as modern humans, but its brain was significantly smaller than that of modern humans.   **3.** Yes, both can be correct. *Homo sapiens* may have established populations outside of Africa as early as 115,000 years ago, as indicated by the fossil record. However, those populations may have left few or no descendants today. Instead, all living humans may have descended from Africans that spread from Africa roughly 50,000 years ago, as indicated by genetic data.

Self-Quiz

1. e **2.** c **3.** a **4.** d **5.** b **6.** c **7.** c

9. (a) Because brain size tends to increase consistently in such lineages, we can conclude that natural selection favored the evolution of larger brains and hence that the benefits outweighed the costs. (b) As long as the benefits of brains that are large relative to body size are greater than the costs, large brains can evolve. Natural selection might favor the evolution of brains that are large relative to body size because such brains confer an advantage in obtaining mates and/or an advantage in survival.

(c) Adult mortality tends to be lower in birds with larger brains.

CHAPTER 35

Figure Questions

Figure 35.9 The finding might suggest that the tawny-colored trichomes deter the beetles by some means other than physically obstructing the beetles. Perhaps they contain a chemical that is harmful or distasteful to the beetles, or their color is a deterrent.   **Figure 35.17** Pith and cortex are defined, respectively, as ground tissue that is internal and external to vascular tissue. Since vascular bundles of monocot stems are scattered throughout the ground tissue, there is no clear distinction between internal and external relative to the vascular tissue.   **Figure 35.19** The vascular cambium produces growth that increases the diameter of a stem or root. The tissues that are exterior to the vascular cambium cannot keep pace with the growth because

their cells no longer divide. As a result, these tissues rupture.   **Figure 35.31** Every root epidermal cell would develop a root hair.

Concept Check 35.1

1. The vascular tissue system connects leaves and roots, allowing sugars to move from leaves to roots in the phloem and allowing water and minerals to move to the leaves in the xylem.   **2.** (a) large axillary buds; (b) petioles; (c) storage leaves; (d) storage roots   **3.** The dermal tissue system is the leaf's protective covering. The vascular tissue system consists of the transport tissues xylem and phloem. The ground tissue system performs metabolic functions such as photosynthesis.   **4.** Here are a few examples: The tubular, hollow structures of the tracheids and vessel elements of the xylem and the sieve plates in the sieve-tube elements of the phloem facilitate transport. Root hairs aid in absorption of water and nutrients. The cuticle in leaves and stems protects these structures from desiccation and pathogens. Leaf trichomes protect from herbivores and pathogens. Collenchyma and sclerenchyma cells have thick walls that provide support for plants.   **5.** To get sufficient energy from photosynthesis, we would need lots of surface area exposed to the sun. This large surface-to-volume ratio, however, would create a new problem—evaporative water loss. We would have to be permanently connected to a water source—the soil, also our source of minerals. In short, we would probably look and behave very much like plants.

Concept Check 35.2

1. Primary growth arises from apical meristems and involves production and elongation of organs. Secondary growth arises from lateral meristems and adds to the girth of roots and stems.   **2.** Your dividing cells are normally limited in the types of cells they can form. In contrast, the products of cell division in a plant meristem can differentiate into all the types of plant cells.   **3.** The largest, oldest leaves would be lowest on the shoot. Since they would probably be heavily shaded, they would not photosynthesize much regardless of their size.   **4.** No, the radish roots will probably be smaller at the end of the second year because the food stored in the root will be used to produce flowers, fruits, and seeds.

Concept Check 35.3

1. Lateral roots emerge from the root's interior (from the pericycle), pushing through cortical and epidermal cells. In contrast, shoot branches arise on the exterior of a shoot (from axillary buds).   **2.** In roots, primary growth occurs in three successive stages, moving away from the tip of the root: the zones of cell division, elongation, and differentiation. In shoots, it occurs at the tip of apical buds, with leaf primordia arising along the sides of an apical meristem. Most growth in length occurs in older internodes below the shoot tip.   **3.** Grazing animals that crop plants close to the ground have more of a detrimental effect on eudicots than on monocots because the removal of the lowest axillary buds prevents the eudicot from recovering. In contrast, the underground stems of grasses and the intercalary meristems of their leaves are less affected by grazing. Thus, the presence of grazing animals selects for the survival of grasses.   **4.** No. Because vertically oriented leaves can capture light equally on both sides of the leaf, you would expect them to have mesophyll cells that are not differentiated into palisade and spongy layers. This is typically the case. Also, vertical leaves usually have stomata on both leaf surfaces.

Concept Check 35.4

1. The sign will still be 2 m above the ground because this part of the tree is no longer growing in length (primary growth); it is now growing only in thickness (secondary growth).   **2.** Stomata must be able to close because evaporation is much more intensive from leaves than from the trunks of woody trees as a result of the higher surface-to-volume ratio in leaves.   **3.** The growth rings of a tree from the tropics would be difficult to discern unless the tree came from an area that had pronounced wet and dry seasons.   **4.** Girdling removes an entire ring of secondary phloem (part of the bark), completely preventing transport of sugars and starches from the shoots to the roots.

Concept Check 35.5

1. *Arabidopsis* is a small, easy-to-grow plant with a small genome and a short generation time.   **2.** Differential gene expression **3.** In *fass* mutants, the arrangement of microtubules is disrupted so that the preprophase band does not form. This results in random planes of cell division, rather than the ordered planes of division that normally occur. Disruption of microtubule organization also prevents the alignment of cellulose microfibrils that sets the plane of cell elongation. Because of this randomness, directional growth is disrupted, and the plant becomes stubby. **4.** In theory, tepals could arise if *B* gene activity was present in all three of the outer whorls of the flower.

Self-Quiz
1. d **2.** c **3.** c **4.** d **5.** a **6.** e **7.** d **8.** d **9.** b **10.** b
11.

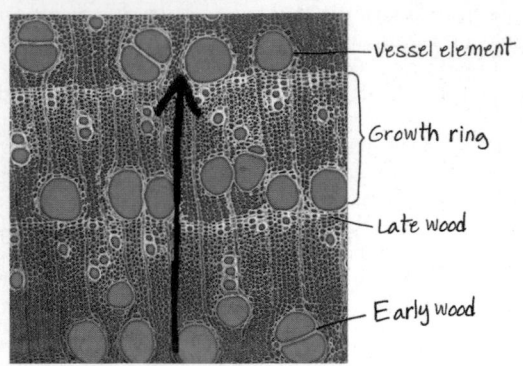

CHAPTER 36

Figure Questions
Figure 36.3 The leaves are being produced in a counterclockwise spiral.
Figure 36.4 A higher leaf area index will not necessarily increase photosynthesis because of upper leaves shading lower leaves. **Figure 36.12** The Casparian strip blocks water and minerals from moving between endodermal cells or moving around an endodermal cell via the cell's wall. Therefore, water and minerals must pass through an endodermal cell's plasma membrane. **Figure 36.21** Because the xylem is under negative pressure (tension), an isolated stylet inserted into a tracheid or vessel element would probably introduce air into the cell. No xylem sap would exude unless pressure was predominant. **Figure 36.22** Such a finding (although not considered likely) would cast doubts on the interpretation of the experiment. If the small fluorescent molecule was cleaved off the larger molecular probe, this small molecule could move through the plasmodesmata without them being dilated.

Concept Check 36.1
1. Vascular plants must transport minerals and water absorbed by the root to all the other parts of the plant. They must also transport sugars from sites of production to sites of use. **2.** Many features of plant architecture affect self-shading, including leaf arrangement, leaf orientation, and leaf area index. **3.** The fungicide may kill the mycorrhizal fungi that help the plants absorb phosphate and other minerals. **4.** Increased stem elongation would raise the plant's upper leaves. Erect leaves and reduced lateral branching would make the plant less subject to shading by the encroaching neighbors. **5.** As described in Chapter 35, pruning the shoot tips will end their apical dominance, allowing axillary buds to grow into lateral shoots (branches). This branching will produce a bushier plant with a higher leaf area index.

Concept Check 36.2
1. The cell's ψ_P is 0.7 MPa. In a solution with a ψ of -0.4 MPa, the cell's ψ_P at equilibrium would be 0.3 MPa. **2.** The cells would still adjust to changes in their osmotic environment, but their responses would be slower. Although aquaporins do not affect the water potential gradient across membranes, they allow for more rapid osmotic adjustments. **3.** If tracheids and vessel elements were living cells, their cytoplasm would impede water movement, preventing rapid long-distance transport. **4.** The protoplasts would burst. Because the cytoplasm has many dissolved solutes, water would enter the protoplast continuously without reaching equilibrium. (When present, the cell wall prevents rupturing by excessive expansion of the protoplast.)

Concept Check 36.3
1. Because water-conducting xylem cells are dead at maturity and form essentially hollow tubes, they offer little resistance to water flow, and their thick walls prevent the cells from collapsing from the negative pressure inside. **2.** At dawn, a drop is exuded because the xylem is under positive pressure due to root pressure. At noon, the xylem is under negative pressure potential due to transpiration and the root pressure cannot keep pace with the increased rate of transpiration. **3.** The en-

dodermis regulates the passage of water-soluble solutes by requiring all such molecules to cross a selectively permeable membrane. Presumably the inhibitor never reaches the plant's photosynthetic cells. **4.** Perhaps greater root mass helps compensate for the lower water permeability of the plasma membranes.

Concept Check 36.4
1. Stomatal aperture is controlled by drought, light, CO_2 concentrations, a circadian rhythm, and the plant hormone abscisic acid. **2.** The activation of the proton pump of stomatal cells would cause the guard cells to take up K^+. The increased turgor of the guard cells would lock the stomata open and lead to extreme evaporation from the leaf. **3.** After the flowers are cut, transpiration from any leaves and from the petals (which are modified leaves) will continue to draw water up the xylem. If cut flowers are transferred directly to a vase, air pockets in xylem vessels prevent delivery of water from the vase to the flowers. Cutting stems again underwater, a few centimeters from the original cut, will sever the xylem above the air pocket. The water droplets prevent another air pocket from forming while placing the flowers in a vase.

Concept Check 36.5
1. In both cases, the long-distance transport is a bulk flow driven by a pressure difference at opposite ends of tubes. Pressure is generated at the source end of a sieve tube by the loading of sugar and resulting osmotic flow of water into the phloem, and this pressure *pushes* sap from the source end to the sink end of the tube. In contrast, transpiration generates a negative pressure potential (tension) as a force that *pulls* the ascent of xylem sap. **2.** The main sources are fully grown leaves (by photosynthesis) and fully developed storage organs (by breakdown of starch). Roots, buds, stems, expanding leaves, and fruits are powerful sinks because they are actively growing. A storage organ may be a sink in the summer when accumulating carbohydrates, but a source in the spring when breaking down starch into sugar for growing shoot tips. **3.** Positive pressure, whether it be in the xylem when root pressure predominates, or in the sieve-tube elements of the phloem, requires active transport. Most long-distance transport in the xylem depends on bulk flow driven by negative pressure potential generated ultimately by the evaporation of water from the leaf and does not require living cells. **4.** The spiral slash prevents optimal bulk flow of the phloem sap to the root sinks. Therefore, more phloem sap can move from the source leaves to the fruit sinks, making them sweeter.

Concept Check 36.6
1. Voltage between cells, cytoplasmic pH, cytoplasmic calcium, and movement proteins all affect symplastic communication, as do developmental changes in plasmodesmatal number. **2.** Plasmodesmata, unlike gap junctions, have the ability to pass RNA, proteins, and viruses from cell to cell. **3.** Although this strategy would eliminate the systemic spread of viral infections, it would also severely impact the development of the plants.

Self-Quiz
1. d **2.** e **3.** c **4.** b **5.** a **6.** d **7.** c **8.** c **9.** b **10.** c
11.

CHAPTER 37

Figure Questions
Figure 37.3 Anions. Because cations are bound to soil particles, they are less likely to be lost from the soil following heavy rains. **Figure 37.10** The legume plants benefit because the bacteria fix nitrogen that is absorbed by their roots. The bacteria benefit because they acquire photosynthetic products from the plants. **Figure 37.11** All three plant tissue systems are affected. Root hairs (dermal tissue) are modified to allow rhizobial penetration. The cortex (ground tissue) and pericycle (vascular tissue) proliferate during nodule formation. The vascular tissue of the nodule links up with the vascular cylinder of the root to allow for efficient nutrient exchange. **Figure 37.13** If phosphate were the only limiting

mineral, then native tree growth would be less severely impacted by the reduction in mycorrhizal associations in soils invaded by garlic mustard.

Concept Check 37.1
1. Overwatering deprives roots of oxygen. Overfertilizing is wasteful and can lead to soil salinization and water pollution. **2.** As lawn clippings decompose, they restore mineral nutrients to the soil. If they are removed, the minerals lost from the soil must be replaced by fertilization. **3.** Because of their small size and negative charge, clay particles would increase the number of binding sites for cations and water molecules and would therefore increase cation exchange and water retention in the soil.

Concept Check 37.2
1. Table 37.1 shows that CO_2 is the source of 90% of a plant's dry weight, supporting Hales's view that plants are nourished mostly by air. **2.** No, because even though macronutrients are required in greater amounts, all essential elements are necessary for the plant to complete its life cycle. **3.** No. Most plants can complete their life cycles in the absence of silicon. Therefore, by definition, it is not an essential nutrient.

Concept Check 37.3
1. The rhizosphere is a narrow zone in the soil immediately adjacent to living roots. This zone is especially rich in both organic and inorganic nutrients and has a microbial population that is many times greater than the bulk of the soil. **2.** Soil bacteria and mycorrhizae enhance plant nutrition by making certain minerals more available for plants. For example, many types of soil bacteria are involved in the nitrogen cycle, whereas the hyphae of mycorrhizae provide a large surface area for the absorption of nutrients, particularly phosphate ions. **3.** Saturating rainfall may deplete the soil of oxygen. A lack of soil oxygen would inhibit nitrogen fixation by the peanut root nodules and decrease the nitrogen available to the plant. Alternatively, heavy rain may leach nitrate from the soil. A symptom of nitrogen deficiency is yellowing of older leaves.

Self-Quiz
1. b **2.** b **3.** c **4.** b **5.** b **6.** c **7.** d **8.** a **9.** d **10.** b
11.

CHAPTER 38

Figure Questions
Figure 38.4 Having a specific pollinator is more efficient because less pollen gets delivered to flowers of the wrong species. However, it is also a risky strategy: If the pollinator population suffers to an unusual degree from predation, disease, or climate change, then the plant may not be able to produce seeds. **Figure 38.6** An inability to produce GABA would also prevent the establishment of a GABA gradient to help direct pollen tube growth. Thus, these mutants would be sterile also. **Figure 38.9** Beans use a hypocotyl hook to push through the soil. The delicate leaves and shoot apical meristem are also protected by being sandwiched between two large cotyledons. The coleoptile of maize seedlings helps protect the emerging leaves.

Concept Check 38.1
1. In angiosperms, pollination is the transfer of pollen from an anther to a stigma. Fertilization is the fusion of the egg and sperm to form the zygote; it cannot occur until after the growth of the pollen tube from the pollen grain. **2.** Seed dormancy prevents the premature germination of seeds. A seed will germinate only when the environmental conditions are optimal for the survival of its embryo as a young seedling. **3.** The fruit types are not completely separate categories because the term *accessory fruit* applies to any fruit that develops not only from one or more carpels but also from additional floral parts. Therefore, a simple, aggregate, or multiple fruit can also be an accessory fruit. The terms *simple*, *aggregate*, and *multiple* refer only to the number of carpels and flowers from which the fruit develops. **4.** Long styles help to weed out pollen grains that are genetically inferior and not capable of successfully growing long pollen tubes.

Concept Check 38.2
1. Sexual reproduction produces genetic variety, which may be advantageous in an unstable environment. The likelihood is better that at least one offspring of sexual reproduction will survive in a changed environment. Asexual reproduction can be advantageous in a stable environment because individual plants that are well suited to that environment pass on all their genes to offspring. Asexual reproduction also generally results in offspring that are less fragile than the seedlings produced by sexual reproduction. However, sexual reproduction offers the advantage of dispersal of tough seeds. **2.** Asexually propagated crops lack genetic diversity. Genetically diverse populations are less likely to become extinct in the face of an epidemic because there is a greater likelihood that a few individuals in the population are resistant. **3.** In the short term, selfing may be advantageous in a population that is so dispersed and sparse that pollen delivery is unreliable. In the long term, however, selfing is an evolutionary dead end because it leads to a loss of genetic diversity that may preclude adaptive evolution. **4.** This might be possible, but satisfactory results would be very unlikely. Both tubers and fruits are tremendous energy sinks. Each plant has only a finite amount of energy to divide between sexual and asexual reproduction. Although a tomato-potato hybrid could, in theory, produce an offspring that makes fruits and tubers equally, these fruits and tubers would be of inferior quality or low yielding.

Concept Check 38.3
1. Traditional breeding and genetic engineering both involve artificial selection for desired traits. However, genetic engineering techniques facilitate faster gene transfer and are not limited to transferring genes between closely related varieties or species. **2.** GM crops may be more nutritious and less susceptible to insect damage or pathogens that invade insect-damaged plants. They also may not require as much chemical spraying. However, unknown risks may include adverse effects on human health and nontarget organisms and the possibility of transgene escape. **3.** *Bt* maize suffers less insect damage; therefore, *Bt* maize plants are less likely to be infected by fumonisin-producing fungi that infect plants through wounds. **4.** In such species, engineering the transgene into the chloroplast DNA would not prevent its escape in pollen; such a method requires that the chloroplast DNA be found only in the egg. An entirely different method of preventing transgene escape would therefore be needed, such as male sterility, apomixis, or self-pollinating closed flowers.

Self-Quiz
1. d **2.** c **3.** a **4.** c **5.** d **6.** c **7.** e **8.** a **9.** c **10.** e
11.

CHAPTER 39

Figure Questions
Figure 39.5 To determine which wavelengths of light are most effective in phototropism, one could use a glass prism to split white light into its component colors and see which colors cause the quickest bending (the answer is blue; see Figure 39.16). **Figure 39.6** The coleoptile would bend toward the side with the TIBA-containing agar bead. **Figure 39.7** No. Polar auxin transport depends on the polar distribution of auxin transport proteins. **Figure 39.17** Yes. The white light, which contains red light, would stimulate seed germination in all treatments. **Figure 39.22** The short-day plant would not flower. The long-day plant would flower. **Figure 39.23** If this were true, florigen would be an inhibitor of flowering, not an inducer.

Concept Check 39.1
1. Dark-grown seedlings have long stems, underdeveloped root systems, and unexpanded leaves, and their shoots lack chlorophyll. **2.** Etiolated growth is beneficial to seeds sprouting under the dark conditions they would encounter underground. By devoting more energy to stem elongation and less to leaf expansion and root growth, a plant increases the likelihood that the shoot will reach the sunlight before its stored foods run out. **3.** Cycloheximide should inhibit

de-etiolation by preventing the synthesis of new proteins necessary for de-etiolation. **4.** No. Applying Viagra, like injecting cyclic GMP as described in the text, should cause only a partial de-etiolation response. Full de-etiolation would require activation of the calcium branch of the signal transduction pathway.

Concept Check 39.2
1. The release of ethylene by the damaged apple stimulates ripening in the other apples. **2.** Because cytokinins delay leaf senescence and floral parts are modified leaves, cytokinins also delay the senescence of cut flowers. **3.** Fusicoccin's ability to cause an increase in plasma H^+ pump activity is similar to an effect of auxin and leads to an auxin-like effect, a promotion of stem cell elongation. **4.** The plant will exhibit a constitutive triple response. Because the kinase that normally prevents the triple response is dysfunctional, the plant will undergo the triple response regardless of whether ethylene is present or the ethylene receptor is functional.

Concept Check 39.3
1. Not necessarily. Many environmental factors, such as temperature and light, change over a 24-hour period in the field. To determine whether the enzyme is under circadian control, the scientist would have to demonstrate that its activity oscillates even when environmental conditions are held constant. **2.** Flowering of the species may have been day-neutral or required multiple exposures to short nights. **3.** You might determine which wavelengths of light are most effective and plot an action spectrum. If the action spectrum indicates phytochrome, you could do further experiments to test for red/far-red photosensitivity. **4.** It is impossible to say. To establish that this species is a short-day plant, it would be necessary to establish the critical night length for flowering and that this species only flowers when the night is longer than the critical night length.

Concept Check 39.4
1. A plant that overproduces ABA would undergo less evaporative cooling because its stomata would not open as widely. **2.** Plants close to the aisles may be more subject to mechanical stresses caused by passing workers and air currents. The plants nearer to the center of the bench may also be taller as a result of shading and less evaporative stress. **3.** Like drought stress, freezing leads to cellular dehydration. Any process that helps mitigate drought stress will tend also to reduce freezing stress. **4.** No. Because root caps are involved in sensing gravity, roots that have their root caps removed are almost completely insensitive to gravity.

Concept Check 39.5
1. Some insects increase plants' productivity by eating harmful insects or aiding in pollination. **2.** Mechanical damage breaches a plant's first line of defense against infection, its protective dermal tissue. **3.** No. Pathogens that kill their hosts would soon run out of victims and might themselves go extinct. **4.** Perhaps the breeze dilutes the local concentration of a volatile defense compound that the plants produce.

Self-Quiz
1. a **2.** c **3.** d **4.** b **5.** e **6.** b **7.** b **8.** c **9.** e **10.** b
11.

CHAPTER 40
Figure Questions
Figure 40.4 Such exchange surfaces are internal in the sense that they are inside the body. However, they are also continuous with openings on the external body surface that contact the environment. **Figure 40.8** The air conditioner would form a second negative-feedback loop, cooling the house when air temperature exceeded the set point. Such opposing, or antagonistic, pairs of negative-feedback loops increase the effectiveness of a homeostatic mechanism. **Figure 40.14** When a female Burmese python is not incubating eggs, her oxygen consumption will decrease with decreasing temperature, as for any other ectotherm. **Figure 40.21** If falling temperatures triggered hibernation, you would predict hibernation would begin earlier than normal. If another seasonal change, such as day length, controlled hibernation, its timing should be unaffected. By controlling these environmental variables in the laboratory, scientists have shown that lowering temperature without a change in day length is sufficient to induce ground squirrel hibernation.

Concept Check 40.1
1. Epithelial cells line a surface, are tightly packed, are situated on top of a basal lamina, and form an active and protective interface with the external environment. **2.** By flattening its ears along its body, the jackrabbit can reduce the total surface area of its body and hence the amount of heat absorbed when environmental temperatures are high, or the amount of heat lost when environmental temperatures are low. **3.** You need the nervous system to perceive the danger and provoke a split-second muscular response to keep from falling. The nervous system, however, does not make a direct connection with blood vessels or liver cells. Instead, the nervous system triggers the release of a hormone (called epinephrine or adrenaline) by the endocrine system, bringing about a change in these tissues in just a few seconds.

Concept Check 40.2
1. No; even though an animal regulates some aspects of its internal environment, the internal environment fluctuates slightly around set points. Homeostasis is a dynamic state. Furthermore, there are sometimes programmed changes in set points, such as those resulting in radical increases in hormone levels at particular times in development. **2.** In negative feedback, a change triggers control mechanisms that counteract further change in that direction. In positive feedback, a change triggers mechanisms that amplify the change. **3.** You would want to locate a thermostat close to where you would be spending time, protected from environmental perturbations, such as direct sunshine, and not right in the path of the output of the heating system. Similarly, the sensors for homeostasis located in the human brain are separated from environmental influences and can monitor conditions in a vital and sensitive tissue.

Concept Check 40.3
1. "Wind chill" involves heat loss through convection. **2.** The hummingbird, being a very small endotherm, has a very high metabolic rate. If by absorbing sunlight certain flowers warm their nectar, a hummingbird feeding on these flowers is saved the metabolic expense of warming the nectar to its body temperature. **3.** The ice water would cool tissues in your head, including blood that would then circulate throughout the body. This effect would accelerate the return to a normal body temperature. If, however, the ice water reached the eardrum and cooled the hypothalamic thermostat, the perceived drop in temperature would inhibit sweating and blood vessel dilation, slowing cooling elsewhere in the body.

Concept Check 40.4
1. The mouse would consume oxygen at a higher rate because it is an endotherm and therefore its basal metabolic rate is higher than the ectothermic lizard's standard metabolic rate. **2.** The house cat; the smaller an animal is, the higher its metabolic rate and its demand for food per unit of body mass are. **3.** Although penguins do not grow as adults, they increase and decrease in size as they repeatedly form and use energy stores. A significant amount of energy might be stored in fat during part of the year but be missing from the pie chart because it is used later in the year.

Self-Quiz
1. b **2.** e **3.** c **4.** e **5.** a **6.** d

7.

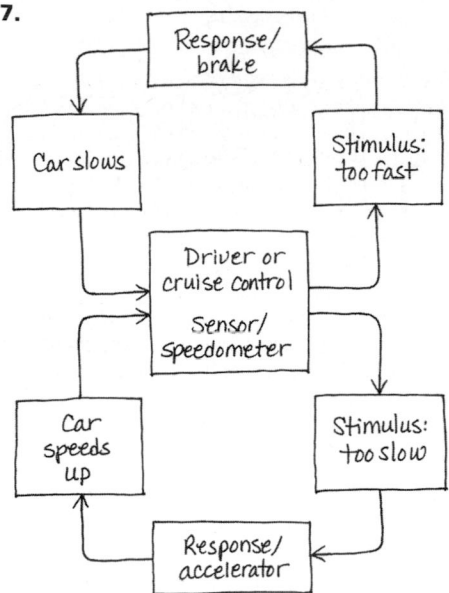

CHAPTER 41

Figure Questions

Figure 41.5 As in the described study, they needed a sample size large enough that they could expect a significant number of neural tube defects in the control group. The information needed to determine the appropriate sample size was the frequency of neural tube defects in first-time pregnancies in the general population. **Figure 41.13** Since enzymes are proteins, and proteins are hydrolyzed in the small intestine, the digestive enzymes in that compartment need to be resistant to cleavage by proteases other than the cleavage required for enzyme activation. **Figure 41.15** None. Since digestion is completed in the small intestine, tapeworms simply absorb predigested nutrients through their large body surface area. **Figure 41.24** The *db* mouse would have higher leptin levels. The wild-type mouse produces leptin after a meal. As the mouse depletes its fat stores, leptin production drops. The mouse eventually regains its appetite, eats another meal, and makes another burst of leptin. Because the *db* mouse cannot respond to leptin, its fat stores are constantly replenished through excessive consumption. As a result, leptin is produced continuously and builds up to a high concentration in the blood.

Concept Check 41.1

1. The only essential amino acids are those that an animal can't synthesize from other molecules containing carbon and nitrogen. **2.** Carbohydrates are needed throughout the body as a source of energy and carbon in the biosynthesis of cellular components, whereas vitamins typically serve as reusable enzyme cofactors or as raw materials for certain specialized cell structures. **3.** To identify the essential nutrient missing from an animal's diet, a researcher could supplement the diet with particular nutrients and determine which nutrient eliminates the signs of malnutrition.

Concept Check 41.2

1. A gastrovascular cavity is a digestive sac with a single opening that functions in both ingestion and elimination; an alimentary canal is a digestive tube with a separate mouth and anus at opposite ends. **2.** As long as nutrients are within the cavity of the alimentary canal, they are in a compartment that is continuous with the outside environment via the mouth and anus and have not yet crossed a membrane to enter the body. **3.** Just as food remains outside the body in a digestive tract, gasoline moves from the fuel tank to the engine and the exhaust without ever entering the passenger compartment of the car. In addition, gasoline, like food, is broken down in a specialized compartment, so that the rest of the body is protected from disassembly. In both cases, high-energy fuels are consumed and waste products are eliminated.

Concept Check 41.3

1. By peristalsis, which can squeeze food through the esophagus even without the help of gravity. **2.** Fats can cross the membranes of epithelial cells by diffusion, whereas proteins and sugars, which are not lipid-soluble, require transport or exchange proteins. **3.** Proteins would be denatured and digested into peptides. Further digestion, to individual amino acids, would require enzymatic secretions found in the small intestine.

Concept Check 41.4

1. The increased time for transit allows for more extensive processing, and the increased surface area provides greater opportunity for absorption. **2.** Mutualistic microbes in the intestines of vertebrates have an environment that is protected against other microbes by saliva and gastric juice, that is held at a constant temperature conducive to enzyme action, and that provides a steady source of nutrients. **3.** For the yogurt treatment to be effective, the bacteria from yogurt would have to establish a mutualistic relationship with the small intestine, where disaccharides are broken down and sugars are absorbed. Conditions in the small intestine are likely to be very different than in a yogurt culture. The bacteria might be killed before they reach the small intestine, or they might not be able to grow there in sufficient numbers to aid in digestion.

Concept Check 41.5

1. Over the long term, the body converts excess calories to fat, whether those calories are consumed as fat, carbohydrate, or protein. **2.** Both hormones have appetite-suppressing effects on the brain's satiety center. During the course of a day, PYY, secreted by the intestine, suppresses appetite after meals. Over the longer term, leptin, produced by adipose tissue, normally reduces appetite as fat storage increases. **3.** In normal individuals, leptin levels decline during fasting. The group with low levels of leptin are likely to be defective in leptin production, so leptin levels would remain low regardless of food intake. The group with high leptin levels are likely to be defective in responding to leptin, but they still should shut off leptin production as fat stores are used up.

Self-Quiz

1. e **2.** a **3.** c **4.** c **5.** c **6.** d **7.** e **8.** b

9.

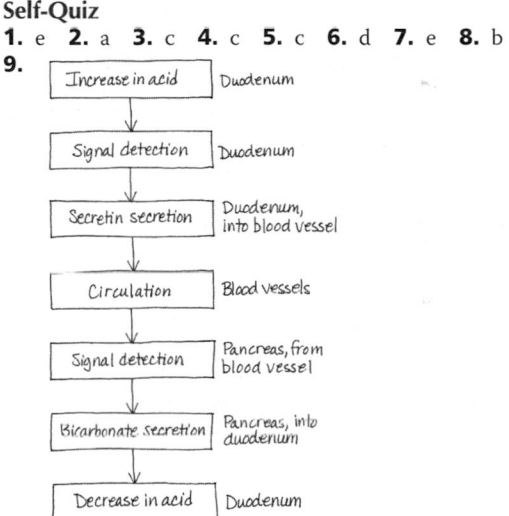

CHAPTER 42

Figure Questions

Figure 42.2 As the name indicates, a gastrovascular cavity functions in both digestion and circulation. Although gas exchange might be improved by a steady, one-way flow of fluid, there would likely be inadequate time for food to be digested and nutrients absorbed if fluids flowed through the cavity in this manner. **Figure 42.12** Because endothelin regulates the smooth muscle cells in blood vessels, you would expect it to be secreted from the basal surface of endothelial cells, a prediction that has been confirmed experimentally. **Figure 42.28** The resulting increase in tidal volume would enhance ventilation within the lungs, increasing P_{O_2} in the alveoli. **Figure 42.30** Some CO_2 is dissolved in plasma, some is bound to hemoglobin, and some is converted to bicarbonate ion (HCO_3^-), which is dissolved in plasma. **Figure 42.31** You might find some fast runners in those with the highest V_{O_2} max, but you might also find some sloths. There are two principal factors that contribute to V_{O_2} max, genetics and exercise. Elite athletes have a very high V_{O_2} max, reflecting not only the strengthening of their cardiovascular system through training but also the genetic circumstance of their having a particular combination of alleles.

Concept Check 42.1

1. In both an open circulatory system and a fountain, fluid is pumped through a tube and then returns to the pump after collecting in a pool. **2.** The ability to shut off blood supply to the lungs when the animal is submerged **3.** The O_2 content would be abnormally low because some oxygen-depleted blood returned to the right ventricle from the systemic circuit would mix with the oxygen-rich blood in the left ventricle.

Concept Check 42.2

1. The pulmonary veins carry blood that has just passed through capillary beds in the lungs, where it accumulated O_2. The venae cavae carry blood that has just passed through capillary beds in the rest of the body, where it lost O_2 to the tissues. **2.** The delay allows the atria to empty completely, filling ventricles fully before they contract. **3.** The heart, like any other muscle, becomes stronger through regular exercise. You would expect a stronger heart to have a greater stroke volume, which would allow for the decrease in heart rate.

Concept Check 42.3

1. The large total cross-sectional area of the capillaries **2.** An increase in blood pressure and cardiac output combined with the diversion of more blood to the skeletal muscles would increase the capacity for action by increasing the rate of blood circulation and delivering more O_2 and nutrients to the skeletal muscles. **3.** Additional hearts could be used to improve blood return from the legs. However, it might be difficult to coordinate the activity of multiple hearts and to maintain adequate blood flow to hearts far from the gas exchange organs.

Concept Check 42.4

1. An increase in the number of white blood cells (leukocytes) may indicate that the person is combating an infection. **2.** Clotting factors do not initiate clotting but are essential steps in the clotting process. Also, the clots that form a thrombus typically result from an inflammatory response to an atherosclerotic plaque, not from clotting at a wound site. **3.** The chest pain results from inadequate blood flow in coronary arteries. Vasodilation promoted by nitric oxide from nitroglycerin increases blood flow, providing the heart muscle with additional oxygen and thus relieving the pain.

Concept Check 42.5

1. Their interior position helps them stay moist. If the respiratory surfaces of lungs extended out into the terrestrial environment, they would quickly dry out, and diffusion of O_2 and CO_2 across these surfaces would stop. **2.** Earthworms need to keep their skin moist for gas exchange, but they need air outside this moist layer. If they stay in their waterlogged tunnels after a heavy rain, they will suffocate because they cannot get as much O_2 from water as from air. **3.** Since exhalation is largely passive, the recoil of the elastic fibers in alveoli helps force air out of the lungs. When alveoli lose their elasticity, as occurs in the disease emphysema, the volume of each breath decreases, lowering the efficiency of gas exchange.

Concept Check 42.6

1. An increase in blood CO_2 concentration causes an increase in the rate of CO_2 diffusion into the cerebrospinal fluid, where the CO_2 combines with water to form carbonic acid. Dissociation of carbonic acid releases hydrogen ions, decreasing the pH of the cerebrospinal fluid. **2.** Increased heart rate increases the rate at which CO_2-rich blood is delivered to the lungs, where CO_2 is removed. **3.** A hole would allow air to enter the space between the inner and outer layers of the double membrane, resulting in a condition called a pneumothorax. The two layers would no longer stick together, and the lung on the side with the hole would collapse and cease functioning.

Concept Check 42.7

1. Differences in partial pressure; gases diffuse from a region of higher partial pressure to a region of lower partial pressure. **2.** The Bohr shift causes hemoglobin to release more O_2 at a lower pH, such as found in the vicinity of tissues with high rates of cellular respiration and CO_2 release. **3.** The doctor is assuming that the rapid breathing is the body's response to low blood pH. Metabolic acidosis, the lowering of blood pH, can have many causes, including complications of certain types of diabetes, shock (extremely low blood pressure), and poisoning.

Self-Quiz

1. c **2.** b **3.** d **4.** e **5.** b **6.** c **7.** a **8.** a

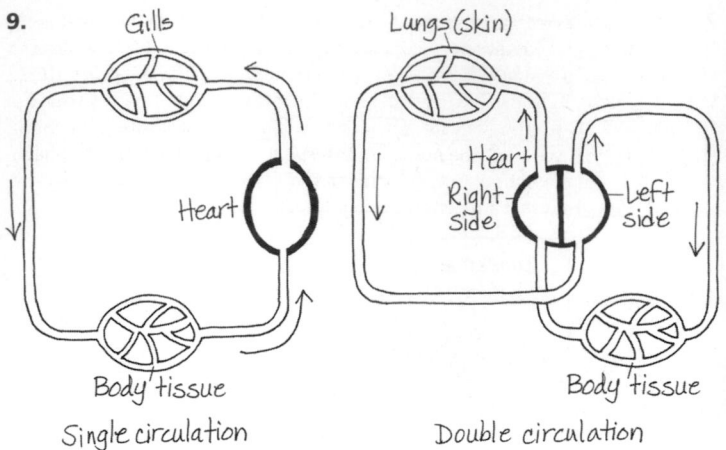

9.

Single circulation

Double circulation

CHAPTER 43

Figure Questions

Figure 43.5 The seemingly inactive peptides might offer protection against pathogens other than those studied. Also, some antimicrobial peptides might work best in combination. **Figure 43.6** Cell surface TLRs recognize pathogens identifiable by surface molecules, whereas TLRs in vesicles recognize pathogens identifiable by internal molecules after the pathogens are broken down. **Figure 43.16** Primary response: arrows extending from Antigen (1st exposure), Antigen-presenting cell, Helper T cell, B cell, Plasma cells, Cytotoxic T cell, and Active Cytotoxic T cells; secondary response: arrows extending from Antigen (2nd exposure), Memory Helper T cells, Memory B cells, and Memory Cytotoxic T cells. **Figure 43.19** Before mounting a secondary immune response, memory cells must become activated by displaying antigen on the cell surface to a helper T cell.

Concept Check 43.1

1. A physical barrier often provides a very effective defense against infection. However, it is necessarily incomplete because animals need openings in their bodies for exchange with the environment. **2.** Because pus contains white blood cells, fluid, and cell debris, it indicates an active and at least partially successful inflammatory response against invading microbes. **3.** A microbe that grew optimally at low pH would be able to colonize the skin or stomach more readily. At the same time, it would not be well adapted to growth in other parts of the body.

Concept Check 43.2

1. See Figure 43.9a. All of the functions shared among receptors map to C regions, whereas the antigen-binding site maps to the V regions. **2.** Generating memory cells ensures both that a receptor specific for a particular epitope will be present and that there will be more lymphocytes with this specificity than in a host that had never encountered the antigen. **3.** If each B cell produced two different light and heavy chains for its antigen receptor, different combinations would make four different receptors. If any one was self-reactive, the lymphocyte would be eliminated in the generation of self-tolerance. For this reason, many more B cells would be eliminated, and those that could respond to a foreign antigen would be less effective at doing so due to the variety of receptors (and antibodies) they express.

Concept Check 43.3

1. A child lacking a thymus would have no functional T cells. Without helper T cells to help activate B cells, the child would be unable to produce antibodies against extracellular bacteria. Furthermore, without cytotoxic T cells or helper T cells, the child's immune system would be unable to kill virus-infected cells. **2.** Since the antigen-binding site is intact, the antibody fragments could neutralize viruses and opsonize bacteria. **3.** If the handler developed immunity to proteins in the antivenin, another injection could provoke a severe immune response. The handler's immune system might also now produce antibodies that could neutralize the venom.

Concept Check 43.4

1. Myasthenia gravis is considered an autoimmune disease because the immune system produces antibodies against self molecules (acetylcholine receptors).

2. A person with a cold is likely to produce oral and nasal secretions that facilitate viral transfer. In addition, since sickness can cause incapacitation or death, a virus that is programmed to exit the host when there is a physiological stress has the opportunity to find a new host at a time when the current host may cease to function. **3.** A person with a macrophage deficiency would have frequent infections. The causes would be poor innate responses, due to diminished phagocytosis and inflammation, and poor acquired responses, due to the lack of macrophages to present antigens to helper T cells.

Self-Quiz
1. b **2.** d **3.** c **4.** b **5.** c **6.** d **7.** b
8. One possible answer:

CHAPTER 44

Figure Questions
Figure 44.7 The body fluids of osmoconformers, such as most marine invertebrates, have the same salt concentration as sea water. Any such animals in the diet of the bird would add to the salt load to be eliminated. In contrast, marine fishes that osmoregulate maintain body fluids that have a much lower salt concentration than the surrounding ocean. By eating such fish, marine birds can obtain nutrients and water without adding as much to their salt load. **Figure 44.15** Tubule cells in the medulla are in contact with extracellular fluid of very high osmolarity. By producing solutes that keep intracellular osmolarity high, these cells achieve homeostasis with regard to volume. **Figure 44.16** Furosemide increases urine volume. The absence of ion transport in the ascending limb leaves the filtrate too concentrated for substantial volume reduction in the distal tubule and collecting duct. **Figure 44.20** The ADH levels would likely be elevated in both sets of patients with mutations because either defect prevents the recapture of water that restores blood osmolarity to normal levels.

Concept Check 44.1
1. Because the salt is moved against its concentration gradient, from low concentration (freshwater) to high concentration (blood) **2.** A freshwater osmoconformer would have body fluids too dilute to carry out life's processes. **3.** Without a layer of insulating fur, the camel must use the cooling effect of evaporative water loss to maintain body temperature, thus linking thermoregulation and osmoregulation.

Concept Check 44.2
1. Because uric acid is largely insoluble in water, it can be excreted as a semisolid paste, thereby reducing an animal's water loss. **2.** Humans produce uric acid from purine breakdown, and reducing purines in the diet often lessens the severity of gout. Birds, however, produce uric acid as a waste product of general nitrogen metabolism. They would therefore need a diet low in all nitrogen-containing compounds, not just purines.

Concept Check 44.3
1. In flatworms, ciliated cells draw interstitial fluids containing waste products into protonephridia. In earthworms, waste products pass from interstitial fluids into the coelom. From there they enter metanephridia by beating of cilia in a funnel surrounding an internal opening. In insects, the Malphigian tubules pump fluids from the hemolymph, which receives waste products during exchange with interstitial fluids in the course of circulation. **2.** Filtration produces a fluid for exchange processes that is free of cells and large molecules which are of benefit to the animal and could not readily be reabsorbed. **3.** The presence of Na^+ and other ions (electrolytes) in the dialysate would limit the extent to which they would be removed from the filtrate during dialysis. Adjusting the electrolytes in the starting dialysate can thus lead to the restoration of proper electrolyte concentrations in the plasma. Similarly, the absence of urea and other waste products in the starting dialysate results in their efficient removal from the filtrate.

Concept Check 44.4
1. The numerous nephrons and well-developed glomeruli of freshwater fishes produce urine at a high rate, while the small numbers of nephrons and smaller glomeruli of marine fishes produce urine at a low rate. **2.** The kidney medulla would absorb less water and thus the drug would increase the amount of water lost in the urine. **3.** A decline in blood pressure in the afferent arteriole would reduce the rate of filtration by moving less material through the vessels.

Concept Check 44.5
1. Alcohol inhibits the release of ADH, causing an increase in urinary water loss and increasing the chance of dehydration. **2.** The consumption of a large amount of water in a very short period of time, coupled with an absence of solute intake, can reduce sodium levels in the blood below tolerable levels. This condition, called hyponatremia, leads to disorientation and, sometimes, respiratory distress. It has been seen in marathon runners who drink water rather than sports drinks. (It has also caused the death of a fraternity pledge as a consequence of a water hazing ritual and the death of a contestant in a water-drinking competition.) **3.** High blood pressure

Self-Quiz
1. d **2.** b **3.** e **4.** d **5.** a **6.** c **7.** b
8.

CHAPTER 45

Figure Questions
Figure 45.4 Because lipid-soluble hormones can freely diffuse across the lipid bilayers of cell membranes, you would expect to see biological activity after microinjection either into cells or into the interstitial space. **Figure 45.5** The hormone is water-soluble and has a cell-surface receptor. Such receptors, unlike those for lipid-soluble hormones, can cause observable changes in cells without hormone-dependent gene transcription. **Figure 45.18** Both diagnoses could be correct. In one case, the thyroid gland may produce excess thyroid hormone despite normal hormonal input from the hypothalamus and anterior pituitary. In the other, abnormally elevated hormonal input may be the cause of the overactive thyroid gland. **Figure 45.22** The result of the surgery would have been the same for both sexes—an absence of sexual differentiation in the genitals.

Concept Check 45.1
1. Water-soluble hormones, which cannot penetrate the plasma membrane, bind to cell-surface receptors. This interaction triggers an intracellular signal transduction pathway that ultimately alters the activity of a preexisting cytoplasmic protein and/or changes transcription of specific genes in the nucleus. Steroid hormones are lipid-soluble and can cross the plasma membrane into the cell interior, where they bind to receptors located in the cytosol or nucleus. The hormone-receptor complex then functions directly as a transcription factor that binds to the cell's DNA and activates or inhibits transcription of specific genes. **2.** Prostaglandins in semen that induce contractions in the uterus are aiding reproduction as signaling molecules that are transferred from one individual to another of the same species, like pheromones. **3.** Whether in different tissues or species, a particular hormone may cause diverse responses in target cells having different receptors for the hormone, different signal transduction pathways, and/or different proteins for carrying out the response.

Concept Check 45.2
1. In a healthy person, insulin released in response to the initial rise in blood glucose stimulates uptake of glucose by body cells. In a person with diabetes, however, inadequate production of insulin or nonresponsiveness of target cells decreases the body's ability to clear excess glucose from the blood. The initial increase in blood glucose is therefore greater in a person with diabetes, and it remains high for a prolonged period. **2.** A pathway governed by a short-lived stimulus would be less dependent on negative feedback. **3.** Since patients with type 2 diabetes produce insulin but fail to maintain normal glucose levels, you might predict that there could be mutations in the genes for the insulin receptor or the signal transduction pathway it activates. Such mutations have in fact been found in type 2 patients.

Concept Check 45.3

1. The posterior pituitary, an extension of the hypothalamus that contains the axons of neurosecretory cells, is the storage and release site for two neurohormones, oxytocin and antidiuretic hormone (ADH). The anterior pituitary, derived from tissues of the embryonic mouth, contains endocrine cells that make at least six different hormones. Secretion of anterior pituitary hormones is controlled by hypothalamic hormones that travel via portal vessels to the anterior pituitary. **2.** Because oxytocin responses involve positive feedback from suckling, the pathway does not require a sustained hormonal input stimulus. **3.** The hypothalamus and pituitary glands function in many different endocrine pathways. Many defects in these glands, such as those affecting growth or organization, would therefore disrupt many hormone pathways. Only a very specific defect, such as a mutation affecting a particular hormone receptor, would alter just one endocrine pathway. The situation is quite different for the final gland in a pathway, such as the thyroid gland. In this case, a wide range of defects that disrupt gland function would disrupt only the one pathway or small set of pathways in which that gland functions.

Concept Check 45.4

1. The adrenal medulla is derived from neural tissue during development. Reflecting this origin, it is an endocrine organ that produces two molecules—epinephrine and norepinephrine—that act both as hormones and as neurotransmitters. **2.** The levels of these hormones in the blood would become very high. This would be due to the diminished negative feedback on the hypothalamic neurons that secrete the releasing hormone that stimulates the secretion of ACTH by the anterior pituitary. **3.** By applying glucocorticoids to tissue by local injection, you in principle exploit their anti-inflammatory activity. Local injection avoids the effects on glucose metabolism that would occur if glucocorticoids were taken orally and transported throughout the body in the bloodstream.

Self-Quiz

1. c **2.** d **3.** d **4.** c **5.** b **6.** b **7.** c **8.** a
9.

CHAPTER 46

Figure Questions

Figure 46.9 According to the graph, about one-third of the females rid themselves of all sperm from the first mating. Thus, two-thirds retain some sperm from the first mating. We would therefore predict that two-thirds of the females would have some offspring exhibiting the small eye phenotype of the dominant mutation carried by the males with which the females mated first. **Figure 46.16** Testosterone can pass from fetal blood to maternal blood via the placental circulation, temporarily upsetting the hormonal balance in the mother. **Figure 46.18** Oxytocin would most likely induce labor and start a positive-feedback loop that would direct labor to completion. Synthetic oxytocin is in fact frequently used to induce labor when prolonged pregnancy might endanger the mother or fetus.

Concept Check 46.1

1. The offspring of sexual reproduction are more genetically diverse. However, asexual reproduction can produce more offspring over multiple generations. **2.** Unlike other forms of asexual reproduction, parthenogenesis involves gamete production. By controlling whether or not haploid eggs are fertilized, species such as honeybees can readily switch between asexual and sexual reproduction. **3.** No. Owing to random assortment of chromosomes during meiosis, the offspring may receive the same copy or different copies of a particular parental chromosome from the sperm and the egg. Furthermore, genetic recombination during meiosis will result in reassortment of genes between pairs of parental chromosomes.

Concept Check 46.2

1. Internal fertilization allows the sperm to reach the egg without either gamete drying out. **2.** (a) Animals with external fertilization tend to release many gametes at once, resulting in the production of enormous numbers of zygotes. This increases the chances that some will survive to adulthood. (b) Animals with internal fertilization produce fewer offspring but generally exhibit greater care of the embryos and the young. **3.** The antimicrobial peptide might serve to protect the sperm before mating, the females with which the male mates, or the eggs those females produce. In all three cases, the reproductive success of the male would be enhanced, providing a mechanism for selection for peptide production over the course of evolution. You might want to think about how you might determine which function is most critical.

Concept Check 46.3

1. Primarily the penis and clitoris, but also the testes, labia, breasts, and outer third of the vagina **2.** Spermatogenesis occurs normally only when the testicles are cooler than normal body temperature. Extensive use of a hot tub (or of very tight-fitting underwear) can cause a decrease in sperm quality and number. **3.** The only effect of sealing off each vas deferens is an absence of sperm in the ejaculate. Sexual response and ejaculate volume are unchanged. The cutting and sealing off of these ducts, a *vasectomy*, is a common surgical procedure for men who do not wish to produce any (more) offspring.

Concept Check 46.4

1. The small size and lack of cytoplasm characteristic of a sperm are adaptations well suited to its function as a delivery vehicle for DNA. The large size and rich cytoplasmic contents of eggs support the growth and development of the embryo. **2.** In humans, the secondary oocyte combines with a sperm before it finishes the second meiotic division. Thus, oogenesis is completed after, not before, fertilization. **3.** The analysis would be informative because the polar bodies contain all of the maternal chromosomes that don't end up in the mature egg. For example, finding two copies of the disease gene in the polar bodies would indicate its absence in the egg. This method of genetic testing is sometimes carried out when oocytes collected from a female are fertilized with sperm in a laboratory dish.

Concept Check 46.5

1. In the testis, FSH stimulates the Sertoli cells, which nourish developing sperm. LH stimulates the production of androgens (mainly testosterone), which in turn stimulate sperm production. In both females and males, FSH encourages the growth of cells that support and nourish developing gametes (follicle cells in females and Sertoli cells in males), and LH stimulates the production of sex hormones that promote gametogenesis (estrogens, primarily estradiol, in females and androgens, especially testosterone, in males). **2.** In estrous cycles, which occur in most female mammals, the endometrium is reabsorbed (rather than shed) if fertilization does not occur. Estrous cycles often occur just one or a few times a year, and the female is usually receptive to copulation only during the period around ovulation. Menstrual cycles are found only in humans and some other primates. **3.** The combination of estradiol and progesterone would have a negative-feedback effect on the hypothalamus, blocking release of GnRH. This would interfere with LH secretion by the pituitary, thus preventing ovulation. This is in fact one basis of action of the most common hormonal contraceptives.

Concept Check 46.6

1. hCG secreted by the early embryo stimulates the corpus luteum to make progesterone, which helps maintain the pregnancy. During the second trimester, however, hCG production drops, the corpus luteum disintegrates, and the placenta completely takes over progesterone production. **2.** Both tubal ligation and vasectomy block the movement of gametes from the gonads to a site where fertilization could take place. **3.** By introducing a spermatid nucleus directly into an oocyte, ICSI bypasses the sperm's acquisition of motility in the epididymis, its swimming to meet the egg in the oviduct, and its fusion with the egg.

Self-Quiz
1. d **2.** b **3.** a **4.** b **5.** c **6.** c **7.** a **8.** d
9.

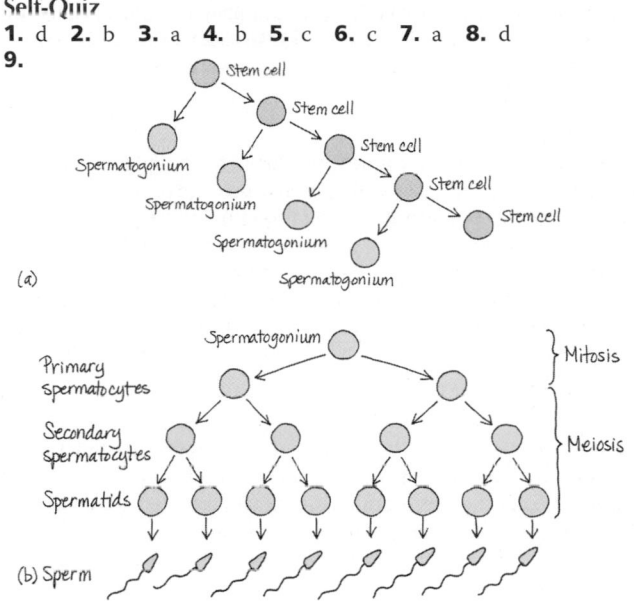

(c) The supply of stem cells would be used up and spermatogenesis would not be able to continue.

CHAPTER 47

Figure Questions
Figure 47.4 You could inject the compound into an unfertilized egg, expose the egg to sperm, and see whether the fertilization envelope forms. **Figure 47.7** The researchers allowed normal cortical rotation to occur, resulting in activation of the "back-forming" determinants. Then they forced the opposite rotation to occur, which established the back on the opposite side as well. Because the molecules on the normal side were already activated, forcing the opposite rotation apparently did not "cancel out" the establishment of the back side by the first rotation. **Figure 47.14** Given that these regions form from ectoderm but are just inside the body, you might propose that they form by an inpocketing of the ectoderm that then meets and fuses with the endoderm. And you would be right! **Figure 47.19** Cadherin is required to hold the cells of the blastula together, and extracellular calcium is required for cadherin function, so in the absence of calcium in the water, you'd expect to see a disorganized embryo like the one shown in the experimental SEM. **Figure 47.20** You could cut out the same tissues from control and injected embryos as was done in experiment 2 and place them between cover slips coated with the artificial fibronectin (FN) matrix. If convergent extension occurred in the tissues from both injected and control embryos, that would support the hypothesis that convergent extension can occur on a preexisting FN matrix in the embryo. **Figure 47.23** In Spemann's control, the two blastomeres were physically separated, and each grew into a whole embryo. In Roux's experiment, remnants of the dead blastomere were still contacting the live blastomere, which developed into a half-embryo. Therefore, molecules present in the dead cell's remnants may have been signaling to the live cell, inhibiting it from making all the embryonic structures. **Figure 47.24** You could inject the isolated protein or an mRNA encoding it into ventral cells of an earlier gastrula. If dorsal structures formed on the ventral side, that would support the idea that the protein is the signaling molecule secreted or presented by the dorsal lip. You should also do a control experiment to make sure the injection process alone did not cause dorsal structures to form. **Figure 47.26** You could remove the AER and look for Sonic

hedgehog mRNA or protein as a marker of the ZPA. If either was absent, that would support your hypothesis. You could also block FGF function and see whether the ZPA formed (by looking for Sonic hedgehog).

Concept Check 47.1
1. The fertilization envelope forms after cortical granules release their contents outside the egg, causing the vitelline membrane to rise and harden. The fertilization envelope serves as a barrier to fertilization by more than one sperm. **2.** During cleavage in frogs and many other animals, the cell cycle is modified so that it virtually skips G_1 and G_2, the growth phases. As a result, the early cleavage divisions divide the zygote's cytoplasm into smaller and smaller cells as the embryo's size remains nearly the same. **3.** Cleavage transforms the single-celled zygote into an embryo consisting of many cells; cleavage does not involve cell or tissue movement. During gastrulation, the cells and tissues of a blastula are extensively rearranged, so that by the late gastrula stage there are three tissue layers positioned in new relationships to each other. **4.** The neural tube forms when a band of ectodermal tissue on the dorsal side along the anterior-posterior axis, called the neural plate, rolls into a tube and pinches off from the rest of the ectoderm. Neural crest cells arise as groups of cells in the regions between the edges of the neural tube and the surrounding ectoderm migrate away from the neural tube. **5.** The increased Ca^{2+} concentration in the egg would cause the cortical granules to fuse with the plasma membrane, releasing their contents and causing a fertilization envelope to form, even though no sperm had entered. This would prevent fertilization. **6.** Conjoined twins develop from monozygotic twins that separate quite late, after part of the embryo has already formed. (This part is shared by the twins.) By this time, both the chorion and amnion have formed, so there is only one of each.

Concept Check 47.2
1. Microtubules elongate, lengthening the cell along one axis, while microfilaments oriented crosswise at one end of the cell contract, making that end smaller and the whole cell wedge-shaped. **2.** The cells of the notochord migrate toward the midline of the embryo (converge), rearranging themselves so there are fewer cells across the notochord, which thus becomes longer overall (extends; see Figure 47.18). **3.** Because microfilaments would not be able to contract and decrease the size of one end of the cell, both the inward bending in the middle of the neural tube and the outward bending of the hinge regions at the edges would be blocked. Therefore, the neural tube probably would not form.

Concept Check 47.3
1. Once the first two axes are specified, the third one is automatically determined. (Think of your own body: If you know where your anterior and posterior ends are and where your left and right sides are, you automatically know which sides are your front and back.) Of course, there still must be a mechanism for determining where asymmetrically placed organs must go, such as the vertebrate stomach or appendix. **2.** Yes, a second embryo could develop because inhibiting BMP-4 activity would have the same effect as transplanting an organizer. **3.** The limb that developed probably would have a mirror-image duplication, with the most posterior digits in the middle and the most anterior digits at either end.

Self-Quiz
1. a **2.** b **3.** e **4.** c **5.** a **6.** c **7.** e
8.

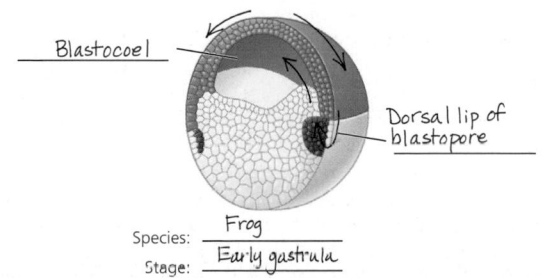

CHAPTER 48

Figure Questions

Figure 48.7 Adding chloride channels makes the membrane potential less negative. Adding sodium or potassium channels would have no effect, because sodium movement is already at equilibrium and there are no potassium ions present. **Figure 48.15** The production and transmission of action potentials would be unaffected. However, action potentials arriving at chemical synapses would be unable to trigger release of neurotransmitter. Signaling at such synapses would thus be blocked. **Figure 48.17** In theory, the results would be similar because the binding studies indicate that both opiates and naloxone, an opiate antagonist, bind directly to the receptor.

Concept Check 48.1

1. Sensors in your ear transmit information to your brain. There the activity of interneurons in processing centers enables you to recognize your name. In response, signals transmitted via motor neurons cause contraction of muscles that turn your neck. **2.** The nervous system is required for control of vital functions, such as circulation and gas exchange, and the transmission of information occurs on a very short time scale. **3.** It would prevent information from being transmitted away from the cell body along the axon.

Concept Check 48.2

1. Ions can flow against a chemical concentration gradient if there is an opposing electrical gradient of greater magnitude. **2.** A decrease in permeability to K^+, an increase in permeability to Na^+, or both. **3.** The activity of the sodium-potassium pump is essential to maintain the resting potential. With the pump inactivated, the sodium and potassium concentration gradients would gradually disappear, and so would the resting potential.

Concept Check 48.3

1. A graded potential has a magnitude that varies with stimulus strength, whereas an action potential has an all-or-none magnitude that is independent of stimulus strength. **2.** Loss of the insulation provided by myelin sheaths leads to a disruption of action potential propagation along axons. Voltage-gated sodium channels are restricted to the nodes of Ranvier, and without the insulating effect of myelin, the inward current produced at one node during an action potential cannot depolarize the membrane to the threshold at the next node. **3.** The maximum frequency would decrease because the refractory period would be extended.

Concept Check 48.4

1. It can bind to different types of receptors, each triggering a specific response in postsynaptic cells. **2.** These toxins would prolong the EPSPs that acetylcholine produces because the neurotransmitter would remain longer in the synaptic cleft. **3.** Such a drug might act as a sedative, decreasing the general level of activity in the brain and hence in the person.

Self-Quiz

1. c **2.** b **3.** c **4.** a **5.** c **6.** e
7. As shown in this pair of drawings, a pair of action potentials would move outward in both directions from each electrode. (Action potentials are unidirectional only if they begin at one end of an axon.) However, because of the refractory period, the two action potentials between the electrodes both stop where they meet. Thus, only one action potential reaches the synaptic terminals.

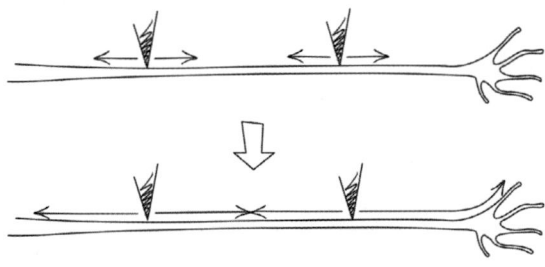

CHAPTER 49

Figure Questions

Figure 49.8 Neurosecretory cells of the adrenal medulla secrete epinephrine in response to preganglionic input from sympathetic neurons. Epinephrine travels in the circulation to reach target tissues throughout the body. Thus, the rapid changes in body tissues required for the "fight-or-flight" response rely on direct input from the nervous system as well as indirect input via neurohormone products of the adrenal medulla. **Figure 49.12** If the new mutation disrupted only pacemaker function, you should be able to restore rhythmic activity by removing the SCN and replacing it with an SCN transplant from either a wild-type or τ mutant hamster. Using the new mutant as the donor would not be as informative, since both failed transplants and successful ones would result in a lack of rhythmic activity. **Figure 49.22** The depolarization should mimic natural stimulation of the brain reward system, resulting in positive and perhaps pleasurable sensations.

Concept Check 49.1

1. The sympathetic division, which mediates the "fight-or-flight" response in stressful situations **2.** The preganglionic neurons use the same neurotransmitter and function similarly in each division (to activate postganglionic neurons). The postganglionic neurons generally have opposing functions and use different neurotransmitters. **3.** Nerves contain bundles of axons, some of which belong to motor neurons that send signals outward from the CNS, and some that belong to sensory neurons that bring signals into the CNS. Therefore, you would expect effects on both motor control and sensation.

Concept Check 49.2

1. The cerebral cortex on the left side of the brain control initiates voluntary movement of the right side of the body. **2.** Alcohol diminishes function of the cerebellum. **3.** Paralysis reflects an inability to carry out motor functions transmitted from the cerebrum to the spinal cord. You would expect these patients to have injuries below the reticular formation. A coma reflects a disruption in the cycles of sleep and arousal regulated by communication between the reticular formation and the cerebrum. You would expect these patients to have injuries at or above the reticular formation.

Concept Check 49.3

1. Brain lesions that disrupt behavior, cognition, memory, or other functions provide evidence that the portion of the brain affected by the damage is important for the normal activity that is blocked or altered. **2.** Broca's area, which is active during the generation of speech, is located near the part of the primary motor cortex that controls muscles in the face. Wernicke's area, which is active when speech is heard, is located near the part of the temporal lobe that is involved in hearing. **3.** Each cerebral hemisphere is specialized for different parts of this task—the right for face recognition and the left for language. Without an intact corpus callosum, neither hemisphere can take advantage of the other's processing abilities.

Concept Check 49.4

1. There can be an increase in the number of synapses between the neurons or an increase in the strength of existing synaptic connections. **2.** If consciousness is an emergent property resulting from the interaction of many different regions of the brain, then it is unlikely that localized brain damage will have a discrete effect on consciousness. **3.** The hippocampus is responsible for organizing newly acquired information. Without hippocampal function, the links necessary to retrieve information from the neocortex will be lacking and no functional memory, short- or long-term, will be formed.

Concept Check 49.5

1. Both are progressive brain diseases whose risk increases with advancing age. Both result from the death of brain neurons and are associated with the accumulation of peptide or protein aggregates. **2.** The symptoms of schizophrenia can be mimicked by a drug that stimulates dopamine-releasing neurons. The brain reward system, which is involved in addiction, is comprised of dopamine-releasing neurons that connect the ventral tegmental area to regions in the cerebrum. Parkinson's disease results from the death of dopamine-releasing neurons. **3.** Not necessarily. It might be that the plaques, tangles, and missing regions of the brain seen at death reflect secondary effects, the consequence of other unseen changes that are actually responsible for the alterations in brain function.

Self-Quiz

1. c **2.** a **3.** d **4.** d **5.** e **6.** c

7. (a)

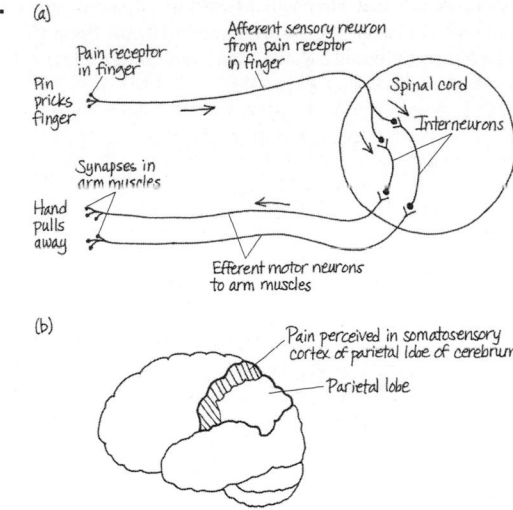

(b)

CHAPTER 50

Figure Questions

Figure 50.10 In the brain. Each note is detected separately in the ear, with each causing vibration of the basilar membrane and deflection of hair cells in a distinct location. Sensory neurons in each location provide output in the form of action potentials that travel along distinct axons in the auditory nerve. It is not until the information reaches the brain that the individual notes are detected and the perception of the chord is generated. **Figure 50.14** The results of the experiment would have been identical. What matters is the activation of particular sets of neurons, not the manner in which they are activated. Any signal from a bitter cell will be interpreted by the brain as a bitter taste, regardless of the nature of the compound and the receptor involved. **Figure 50.15** Only perception. Binding of an odorant to its receptor will cause action potentials to be sent to the brain. Although an excess of that odorant might cause a diminished response through adaptation, another odorant can mask the first only at the level of perception in the brain. **Figure 50.22** Each of the three types of cones is most sensitive to a distinct wavelength of light. A cone might be fully depolarized when there is light present if the light is of a wavelength far from its optimum. **Figure 50.27** Hundreds of myosin heads participate in sliding each pair of thick and thin filaments past each other. Because cross-bridge formation and breakdown are not synchronized, many myosin heads are exerting force on the thin filaments at all times during muscle contraction. **Figure 50.37** Since a duck is more specialized for flying than for swimming, you might expect that it would consume more energy per unit body mass and distance in swimming than would, for example, a fish. (In fact, if the value for a 10^3 g swimming duck were plotted on this graph, it would appear well above the line for swimmers and just above the line for runners.)

Concept Check 50.1

1. Electromagnetic receptors in general detect only external stimuli. Non-electromagnetic receptors, such as chemoreceptors or mechanoreceptors, can act as either internal or external sensors. **2.** The capsaicin present in the spice mix activates the thermoreceptor for high temperatures. In response to the perceived high temperature, the nervous system triggers sweating to achieve evaporative cooling. **3.** You would perceive the electrical stimulus as if the sensory receptors that regulate that neuron had been activated. For example, electrical stimulation of the sensory neuron controlled by the thermoreceptor activated by menthol would likely be perceived as a local cooling.

Concept Check 50.2

1. Statocysts detect the animal's orientation with respect to gravity, providing information that is essential in environments such as these, where light cues are absent. **2.** As a sound that changes gradually from a very low to a very high pitch **3.** The stapes and the other middle ear bones transmit vibrations from the tympanic membrane to the oval window. Fusion of these bones, as occurs in otosclerosis, would block this transmission and result in hearing loss.

Concept Check 50.3

1. Both taste cells and olfactory cells have receptor proteins in their plasma membrane that bind certain substances, leading to membrane depolarization through a signal transduction pathway involving a G protein. However, olfactory cells are sensory neurons, whereas taste cells are not. **2.** Since animals rely on chemical signals for behaviors that include finding mates, marking territories, and avoiding dangerous substances, it is adaptive for the olfactory system to have a robust response to a very small number of molecules of a particular odorant. **3.** Because the sweet, bitter, and umami tastes involve GPCR proteins but the sour taste does not, you might predict that the mutation is in a molecule that acts in the signal transduction pathway common to the different GPCR receptors.

Concept Check 50.4

1. Planarians have ocelli that cannot form images but can sense the intensity and direction of light, providing enough information to enable the animals to find protection in shaded places. Flies have compound eyes that form images and excel at detecting movement. **2.** The person can focus on distant objects but not close objects (without glasses) because close focusing requires the lens to become almost spherical. This problem is common after age 50. **3.** Close each eye in turn. An object floating on the surface of an eyeball will appear only when that eye is open.

Concept Check 50.5

1. By causing all of the motor neurons that control the muscle to generate action potentials at a rate high enough to produce tetanus in all of the muscle fibers **2.** In a skeletal muscle fiber, Ca^{2+} binds to the troponin complex, which moves tropomyosin away from the myosin-binding sites on actin and allows cross-bridges to form. In a smooth muscle cell, Ca^{2+} binds to calmodulin, which activates an enzyme that phosphorylates the myosin head and thus enables cross-bridge formation. **3.** *Rigor mortis*, a Latin phrase meaning "stiffness of death," results from the complete depletion of ATP in skeletal muscle. Since ATP is required for release of myosin from actin and to pump Ca^{2+} out of the cytosol, muscles become chronically contracted beginning about 3 or 4 hours after death.

Concept Check 50.6

1. Septa provide the divisions of the coelom that allow for peristalsis, a form of locomotion requiring independent control of different body segments. **2.** The main problem in swimming is drag; a fusiform body minimizes drag. The main problem in flying is overcoming gravity; wings shaped like airfoils provide lift, and adaptations such as air-filled bones reduce body mass. **3.** You could start by standing with your upper arm against your side and your lower arm extended out at a ninety degree angle from your hip. You could then slowly lower your hand toward the ground. Because you are holding the weight of your hand and lower arm against gravity, you need to maintain tetanus in the biceps muscle. As you lower your hand, you are gradually decreasing the number of motor units in the biceps that are contracted. The triceps is not involved because gravity is providing the force for arm extension.

Self Quiz

1. e **2.** d **3.** b **4.** a **5.** c **6.** b
7.

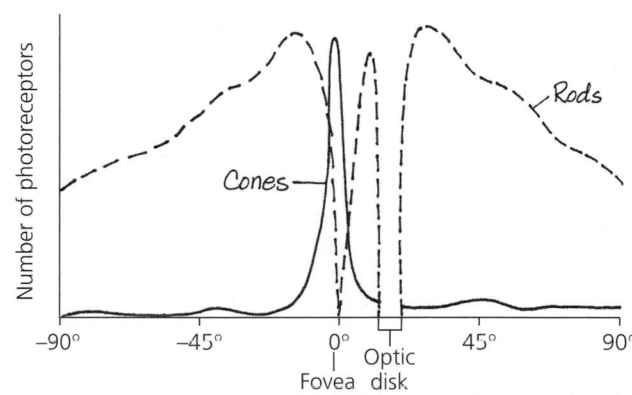

The answer shows the actual distribution of rods and cones in the human eye. Your graph may differ but should have the following properties: Only cones at the fovea; fewer cones and more rods at both ends of the *x*-axis; no photoreceptors in the optic disk.

CHAPTER 51

Figure Questions

Figure 51.3 The fixed action pattern based on the sign stimulus of a red belly ensures that the male will chase away any invading males of his species. By chasing away such males, the defender decreases the chance that eggs laid in his nesting territory will be fertilized by another male. **Figure 51.10** There should be no effect. Imprinting is an innate behavior that is carried out anew in each generation. Assuming the nest was not disturbed, the offspring of the Lorenz followers would imprint on the mother goose. **Figure 51.11** Perhaps the wasp doesn't use visual cues. It might also be that wasps recognize objects native to their environment, but not foreign objects, such as the pinecones. Tinbergen addressed these ideas before carrying out the pinecone study. When he swept away the pebbles and sticks around the nest, the wasps could no longer find their nests. If he shifted the natural objects in their natural arrangement, the shift in the landmarks caused a shift in the site to which the wasps returned. Finally, if the natural objects around the nest site were replaced with pinecones while the wasp was in the burrow, the wasp nevertheless found her way back to the nest site. **Figure 51.14** Courtship song generation must be coupled to courtship song recognition. Unless the genes that control generation of particular song elements also control recognition, the hybrids might be unlikely to find mating partners, depending on what aspects of the songs are important for mate recognition and acceptance. **Figure 51.15** It might be that the birds require stimuli during flight to exhibit their migratory preference. If this were true, the birds would show the same orientation in the funnel experiment despite their distinct genetic programming. **Figure 51.28** It holds true for some, but not all individuals. If a parent has more than one reproductive partner, the offspring of different partners will have a coefficient of relatedness less than 0.5.

Concept Check 51.1

1. It is an example of a fixed action pattern. The proximate explanation might be that nudging and rolling are released by the sign stimulus of an object outside the nest, and the behavior is carried to completion once initiated. The ultimate explanation might be that ensuring that eggs remain in the nest increases the chance of producing healthy offspring. **2.** Circannual rhythms are typically based on the cycles of light and dark in the environment. As the global climate changes, animals that migrate in response to these rhythms may shift to a location before or after local environmental conditions are optimal for reproduction and survival. **3.** There might be selective pressure for other prey fish to detect an injured fish because the source of the injury might threaten them as well. There might be selection for predators to be attracted to the alarm substance because they would be more likely to encounter crippled prey than would be predators that can't respond. Fish with adequate defenses might show no change because they have a selective advantage if they do not waste energy responding to the alarm substance.

Concept Check 51.2

1. Natural selection would tend to favor convergence in color pattern because a predator learning to associate a pattern with a sting or bad taste would avoid all other individuals with that same color pattern, regardless of species. **2.** Forgetting the location of some caches, which consist of pine seeds buried in the ground, might benefit the nutcracker by increasing the number of pines growing in its habitat. This example points out one of the difficulties in making simplistic assumptions about the purpose of a behavior. **3.** You might move objects around to establish an abstract rule, such as "past landmark A, the same distance as A is from the starting point," while maintaining a minimum of fixed metric relationships, that is, avoiding having the food directly adjacent to or a set distance from a landmark. As you might surmise, designing an informative experiment of this kind is not easy.

Concept Check 51.3

1. Because this geographic variation corresponds to differences in prey availability between two garter snake habitats, it seems likely that snakes with characteristics enabling them to feed on the abundant prey in their locale would have had increased survival and reproductive success, and thus natural selection would have resulted in the divergent foraging behaviors. **2.** Courtship is easier to study because it is essential for reproduction, but

not for growth, development, and survival. Mutations disrupting many other behaviors would be lethal. **3.** You would need to know the percentage of time that unrelated individuals behave identically when performing this behavior.

Concept Check 51.4

1. Certainty of paternity is higher with external fertilization. **2.** Natural selection acts on genetic variation in the population. **3.** Because females would now be present in much larger numbers than males, all three types of males should have some reproductive success. Nevertheless, since the advantage that the blue-throats rely on—a limited number of females in their territory—will be absent, the yellow-throats are likely to increase in frequency in the short term.

Concept Check 51.5

1. Reciprocal altruism, the exchange of helpful behaviors for future similar behaviors, can explain cooperative behaviors between unrelated animals, though often the behavior has some potential benefit to the benefactor as well. **2.** Yes. Kin selection does not require any recognition or awareness of relatedness. **3.** The older individual cannot be the beneficiary because he or she cannot have extra offspring. However, the cost is low for an older individual performing the altruistic act because that person has already reproduced (but perhaps is still caring for a child or grandchild). There can therefore be selection for an altruistic act by a postreproductive individual that benefits a young relative.

Self-Quiz

1. d **2.** a **3.** c **4.** a **5.** c **6.** b **7.** c
8.

You could measure the size of mussels that oystercatchers successfully open and compare that with the size distribution in the habitat.

CHAPTER 52

Figure Questions

Figure 52.6 Some factors, such as fire, are relevant only for terrestrial systems. At first glance, water availability is primarily a terrestrial factor, too. However, species living along the intertidal zone of oceans or along the edge of lakes suffer desiccation as well. Salinity stress is important for species in some aquatic and terrestrial systems. Oxygen availability is an important factor primarily for species in some aquatic systems and in soils and sediments. **Figure 52.8** When only urchins were removed, limpets may have increased in abundance and reduced seaweed cover somewhat (the difference between the purple and blue lines on the graph). **Figure 52.14** Dispersal limitations, the activities of people (such as a broad-scale conversion of forests to agriculture or selective harvesting), or other factors listed in Figure 52.6

Concept Check 52.1

1. *Ecology* is the scientific study of the interactions between organisms and their environment; *environmentalism* is advocacy for the environment. Ecology provides scientific understanding that can inform decision making about environmental issues. **2.** Interactions in ecological time that affect the survival or reproduction of organisms can result in changes to the population's gene pool and ultimately result in a change in the population on an evolutionary time scale. **3.** If the fungicides are used together, fungi will likely evolve resistance to all four much more quickly than if the fungicides are used individually at different times.

Concept Check 52.2

1. a. Humans could transplant a species to a new area that it could not previously reach because of a geographic barrier (dispersal change). b. Humans could change a species' biotic interactions by eliminating a predator or herbivore species, such as sea urchins, from an area. **2.** The sun's unequal heating of Earth's surface produces temperature variations between the warmer tropics and colder polar regions, and it influences the movement of air masses and thus the distribution of moisture at different latitudes. **3.** One test would be to build a fence around a plot of land in an area that has trees of that species, excluding all deer from the plot. You could then compare the abundance of tree seedlings inside and outside the fenced plot over time.

Concept Check 52.3

1. Rapid changes in salinity can cause salt stress in many organisms. **2.** In the oceanic pelagic zone, the ocean bottom lies below the photic zone, so there is too little light to support benthic algae or rooted plants. **3.** In a river below a dam, the fish are more likely to be species that prefer colder water. In summer, the deep layers of a reservoir are colder than the surface layers, so a river below a dam will be colder than an undammed river.

Concept Check 52.4

1. Higher average temperature in deserts **2.** Answers will vary by location but should be based on the information and maps in Figure 52.21. How much your local area has been altered from its natural state will influence how much it reflects the expected characteristics of your biome, particularly the expected plants and animals. **3.** Northern coniferous forest is likely to replace tundra along the boundary between these biomes. To see why, note that northern coniferous forest is adjacent to tundra throughout North America, northern Europe, and Asia (see Figure 52.19) and that the temperature range for northern coniferous forest is just above that for tundra (see Figure 52.20).

Self-Quiz

1. c **2.** d **3.** a **4.** d **5.** b **6.** d **7.** d **8.** e **9.** a
10.

Based on what you learned from Figure 52.8 and on the positive relationship you observed in the field between kelp abundance and otter density, you could hypothesize that otters lower sea urchin density, reducing feeding of the urchins on kelp.

CHAPTER 53

Figure Questions

Figure 53.4 The dispersion of the penguins would likely appear clumped as you flew over densely populated islands and sparsely populated ocean. **Figure 53.8** If male European kestrels provided no parental care, brood size should not affect their survival. Therefore, the three bars representing male survival in Figure 53.8 should have similar heights. In contrast, female survival should still decline with increasing brood size, as shown in the current figure. **Figure 53.19** The moose population grew quickly because food was abundant and predators were absent. During this period, the population experienced exponential growth. **Figure 53.20** Hare numbers typically peaked slightly before lynx numbers did. The lynx depend on the hares for food, but there is a delay between increased food availability and increased reproduction by the lynx.

Concept Check 53.1

1. The territorial species likely has a uniform pattern of dispersion, since the interactions between individuals will maintain constant space between

them. The flocking species is probably clumped, since most individuals probably live in one of the clumps (flocks).
2.

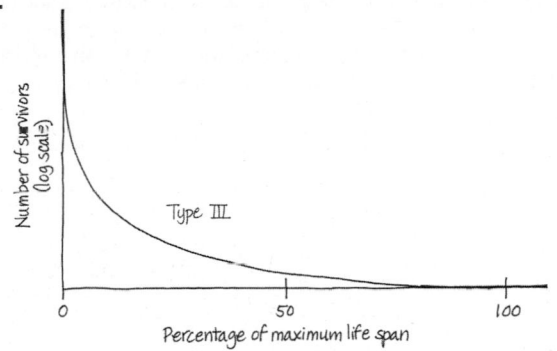

A type III survivorship curve is most likely because very few of the young probably survive. **3.** If an animal is captured by attracting it with food, it may be more likely to be recaptured if it seeks the same food. The number of marked animals recaptured (x) would be an overestimate, and because the population size $(N) = mn/x$, N would be an underestimate. Alternatively, if an animal has a negative experience during capture and learns from that experience, it may be less likely to be recaptured. In this case, x would be an underestimate and N would be an overestimate.

Concept Check 53.2

1. The constant, spring-fed stream. In more constant physical conditions, where populations are more stable and competition for resources is more likely, larger well-provisioned young, which are more typical of iteroparous species, have a better chance of surviving. **2.** By preferentially investing in the eggs it lays in the nest, the peacock wrasse increases their probability of survival. The eggs it disperses widely and does not provide care for are less likely to survive, at least some of the time, but require a lower investment by the adults. (In this sense, the adults avoid the risk of placing all their eggs in one basket.) **3.** If a parent's survival is compromised greatly by bearing young during times of stress, the animal's fitness may increase if it abandons its current young and survives to produce healthier young at a later time.

Concept Check 53.3

1. Though r_{max} is constant, N, the population size, is increasing. As r_{max} is applied to an increasingly large N, population growth $(r_{max}N)$ accelerates, producing the J-shaped curve. **2.** On the new island. The first plants that found suitable habitat on the island would encounter an abundance of space, nutrients, and light. In the rain forest, competition among plants for these resources is intense. **3.** The net population growth is $\Delta N/\Delta t = bN - dN$. The annual per capita birth rate, b, equals $14/1,000$, or 0.014, and the per capita death rate, d, equals $8/1,000$, or 0.008. Therefore, the net population growth in 2006 is

$$\frac{\Delta N}{\Delta t} = (0.014 \times 300,000,000) - (0.008 \times 300,000,000)$$

or 1.8 million people. A population is growing exponentially only if its per capita rate of increase equals its maximum rate. That is not the case for the United States currently.

Concept Check 53.4

1. When N (population size) is small, there are relatively few individuals producing offspring. When N is large, near the carrying capacity, per capita growth is relatively small because it is limited by available resources. The steepest part of the logistic growth curve corresponds to a population with a number of reproducing individuals that is substantial but not yet near carrying capacity. **2.** r-selected. Weeds that colonize an abandoned field face little competition, and their initial populations are well below carrying capacity. These are characteristics of environments that favor r-selected species. **3.** Using a population size of 1,600 as an example,

$$\frac{dN}{dt} = r_{max}N \frac{(K-N)}{K} = \frac{1(1,600)(1,500 - 1,600)}{1,500}$$

and the population "growth" rate is −107 individuals per year. The population shrinks even faster when N is farther from the carrying capacity; when N equals 1,750 and 2,000 individuals, the population shrinks by 292 and 667 individuals per year, respectively. These negative growth rates correspond most closely to the time when the *Daphnia* population has overshot its carrying capacity and is shrinking, about days 65–100 in Figure 53.13b.

Concept Check 53.5
1. Competition for resources and space can negatively impact population growth by limiting reproductive output. Diseases that are transmitted more easily in crowded populations can exert negative feedback on increasing population size. Some predators feed preferentially on species at higher population densities, since those prey are easier to find than are prey in less dense populations. In crowded populations, toxic metabolic wastes can build up and poison the organisms.   **2.** Three attributes are the size, quality, and isolation of patches. A patch that is larger or of higher quality is more likely to attract individuals and to be a source of individuals for other patches. A patch that is relatively isolated will undergo less exchange of individuals with other patches.   **3.** You would need to study the population for more than one cycle (longer than 10 years and probably at least 20) before having sufficient data to examine changes through time. Otherwise, it would be impossible to know whether an observed decrease in the population size reflected a long-term trend or was part of the normal cycle.

Concept Check 53.6
1. A bottom-heavy age structure, with a disproportionate number of young people, portends continuing growth of the population as these young people begin reproducing. In contrast, a more evenly distributed age structure predicts a more stable population size.   **2.** The growth rate of Earth's human population has dropped by half since the 1960s, from 2.2% in 1962 to 1.15% today. Nonetheless, growth has not slowed much because the smaller growth rate is counterbalanced by increased population size; the number of extra people on Earth each year remains enormous—approximately 75 million.   **3.** Each of us influences our ecological footprint by how we live—what we eat, how much energy we use, and the amount of waste we generate—as well as by how many children we have. Making choices that reduce our demand for resources makes our ecological footprint smaller.

Self-Quiz
1. c   **2.** c   **3.** c   **4.** d   **5.** d   **6.** b   **7.** c   **8.** d   **9.** c   **10.** d
11.

The total number of female offspring produced is greatest in females 1–2 years of age. Sample calculation for females of this age group: 252 indiv. × 1.07 female offspring/indiv. = 270 female offspring.

CHAPTER 54

Figure Questions
Figure 54.3 Its realized and fundamental niches would be similar. **Figure 54.4** If both species were feeding on seeds of the same size, you would expect differences in beak size to disappear over evolutionary time. The species could not specialize on seeds of different sizes.   **Figure 54.14** The low-productivity treatment had the shortest food chain, so that food chain should be the most stable.   **Figure 54.15** The death of individuals

of *Mytilus*, a dominant species, should open up space for other species and increase species richness even in the absence of *Pisaster*.   **Figure 54.19** Because the abundance of the second predatory species is unaffected by soil warming, there would be a less dramatic decrease in total predator numbers. Therefore, if the top-down model applies in this community, you would expect a smaller increase in *S. lindsayae* density than was actually observed. **Figure 54.28** Other factors not included in the model must contribute to the unexplained variation in the results.

Concept Check 54.1
1. Interspecific competition has negative effects on both species (−/−). In predation, the predator population benefits at the expense of the prey population (+/−). Mutualism is a symbiosis in which both species benefit (+/+).   **2.** One of the competing species will become locally extinct because of the greater reproductive success of the more efficient competitor.   **3.** Examples of relevant interactions include competition between weeds and food crops; predation by humans on herbivores, such as cattle; herbivory by humans on leafy vegetables, such as lettuce or spinach; and the planting of symbiotic nitrogen-fixing plants, such as beans or peas.

Concept Check 54.2
1. Species richness, the number of species in the community, and relative abundance, the proportions of the community represented by the various species, both contribute to species diversity. Compared to a community with a very high proportion of one species, one with a more even proportion of species is considered to be more diverse.   **2.** The energetic hypothesis suggests that the length of a food chain is limited by the inefficiency of energy transfer along the chain, while the dynamic stability hypothesis proposes that long food chains are less stable than short chains. The energetic hypothesis predicts that food chains will be longer in habitats with higher primary productivity. The dynamic stability hypothesis predicts that food chains will be longer in more predictable environments.   **3.** According to the bottom-up model, adding extra predators would have little effect on lower trophic levels, particularly vegetation. If the top-down model applied, increased bobcat numbers would decrease raccoon numbers, increase snake numbers, decrease grasshopper numbers, and increase plant biomass.

Concept Check 54.3
1. High levels of disturbance are generally so disruptive that they eliminate many species from communities, leaving the community dominated by a few tolerant species. Low levels of disturbance permit competitively dominant species to exclude other species from the community. In contrast, moderate levels of disturbance can facilitate coexistence of a greater number of species in a community by preventing competitively dominant species from becoming abundant enough to eliminate other species from the community.   **2.** Early successional species can facilitate the arrival of other species in many ways, including increasing the fertility or water-holding capacity of soils or providing shelter to seedlings from wind and intense sunlight.   **3.** The absence of fire for 100 years would represent a change to a low level of disturbance. According to the intermediate disturbance hypothesis, this change should cause diversity to decline as competitively dominant species gain sufficient time to exclude less competitive species.

Concept Check 54.4
1. Ecologists propose that the greater species richness of tropical regions is the result of their longer evolutionary history and the greater solar energy input and water availability in tropical regions.   **2.** Immigration of species to islands declines with distance from the mainland and increases with island area. Extinction of species is lower on larger islands and on less isolated islands. Since the number of species on islands is largely determined by the difference between rates of immigration and extinction, the number of species will be highest on large islands near the mainland and lowest on small islands far from the mainland.   **3.** Because of their greater mobility, birds disperse to islands more often than snakes or mammals, so birds should have greater richness.

Concept Check 54.5
1. Pathogens are microorganisms, viruses, viroids, or prions that cause disease.   **2.** If the parasite requires contact with a human and another animal, the parasite might be an especially likely vector for the pathogens that cause zoonotic diseases.   **3.** If you can identify the host or hosts of the disease as well as any intermediate vectors, such as mosquitoes or fleas, you can reduce

the rate of infection by decreasing the abundance of the host and vector or by reducing their contact with people.

Self-Quiz
1. c **2.** d **3.** b **4.** c **5.** c **6.** d **7.** b **8.** c
9. Community 1: $H = -[(0.05)(\ln 0.05) + (0.05)(\ln 0.05) + (0.85)(\ln 0.85) + (0.05)(\ln 0.05)] = 0.59$. Community 2: $H = -[(0.30)(\ln 0.30) + (0.40)(\ln 0.40) + (0.30)(\ln 0.30)] = 1.1$. Community 2 is more diverse.
10.

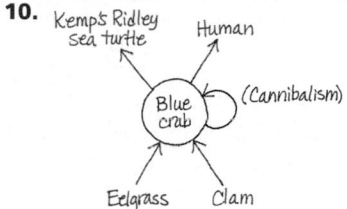

Crab numbers should increase, reducing the abundance of eelgrass.

CHAPTER 55

Figure Questions
Figure 55.6 Wetlands, coral reefs, and coastal zones cover areas too small to show up clearly on global maps. **Figure 55.7** If the new duck farms made nitrogen available in rich supply, as phosphorus already is, then adding extra nitrogen in the experiment would not increase phytoplankton density. **Figure 55.13** By dissolving minerals, the fungi move nutrients from reservoir D (inorganic materials unavailable as nutrients) to reservoir C (inorganic materials available as nutrients). **Figure 55.15** Water availability is probably another factor that varied across the sites. Such factors not included in the experimental design could make the results more difficult to interpret. Multiple factors can also covary in nature, so ecologists must be careful that the factor they are studying is actually causing the observed response and is not just correlated with it.

Concept Check 55.1
1. Energy passes through an ecosystem, entering as sunlight and leaving as heat. It is not recycled within the ecosystem. **2.** The second law states that in any energy transfer or transformation, some of the energy is dissipated to the surroundings as heat. This "escape" of energy from an ecosystem is offset by the continuous influx of solar radiation. **3.** You would need to know how much biomass the wildebeests ate from your plot and how much nitrogen was contained in that biomass. You would also need to know how much nitrogen they deposited in urine or feces.

Concept Check 55.2
1. Only a fraction of solar radiation strikes plants or algae, only a portion of that fraction is of wavelengths suitable for photosynthesis, and much energy is lost as a result of reflection or heating of plant tissue. **2.** By manipulating the level of the factors of interest, such as phosphorus availability or soil moisture, and measuring responses by primary producers **3.** The student is missing the plant biomass eaten by herbivores and the production allocated to plant roots and other belowground tissues.

Concept Check 55.3
1. 20 J; 40% **2.** Nicotine protects the plant from herbivores. **3.** There are many things they could do to reduce their production efficiency. For example, exercising vigorously will use energy that might otherwise go to biomass, and keeping the house cool will force their bodies to use energy to stay warm.

Concept Check 55.4
1. For example, for the carbon cycle:

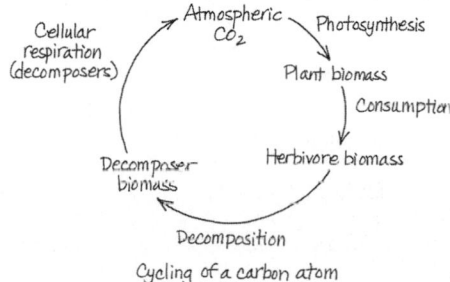

2. Removal of the trees stops nitrogen uptake from the soil, allowing nitrate to accumulate there. The nitrate is washed away by precipitation and enters the streams. **3.** Most of the nutrients in a tropical rain forest are contained in the trees, so removing the trees by logging rapidly depletes nutrients from the ecosystem. The nutrients that remain in the soil are quickly carried away into streams and groundwater by the abundant precipitation.

Concept Check 55.5
1. Adding nutrients causes population explosions of algae and the organisms that feed on them. Increased respiration by algae and consumers, including detritivores, depletes the lake's oxygen, which the fish require. **2.** At a lower trophic level, because biological magnification increases the concentration of toxins up the food chain **3.** Because higher temperatures lead to faster decomposition, organic matter in these soils could be quickly decomposed to CO_2, speeding up global warming.

Self-Quiz
1. c **2.** b **3.** d **4.** c **5.** e **6.** a **7.** d
8.

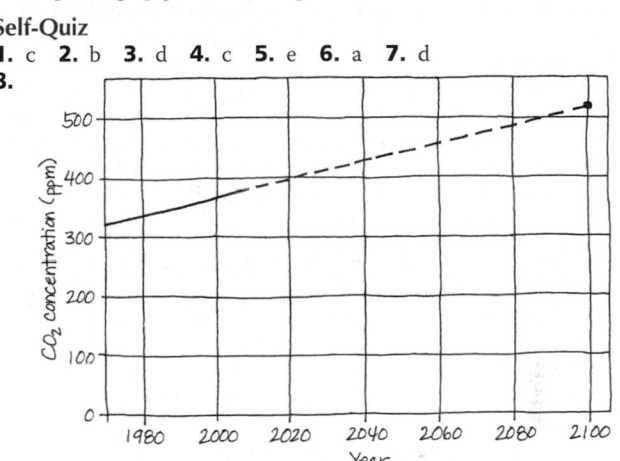

Between 1974 and 2007, Earth's atmospheric CO_2 concentration increased from approximately 330 ppm to 385 ppm. If this rate of increase of 1.7 ppm/yr continues, the concentration in 2100 will be about 540 ppm. The actual rise in CO_2 concentration could be larger or smaller, depending on Earth's human population, per capita energy use, and the extent to which societies take steps to reduce CO_2 emissions, including replacing fossil fuels with renewable or nuclear fuels. Additional scientific data will be important for many reasons, including determining how quickly greenhouse gases such as CO_2 are removed from the atmosphere by the biosphere.

CHAPTER 56

Figure Questions
Figure 56.4 You would need to know the complete range of the species and that it is missing across all of that range. You would also need to be certain that the species isn't hidden, as might be the case for an animal that is hibernating underground or a plant that is present in the form of seeds or spores. **Figure 56.11** Because the population of Illinois birds has a different genetic makeup than birds in other regions, you would want to maintain to the greatest extent possible the frequency of beneficial genes or alleles found only in that population. In restoration, preserving genetic diversity in a species is as important as increasing organism numbers. **Figure 56.13** The natural disturbance regime in this habitat included frequent fires that cleared undergrowth but did not kill mature pine trees. Without these fires, the undergrowth quickly fills in and the habitat becomes unsuitable for red-cockaded woodpeckers.

Concept Check 56.1
1. In addition to species loss, the biodiversity crisis includes the loss of genetic diversity within populations and species and the degradation of entire ecosystems. **2.** Habitat destruction, such as deforestation, channelizing of rivers, or conversion of natural ecosystems to agriculture or cities, deprives species of places to live. Introduced species, which are transported by humans to regions outside their native range, where they are not controlled by their natural pathogens or predators, often reduce the population sizes of native species through competition or predation. Overexploitation has reduced populations of plants and animals or driven them to extinction. **3.** If both

populations breed separately, then gene flow between the populations would not occur and genetic differences between them would be greater. As a result, the loss of genetic diversity would be greater than if the populations interbreed.

Concept Check 56.2
1. Reduced genetic variation decreases the capacity of a population to evolve in the face of change.   **2.** The effective population size, N_e, is $4(35 \times 10)/(35 + 10) = 31$ birds.   **3.** Because millions of people use the greater Yellowstone ecosystem each year, it would be impossible to eliminate all contact between people and bears. Instead, you might try to reduce the kinds of encounters where bears are killed. You might recommend lower speed limits on roads in the park, adjust the timing or location of hunting seasons (where hunting is allowed outside the park) to minimize contact with mother bears and cubs, and provide financial incentives for livestock owners to try alternative means (such as guard dogs) of protecting livestock.

Concept Check 56.3
1. A small area supporting an exceptionally large number of endemic species as well as a disproportionate number of endangered and threatened species   **2.** Zoned reserves may provide sustained supplies of forest products, water, hydroelectric power, educational opportunities, and income from ecotourism.   **3.** Habitat corridors can increase the rate of movement or dispersal of organisms between habitat patches and thus the rate of gene flow between subpopulations. They thus help prevent a decrease in fitness attributable to inbreeding. They can also minimize interactions between organisms and humans as the organisms disperse; in cases involving potential predators, such as bears or large cats, minimizing such interactions is desirable.

Concept Check 56.4
1. The main goal is to restore degraded ecosystems to a more natural state.   **2.** Bioremediation uses organisms, generally prokaryotes, fungi, or plants, to detoxify or remove pollutants from ecosystems. Biological augmentation uses organisms, such as nitrogen-fixing plants, to add essential materials to degraded ecosystems.   **3.** The Kissimmee River project returns the flow of water to the original channel and restores natural flow, a self-sustaining outcome. Ecologists at the Maungatautari reserve will need to maintain the integrity of the fence indefinitely, an outcome that is not self-sustaining in the long term.

Concept Check 56.5
1. Sustainable development is an approach to development that works toward the long-term prosperity of human societies and the ecosystems that support them, which requires linking the biological sciences with the social sciences, economics, and humanities.   **2.** Biophilia, our sense of connection to nature and other forms of life, may act as a significant motivation for the development of an environmental ethic that resolves not to allow species to become extinct or ecosystems to be destroyed. Such an ethic is necessary if we are to become more attentive and effective custodians of the environment.   **3.** At a minimum, you would want to know the size of the population and the average reproductive rate of individuals in it. To develop the fishery sustainably, you would seek a harvest rate that maintains the population near its original size and maximizes its harvest in the long term rather than the short term.

Self-Quiz
1. c **2.** e **3.** d **4.** d **5.** d **6.** e **7.** c **8.** a
10.

To minimize the area of forest into which the cowbirds penetrate, you should locate the road along one edge of the reserve. Any other location would increase the area of affected habitat. Similarly, the maintenance building should be in a corner of the reserve to minimize the area susceptible to cowbirds.

B Periodic Table of the Elements

Representative elements

Alkali metals → 1

Alkaline earth metals → 2

Halogens Noble gases

18

Period number

Group 1A	Group 2A											Group 3A	Group 4A	Group 5A	Group 6A	Group 7A	Group 8A

Period 1
| 1 H 1.008 | | | | | | | | | | | | | | | | | 2 He 4.003 |

Period 2 — Transition elements
| 3 Li 6.941 | 4 Be 9.012 | | | | | | | | | | | 5 B 10.81 | 6 C 12.01 | 7 N 14.01 | 8 O 16.00 | 9 F 19.00 | 10 Ne 20.18 |

Period 3
| 11 Na 22.99 | 12 Mg 24.31 | 3 3B | 4 4B | 5 5B | 6 6B | 7 7B | 8 | 9 —8B— | 10 | 11 1B | 12 2B | 13 Al 26.98 | 14 Si 28.09 | 15 P 30.97 | 16 S 32.07 | 17 Cl 35.45 | 18 Ar 39.95 |

Period 4
| 19 K 39.10 | 20 Ca 40.08 | 21 Sc 44.96 | 22 Ti 47.87 | 23 V 50.94 | 24 Cr 52.00 | 25 Mn 54.94 | 26 Fe 55.85 | 27 Co 58.93 | 28 Ni 58.69 | 29 Cu 63.55 | 30 Zn 65.41 | 31 Ga 69.72 | 32 Ge 72.64 | 33 As 74.92 | 34 Se 78.96 | 35 Br 79.90 | 36 Kr 83.80 |

Period 5
| 37 Rb 85.47 | 38 Sr 87.62 | 39 Y 88.91 | 40 Zr 91.22 | 41 Nb 92.91 | 42 Mo 95.94 | 43 Tc (98) | 44 Ru 101.1 | 45 Rh 102.9 | 46 Pd 106.4 | 47 Ag 107.9 | 48 Cd 112.4 | 49 In 114.8 | 50 Sn 118.7 | 51 Sb 121.8 | 52 Te 127.6 | 53 I 126.9 | 54 Xe 131.3 |

Period 6
| 55 Cs 132.9 | 56 Ba 137.3 | 57* La 138.9 | 72 Hf 178.5 | 73 Ta 180.9 | 74 W 183.8 | 75 Re 186.2 | 76 Os 190.2 | 77 Ir 192.2 | 78 Pt 195.1 | 79 Au 197.0 | 80 Hg 200.6 | 81 Tl 204.4 | 82 Pb 207.2 | 83 Bi 209.0 | 84 Po (209) | 85 At (210) | 86 Rn (222) |

Period 7
| 87 Fr (223) | 88 Ra (226) | 89† Ac (227) | 104 Rf (261) | 105 Db (262) | 106 Sg (266) | 107 Bh (264) | 108 Hs (269) | 109 Mt (268) | 110 Ds (271) | 111 — (272) | 112 — (285) | 113 (284) | 114 (289) | 115 (288) | | | |

*Lanthanides
| 58 Ce 140.1 | 59 Pr 140.9 | 60 Nd 144.2 | 61 Pm (145) | 62 Sm 150.4 | 63 Eu 152.0 | 64 Gd 157.3 | 65 Tb 158.9 | 66 Dy 162.5 | 67 Ho 164.9 | 68 Er 167.3 | 69 Tm 168.9 | 70 Yb 173.0 | 71 Lu 175.0 |

†Actinides
| 90 Th 232.0 | 91 Pa 231.0 | 92 U 238.0 | 93 Np (237) | 94 Pu (244) | 95 Am (243) | 96 Cm (247) | 97 Bk (247) | 98 Cf (251) | 99 Es 252 | 100 Fm 257 | 101 Md 258 | 102 No 259 | 103 Lr 260 |

▢ Metals   ▢ Metalloids   ▢ Nonmetals

Name (Symbol)	Atomic Number	Name (Symbol)	Atomic Number	Name (Symbol)	Atomic Number	Name (Symbol)	Atomic Number	Name (Symbol)	Atomic Number
Actinium (Ac)	89	Cobalt (Co)	27	Iodine (I)	53	Osmium (Os)	76	Silicon (Si)	14
Aluminum (Al)	13	Copper (Cu)	29	Iridium (Ir)	77	Oxygen (O)	8	Silver (Ag)	47
Americium (Am)	95	Curium (Cm)	96	Iron (Fe)	26	Palladium (Pd)	46	Sodium (Na)	11
Antimony (Sb)	51	Darmstadtium (Ds)	110	Krypton (Kr)	36	Phosphorus (P)	15	Strontium (Sr)	38
Argon (Ar)	18	Dubnium (Db)	105	Lanthanum (La)	57	Platinum (Pt)	78	Sulfur (S)	16
Arsenic (As)	33	Dysprosium (Dy)	66	Lawrencium (Lr)	103	Plutonium (Pu)	94	Tantalum (Ta)	73
Astatine (At)	85	Einsteinium (Es)	99	Lead (Pb)	82	Polonium (Po)	84	Technetium (Tc)	43
Barium (Ba)	56	Erbium (Er)	68	Lithium (Li)	3	Potassium (K)	19	Tellurium (Te)	52
Berkelium (Bk)	97	Europium (Eu)	63	Lutetium (Lu)	71	Praseodymium (Pr)	59	Terbium (Tb)	65
Beryllium (Be)	4	Fermium (Fm)	100	Magnesium (Mg)	12	Promethium (Pm)	61	Thallium (Tl)	81
Bismuth (Bi)	83	Fluorine (F)	9	Manganese (Mn)	25	Protactinium (Pa)	91	Thorium (Th)	90
Bohrium (Bh)	107	Francium (Fr)	87	Meitnerium (Mt)	109	Radium (Ra)	88	Thulium (Tm)	69
Boron (B)	5	Gadolinium (Gd)	64	Mendelevium (Md)	101	Radon (Rn)	86	Tin (Sn)	50
Bromine (Br)	35	Gallium (Ga)	31	Mercury (Hg)	80	Rhenium (Re)	75	Titanium (Ti)	22
Cadmium (Cd)	48	Germanium (Ge)	32	Molybdenum (Mo)	42	Rhodium (Rh)	45	Tungsten (W)	74
Calcium (Ca)	20	Gold (Au)	79	Neodymium (Nd)	60	Rubidium (Rb)	37	Uranium (U)	92
Californium (Cf)	98	Hafnium (Hf)	72	Neon (Ne)	10	Ruthenium (Ru)	44	Vanadium (V)	23
Carbon (C)	6	Hassium (Hs)	108	Neptunium (Np)	93	Rutherfordium (Rf)	104	Xenon (Xe)	54
Cerium (Ce)	58	Helium (He)	2	Nickel (Ni)	28	Samarium (Sm)	62	Ytterbium (Yb)	70
Cesium (Cs)	55	Holmium (Ho)	67	Niobium (Nb)	41	Scandium (Sc)	21	Yttrium (Y)	39
Chlorine (Cl)	17	Hydrogen (H)	1	Nitrogen (N)	7	Seaborgium (Sg)	106	Zinc (Zn)	30
Chromium (Cr)	24	Indium (In)	49	Nobelium (No)	102	Selenium (Se)	34	Zirconium (Zr)	40

Measurement	Unit and Abbreviation	Metric Equivalent	Metric-to-English Conversion Factor	English-to-Metric Conversion Factor
Length	1 kilometer (km)	= 1000 (10^3) meters	1 km = 0.62 mile	1 mile = 1.61 km
	1 meter (m)	= 100 (10^2) centimeters	1 m = 1.09 yards	1 yard = 0.914 m
		= 1000 millimeters	1 m = 3.28 feet	1 foot = 0.305 m
			1 m = 39.37 inches	
	1 centimeter (cm)	= 0.01 (10^{-2}) meter	1 cm = 0.394 inch	1 foot = 30.5 cm
				1 inch = 2.54 cm
	1 millimeter (mm)	= 0.001 (10^{-3}) meter	1 mm = 0.039 inch	
	1 micrometer (μm) (formerly micron, μ)	= 10^{-6} meter (10^{-3} mm)		
	1 nanometer (nm) (formerly millimicron, mμ)	= 10^{-9} meter (10^{-3} μm)		
	1 angstrom (Å)	= 10^{-10} meter (10^{-4} μm)		
Area	1 hectare (ha)	= 10,000 square meters	1 ha = 2.47 acres	1 acre = 0.405 ha
	1 square meter (m^2)	= 10,000 square centimeters	1 m^2 = 1.196 square yards	1 square yard = 0.8361 m^2
			1 m^2 = 10.764 square feet	1 square foot = 0.0929 m^2
	1 square centimeter (cm^2)	= 100 square millimeters	1 cm^2 = 0.155 square inch	1 square inch = 6.4516 cm^2
Mass	1 metric ton (t)	= 1000 kilograms	1 t = 1.103 tons	1 ton = 0.907 t
	1 kilogram (kg)	= 1000 grams	1 kg = 2.205 pounds	1 pound = 0.4536 kg
	1 gram (g)	= 1000 milligrams	1 g = 0.0353 ounce	1 ounce = 28.35 g
			1 g = 15.432 grains	
	1 milligram (mg)	= 10^{-3} gram	1 mg = approx. 0.015 grain	
	1 microgram (μg)	= 10^{-6} gram		
Volume (solids)	1 cubic meter (m^3)	= 1,000,000 cubic centimeters	1 m^3 = 1.308 cubic yards	1 cubic yard = 0.7646 m^3
			1 m^3 = 35.315 cubic feet	1 cubic foot = 0.0283 m^3
	1 cubic centimeter (cm^3 or cc)	= 10^{-6} cubic meter	1 cm^3 = 0.061 cubic inch	1 cubic inch = 16.387 cm^3
	1 cubic millimeter (mm^3)	= 10^{-9} cubic meter (10^{-3} cubic centimeter)		
Volume (liquids and gases)	1 kiloliter (kl or kL)	= 1000 liters	1 kL = 264.17 gallons	1 gallon = 3.785 L
	1 liter (l or L)	= 1000 milliliters	1 L = 0.264 gallons	1 quart = 0.946 L
			1 L = 1.057 quarts	
	1 milliliter (ml or mL)	= 10^{-3} liter	1 mL = 0.034 fluid ounce	1 quart = 946 mL
		= 1 cubic centimeter	1 mL = approx. 1/4 teaspoon	1 pint = 473 mL
				1 fluid ounce = 29.57 mL
			1 mL = approx. 15-16 drops (gtt.)	1 teaspoon = approx. 5 mL
	1 microliter (μl or μL)	= 10^{-6} liter (10^{-3} milliliters)		
Time	1 second (s)	= 1/60 minute		
	1 millisecond (ms)	= 10^{-3} second		
Temperature	Degrees Celsius (°C) (Absolute zero, when all molecular motion ceases, is − 273°C. The Kelvin [K] scale, which has the same size degrees as Celsius, has its zero point at absolute zero. Thus, 0°K = −273°C.)		°F = 9/5°C + 32	°C = 5/9 (°F − 32)

A Comparison of the Light Microscope and the Electron Microscope

Light Microscope

In light microscopy, light is focused on a specimen by a glass condenser lens; the image is then magnified by an objective lens and an ocular lens, for projection on the eye, digital camera, digital video camera, or photographic film.

Electron Microscope

In electron microscopy, a beam of electrons (top of the microscope) is used instead of light, and electromagnets are used instead of glass lenses. The electron beam is focused on the specimen by a condenser lens; the image is magnified by an objective lens and a projector lens for projection on a digital detector, fluorescent screen, or photographic film.

Classification of Life

This appendix presents a taxonomic classification for the major extant groups of organisms discussed in this text; not all phyla are included. The classification presented here is based on the three-domain system, which assigns the two major groups of prokaryotes, bacteria and archaea, to separate domains (with eukaryotes making up the third domain). This classification contrasts with the traditional five-kingdom system, which groups all prokaryotes in a single kingdom, Monera. Systematists no longer recognize the kingdom Monera because it would have members in two different domains (see Chapter 26).

Various alternative classification schemes are discussed in Unit Five of the text. The taxonomic turmoil includes debates about the number and boundaries of kingdoms and about the alignment of the Linnaean classification hierarchy with the findings of modern cladistic analysis. In this review, asterisks (*) indicate currently recognized phyla thought by some systematists to be paraphyletic.

DOMAIN BACTERIA

► **Proteobacteria**

► **Chlamydia**

► **Spirochetes**

► **Gram-positive Bacteria**

► **Cyanobacteria**

DOMAIN ARCHAEA

► **Korarchaeota**

► **Euryarchaeota**

► **Crenarchaeota**

► **Nanoarchaeota**

DOMAIN EUKARYA

In the phylogenetic hypothesis we present in Chapter 28, major clades of eukaryotes are grouped together in the five "supergroups" listed below in bold type. The traditional five-kingdom classification scheme united all the eukaryotes generally called protists in a single kingdom, Protista. However, advances in systematics have made it clear that Protista is in fact polyphyletic: Some protists are more closely related to plants, fungi, or animals than they are to other protists. As a result, the kingdom Protista has been abandoned. In contrast, the kingdoms Plantae (land plants), Fungi, and Animalia (animals) have survived from the five-kingdom system.

Excavata
► Diplomonadida (diplomonads)
► Parabasala (parabasalids)
► Euglenozoa (euglenozoans)
    Euglenophyta (euglenids)
    Kinetoplastida (kinetoplastids)

Chromalveolata
► Alveolata (alveolates)
    Dinoflagellata (dinoflagellates)
    Apicomplexa (apicomplexans)
    Ciliophora (ciliates)
► Stramenopila (stramenopiles)
    Bacillariophyta (diatoms)
    Chrysophyta (golden algae)
    Phaeophyta (brown algae)
    Oomycota (water molds)

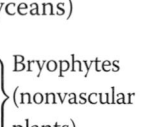

Archaeplastida
► Rhodophyta (red algae)
► Chlorophyta (green algae: chlorophytes)
► Charophyceae (green algae: charophyceans)
► Plantae

Phylum Hepatophyta (liverworts)	Bryophytes
Phylum Anthocerophyta (hornworts)	(nonvascular
Phylum Bryophyta (mosses)	plants)
Phylum Lycophyta (lycophytes)	Seedless vascular
Phylum Pterophyta (ferns, horsetails, whisk ferns)	plants
Phylum Ginkgophyta (ginkgo)	
Phylum Cycadophyta (cycads)	Gymnosperms
Phylum Gnetophyta (gnetophytes)	
Phylum Coniferophyta (conifers)	
Phylum Anthophyta (flowering plants)	Angiosperms

See pla►

Rhizaria
- Chlorarachniophyta (chlorarachniophytes)
- Foraminifera (forams)
- Radiolaria (radiolarians)

Unikonta
- Amoebozoa (amoebozoans)
    - Myxogastrida (plasmodial slime molds)
    - Dictyostelida (cellular slime molds)
    - Gymnamoeba (gymnamoebas)
    - Entamoeba (entamoebas)
    - Nucleariida (nucleariids)

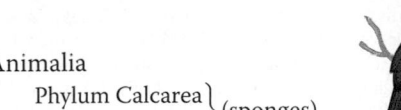

- Fungi
    - *Phylum Chytridiomycota (chytrids)
    - Phylum Zygomycota (zygomycetes)
    - Phylum Glomeromycota (glomeromycetes)
    - Phylum Ascomycota (sac fungi)
    - Phylum Basidiomycota (club fungi)

- Choanoflagellata (choanoflagellates)

- Animalia
    - Phylum Calcarea ⎫
    - Phylum Silicea ⎬ (sponges)
    - Phylum Cnidaria (cnidarians)
        - Class Hydrozoa (hydrozoans)
        - Class Scyphozoa (jellies)
        - Class Cubozoa (box jellies and sea wasps)
        - Class Anthozoa (sea anemones and most corals)
    - Phylum Ctenophora (comb jellies)
    - Phylum Acoela (acoel flatworms)
    - Lophotrochozoa (lophotrochozoans)
        - Phylum Placozoa (placozoans)
        - Phylum Kinorhyncha (kinorhynchs)
        - Phylum Platyhelminthes (flatworms)
            - Class Turbellaria (free-living flatworms)
            - Class Trematoda (flukes)
            - Class Monogenea (monogeneans)
            - Class Cestoda (tapeworms)
        - Phylum Nemertea (proboscis worms)
        - Phylum Ectoprocta (ectoprocts)
        - Phylum Phoronida (phoronids)
        - Phylum Brachiopoda (brachiopods)
        - Phylum Rotifera (rotifers)
        - Phylum Cycliophora (cycliophorans)
        - Phylum Mollusca (molluscs)
            - Class Polyplacophora (chitons)
            - Class Gastropoda (gastropods)
            - Class Bivalvia (bivalves)
            - Class Cephalopoda (cephalopods)
        - Phylum Annelida (segmented worms)
            - Class Oligochaeta (oligochaetes)
            - Class Polychaeta (polychaetes)
            - Class Hirudinea (leeches)
        - Phylum Acanthocephala (spiny-headed worms)
    - Ecdysozoa (ecdysozoans)
        - Phylum Loricifera (loriciferans)
        - Phylum Priapula (priapulans)
        - Phylum Nematoda (roundworms)
        - Phylum Arthropoda (This survey groups arthropods into a single phylum, but some zoologists now split the arthropods into multiple phyla.)
            - Subphylum Cheliceriformes (horseshoe crabs, arachnids)
            - Subphylum Myriapoda (millipedes, centipedes)
            - Subphylum Hexapoda (insects, springtails)
            - Subphylum Crustacea (crustaceans)
        - Phylum Tardigrada (tardigrades)
        - Phylum Onychophora (velvet worms)
    - Deuterostomia (deuterostomes)
        - Phylum Hemichordata (hemichordates)
        - Phylum Echinodermata (echinoderms)
            - Class Asteroidea (sea stars)
            - Class Ophiuroidea (brittle stars)
            - Class Echinoidea (sea urchins and sand dollars)
            - Class Crinoidea (sea lilies)
            - Class Concentricycloidea (sea daisies)
            - Class Holothuroidea (sea cucumbers)
        - Phylum Chordata (chordates)
            - Subphylum Cephalochordata (cephalochordates: lancelets)
            - Subphylum Urochrodata (urochordates: tunicates)
            - Subphylum Craniata (craniates)
                - Class Myxini (hagfishes)
                - Class Cephalaspidomorphi (lampreys) ⎫
                - Class Chondrichthyes (sharks, rays, chimaeras)
                - Class Acinopterygii (ray-finned fishes)
                - Class Actinistia (coelacanths)
                - Class Dipnoi (lungfishes) ⎬ Vertebrates
                - Class Amphibia (amphibians)
                - Class Reptilia (tuataras, lizards, snakes, turtles, crocodilians, birds)
                - Class Mammalia (mammals) ⎭

Credits

ILLUSTRATION CREDITS

Credits

Jurassic and evolution of mammalian characteristics. *Science* 292: 1535; **25.7** Adapted from D. J. Des Marais. September 8, 2000. When did photosynthesis emerge on Earth? *Science* 289: 1703—1705; **25.10** Data from A. H. Knoll and S. B. Carroll, June 25, 1995. *Science* 284: 2129—2137; **25.12** Map adapted from http://gelology.er.usgs.gov/eastern/plates.html; **25.14** Graph created from D. M. Raup and J. J. Sepkoski, Jr. 1982. Mass extinctions in the marine fossil record. *Science.* 215: 1501-1503 and J. J. Sepkoski, Jr. 1984. A kinetic model of Phanerozoic taxonomic diversity. III. Post-Paleozoic families and mass extinctions. *Paleobiology.* Vol 10, No. 2, pp. 246-267 in D. J. Futuyma, fig. 7.3a, p. 143 and fig. 7.6, p. 145, Sunderland, MA: Sinauer Associates; **25.16** Graph from R. K. Bambach et al. 2002. Anatomical and ecological constraints on Phanerozoic animal diversity in the marien realm. *PNAS* 99: 6854-6859; **25.17** Adapted from Hickman, Roberts, and Larson.1997, *Zoology*, 10th ed, Wm. C. Brown, fig. 31.1; **25.22** Adapted from M. Ronshaugen et al. Feb. 21, 2002. Hox protein mutation and macroevolution of the insect body plan. *Nature* 415: 914-917, fig. 1a; **25.24** Adapted from M. Strickberger, 1990. *Evolution*, Boston: Jones & Bartlett. **Chapter 26 26.6** Adapted from C. S. Baker and S. R. Palumbi. 1994. Which whales are hunted? A molecular genetic approach to monitoring whaling. *Science* 265: 1538-1539, fig. 1. Copyright © 1994. Reprinted with permission from AAAS; **26.12** Adapted from S. M. Shimeld. 1999. The evolution of the hedgehog gene family in chordates: Insights from amphioxus hedgehog. *Development Genes and Evolution* 209: 40-47, fig. 3; **26.19** Adapted from J. C. Avise, 2004. *Molecular Markers, Natural History, and Evolution*, 2/e, fig. 4.3c. Copyright © Sinauer Associates, Inc. Used with permission; **26.20a** Graph adapted from B. Korber et al. Timing the ancestor of the HIV-1 pandemic strains. *Science* 288: 1789-1796. June 9, 2000. Copyright © 2000. Reprinted with permission from AAAS. **26.21** Adapted from S. L. Baldauf et al. 2004. The Tree of Life: An Overview. In *Assembling the Tree of Life* by J. Cracraft and MJ Donoghue (eds), Oxford University Press, NY; **26.22** Adapted from S. Blair Hedges. The origin and evolution of model organisms. *Nature Reviews Genetics* 3: 838-848, fig. 1, p. 840; **26.23** Adapted from M. C. Rivera and J. A. Lake. 2004. The ring of life provides evidence for a genome fusion origin of eukaryotes. *Nature* 431: 152-155, fig. 3. Copyright © 2004. Reprinted by permission of Macmillan Publishers, Ltd. **Chapter 27 27.10b** Graph adapted from V. S. Cooper and R. E. Lenski. 2000. The population genetics of ecological specialization in evolving *E. coli* populations. *Nature* 407: 736-739; **27.19** Graph created from data in C. Calvaruso et al. 2006. Root-associated bacteria contribute to mineral weathering and to mineral nutrition in trees: A budgeting analysis. *Applied and Environmental Microbiology* 72: 1258-1266. **Chapter 28 28.2** From Archibald and Keeling, "Recycled Plastids," *Trends in Genetics*, Vol. 18, No. 11, 2002. Copyright © 2002, with permission from Elsevier; **28.11** Adapted from R. W. Bauman. 2004. *Microbiology*, fig. 12.7, p. 350. Copyright © 2004 Pearson Education, Inc., publishing as Pearson Benjamin Cummings; **28.23** Data from A. Stechman and T. Cavalier-Smith. 2002. Rooting the eukaryote tree by using a derived gene fusion, *Science* 297: 89-91; **28.27** Copyright © 2004 The Nature Conservancy. Map produced by N. Law – Global Priorities Group – 08/14/2004. **Chapter 29 29.10** Source: R. D. Bowden. 1991. Inputs, outputs and accumulation of nitrogen in an early successional moss *(Polytrichum)* ecosystem. *Ecological Monographs* 61: 207-223; **29.14** Adapted from Raven et al. *Biology of Plants*, 6th ed., fig. 19.7. **Chapter 30 30.12a** Adapted from Soltis et al., 2005. *Phylogeny and Evolution of Angiosperms*, Sinauer Associates, pp. 17, fig. 1.11 from Crane 1985, which is based on Harris, 1964; **30.12b** Adapted from Soltis et al., *Phylogeny and Evolution of Angiosperms*, p. 28, fig. 2.3. Copyright © 2005. Reprinted by permission of Sinauer Associates, Inc.; **Table 30.1** Adapted from Randy Moore et al., *Botany*, 2nd ed. Dubuque, IA: Brown, 1998, Table 2.2, p. 37. **Chapter 31 31.21** Graphs adapted from A. E. Arnold et al. 2003. Fungal endophytes limit pathogen damage in a tropical tree. *PNAS* 100: 15649-15654, figs. 4 and 5. **Chapter 33 33.28a** From J. K. Grenier et al. 1997. Evolution of the entire arthropod *Hox* gene set predated the origin and radiation of the onychophoran/arthropod clade, *Current Biology* 7: 547-553, fig. 3c, p. 551. Copyright © 1997, with permission from Elsevier, Inc. **Chapter 34 34.8b** Adapted from J. Mallatt and J. Chen. 2003. Fossil sister group of craniates: Predicted and found. *Journal of Morphology* 258: 1-31, fig. 1, 5/15/03. Copyright © 2003. Reprinted with permission of Wiley-Liss, Inc., a subsidiary of John Wiley & Sons, Inc.; **34.12** Adapted from K. Kardong. 2001. *Vertebrates: Comparative Anatomy, Function, and Evolution*, 3/e. © 2001 McGraw-Hill Science/Engineering/Mathematics.; **34.19** and **34.20** From C. Zimmer. *At the Water's Edge.* Copyright © 1999 by Carl Zimmer. Reprinted by permission of Jankow & Nesbit; **34.31a** Adapted from D. J. Futuyma. 2005. *Evolution*, 1/e. Sunderland, MA: Sinauer Associates; **34.40** Drawn from photos of fossils: *O. tugenensis* photo in Michael Balter, Early hominid sows division, *ScienceNow*, Feb. 22, 2001, © 2001 American Association for the Advancement of Science. *A. ramidus kadabba* photo by Timothy White, 1999/Brill Atlanta. *A. anamensis, A. garhi,* and *H. neanderthalensis* adapted from *The Human Evolution Coloring Book. K platyops* drawn from photo in Meave Leakey et al., New hominid genus from eastern Africa shows diverse middle Pliocene lineages, *Nature*, March 22, 2001, 410: 433. *P. boisei* drawn from a photo by David Bill. *H. ergaster* drawn from a photo at www.inhandmuseum.com. *S. tchadensis* drawn from a photo in Michel Brunet et al., A new hominid from the Upper Miocene of Chad, Central Africa, *Nature*, July 11, 2002, 418: 147, fig. 1b.; **34.43a** and **b** Adapted from I. V. Ovchinnikov et al. 2000. Molecular analysis of Neanderthal DNA from the northern Caucasus. *Nature* 404: 492, fig.3a and b. **Chapter 35 35.24 (right)** Pie chart adapted from *Nature*, Dec. 14, 2000, 408: 799. New data from The Arabidopsis Information Resource (TAIR). **Chapter 39 39.16 (top)** Adapted from M. Wilkins. 1988. *Plant Watching*, Facts of File Publ.; **39.28** Reprinted with permission from Edward Farmer, 1997, *Science* 279: 912. Copyright © 1997 American Association for the Advancement of Science. **Chapter 40 40.14** Adapted from fig. 2 in V. H. Hutchinson et al. Thermoregulation in a brooding female Indian python, *Python molurus bivittatus. Science* 151: 694-695, fig. 2. Copyright © 1966. Reprinted with permission from AAAS; **40.15** Adapted with permission from B. Heinrich. 1974. Thermoregulation in endothermic insects. *Science* 185: 747-756, fig. 7. © 1974 American Association for the Advancement of Science. **Chapter 41 41.5** Source: R. W. Smithells et al. 1980. Possible prevention of neural-tube defects by periconceptual vitamins supplementation. *Lancet* 315: 339-340; **41.10** Adapted from R. A. Rhoades and R.G. Pflanzer, *Human Physiology*, 3/e, fig. 22-1, p. 666. Copyright © 1996. Reprinted by permission of Brooks/Cole, a division of Thomson Learning: www.thomsonrights.comFax 800 732-2215; **41.23** Adapted from J. Marx, "Cellular Warriors at the Battle of the Bulge," *Science*, Vol. 299, p. 846. Copyright © 2003 American Association for the Advancement of Science. Illustration: Katharine Sutliff. **Chapter 42 42.31** Adapted from S. L. Lindstedt et al. 1991. Running energetics in the pronghorn antelope. *Nature* 353: 748–750. Copyright © 1991. Reprinted by permission of Macmillan Publishers, Ltd. **Chapter 43 43.5** Adapted from Phoebe Tzou et al, "Constitutive expression of a single antimicrobial peptide can restore wild-type resistance to infection in immuno-deficient *Drosophila* mutants," *PNAS*, 99: 2152-2157, figs. 2a and 4a. Copyright © 2002 National Academy of Sciences, U.S.A. Used with permission. **Chapter 44 44.6** Kangaroo rat data adapted from K. B. Schmidt-Nielson. 1990. *Animal Physiology: Adaptation and Environment*, 4th ed., p. 339. Cambridge: Cambridge University Press; **44.7** Adapted from K. B. Schmidt-Nielsen et al. 1958. Extrarenal salt excretion in birds. *American Journal of Physiology* 193: 101-107; **44.20** Table adapted from P. M. T. Deen et al. 1994. Requirement of human renal water channel aquaporin-2 for vasopressin-dependent concentration in urine. *Science* 264: 92-95, table 1. Copyright © 1994. Reprinted with permission from AAAS; **44 EOC** (visual summary) Adapted from W. S. Beck et al. 1991. *Life: An Introduction to Biology*, p. 649. Copyright © 1991 HarperCollins. Reprinted by permission of Pearson Education. **Chapter 45 45.4** J. M. Horowitz, et al. 1980. The Response of Single Melanophores to Extracellular and Intracellular Iontophoretic Injection of Melanocyte-Stimulating Hormone. *Endocrinology* 106: 771, fig. B. © 1980 by The Endocrine Society; **45.22** A. Jost, Recherches sur la differenciation sexuelle de l'embryon de lapin (Studies on the sexual differentiation of the rabbit embryo). *Arch. Anat. Microsc. Morphol. Exp (Archives d'anatomie microscopique et de biologie expérimentale*). 36: 271-316, 1947. **Chapter 46 46.9** Figure adapted from R. R. Snook and D. J. Hosken. 2004. Sperm death and dumping in *Drosophila.. Nature* 428: 939—941, fig. 2. Copyright © 2004. Reprinted by permission of Macmillan Publishers, Ltd. **Chapter 47 47.18** From Wolpert, et al. 1998. *Principles of Development*, fig. 8.25, p. 251 (right). Oxford: Oxford University Press. By permission of Oxford University Press; **47.21a** Copyright © 1989 from *Molecular Biology of the Cell*, 2nd ed. by Bruce Alberts et al. Reproduced by permission of Garland Science/Taylor & Francis Books, Inc.; **47.21b** From Hiroki Nishida, "Cell lineage analysis in ascidian embryos by intracellular injection of a tracer enzyme: III. Up to the tissue restricted stage," *Developmental Biology*, Vol. 121, p. 526, June, 1987. Copyright © 1987 with permission from Elsevier, Inc.; **47.22** Copyright © 2002 from *Molecular Biology of the Cell*, 4th ed. by Bruce Alberts et al., fig. 21.17, p. 1172. Reproduced by permission of Garland Science/Taylor & Francis Books, Inc.; **47.24 experiment** and **left side of results** From Wolpert et al. 1998. *Principles of Development*, fig. 1.10, Oxford: Oxford University Press. By permission of Oxford University Press; **47.24 right side of results** Figure 15.12, p. 604 from *Developmental Biology*, 5th ed. by Gilbert et al. Copyright © 1997 Sinauer Associates. Used with permission. **Chapter 48 48.10** Adapted from G. Matthews, 1986. *Cellular Physiology of Nerve and Muscle*, Cambridge, MA: Blackwell Scientific Publications. © 1986 Blackwell Science. Used with permission of Blackwell Science, Inc.; **48.17** Adapted from C. B. Pert and S. H. Snyder. 1973. Opiate receptor: Demonstration in nervous tissue. *Science* 179: 1011-1014, Table 1. **Chapter 49 49.11** Adapted from L. M. Mukhametov. 1984. Sleep in marine mammals. In *Sleep Mechanisms*, by A. A. Borbéley and J. L. Valatx (eds.). Munich: Springer-Verlag, pp 227-238; **49.12** Adapted from M. R. Ralph et al. 1990. Transplanted suprachiasmatic nucleus determines circadian period. *Science* 247: 975-978, fig. 2; **49.14** Adapted from E. D. Jarvis et al. 2005. Avian brains and a new understanding of vertebrate brain evolution. *Nature Reviews Neuroscience* 6: 151-159, fig. 1c. **Chapter 50 50.14** Adapted from K. L. Mueller et al. 1975. The receptors and coding logic for bitter taste. *Nature* 434: 225-229;

50.19 Adapted from Bear et al. 2001. *Neuroscience: Exploring the Brain,* 2nd ed., figs. 11.8 and 11.9, pp. 281 and 283. Hagerstown,MD: Lippincott Williams & Wilkins. © 2001 Lippincott Williams and Wilkins; **50.22** Adapted from Shepherd. 1988. *Neurobiology,* 2nd ed., fig. 11.4, p. 227. Oxford University Press. (From V. G. Dethier. 1976. *The Hungry Fly.* Cambridge, MA: Harvard University Press.); **50.23** Adapted from Bear et al. 2001, Neuroscience: Exploring the Brain, 2nd ed., fig. 8.7, p. 196. Hagerstown,MD: Lippincott Williams & Wilkins. © 2001 Lippincott Williams and Wilkins; **50.32** Grasshopper adapted from Hickman et al. 1993. *Integrated Principles of Zoology,* 9th ed., Fig. 22.6, p. 518. New York: McGraw-Hill Higher Education. © 1993 The McGraw-Hill Companies; **50.37** K. Schmidt-Nielsen. 1972. Locomotion: Energy cost of swimming, flying, and running. *Science* 177: 222-228. **Chapter 51 51.3b** Adapted from N. Tinbergen. 1951. *The Study of Instinct.* Oxford: Oxford University Press. By permission of Oxford University Press; **51.7** Adapted from M. B. Sokolowski, 2001. *Drosophila: Genetics meets behavior. Nature Reviews: Genetics* 2: 881, fig. 1. Copyright © 2001 McMillan Publishing. Used with permission; **51.14 (left)** Adapted from C. S. Henry et al. 2002. The inheritance of mating songs in two cryptic, sibling lacewings species (Neuroptera: Chrysopidae: *Chrysoperla*). *Genetica* 116: 269-289, fig. 2. Copyright © 2002. Reprinted by permission of Springer Verlag; **51.15 (top)** Adapted from a photograph by Jonathan Blair in Alcock, 2002. *Animal Behavior,* 7th ed. Sinauer Associates, Inc., Publiishers. **51.15 (bottom)** Adapted from P. Berthold et al. 1992. Rapid microevolution of migratory behaviour in a wild bird species. *Nature* 360, 12/17,/92, p. 668, fig. 1. Copyright © 1992 Nature Publishing, Inc., used with permission; **51.18** Adapted from M. B. Sokolowski et al. 1997. Evolution of foraging behavior in *Drosophila* by density-dependent selection. Proceedings of the National Academy of Sciences of the United States of America. 94: 7373-7377. Copyright © 1997 National Academy of Sciences, U.S.A.; **51.24** K. Witte and N. Sawka. 2003. Sexual imprinting on a novel trait in the dimorphic zebra finch: sexes differ. *Animal Behaviour* 65: 195-203. Art adapted from http://www.uni-bielefeld.de/biologue/vhf/KW/Forschungsprojekte2.html. **Chapter 52 52.3** Adapted from figure at http://tde.ornl.gov. Project supported by the U.S. Dept. of Energy's Office of Science (BER); **52.5** Map adapted from G. Caughly et al. 1987. *Kangaroos: Their Ecology and Management in the Sheep Rangelands of Australia,* p. 12, fig. 1.2, Cambridge: Cambridge University Press. Copyright © 1987 Cambridge University Press. Used with permission; **52.7** Map adapted from R. L. Smith. 1974. *Ecology and Field Biology,* fig. 11.19, p. 353. Harper and Row Publishers. Map updated from D. A. Sibley. 2000. National Audubon Society *The Sibley Guide to Birds,* Alfred A. Knopf: New York; **52.8** Data from W. J. Fletcher. 1987. Interactions among subtidal Australian sea urchins, gastropods and algae: effects of experimental removals. *Ecological Monographs* 57: 89–109; **52.11** Map adapted from Physicists track great ocean conveyor belt. http://www.anl.gov/Media_Center/Frontiers/2003/d8ee.html; **52.14** Adapted from L. Roberts. 1989. How fast can trees migrate? *Science* 243: 736, fig. 2. © 1989 by the American Association for the Advancement of Science; **52.19** Adapted from Heinrich Walter and Siegmar-Walter Breckle. 2003. *Walter's Vegetation of the Earth,* fig. 16, p. 36. Springer-Verlag, © 2003; **Un. 52.2** Data from J. Clausen, D. D. Keck, and W. M. Hiesey. 1948. Experimental studies on the nature of species. III. Environmental responses of climatic races of *Achillea.* Carnegie Institution of Washington Publication 581. **Chapter 53 53.5** Adapted from P. W. Sherman and M. L. Morton, "Demography of Belding's ground squirrels," *Ecology,* Vol. 65, No. 5, p. 1622, fig. 1a, 1984. Copyright © 1984 Ecological Society of America. Used by permission. **53.15** Adapted from J. T. Enright. 1976. Climate and population regulation: The biogeographer's dilemma. *Oecologia* 24: 295-310; **53.16** and **53.18** Adapted from T. Clutton-Brock and J. Pemberton. 2004. Soay Sheep: Dynamics and selection in an island population. Cambridge University Press. Used with permission; **53.19** Data courtesy of Rolf O. Peterson, Michigan Technological University; **53.23** Data from U. S. Census Bureau International Data Base; **53.24** Data from Population Reference Bureau 2000 and U. S. Census Bureau International Data Base, 2003; **53.25** Data from U. S. Census Bureau International Data Base; **53.26** Data from U. S. Census Bureau International Data Base 2003; **53.27** Adapted from M. L. Imhoff et al. 2004. Global patterns in human consumption of net primary production. *Nature* 429: 870-873, fig. 1a; **Tables 53.1** and **53.2** Data from P. W. Sherman and M. L. Morton, "Demography of Belding's ground squirrels," *Ecology,* Vol. 65, No. 5, p. 1622, fig. 1a, 1984. Copyright © 1984 Ecological Society of America. **Chapter 54 54.2** A. S. Rand and E. E. Williams. 1969. The anoles of La Palma: Aspects of their ecological relationships. *Breviora* 327. Museum of Comparative Zoology, Harvard University. Copyright © 1969 by the President and Fellows of Harvard College. Reprinted with permission from the Museum of Comparative Zoology; **54.10** Adapted from N.

Fierer and R. B. Jackson. 2006. The diversity and biogeography of soil bacterial communities. *Proceedings of the National Academy of Sciences USA* 103: 626–631 fig. 1a. Copyright © 2006 National Academy of Sciences, U.S.A. Used with permission; **54.12** Adapted from E. A, Knox. 1970. Antarctic marine ecosystems. In *Antarctic Ecology,* ed. M. W. Holdgate, 69-96. London: Academic Press; **54.13** Adapted from D. L. Breitburg et al. 1997. Varying effects of low dissolved oxygen on trophic interactions in an estuarine food web. *Ecological Monographs* 67: 490. Copyright © 1997 Ecological Society of America; **54.14** Adapted from B. Jenkins. 1992. Productivity, disturbance and food web structure at a local spatial scale in experimental container habitats. *Oikos* 65: 252. Copyright © 1992 Oikos, Sweden; **54.15** Adapted from R. T. Paine. 1966. Food web complexity and species diversity. *American Naturalist* 100: 65-75; **54.16** Adapted from J. A. Estes et al. 1998. Killer whale predation on sea otters linking oceanic and nearshore ecosystems. *Science* 282: 474. Copyright © 1998 by the American Association for the Advancement of Science. Reprinted with permission from AAAS; **54.18** Data for graph from S. D. Hacker and M. D. Bertness. 1999. Experimental evidence for factors maintaining plant species diversity in a New England salt marsh. *Ecology* 80: 2064-2073; **54.19** Data from D. Wall Freckman and R. A. Virginia 1997. Low-diversity Antarctic soil nematode communities: distribution and response to disturbance. *Ecology* 78: 363-369; **54.20** Graph adapted from A. R. Townsend et al. 1997. The intermediate disturbance hypothesis, refugia, and diversity in streams. *Limnology and Oceanography* 42: 938-949. Copyright © 1997 by the American Society of Limnology and Oceanography, Inc. Used with permission; **54.22** Adapted from R. L. Crocker and J. Major. 1955. Soil Development in relation to vegetation and surface age at Glacier Bay, Alaska. *Journal of Ecology* 43: 427-448; **54.23** Data from F. S. Chapin, III, et al. 1994. Mechanisms of primary succession following deglaciation at Glacier Bay, Alaska. *Ecological Monographs* 64: 149-175; **54.25** Adapted from D. J. Currie. 1991. Energy and large-scale patterns of animal- and plant-species richness. *American Naturalist* 137: 27-49; **54.26** Adapted from F. W. Preston. 1960. Time and space and the variation of species. *Ecology* 41: 611-627; **54.28** Adapted from F. W. Preston. 1962. The canonical distribution of commonness and rarity. *Ecology* 43: 185-215, 410-432. **Chapter 55 55.4** and **Un 55.1** Adapted from D. L. DeAngelis. 1992. *Dynamics of Nutrient Cycling and Food Webs.* New York: Chapman & Hall; **55.7** Adapted from J. H. Ryther and W. M. Dunstan. 1971. Nitrogen, phosphorus, and eutrophication in the coastal marine environment. *Science* 171: 1008-1013. Copyright © 1971. Reprinted with permission from AAAS; **55.8** Data from M. L. Rosenzweig. 1968. New primary productivity of terrestrial environments: Predictions from climatologic data, *American Naturalist* 102: 67-74; **55.14a** Adapted from R. E. Ricklefs. 1997. *The Economy of Nature,* 4th ed. © 1997 by W. H. Freeman and Company. Used with permission; **55.15** Map adapted from Moore et al. 1999. Litter decomposition rates in Canadian forests, Global Change Biology 5: 75-82. Trofymow et al. 1998. Canadian Intersite Decomposition Experiment (CIDET): Project and site establishment. Information Report BC-X-378. NRCAN CFS Victoria. 126pp. Produced under license from Her Majesty the Queen in Right of Canada, with permission of Natural Resources Canada. The Canadian Intersite Decomposition Experiment (CIDET) - http://cfs.nrcan.gc.ca/subsite/cidet; **55.21** CO_2 data from C. D. Keeling and T. P. Whorf, Scripps Institution of Oceanography. Temperature data from www.earth-policy.org/Indicators/Temp/Temp_data.htm. **55.23** Data from ozonewatch.gsfc.nasa.gov/facts/history/htmml; **Table 55.1** Data from Menzel and Ryther. 1961. *Deep Sea Ranch* 7: 276-281. **Chapter 56 56.10** Adapted from C. J. Krebs. 2001. *Ecology,* 5th ed., fig. 19.1. Copyright © 2001 Pearson Education, Inc., publishing as Pearson Benjamin Cummings; **56.11** Adapted from R. L. Westemeiier et al. 1998. Tracking the long-term decline and recovery of an isolated population. *Science* 282: 1696. © 1998 by the American Association for the Advancement of Science; **56.17** Adapted from N. Myers et al., "Biodiversity hotspots for conservation priorities," *Nature,* Vol. 403, p. 853, 2/24/2000. Copyright © 2000 Nature Publishing, Inc. Used with permission. Updated with data from C. H. Roberts et al. 2002. Marine biodiversity hotspots and conservation priorities for tropical reefs. *Science* 295: 1280-1284; **56.18** Adapted from W.D. Newmark, "Legal and biotic boundaries of western North American national parks: A problem of congruence." *Biological Conservation* 33: 199, 1985. © 1985 Elsevier, with kind permission; **56.19a** Map adapted from W. Purves and G. Orians, *Life, The Science of Biology,* 5th ed., fig. 55.23, p. 1239. © 1998 by Sinauer Associates, Inc. Used with permission; **56.22b** Graph adapted from http://news-service.standford.edu/news/2006/may24/gcriddle_ponds.jpg; **56.24** Data from Instituto Nacional de Estadistica y Censos de Costa Rica and Centro Centroamericano de Poblacion, Universidad de Costa Rica.

Glossary

G-1

Pronunciation Key
Pronounce

ā	as in	ace
a		ash
ch		chose
ē		meet
e/eh		bet
g		game
ī		ice
i		hit
ks		box
kw		quick
ng		song
ō		robe
o		ox
oy		boy
s		say
sh		shell
th		thin
ū		boot
u/uh		up
z		zoo

′ = primary accent
′ = secondary accent

5′ cap A modified form of guanine nucleotide added onto the nucleotide at the 5′ end of a pre-mRNA molecule.

A site One of a ribosome's three binding sites for tRNA during translation. The A site holds the tRNA carrying the next amino acid to be added to the polypeptide chain. (A stands for aminoacyl tRNA.)

ABC model A model of flower formation identifying three classes of organ identity genes that direct formation of the four types of floral organs.

abiotic (ā′-bī-ot′-ik) Nonliving; referring to physical and chemical properties of an environment.

abortion The termination of a pregnancy in progress.

abscisic acid (ABA) (ab-sis′-ik) A plant hormone that slows growth, often antagonizing actions of growth hormones. Two of its many effects are to promote seed dormancy and facilitate drought tolerance.

absorption The third stage of food processing in animals: the uptake of small nutrient molecules by an organism's body.

absorption spectrum The range of a pigment's ability to absorb various wavelengths of light; also a graph of such a range.

abyssal zone (uh-bis′-ul) The part of the ocean's benthic zone between 2,000 and 6,000 m deep.

acanthodian (ak′-an-thō′-d ē-un) Any of a group of ancient jawed aquatic vertebrates from the Devonian period.

accessory fruit A fruit, or assemblage of fruits, in which the fleshy parts are derived largely or entirely from tissues other than the ovary.

acclimatization (uh-klī′-muh-tī-zā′-shun) Physiological adjustment to a change in an environmental factor.

acetyl CoA Acetyl coenzyme A; the entry compound for the citric acid cycle in cellular respiration, formed from a fragment of pyruvate attached to a coenzyme.

acetylcholine (as′-uh-til-kō′-lēn) One of the most common neurotransmitters; functions by binding to receptors and altering the permeability of the postsynaptic membrane to specific ions, either depolarizing or hyperpolarizing the membrane.

acid A substance that increases the hydrogen ion concentration of a solution.

acid precipitation Rain, snow, or fog that is more acidic than pH 5.2.

acoelomate (uh-sē′-lō-māt) A solid-bodied animal lacking a cavity between the gut and outer body wall.

acquired immunity A vertebrate-specific defense that is mediated by B lymphocytes (B cells) and T lymphocytes (T cells). It exhibits specificity, memory, and self-nonself recognition. Also called adaptive immunity.

acrosomal reaction (ak′-ruh-sōm′-ul) The discharge of hydrolytic enzymes from the acrosome, a vesicle in the tip of a sperm, when the sperm approaches or contacts an egg.

acrosome (ak′-ruh-sōm) A vesicle in the tip of a sperm containing hydrolytic enzymes and other proteins that help the sperm reach the egg.

actin (ak′-tin) A globular protein that links into chains, two of which twist helically about each other, forming microfilaments (actin filaments) in muscle and other kinds of cells.

action potential A rapid change in the membrane potential of an excitable cell, caused by stimulus-triggered, selective opening and closing of voltage-sensitive gates in sodium and potassium ion channels.

action spectrum A graph that profiles the relative effectiveness of different wavelengths of radiation in driving a particular process.

activation energy The amount of energy that reactants must absorb before a chemical reaction will start; also called free energy of activation.

activator A protein that binds to DNA and stimulates gene transcription. In prokaryotes, activators bind in or near the promoter; in eukaryotes, activators bind to control elements in enhancers.

active immunity Long-lasting immunity conferred by the action of B cells and T cells and the resulting B and T memory cells specific for a pathogen. Active immunity can develop as a result of natural infection or immunization.

active site The specific portion of an enzyme that binds the substrate by means of multiple weak interactions and that forms the pocket in which catalysis occurs.

active transport The movement of a substance across a cell membrane, with an expenditure of energy, against its concentration or electrochemical gradient; mediated by specific transport proteins.

actual evapotranspiration The amount of water transpired by plants and evaporated from a landscape over a given period of time, usually measured in millimeters and estimated for a year.

adaptation Inherited characteristic of an organism that enhances its survival and reproduction in specific environments.

adaptive radiation Period of evolutionary change in which groups of organisms form many new species whose adaptations allow them to fill vacant ecological roles in their communities.

adenylyl cyclase (uh-den′-uh-lil) An enzyme that converts ATP to cyclic AMP in response to a signal.

adhesion The attraction between different kinds of molecules.

adipose tissue A connective tissue that insulates the body and serves as a fuel reserve; contains fat-storing cells called adipose cells.

adrenal gland (uh-drē′-nul) One of two endocrine glands located adjacent to the kidneys in mammals. Endocrine cells in the outer portion (cortex) respond to ACTH by secreting steroid hormones that help maintain homeostasis during long-term stress. Neurosecretory cells in the central portion (medulla) secrete epinephrine and norepinephrine in response to nervous inputs triggered by short-term stress.

adrenocorticotropic hormone (ACTH) A tropic hormone that is produced and secreted by the anterior pituitary and that stimulates the production and secretion of steroid hormones by the adrenal cortex.

aerobic respiration A catabolic pathway that consumes oxygen (O_2) and organic molecules, producing ATP. This is the most efficient catabolic pathway and is carried out in most eukaryotic cells and many prokaryotic organisms.

afferent arteriole (af′-er-ent) In the kidney, the blood vessel supplying a nephron.

age structure The relative number of individuals of each age in a population.

aggregate fruit A fruit derived from a single flower that has more than one carpel.

agonistic behavior (a'-gō-nis'-tik) In animals, an often ritualized contest that determines which competitor gains access to a resource, such as food or mates.

AIDS (acquired immunodeficiency syndrome) The symptoms and signs present during the late stages of HIV infection, defined by a specified reduction in the number of T cells and the appearance of characteristic secondary infections.

alcohol fermentation Glycolysis followed by the conversion of pyruvate to carbon dioxide and ethyl alcohol.

aldosterone (al-dos'-tuh-rōn) A steroid hormone that acts on tubules of the kidney to regulate the transport of sodium ions (Na^+) and potassium ions (K^+).

alimentary canal (al'-uh-men'-tuh-rē) A digestive tract consisting of a tube running between a mouth and an anus; also called a complete digestive tract.

allantois (al-an'-tō'-is) One of four extra-embryonic membranes; serves as a repository for the embryo's nitrogenous waste and functions in gas exchange.

allele (uh-lē'-ul) Any of the alternative versions of a gene that produce distinguishable phenotypic effects.

allopatric speciation (al'-uh-pat'-rik) The formation of new species in populations that are geographically isolated from one another.

allopolyploid (al'-ō-pol'-ē-ployd) A fertile individual that has more than two chromosome sets as a result of two different species interbreeding and combining their chromosomes.

allosteric regulation The binding of a regulatory molecule to a protein at one site that affects the function of the protein at a different site.

alpha (α) helix (al'-fuh hē'-liks) A spiral shape constituting one form of the secondary structure of proteins, arising from a specific pattern of hydrogen bonding.

alternation of generations A life cycle in which there is both a multicellular diploid form, the sporophyte, and a multicellular haploid form, the gametophyte; characteristic of plants and some algae.

alternative RNA splicing A type of eukaryotic gene regulation at the RNA-processing level in which different mRNA molecules are produced from the same primary transcript, depending on which RNA segments are treated as exons and which as introns.

altruism (al'-trū-iz-um) Selflessness; behavior that reduces an individual's fitness while increasing the fitness of another individual.

alveolate (al-vē'-uh-let) A protist with membrane-bounded sacs (alveoli) located just under the plasma membrane.

alveolus (al-vē'-uh-lus) (plural, **alveoli**) One of the dead-end, multilobed air sacs where gas exchange occurs in a mammalian lung.

Alzheimer's disease (alts'-hī-merz) An age-related dementia (mental deterioration) characterized by confusion, memory loss, and other symptoms.

amacrine cell (am'-uh-krin) A neuron of the retina that helps integrate information before it is sent to the brain.

amino acid (uh-mēn'-ō) An organic molecule possessing both carboxyl and amino groups. Amino acids serve as the monomers of polypeptides.

amino group A chemical group consisting of a nitrogen atom bonded to two hydrogen atoms; can act as a base in solution, accepting a hydrogen ion and acquiring a charge of $1+$.

aminoacyl-tRNA synthetase An enzyme that joins each amino acid to the appropriate tRNA.

ammonia A small, very toxic molecule (NH_3) produced by nitrogen fixation or as a metabolic waste product of protein and nucleic acid metabolism.

ammonite A member of a group of shelled cephalopods that were important marine predators for hundreds of millions of years until their extinction at the end of the Cretaceous period (65.5 mya).

amniocentesis (am'-nē-ō-sen-tē'-sis) A technique of prenatal diagnosis in which amniotic fluid, obtained by aspiration from a needle inserted into the uterus, is analyzed to detect certain genetic and congenital defects in the fetus.

amnion (am'-nē-on) One of four extraembryonic membranes. It surrounds a fluid-filled cavity that cushions the embryo.

amniote (am'-nē-ōt) Member of a clade of tetrapods named for a key derived character, the amniotic egg, which contains specialized membranes, including the fluid-filled amnion, that protect the embryo. Amniotes include mammals as well as birds and other reptiles.

amniotic egg A shelled egg in which an embryo develops within a fluid-filled amniotic sac and is nourished by yolk. Produced by reptiles (including birds) and egg-laying mammals, it enables them to complete their life cycles on dry land.

amoeba (uh-mē'-buh) A protist grade characterized by the presence of pseudopodia.

amoebocyte (uh-mē'-buh-sīt') An amoeba-like cell that moves by pseudopodia and is found in most animals. Depending on the species, it may digest and distribute food, dispose of wastes, form skeletal fibers, fight infections, and change into other cell types.

amoebozoan (uh-mē'-buh-zō'-an) A protist in a clade that includes many species with lobe- or tube-shaped pseudopodia.

amphibian Member of the tetrapod class Amphibia, including salamanders, frogs, and caecilians.

amphipathic (am'-fē-path'-ik) Having both a hydrophilic region and a hydrophobic region.

amplification The strengthening of stimulus energy during transduction.

amygdala (uh-mig'-duh-luh) A structure in the temporal lobe of the vertebrate brain that has a major role in the processing of emotions.

amylase (am'-uh-lās') An enzyme in saliva that hydrolyzes starch (a glucose polymer from plants) and glycogen (a glucose polymer from animals) into smaller polysaccharides and the disaccharide maltose.

anabolic pathway (an'-uh-bol'-ik) A metabolic pathway that consumes energy to synthesize a complex molecule from simpler compounds.

anaerobic respiration (an-er-ō'-bik) The use of inorganic molecules other than oxygen to accept electrons at the "downhill" end of electron transport chains.

analogous Having characteristics that are similar because of convergent evolution, not homology.

analogy (an-al'-uh-jē) Similarity between two species that is due to convergent evolution rather than to descent from a common ancestor with the same trait.

anaphase The fourth stage of mitosis, in which the chromatids of each chromosome have separated and the daughter chromosomes are moving to the poles of the cell.

anatomy The structure of an organism and its study.

anchorage dependence The requirement that a cell must be attached to a substratum in order to divide.

androgen (an'-drō-jen) Any steroid hormone, such as testosterone, that stimulates the development and maintenance of the male reproductive system and secondary sex characteristics.

aneuploidy (an'-yū-ploy'-dē) A chromosomal aberration in which one or more chromosomes are present in extra copies or are deficient in number.

angiosperm (an'-jē-ō-sperm) A flowering plant, which forms seeds inside a protective chamber called an ovary.

angiotensin II A peptide hormone that stimulates constriction of precapillary arterioles and increases reabsorption of NaCl and water by the proximal tubules of the kidney, increasing blood pressure and volume.

anhydrobiosis (an-hī'-drō-bī-ō'-sis) A dormant state involving loss of almost all body water.

animal pole The point at the end of an egg in the hemisphere where the least yolk is concentrated; opposite of vegetal pole.

Animalia The kingdom that consists of multicellular eukaryotes that ingest their food.

anion (an'-ī-on) A negatively charged ion.

annual A flowering plant that completes its entire life cycle in a single year or growing season.

anterior Pertaining to the front, or head, of a bilaterally symmetrical animal.

anterior pituitary Also called the adenohypophysis; portion of the pituitary that develops from nonneural tissue; consists of endocrine cells that synthesize and secrete several tropic and nontropic hormones.

anther In an angiosperm, the terminal pollen sac of a stamen, where pollen grains containing sperm-producing male gametophytes form.

antheridium (an'-thuh-rid'-ē-um) (plural, **antheridia**) In plants, the male gametangium, a moist chamber in which gametes develop.

anthropoid (an'-thruh-poyd) Member of a primate group made up of the monkeys and the apes (gibbons, orangutans, gorillas, chimpanzees, bonobos, and humans).

antibody A protein secreted by plasma cells (differentiated B cells) that binds to a particular antigen; also called immunoglobulin. All antibody molecules have the same Y-shaped structure and in their monomer form consist of two identical heavy chains and two identical light chains.

anticodon (an'-tī-kō'-don) A nucleotide triplet at one end of a tRNA molecule that recognizes a particular complementary codon on an mRNA molecule.

antidiuretic hormone (ADH) (an'-tī-dī-yū-ret'-ik) A peptide hormone, also known as vasopressin, that promotes water retention by the kidneys. Produced in the hypothalamus and released from the posterior pituitary, ADH also has activities in the brain.

antigen (an'-ti-jen) A macromolecule that elicits an immune response by binding to receptors of B cells or T cells.

antigen presentation The process by which an MHC molecule binds to a fragment of an intracellular protein antigen and carries it to the cell surface, where it is displayed and can be recognized by a T cell.

antigen receptor The general term for a surface protein, located on B cells and T cells, that binds to antigens, initiating acquired immune responses. The antigen receptors on B cells are called B cell receptors, and the antigen receptors on T cells are called T cell receptors.

antigen-presenting cell A cell that upon ingesting pathogens or internalizing pathogen proteins generates peptide fragments that are bound by class II MHC molecules and subsequently displayed on the cell surface to T cells. Macrophages, dendritic cells, and B cells are the primary antigen-presenting cells.

antiparallel The opposite arrangement of the sugar-phosphate backbones in a DNA double helix.

aphotic zone (ā'-fō'-tik) The part of an ocean or lake beneath the photic zone, where light does not penetrate sufficiently for photosynthesis to occur.

apical bud (ā'-pik-ul) A bud at the tip of a plant stem; also called a terminal bud.

apical dominance Concentration of growth at the tip of a plant shoot, where a terminal bud partially inhibits axillary bud growth.

apical ectodermal ridge (AER) A thickened area of ectoderm at the tip of a limb bud that promotes outgrowth of the limb bud.

apical meristem (mār'-uh-stem) Embryonic plant tissue in the tips of roots and the buds of shoots. The dividing cells of an apical meristem enable the plant to grow in length.

apicomplexan (ap'-ē-kom-pleks'-un) A protist in a clade that includes many species that parasitize animals. Some apicomplexans cause human disease.

apomixis (ap'-uh-mik'-sis) The ability of some plant species to reproduce asexually through seeds without fertilization by a male gamete.

apoplast (ap'-ō-plast) In plants, the continuum of cell walls plus the extracellular spaces.

apoptosis (ā-puh-tō'-sus) A program of controlled cell suicide, which is brought about by signals that trigger the activation of a cascade of suicide proteins in the cell destined to die.

aposematic coloration (ap'-ō-si-mat'-ik) The bright coloration of animals with effective physical or chemical defenses that acts as a warning to predators.

appendix A small, finger-like extension of the vertebrate cecum; contains a mass of white blood cells that contribute to immunity.

aquaporin A channel protein in the plasma membrane of a plant, animal, or microorganism cell that specifically facilitates osmosis, the diffusion of water across the membrane.

aqueous humor Plasma-like liquid in the space between the lens and the cornea in the vertebrate eye; helps maintain the shape of the eye, supplies nutrients and oxygen to its tissues, and disposes of its wastes.

aqueous solution (ā'-kwē-us) A solution in which water is the solvent.

arachnid A member of a major arthropod group, the cheliceriforms. Arachnids include spiders, scorpions, ticks, and mites.

arbuscular mycorrhiza (ar-bus'-kyū-lur mī'-kō-rī'-zuh) Association of a fungus with a plant root system in which the fungus causes the invagination of the host (plant) cells' plasma membranes.

arbuscular mycorrhizal fungus A symbiotic fungus whose hyphae grow through the cell wall of plant roots and extend into the root cell (enclosed in tubes formed by invagination of the root cell plasma membrane).

Archaea (ar'-kē'-uh) One of two prokaryotic domains, the other being Bacteria.

archaean Member of the prokaryotic domain Archaea.

Archaeplastida (ar'-kē-plas'-tid-uh) One of five supergroups of eukaryotes proposed in a current hypothesis of the evolutionary history of eukaryotes. This monophyletic group, which includes red algae, green alage, and land plants, descended from an ancient protist ancestor that engulfed a cyanobacterium. *See also* Excavata, Chromalveolata, Rhizaria, and Unikonta.

archegonium (ar-ki-gō'-nē-um) (plural, **archegonia**) In plants, the female gametangium, a moist chamber in which gametes develop.

archenteron (ar-ken'-tuh-ron) The endoderm-lined cavity, formed during gastrulation, that develops into the digestive tract of an animal.

archosaur (ar'-kō-sōr) Member of the reptilian group that includes crocodiles, alligators, dinosaurs, and birds.

arteriole (ar-ter'-ē-ōl) A vessel that conveys blood between an artery and a capillary bed.

artery A vessel that carries blood away from the heart to organs throughout the body.

arthropod A segmented ecdysozoan with a hard exoskeleton and jointed appendages. Familiar examples include insects, spiders, millipedes, and crabs.

artificial selection The selective breeding of domesticated plants and animals to encourage the occurrence of desirable traits.

ascocarp The fruiting body of a sac fungus (ascomycete).

ascomycete (as'-kuh-mī'-sēt) Member of the fungal phylum Ascomycota, commonly called sac fungus. The name comes from the saclike structure in which the spores develop.

ascus (plural, **asci**) A saclike spore capsule located at the tip of a dikaryotic hypha of a sac fungus.

asexual reproduction The generation of offspring from a single parent that occurs without the fusion of gametes (by budding, division of a single cell, or division of the entire organism into two or more parts). In most cases, the offspring are genetically identical to the parent.

assisted reproductive technology A fertilization procedure that generally involves surgically removing eggs (secondary oocytes) from a woman's ovaries after hormonal stimulation, fertilizing the eggs, and returning them to the woman's body.

associative learning The acquired ability to associate one environmental feature (such as a color) with another (such as danger).

aster A radial array of short microtubules that extends from each centrosome toward the plasma membrane in an animal cell undergoing mitosis.

astrocyte A glial cell with diverse functions, including providing structural support for neurons, regulating the interstitial environment, facilitating synaptic transmission, and assisting in regulating the blood supply to the brain.

atherosclerosis A cardiovascular disease in which fatty deposits called plaques develop in the inner walls of the arteries, obstructing the arteries and causing them to harden.

atom The smallest unit of matter that retains the properties of an element.

atomic mass The total mass of an atom, which is the mass in grams of 1 mole of the atom.

atomic nucleus An atom's dense central core, containing protons and neutrons.

atomic number The number of protons in the nucleus of an atom, unique for each element and designated by a subscript to the left of the elemental symbol.

ATP (adenosine triphosphate) (a-den'-ō-sēn trī-fos'-fāt) An adenine-containing nucleoside triphosphate that releases free energy when its phosphate bonds are hydrolyzed. This energy is used to drive endergonic reactions in cells.

ATP synthase A complex of several membrane proteins that provide a port through which protons diffuse. This complex functions in chemiosmosis with adjacent electron transport chains, using the energy of a hydrogen ion (proton) concentration gradient to make ATP. ATP synthases are found in the inner mitochondrial membrane of eukaryotic cells and in the plasma membrane of prokaryotes.

atrial natriuretic peptide (ANP) (ā'-trē-ul na'-trē-yū-ret'-ik) A peptide hormone secreted by cells of the atria of the heart in response to high blood pressure. ANP's effects on the kidney alter ion and water movement and thereby reduce blood pressure.

atrioventricular (AV) node A region of specialized heart muscle tissue between the left and right atria where electrical impulses are delayed for about 0.1 second before spreading to both ventricles and causing them to contract.

atrioventricular (AV) valve A heart valve located between each atrium and ventricle that prevents a backflow of blood when the ventricle contracts.

atrium (ā'-trē-um) (plural, **atria**) A chamber of the vertebrate heart that receives blood from the veins and transfers blood to a ventricle.

autocrine Referring to a secreted molecule that acts on the cell that secreted it.

autoimmune disease An immunological disorder in which the immune system turns against self.

autonomic nervous system (ot'-ō-nom'-ik) An efferent branch of the vertebrate peripheral nervous system that regulates the internal environment; consists of the sympathetic, parasympathetic, and enteric divisions.

autopolyploid (ot'-ō-pol'-ē-ployd) An individual that has more than two chromosome sets that are all derived from a single species.

autosome (ot'-ō-sōm) A chromosome that is not directly involved in determining sex; not a sex chromosome.

autotroph (ot'-ō-trōf) An organism that obtains organic food molecules without eating other organisms or substances derived from other organisms. Autotrophs use energy from the sun or from the oxidation of inorganic substances to make organic molecules from inorganic ones.

auxin (ok'-sin) A term that primarily refers to indoleacetic acid (IAA), a natural plant hormone that has a variety of effects, including cell elongation, root formation, secondary growth, and fruit growth.

average heterozygosity (het'-er-ō-zī-gō'-si-tē) The percent, on average, of a population's loci that are heterozygous in members of the population.

avirulent Describing a pathogen that can only mildly harm, but not kill, the host.

axillary bud (ak'-sil-ār-ē) A structure that has the potential to form a lateral shoot, or branch. The bud appears in the angle formed between a leaf and a stem.

axon (ak'-son) A typically long extension, or process, of a neuron that carries nerve impulses away from the cell body toward target cells.

axon hillock The conical region of a neuron's axon where it joins the cell body; typically the region where nerve impulses are generated.

B cell receptor The antigen receptor on B cells: a Y-shaped, membrane-bound molecule consisting of two identical heavy chains and two identical light chains linked by disulfide bridges and containing two antigen-binding sites.

B cells The lymphocytes that complete their development in the bone marrow and become effector cells for the humoral immune response.

Bacteria One of two prokaryotic domains, the other being Archaea.

bacterial artificial chromosome (BAC) A large plasmid that acts as a bacterial chromosome and can carry inserts of 100,000 to 300,000 base pairs.

bacteriophage (bak-tēr'-ē-ō-fāj) A virus that infects bacteria; also called a phage.

bacterium Member of the prokaryotic domain Bacteria.

bacteroid A form of the bacterium *Rhizobium* contained within the vesicles formed by the root cells of a root nodule.

balancing selection Natural selection that maintains two or more phenotypic forms in a population.

bark All tissues external to the vascular cambium, consisting mainly of the secondary phloem and layers of periderm.

Barr body A dense object lying along the inside of the nuclear envelope in cells of female mammals, representing a highly condensed, inactivated X chromosome.

barrier method Contraception that relies on a physical barrier to block the passage of sperm. Examples include condoms and diaphragms.

basal angiosperm Member of a clade of three early-diverging lineages of flowering plants. Examples are *Amborella*, water lilies, and star anise and its relatives.

basal body (ba'-sul) A eukaryotic cell structure consisting of a 9 + 0 arrangement of microtubule triplets. The basal body may organize the microtubule assembly of a cilium or flagellum and is structurally very similar to a centriole.

basal metabolic rate (BMR) The metabolic rate of a resting, fasting, and non-stressed endotherm at a comfortable temperature.

base A substance that reduces the hydrogen ion concentration of a solution.

base-pair substitution A type of point mutation; the replacement of one nucleotide and its partner in the complementary DNA strand by another pair of nucleotides.

basidiocarp Elaborate fruiting body of a dikaryotic mycelium of a club fungus.

basidiomycete (buh-sid'-ē-ō-mī'-sēt) Member of the fungal phylum Basidiomycota, commonly called club fungus. The name comes from the club-like shape of the basidium.

basidium (plural, **basidia**) (buh-sid'-ē-um, buh-sid'-ē-ah) A reproductive appendage that produces sexual spores on the gills of mushrooms (club fungi).

Batesian mimicry (bāt'-zē-un mim'-uh-krē) A type of mimicry in which a harmless species looks like a species that is poisonous or otherwise harmful to predators.

behavior (in animals) Individually, an action carried out by muscles or glands under control of the nervous system in response to a stimulus; collectively, the sum of an animal's responses to external and internal stimuli.

behavioral ecology The study of the evolution of and ecological basis for animal behavior.

benign tumor A mass of abnormal cells that remains at the site of its origin.

benthic zone The bottom surface of an aquatic environment.

benthos (ben'-thōz) The communities of organisms living in the benthic zone of an aquatic biome.

beta (β) pleated sheet One form of the secondary structure of proteins in which the polypeptide chain folds back and forth. Two regions of the chain lie parallel to each other and are held together by hydrogen bonds.

beta oxidation A metabolic sequence that breaks fatty acids down to two-carbon fragments that enter the citric acid cycle as acetyl CoA.

bicoid A maternal effect gene that codes for a protein responsible for specifying the anterior end in *Drosophila*.

biennial (bī-en'-ē-ul) A flowering plant that requires two years to complete its life cycle.

big-bang reproduction Reproduction in which an organism produces all of its offspring in a single event; also known as semelparity.

bilateral symmetry Body symmetry in which a central longitudinal plane divides the body into two equal but opposite halves.

bilaterian (bī'-luh-ter'-ē-uhn) Member of a clade of animals with bilateral symmetry and three germ layers.

bile A mixture of substances that is produced in the liver but stored in the gallbladder and that enables formation of fat droplets in water as an aid in the digestion and absorption of fats.

binary fission A method of asexual reproduction by "division in half." In prokaryotes, binary fission does not involve mitosis; but in single-celled eukaryotes that undergo binary fission, mitosis is part of the process.

binomial The two-part latinized name of a species, consisting of the genus and specific epithet.

biodiversity hot spot A relatively small area with an exceptional concentration of endemic species and often a large number of endangered and threatened species.

bioenergetics (1) The overall flow and transformation of energy in an organism. (2) The study of how energy flows through organisms.

biofilm A surface-coating colony of one or more species of prokaryotes that engage in metabolic cooperation.

biofuel A fuel produced from dry organic matter or combustible oils produced by plants.

biogenic amine A neurotransmitter derived from an amino acid.

biogeochemical cycle Any of the various chemical cycles, which involve both biotic and abiotic components of ecosystems.

biogeography The study of the past and present distribution of species.

bioinformatics The use of computers, software, and mathematical models to process and integrate biological information from large data sets.

biological augmentation An approach to restoration ecology that uses organisms to add essential materials to a degraded ecosystem.

biological clock An internal timekeeper that controls an organism's biological rhythms. The biological clock marks time with or without environmental cues but often requires signals from the environment to remain tuned to an appropriate period. *See also* circadian rhythm.

biological magnification A process in which retained substances become more concentrated at each higher trophic level in a food chain.

biological species concept Definition of a species as a population or group of populations whose members have the potential to interbreed in nature and produce viable, fertile offspring, but do not produce viable, fertile offspring with members of other such groups.

biology The scientific study of life.

biomanipulation An approach that applies the top-down model of community organization to alter ecosystem characteristics. For example, ecologists can prevent algal blooms and eutrophication by altering the density of higher-level consumers in lakes instead of by using chemical treatments.

biomass The total mass of organic matter comprising a group of organisms in a particular habitat.

biome (bī'-ōm) Any of the world's major ecosystems, often classified according to the predominant vegetation and characterized by adaptations of organisms to that particular environment.

bioremediation The use of organisms to detoxify and restore polluted and degraded ecosystems.

biosphere The entire portion of Earth inhabited by life; the sum of all the planet's ecosystems.

biotechnology The manipulation of organisms or their components to produce useful products.

biotic (bī-ot'-ik) Pertaining to the living organisms in the environment.

bipolar cell A neuron that relays information between photoreceptors and ganglion cells in the retina.

bipolar disorder Depressive mental illness characterized by swings of mood from high to low; also called manic-depressive disorder.

birth control pill A chemical contraceptive that inhibits ovulation, retards follicular development, or alters a woman's cervical mucus to prevent sperm from entering the uterus.

blade (1) A leaflike structure of a seaweed that provides most of the surface area for photosynthesis. (2) The flattened portion of a typical leaf.

blastocoel (blas'-tuh-sēl) The fluid-filled cavity that forms in the center of a blastula.

blastocyst (blas'-tuh-sist) The blastula stage of mammalian embryonic development, consisting of an inner cell mass, a cavity, and an outer layer, the trophoblast. In humans, the blastocyst forms one week after fertilization.

blastomere An early embryonic cell arising during the cleavage stage of an early embryo.

blastopore (blas'-tō-pōr) In a gastrula, the opening of the archenteron that typically develops into the anus in deuterostomes and the mouth in protostomes.

blastula (blas'-tyū-luh) A hollow ball of cells that marks the end of the cleavage stage during early embryonic development in animals.

blood A connective tissue with a fluid matrix called plasma in which red blood cells, white blood cells, and cell fragments called platelets are suspended.

blood-brain barrier A specialized capillary arrangement in the brain that restricts the passage of most substances into the brain, thereby preventing dramatic fluctuations in the brain's environment.

blue-light photoreceptor A type of light receptor in plants that initiates a variety of responses, such as phototropism and slowing of hypocotyl elongation.

body cavity A fluid- or air-filled space between the digestive tract and the body wall.

body plan In animals, a set of morphological and developmental traits that are integrated into a functional whole—the living animal.

Bohr shift A lowering of the affinity of hemoglobin for oxygen, caused by a drop in pH. It facilitates the release of oxygen from hemoglobin in the vicinity of active tissues.

bolus A lubricated ball of chewed food.

bone A connective tissue consisting of living cells held in a rigid matrix of collagen fibers embedded in calcium salts.

book lung An organ of gas exchange in spiders, consisting of stacked plates contained in an internal chamber.

bottleneck effect Genetic drift that occurs when the size of a population is reduced, as by a natural disaster or human actions. Typically, the surviving population is no longer genetically representative of the original population.

bottom-up model A model of community organization in which mineral nutrients influence community organization by controlling plant or phytoplankton numbers, which in turn control herbivore numbers, which in turn control predator numbers.

Bowman's capsule (bō'-munz) A cup-shaped receptacle in the vertebrate kidney that is the initial, expanded segment of the nephron where filtrate enters from the blood.

brachiopod (bra'-kē-uh-pod') A marine lophophorate with a shell divided into dorsal and ventral halves. Brachiopods are also called lamp shells.

brain Organ of the central nervous system where information is processed and integrated.

brainstem Collection of structures in the vertebrate brain, including the midbrain, the pons, and the medulla oblongata; functions in homeostasis, coordination of movement, and conduction of information to higher brain centers.

branch point The representation on a phylogenetic tree of the divergence of two or more taxa from a common ancestor. Most branch points are shown as dichotomies, in which a branch representing the ancestral lineage splits (at the branch point) into two branches, one for each of the two descendant taxa.

brassinosteroid A steroid hormone in plants that has a variety of effects, including cell elongation, retarding leaf abscission, and promoting xylem differentiation.

breathing Ventilation of the lungs through alternating inhalation and exhalation.

breathing control center A brain center that directs the activity of organs involved in breathing.

bronchiole (brong'-kē-ōl') A fine branch of the bronchi that transports air to alveoli.

bronchus (brong'-kus) (plural, **bronchi**) One of a pair of breathing tubes that branch from the trachea into the lungs.

brown alga A multicellular, photosynthetic protist with a characteristic brown or olive color that results from carotenoids in its plastids. Most brown algae are marine, and some have a plantlike body (thallus).

bryophyte (brī'-uh-fīt) An informal name for a moss, liverwort, or hornwort; a nonvascular plant that lives on land but lacks some of the terrestrial adaptations of vascular plants.

budding Asexual reproduction in which outgrowths from the parent form and pinch off to live independently or else remain attached to eventually form extensive colonies.

buffer A substance that consists of acid and base forms in a solution and that minimizes changes in pH when extraneous acids or bases are added to the solution.

bulk feeder An animal that eats relatively large pieces of food.

bulk flow The movement of a fluid due to a difference in pressure between two locations.

bundle-sheath cell In C_4 plants, a type of photosynthetic cell arranged into tightly packed sheaths around the veins of a leaf.

C_3 plant A plant that uses the Calvin cycle for the initial steps that incorporate CO_2 into organic material, forming a three-carbon compound as the first stable intermediate.

C_4 plant A plant in which the Calvin cycle is preceded by reactions that incorporate CO_2 into a four-carbon compound, the end product of which supplies CO_2 for the Calvin cycle.

cadherin (kad-hēr'-in) A member of an important class of cell adhesion molecules that requires extracellular calcium ions for its function.

calcitonin (kal'-si-tō'-nin) A hormone secreted by the thyroid gland that lowers blood calcium levels by promoting calcium deposition in bone and calcium excretion from the kidneys; nonessential in adult humans.

callus A mass of dividing, undifferentiated cells at the cut end of a shoot.

calorie (cal) The amount of heat energy required to raise the temperature of 1 g of water by 1°C; also the amount of heat energy that 1 g of water releases when it cools by 1°C. The Calorie (with a capital C), usually used to indicate the energy content of food, is a kilocalorie.

Calvin cycle The second of two major stages in photosynthesis (following the light reactions), involving fixation of atmospheric CO_2 and reduction of the fixed carbon into carbohydrate.

CAM plant A plant that uses crassulacean acid metabolism, an adaptation for photosynthesis in arid conditions. In this process, carbon dioxide entering open stomata during the night is converted to organic acids, which release CO_2 for the Calvin cycle during the day, when stomata are closed.

Cambrian explosion A relatively brief time in geologic history when large, hard-bodied forms of animals with most of the major body plans known today appeared in the fossil record. This burst of evolutionary change occurred about 535–525 million years ago.

canopy The uppermost layer of vegetation in a terrestrial biome.

capillary (kap′-il-ār′-ē) A microscopic blood vessel that penetrates the tissues and consists of a single layer of endothelial cells that allows exchange between the blood and interstitial fluid.

capillary bed A network of capillaries in a tissue or organ.

capsid The protein shell that encloses a viral genome. It may be rod-shaped, polyhedral, or more complex in shape.

capsule (1) A sticky layer that surrounds the cell wall of some prokaryotes, protecting the cell surface and sometimes helping to glue the cell to surfaces. (2) The sporangium of a bryophyte (moss, liverwort, or hornwort).

carbohydrate (kar′-bō-hī′-drāt) A sugar (monosaccharide) or one of its dimers (disaccharides) or polymers (polysaccharides).

carbon fixation The initial incorporation of carbon from CO_2 into an organic compound by an autotrophic organism (a plant, another photosynthetic organism, or a chemoautotrophic prokaryote).

carbonyl group (kar′-buh-nēl′) A chemical group present in aldehydes and ketones and consisting of a carbon atom double-bonded to an oxygen atom.

carboxyl group (kar-bok′-sil) A chemical group present in organic acids and consisting of a single carbon atom double-bonded to an oxygen atom and also bonded to a hydroxyl group.

cardiac cycle (kar′-dē-ak) The alternating contractions and relaxations of the heart.

cardiac muscle A type of muscle that forms the contractile wall of the heart. Its cells are joined by intercalated disks that relay each heartbeat.

cardiac output The volume of blood pumped per minute by each ventricle of the heart.

cardiovascular system A closed circulatory system with a heart and branching network of arteries, capillaries, and veins. The system is characteristic of vertebrates.

carnivore An animal that mainly eats other animals.

carotenoid (kuh-rot′-uh-noyd′) An accessory pigment, either yellow or orange, in the chloroplasts of plants and in some prokaryotes. By absorbing wavelengths of light that chlorophyll cannot, carotenoids broaden the spectrum of colors that can drive photosynthesis.

carpel (kar′-pul) The ovule-producing reproductive organ of a flower, consisting of the stigma, style, and ovary.

carrier In genetics, an individual who is heterozygous at a given genetic locus, with one normal allele and one recessive allele. The heterozygote is phenotypically dominant for the character determined by the gene but can pass on the recessive allele to offspring.

carrying capacity The maximum population size that can be supported by the available resources, symbolized as *K*.

cartilage (kar′-til-ij) A flexible connective tissue with an abundance of collagenous fibers embedded in chondroitin sulfate.

Casparian strip (kas-pār′-ē-un) A water-impermeable ring of wax in the endodermal cells of plants that blocks the passive flow of water and solutes into the stele by way of cell walls.

catabolic pathway (kat′-uh-bol′-ik) A metabolic pathway that releases energy by breaking down complex molecules to simpler compounds.

catalyst (kat′-uh-list) A chemical agent that increases the rate of a reaction without being consumed by the reaction.

catastrophism (kuh-tas′-truh-fiz′-um) The principle that events in the past occurred suddenly and were caused by different mechanisms than those operating today. *See* uniformitarianism.

catecholamine (kat′-uh-kōl′-uh-mēn) Any of a class of neurotransmitters and hormones, including the hormones epinephrine and norepinephrine, that are synthesized from the amino acid tyrosine.

cation (cat′-ī-on) A positively charged ion.

cation exchange A process in which positively charged minerals are made available to a plant when hydrogen ions in the soil displace mineral ions from the clay particles.

CD4 A surface protein, present on most helper T cells, that binds to class II MHC molecules, enhancing the interaction between the T cell and an antigen-presenting cell.

CD8 A surface protein, present on most cytotoxic T cells, that binds to class I MHC molecules, enhancing the interaction between the T cell and a target cell.

cDNA library A gene library containing clones that carry complementary DNA (cDNA) inserts. The library includes only the genes that were transcribed in the cells whose mRNA was isolated to make the cDNA.

cecum (sē′-kum) (plural, **ceca**) The blind pouch at the beginning of the large intestine.

cell adhesion molecule (CAM) A transmembrane, cell-surface glycoprotein that binds to CAMs on other cells. The resulting cell-to-cell attachments contribute to stable tissue structure.

cell body The part of a neuron that houses the nucleus and most other organelles.

cell cycle An ordered sequence of events in the life of a cell, from its origin in the division of a parent cell until its own division into two; the eukaryotic cell cycle is composed of interphase (including G_1, S, and G_2 subphases) and M phase (including mitosis and cytokinesis).

cell cycle control system A cyclically operating set of molecules in the eukaryotic cell that both triggers and coordinates key events in the cell cycle.

cell differentiation The structural and functional divergence of cells as they become specialized during a multicellular organism's development. Cell differentiation depends on the control of gene expression.

cell division The reproduction of cells.

cell fractionation The disruption of a cell and separation of its parts by centrifugation.

cell plate A double membrane across the midline of a dividing plant cell, between which the new cell wall forms during cytokinesis.

cell wall A protective layer external to the plasma membrane in the cells of plants, prokaryotes, fungi, and some protists. Polysaccharides such as cellulose (in plants and some protists), chitin (in fungi), and peptidoglycan (in bacteria) are an important structural component of cell walls.

cell-mediated immune response The branch of acquired immunity that involves the activation of cytotoxic T cells, which defend against infected cells.

cellular respiration The catabolic pathways of aerobic and anaerobic respiration, which break down organic molecules for the production of ATP.

cellular slime mold A type of protist that has unicellular amoeboid cells and aggregated reproductive bodies in its life cycle.

cellulose (sel′-yū-lōs) A structural polysaccharide of plant cell walls, consisting of glucose monomers joined by β glycosidic linkages.

Celsius scale (sel′-sē-us) A temperature scale (°C) equal to $\frac{5}{9}$(°F − 32) that measures the freezing point of water at 0°C and the boiling point of water at 100°C.

central canal The narrow cavity in the center of the spinal cord that is continuous with the fluid-filled ventricles of the brain.

central vacuole A membranous sac in a mature plant cell with diverse roles in reproduction, growth, and development.

centriole (sen′-trē-ōl) A structure in the centrosome of an animal cell composed of a cylinder of microtubule triplets arranged in a 9 + 0 pattern. A centrosome has a pair of centrioles.

centromere (sen′-trō-mēr) The specialized region of the chromosome where two sister chromatids are most closely attached.

centrosome (sen′-trō-sōm) Structure present in the cytoplasm of animal cells, important during cell division; functions as a microtubule-organizing center. A centrosome has two centrioles.

cephalization (sef′-uh-luh-zā′-shun) An evolutionary trend toward the concentration of sensory equipment at the anterior end of the body.

cerebellum (sār′-ruh-bel′-um) Part of the vertebrate hindbrain located dorsally; functions in unconscious coordination of movement and balance.

cerebral cortex (suh-rē′-brul) The surface of the cerebrum; the largest and most complex part of the mammalian brain, containing nerve cell bodies of the cerebrum; the part of the vertebrate brain most changed through evolution.

cerebral hemisphere The right or left side of the cerebrum.

cerebrospinal fluid (suh-rē′-brō-spī′-nul) Blood-derived fluid that surrounds, protects against infection, nourishes, and cushions the brain and spinal cord.

cerebrum (suh-rē′-brum) The dorsal portion of the vertebrate forebrain, composed of right and left hemispheres; the integrating center for memory, learning, emotions, and other highly complex functions of the central nervous system.

cervix (ser′-viks) The neck of the uterus, which opens into the vagina.

chaparral A scrubland biome of dense, spiny evergreen shrubs found at midlatitudes along coasts where cold ocean currents circulate offshore; characterized by mild, rainy winters and long, hot, dry summers.

chaperonin (shap′-er-ō′-nin) A protein molecule that assists in the proper folding of other proteins.

character An observable heritable feature.

character displacement The tendency for characteristics to be more divergent in sympatric populations of two species than in allopatric populations of the same two species.

checkpoint A control point in the cell cycle where stop and go-ahead signals can regulate the cycle.

chelicera (kē-lih′-suh-ruh) (plural, **chelicerae**) One of a pair of clawlike feeding appendages characteristic of cheliceriforms.

cheliceriform (kē-lih-suh′-ri-form) An arthropod that has chelicerae and a body divided into a cephalothorax and an abdomen. Living cheliceriforms include sea spiders, horseshoe crabs, scorpions, ticks, and spiders.

chemical bond An attraction between two atoms, resulting from a sharing of outer-shell electrons or the presence of opposite charges on the atoms. The bonded atoms gain complete outer electron shells.

chemical energy Energy available in molecules for release in a chemical reaction; a form of potential energy.

chemical equilibrium In a chemical reaction, the state in which the rate of the forward reaction equals the rate of the reverse reaction, so that the relative concentrations of the reactants and products do not change with time.

chemical reaction The making and breaking of chemical bonds, leading to changes in the composition of matter.

chemiosmosis (kem′-ē-oz-mō′-sis) An energy-coupling mechanism that uses energy stored in the form of a hydrogen ion gradient across a membrane to drive cellular work, such as the synthesis of ATP. Most ATP synthesis in cells occurs by chemiosmosis.

chemoautotroph (kē′-mō-ot′-ō-trōf) An organism that needs only carbon dioxide as a carbon source but obtains energy by oxidizing inorganic substances.

chemoheterotroph (kē′-mō-het′-er-ō-trōf) An organism that must consume organic molecules for both energy and carbon.

chemoreceptor A sensory receptor that responds to a chemical stimulus, such as a solute or an odorant.

chiasma (plural, **chiasmata**) (kī-az′-muh, kī-az′-muh-tuh) The X-shaped, microscopically visible region where homologous nonsister chromatids have exchanged genetic material through crossing over during meiosis, the two homologs remaining associated due to sister chromatid cohesion.

chitin (kī′-tin) A structural polysaccharide, consisting of amino sugar monomers, found in many fungal cell walls and in the exoskeletons of all arthropods.

chlorophyll (klōr′-ō-fil) A green pigment located within the chloroplasts of plants and algae and in the membranes of certain prokaryotes. Chlorophyll *a* participates directly in the light reactions, which convert solar energy to chemical energy.

chlorophyll *a* A photosynthetic pigment that participates directly in the light reactions, which convert solar energy to chemical energy.

chlorophyll *b* An accessory photosynthetic pigment that transfers energy to chlorophyll *a*.

chloroplast (klōr′-ō-plast) An organelle found in plants and photosynthetic protists that absorbs sunlight and uses it to drive the synthesis of organic compounds from carbon dioxide and water.

choanocyte (kō-an′-uh-sīt) A flagellated feeding cell found in sponges. Also called a collar cell, it has a collar-like ring that traps food particles around the base of its flagellum.

cholesterol (kō-les′-tuh-rol) A steroid that forms an essential component of animal cell membranes and acts as a precursor molecule for the synthesis of other biologically important steroids, such as hormones.

chondrichthyan (kon-drik′-thē-an) Member of the class Chondrichthyes, vertebrates with skeletons made mostly of cartilage, such as sharks and rays.

chordate Member of the phylum Chordata, animals that at some point during their development have a notochord; a dorsal, hollow nerve cord; pharyngeal slits or clefts; and a muscular, post-anal tail.

chorion (kōr′-ē-on) The outermost of four extraembryonic membranes. It functions in gas exchange and contributes to the formation of the mammalian placenta.

chorionic villus sampling (CVS) (kōr′-ē-on′-ik vil′-us) A technique of prenatal diagnosis in which a small sample of the fetal portion of the placenta is removed and analyzed to detect certain genetic and congenital defects in the fetus.

choroid (kor′-oyd) A thin, pigmented inner layer of the vertebrate eye.

Chromalveolata One of five supergroups of eukaryotes proposed in a current hypothesis of the evolutionary history of eukaryotes. Chromalveolates may have originated by secondary endosymbiosis and include two large protist clades, the alveolates and the stramenopiles. *See also* Excavata, Rhizaria, Archaeplastida, and Unikonta.

chromatin (krō′-muh-tin) The complex of DNA and proteins that makes up a eukaryotic chromosome. When the cell is not dividing, chromatin exists in its dispersed form, as a mass of very long, thin fibers that are not visible with a light microscope.

chromosome (krō′-muh-sōm) A cellular structure carrying genetic material, found in the nucleus of eukaryotic cells. Each chromosome consists of one very long DNA molecule and associated proteins. (A bacterial chromosome usually consists of a single circular DNA molecule and associated proteins. It is found in the nucleoid region, which is not membrane bounded.) *See also* chromatin.

chromosome theory of inheritance A basic principle in biology stating that genes are located on chromosomes and that the behavior of chromosomes during meiosis accounts for inheritance patterns.

chylomicron (kī′-lō-mī′-kron) A small globule that transports lipids. Chylomicrons are composed of fats mixed with cholesterol and coated with proteins.

chyme (kīm) The mixture of partially digested food and digestive juices formed in the stomach.

chytrid (kī′-trid) Member of the fungal phylum Chytridiomycota, mostly aquatic fungi with flagellated zoospores that represent an early-diverging fungal lineage.

ciliary body A portion of the vertebrate eye associated with the lens. It produces the clear, watery aqueous humor that fills the anterior cavity of the eye.

ciliate (sil′-ē-it) A type of protist that moves by means of cilia.

cilium (sil′-ē-um) (plural, **cilia**) A short cellular appendage containing microtubules. A motile cilium is specialized for locomotion and is formed from a core of nine outer doublet microtubules and two inner single microtubules (the "9 + 2" arrangement) ensheathed in an extension of the plasma membrane. A primary cilium is usually nonmotile and plays a sensory and signaling role; it lacks the two inner microtubules (the "9 + 0" arrangement).

circadian rhythm (ser-kā'-dē-un) A physiological cycle of about 24 hours that is present in all eukaryotic organisms and that persists even in the absence of external cues.

citric acid cycle A chemical cycle involving eight steps that completes the metabolic breakdown of glucose molecules begun in glycolysis by oxidizing pyruvate to carbon dioxide; occurs within the mitochondrion in eukaryotic cells and in the cytosol of prokaryotes; the second major stage in cellular respiration.

clade (klayd) A group of species that includes an ancestral species and all its descendants.

cladistics (kluh-dis'-tiks) An approach to systematics in which organisms are placed into groups called clades based primarily on common descent.

class In classification, the taxonomic category above the level of order.

class I MHC molecule A type of MHC molecule found on the surface of nearly all nucleated cells and that functions in identification of infected cells by cytotoxic T cells.

class II MHC molecule A type of MHC molecule restricted to a few specialized immune cell types (dendritic cells, macrophages, and B cells) that serve as antigen-presenting cells.

classical conditioning A type of associative learning in which an arbitrary stimulus becomes associated with a particular outcome.

cleavage (1) The process of cytokinesis in animal cells, characterized by pinching of the plasma membrane. (2) The succession of rapid cell divisions without significant growth during early embryonic development that converts the zygote to a ball of cells.

cleavage furrow The first sign of cleavage in an animal cell; a shallow groove in the cell surface near the old metaphase plate.

climate The long-term prevailing weather conditions at a locality.

climograph A plot of the temperature and precipitation in a particular region.

cline A graded change in a character along a geographic axis.

clitoris (klit'-uh-ris) An organ at the upper intersection of the labia minora that engorges with blood and becomes erect during sexual arousal.

cloaca (klō-ā'-kuh) A common opening for the digestive, urinary, and reproductive tracts found in many nonmammalian vertebrates but in few mammals.

clonal selection The process by which an antigen selectively binds to and activates only those lymphocytes bearing receptors specific for the antigen. The selected lymphocytes proliferate and differentiate into a clone of effector cells and a clone of memory cells specific for the stimulating antigen.

clone (1) A lineage of genetically identical individuals or cells. (2) In popular usage, a single individual organism that is genetically identi-

cal to another individual. (3) As a verb, to make one or more genetic replicas of an individual or cell. *See also* gene cloning.

cloning vector In genetic engineering, a DNA molecule that can carry foreign DNA into a host cell and replicate there. Cloning vectors include plasmids that move recombinant DNA from a test tube back into a cell and viruses that transfer recombinant DNA by infection.

closed circulatory system A circulatory system in which blood is confined to vessels and is kept separate from the interstitial fluid.

club fungus *See* basidiomycete.

cnidocyte (nī'-duh-sīt) A specialized cell unique to the phylum Cnidaria; contains a capsule-like organelle housing a coiled thread that, when discharged, explodes outward and functions in prey capture or defense.

cochlea (kok'-lē-uh) The complex, coiled organ of hearing that contains the organ of Corti.

codominance The situation in which the phenotypes of both alleles are exhibited in the heterozygote because both alleles affect the phenotype in separate, distinguishable ways.

codon (kō'-don) A three-nucleotide sequence of DNA or mRNA that specifies a particular amino acid or termination signal; the basic unit of the genetic code.

coefficient of relatedness The fraction of genes that, on average, are shared by two individuals.

coelom (sē'-lōm) A body cavity lined by tissue derived only from mesoderm.

coelomate (sē'-lō-māt) An animal that possesses a true coelom (a body cavity lined by tissue completely derived from mesoderm).

coenocytic fungus (sō'-no-si'-tic) A fungus that lacks septa and hence whose body is made up of a continuous cytoplasmic mass that may contain hundreds or thousands of nuclei.

coenzyme (kō-en'-zīm) An organic molecule serving as a cofactor. Most vitamins function as coenzymes in metabolic reactions.

cofactor Any nonprotein molecule or ion that is required for the proper functioning of an enzyme. Cofactors can be permanently bound to the active site or may bind loosely with the substrate during catalysis.

cognition The process of knowing that may include awareness, reasoning, recollection, and judgment.

cognitive map A neural representation of the abstract spatial relationships between objects in an animal's surroundings.

cohesion The binding together of like molecules, often by hydrogen bonds.

cohort A group of individuals of the same age in a population.

coitus (kō'-uh-tus) The insertion of a penis into a vagina; also called sexual intercourse.

coleoptile (kō-lē-op'-tul) The covering of the young shoot of the embryo of a grass seed.

coleorhiza (kō'-lē-uh-rī'-zuh) The covering of the young root of the embryo of a grass seed.

collagen A glycoprotein in the extracellular matrix of animal cells that forms strong fibers,

found extensively in connective tissue and bone; the most abundant protein in the animal kingdom.

collecting duct The location in the kidney where processed filtrate, called urine, is collected from the renal tubules.

collenchyma cell (kō-len'-kim-uh) A flexible plant cell type that occurs in strands or cylinders that support young parts of the plant without restraining growth.

colloid A mixture made up of a liquid and particles that (because of their large size) remain suspended rather than dissolved in that liquid.

colon (kō'-len) The largest section of the vertebrate large intestine; functions in water absorption and formation of feces.

commensalism (kuh-men'-suh-lizm) A symbiotic relationship in which one organism benefits but the other is neither helped nor harmed.

communication In animal behavior, a process involving transmission of, reception of, and response to signals. The term is also used in connection with other organisms, as well as individual cells of multicellular organisms.

community All the organisms that inhabit a particular area; an assemblage of populations of different species living close enough together for potential interaction.

community ecology The study of how interactions between species affect community structure and organization.

companion cell A type of plant cell that is connected to a sieve-tube element by many plasmodesmata and whose nucleus and ribosomes may serve one or more adjacent sieve-tube elements.

competitive exclusion The concept that when populations of two similar species compete for the same limited resources, one population will use the resources more efficiently and have a reproductive advantage that will eventually lead to the elimination of the other population.

competitive inhibitor A substance that reduces the activity of an enzyme by entering the active site in place of the substrate whose structure it mimics.

complement system A group of about 30 blood proteins that may amplify the inflammatory response, enhance phagocytosis, or directly lyse extracellular pathogens.

complementary DNA (cDNA) A double-stranded DNA molecule made *in vitro* using mRNA as a template and the enzymes reverse transcriptase and DNA polymerase. A cDNA molecule corresponds to the exons of a gene.

complete digestive tract A digestive tube that runs between a mouth and an anus; also called an alimentary canal.

complete dominance The situation in which the phenotypes of the heterozygote and dominant homozygote are indistinguishable.

complete flower A flower that has all four basic floral organs: sepals, petals, stamens, and carpels.

complete metamorphosis The transformation of a larva into an adult that looks very different, and often functions very differently in its environment, than the larva.

compound A substance consisting of two or more different elements combined in a fixed ratio.

compound eye A type of multifaceted eye in insects and crustaceans consisting of up to several thousand light-detecting, focusing ommatidia; especially good at detecting movement.

concentration gradient A region along which the density of a chemical substance increases or decreases.

conception The fertilization of an egg by a sperm in humans.

condensation reaction A reaction in which two molecules become covalently bonded to each other through the loss of a small molecule, usually water, in which case it is also called a dehydration reaction.

condom A thin, latex rubber or natural membrane sheath that fits over the penis to collect semen.

conduction The direct transfer of thermal motion (heat) between molecules of objects in direct contact with each other.

cone A cone-shaped cell in the retina of the vertebrate eye, sensitive to color.

conformer An animal for which an internal condition conforms with a change in an environmental variable.

conidium (plural, **conidia**) A haploid spore produced at the tip of a specialized hypha in ascomycetes during asexual reproduction.

conifer Member of the largest gymnosperm phylum. Most conifers are cone-bearing trees, such as pines and firs.

conjugation (kon´-jū-gā´-shun) In prokaryotes, the direct transfer of DNA between two cells (of the same or different species) that are temporarily joined. In ciliates, a sexual process in which two cells exchange haploid micronuclei.

connective tissue Animal tissue that functions mainly to bind and support other tissues, having a sparse population of cells scattered through an extracellular matrix.

conodont An early, soft-bodied vertebrate with prominent eyes and dental elements.

conservation biology The integrated study of ecology, evolutionary biology, physiology, molecular biology, and genetics to sustain biological diversity at all levels.

continental drift The slow movement of the continental plates across Earth's surface.

contraception The deliberate prevention of pregnancy.

contractile vacuole A membranous sac that helps move excess water out of certain freshwater protists.

control element A segment of noncoding DNA that helps regulate transcription of a gene by binding a transcription factor. Multiple control elements are present in a eukaryotic gene's enhancer.

controlled experiment An experiment in which an experimental group is compared with a control group that varies only in the factor being tested.

convection The mass movement of warmed air or liquid to or from the surface of a body or object.

convergent evolution The evolution of similar features in independent evolutionary lineages.

convergent extension A process in which the cells of a tissue layer rearrange themselves, so that the sheet of cells becomes narrower (converges) and longer (extends).

cooperativity A kind of allosteric regulation whereby a shape change in one subunit of a protein caused by substrate binding is transmitted to all the others, facilitating binding of subsequent substrate molecules.

copepod (cō´-puh-pod) Any of a group of small crustaceans that are important members of marine and freshwater plankton communities.

coral reef Typically a warm-water, tropical ecosystem dominated by the hard skeletal structures secreted primarily by the resident cnidarians. Some reefs also exist in cold, deep waters.

corepressor A small molecule that binds to a bacterial repressor protein and changes its shape, allowing it to switch an operon off.

cork cambium (kam´-bē-um) A cylinder of meristematic tissue in woody plants that replaces the epidermis with thicker, tougher cork cells.

cornea (kor´-nē-uh) The transparent frontal portion of the sclera, which admits light into the vertebrate eye.

corpus callosum (kor´-pus kuh-lō´-sum) The thick band of nerve fibers that connects the right and left cerebral hemispheres in mammals, enabling the hemispheres to process information together.

corpus luteum (kor´-pus lū´-tē-um) A secreting tissue in the ovary that forms from the collapsed follicle after ovulation and produces progesterone.

cortex (1) The outer region of cytoplasm in a eukaryotic cell, lying just under the plasma membrane, that has a more gel-like consistency than the inner regions, due to the presence of multiple microfilaments. (2) In plants, ground tissue that is between the vascular tissue and dermal tissue in a root or eudicot stem.

cortical granule A vesicle containing enzymes and other macromolecules located in the cortex (the region just under the plasma membrane) of an egg. Cortical granules undergo exocytosis during the cortical reaction.

cortical nephron In mammals and birds, a nephron with a loop of Henle located almost entirely in the renal cortex.

cortical reaction Exocytosis of enzymes and other macromolecules from cortical granules in the egg cytoplasm during fertilization, leading to the formation of a fertilization envelope.

corticosteroid Any steroid hormone produced and secreted by the adrenal cortex.

cotransport The coupling of the "downhill" diffusion of one substance to the "uphill" transport of another against its own concentration gradient.

cotyledon (kot´-uh-lē´-dun) A seed leaf of an angiosperm embryo. Some species have one cotyledon, others two.

countercurrent exchange The exchange of a substance or heat between two fluids flowing in opposite directions. For example, blood in a fish gill flows in the opposite direction of water passing over the gill, maximizing diffusion of oxygen into and carbon dioxide out of the blood.

countercurrent multiplier system A countercurrent system in which energy is expended in active transport to facilitate exchange of materials and generate concentration gradients.

covalent bond (kō-vā´-lent) A type of strong chemical bond in which two atoms share one or more pairs of valence electrons.

cranial nerve A nerve that originates in the brain and terminates in an organ of the head or upper body.

craniate A chordate with a head.

crassulacean acid metabolism (CAM) An adaptation for photosynthesis in arid conditions, first discovered in the family Crassulaceae. In this process, a plant takes up CO_2 and incorporates it into a variety of organic acids at night; during the day, CO_2 is released from organic acids for use in the Calvin cycle.

crista (plural, **cristae**) (kris´-tuh, kris´-tē) An infolding of the inner membrane of a mitochondrion that houses electron transport chains and molecules of the enzyme catalyzing the synthesis of ATP (ATP synthase).

critical load The amount of added nutrient, usually nitrogen or phosphorus, that can be absorbed by plants without damaging ecosystem integrity.

crop rotation The practice of planting nonlegumes one year and legumes in alternating years to restore concentrations of fixed nitrogen in the soil.

cross-fostering study A behavioral study in which the young of one species are placed in the care of adults from another species.

crossing over The reciprocal exchange of genetic material between nonsister chromatids during prophase I of meiosis.

cross-pollination In angiosperms, the transfer of pollen from an anther of a flower on one plant to the stigma of a flower on another plant of the same species.

crustacean (kruh-stā´-shun) A member of a subphylum of mostly aquatic arthropods that includes lobsters, crayfishes, crabs, shrimps, and barnacles.

cryptic coloration Camouflage that makes a potential prey difficult to spot against its background.

culture A system of information transfer through social learning or teaching that influences the behavior of individuals in a population.

cuticle (kyū´-tuh-kul) (1) A waxy covering on the surface of stems and leaves that acts as an adaptation that prevents desiccation in terrestrial plants. (2) The exoskeleton of an arthropod, consisting of layers of protein and chitin that are variously modified for different functions. (3) A tough coat that covers the body of a nematode.

cyclic AMP (cAMP) Cyclic adenosine monophosphate, a ring-shaped molecule made from ATP that is a common intracellular signaling molecule (second messenger) in eukaryotic cells. It is also a regulator of some bacterial operons.

cyclic electron flow A route of electron flow during the light reactions of photosynthesis that involves only photosystem I and that produces ATP but not NADPH or O_2.

cyclin (sī'-klin) A cellular protein that occurs in a cyclically fluctuating concentration and that plays an important role in regulating the cell cycle.

cyclin-dependent kinase (Cdk) A protein kinase that is active only when attached to a particular cyclin.

cystic fibrosis (sis'-tik fī-brō'-sis) A human genetic disorder caused by a recessive allele for a chloride channel protein; characterized by an excessive secretion of mucus and consequent vulnerability to infection; fatal if untreated.

cytochrome (sī'-to-krom) An iron-containing protein that is a component of electron transport chains in the mitochondria and chloroplasts of eukaryotic cells and the plasma membranes of prokaryotic cells.

cytogenetic map A chart of a chromosome that locates genes with respect to chromosomal features distinguishable in a microscope.

cytokine (sī'-tō-kīn') Any of a group of proteins secreted by a number of cell types, including macrophages and helper T cells, that regulate the function of lymphocytes and other cells of the immune system.

cytokinesis (sī'-tō-kuh-nē'-sis) The division of the cytoplasm to form two separate daughter cells immediately after mitosis, meiosis I, or meiosis II.

cytokinin (sī'-tō-kī'-nin) Any of a class of related plant hormones that retard aging and act in concert with auxin to stimulate cell division, influence the pathway of differentiation, and control apical dominance.

cytoplasm (sī'-tō-plaz'-um) The contents of the cell, exclusive of the nucleus and bounded by the plasma membrane.

cytoplasmic determinant A maternal substance, such as a protein or RNA, placed into an egg that influences the course of early development by regulating the expression of genes that affect the developmental fate of cells.

cytoplasmic streaming A circular flow of cytoplasm, involving myosin and actin filaments, that speeds the distribution of materials within cells.

cytoskeleton A network of microtubules, microfilaments, and intermediate filaments that branch throughout the cytoplasm and serve a variety of mechanical, transport, and signaling functions.

cytosol (sī'-tō-sol) The semifluid portion of the cytoplasm.

cytotoxic T cell A type of lymphocyte that, when activated, kills infected cells as well as certain cancer cells and transplanted cells.

dalton A measure of mass for atoms and subatomic particles; the same as the atomic mass unit, or amu.

data Recorded observations.

day-neutral plant A plant in which flower formation is not controlled by photoperiod or day length.

decapod A member of the group of crustaceans that includes lobsters, crayfishes, crabs, and shrimps.

decomposer An organism that absorbs nutrients from nonliving organic material such as corpses, fallen plant material, and the wastes of living organisms and converts them to inorganic forms; a detritivore.

deductive reasoning A type of logic in which specific results are predicted from a general premise.

deep-sea hydrothermal vent A dark, hot, oxygen-deficient environment associated with volcanic activity on or near the seafloor. The producers in a vent community are chemoautotrophic prokaryotes.

de-etiolation The changes a plant shoot undergoes in response to sunlight; also known informally as greening.

dehydration reaction A chemical reaction in which two molecules covalently bond to each other with the removal of a water molecule.

deletion (1) A deficiency in a chromosome resulting from the loss of a fragment through breakage. (2) A mutational loss of one or more nucleotide pairs from a gene.

demographic transition A shift from rapid population growth in which birth rate outpaces death rate to zero population growth characterized by low birth and death rates.

demography The study of statistics relating to births and deaths in populations.

denaturation (dē-nā'-chur-ā'-shun) In proteins, a process in which a protein unravels and loses its native shape, thereby becoming biologically inactive; in DNA, the separation of the two strands of the double helix. Denaturation occurs under extreme (noncellular) conditions of pH, salt concentration, and temperature.

dendrite (den'-drīt) One of usually numerous, short, highly branched extensions of a neuron that receive signals from other neurons.

dendritic cell An antigen-presenting cell, located mainly in lymphatic tissues and skin, that is particularly efficient in presenting antigens to helper T cells, thereby initiating a primary immune response.

density The number of individuals per unit area or volume.

density dependent Referring to any characteristic that varies according to an increase in population density.

density independent Referring to any characteristic that is not affected by population density.

density-dependent inhibition The phenomenon observed in normal animal cells that causes them to stop dividing when they come into contact with one another.

deoxyribonucleic acid (DNA) (dē-ok'-sē-rī'-bō-nū-klā'-ik) A double-stranded, helical nucleic acid molecule consisting of nucleotide monomers with a deoxyribose sugar and the nitrogenous bases adenine (A), cytosine (C), guanine (G), and thymine (T); capable of replicating and determining the inherited structure of a cell's proteins.

deoxyribose (dē-ok'-si-rī'-bōs) The sugar component of DNA nucleotides, having one fewer hydroxyl group than ribose, the sugar component of RNA nucleotides.

depolarization A change in a cell's membrane potential such that the inside of the membrane is made less negative relative to the outside. For example, a neuron membrane is depolarized if a stimulus decreases its voltage from the resting potential of −70 mV in the direction of zero voltage.

dermal tissue system The outer protective covering of plants.

desert A terrestrial biome characterized by very low precipitation.

desmosome A type of intercellular junction in animal cells that functions as a rivet.

determinate cleavage A type of embryonic development in protostomes that rigidly casts the developmental fate of each embryonic cell very early.

determinate growth A type of growth characteristic of most animals and some plant organs, in which growth stops after a certain size is reached.

determination The progressive restriction of developmental potential in which the possible fate of each cell becomes more limited as an embryo develops. At the end of determination, a cell is committed to its fate.

detritivore (deh-trī'-tuh-vōr) A consumer that derives its energy and nutrients from nonliving organic material such as corpses, fallen plant material, and the wastes of living organisms; a decomposer.

detritus (di-trī'-tus) Dead organic matter.

deuteromycete (dū'-tuh-rō-mī'-sēt) Traditional classification for a fungus with no known sexual stage. When a sexual stage for a so-called deuteromycete is discovered, the species is assigned to a phylum.

deuterostome development (dū'-tuh-rō-stōm') In animals, a developmental mode distinguished by the development of the anus from the blastopore; often also characterized by radial cleavage and by the body cavity forming as outpockets of mesodermal tissue.

diabetes mellitus (dī'-uh-bē'-tis mel'-uh-tus) An endocrine disorder marked by inability to maintain glucose homeostasis. The type 1 form results from autoimmune destruction of insulin-secreting cells; treatment usually requires daily insulin injections. The type 2 form most commonly results from reduced responsiveness of target cells to insulin; obesity and lack of exercise are risk factors.

diacylglycerol (DAG) (dī-a′-sil-glis′-er-ol) A second messenger produced by the cleavage of a certain kind of phospholipid in the plasma membrane.

diaphragm (dī′-uh-fram′) (1) A sheet of muscle that forms the bottom wall of the thoracic cavity in mammals. Contraction of the diaphragm pulls air into the lungs. (2) A dome-shaped rubber cup fitted into the upper portion of the vagina before sexual intercourse. It serves as a physical barrier to the passage of sperm into the uterus.

diapsid (dī-ap′-sid) Member of an amniote clade distinguished by a pair of holes on each side of the skull. Diapsids include the lepidosaurs and archosaurs.

diastole (dī-as′-tō-lē) The stage of the cardiac cycle in which a heart chamber is relaxed and fills with blood.

diastolic pressure Blood pressure in the arteries when the ventricles are relaxed.

diatom (dī′-uh-tom) A unicellular photosynthetic alga with a unique glassy cell wall containing silica.

dicot A term traditionally used to refer to flowering plants that have two embryonic seed leaves, or cotyledons. Recent molecular evidence indicates that dicots do not form a clade; species once classified as dicots are now grouped into eudicots, magnoliids, and several lineages of basal angiosperms.

differential gene expression The expression of different sets of genes by cells with the same genome.

diffusion The spontaneous movement of a substance down its concentration gradient, from a region where it is more concentrated to a region where it is less concentrated.

digestion The second stage of food processing in animals: the breaking down of food into molecules small enough for the body to absorb.

dihybrid (dī′-hī′-brid) An organism that is heterozygous with respect to two genes of interest. All the offspring from a cross between parents doubly homozygous for different alleles are dihybrids. For example, parents of genotypes *AABB* and *aabb* produce a dihybrid of genotype *AaBb*.

dikaryotic (dī′-kār-ē-ot′-ik) Referring to a fungal mycelium with two haploid nuclei per cell, one from each parent.

dinoflagellate (dī′-nō-flaj′-uh-let) Member of a group of mostly unicellular photosynthetic algae with two flagella situated in perpendicular grooves in cellulose plates covering the cell.

dinosaur Member of an extremely diverse clade of reptiles varying in body shape, size, and habitat. Birds are the only extant dinosaurs.

dioecious (dī-ē′-shus) In plant biology, having the male and female reproductive parts on different individuals of the same species.

diploblastic Having two germ layers.

diploid cell (dip′-loyd) A cell containing two sets of chromosomes (*2n*), one set inherited from each parent.

diplomonad A protist that has modified mitochondria, two equal-sized nuclei, and multiple flagella.

directional selection Natural selection in which individuals at one end of the phenotypic range survive or reproduce more successfully than do other individuals.

disaccharide (dī-sak′-uh-rī d) A double sugar, consisting of two monosaccharides joined by a glycosidic linkage formed during dehydration synthesis.

discovery science The process of scientific inquiry that focuses on describing nature.

dispersal The movement of individuals (or gametes) away from their parent location. This movement sometimes expands the geographic range of a population or species.

dispersion The pattern of spacing among individuals within the boundaries of the geographic population.

disruptive selection Natural selection in which individuals on both extremes of a phenotypic range survive or reproduce more successfully than do individuals with intermediate phenotypes.

distal tubule In the vertebrate kidney, the portion of a nephron that helps refine filtrate and empties it into a collecting duct.

disturbance A natural or human-caused event that changes a biological community and usually removes organisms from it. Disturbances, such as fires and storms, play a pivotal role in structuring many communities.

disulfide bridge A strong covalent bond formed when the sulfur of one cysteine monomer bonds to the sulfur of another cysteine monomer.

DNA (deoxyribonucleic acid) (dē-ok′-sē-rī′-bō-nū-klā′-ik) A double-stranded, helical nucleic acid molecule, consisting of nucleotide monomers with a deoxyribose sugar and the nitrogenous bases adenine (A), cytosine (C), guanine (G), and thymine (T); capable of being replicated and determining the inherited structure of a cell's proteins.

DNA ligase (lī′-gās) A linking enzyme essential for DNA replication; catalyzes the covalent bonding of the 3′ end of one DNA fragment (such as an Okazaki fragment) to the 5′ end of another DNA fragment (such as a growing DNA chain).

DNA microarray assay A method to detect and measure the expression of thousands of genes at one time. Tiny amounts of a large number of single-stranded DNA fragments representing different genes are fixed to a glass slide and tested for hybridization with samples of labeled cDNA.

DNA polymerase (puh-lim′-er-ās) An enzyme that catalyzes the elongation of new DNA (for example, at a replication fork) by the addition of nucleotides to the 3′ end of an existing chain. There are several different DNA polymerases; DNA polymerase III and

DNA polymerase I play major roles in DNA replication in prokaryotes.

domain (1) A taxonomic category above the kingdom level. The three domains are Archaea, Bacteria, and Eukarya. (2) An independently folding part of a protein.

dominant allele An allele that is fully expressed in the phenotype of a heterozygote.

dominant species A species with substantially higher abundance or biomass than other species in a community. Dominant species exert a powerful control over the occurrence and distribution of other species.

dopamine A neurotransmitter that is a catecholamine, like epinephrine and norepinephrine.

dormancy A condition typified by extremely low metabolic rate and a suspension of growth and development.

dorsal Pertaining to the top of an animal with radial or bilateral symmetry.

dorsal lip The region above the blastopore on the dorsal side of the amphibian embryo.

double bond A double covalent bond; the sharing of two pairs of valence electrons by two atoms.

double circulation A circulatory system consisting of separate pulmonary and systemic circuits, in which blood passes through the heart after completing each circuit.

double fertilization A mechanism of fertilization in angiosperms in which two sperm cells unite with two cells in the female gametophyte (embryo sac) to form the zygote and endosperm.

double helix The form of native DNA, referring to its two adjacent antiparallel polynucleotide strands wound around an imaginary axis into a spiral shape.

Down syndrome A human genetic disease caused by the presence of an extra chromosome 21; characterized by mental retardation and heart and respiratory defects.

Duchenne muscular dystrophy (duh-shen′) A human genetic disease caused by a sex-linked recessive allele; characterized by progressive weakening and a loss of muscle tissue.

duodenum (dū′-uh-dēn′-um) The first section of the small intestine, where chyme from the stomach mixes with digestive juices from the pancreas, liver, and gallbladder as well as from gland cells of the intestinal wall.

duplication An aberration in chromosome structure due to fusion with a fragment from a homologous chromosome, such that a portion of a chromosome is duplicated.

dynamic stability hypothesis The idea that long food chains are less stable than short chains.

dynein (dī′-nē-un) In cilia and flagella, a large contractile protein extending from one microtubule doublet to the adjacent doublet. ATP hydrolysis drives changes in dynein shape that lead to bending of cilia and flagella.

E site One of a ribosome's three binding sites for tRNA during translation. The E site is the place where discharged tRNAs leave the ribosome. (E stands for exit.)

ecdysone (ek′-duh-sōn) A steroid hormone, secreted by the prothoracic glands, that triggers molting in arthropods.

ecdysozoan Member of a group of animal phyla identified as a clade by molecular evidence. Many ecdysozoans are molting animals.

echinoderm (i-kī′-nō-derm) A slow-moving or sessile marine deuterostome with a water vascular system and, in larvae, bilateral symmetry. Echinoderms include sea stars, brittle stars, sea urchins, feather stars, and sea cucumbers.

ecological footprint The aggregate land and water area required by a person, city, or nation to produce all of the resources it consumes and to absorb all of the waste it generates.

ecological niche (nich) The sum of a species' use of the biotic and abiotic resources in its environment.

ecological species concept A definition of species in terms of ecological niche, the sum of how members of the species interact with the nonliving and living parts of their environment.

ecological succession Transition in the species composition of a community following a disturbance; the establishment of a community in an area virtually barren of life.

ecology The study of how organisms interact with each other and their environment.

ecosystem All the organisms in a given area as well as the abiotic factors with which they interact; one or more communities and the physical environment around them.

ecosystem ecology The study of energy flow and the cycling of chemicals among the various biotic and abiotic components in an ecosystem.

ecosystem service A function performed by an ecosystem that directly or indirectly benefits humans.

ecotone The transition from one type of habitat or ecosystem to another, such as the transition from a forest to a grassland.

ectoderm (ek′-tō-durm) The outermost of the three primary germ layers in animal embryos; gives rise to the outer covering and, in some phyla, the nervous system, inner ear, and lens of the eye.

ectomycorrhiza (ek′-tō-mī′-kō-rī′-zuh) Association of a fungus with a plant root system in which the fungus surrounds the roots but does not cause invagination of the host (plant) cells' plasma membranes.

ectomycorrhizal fungus A symbiotic fungus that forms sheaths of hyphae over the surface of plant roots and also grows into extracellular spaces of the root cortex.

ectoparasite A parasite that feeds on the external surface of a host.

ectopic Occurring in an abnormal location.

ectoproct A sessile, colonial lophophorate commonly called a bryozoan.

ectothermic Referring to organisms for which external sources provide most of the heat for temperature regulation.

Ediacaran biota (ē′-dē-uh-keh′-run bī-ō′-tuh) An early group of soft-bodied, multicellular eukaryotes known from fossils that range in age from 565 million to 545 million years old.

effective population size An estimate of the size of a population based on the numbers of females and males that successfully breed; generally smaller than the total population.

effector cell (1) A muscle cell or gland cell that performs the body's response to stimuli as directed by signals from the brain or other processing center of the nervous system. (2) A lymphocyte that has undergone clonal selection and is capable of mediating an acquired immune response.

efferent arteriole In the kidney, the blood vessel draining a nephron.

egg The female gamete.

egg-polarity gene A gene that helps control the orientation (polarity) of the egg; also called a maternal effect gene.

ejaculation The propulsion of sperm from the epididymis through the muscular vas deferens, ejaculatory duct, and urethra.

ejaculatory duct In mammals, the short section of the ejaculatory route formed by the convergence of the vas deferens and a duct from the seminal vesicle. The ejaculatory duct transports sperm from the vas deferens to the urethra.

electrocardiogram (ECG or EKG) A record of the electrical impulses that travel through heart muscle during the cardiac cycle.

electrochemical gradient The diffusion gradient of an ion, which is affected by both the concentration difference of the ion across a membrane (a chemical force) and the ion's tendency to move relative to the membrane potential (an electrical force).

electrogenic pump An ion transport protein that generates voltage across a membrane.

electromagnetic receptor A receptor of electromagnetic energy, such as visible light, electricity, or magnetism.

electromagnetic spectrum The entire spectrum of electromagnetic radiation ranging in wavelength from less than a nanometer to more than a kilometer.

electron A subatomic particle with a single negative electrical charge and a mass about $1/_{2,000}$ that of a neutron or proton. One or more electrons move around the nucleus of an atom.

electron microscope (EM) A microscope that uses magnets to focus an electron beam on or through a specimen, resulting in resolving power a thousandfold greater than that of a light microscope. A transmission electron microscope (TEM) is used to study the internal structure of thin sections of cells. A scanning electron microscope (SEM) is used to study the fine details of cell surfaces.

electron shell An energy level of electrons at a characteristic average distance from the nucleus of an atom.

electron transport chain A sequence of electron carrier molecules (membrane proteins) that shuttle electrons during the redox reactions that release energy used to make ATP.

electronegativity The attraction of a given atom for the electrons of a covalent bond.

electroporation A technique to introduce recombinant DNA into cells by applying a brief electrical pulse to a solution containing the cells. The pulse creates temporary holes in the cells' plasma membranes, through which DNA can enter.

element Any substance that cannot be broken down to any other substance by chemical reactions.

elimination The fourth and final stage of food processing in animals: the passing of undigested material out of the digestive system.

embryo sac (em′-brē-ō) The female gametophyte of angiosperms, formed from the growth and division of the megaspore into a multicellular structure that typically has eight haploid nuclei.

embryonic lethal A mutation with a phenotype leading to death of an embryo or larva.

embryophyte Alternate name for land plants that refers to their shared derived trait of multicellular, dependent embryos.

emergent properties New properties that arise with each step upward in the hierarchy of life, owing to the arrangement and interactions of parts as complexity increases.

emigration The movement of individuals out of a population.

enantiomer (en-an′-tē-ō-mer) One of two compounds that are mirror images of each other.

endangered species A species that is in danger of extinction throughout all or a significant portion of its range.

endemic (en-dem′-ik) Referring to a species that is confined to a specific, relatively small geographic area.

endergonic reaction (en′-der-gon′-ik) A nonspontaneous chemical reaction, in which free energy is absorbed from the surroundings.

endocrine gland (en′-dō-krin) A ductless gland that secretes hormones directly into the interstitial fluid, from which they diffuse into the bloodstream.

endocrine system The internal system of communication involving hormones, the ductless glands that secrete hormones, and the molecular receptors on or in target cells that respond to hormones; functions in concert with the nervous system to effect internal regulation and maintain homeostasis.

endocytosis (en′-dō-sī-tō′-sis) Cellular uptake of biological molecules and particulate matter via formation of new vesicles from the plasma membrane.

endoderm (en′-dō-durm) The innermost of the three primary germ layers in animal embryos; lines the archenteron and gives rise to the liver, pancreas, lungs, and the lining of the digestive tract in species that have these structures.

endodermis The innermost layer of the cortex in plant roots; a cylinder one cell thick that forms the boundary between the cortex and the vascular cylinder.

endomembrane system The collection of membranes inside and around a eukaryotic cell, related either through direct physical contact or by the transfer of membranous vesicles; includes the smooth and rough endoplasmic reticulum, the Golgi apparatus, lysosomes, and vacuoles.

endometriosis (en′-dō-mē-trē-ō′-sis) The condition resulting from the presence of endometrial tissue outside of the uterus.

endometrium (en′-dō-mē′-trē-um) The inner lining of the uterus, which is richly supplied with blood vessels.

endoparasite A parasite that lives within a host.

endophyte A fungus that lives inside a leaf or other plant part without causing harm to the plant.

endoplasmic reticulum (ER) (en′-dō-plaz′-mik ruh-tik′-yū-lum) An extensive membranous network in eukaryotic cells, continuous with the outer nuclear membrane and composed of ribosome-studded (rough) and ribosome-free (smooth) regions.

endorphin (en-dōr′-fin) Any of several hormones produced in the brain and anterior pituitary that inhibits pain perception.

endoskeleton A hard skeleton buried within the soft tissues of an animal, such as the spicules of sponges, the plates of echinoderms, and the bony skeletons of vertebrates.

endosperm In angiosperms, a nutrient-rich tissue formed by the union of a sperm with two polar nuclei during double fertilization. The endosperm provides nourishment to the developing embryo in angiosperm seeds.

endospore A thick-coated, resistant cell produced by a bacterial cell exposed to harsh conditions.

endosymbiosis A process in which a unicellular organism (the "host") engulfs another cell, which lives within the host cell and ultimately becomes an organelle in the host cell; also refers to the hypothesis that mitochondria and plastids were formerly small prokaryotes that began living within larger cells.

endothelin A peptide produced by a blood vessel's endothelium that causes the vessel to constrict.

endothelium (en′-dō-thē′-lē-um) The simple squamous layer of cells lining the lumen of blood vessels.

endothermic Referring to organisms with bodies that are warmed by heat generated by metabolism. This heat is usually used to maintain a relatively stable body temperature higher than that of the external environment.

endotoxin A toxic component of the outer membrane of certain gram-negative bacteria that is released only when the bacteria die.

energetic hypothesis The concept that the length of a food chain is limited by the inefficiency of energy transfer along the chain.

energy The capacity to cause change, especially to do work (to move matter against an opposing force).

energy coupling In cellular metabolism, the use of energy released from an exergonic reaction to drive an endergonic reaction.

enhancer A segment of eukaryotic DNA containing multiple control elements, usually located far from the gene whose transcription it regulates.

enteric division Networks of neurons in the digestive tract, pancreas, and gallbladder; normally regulated by the sympathetic and parasympathetic divisions of the autonomic nervous system.

entropy A measure of disorder, or randomness.

enzymatic hydrolysis The process in digestion that splits macromolecules from food by the enzymatic addition of water.

enzyme (en′-zīm) A macromolecule serving as a catalyst, a chemical agent that changes the rate of a reaction without being consumed by the reaction.

enzyme-substrate complex A temporary complex formed when an enzyme binds to its substrate molecule(s).

eosinophil (ē′-ō-sin′-ō-fil) A type of white blood cell with low phagocytic activity that is thought to play a role in defense against parasitic worms by releasing enzymes toxic to these invaders.

epicotyl (ep′-uh-kot′-ul) In an angiosperm embryo, the embryonic axis above the point of attachment of the cotyledon(s) and below the first pair of miniature leaves.

epidemic A general outbreak of a disease.

epidermis (1) The dermal tissue system of nonwoody plants, usually consisting of a single layer of tightly packed cells. (2) The outermost layer of cells in an animal.

epididymis (ep′-uh-did′-uh-mus) A coiled tubule located adjacent to the mammalian testis where sperm are stored.

epigenetic inheritance Inheritance of traits transmitted by mechanisms not directly involving the nucleotide sequence of a genome.

epinephrine (ep′-i-nef′-rin) A catecholamine that, when secreted as a hormone by the adrenal medulla, mediates "fight-or-flight" responses to short-term stresses; also released by some neurons as a neurotransmitter; also known as adrenaline.

epiphyte (ep′-uh-fīt) A plant that nourishes itself but grows on the surface of another plant for support, usually on the branches or trunks of tropical trees.

epistasis (ep′-i-stā′-sis) A type of gene interaction in which one gene alters the phenotypic effects of another gene that is independently inherited.

epithelial tissue (ep′-uh-thē′-lē-ul) Sheets of tightly packed cells that line organs and body cavities as well as external surfaces.

epithelium An epithelial tissue.

epitope A small, accessible region of an antigen to which an antigen receptor or antibody binds; also called an antigenic determinant.

EPSP *See* excitatory postsynaptic potential.

equilibrium potential (E_{ion}) The magnitude of a cell's membrane voltage at equilibrium; calculated using the Nernst equation.

erythrocyte (eh-rith′-ruh-sīt) A blood cell that contains hemoglobin, which transports oxygen; also called a red blood cell.

erythropoietin (EPO) (eh-rith′-rō-poy′-uh-tin) A hormone that stimulates the production of erythrocytes. It is secreted by the kidney when body tissues do not receive enough oxygen.

esophagus (eh-sof′-uh-gus) A channel that conducts food, by peristalsis, from the pharynx to the stomach.

essential amino acid An amino acid that an animal cannot synthesize itself and must be obtained from food in prefabricated form. Eight amino acids are essential in the human adult.

essential element In plants, a chemical element required for the plant to grow from a seed and complete its life cycle, producing another generation in the form of seeds.

essential fatty acid An unsaturated fatty acid that an animal needs but cannot make.

essential nutrient A substance that an organism must absorb in preassembled form because it cannot be synthesized from any other material. In humans, there are essential vitamins, minerals, amino acids, and fatty acids.

estradiol (es′-truh-dī′-ol) A steroid hormone that stimulates the development and maintenance of the female reproductive system and secondary sex characteristics; the major estrogen in mammals.

estrogen (es′-trō-jen) Any steroid hormone, such as estradiol, that stimulates the development and maintenance of the female reproductive system and secondary sex characteristics.

estrous cycle (es′-trus) A reproductive cycle characteristic of female mammals except humans and certain other primates, in which the nonpregnant endometrium is reabsorbed rather than shed, and sexual response occurs only during mid-cycle at estrus.

estuary The area where a freshwater stream or river merges with the ocean.

ethology The scientific study of how animals behave, particularly in their natural environments.

ethylene (eth′-uh-lēn) The only gaseous plant hormone. Among its many effects are response to mechanical stress, programmed cell death, leaf abscission, and fruit ripening.

etiolation Plant morphological adaptations for growing in darkness.

euchromatin (yū-krō′-muh-tin) The less condensed form of eukaryotic chromatin that is available for transcription.

eudicot (yū-dī′-kot) Member of a clade consisting of the vast majority of flowering plants that have two embryonic seed leaves, or cotyledons.

euglenid (yū′-glen-id) A protist, such as *Euglena* or its relatives, characterized by an anterior pocket from which one or two flagella emerge.

euglenozoan Member of a diverse clade of flagellated protists that includes predatory heterotrophs, photosynthetic autotrophs, and pathogenic parasites.

Eukarya (yū-kar′-ē-uh) The domain that includes all eukaryotic organisms.

eukaryotic cell (yū′-ker-ē-ot′-ik) A type of cell with a membrane-enclosed nucleus and membrane-enclosed organelles. Organisms with eukaryotic cells (protists, plants, fungi, and animals) are called eukaryotes.

eumetazoan (yū′-met-uh-zō′-un) Member of a clade of animals with true tissues. All animals except sponges and a few other groups are eumetazoans.

euryhaline (yur′-i-hā′-līn) Referring to organisms that tolerate substantial changes in external osmolarity.

eurypterid (yur-ip′-tuh-rid) An extinct carnivorous cheliceriform also called a water scorpion.

Eustachian tube (yū-stā′-shun) The tube that connects the middle ear to the pharynx.

eutherian (yū-thēr′-ē-un) Placental mammal; mammal whose young complete their embryonic development within the uterus, joined to the mother by the placenta.

eutrophic lake (yū-trōf′-ik) A lake that has a high rate of biological productivity supported by a high rate of nutrient cycling.

eutrophication A process by which nutrients, particularly phosphorus and nitrogen, become highly concentrated in a body of water, leading to increased growth of organisms such as algae or cyanobacteria.

evaporation The process by which a liquid changes to a gas.

evaporative cooling The process in which the surface of an object becomes cooler during evaporation, owing to a change of the molecules with the greatest kinetic energy from the liquid to the gaseous state.

evapotranspiration The total evaporation of water from an ecosystem, including evaporation from soil and the outside of plants, as well as the transpiration of water from within plants through stomata.

evo-devo Evolutionary developmental biology; a field of biology that compares developmental processes of different multicellular organisms to understand how these processes have evolved and how changes can modify existing organismal features or lead to new ones.

evolution Descent with modification; the idea that living species are descendants of ancestral species that were different from the present-day ones; also defined more narrowly as the change in the genetic composition of a population from generation to generation.

evolutionary tree A branching diagram that reflects a hypothesis about evolutionary relationships among groups of organisms.

Excavata One of five supergroups of eukaryotes proposed in a current hypothesis of the evolutionary history of eukaryotes. Excavates have unique cytoskeletal features, and some species have an "excavated" feeding groove on one side of the cell body. *See also* Chromalveolata, Rhizaria, Archaeplastida, and Unikonta.

excitatory postsynaptic potential (EPSP) An electrical change (depolarization) in the membrane of a postsynaptic cell caused by the binding of an excitatory neurotransmitter from a presynaptic cell to a postsynaptic receptor; makes it more likely for a postsynaptic cell to generate an action potential.

excretion The disposal of nitrogen-containing metabolites and other waste products.

exergonic reaction (ek′-ser-gon′-ik) A spontaneous chemical reaction, in which there is a net release of free energy.

exocytosis (ek′-sō-sī-tō′-sis) The cellular secretion of biological molecules by the fusion of vesicles containing them with the plasma membrane.

exon A sequence within a primary transcript that remains in the RNA after RNA processing; also refers to the region of DNA from which this sequence was transcribed.

exoskeleton A hard encasement on the surface of an animal, such as the shell of a mollusc or the cuticle of an arthropod, that provides protection and points of attachment for muscles.

exotoxin (ek′-sō-tok′-sin) A toxic protein that is secreted by a prokaryote or other pathogen and that produces specific symptoms, even if the pathogen is no longer present.

expansin Plant enzyme that breaks the cross-links (hydrogen bonds) between cellulose microfibrils and other cell wall constituents, loosening the wall's fabric.

exponential population growth Growth of a population in an ideal, unlimited environment, represented by a J-shaped curve when population size is plotted over time.

expression vector A cloning vector that contains the requisite bacterial promoter just upstream of a restriction site where a eukaryotic gene can be inserted, allowing the gene to be expressed in a bacterial cell.

external fertilization The fusion of gametes that parents have discharged into the environment.

extinction vortex A downward population spiral in which inbreeding and genetic drift combine to cause a small population to shrink and, unless the spiral is reversed, to become extinct.

extracellular digestion The breakdown of food in compartments that are continuous with the outside of an animal's body.

extracellular matrix (ECM) The substance in which animal cells are embedded, consisting of protein and polysaccharides synthesized and secreted by cells.

extraembryonic membrane One of four membranes (yolk sac, amnion, chorion, and allantois) located outside the embryo that support the developing embryo in reptiles and mammals.

extreme halophile An organism that lives in a highly saline environment, such as the Great Salt Lake or the Dead Sea.

extreme thermophile An organism that thrives in hot environments (often 60–80°C or hotter).

extremophile An organism that lives in an environment whose conditions are so extreme that few other species can survive there. Extremophiles include extreme halophiles and extreme thermophiles.

F factor In bacteria, the DNA segment that confers the ability to form pili for conjugation and associated functions required for the transfer of DNA from donor to recipient. The F factor may exist as a plasmid or be integrated into the bacterial chromosome.

F plasmid The plasmid form of the F factor.

F_1 generation The first filial, or hybrid, offspring in a series of genetic crosses.

F_2 generation Offspring resulting from interbreeding of the hybrid F_1 generation.

facilitated diffusion The spontaneous passage of molecules or ions across a biological membrane with the assistance of specific transmembrane transport proteins.

facilitator A species that has a positive effect on the survival and reproduction of other species in a community and that influences community structure.

facultative anaerobe (fak′-ul-tā′-tiv an′-uh-rōb) An organism that makes ATP by aerobic respiration if oxygen is present but that switches to anaerobic respiration or fermentation if oxygen is not present.

family In classification, the taxonomic category above genus.

fast block to polyspermy The depolarization of the egg plasma membrane that begins within 1–3 seconds after a sperm binds to an egg membrane protein. The depolarization lasts about 1 minute and prevents additional sperm from fusing with the egg during that time.

fast-twitch fiber A muscle fiber used for rapid, powerful contractions.

fat A lipid consisting of three fatty acids linked to one glycerol molecule; also called a triacylglycerol or triglyceride.

fate map A territorial diagram of embryonic development that displays the future derivatives of individual cells and tissues.

fatty acid A long carbon chain carboxylic acid. Fatty acids vary in length and in the number and location of double bonds; three fatty acids linked to a glycerol molecule form a fat molecule, also known as a triacylglycerol or triglyceride.

feces (fē′-sēz) The wastes of the digestive tract.

feedback inhibition A method of metabolic control in which the end product of a metabolic pathway acts as an inhibitor of an enzyme within that pathway.

fermentation A catabolic process that makes a limited amount of ATP from glucose without an electron transport chain and that produces a characteristic end product, such as ethyl alcohol or lactic acid.

fertilization (1) The union of haploid gametes to produce a diploid zygote. (2) The addition of mineral nutrients to the soil.

fertilization envelope The protective layer formed when the vitelline layer of an egg is pushed away from the plasma membrane and hardened after fertilization by molecules exocytosed during the cortical reaction.

fetus (fē'-tus) A developing mammal that has all the major structures of an adult. In humans, the fetal stage lasts from the 9th week of gestation until birth.

fiber A lignified cell type that reinforces the xylem of angiosperms and functions in mechanical support; a slender, tapered sclerenchyma cell that usually occurs in bundles.

fibrin (fī'-brin) The activated form of the blood-clotting protein fibrinogen. Fibrin aggregates into threads that form the fabric of the clot.

fibroblast (fī'-brō-blast) A type of cell in loose connective tissue that secretes the protein ingredients of the extracellular fibers.

fibronectin A glycoprotein that helps animal cells attach to the extracellular matrix.

filament In an angiosperm, the stalk portion of the stamen, the pollen-producing reproductive organ of a flower.

filtrate Cell-free fluid extracted from the body fluid by the excretory system.

filtration In excretory systems, the extraction of water and small solutes, including metabolic wastes, from the body fluid.

fimbria (plural, **fimbriae**) A short, hairlike appendage of a prokaryotic cell that helps it adhere to the substrate or to other cells; also known as an attachment pilus.

first law of thermodynamics The principle of conservation of energy: Energy can be transferred and transformed, but it cannot be created or destroyed.

fission The separation of an organism into two or more individuals of approximately equal size.

fixed action pattern In animal behavior, a sequence of unlearned acts that is essentially unchangeable and, once initiated, usually carried to completion.

flaccid (flas'-id) Limp. Lacking in stiffness or firmness, as in a plant cell in surroundings where there is no tendency for water to enter the cell.

flagellum (fluh-jel'-um) (plural, **flagella**) A long cellular appendage specialized for locomotion. Like motile cilia, eukaryotic flagella have a core with nine outer doublet microtubules and two inner single microtubules ensheathed in an extension of the plasma membrane. Prokaryotic flagella have a different structure.

florigen A flowering signal, not yet chemically identified, that may be a hormone or may be a change in relative concentrations of multiple hormones.

flower In an angiosperm, a short stem with up to four sets of modified leaves, bearing structures that function in sexual reproduction.

fluid feeder An animal that lives by sucking nutrient-rich fluids from another living organism.

fluid mosaic model The currently accepted model of cell membrane structure, which envisions the membrane as a mosaic of protein molecules drifting laterally in a fluid bilayer of phospholipids.

follicle (fol'-uh-kul) A microscopic structure in the ovary that contains the developing oocyte and secretes estrogens.

follicle-stimulating hormone (FSH) A tropic hormone that is produced and secreted by the anterior pituitary and that stimulates the production of eggs by the ovaries and sperm by the testes.

follicular phase That part of the ovarian cycle during which follicles are growing and oocytes maturing.

food chain The pathway along which food energy is transferred from trophic level to trophic level, beginning with producers.

food vacuole A membranous sac formed by phagocytosis of microorganisms or particles to be used as food by the cell.

food web The interconnected feeding relationships in an ecosystem.

foot (1) The portion of a bryophyte sporophyte that gathers sugars, amino acids, water, and minerals from the parent gametophyte via transfer cells. (2) One of the three main parts of a mollusc; a muscular structure usually used for movement. *See also* mantle, visceral mass.

foraging The seeking and obtaining of food.

foram (foraminiferan) An aquatic protist that secretes a hardened shell containing calcium carbonate and extends pseudopodia through pores in the shell.

foraminiferan *See* foram.

forebrain One of three ancestral and embryonic regions of the vertebrate brain; develops into the thalamus, hypothalamus, and cerebrum.

fossil A preserved remnant or impression of an organism that lived in the past.

founder effect Genetic drift that occurs when a few individuals become isolated from a larger population and form a new population whose gene pool composition is not reflective of that of the original population.

fovea (fō'-vē-uh) The place on the retina at the eye's center of focus, where cones are highly concentrated.

fragmentation A means of asexual reproduction whereby a single parent breaks into parts that regenerate into whole new individuals.

frameshift mutation A mutation occurring when the number of nucleotides inserted or deleted is not a multiple of three, resulting in the improper grouping of the subsequent nucleotides into codons.

free energy The portion of a biological system's energy that can perform work when temperature and pressure are uniform throughout the system. (The change in free energy of a system is calculated by the equation $\Delta G = \Delta H -$

$T\Delta S$, where H is enthalpy [in biological systems, equivalent to total energy], T is absolute temperature, and S is entropy.)

frequency-dependent selection A decline in the reproductive success of individuals that have a phenotype that has become too common in a population.

fruit A mature ovary of a flower. The fruit protects dormant seeds and often aids in their dispersal.

functional group A specific configuration of atoms commonly attached to the carbon skeletons of organic molecules and usually involved in chemical reactions.

Fungi (fun'-jē) The eukaryotic kingdom that includes organisms that absorb nutrients after decomposing organic material.

G_0 phase A nondividing state occupied by cells that have left the cell cycle.

G_1 phase The first gap, or growth phase, of the cell cycle, consisting of the portion of interphase before DNA synthesis begins.

G_2 phase The second gap, or growth phase, of the cell cycle, consisting of the portion of interphase after DNA synthesis occurs.

gallbladder An organ that stores bile and releases it as needed into the small intestine.

game theory An approach to evaluating alternative strategies in situations where the outcome of a particular strategy depends on the strategies used by other individuals.

gametangium (gam'-uh-tan'-jē-um) (plural, **gametangia**) Multicellular plant structure in which gametes are formed. Female gametangia are called archegonia, and male gametangia are called antheridia.

gamete (gam'-ēt) A haploid reproductive cell, such as an egg or sperm. Gametes unite during sexual reproduction to produce a diploid zygote.

gametogenesis The process by which gametes are produced.

gametophore (guh-mē'-tō-fōr) The mature gamete-producing structure of a moss gametophyte.

gametophyte (guh-mē'-tō-fīt) In organisms (plants and some algae) that have alternation of generations, the multicellular haploid form that produces haploid gametes by mitosis. The haploid gametes unite and develop into sporophytes.

gamma-aminobutyric acid (GABA) An amino acid that functions as a CNS neurotransmitter in the central nervous system of vertebrates.

ganglion (gang'-glē-un) (plural, **ganglia**) A cluster (functional group) of nerve cell bodies in a centralized nervous system.

ganglion cell A type of neuron in the retina that synapses with bipolar cells and transmits action potentials to the brain via axons in the optic nerve.

gap junction A type of intercellular junction in animals that allows the passage of materials between cells.

gas exchange The uptake of molecular oxygen from the environment and the discharge of carbon dioxide to the environment.

gastric juice A digestive fluid secreted by the stomach.

gastrovascular cavity A central cavity with a single opening in the body of certain animals that functions in both the digestion and distribution of nutrients.

gastrula (gas′-trū-luh) An embryonic stage in animal development encompassing the formation of three layers: ectoderm, mesoderm, and endoderm.

gastrulation (gas′-trū-lā′-shun) In animal development, a series of cell and tissue movements in which the blastula-stage embryo folds inward, producing a three-layered embryo, the gastrula.

gated channel A transmembrane protein channel that opens or closes in response to a particular stimulus.

gated ion channel A gated channel for a specific ion. The opening or closing of such channels may alter the membrane potential.

gel electrophoresis (ē-lek′-trō-fōr-ē′-sis) A technique for separating nucleic acids or proteins on the basis of their size and electrical charge, both of which affect their rate of movement through an electric field in a gel.

gene A discrete unit of hereditary information consisting of a specific nucleotide sequence in DNA (or RNA, in some viruses).

gene cloning The production of multiple copies of a gene.

gene expression The process by which DNA directs the synthesis of proteins or, in some cases, just RNAs.

gene flow The transfer of alleles from one population to another, resulting from the movement of fertile individuals or their gametes.

gene pool The aggregate of all of the alleles for all of the loci in all individuals in a population. The term is also used in a more restricted sense as the aggregate of alleles for just one or a few loci in a population.

gene therapy The introduction of genes into an afflicted individual for therapeutic purposes.

gene-for-gene recognition A widespread form of plant disease resistance involving recognition of pathogen-derived molecules by the protein products of specific plant disease resistance genes.

genetic drift A process in which chance events cause unpredictable fluctuations in allele frequencies from one generation to the next. Effects of genetic drift are most pronounced in small populations.

genetic engineering The direct manipulation of genes for practical purposes.

genetic map An ordered list of genetic loci (genes or other genetic markers) along a chromosome.

genetic profile An individual's unique set of genetic markers, detected most often today by PCR or, previously, by electrophoresis and nucleic acid probes.

genetic recombination General term for the production of offspring with combinations of traits that differ from those found in either parent.

genetically modified (GM) organism An organism that has acquired one or more genes by artificial means; also known as a transgenic organism.

genetics The scientific study of heredity and hereditary variation.

genome (jē′-nōm) The genetic material of an organism or virus; the complete complement of an organism's or virus's genes along with its noncoding nucleic acid sequences.

genomic imprinting A phenomenon in which expression of an allele in offspring depends on whether the allele is inherited from the male or female parent.

genomic library A set of cell clones containing all the DNA segments from a genome, each within a plasmid, phage, or other cloning vector.

genomics (juh-nō′-miks) The study of whole sets of genes and their interactions.

genotype (jē′-nō-tīp) The genetic makeup, or set of alleles, of an organism.

genus (jē′-nus) (*plural,* **genera**) A taxonomic category above the species level, designated by the first word of a species' two-part scientific name.

geographic variation Differences between the gene pools of geographically separate populations or population subgroups.

geologic record The division of Earth's history into time periods, grouped into three eons—Archaean, Proterozoic, and Phanerozoic—and further subdivided into eras, periods, and epochs.

geometric isomer One of several compounds that have the same molecular formula and covalent arrangements but differ in the spatial arrangements of their atoms owing to the inflexibility of double bonds.

germ layer One of the three main layers in a gastrula that will form the various tissues and organs of an animal body.

gestation (jes-tā′-shun) Pregnancy; the state of carrying developing young within the female reproductive tract.

gibberellin (jib′-uh-rel′-in) Any of a class of related plant hormones that stimulate growth in the stem and leaves, trigger the germination of seeds and breaking of bud dormancy, and (with auxin) stimulate fruit development.

glans The rounded structure at the tip of the clitoris or penis that is involved in sexual arousal.

glial cells (glia) Supporting cells that are essential for the structural integrity of the nervous system and for the normal functioning of neurons.

global ecology The study of the functioning and distribution of organisms across the biosphere and how the regional exchange of energy and materials affects them.

glomeromycete (glō′-mer-ō-mī′-sēt) Member of the fungal phylum Glomeromycota, characterized by a distinct branching form of mycorrhizae (mutualistic relationships with plant roots) called arbuscular mycorrhizae.

glomerulus (glō-mār′-yū-lus) A ball of capillaries surrounded by Bowman's capsule in the nephron and serving as the site of filtration in the vertebrate kidney.

glucagon (glū′-kuh-gon) A hormone secreted by pancreatic alpha cells that raises blood glucose levels. It promotes glycogen breakdown and release of glucose by the liver.

glucocorticoid A steroid hormone that is secreted by the adrenal cortex and that influences glucose metabolism and immune function.

glutamate An amino acid that functions as a neurotransmitter in the central nervous system.

glyceraldehyde-3-phosphate (G3P) (glis′-er-al′-de-hīd) A three-carbon carbohydrate that is the direct product of the Calvin cycle; it is also an intermediate in glycolysis.

glycogen (glī′-kō-jen) An extensively branched glucose storage polysaccharide found in the liver and muscle of animals; the animal equivalent of starch.

glycolipid A lipid with covalently attached carbohydrate(s).

glycolysis (glī-kol′-uh-sis) The splitting of glucose into pyruvate. Glycolysis occurs in almost all living cells, serving as the starting point for fermentation or cellular respiration.

glycoprotein A protein with one or more carbohydrates covalently attached to it.

glycosidic linkage A covalent bond formed between two monosaccharides by a dehydration reaction.

gnathostome (na′-thu-stōm) Member of the vertebrate subgroup possessing jaws.

golden alga A biflagellated, photosynthetic protist named for its color, which results from its yellow and brown carotenoids.

Golgi apparatus (gol′-jē) An organelle in eukaryotic cells consisting of stacks of flat membranous sacs that modify, store, and route products of the endoplasmic reticulum and synthesize some products, notably noncellulose carbohydrates.

gonads (gō′-nadz) The male and female sex organs; the gamete-producing organs in most animals.

G protein A GTP-binding protein that relays signals from a plasma membrane signal receptor, known as a G protein-coupled receptor, to other signal transduction proteins inside the cell.

G protein-coupled receptor A signal receptor protein in the plasma membrane that responds to the binding of a signaling molecule by activating a G protein. Also called a G protein-linked receptor.

grade A group of organisms that share the same level of organizational complexity or share a key adaptation.

Gram stain A staining method that distinguishes between two different kinds of bacterial cell walls.

gram-negative Describing the group of bacteria that have a cell wall that is structurally more complex and contains less peptidoglycan than the cell wall of gram-positive bacteria. Gram-negative bacteria are often more toxic than gram-positive bacteria.

gram-positive Describing the group of bacteria that have a cell wall that is structurally less complex and contains more peptidoglycan than the cell wall of gram-negative bacteria. Gram-positive bacteria are usually less toxic than gram-negative bacteria.

granum (gran′-um) (plural, **grana**) A stack of membrane-bounded thylakoids in the chloroplast. Grana function in the light reactions of photosynthesis.

gravitropism (grav′-uh-trō′-pizm) A response of a plant or animal to gravity.

gray crescent A light gray, crescent-shaped region of cytoplasm that becomes exposed after cortical rotation, located near the equator of an egg on the side opposite sperm entry, marking the future dorsal side of the embryo.

gray matter Regions of dendrites and clustered neuron cell bodies within the CNS.

green alga A photosynthetic protist, named for green chloroplasts that are similar in structure and pigment composition to those of land plants. Green algae are a paraphyletic group, some of whose members are more closely related to land plants than they are to other green algae.

green world hypothesis The conjecture that terrestrial herbivores consume relatively little plant biomass because they are held in check by a variety of factors, including predators, parasites, and disease.

greenhouse effect The warming of Earth due to the atmospheric accumulation of carbon dioxide and certain other gases, which absorb reflected infrared radiation and reradiate some of it back toward Earth.

gross primary production (GPP) The total primary production of an ecosystem.

ground tissue system Plant tissues that are neither vascular nor dermal, fulfilling a variety of functions, such as storage, photosynthesis, and support.

growth factor (1) A protein that must be present in the extracellular environment (culture medium or animal body) for the growth and normal development of certain types of cells. (2) A local regulator that acts on nearby cells to stimulate cell proliferation and differentiation.

growth hormone (GH) A hormone that is produced and secreted by the anterior pituitary and that has both direct (nontropic) and tropic effects on a wide variety of tissues.

guard cells The two cells that flank the stomatal pore and regulate the opening and closing of the pore.

gustation The sense of taste.

guttation The exudation of water droplets, caused by root pressure in certain plants.

gymnosperm (jim′-nō-sperm) A vascular plant that bears naked seeds—seeds not enclosed in specialized chambers.

habituation A simple type of learning that involves a loss of responsiveness to stimuli that convey little or no new information.

half-life The amount of time it takes for 50% of a sample of a radioactive isotope to decay.

Hamilton's rule The principle that for natural selection to favor an altruistic act, the benefit to the recipient, devalued by the coefficient of relatedness, must exceed the cost to the altruist.

haploid cell (hap′-loyd) A cell containing only one set of chromosomes (n).

Hardy-Weinberg equilibrium The condition describing a nonevolving population (one that is in genetic equilibrium).

Hardy-Weinberg principle The principle that frequencies of alleles and genotypes in a population remain constant from generation to generation, provided that only Mendelian segregation and recombination of alleles are at work.

haustorium (plural, **haustoria**) (ho-stōr′-ē-um, ho-stōr′-ē-uh) In certain symbiotic fungi, a specialized hypha that can penetrate the tissues of host organisms.

heart A muscular pump that uses metabolic energy to elevate the hydrostatic pressure of the circulatory fluid (blood or hemolymph). The fluid then flows down a pressure gradient through the body and eventually returns to the heart.

heart attack The damage or death of cardiac muscle tissue resulting from prolonged blockage of one or more coronary arteries.

heart murmur A hissing sound that most often results from blood squirting backward through a leaky valve in the heart.

heart rate The frequency of heart contraction.

heat The total amount of kinetic energy due to the random motion of atoms or molecules in a body of matter; also called thermal energy. Heat is energy in its most random form.

heat of vaporization The quantity of heat a liquid must absorb for 1 g of it to be converted from the liquid to the gaseous state.

heat-shock protein A protein that helps protect other proteins during heat stress. Heat-shock proteins are found in plants, animals, and microorganisms.

heavy chain One of the two types of polypeptide chains that make up an antibody molecule and B cell receptor; consists of a variable region, which contributes to the antigen-binding site, and a constant region.

helicase An enzyme that untwists the double helix of DNA at the replication forks, separating the two strands and making them available as template strands.

helper T cell A type of T cell that, when activated, secretes cytokines that promote the response of B cells (humoral response) and cytotoxic T cells (cell-mediated response) to antigens.

hemoglobin (hē′-mō-glō′-bin) An iron-containing protein in red blood cells that reversibly binds oxygen.

hemolymph (hē′-mō-limf′) In invertebrates with an open circulatory system, the body fluid that bathes tissues.

hemophilia (hē′-muh-fil′-ē-uh) A human genetic disease caused by a sex-linked recessive allele resulting in the absence of one or more blood-clotting proteins; characterized by excessive bleeding following injury.

hepatic portal vein A large circulatory channel that conveys nutrient-laden blood from the small intestine to the liver, which regulates the blood's nutrient content.

herbivore (hur′-bi-vōr′) An animal that mainly eats plants or algae.

herbivory An interaction in which an organism eats parts of a plant or alga.

heredity The transmission of traits from one generation to the next.

hermaphrodite (hur-maf′-ruh-dīt′) An individual that functions as both male and female in sexual reproduction by producing both sperm and eggs.

hermaphroditism (hur-maf′-rō-dī-tizm) A condition in which an individual has both female and male gonads and functions as both a male and female in sexual reproduction by producing both sperm and eggs.

heterochromatin (het′-er-ō-krō′-muh-tin) Eukaryotic chromatin that remains highly compacted during interphase and is generally not transcribed.

heterochrony (het′-uh-rok′-ruh-nē) Evolutionary change in the timing or rate of an organism's development.

heterocyte (het′-er-ō-sīt) A specialized cell that engages in nitrogen fixation in some filamentous cyanobacteria; formerly called heterocyst.

heterokaryon (het′-er-ō-kār′-ē-un) A fungal mycelium that contains two or more haploid nuclei per cell.

heteromorphic (het′-er-ō-mōr′-fik) Referring to a condition in the life cycle of plants and certain algae in which the sporophyte and gametophyte generations differ in morphology.

heterosporous (het-er-os′-pōr-us) Referring to a plant species that has two kinds of spores: microspores, which develop into male gametophytes, and megaspores, which develop into female gametophytes.

heterotroph (het′-er-ō-trōf) An organism that obtains organic food molecules by eating other organisms or substances derived from them.

heterozygote advantage Greater reproductive success of heterozygous individuals compared with homozygotes; tends to preserve variation in a gene pool.

heterozygous (het′-er-ō-zī′-gus) Having two different alleles for a given gene.

hexapod An insect or closely related wingless, six-legged arthropod.

hibernation A physiological state in which metabolism decreases, the heart and respiratory system slow down, and body temperature is maintained at a lower level than normal.

high-density lipoprotein (HDL) A particle in the blood made up of cholesterol and other lipids surrounded by a single layer of phospholipids in which proteins are embedded. HDL carries less cholesterol than a related lipoprotein, LDL, and high HDL levels in the blood may be correlated with a decreased risk of blood vessel blockage.

hindbrain One of three ancestral and embryonic regions of the vertebrate brain; develops into the medulla oblongata, pons, and cerebellum.

histamine (his'-tuh-mēn) A substance released by mast cells that causes blood vessels to dilate and become more permeable in inflammatory and allergic responses.

histone (his'-tōn) A small protein with a high proportion of positively charged amino acids that binds to the negatively charged DNA and plays a key role in chromatin structure.

histone acetylation The attachment of acetyl groups to certain amino acids of histone proteins.

HIV (human immunodeficiency virus) The infectious agent that causes AIDS. HIV is a retrovirus.

holdfast A rootlike structure that anchors a seaweed.

holoblastic cleavage (hō'-lō-blas'-tik) A type of cleavage in which there is complete division of the egg; occurs in eggs that have little yolk (such as those of the sea urchin) or a moderate amount of yolk (such as those of the frog).

homeobox (hō'-mē-ō-boks') A 180-nucleotide sequence within homeotic genes and some other developmental genes that is widely conserved in animals. Related sequences occur in plants and yeasts.

homeostasis (hō'-mē-ō-stā'-sis) The steady-state physiological condition of the body.

homeotic gene (ho'-mē-o'-tik) Any of the master regulatory genes that control placement and spatial organization of body parts in animals, plants, and fungi by controlling the developmental fate of groups of cells.

hominin (ho'-mi-nin) A species on the human branch of the evolutionary tree. Hominins include *Homo sapiens* and our ancestors, a group of extinct species that are more closely related to us than to chimpanzees.

homologous chromosomes (hō-mol'-uh-gus) A pair of chromosomes of the same length, centromere position, and staining pattern that possess genes for the same characters at corresponding loci. One homologous chromosome is inherited from the organism's father, the other from the mother. Also called homologs, or a homologous pair.

homologous structures Structures in different species that are similar because of common ancestry.

homology (hō-mol'-uh-jē) Similarity in characteristics resulting from a shared ancestry.

homoplasy (hō'-muh-play'-zē) Similar (analogous) structure or molecular sequence that has evolved independently in two species.

homosporous (hō-mos'-puh-rus) Referring to a plant species that has a single kind of spore, which typically develops into a bisexual gametophyte.

homozygous (hō'-mō-zī'-gus) Having two identical alleles for a given gene.

horizontal cell A neuron of the retina that helps integrate information before it is sent to the brain.

horizontal gene transfer The transfer of genes from one genome to another through mechanisms such as transposable elements, plasmid exchange, viral activity, and perhaps fusions of different organisms.

hormone In multicellular organisms, one of many types of secreted chemicals that are formed in specialized cells, travel in body fluids, and act on specific target cells in other parts of the body to change their functioning.

hornwort A small, herbaceous nonvascular plant that is a member of the phylum Anthocerophyta.

host The larger participant in a symbiotic relationship, serving as home and food source for the smaller symbiont.

host range The limited range of host cells that each type of virus can infect.

human chorionic gonadotropin (hCG) (kōr'-ē-on'-ik gō-na'-dō-trō'-pin) A hormone secreted by the chorion that maintains the corpus luteum of the ovary during the first three months of pregnancy.

Human Genome Project An international collaborative effort to map and sequence the DNA of the entire human genome.

humoral immune response (hyū'-mer-ul) The branch of acquired immunity that involves the activation of B cells and that leads to the production of antibodies, which defend against bacteria and viruses in body fluids.

humus (hyū'-mus) Decomposing organic material that is a component of topsoil.

Huntington's disease A human genetic disease caused by a dominant allele; characterized by uncontrollable body movements and degeneration of the nervous system; usually fatal 10 to 20 years after the onset of symptoms.

hybrid Offspring that results from the mating of individuals from two different species or two true-breeding varieties of the same species.

hybrid zone A geographic region in which members of different species meet and mate, producing at least some offspring of mixed ancestry.

hybridization In genetics, the mating, or crossing, of two true-breeding varieties.

hydration shell The sphere of water molecules around a dissolved ion.

hydrocarbon An organic molecule consisting only of carbon and hydrogen.

hydrogen bond A type of weak chemical bond that is formed when the slightly positive hydrogen atom of a polar covalent bond in one molecule is attracted to the slightly negative atom of a polar covalent bond in another molecule.

hydrogen ion A single proton with a charge of $1+$. The dissociation of a water molecule (H_2O) leads to the generation of a hydroxide ion (OH^-) and a hydrogen ion (H^+).

hydrolysis (hī-drol'-uh-sis) A chemical process that lyses, or splits, molecules by the addition of water, functioning in disassembly of polymers to monomers.

hydronium ion A water molecule that has an extra proton bound to it; H_3O^+.

hydrophilic (hī'-drō-fil'-ik) Having an affinity for water.

hydrophobic (hī'-drō-fō'-bik) Having an aversion to water; tending to coalesce and form droplets in water.

hydrophobic interaction A type of weak chemical bond formed when molecules that do not mix with water coalesce to exclude water.

hydroponic culture A method in which plants are grown in mineral solutions rather than in soil.

hydrostatic skeleton A skeletal system composed of fluid held under pressure in a closed body compartment; the main skeleton of most cnidarians, flatworms, nematodes, and annelids.

hydroxide ion A water molecule that has lost a proton; OH^-.

hydroxyl group (hī-drok'-sil) A chemical group consisting of an oxygen atom joined to a hydrogen atom. Molecules possessing this group are soluble in water and are called alcohols.

hymen A thin membrane that partly covers the vaginal opening in the human female. The hymen is ruptured by sexual intercourse or other vigorous activity.

hyperpolarization A change in a cell's membrane potential such that the inside of the membrane becomes more negative relative to the outside. Hyperpolarization reduces the chance that a neuron will transmit a nerve impulse.

hypersensitive response A plant's localized defense response to a pathogen, involving the death of cells around the site of infection.

hypertension A disorder in which blood pressure remains abnormally high.

hypertonic Referring to a solution that, when surrounding a cell, will cause the cell to lose water.

hypha (plural, **hyphae**) (hī'-fuh, hī'-fē) One of many connected filaments that collectively make up the mycelium of a fungus.

hypocotyl (hī'-puh-cot'-ul) In an angiosperm embryo, the embryonic axis below the point of attachment of the cotyledon(s) and above the radicle.

hypothalamus (hī'-pō-thal'-uh-mus) The ventral part of the vertebrate forebrain; functions in maintaining homeostasis, especially in coordinating the endocrine and nervous systems; secretes hormones of the posterior pituitary and releasing factors that regulate the anterior pituitary.

hypothesis (hī-poth'-uh-sis) A tentative answer to a well-framed question, narrower in scope than a theory and subject to testing.

hypotonic Referring to a solution that, when surrounding a cell, will cause the cell to take up water.

imbibition The physical adsorption of water onto the internal surfaces of structures.

immigration The influx of new individuals into a population from other areas.

immune system An animal body's system of defenses against agents that cause disease.

immunization The process of generating a state of immunity by artificial means. In active immunization, also called vaccination, an inactive or weakened form of a pathogen is administered, inducing B and T cell responses and immunological memory. In passive immunization, antibodies specific for a particular microbe are administered, conferring immediate but temporary protection.

immunodeficiency A disorder in which the ability of an immune system to protect against pathogens is defective or absent.

immunoglobulin (Ig) (im'-yū-nō-glob'-yū-lin) Any of the class of proteins that function as antibodies. Immunoglobulins are divided into five major classes that differ in their distribution in the body and antigen disposal activities.

imprinting In animal behavior, the formation at a specific stage in life of a long-lasting behavioral response to a specific individual or object. (*See also* genomic imprinting.)

in situ hybridization A technique used to detect the location of a specific mRNA using nucleic acid hybridization with a labeled probe in an intact organism.

in vitro fertilization (IVF) (vē'-trō) Fertilization of oocytes in laboratory containers followed by artificial implantation of the early embryo in the mother's uterus.

in vitro mutagenesis A technique used to discover the function of a gene by cloning it, introducing specific changes into the cloned gene's sequence, reinserting the mutated gene into a cell, and studying the phenotype of the mutant.

inclusive fitness The total effect an individual has on proliferating its genes by producing its own offspring and by providing aid that enables other close relatives to increase the production of their offspring.

incomplete dominance The situation in which the phenotype of heterozygotes is intermediate between the phenotypes of individuals homozygous for either allele.

incomplete flower A flower in which one or more of the four basic floral organs (sepals, petals, stamens, or carpels) are either absent or nonfunctional.

incomplete metamorphosis A type of development in certain insects, such as grasshoppers, in which the young (called nymphs) resemble adults but are smaller and have different body proportions. The nymph goes through a series of molts, each time looking more like an adult, until it reaches full size.

incus The second of three bones in the middle ear of mammals; also called the anvil.

indeterminate cleavage A type of embryonic development in deuterostomes in which each cell produced by early cleavage divisions retains the capacity to develop into a complete embryo.

indeterminate growth A type of growth characteristic of plants, in which the organism continues to grow as long as it lives.

induced fit Induced by entry of the substrate, the change in shape of the active site of an enzyme so that it binds more snugly to the substrate.

inducer A specific small molecule that binds to a bacterial repressor protein and changes the repressor's shape so that it cannot bind to an operator, thus switching an operon on.

induction The process in which one group of embryonic cells influences the development of another, usually by causing changes in gene expression.

inductive reasoning A type of logic in which generalizations are based on a large number of specific observations.

inflammatory response An innate immune defense triggered by physical injury or infection of tissue involving the release of substances that promote swelling, enhance the infiltration of white blood cells, and aid in tissue repair and destruction of invading pathogens.

inflorescence A group of flowers tightly clustered together.

ingestion The first stage of food processing in animals: the act of eating.

ingroup A species or group of species whose evolutionary relationships we seek to determine.

inhibin A hormone produced in the male and female gonads that functions in part by regulating the function of the anterior pituitary by negative feedback.

inhibitory postsynaptic potential (IPSP) An electrical change (usually hyperpolarization) in the membrane of a postsynaptic neuron caused by the binding of an inhibitory neurotransmitter from a presynaptic cell to a postsynaptic receptor; makes it more difficult for a postsynaptic neuron to generate an action potential.

innate behavior Animal behavior that is developmentally fixed and under strong genetic control. Innate behavior is exhibited in virtually the same form by all individuals in a population despite internal and external environmental differences during development and throughout their lifetimes.

innate immunity A form of defense common to all animals that is active immediately upon exposure to pathogens and that is the same whether or not the pathogen has been encountered previously.

inner cell mass An inner cluster of cells at one end of a mammalian blastocyst that subsequently develops into the embryo proper and some of the extraembryonic membranes.

inner ear One of three main regions of the vertebrate ear; includes the cochlea (which in turn contains the organ of Corti) and the semicircular canals.

inositol trisphosphate (IP₃) (in-ō'-suh-tol) A second messenger that functions as an intermediate between certain nonsteroid hormones and a third messenger, a rise in cytoplasmic Ca^{2+} concentration.

inquiry The search for information and explanation, often focused by specific questions.

insertion A mutation involving the addition of one or more nucleotide pairs to a gene.

insulin (in'-suh-lin) A hormone secreted by pancreatic beta cells that lowers blood glucose levels. It promotes the uptake of glucose by most body cells and the synthesis and storage of glycogen in the liver and also stimulates protein and fat synthesis.

integral protein Typically a transmembrane protein with hydrophobic regions that extend into and often completely span the hydrophobic interior of the membrane and with hydrophilic regions in contact with the aqueous solution on either side of the membrane (or lining the channel in the case of a channel protein).

integrin In animal cells, a transmembrane receptor protein that interconnects the extracellular matrix and the cytoskeleton.

integument (in-teg'-yū-ment) Layer of sporophyte tissue that contributes to the structure of an ovule of a seed plant.

integumentary system The outer covering of a mammal's body, including skin, hair, and nails.

intercalated disk (in-ter'-kuh-lā'-ted) A special junction between cardiac muscle cells that provides direct electrical coupling between the cells.

interferon (in'-ter-fēr'-on) A protein that has antiviral or immune regulatory functions. Interferon-α and interferon-β, secreted by virus-infected cells, help nearby cells resist viral infection; interferon-γ, secreted by T cells, helps activate macrophages.

intermediate disturbance hypothesis The concept that moderate levels of disturbance can foster greater species diversity than low or high levels of disturbance.

intermediate filament A component of the cytoskeleton that includes filaments intermediate in size between microtubules and microfilaments.

internal fertilization The fusion of eggs and sperm within the female reproductive tract. The sperm are typically deposited in or near the tract.

interneuron An association neuron; a nerve cell within the central nervous system that forms synapses with sensory and/or motor neurons and integrates sensory input and motor output.

internode A segment of a plant stem between the points where leaves are attached.

interphase The period in the cell cycle when the cell is not dividing. During interphase, cellular metabolic activity is high, chromosomes and organelles are duplicated, and cell size may increase. Interphase accounts for 90% of the cell cycle.

intersexual selection Selection whereby individuals of one sex (usually females) are choosy in selecting their mates from individuals of the other sex; also called mate choice.

interspecific competition Competition for resources between individuals of two or more species when resources are in short supply.

interspecific interaction A relationship between individuals of two or more species in a community.

interstitial fluid The fluid filling the spaces between cells in an animal.

intertidal zone The shallow zone of the ocean adjacent to land and between the high- and low-tide lines.

intracellular digestion The hydrolysis of food inside vacuoles.

intracytoplasmic sperm injection (ICSI) The fertilization of an egg in the laboratory by the direct injection of a single sperm.

intrasexual selection A direct competition among individuals of one sex (usually the males in vertebrates) for mates of the opposite sex.

introduced species A species moved by humans, either intentionally or accidentally, from its native location to a new geographic region; also called non-native or exotic species.

intron (in'-tron) A noncoding, intervening sequence within a primary transcript that is removed from the transcript during RNA processing; also refers to the region of DNA from which this sequence was transcribed.

invagination The infolding, or pushing inward, of cells due to changes in cell shape.

invasive species A species, often introduced by humans, that takes hold outside its native range.

inversion An aberration in chromosome structure resulting from reattachment of a chromosomal fragment in a reverse orientation to the chromosome from which it originated.

invertebrate An animal without a backbone. Invertebrates make up 95% of animal species.

involution The process by which sheets of cells roll over the edge of the lip of the blastopore into the interior of the embryo during gastrulation.

ion (ī'-on) An atom or group of atoms that has gained or lost one or more electrons, thus acquiring a charge.

ion channel A transmembrane protein channel that allows a specific ion to flow across the membrane down its concentration gradient.

ionic bond (ī-on'-ik) A chemical bond resulting from the attraction between oppositely charged ions.

ionic compound A compound resulting from the formation of an ionic bond; also called a salt.

IPSP *See* inhibitory postsynaptic potential.

iris The colored part of the vertebrate eye, formed by the anterior portion of the choroid.

islets of Langerhans Clusters of endocrine cells within the pancreas that produce and secrete the hormones glucagon (from alpha cells) and insulin (from beta cells).

isomer (ī'-sō-mer) One of several compounds with the same molecular formula but different structures and therefore different properties. The three types of isomers are structural isomers, geometric isomers, and enantiomers.

isomorphic Referring to alternating generations in plants and certain algae in which the sporophytes and gametophytes look alike, although they differ in chromosome number.

isopod A member of one of the largest groups of crustaceans, which includes terrestrial, freshwater, and marine species. Among the terrestrial isopods are the pill bugs, or wood lice.

isotonic (ī'-sō-ton'-ik) Referring to a solution that, when surrounding a cell, has no effect on the passage of water into or out of the cell.

isotope (ī'-sō-tōp') One of several atomic forms of an element, each with the same number of protons but a different number of neutrons, thus differing in atomic mass.

iteroparity Reproduction in which adults produce offspring over many years; also known as repeated reproduction.

joule (J) A unit of energy: 1 J = 0.239 cal; 1 cal = 4.184 J.

juvenile hormone A hormone in arthropods, secreted by the corpora allata (a pair of glands), that promotes the retention of larval characteristics.

juxtaglomerular apparatus (JGA) (juks'-tuh-gluh-mār'-yū-ler) A specialized tissue in nephrons that releases the enzyme renin in response to a drop in blood pressure or volume.

juxtamedullary nephron In mammals and birds, a nephron with a loop of Henle that extends far into the renal medulla.

karyogamy (kār'-ē-og'-uh-mē) The fusion of two nuclei, as part of syngamy (fertilization).

karyotype (kār'-ē-ō-tīp) A display of the chromosome pairs of a cell arranged by size and shape.

keystone species A species that is not necessarily abundant in a community yet exerts strong control on community structure by the nature of its ecological role or niche.

kilocalorie (kcal) A thousand calories; the amount of heat energy required to raise the temperature of 1 kg of water by 1°C.

kin selection Natural selection that favors altruistic behavior by enhancing the reproductive success of relatives.

kinesis (kuh-nē'-sis) A change in activity or turning rate in response to a stimulus.

kinetic energy (kuh-net'-ik) The energy associated with the relative motion of objects. Moving matter can perform work by imparting motion to other matter.

kinetochore (kuh-net'-uh-kōr) A structure of proteins attached to the centromere that links each sister chromatid to the mitotic spindle.

kinetoplastid A protist, such as a trypanosome, that has a single large mitochondrion that houses an organized mass of DNA.

kingdom A taxonomic category, the second broadest after domain.

***K*-selection** Selection for life history traits that are sensitive to population density; also called density-dependent selection.

labia majora A pair of thick, fatty ridges that encloses and protects the rest of the vulva.

labia minora A pair of slender skin folds that surrounds the openings of the vagina and urethra.

labor A series of strong, rhythmic contractions of the uterus that expel a baby out of the uterus and vagina during childbirth.

lactation The continued production of milk from the mammary glands.

lacteal (lak'-tē-ul) A tiny lymph vessel extending into the core of an intestinal villus and serving as the destination for absorbed chylomicrons.

lactic acid fermentation Glycolysis followed by the conversion of pyruvate to lactate, with no release of carbon dioxide.

lagging strand A discontinuously synthesized DNA strand that elongates by means of Okazaki fragments, each synthesized in a 5'→3' direction away from the replication fork.

lancelet Member of the subphylum Cephalochordata, small blade-shaped marine chordates that lack a backbone.

landmark A location indicator—a point of reference for orientation during navigation.

landscape An area containing several different ecosystems linked by exchanges of energy, materials, and organisms.

landscape ecology The study of how the spatial arrangement of habitat types affects the distribution and abundance of organisms and ecosystem processes.

large intestine The tubular portion of the vertebrate alimentary canal between the small intestine and the anus; functions mainly in water absorption and the formation of feces.

larva (lar'-vuh) (plural, **larvae**) A free-living, sexually immature form in some animal life cycles that may differ from the adult animal in morphology, nutrition, and habitat.

larynx (lār'-inks) The portion of the respiratory tract containing the vocal cords; also called the voice box.

lateral geniculate nucleus One of a pair of structures in the brain that are the destination for most of the ganglion cell axons that form the optic nerves.

lateral inhibition A process that sharpens the edges and enhances the contrast of a perceived image by inhibiting receptors lateral to those that have responded to light.

lateral line system A mechanoreceptor system consisting of a series of pores and receptor units along the sides of the body in fishes and aquatic amphibians; detects water movements made by the animal itself and by other moving objects.

lateral meristem (mār'-uh-stem) A meristem that thickens the roots and shoots of woody plants. The vascular cambium and cork cambium are lateral meristems.

lateral root A root that arises from the pericycle of an established root.

lateralization Segregation of functions in the cortex of the left and right hemispheres of the brain.

law of conservation of mass A physical law stating that matter can change form but cannot be created or destroyed. In a closed system, the mass of the system is constant.

law of independent assortment Mendel's second law, stating that each pair of alleles segregates, or assorts, independently of each other pair during gamete formation; applies when genes for two characters are located on different pairs of homologous chromosomes.

law of segregation Mendel's first law, stating that the two alleles in a pair segregate (separate) into different gametes during gamete formation.

leading strand The new complementary DNA strand synthesized continuously along the template strand toward the replication fork in the mandatory 5′→3′ direction.

leaf The main photosynthetic organ of vascular plants.

leaf primordium A finger-like projection along the flank of a shoot apical meristem, from which a leaf arises.

learning The modification of behavior based on specific experiences.

lens The structure in an eye that focuses light rays onto the photoreceptors.

lenticel (len′-ti-sel) A small raised area in the bark of stems and roots that enables gas exchange between living cells and the outside air.

lepidosaur (leh-pid′-uh-sōr) Member of the reptilian group that includes lizards, snakes, and two species of New Zealand animals called tuataras.

leukocyte (lū′-kō-sīt′) A blood cell that functions in fighting infections; also called a white blood cell.

Leydig cell (lī′-dig) A cell that produces testosterone and other androgens and is located between the seminiferous tubules of the testes.

lichen The symbiotic collective formed by the mutualistic association between a fungus and a photosynthetic alga or cyanobacterium.

life cycle The generation-to-generation sequence of stages in the reproductive history of an organism.

life history The traits that affect an organism's schedule of reproduction and survival.

life table A table of data summarizing mortality in a population.

ligament A fibrous connective tissue that joins bones together at joints.

ligand (lig′-und) A molecule that binds specifically to another molecule, usually a larger one.

ligand-gated ion channel A protein pore in cellular membranes that opens or closes in response to a signaling chemical (its ligand), allowing or blocking the flow of specific ions.

light chain One of the two types of polypeptide chains that make up an antibody molecule and B cell receptor; consists of a variable region, which contributes to the antigen-binding site, and a constant region.

light microscope (LM) An optical instrument with lenses that refract (bend) visible light to magnify images of specimens.

light reactions The first of two major stages in photosynthesis (preceding the Calvin cycle). These reactions, which occur on the thylakoid membranes of the chloroplast or on membranes of certain prokaryotes, convert solar energy to the chemical energy of ATP and NADPH, releasing oxygen in the process.

light-harvesting complex A complex of proteins associated with pigment molecules (including chlorophyll *a*, chlorophyll *b*, and carotenoids) that captures light energy and

transfers it to reaction-center pigments in a photosystem.

lignin (lig′-nin) A hard material embedded in the cellulose matrix of vascular plant cell walls that provides structural support in terrestrial species.

limiting nutrient An element that must be added for production to increase in a particular area.

limnetic zone In a lake, the well-lit, open surface waters farther from shore.

linear electron flow A route of electron flow during the light reactions of photosynthesis that involves both photosystems (I and II) and produces ATP, NADPH, and O_2. The net electron flow is from H_2O to $NADP^+$.

linkage map A genetic map based on the frequencies of recombination between markers during crossing over of homologous chromosomes.

linked genes Genes located close enough together on a chromosome that they tend to be inherited together.

lipid (lip′-id) One of a group of compounds, including fats, phospholipids, and steroids, that mix poorly, if at all, with water.

littoral zone In a lake, the shallow, well-lit waters close to shore.

liver The largest internal organ in the vertebrate body. The liver performs diverse functions, such as producing bile, preparing nitrogenous wastes for disposal, and detoxifying poisonous chemicals in the blood.

liverwort A small, herbaceous nonvascular plant that is a member of the phylum Hepatophyta.

loam The most fertile soil type, made up of roughly equal amounts of sand, silt, and clay.

lobe-fin Member of the vertebrate subgroup Sarcopterygii, osteichthyans with rod-shaped muscular fins, including coelacanths and lungfishes as well as the lineage that gave rise to tetrapods.

local regulator A secreted molecule that influences cells near where it is secreted.

locomotion Active motion from place to place.

locus (lō′-kus) (plural, **loci**) A specific place along the length of a chromosome where a given gene is located.

logistic population growth Population growth that levels off as population size approaches carrying capacity.

long-day plant A plant that flowers (usually in late spring or early summer) only when the light period is longer than a critical length.

long-term memory The ability to hold, associate, and recall information over one's lifetime.

long-term potentiation (LTP) An enhanced responsiveness to an action potential (nerve signal) by a receiving neuron.

loop of Henle The hairpin turn, with a descending and ascending limb, between the proximal and distal tubules of the vertebrate kidney; functions in water and salt reabsorption.

lophophore (lof′-uh-fōr) In some lophotrochozoan animals, including brachiopods, a crown of ciliated tentacles that surround the mouth and function in feeding.

lophotrochozoan Member of a group of animal phyla identified as a clade by molecular evidence. Lophotrochozoans include organisms that have lophophores or trochophore larvae.

low-density lipoprotein (LDL) A particle in the blood made up of cholesterol and other lipids surrounded by a single layer of phospholipids in which proteins are embedded. LDL carries more cholesterol than a related lipoprotein, HDL, and high LDL levels in the blood correlate with a tendency to develop blocked blood vessels and heart disease.

lung An infolded respiratory surface of a terrestrial vertebrate, land snail, or spider that connects to the atmosphere by narrow tubes.

luteal phase That portion of the ovarian cycle during which endocrine cells of the corpus luteum secrete female hormones.

luteinizing hormone (LH) (lū′-tē-uh-nī′-zing) A tropic hormone that is produced and secreted by the anterior pituitary and that stimulates ovulation in females and androgen production in males.

lycophyte (lī′-kuh-fīt) An informal name for a member of the phylum Lycophyta, which includes club mosses, spike mosses, and quillworts.

lymph The colorless fluid, derived from interstitial fluid, in the lymphatic system of vertebrates.

lymph node An organ located along a lymph vessel. Lymph nodes filter lymph and contain cells that attack viruses and bacteria.

lymphatic system A system of vessels and nodes, separate from the circulatory system, that returns fluid, proteins, and cells to the blood.

lymphocyte A type of white blood cell that mediates acquired immunity. The two main classes are B cells and T cells.

lysogenic cycle (lī′-sō-jen′-ik) A type of phage reproductive cycle in which the viral genome becomes incorporated into the bacterial host chromosome as a prophage and does not kill the host.

lysosome (lī′-suh-sōm) A membrane-enclosed sac of hydrolytic enzymes found in the cytoplasm of animal cells and some protists.

lysozyme (lī′-sō-zīm) An enzyme that destroys bacterial cell walls; in mammals, found in sweat, tears, and saliva.

lytic cycle (lit′-ik) A type of phage reproductive cycle resulting in the release of new phages by lysis (and death) of the host cell.

macroclimate Large-scale patterns in climate; the climate of an entire region.

macroevolution Evolutionary change above the species level, including the origin of a new group of organisms or a shift in the broad pattern of evolutionary change over a long period of time. Examples of macroevolutionary change include the appearance of major new features of organisms and the impact of mass extinctions on the diversity of life and its subsequent recovery.

macromolecule A giant molecule formed by the joining of smaller molecules, usually by a condensation reaction. Polysaccharides, proteins, and nucleic acids are macromolecules.

macronutrient A chemical substance that an organism must obtain in relatively large amounts. *See also* micronutrient.

macrophage (mak'-rō-fāj) A phagocytic cell present in many tissues that functions in innate immunity by destroying microbes and in acquired immunity as an antigen-presenting cell.

magnoliid Member of the angiosperm clade most closely related to eudicots. Extant examples are magnolias, laurels, and black pepper plants.

major depressive disorder A mood disorder characterized by feelings of sadness, lack of self-worth, emptiness, or loss of interest in nearly all things.

major histocompatibility complex (MHC) A family of genes that encode a large set of cell-surface proteins that function in antigen presentation. Foreign MHC molecules on transplanted tissue can trigger T cell responses that may lead to rejection of the transplant.

malignant tumor A cancerous tumor that is invasive enough to impair the functions of one or more organs.

malleus The first of three bones in the middle ear of mammals; also called the hammer.

malnourishment The long-term absence from the diet of one or more essential nutrients.

Malpighian tubule (mal-pig'-ē-un) A unique excretory organ of insects that empties into the digestive tract, removes nitrogenous wastes from the hemolymph, and functions in osmoregulation.

mammal Member of the class Mammalia, amniotes with mammary glands—glands that produce milk.

mammary glands Exocrine glands that secrete milk to nourish the young. These glands are characteristic of mammals.

mandible One of a pair of jaw-like feeding appendages found in myriapods, hexapods, and crustaceans.

mantle One of the three main parts of a mollusc; a fold of tissue that drapes over the mollusc's visceral mass and may secrete a shell. *See also* foot, visceral mass.

mantle cavity A water-filled chamber that houses the gills, anus, and excretory pores of a mollusc.

map unit A unit of measurement of the distance between genes. One map unit is equivalent to a 1% recombination frequency.

marine benthic zone The ocean floor.

mark-recapture method A sampling technique used to estimate the size of animal populations.

marsupial (mar-sū'-pē-ul) A mammal, such as a koala, kangaroo, or opossum, whose young complete their embryonic development inside a maternal pouch called the marsupium.

mass extinction Period of time when global environmental changes lead to the elimination of a large number of species throughout Earth.

mass number The sum of the number of protons and neutrons in an atom's nucleus.

mast cell A vertebrate body cell that produces histamine and other molecules that trigger inflammation in response to infection and in allergic reactions.

mate choice copying Behavior in which individuals in a population copy the mate choice of others, apparently as a result of social learning.

maternal effect gene A gene that, when mutant in the mother, results in a mutant phenotype in the offspring, regardless of the offspring's genotype. Maternal effect genes were first identified in *Drosophila*.

matter Anything that takes up space and has mass.

maximum likelihood As applied to systematics, a principle that states that when considering multiple phylogenetic hypotheses, one should take into account the hypothesis that reflects the most likely sequence of evolutionary events, given certain rules about how DNA changes over time.

maximum parsimony A principle that states that when considering multiple explanations for an observation, one should first investigate the simplest explanation that is consistent with the facts.

mechanoreceptor A sensory receptor that detects physical deformation in the body's environment associated with pressure, touch, stretch, motion, or sound.

medulla oblongata (meh-dul'-uh ob'-long-go'-tuh) The lowest part of the vertebrate brain, commonly called the medulla; a swelling of the hindbrain anterior to the spinal cord that controls autonomic, homeostatic functions, including breathing, heart and blood vessel activity, swallowing, digestion, and vomiting.

medusa (muh-dū'-suh) The floating, flattened, mouth-down version of the cnidarian body plan. The alternate form is the polyp.

megapascal (MPa) (meg'-uh-pas-kal') A unit of pressure equivalent to about 10 atmospheres of pressure.

megaphyll (meh'-guh-fil) A leaf with a highly branched vascular system, characteristic of the vast majority of vascular plants.

megaspore A spore from a heterosporous plant species that develops into a female gametophyte.

meiosis (mī-ō'-sis) A modified type of cell division in sexually reproducing organisms consisting of two rounds of cell division but only one round of DNA replication. It results in cells with half the number of chromosome sets as the original cell.

meiosis I The first division of a two-stage process of cell division in sexually reproducing organisms that results in cells with half the number of chromosome sets as the original cell.

meiosis II The second division of a two-stage process of cell division in sexually reproducing organisms that results in cells with half the number of chromosome sets as the original cell.

melanocyte-stimulating hormone (MSH) A hormone produced and secreted by the anterior pituitary that regulates the activity of pigment-containing cells in the skin of some vertebrates.

melatonin A hormone secreted by the pineal gland that regulates body functions related to seasonal day length.

membrane potential The difference in electrical charge (voltage) across a cell's plasma membrane, due to the differential distribution of ions. Membrane potential affects the activity of excitable cells and the transmembrane movement of all charged substances.

memory cell One of a clone of long-lived lymphocytes, formed during the primary immune response, that remains in a lymphoid organ until activated by exposure to the same antigen that triggered its formation. Activated memory cells mount the secondary immune response.

menopause The cessation of ovulation and menstruation marking the end of a human female's reproductive years.

menstrual cycle (men'-strū-ul) In humans and certain other primates, a type of reproductive cycle in which the nonpregnant endometrium is shed through the cervix into the vagina.

menstrual flow phase That portion of the uterine (menstrual) cycle when menstrual bleeding occurs.

menstruation The shedding of portions of the endometrium during a uterine (menstrual) cycle.

meristem (mar'-uh-stem) Plant tissue that remains embryonic as long as the plant lives, allowing for indeterminate growth.

meristem identity gene A plant gene that promotes the switch from vegetative growth to flowering.

meroblastic cleavage (mar'-ō-blas'-tik) A type of cleavage in which there is incomplete division of a yolk-rich egg, characteristic of avian development.

mesoderm (mez'-ō-derm) The middle primary germ layer in an animal embryo; develops into the notochord, the lining of the coelom, muscles, skeleton, gonads, kidneys, and most of the circulatory system in species that have these structures.

mesohyl (mez'-ō-hīl) A gelatinous region between the two layers of cells of a sponge.

mesophyll (mez'-ō-fil) The ground tissue of a leaf, sandwiched between the upper and lower epidermis and specialized for photosynthesis.

mesophyll cell In C₄ plants, a type of loosely arranged photosynthetic cell located between the bundle sheath and the leaf surface.

messenger RNA (mRNA) A type of RNA, synthesized using a DNA template, that attaches to ribosomes in the cytoplasm and specifies the primary structure of a protein.

metabolic pathway A series of chemical reactions that either builds a complex molecule (anabolic pathway) or breaks down a complex molecule into simpler compounds (catabolic pathway).

metabolic rate The total amount of energy an animal uses in a unit of time.

metabolism (muh-tab'-uh-lizm) The totality of an organism's chemical reactions, consisting of catabolic and anabolic pathways, which manage the material and energy resources of the organism.

metamorphosis (met'-uh-mōr'-fuh-sis) A developmental transformation that turns an animal larva into either an adult or an adult-like stage that is not yet sexually mature.

metanephridium (met'-uh-nuh-frid'-ē-um) (plural, **metanephridia**) An excretory organ found in many invertebrates that typically consists of tubules connecting ciliated internal openings to external openings.

metaphase The third stage of mitosis, in which the spindle is complete and the chromosomes, attached to microtubules at their kinetochores, are all aligned at the metaphase plate.

metaphase plate An imaginary plane midway between the two poles of a cell in metaphase on which the centromeres of all the duplicated chromosomes are located.

metapopulation A group of spatially separated populations of one species that interact through immigration and emigration.

metastasis (muh-tas'-tuh-sis) The spread of cancer cells to locations distant from their original site.

methanogen (meth-an'-ō-jen) An organism that obtains energy by using carbon dioxide to oxidize hydrogen, producing methane as a waste product; all known methanogens are in domain Archaea.

methyl group A chemical group consisting of a carbon bonded to three hydrogen atoms. The methyl group may be attached to a carbon or to a different atom.

microclimate Very fine scale patterns of climate, such as the specific climatic conditions underneath a log.

microevolution Evolutionary change below the species level; change in the allele frequencies in a population over generations.

microfilament A cable composed of actin proteins in the cytoplasm of almost every eukaryotic cell, making up part of the cytoskeleton and acting alone or with myosin to cause cell contraction; also known as an actin filament.

micronutrient An element that an organism needs in very small amounts and that functions as a component or cofactor of enzymes. *See also* macronutrient.

microphyll (mī'-krō-fil) In lycophytes, a small leaf with a single unbranched vein.

micropyle A pore in the integument(s) of an ovule.

microRNA (miRNA) A small, single-stranded RNA molecule, generated from a hairpin structure on a precursor RNA transcribed from a particular gene. The miRNA associates with one or more proteins in a complex that can degrade or prevent translation of an mRNA with a complementary sequence.

microspore A spore from a heterosporous plant species that develops into a male gametophyte.

microtubule A hollow rod composed of tubulin proteins that make up part of the cytoskeleton in all eukaryotic cells and is found in cilia and flagella.

microvillus (plural, **microvilli**) One of many fine, finger-like projections of the epithelial cells in the lumen of the small intestine that increase its surface area.

midbrain One of three ancestral and embryonic regions of the vertebrate brain; develops into sensory integrating and relay centers that send sensory information to the cerebrum.

middle ear One of three main regions of the vertebrate ear; in mammals, a chamber containing three small bones (the malleus, incus, and stapes) that convey vibrations from the eardrum to the oval window.

middle lamella (luh-mel'-uh) In plants, a thin layer of adhesive extracellular material, primarily pectins, found between the primary walls of adjacent young cells.

migration A regular, long-distance change in location.

mineral In nutrition, a simple nutrient that is inorganic and therefore cannot be synthesized.

mineralocorticoid A steroid hormone secreted by the adrenal cortex that regulates salt and water homeostasis.

minimum viable population (MVP) The smallest population size at which a species is able to sustain its numbers and survive.

mismatch repair The cellular process that uses specific enzymes to remove and replace incorrectly paired nucleotides.

missense mutation A base-pair substitution that results in a codon that codes for a different amino acid.

mitochondrial matrix The compartment of the mitochondrion enclosed by the inner membrane and containing enzymes and substrates for the citric acid cycle.

mitochondrion (mī'-tō-kon'-drē-un) (plural, **mitochondria**) An organelle in eukaryotic cells that serves as the site of cellular respiration.

mitosis (mī-tō'-sis) A process of nuclear division in eukaryotic cells conventionally divided into five stages: prophase, prometaphase, metaphase, anaphase, and telophase. Mitosis conserves chromosome number by allocating replicated chromosomes equally to each of the daughter nuclei.

mitotic (M) phase The phase of the cell cycle that includes mitosis and cytokinesis.

mitotic spindle An assemblage of microtubules and associated proteins that is involved in the movements of chromosomes during mitosis.

mixotroph An organism that is capable of both photosynthesis and heterotrophy.

model A representation of a theory or process.

model organism A particular species chosen for research into broad biological principles because it is representative of a larger group and usually easy to grow in a lab.

molarity A common measure of solute concentration, referring to the number of moles of solute per liter of solution.

mold Informal term for a fungus that grows as a filamentous fungus, producing haploid spores by mitosis and forming a visible mycelium.

mole (mol) The number of grams of a substance that equals its molecular weight in daltons and contains Avogadro's number of molecules.

molecular clock A method for estimating the time required for a given amount of evolutionary change, based on the observation that some regions of genomes appear to evolve at constant rates.

molecular formula A type of molecular notation representing the quantity of constituent atoms, but not the nature of the bonds that join them.

molecular mass The sum of the masses of all the atoms in a molecule; sometimes called molecular weight.

molecular systematics A scientific discipline that uses nucleic acids or other molecules in different species to infer evolutionary relationships.

molecule Two or more atoms held together by covalent bonds.

molting A process in ecdysozoans in which the exoskeleton is shed at intervals, allowing growth by the production of a larger exoskeleton.

monoclonal antibody (mon'-ō-klōn'-ul) Any of a preparation of antibodies that have been produced by a single clone of cultured cells and thus are all specific for the same epitope.

monocot Member of a clade consisting of flowering plants that have one embryonic seed leaf, or cotyledon.

monogamous (muh-nog'-uh-mus) Referring to a type of relationship in which one male mates with just one female.

monohybrid An organism that is heterozygous with respect to a single gene of interest. All the offspring from a cross between parents homozygous for different alleles are monohybrids. For example, parents of genotypes *AA* and *aa* produce a monohybrid of genotype *Aa*.

monomer (mon'-uh-mer) The subunit that serves as the building block of a polymer.

monophyletic (mon'-ō-fī-let'-ik) Pertaining to a group of taxa that consists of a common ancestor and all its descendants. A monophyletic taxon is equivalent to a clade.

monosaccharide (mon'-ō-sak'-uh-rīd) The simplest carbohydrate, active alone or serving as a monomer for disaccharides and polysaccharides. Also known as simple sugars, monosaccharides have molecular formulas that are generally some multiple of CH_2O.

monosomic Referring to a cell that has only one copy of a particular chromosome instead of the normal two.

morphogen A substance, such as Bicoid protein in *Drosophila*, that provides positional information in the form of a concentration gradient along an embryonic axis.

morphogenesis (mōr'-fō-jen'-uh-sis) The development of body shape and organization.

morphological species concept A definition of species in terms of measurable anatomical criteria.

morphology An organism's external form.

moss A small, herbaceous nonvascular plant that is a member of the phylum Bryophyta.

motor neuron A nerve cell that transmits signals from the brain or spinal cord to muscles or glands.

motor protein A protein that interacts with cytoskeletal elements and other cell components, producing movement of the whole cell or parts of the cell.

motor system An efferent branch of the vertebrate peripheral nervous system composed of motor neurons that carry signals to skeletal muscles in response to external stimuli.

motor unit A single motor neuron and all the muscle fibers it controls.

movement corridor A series of small clumps or a narrow strip of quality habitat (usable by organisms) that connects otherwise isolated patches of quality habitat.

MPF Maturation-promoting factor (M-phase-promoting factor); a protein complex required for a cell to progress from late interphase to mitosis. The active form consists of cyclin and a protein kinase.

mucus A viscous and slippery mixture of glycoproteins, cells, salts, and water that moistens and protects the membranes lining body cavities that open to the exterior.

Müllerian mimicry (myū-lār′-ē-un) A mutual mimicry by two unpalatable species.

multifactorial Referring to a phenotypic character that is influenced by multiple genes and environmental factors.

multigene family A collection of genes with similar or identical sequences, presumably of common origin.

multiple fruit A fruit derived from an inflorescence, a group of flowers tightly clustered together.

muscle tissue Tissue consisting of long muscle cells that can contract, either on its own or when stimulated by nerve impulses.

mutagen (myū′-tuh-jen) A chemical or physical agent that interacts with DNA and causes a mutation.

mutation (myū-tā′-shun) A change in the nucleotide sequence of an organism's DNA, ultimately creating genetic diversity. Mutations also can occur in the DNA or RNA of a virus.

mutualism (myū′-chū-ul-izm) A symbiotic relationship in which both participants benefit.

mycelium (mī-sē′-lē-um) The densely branched network of hyphae in a fungus.

mycorrhiza (mī′-kō-rī′-zuh) (plural, **mycorrhizae**) A mutualistic association of plant roots and fungus.

mycosis (mī-kō′-sis) General term for a fungal infection.

myelin sheath (mī′-uh-lin) Around the axon of a neuron, an insulating coat of cell membranes from Schwann cells or oligodendrocytes. It is interrupted by nodes of Ranvier, where action potentials are generated.

myofibril (mī′-ō-fī′-bril) A fibril collectively arranged in longitudinal bundles in muscle cells (fibers); composed of thin filaments of actin and a regulatory protein and thick filaments of myosin.

myoglobin (mī′-uh-glō′-bin) An oxygen-storing, pigmented protein in muscle cells.

myosin (mī′-uh-sin) A type of protein filament that acts as a motor protein with actin filaments to cause cell contraction.

myotonia (mī′-uh-tō′-nī-uh) Increased muscle tension, characteristic of sexual arousal in certain human tissues.

myriapod (mir′-ē-uh-pod′) A terrestrial arthropod with many body segments and one or two pairs of legs per segment. Millipedes and centipedes comprise the two classes of living myriapods.

NAD$^+$ Nicotinamide adenine dinucleotide, a coenzyme that can accept an electron and acts as an electron carrier in the electron transport chain.

NADP$^+$ Nicotinamide adenine dinucleotide phosphate, an electron acceptor that, as NADPH, temporarily stores energized electrons produced during the light reactions.

natural family planning A form of contraception that relies on refraining from sexual intercourse when conception is most likely to occur; also called the rhythm method.

natural killer (NK) cell A type of white blood cell that can kill tumor cells and virus-infected cells as part of innate immunity.

natural selection A process in which organisms with certain inherited characteristics are more likely to survive and reproduce than are organisms with other characteristics.

negative feedback A primary mechanism of homeostasis, whereby a change in a physiological variable triggers a response that counteracts the initial change.

negative pressure breathing A breathing system in which air is pulled into the lungs.

nematocyst (nem′-uh-tuh-sist′) In a cnidocyte of a cnidarian, a specialized capsule-like organelle containing a coiled thread that when discharged can penetrate the body wall of the prey.

nephron (nef′-ron) The tubular excretory unit of the vertebrate kidney.

neritic zone The shallow region of the ocean overlying the continental shelf.

nerve A ropelike bundle of neuron fibers (axons) tightly wrapped in connective tissue.

nerve net A weblike system of neurons, characteristic of radially symmetrical animals, such as hydra.

nervous system The fast-acting internal system of communication involving sensory receptors, networks of nerve cells, and connections to muscles and glands that respond to nerve signals; functions in concert with the endocrine system to effect internal regulation and maintain homeostasis.

nervous tissue Tissue made up of neurons and supportive cells.

net primary production (NPP) The gross primary production of an ecosystem minus the energy used by the producers for respiration.

neural crest cells In vertebrates, groups of cells along the sides of the neural tube where it pinches off from the ectoderm. The cells migrate to various parts of the embryo and form pigment cells in the skin and parts of the skull, teeth, adrenal glands, and peripheral nervous system.

neural plasticity The capacity of a nervous system to change with experience.

neural tube A tube of infolded ectodermal cells that runs along the anterior-posterior axis of a vertebrate, just dorsal to the notochord. It will give rise to the central nervous system.

neurohormone A molecule that is secreted by a neuron, travels in body fluids, and acts on specific target cells to change their functioning.

neuron (nyūr′-on) A nerve cell; the fundamental unit of the nervous system, having structure and properties that allow it to conduct signals by taking advantage of the electrical charge across its plasma membrane.

neuropeptide A relatively short chain of amino acids that serves as a neurotransmitter.

neurotransmitter A molecule that is released from the synaptic terminal of a neuron at a chemical synapse, diffuses across the synaptic cleft, and binds to the postsynaptic cell, triggering a response.

neutral theory The hypothesis that much evolutionary change in genes and proteins has no effect on fitness and therefore is not influenced by Darwinian natural selection.

neutral variation Genetic variation that does not appear to provide a selective advantage or disadvantage.

neutron A subatomic particle having no electrical charge (electrically neutral), with a mass of about 1.7×10^{-24} g, found in the nucleus of an atom.

neutrophil The most abundant type of white blood cell. Neutrophils are phagocytic and tend to self-destruct as they destroy foreign invaders, limiting their life span to a few days.

nitric oxide (NO) A gas produced by many types of cells that functions as a local regulator and as a neurotransmitter.

nitrogen cycle The natural process by which nitrogen, either from the atmosphere or from decomposed organic material, is converted by soil bacteria to compounds that can be assimilated by plants. This incorporated nitrogen is then taken in by other organisms and subsequently released, acted on by bacteria, and made available again to the nonliving environment.

nitrogen fixation The conversion of atmospheric nitrogen (N_2) to ammonia (NH_3). Biological nitrogen fixation is carried out by certain prokaryotes, some of which have mutualistic relationships with plants.

nociceptor (nō′-si-sep′-tur) A sensory receptor that responds to noxious or painful stimuli; also called a pain receptor.

node A point along the stem of a plant at which leaves are attached.

node of Ranvier (ron′-vē-ā′) Gap in the myelin sheath of certain axons where an action potential may be generated. In saltatory conduction, an action potential is regenerated at each node, appearing to "jump" along the axon from node to node.

nodule A swelling on the root of a legume. Nodules are composed of plant cells that contain nitrogen-fixing bacteria of the genus *Rhizobium*.

noncompetitive inhibitor A substance that reduces the activity of an enzyme by binding to a location remote from the active site, changing the enzyme's shape so that the active site no longer functions effectively.

nondisjunction An error in meiosis or mitosis in which members of a pair of homologous chromosomes or a pair of sister chromatids fail to separate properly from each other.

nonequilibrium model A model that maintains that communities change constantly after being buffeted by disturbances.

nonpolar covalent bond A type of covalent bond in which electrons are shared equally between two atoms of similar electronegativity.

nonsense mutation A mutation that changes an amino acid codon to one of the three stop codons, resulting in a shorter and usually nonfunctional protein.

norepinephrine A catecholamine that is chemically and functionally similar to epinephrine and acts as a hormone or neurotransmitter; also known as noradrenaline.

norm of reaction The range of phenotypes produced by a single genotype, due to environmental influences.

normal range An upper and lower limit of a variable.

Northern blotting A technique that enables specific nucleotide sequences to be detected in a sample of mRNA. It involves gel electrophoresis of RNA molecules and their transfer to a membrane (blotting), followed by nucleic acid hybridization with a labeled probe.

northern coniferous forest A terrestrial biome characterized by long, cold winters and dominated by cone-bearing trees.

no-till agriculture A plowing technique that involves creating furrows, resulting in minimal disturbance of the soil.

notochord (nō′-tuh-kord′) A longitudinal, flexible rod made of tightly packed mesodermal cells that runs along the anterior-posterior axis of a chordate in the dorsal part of the body.

nuclear envelope The double membrane in a eukaryotic cell that encloses the nucleus, separating it from the cytoplasm.

nuclear lamina A netlike array of protein filaments lining the inner surface of the nuclear envelope; it helps maintain the shape of the nucleus.

nucleariid Member of a group of unicellular, amoeboid protists that are more closely related to fungi than they are to other protists.

nuclease An enzyme that cuts DNA or RNA, either removing one or a few bases or hydrolyzing the DNA or RNA completely into its component nucleotides.

nucleic acid (nū-klā′-ik) A polymer (polynucleotide) consisting of many nucleotide monomers; serves as a blueprint for proteins and, through the actions of proteins, for all cellular activities. The two types are DNA and RNA.

nucleic acid hybridization The process of base pairing between a gene and a complementary sequence on another nucleic acid molecule.

nucleic acid probe In DNA technology, a labeled single-stranded nucleic acid molecule used to locate a specific nucleotide sequence in a nucleic acid sample. Molecules of the probe hydrogen-bond to the complementary sequence wherever it occurs; radioactive or other labeling of the probe allows its location to be detected.

nucleoid (nū′-klē-oyd) A dense region of DNA in a prokaryotic cell.

nucleolus (nū-klē′-ō-lus) (plural, **nucleoli**) A specialized structure in the nucleus, consisting of chromatin regions containing ribosomal RNA genes along with ribosomal proteins imported from the cytoplasmic site of rRNA synthesis and ribosomal subunit assembly. *See also* ribosome.

nucleosome (nū′-klē-ō-sōm′) The basic, bead-like unit of DNA packing in eukaryotes, consisting of a segment of DNA wound around a protein core composed of two copies of each of four types of histone.

nucleotide (nū′-klē-ō-tīd′) The building block of a nucleic acid, consisting of a five-carbon sugar covalently bonded to a nitrogenous base and a phosphate group.

nucleotide excision repair A repair system that removes and then correctly replaces a damaged segment of DNA using the undamaged strand as a guide.

nucleus (1) An atom's central core, containing protons and neutrons. (2) The chromosome-containing organelle of a eukaryotic cell. (3) A cluster of neurons.

nutrition The process by which an organism takes in and makes use of food substances.

obligate aerobe (ob′-lig-et ār′-ōb) An organism that requires oxygen for cellular respiration and cannot live without it.

obligate anaerobe (ob′-lig-et an′-uh-rōb) An organism that only carries out fermentation or anaerobic respiration. Such organisms cannot use oxygen and in fact may be poisoned by it.

oceanic pelagic zone Most of the ocean's waters far from shore, constantly mixed by ocean currents.

odorant A molecule that can be detected by sensory receptors of the olfactory system.

Okazaki fragment (ō′-kah-zah′-kē) A short segment of DNA synthesized away from the replication fork on a template strand during DNA replication, many of which are joined together to make up the lagging strand of newly synthesized DNA.

olfaction The sense of smell.

oligodendrocyte A type of glial cell that forms insulating myelin sheaths around the axons of neurons in the central nervous system.

oligotrophic lake A nutrient-poor, clear lake with few phytoplankton.

ommatidium (ōm′-uh-tid′-ē-um) (plural, **ommatidia**) One of the facets of the compound eye of arthropods and some polychaete worms.

omnivore An animal that regularly eats animals as well as plants or algae.

oncogene (on′-kō-jēn) A gene found in viral or cellular genomes that is involved in triggering molecular events that can lead to cancer.

oocyte A cell in the female reproductive system that differentiates to form an egg.

oogenesis (ō′-uh-jen′-uh-sis) The process in the ovary that results in the production of female gametes.

oogonium (ō′-uh- gō′-nē-em) A cell that divides mitotically to form oocytes.

oomycete (ō′-uh-mī′- sēt) A protist with flagellated cells, such as a water mold, white rust, or downy mildew, that acquires nutrition mainly as a decomposer or plant parasite.

open circulatory system A circulatory system in which fluid called hemolymph bathes the tissues and organs directly and there is no distinction between the circulating fluid and the interstitial fluid.

operant conditioning (op′-er-ent) A type of associative learning in which an animal learns to associate one of its own behaviors with a reward or punishment and then tends to repeat or avoid that behavior; also called trial-and-error learning.

operator In bacterial DNA, a sequence of nucleotides near the start of an operon to which an active repressor can attach. The binding of the repressor prevents RNA polymerase from attaching to the promoter and transcribing the genes of the operon.

operculum (ō-per′-kyuh-lum) In aquatic osteichthyans, a protective bony flap that covers and protects the gills.

operon (op′-er-on) A unit of genetic function found in bacteria and phages, consisting of a promoter, an operator, and a coordinately regulated cluster of genes whose products function in a common pathway.

opisthokont (uh-pis′-thuh-kont′) Member of the diverse clade Opisthokonta, organisms that descended from an ancestor with a posterior flagellum, including fungi, animals, and certain protists.

opposable thumb A thumb that can touch the ventral surface of the fingertips of all four fingers.

opsin A membrane protein bound to a light-absorbing pigment molecule.

optic chiasm The place where the two optic nerves meet and where the sensations from the left visual field of both eyes are transmitted to the right side of the brain and the sensations from the right visual field of both eyes are transmitted to the left side of the brain.

optimal foraging model The basis for analyzing behavior as a compromise between feeding costs and feeding benefits.

oral cavity The mouth of an animal.

orbital The three-dimensional space where an electron is found 90% of the time.

order In classification, the taxonomic category above the level of family.

organ A specialized center of body function composed of several different types of tissues.

organ identity gene A plant homeotic gene that uses positional information to determine which emerging leaves develop into which types of floral organs.

organ of Corti The actual hearing organ of the vertebrate ear, located in the floor of the cochlear duct in the inner ear; contains the receptor cells (hair cells) of the ear.

organ system A group of organs that work together in performing vital body functions.

organelle (ōr-guh-nel′) Any of several membrane-enclosed structures with specialized functions, suspended in the cytosol of eukaryotic cells.

organic chemistry The study of carbon compounds (organic compounds).

organismal ecology The branch of ecology concerned with the morphological, physiological, and behavioral ways in which individual organisms meet the challenges posed by their biotic and abiotic environments.

organogenesis (ōr-gan′-ō-jen′-uh-sis) The process in which organ rudiments develop from the three germ layers after gastrulation.

orgasm Rhythmic, involuntary contractions of certain reproductive structures in both sexes during the human sexual response cycle.

origin of replication Site where the replication of a DNA molecule begins, consisting of a specific sequence of nucleotides.

orthologous genes Homologous genes that are found in different species because of speciation.

osculum (os′-kyuh-lum) A large opening in a sponge that connects the spongocoel to the environment.

osmoconformer An animal that is isoosmotic with its environment.

osmolarity (oz′-mō-lār′-uh-tē) Solute concentration expressed as molarity.

osmoregulation Regulation of solute concentrations and water balance by a cell or organism.

osmoregulator An animal that controls its internal osmolarity independent of the external environment.

osmosis (oz-mō′-sis) The diffusion of water across a selectively permeable membrane.

osmotic potential A component of water potential that is proportional to the osmolarity of a solution and that measures the effect of solutes on the direction of water movement; also called solute potential, it can be either zero or negative.

osteichthyan (os′-tē-ik′-thē-an) Member of a vertebrate subgroup with jaws and mostly bony skeletons.

outer ear One of three main regions of the ear in reptiles (including birds) and mammals; made up of the auditory canal and, in many birds and mammals, the pinna.

outgroup A species or group of species from an evolutionary lineage that is known to have diverged before the lineage that contains the group of species being studied. An outgroup is selected so that its members are closely related to the group of species being studied, but not as closely related as any study-group members are to each other.

oval window In the vertebrate ear, a membrane-covered gap in the skull bone, through which sound waves pass from the middle ear to the inner ear.

ovarian cycle (ō-vār′-ē-un) The cyclic recurrence of the follicular phase, ovulation, and the luteal phase in the mammalian ovary, regulated by hormones.

ovary (ō′-vuh-rē) (1) In flowers, the portion of a carpel in which the egg-containing ovules develop. (2) In animals, the structure that produces female gametes and reproductive hormones.

overnourishment The consumption of more calories than the body needs for normal metabolism.

oviduct (ō′-vuh-duct) A tube passing from the ovary to the vagina in invertebrates or to the uterus in vertebrates, where it is also known as a fallopian tube.

oviparous (ō-vip′-uh-rus) Referring to a type of development in which young hatch from eggs laid outside the mother's body.

ovoviviparous (ō′-vō-vī-vip′-uh-rus) Referring to a type of development in which young hatch from eggs that are retained in the mother's uterus.

ovulation The release of an egg from an ovary. In humans, an ovarian follicle releases an egg during each uterine (menstrual) cycle.

ovule (o′-vyūl) A structure that develops within the ovary of a seed plant and contains the female gametophyte.

oxidation The loss of electrons from a substance involved in a redox reaction.

oxidative phosphorylation (fos′-fōr-uh-lā′-shun) The production of ATP using energy derived from the redox reactions of an electron transport chain; the third major stage of cellular respiration.

oxidizing agent The electron acceptor in a redox reaction.

oxytocin (ok′-si-tō′-sen) A hormone produced by the hypothalamus and released from the posterior pituitary. It induces contractions of the uterine muscles during labor and causes the mammary glands to eject milk during nursing.

P generation The parent individuals from which offspring are derived in studies of inheritance; P stands for "parental."

P site One of a ribosome's three binding sites for tRNA during translation. The P site holds the tRNA carrying the growing polypeptide chain. (P stands for peptidyl tRNA.)

p53 gene A tumor-suppressor gene that codes for a specific transcription factor that promotes the synthesis of cell cycle inhibiting proteins.

paedomorphosis (pē′-duh-mōr′-fuh-sis) The retention in an adult organism of the juvenile features of its evolutionary ancestors.

pain receptor A sensory receptor that responds to noxious or painful stimuli; also called a nociceptor.

paleoanthropology The study of human origins and evolution.

paleontology (pā′-lē-un-tol′-ō-jē) The scientific study of fossils.

pancreas (pan′-krē-us) A gland with the following dual functions: The nonendocrine portion functions in digestion, secreting enzymes and an alkaline solution into the small intestine via a duct; the ductless endocrine portion functions in homeostasis, secreting the hormones insulin and glucagon into the blood.

pandemic A global epidemic.

Pangaea (pan-jē′-uh) The supercontinent that formed near the end of the Paleozoic era, when plate movements brought all the landmasses of Earth together.

parabasalid A protist, such as a trichomonad, with modified mitochondria.

paracrine Referring to a secreted molecule that acts on a neighboring cell.

paralogous genes Homologous genes that are found in the same genome as a result of gene duplication.

paraphyletic (pār′-uh-fī-let′-ik) Pertaining to a group of taxa that consists of a common ancestor and some, but not all, of its descendants.

parareptile First major group of reptiles to emerge, consisting mostly of large, stocky quadrupedal herbivores; died out in the late Triassic period.

parasite (pār′-uh-sīt) An organism that feeds on the cell contents, tissues, or body fluids of another species (the host) while in or on the host organism. Parasites harm but usually do not kill their host.

parasitism (pār′-uh-sit-izm) A symbiotic relationship in which one organism, the parasite, benefits at the expense of another, the host, by living either within or on the host.

parasympathetic division One of three divisions of the autonomic nervous system; generally enhances body activities that gain and conserve energy, such as digestion and reduced heart rate.

parathyroid gland Any of four small endocrine glands, embedded in the surface of the thyroid gland, that secrete parathyroid hormone.

parathyroid hormone (PTH) A hormone secreted by the parathyroid glands that raises blood calcium level by promoting calcium release from bone and calcium retention by the kidneys.

parenchyma cell (puh-ren′-ki-muh) A relatively unspecialized plant cell type that carries out most of the metabolism, synthesizes and stores organic products, and develops into a more differentiated cell type.

parental type An offspring with a phenotype that matches one of the parental phenotypes; also refers to the phenotype itself.

Parkinson's disease A progressive brain disease characterized by difficulty in initiating movements, slowness of movement, and rigidity.

parthenogenesis (par'-thuh-nō'-jen'-uh-sis) Asexual reproduction in which females produce offspring from unfertilized eggs.

partial pressure The pressure exerted by a particular gas in a mixture of gases (for instance, the pressure exerted by oxygen in air).

passive immunity Short-term immunity conferred by the transfer of antibodies, as occurs in the transfer of maternal antibodies to a fetus or nursing infant.

passive transport The diffusion of a substance across a biological membrane with no expenditure of energy.

pathogen An organism or virus that causes disease.

pattern formation The development of a multicellular organism's spatial organization, the arrangement of organs and tissues in their characteristic places in three-dimensional space.

peat Extensive deposits of partially decayed organic material formed primarily from the wetland moss *Sphagnum*.

pedigree A diagram of a family tree showing the occurrence of heritable characters in parents and offspring over multiple generations.

penis The copulatory structure of male mammals.

PEP carboxylase An enzyme that adds CO_2 to phosphoenolpyruvate (PEP) to form oxaloacetate in C_4 plants. It acts prior to photosynthesis.

pepsin An enzyme present in gastric juice that begins the hydrolysis of proteins.

pepsinogen The inactive form of pepsin that is first secreted by chief cells located in gastric pits of the stomach.

peptide bond The covalent bond between the carboxyl group on one amino acid and the amino group on another, formed by a dehydration reaction.

peptidoglycan (pep'-tid-ō-glī'-kan) A type of polymer in bacterial cell walls consisting of modified sugars cross-linked by short polypeptides.

perception The interpretation of sensory system input by the brain.

perennial (puh-ren'-ē-ul) A flowering plant that lives for many years.

pericycle The outermost layer in the vascular cylinder from which lateral roots arise.

periderm (par'-uh-derm') The protective coat that replaces the epidermis in woody plants during secondary growth, formed of the cork and cork cambium.

peripheral nervous system (PNS) The sensory and motor neurons that connect to the central nervous system.

peripheral protein A protein loosely bound to the surface of a membrane or to part of an integral protein and not embedded in the lipid bilayer.

peristalsis (par'-uh-stal'-sis) (1) Alternating waves of contraction and relaxation in the smooth muscles lining the alimentary canal that push food along the canal. (2) A type of movement on land produced by rhythmic waves of muscle contractions passing from front to back, as in many annelids.

peristome A ring of interlocking, tooth-like structures on the upper part of a moss capsule (sporangium), often specialized for gradual spore discharge.

peritubular capillary One of the tiny blood vessels that form a network surrounding the proximal and distal tubules in the kidney.

permafrost A permanently frozen soil layer.

peroxisome (puh-rok'-suh-sōm') An organelle containing enzymes that transfer hydrogen (H_2) from various substrates to oxygen (O_2), producing and then degrading hydrogen peroxide (H_2O_2).

petal A modified leaf of a flowering plant. Petals are the often colorful parts of a flower that advertise it to insects and other pollinators.

petiole (pet'-ē-ōl) The stalk of a leaf, which joins the leaf to a node of the stem.

pH A measure of hydrogen ion concentration equal to $-\log [H^+]$ and ranging in value from 0 to 14.

phage (fāj) A virus that infects bacteria; also called a bacteriophage.

phagocytosis (fag'-ō-sī-tō'-sis) A type of endocytosis in which large particulate substances are taken up by a cell. It is carried out by some protists and by certain immune cells of animals (in mammals, mainly macrophages, neutrophils, and dendritic cells).

pharyngeal cleft (fuh-rin'-jē-ul) In chordate embryos, one of the grooves that separate a series of pouches along the sides of the pharynx and may develop into a pharyngeal slit.

pharyngeal slit (fuh-rin'-jē-ul) In chordate embryos, one of the slits that form from the pharyngeal clefts and communicate to the outside, later developing into gill slits in many vertebrates.

pharynx (far'-inks) (1) An area in the vertebrate throat where air and food passages cross. (2) In flatworms, the muscular tube that protrudes from the ventral side of the worm and ends in the mouth.

phase change A shift from one developmental phase to another.

phenotype (fē'-nō-tīp) The physical and physiological traits of an organism, which are determined by its genetic makeup.

pheromone (far'-uh-mōn) In animals and fungi, a small molecule released into the environment that functions in communication between members of the same species. In animals, it acts much like a hormone in influencing physiology and behavior.

phloem (flō'-em) Vascular plant tissue consisting of living cells arranged into elongated tubes that transport sugar and other organic nutrients throughout the plant.

phloem sap The sugar-rich solution carried through sieve tubes.

phosphate group A chemical group consisting of a phosphorus atom bonded to four oxygen atoms; important in energy transfer.

phospholipid (fos'-fō-lip'-id) A lipid made up of glycerol joined to two fatty acids and a phosphate group. The hydrocarbon chains of the fatty acids act as nonpolar, hydrophobic tails, while the rest of the molecule acts as a polar, hydrophilic head. Phospholipids form bilayers that function as biological membranes.

phosphorylated Referring to a molecule that is covalently bonded to a phosphate group.

photic zone (fō'-tic) The narrow top layer of an ocean or lake, where light penetrates sufficiently for photosynthesis to occur.

photoautotroph (fō'-tō-ot'-ō-trōf) An organism that harnesses light energy to drive the synthesis of organic compounds from carbon dioxide.

photoheterotroph (fō'-tō-het'-er-ō-trōf) An organism that uses light to generate ATP but must obtain carbon in organic form.

photomorphogenesis Effects of light on plant morphology.

photon (fō'-ton) A quantum, or discrete quantity, of light energy that behaves as if it were a particle.

photoperiodism (fō'-tō-pēr'-ē-ō-dizm) A physiological response to photoperiod, the relative lengths of night and day. An example of photoperiodism is flowering.

photophosphorylation (fō'-tō-fos'-fōr-uh-lā'-shun) The process of generating ATP from ADP and phosphate by means of a proton-motive force generated across the thylakoid membrane of the chloroplast or the membrane of certain prokaryotes during the light reactions of photosynthesis.

photoreceptor An electromagnetic receptor that detects the radiation known as visible light.

photorespiration A metabolic pathway that consumes oxygen and ATP, releases carbon dioxide, and decreases photosynthetic output. Photorespiration generally occurs on hot, dry, bright days, when stomata close and the oxygen concentration in the leaf exceeds that of carbon dioxide.

photosynthesis (fō'-tō-sin'-thi-sis) The conversion of light energy to chemical energy that is stored in sugars or other organic compounds; occurs in plants, algae, and certain prokaryotes.

photosystem A light-capturing unit located in the thylakoid membrane of the chloroplast or in the membrane of some prokaryotes, consisting of a reaction-center complex surrounded by numerous light-harvesting complexes. There are two types of photosystems, I and II; they absorb light best at different wavelengths.

photosystem I (PS I) One of two light-capturing units in a chloroplast's thylakoid membrane or in the membrane of some prokaryotes; it has two molecules of P700 chlorophyll *a* at its reaction center.

photosystem II (PS II) One of two light-capturing units in a chloroplast's thylakoid membrane or in the membrane of some prokaryotes; it has two molecules of P680 chlorophyll *a* at its reaction center.

phototropism (fō'-tō-trō'-pizm) Growth of a plant shoot toward or away from light.

phragmoplast (frag'-mō-plast') An alignment of cytoskeletal elements and Golgi-derived vesicles that forms across the midline of a dividing plant cell.

phyllotaxy (fil'-uh-tak'-sē) The arrangement of leaves on the shoot of a plant.

PhyloCode System of classification of organisms based on evolutionary relationships: Only groups that include a common ancestor and all of its descendents are named.

phylogenetic bracketing An approach in which features shared by two groups of organisms are predicted (by parsimony) to be present in their common ancestor and all of its descendants.

phylogenetic species concept A definition of species as the smallest group of individuals that share a common ancestor, forming one branch on the tree of life.

phylogenetic tree A branching diagram that represents a hypothesis about the evolutionary history of a group of organisms.

phylogeny (fī-loj'-uh-nē) The evolutionary history of a species or group of related species.

phylum (fī'-lum) (plural, **phyla**) In classification, the taxonomic category above class.

physical map A genetic map in which the actual physical distances between genes or other genetic markers are expressed, usually as the number of base pairs along the DNA.

physiology The processes and functions of an organism and their study.

phytochrome (fī'-tuh-krōm) A type of light receptor in plants that mostly absorbs red light and regulates many plant responses, such as seed germination and shade avoidance.

phytoremediation An emerging nondestructive biotechnology that seeks to cheaply reclaim contaminated areas by taking advantage of some plant species' ability to extract heavy metals and other pollutants from the soil and to concentrate them in easily harvested portions of the plant.

pineal gland (pī'-nē-ul) A small gland on the dorsal surface of the vertebrate forebrain that secretes the hormone melatonin.

pinocytosis (pī'-nō-sī-tō'-sis) A type of endocytosis in which the cell ingests extracellular fluid and its dissolved solutes.

pistil A single carpel or a group of fused carpels.

pith Ground tissue that is internal to the vascular tissue in a stem; in many monocot roots, parenchyma cells that form the central core of the vascular cylinder.

pituitary gland (puh-tū'-uh-tār'-ē) An endocrine gland at the base of the hypothalamus; consists of a posterior lobe (neurohypophysis), which stores and releases two hormones produced by the hypothalamus, and an anterior lobe (adenohypophysis), which produces and secretes many hormones that regulate diverse body functions.

placenta (pluh-sen'-tuh) A structure in the pregnant uterus for nourishing a viviparous fetus with the mother's blood supply; formed from the uterine lining and embryonic membranes.

placental transfer cell A plant cell that enhances the transfer of nutrients from parent to embryo.

placoderm A member of an extinct class of fishlike vertebrates that had jaws and were enclosed in a tough outer armor.

planarian A free-living flatworm found in unpolluted ponds and streams.

Plantae (plan'-tā) The kingdom that consists of multicellular eukaryotes that carry out photosynthesis.

plasma (plaz'-muh) The liquid matrix of blood in which the cells are suspended.

plasma cell The antibody-secreting effector cell of humoral immunity; arises from antigen-stimulated B cells.

plasma membrane The membrane at the boundary of every cell that acts as a selective barrier, regulating the cell's chemical composition.

plasmid (plaz'-mid) A small, circular, double-stranded DNA molecule that carries accessory genes separate from those of a bacterial chromosome. Plasmids are also found in some eukaryotes, such as yeasts.

plasmodesma (plaz'-mō-dez'-muh) (plural, **plasmodesmata**) An open channel in the cell wall of a plant through which strands of cytosol connect from an adjacent cell.

plasmodial slime mold (plaz-mō'-dē-ul) A type of protist that has amoeboid cells, flagellated cells, and a plasmodial feeding stage in its life cycle.

plasmodium A single mass of cytoplasm containing many diploid nuclei that forms during the life cycle of some slime molds.

plasmogamy (plaz-moh'-guh-mē) The fusion of the cytoplasm of cells from two individuals; occurs as one stage of syngamy (fertilization).

plasmolysis (plaz-mol'-uh-sis) A phenomenon in walled cells in which the cytoplasm shrivels and the plasma membrane pulls away from the cell wall; occurs when the cell loses water to a hypertonic environment.

plastid One of a family of closely related organelles that includes chloroplasts, chromoplasts, and amyloplasts (leucoplasts). Plastids are found in cells of photosynthetic organisms.

platelet A pinched-off cytoplasmic fragment of a specialized bone marrow cell. Platelets circulate in the blood and are important in blood clotting.

pleiotropy (plī-o'-truh-pē) The ability of a single gene to have multiple effects.

pluripotent Describing a cell that can give rise to many, but not all, parts of an organism.

point mutation A change in a gene at a single nucleotide pair.

polar covalent bond A covalent bond between atoms that differ in electronegativity. The shared electrons are pulled closer to the more electronegative atom, making it slightly negative and the other atom slightly positive.

polar molecule A molecule (such as water) with opposite charges on different ends of the molecule.

polarity A lack of symmetry; structural differences in opposite ends of an organism or structure, such as the root end and shoot end of a plant.

pollen grain In seed plants, a structure consisting of the male gametophyte enclosed within a pollen wall.

pollen tube A tube formed after germination of the pollen grain that functions in the delivery of sperm to the ovule.

pollination (pol'-uh-nā'-shun) The transfer of pollen to the part of a seed plant containing the ovules, a process required for fertilization.

poly-A tail A sequence of 50 to 250 adenine nucleotides added onto the 3' end of a pre-mRNA molecule.

polyandry (pol'-ē-an'-drē) A polygamous mating system involving one female and many males.

polygamous Referring to a type of relationship in which an individual of one sex mates with several of the other.

polygenic inheritance (pol'-ē-jen'-ik) An additive effect of two or more genes on a single phenotypic character.

polygyny (puh-lij'-en-ē) A polygamous mating system involving one male and many females.

polymer (pol'-uh-mer) A long molecule consisting of many similar or identical monomers linked together.

polymerase chain reaction (PCR) (puh-lim'-uh-rās) A technique for amplifying DNA *in vitro* by incubating it with specific primers, a heat-resistant DNA polymerase, and nucleotides.

polynucleotide (pol'-ē-nū'-klē-ō-tīd) A polymer consisting of many nucleotide monomers in a chain; nucleotides can be those of DNA or RNA.

polyp The sessile variant of the cnidarian body plan. The alternate form is the medusa.

polypeptide (pol'-ē-pep'-tīd) A polymer (chain) of many amino acids linked together by peptide bonds.

polyphyletic (pol'-ē-fī-let'-ik) Pertaining to a group of taxa derived from two or more different ancestors.

polyploidy (pol'-ē-ploy'-dē) A chromosomal alteration in which the organism possesses more than two complete chromosome sets. It is the result of an accident of cell division.

polyribosome (polysome) (pol'-ē-rī'-bō-sōm') A group of several ribosomes attached to, and translating, the same messenger RNA molecule.

polysaccharide (pol'-ē-sak'-uh-rīd) A polymer of many monosaccharides, formed by dehydration reactions.

polytomy (puh-lit'-uh-mē) In a phylogenetic tree, a branch point from which more than two descendant taxa emerge. A polytomy indicates that the evolutionary relationships among the descendant taxa are not yet clear.

pons Portion of the brain that participates in certain automatic, homeostatic functions, such as regulating the breathing centers in the medulla.

population A localized group of individuals of the same species that can interbreed, producing fertile offspring.

population dynamics The study of how complex interactions between biotic and abiotic factors influence variations in population size.

population ecology The study of populations in relation to their environment, including environmental influences on population density and distribution, age structure, and variations in population size.

positional information Molecular cues that control pattern formation in an animal or plant embryonic structure by indicating a cell's location relative to the organism's body axes. These cues elicit a response by genes that regulate development.

positive feedback A physiological control mechanism in which a change in a variable triggers mechanisms that amplify the change.

positive pressure breathing A breathing system in which air is forced into the lungs.

posterior Pertaining to the rear, or tail end, of a bilaterally symmetrical animal.

posterior pituitary Also called the neurohypophysis; an extension of the hypothalamus composed of nervous tissue that secretes oxytocin and antidiuretic hormone made in the hypothalamus; a temporary storage site for these hormones.

postsynaptic cell The target cell at a synapse.

postzygotic barrier (pōst'-zī-got'-ik) A reproductive barrier that prevent hybrid zygotes produced by two different species from developing into viable, fertile adults.

potential energy The energy that matter possesses as a result of its location or spatial arrangement (structure).

predation An interaction between species in which one species, the predator, eats the other, the prey.

pregnancy The condition of carrying one or more embryos in the uterus.

preprophase band Microtubules in the cortex (outer cytoplasm) of a cell that are concentrated into a ring.

prepuce (prē'-pyūs) A fold of skin covering the head of the clitoris or penis.

pressure potential (Ψ_P) A component of water potential that consists of the physical pressure on a solution, which can be positive, zero, or negative.

presynaptic cell The transmitting cell at a synapse.

prezygotic barrier (prē'-zī-got'-ik) A reproductive barrier that impedes mating between species or hinders fertilization if interspecific mating is attempted.

primary cell wall In plants, a relatively thin and flexible layer first secreted by a young cell.

primary consumer An herbivore; an organism that eats plants or other autotrophs.

primary electron acceptor In the thylakoid membrane of a chloroplast or in the membrane of some prokaryotes, a specialized molecule that shares the reaction-center complex with a pair of chlorophyll *a* molecules and that accepts an electron from them.

primary growth Growth produced by apical meristems, lengthening stems and roots.

primary immune response The initial acquired immune response to an antigen, which appears after a lag of about 10 to 17 days.

primary oocyte (ō'-uh-sīt) An oocyte prior to completion of meiosis I.

primary plant body The tissues produced by apical meristems, which lengthen stems and roots.

primary producer An autotroph, usually a photosynthetic organism. Collectively, autotrophs make up the trophic level of an ecosystem that ultimately supports all other levels.

primary production The amount of light energy converted to chemical energy (organic compounds) by autotrophs in an ecosystem during a given time period.

primary structure The level of protein structure referring to the specific sequence of amino acids.

primary succession A type of ecological succession that occurs in an area where there were originally no organisms present and where soil has not yet formed.

primary transcript An initial RNA transcript; also called pre-mRNA when transcribed from a protein-coding gene.

primary visual cortex The destination in the occipital lobe of the cerebrum for most of the axons from the lateral geniculate nuclei.

primase An enzyme that joins RNA nucleotides to make the primer using the parental DNA strand as a template.

primer A short stretch of RNA with a free 3' end, bound by complementary base pairing to the template strand, that is elongated with DNA nucleotides during DNA replication.

primitive streak A thickening along the future anterior-posterior axis on the surface of an early avian or mammalian embryo, caused by a piling up of cells as they congregate at the midline before moving into the embryo.

prion An infectious agent that is a misfolded version of a normal cellular protein. Prions appear to increase in number by converting correctly folded versions of the protein to more prions.

problem solving The cognitive activity of devising a method to proceed from one state to another in the face of real or apparent obstacles.

producer An organism that produces organic compounds from CO_2 by harnessing light energy (in photosynthesis) or by oxidizing inorganic chemicals (in chemosynthetic reactions carried out by some prokaryotes).

product A material resulting from a chemical reaction.

production efficiency The percentage of energy stored in food that is not used for respiration or eliminated as waste.

progesterone A steroid hormone that prepares the uterus for pregnancy; the major progestin in mammals.

progestin Any steroid hormone with progesterone-like activity.

progymnosperm (prō'-jim'-nō-sperm) An extinct seedless vascular plant that may be ancestral to seed plants.

prokaryotic cell (prō-kār'-ē-ot'-ik) A type of cell lacking a membrane-enclosed nucleus and membrane-enclosed organelles. Organisms with prokaryotic cells (bacteria and archaea) are called prokaryotes.

prolactin (PRL) A hormone produced and secreted by the anterior pituitary with a great diversity of effects in different vertebrate species. In mammals, it stimulates growth of and milk production by the mammary glands.

proliferative phase That portion of the uterine (menstrual) cycle when the endometrium regenerates and thickens.

prometaphase The second stage of mitosis, in which discrete chromosomes consisting of identical sister chromatids appear, the nuclear envelope fragments, and the spindle microtubules attach to the kinetochores of the chromosomes.

promiscuous Referring to a type of relationship in which mating occurs with no strong pair-bonds or lasting relationships.

promoter A specific nucleotide sequence in DNA that binds RNA polymerase, positioning it to start transcribing RNA at the appropriate place.

prophage (prō'-fāj) A phage genome that has been inserted into a specific site on a bacterial chromosome.

prophase The first stage of mitosis, in which the chromatin condenses, the mitotic spindle begins to form, and the nucleolus disappears, but the nucleus remains intact.

prostaglandin (PG) (pros'-tuh-glan'-din) One of a group of modified fatty acids secreted by virtually all tissues and performing a wide variety of functions as local regulators.

prostate gland (pros'-tāt) A gland in human males that secretes an acid-neutralizing component of semen.

protease An enzyme that digests proteins by hydrolysis.

proteasome A giant protein complex that recognizes and destroys proteins tagged for elimination by the small protein ubiquitin.

protein (prō'-tēn) A functional biological molecule consisting of one or more polypeptides folded and coiled into a specific three-dimensional structure.

protein kinase An enzyme that transfers phosphate groups from ATP to a protein, thus phosphorylating the protein.

protein phosphatase An enzyme that removes phosphate groups from (dephosphorylates) proteins, often functioning to reverse the effect of a protein kinase.

proteoglycan (prō'-tē-ō-glī'-kan) A glycoprotein consisting of a small core protein with many carbohydrate chains attached, found in the

extracellular matrix of animal cells. A proteoglycan may consist of up to 95% carbohydrate.

proteomics (prō'-tē-ō'-miks) The systematic study of the full protein sets (proteomes) encoded by genomes.

protist An informal term applied to any eukaryote that is not a plant, animal, or fungus. Most protists are unicellular, though some are colonial or multicellular.

protobiont A collection of abiotically produced molecules surrounded by a membrane or membrane-like structure.

proton (prō'-ton) A subatomic particle with a single positive electrical charge, with a mass of about 1.7×10^{-24} g, found in the nucleus of an atom.

proton pump An active transport protein in a cell membrane that uses ATP to transport hydrogen ions out of a cell against their concentration gradient, generating a membrane potential in the process.

protonema (plural, **protonemata**) A mass of green, branched, one-cell-thick filaments produced by germinating moss spores.

protonephridia (prō'-tō-nuh-frid'-ē-uh) (singular, **protonephridium**) An excretory system, such as the flame bulb system of flatworms, consisting of a network of tubules lacking internal openings.

proton-motive force The potential energy stored in the form of an electrochemical gradient, generated by the pumping of hydrogen ions across a biological membrane during chemiosmosis.

proto-oncogene (prō'-tō-on'-kō-jēn) A normal cellular gene that has the potential to become an oncogene.

protoplast fusion The fusing of two protoplasts from different plant species that would otherwise be reproductively incompatible.

protostome development In animals, a developmental mode distinguished by the development of the mouth from the blastopore; often also characterized by spiral cleavage and by the body cavity forming when solid masses of mesoderm split.

provirus A viral genome that is permanently inserted into a host genome.

proximal tubule In the vertebrate kidney, the portion of a nephron immediately downstream from Bowman's capsule that conveys and helps refine filtrate.

proximate causation The mechanistic explanation of "how" a behavior (or other aspect of an organism's biology) occurs or is modified; that is, how a stimulus elicits a behavior, what physiological mechanisms mediate the response, and how experience influences the response.

pseudocoelomate (sū'-dō-sē'-lō-māt) An animal whose body cavity is lined by tissue derived from mesoderm and endoderm.

pseudogene (sū'-dō-jēn) A DNA segment very similar to a real gene but which does not yield a functional product; a DNA segment that formerly functioned as a gene but has become inactivated in a particular species because of mutation.

pseudopodium (sū'-dō-pō'-dē-um) (plural, **pseudopodia**) A cellular extension of amoeboid cells used in moving and feeding.

pterophyte (ter'-uh-fīt) An informal name for a member of the phylum Pterophyta, which includes ferns, horsetails, and whisk ferns and their relatives.

pterosaur Winged reptile that lived during the Mesozoic era.

pulmocutaneous circuit A branch of the circulatory system in many amphibians that supplies the lungs and skin.

pulmonary circuit The branch of the circulatory system that supplies the lungs.

pulse The rhythmic bulging of the artery walls with each heartbeat.

punctuated equilibria In the fossil record, long periods of apparent stasis, in which a species undergoes little or no morphological change, interrupted by relatively brief periods of sudden change.

Punnett square A diagram used in the study of inheritance to show the predicted results of random fertilization in genetic crosses.

pupil The opening in the iris, which admits light into the interior of the vertebrate eye. Muscles in the iris regulate its size.

purine (pyū'-rēn) One of two types of nitrogenous bases found in nucleotides, characterized by a six-membered ring fused to a five-membered ring. Adenine (A) and guanine (G) are purines.

pyrimidine (puh-rim'-uh-dēn) One of two types of nitrogenous bases found in nucleotides, characterized by a six-membered ring. Cytosine (C), thymine (T), and uracil (U) are pyrimidines.

quantitative character A heritable feature that varies continuously over a range rather than in an either-or fashion.

quaternary structure (kwot'-er-nār-ē) The particular shape of a complex, aggregate protein, defined by the characteristic three-dimensional arrangement of its constituent subunits, each a polypeptide.

R plasmid A bacterial plasmid carrying genes that confer resistance to certain antibiotics.

radial cleavage A type of embryonic development in deuterostomes in which the planes of cell division that transform the zygote into a ball of cells are either parallel or perpendicular to the vertical axis of the embryo, thereby aligning tiers of cells one above the other.

radial glia In an embryo, supporting cells that form tracks along which newly formed neurons migrate from the neural tube; can also act as stem cells that give rise to other glia and neurons.

radial symmetry Symmetry in which the body is shaped like a pie or barrel (lacking a left side and a right side) and can be divided into mirror-image halves by any plane through its central axis.

radiation The emission of electromagnetic waves by all objects warmer than absolute zero.

radicle An embryonic root of a plant.

radioactive isotope An isotope (an atomic form of a chemical element) that is unstable; the nucleus decays spontaneously, giving off detectable particles and energy.

radiolarian A protist, usually marine, with a shell generally made of silica and pseudopodia that radiate from the central body.

radiometric dating A method for determining the absolute ages of rocks and fossils, based on the half-life of radioactive isotopes.

radula A straplike rasping organ used by many molluscs during feeding.

***ras* gene** A gene that codes for Ras, a G protein that relays a growth signal from a growth factor receptor on the plasma membrane to a cascade of protein kinases, ultimately resulting in stimulation of the cell cycle.

ratite (rat'-īt) Member of the group of flightless birds.

ray-finned fish Member of the class Actinopterygii, aquatic osteichthyans with fins supported by long, flexible rays, including tuna, bass, and herring.

reabsorption In excretory systems, the recovery of solutes and water from filtrate.

reactant A starting material in a chemical reaction.

reaction-center complex A complex of proteins associated with a special pair of chlorophyll *a* molecules and a primary electron acceptor. Located centrally in a photosystem, this complex triggers the light reactions of photosynthesis. Excited by light energy, the pair of chlorophylls donates an electron to the primary electron acceptor, which passes an electron to an electron transport chain.

reading frame On an mRNA, the triplet grouping of ribonucleotides used by the translation machinery during polypeptide synthesis.

receptacle The base of a flower; the part of the stem that is the site of attachment of the floral organs.

receptor potential An initial response of a receptor cell to a stimulus, consisting of a change in voltage across the receptor membrane proportional to the stimulus strength. The intensity of the receptor potential determines the frequency of action potentials traveling to the nervous system.

receptor tyrosine kinase A receptor protein in the plasma membrane, the cytoplasmic (intracellular) part of which can catalyze the transfer of a phosphate group from ATP to a tyrosine on another protein. Receptor tyrosine kinases often respond to the binding of a signaling molecule by dimerizing and then phosphorylating a tyrosine on the cytoplasmic portion of the other receptor in the dimer. The phosphorylated tyrosines on the receptors then activate other signal transduction proteins within the cell.

receptor-mediated endocytosis (en'-dō-sī-tō'-sis) The movement of specific molecules into a cell by the inward budding of membranous vesicles containing proteins with receptor sites specific to the molecules being taken in; enables a cell to acquire bulk quantities of specific substances.

recessive allele An allele whose phenotypic effect is not observed in a heterozygote.

reciprocal altruism Altruistic behavior between unrelated individuals, whereby the altruistic individual benefits in the future when the beneficiary reciprocates.

recombinant chromosome A chromosome created when crossing over combines the DNA from two parents into a single chromosome.

recombinant DNA A DNA molecule made *in vitro* with segments from different sources.

recombinant type (recombinant) An offspring whose phenotype differs from that of the parents; also refers to the phenotype itself.

recruitment The process of progressively increasing the tension of a muscle by activating more and more of the motor neurons controlling the muscle.

rectum The terminal portion of the large intestine where the feces are stored until they are eliminated.

red alga A photosynthetic protist, named for its color, which results from a red pigment that masks the green of chlorophyll. Most red algae are multicellular and marine.

redox reaction (rē′-doks) A chemical reaction involving the complete or partial transfer of one or more electrons from one reactant to another; short for oxidation-reduction reaction.

reducing agent The electron donor in a redox reaction.

reduction The addition of electrons to a substance involved in a redox reaction.

reflex An automatic reaction to a stimulus, mediated by the spinal cord or lower brain.

refractory period (rē-frakt′-ōr-ē) The short time immediately after an action potential in which the neuron cannot respond to another stimulus, owing to the inactivation of voltage-gated sodium channels.

regulator An animal for which mechanisms of homeostasis moderate internal changes in the face of external fluctuations.

regulatory gene A gene that codes for a protein, such as a repressor, that controls the transcription of another gene or group of genes.

reinforcement A process in which natural selection strengthens prezygotic barriers to reproduction, thus reducing the chances of hybrid formation. Such a process is likely to occur only if hybrid offspring are less fit than members of the parent species.

relative abundance The proportional abundance of different species in a community.

relative fitness The contribution an individual makes to the gene pool of the next generation, relative to the contributions of other individuals in the population.

renal artery The blood vessel bringing blood to the kidney.

renal cortex The outer portion of the vertebrate kidney.

renal medulla The inner portion of the vertebrate kidney, beneath the renal cortex.

renal pelvis The funnel-shaped chamber that receives processed filtrate from the vertebrate kidney's collecting ducts and is drained by the ureter.

renal vein The blood vessel that carries blood away from the kidney.

renin-angiotensin-aldosterone system (RAAS) A hormone cascade pathway that helps regulate blood pressure and blood volume.

repeated reproduction Reproduction in which adults produce offspring over many years; also known as iteroparity.

repetitive DNA Nucleotide sequences, usually noncoding, that are present in many copies in a eukaryotic genome. The repeated units may be short and arranged tandemly (in series) or long and dispersed in the genome.

replication fork A Y-shaped region on a replicating DNA molecule where the parental strands are being unwound and new strands are growing.

repressor A protein that inhibits gene transcription. In prokaryotes, repressors bind to the DNA in or near the promoter. In eukaryotes, repressors may bind to control elements within enhancers, to activators, or to other proteins in a way that blocks activators from binding to DNA.

reproductive isolation The existence of biological factors (barriers) that impede members of two species from producing viable, fertile offspring.

reproductive table An age-specific summary of the reproductive rates in a population.

reptile Member of the clade of amniotes that includes tuataras, lizards, snakes, turtles, crocodilians, and birds.

residual volume The amount of air that remains in the lungs after forceful exhalation.

resource partitioning The division of environmental resources by coexisting species such that the niche of each species differs by one or more significant factors from the niches of all coexisting species.

respiratory pigment A protein that transports oxygen in blood or hemolymph.

response (1) In cellular communication, the change in a specific cellular activity brought about by a transduced signal from outside the cell. (2) In homeostasis, a physiological activity that helps return a variable to a set point.

resting potential The membrane potential characteristic of a nonconducting excitable cell, with the inside of the cell more negative than the outside.

restoration ecology Applying ecological principles in an effort to return ecosystems that have been disturbed by human activity to a condition as similar as possible to their natural state.

restriction enzyme An endonuclease (type of enzyme) that recognizes and cuts DNA molecules foreign to a bacterium (such as phage genomes). The enzyme cuts at specific nucleotide sequences (restriction sites).

restriction fragment A DNA segment that results from the cutting of DNA by a restriction enzyme.

restriction fragment length polymorphism (RFLP) A single nucleotide polymorphism (SNP) that exists in the restriction site for a particular enzyme, thus making the site unrecognizable by that enzyme and changing the lengths of the restriction fragments formed by digestion with that enzyme. A RFLP can be in coding or noncoding DNA.

restriction site A specific sequence on a DNA strand that is recognized and cut by a restriction enzyme.

reticular formation (re-tik′-yū-ler) A diffuse network of neurons in the core of the brainstem that filters information traveling to the cerebral cortex.

retina (ret′-i-nuh) The innermost layer of the vertebrate eye, containing photoreceptor cells (rods and cones) and neurons; transmits images formed by the lens to the brain via the optic nerve.

retinal The light-absorbing pigment in rods and cones of the vertebrate eye.

retrotransposon (re′-trō-trans-pō′-zon) A transposable element that moves within a genome by means of an RNA intermediate, a transcript of the retrotransposon DNA.

retrovirus (re′-trō-vī′-rus) An RNA virus that reproduces by transcribing its RNA into DNA and then inserting the DNA into a cellular chromosome; an important class of cancer-causing viruses.

reverse transcriptase (tran-skrip′-tās) An enzyme encoded by certain viruses (retroviruses) that uses RNA as a template for DNA synthesis.

reverse transcriptase–polymerase chain reaction (RT-PCR) A technique for determining expression of a particular gene. It uses reverse transcriptase and DNA polymerase to synthesize cDNA from all the mRNA in a sample and then subjects the cDNA to PCR amplification using primers specific for the gene of interest.

Rhizaria (rī-za′-rē-uh) One of five supergroups of eukaryotes proposed in a current hypothesis of the evolutionary history of eukaryotes; a morphologically diverse protist clade that is defined by DNA similarities. *See also* Excavata, Chromalveolata, Archaeplastida, and Unikonta.

rhizobacterium A soil bacterium whose population size is much enhanced in the rhizosphere, the soil region close to a plant's roots.

rhizoid (rī′-zoyd) A long, tubular single cell or filament of cells that anchors bryophytes to the ground. Unlike roots, rhizoids are not composed of tissues, lack specialized conducting cells, and do not play a primary role in water and mineral absorption.

rhizosphere The soil region close to plant roots and characterized by a high level of microbiological activity.

rhodopsin (rō-dop′-sin) A visual pigment consisting of retinal and opsin. When rhodopsin absorbs light, the retinal changes shape and dissociates from the opsin, after which it is converted back to its original form.

rhythm method A form of contraception that relies on refraining from sexual intercourse when conception is most likely to occur; also called natural family planning.

ribonucleic acid (RNA) (rī′-bō-nū-klā′-ik) A type of nucleic acid consisting of nucleotide monomers with a ribose sugar and the nitrogenous bases adenine (A), cytosine (C), guanine (G), and uracil (U); usually single-stranded; functions in protein synthesis, gene regulation, and as the genome of some viruses.

ribose The sugar component of RNA nucleotides.

ribosomal RNA (rRNA) (rī′-buh-sō′-mul) The most abundant type of RNA, which together with proteins makes up ribosomes.

ribosome (rī′-buh-sōm′) A complex of rRNA and protein molecules that functions as a site of protein synthesis in the cytoplasm; consists of a large and a small subunit. In eukaryotic cells, each subunit is assembled in the nucleolus. *See also* nucleolus.

ribozyme (rī′-bō-zīm) An RNA molecule that functions as an enzyme, catalyzing reactions during RNA splicing.

RNA interference (RNAi) A technique used to silence the expression of selected genes. RNAi uses synthetic double-stranded RNA molecules that match the sequence of a particular gene to trigger the breakdown of the gene's messenger RNA.

RNA polymerase An enzyme that links ribonucleotides into a growing RNA chain during transcription.

RNA processing Modification of RNA transcripts, including splicing out of introns, joining together of exons, and alteration of the 5′ and 3′ ends.

RNA splicing After synthesis of a eukaryotic primary RNA transcript, the removal of portions (introns) of the transcript that will not be included in the mRNA.

rod A rodlike cell in the retina of the vertebrate eye, sensitive to low light intensity.

root An organ in vascular plants that anchors the plant and enables it to absorb water and minerals from the soil.

root cap A cone of cells at the tip of a plant root that protects the apical meristem.

root hair A tiny extension of a root epidermal cell, growing just behind the root tip and increasing surface area for absorption of water and minerals.

root pressure The upward push of xylem sap in the vascular tissue of roots.

root system All of a plant's roots, which anchor it in the soil, absorb and transport minerals and water, and store food.

rooted Describing a phylogenetic tree that contains a branch point (typically, the one farthest to the left) representing the last common ancestor of all taxa in the tree.

rough ER That portion of the endoplasmic reticulum studded with ribosomes.

round window In the mammalian ear, the point of contact between the stapes and the cochlea, where vibrations of the stapes create a traveling series of pressure waves in the fluid of the cochlea.

r-selection Selection for life history traits that maximize reproductive success in uncrowded environments; also called density-independent selection.

rubisco (rū-bis′-kō) Ribulose bisphosphate (RuBP) carboxylase, the enzyme that catalyzes the first step of the Calvin cycle (the addition of CO_2 to RuBP).

ruminant (rū′-muh-nent) An animal, such as a cow or a sheep, with an elaborate, multicompartmentalized stomach specialized for an herbivorous diet.

S phase The synthesis phase of the cell cycle; the portion of interphase during which DNA is replicated.

sac fungus *See* ascomycete.

saccule In the vertebrate ear, a chamber in the vestibule behind the oval window that participates in the sense of balance.

salicylic acid (sal′-i-sil′-ik) A signaling molecule in plants that may be partially responsible for activating systemic acquired resistance to pathogens.

salivary gland A gland associated with the oral cavity that secretes substances to lubricate food and begin the process of chemical digestion.

salt A compound resulting from the formation of an ionic bond; also called an ionic compound.

saltatory conduction (sol′-tuh-tōr′-ē) Rapid transmission of a nerve impulse along an axon, resulting from the action potential jumping from one node of Ranvier to another, skipping the myelin-sheathed regions of membrane.

sarcomere (sar′-kō-mēr) The fundamental, repeating unit of striated muscle, delimited by the Z lines.

sarcoplasmic reticulum (SR) (sar′-kō-plaz′-mik ruh-tik′-yū-lum) A specialized endoplasmic reticulum that regulates the calcium concentration in the cytosol of muscle cells.

saturated fatty acid A fatty acid in which all carbons in the hydrocarbon tail are connected by single bonds, thus maximizing the number of hydrogen atoms that are attached to the carbon skeleton.

savanna A tropical grassland biome with scattered individual trees and large herbivores and maintained by occasional fires and drought.

scaffolding protein A type of large relay protein to which several other relay proteins are simultaneously attached, increasing the efficiency of signal transduction.

scanning electron microscope (SEM) A microscope that uses an electron beam to scan the surface of a sample to study details of its topography.

schizophrenia (skit′-suh-frē′-nē-uh) Severe mental disturbance characterized by psychotic episodes in which patients lose the ability to distinguish reality from hallucination.

Schwann cell A type of glial cell that forms insulating myelin sheaths around the axons of neurons in the peripheral nervous system.

scion (sī′-un) The twig grafted onto the stock when making a graft.

sclera (sklar′-uh) A tough, white outer layer of connective tissue that forms the globe of the vertebrate eye.

sclereid (sklar′-ē-id) A short, irregular sclerenchyma cell in nutshells and seed coats. Sclereids are scattered throughout the parenchyma of some plants.

sclerenchyma cell (skluh-ren′-kim-uh) A rigid, supportive plant cell type usually lacking a protoplast and possessing thick secondary walls strengthened by lignin at maturity.

scrotum A pouch of skin outside the abdomen that houses the testes; functions in maintaining the testes at the lower temperature required for spermatogenesis.

second law of thermodynamics The principle stating that every energy transfer or transformation increases the entropy of the universe. Ordered forms of energy are at least partly converted to heat.

second messenger A small, nonprotein, water-soluble molecule or ion, such as a calcium ion (Ca^{2+}) or cyclic AMP, that relays a signal to a cell's interior in response to a signaling molecule bound by a signal receptor protein.

secondary cell wall In plants, a strong and durable matrix often deposited in several laminated layers for cell protection and support.

secondary consumer A carnivore that eats herbivores.

secondary endosymbiosis A process in eukaryotic evolution in which a heterotrophic eukaryotic cell engulfed a photosynthetic eukaryotic cell, which survived in a symbiotic relationship inside the heterotrophic cell.

secondary growth Growth produced by lateral meristems, thickening the roots and shoots of woody plants.

secondary immune response The acquired immune response elicited on second or subsequent exposures to a particular antigen. The secondary immune response is more rapid, of greater magnitude, and of longer duration than the primary immune response.

secondary oocyte (ō′-uh-sīt) An oocyte that has completed the first of the two meiotic divisions.

secondary plant body The tissues produced by the vascular cambium and cork cambium, which thicken the stems and roots of woody plants.

secondary production The amount of chemical energy in consumers' food that is converted to their own new biomass during a given time period.

secondary structure The localized, repetitive coiling or folding of the polypeptide backbone of a protein due to hydrogen bond formation between constituents of the backbone.

secondary succession A type of succession that occurs where an existing community has been cleared by some disturbance that leaves the soil or substrate intact.

secretion (1) The discharge of molecules synthesized by a cell. (2) The discharge of wastes from the body fluid into the filtrate.

secretory phase That portion of the uterine (menstrual) cycle when the endometrium continues to thicken, becomes more vascularized, and develops glands that secrete a fluid rich in glycogen.

seed An adaptation of some terrestrial plants consisting of an embryo packaged along with a store of food within a protective coat.

seed coat A tough outer covering of a seed, formed from the outer coat of an ovule. In a flowering plant, the seed coat encloses and protects the embryo and endosperm.

seedless vascular plant An informal name for a plant that has vascular tissue but lacks seeds. Seedless vascular plants form a paraphyletic group that includes the phyla Lycophyta (club mosses and their relatives) and Pterophyta (ferns and their relatives).

selective permeability A property of biological membranes that allows them to regulate the passage of substances.

self-incompatibility The ability of a seed plant to reject its own pollen and sometimes the pollen of closely related individuals.

semelparity Reproduction in which an organism produces all of its offspring in a single event; also known as big-bang reproduction.

semen (sē′-mun) The fluid that is ejaculated by the male during orgasm; contains sperm and secretions from several glands of the male reproductive tract.

semicircular canals A three-part chamber of the inner ear that functions in maintaining equilibrium.

semiconservative model Type of DNA replication in which the replicated double helix consists of one old strand, derived from the old molecule, and one newly made strand.

semilunar valve A valve located at each exit of the heart, where the aorta leaves the left ventricle and the pulmonary artery leaves the right ventricle.

seminal vesicle (sem′-i-nul ves′-i-kul) A gland in males that secretes a fluid component of semen that lubricates and nourishes sperm.

seminiferous tubule (sem′-i-nif′-er-us) A highly coiled tube in the testis in which sperm are produced.

senescence (se-nes′-ens) The growth phase in a plant or plant part (as a leaf) from full maturity to death.

sensitive period A limited phase in an individual animal's development when learning of particular behaviors can take place; also called a critical period.

sensor In homeostasis, a receptor that detects a stimulus.

sensory adaptation The tendency of sensory neurons to become less sensitive when they are stimulated repeatedly.

sensory neuron A nerve cell that receives information from the internal or external environment and transmits signals to the central nervous system.

sensory reception The detection of the energy of a stimulus by sensory cells.

sensory receptor An organ, cell, or structure within a cell that responds to specific stimuli from an organism's external or internal environment.

sensory transduction The conversion of stimulus energy to a change in the membrane potential of a sensory receptor cell.

sepal (sē′-pul) A modified leaf in angiosperms that helps enclose and protect a flower bud before it opens.

septum (plural, **septa**) One of the cross-walls that divide a fungal hypha into cells. Septa generally have pores large enough to allow ribosomes, mitochondria, and even nuclei to flow from cell to cell.

serial endosymbiosis A hypothesis for the origin of eukaryotes consisting of a sequence of endosymbiotic events in which mitochondria, chloroplasts, and perhaps other cellular structures were derived from small prokaryotes that had been engulfed by larger cells.

serotonin (ser′-uh-tō′-nin) A neurotransmitter, synthesized from the amino acid tryptophan, that functions in the central nervous system.

set point In animal bodies, a value maintained for a particular variable, such as body temperature or solute concentration, to achieve homeostasis.

seta (sē′-tuh) (plural, **setae**) The elongated stalk of a bryophyte sporophyte.

sex chromosome A chromosome responsible for determining the sex of an individual.

sex pilus (plural, **sex pili**) (pī′-lus, pī′-lī) In bacteria, a structure that links one cell to another at the start of conjugation; also known as a conjugation pilus.

sex-linked gene A gene located on a sex chromosome (usually the X chromosome), resulting in a distinctive pattern of inheritance.

sexual dimorphism (dī-mōr′-fizm) Marked differences between the secondary sex characteristics of males and females.

sexual reproduction A type of reproduction in which two parents give rise to offspring that have unique combinations of genes inherited from the gametes of the parents.

sexual selection A form of natural selection in which individuals with certain inherited characteristics are more likely than other individuals to obtain mates.

Shannon diversity An index of community diversity symbolized by H and represented by the equation $H = [(p_A \ln p_A) + (p_B \ln p_B) + (p_C \ln p_C) + \ldots]$, where A, B, C . . . are the species in the community, p is the relative abundance of each species, and ln is the natural logarithm.

shared ancestral character A character, shared by members of a particular clade, that originated in an ancestor that is not a member of that clade.

shared derived character An evolutionary novelty that is unique to a particular clade.

shoot system The aerial portion of a plant body, consisting of stems, leaves, and (in angiosperms) flowers.

short tandem repeat (STR) Simple sequence DNA containing multiple tandemly repeated units of two to five nucleotides. Variations in STRs act as genetic markers in STR analysis, used to prepare genetic profiles.

short-day plant A plant that flowers (usually in late summer, fall, or winter) only when the light period is shorter than a critical length.

short-term memory The ability to hold information, anticipations, or goals for a time and then release them if they become irrelevant.

sickle-cell disease A human genetic disease caused by a recessive allele that results in the substitution of a single amino acid in a globin polypeptide that is part of the hemoglobin protein; characterized by deformed red blood cells (due to protein aggregation) that can lead to numerous symptoms.

sieve plate An end wall in a sieve-tube element, which facilitates the flow of phloem sap in angiosperm sieve tubes.

sieve-tube element A living cell that conducts sugars and other organic nutrients in the phloem of angiosperms; also called a sieve-tube member. Connected end to end, they form sieve tubes.

sign stimulus An external sensory cue that triggers a fixed action pattern by an animal.

signal In animal behavior, transmission of a stimulus from one animal to another. The term is also used in the context of communication in other kinds of organisms and in cell-to-cell communication in all multicellular organisms.

signal peptide A sequence of about 20 amino acids at or near the leading (amino) end of a polypeptide that targets it to the endoplasmic reticulum or other organelles in a eukaryotic cell.

signal transduction The linkage of a mechanical, chemical, or electromagnetic stimulus to a specific cellular response.

signal transduction pathway A series of steps linking a mechanical or chemical stimulus to a specific cellular response.

signal-recognition particle (SRP) A protein-RNA complex that recognizes a signal peptide as it emerges from a ribosome and helps direct the ribosome to the endoplasmic reticulum (ER) by binding to a receptor protein on the ER.

simple fruit A fruit derived from a single carpel or several fused carpels.

simple sequence DNA A DNA sequence that contains many copies of tandemly repeated short sequences.

single bond A single covalent bond; the sharing of a pair of valence electrons by two atoms.

single circulation A circulatory system consisting of a single pump and circuit, in which blood passes from the sites of gas exchange to the rest of the body before returning to the heart.

single nucleotide polymorphism (SNP) A single base-pair site in a genome where nucleotide variation is found in at least 1% of the population.

single-lens eye The camera-like eye found in some jellies, polychaetes, spiders, and many molluscs.

single-strand binding protein A protein that binds to the unpaired DNA strands during DNA

replication, stabilizing them and holding them apart while they serve as templates for the synthesis of complementary strands of DNA.

sinoatrial (SA) node A region in the right atrium of the heart that sets the rate and timing at which all cardiac muscle cells contract; the pacemaker.

sister chromatid Either of two copies of a duplicated chromosome attached to each other by proteins at the centromere and, sometimes, along the arms. While joined, two sister chromatids make up one chromosome; chromatids are eventually separated during mitosis or meiosis II.

sister taxa Groups of organisms that share an immediate common ancestor and hence are each other's closest relatives.

skeletal muscle Muscle that is generally responsible for the voluntary movements of the body; one type of striated muscle.

sliding-filament model The theory explaining how muscle contracts, based on change within a sarcomere, the basic unit of muscle organization. According to this model, thin (actin) filaments slide across thick (myosin) filaments, shortening the sarcomere. The shortening of all sarcomeres in a myofibril shortens the entire myofibril.

slow block to polyspermy The formation of the fertilization envelope and other changes in an egg's surface that prevent fusion of the egg with more than one sperm. The slow block begins about 1 minute after fertilization.

slow-twitch fiber A muscle fiber that can sustain long contractions.

small interfering RNA (siRNA) A small, single-stranded RNA molecule generated by cellular machinery from a long, double-stranded RNA molecule. The siRNA associates with one or more proteins in a complex that can degrade or prevent translation of an mRNA with a complementary sequence. In some cases, siRNA can also block transcription by promoting chromatin modification.

small intestine The longest section of the alimentary canal, so named because of its small diameter compared with that of the large intestine; the principal site of the enzymatic hydrolysis of food macromolecules and the absorption of nutrients.

smooth ER That portion of the endoplasmic reticulum that is free of ribosomes.

smooth muscle A type of muscle lacking the striations of skeletal and cardiac muscle because of the uniform distribution of myosin filaments in the cell; responsible for involuntary body activities.

social learning Modification of behavior through the observation of other individuals.

sociobiology The study of social behavior based on evolutionary theory.

sodium-potassium pump A transport protein in the plasma membrane of animal cells that actively transports sodium out of the cell and potassium into the cell.

soil horizon A soil layer that parallels the land surface and has physical characteristics that differ from those of the layers above and beneath.

solute (sol'-yūt) A substance that is dissolved in a solution.

solute potential (Ψ_S) A component of water potential that is proportional to the osmolarity of a solution and that measures the effect of solutes on the direction of water movement; also called osmotic potential, it can be either zero or negative.

solution A liquid that is a homogeneous mixture of two or more substances.

solvent The dissolving agent of a solution. Water is the most versatile solvent known.

somatic cell (sō-mat'-ik) Any cell in a multicellular organism except a sperm or egg.

somite One of a series of blocks of mesoderm that exist in pairs just lateral to the notochord in a vertebrate embryo.

soredium (plural, **soredia**) In lichens, a small cluster of fungal hyphae with embedded algae.

sorus (plural, **sori**) A cluster of sporangia on a fern sporophyll. Sori may be arranged in various patterns, such as parallel lines or dots, which are useful in fern identification.

Southern blotting A technique that enables specific nucleotide sequences to be detected in a sample of DNA. It involves gel electrophoresis of DNA molecules and their transfer to a membrane (blotting), followed by nucleic acid hybridization with a labeled probe.

spatial learning The establishment of a memory that reflects the environment's spatial structure.

spatial summation A phenomenon of neural integration in which the membrane potential of the postsynaptic cell is determined by the combined effect of EPSPs or IPSPs produced nearly simultaneously by different synapses.

speciation (spē'-sē-ā'-shun) An evolutionary process in which one species splits into two or more species.

species (spē'-sēz) A population or group of populations whose members have the potential to interbreed in nature and produce viable, fertile offspring, but do not produce viable, fertile offspring with members of other such groups.

species diversity The number and relative abundance of species in a biological community.

species richness The number of species in a biological community.

species-area curve The biodiversity pattern, first noted by Alexander von Humboldt, that shows that the larger the geographic area of a community is, the more species it has.

specific heat The amount of heat that must be absorbed or lost for 1 g of a substance to change its temperature by 1°C.

spectrophotometer An instrument that measures the proportions of light of different wavelengths absorbed and transmitted by a pigment solution.

sperm The male gamete.

spermatheca (sper'-muh-thē'-kuh) In many insects, a sac in the female reproductive system where sperm are stored.

spermatogenesis The continuous and prolific production of mature sperm cells in the testis.

spermatogonium A cell that divides mitotically to form spermatocytes.

sphincter (sfink'-ter) A ringlike valve, consisting of modified muscles in a muscular tube, that regulates passage between some compartments of the alimentary canal.

spinal nerve In the vertebrate peripheral nervous system, a nerve that carries signals to or from the spinal cord.

spiral cleavage A type of embryonic development in protostomes in which the planes of cell division that transform the zygote into a ball of cells are diagonal to the vertical axis of the embryo. As a result, the cells of each tier sit in the grooves between cells of adjacent tiers.

spliceosome (splī'-sē-ō-sōm) A large complex made up of proteins and RNA molecules that splices RNA by interacting with the ends of an RNA intron, releasing the intron and joining the two adjacent exons.

spongocoel (spon'-jō-sēl) The central cavity of a sponge.

sporangium (spōr-an'-jē-um) (plural, **sporangia**) A multicellular organ in fungi and plants in which meiosis occurs and haploid cells develop.

spore (1) In the life cycle of a plant or alga undergoing alternation of generations, a haploid cell produced in the sporophyte by meiosis. A spore can divide by mitosis to develop into a multicellular haploid individual, the gametophyte, without fusing with another cell. (2) In fungi, a haploid cell, produced either sexually or asexually, that produces a mycelium after germination.

sporocyte A diploid cell, also known as a spore mother cell, that undergoes meiosis and generates haploid spores.

sporophyll (spō'-ruh-fil) A modified leaf that bears sporangia and hence is specialized for reproduction.

sporophyte (spō-ruh-fīt') In organisms (plants and some algae) that have alternation of generations, the multicellular diploid form that results from the union of gametes. The sporophyte produces haploid spores by meiosis that develop into gametophytes.

sporopollenin (spōr-uh-pol'-eh-nin) A durable polymer that covers exposed zygotes of charophyte algae and forms the walls of plant spores, preventing them from drying out.

stabilizing selection Natural selection in which intermediate phenotypes survive or reproduce more successfully than do extreme phenotypes.

stamen (stā'-men) The pollen-producing reproductive organ of a flower, consisting of an anther and a filament.

standard metabolic rate (SMR) The metabolic rate of a resting, fasting, and nonstressed ectotherm at a particular temperature.

stapes The third of three bones in the middle ear of mammals; also called the stirrup.

starch A storage polysaccharide in plants, consisting entirely of glucose monomers joined by α glycosidic linkages.

statocyst (stat'-uh-sist') A type of mechanoreceptor that functions in equilibrium in invertebrates by use of statoliths, which stimulate hair cells in relation to gravity.

statolith (stat'-uh-lith') (1) In plants, a specialized plastid that contains dense starch grains and may play a role in detecting gravity. (2) In invertebrates, a grain or other dense granule that settles in response to gravity and is found in sensory organs that function in equilibrium.

stele (stēl)The vascular tissue of a stem or root.

stem A vascular plant organ consisting of an alternating system of nodes and internodes that support the leaves and reproductive structures.

stem cell Any relatively unspecialized cell that can produce, during a single division, one identical daughter cell and one more specialized daughter cell that can undergo further differentiation.

stenohaline (sten'-ō-hā'-līn) Referring to organisms that cannot tolerate substantial changes in external osmolarity.

steroid A type of lipid characterized by a carbon skeleton consisting of four rings with various chemical groups attached.

sticky end A single-stranded end of a double-stranded restriction fragment.

stigma (plural, **stigmata**) The sticky part of a flower's carpel, which traps pollen grains.

stimulus In homeostasis, a fluctuation in a variable that triggers a return to a set point.

stipe A stemlike structure of a seaweed.

stock The plant that provides the root system when making a graft.

stoma (stō'-muh) (plural, **stomata**) A microscopic pore surrounded by guard cells in the epidermis of leaves and stems that allows gas exchange between the environment and the interior of the plant.

stomach An organ of the digestive system that stores food and performs preliminary steps of digestion.

stramenopile A protist in which a "hairy" flagellum (one covered with fine, hairlike projections) is paired with a shorter, smooth flagellum.

stratum (strah'-tum) (plural, **strata**) A rock layer formed when new layers of sediment cover older ones and compress them.

striated muscle Muscle in which the regular arrangement of filaments creates a pattern of light and dark bands.

strobilus (strō-bī'-lus) (plural, **strobili**) The technical term for a cluster of sporophylls known commonly as a cone, found in most gymnosperms and some seedless vascular plants.

stroke The death of nervous tissue in the brain, usually resulting from rupture or blockage of arteries in the head.

stroke volume The volume of blood pumped by a heart ventricle in a single contraction.

stroma (strō'-muh) Within the chloroplast, the dense fluid of the chloroplast surrounding the thylakoid membrane; involved in the synthesis of organic molecules from carbon dioxide and water.

stromatolite Layered rock that results from the activities of prokaryotes that bind thin films of sediment together.

structural formula A type of molecular notation in which the constituent atoms are joined by lines representing covalent bonds.

structural isomer One of several compounds that have the same molecular formula but differ in the covalent arrangements of their atoms.

style The stalk of a flower's carpel, with the ovary at the base and the stigma at the top.

substance P A neuropeptide that is a key excitatory neurotransmitter that mediates the perception of pain.

substrate The reactant on which an enzyme works.

substrate feeder An animal that lives in or on its food source, eating its way through the food.

substrate-level phosphorylation The formation of ATP by an enzyme directly transferring a phosphate group to ADP from an intermediate substrate in catabolism.

sugar sink A plant organ that is a net consumer or storer of sugar. Growing roots, shoot tips, stems, and fruits are sugar sinks supplied by phloem.

sugar source A plant organ in which sugar is being produced by either photosynthesis or the breakdown of starch. Mature leaves are the primary sugar sources of plants.

sulfhydryl group A chemical group consisting of a sulfur atom bonded to a hydrogen atom.

suprachiasmatic nucleus (SCN) A group of neurons in the hypothalamus of mammals that functions as a biological clock.

surface tension A measure of how difficult it is to stretch or break the surface of a liquid. Water has a high surface tension because of the hydrogen bonding of surface molecules.

surfactant A substance secreted by alveoli that decreases surface tension in the fluid that coats the alveoli.

survivorship curve A plot of the number of members of a cohort that are still alive at each age; one way to represent age-specific mortality.

suspension feeder An aquatic animal, such as a sponge, clam, or baleen whale, that feeds by sifting small food particles from the water.

sustainable agriculture Long-term productive farming methods that are environmentally safe.

sustainable development Development that meets the needs of people today without limiting the ability of future generations to meet their needs.

swim bladder In aquatic osteichthyans, an air sac that enables the animal to control its buoyancy in the water.

symbiont (sim'-bē-ont) The smaller participant in a symbiotic relationship, living in or on the host.

symbiosis An ecological relationship between organisms of two different species that live together in direct and intimate contact.

sympathetic division One of three divisions of the autonomic nervous system of vertebrates; generally increases energy expenditure and prepares the body for action.

sympatric speciation (sim-pat'-rik) The formation of new species in populations that live in the same geographic area.

symplast In plants, the continuum of cytoplasm connected by plasmodesmata between cells.

synapse (sin'-aps) The junction where one neuron communicates with another cell across a narrow gap. Neurotransmitter molecules released by the neuron diffuse across the synapse, relaying messages to the other cell.

synapsid Member of an amniote clade distinguished by a single hole on each side of the skull. Synapsids include the mammals.

synapsis (si-nap'-sis) The pairing and physical connection of replicated homologous chromosomes during prophase I of meiosis.

synaptic cleft (sin-ap'-tik) A narrow gap separating the synaptic terminal of a transmitting neuron from a receiving neuron or an effector cell.

synaptic terminal A bulb at the end of an axon in which neurotransmitter molecules are stored and from which they are released.

synaptic vesicle Membranous sac containing neurotransmitter molecules at the tip of an axon.

systematics A scientific discipline focused on classifying organisms and determining their evolutionary relationships.

systemic Occurring throughout the body and affecting many or all body systems or organs.

systemic acquired resistance A defensive response in infected plants that helps protect healthy tissue from pathogenic invasion.

systemic circuit The branch of the circulatory system that supplies all body organs except those involved in gas exchange.

systems biology An approach to studying biology that aims to model the dynamic behavior of whole biological systems.

systole (sis'-tō-lē) The stage of the cardiac cycle in which a heart chamber contracts and pumps blood.

systolic pressure Blood pressure in the arteries during contraction of the ventricles.

T cell receptor The antigen receptor on T cells; a membrane-bound molecule consisting of one α chain and one β chain linked by a disulfide bridge and containing one antigen-binding site.

T cells The class of lymphocytes that mature in the thymus and that includes both effector cells for the cell-mediated immune response and helper cells required for both branches of adaptive immunity.

taproot A main vertical root that develops from an embryonic root and gives rise to lateral (branch) roots.

tastant Any chemical that stimulates the sensory receptors in a taste bud.

taste bud A collection of modified epithelial cells on the tongue or in the mouth that are receptors for taste in mammals.

TATA box A DNA sequence in eukaryotic promoters crucial in forming the transcription initiation complex.

taxis (tak′-sis) An oriented movement toward or away from a stimulus.

taxon (plural, **taxa**) A named taxonomic unit at any given level of classification.

taxonomy (tak-son′-uh-mē) A scientific discipline concerned with naming and classifying the diverse forms of life.

Tay-Sachs disease A human genetic disease caused by a recessive allele for a dysfunctional enzyme, leading to accumulation of certain lipids in the brain. Seizures, blindness, and degeneration of motor and mental performance usually become manifest a few months after birth, followed by death within a few years.

technology The application of scientific knowledge for a specific purpose, often involving industry or commerce but also including uses in basic research.

telomerase An enzyme that catalyzes the lengthening of telomeres in eukaryotic germ cells.

telomere (tel′-uh-mēr) The tandemly repetitive DNA at the end of a eukaryotic chromosome's DNA molecule that protects the organism's genes from being eroded during successive rounds of replication. *See also* repetitive DNA.

telophase The fifth and final stage of mitosis, in which daughter nuclei are forming and cytokinesis has typically begun.

temperate broadleaf forest A biome located throughout midlatitude regions where there is sufficient moisture to support the growth of large, broadleaf deciduous trees.

temperate grassland A terrestrial biome dominated by grasses and forbs.

temperate phage A phage that is capable of reproducing by either a lytic or lysogenic cycle.

temperature A measure of the intensity of heat in degrees, reflecting the average kinetic energy of the molecules.

template strand The DNA strand that provides the pattern, or template, for ordering the sequence of nucleotides in an RNA transcript.

temporal summation A phenomenon of neural integration in which the membrane potential of the postsynaptic cell in a chemical synapse is determined by the combined effect of EPSPs or IPSPs produced in rapid succession.

tendon A fibrous connective tissue that attaches muscle to bone.

terminator In bacteria, a sequence of nucleotides in DNA that marks the end of a gene and signals RNA polymerase to release the newly made RNA molecule and detach from the DNA.

territoriality A behavior in which an animal defends a bounded physical space against encroachment by other individuals, usually of its own species.

tertiary consumer (ter′-shē-ār′-ē) A carnivore that eats other carnivores.

tertiary structure Irregular contortions of a protein molecule due to interactions of side chains involved in hydrophobic interactions, ionic bonds, hydrogen bonds, and disulfide bridges.

testcross Breeding an organism of unknown genotype with a homozygous recessive individual to determine the unknown genotype. The ratio of phenotypes in the offspring reveals the unknown genotype.

testis (plural, **testes**) The male reproductive organ, or gonad, in which sperm and reproductive hormones are produced.

testosterone A steroid hormone required for development of the male reproductive system, spermatogenesis, and male secondary sex characteristics; the major androgen in mammals.

tetanus (tet′-uh-nus) The maximal, sustained contraction of a skeletal muscle, caused by a very high frequency of action potentials elicited by continual stimulation.

tetrapod A vertebrate with two pairs of limbs. Tetrapods include mammals, amphibians, and birds and other reptiles.

thalamus (thal′-uh-mus) One of two integrating centers of the vertebrate forebrain. Neurons with cell bodies in the thalamus relay neural input to specific areas in the cerebral cortex and regulate what information goes to the cerebral cortex.

thallus (plural, **thalli**) A seaweed body that is plantlike, consisting of a holdfast, stipe, and blades, yet lacks true roots, stems, and leaves.

theory An explanation that is broad in scope, generates new hypotheses, and is supported by a large body of evidence.

thermal energy *See* heat.

thermocline A narrow stratum of rapid temperature change in the ocean and in many temperate-zone lakes.

thermodynamics (ther′-mō-dī-nam′-iks) The study of energy transformations that occur in a collection of matter. *See* first law of thermodynamics; second law of thermodynamics.

thermoreceptor A receptor stimulated by either heat or cold.

thermoregulation The maintenance of internal body temperature within a tolerable range.

theropod Member of an ancient group of dinosaurs that were bipedal carnivores.

thick filament A filament composed of staggered arrays of myosin molecules; a component of myofibrils in muscle fibers.

thigmomorphogenesis A response in plants to chronic mechanical stimulation, resulting from increased ethylene production. An example is thickening stems in response to strong winds.

thigmotropism (thig-mo′-truh-pizm) A directional growth of a plant in response to touch.

thin filament A filament consisting of two strands of actin and two strands of regulatory protein coiled around one another; a component of myofibrils in muscle fibers.

threatened species A species that is considered likely to become endangered in the foreseeable future.

threshold The potential that an excitable cell membrane must reach for an action potential to be initiated.

thrombus A fibrin-containing clot that forms in a blood vessel and blocks the flow of blood.

thylakoid (thī′-luh-koyd) A flattened membranous sac inside a chloroplast. Thylakoids exist in an interconnected system in the chloroplast and contain the molecular "machinery" used to convert light energy to chemical energy.

thymus (thī′-mus) A small organ in the thoracic cavity of vertebrates where maturation of T cells is completed.

thyroid gland An endocrine gland, located on the ventral surface of the trachea, that secretes two iodine-containing hormones, triiodothyronine (T_3) and thyroxine (T_4), as well as calcitonin.

thyroxine (T_4) One of two iodine-containing hormones that are secreted by the thyroid gland and that help regulate metabolism, development, and maturation in vertebrates.

Ti plasmid A plasmid of a tumor-inducing bacterium (the plant pathogen *Agrobacterium*) that integrates a segment of its DNA (T DNA) into a chromosome of a host plant. The Ti plasmid is frequently used as a vector for genetic engineering in plants.

tidal volume The volume of air a mammal inhales and exhales with each breath.

tight junction A type of intercellular junction in animal cells that prevents the leakage of material between cells.

tissue An integrated group of cells with a common function, structure, or both.

tissue system One or more tissues organized into a functional unit connecting the organs of a plant.

TLR Toll-like receptor. A membrane receptor on a phagocytic white blood cell that recognizes fragments of molecules common to a set of pathogens.

tonicity The ability of a solution surrounding a cell to cause that cell to gain or lose water.

top-down model A model of community organization in which predation influences community organization by controlling herbivore numbers, which in turn control plant or phytoplankton numbers, which in turn control nutrient levels; also called the trophic cascade model.

topoisomerase A protein that breaks, swivels, and rejoins DNA strands. During DNA replication, topoisomerase helps to relieve strain in the double helix ahead of the replication fork.

topsoil A mixture of particles derived from rock, living organisms, and decaying organic material (humus).

torpor A physiological state in which activity is low and metabolism decreases.

torsion In gastropods, a developmental process in which the visceral mass rotates up to 180°, causing the animal's anus and mantle cavity to be positioned above its head.

totipotent (tō′-tuh-pōt′-ent) Describing a cell that can give rise to all parts of the embryo and adult, as well as extraembryonic membranes in species that have them.

trace element An element indispensable for life but required in extremely minute amounts.

trachea (trā′-kē-uh) The portion of the respiratory tract that passes from the larynx to the bronchi; also called the windpipe.

tracheal system In insects, a system of branched, air-filled tubes that extends throughout the body and carries oxygen directly to cells.

tracheid (trā′-kē-id) A long, tapered water-conducting cell found in the xylem of nearly all vascular plants. Functioning tracheids are no longer living.

trait Any detectable variant in a genetic character.

trans fat An unsaturated fat containing one or more *trans* double bonds.

transcription The synthesis of RNA using a DNA template.

transcription factor A regulatory protein that binds to DNA and affects transcription of specific genes.

transcription initiation complex The completed assembly of transcription factors and RNA polymerase bound to a promoter.

transcription unit A region of DNA that is transcribed into an RNA molecule.

transduction (1) A type of horizontal gene transfer in which phages (viruses) carry bacterial DNA from one host cell to another. (2) In cellular communication, the conversion of a signal from outside the cell to a form that can bring about a specific cellular response.

transfer cell In a plant, a companion cell with numerous ingrowths of its wall, which increase the cell's surface area and enhance the transfer of solutes between apoplast and symplast.

transfer RNA (tRNA) An RNA molecule that functions as an interpreter between nucleic acid and protein language by picking up specific amino acids and recognizing the appropriate codons in the mRNA.

transformation (1) The conversion of a normal animal cell to a cancerous cell. (2) A change in genotype and phenotype due to the assimilation of external DNA by a cell.

transgenic Pertaining to an organism whose genome contains a gene introduced from another organism of the same or a different species.

translation The synthesis of a polypeptide using the genetic information encoded in an mRNA molecule. There is a change of "language" from nucleotides to amino acids.

translocation (1) An aberration in chromosome structure resulting from attachment of a chromosomal fragment to a nonhomologous chromosome. (2) During protein synthesis, the third stage in the elongation cycle when the RNA carrying the growing polypeptide moves from the A site to the P site on the ribosome. (3) The transport of organic nutrients in the phloem of vascular plants.

transmission The passage of a nerve impulse along axons.

transmission electron microscope (TEM) A microscope that passes an electron beam through very thin sections and is primarily used to study the internal ultrastructure of cells.

transpiration The evaporative loss of water from a plant.

transport epithelium One or more layers of specialized epithelial cells that regulate solute movements.

transport protein A transmembrane protein that helps a certain substance or class of closely related substances to cross the membrane.

transport vesicle A tiny membranous sac in a cell's cytoplasm carrying molecules produced by the cell.

transposable element A segment of DNA that can move within the genome of a cell by means of a DNA or RNA intermediate; also called a transposable genetic element.

transposon A transposable element that moves within a genome by means of a DNA intermediate.

transverse (T) tubule An infolding of the plasma membrane of skeletal muscle cells.

triacylglycerol (trī-as′-ul-glis′-uh-rol) Three fatty acids linked to one glycerol molecule; also called a fat or a triglyceride.

triiodothyronine (T_3) (trī′-ī-ō′-dō-thī′-rō-nēn) One of two iodine-containing hormones that are secreted by the thyroid gland and that help regulate metabolism, development, and maturation in vertebrates.

trimester In human development, one of three 3-month-long periods of pregnancy.

triple response A plant growth maneuver in response to mechanical stress, involving slowing of stem elongation, a thickening of the stem, and a curvature that causes the stem to start growing horizontally.

triplet code A set of three-nucleotide-long words that specify the amino acids for polypeptide chains.

triploblastic Possessing three germ layers: the endoderm, mesoderm, and ectoderm. Most eumetazoans are triploblastic.

trisomic Referring to a diploid cell that has three copies of a particular chromosome instead of the normal two.

trochophore larva (trō′-kuh-fōr) Distinctive larval stage observed in some lophotrochozoan animals, including some annelids and molluscs.

trophic efficiency The percentage of production transferred from one trophic level to the next.

trophic structure The different feeding relationships in an ecosystem, which determine the route of energy flow and the pattern of chemical cycling.

trophoblast The outer epithelium of a mammalian blastocyst. It forms the fetal part of the placenta, supporting embryonic development but not forming part of the embryo proper.

tropic hormone A hormone that has another endocrine gland as a target.

tropical rain forest A terrestrial biome characterized by high levels of precipitation and high temperatures year-round.

tropics Latitudes between 23.5° north and south.

tropism A growth response that results in the curvature of whole plant organs toward or away from stimuli due to differential rates of cell elongation.

tropomyosin The regulatory protein that blocks the myosin-binding sites on actin molecules.

troponin complex The regulatory proteins that control the position of tropomyosin on the thin filament.

true-breeding Referring to plants that produce offspring of the same variety when they self-pollinate.

tubal ligation A means of sterilization in which a woman's two oviducts (fallopian tubes) are tied closed to prevent eggs from reaching the uterus. A segment of each oviduct is removed.

tube foot One of numerous extensions of an echinoderm's water vascular system. Tube feet function in locomotion, feeding, and gas exchange.

tumor-suppressor gene A gene whose protein product inhibits cell division, thereby preventing the uncontrolled cell growth that contributes to cancer.

tundra A terrestrial biome at the extreme limits of plant growth. At the northernmost limits, it is called arctic tundra, and at high altitudes, where plant forms are limited to low shrubby or matlike vegetation, it is called alpine tundra.

tunicate Member of the subphylum Urochordata, sessile marine chordates that lack a backbone.

turgid (ter′-jid) Swollen or distended, as in plant cells. (A walled cell becomes turgid if it has a greater solute concentration than its surroundings, resulting in entry of water.)

turgor pressure The force directed against a plant cell wall after the influx of water and swelling of the cell due to osmosis.

turnover The mixing of waters as a result of changing water-temperature profiles in a lake.

turnover time The time required to replace the standing crop of a population or group of populations (for example, of phytoplankton), calculated as the ratio of standing crop to production.

twin study A behavioral study in which researchers compare the behavior of identical twins raised apart with that of identical twins raised in the same household.

tympanic membrane Another name for the eardrum, the membrane between the outer and middle ear.

ultimate causation The evolutionary explanation of "why" a behavior (or other aspect of an organism's biology) occurs, that is, the benefit to survival and reproduction or the evolutionary significance of the behavioral act.

undernourishment A condition that results from a diet that consistently supplies less chemical energy than the body requires.

uniformitarianism The principle stating that mechanisms of change are constant over time. *See* catastrophism.

Unikonta (yū′-ni-kon′-tuh) One of five supergroups of eukaryotes proposed in a current hypothesis of the evolutionary history of eukaryotes. This clade, which is supported by studies of myosin proteins and DNA, consists of amoebozoans and opisthokonts. *See also* Excavata, Chromalveolata, Rhizaria, and Archaeplastida.

unsaturated fatty acid A fatty acid possessing one or more double bonds between the carbons in the hydrocarbon tail. Such bonding reduces the number of hydrogen atoms attached to the carbon skeleton.

urea A soluble nitrogenous waste produced in the liver by a metabolic cycle that combines ammonia with carbon dioxide.

ureter (yū-rē′-ter) A duct leading from the kidney to the urinary bladder.

urethra (yū-rē′-thruh) A tube that releases urine from the mammalian body near the vagina in females and through the penis in males; also serves in males as the exit tube for the reproductive system.

uric acid A product of protein and purine metabolism and the major nitrogenous waste product of insects, land snails, and many reptiles. Uric acid is relatively nontoxic and largely insoluble.

urinary bladder The pouch where urine is stored prior to elimination.

uterine cycle The changes that occur in the uterus during the reproductive cycle of the human female; also called the menstrual cycle.

uterus A female organ where eggs are fertilized and/or development of the young occurs.

utricle In the vertebrate ear, a chamber in the vestibule behind the oval window that opens into the three semicircular canals.

vaccination *See* immunization.

vaccine A harmless variant or derivative of a pathogen that stimulates a host's immune system to mount defenses against the pathogen.

vacuole (vak′-yū-ōl′) A membrane-bounded vesicle whose function varies in different kinds of cells.

vagina Part of the female reproductive system between the uterus and the outside opening; the birth canal in mammals. During copulation, the vagina accommodates the male's penis and receives sperm.

valence The bonding capacity of a given atom; usually equals the number of unpaired electrons required to complete the atom's outermost (valence) shell.

valence electron An electron in the outermost electron shell.

valence shell The outermost energy shell of an atom, containing the valence electrons involved in the chemical reactions of that atom.

van der Waals interactions Weak attractions between molecules or parts of molecules that result from localized charge fluctuations.

variation Differences between members of the same species.

vas deferens In mammals, the tube in the male reproductive system in which sperm travel from the epididymis to the urethra.

vasa recta The capillary system in the kidney that serves the loop of Henle.

vascular cambium A cylinder of meristematic tissue in woody plants that adds layers of secondary vascular tissue called secondary xylem (wood) and secondary phloem.

vascular plant A plant with vascular tissue. Vascular plants include all living plant species except mosses, liverworts, and hornworts.

vascular tissue Plant tissue consisting of cells joined into tubes that transport water and nutrients throughout the plant body.

vascular tissue system A transport system formed by xylem and phloem throughout a vascular plant. Xylem transports water and minerals; phloem transports sugars, the products of photosynthesis.

vasectomy The cutting and sealing of each vas deferens to prevent sperm from entering the urethra.

vasocongestion The filling of a tissue with blood, caused by increased blood flow through the arteries of that tissue.

vasoconstriction A decrease in the diameter of blood vessels caused by contraction of smooth muscles in the vessel walls.

vasodilation An increase in the diameter of blood vessels caused by relaxation of smooth muscles in the vessel walls.

vector An organism that transmits pathogens from one host to another.

vegetal pole The point at the end of an egg in the hemisphere where most yolk is concentrated; opposite of animal pole.

vegetative reproduction Cloning of plants by asexual means.

vein (1) In animals, a vessel that carries blood toward the heart. (2) In plants, a vascular bundle in a leaf.

ventilation The flow of air or water over a respiratory surface.

ventral Pertaining to the underside, or bottom, of an animal with bilateral symmetry.

ventricle (ven′-tri-kul) (1) A heart chamber that pumps blood out of the heart. (2) A space in the vertebrate brain, filled with cerebrospinal fluid.

venule (ven′-yūl) A vessel that conveys blood between a capillary bed and a vein.

vernalization The use of cold treatment to induce a plant to flower.

vertebrate A chordate animal with a backbone: the mammals, reptiles (including birds), amphibians, sharks and rays, ray-finned fishes, and lobe-fins.

vesicle (ves′-i-kul) A sac made of membrane in the cytoplasm.

vessel A continuous water-conducting micropipe found in most angiosperms and a few nonflowering vascular plants.

vessel element A short, wide water-conducting cell found in the xylem of most angiosperms and a few nonflowering vascular plants. Dead at maturity, vessel elements are aligned end to end to form micropipes called vessels.

vestigial structure A structure of marginal, if any, importance to an organism. Vestigial structures are historical remnants of structures that had important functions in ancestors.

villus (plural, **villi**) (1) A finger-like projection of the inner surface of the small intestine. (2) A finger-like projection of the chorion of the mammalian placenta. Large numbers of villi increase the surface areas of these organs.

viral envelope A membrane that cloaks the capsid that in turn encloses a viral genome.

viroid (vī′-royd) A plant pathogen consisting of a molecule of naked, circular RNA a few hundred nucleotides long.

virulent Describing a pathogen against which an organism has little specific defense.

virulent phage A phage that reproduces only by a lytic cycle.

visceral mass One of the three main parts of a mollusc; the part containing most of the internal organs. *See also* foot, mantle.

visible light That portion of the electromagnetic spectrum that can be detected as various colors by the human eye, ranging in wavelength from about 380 nm to about 750 nm.

vital capacity The maximum volume of air that a mammal can inhale and exhale with each breath.

vitamin An organic molecule required in the diet in very small amounts. Vitamins serve primarily as coenzymes or as parts of coenzymes.

vitreous humor The jellylike material that fills the posterior cavity of the vertebrate eye.

viviparous (vī-vip′-uh-rus) Referring to a type of development in which the young are born alive after having been nourished in the uterus by blood from the placenta.

vocal cord One of a pair of bands of elastic tissue in the larynx. Air rushing past the tensed vocal cords makes them vibrate, producing sounds.

voltage-gated ion channel A specialized ion channel that opens or closes in response to changes in membrane potential.

vulva Collective term for the female external genitalia.

water potential (Ψ) The physical property predicting the direction in which water will flow, governed by solute concentration and applied pressure.

water vascular system A network of hydraulic canals unique to echinoderms that branches into extensions called tube feet, which function in locomotion, feeding, and gas exchange.

wavelength The distance between crests of waves, such as those of the electromagnetic spectrum.

wetland A habitat that is inundated by water at least some of the time and that supports plants adapted to water-saturated soil.

white matter Tracts of axons within the CNS.

wild type An individual with the phenotype most commonly observed in natural populations; also refers to the phenotype itself.

wilting The drooping of leaves and stems as a result of plant cells becoming flaccid.

wobble Flexibility in the base-pairing rules in which the nucleotide at the 5′ end of a tRNA anticodon can form hydrogen bonds with more than one kind of base in the third position (3′ end) of a codon.

xerophyte A plant adapted to an arid climate.

X-ray crystallography A technique that depends on the diffraction of an X-ray beam by the individual atoms of a crystallized molecule to study the three-dimensional structure of the molecule.

xylem (zī′-lum) Vascular plant tissue consisting mainly of tubular dead cells that conduct most of the water and minerals upward from the roots to the rest of the plant.

xylem sap The dilute solution of water and dissolved minerals carried through vessels and tracheids.

yeast Single-celled fungus that reproduces asexually by binary fission or by the pinching of small buds off a parent cell; some species exhibit cell fusion between different mating types.

yeast artificial chromosome (YAC) A cloning vector that combines the essentials of a eukaryotic chromosome—an origin for DNA replication, a centromere, and two telomeres—with foreign DNA.

yolk Nutrients stored in an egg.

yolk plug A group of large, nutrient-laden endodermal cells surrounded by the completed blastopore in an amphibian gastrula. These cells will be covered by ectoderm and end up inside the embryo.

yolk sac One of four extraembryonic membranes. It encloses the yolk in reptiles and is the first site of blood cell and circulatory system function.

zero population growth (ZPG) A period of stability in population size, when the per capita birth rate and death rate are equal.

zona pellucida The extracellular matrix surrounding a mammalian egg.

zone of polarizing activity (ZPA) A block of mesoderm located just under the ectoderm where the posterior side of a limb bud is attached to the body; required for proper pattern formation along the anterior-posterior axis of the limb.

zoned reserve An extensive region that includes areas relatively undisturbed by humans surrounded by areas that have been changed by human activity and are used for economic gain.

zoonotic pathogen A disease-causing agent that is transmitted to humans from other animals.

zoospore Flagellated spore found in chytrid fungi and some protists.

zygomycete (zī′-guh-mī′-sēt) Member of the fungal phylum Zygomycota, characterized by the formation of a sturdy structure called a zygosporangium during sexual reproduction.

zygosporangium (zī′-guh-spōr-an′-jē-um) In zygomycete fungi, a sturdy multinucleate structure in which karyogamy and meiosis occur.

zygote (zī′-gōt) The diploid product of the union of haploid gametes during fertilization; a fertilized egg.

Index

Index

Index

Index

sets of, in human cells, 250–51
sex determination and, 289–90
synthetic bacterial, 573
Chromosome theory of inheritance, **286**
Chronic myelogenous leukemia (CML), 300, 300f, 418
Chylomicrons, **889**
Chyme, **885**
Chytridiomycota, 641
Chymotrypsin, 888
Chytrids, **641**, 642f
Cichlids
sexual selection in, 497
weakening of reproductive barriers and, 500, 501f
Cilia, **114**
ciliates and, 584–85
dynein motor proteins and movement of, 116f
in eukaryotes, 14f
ultrastructure, 115f
Ciliary body, **1101**
Ciliates, **584–85**
Circadian rhythms, **777**, **838**, 994, 1122. *See also* Biological clock
suprachiasmatic nucleus control of, 1072–73
Circannual rhythms, 1122–23
Circulatory system, **898–915**
adaptations of, for thermoregulation, 864–65
blood composition and function, 911–14 (*see also* Blood)
blood vessels, blood flow velocity, and blood pressure in, 906–10
diseases of, in humans, 914–15
gas exchange and, 898, 923 (*see also* Gas exchange)
gastrovascular cavities related to, 899
heart and, 903–5
lymphatic system and, 910–11
mammalian, 903–15
open and closed, 899, 900f
placental, and fetal, 1014f
review, 927–28
vertebrate, 900–903
Cis double bond, fatty acids and, 76
Cis face, Golgi apparatus, 106–7, 106f
Cis isomers, 62
Cisternae
ER, 104, 105f
Golgi apparatus, 105–7
Cisternal maturation model, 106–7
Citric acid, 651
Citric acid cycle, **166**, 170, 172
ATP yield, 176f
cellular respiration and, 166f
connection of, to other metabolic pathways, 180–82
overview of, 170f, 171f
Citrulline, 327f
Clades (taxonomy), **542–43**
animal phylogeny and, 661–62
grades vs., 659, 660
Cladistics, **542–43**
Clam, 679f
Clark's nutcracker, 1127
Classes (taxonomy), **537**
Classical conditioning, **1127**
Classification of life, 12f, 537–38, E-1–E-2. *See also* Taxonomy
early schemes for, 453
links between phylogeny and, 538–39
Class I MHC molecules, **938**
Class II MHC molecules, **938**

Cleavage, **234**, 235f, **655**, **1013**, 1022, **1025–27**
in echinoderm embryo, 1025f
embryonic development and, 655f
in frog embryo, 1027f
holoblastic, and microblastic, 1027
in protostomes vs. in deuterostomes, 660, 661f
Cleavage furrow, **234**, 235f
Clements, F. E., 1211
Climate, **1155–59**
changes in, 520, 1159, 1239–41
continental drift and, 520
effects of bodies of water and ocean currents on, 1155, 1158f
effects of bodies of water on, 49f
effects of mountains on, 1158
global patterns of, 1155–58
global warming and, 1239–41
macroclimate, 1155
microclimate, 1155, 1158–59
reconstructing ancient, 615
seasonality and, 1158
studying past, using tree rings, 753f
Climax community, 1211
Climograph, **1166**
for major types of North American biomes, 1167f
Cline, **470**
Clitoris, **1004**
Cloaca, **708**, **1002**
Clock, biological. *See* Biological clock
Clock, floral, 821
Clonal analysis, 759
Clonal selection, **940**
amplifying lymphocytes by, 940–41
of B cells, 941f
Clone(s), **249**, **250**
cuttings and, 814
DNA (*see* DNA cloning)
fragmentation and, 812
meaning of term, 412
test-tube, 814–15
P. Zambryski on, 736–37
Cloning vector, **398**
Closed circulatory system, 899–**900**, 900f
Clotting, blood, 11, 397f, 913
Clownfish, 709f
Club fungus, **646–48**
Club mosses, 613, 614f
Clumped dispersion, 1176
Cnidarians (Cnidaria), 518, 667f, 671–73
classes of, 672t
gastrovascular cavities, 899f
polyp and medusa forms of, 671f
role of β-catenin in control of gastrulation in, 658f
Cnidocytes, **671**
CO₂. *See* Carbon dioxide (CO₂)
Coal, 615
Coated pits, endocytosis and, 139f
Coat proteins, 139f
Coccidioidomycosis, 651
Cochlea, **1093f**
transduction in, 1095f
Coconut palm, 1181f
Cocktails, multidrug HIV, 391
Cod, 709
Codominance, **272**
Codons, 329, **330**
anticodons, 337
codon recognition, 341
dictionary of, 330f
Coefficient of relatedness, **1139**

Coelacanth, 709f
Coelom, **659–60**
earthworm, 681f
formation, 660, 661f
Coelomates, **659**, 660f
Coenocytic fungi, **637–38**
Coenzyme, **156**
Cofactors, enzyme, **156**
Cognition, **1128**
brain regions for, in birds and humans, 1074f
consciousness and, 1078
FOXP2 genes and, 733
problem solving and, 1128
vertebrate, 1074
Cognitive maps, **1127**
Cohesins, 229, 257
Cohesion, **47**
rise of xylem sap and, 775–76
Cohort, **1177**
Coitus, **1006**
Coitus interruptus, 1016
Cold, plant response to excessive, 844–45
Coleman, Doug, 894–95
Coleoptera, 690f
Coleoptile, **808**
action spectrum for blue-light-stimulated phototropism in, 835f
signal transduction in growth of, 825–26
Coleorhiza, **808**
Collagen, 78t, 83f, **119**, 654
extracellular matrix and, 120f
quaternary protein structure of, 83f
Collagenous fibers, 857
Collar cells, 656f
Collecting duct, **964**, 965f, 966
Collenchyma cells, **744f**, 750
Colloid, **51**
Colon, **890**
Colonies, ant, 28–29
Colonies, green algae, 591
Coloration, defensive, 1201–2
Color blindness, 291f
Colorectal cancer, model for development of, 376f
Columnar cells, 856
Columnar epithelium, 856f
Combinatorial gene expression regulation, 361
Comet collision, mass extinction by, 522
Commensalism, **570**, **1203**
Commercial applications
DNA technology and development of pharmaceutical products, 418–19
of fungi, 651–52
of mosses, 609–10
Common arrowhead, 813f
Common juniper, 623f
Common scaly-foot, 536
Communicating junctions, 121f
Communication, **1123**
animal signals and, 1123–25
cell-cell (*see* Cell signaling)
chemical, in ants, 28–29
by neurons, 1047, 1048
symplastic, 781–82
Community(ies), **1149f**, **1198**
biogeographic factors affecting diversity in, 1214–17
bottom-up and top-down controls in, 1209–10
competition in, 1199–1200
dominant species in, 1207
ecological succession in, 1212–14
foundation species in, 1208–9

Index

Index

DNA technology and, 422–23
gene therapy, 418
plant extinctions, 634
science and, 24
Ethology, **1121**. *See also* Behavior
Ethylene, 827*t*, **832**–34
    fruit ripening and role of, 834
    leaf abscission and role of, 833
    plant response to flooding and, 844, 844*f*
    senescence and role of, 833
    triple response to mechanical stress and role
        of, 832–33
Etiolation, **822**. *See also* De-etiolation
Euchromatin, **322**
Eudicots, **630**, 631*f*
    embryo development, 807*f*
    root, 748*f*
    seed structure, 808*f*
    shoots, 750*f*
Euglenids, **581**, 581*f*
Euglenozoans, **580**–81, 581*f*
    euglenids, 581
    kinetoplastids, 580–81
Eukaryotic cell(s)
    differential gene expression in, 356, 366–73
    mechanisms of post-transcriptional regula-
        tion of gene expression in, 362–64
    noncoding RNAs in regulation of gene
        expression in, 364–66
    regulation of chromatin structure in, 356–58
    regulation of transcription initiation in,
        358–62
    stages of gene expression regulated in, 357*f*
Eukarya domain, **13**, 13*f*, **14**, 551–52, 552*f*. *See
        also* Eukaryotes
    compared with Bacteria and Archaea, 567*tf*
    gene expression, compared with other life do-
        mains, 346–47
    genome size in, 432, 433*t*
    protists, 575–76 (*see also* Protist(s))
Eukaryotes. *See also* Eukarya domain
    animals as, 654–56
    cells of (*see* Eukaryotic cell(s))
    chromatin packing in, 320–21*f*
    chromosomes of, vs. bacterial chromosomes,
        320–23
    cilia in, 14*f*
    classification of, 551–52
    coordinately controlled genes in, 362
    domain, 14
    domain Eukarya and, 13–14
    endosymbiosis in evolution of, 576, 577*f*
    evolution of mitosis in, 237*f*
    gene expression in, compared with other life
        domains, 346–47
    genes of (*see* Eukaryotic genes)
    organization of typical gene in, 359
    origins of DNA replication in, 313*f*
    origins of first, 516–17
    origins of multicellular, 517–18
    phylogenetic tree, 593*f*
    plants as (*see* Plant(s))
    protists as, 575 (*see also* Protist(s))
    as single-celled organisms, 575–77
    unikonts as common ancestor for, 593–94, 593*f*
Eukaryotic cell(s), **8**, **98**–121. *See also* Cell(s)
    animal, 100*f* (*see also* Animal cell(s))
    cell cycle in, 238–43
    cell division in, 229–43
    chromosomes, 229*f*
    cytoskeleton, 112–18
    endomembrane system, 104–9

extracellular components, 118–22
initiation of transcription in, 333*f*
as living unit, 122
mitochondria and chloroplasts, 109–11
nucleus and ribosomes, 102–4
P. Nurse on reproduction in, 92–93
panoramic view of, 99
plant, 101*f* (*see also* Plant cell(s))
post-transcription modification of RNA in,
    334–36
prokaryotic cell compared with, 8*f*, 98–99
review, 122–24
summary of gene expression in, 348*f*
transcription and translation as gene
    expression in, 329*f*, 331–34, 337–44
Eukaryotic genes
    cloning of, 398–403
    expression of cloned, 403
    making complementary DNA for, 401*f*
Eukaryotic genome, **434**–38. *See also* Genome(s)
    DNA changes leading to evolution
        of, 438–42
    gene and multigene families in, 436–38
    gene expression in (*see* Gene expression)
    human (*see* Human genome)
    noncoding DNA sequences in, 434–36
    repetitive DNA in, 436
    transposable elements and related sequences
        in, 435–36
Eulipotyphla, 725*f*
Eumetazoa clade, 671–73
Eumetazoans, **662**
European kestrels, 1180*f*
European larch, 623*f*
European Molecular Biology Laboratory, 429
Euryarchaeota clade, 567
Euryhaline, **955**, 955*f*
Eurypterids, **686**
Eustachian tube, **1093***f*
Eutherians (placental mammals), **723**–28, 1001
    adaptive radiation of, 523*f*
    convergent evolution of marsupials and, 465*f*
    evolutionary convergence of marsupials
        and, 723*f*
    humans, 728–33
    primates, 723–27
Eutrophication, **1227**
Eutrophic lakes, **1162***f*
Evans, Martin, 411
Evaporation, 47*f*, 49, **863***f*
Evaporative cooling, **49**
    in animals, 865–66
Evapotranspiration, **1215**
Evo-devo (evolutionary developmental biology),
    445–47, 525–29
Evolution, **1**, 450–67, **452**, **613**
    adaptation and (*see* Evolutionary adaptation)
    angiosperm, 628, 629*f*, 630
    of animals, 656–58
    ant colonies and, 29
    C. Darwin's field research and his ideas
        about, 455–57
    C. Darwin's theory of, 457–60
    of cell signaling, 206–7
    of cognition in vertebrates, 1074
    comparing genome sequences to study,
        442–44, 443*f*, 444*f*
    as core biological theme, 3, 12–18
    convergent, 464–65
    descent with modification as, 452, 457–58 (*see
        also* Descent with modification concept)
development and, 527–28, 534

direct observations of change, 460–61
diversity of life histories and, 1179–80
DNA and proteins as measures of, 89
early chordate, 701–2
S. Edwards on, 450–51
evolutionary time, 1150
of fungi, 640–41
gene flow and human, 478*f*
of genomes, 438–42
gymnosperm, 621
historical context of Darwinian revolution in,
    452–55
of human culture, 1142
influence of, on nitrogenous wastes, 960
J. B. Lamarck's theory of, 454
of land plants from green algae, 600–606, 605*f*
of life on Earth (*see* Macroevolution)
of mammals, 721
molecular clock and rate of, 549–51
natural selection and, 458–60 (*see also* Nat-
    ural selection)
obesity and, 895–96
origin of plants, 604–6
origin of species and, 457–60 (*see also* Speci-
    ation; Species)
phylogenies and, 537–40
of populations (*see* Microevolution; Popula-
    tion genetics)
prokaryotic, in response to environmental
    conditions, 560*f*
of reptiles, 716
review, 466–67
role of genetic variation in, 258–60
of roots and leaves, 612, 613*f*
scientific evidence for, 460–66
secondary endosymbiosis in eukaryotic,
    576, 577*f*
sexual reproduction as enigma of, 998–99
significance of glycolysis in, 179*f*
significance of introns in, 336
trends in, 530–31
of viruses, 390
of visual perception, 1105
Evolutionary adaptation, **456**, 458–59. *See also*
    Adaptation; Natural selection
    in bats, 16*f*
    C. Darwin's theory of natural selection and,
        456–57
    enabling move to land, 601
    in prokaryotes, 559–60
    as property of life, 2*f*
    of vertebrate digestive systems, 891–93
Evolutionary biology, linking ecology and,
    1148, 1150
Evolutionary developmental biology (evo-devo),
    445–47, 525–29
Evolutionary tree, **464**. *See also* Phylogenetic trees
    C. Darwin on, 457*f*
    S. Edwards on, 451
    homologies and, 464
Exaptation, 530
Excavata (excavates), 578*f*, **580**–81
    diplomonads and parabasalids, 580
    euglenozoans, 580–81
Exchange surfaces, 854, 898, 916
Excitatory postsynaptic potentials (EPSPs),
    1058, **1059**
Excretion, **954**, 961*f*. *See also* Excretory systems
    of excess salt in seabirds, 958*f*
    in fish, 956*f*
    nitrogenous wastes, 959–60

Index

heredity and role of, 248–49
homeotic, 370, 371*f*, 445–46, 445*f*, 526–27
homologous, 541
homologous, origins of, 548, 549*f*
Hox, 1044 (*see Hox* genes)
identifying protein-coding, 429–31
importance of concept of, 281
linked, 292–300
locating, along chromosomes, 286
lymphocyte diversity generated by rearrangement of, 939, 940*f*
major histocompatibility complex (MHC), 450–51
mapping distance between, 294–96
maternal effect, 371, 372–73
Mendelian inheritance and, 262
meristem identity, 760
microevolution due to mutations altering number of, 471
multigene families, 436–38
number of, in genomes, 432–33, 433*t*
ob and *db* genes and appetite regulation, 895*f*
organelle (extranuclear), 301–2
organ identity, 760
organization of typical eukaryotic, 359, 359*f*
orthologous, 548–49, 549*f*
p53, 376
paralogous, 548–49, 549*f*
pattern formation, 371–72, 372*f*
protein synthesis and (*see* Gene expression; Protein synthesis)
pseudogenes, 434
ras gene, **376**
rearrangement of parts of, 440–41
regulatory, 353
sex-linked, 289–92
single-gene speciation, 503, 503*f*
split, 334–36
systems approach to studying, 431
transplanting, into different species, 331*f*
types of, associated with cancer, 373–74
unequal crossing over of, 439*f*
universality in concept of, 346–48
Genealogy, molecular, 89
Gene cloning, **397**, 397
cloning eukaryotic gene in bacterial plasmid, 398–400, 399*f*
polymerase chain reaction vs., 404
screening DNA libraries for specific cloned genes, 401–3
storing clones genes in DNA libraries, 400*f*, 401
uses of cloned genes, 397–98, 397*f*
Gene expression, **325**–50. *See also* Protein synthesis; Transcription; Translation
analysis of interacting groups of genes and their, 410–11
analysis of single genes and their, 409*f*, 410
in bacteria, Archaea, and Eukarya, 346–47
of cloned eukaryotic genes, 403
differential (*see* Differential gene expression)
in different species, 331*f*
evolution due to changes in, 527–28, 528*f*
faulty genes and, 325, 325*f*
flow of genetic information and, 325
gene concept and, 346–47, 348*f*
gene specification of proteins via transcription and translation as, 325–31
genetic code and, 328–31
in plants, 758, 759*f*
point mutations and, 344–46

polypeptide synthesis via RNA-directed translation as, 337–44
regulation of (*see* Gene expression, regulation of)
review, 349–50
RNA modification after transcription by eukaryotic cells, 334–36
RNA synthesis via DNA-directed transcription, 331–34
stages of eukaryotic, that can be regulated, 357*f*
steroid hormones and regulation of, 979*f*
summary of, in eukaryotic cells, 348*f*
as transcription, 356
using DNA technology to study, 405–11
Gene expression, regulation of, 351–80
in bacterial transcription, 351–56
cancer due to faulty, 373–77
different cell types in multicellular organisms from differential gene expression, 366–73
in eukaryotic cells, 356–64
review, 378–79
role of noncoding RNAs in, 364–66
Gene families, 548–49
Gene flow, **478**
alteration of population allele frequencies due to, 475–78
human evolution and, 478*f*
natural selection and, 479*f*
over geographic distance, 489*f*
selection and, 479*f*
speciation and, 488
Gene-for-gene recognition, **846**, 847*f*
Gene guns, P. Zambryski on, 736
Gene pool, **472**–75
random selection of alleles from, 473*f*
General transcription factors, 359
Generative cells, angiosperm, 627
Gene therapy, **417**–19, 417*f*
Genetically modified organisms (GMOs), **422**–23, 816–19. *See also* Transgenic organisms
P. Zambryski on, 737
Genetically unlinked genes, 295. *See* Genetic disorders
Genetic change, phylogenetic tree branch lengths and, 544, 544*f*
Genetic code, 328–31
codons and triplet code of, 329
deciphering, 330–31
dictionary of, 330*f*
evolution and universality of, 463
evolution of, 331
reading frame for, 331
Genetic disorders
abnormal chromosome number as cause of, 297, 298*f*, 299
abnormal chromosome structure as cause of, 298, 299–300
achondroplasia, 278, 279*f*
alkaptonuria, 325–26
chromosomal alterations and, 297–300
chronic myelogenous leukemia, 300*f*
counseling and testing to avoid, 279–81
cystic fibrosis, 278
diagnosing fetal, 1018
DNA technology for, 416–19
dominantly inherited, 278–79
Down syndrome (trisomy 21), 299
Duchenne muscular dystrophy, 291

genetic testing and counseling for, 279–81
hemophilia, 291
Huntington's disease, 279
Klinefelter and Turner syndromes, 299
mitochondrial genes and, 300–301
multifactorial, 279
point mutations and, 344–46
recessively inherited, 277–78, 277–78
sex-linked genes and, 291
sickle-cell disease, 84, 278, 344, 344*f*
Tay-Sachs disease, 272
xeroderma pigmentosa, 318
Genetic diversity, 1246. *See* Genetic variation
benefits of, 1248
Genetic drift, **476**, 476*f*
alteration of population allele frequencies due to, 475–78
effects of, summarized, 478
Genetic engineering, **396**. *See also* DNA technology
of crop plants, 801, 816–17, 817*f*
fungi and, 651–52
of plants, 421–22, 792, 792*f*
P. Zambryski on, 736–37
Genetic map, **294**
Genetic markers, 416–17, 419–20
Genetic profiles, **419**–20
Genetic prospecting, with polymerase chain reaction (PCR), 566
Genetic recombination
gene linkage and, 293–94
mapping distance between genes using data from, 294–96
in prokaryotes, 561–64
Genetics, **248**, 260. *See also* Heredity; Inheritance
behavior and, 1130–32
chromosomal basis of inheritance (*see* Chromosomal basis of inheritance)
DNA technology (*see* DNA technology)
gene expression (*see* Gene expression)
genome (*see* Genome(s))
importance of Gregor Mendel's work, 281
Mendelian (*see* Mendelian inheritance)
molecular basis of inheritance (*see* Molecular basis of inheritance)
nervous system disorders and, 1080–81
regulation of gene expression (*see* Gene expression, regulation of)
schizophrenia and, 1081
sexual life cycle (*see* Sexual life cycle)
of speciation, 503–4
terms related to, 266–67
T. Orr-Weaver on, 246–47
variation in (*see* Genetic variation)
viruses (*see* Viruses)
Genetics Society of America, 247
Genetic testing and counseling, 279–81, 299
based on Mendelian genetics and probability rules, 279–80
fetal testing, 280, 281*f*
newborn screening, 280–81
tests for identifying carriers, 280
Genetic variation, 248, 468–71
bottleneck effect and reduction of, 477*f*
evolution and role of, 258–60
integrating Mendelian view into heredity and, 275
mutations as source of, 470–71
natural selection, genetic drift, and gene flow as causes of, 475–79

Index

Nitrogenous wastes, 954, 959–60
    forms of, 959–60, 959*f*
    influence of evolution and environment on, 960
Nitrogen recycling, 568*f*
Nobel Prize winners
    R. Axel and L. Buck, 1099
    S. Brenner, R. Horvitz, and J. Sulston, 1039
    M. Capecchi, M. Evans, and O. Smithies, 441
    R. Furchgott, L. Ignarro, and F. Murad, 908
    F. Jacob, 529
    R. Kornberg, 86*f*
    B. Marshall and R. Warren, 887
    B. McClintock, 435*f*
    M. Meselson, 677
    P. Mitchell, 176
    P. Nurse, L. Hartwell, and R. Hunt, 92
    C. Nüsslein-Volhard and E. Wieschaus, 371
    S. Prusiner, 394
    F. Sanger, 409
    M. Wilkins, J. Watson, F. Crick, 309*f*
Nociceptors, **1091**
Nodes, **740**
Nodes of Ranvier, **1056**
Nodules, **794**–95, 794*f*, 795*f*
Nomarski microscopy, 96*f*
Noncoding DNA, 433–34
Noncoding RNAs, 364–66
Noncompetitive inhibition, 156*f*
Nondisjunction, **297**
Nondividing state, cell, 239
Nonequilibrium model, **1211**
Nonheritable variation, 469*f*
Nonidentical DNA sequences, 437
Nonpolar amino acids, 79*f*
Nonpolar covalent bonds, **39**
Nonreciprocal crossovers, 298
Nonsense mutations, **345**, 345*f*
Nonshivering thermogenesis, 866
Nonsteroidal anti-inflammatory drugs
    (NSAIDS), 993
Nontemplate strand, DNA, 330
Nontropic hormones, 989
Nonvascular plants, 605*t*, 606–10
Noradrenaline, 991–92
Norepinephrine, **991**–92, **1060**
Normal range, **861**
Norm of reaction, **275**, 275*f*
Northern blotting, **409**
Northern coniferous forest, **1170***f*
No-till agriculture, **789**
Notochord, **699**, 699*f*, 880, **1030**
N-terminus, 80, 129*f*, 340, 357–58
Nuclear envelope, **102**
    animal cell, 100*f*
    endomembrane system and, 109*f*
    nucleus and, 103*f*
    plant cell, 101*f*
Nucleariids, **640**
Nuclear lamina, **102**, 103*f*
Nuclear magnetic resonance (NMR) spec-
    troscopy, 86
Nuclear matrix, 102
Nuclear transplantation, animal cloning and,
    412–15, 414*f*
Nuclease, **318**
Nucleic acid(s), **86**–89
    components of, 87*f*
    digestion, 887*f*
    DNA, 88, 89*f* (*see also* DNA (deoxyribonu-
        cleic acid))
    DNA and, 305
    RNA (*see* RNA (ribonucleic acid))

    role of, 86
    separating, with gel electrophoresis, 405*f*
    structure of, 87*f*, 88
    viroids as, 393
    viruses as molecules of, 382
Nucleic acid hybridization, **401**–3, 406
Nucleic acid probe, **402**–3
    detecting specific DNA sequence using, 402*f*
Nucleoid, **98**, 98*f*, **321**, 559
Nucleolus, **102**
    animal cell, 100*f*
    nucleus and, 103*f*
    plant cell, 101*f*
Nucleomorphs, 576
Nucleosides, 88
    components of, 87*f*
Nucleosomes, 320*f*
Nucleotide(s), 87*f*, **88**. *See also* DNA sequences
    amino acids specified by triplets of,
        329*f*, 330
    base-pair insertions and deletions as point
        mutation in, 345*f*, 346
    base-pair substitutions as point mutation in,
        344, 345*f*
    coding and noncoding, 334–35
    determining sequences of, in DNA, 408*f*, 409
    DNA and, 9*f*
    excision repair, 318*f*
    incorporation of, into DNA strand, 315*f*
    monomers, 88
    polymers, 88
    triplet code for, 330*f*
    variability, 469–70
Nucleus, atomic, **33**, 33*f*
Nucleus, eukaryotic cell, 98, **102**, 103*f*
    animal cell, 100*f*
    genetic information in, 102
    organismal development from
        differentiated, 413*f*
    plant cell, 101*f*
    reproductive cloning by transplantation
        of, 414*f*
    responses to cell signaling in, 218–20, 219*f*
    structure, 103*f*
Nurse, Paul, 92–93, 238, 240*f*
Nüsslein-Volhard, Chistiane, 371, 372–73, 372*f*
Nutrients
    cycling of, and decomposition, 1234
    cycling of, and role of prokaryotes, 570–71
    cycling of, in ecosystems, 6*f*, 1231, 1231*f*,
        1232–33*f*
    cycling of, in Hubbard Brook Experimental
        Forest, 1234–36
    enrichment experiment, 1227*t*
    enrichment of, by humans, 1236–37
    primary production in aquatic ecosystems
        and limitations of, 1226, 1227*f*
Nutrition, 896–97
    animal, **875**
    of fungi, 636–37
    major modes of, 564*t*
    plant, **785** (*see also* Plant nutrition)
    in prokaryotes, 564–65
    of protists, 576
    transgenic plants and, 422

O

Obesity, 894–96
    evolution and, 895–96
Ob gene, 895*f*
Obligate aerobes, **564**
Obligate anaerobes, **179**, **564**

Obligate mutualism, 1203
Occam's razor, 544
Oceans
    benthic zone, 1165*f*
    coral reefs, 1165*f*
    effect of, on climate, 49*f*
    effects of currents of, on climate, 1155*f*
    great ocean conveyer belt, 1155, 1155*f*
    pelagic zone, **1164***f*
    zonation in, 1160*f*, 1161
Ocelli, 1099–1100
Ocotillo, 778*f*
Octopuses, 680*f*
Odonata, 691*f*
Odorant receptors (ORs), 1098–99
Odorants, **1097**
Odum, Eugene, 1199
Okazaki fragments, **316**
Oleander, 778*f*
Oleic acid, 75*f*
Olfaction, **1097**, 1098, 1099*f*
Oligochaeta, 680*t*
Oligochaetes, 681–82. *See also* Earthworm
Oligodendrocytes, **1056**
Oligotrophic lakes, **1162***f*
Omasum, 892*f*
Ommatidia, **1100**
Omnivores, **875**
    diet and dentition in, 891*f*
Oncogenes, **374**, 374*f*, 375*f*, 376*f*
One gene–one enzyme hypothesis, 326
    bread mold and, 646
One gene–one polypeptide hypothesis, 326
One gene–one protein hypothesis, 326
*On the Origin of Species by Means of Natural Se-
    lection*, 14–15, 456–57, 457*f*
Onychophora, 669*f*
Oocyte, **1003**, 1007
Oogenesis, **1003**, **1007**
    in human females, 1009*f*
Oogonia, **1009***f*
Oomycetes, **588**–89, 588*f*
Oost, Bernard van, 970, 971*f*
Oparin, A. I., 508
Open circulatory system, 899–**900**, 900*f*
    arthropod, **685**
Open system, 144, 148*f*
Operant conditioning, **1127**, 1128*f*
Operator, **352**
Operculum, **708**, 708*f*
Operon model, 352
Operons, **352**
    basic concept of bacterial gene regulation and
        role of, 352–53
    negative gene regulation and repressible, and
        inducible, 353–55
    positive gene regulation and, 355–56
Ophiuroidea, 694*t*
Opiates, 42
    protein receptor for, in mammalian brain,
        1060–61, 1061*f*
Opisthokonts, **596**
    fungi as, **640**
Opposable thumb, **723**
Opposite phyllotaxy, 766
Opsin, **1102**
Opsonization, 946, 946*f*
Optical sectioning microscopy, 96*f*
Optic chiasm, **1104**
Optimal conditions, enzyme activity, 155
Optimal foraging model, **1133**–34
Oral cavity, **884**, 885*f*

Index

Index

Index

Index

Index

Index

PRIDE OF PLACE

PRIDE OF PLACE

BUILDING THE AMERICAN DREAM

ROBERT A. M. STERN

Assisted by Thomas Mellins and Raymond Gastil

HOUGHTON MIFFLIN COMPANY · BOSTON
AMERICAN HERITAGE · NEW YORK
1986

Page design by Marleen Adlerblum
Format design by Chermayeff &
Geismar Associates
Picture editing by Sabra Moore

*Library of Congress Cataloging in
Publication Data*
Stern, Robert A. M.
Pride of place.
1. Architecture — United States —
Themes, motives.   I. Title.
NA705.S74   1986   720'.973   85-27342
ISBN 0-395-36696-8

Printed in the United States of
America

R 10 9 8 7 6 5 4 3 2 1

HALF-TITLE PAGE:
A nineteenth-century engraving of
a conservatory at Golden Gate Park
in San Francisco

TITLE PAGE:
New York City at night, a panorama
of light and color

EPIGRAPH:
A whaling captain's house built in
the early nineteenth century on
Nantucket Island, Massachusetts

Contents

The shapes arise!
Shapes of factories, arsenals, foundries, markets,
Shapes of . . . bridges, vast frameworks, girders, arches . . .
Shapes of Democracy total, result of centuries,
Shapes ever projecting other shapes,
Shapes of turbulent . . . cities,
Shapes of the friends and home-givers of the whole earth,
Shapes bracing the earth and braced with the whole earth.

Walt Whitman, "Song of the Broad-Axe," *Leaves of Grass*

1 The Search for a Usable Past

Mount Vernon, built by George Washington in the mid-eighteenth century, remains the most emulated building in America. The two-storey columned porch is the most outstanding feature of the house. Added in 1787, it completed the perfect house portrait, connecting Washington's private realm to the public space of nature.

Pride of Place is the story of the way a young nation has built its country. We as Americans have faced a particular challenge in our lives and in our architecture. Architecture, like all culture, grows out of a people's past — out of shared traditions and conventions — altered and reinterpreted to reflect circumstances and interests of the present. But in America, ties to ancient cultures have been broken. We have had not only to make our world on a vast, unbuilt continent but also to make a history for ourselves.

Our buildings tell the story of the great energy we have devoted to inventing and reinventing our past. In the country of the self-made man, aspirations to reinvent personal as well as national history are high. The story of our architecture, then, is also in large part the story of individuals — of strong-willed, impassioned clients and of individual architects with particular visions. Each work of architecture is colored by the dreams and experiences of its creators. In a similar way, my telling of the story of American architecture is colored by my experiences as an American and an architect, by the way I studied architecture, by the people and buildings that have influenced me, and by the dreams they have helped me dream. Before beginning the tale, then, let me introduce the teller.

I became an architect because I loved the architecture of my native city, New York. When I was growing up, the skyscrapers of Manhattan seemed to me the peaks of an astonishing mountain range: fabulous buildings — the Woolworth, the Chrysler, the Empire State — were wonderfully intermeshed in my schoolboy's imagination with images of King Kong and the experience of Fifth Avenue shopping sprees. From my childhood home in Brooklyn in the 1940s and 1950s, the proud towers across the East River seemed part of an Emerald City. They were my personal Oz — a great movie set through which I could wander freely. As I walked around lower Manhattan, the thrill I felt at the sight of those skyscrapers rising to transform the streets into canyons was like what the first pioneers to see the Grand Canyon must have known.

New York is still my city. I live there. I work there. The screeching, graffiti-laden subway trains, the seemingly endless, low-lying sprawl of the outer borough's hundred-year-old suburbia, as well as the proud, shimmering towers that rise above the bay to form Manhattan's skyline — all are part of the scene that continues to thrill and inspire me. Of all the places that I love, I am most proud, as an architect and an American, of this great city.

I always wanted to be an architect, to make buildings like those I saw in the

This view of lower Manhattan, circa 1907, was taken from Jersey City. Ernest Flagg's slender Singer Tower (*center*) dominated the skyline until it was replaced by the anonymous, boxlike buildings of the Modernist world.

Manhattan skyline of the twenties and thirties, soaring towers filled with dreams of modern power married to ancient form. I loved these buildings for what they were and for what they aspired to. What I couldn't understand was why the new buildings of the fifties were so drained of quality and of aspiration, why they were so bland, so inarticulate, and so boring. To me they seemed like the empty boxes the original skyscrapers would have come in. These new, boxlike buildings were the same at the bottom as they were at the top, the same on one side as on the other. Their anonymous window-walls suggested neither joy nor dignity in work. Sadly, even the swaggering corporate capitalism that created them and the astonishing hierarchies they housed had repressed itself into a bland uniformity. I had dreamed of seeing new buildings rise like foothills to the mountain ranges of the 1920s towers, in the manner of the stepping masses of buildings like Buchman and Kahn's 120 Wall Street. Instead, I found a new generation of insensitive, uniform boxes that interfered with formerly grand relationships between older buildings and seemed to contradict all that had come before.

Just what had happened? I soon learned that it wasn't cost-cutting accountants or dimwitted architects who gave us the bland box, but rather a generation of inspired idealists. I learned that to understand the demise of a great and unique American building type and the dreams it embodied, we had to look to Europe just before and after the First World War. For it was there that a number of dreamers and visionaries, disenchanted with an old order and with what was felt to be moribund tradition, began impatiently to plan a new world. Their spirit was captured in the drawings of Antonio Sant'Elia, a young Italian architect. Drawn just before World War I, they show his dream-vision of an American city, a nirvana of widely spaced towers served by avenues of swift-moving traffic and high-flown bridges. While the Europeans were inspired by the futuristic images of American cities projected in 1908 by H. M. Petit, for King's *Views of New York,* the cathartic minimalism of the technologically and functionally determined architecture that Sant'Elia and others drew was very different from its American sources. The Europeans admired New York's Grand Central Terminal (1903–13) only for its engineering and circulation patterns, ignoring the Classical masonry shell that was so fundamental to the terminal's success as a gateway to America's greatest metropolis.

Disillusionment with the European city was even more intense following World War I. In both Germany and France, young architects yearned to forget the past and build a new order. In Berlin and at the Bauhaus in Dessau, Germany, artists in many disciplines devoted themselves to developing new forms innocent of all preexisting conventions. Ludwig Mies van der Rohe's Berlin designs confound traditional notions of space and mass, with extruded crystalline towers rising free from their physical settings. In France, Charles-Édouard Jeanneret-Gris, a Swiss-born painter and polemicist, self-styled as Le Corbusier in his architectural incarnation, celebrated managerial and technological efficiency in an idealized architecture that took its formal inspiration from machines. For Le Corbusier the street life of Paris, where he had settled during the First World War, was intolerable. In his proposals for a new architecture of perfect circulation, he wrote: "Cafés and places for recreation would no longer be that fungus which eats up the pavements."[1] His 1921–22 "Plan for a Contemporary City of Three Million" and his 1925 "Plan Voisin de Paris" show boulevards uncompromised by the clutter of grocery-carrying housewives and sidewalk-café sitters. He planned a Paris as efficient and uniform and impersonal as the new American Ford motorcars — in fact, as efficient as the assembly lines of the Ford factories themselves.

The explanations for America's open-armed reception of the antihistoricist ideals of Le Corbusier and Mies are various. Most important, perhaps, was the fact of the Depression, which had broken American self-confidence much as World War I had shaken Europe's. Bare-boned, functionalist Modernism may have been a tonic to the luxurious architectural expression of a consumer society that seemed, at least in the 1930s, to have failed. The puritanism of Mies's and Le Corbusier's visions, then, appealed to fundamental American values that had been debunked by the generation following the war. In addition, the allure of the latest European trend — a constant in the history of American architecture — was greatly enhanced when leaders of the European movement, refugees from the rise of Nazism and the ensuing war, arrived to practice in America. They were received by much of the architectural community as cultural ambassadors, bringing gifts of authentic twentieth-century culture to the historically referential colonies. Mies ended up in Chicago at the Illinois Institute of Technology, while Walter Gropius, founder of the Bauhaus, settled at Harvard. Both enjoyed enormous prestige among younger architects, who helped translate their visions of a brave new world into a rationalized, functionally articulate building style.

By the time I went to architecture school at Yale, the antihistoricist, functionally and technologically determined Modernism of these architects was institutionalized as the only legitimate, authentic form of *Modernism*. I was encouraged to believe that the proud towers of New York were little more than antediluvian artifacts of a spurious romanticism and that my dream of adding new pinnacles to Manhattan's skyline was a childish one from which I should awake. A new postwar world had dawned, I was reminded, and just as I must learn to love the bomb — or at least live with it — I must learn to love an architecture that exalted function and structural technique as the determinants of significant form.

Fortunately for me, there were some great teachers at Yale — Vincent Scully, Louis Kahn, Paul Rudolph — who saw beyond the rigid doctrines of my era. In a sense, the very buildings in which I was taught were my instructors. For the campus of Yale stands as contradictory evidence to the assertion that traditional buildings lack value and meaning and that it is impossible to adapt old forms to contemporary purposes. Its most representative portions were built between 1918 and 1940. Largely Gothic in styling, they evoke the medieval campuses of Cambridge and Oxford universities in England. Yale's campus is an inspiring, remarkably coherent collection of academic and residential buildings, so skillfully inserted into the city of New Haven's Colonial gridiron plan that the illusion of a place of pastoral contemplation is held in near-perfect balance with urban vitality. Yet the campus that I admired and that clearly continued to serve and even inspire students and faculty was given the silent treatment by most of my teachers, who seemed to think that its buildings were neither good nor bad but existed in a kind of limbo of nonarchitecture. Buildings like Egerton Swartwout's Old Art Gallery of 1927, which contained the art and architecture library as well as many of our classrooms, weren't even discussed. It was as if nothing about their design had anything to teach us. But the lessons were there for those who would learn them. With walls thick with moldings, detail, and plastic complexity, they met the ground softly, so to speak, and there were benches on the street where you could sit and read the paper. Such design represented an architecture of civic responsibility, in which each building was about more than itself, about more, that is, than function and constructional technique. It was an approach that regarded each building as a character in the ongoing drama of culture.

Vincent Scully, the historian and critic, was one teacher at Yale who could make the great buildings of the past and present come alive as a continuum of artistic passion and cultural concern. He taught me that the sometimes grand, sometimes indescribably modest buildings and places I knew and admired were architecture after all: the shingled summer cottages of Long Island beach towns were part of a tradition that had reached its highest expression in the 1870s and 1880s in Newport, Rhode Island; the Gothic quadrangles of Yale were as rigorously planned — if not more so — than any suburban office building by Skidmore, Owings & Merrill; the towers of lower Manhattan were not only the inspiration for the European Modernists but also had value in their own right. Most important, Scully constantly reminded his students that architecture is a civilized conversation across time, across continents, across cultures. It is an art with its own culture, but not one hermetically sealed against life. It is a social art, with forms that can mean

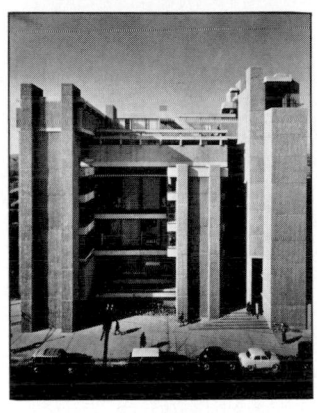

Top. Louis Kahn's 1953 addition (left) to Egerton Swartwout's Old Art Gallery (1927) is starkly reductive. However, its contrasting use of sheer and solid façades and its geometrical clarity synthesized Modernist and traditional values.

Bottom. The vertical elements and jagged silhouette of Paul Rudolph's Art Gallery and Design Center (1963) evoke Yale's Gothic-style buildings, thereby more ambitiously proclaiming architecture a dialogue between the past and present.

Overleaf. "This log will cut forty thousand shingles." The ability to transform abundant natural resources has contributed to the qualities of a uniquely American architecture.

one thing in a totalitarian system and another in a democracy. It is a reality and a dream.

Louis Kahn was no longer teaching in New Haven when I began to study architecture there, but his ideas and ideals were still strongly felt. They were sustained by brilliant students of his still at Yale, such as Jaquelin Robertson, who has continued to play an influential role in the evolution of contemporary architecture. Kahn's visions and struggles were keenly represented in his Art Gallery and Design Center (1953), which housed the school's drafting studios. Starkly reductive though it is in many ways, brutally scaled, and with an almost mute, blank-walled façade turned toward the street, the building nonetheless powerfully, if clumsily, pointed the way toward a renewed sense of architectural purpose. For unlike its orthodox Modernist predecessors, the expression of the building's structure was not the prime intent of its design. Rather, structure was secondary to the composition of its massing, surfaces, and details. Though Kahn's architectural vocabulary is emptily reductive compared to Swartwout's, his contrasting use of glazed and solid gridded façades and his design's geometrical clarity reveal a sincere effort to recapture traditional values of monumentality, urbanism, and architectural detail. Kahn, who had been trained as a Classicist but had later embraced the structural and functional determinism of Modernism, was trying to begin again in the middle of the twentieth century by synthesizing the two approaches.

In the drafting studios, Paul Rudolph, the architecture department's brilliant chairman, insisted, as Scully did in the lecture hall, that for architecture to succeed it must aspire to more than mere utilitarianism. While in New Haven I was privileged to see Rudolph struggle with the design of his masterwork, the Art and Architecture Building (1963), for which he was, in a sense, both architect and client. To connect with the best of modern architecture, Rudolph compressed the designs of three buildings by Le Corbusier and one by Frank Lloyd Wright into a densely compacted composition of deliberately crude reinforced concrete. Though rugged in its massing and in the texture of its ribbed concrete walls, the Art and Architecture Building is less primordial than Kahn's art gallery. Rudolph also attempted to connect with the past that defined the context: Yale's Oxbridge-style buildings. The vertical elements suggesting towers give the building the sort of upward thrust reminiscent of the spires of the campus's Gothic buildings; its jagged silhouette against the sky evokes their crenelations. But while its gestures toward Yale's traditional Gothicism are much more overt than Kahn's, the final effect is not so engaging. Rudolph's ambition to connect the building with things and ideas outside its own utilitarian purposes, however, was far more impassioned, and the design compels our respect even as it rejects our potentially admiring advances. Rudolph yearned to make significant public architecture in the grand manner, and his ultimate failure to win the affections of the building's users and the public is the stuff of tragedy. Loved and hated from its inception, the building has been condemned as a blatant expression of the university's arrogant power — a group of students tried to burn it down in 1969 — but it has outlived its critics to succeed as a powerful landmark, marking a boundary both of Yale and of New Haven's original nine-square grid.

However tentatively, Kahn and Rudolph proclaimed architecture as an ongoing dialogue across time between the present and the past. In this they were

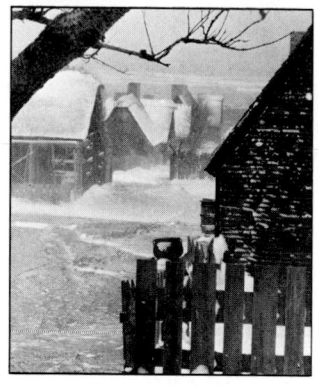

Top. Stanford White's granite Classical temple provides an appropriate shelter for Plymouth Rock (here covered in snow), the "foundation stone of the American dream."

Bottom. The buildings on Main Street at reconstructed Plimoth Plantation adapted Old World building techniques to the harsher New England conditions.

pioneers, seeking a way out of a problem inherent in the very structure of Modernism, which fiercely negated past reference in favor of a single-minded orientation to the present. For to me it seems impossible that enduring art can be founded on a negative statement. Art requires an assertion of belief. Even the iconoclastic aesthetic experiments of Le Corbusier and of Mies, both of whom railed against historical representation in architecture, were positive in their glorification of the machine. But the machine — taken either as a formal phenomenon or *objet type,* as Le Corbusier would have it, or as a means of production rendering individuality obsolete — is inadequate to architecture's traditional task of place-making. As a result, almost from its inception, machine-style Modernism faced a crisis of representation. For most Modernists, traditional architectural styles were irrelevant because they did not represent the tumultuous issues of the day and because they were ingrained in a bourgeois culture that Modernists professed to abhor. Yet in banishing history, Modernists left themselves little with which to evolve a new style. At first Le Corbusier and Mies sought to subvert the grid system of Classical composition with diagonal and curved plans that were intended to represent the randomness of everyday life. The ramp, the strip window, the pipe, and the pipe rail were served up as posthistorical elements to replace the columns and pediments of Classical representation. But Le Corbusier and Mies were soon frustrated by the reductiveness of this invented vocabulary and conscious of the futility of an art based on the eradication of the past. Their best work thereafter sought to reconnect contemporary art with the past. For Le Corbusier, this culminated in his lyrically evocative mature, post–World War II work, such as the highly associational Church of Notre-Dame-du-Haut at Ronchamp in France. Unfortunately, while Le Corbusier struggled in his architecture to come to grips with the past, his polemical Modernist texts proliferated, inspiring legions of dragon-slaying young architects to ignore their own architectural traditions as well as the lessons the master himself had quietly learned.

What I began to understand at Yale was that architecture is a narrative art, and that architectural style is analogous to poetic diction. While straightforward prose may serve the purposes of communication, it does not necessarily give much pleasure. "Just the facts, ma'am," may be enough for hardboiled detectives and investigative reporters from big city dailies, but most of us need a metaphor, a simile, or even a pun here and there to engage our attention and delight our imaginations. In evoking convention and tradition, these elements help us reaffirm our moment in time by placing it within a historical continuum, assuring us that we are not an isolated accident of existence. Storytellers since the Greek tragedians have embroidered their tales with references to works of the past in order to connect with tradition. The complexity of a narrative, its allusiveness, resonance, and aggrandizement of the reader's own experience, raises the statement of a simple literary theme to the realm of art. When Louis Sullivan, considering the stridently American architectural proposition of the skyscraper in 1896, declared, "Form ever follows function," he still aspired to a complex architectural narrative and condemned materialist solutions: "Problem: How should we impart to this sterile pile [the tall office building], this crude, harsh, brutal agglomeration, this stark, staring exclamation of eternal style, the graciousness of those higher forms of sensibility and culture that rest on the lower and fiercer passions?"[2]

Many artists and philosophers of the modern age have attempted to escape the complexities of history and build a utopian dreamworld of the future, with forms deliberately shaped to be free of all relationships to those inherited from the past. But most of these efforts have quickly become as dated as the futurism of Buck Rogers's twenty-fifth century. Those dreams for a better future that have endured, in architecture as in other arts, are those that have reshaped the familiar strands of inherited culture in order to open for us new visions of the present and new hope for the future. While great architecture must, it seems to me, reverberate with inherent fitness to purpose and fineness of construction, it must also resonate with an external commentary, a narrative, and a dream, drawn up from the wellsprings of culture by the imaginings of the architect in order to help realize his own and his patrons' conception of the present and the future.

Art cannot be the product of spontaneous combustion; art always comes from other art. The ways in which one generation puts to use the forms and symbols of the past are fundamental not only to the progress of art but to its existence as a language capable of conveying and continuing meanings through and across time. Like a biological culture, the culture of art is a living substance, and only by working with inherited culture can an artist hope to evolve a new synthesis. The *continuity* of imagery gives art much of its meaning; it is the source of its *intelligibility*. What gives art its *vitality* is simply and ineffably the capacity of individuals to interpret and transform the language to express new ideas or restate old ones in a compelling way. I believe that architecture, that is, the art of building, reaches lyrical heights when it embodies some sense of otherness, something beyond mere bricks and mortar — when it builds a dream.

The American dream has always depended on the dialogue between the present and the past. In our architecture, as in all our other arts — indeed, as in our political and social culture as a whole — ours has been a struggle to formulate and sustain a usable past. *Pride of Place* is the story of how Americans, confronted with the overwhelming natural history of the new continent, have constructed a human past of commensurate age and authenticity. Architecture, as an art of materialism and myth, has played a leading role in that struggle. And our greatest architects, working with individual clients of great conviction and vision, have traditionally taken this task upon themselves — to interpret the past in its fullest complexity in order to turn the assemblage of bricks and mortar into art, to lift mere building into the realm of architecture.

For a while we seem to have lost that capacity, but we can bring it back again. Contemporary developments suggest that ours is an age of architectural excellence; it may be more than that — I think that we are in the midst of a new era of dreaming, of making art out of circumstance, of preserving the special places we have carved out on this continent and of making new ones as powerfully resonant as those we made in the past.

This has been my story and my hope and dream for the future of American architecture. The story itself must now be told, the story of *Pride of Place*.

"The hideous and desolate wilderness"[3] of Cape Cod that William Bradford saw from the *Mayflower* may have seemed in some way an appropriately biblical setting for a mission intent on establishing a community along strict scriptural lines. To Bradford's wife, Dorothy, however, so far from Eden did this wilderness

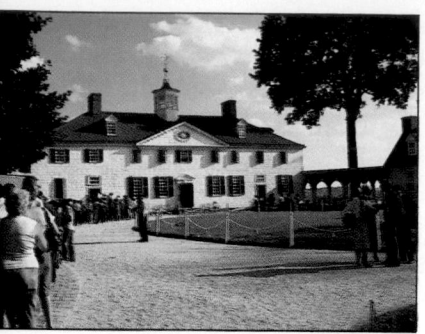

Mount Vernon is visited by one million tourists every year. George Washington's Classical estate has become a national shrine, an important symbol of our relatively recent birth as a nation and our continued national unity.

on the horizon appear to be that she leapt overboard in an apparent suicide.

In architecture, the harsh circumstances of the new country immediately began to play their part. When the first ninety-eight settlers disembarked from the *Mayflower* in 1620, they put up houses like those they had known in England: exposed-frame, wattle-and-daub cottages covered with thatch roofs. But very quickly they began to adapt what they knew to what they discovered and the house forms of Elizabethan England were adapted to better suit conditions in the New World. Efficiency was stressed from the start: carpenters figured out how to build a comfortable house during the brief building season, using the fewest men in the least amount of time. With lighter, shorter beams and simple joinery, houses could be more readily assembled and required just four men instead of the whole town. To provide a more efficient distribution of heat, the hearth, traditionally located at the side of the house in England, became more frequently placed at the center. Materials changed as well. Clapboard was employed to make the houses warmer. Thatch roofs, a commonplace in England where wood was in short supply, were banned in Plymouth in 1629 as a fire hazard; shingles were used instead, made from the abundant local timber that also evoked the clay tiles used to sheathe cottages in Kent.

As the Pilgrims transformed the vernacular of their English homeland to soften American conditions, they exhibited a direct approach to problems of craft and technology that would become the hallmark of American building. As such, the Plymouth experience is a model of cultural expression, in which civilized action is always undertaken within the constraints of history and circumstance. But alterations of the English model were to some degree troubling deviations from the familiar in a strange world built, as John Donne wrote to the founders of Jamestown in 1622, to be "but the suburb of the Old World."[4] Even in the eighteenth century, when Georgian styling began to replace the medieval models followed in the seventeenth century, Colonial architecture was still but a provincial manifestation of English trends, caught between the scholarly refinement of the Old World and the untutored primitivism of the New. The "split personality" engendered by ingenuity and invention in the face of challenge, on the one hand, and the aspiration to maintain a connection with a more ancient culture, on the other, have been the source both of America's strength and its sense of cultural inferiority ever since.

When the English colonists burned the bridges between Europe and America in 1776 and declared their political independence, they set in motion the world's first wholly modern culture — not a relatively coherent culture like that of Italy or France, gradually evolved from the tribal origins of a unified, shared past, but a complex, heterogeneous admixture held together by allegiance to a flag, a few sheets of paper declaring a new nation, a dream of continental empire, and a conviction that the New World represented the last best hope of the Old. Americans, suddenly a new breed, were effectively without a past, without a history. Politically self-invented, America felt a painful need to forge an identity for itself. Nothing could be explained as native, vernacular, or instinctual. As the critic and historian Perry Miller has written, "Being American is not something to be inherited so much as something to be achieved."[5]

The longevity and strength of this will to explain ourselves in the present by defining or redefining our past could be seen three hundred years after the

Mount Vernon's modified Palladian design has spawned countless imitations. Among them, *top to bottom:* Yellow Top Farms, Long Island, New York; Howard Johnson's, Mineola, New York; and the Ewing Ranch from TV's "Dallas."

Pilgrims alighted at Plymouth Rock. For the tricentennial of the landing, the National Society of Colonial Dames sponsored the building of a shelter over what has come to be seen as the foundation stone of the American dream. The distinguished architectural firm of McKim, Mead, and White designed, not a reproduction of the rude huts like those of the first settlers, but rather a grand Classical temple built of granite. The Colonial Dames and the architects wanted a monument that represented the dream of an America greater than its modest beginnings as a new England. For by 1920, flush with its triumphant role in the First World War, America was apparently well on its way toward achieving its destiny as a new Rome, a continental empire that much of the world believed was Western humanism's last best hope.

The magnificence of the temple erected over Plymouth Rock is also a testament to the importance we as Americans invest in the symbols of our relatively recent beginnings. Even more striking is the status accorded to a relatively modest house on the Potomac River in Virginia. Visited by one million tourists every year, Mount Vernon, George Washington's Classical estate, is arguably the Lenin's tomb of American architecture, the pilgrimage point that by consensus has come to represent our birth as a nation and our continued national unity. As Henry James observed, Mount Vernon is "our supreme example of the rich interference of association. Association does, at Mount Vernon, simply what it likes with us — it is of so beautiful and noble a sort; and to this end it begins by making us unfit to say whether or no we would in its absence have noticed the house for any material grace at all."[6]

What "material grace" there is to be found at Mount Vernon draws on the designs of the Renaissance architect Andrea Palladio, whose villas in the Veneto had been built for Venetian noblemen seeking escape from their economically and politically troubled city. Palladio's clients, like our first president, were gentlemen farmers. The villas are distinguished by perfect order and symmetry in their plans, carefully proportioned Classical columns and pediments, and, frequently, the graceful gathering of dependencies into extended building compositions. Palladio's designs, published in his *Four Books of Architecture,* were enormously influential in England, where they were adapted to native building materials and motifs. The resulting style, known as Georgian, synthesized typical English elements such as frequently spaced, vertically proportioned windows and the use of red brick. Palladio's designs, with their high casements and central halls, were even better suited for the mild, humid climate of Virginia than they were for England.

Washington adjusted the grandiose visions of published Palladian designs to practical concerns. Wood cladding was milled to look like stone. The grandeur of Mount Vernon's porch colonnade, pedimented entrance, and embracing hyphenated plan is undercut by the casual construction of the house, with its expeditiously disposed window patterns. An enormous pediment at the entrance seems to have been proportioned at such a large scale in an attempt to unify the slightly skewed placement of windows and doors, legacies of the house's renovations and interior rearrangements. The pediment is so large, however, that it appears almost disconnected from the house, as though it might sail out from it. The greatest architectural feature of Mount Vernon is the grand double-height porch overlooking a bend in the Potomac River. Washington added the porch in 1787, just before his election to the presidency. It quickly became a front porch for the nation, the place where he received his official guests in the middle landscape between the private realm of the house and the public space of nature. As both a public and private outdoor space, and above all as a frame for America's seemingly unbounded landscape, Washington's square-columned loggia completed a perfect house portrait, raising a private dwelling to the status of a public institution as the private individual became the nation's first citizen.

As both villa and village — with its curving colonnades serving to link a number of dependencies — Mount Vernon raises critical questions about American architecture and planning. In fact, it is not much as architecture. At once ordered and disordered, formal in its intentions and ragtag in its realization, it is an expedient patchwork of high aesthetic ambition and relatively modest circumstances. It is also the most widely emulated building in America: we see it in everything from Howard Johnson's roadside restaurants to the Ewing ranch on TV's "Dallas."

In a sense it is ironic that Mount Vernon has become so widespread a model for American building, for it was not Washington but his peer Thomas Jefferson who self-consciously undertook a search for an architectural expression for the new nation. Palladio was Jefferson's architectural hero, and he carefully studied the *Four Books of Architecture*. He was appalled by the divergence from the original models not only in Colonial copies but in the far grander English examples as well. After a visit to England in 1785, he declared, "Their architecture is in the most wretched style I ever saw, not meaning to except America, where it is bad, nor here in Virginia, where it is worse than in any other part of America I have seen."[7] In 1767, at the age of twenty-four, Jefferson set out to put his studies into practice, designing a house to be built on a hilltop across the Rivanna River from his father's plantation, looking westward to the Indian country beyond the Piedmont. The decision to build on a hilltop site, despite numerous practical problems including a shortage of water, reflected Jefferson's soaring imagination and belief in the nearly limitless possibilities inherent in the vast continental expanse.

The name Jefferson chose for his new plantation — Monticello — and to some extent its siting, paid homage to Palladio, who recommended that a house be built in an "elevated and cheerful" place (a choice he deemed second only to a site along a river).[8] "Monticello" translates as "little mountain"; but where Palladio would have applied the term to hillocks such as those along the Venetian coastline, Jefferson used it to describe a looming eight-hundred-foot promontory that was, despite its height, merely a foothill to the mountains that lay beyond. In the New World, even Arcadia was superscaled. Jefferson cropped and terraced the hill, planting gardens and orchards that contrasted with the surrounding forest to create a village for his "family," which by 1774 included twenty-nine slaves assigned to the house.

Jefferson began to sketch the original Monticello in 1767. Conventional though the design was in comparison to the great work of Jefferson's maturity, it nonetheless hinted at the vivacity of its owner-architect's imagination. From the first, Jefferson was after something very special: though his budget was small, his artistic ambitions were unbounded. Monticello was to surpass the typical provincial Georgian houses of the Virginia planters and to pay aesthetic homage to Palladio. Indeed, Jefferson's designs for the first Monticello stretched the fashionable Palladianism of the day to its limits: its proportions were

Jefferson began to sketch Monticello in 1767. After he saw Roman architecture in France, however, the early version, as represented in this 1770 drawing, gave way to a more refined, dignified design.

extraordinarily refined; the interlocking polygonal rooms of its plan more interesting and varied than the typical boxlike rooms of Georgian houses; the details more scholarly than in the typical plantation house. The first Monticello impressed the urbane Marquis de Chastellux enough for him to remark after a visit in 1782, "Mr. Jefferson is the first American who has consulted the fine arts to know how he should shelter himself from the weather."[9]

The original Monticello reflected Jefferson's dissatisfaction with the taste for Colonial Georgian architecture, which, he stated in his *Notes on Virginia*, published in 1782, "seems to have its maledictions over this land."[10] Yet his own design would seem completely provincial to him once he had experienced the treasures of France, where he served as American Minister Plenipotentiary between 1784 and 1789. In France, Jefferson was able to study masterworks of Western architecture first hand and share ideas with the great architects of his time. Jefferson's sojourn in France liberated his imagination, allowing him to fully realize his architectural genius.

Even before returning to Virginia, Jefferson indelibly stamped his ideas on the civic architecture of the new democracy by proposing that the design for the new capitol building for the State of Virginia at Richmond be based on a Roman model. Soon after his arrival in France, Jefferson was asked by the Directors of Public Buildings in Virginia "to consult an able Architect on a plan fit for a Capitol."[11] Realizing the importance of the capitol as the first significant public building to be undertaken after Independence — potentially the first public manifestation of the new nation's cultural sophistication — Jefferson took it upon himself to act as that "able Architect." To evoke the authority of a purely Classical design, he chose to copy a Roman temple, the so-called Maison Carrée, believed to be the best-preserved exemplar of ancient architecture. He knew the temple only from the illustrations in Palladio's *Four Books of Architecture* and in *Antiquités du Midi de la France* (1778) by the French architect Charles-Louis Clérisseau. After conferring with Clérisseau, he altered the temple's design significantly, for both functional

In his design of Monticello, Jefferson was influenced by the work of the Italian late-Renaissance architect Andrea Palladio, as evidenced by this plan from Palladio's *Four Books of Architecture*, published in 1581.

Right. With Monticello, Thomas Jefferson sought to articulate an architectural expression for the new nation. The principal façade of the building presents his noble, if somewhat grand, vision in the form of Doric columns, a Roman dome, and long parallel wings, which project in a U shape to embrace the expansive lawn.

and aesthetic reasons. When he returned to America in 1789, Jefferson saw the half-finished edifice and reacted with optimism: "Whenever it shall be finished with the proper ornaments belonging to it (which shall not be in this age); it will be worthy of being exhibited alongside the most celebrated remains of antiquity."[12] The exigent building, finished in 1797, never acquired the ornaments Jefferson desired, but it was nonetheless the purest contemporary example of Classical architecture in the world. By the very authority of its antique associations and the monumental dignity of its design, Jefferson had succeeded in giving the new republic its first identifiable architectural form: not a provincial version of a royal palace but a pure replication of a temple, which elevated statecraft to the symbolic status of religion. As Fiske Kimball has written, "The columns were used not only as elements of intrinsic magnificence, but as trophies of the Classical culture of the builders. The portico was to be a frontispiece to all Virginia."[13]

In reaching back to Classical sources, Jefferson also set American architecture on an independent course, free of associations with English Georgian architecture. Jefferson intended not only to establish a new aesthetic for the democratic nation but to put the very issue of aesthetics on sure ground. Through Classicism Jefferson struggled to bring together the order of things as they might be and the order of things as they are. His dream of a democratic empire on the American continent was as much a product of an eclectic imagination as of an idealistic

Left. Frank Lloyd Wright's studio-home Taliesin, in Spring Green, Wisconsin, is completely integrated with the surrounding landscape. Nestled into the brow of a hill, its roughhewn stone façades, low-slung roofs, and insistent horizontality blur the distinction between the manmade and the natural.

Right. This perspective view of Taliesin drawn by Frank Lloyd Wright around 1911 was later reproduced in a Japanese publication. Wright's appreciation for Japanese architecture was manifest in the horizontal forms of his own buildings.

米國ウイスコンシン州スプリング、グリーン、に於けるライト氏邸宅（其の一）鳥瞰圖
Home of Frank Lloyd Wright, Spring Green, Wisconsin.

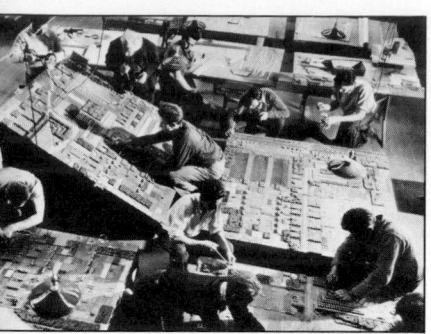

Wright transformed his studio-home into a school of architecture in 1932. It provided students with an ideal environment in which to practice their craft and to live by the visionary principles taught by their master.

nature. To a friend, Jefferson wrote that America, and her architecture, constituted not so much a new beginning as a new synthesis: "I know nothing so charming as our own country. The learned say it is a new creation; and I believe them; not for their reasons, but because it is made on an improved plan. Europe is a first idea, a crude production, before the maker knew his trade, or had made up his mind as to what he wanted."[14]

Jefferson's Paris sojourn, though motivated by affairs of state, opened his eyes wide to the breadth of European culture and introduced him to the most sophisticated architecture of his day, exemplified by the writings and designs of his confidant Clérisseau, as well as the work of the revolutionaries of French Classicism, Claude-Nicolas Ledoux and Étienne-Louis Boullée. Europe stimulated him to rebuild Monticello as an American symbol; in so doing, he transformed an elegant country house into an architectural epiphany. Whereas the first Monticello was the work of a devoted student of Palladio, the second version would be that of a colleague across time. Jefferson's direct exposure to Roman architecture made him aware for the first time of the degree to which it had inspired Palladio. From that point on, William Pierson has written, "Palladio shifted from his role of teacher to that of fellow Romanist."[15]

While Jefferson relied in part on his brief encounters with the work of French architects and with the remains of ancient Classical monuments, the facts of geography confined most of his architectural investigations to the pages of books. It is therefore not surprising that he became a rather eclectic designer, who incorporated conventional elements in a synthesis that was frequently inspired if not entirely resolved. In this sense his was the paradigm for American architecture. For it is not in the specific elements of Jefferson's Monticello, or of his equally compelling University of Virginia campus, discussed in chapter 2, that we look for originality; rather, Jefferson's genius is to be found in the way those elements were put together. From the first, American architects would not invent a new language; but they would struggle to say new things.

Jefferson's reconfiguration of Monticello took the form of a Classical temple surmounted by a noble if somewhat incongruous dome, from which two long parallel wings, tucked into the hillside, project to embrace a U-shaped courtyard. He covered the wings with nearly flat roofs so that, at first glance, they seem little more than terraced walkways leading to isolated gazebo-like dependencies that appear to punctuate a great lawn. The design offers commanding views of the distant landscape, which for Jefferson was a continental garden unparalleled in its beauty and promise.

Like Palladio's Villa Barbaro, Monticello's Classical design is rendered in the local argot. Palladio used red tile roofs and stucco walls; Jefferson covered his roofs in tin and built his walls of red brick trimmed in white-painted wood. Jefferson's artistic daring, and his amateurism, were most vividly manifested in his placement of the low Roman dome atop the pedimented Doric portico that forms the entrance — in effect making the house-temple into a church as well. (Both the Pantheon in Rome and Palladio's chapel at the Villa Barbaro used a similar device.) The dome is not part of a grand, lofty space in the house but merely shelters what Jefferson called his "sky room," a largely inaccessible space raised from mundane status as an attic to a magnificently purposeless place of meeting, far beyond the ordinary ambitions of a wilderness house. The construction of the crowning dome proved

Wright is seated at one of the six grand pianos at Taliesin. The huge hearth was placed in the center of the house as a monument to family life in America.

that the grand ideas of Classicism could be realized by the rude carpentry of the frontier. However, the overscaled detailing that Jefferson used to articulate his design — based in part on the ancient Temple of Vesta, with a baselike wainscoting large enough to support columns four times as high as the room itself — suggests that his ideas were sometimes too big for their reality. As Jaquelin Robertson has observed, Jefferson's giantism of scale and detail seems to be his way of saying that "out here in the wilderness, I must exaggerate Classical reference or no one will hear me."[16]

For forty years, Monticello's peaceful hilltop resounded with the blows of construction hammers, evidence of a restless mind that took as much pleasure in the process as the product. As Jefferson reportedly said to a visitor in 1809, "Architecture is my chief delight, and putting up and pulling down one of my favorite amusements."[17] To unravel Monticello's complexities is not only to fathom Jefferson's dialogue between ideal reason and empirical fact but also to understand the unresolved psychological complexities of its architect. Though a monument to the agrarian republic of Jefferson's imagination and to the family farmers he considered the moral concomitant of democracy, Monticello was also a temple dedicated to its architect — a self-portrait in bricks and mortar. For all its aspirations to the magisterial resolution of national culture, Monticello, like the best American houses that followed it, celebrates the eccentricities of its strong-willed owner's personality. It reveals the obsessive nature of its builder as he relentlessly invented and reinvented himself and his environment at the edge of civilization.

Over a century later, Frank Lloyd Wright's work on the studio-home he called Taliesin, at Spring Green, Wisconsin, sought to rival Jefferson's Monticello as autobiography and as blueprint for America's architectural and cultural destiny.

Wright was born in 1867, one hundred years after Jefferson broke ground for the first Monticello. Before he began work on Taliesin in 1911, he had been living in Oak Park, a Chicago suburb, for more than twenty years and had designed over one hundred houses as well as a handful of important large buildings, including an office building for the Larkin Company in Buffalo, New York (1904), and the Unity Temple in Oak Park (1906). In 1909 he decided to leave his wife, Catherine, and his six children in Oak Park in order to begin a new life with Mamah Borthwick Cheney, the wife of a neighbor and former client. After a year in Europe, he returned to the Wisconsin countryside where he had grown up.

To Jefferson, a firm believer in material progress, Monticello was a paean to ideal mathematics and a lodestar for the progress of civilization across the continental empire. Wright's assessment of the situation was less optimistic. Appalled by much that he saw in the industrialized world, he retreated into nature. He nestled his house into the hill and gave it the topographically explicit name of Taliesin, meaning "shining brow" in Welsh. Taliesin was also the name of a legendary fifth-century Welsh poet, an identification that firmly expressed Wright's anti-Classical bias. In his autobiography, Wright described his return to "the hill in the Valley as my Grandfather before me had turned to America — as a hope and a haven."[18]

As Vincent Scully described it, Taliesin was "the expression of a return, beyond the suburb, not only to the land of the only ancestors Wright would acknowledge . . . but also to his beloved Jeffersonian tradition of moral strength to be derived from the earth."[19] But where Jefferson believed the dialogue between man and nature was mutually edifying, in Wright's view nature was primary.

Taliesin was built not on top of the hill, where it would dominate the site, but rather on its brow, with façades of coarsely hewn local stone, low-slung roofs, and an insistent horizontality that make the building seem part of the landscape. Monticello was an object in space, its long service wings defining the edges of the manmade world and keeping nature safely at bay; Taliesin was a work of environmental integration, its broad wings defining a courtyard that shone as the brow of the hill, deliberately blurring the edges between the manmade and the natural.

Every element of Wright's design corresponded to the surrounding landscape. The yellow stone came from a quarry a mile away, and, when finished, Taliesin looked like the outcroppings on the local hills. To Wright, the "finished wood outside was the color of gray tree-trunks, in violet light,"[20] and the plastered walls above the stone had the same tawny color as the sand banks in the river below. Taliesin was the first American building completely at peace with the continent.

Wright pegged his dream to the solid core of Colonial domesticity, developing a personal reinterpretation of the saltbox's primitive sense of protection. At the center of Wright's house, he monumentalized family life with a huge hearth surmounted by a stone lintel. But he also reacted against the boxlike forms and interiors of Colonial houses and the Victorian frame buildings widespread in the Midwest. For inspiration, he turned to sources as eclectic as Jefferson's. Taliesin's sense of earthbound permanence, the low, broad overhanging roofs and gently contoured courtyard punctuated with statuary, all suggested the Italian farmhouse villas Wright knew from his travels in Tuscany. The open, flowing spaces were in

Taliesin West, an oasis set in the primitive landscape of the Arizona desert, represented Wright's utopian dream of America before the invasion of the white man. Wright's young apprentices, who migrated there with him every winter, constructed the tented pavilions out of local stone.

Theodate Pope Riddle stands in front of Mount Vernon, the model for Hill-Stead, the house she designed with Stanford White in Farmington, Connecticut. Not slavish to her model, however, she copied only its front porch and based the rest of the plan on her own vision of the perfect New England farmhouse.

part inspired by his admiration for the architecture of Japan, which he had visited in 1906.

Taliesin's story is one of heroic passions, both architectural and personal. The first Taliesin was destroyed in 1914 by a servant who went mad when he belatedly discovered that the mistress of the house was not married to the master. While Wright was at work in Chicago, the servant, a religious fanatic, butchered Cheney and her children and then set the house on fire. Wright eventually rebuilt Taliesin and lived there with Miriam Noel, whom he eventually married in 1923. That marriage dissolved in a few months, and in 1925, Taliesin burned to the ground again. With the third and last Mrs. Wright, Olga Molanoff Hinzenberg, or Olgivanna, as Wright called her, Taliesin was rebuilt again.

In 1932, at the age of sixty-five, with his career at an all-time low and his finances virtually nonexistent, Wright seized on the idea of transforming Taliesin into a school for architects. Wright's school was an idealistic community, dedicated to the study and practice of architecture. Since there was no money to hire help, it was also dedicated to the management of the great house, as well as to agriculture and animal husbandry. The female apprentice-architects performed all the household chores and the young men tilled the fields, tended the flocks, and kept the buildings in repair. From the first, apprentices eagerly responded to Wright's national invitation. As he cast himself as the self-appointed heir to Thomas Jefferson's Arcadian vision, the Taliesin Fellowship was a stroke of genius, a brilliant piece of enabling legislation in a nation rent by economic depression. By replacing Jefferson's slaves with aspiring student-architects and putting them to work in the household and on the farm, Wright extended Jefferson's vision into the twentieth century. His community was also, in a sense, an expression of Wright's idealization of the American pioneer experience. Indeed, he tried to re-create the antimaterialist communality that the Pilgrims had hastened to abandon almost as soon as they disembarked at Plymouth three centuries before.

When his financial situation improved in the late thirties, Wright began to create a permanent winter home in the Arizona desert outside Scottsdale. Yet another dream of America before the invasion of the white man, Taliesin West was like an Apache chief's encampment. The complex was built of stones collected from the desert, set in concrete by the brawn and muscle of young apprentices. A series of tented pavilions with swags of canvas hung from enormous wooden trusses to shelter the draftsmen from the sun. A petroglyph-covered boulder found on the site marks the processional way to the entrance; nearly two hundred feet of shaded pathways penetrate ever more deeply into the heart of the encampment. The entire plan showed what the architect Philip Johnson has characterized as Wright's absolute mastery of "the arrangements of the secrets of space."[21] At the core of the complex, on a loggia that flows through to a terrace commanding a ninety-mile view of desert, Wright's guests would be greeted and led through a turning, gold-leaf concrete tunnel to a great redwood-trussed living hall. Here they would find Wright and his consort ensconced beneath the wood-louver- and canvas-screen ceiling, amidst animal skins and other symbols of desert life, as well as an elaborately decorated grand piano, seemingly dragged from the East as the pioneers had brought household objects nearly a hundred years before. To the side of the imposing room, isolated from views of the outside world, Wright would open a tent flap to reveal, as Johnson has described it, a "private secret garden . . . where water is playing unlike any water in the desert. The plants are twenty feet high in this garden, and there is a lawn such as you have only seen in New England."[77]

For Wright, architecture was the reenacting of the American experience: the primitive world of the native Indian, the tenuous grasp on European culture that was the pioneers', the vulnerability of both before the majesty and force of the desert and the mountains beyond. Each year, after Thanksgiving, Wright would evoke the pioneers' hegira across the desert, packing up the studios in Wisconsin and leading his apprentices in a caravan westward across the barren prairie landscape to his lush desert oasis. Here Wright felt liberated at last of the baggage of inherited Western culture, free to carry the dream of Arcadia beyond Jeffersonian ambivalence to a wholly primitive, wholly American landscape.

To a remarkable extent both Jefferson, the amateur architect and professional politician, and Wright, the amateur politician and professional architect, were eager to convince America to follow their architectural and agrarian imperatives. The breadth of their ambitions for a national culture, for the evolution of a national mythology, charged their architecture with meaning. So too did their shared impulse to re-create their personal histories through architecture. The same impulses can be seen in the life and work of Theodate Pope Riddle, one of America's first important women architects. As amateur as Jefferson and as arrogant as Wright, Riddle, who was born in 1868, a year after Wright, into a wealthy Cleveland family, first revealed her precocious nature when, at age twelve, she changed her name from the drab "Effie" to the imperious "Theodate." (The name, which means "gift of God" in Greek, belonged to her maternal grandmother from Maine.) Although Riddle's work and influence are slight compared to that of Jefferson and Wright, and although her very effort to practice architecture was met with derision in her era, the sweep of her ambition

Avon Old Farms is shown under construction (*above*) and completed (*right*). Built with a near fanatical commitment to the techniques and tools of preindustrial times, the school opened in 1927 and was intended to instill its students with a sense of community untainted by the mechanization of the modern world.

approached theirs. For Riddle not only sought to express a revised personal history through architecture; she also sought, particularly in her work at Avon Old Farms, to alter its future by creating an environment for its schoolchildren based on her own reinvention of a European past.

Educated at Miss Porter's in Farmington, Connecticut, Riddle was so inspired by the New England landscape that by age sixteen she was drawing up plans for her dream house in Connecticut. After graduation came the customary Grand Tour of Europe with her parents and subsequent presentation to high society back in Cleveland. As quickly as possible, she escaped the hometown she detested to return to Farmington in order to realize her architectural dream. She bought and restored two seventeenth-century cottages on forty-two acres of land, finishing them in the manner of an early-nineteenth-century Connecticut farmhouse.

But ambitious Riddle found that the renovation had not satiated her need to create, and she decided that the only way to sufficiently utilize her artistic talents, idealistic nature, and determination was to become a professional architect. Refused admission to all-male Princeton, she enlisted private tutors. In 1898 she arranged to have the country's most fashionable architect, Stanford White, build a retirement house for her parents on her property in Farmington. She was to be the apprentice. The building of Hill-Stead with White marked Riddle's transformation into a professional in the field of architecture.

Riddle was determined to make Hill-Stead the definitive American house. In trying to decide on the form such a house would take, she rejected the European palace model popular in the late nineteenth century, which for her reeked of the new money and pretensions she had detested since childhood. On the other hand, like Jefferson, she was loath to be dubbed provincial and felt that a personal interpretation of a generic rural vernacular — the sort Wright was developing — would fail to adequately convey her sense of pride of place. For her, the historical links had to be more explicit. Ultimately she settled on Mount Vernon as the appropriate model — nothing short of the Founding Father's house would do.

Theodate Riddle deeply believed that historical allusion could give meaning to the present. She was rewriting her past with her parents in the role of New England country gentry, just as she had once reformulated herself from Effie to Theodate. Her design for Hill-Stead did not slavishly copy her model; she repeated only the most essential symbol, the two-story porch. She based the rest of her design on her vision of the perfect New England farmhouse. Explicit though its associations are, White and Riddle's design is nonetheless fresh. The bay windows establish a syncopated rhythm with the "Mount Vernon" colonnade. The interiors have little of the symmetrical planning of Palladian design; instead, spacious, formal rooms interconnect in a meandering, informal way.

For her next architectural endeavor, Riddle convinced her ever-malleable father to finance the construction of Westover (1909–12), a girls' school in nearby Middlebury, Connecticut. Although an architectural achievement of some note, as we will see in chapter 2, Westover was considered at the time, after all, only a girls' school in a man's world — a point Cass Gilbert, the well-known architect, made all too clear when, after praising the design for "refined and scholarly" details and proportions that were "exceedingly well sustained throughout," he qualified his assessment by labeling it "in fact the best girls' school that I know in the country."[23]

Riddle, who had struggled to escape the conventional "woman's place" of her generation by becoming an architect, could not rest on these delimited laurels. The hubris that had led her to an architectural self-identification with the father of the country sustained her ambition to go beyond the gentlewomanly design of a girls' school. Registered in 1910 as Connecticut's first woman architect, Riddle inherited a fortune after her father's death in 1913 and secured her social position in 1916 with her marriage to a diplomat, John Wallace Riddle. She was now rich enough and established enough to fulfill her chief fantasy: to build a dreamworld for *men* to inhabit, where she designed all the buildings and wrote all the rules. Avon Old Farms was to be more than a school; it was to be a place where the coddled sons of wealthy American industrialists could recapture the Puritan work ethic, a farm village that reflected old England and New England in equal measure.

Riddle designed the school in 1918. By 1920 she had three thousand acres of rural Connecticut at her disposal, and the next year construction began. Riddle didn't let her desire to create an educational farming village in New England confine her architectural imagination to the problematic American past. In her own life, she had chosen to arrange her origins to her own taste, and she would do no less for American schoolboys, who would study, work, and play surrounded by manifestations of preindustrial England, with only the better elements of northern Europe allowed. In a sense, Avon Old Farms was to be a rewrite of the Pilgrims' experience — a continuation of the craftsmanship and formal traditions of the medieval world the Pilgrims knew but were unable to sustain as they confronted the harsh realities of the American wilderness. Three hundred years later, Riddle could set things straight, using her talent and cash to help make a new New England, far more coherent and beautiful than any the Pilgrims could have afforded or even imagined. In true American fashion, she would get it right the second time around. American life would be reborn as an idealistic communitarianism untainted by mechanization. At Avon Old Farms, the medieval architecture would be the real thing, or as close to it as scholarship and money could make it: in its construction methods, architectural styles, and charter, the school would send up a permanent protest against the evils of the very industrialism that financed it.

The school had its own carpentry shop and forge. Stone was quarried and timber felled for construction within the boundaries of the campus. To start the project off in the right way, Riddle imported six English workmen bearing seventeenth-century tools. They soon returned home after finishing only the train station, ironically the building that perhaps more than any at the school betrayed Riddle's anti-industrial ideal. Undaunted by their defection, Riddle — a woman who had survived the sinking of the *Lusitania* in 1915 — marshaled an army of five hundred American workers and ordered them to show the same devotion to their craft. Instructed to "work by rule of thumb and to gauge all verticals by eye,"[24] the men, who could take only so much of Riddle's dream, were said to use twentieth-century techniques on the sly.

Located five miles from Farmington, and approached through a dense forest, Avon Old Farms confronts the arriving visitor with the high cylinder of a brick water tower, a hulking mass that looks like a medieval castle keep. At its base, the forge and carpentry shop are clustered like barnacles, superbly crafted, ancient-looking buildings. The carpentry shop, a half-timbered structure with the spaces filled by brickwork artfully bonded horizontally, vertically, and in herringbone,

Overleaf. Johnson's Glass House, an almost entirely transparent composition in glass and steel, challenged traditional notions of house as shelter. The Classical pavilion set in the pond (*lower right*) was underscaled to create the illusion of distance.

was so reverently formed that when Riddle was forced to cut back on her plans, it was easily transformed into a chapel. Beyond the water tower group, a square stone Gothic tower rises to mark the principal entrance to the quadrangle. The quad is neatly quartered by flagstone paths; but as for the buildings themselves, Riddle brooked few right angles. Irregularly disposed trees graced the lawn, which was bounded by picturesquely detailed common rooms, masters' cottages, and dormitories. Dormers plunk out perverse rhythms through the red slate roofs above, the eaves drop almost to the ground, and the red sandstone walls are beautifully carved to articulate the entrances and frame the small windows that puncture the two-foot-thick walls. Passing through the quadrangle, the visitor arrives at the Village Green. The headmaster's and dean's houses, opposite one another, open onto the Green. Each has an elevated court, enclosed by a low stone wall. The communal center designed for the school was the big Gothic hall of the refectory. Outside, buttressed stone walls rise one storey to a slate roof and a band of clerestory windows. Inside, Riddle wed the late-Gothic forms to a voluptuously Baroque sensibility, with enormous arched braces sprung over the room and ending in grotesquely overscaled spirals. Despite the plane-honed oak and the relatively spare detailing, the refectory has a luxurious fluidity of form.

For all her concern with traditional craftsmanship, Riddle was interested not in archaeological reconstruction but rather in the role historical styles could play in articulating the dialogue across time that she thought would best develop the character of the school's students. So it was that next to the refectory Riddle undercut the school's medieval styling with an anomaly — a bank, located where one might have expected a chapel or library. Riddle deemed a bank fundamental to an educational program intent on teaching wealthy young citizens how to come to terms, practically as well as philosophically, with their industrial age inheritances. Riddle's bank was the school's one break with medievalism: a modern function required an appropriate form and Riddle chose a Classical Doric portico modeled after America's earliest temple of finance, the First Bank of the United States, in Philadelphia. The casting of financial institutions in the form of Classical temples has been a convention in Western architecture since the eighteenth century, perhaps because of the association of Classical architecture with the stability and longevity of our most ancient architectural civilization, and the value assigned to the historic. It was precisely such associations that Jefferson sought to evoke as representative of the young America when he fashioned its first public building, the Virginia State Capitol.

By 1930, Riddle had spent nine years and the lion's share of her fortune constructing Avon Old Farms, which had opened in 1927. Incomplete though it is, lacking the Gothic chapel and with only one of the two quadrangles built, it stands as a radically inventive expression of American optimism. For with the open book of the past before her, Riddle had used architecture to define the present as she desired and presumed such definition could affect the future.

Philip Johnson, like his cousin Theodate Pope Riddle before him, set out to reconstruct the past in order to define the present, but in a radically different way. To Johnson, the materials and historical styles of Avon Old Farms were anathema. A campaigning Modernist, Johnson's work as the first curator of the Museum of Modern Art's Department of Architecture and his exhibition and accompanying book of 1932, *The International Style*, co-authored with Henry-Russell Hitchcock, are

A *New York Times* cartoon depicts the hazards of life in Johnson's Glass House. In the first two frames, the house is beset by curious neighbors and relentless salesmen. At bottom, the architect sits down to a less-than-private breakfast.

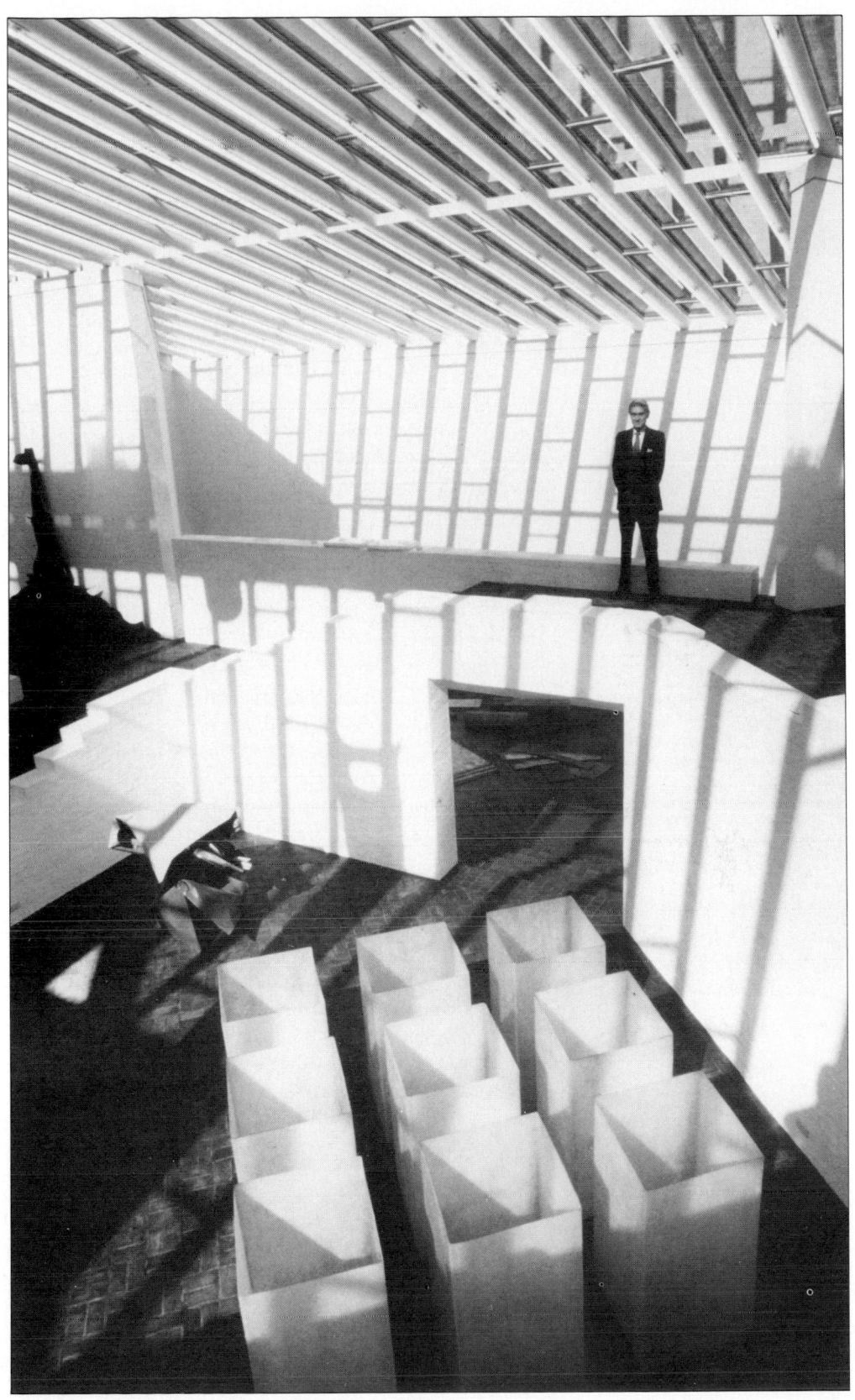

Philip Johnson stands in the sculpture gallery, his favorite building on the New Canaan compound.

widely credited with launching in America the radical European concepts of Modernism. The youthful Johnson's rebellious aestheticism, combined with the contempt in which Johnson's family held their well-traveled, aristocratic cousin Theodate — whom they always referred to as Effie — blinded him to Riddle's achievement. He despised Hill-Stead, taking no interest in the architecture except as a container for what he deemed "a collection of bad pictures,"[25] which included the Impressionist works of Claude Monet, Édouard Manet, and Edgar Degas, set off in gold frames designed by Stanford White.

Yet however unaware he was of it at the time, Johnson's career matched the substance of his cousin's in many ways. The Cleveland-born Johnson was also educated in the East, and also refused to go home again. Like Riddle, he at first pursued architecture as an amateur, returning to Harvard when he was thirty-three years old to study it formally and receive a professional degree. In 1948, fifty years after Riddle commenced Hill-Stead, he, too, began to build a house for himself in the Connecticut countryside. In its intentions and execution, the complex exudes the same individualism Riddle displayed throughout her life. As Johnson himself has noted, "Coming here was a statement of defiance to the world and to my family and to the sales value, the market value of the house because you never build a house unless you know you can sell it."[26]

His first building on the site, a steel and glass pavilion — entirely transparent save for a cylindrical form containing the fireplace and bath — suggests a Modernist version of Jefferson's ideal. Johnson sited the Glass House like a temple: rather than relating the structure to nature in the nestling manner that Wright favored, Johnson blasted a level shelf where he set his house on a podium — a Classical stance more closely resembling Monticello, where the works of man stand in stark contrast to the natural world. Jefferson had spent decades rearranging his landscape, hauling earth and planting to make sure that every window had a good view, while Johnson, in a landscape that had reverted from farming to forest, cleared and thinned. Johnson's splendid isolation, like Jefferson's, didn't call for roughing it. As Johnson put it, "It's nice to be out in nature without having to go into one of these horrible sleeping bags."[27]

Predictably, when Frank Lloyd Wright visited Johnson's Glass House, he minced no words, describing the house as "a monkey cage for a monkey."[28] Johnson tells the story of Wright's visit:

He was so perplexed. He'd heard this was a famous house and so he felt that he was wrong in his hatred of it, but it bothered him . . . and he came in one day and looked around . . . [and] said "Here I am, Philip, am I indoors or am I out? Do I leave my hat on or do I take it off?" You see how clever that is because to him there couldn't be a house without a sense of shelter. And to me a house doesn't need that, a house needs a presence on a cliff.[29]

As Jefferson's explorations and inventions paid homage to the Renaissance Classicism of Palladio, so Johnson's Glass House paid tribute to the industrial age Classicism of *his* architect-hero, Mies van der Rohe. Today, Johnson somewhat self-deprecatingly explains his early ambitions: since construction of Mies's own design for a glass house — the Farnsworth House — had been delayed, Johnson saw his chance to build the world's first example. But Johnson's Glass House is far different from Mies's design. Where Mies's building floats above the ground, Johnson's anchors itself to the earth with a brick podium. The interior,

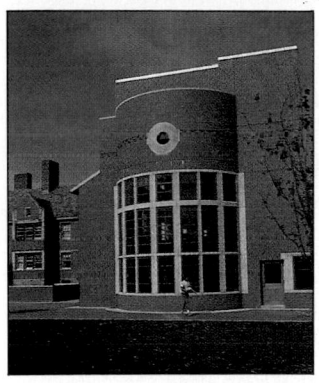

Top. Princeton's Whig Hall, gutted by fire in 1969, was remodeled by Charles Gwathmey and Robert Siegel. They retained the surviving Greek Revival temple façade as a frame for their new Modernist composition. The combative dialogue between styles that resulted was appropriate to a building that housed the debating society.

Bottom. This view of Wu Hall's dining room bay window, with limestone insets floating above it, represents a more ironic treatment of history. Venturi, Rauch & Scott Brown playfully reinterpreted Princeton's Collegiate Gothic visage with decorative elements borrowed from the Elizabethan manor house.

unmistakably an *homage à* Mies, includes pieces of the master's furniture in an arrangement that gives the illusion of flexibility, although their asymmetrical placement is as permanent as the distinctly un-Miesian cylindrical fireplaced bathroom that rises through the roof.

When Johnson published the house in the English magazine *Architectural Review* in 1950, he declared it "frankly derivative."[30] Given the antihistoricism of the Modernist point of view, the iconoclasm behind this statement cannot be overemphasized. Modernism grew up in Europe, where architects and other intellectuals regarded the masterpieces of the past as smothering fetters: to be free of history was to make history. For Johnson, an American, the new style was not a rejection of the past but a challenge to reinvent it. In designing the house and its complementary boxlike, nearly windowless brick guest house, Johnson employed a dazzling display of historical references: Mies van der Rohe, Ledoux, Schinkel, von Doesberg, and Le Corbusier, not to mention the principles of Greek site planning and architecture.

The Glass House was only the first chapter of what would become the greatest architectural autobiography of our time. At New Canaan, Connecticut, Johnson created nothing less than an industrial age Monticello — or, perhaps, a machine age Hadrian's villa, the emperor's estate that spread its rich and slightly disconnected geometries across the plan of Tivoli, outside Rome, in the second century A.D. Like Jefferson, Johnson borrowed freely from the architecture of the past, choosing from various traditions rather than submitting to a strict interpretation of any one in particular. But unlike Jefferson, he treated the artifacts of the past not as words to be recomprised into new sentences but as objects to be abstracted, to be reconfigured in terms of industrial era building techniques and, more critically — at least in terms of a Modernist impulse to see the value of art in inverse relation to its expression of the past — to value art as it shapes rather than embodies the conventions of its time.

In the thirty-five years Johnson has lived in New Canaan, what started out as a suburban house on a suburban lot has become the nucleus of a thirty-two-acre estate with a collection of Modernist buildings, each throwing down a challenge to history: the brick guest house (1952), with its famous plaster-vaulted bedroom derived from the work of Sir John Soane; the Classical pavilion (1962), set in a pond below the house and falsely underscaled to make it seem more distant; the underground Minoan tumulus (1965), used as a painting gallery; a Spanish farmhouse married to a glazed shed, used as a sculpture gallery (1970); and a Scottish castle with a Mediterranean roof cone (1983), used for a studio and library.

In the way landscape and architecture are made to interact, Johnson firmly identifies himself with the Arcadian architectural tradition in America begun by Jefferson. Yet for all its aspirations to a pastoral ideal, the New Canaan estate, even more than Monticello, exudes restless intelligence rather than repose. For Johnson, like Jefferson, "the only way you can test these things is by yourself. I couldn't prove to anybody that the only way to hang pictures was to see only six at a time and to swing the things around. I couldn't prove all my points about sculpture being clogged up except by doing [the sculpture gallery]."[31] This kind of urgent experimentation is in evidence throughout the estate, making it a revealing portrait of its owner's mercurial imagination.

While Johnson's Glass House pushed architecture to the furthest reaches of

The San Juan Capistrano Mission (*above*) was a source of inspiration for Michael Graves's Regional Library (1983) nearby. The Spanish elements are typical of Southern California architecture.

Right. The Regional Library is a world apart. Graves's humanistic design includes sculpted, enclosed places that encourage the reader's imagination to wander, such as this cloistered courtyard with a fountain.

structural minimalism and, by virtue of the extreme abstraction of its forms, seemed to break the conversation with the past that had for so long been an essential ingredient of American architecture, in reality it was the by-product of a struggle to restate traditional architectural values in a new language. As Johnson's architectural autobiography has unfolded in New Canaan, that struggle to reiterate history in exclusively contemporary terms has been the continuous thread linking together the disparate buildings. Johnson's abstract recapitulation of history opened the way for architects trained in the reductionist vocabulary of Modernism to renew the "dialogue across time" that, as Vincent Scully has stated, is "what architecture is all about."[32]

In its challenge to history, Johnson's estate closes the book on a disconnected Modernism, reaffirming that the past is *the* compelling theme of American architecture, not as nostalgia, but as necessity. Under the sway of Modernism, American architects less cogent than Johnson thought they had license to break architecture's contract with the past; the grim result, visible to every American, and shocking to most, was a bland, anonymous, meretriciously constructed environment, exalted by its proponents as up-to-date, functional, and technologically advanced, but brilliantly castigated by Norman Mailer as "the empty landscape of psychosis."[33]

Shocked by the wanton destruction of such notable public monuments as New York's Pennsylvania Station in 1963 and by the threat of further violence to the architectural art of their past, such as proposals to build a mediocre skyscraper atop Grand Central Station, the general public has lobbied vigorously and successfully to preserve old buildings and to force architects to recognize the existing physical context as a component of new building. The motivations behind the historic preservation movement in America are complex, but one thing is clear: its widespread popularity is a grassroots vote of no confidence for the near-hysterical rejection of tradition that characterized American architectural practice in the era immediately following World War II.

The preservation movement and public preference, as well as the pioneering work of advocates of historically based form such as Robert Venturi, have had their effect, and the best contemporary architecture once again, in one way or another, takes the past as a point of aesthetic departure. Venturi's seminal *Complexity and Contradiction in Architecture* of 1965 proposed a serious reappraisal of Modernism, calling into question its rigidity, its abstractness, and the way in which it ignores context and history in favor of an entirely new order. At the time, Venturi's observations seemed radical: "A valid order accommodates the circumstantial contradictions of a complex reality. It accommodates as well as imposes. It thereby admits control and spontaneity, correctness and ease."[34] But now, largely as a result of Venturi's powerful polemic, American architecture has come to its senses, has rediscovered its destiny as a dialogue between the past and the present. The critical issue today is the relationship of new buildings to the past. In a sense it is fitting that the architects of America — a country whose most consistent architectural tradition has been a search *for* tradition — have become world leaders in a search for the means of reinvesting architecture with its past and its conventions.

Two representative explorations in this search can be found on the campus of Princeton University. As we will see in chapter 2, the overall architectural character

of Princeton's campus is a historicist invention: as a result of the decision by faculty and trustees in 1896 to transform the provincial college into a great university based on the English model, the campus was transformed physically as well, into something overwhelmingly "Collegiate Gothic" in style. But by the 1950s, under the antihistoricist arguments of Modernism, Princeton's Gothic dreamworld, once one of the glories of our architecture, was deemed an irrelevant fantasy to be cured with a bitter pill of structural earnestness.

One of the earliest deviations from the banalities of the campus's Modernist architecture ironically came from a firm famed for its exquisite mastery of that aesthetic: the firm of Charles Gwathmey and Robert Siegel. At Princeton, they used a historical building as a kind of cage for a Modernist construction within. Whig Hall, a marble Greek Revival temple housing an undergraduate debating society, was designed in 1893 by A. Page Brown, who based his work on an earlier version built in wood. Although Whig Hall was gutted by fire in 1969, the temple front was not visibly affected. When Gwathmey and Siegel were asked to remodel it for use as a lecture hall, they removed the fire-damaged east wall of the original building, leaving only the masonry base, piers, and entablature to frame a new, stylistically contrasting composition of pipe railing, curving wall, and strip windows. A somewhat combative dialogue between the styles resulted, perhaps not inappropriate to a building devoted to the grand tradition of collegiate debating. In the course of achieving this representation of the building's function, Gwathmey and Siegel orchestrated a collision between the past and the present that stumbles like a servant with two masters.

As distressing as the jarring aesthetics of Princeton's Modernist buildings was their failure to contribute, by their forms and siting, to the creation of special places — quadrangles and courts — which is a hallmark of Princeton's older buildings. To restore the ailing campus to health, the university turned to the firm of Venturi, Rauch, and Scott Brown, who created Butler College, a coherent environmental entity, out of a heterogeneous collection of buildings that ran the full range of the university's post–World War II banalities. The confident irony of the Venturi firm's manipulation of architectural precedent is apparent in the siting of the new college's centerpiece, Gordon Wu Hall (1983). Both spatially and stylistically, the site unites the college's inherited stock of cliché buildings, including the completely nonrepresentational dormitories by Hugh Stubbins (1964).

The Wu Hall building itself summons up the grandeur of Princeton's Gothic dream, which reached its greatest expression in the graduate school by Ralph Adams Cram (1913). Rather than assuming the combative pose of Gwathmey and Siegel's Whig Hall, it suggests an ironic relationship to the past. Throughout the building, Venturi and his partners play with the idea of a great hall manqué: the entrance lies beneath a flat granite and marble coat of arms, depicting primary shapes distantly related to the decoration of an Elizabethan manor house. It stands as a heraldic banner frozen in stone, arrestingly bisected by a strip of horizontal windows running the length of the façade. Limestone insets float above the dining hall's glass wall, revealing their purely decorative function. But there is sensuousness here as well: both the spacious, bay-windowed dining hall and the broad, inviting staircase are worthy of their Elizabethan prototypes and perfectly suited to their collegiate purposes.

Venturi and his partners look at the past with a twisted smile. Yet to use the past honestly, our architecture must go beyond the sly ironies of Butler College and the stylistic combativeness of Whig Hall to meet tradition head on. Michael Graves's Regional Library in San Juan Capistrano, California, completed in 1983, represents such an effort.

Graves's design is a distinctly humanist, if perhaps overly personal, response to the neighboring San Juan Capistrano Mission, which Graves describes as being "like the Alamo, but without the kitsch."[35] The mission provided the architect with much of the inspiration for the library's red-tiled roofs, tiny windows, heavy masses, and cloistered courtyards. It also bolstered his own conviction that sequences of sculpted, enclosing spaces provide the most appropriate and reassuring environment for human endeavor.

Abandoning the "supermarket" plans of allegedly flexible space offered by Modernist libraries, Graves provides readers with an architectural promenade through a hierarchical pattern of clearly defined indoor and outdoor rooms. His concern for creating places for private study within a public interior yielded the charming, toylike reading nooks alongside the stacks, the well-delineated study carrels, and, in an almost embarrassing climax of cuteness, the inglenooks beside the fireplace in the adult lounge. The multilevel courtyard serves as an outdoor reading room as well as a lobby for the auditorium on the north side. Water is its theme, with a circular fountain that comes as welcome relief to the almost ascetic plainness of the surrounding columns. Past the cloister that encloses the courtyard on the west, Graves placed three outdoor rooms in the form of lattice gazebos, which will eventually be covered with bougainvillea and trumpet vines.

Graves's library transports its users from the familiarity of domestic enclosure to the dreamworld possibilities of California's Arcadian landscape, and also to the farthest reaches of their own imaginings. The structure is more than simply a library; it is a world apart, created through its architect's original reinterpretation of historic form. With its carrel towers, its monastic cloister, and its garden bower, it is a world of places, not spaces. In it the reader's own imagination can wander freely, unhindered by the realities of information processing.

Overleaf. Philip Johnson's sixty-five-storey Transco Tower glows against the Houston skyline. In the late seventies and early eighties, America witnessed a comeback of the skyscraper, its only real claim to a unique building style. Unlike the towering, boxlike structures of the postwar era, however, new designs incorporated a sense of play between the past and the present.

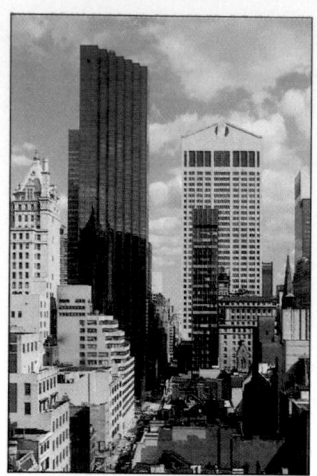

Johnson & Burgee's towering AT&T Building (1978–84) signaled the return of narrative to the architecture of New York City. Ordered like a column, with a base, shaft, and capital, it reasserted the aspirational quality of an earlier era of skyscrapers.

The rediscovery of architecture's obligation to define its present in terms of the past that Venturi and Graves have ably demonstrated is most striking in the new generation of skyscrapers in American cities. The skyscraper holds the clearest claim to being a uniquely American building type, and its devaluation in the 1950s and 1960s revealed how far confidence in American architecture had fallen. By the early seventies, New York's status as America's prototypical skyscraper city seemed threatened by the exploding skyline of Houston, Texas, where the glass façades of depersonalized packing-crate high-rises reflected the region's immobilizing heat and light onto the empty sidewalks of a totally automobilized megalopolis. With their Pennzoil Place (1974–76), Philip Johnson and John Burgee showed Houston that even the glass and steel tower could rise above anonymity toward the mythopoeic level of traditional skyscrapers. The architects' bold design of twin thirty-six-storey trapezoidal towers, each sliced off at a forty-five-degree angle at the top, was at first dismissed by developer Gerald D. Hines, who, according to Johnson, said, "Take the funny tops off and I'll rent it tomorrow."[36] Pennzoil chairman J. Hugh Liedtke felt differently, however, recognizing the usefulness of the building's silhouette as a corporate symbol for a small, independent oil company without a public image. Further, Liedtke's pride was at stake: having rejected an earlier Skidmore, Owings & Merrill design as "just another inverted cigar box," he told himself, "I'm probably only going to build one major building in my lifetime, and I want it to be good."[37] The result proved to be good architecture and good business, attracting so many tenants that two floors were added to the design when the building was half erected.

For Houstonians driving the freeways that ring the downtown, Pennzoil was an abstract sculpture, enlivened by the ever-shifting slot of sky between the two gray-bronze towers. For those who drove into the downtown core and got out of their cars, Pennzoil repeated the eight-storey slope of its roof with eight-storey glass-enclosed courtyards at the base of the towers, filled with trees and greenery beneath the white-painted aluminum space frame, providing a light-flooded lobby for office workers who pass through air-conditioned underground "tubes" to get from one downtown tower to another.

Johnson and Burgee, again working with the developer Gerald Hines, have further contributed to Houston's skyline, adding the uncompromisingly historicist RepublicBank Center (1984) across the street from Pennzoil. Its red-granite skin and superscaled Dutch gables grin with pride beside the cool glass and geometric purity of Pennzoil. Their sixty-five-storey glass-sheathed Transco Tower in the Post Oak district of Houston adds a super-scaled church steeple reminiscent of the best 1920s skyscrapers to the suburban "village" below. After the bland boxes that threatened to define the Sunbelt, Houston now has buildings that aspire to be more, skyscrapers that really climb and assume a position on the skyline, buildings that stand for the corporation, for the individual, and for art.

It is not only the Sunbelt cities that have benefited from the renewed interest of architects and builders in history and symbolism. At PPG Place (1985) in Pittsburgh, Johnson and Burgee have carried the synthesis between old and new even further. The corporate headquarters of PPG Industries, formerly known as the Pittsburgh Plate Glass Company, the building is a brazen display of the company's best-known product. The tower's reflective skin is not just an uncommunicative mirror, beautiful only in its reflection of neighboring buildings or the sky; its "pleated" walls form an intricate Gothic tower in glass. The building takes its stylistic inspiration from the early-nineteenth-century tower of Sir Charles Barry and Augustus Welby Pugin's Houses of Parliament and refers to Pittsburgh's own early-twentieth-century Cathedral of Learning, by Day & Klauder. It is thus aligned to both the international traditions of Western architecture and the architecture of its particularly American place.

In New York, my city, where I had despaired over the boring, dreamless high-rises that blocked off the towers of lower Manhattan, the dialogue between past and present has been revived and with it the skyscraper thrills of my youthful fantasies. Sadly, some great work has been lost: Ernest Flagg's Singer Tower (1907), once a symbol of New York's downtown skyline, toppled to make way for a steel behemoth. But the motivating spark that gave the world its great swaggering corporate towers seems to have ignited once again.

Johnson and Burgee's AT&T Building (1978–84) marked a turning point. From its first appearance as a sketch on the front page of the *New York Times* in 1978, the design signaled the return of narrative to the architecture of the city. The AT&T Building, ordered as a column with a base, shaft, and capital, was the first New York skyscraper in forty years to inhabit its height proudly. Its pedimented top, pierced by a vapor-filled oculus, reasserted the aspirational quality of an earlier era's skyscraper towers, while at its base, the overscaled archway marked a grand entrance to the corporate citadel. Its colossal columns define a luxurious urban loggia scaled to the lunch-time dreams of the brown-bagging citizens of the world's capital. Once again, our architecture amuses and challenges us. Once again, it represents our pride of place.

2

Academical Villages: The Places Apart

American campuses — ideal, independent villages, socially and culturally coherent communities for learning and research — are among the greatest dream places of our civilization and a distinctly American invention. At the core of the American experience is the sense of the continent as a place of new beginnings and of the need for new institutions to represent our democracy. Given America's cultural diversity, the campus and the rituals that it supports — from sitting on the Yale fence to walking the line at the United States Air Force Academy — provide an essential sense of community, uniting people in a common pursuit.

Where universities in Europe and Latin America grew out of the religious orders, with the ratification of the Constitution, Thomas Jefferson pioneered for America a new type — a university rooted in a humanist, as opposed to religious, conception of society. Acting as both educator and architect, Jefferson brought a new kind of university to fruition: a nearly self-sufficient secular cloister, a place apart. To isolate his "Academical village" from the bustle, temptations, and conflicts of the city, Jefferson located the university he founded in 1817, the University of Virginia, a mile outside the barely settled village of Charlottesville.

Jefferson's design for the University of Virginia (1817–26) followed a plan he first outlined in 1810. Advising the trustees of a lottery for East Tennessee College, he wrote:

I consider the common plan, followed in this country, but not in others, of making one large and expensive building as unfortunately erroneous. It is infinitely better to erect a small and separate lodge for each professorship, with only a hall below for his class, and two chambers above for himself; joining these lodges by barracks for a certain portion of the students opening into a covered way to give a dry communication between all the schools the whole of these arranged around an open square of grass and trees would make it, what it should be in fact, an academical village, instead of a large and common den of noise, of filth, and of fetid air.[1]

The University of Virginia was such a village. At the head of its village green, the Lawn, Jefferson placed a rotunda — a half-scale adaptation of the Pantheon — built to house the university's library. The monumental scale of the great Rotunda and its central, dominant position announced the single-minded intent and focus of the enterprise with then-revolutionary clarity. The Rotunda was devoted not to the worship of the gods or even to a singular religion but rather to the common purpose of the village — learning. Through its architectural dignity, its grandly

The University of Virginia was founded by Thomas Jefferson in 1817. The Pantheon provided the model for its central building, the library, complete with Corinthian columns.

The Observatory at Vassar College, circa 1870. At that time, focal buildings on American university campuses were more apt to be devoted to scientific pursuit than to spiritual enlightenment.

scaled details, such as its Corinthian columns (realized in the only available materials, cast iron and wood, assembled and whitewashed to resemble marble), its form derived from the pure geometric figure of a sphere, and its evocation of the temple on which its design is based, the Rotunda made it clear that worldliness of learning rather than religion was the symbolic heart of university life. And, in a further break from the cloisterlike tradition of college planning and a reaffirmation of its founder's faith in the future of the new nation, the Lawn is not closed in as a quadrangle; from the Rotunda, across the Lawn, a view beyond lay open to the continental empire that Jefferson believed to be America's destiny.

In developing the architectural style of the university, Jefferson, anxious to distance the new nation from English origins as well as from the monarchical traditions of continental Europe, sought inspiration from the Classical world. The architecture of the entire village was meant as a model for the instruction of the students in great architecture, which for Jefferson was synonymous with the Classical tradition. As Jefferson wrote to Benjamin Latrobe, the young English-trained architect who advised him in the design of the buildings, the faculty houses in particular were meant to "be models of taste and correct architecture — and of a variety of appearance, no two alike, so as to serve as specimens of orders for the architectural lectures."[2]

Although the University of Virginia provided a strong model, it was only after the Civil War that campuses — designed to be spatially, symbolically, and stylistically coherent places set apart and somehow independent of their surroundings — became the norm. For it was then that a great burst of funding from private benefactors enabled the established but provincial colleges of the East to transcend their origins as church-sponsored institutions and to transform themselves into secular world-class institutions of higher learning.

The increasing national wealth that made the transformation of the old colleges into universities possible also cast a pall over the old towns in which they were located, threatening to engulf both the towns and the colleges in them. Even more than Jefferson, the college trustees and architects who presided over the post–Civil War expansion did so in defiance of the city. One characteristic reaction to the city was to flee it.

When Columbia University was founded as King's College in 1754, it was located at what was then the outskirts of New York City on Murray Street, about one-half mile from the Battery. By 1859, the city had so closed in around the college that it moved uptown to the new residential district near Forty-ninth Street. It was in this retreat from the city that the ancient model of the college as a monastic cloister had a particularly functional appeal. Charles Coolidge Haight, the architect retained by Columbia to create its new campus, carved out of New York's gridiron plan a cloister that achieved what nineteenth-century critic Montgomery Schuyler described as an "air of seclusion of repose . . . as completely attained on a bustling New York avenue as in the sleepiest university towns."[3]

But by 1890, when Seth Low was elected Columbia's president, the college had again outgrown its campus. Low, a former mayor of Brooklyn and a future mayor of a unified Greater New York after it had merged with Brooklyn and the other neighboring counties in 1898, masterminded Columbia's transformation into a university and, simultaneously, a move from its midtown cloister to a spacious campus atop Morningside Heights. It was Low's dream that Jefferson's academical village could retain its independence yet be a part of the metropolis. Hence the college was rechristened Columbia University in the City of New York.

The university retained Charles Follen McKim, a partner in McKim, Mead & White, America's most popular and influential architectural firm at the turn of the century, to establish a master plan. His 1894 plan for a university envisaged as a school for commuting scholars arranged the campus between 116th and 120th streets, and Broadway and Amsterdam avenues. A tight urban ensemble, it left almost a third of the site open for future expansion. Buildings ran right to the lot line, except where a grand cour d'honneur opened before the monumental Low Library, which faced south to the city beyond over what was still open country. The master plan was tense with ambiguity. On the one hand, it tied the university to the city in the density with which its buildings were to be closely packed and in its use of the city's grid system as its organization. But on the other hand, it created a cloistral wall against the city's vitality with its buildings' backs to the streets, facing into the campus center. To the critic Montgomery Schuyler, the tension was too much, the price paid for its success as an essay in civics was too great in terms of a lost collegiality: "The group of Columbia, in so far as it is carrying out a special intention, is a failure. One might take it for a hospital, for a group of official buildings, for almost anything but what it is. You may admit that it is 'municipal.' You cannot possibly maintain that it is 'collegiate.'"[4]

McKim's revised master plan of 1903 reflected the university's decision to establish a residential campus. On the two blocks directly south of its original property, McKim planned for rows of dormitories along the east and west edges of the site, forming two tight, elongated quadrangles with a large open courtyard

Overleaf. At the University of Virginia, rows of dormitories and faculty houses surround the great lawn to create an academic village. Each house is of a different architectural style and serves as a model for learning. Gardens are enclosed by curved walls, echoing the rolling hills of the surrounding countryside.

centered between them. The cour d'honneur in front of the library elongated into a mall traversed by 116th Street, becoming the core of a far greener and more inwardly centered campus — a garden in the grid.

With the opening of the subway along Broadway in 1904, the city swept northward in a surge, and Columbia has once again been faced with an obligation to try to maintain an atmosphere of scholarly repose by sequestering students from the city's noise. Inevitably, this change in policy and its architectural expressions — gates, blank walls to the street — foster a decline in town-gown relations that seems to haunt every urban academic village.

The founders of the College of New Jersey at Princeton appear to have anticipated the metropolitan crisis very early on: in 1752 they moved their fledgling institution from a room above the Newark jail to a country village that the trustees found "more sequestered from the various temptations attending a promiscuous commerce with the world, that theatre of folly and dissipation."[5] Furthermore, the Princeton trustees set the main building, Nassau Hall (1755–57), far back from the road amid eleven acres — creating the first leafy setting for collegiate life to be called by the name "campus."[6]

Throughout the nineteenth century Princeton fleshed out its campus with modest buildings. Benjamin Latrobe, who restored Nassau Hall after it was gutted by fire in 1802, framed it with a library and refectory. In the 1830s the local builder and architect Charles Steadman helped define a green behind Nassau Hall by executing Whig and Clio halls (1837–38) opposite it, Greek temples constructed of white clapboard. After the Civil War, the architect William Appleton Potter set the college in a very different stylistic direction, sacrificing its Classical tradition with richly sensuous, individualistic statements. Potter's octagonal Chancellor Green Library (1873) evoked Venice, while the hulking Alexander Hall (1892) recalled medieval France, but both designs were freely composed, using bright tiles, terra-cotta bas reliefs, towers, and lanterns in eclectic array.

Jefferson employed Classical elements to create an ideal, wholly American institution at the University of Virginia. The grandly scaled columns of the Rotunda are of cast iron and wood, whitewashed to resemble marble.

Classics professor Andrew F. West, who would later become dean of the Graduate School, took the celebrations of Princeton's sesquicentennial in 1896 as an opportunity to put an end to this stylistic eclecticism in its campus architecture. West persuaded the college trustees that the time had come for Princeton to become a modern university and that, in so doing, it should also put its architectural house in order. West believed that the new university would most easily become a great and venerable institution if it looked like one, specifically like Oxford and Cambridge.

These English universities, whose architectural style was known collectively as Oxbridge, comprised individual, nearly independent colleges each of which had an essentially ecclesiastical foundation with an almost monastic life. Developed over centuries, the Oxbridge colleges have attained a richness in their variety. In each college the blocks of student cells around the intimately scaled quadrangles are punctuated and dominated by the communal hall and the sponsoring chapel. Because much construction was done in the fifteenth and sixteenth centuries, stylistically the buildings have many elements described as Gothic: slender vertical proportions, pointed arches, and vaults built in stone. These elements, and the suggestion of a place that evolved in a coherent way over time, were the kinds of things West strived to re-create.

The work of adding a millennium to Princeton's architectural history began in earnest with the work of Cope & Stewardson, a firm instrumental in the rising popularity of "Collegiate Gothic" — an American style invented to meet precisely the challenge of evoking an aura of venerability on young American campuses. As a result of its successes at Bryn Mawr (1886) and the University of Pennsylvania (1895), Cope & Stewardson was employed in 1897 to design Dillon Gymnasium as well as Blair and Stafford Little halls. The buildings' picturesque masses form a series of greens and quadrangles interconnected by a series of arched passageways. In addition, the buildings both screened the campus and provided

The great tree-lined Lawn of the University of Virginia campus served as a kind of village green, but was open at one end. The Rotunda stands at the head of the lawn, with faculty housing lining both sides.

an entrance from the spur line of the Pennsylvania railroad, which deposited travelers at what had theretofore been the "backyard" of the campus. Blair Arch, which formed the gateway of the university for those arriving by train, with its crenelated, fortresslike towers, the pointed arches of its inset window frames and of its great vaulted passageway, the sculpture groups set into its façade, and its great flight of steps pouring down from the arch, creates by association if not by mimicry a strong evocation of medieval churches, castles, and cloisters. And it was thus with an image of medieval and monastic retreat and seclusion that the university literally and symbolically prevented the machine from intruding upon its garden.

The appointment of Ralph Adams Cram in 1902 as supervisory architect insured the continuation of Princeton's architectural "aging" process. Cram's devotion to Gothic forms was more than stylistic. While to many the appeal of Gothic styling may have seemed a pretty and appropriate way of evoking established age and wisdom, for Cram it embodied moral and philosophical values. He idealized the medieval, a moral focus to the modern world, as an organically whole, spiritually pure communal environment. It seemed a just and necessary environment in which future leaders of a nation threatened by a rapidly industrializing world could be trained. He wrote that Princeton was "a place . . . containing within itself all necessary influences towards the making of character, repelling all those that work against the same: a walled city against materialism and all its works."[7]

Cram brought his vision to life in his Graduate College (1910–13), arguably one of the most beautiful "Gothic" quadrangles ever constructed. It captured both the isolation of monastic retreat and a sense of purposefulness, but where Chartres and Salisbury rise up from grassy plains devoted to agriculture, Princeton's Graduate College is approached across a meticulously landscaped golf course.

Dominated by the 173-foot Cleveland Tower, the complex is designed to appear as a collection of buildings grown up together over time. Inside the main entrance, the main quadrangle is enclosed by ranges of living accommodations; towers, arched cloisters, oriels, and an array of variously scaled gables and dormers breathe life into the composition, rendering it convincingly picturesque. The most ceremonial building is Proctor Hall, a refectory modeled after an English Gothic chapel. Entered through an ornately carved wooden screen, the hall has an "Upper Table" for masters set on a dais at the far end, lighted by an enormous window mullioned in Gothic tracery and paned in stained glass. The hall's formality was relieved by humorous but stylistically appropriate carved wooden grotesques placed at the beam ends of the open trusswork supporting the slate roof above.

Cram's design set the standard for every campus aspiring to medieval venerability. Although Yale had been constructing Gothic buildings since 1842, it had never sought to bind itself to a single image. But in an effort to compensate for its urban setting, and, perhaps, chastened by Columbia's failure to establish a coherent collegiality, Yale, as it grew to university status, adopted the cloistral Gothicism that had been so successfully exploited by its rival, Princeton.

The appeal of Gothic-style planning, with its secure, quiet cloisters and sense of place and of overall coherence created by consistent styling, was heightened by Yale's situation within a town that was rapidly changing into a city.

Founded in 1701 in Saybrook, Connecticut, by Congregational ministers, Yale relocated in 1717 to New Haven. One of the first geometrically planned cities in America, New Haven was laid out in 1641 in a nine-square grid, its central square reserved as a public green with a church in the middle. In an effort to attract Yale, New Haven had outbid other Connecticut towns by offering to pay for a new college building. A 162-foot-long, 23-foot-deep Georgian structure facing the Green, it housed an assembly hall, library, dining hall, kitchen, and twenty-two bedrooms. By 1782 Yale had grown so much that the original building was removed to make way for College Row, an alternating pattern of dormitories and meeting halls that established a nearly continuous wall along the street. With painter John Trumbull acting as informal aesthetic adviser, College Row was in essence the first example of an American campus deliberately planned to meet both functional and aesthetic criteria. The red brick dormitories and classrooms had small, symmetrical yards in front, along College Street, bordered by a low wood fence. In the back, beyond the privies, Trumbull planted a picturesque English garden.

Yale's honeymoon with New Haven didn't lead to a particularly happy marriage. Despite a good start, relations between the town and the college were never very cordial. Students rioted regularly during the eighteenth century and New Havenites resented being taxed for the repairs. By 1799 their resentment had reached such a state that sailors from nearby Bridgeport were encouraged to lead a mob up the Green to "whip the scholars." Riots broke out so often that Yale undergraduates elected a "college bully" each year to lead them in the melees. By the 1850s the situation had gotten pretty out of hand, with students encountering firemen in kicking and shoving fights. One scuffle in 1854 resulted in a town mob leader being stabbed to death, and in 1856 a fireman was shot and killed by a student. After the stabbing, the angry mob dragged cannons up to the edge of the campus, ready and willing but in the end unable to fire. While it is not clear who was more at fault — the town or the gown — by the end of the Civil War, as New Haven prospered, it was clear that Yale needed a greater barrier than a wood fence to maintain its collegiate tone in the bustling city.

In the 1840s Gothic styling began to make an appearance on Yale's campus, competing with its older red brick buildings. The latter were beginning to be associated with the all-too-recent Colonial past, remembered from that perspective as less than grand. Further, red brick had become the preferred material for mill construction in New England. Gothic styling, which was growing in popularity as a revival style in England as well, suggested a shared cultural tradition.

Finished in 1846, Henry Austin's library is evocative of a Gothic cathedral and was called the first college building to make any "pretensions to architectural beauty."[8] Six years later, Alumni Hall by Alexander Jackson Davis, while associated with Gothic styling by its pointed arches and vertical proportions, added a more militaristic edifice — reminiscent of medieval castles rather than churches — to the campus with its battlements and crenelated towers.

At the end of the Civil War, under the direction of Noah Porter, Yale's president from 1871 to 1886, and a staunch advocate of planning facilities around quadrangles, Yale went even further in its efforts to disassociate itself from its Colonial past. The university systematically tore down its Georgian buildings, replacing them with "modern" structures that formed a solid wall between the

New Haven Green and the campus. Most of the components of it were designed by Russell Sturgis in a tightly ordered, somewhat forbidding Gothic style. By 1900 only one vestige was left of the "Old Brick Row": Connecticut Hall (1752), the campus's sole pre-Revolutionary structure, which in 1925, as America fell back in love with its Colonial past, was paired by an uninspired twin, McClennan Hall.

Even though Yale had embraced the Gothic in the 1840s, by the 1890s its campus as a whole was as stylistically wayward as contemporary Princeton. In fact, Yale entered the new century with a brief but violent swerve from Gothic to Classical architecture. The sponsors of the university's Bicentennial Buildings (1901–2) rejected a field of romanticized Collegiate Gothic entries in favor of a grandiose Modern French Classical design, which seemed more appropriate to their image of America's world-power status in the wake of the Spanish-American War. As designed by Carrère & Hastings — the New York architectural firm that was already at work on what would be the apogee of civic grandeur, the New York Public Library (1897–1911) — the winning scheme provided two cavernous halls, the Commons and Woolsey Hall, united by a circular War Memorial, which was topped by a domed rotunda. While they are sheathed in dazzlingly white limestone, pilastered and cartouched, their interiors, at least in the Commons, are more conventionally "collegiate": paneled in wood after the manner of Inigo Jones or Christopher Wren, they look, if not Gothic, at least very English.[9] The laboratories, dormitories, and classrooms of the next two decades, however, were almost all built in a Gothic style, culminating in the Harkness Memorial Quadrangle, begun in 1917.

Located across the street from the existing Yale campus and in the middle of the city, the quadrangle's setting was, as opposed to the pastures in which Gothic-style quadrangles were erected at Princeton, more like Oxford itself. But it was the history of Yale and its relationship to the city of New Haven that brilliantly informed James Gamble Rogers's conception. He enriched and transformed what had begun as only a little more than a vaguely conceived essay in associationalism into a complicated and successful effort to unite the Jeffersonian ideal of academic Arcadia with the gridded realities of an industrialized city. An unprecedentedly lavish complex of buildings, it set a new standard for collegiate architecture.

The complex was a gift of Mrs. Stephen V. Harkness as a memorial to her son, Charles, a Yale graduate who had died the year before; the buildings' grandeur reflected the virtually limitless oil gushes that were the source of the family's fortune. It was agreed that the buildings should be Gothic, and that Rogers, an 1889 Yale graduate, who was a favorite of both the Harkness family and the university, should be the architect. It was also agreed that cost was no object.

Though Rogers in his scheme for the new quadrangle concerned himself with the security of its 630 students, he eschewed the battlemented austerity of Sturgis's paramilitary Gothicism. His version of Gothic styling and Classical planning aimed at a softer, dreamier intimacy that might serve to reassure undergraduates that Yale was a genteel child born of the marriage of American money and English antiquity. To achieve this, he took a freehanded approach to the Gothic. Indeed, the Memorial Quadrangle's success as a collegiate retreat depended on Rogers's masterly layout, which was rigorously Classical in plan, as much as on the luxurious historicizing and iconographic detail. Articulated into six enclosed courtyards, the plan provided a small scale and variety that the old campus lacked.

In the early 1890s, Columbia University in New York City retained Charles Follen McKim to create an independent academic village that could interact with the urban environment. Instead, as shown in this aerial view, its buildings formed a wall to the street, enclosing the campus against the threat of the rapidly expanding city.

The students and alumni praised it over Yale's existing buildings as "a more beautiful, a more intimate and lovable place — a retreat of courts and towers, entries and walks."[10] Indeed, it gave the students a daily routine that was an idyll fit for a princeling: a trip from Library Street took one across a landscaped moat, through a long vaulted passageway, up three steps, and into an intimate court, whose brick bounding walls were trimmed with Briar Hill sandstone, which harmonized with the quadrangle's pervasive granite. Another vaulted passage led out to the southeast corner of the great lawn of the main courtyard, 271 by 131 feet large, off of which opened two other small courtyards, similar to and aligned with Linonia, while at the northwest corner a close, lined with sculptures of Yale's mascot, the English bulldog, led to the larger, fortresslike northern courts.

To mark the entrance to the quadrangle from Yale's old campus, Rogers designed Harkness Tower. Not one to be fettered by historical precision, Rogers rejected Oxford's Magdalen Tower, the usual model for Collegiate Gothic towers. Instead Rogers stacked an improbable mixture of details and elements mined from different eras of both French and English architecture, to achieve a consummate blending that was pure poetic invention. Not all have found the result laudable.

Above. A nineteenth-century view of students at what was then rural Princeton College. The term *campus,* Latin for "field," was an American coinage, first used in 1775 to describe Princeton's leafy grounds.

Right. By the mid–nineteenth century, Princeton enjoyed an eclectic array of architectural styles. The Pennsylvania Railroad ran directly to the center of the campus, a reminder of America's increasing industrialization. The foreground shows the proximity of the town's buildings.

53   ACADEMICAL VILLAGES

Princeton as it appears today. At the turn of the century, attempts to unify the school architecturally took the form of the Collegiate Gothic style, modeled after Cambridge and Oxford universities. The campus was carefully composed to suggest a collection of buildings that had grown up together over the course of time.

Frank Lloyd Wright is reputed to have declared that if he taught at Yale, he'd have his office in Harkness Tower so that he wouldn't have to look at it.

Rogers was more interested in the feeling of history than the facts. Yet he knew precisely how to achieve an approximation of the visual effect that Oxford's and Cambridge's colleges had gained through centuries of weathering. He employed ceramic tiles rather than slate for his roofs because they looked more like his idealized vision of slate roofs than did the real thing. To give his quadrangle more history than Yale's remaining two-hundred-year-old building, Connecticut Hall, across the street, Rogers instantly wore down the stone steps of the staircases with acid and dung. He designed irregularly paned leaded windows. And, in one of architectural history's great non sequiturs, Rogers's medieval Gothic design used early-nineteenth-century brick from a demolished Yale building.

Seven years after the Memorial Quadrangle was built, Rogers took over the design of the Sterling Library when Bertram Grosvenor Goodhue, the original architect, died. Streamlining Goodhue's early sketches into a Modern Gothic mass, Rogers made the building distinctly collegiate and distinctly Yale's, using architecture to tell the university's history in a sequence of allusive, iconographically splendid spaces, embellished with genuine and invented memorabilia. If Yale's old library, by Austin, was a chapel, the Sterling Library was a cathedral; here Jefferson's appropriation of a Roman temple to serve as a working symbol of the university as a scholarly city of heaven on earth was restated in the modern university. Inside the library, one could proceed down a nave to the call desk, above which Yale art professor Eugene F. Savage's mural depicted the allegory of the female spirit of learning attended by the arts and sciences. The length of the nave was lit by stained glass that featured famous graduates and lined with brass-trimmed glass cases displaying the university's gilded relics. The main reading room, off the transept to the left, was Gothic in its thin, taut length but pure invention in its position: it ran parallel to the main nave, constituting, in effect, a twin cathedral, devoted to the practical task of research. To the right of the main entrance, a dark vestibule led to a low, cramped portal through which the light, two-storey, book-lined Linonia and Brothers Library exploded into view as a great library in an English manor house. In good weather, scholars could take their books outside into a cloistered, landscaped courtyard.

Beyond the library, past the spatially intricate Sterling Law Buildings (1930–31) and the modernized Gothic tower of the Graduate School (1930–32), which was paid for by but not named after Sterling, rose a tribute to the millionaire sportsman Harry Payne Whitney, who was fittingly memorialized by a gymnasium — certainly the largest Gothic gymnasium in the world. Rogers's Sterling Library was modestly scaled compared to John Russell Pope's realization of the Whitney gymnasium as a colossal cathedral of sweat. With a base almost as tall as the library's stack tower and a two-hundred-foot-high tower, only twenty feet lower than the Harkness Memorial Tower, the gymnasium equated the status of physical culture with that of the intellectual and the spiritual.

In 1926 Edward S. Harkness extended his family's generosity to insure Gothic collegiality to all students by building a series of new residential colleges based on the pattern established in the Memorial Quadrangle. At that time, boarding off campus was the norm for most Yale undergraduates. Harkness felt that "average men" like himself were thus missing out on much of the fraternal experience

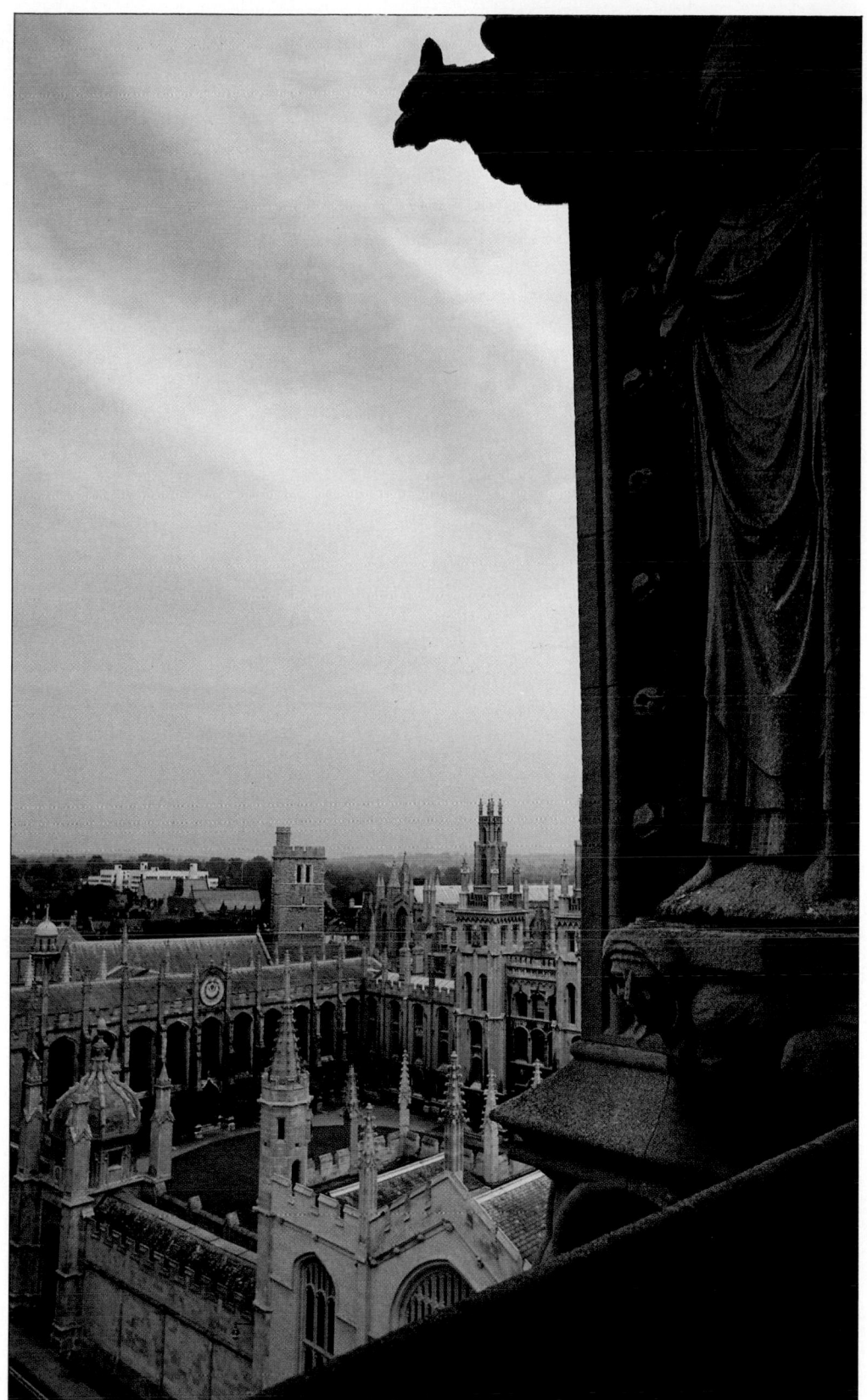

Oxford University was often used as a model for American Gothic-style campuses. Pointed arches, stone vaults, and vertical proportions are typical elements within the many independent colleges. Note the use of gargoyles (*foreground*) to drain rainwater clear of building walls.

New Haven was one of the first geometrically planned cities in America. The town attracted Yale with its offer to build a college facing the public Green that occupied the center of its nine-square configuration, shown in this 1748 plan.

college life should include. Together with Yale's president, James Rowland Angell, Harkness and Rogers traveled to England to study the residential life of colleges at Oxford and Cambridge. At them they found individual scholastic environments, with each college containing housing, dining areas, and study commons for a relatively small, cohesive group of students — an organic communal experience derived from monastic models. But Yale's trustees were reluctant to further indulge Harkness's dream of a medieval Oxbridge in Connecticut. An angered Harkness took his money to rival Harvard, donating, in December 1928, eleven million dollars to a university where neither he nor any of his family had studied. Harvard enacted a residential plan — democratically called a "house system" — as Harkness had intended to sponsor at Yale and built with his funds two on-campus dormitory houses. Yale subsequently applied to Harkness to fund a residential college program, which seemed more desirable after the humiliation of losing the bequest to Harvard. Remarkably, Harkness still had enough money left over — fifteen million dollars — to pay for eight new quadrangle colleges for Yale, begun in 1930. The budget was far less lavish than the Memorial Quadrangle's had been, but Yale made do.

Under Rogers's direction, Yale's expansion of the early 1930s enabled it to reinvent its own history in steel and stone as it carved out of one corner of the historic New Haven grid a remarkable, if introspective, city within a city. As Rogers designed them, Yale's colleges made up an architectural pedigree for the university that took students on a journey through centuries of architectural history but which took little more than a decade to build. Rogers used architecture to provide Yale with a kind of WASP version of *Roots*. As red brick Georgian returned to fashion under the impact of restored Colonial Williamsburg, Rogers propelled Yale past its opening medieval chapters into a recapitulation of its past. Davenport College, across the street from the Memorial Quadrangle, was a brilliant tour de force, designed as a deliberately transitional work, with a Gothic street façade giving way to a Colonial Georgian courtyard. The entrance passage was a masterly architectural version of a cinematic slow dissolve, with Gothic details melding almost imperceptibly to Georgian. Rogers also added an entirely Georgian quadrangle, Pierson College (1933), to the west side of Davenport College. Many of Rogers's Georgian inspirations came from Colonial America, particularly the South — an evocation furthered by the placement of a building group suggesting slave quarters off Pierson's main courtyard. The questionable taste and symbolic crassness of the gesture aside, the walls of whitewashed brick' fronted by iron stairways and railings resulted in a courtyard as successfully intimate and collegiate as the smaller courts at Branford College. Continuing his eclectic stylistic explorations at Timothy Dwight College (1934), Rogers inserted a cupola-topped New England meeting house in the crook of its L-shaped courtyard.

Whether Georgian or Gothic, Yale's quadrangles were a compromise between a pastoral ideal and urban circumstances. Hemmed in by the city at its campus borders, it was by instituting the college system and thus by turning inward that Yale's campus established and preserved its identity as a place apart. For each residential college, through its intimacy and the private preserve of its quadrangle, served its slice of the Arcadian pie. By the end of the 1930s, however, Yale, by the extent and complexity of its growth, was an academical village no more but rather a university city, diverse in its parts, a place made of many small places.

As a majority of colleges have, like Yale, grown in size and become penned in by their surroundings, many of the pastoral campuses surviving in the twentieth century are those of the exclusive preparatory schools of New England, established in the last half of the nineteenth century. The impetus for their founding was born of a variation on the Arcadian dream. Where the University of Virginia was

Nineteenth-century Yale students lounge along the old wood fence in front of College Row, an alternating series of red brick dormitories and classrooms dating from the eighteenth century. By 1900, the school had demolished all but one of the buildings in an effort to disassociate itself from its Colonial past, making way for a more unified, Gothic-style campus.

intended as a beacon of enlightened civilization for a new continent, the isolated campuses of leading preparatory schools were built as retreats from the ill effects of the increasing industrialization with which that continent was being developed. While the preparatory schools established in the eighteenth century had, like many Colonial colleges, been built facing their town's green in harmony with its architecture, those established in the nineteenth century were built as independent rural enclaves. And, given their slower rates of expansion, they offer interesting insights into the way twentieth-century architects, in adding facilities to these nineteenth-century retreats, respond to a preserved pastoral ideal.

The setting chosen by Dr. George Shattuck in 1855 for the St. Paul's School was thirteen hundred rural acres located three miles outside Concord, New Hampshire. Its first purpose-built building was a simple brick Gothic Revival chapel designed by the Boston architect George Snell. With the nurture of post–Civil War prosperity, the school expanded. Beginning with two austere, vaguely Tudoresque school buildings built in the early 1870s, gradually the school's main thoroughfare increasingly came to resemble a village street.

As the school prospered, its architecture furthered its self-image as an oasis from the industrial age. In 1886 Henry Vaughan was asked to design a new chapel for St. Paul's School. Completed in 1894 on a site set back from the road, the Chapel of St. Peter and St. Paul was a lyrical evocation of the Middle Ages, a sylvan setting as tranquil and beautiful as any in England. In 1901, the Sheldon Library, designed by Ernest Flagg, was built to face the chapel across the pond. Resembling a Renaissance temple or casino, the library provided a Classical counterpoint to Vaughan's Gothic. While at the University of Virginia, Jefferson had boldly crowned the campus with a pantheonic library that symbolized the triumph of the secular over the religious, at St. Paul's, Classical knowledge and medieval spirituality were held in careful balance. More than twenty-five years later, the complex nature of the industrial age was redefined in Charles Z. Klauder's design for a power plant, which was completed in 1927. Klauder would also design a power plant for Yale University (1929) and had designed buildings at numerous colleges and universities during the teens and twenties, most notably the forty-two-storey Gothic Cathedral of Learning at the University of Pittsburgh (1926). Klauder's power plant for St. Paul's exploited the vertical thrust of its smokestack in a Gothic scheme that related to Vaughan's chapel. It provided a perfect resolution to Henry Adams's dialectic of the Dynamo and the Virgin, in which the Virgin represented the medieval world's spirituality and communality and the Dynamo represented the confusion, materialism, and fierce energy of the modern world. How Henry Adams would have smiled at St. Paul's where the Dynamo and the Virgin were united, at least in terms of architectural style, in Gothic embrace.

As early as the close of the nineteenth century, St. Paul's had grown in a sufficiently haphazard manner that it was in danger of losing a sense of spatial coherence. In 1898 the school hired the office of Frederick Law Olmsted, the landscape architect of New York City's Central Park, to devise a proposal for the school's future growth. Olmsted's report advocated the abandonment of an increasingly urban, street-oriented scheme in favor of a more Arcadian development, consisting of a grouping of buildings arranged around a central open area. The report suggested a small river valley located to the south of the main road as an advantageous site for future expansion. While buildings, including the library and the large Jacobean-style New Upper School (1902–4) designed by Vaughan did not strictly conform to the proposed plan, a series of buildings erected in the 1920s and 1930s realized Olmsted's vision, while the campus as a whole maintained an informal and naturalistically laid-out plan.

Within St. Paul's Arcadian setting, historically referential architecture designed during its first hundred years of existence furthered Shattuck's original aim of establishing a place apart. In 1937 James Gamble Rogers's School House continued the Gothic dreamworld, extending architectural themes he had established at Yale. But since the 1960s, the dream has become diffuse. There is still

Below are two exceptions to Yale's typically Gothic-style campus. *Left:* Architect Alexander Jackson Davis added battlements and crenelated towers to Alumni Hall in 1852, imparting a more militaristic, castlelike appearance. *Right:* Students gather at Romanesque Osborne Hall at the turn of the century.

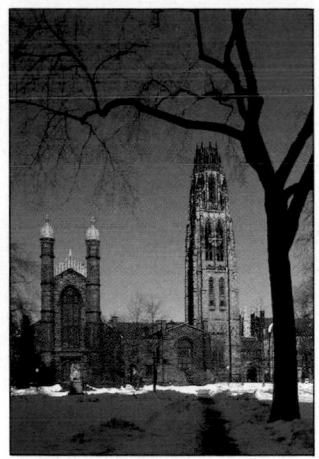

Entry to Memorial Quadrangle is marked by Harkness Tower, an improbable but inspired mixture of details and elements from different eras of English and French architecture. The architect "aged" his creation by applying acid to its stone steps, designing irregularly shaped leaded windows, and using early-nineteenth-century brick taken from a demolished Yale building.

Left. The arch of Harkness Memorial Quadrangle at Yale University opens onto one of six enclosed courtyards. Designed by Yale graduate James Gamble Rogers and begun in 1917, the quadrangle plan provided a small scale and variety that the old campus lacked.

an intimate scale to the campus, but the newer buildings have abandoned Vaughan's medievalism for the red brick of the mills and mercantilism that Shattuck had struggled to escape from one hundred years before. Dormitories and faculty apartments (1961–63) designed by Edward Larrabee Barnes and facilities for the study of music and dance (1980) designed by Hardy, Holzman & Pfeiffer look more like the gritty red brick factories of nearby Manchester than the cloistral enclaves of Oxbridge. As at Yale, where during the nineteenth century Colonial architecture, now the beloved model for so much American building, was considered too raw and crude for the high aspirations of a major university, at St. Paul's it seems that the once-loathed brick factories of New England have been sufficiently romanticized to become the source material for an Arcadian dream.

While the haphazard growth of St. Paul's has lent it an air of rural informality that is part of its strength as a place, certain original visions are so strong as to impede successful expansion. Fortunately for the Westover School, which occupies a ninety-acre site near Middlebury, Connecticut, its late-twentieth-century expansion augments rather than detracts from its original coherence as a campus. As designed by Theodate Pope Riddle in 1912, the school followed the model of English hospitals and almshouses, with all facilities housed in a single building enclosing a quadrangle. Domestic rather than monumental in its architectural vocabulary, the building was sheathed in ecru stucco, its windows adorned with dark green shutters, and its mass surmounted by a gabled roof of Pennsylvania slate, which was punctuated by numerous dormers, chimneys, and a cupola over the main entrance. Inside the building, an English Cotswold-inspired arcade along the ground floor created a cloistered walkway. As the student body and function of the school changed from girls' finishing school to young women's preparatory institution, it became both functionally and symbolically important to extend the school beyond Riddle's cloister. A bland, boxlike activities building awkwardly attached in the 1960s to the original building at its southwest corner had not provided a promising beginning. In the late 1970s the architects Charles Gwathmey and Robert Siegel provided an ingenious, contextually sensitive design for expansion. They extended one of the original building's interior arcades beyond the cloister out to a wing containing new science laboratories and a library. While it replicated the materials of the original arcade, its forms created a volumetric, sculptural quality that even Riddle's design lacked.

Between the cloister and the science building, the arcades succeed in both masking the unattractive activities building and simultaneously binding this once-foreign building into the sort of architectural coherence originally created by Riddle. At midpoint along the arcade, a grandstand spills down to one side, providing a vantage point from which to view the playing field and the countryside beyond. Terminating the arcade, the tower of an observatory provides a visual coda for the arcade and a deferential nod to the cupola Riddle installed above the entrance to her cloister. The observatory, like the grandstand, both literally and symbolically provides views of the world beyond the campus.

In planning the University of Virginia, Jefferson had imagined it as a model for all American campuses, but it was, after all, only a state university. From the Revolution until the election of Andrew Jackson as president in 1828, the new nation's leaders repeatedly proposed a national university. George Washington mentioned it in his message to Congress in 1790, and one of the most impressive

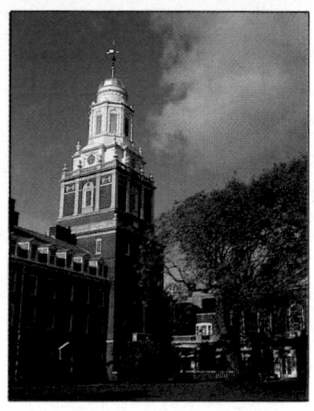

Top. For Branford College in Harkness Memorial Quadrangle, architect James Gamble Rogers employed the Gothic style.

Center. Davenport College was built by Rogers in the 1930s. A deliberately transitional work, its Gothic exterior gradually gives way to a Colonial Georgian courtyard.

Bottom. Pierson College (1933), Rogers's entirely Georgian quadrangle, was inspired by buildings of the Colonial South.

groups of proposals came in 1799 in response to an essay competition sponsored by the American Philosophical Society. Minister and educator Samuel Knox wrote an essay that included an architectural description imbued with the Enlightenment's respect for science and the applied arts. Set a few miles outside Washington, D.C., Knox's campus for a national university would have consisted of two concentric quadrangles enclosing a square building, with classrooms, library, and faculty housing in the outer quadrangle, student residences in the interior one, and at the center, a building for teaching decorative arts, a printing office, and an astronomical observatory situated in a dome.[11] In 1816 Benjamin Henry Latrobe, who had contributed to the college designs of the University of Pennsylvania (1802–5), Princeton (1802), and Dickinson College (1803) as well as the University of Virginia, drew up a scheme for a national university at the end of the Mall in Washington, D.C. Latrobe's design followed many of the enlightened collegiate principles that inspired Jefferson's University of Virginia. A great "U" on axis to the Capitol, its central building was not a chapel but an entrance hall crowned by a symbol of science: an observatory. Religion was sequestered outside the campus gates and aligned with the observatory and Capitol. A library and refectory flanked the colonnaded entrance hall, while the identical perpendicular wings followed a pattern of two projecting professors' houses, lodging rooms, and hall. The parallel arrangement of faculty house–dormitory–faculty house, a rational articulation of collegiate ideals, would only be realized a decade later in Latrobe's contributions to a state institution, the University of Virginia.

But instead of a federal university in the nation's capital dedicated to the humanistic disciplines, America's only national educational institutions were realized in service academies dedicated to military science, with cadets from every state in the nation, nominated by the country's elected officials. In 1802 the United States Military Academy was founded at West Point; forty-three years later, the Naval Academy opened at Annapolis. At their founding neither academy benefited from an architectural plan as coherent as Knox's or Latrobe's, but following the Spanish-American War, which had provided the nation's military forces with their first opportunity to reunite on the battlefield since the Civil War, a Congress inspired with newfound national pride provided West Point and Annapolis with the means to transform their haphazard grounds into monumental, unified campuses befitting America's new role as a world power.

In 1845, the U.S. Naval Academy was established at Fort Severn in Annapolis, rather than at the Naval Asylum in Philadelphia, reputedly on the decision of Secretary of the Navy George Bancroft. A university man, he was convinced that a campus should be designed at a "healthy and secluded" site away from the "temptations and distractions that necessarily connect with a large and populous city."[12] The small and not very populous town of Annapolis had an orthogonal pattern to its quiet streets. The vacated army buildings of Fort Severn — which included a circular stone battery and seven other, mostly red brick buildings — within walls aligned with the town's streets were askew, oriented instead to the riverbank. Throughout the nineteenth century, many of the buildings added by the navy continued to be sited facing the riverbank, while others spread along the town's streets as new land was acquired for expansion. Architecturally, the new buildings reflected the growing success and status of the navy, with many buildings of fine civic character and stylistic aspirations.

The chapel built in 1854, for example, was an elegant Greek Revival building. Adjacent to it was the meandering Seamanship Hall, one gable-end of which sported the elaborate corner quoins of a fortified Italian palazzo. Later buildings include a Victorian Gothic red brick chapel (1868) and a four-storey vestigially Georgian brick edifice with an octagonal pediment and wrought iron balconies. But the hodgepodge of architectural styles and the two different geometries by which different buildings were organized created neither visual coherence nor any strong sense of place.

On the heels of the navy's great success in the Spanish-American War, Congress granted funds for essentially a complete reconstruction of the academy. The project architect, Ernest Flagg, French trained and New York based, found little to praise in the existing situation, removing all but three gatehouses from the original campus in the course of completing his work. The question of the conflicting campus geometries was resolved by dredging and landfilling until the river's edge aligned with that of the town and the new academy. What had been an open, treed lawn at the point where the two orders collided was reshaped into a square by the new buildings and boat basin defining its perimeter. Flagg's scheme flaunted the arts and sciences of war in full Roman regalia. Jefferson had to content himself with a continental empire. Ernest Flagg had all the seven seas. The Naval Academy prepared midshipmen to administer the oceanic empire that America had acquired almost overnight in 1899 when Admiral Dewey triumphantly sailed into Manila Harbor.

Whereas Jefferson had turned pretty directly to Rome for inspiration, Flagg looked to Paris. The academy's buildings and their siting were based on the great military buildings of Paris, the Hôtel des Invalides (main building by Liberal Bruant [1670–77], dome by Jules Hardouin-Mansart [1680–91]) and L'École Militaire (1750–68) by Jacques-Ange Gabriel. The academy's chapel (1908), under a huge dome inspired by Mansart, sat at the center of the town side of the campus, facing the Severn River beyond, while the dormitory and academic buildings perpendicular to it defined the other two sides of the quadrangle bounded by the boat basin.

Even more than Jefferson's, Flagg's was a modern Classicism, invigorating historical precedent with advanced construction technology. Granite was machine cut into crisp cornered blocks and steel roof trusses were employed. Bancroft Hall, built as the midshipmen's dormitory, is five storeys high and 733 feet wide. Its campus entrance consists of two rampways bowed around a central flight of stairs which lead to three doorways framed by massive columns. An ornate frieze and cornice above the entrance is topped by a balustrade through which project as decor and iconography the prows of elaborate vessels.

Despite budget restrictions on the library and flanking classroom buildings, which faced Bancroft Hall across the quadrangle, Flagg sustained the campus's monumental scale. Although the library was smaller than planned and gray brick was substituted for granite, elements like the 140-foot-high clock tower atop the library succeed in providing some balance to the domed chapel and the vast Bancroft Hall. The French Classical façades face what is formally a cour d'honneur, although with its lawn, trees, and meandering paths retained from the original campus, it suggests the mighty transformation to which it was subject.

Like the Naval Academy, the U.S. Military Academy at West Point developed in its early years without a formal plan or architectural distinction. As increasingly finer buildings were constructed, their styles were, as at Annapolis, eclectic: a Greek Revival chapel in 1836, a Georgian academic building (1838), and, with the library of 1841, a martial Gothic architecture created from the grim local granite. Through the century, fine exemplars of both Classical and Gothic styling were built. Richard Morris Hunt's Gothic trio of gymnasium, academic building, and guardhouse (1893–97), for example, contrasted with McKim, Mead & White's Classical pink granite box, Cullum Memorial Hall (1893–98).

At the turn of the century, however, the army, like the navy, chose to turn its collection of buildings into a campus. It was to be as grand and imposing as the academy's site on a high bluff above a bend in the Hudson River. Those empowered to determine the form and style of the campus felt that it was the Gothic buildings on campus that set the most appropriate tone. As one report on the subject insisted: "It is not desirable that any scheme should attempt to sweep the field clean and destroy architectural associations made honorable by generations of great men, while it is of the highest importance to preserve intact the structural sentiment which gives character and individuality to the Academy."[13]

The architects selected, Cram, Goodhue & Ferguson, incorporated existing buildings into the design of a romantic vision of a medieval fortress. Buildings rising from sheer cliff faces and retaining walls, roof lines crenelated like battlements, walls buttressed — all combined to create a citadel above the American Rhine. Unencumbered by the moral vision that governed his partner, Ralph Adams Cram, in his work at Princeton, Bertram Goodhue created stylistic and imagistic coherence through free reinterpretation of the Gothic idiom. As a contemporary journal reported:

It may be said at once that nowhere does the style verge on archaeology or copying of any sort. The work is, of course, Gothic (whatever that may mean) in that it has no affiliations with any other historic style; its composition and details are based very solidly on the medieval work of England and the Continent. If it is Gothic, it is Gothic used with extreme flexibility; the Gothic idea and method, rather than the assembling of traditionally Gothic forms.[14]

At West Point, the natural site, the client's sentiment, and some preexisting buildings led toward an architectural idiom capable of sustaining a coherent environment of appropriate symbolic connotations. In their work later at William Marsh Rice Institute in the raw, new city of Houston, Cram and Goodhue were faced with the challenge of creating a place with no clues as to the appropriate character. As Cram described it:

A college was to be created *de novo* in Texas. What to do? Here was a plane-like area with no cultural traditions except those of the flimsiest with Mexico. Racially it was New England, culturally it was Middle West. What style could be used as a *point d'appui*? The so-called Mission style . . . the strange and effulgent Renaissance of Mexico . . . the Colonial of New England, the "Collegiate Gothic"? None seemed really possible under the circumstances, either because of obvious affectation, inapplicability to climatic conditions, prohibitive costs, or just obvious impropriety.[15]

The task was particularly arduous. Though at first the relatively undeveloped Western territories seemed to offer the designer and planner greater freedom than was allowed in the rebuilding of the older colleges and service academies of the East, it was, as in Jefferson's time, precisely the sense of placelessness that drove architects back into history in search of real or imagined traditions.

Founded in 1889 as a polytechnic school, Rice University in Houston, Texas, had much more modest beginnings than Stanford, but by 1909 the institute's endowment had grown to be the seventh largest in the country. In addition, Rice had an ambitious former Princeton professor, Edgar Odell Lovett, as president, who reshaped Rice into a major university.

The challenge of a Western setting pushed the Eastern architects Cram, Goodhue, and Ferguson, well known for their Gothicism, toward a new synthesis that combined Classical order with exotic styles reflecting their dreamy imaginings of south Texas as an American Venice. A tree-lined driveway extending through the Texas plain for a quarter mile passes through a central portal cut through the Administration Building onto an equally long campus mall, called the Academic Court, which is flanked along its length by long, narrow buildings. Opposite the Administration Building, a huge auditorium was to close the mall and terminate the long entrance axis; a library eventually filled the site. Building groups at both ends of the court are linked with arcades, a gesture in response not only to cloistral collegiality but also to Houston's semitropical climate, in which shaded walkways have particular appeal.

The Administration Building, which opened in 1912, condensed a few thousand years of Venetian cross-cultural synthesis into a narrow, colonnaded slab. With a cloister of Romanesque arches on one elevation and with a second-storey loggia behind Classical piers and columns on another, with masonry so decoratively and colorfully combined as to appear almost a relic from Byzantium, and with balusters derived from medieval Venetian palaces, the building is an associational mix of scholarship, piety, and power. If the architectural borrowings failed to instruct, students could take their lessons from the reliefs of great men and allegorical figures carved in tablets set into the brick walls of its second storey. For the auditorium, planned but never constructed, Goodhue looked to Persian Isfahan for inspiration: its towering spherical dome faced with multicolored tile and marble would have dominated the campus. For East Hall (1913–15), Cram, the principal designer, took Goodhue's exoticism further and turned to the Orient for architectural inspiration, lifting the third storey's dark wooden window bays from a Bhutanese building illustrated in the April 1914 issue of *National Geographic*.[16]

The Morrill Act of 1862 granted each state federal land as an endowment for one or more state colleges offering instruction in the democratic disciplines of agriculture and the mechanic arts in addition to the traditional liberal arts curriculum. The campuses built under the Morrill Act generally spurned antique, Gothic, or Classical styling for a thoroughgoing eclecticism believed to express more democratic ideals. The president of one land grant college, John Anderson, at Kansas State Agricultural College, stated that his campus's architecture should be as democratic as its principles, "cheap, stone buildings, one or two stories, scattered among the trees."[17] In reality, this translated into the massive, towered, Victorian Gothic pile of College Hall (1877). At least a few times, as under the prodding of a bold, rich visionary like Phoebe Apperson Hearst, or with the

Ernest Flagg reconstructed the U.S. Naval Academy at Annapolis on the heels of the navy's great success in the Spanish-American War. Flagg's scheme derived from the great military buildings of Paris. Despite budget restrictions, the library (*above*) sustained the campus's monumental scale.

dogged search for an image by an institution like the University of Texas, new universities in the West rose to the challenge of invention, and — as at the University of Virginia — special places of character, memorable, distinct environments for learning, were created in the wilderness.

The planners of privately funded universities, endowed with more cash and more leisure to think, recognized architecture's capacity to transform a collection of buildings and a curriculum into an identifiable place. In 1886, Leland Stanford, a railroad baron, former governor of and United States senator from California, founded a university to memorialize his only son, Leland Stanford, Jr., who had died two years before. To lay out the university, which was to be located on Stanford's eight-thousand-acre Palo Alto estate, he hired Frederick Law Olmsted, who drew up a plan incorporating domestically scaled buildings picturesquely distributed along winding paths in the hilly uplands. Olmsted's inherently modest proposal disappointed Stanford, who insisted on a monumental grouping on the flat plain below. Olmsted obliged him with a mile-long approach lined by palm trees, which ended in a memorial arch that would have satisfied an emperor.

Stanford chose as his university's architect Charles A. Coolidge, a partner in the Boston firm of Shepley, Rutan & Coolidge, which had taken over Henry Hobson Richardson's practice. In his design for the main campus group, Coolidge emulated the Romanesque manner of Richardson but moved beyond it toward a more rigidly Classical massing that incorporated the images of a cloistered Romanesque monastery, California's missions, and English collegiate quadrangles. The triple-arched porch and steeply pitched crossing tower of the Memorial Church rose on axis with the campus's monumental entrance. (Both the church and arch were felled by the 1906 earthquake. The church was rebuilt without a tower in 1913, while the Memorial Arch was never reconstructed, leaving the campus with a much more horizontal character than was Coolidge's intention.) Crossing the axis was a long rectangle of lawn, rimmed by continuous arcades whose squat columns and heavy masonry managed to evoke both the stone monasteries of southern France and the adobe missions of California.

Just as the universities of the West challenged architects seeking to provide a convincing sense of collegiality and an appropriate sense of place, the emergence of technological institutes, which were almost exclusively concerned with the present and the future as represented by the relentless pursuit of quantifiable progress in science and engineering, also posed new architectural challenges. The Massachusetts Institute of Technology, founded in 1859 with a curriculum that was relentlessly future-oriented, nonetheless delved into the past to establish its institutional identity through architecture. At first, MIT was located in Boston's Back Bay in a not particularly distinguished building designed by Jonathan and William G. Preston in 1866. It was a richly decorated composition with a Corinthian portico above a rusticated base. But it was not until the first decade of the twentieth century, when MIT outgrew its quarters and moved across the Charles River to become Harvard's neighbor in Cambridge, that MIT set out in earnest to create a symbol of rational modernity. As designed by William Welles Bosworth, the institute's building complex was a stark limestone monument. While MIT abandoned the Jeffersonian tradition of humanist education, its campus recalled the University of Virginia. But unlike Jefferson's campus, MIT made no gestures to the local vernacular. Bosworth rejected the Arcadian village ideal,

The Gothic-style Military Academy at West Point, designed by Bertram Goodhue, created the illusion of a medieval fortress, here seen in a contemporary photograph. Buildings that rise from cliff faces, crenelated roof lines, and buttressed retaining walls combine to form a citadel on the Hudson River.

losing both its domestic scale and stylistic variety in favor of the Ionic order wrapped around a single enormous megastructure. MIT's was a self-referential Classicism, which in its aspiration to be a pure architecture recalled the visionary work of French architects Claude-Nicolas Ledoux and Étienne-Louis Boulée. But while Ledoux and Boulée had redefined their buildings' vast scale with arches and ornaments, Bosworth left it to lettering, dentils, moldings, and Ionic volutes. Arranged around a central court, MIT's connected pavilions were inscribed with the names of the heroes of science — Archimedes, Leonardo, Darwin — but beyond that the buildings were uncorrupted by the associational mumbo jumbo that characterized the liberal arts universities. Its halls were nameless, flexible for an ever-expanding curriculum, only qualified as Building A, Building B, and so on.

While in 1916 MIT's stone architecture had "an austerity that suggests steel and concrete,"[18] twenty years later architects argued that the structure should *be* steel and concrete. Architecture began to feel an obligation less to the age-old continuities and more to the uniqueness of the present. In 1937 Ludwig Mies van der Rohe, the German architect who had served as the last director of the Bauhaus, a school and workshop which was the greatest hotbed of Modernist architectural thought and design in Europe, immigrated to the United States at the invitation of the Illinois Institute of Technology, which had just been founded as a result of the merger of the Lewis and Armour institutes. Mies was asked to head IIT's architecture school and to design the institute's new campus on a hundred-acre site on Chicago's South Side, which was degenerating into one of the city's worst slums.

As Mies designed it, IIT became an industrial age answer to Jefferson's University of Virginia, substituting technology for history as the subject of design. Mies's glass-steel-and-concrete buildings mirrored his clients' hard-headed pragmatism as precisely as Jefferson had reflected his own dreams for the new nation's institutions of learning. No matter their function — laboratory, office, or

Charles A. Coolidge designed the main campus group of Stanford University in Palo Alto, California. The buildings, massed in a Classical manner, evoke images of a cloistered Romanesque monastery, California's missions — represented here by red tile roofs — and English collegiate quadrangles.

workshop — the buildings were based on a spatial module of twenty feet square and twelve feet high. While IIT's formal purity clearly reflected Mies's view that "where technology attains its true fulfilment, it transcends into architecture,"[19] its minimalism and relentless consistency rendered the buildings inarticulate to the public. At IIT, the critic Charles Jencks has pointed out, "you can't tell the church from the boilerhouse and the boilerhouse looks very much like a church because it has a campanile, it has clerestory windows and in effect, an aisle."[20] Mies seemed to be arguing that, in the terms of Henry Adams's dialectic, the force of modern technology had replaced the medieval power of the Virgin as the principal focus of contemporary life. However, it can also be seen as Mies's simply replacing the Virgin with agnosticism.

Mies rejected as sentimental the historic associationalism of American university architecture. In contrast to Jefferson's scheme for the University of Virginia, where each building facing the lawn served as a distinct model of architectural excellence, Mies's buildings at IIT instructed only in the lessons of technology and construction. Mies willingly condemned architecture to an existential world without past or future: "We reject all aesthetic speculation. . . . Not yesterday, not tomorrow, only today can be given form," he had proclaimed in 1923, stating in the following year that "ours is not an age of pathos; we do not respect flights of the spirit as much as we value reason and realism."[21] But however rooted in the concrete and the practical, the technology that Mies deified was itself not an eternal truth but a variable, a constantly evolving standard. Mies's escape from the past into the technological present in time became subject to history as well, taking on, in less than half a century, a dreamlike, almost quaint quality, evoking the nostalgia for the machine age one now feels when watching Charlie Chaplin's 1936 film *Modern Times*.

Mies was trained as a Classicist architect and he understood the use of stone and other traditional building materials to a far greater extent than most of his contemporaries. In his designs for IIT, he struggled to create an order based on the steel I-beam that could compare with the traditional orders of Classicism. In his new architectural lexicon, the order of the I-beam enjoyed the status that the Greek Doric or Tuscan orders had had for Jefferson. Crown Hall was IIT's Parthenon. Housing the departments of architecture, planning, and design, it symbolized Mies's belief that humanistic concerns were at the core of even the purest technology. The roof was suspended from four mammoth plate-girder trusses and a colonnade of freestanding I-beams was reduced to the status of window mullions placed at ten-foot intervals largely to ornament the façades.

Despite its self-referential Modernist attitude toward form, the placement of Mies's buildings on the site seems, at first, as limpid as Jefferson's. Mies's original site plan called for a symmetrical and axial arrangement of buildings, shaping a central quadrangle flanked by subsidiary building groups. However, Chicago's denial of permission to close a thoroughfare that crossed the campus resulted in the omission of a central open space. The revised enlarged scheme of 1940 resulted in a somewhat less formal design, which further blurred the initial clarity of Mies's approach. By denying the campus a physical and symbolic focus like Jefferson's Rotunda and Lawn, Mies denied the campus one of its primary functions, that of bringing people together in a cloistered world, apart from the surrounding context, whether urban or rural.

Above. The Memorial Church at Stanford University was felled by the 1906 earthquake and reconstructed in 1913 without its steeply pitched tower, giving the campus a more horizontal character. Here, the church is framed by one of the arches that surround the courtyard.

Right. Cram, Goodhue & Ferguson designed the building groups at Rice University in Houston, Texas. They are linked together with arcades, a gesture not only to cloistral collegiality but also to the semitropical climate in which shaded walkways have particular appeal.

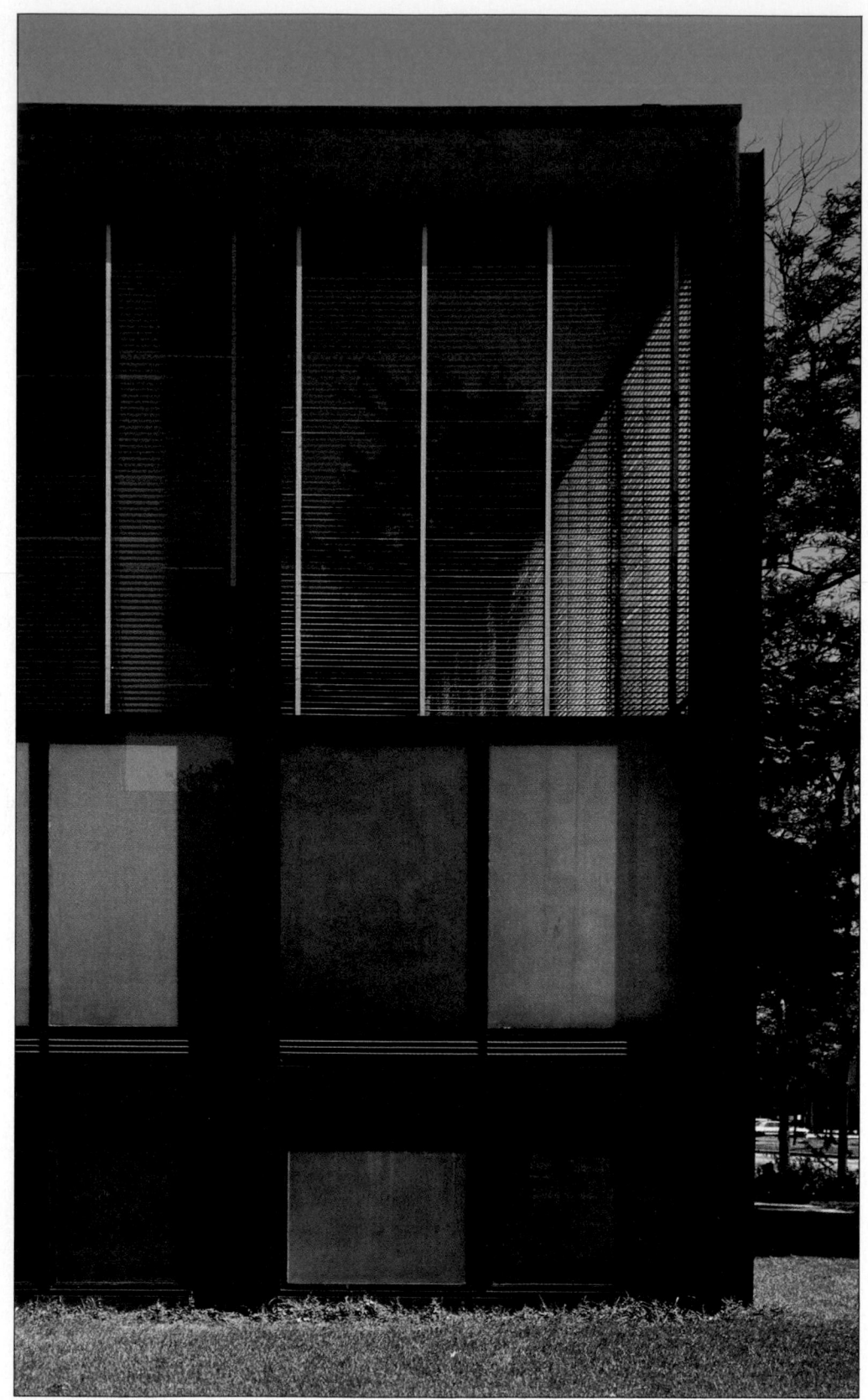

Mies van der Rohe's Modernist buildings are lessons in technology and construction. This corner detail of Crown Hall at the Illinois Institute of Technology shows that the steel I-beam was to Mies what the Classical column was to Jefferson at the University of Virginia.

Mies considered the architecture of most American universities sentimental in its historical associations. His 1940 design for the Illinois Institute of Technology on Chicago's South Side was organized on a grid pattern, echoed in the details of each building module.

Under the influence of Mies's rigorously Modernist scheme for IIT, a generation of architects sought to rid the American campus of its traditionally "collegiate" look, as well as of any regional identity, retaining only the central notion of a planned, self-contained community. After World War II, the increased automobility of Americans made it possible for many corporations to contemplate a move away from the cities. Lured by large tracts of available land as well as by tax incentives, corporations like General Motors, swelled by new profits, aggrandized themselves by building office complexes that emulated college campuses. When Eero Saarinen designed the General Motors Technical Center (1946–56), he based his work on IIT, yet much of Mies's structural and intellectual rigor was sacrificed to the requirements and tastes of America's mightiest corporation. Located on a nine-hundred-acre site in Warren, Michigan, just north of Detroit, the Tech Center's elaborately landscaped grounds were, not surprisingly, scaled to the automobile. For General Motors's "campus," Saarinen arranged forty-one buildings around a twenty-two-acre rectilinear pool, punctuated by islands landscaped with willow trees and by a fountain — a 115-foot-wide, 50-foot-high "wall" of water designed by the sculptor Alexander Calder. But just in case the manmade landscape appeared indulgent, the pool was also equipped with a water tower and served the eminently practical function of water recirculation for the center's vast air-conditioning system.

Souping up the Miesian vocabulary with brightly colored exterior walls and slickly finished materials, including glazed bricks and porcelain panels, Saarinen's architecture perfectly reflected the car industry's consumerist pitch. For the Tech Center, Saarinen designed a grand dome, casually placed off-center in the composition, which nonetheless powerfully evoked Jefferson's Rotunda. But if for Jefferson form followed philosophy, for Saarinen, poet-pragmatist of the American consumerist dream, form followed fantasy. At GM, the dome did not enshrine books but late-model cars, which were displayed on revolving turntables.

The Connecticut General Life Insurance Company also moved to the country during the fifties, isolating its staff on a 280-acre campus so remote from urban pleasures and conveniences that it had to provide shops, restaurants, and beauty salons for its three thousand employees. In the Bloomfield hills, five miles from the center of America's insurance capital — Hartford, Connecticut — Skidmore, Owings & Merrill's 1952 design for Connecticut General Life's headquarters stripped away even more of Mies's symbolism, wrapping acres of anonymous office space in thin, slickly finished skins of glass, aluminum, and stainless steel. While the scheme's cool elegance was everywhere apparent, the relentless reductivism led some to label the Skidmore triumvirate the "three blind Mies." No domes, no water tower campaniles here; inside and out, the grid dominated all. Florence Knoll, the interior designer, provided the standardized furniture, which, should it be unintentionally moved by an actuarial quirk, could be realigned to the two-centimeter-wide bands that defined the grid on the floor and ceiling. To realize the grid's full potential of placelessness, the walls were demountable planes of red, blue, yellow, and gray plastic laminate that could be anchored anywhere in

The General Motors Technical Center was located on nine hundred acres north of Detroit. In the tradition of Mies at IIT, architect Eero Saarinen rid the design of the traditional collegiate campus look, while retaining the sense of a self-contained community. The car is parked outside the glossy showroom.

this vast sea of bureaucracy. Gordon Bunshaft, the architect in charge of the project, chose to monumentalize only one corporate activity — lunch. Projecting from a corner of the main building, the cafeteria was a glass-walled lunch box–like pavilion.

By the 1950s corporate America had so completely come to embody American values that Charles E. Wilson, president of General Motors, could publicly state that what was good for GM was good for the country. When the United States Army Air Corps, which had just been elevated to independent status as the Air Force, set out to build its own academy, it turned to SOM — the corporate architects par excellence — to realize on earth its dream of a heavenly — or perhaps outer-space — city, a dream not of the past but of the future. With the Naval Academy clothed in Classicism and the army's West Point military academy in Gothic, the air force rejected associations with the architectural past and chose to realize a dream of the future in International Style Modernism. SOM's gloss on Modernism perfectly suited the "scientific-technological elite" of the growing "military-industrial complex" that President Eisenhower would warn against in his farewell message to the country in 1961. The Air Force Academy (1956–63) was set on nearly eighteen thousand acres, at the foot of the Rampart Range of the Rocky Mountains in Colorado. The site and the need to instantly create an institution with its own traditions conspired to raise the inherent materialism of the architecture to the level of fantasy, albeit of the glitzy Hollywood variety. With Cecil B. De Mille designing the cadet uniforms, it was as if the Chocolate Soldier had gotten lost in Buck Rogers's twenty-fifth century.

Abandoning the greenery of traditional campus design, Walter Netsch, SOM's architect in charge, set the academy on a powerfully massed podium, the rough concrete surface of which was crisscrossed by a grid of foot-wide marble paths. While the paved surface was largely a response to the need to plow during the long, snowy Colorado winters, it also reflected the academy's inherent bias toward rationalism and timeless modernity. Yet architecture has a power to forge traditions: the grid has created a daily ritual for freshmen cadets, who must march only along the lines while upperclassmen, having paid their dues, roam the entire field.

The academy's classrooms and residence halls, like the buildings at the General Motors Technical Center, were the familiar corporate slicked-up versions of Mies's IIT, apparently arbitrarily cordoned-off blocks of space within a larger grid. Long horizontal buildings — such as Mitchell Hall, the vast 252-foot-square column-free pavilion in which all of the academy's cadets and officers, numbering nearly four thousand, could dine at once — marked off various portions of the grid, capturing paved courtyards of sorts from the undifferentiated space. For the chapel, Walter Netsch sought to render the aspirational verticality of traditional Gothic form in the materiality of steel pipe, aluminum, and glass, folded in tetrahedrons. Against the overwhelming majesty of the mountainscape, however, that which was no doubt undertaken as a grand search comes off as a trivial pursuit. For Frank Lloyd Wright, who mocked SOM as "Skiddings, Owe More, and Sterile,"[22] the campus was clear evidence that "commercialization has eaten pretty deep into our architectural inspiration." Neither harmonious with its surroundings nor aspirational in its own right, the academy, despite its massive scale, seemed to Wright like little more than a "wayside market."[23]

Walter Netsch had a second opportunity to design a campus in the 1960s, not in the wilderness of the American West, but on the new frontier — the concrete jungle of a typical American city, Chicago. The University of Illinois, whose fine, traditional main campus is in the small town of Champaign, sought for their Chicago campus a suburban site with lawns, trees, and open space. But Chicago's mayor, Richard J. Daley, made the university an offer it couldn't refuse: 118 acres of land in a depressed neighborhood to be transformed by urban renewal — or "urban removal," the term preferred by critics to describe the savage mid-century destruction of declining urban areas.

Netsch, seeking to resolve the conflict between the university's dream of a suburban setting and the realities of an urban commuter college, devised a highly disciplined multilevel gridiron plan buffered from the surrounding city on all sides by wide bands of greenery. His design struggled to realize an academic village that would be an oasis from the relentless gridiron of Chicago. Though the campus, opened in 1965, was the product of a meticulous consideration of the material needs of students and faculty, it does little to symbolize their aspirations. From the peripheral parking garages, the university community circulates on second-storey pedestrian "expressways" — no exits or intersections — which lead to the center of the campus: a 450-by-300-foot rooftop plaza. Unfortunately, the elevated granite walkways are blazing infernos of reflected heat in summer and snow-and-ice-covered nightmares in winter. It was as if Netsch and his colleagues had never been to Chicago, though their offices were only about a mile away. The pedestrian circulation system not only failed to function well in the extremes of Chicago's harsh climate but it trivialized the technological advances of engineering that had inspired it. Most significantly, it denied the campus its principal function of bringing people together in a self-contained environment conducive to learning.

The campus as a whole was riddled by a geometry gone mad. While geometry disciplined Jefferson's cultural aspirations for the University of Virginia, at the University of Illinois at Chicago its pervasiveness not only created spaces that were psychologically alienating and physically disorienting but also eliminated any wider cultural meaning from the design. The campus's original name, the University of Illinois at Chicago Circle, was telling. It referred to the adjacent intersection of three expressways that provided access to downtown, the suburbs, and outlying areas — not a place but a nonplace, through which motorists sped on their way to someplace else. Perhaps Netsch's scheme was intended as a training ground, or as a tribute to the more than twenty thousand students who daily commuted to the campus, many of whom would go on to work in suburban offices located next to anonymous highways — which just might, after four years at the Circle campus, feel like home. In the midst of this geometric jungle, Jefferson Hall stood as a bungled tribute to a man and a tradition that seemed to be remembered in name only.

Netsch's campus took us as far as we could go from Jefferson's Arcadia. Instead of students and faculty meeting at individual house-temples and enjoying the casual sociality of lawn and arcade, the University of Illinois at Chicago Circle offered only the impersonality of the superhighway. If IIT had the quirky charm of *Modern Times,* Chicago Circle was portentous, like the film of H. G. Wells's *Things to Come* (1936), all too powerfully warning of a future without a past.

By mid-century the ominous possibility that denying the past would condemn us to a future without dreams was perceived with increasing discomfort by growing numbers of architects and patrons. Efforts to reinvest campus planning with acknowledgments of a shared and meaningful history took many forms. The campus as an ideal survives because, for most of us, it is our last best hope to dream. At its best, the campus is an escape from the everyday that elevates even the most banal tastes to the level of dedicated scholarship. Since the 1940s two concepts of the ideal campus have competed for Americans' attention, if not necessarily for their affection: one is the campus as a place where the past, ancient or recent, informs the present; the other is a place of abstract principles, a place in which the future is discovered in the context of an eternal present. The competition between these ideals is perhaps most clearly illustrated by two research institutions dedicated to scientific study: the Salk Institute in La Jolla, California, and the Cold Spring Harbor Laboratories on the north shore of Long Island. Their directors, Dr. Francis Crick and Dr. James D. Watson, respectively, once worked together and shared the 1962 Nobel Prize in physiology and medicine for their discovery of DNA.

At the Salk Institute, Louis Kahn tried to create a campus in which history was transcended into the realm of pure geometry. Completed in 1965, the Salk Institute consists of a superbly rational structural and spatial matrix. Open, highly flexible, column-free spaces for labs alternate with spaces through which full-storey-high ducts containing all utilities can be moved around at will. Individual studies and seminar rooms form the only traditional rooms — except for the "room" of the magnificently barren central court, in which the only adornment is a tiny rill that seems to carry water from the distant hills that form the institute's backdrop down to the sea below. This institute is one of the most perfectly constructed works in concrete ever. The normally obdurate mix of cement, sand, and water has been coaxed into a marblelike density and meticulously poured to suggest industrial age masonry, which gives the building the dignity and chthonic majesty of an ancient ruin. Kahn strove for this effect even in his earliest designs, derived from his studies of the remains of the emperor Hadrian's first-century villa outside Rome. Its Roman sources notwithstanding, Kahn's scheme for the Salk Institute contains no sentimentality, no cozy contextualism. In fact, it suggests a stance consistent with the theory of dreams Crick had co-authored with Dr. Graeme Mitchison while at the Salk Institute. In it, they reason that man must dream in order to "unlearn" or purge the mind of unwanted connections. To remember a dream of the night before may damage our daily present-oriented life, argues Crick, who has said, "We dream in order to forget."[24]

On the opposite side of the country, the Cold Spring labs occupy a one-hundred-acre site that contains nine nineteenth-century buildings first used by the Cold Spring Whaling Company and then by textile manufacturers, as well as research buildings built in the early part of the century by the Carnegie Foundation. Dr. Watson turned to Charles Moore, whose work, particularly at the University of California at Santa Cruz, suggested his respect for traditional campus forms and his ability to update them by expanding the necessary technical laboratory facilities. In 1975 Moore and his partners began by providing a house for Dr. Watson and his family, restoring and adding to Airslie House (1806), which was built for a sea captain and which later served as the guest house for an estate with grounds landscaped by Frederick Law Olmsted. Moore then designed a

Overleaf. The Salk Institute's magnificently barren central court is lined with study towers, angled to provide views of the Pacific Ocean. A rill of water runs down its center.

sewage treatment plant for the research center, which technical considerations required be built on a prominent hillside site. The concrete structure was submerged, with only a charming wooden gazebo marking its presence. The gazebo is surmounted not by a traditional weather vane but by a replica of a DNA particle. An 1893 barnlike building was renovated into the Jones Laboratory, the first building on the site constructed for scientific work. Moore left the shell untouched, slipping five sealable aluminum "pods" inside to house lab facilities. At Cold Spring Harbor, the architecture confronts the activities of the present with the achievements of the past.

One of the earliest notable efforts to recapture the Arcadian campus ideal was Eero Saarinen's design for two new residential colleges, Morse and Stiles (1960–62), at Yale University. Before Saarinen's work in the sixties, the last college to be built on campus was Silliman College, completed in the Georgian style in 1940. In response to an unattractive site and perhaps in deference to the value of the traditional colleges on campus he had enjoyed as a student at Yale, Saarinen made a decisive break with the orthodox Modernism of his work for corporations like GM and IBM. Instead he created two cloistered groupings, which consisted of low buildings punctuated by towers separated by a pedestrian street. The walkway's ups and downs and its manipulations of scale and perspective brought the cacophonous surroundings into near-perfect scale in the manner of a medieval Italian hill town like San Gimignano.

But Saarinen's vision took him only so far toward a modern medievalism. Though he "conceived of the colleges as Citadels of Masonry,"[25] there was not the money — or perhaps the will — to sheathe them in stone as Rogers had done when he designed steel-framed Gothic structures for the campus forty years earlier. To achieve the effect he wanted, Saarinen experimented until he devised "masonry walls made without masons"[26] by spraying concrete around rough boulders casually laid up. This technique results in a material that looks more like peanut brittle than stone, one that might be more in context in Santa Fe, New Mexico, than at Oxbridge or Yale.

Because Modernist minimalism frowned on applied ornament, Saarinen achieved variety by providing irregularly shaped rooms within each college, thus permitting the building to be both functionally frank and visually varied. Always the intuitive artist, much to the shock of his more conservative contemporaries,

Below. Charles Moore began to redesign the one-hundred-acre site of Cold Spring Harbor Laboratories on the north shore of Long Island in 1975. It contained nine nineteenth-century buildings, including the 1893 barnlike structure (*left*), which is now Jones Laboratory, as well as such modern buildings as Sammis Hall (*right*).

Saarinen is said to have arrived at the skyline design empirically, not from a structural or functional program but by floating balloons at various heights to see how the projected buildings would look. Saarinen was more successful in emulating the courtyards of the Gothic colleges than in re-creating their walls. Offering places to walk, to sit, and to enact the role of being a student, the courtyards make a convincing statement for the collegiality and interaction of groups gathering together.

Saarinen's chief complaint about the older colleges at Yale was that they closed themselves off from the city. He wanted the citizens of New Haven to walk right through his colleges. After his death, his widow fought to keep the university from building gates across the entrances. Yale compromised, promising to keep the gates open. Now they are always locked, a return to the realistic appraisal of the gulf between the town and campus that had spurred Rogers to include moats and bars in his original designs for Yale forty years before and had driven Jefferson deep into the countryside to lay out the University of Virginia at the dawn of the Republic.

Something very fundamental and precious was at stake at Yale, much more than the issue of collegiality — the freedom to dream. While Rogers fed his dreams with and found inspiration in the treasures of five hundred years of university architecture, Saarinen had been taught that these treasures were off-limits to him as a twentieth-century architect. At Yale, however, he created a place that had a distinct identity, yet one that related not only to the surrounding buildings but to the history of architecture as well. Although Morse and Stiles were perhaps more successful in concept than in reality, they nonetheless constituted a watershed, representing, as Vincent Scully, Yale's preeminent professor of architectural history, has stated, "a beginning toward picking up that dialogue with the past which architecture is all about."[27]

When the University of California extended its chain of campuses, creating a new campus at Santa Cruz, it sought to preserve the site's Arcadian quality. On a spectacular two-thousand-acre site embracing wooded, rolling hills and open meadows, the Santa Cruz campus (1963–77) was divided into a series of eight colleges, in effect eight academical villages, each designed by a different architect, who would consult with faculty and students to evolve a workable and meaningful form. The master plan, prepared by the San Francisco architect John Carl Warnecke, grouped together dormitories, classrooms, and faculty offices in each college. As a whole, the university's architecture wavers between evocations of disparate styles, places, and characters; phrases like "Mediterranean Modernism" and "commercialized Bay Region funkiness" begin to suggest their variety.

Only Charles Moore, with his design for Kresge College (1972–74), suggested new and inspired efforts to achieve a genuine sense of place. The college turns an earth-colored wall to the exterior to blend its architecture with the surrounding forests and create an enclosure and a suggestion of remarkable secrets for those permitted to enter. Inside, an eclectic array of building forms are disposed to create as richly articulated a stage set for human action as any ever offered by Hollywood. Kresge, even more than the residential colleges at Yale, is a self-contained village within a larger university, lacking only a chapel, a major library, and a gym to achieve complete independence from the rest of the campus. But without these symbolic and functional foci, Moore aggrandized the laundry and

Eero Saarinen stands
behind his model of Yale's
Morse and Stiles colleges.
His plan for two cloistered
groupings, consisting of
low buildings punctuated
by towers, reopened a
dialogue with the past that
had long been lost to
Modern architecture.

canteen, which later became a Chinese restaurant, to provide moments of architectural grandeur. An amphitheater, a red-white-and-blue rostrum, two-storey dormitories that vaguely resemble roadside motels, administrative offices, shops, and a mailroom — all decorated with strips of neon — and freestanding walls with rectangular openings that visually frame the sky complete the assembly. The buildings are arranged along a grand thousand-foot-long street — the thoroughfare of the college, intended to serve as its symbolic and functional nexus, the sort of linear quadrangle guaranteed liveliness by the movement of students along it.

Unfortunately, the use of highly abstract forms robs the scheme of much of its power. While the creation of a street and of a sheltered compound were derived from a careful study and evocation of historic precedent, a translation of such precedent into the details and character of the buildings would have been wildly daring at the time of its construction. Instead, walls in general are planar and unadorned. Variety was sought exclusively in color, overall massing, and siting. As a result, the cacophonous color and the play of scale seem a bit too much like Disney or a Mel Brooks version of *High Noon*. The sophisticated irony of the assembly combined with the calculated spontaneity it requires of the students seems to mock rather than glorify the students' role. As Charles Jencks, a generally ardent admirer of the ironic, has observed:

Whereas the southern European village gives stability and a sense of permanence, because it is built of an encompassing stone, Kresge is made from a cardboard-like wood, that "cheapskate" material that has always plagued Modernism. Thus a feeling of insubstantiality is created at the very point that the metaphor of enclosure is about to be consummated, and the image of the Italian hill town criticizes, not reinforces, the meanings intended.[28]

The failure of Kresge College to function effectively as a setting for college life, which Moore has described as "an urgently important four-year-long operetta,"[29] is now reflected in many students' requests to live in the far more conventional complexes of some of the other colleges on the campus, leaving Kresge's "streets" frequently deserted, devoid of life. Despite the architecture's vitality and brave attempt to define a place, the scheme is too strident and self-consciously clever to fully serve an academic community isolated in an Arcadian setting.

Architecture must be both abstract and representational, practical and expressive, real and surreal. Architects need to work within the conventions of meaning that are shared by their audiences — the public. To do so does not, however, condemn them to playing it safe. Frank Gehry's buildings for Loyola Marymount University's law school create, with an ingenious site plan, a real and ideal campus. The preexisting campus, at the edge of downtown Los Angeles, could not have been less dreamlike or less promising. The low-rise buildings on campus were contextually responsive in that they reflected the banality of the surrounding neighborhood, which Gehry has described as "in transition for so long it's not in transition."[30]

The client asked for a single building to be built within a limited budget. But in interviews with faculty and students, it became clear that the facility was grievously lacking something that it became critical to the architect to address directly: Loyola had buildings but it had no campus. As a result, the process of learning was impaired, for students had no incentive to remain at school, no place to gather for the informal discussions critical to the quality of higher education.

As Charles Moore had at Kresge College, Gehry felt a necessary first component was a central focus of activity. His scheme, then, was to house some of the required facilities in small-scale individual buildings, arranged in a central open area created between his new large classroom/office building and the parking garages to the north. The result, as he describes it, is "a pileup of buildings like an acropolis,"[31] which constitutes a miniature campus that simultaneously provides the university with a distinct place of its own and maintains an appropriately low scale and understated street façades that are harmonious with the city outside.

Until Frank Gehry designed the interior court for Loyola Marymount University's Law School in Los Angeles, the school lacked any sense of a campus. He successfully defined the site as both a part of the city and a scholarly retreat, with a small-scale plan that was sensitive to its surroundings. The freestanding concrete columns in front of Merrifield Hall provide an enriching historical reference.

The largest building in Gehry's campus plan, the Burns Building, has a street façade clad in light gray stucco. Facing the campus, however, it presents a bright ochre screen façade, which serves as a backdrop to the smaller buildings arranged in front of it. The façade "splits open" with a trio of deviantly asymmetrical staircases, with the middle one climbing to the building's "pediment" — a glass greenhouse-like structure. The main stair of the Burns Building, in addition to adding a lively and enlivening element to the "acropolis" and binding it to the larger building, also angles toward the adjacent boulevard running by perpendicular to it. Thus the campus, while maintaining a sense of an enclosed, private space, is also turned toward the city, a relationship previously ignored by the law school's facilities.

To invest the anonymous urban setting with some of the dignity of the subject studied on the campus, Gehry sought to suggest some historical symbolic forms. The school's dual foundation in religion and law is reflected in the prominence of a chapel and a moot court building. The chapel projects a windowless curved façade of polished plywood to the street, while its campus façade is all glass and reveals the exposed wooden structural elements within. Next to the chapel, a rectilinear tower forms a campanile without bells that clearly expresses the building's function and connects it to a formal tradition. In the center of the campus, Merrifield Hall, a gable-roofed brick box, is rotated off-axis and fronted by a "screen" of freestanding, squat, eighteen-foot-high concrete columns. While stark in their lack of bases and capitals, they, like the forms of the chapel, delve into the past to evoke a formal language, related to the practical function for which the building was designed — to hold a moot court. Symbolically these columns elevate the structure to a temple of justice.

Like Jefferson at the University of Virginia, Gehry has taken the circumstances of a particular place and time and, using the forms and symbols of the past, raised the real to the ideal. At Loyola Marymount, these circumstances included a limited budget, necessitating the use of humble materials, and a rather bleak but visually complex urban context. While Jefferson's campus included bold acts of architectural synthesis, Gehry's, in its heterogeneous urban setting, is more fragmented. Each structure is isolated and yet all are closely interrelated like the elements of a still life or a Cubist collage. Still, in its very heterogeneity and its fond deference to the city's complexity, the campus has achieved a critical balance: it is at once open to its context and protected as a special domain, reassuring in its associations with the past and provocative in its startling juxtapositions of forms and materials, a part of the city and a scholarly retreat. Indeed, Loyola has been designed by remembering and comes close to fulfilling a particular American dream: it realizes the American campus's potential to bring people together united by a common purpose, in a place apart. While the opportunity to build a campus that would shape an emerging culture — an opportunity so brilliantly seized by Thomas Jefferson — may not belong to us, Loyola stands as a compelling symbol of the possibility of creating an oasis of civility within our modern urban frontier. It promises that we can recapture the sense of a special place. It suggests that it may still be possible to create alternatives to the senseless impersonality and placelessness that have destroyed so many of our cities, to make places apart, places informed by the past but continuously renewed by the realities, the ideals, and the dreams of the present.

3   Dream Houses

America is the most "house proud" of nations. The single-family house is the most visible image of our wealth and liberty. The typical American house, no matter how modest, reveals in its architectural conventions subliminal expressions of the themes — the myths, even — of our history, our traditions, and our dreams: lapped siding, for example, denotes a farmhouse, while natural shingles conjure up houses confronting a storm-tossed sea. Red tile roofs and porches suggest the haciendas of the Southwest, where Spaniard and Indian forged a socially uneasy but physically beguiling architectural synthesis. Every detail of the American single-family house — the American dream house — from the handling of the bricks or stone or stucco to the hurricane lamps in the picture windows and the decorative wagon wheel on the front lawn, defines who we are in terms of our need to appropriate the past, raise it to mythic proportions, and make it our own. As Robert Venturi, Denise Scott Brown, and Steven Izenour, pioneers in advocating that architects study and learn from the vitality of ordinary tract housing, have pointed out, "Pitched-roof houses, Colonial doorways, and shuttered windows tell us without need of signs that here is a community that values tradition, pride of ownership, and the rural life."[1] We add bedrooms, sun decks, pools, landscaping, and whatever else might stand as evidence of our achievements, aspirations, and personalities, our idiosyncrasies and conformity. With modest means or great wealth, each American homeowner embarks on the creation of a testimonial to his or her dreams.

Two houses, built nearly three hundred years apart, symbolize the fundamental contradictions that define the American dream house: our simultaneous need to define ourselves through history and yet escape entirely from the past, and the conflict between the real and an imagined past that renders us at once the youngest and oldest nation on earth. One house is a saltbox lean-to in East Hampton, New York, built sometime between 1680 and 1690 by Robert Dayton, a Colonial settler; the other is House VI, built in Cornwall, Connecticut, in 1976 by the architect Peter Eisenman. Each carries the house beyond the rudiments of shelter to provide a means of transcending daily reality; but the two houses achieve this end in diametrically opposite ways. At first glance the Dayton House appears to be the quintessential cozy cottage, but a second look reveals that it can barely be called architecture at all. A rude shelter, its every feature attests to the needs to protect the householders against the elements and to build with local materials in the most economical manner. Small windows and doors are set flush

The Henry Davis Sleeper house, known as Beauport, was set on the edge of a cliff overlooking the harbor in Gloucester, Massachusetts. This exterior view, with its profusion of chimneys, turrets, and gables, hints at the mosaic of its interior plan.

with the wood shingle sheathing to seal the house tightly, while inside a brick fireplace dominates, at once an environmental necessity and a symbol of family life. Yet in its own modest way, the Dayton House is a work of architecture embodying both memory and aspiration: the colonists' memory of the stable if inhospitable world they left behind in England and their aspiration for a new, dreamlike existence, a heaven on earth. What has enabled us to see the Dayton House, and others like it, as more than mere shelter is our ability to launder it of the grim realities of life in Colonial America. It was not until after the founding of the Republic, when the nation had gone sufficiently beyond its humble beginnings, that it could afford the luxury of elevating ordinary buildings to the level of architecture. Likewise, it was not until the nineteenth century, when the success of the national experiment had been established, that we could look at ourselves as a nation and create a mythology out of the cultural ambiguities of our Colonial past. John Howard Payne, an American actor and lyricist, was reputed to have been born in Dayton's saltbox house. When in 1823 Payne, who immigrated to Europe as a young man, immortalized his birthplace in his most enduring work, the ballad "Home Sweet Home." Since then, the house, now known as Home Sweet Home and burnished by an additional 160 years of weathering and mythmaking, veritably drips with charm, powerfully evoking for all Americans a memory of a past that was theirs only in mythic terms. Home Sweet Home represents a particularly complex and hard-won aspect of the American dream: the dream of a shared history. As a polyglot nation of immigrants, unlike other nations whose culture evolved over a long time, we are without a collective past. Seeking to transcend our hybrid national identity, we look to the Colonial experience that only a small segment of our population can trace its lineage back to. We clutch at the Colonial past as a common denominator, a binding heritage. Yet as we do so, we are made uncomfortable: the Colonial past confronts us all too directly with our nation's fundamental cultural dichotomy: we are part Europe and part America, part old and part new.

House VI strips us of our illusions, propelling the American dream into a world free of the environmental, cultural, and psychological constraints that give the Dayton House its poignant urgency. Democratic capitalism has provided us with an unprecedented degree of affluence and freedom. The act of building has been so thoroughly unleashed from the requirements of shelter that some

Extending beyond the rudiments of shelter, the typical American house stands as evidence of individual personalities and aspirations. *Below, left to right,* are four examples of proud ownership: Mr. M's house in Chicago; red awnings in Birmingham, Alabama; red-white-and-blue house in Anaconda, Montana; and a modest hacienda in the Watts section of Los Angeles.

architects have pushed it beyond history and even beyond mythology to become
the architectural equivalent of an interior monologue, or perhaps of the
analysand's stream of consciousness. Eisenman rejects traditional notions of
memory and place; as he has stated, House VI "basically attempts to destabilize
the notion of home."[2] Instead of creating a memory-laden shrine to the family,
Eisenman has used the house to rigorously explore the formal possibilities of pure,
undecorated geometry, the nature of perception, and his own psyche. Throwing
up planes of structure that defy the rules of construction, Eisenman's house,
designed as a weekend retreat for a photographer and an art historian, is
ultimately made possible only by artifice. Not only is the distinction between
indoors and outdoors obscured, but even right-side-up and upside-down are
inverted, as a bright red "fake" step formation is suspended above its "real"
counterpart, a green staircase leading to the house's second storey. In the kitchen,
a column, serving no structural purpose, is placed in the only convenient location
for a dining table, hindering conversation and putting to the test even the
congeniality of family mealtime, while outside, one column supports nothing but
the sky and another is suspended, stopping short of the ground below. Eisenman's
polemical gymnastics continue in the bedroom, where a "floor light" rather
menacingly cleaves the conjugal bed.

Dayton's saltbox cottage represents the fact of building raised to the level of
architecture through mythology; House VI goes beyond architecture in a
conventional sense to create a model of the mind liberated from physical reality.
Between the poles of maximum memory and aesthetic amnesia lies the broad plain
of dream and myth, upon which most Americans seek to give architectural
expression to their hopes and goals. While most of us have to content ourselves
with realizing but a fraction of what we aspire to, a handful of Americans have had
the imagination, the intelligence, the cash, the arrogance, and most of all the
singular, obsessive passion to build houses that go well beyond the ordinary
definitions of shelter. They built houses that elevate architecture to autobiography,
conflating personal taste with national destiny to transform their dreams into
blueprints for American life.

Thomas Jefferson's Monticello was the first American dream house, an
aesthetic and philosophical exemplar for the new nation. Jefferson believed that
each American family should live in its own house on its own piece of land. While

FIRST FLOOR

SECOND FLOOR

THIRD FLOOR

This 1874 plan by architect Edward T. Potter for the Samuel Clemens (a.k.a. Mark Twain) house in Hartford, Connecticut, fit more than twenty rooms into a compact three-storey building that rose asymmetrically to steeply pitched roofs. The design reflected its owner's taste for functional perfection combined with flamboyant aesthetics.

Right. The upper windows of the Clemens house were surrounded by brickwork that incorporated bold bands of black and vermilion as well as patterns both worked into its surface and as reliefs. One critic wrote that the house "looked as if it had been tattooed."

it is unlikely that Jefferson ever imagined that the majority of his fellow citizen-farmers would own six-thousand-acre estates like his own, he nevertheless built his mountaintop dream house as a paradigm: a demonstration that in Arcadia, Classical beauty could be coupled with New World practicality to provide every family with its own house-temple.

When Jefferson chose to leave his father's plantation and build his own house on a wilderness hilltop, he established what through the centuries has proved to be one of the most enduring American occupations — that of expressing one's individuality through the medium of a house of one's own. To build one's own house is to start anew as an individual, and to build a house in the upcountry, a house facing westward, was to pioneer, as each subsequent generation would do. As Lewis Mumford wrote in *The Golden Day*, it was on the frontier that "America became . . . a place . . . where the social man could become an "individual," where the settled man could become a nomad, and the family man could forget his old connections. With pioneering, America ceased to be an outpost of Europe."[3]

Jefferson worked on the new Monticello for thirty years, much like any inspired do-it-yourselfer today who undertakes the long process of customizing his typical tract house, or the hot-rodder who transforms his ordinary car into a unique personal statement. For Jefferson, Monticello was a working laboratory and an abiding passion. The quintessential do-it-yourselfer, he was also a madly inspired gadgeteer whose devices anticipated the increasingly servantless world of democratic society.

Jefferson's bedroom reveals the self-consciously obsessional side of his personality. In many ways a command post, with a clear view throughout the house and out to the landscape beyond, it reveals him as much a tinker as a thinker: at his desk a polygraph made copies of his letters as he wrote them, one copy for the correspondent, one for history; a rotating book stand let him read four books at a time; and, on a shelf at the foot of the bed, a clock served as a constant reminder of work to be done.

Nowhere at Monticello is Jefferson's dream for America more evident than in the entrance hall, where the Classical tradition of the ancient world and the natural history of the new are given equal status. A spacious vestibule, it contains plaster casts of Jean-Antoine Houdon's busts of Voltaire and Turgot, as well as Cerrachi's busts of Alexander Hamilton — Jefferson's old political rival, who, despite bitter ideological differences, had supported him against Aaron Burr in 1800 and after his fatal duel in 1804 had become a national hero — and a bust of Jefferson himself, set on a truncated Classical column that was a gift to him from Madame de Tessé when he left Paris. The Classicizing conventions of representation lift the subjects to deistic status. Side by side with Jefferson's heroes, elk horns, a bison's head, a mastodon's jaw, and Indian artifacts including wampum belts, peace pipes, and bows represent the primitive world of nature. Nowhere is the dialogue between ideal and real, rationalism and naturalism, more vividly seen than in Jefferson's famous, seven-day cannonball hall clock. An ingenious yet compositionally flawed timepiece, it told the time and the days of the week by counting off cannonballs. But it was too big for the room that contained it, forcing Jefferson to compromise his architectural ideal by cutting holes into the floor to accommodate Saturday's cannonballs.

Jefferson died at Monticello in 1826, fifty years to the day since he had signed

Top. Clemens called the prominent veranda surrounding his house the ombra, after the Latin root meaning "shadow." The third floor of the turret (*upper left*) was his private study.

Bottom. The greenhouse extended from the living room on the first floor, which was the domain of Clemens's wife.

Left. In 1881, only seven years after the completion of his home, Clemens commissioned the Associated Artists of New York to redecorate its interiors. The main stairway rises amid the intricate stenciling and rich variety of decorative motifs applied to walls and ceilings throughout the house.

his definitive draft of the Declaration of Independence. His family was swiftly overwhelmed by debts, and Monticello was sold and soon neglected. Ten years later, just as the house teetered at the edge of decrepitude, it was bought by a proud and fiery naval officer, Uriah Levy, who conscientiously protected the house's legacy. But by the 1920s, Monticello had once again slipped into decay. With cows herded in its portico, it became a ruin worthy of the great eighteenth-century Neo-Classical painters, or perhaps of Palladio himself, who had first seen the marvels of the ancient Roman world under similar circumstances. After numerous unsuccessful attempts, Monticello's restoration was finally insured in 1923 with the creation of the Thomas Jefferson Memorial Foundation, headed by two New York lawyers. The foundation purchased Monticello in 1924 with the help of thousands of small contributions — a fitting tribute to Jefferson's belief in the power of the individual in a democracy. In 1926, on the one-hundredth anniversary of Jefferson's death and the one-hundred-fiftieth of the Declaration of Independence, Monticello was dedicated as a public memorial. The restoration of the house and grounds was guided by Fiske Kimball, the noted architectural historian and director of the Philadelphia Museum of Art, whose seminal work, *Thomas Jefferson: Architect,* published in 1915, greatly contributed to establishing Jefferson's reputation as an architect and to galvanizing national interest in Monticello's fate.

Not only does Monticello embody its owner's vision of America, but its essentially incomplete state appropriately reflects its owner's need to express his ever-evolving dreams and idiosyncrasies. While Jefferson never completed his dream house, his goal of establishing Classical architecture as a model for the new nation was realized in the Greek Revival movement of the early Republic. Classical house-temples moved westward with the pioneers across the uncharted wilderness, symbolizing the ideal of the new democracy. But by the time of the Civil War, the house as temple proved too constraining: it seemed there were as many kinds of family self-portraits to be built as there were sites to build them on. The architects Andrew Jackson Downing and Alexander Jackson Davis were among the first to suggest a variety of picturesque architectural styles to suit not only the site but the individual homeowner's character and mood. Fueled by post–Civil War prosperity, Victorian Americans took their cues from Downing's and Davis's medievalized designs, indulging themselves in an orgy of self-expression. The house became a self-portrait, as near to pure autobiography as possible.

Perhaps the most powerfully expressive autobiographical house of the era was the portrait house that Edward T. Potter designed in 1874 for Samuel Clemens in Hartford, Connecticut. At once a monument to Victorian respectability and a raffish Mississippi steamboat, this restlessly configured, boldly colorful, idiosyncratic dream house perfectly mirrored the twin personae of its owner Samuel Clemens and his alter ego Mark Twain. When Missouri-born Clemens first visited Hartford in 1868, the West's greatest mythologizer fell in love with it immediately: "You do not know what beauty is," he wrote, "if you have not been here."[4] Three years later, after the success of *The Innocents Abroad,* the Clemens family moved from Buffalo, New York, to Nook Farm, a genteel literary enclave situated between the center of Hartford and the open countryside to its west. Neighbors in the community included Charles Dudley Warner, the editor of the *Hartford Courant,* and Harriet Beecher Stowe, author of *Uncle Tom's Cabin.*

Separated from the domestic concerns of the first two floors, the billiard room on the third floor of Clemens's house was his private domain. Here he would retire to read, write, and entertain friends.

Ironically, it was in the midst of this environment — intellectual, affluent, and Eastern — that Clemens found the voice of Mark Twain, the man of the West, who created a national mythology of rough-and-tumble, carefree youth in *The Adventures of Tom Sawyer, Huckleberry Finn,* and *Life on the Mississippi.*

From its inception, Clemens undertook the construction of his house as a major — and very personal — project. Indeed, he compared its design and construction with the task that had originally confronted the Almighty. "It is likely," he speculated, "that if more time had been taken, in the first place, the world would have been made right, and this ceaseless improving and repairing would not be necessary now. But if you hurry a world or a house, you are nearly sure to find out, by and by, that you have left out a towhead, or a broom-closet, or some other little convenience, here and there, which has got to be supplied, no matter how much expense or vexation it may cost."[5] Clearly, Clemens intended to do it correctly, more correctly, in fact, than his heavenly predecessor.

Clemens's desire for functional perfection was matched by a taste for flamboyant aesthetics. For assistance, he turned to Edward T. Potter, a talented architect who was also an accomplished writer and musician and a serious student of theology. The son of an Episcopal bishop, Potter treated the church commissions that flowed his way as opportunities to investigate the relationship between the spiritual and secular. For example, his Hartford Church of the Good Shepherd (1867–69), built for the widow of arms manufacturer Samuel Colt, was adorned with carved gun parts.

Potter's design for Clemens reflected the personality of his client — exuberant and bursting with vitality. In part it was not so much a family temple as a family church. In part it was a demonstration of the ideas of Clemens's neighbor, Harriet Beecher Stowe, who, with her sister Catherine Beecher, published the highly influential book *The American Woman's House* in 1869. In it they stressed the importance of efficient spatial planning and firmly advocated that a woman should be the "minister of the home,"[6] relying on neither servants nor men for help and advice. More than twenty rooms were fitted into a three-storey building that is relatively compact and straightforward in plan but churchlike in its massing, which rises asymmetrically to steeply pitched roofs. Its forms include projecting bay windows, gables and turrets, decorative wooden tracery, balconies carved into the roofs, and a prominent low-slung veranda, which Clemens called the ombra after the Latin root meaning "shadow." The brickwork incorporates bold bands of black and vermilion and patterns both worked into its surface and as reliefs. One critic writing in the *American Architect and Building News* stated that it "looked as if it had been tattooed!" while another from the same journal observed: "I do not know whether it was in reference to this house that the scorner said that American humor had never found its full expression except in architecture."[7]

But Clemens was well pleased. Seven years later, his purse swelling with royalties, he extended the kitchen wing and had all the interiors redecorated by the Associated Artists, a collaborative of New York artists and craftsmen that included Louis Comfort Tiffany, Lockwood de Forest, Candace Thurber Wheeler, and Samuel Colman. The new interiors made extensive use of wall and ceiling stenciling and a rich variety of decorative motifs including many drawn from Oriental sources, a hallmark of the collaboration's work. The vividly colored and patterned rooms were even more exuberant than the exterior. Thrilled with the results, Clemens boasted that the more staid, restrained domestic interiors he had seen in Europe were "ugly, tasteless, repulsive . . . compared with the perfect taste of this grand floor, with its delicious dream of harmonious color, and its all-prevailing spirit of peace and serenity and deep contentment."[8]

On the first two floors of the house, which were devoted to conventional family life, Olivia Langdon Clemens applied herself to the "woman's profession" of household management as described by the Beecher sisters. On the third floor, Clemens, transmogrified into Mark Twain, ruled a world of his own invention. Using the billiard room as his study, Mark Twain, now the nation's principal mythmaker, read and wrote. Here he also shared glasses of warm Scotch with friends and challenged them to games of pool, often played by his own rules. Just outside was a richly fretted balcony, where he could imagine that he was charting a course from the pilothouse of a grand side-wheeler improbably sailing to safe harbor across the peaceful Connecticut River Valley.

So accurate was Potter's portrait of Twain that Clemens began to think he had designed the house himself, going so far as to publish a verse titled "This Is the House That Mark Built":

> This is the sunny and snug retreat,
> At once both city and country seat,
> Where he grinds out many a comical grist,
> The author, architect, humorist,
> The auctioneer and dramatist,
> Who lives in the house that Mark built . . .

Samuel L. Clemens his maiden name;
As a humorist not unknown to fame,
As author or architect all the same,
At auction or drama always game,
An extravagant wag whom none can tame:
He lives in the house that Mark built.[9]

Financial reversals forced Clemens to abandon his beloved house in 1891 in order to embark on a worldwide lecture tour. But he could not bear to sell it, even after the death of his eldest daughter, Susy, in 1896 at Nook Farm shattered any possibility of resuming life there. Even after he did sell the house in 1903, it still obsessed him: "It had a heart, and a soul, and eyes to see us with . . . it was of us; and we were in its grace and in the peace of its benediction."[10]

While the Clemens/Twain house was a vivid example of the autobiographical strain that Jefferson introduced into American house architecture, Henry Davis Sleeper's house, Beauport, in Gloucester, Massachusetts, more directly picked up on Jefferson's notion of the house as a personal vision and a repository of national culture. Like Monticello, Beauport took almost a lifetime to build: begun in 1907, it was worked on almost continuously until Sleeper's death in 1934.

In 1907, Sleeper purchased a modest strip of land by the rocky cliffs that overhang the harbor near the end of Gloucester's Eastern Point. A man of independent means, he had studied architecture in Paris only briefly. With the help of Gloucester architect Halfdan M. Hanson, Sleeper erected a relatively small shingle and stucco cottage, which gradually grew to forty rooms. Its name, Beauport, meaning Handsome Harbor, was the title Samuel Champlain had given to Gloucester Harbor when he discovered it three hundred years before. Beauport is as significant for the things it contains as for the architecture that surrounds it.

Approached from the sea, or from the narrow road that circles Eastern Point, Beauport's profusion of chimneys, gables, and turrets offers a tantalizing hint of the interior mosaic of its plan where rooms are strung together in accordance with a process that can be regarded, depending on the observer's point of view, as either organic or haphazard. Despite the looseness of the overall plan, each room was organized down to the smallest details before it was executed. From the outset, Sleeper's goal was as much aesthetic as it was cultural: "Mightn't it be fun to have a house in which each room could recapture some of the spirit of a specific mood or phase or 'period' of our American life from the time of Plymouth down through the Revolution and the early Republic?"[11] This was to be not a museum of old rooms but a work of architectural synthesis, in which the past was seen as the springboard for a highly original work of art.

At the same time that Braque and Picasso were developing their technique of collage, using artifacts of everyday life to create two- and three-dimensional works on canvas of great plastic and narrative complexity, Sleeper proceeded to develop similar techniques on the architectural level. For Sleeper, architecture was but the canvas for an assemblage of precious objects that were not only inherently beautiful but also rich in historic association.

If Monticello is a temple dedicated to the continent, Beauport can be seen as an architectural biography of preindustrial America seen through the filter of one man's psyche, an idiosyncratic and individualistic assemblage of objects, furniture, and even whole rooms that reflects Sleeper's hyper-aestheticism and his highly

The original shingle and stucco summer cottage built by Henry Davis Sleeper in 1907 was developed over the course of twenty-seven years into the rambling, forty-room Beauport mansion. This photograph shows the front entrance.

personal interpretation of early American history. When the William Cogswell house, a decaying gambrel-roofed structure in nearby Essex, went up for sale in 1907, Sleeper purchased its pine paneling and installed it the next year in Beauport's front hall, thus beginning the obsessive process through which he transformed his summer cottage into an inspired history lesson. Throughout the house, objects steeped in history and legend, such as Lord Bryon's bed, vie for the visitor's attention with carvings from Yankee sailing ships, Chinese export porcelain, and curiosities such as a Troy iron heating stove, cast to represent George Washington draped in a toga.

But Beauport is no ordinary antiquarian assemblage; to proceed through the mazelike configuration of its rooms is to walk through Sleeper's mind. At Beauport, eccentricity is elevated to the level of genius. Its dense assembly of artifacts from different eras telescopes time in an effort to render history readable in a moment's glance. The decoration is complemented by a disorienting plan, in which constricted spaces are carefully juxtaposed with larger, expansive ones. The journey through the house takes on metaphorical meaning as an individual temperament and a national heritage are gradually revealed and intertwined. The collection is exhibited in deliberately mysterious spaces that are rendered sublime by natural light emanating from concealed sources. For example, a collection of amber glass, displayed in a showcase made from a leaded-glass doorway from another house, has been back-lit to become, in accordance with the weather, either as transcendent as the windows at Chartres or as eerie as the monumental sculpture inside the Great Temple at Abu Simbel.

The merger of the historic and the personal is nowhere more evident than in Beauport's Pembroke Room, a pine-paneled kitchen that Sleeper named after the Massachusetts town where his ancestor Robert Barker had built a saltbox house in 1650, and where seven generations of his ancestors had lived for over two centuries. Although the contents of the family homestead had already been sold at auction, Sleeper is said to have found the auctioneer, traced the scattered objects, and bought many of them back. In any case, he used the disintegrating house's doors and paneling, chimney, and ceiling beams to reconstruct what came to be his favorite room — the Pembroke Room, a romanticized evocation of early American domesticity.

In a similar manner, the materials used to construct other rooms were culled from old buildings, junk stores, and auctions. The walls of one room, which Sleeper called the China Trade Room, were covered with wallpaper that Sleeper discovered packed in its original boxes in the attic of a house in Marblehead. The paper had been ordered from China by Robert Morris, one of the signers of the Declaration of Independence and appointed financier for the Revolutionary War. Morris had opened trade between the new republic and the Chinese empire, but through a series of financial reversals ended in debtors' prison and never completed the house for which the wallpaper was intended. In the window recess of another room, the so-called Little Lady Room, is a rug designed by Edward Sands Frost, the first commercial designer of hooked rugs. Frost had been a tin peddler in Maine when he perceived a market for good rug designs. He maximized his profits by devising stencils of separate motifs, rather than complete designs, that could be combined in different ways to create a multitude of patterns, albeit rather piecemeal ones. The tale of Frost's rug-making typifies the stories associated with Beauport's rooms, which honor traditional American values, "Yankee ingenuity," and history.

During World War I, Sleeper devoted great energy to cofounding and raising funds for the American Field Service, whose volunteers operated ambulances in France. The project nearly ruined him financially; after the war, he became a professional interior decorator, interpreting the early American experience for affluent North Shore suburbanites and exerting a strong influence on popular taste. But his primary focus and his greatest work remained Beauport.

Sleeper died in debt in 1934, leaving Beauport to his brother Stephen. The following year, the house was sold to Charles E. F. McCann and his wife, Helena, Frank Woolworth's daughter, who was ardently dedicated to preserving the house. In 1942, four years after Mrs. McCann's death, her children insured the protection of Sleeper's dream house by transferring ownership of it to the Society for the Preservation of New England Antiquities in Boston to be maintained as a public museum.

Sleeper's devotion to early American architecture and decor ran counter to the tastes of many Americans, especially those of the late nineteenth and early twentieth centuries — an era whose ostentatious displays of wealth earned it the title of the Gilded Age. By the end of the nineteenth century, fortunes had been drawn out of the very substance of the continent. Many of the newly rich came to feel that America simply was not grand enough to match their aspirations for it. Like Jefferson, they traveled to Europe to equip themselves with a more venerable, and therefore presumably more valuable, culture. But while Jefferson wanted to synthesize European traditions in order to create a complex American culture, these newly wealthy citizens simply imported pieces of European history to create a dreamworld of European culture on American soil. As Lewis Mumford has written: "Hunting for pictures, statues, tapestries, clothes, pieces of furniture, for the epidermis and entrails of palaces and cottages and churches, satisfied the two capital impulses of the Gilded Age: it gave full play to the acquisitive instinct . . . At the same time, it satisfied a starved desire for beauty and raised the pursuer an estimable step or two in the social scale."[12]

But while many were content to purchase some part of Europe's past as a glittering prize, a few raised their sights higher, using the past as a touchstone for a better life for themselves and for the public at large. One such visionary representative of the era was George Washington Vanderbilt II, the scholarly grandson of Cornelius Vanderbilt, the Commodore. In 1891 the younger Vanderbilt set out to build a dream house that would outdo not only in size and splendor but also in significance the mansions that his older and much richer brothers William and Cornelius II had built on New York's Fifth Avenue and in Newport, Rhode Island. Eschewing the social whirl of his family, the twenty-six-year-old bachelor, who had traveled throughout Europe pursuing his interest in architecture, chose to build his estate, which he called Biltmore, in the backwoods of North Carolina's Blue Ridge Mountains. Vanderbilt had discovered the Asheville mountain site while on vacation with his mother. Once he decided to build there, he began to acquire land to protect his privacy, finally accumulating 125,000 acres. He then began simultaneously to build a grand medieval manor and to explore and implement far-sighted innovations in forestry and farming.

It was Frederick Law Olmsted, the designer of New York's Central Park, who suggested land management as an avocation for the young lord of the manor. As Olmsted explained it: "That would be a suitable and dignified business for you to engage in: it would, in the long run, be probably a fair investment of capital and it would be of great value to the country to have a thoroughly well organized and systematically conducted attempt in forestry made on a large scale."[13] Olmsted laid out Biltmore's grounds and devised a program of scientific forestry for the vast estate. He rejected Vanderbilt's suggestion for a large park, finding the land "a generally poor and vagabondish region."[14] Instead he developed a setting for the house that combined naturalistic plantings with formal, axially arranged gardens. But Olmsted's suggestion went far beyond the immediate domain of the house to include a far-reaching program for the full acreage and for its management. He began a nursery, reforested depleted fields, and thinned poor stock from forests, all with the aim of working with nature to reap maximum long-term benefits. In this way, his methods foreshadowed the agribusiness of the mid–twentieth century. Vanderbilt allowed more money for the improvement of his land than was provided in the entire United States Department of Agriculture's budget during the time of Biltmore's construction, and he spent it wisely. At the very least, the grounds of Biltmore represented, as Olmsted said, "an Experiment Station and Museum of living trees."[15] At the most, it helped awaken the nation to the need for conservation and to the aesthetic commercial value of the natural environment. A generation of foresters was trained at the school Vanderbilt established on its grounds in 1898.

This detail plan of Biltmore shows diagonally set windows that give exterior expression to the spiral staircase. The staircase was housed in the foyer, adjacent to the elaborate tower containing the elevator.

Biltmore stands as a coherent expression of Jefferson's dream of America as a continental agricultural empire. Vanderbilt realized the Jeffersonian ideal of living both practically and nobly off the land. Just as Monticello had compelled Jefferson, so Biltmore was to become Vanderbilt's abiding passion, costing him much of his fortune. His involvement with the design, planning, and construction was intense. While the management of the land was eventually entrusted to Gifford Pinchot, who would later become the governor of Pennsylvania and the first chief of the United States Forest Service, Vanderbilt himself worked alongside the lumberjacks to clear a site for the mansion and to realize Olmsted's scientifically ordered forest plan. Vanderbilt lorded over his agricultural dreamworld from Biltmore House (1895), the largest private house ever built in America.

Biltmore is a 250-room château designed by the Vanderbilt family's favorite architect, Richard Morris Hunt, the first American to graduate from the École des Beaux-Arts in Paris. Hunt and Vanderbilt enjoyed a particularly close relationship, with Hunt assuming a paternal role with his young client. Vanderbilt was even more closely involved in the design and construction of his house than he had been in the management of his land. He scrupulously studied and corrected Hunt's contract drawings and labored alongside the workers in the stone yard as he had in his forests.

Hunt's design for the mansion, built of Indiana limestone, evokes the châteaux of Chambord, Chenonceau, and Blois. Aspects of their forms and details — steeply pitched roofs and towers, dormers richly decorated with tracery — are carefully composed into a distinctive new work. The house is approached by means of Olmsted's artful entrance road, which winds through three miles of woodlands. The principal façade, with a loggia along its ground floor, is dominated by an elaborate entrance tower. Adjacent to it, diagonally arranged windows give exterior expression to the spiral staircase housed in Biltmore's foyer, which was modeled on that of the Blois château. The interior shows an even greater diversity of styling and composition. Just off the entrance hall lies the polygonal glass-domed Palm Court, worthy of a metropolitan hotel. The grandest of the interior spaces is the seventy-five-foot-high Banquet Hall, where an imposing triple fireplace, medieval tapestries, and hunting trophies attest to Vanderbilt's passion for history as well as his deep interest in nature. After a strenuous day of hiking, fishing, and horseback riding, or touring his grounds — which included a village he had rebuilt with schools, churches, a railroad station, and housing for the estate workers — Vanderbilt could retreat to the privacy of his favorite room, a Baroque-style library, where, surrounded by twenty thousand volumes, he could engage in the peculiar pursuit of translating modern literature into ancient Greek. Although Vanderbilt chose to build his castle on a remote site and evoke the grandeur of another age, he did not deny himself any of the practical pleasures state-of-the-art American technology could provide. Water piped in six miles from the Busbee Mountains was stored in reservoirs and treated in the estate's own filtration plant.

So large was Biltmore that, as Hunt wryly observed, the surrounding mountains were "just the right size and scale for the château!"[16] But not everyone found the building's palatial grandeur appropriate in the context of its surroundings. Even Pinchot, who found the house "magnificent," faulted it for being in disjunction with its time and place, stating that "in the United States of the nineteenth century and among the one-room cabins of the Appalachian mountaineers, it did not belong. The contrast was a devastating commentary on the injustice of concentrated wealth."[17] But whatever its incongruities and shortcomings, Hunt's last building represented a crowning achievement. Here America's first native-born, European-trained architect was able to realize a private vision whose scope was without parallel in its century.

When Vanderbilt died in 1914, he willed part of his estate to the federal government for the Pisgah National Forest. Some of the land was later sold to become the Blue Ridge Parkway. The house itself, along with fifty million dollars, was left to his only child, Cornelia, who had married an Englishman, John Cecil, son of Baroness Amherst of Hackney and Lord William Cecil. Vanderbilt stipulated, however, that Cornelia live in the mansion for at least half of every year, as if to insure that his dreamworld would not simply become an occasional stage set for spectacular events. Preferring to lead a simpler life in London, Cornelia relinquished her interest in the estate, leaving it to her two sons, who at last realized Vanderbilt's hope of establishing a landed aristocracy, combining American wealth and English ancestry. The brothers took up residence at the estate, running dairy and forestry operations. In 1930, stating that they sought to revitalize the region's Depression-devastated economy, they opened the house and gardens to the public.

Henry James, who disapproved of Biltmore, calling it "a glacial phantasy . . . a phenomenon of brute achievement . . . utterly unaddressed to any possible arrangement of life or state of society,"[18] was both fascinated and repelled by the excesses of America's Gilded Age. In 1895, the year George Washington Vanderbilt II finished building his grand château, James was writing critically in his journals of the woman who for him most personified the restlessness and excessive materialism of Victorian America, which he abhorred as it enthralled him: Isabella Stewart Gardner. For James, she was "not a woman but a locomotive with a pullman car attached."[19] Indeed, for him she stood as a symbol of the era, as he wrote: ". . . the deluge of people, the insane movement for movement, the ruin of thought, of life, the negation of work, of literature, the swelling roaring crowds, the 'where are you going?' the age of Mrs. Jack, the figure of Mrs. Jack, the American, the nightmare . . ."[20] But it was precisely Mrs. Jack's quintessentially American ambition that drove her to assemble one of the nation's most notable art collections and to build one of its great dream houses, Fenway Court.

Isabella Stewart had moved from New York to Boston in 1860, when she married John Lowell Gardner, a reserved and proper Bostonian who had gone into his family's prosperous shipping business. Caught with a double fever for culture and socializing, the young Mrs. Gardner, who, as the New York society journal *Town Topics* wrote, "exercised a certain personal hypnotism in the ranks of swelldom,"[21] held salons where Henry Adams, Oliver Wendell Holmes, Henry and William James, and Bernard Berenson gathered.

Known as "Belle," "Donna Isabella," "Queen of Holy Back Bay," "The Dollar Princess," and by Berenson as "The Serpent of the Charles," Gardner was most often referred to simply and respectfully as "Mrs. Jack." Mrs. Jack alternately delighted and outraged her fellow Bostonians when she drank beer in public, sat in the front row at a Jim Corbett boxing match, and, as Van Wyck Brooks recounted, "walked down Tremont Street with a lion in leash . . . hired

Above, top. This early photograph shows Fenway Court, later the Isabella Stewart Gardner Museum, which was built facing a tributary of the Charles River in Boston. *Bottom.* The design of Fenway Court was based on the Italian palazzos Mrs. Gardner admired. This cross section of the four-storey house looks toward the rear through the court and Tapestry Room.

locomotives when coaches were not fast enough, and appeared at balls with a page to bear her train."[22] Compelled by the exotic, Mrs. Jack delved into Buddhism. While she later participated in more conventional religious activities, she did so with her characteristic style: each Lenten season she sent out black-bordered invitations to Holy Communion and, under the eyes of an amazed public, piously atoned for her transgressions by scrubbing the steps of the Church on the Advent on Boston's proper and elegant Beacon Hill.

Mrs. Jack's avocation as collector and builder was sparked by her attendance at the classes of Charles Eliot Norton, Harvard's first professor of art history.

Left. The interior courtyard of Fenway Court was elaborately landscaped with lush floral displays in perpetual bloom. It also contained a bubbling fountain surrounded by ancient mosaics and statuary. The glass roof was designed so that the light in the courtyard was reminiscent of Venice.

Revered by his friends as "Pope Charles," Norton discussed art, as Van Wyck Brooks has written, as "his forebears preached salvation. . . . If the modern world was ugly, it was also base: its baseness and ugliness went together. Taste alone could redeem it."[23] Armed with such an ideal, Mrs. Jack turned for assistance in assembling a collection of redeeming good taste to the youthful Bernard Berenson, the brilliant Lithuanian-born art historian who would amass a fortune advising wealthy Americans on their purchases while authenticating art dealers' attributions. It was Berenson who inspired James's portrayal of Breckenridge Bender in his popular novel *The Outcry.* As art adviser, Bender was a "Yankee on the spend," and a part of "such a conquering horde as invaded the old civilization, only armed now with huge chequebooks instead of with spears and battle-axes."[24]

Gardner built Fenway Court as a museum-palace to house her cultural trophies. Situated on a small site beyond the center of Boston's fashionable Back Bay, where the Gardners had previously lived, Fenway Court faced a tributary of the Charles River that meandered through Olmsted's Back Bay Fens. A four-storey Italian palazzo, Fenway Court climaxed a life of collecting and patronage. Gardner wanted her house to be a Venetian palace similar to the kind that might originally have housed her works of art and suitable to the passionately pro-Italian world view of the intellectual circle with which she had allied herself. So clear was Gardner's vision that her architects, Willard T. Sears and Edward Nichols, were reduced to draftsmen and engineering consultants. Although Gardner's palace was based in part on a palazzo in Venice that she had rented annually since 1890, she was not content with a copy or even an interpretation. Unable to buy a palazzo outright and rebuild it in Boston, she traveled through Europe, collecting architectural fragments such as mosaics, columns, and balustrades. She then had Sears and Nichols arrange the various elements into a coherent whole, as though architecture were another kind of art collecting.

As built, Fenway Court is a palazzo type turned inside out. The palace's severe exterior gives no hint of the luxurious interior, where pink-and-white façades turn inward upon a courtyard that is roofed in glass so that the mottled surfaces simulate the effects of light reflected from Venetian canals. From tripartite windows articulated by balustrades or balconies, Gardner looked down on a landscaped courtyard containing a bubbling fountain, ancient mosaics, and statuary, as well as lush floral displays in perpetual bloom regardless of the unpredictable New England weather. The rooms grouped around the court incorporate architectural fragments appropriate to the paintings. And what paintings they were: Piero della Francesca, Botticelli, Raphael, Titian, Rembrandt, and Vermeer were presented to American eyes as though the Renaissance had happened only yesterday. To its critics, Fenway Court was, as Mary Logan Smith Costelloe, Berenson's wife, commented in 1920, "in spite of the marvellous pictures in it . . . *like a junk shop.* There is something horrible in these American collections, in snatching this and that away from its real home and hanging it on a wall of priceless damask made for something else, above furniture higgle-dipiggled from other places, strewn with *objets d'art* ravished from still other realms, Chinese, Japanese, Persian, Indian objects, that seem as if they were bleeding to death in those dreary super-museums."[25]

But unlike other collectors who completely turned their backs on the art of their moment, Mrs. Jack fostered the careers of contemporary American artists,

hanging their works in her palace beside her Renaissance treasures. Among the
painters she favored was John Singer Sargent, who maintained a studio in her
house-museum and painted a portrait of her that was so seductive that one critic
said it "challenged speculation regarding the audacity of both sitter and artist."[26]
Mr. Gardner ordered that the portrait, of which his wife was deeply proud, be
removed from public display at the staid Saint Botolph's Club, further stipulating
that it not be publicly shown during his lifetime. It was the only known occasion
when her husband — or anyone else — told Mrs. Jack what to do. She later hung
the flattering painting in the Gothic Room of her palace, but the public was not
permitted to enter the room until after her death.

Her involvement with every detail of her house was so great that during

Mrs. Gardner was a patron of contemporary American artists and hung their paintings alongside her Renaissance treasures. Among them was her commissioned portrait by John Singer Sargent (*above*). Considered seductive and therefore not suitable for public display, the painting was removed by her husband's order and was not allowed to be viewed again until after her death in 1924.

construction, she was daily on the site of what the workmen called her "Eyetalian palace," bringing her own lunch and paying her ten cents for oatmeal used to purify the drinking water. On one occasion she wielded a paintbrush, while on another she took an ax to a wooden beam to show the workmen just how she wanted things done. During construction, Mrs. Jack kept the interior appearance of her mansion such a guarded secret that in order to test the acoustics of the Music Room before the palace's official opening gala on New Year's Day 1903, she invited members of the Boston Symphony Orchestra to play for a very special audience: children from the Perkins Institution for the Blind.

Henry James offered what is perhaps the most trenchant observation on Mrs. Jack and her dream house: he praised Fenway Court as a "tour-de-force — no Evolution at all — but pure Special Creation in an adverse environment."[27] She was among the first major collectors to open her house to the public. To the end, Mrs. Jack had it on her own terms. Her motto, engraved on her palace's wall beside a representation of a phoenix, symbolizing immortality, was "C'est mon plaisir." From its dedication in 1903, Fenway Court was open to the public, if only on a capricious schedule. Democracy went just so far: on the rare days when she willed it, tourists could purchase one-dollar tickets from brokers. Whatever her idiosyncrasies, Mrs. Jack set the tone in an era marked by a blossoming of American culture. And she insured that Fenway Court would remain a monument to her unique sensibility even after her death. Her will stipulated that her palace become a full-fledged museum open to the public, but that any change in the collection or its arrangement, no matter how minute or inconsequential, would result in the museum's dissolution. Only after her death in 1924 were the clarity and generosity of her vision fully revealed, when the inscription "The Isabella Stewart Gardner Museum MDCCCC" carved in stone above the front door was uncovered for the first time.

Another Italian palazzo created on American shores to house a vast collection of European artifacts was built as a retreat from, rather than a resource for, the society of the Northeast. James Deering, vice president of the International Harvester Company — which had been founded ten years earlier when his father's company, the Deering Harvester Company, merged with the McCormick Harvester Company to become the world's largest manufacturer of farm machinery — had been told by his physician in 1910 that he must move to a warmer climate. After considering the French Riviera, Monte Carlo, southern Italy, and northern Africa, the fifty-three-year-old bachelor from Chicago decided to build a house on Biscayne Bay, south of Miami, Florida, which, despite the completion of Henry Morrison Flagler's railroad in 1896, was still a rather sleepy town of about ten thousand inhabitants. There Deering built a seventy-room palazzo, Vizcaya, named after the Basque province from which the Spanish explorers who charted the coast of southern Florida first sailed.

Before building began, Deering traveled in Europe for two years surveying architecture with Paul Chalfin. Chalfin was a complex personality, not only a talented and highly trained painter and art scholar but also a socially ambitious *saloniste*. He had been a Fellow of the American Academy in Rome and a curator at the Boston Museum of Fine Arts before being employed as an assistant to Elsie de Wolfe, the decorator, who introduced him to Deering. After assembling a collection of furnishings and architectural fragments, Deering and Chalfin joined

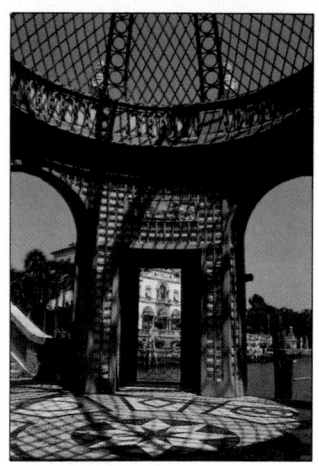

This domed pavilion is only one of the many small buildings that adorned the formal gardens of James Deering's 180-acre Vizcaya estate. The surrounding landscape, designed by Diego Suarez, also incorporated a series of stepped pools, a casino, an orchid garden, two teahouses, and a gondola canal.

forces with F. Burrall Hoffman, Jr., an American architect trained in Paris at the École des Beaux-Arts, and Hoffman's partner, Harry Creighton Ingalls, to design an appropriate setting for the vast treasury of European furnishings and architectural fragments that had been shipped to New York and stored in warehouses. Although Hoffman's design for Vizcaya was inspired by villas in many parts of Italy, its principal source was the seventeenth-century Villa Rezzonico, located northwest of Venice in the Brenta River country, which Deering and Chalfin visited in 1911. The building program and the tropical climate, however, required that Hoffman move far beyond his model. The mansion's façades, its four corner towers, and a central court are Vizcaya's chief legacy from the Villa Rezzonico. Under Hoffman's inspired direction, Vizcaya departed from its model's rather austere and rigorous styling to attain a gentle lyricism appropriate to the lush greenery of south Florida. Constructed of reinforced concrete and stucco, and surmounted by red half-barrel tile roofs, the villa is trimmed in local oolitic limestone, while the steps leading to the mansion were built of Florida quarry keystone, incorporating coral formations. Weight-bearing columns were made of denser limestone imported from Cuba. The mansion's boldest façade, which faced the bay because Deering wanted the most striking view of his villa to be the one seen from his yachts, culminates in a broken pediment flanked by finial-like statues and volutes.

To accommodate Miami's year-round heat, Hoffman ranged principal rooms in a single layer around a courtyard. Unlike its Italian prototype's covered two-storey court, at Vizcaya the courtyard is open to the sky, facilitating ventilation.

Left. Deering protected his two yachts against the turbulent tides of Biscayne Bay with a breakwater in the form of a 176-foot-long stone barge. He commissioned sculptor A. Stirling Calder to decorate it with exotic carvings depicting mythic sea creatures. Deering's estate was further protected by a seawall 300 feet long.

The main living quarters are on the ground floor, while the mansion's large kitchens are on the second floor in a tower area screened from the court to dissipate the heat and odors caused by cooking. Vizcaya's interiors were designed by Chalfin, who skillfully blended four centuries of Italian and French decorative arts. Among the objects housed at Vizcaya were a set of seventeenth-century wrought iron gates from the Palazzo Pisani in Venice, an eighteenth-century modeled plaster ceiling from the Venetian Palazzo Rossi, and an Empire-style bed from the Palace of Malmaison.

Like the villas along the Brenta, Vizcaya incorporated a working farm, which rendered the 180-acre estate nearly self-sufficient. To house Vizcaya's key personnel, Hoffman designed outbuildings that resembled those in a northern Italian village. But it was the formal gardens that gave the estate its dreamlike ethereality. Draining the mangrove swamp that immediately surrounded Deering's mansion, landscape architect Diego Suarez created gardens echoing those of the Villa d'Este in Tivoli and the Villa Albani in Rome. In Suarez's design the fan-shaped main garden had a central axis, defined by an elevated "island" of lawn and flanked by elaborately patterned low-clipped hedges, which terminated in an artificial hill. The mount incorporated an elegant series of stepped pools and was surmounted by a fanciful casino, containing a loggia and two small rooms decorated in a Rococo style. Chalfin described the casino as a place "to dream in or perhaps weep; for two to steal to; for three to sing and for eight to dance in . . . [it] held itself a household in miniature . . . a playhouse for an hour, the great establishment with all its etiquette abbreviated and curtailed, but unbroken."[28] Suarez's scheme also incorporated a walled orchid garden, grottoes adorned with statuary carved of rough-surfaced quarry keystone, a teahouse built of French *treillage* and another of stucco and latticework, and a domed pavilion known as the Casba. A gondola canal that meandered through the grounds provided Deering and his guests with opportunities for moonlight boating. A footbridge over the waterway was ornamented with twisted columns surmounted by stone peacocks sculpted by Gaston Lachaise.

Deering kept his two yachts, the *Nepenthe* and the *Psyche*, in a private harbor, dredged to accommodate oceangoing schooners and bordered by a three-hundred-foot-long seawall. To further protect his estate from the turbulent tides of Biscayne Bay, Deering built a breakwater; but this was no ordinary breakwater. In keeping with the extravagant spirit of the site, Chalfin commissioned the sculptor A. Stirling Calder to decorate a 176-foot-long stone barge inspired by the one at the Villa Borromeo on Lake Maggiore in Italy. The barge, embellished with elaborate carvings depicting mythic sea creatures both benign and malevolent, also evoked one that the dowager empress of China built at the Summer Palace in Peking at the end of the nineteenth century, and was no less exotic.

In all its lush extravagance, no estate could have been less suited to its client than Vizcaya. Deering, who spent only ninety days a year there, was hardly a hedonist. A sign posted in the servants' dining room admonished, "Singing and Whistling Will Not Be Indulged in While Mr. Deering or Guests Are in the House." While Deering did entertain the rich and famous, his parties were notoriously staid, always ending, at least officially, at 10:30 P.M. Deering was apparently not interested in staging elaborate follies at Vizcaya or even in taking great pleasure in living there privately. Indeed, the environment he created for

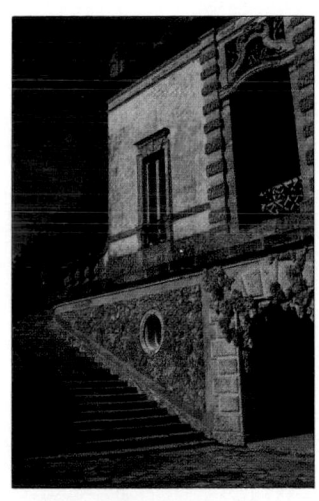

A seventeenth-century Italian villa inspired F. Burrall Hoffman, Jr.'s design of Vizcaya. Constructed of concrete and stucco, the Florida villa was trimmed in local limestone, while the steps leading to the mansion were built of indigenous quarry keystone, laid to represent coral formations.

himself seemed strangely at odds with the man. Photographer Nell Dorr visited Vizcaya with Lillian Gish, star of D. W. Griffith's epic films *Birth of a Nation* and *Intolerance*. Dorr recalled that Deering "was a man who wanted to have beauty around him . . . but he didn't know what to do with it. He wasn't able to live with it. It was simply there. . . . The whole place was magic. Everything except poor Mr. Deering . . . there was not a magic thing about him."[29] What Deering shared with Gardner, and with Jefferson, Clemens, and Vanderbilt, was a passion about his building project, a singular intent to see his personal dream made real. Suffering from pernicious anemia, Deering rationed his energy judiciously but seemed to his friends to be invigorated rather than daunted by the immense project, for which he would employ nearly ten percent of Miami's population and spend almost as much money as Frank W. Woolworth paid at about the same time for his famed New York skyscraper. The thirteen years it took to plan and build the estate were, Hoffman said, "Deering's greatest years. . . . He seemed so alive then. It was a time of great excitement for him."[30] The project's complex logistics, which included building a railroad spur and operating a quarry, appealed to Deering's mathematical turn of mind. Not surprisingly, Deering, unlike William Randolph Hearst and many others who built vast dream houses, was able to complete his palace, resolutely setting limits on his own dream. The building of Vizcaya ultimately seemed to be a battle for life: it sustained Deering until two years after its completion, when he died in 1923, willing his dream house to his nieces and nephews. The following year, the devastating hurricane that dealt a final blow to Florida's faltering real estate boom significantly damaged the mansion. For nearly three decades Vizcaya stood generally vacant. In 1952, however, its restoration and preservation were insured when two of Deering's nieces, Mrs. Marion Deering McCormick and Mrs. Barbara Deering Danielson, who had bought out the other heirs' interests, conveyed their uncle's private dreamworld to Dade County to be maintained as a public museum.

Ironically, considering Deering's fairly conservative life at Vizcaya, it was immortalized on film as the site of one of America's most extravagant dreams of empire. *Citizen Kane*, Orson Welles's thinly disguised portrait of newspaper tycoon William Randolph Hearst, used Vizcaya for some of the film's representation of Xanadu, itself a portrait of Hearst's San Simeon. In a sense, the use of Vizcaya was appropriate, for it was there that Hearst's romance with Marion Davies blossomed. Three years after their meeting at Vizcaya, Hearst set out to create for himself and his consort an even more breathtaking dreamworld overlooking the Pacific Ocean in California, "La Cuesta Encantada," the enchanted hill, San Simeon.

Not only a newspaper czar, Hearst was also an art connoisseur, an amateur architect, a bon vivant, a statesman, a pal to movie stars, a horticulturist, a zoologist, and a rancher. Building on the ranch he'd inherited from his parents, he began San Simeon when he was fifty-six years old. His dream was based on somewhat contradictory terms: Hearst believed that by expending great wealth, he could recapture the simple life. His reasons for undertaking the project were rooted not in the quest for power but in nostalgia for his childhood, when he had spent holidays on the ranch with his parents, picnicking and sleeping in tents. Set sixteen thousand feet above the sea, amidst more than a quarter-million acres of open land — nearly one-third as large as the entire state of Rhode Island — San Simeon was like nothing ever built before, a ranch fit for a king. Here, beginning in

William Randolph Hearst's elaborate San Simeon estate, designed by Julia Morgan, was built on a hilltop overlooking the Pacific Ocean. The twin towers that loomed over the entrance to the main house were directly based on the tower of a Spanish cathedral. The statue in the foreground is only one of countless pieces from Hearst's collection that were placed throughout the estate.

In the movie *Citizen Kane,* John Deering's Vizcaya estate in Florida substituted for San Simeon, the monumental dream castle William Randolph Hearst built for actress Marion Davies in California. Hearst had first met Davies at Vizcaya, and the oversize architectural grandeur of its interiors, as seen in this still photograph from the movie, matched that of San Simeon.

1920, Hearst and his architect, Julia Morgan, created a dreamworld without parallel, furiously building until 1937, when, like millions of other Americans, he ran out of money during the Great Depression. Hearst's castle was an eclectic mixture that only approached synthesis. As a piece of architectural bravado, it knew no rivals: a castle in function, by design it was a cathedral lording over a hilltop village high above the sea.

Hearst did not feel free — or rich enough — to undertake his greatest building project until after his mother's death in 1919. An only child, he had been extremely close to his mother, Phoebe Apperson Hearst. A tiny, well-mannered, but ambitious schoolteacher from Franklin County, Missouri, she had eloped in 1862 with George Hearst, a hard-working, heavy-drinking tycoon. Like most of America's richest men, George Hearst culled his riches from the earth itself. Going to California to seek his fortune during the gold rush of '49, Hearst first hit pay dirt mining silver at the Comstock Lode in Virginia City, Nevada, and later ended up with interests in the Homestake gold mines in South Dakota and the Anaconda copper mines in Montana. From his father, young William inherited the fortune with which to finance his dreams; from his mother he inherited the strong will and passionate aestheticism with which to render his dreams beautiful. Hearst's mother was one of several strong-willed women to play an influential role in his life. She had provided a model for shaping and building dreams on a grand scale with her work on one of her pet projects, the campus of the University of California at Berkeley. It was appropriate, then, that Hearst should turn to a woman architect, Julia Morgan, whose career had been strongly supported by his mother. The first woman to graduate from Berkeley's School of Engineering, Morgan, encouraged by her drafting teacher, the prominent Bay Area architect Bernard Maybeck, went on to become the first woman to graduate from the École des Beaux-Arts in Paris. Phoebe Hearst, who met Morgan in Paris, was impressed by her tenacity. When Morgan became the first woman licensed to practice architecture in California, Phoebe Hearst prompted her to open her own office. Boosted by Hearst's patronage, Morgan became one of California's most well-known and prolific architects, designing hundreds of buildings, including the Mission-style offices of the Hearst-owned *Examiner* in Los Angeles (1912).

In 1919, soon after his mother's death, Hearst visited Morgan's office in San Francisco to discuss a building project for the San Simeon property, which he had just inherited. Walter Steilberg, an employee of Morgan's, recalled the physically imposing Hearst's saying in his incongruously high-pitched voice:

I would like to build something up on the hill at San Simeon. I get tired of going up there and camping in tents. I'm getting a little old for that. I'd like to get something that would be more comfortable. The other day I was in Los Angeles, prowling around second-hand book stores . . . and I came upon this stack of books called Bungalow Books. Among them I saw this one which has a picture — this isn't what I want, but it gives you an idea of my thought about the thing, keeping it simple — sort of a Jappo-Swisso bungalow.[31]

Morgan's first sketches depicted a modestly scaled, one-storey house that, as historians David Gebhard and Robert Winter have pointed out, would have looked fully appropriate on any residential street in Pasadena.[32] But Hearst's desire to build a bungalow soon vanished, to be replaced by a grand, elaborate vision. Changing the name of the site from Camp Hill to La Cuesta Encantada, Hearst

This 1937 photograph shows Hearst at dinner with his guests in the Refectory at San Simeon. The long table seated forty people beside a huge Gothic fireplace and beneath rows of brilliantly colored flags based on thirteenth-century Sienese banners.

Overleaf. Beyond the central complex of San Simeon was a series of elegantly landscaped terraces. The most remarkable of these contained the Neptune Pool, a vast Roman-style swimming pool of white marble and green tile. It was bordered by two made-to-order Classical colonnades.

began to envision a complex that would dwarf all other American estates, including George Vanderbilt's Biltmore in North Carolina. The castlelike mansion he built, San Simeon, would accurately be compared to Versailles and Frederick the Great's Sans Souci.

Like Gardner's and Deering's architects before her, Morgan was faced with designing not only a house but also a repository for an enormous collection of European artifacts, furnishings, and architectural fragments. For Hearst, too, was a voracious collector. It is reported that when the ten-year-old Willie Hearst was traveling with his mother in Europe, he remarked, upon seeing the Louvre in Paris, "Buy it for me, Mom! We can afford it."[33] As an adult, Hearst satisfied his ambition by compulsively collecting architectural fragments and objects. Filling up his New York triplex apartment until it was chock-a-block, Hearst stored the rest of his collection in warehouses in the Bronx. His passion for beautiful things was obsessional: his wife, Millicent, once commented, "I think he went out and bought things whenever he was worried."[34] Much of Hearst's collection stayed in the Bronx, but he eventually sent his favorite pieces to be used in his California dream house, temporarily storing them in an immense pier warehouse in San Simeon Bay. Incorporating a large portion of Hearst's vast and varied collection into the design for the mansion, Morgan brilliantly combined the ancient and the contemporary, the found and the commissioned, the genuine and the ersatz into a seamless, coherent compositional whole glued together in poured concrete. San Simeon was like a museum of architecture, its treasures subsumed by the Spanish and Spanish Colonial architecture — a not inappropriate choice of style, given the castle's location along the coast between important missions at San Luis Obispo and Carmel.

As Morgan designed it, San Simeon was a Mediterranean hilltop village, incorporating three guest houses romantically named the Casa del Mar, the Casa del Monte, and the Casa del Sol. The main house, La Casa Grande, embodied the ultimate in arrogance: it was designed to look like a cathedral. The twin towers that loomed above the main entrance derived directly from the tower of the cathedral in Ronda, Spain. The basic organization of the house, which contained more than one hundred rooms and a total area almost one and a half times the size of a football field, derived from the plan of an early Christian basilica: the Main Vestibule was the apse, the Assembly Room the transept, the Refectory the nave without side aisles, and the Morning Room, flanked by the pantry and Billiard Room, the narthex. To enhance the churchlike ambiance, there were no great stairways and even an elevator was carefully concealed. La Casa Grande's second floor was dominated by a library and four bedroom suites known collectively as the Cloisters. A large part of the third floor was occupied by Hearst's private Gothic Study and Gothic Suite, as well as by Hearst's and Davies's bedrooms. Before the towers were completed, Hearst became so enchanted by the view they afforded that he asked Morgan to place living quarters there. "But, Mr. Hearst, this is the roof," the usually unflappable architect is said to have observed. To which Hearst replied, "Then put on another story. We'll call it the Celestial Suite."[35]

Beyond the central complex, a series of elegantly landscaped terraces stepped down the hill, the most remarkable of which contained the Neptune Pool. An oval white marble and green tile swimming pool in the Roman manner, its waters reflected an ancient temple façade, as well as two made-to-order Classical colonnades. Also at the Neptune was one of the battery of telephones that connected Hearst's secluded dreamworld with his far-flung editors, who always referred to him as "The Chief." There were telephones everywhere — beside his chair in his private movie theater, even in the trees that lined the mile-long vine-covered pergola — claimed by its owner to be the "longest pergola in captivity"[36] — through which Hearst and his guests would ride on horseback protected from the glaring California sun.

Marion Davies remained Hearst's companion for the last thirty-two years of his life. They invited a steady stream of visitors to San Simeon. Some of them came by plane, landing on the private air strip; others took the steamer from San Francisco, arriving at a dock large enough to accommodate Hearst's oceangoing yachts as well as the boats that ferried in building supplies. Davies's Hollywood pals would depart on Friday afternoons from Los Angeles aboard a train that Hearst leased from the Southern Pacific Railroad for his private use, arriving five hours later at San Luis Obispo, forty miles down the coast from San Simeon. A fleet of limousines would meet the train and take the guests for the final leg of the journey up the coast. Turning off the coast road, they could see the floodlit castle rising in the distance. The five-mile-long winding approach road led up the enchanted hill through a landscape where Hearst had impatiently rewritten natural history. In the shadow of towering cypress trees, which Hearst had shipped in as mature thirty-five-foot-tall specimens, herds of cattle grazed alongside exotic animals from Hearst's menagerie, including zebras and camels. Travel-weary guests — visiting heads of state as well as reigning Hollywood royalty — were deposited at San Simeon's front door, where Hearst and Davies would initiate them into their dreamworld with the rather disarming greeting, "Welcome to the ranch!"

The evening rituals began in the Assembly Room, where guests would imbibe the one cocktail allotted by their host while they waited for his dramatic entrance by way of the hidden elevator. Upon his arrival, Hearst would lead his guests into the Refectory, a room so splendid that even the somewhat jaded film star Louise Brooks, who was a frequent guest, confessed to having "never entered without a little shiver of delight."[37] The Refectory's long table seated forty people beside a huge Gothic fireplace and beneath rows of brilliantly colored flags based on thirteenth-century Sienese banners. Despite the splendor of the room, the cuisine was decidedly down-home, with hearty ranch-style dishes accompanied by catsup served from the bottle. After dinner, all guests, movie stars and dignitaries alike, were required to go to the private movie theater, where a film, often one starring Marion Davies, was shown. Afterward, while many of his guests splashed about in the enclosed Roman pool, Hearst customarily retreated to his Gothic Study, where he would give himself over to his abiding passion — newspapers — and work until three or four o'clock in the morning.

Hearst's restless intelligence and obsessive nature resulted in an approach to building reminiscent of Jefferson's. He frequently had sections torn down and rebuilt if they did not meet his or Morgan's complete approval. Throughout the Depression, hundreds of workmen were employed in what was the largest private construction project in California. Construction was slow and costly. Building supplies had to be shipped by coastal steamers overnight from San Francisco. By 1937, even Hearst's fortune was spent, and construction on La Cuesta Encantada stopped. Between 1942 and 1944, Hearst and Davies had abandoned San Simeon in order to save money and in fear that the coast might be shelled by Japanese submarines. They escaped to the forests of northern California, where they stayed at another family property, Wyntoon. After an eight-year hiatus, Hearst and Davies returned to their castle and resumed construction with the aid of Warren McClure, an assistant of Morgan's. By this time, however, Hearst's sons had gained positions of power within their father's business empire and were able to significantly curb his insatiable appetite for building.

No matter that the ranch and his other holdings made him richer than most of his guests, Hearst portrayed himself as the man who comes from nowhere, whose existence is defined by constant action and who is liberated by the vast expanses and inherent possibilities of the continent. If Jefferson was the first Westerner, perhaps Hearst was the last. Living during a time when the nation's desire for global territorial expansion subsided, and suffering great personal failures amidst his successes, Hearst invented a "frontier" to replace the vanished opportunities his father had exploited. While San Simeon was built as a showplace and continually visited by the power elite, it was the very private vision of a single man, built ultimately for his pleasure alone.

So intensely personal was his dream that his sons did not care to take possession of San Simeon when Hearst died in 1951 at age eighty-eight; besides, it was too costly to maintain. Hearst suggested in his will that it be given to the University of California as a memorial to his mother, but even the regents of a major public institution whose very existence was owed in large measure to Mrs. Hearst were reluctant to assume the enormous operating expense. Eventually the state government took title, and today San Simeon is, with the exception of Disneyland, the biggest single tourist draw in California.

Perhaps the greatest fantasy in home building — one that eluded Hearst — is to create a self-perpetuating dreamworld. In America, both the tax laws and tradition discourage the passage of houses from one generation to the next. The relative unimportance of inherited wealth and family lineage, compared with Europe, has gone hand in hand with the uniquely American cult of individualism. Every American seeks to create his own identity, his own relationship to the realities and myths of American life. Founding an institution, as Isabella Stewart Gardner did, is perhaps the only way to create a lasting dream. Some American dreamers have realized the goal of creating self-perpetuating dreamworlds by extending their houses to encompass whole regenerating communities — schools and artists' enclaves such as Frank Lloyd Wright's Taliesin — through which they could insure that their ideals would not die with them. Those who use their own homes as the catalysts for the creation of such larger entities are at once the most altruistic and egotistical of individuals, sacrificing their privacy in order to perpetuate their dreams.

Aline Barnsdall, an oil heiress from Pennsylvania, sought to build and immortalize her dreams on a Los Angeles hillside. Her residential complex was designed from its inception to be home not only for Barnsdall but for the arts as well — an institution that was to initiate a new era in American theater. For Barnsdall, the Midwest wasn't far enough from the restrictive commercialism of New York to nurture a community dedicated to elevating America's theater from mere entertainment to art. Southern California offered the artistic freedom her imagination demanded after years of study and travel with European theater's avant-garde. To create this world for Art, Barnsdall chose the architect Frank Lloyd Wright, whom she had met in Chicago and first commissioned to design a theater there. For Barnsdall, Wright was the only architect worthy of the "great force"[38] of American theater she wished to harness.

The site she selected was called Olive Hill, a thirty-six-acre mound in the middle of Hollywood that Barnsdall purchased in 1919. With an olive grove overlooking the Pacific to the west and snowcapped mountains to the east, the site was a miracle of landscape, described by one observer as a Maxfield Parrish painting come alive. Between 1915 and 1925, Wright worked on plans for an art village consisting of two principal structures, Hollyhock House and a 1,250-seat theater, as well as apartments, studios, cottages, and terraced stores. Most of the complex, including the theater, was never built, but Hollyhock House itself was finished in 1921, although not without more than a fair share of struggle between the strong-willed architect and client.

The house itself was a collaborative performance integrating Barnsdall's and Wright's respective ambitions to express a uniquely American vision in theater and architecture; the house was, in essence, as Vincent Scully has observed, "a temple dedicated to the American continent."[39] Olive Hill went far beyond Barnsdall's initial conception of a refuge from Broadway commercialism: for Wright it was a refuge from personal tragedy and artistic anxiety. With his only other substantial work being built within the completely alien cultural context of Japan, Wright transformed Olive Hill into an archetypal American place. Dipping deep into the American experience, he conceived of the house as an ancient temple and a Spanish Colonial hacienda, uniting the antitheses of America's southwestern experience and manipulating the ordinary lightweight stucco-on-lath construction

of builders' bungalows and Hollywood stage sets to achieve so extraordinary an impression of monumental permanence that a generation of observers took it to be built of reinforced concrete. From the outside it seems almost a solid mass, with long, heavy lintels crowned by a frieze of abstracted hollyhocks — Barnsdall's favorite flower. The effect is distinctly forbidding, although the house is eminently accessible through wide portals. Inside, it appears, in contrast, magically hollow. With its rooms ranged around a central court and ancillary patio, it is a vessel for light, which streams in through skylights. At the head of the long axis of the court stands the living room. Its glass doors could be folded away so that the interior flowed through a loggia to the garden court, in keeping with Wright's belief that a "California house should be half house, half garden,"[40] a view Barnsdall shared. Beyond the court an elevated lawn served as a stage, second-storey terraces as the balconies, an electrically operated fountain as the curtain, and tall trees as a cyclorama. The house itself, then, was frankly theatrical, creating a domestic version of the large public theater that Wright also hoped to build for Barnsdall.

To the extent that the Hollyhock House succeeded as a regional portrait, it also succeeded as a portrait of its thirty-five-year-old owner, Aline Barnsdall, whom Wright described as "neither neo, quasi, nor pseudo. She was as near American as any Indian, as developed and traveled in appreciation of the beautiful as any European. As domestic as a shooting star."[41] Wright's interest in architectural portraiture was quite explicit: his son, Lloyd, who was responsible for much of the

Left. Hollyhock House, designed by Frank Lloyd Wright for oil heiress Aline Barnsdall, presents a forbidding façade of monumental proportions. Its seemingly solid mass is constructed of lightweight stucco. The long, heavy lintels are crowned by a frieze of abstracted hollyhocks, the owner's favorite flower.

Right. Barnsdall intended her estate to be not only a personal residence but a community for the arts that would initiate a new era of theater in America. The original design — never completed — included a theater, studios, stores, and apartments in addition to Hollyhock House. This pencil sketch dates from about 1919.

The dining room at Hollyhock House contained furniture designed for the house by Frank Lloyd Wright.

In contrast to its solid exterior, Hollyhock House appears magically hollow inside. In the living room, light pouring in from a skylight above the hearth is reflected in a pool below. The ornamental panel that served as a mantel was developed with architectural tools.

site's landscaping, claimed that the design over the fireplace — an ornamental panel developed with the tools of the architect — the triangle, compass, and T-square — was an abstract portrait of Barnsdall, the hollyhock turned into a footloose American. This may be too broad an interpretation, but the mantel was without doubt a marvelous composition expressing the formal elements of design. Below it, the hearth was made as a pool reflecting the light pouring in from a skylight above. In short, Wright sought to reconcile the coziness of a suburban home with the dark mysteries of an ancient temple, linking together earth, air, fire, and water in a dynamic geometric outpouring.

Barnsdall was ultimately unsuccessful in her dream of altering either the course of American theater or her own mortality. In 1927, the City of Los Angeles received the grounds as a park, and the California Arts Club transformed the house into its headquarters. On the plaque dedicating the park to Barnsdall's father, Theodore, the daughter wrote: "Our fathers mined for the gold of this country. We should mine for its beauty." Barnsdall maintained ownership of one of the outbuildings on Olive Hill, which she called the Oleanders House, dying there in 1946.

The newspaper publisher George G. Booth and his wife, Ellen Scripps Booth, a newspaper heiress, succeeded where Barnsdall had failed, ultimately fulfilling their dream of building an independent community dedicated to the arts. Within twenty-five years of building their country house in Bloomfield Hills, twenty miles outside Detroit, the Booths had transformed it into the nucleus of an eclectic dreamworld founded upon their belief that good design led to good living. The Booths' house, a Tudoresque country house designed by Albert Kahn and completed in 1908, was named Cranbrook after the English village where Booth's grandfather had been the coppersmith. Recognizing that his squirearchy lacked a context, Booth set out to make a country village similar to the one his ancestors had left behind. He built an elementary school and commissioned a Gothic church from Bertram Grosvenor Goodhue, but Cranbrook, neither farm nor market town, still lacked a sense of purpose. In 1924, after several false starts in spreading the gospel of good design, Booth's moralistic faith in aesthetics and his search for context coalesced: from then on, the Cranbrook estate would be an art village. At the suggestion of his son Henry, who was studying architecture at the University of Michigan, Booth hired the Finnish architect Eliel Saarinen to structure his dream. Saarinen had a plan for Cranbrook ready in 1925, and construction began the next year.

Inspired by the American Academy in Rome, which they had visited in 1922, the Booths wanted Cranbrook to be a place where students and artists could work together and trade ideas. The American Academy, however, was steeped in the architecture of the Eternal City, where antiquity stood side by side with the work of modern times. Saarinen couldn't quite bring Rome to Detroit, but he did supply Cranbrook with an architectural past that gives it the appearance of having developed over hundreds of years and not the twenty it actually took to build it.

The academy itself, where resident artisans lived and worked, was strung out along a street, Academy Way. If their work wasn't displayed outside as part of the architectural ensemble, it could be seen in the studios and museum. Saarinen's own house (1928) was a group effort, with Saarinen designing the building and some of its furnishings, which were executed by Tor Berglund, a Swedish cabinet-maker. Saarinen's wife, Loja, wove the rug, and the distinctive tiles that framed the fireplace were executed by Mary Chase Stratton.

Under Booth and Saarinen, Cranbrook flourished, with well-known European artisans training dozens of important American designers, including Saarinen's own brilliant son, Eero. In addition to the academy, Booth founded two preparatory schools. Adjacent to the academy, the boys' school was English Gothic in feeling. Across the lake from Cranbrook House, Saarinen's growing respect for Frank Lloyd Wright was reflected in an expanded Prairie-style design for the Kingswood girls' school. After Kingswood School was completed in 1931, Saarinen began the design of the Cranbrook Institute of Science. Intended for both exhibiting and research, the institute had a much more modest budget than Kingswood, and perhaps as a consequence far less architectural detail. It was a transitional design, suggesting that Saarinen was moving away from the Midwestern sources of the Kingswood School and closer to European Modernism. In effect, Saarinen was not attracted by the machine-style Modernism of Le Corbusier or Mies van der Rohe; rather, he was interested in the Modern Classicism that first flourished in Germany and Italy as well as in the United States, as can be seen clearly in the last of his Cranbrook buildings, the library and art museum of 1942, which provided a monumental centerpiece for the village — its metaphoric civic link. The building's stripped Classicism reverberated to distant architectural thunderclaps from Italy and Germany, while it was complexly counterpointed by grace notes from pre-Columbian America and patterning based on the De Stijl master Piet Mondrian. A stage set worthy of the German filmmaker Leni Riefenstahl, perhaps, Saarinen's last building for Cranbrook was also sweetly gentle, a sandstone temple carved by the wind. As realized by the Booths, Cranbrook is a quintessential American dream house, establishing a sense of place, memory, and the owner's personality as it reaches out to establish a complex communal vision that endures over time.

4   Suburbs: Arcadia for Everyone

For most Americans, the suburb is an impersonal subdivision, populated by hundreds of virtually identical houses with gimcrack ornament, set on sunbaked, treeless sites, with neither city nor open country close at hand. While the suburban ideal speaks of the permanence of home and hearth and of the cultivation of nature, today's suburban experience is often defined by rootlessness, with families moving once every seven years on the average. Yet the house on its suburban lot remains central to the American dream, a fundamental representation of the American search for an ideal community in nature, a *rus in urbe.*

At their best, our suburbs have been so much more than the monotonous post–World War II tract developments disparaged by Pete Seeger, who sang of "Little Boxes on the hillside, Little Boxes made of ticky tacky . . . Little Boxes all the same."[1]

For Seeger and millions of Americans, suburban imagery is familiar; yet its role in culture is little studied and even less understood. At its best, the suburb is an attainable, inhabitable Arcadia in the form of a village, only a short ride from the city, where the American family can dwell in its individual house-temple. The movies fixed an idealized image of suburbia in the mind's eye of a generation of Americans raised in the Depression of the 1930s: a converted farmhouse miles from any neighbor in the Connecticut countryside, like the one that belonged to Katharine Hepburn in *Bringing Up Baby* (1938) or Barbara Stanwyck in *Christmas in Connecticut* (1945). But the suburb is more than a collection of cozy castles on celluloid; as Denise Scott Brown, the architect and urban planner, has written: "Curving roads and tended lawns . . . houses with pitched roofs, colonial doorways and shutters, tell us, without need of further signs, that here is a community that values tradition, pride of ownership, and the rural life."[2]

The suburb is a remarkable achievement, a complex physical embodiment of American aspirations deeply rooted in the national psyche. Yet in the last half century, our newer suburbs seem cut off from their original, wider and deeper meanings; they no longer are built as an identifiably distinct form of urbanism. We have held on to the myth but we seem to have lost the fact of the suburb — the Arcadian village at the edge of or even inside the town. Lost also is the ability to flesh out the suburb with houses, streets, and gardens that can breathe life — the gift of individuality — into it. Yet what a glorious past the American suburb had.

The planned suburb in America brought commerce, social reform, and art together in intimate embrace. While suburban villas were built as early as the

This 1924 painting by Molly Luce entitled *Suburbia* represents the ideal community in nature as it was originally intended to be, a synthesis of two preindustrial environments: the artisan's village and the open countryside.

fifteenth century in Italy, the development of residential villages in areas just surrounding cities, for families whose source of income was not agriculture but commerce undertaken in the city, dates only from the industrial age. Industrialization contributed to the growth of suburbs in four ways: it brought increased prosperity to a large segment of the population; it brought improved public transportation; it created environmental problems that made large portions of the urban centers less desirable for habitation; and it transformed the city into an environment that seemed to many to be contrary to domestic harmony. Technological advances, particularly in transportation and communications, made it possible for large numbers of people dependent on the city for their livelihood to live outside its center, generating a previously unknown settlement pattern that was neither rural nor urban. Although there are a few important early examples of planned suburban development in England, such as John Nash's Park Villages (ca. 1820), built as part of the Regents' development in London, by and large the idea of inventing a new, ideal, industry-free town from scratch was a uniquely American phenomenon. At their best, America's planned suburban villages constitute a tapestry of architecture and landscape that weave together contradicting but not necessarily irreconcilable strains of romance, reform, and dollars-and-cents realism.

Perhaps the strongest influence on the development of suburbs was a desire widespread in American society to maintain traditional preindustrial values and environments. It was this impetus that most directly affected the physical character of the planned suburban communities built between the middle of the nineteenth century and the Second World War. Typically, these suburbs attempted to

Alexander Jackson Davis's design for an American cottage (*above*) was published in an 1837 book entitled *Rural Residences*.

Right. Today, Davis's influence is apparent in suburban houses such as those at the corner of Atlantic Boulevard and Coronado Street in Atlantic Beach, Long Island.

synthesize two distinct preindustrial environments: the artisan's village and the open countryside. The merger of these two patterns had the positive effect of creating a rich and visually varied environment comparable to the texture of the surrounded urban areas. Because each new suburb was created as an entirely new and large-scale entity, it required professional planning, which had hitherto been reserved for the design of cities and large-scale landscapes. Ironically, these trained professional planners who undertook the design of such new communities for the most part employed naturalistic plans and vernacular architecture to create the illusion of country villages set in picture-perfect landscapes that had developed organically over long periods of time.

One powerful inspiration for the planned suburb in America was, rather curiously, the large suburban cemeteries that began to be built just outside city centers in the 1830s. Pastoral cities for the dead — such as Mount Auburn Cemetery in Cambridge, Massachusetts (1831), and Greenwood Cemetery in Brooklyn, New York (1838) — in their cultivated beauty and careful planning struck a responsive chord for many American city dwellers. In 1849, Andrew Jackson Downing, whose ideas about gardens and villa design revolutionized domestic architecture, observed that

one of the most remarkable illustrations of the popular taste . . . is to be found in the rise and progress of our rural cemeteries. . . . Twenty years ago, nothing better than a common grave-yard, filled with high grass, and a chance sprinkling of weeds and thistles, was to be found in the Union. . . . At the present moment, there is scarcely a city of note in the whole country that has not its rural cemetery.[3]

In the first of these cemeteries, Mount Auburn in Cambridge, a plan was adopted that epitomized romantic landscape architecture: winding drives following the earth's contours meandered through a naturalistically orchestrated landscape, incorporating groves of trees and ponds. At Greenwood in Brooklyn, nearly twenty miles of winding roads were laid out by Major D. B. Douglas on a 478-acre site overlooking New York Harbor. Greenwood was a pastoral community. The very street names evoked nature. This idyllic setting was also a real estate development: to house their dead, the rich bought grassy lots and built house-temple tombs. Greenwood was not so much a city as a suburb for the dead. It was immediately popular as a park, attracting crowds of pleasure-seekers escaping the city each Sunday. Based on personal observation, Downing commented that nearly sixty thousand people visited Greenwood between April and December 1848, and while some no doubt went "to twine the votive garland,"[4] most went simply to enjoy themselves.

In the decades before the Civil War, planned, landscaped cemeteries made clear that there was a widespread hunger to escape into nature from the social and aesthetic rigors of the urban gridiron. That same hunger ultimately also gave birth to the resettlement of the middle class in suburbs. Much of the impetus for the landscapes and buildings developed as alternatives to the city came from the designs and publications of a group of several designers: Andrew Jackson Downing, Alexander Jackson Davis, Calvert Vaux, and Frederick Law Olmsted.

Throughout the 1840s and 1850s, Downing published a series of highly influential books, promoting a modest, naturalistic approach to the cultivation of landscapes. He argued that landscapes should not be subjected to rigid geometric disciplines but that the asymmetrical and freely growing appearance of untrammeled nature should be fostered. He further argued that in encouraging contemplative calm, these environments had a moral and social value.

Downing's books promoted a complementary architectural style, typified by the work of Alexander Jackson Davis, who illustrated Downing's ideas. Davis proposed an architectural equivalent of Downingesque naturalism, repudiating Classical symmetry in favor of picturesque, "naturalistic" composition and rustic modesty. Davis's designs for Downing, representing what was sometimes called the American Style, used wide plank siding overlaid with wooden battens, deep roof eaves supported by brackets, and generous verandas, towers, and cupolas to create a picturesque effect. These architectural trends were furthered by Calvert Vaux, an English architect who had immigrated to the United States in the early 1850s to form a partnership with Downing.

After Downing's death in 1857, in a Hudson River steamboat explosion, Vaux teamed up with Frederick Law Olmsted, who succeeded Downing as America's most influential landscape architect. Olmsted, whose work on estates like Biltmore and campuses like Stanford has been seen in earlier chapters, was a wealthy, socially and politically involved intellectual with no formal training in architecture or landscape architecture. His only direct experience with a related field was a six-year stint as a farmer on Staten Island. But his extensive travels in the American South as well as in England in 1850 made him acutely aware of the sociological consequences of environmental abuse, whether slavery or industrialization. Olmsted's English journeys familiarized him with a number of early attempts to reverse the ill effects of industrialization by enlightened town planning. His observations during his trip to England were published two years later in *Walks and Talks of an American Farmer in England*. Despite the title, Olmsted's book was not really much about farming but about urbanism and, most important, suburbanism, as exemplified by Joseph Paxton's successful synthesis of artistic and practical considerations at Birkenhead, a model development outside Liverpool. For Olmsted, the success and potential of Birkenhead were so great that it could "be held up as an example not only to philanthropists and men of taste but to speculators and men of business."[5] The central focus of the development was Birkenhead Park (1857), a former clay pit that Paxton transformed into a lush, naturalistic landscape devoted to public recreation. But Olmsted was equally compelled by the park's social implications: Birkenhead Park was "entirely, unreservedly, and for ever the people's own. The poorest British peasant is as free to enjoy it in all its parts as the British queen. More than that, the baker of Birkenhead has the pride of an OWNER in it."[6]

It was as co-designer, with Vaux, of the winning entry in the competition for New York's Central Park in 1858 that Olmsted was able to transform his intellectual interest in land management and the sociological aspects of urbanism into a professional career as a landscape architect. The dedication of 840 acres to natural parkland in the middle of Manhattan reflected the widespread perception that the spread of the industrialized city was a threat to health and to traditional morality and aesthetics — the same perception that fueled the growth of suburbia. To this day Central Park provides the only significant interruption of the city's insistently regular gridiron plan and is one of its most treasured civic amenities. The park as designed and realized represents a remarkable achievement, combining enlightened social concern, superb aesthetic control, and brilliantly ambitious engineering. To transform what Olmsted described as "a very nasty place . . . steeped in the overflow and mush of pigsties, slaughter houses, and bone-boiling works [where] the stench was sickening,"[7] millions of tons of earth were shifted by horse and cart. A romantic landscape of rolling hills, forests, and even a vast lawn trimmed by a flock of sheep administered by a shepherd epitomized Olmsted's vision of Central Park as a slice of nature from preindustrial Manhattan frozen in time, an idealized version of the open country made accessible to urbanites of all classes. Yet its "naturalism" was carefully orchestrated and laboriously achieved. Within the park, bridges and tunnels separated various types of traffic so that pedestrians, horseback riders, and carriages were provided with their own pathways. A gracious carriage road looped through the park, while through traffic was served by traverse roads ingeniously sunk below the surface to minimize the presence of the workaday world of commerce. Yet a quarter-mile-long straight and wide pedestrian mall, linking the expanding city at its southern end with a mock castle, perched high above a manmade lake and built intentionally small so as to appear more distant when seen in a false perspective through the woods, made absolutely clear that the park was an artifact of man and not an accident of elapsed time. All the effort to create an illusion of an untamed romantic wilderness notwithstanding, Central Park's design proposed neither urbanity nor wilderness but a synthesis of the two into a new and special civility. In this marriage of natural, picturesque landscaping and rational, technologically advanced planning, a highly visible model for the American planned suburb was created.

In 1853 Llewellyn Haskell, a friend of Davis's and an ardent supporter of

Today, the planned suburb is an impersonal subdivision filled with identical houses, with neither city nor open country close at hand. *Above, top to bottom:* Sun City near Phoenix, Arizona; Dominguez Hills, Los Angeles; and a housing development on Staten Island, New York. *Right:* "Little Boxes on the hillside" in Daly City, California.

The houses of Forest Hills Gardens, New York, were laid out along gently curving streets arranged in a modified grid. The model community was planned as a tranquil residential retreat for commuters from nearby Manhattan.

proposals to create Central Park, established a residential enclave in West Orange, New Jersey, that crystallized the ideals of the planned suburb. Haskell abandoned his estate on the nearby Passaic River after concluding that its swampy site was at least partly to blame for the deaths of four of his five sons and his own bouts with rheumatism. Seeking a higher site, where he hoped to find restorative fresh air, he bought and renovated a farmhouse on Orange Mountain, twelve miles from midtown Manhattan, near mineral springs that had been the nucleus of a popular resort area since the 1820s. Around his new home, Haskell developed Llewellyn Park as a residential enclave of "country homes for city people."[8]

Llewellyn Park was laid out by Haskell, assisted by Davis, who may have suggested the idea to Haskell. The core of the development encompassed 350 acres, including a 50-acre linear strip of common parkland known as the Ramble, which served as the community's spine. Ten miles of curving streets encircled the Ramble and branched out to the house sites, which were laid out in a largely unmanicured landscape that flew in the face of conventional mid-Victorian practice. Covenants not only protected the park area but also, to help preserve the area's pastoral character, stipulated that no house be on less than one acre.

It was the unique relationship of Davis with Llewellyn Park's early days that was in large part responsible for the enclave's architectural consistency. Davis renovated Haskell's farmhouse, transforming it into a picturesque cottage. He also designed a summer house for himself on an adjacent site. Thus established at Llewellyn Park, he no doubt exercised substantial influence on the development of the community's planning as well as, by design and example, the villas built there. But Llewellyn Park's architectural unity resulted not only from close collaboration between architect and developer but also because the smallish Gothic-style houses tended to be subsumed by the landscape. Davis's turreted, stone gate lodge, flanking a willow pond, guarded Llewellyn Park's fenced-in preserve and set the architectural tone so that even the more elaborate houses, such as Castlewood, a mock-Gothic castle that Davis designed in 1859 for the prominent local businessman Joseph C. Howard, were so intricately composed as to seem modest — as modest as the Park's board and batten villas, including one Davis designed in 1859 that was purchased seven years later by James Miller McKim, minister, ardent abolitionist, and father of the future architect Charles Follen McKim. Complete with two massive towers, constructed of roughhewn stone from the Park's quarries, and a long "cloister" connecting the main house to its stone stables, Castlewood was a wonderful evocation of an imaginary past, an American dream of the English Middle Ages as it never was. Of the two, Castlewood and not the McKim cottage was the more premonitory: by the 1880s the suburb began to throw off its cloak of modesty and emerge as an enclave whose exclusivity was defined principally by material wealth, not romantic ideals.

In 1886 Thomas Alva Edison, filled with the first flush of success, settled in the Park, from which he commuted to the factory he built just outside the gates in West Orange. Edison's house, Glenmont, had been completed in 1881 for Henry C. Peddler, who was later convicted of building the house with funds he had embezzled from his employer, Arnold Constable, the New York department store tycoon. In order to retrieve some of his losses, Constable, who acquired the house, sold it fully furnished to Edison. Glenmont was a vast, turreted, red-painted wood palace, designed by Henry Hudson Holly. Like Downing before him, Holly published many books on suburban house design, in which he advocated rational planning and more grandiloquent architectural expression. Their popularity was to make him one of the most influential house architects of his generation. In keeping with the evolution of such changing preferences, Llewellyn Park's trend toward more extravagant architectural expression accelerated rapidly around the turn of the century, when many of the original houses were torn down and replaced with much larger Georgian and Tudor mansions, culminating in Delano & Aldrich's limestone mansion, Landmore, completed in 1931 for Edison's son Charles, one-time governor of New Jersey. Few of the Gothic cottages survived; neither did the sense of intimacy between nature and architecture seen in the early planning. Instead, homeowners increasingly came to find appropriate self-expression in the dominance of individual buildings over the adjacent landscape.

Despite Llewellyn Park's naturalistic plan and Arcadian spirit, the absence of any public or commercial facilities and the nearly two miles from its entrance to the nearest railroad station prevented it from ever functioning as a fully developed village, a distinction that belongs to Olmsted and Vaux's Riverside, the brainchild of E. E. Childs, whose Riverside Improvement Company undertook to transform

This advertisement for Forest Hills Gardens shows its assortment of architectural styles. Although advanced industrial techniques were employed in their construction, the houses were deliberately nostalgic, evoking images of old, handcrafted buildings.

One powerful if curious inspiration for suburban planning in America was the cemetery. The entrance to Greenwood Cemetery in Brooklyn (*above*) led to the idyllic setting pictured in this 1852 bird's-eye view (*right*). The asymmetrical, freely growing appearance of the landscape design provided an escape from the urban grid — a naturalistic approach advocated for the design of suburbs.

an unattractive, flat, flood-prone 1,600-acre agricultural site on the Des Plaines River in Illinois into a model suburb. An observer of 1869 noted that the site, nine miles from Chicago, presented "an overwhelming generosity of raw prairie wind and waste prairie land which were anything but inviting." Under Olmsted and Vaux's direction, Riverside would soon emerge as "at once an elegant drive, a handsome park, and a delightful suburban city."[9]

Childs and his designers were convinced that an ideal suburb offered not only the pleasures of rural retreat but also the convenience of all the latest advances in public utilities and transportation and the conviviality of a community to which city dwellers had become accustomed.

As in the case of Central Park, Olmsted's scheme was both idealistic and practical. Olmsted thought that the gridiron plan, though sensible from the point of view of real estate development, was "too stiff and formal for such adornment and rusticity as should be combined in a model suburb."[10] In a brilliantly pragmatic move — one that became a standard of suburban planning — he modified the grid by curving it, thereby providing both easily divisible real estate and the illusion of a naturally evolved rural settlement pattern. Olmsted then took his pragmatism one step further, turning the site's principal deficit into an incomparable advantage: he transformed the useless flood plains into parkland.

The plan for Riverside was metropolitan in scale, calling for a landscaped roadway connecting it to Chicago, with separate lanes for pleasure and commercial vehicles. Olmsted called this road the "park way," a term he may have picked up from Llewellyn Park, whose Park Way ran along one side of the Ramble. Olmsted's parkway was never carried out, nor were many of the buildings Vaux designed for the village center. Financial troubles, including the nationwide panic of 1873, plagued Riverside's growth. A town center did eventually grow up around the railroad station. It included stores, offices, a chalet-style hotel, and public works buildings, such as a vaguely Germanic turreted water tower that became the community's symbol.

Olmsted and Vaux did not include any stylistic stipulations in their plan, but they did impose certain environmental and economic controls to insure both the town's appearance of affluent spaciousness and a general visual coherence by keeping landscaped areas primary. It was stipulated that houses were to be set at least 30 feet from the private property line; building lots were to be at least 100 feet wide and about 200 feet deep; the construction of fences in front yards was prohibited; houses were required to cost at least $3,000 and to be owner-occupied; and 700 of the suburb's 1,600 acres were to be devoted to roads, some of which were depressed below grade, as well as to parks and ornamental greenswards, including the nucleus of the plan, Long Common. Although the suburb as a whole lacked architectural distinction or even coherence, several notable houses were built, including Louis Sullivan's Babson house (1907) and Frank Lloyd Wright's complex for the Coonley family (1907, 1911) and his house for F. F. Tomek (1907). Ironically, the low-lying hipped roofs of his houses, which Wright claimed had evolved to suit the uninterrupted flatness and sweep of the Midwestern prairie, seem quite at home in Riverside, where Olmsted had transformed the prairie into a picturesque landscape based on the eighteenth-century estate parks he had visited in England.

From a sociological point of view, Riverside institutionalized the trends that Llewellyn Park had pioneered: an idealized alternative to conventional city living, Riverside was not just a residential enclave; it was a community with shops, schools, and a town hall, an evocation rather than a bread-and-butter realization of an autonomous community, for none of its inhabitants did any of their useful work there. In this sense, Riverside exemplified the essential fantasy of the suburban ideal. A dream town come true, Riverside was a village without an economy — a village that could never have actually existed in the past. As both a practically laid-out, independent village and a brilliantly designed stage set for enacting the Good Life in industrial America, Riverside set the standard for future suburban developments throughout the nation and the industrial world.

An alternative to the commuter's world of Riverside could be found nearby, thirteen miles south of Chicago. There, on a four-thousand-acre site located between the Illinois Central Railroad tracks and Lake Calumet, George M. Pullman, the railroad car tycoon, built the first planned industrial village in the United States, a suburban factory town housing eight thousand people. Pullman's company produced Pullman Palace Cars, which not only provided gourmet meals and comfortable berths but also revolutionized rail travel by stimulating competing rail lines to adopt standard-width tracks across the country. By 1880 Pullman's fortune was so large and his success so great that he was referred to as a "satiated Alexander with no more worlds to conquer."[11] Yet three years later, while planning to build a new factory, Pullman embarked on one more great project: he would build a model town unlike any ever built before, combining in one harmonic, economically sound whole a railroad car construction plant and housing for the workers needed to keep it going. His dream town reflected his belief, both

Squatter's shacks like this one dotted the site of Central Park before Frederick Law Olmsted and Calvert Vaux transformed it into an oasis within the city.

THE ARCH

BRIDGE AT THE
7TH AVENUE ENTRANCE.

As envisioned by designers Olmsted and Vaux, Central Park became an idealized version of the open country. Within the park, bridges and tunnels such as those pictured in the engravings above accommodated different types of traffic, so that pedestrians, horseback riders, and carriages were provided with separate pathways.

Right. A 1979 painting by Rackstraw Downes shows the Oval Lawn in Central Park. From the time of its dedication in the mid–nineteenth century, the park has been one of the city's most treasured amenities.

idealistic and opportunistic, that well-designed workers' communities would benefit wage earners and management alike. Pullman saw the development of his ideal town as the logical extension of his previous achievements. As a Pullman Palace Car Company brochure distributed in 1893 stated, "The story of Pullman naturally divides itself into three parts — the building of a car, the building of the operating system, and the building of the town."[12]

Pullman set out to build his town in a typically shrewd buccaneer fashion, buying the land in secret. He hired the twenty-seven-year-old architect Solon S. Beman, who had recently remodeled Pullman's Chicago mansion, to design the factory — an uncommon task for an architect at the time. Aided by the landscape designer Nathan Barrett, Beman then laid out the town. The town's major streets ran north and south and were, in effect, continuations of the gridiron in Chicago, the realist's city par excellence. Nonetheless, Pullman, Beman, and Barrett believed in the commercial value of beauty. Pullman's town was distinguished by such amenities as a public square across from the railroad station and the Hotel Florence (named for Pullman's daughter), a handsome brick building with a broad, ornamented veranda that was largely off-bounds to workers. Pullman's grandest building was the critically acclaimed 250-foot-long Arcade, a 90-foot-high glass-roofed building housing a theater and a library containing eight thousand books donated by Pullman. He also built a farmers' market in 1882, which, when it burned down ten years later, he had rebuilt in the Classical style. The market constituted an important community focus on its site, which interrupted the town's grid of streets.

Pullman established as a development principle that sound housing was fundamental to the well-being and productivity of each and every worker. The town's housing reflected the company's hierarchy. Decent accommodations were provided at moderate rents for workers at all pay levels, from freestanding houses, to row houses, to two- and three-room tenements. By varying roofs and the way in which standardized windows, doors, and trim were composed on different buildings, visual monotony was avoided. Consistency, however, was maintained by the repeated use of brick as a building material and the use of standardized building elements. Most important, Pullman was the nation's first fully functioning instantly created city. Pullman's sophisticated infrastructure was founded on scientific and sanitary principles. Separate storm and sewage systems carried storm water from roofs and streets through cobblestone gutters into Lake Calumet and sent sewage in glazed pipes to a 300,000-gallon reservoir. The water was then fermented, the unpolluted effluent recycled, and the remainder used as fertilizer for nearby farms owned by Pullman. Power for the factory and the town was supplied by the 700-ton Corliss engine that had powered the 1876 Centennial Exposition in Philadelphia.

As the new town began to take shape, George Pullman was hailed as an idealist. A London newspaper reporter called the town the most perfect city in the world[13] and Henry Demarest Lloyd, financial editor of the *Chicago Tribune*, whose virulent criticism of the ruthlessly managed Standard Oil Company had made him famous, stated that Pullman need not fear strikes. In the initial euphoria, no one seemed to see Pullman's tragic flaw: for better or worse, Pullman was the quintessential "company town." The company owned everything. George Pullman liked to claim that even the churches in his town were required to return six percent on his investment. As a result, church buildings stood vacant because no congregation could afford the rent. Pullman's refusal to sell the houses to the workers conflicted with the fundamental American dream of home ownership. Richard T. Ely, an economics professor whose career as a social critic was launched by an analysis of Pullman in *Harper's Magazine*, felt that "the idea of Pullman is un-American" in the way it divested the worker of independence, making every aspect of his life subject to legislation by company authority.[14]

In boom times, Pullman's policies were grudgingly tolerated by workers, but when the Depression of the 1890s came and the company laid off workers and simultaneously increased rents, all hell broke loose. When a strike erupted, Pullman, failing to recognize its significance, ignored the advice of the eminently pragmatic Republican politician Mark Hanna, who told him to "arbitrate, arbitrate, arbitrate." Hanna wrote him off, saying that "a man who won't meet his own men halfway is a God-damn fool."[15] After repeated walkouts, a prolonged strike culminated in violence in 1894, bringing the National Guard armed with Gatling guns into the town. Although the strikers ultimately capitulated, they had succeeded in attracting national attention and the support of the pioneer labor leaders Eugene Debs and Samuel Gompers. Pullman and his town, once lionized as progressive, now symbolized corporate feudalism. Within four years, the Illinois Supreme Court upheld the workers' demand that Pullman sell them their houses. When he died, shortly thereafter, Pullman had become so hated as a symbol of capitalist abuse that his family feared for his mortal remains and had his coffin bound in steel and embedded in asphalt.

The bitter aftertaste of the Pullman strike stigmatized the town for generations to come. The housing deteriorated; the Arcade was torn down in 1926. By the 1960s, with passenger railroading in deep decline, the long-neglected town was threatened with demolition. Yet the fundamental humanity of Pullman's vision endured. Town residents — now homeowners — stuck it out, and preservationists began to lobby on its behalf. One hundred years after its construction, Pullman is being gentrified as an affordable suburb. A new middle class that punches computer keys in Chicago's offices instead of rivets in Pullman's factories is bringing it back to life. However, the remarkable balance of workplace and dwelling that was Pullman's original goal and achievement has been lost, a preponderance of its citizens commuting to their jobs by train or freeway.

Following Pullman, a surprising number of workers' towns were built in suburban areas throughout the nation: McKim, Mead & White's vaguely Colonial-style Echota, built in 1892 for the Niagara Power Company in the town of Niagara Falls, New York, and Kohler, Wisconsin, built at the edge of the town of Sheboygan and incorporated in 1912 by its namesake, the well-known plumbing manufacturers. Even the federal government co-opted the suburban ideal for workers housing. As part of the mobilization effort for World War I, the United States Housing Corporation undertook a series of emergency projects at East Coast port cities to handle the influx of shipyard workers. So short was our participation in the war that most of these suburbs remained on paper. Yet the few that were at least partially realized — most notably the series of enclaves built in Bridgeport, Connecticut, as well as Yorkship Village in Camden, New Jersey, completed in 1918 — testified to the efficacy of the suburban dream: enlightened architects could emulate the houses and towns of the rich to create an affordable and desirable working and dwelling environment for the less prosperous classes.

Another variation on the theme of a low-density residential area in a natural setting was the development of enclaves of suburbanity within the heart of gridded cities. The most interesting of these enclaves are the "private places" of St. Louis, where suburbia was married to the convenience of an in-town location in a gesture that celebrated at once the power of the individual and the power of the metropolitan city to embrace a wide variety of planning types. Entered from the surrounding streets of commercial and comparatively high-density development, each of St. Louis's nearly fifty private places offered a tranquil, well-ordered alternative to the surrounding urban context. St. Louis's private places typically consist of a broad boulevard only a few blocks in length but divided by a generous planting strip and marked at both ends by exuberant, ceremonial gates, which guard broad boulevards along which were set large houses on small lots. Strict development regulations were usually established by the street association. Collectively, the enclaves formed a chain of grassy oases leading from the central city to the outlying open country.

Lucas Place, planned in 1851, was St. Louis's first private place. It was developed by James B. C. Lucas, who had been appointed Justice for the Northern District of Louisiana by Thomas Jefferson. The development did not differ physically from the typical St. Louis street; it was its internal regulation that was innovative. Lucas Place, which extended for four blocks, prohibited any commercial development, while part of the street was zoned exclusively for schools and churches. Benton Place, however, founded in 1867 by Montgomery Blau, broke with the city's grid. From its single-gated entry, its street divided to create a boulevard encircling a lushly planted mall. Around the mall were freestanding houses. In form, plan, and styling, the houses maintained a relationship to an urban prototype, appearing much like detached row houses.

Benton Place was quickly followed by a succession of kindred developments. Vandeventer Place (1870) was conceived by Charles Peck in association with Joseph McCune and Napoleon Mullikin and planned by Julius Pitzman, an engineer and major in the Union Army who had surveyed the city of St. Louis. Its plan was like that of Benton Place, but many of the houses were conceived as suburban villas rather than town houses. They were built by such notable architects as Peabody & Stearns, Henry Hobson Richardson, and Burnham & Root. Pitzman took the private place concept one step further in his design for Compton Heights (1889), capitalizing on the existing topography to create a winding street free from the city gridiron. Houses built in subsequent developments ranged from modest villas (Lewis Place, 1890) to very large and imposing houses (Westmoreland and Portland places of 1889 and Kingsbury Place of 1908). Consistently, however, each new enclave was graced with a grand and stylistically distinctive set of gates or a gatehouse. The attention lavished on these adornments was symbolic of a critical attraction of suburban communities, one that it was necessary to underscore in the

The design of Central Park synthesized urbanity and wilderness into a new, special civility. *Above* is a view of Central Park Lake circa 1890; *left*, today, skaters enjoy the same spot.

urban sites of St. Louis: the escape from the pressures, crush, and monotony of the city to a protected place of one's own.

While the residents of St. Louis's enclaves entered their communities through monumental gateways, at many of the great American suburbs of the nineteenth century the community's gate was its railroad station. As at Riverside, numerous suburbs developed with their "village" centers clustered around the station, so crucial to residents' daily lives. These railroad suburbs were perhaps the most successful at establishing visually and socially cohesive communities. With a single primary link to the city, one primary village center could be maintained by it, with most residents passing through it daily. The parkland and roadways beyond were quiet and leisurely.

The concept of the railway suburb was initiated at Riverside; it was given its most complex and finely articulated expression nine miles from the heart of midtown Manhattan, at Forest Hills Gardens. A high point as well as a watershed in the planner's art, Forest Hills Gardens was begun in 1909 with its principal features in place by 1912. Its developer, the Russell Sage Foundation, recognized the potential for less affluent urban workers to escape from the city when the Long Island Railroad was electrified and for the first time directly connected via a tunnel to Manhattan, where Pennsylvania Station was just being completed. Forest Hills Gardens was intended to be a suburban village for wage earners that would not only satisfy the needs of its inhabitants but serve as a paradigm for future ventures elsewhere. After purchasing two hundred acres of farmland, the foundation hired the Olmsted Brothers — Frederick Law Olmsted's firm as it operated after its founder's death — as planners and Grosvenor Atterbury as architect of the village.

Forest Hills Gardens was to be comparable in scope and quality to both the industrial suburb of Margarethenhohe outside Essen, Germany, which had been built by the Krupp family to house workers for its nearby munitions factories, and the great English experiment at Hampstead Garden Suburb outside London, where a social worker, Henrietta Barnett, assisted by the architect-planners Parker & Unwin as well as by the architects Edwin Lutyens and M. H. Baillie-Scott, had set out to create a workers village accessible to central London via the newly extended Underground. Though in many respects the most European of American suburbs, Forest Hills Gardens clearly reflected American civic-mindedness by incorporating into an otherwise cozy domesticity an emphasis on monumental urban planning that had gained momentum after the 1893 World's Columbian Exposition in Chicago. Like its English prototype, Forest Hills Gardens was an aesthetic triumph but a failure at social reform: the proximity to central London in the one case and to Manhattan in the other rendered the property values too high. Almost as soon as the developments commenced, they became upper-middle-class preserves.

The railroad station was designed by Atterbury as the gateway to the suburban community. Home-bound commuters arrived at Station Square, a brick plaza bordered on one side by the railroad embankment and on the other three sides by continuous arcaded buildings that housed apartments, shops, and the Forest Hills Inn, whose tower dominated the square and provided a visual focus for the community. The buildings spanned the two principal streets that radiated from the square to the residential neighborhoods. Eclectic in its sources of planning and architectural expression, the square is perhaps most evocative of a German medieval village. Beyond Station Square, houses were laid out along streets arranged in a modified grid that incorporated long curving avenues. While the Olmsteds' plan did not totally succumb to the hegemony of the urban grid, it stood in marked contrast to more romantic schemes like those of Llewellyn Park and Riverside. In the prospectus of 1911, Forest Hills Gardens's sponsors stated that "fantastically crooked layouts have been abandoned for the cozy, domestic character of local streets, not perfectly straight for long stretches, but gently curving to avoid monotony."[16]

Forest Hills Gardens was an idealized metropolis in miniature. Passing through the suburb from Station Square to Forest Park at the community's edge suggested a metaphoric journey from town to country.

At once a model community and a practical business proposition, Forest Hills Gardens represented a more complex kind of suburbanism than ever before attempted. Atterbury, working with other architects, provided a wide variety of housing types, from the hotel at Station Square to apartment buildings and row houses as well as attached and single-family dwellings. A number of housing groups were clustered around shared garden spaces in a bold and largely successful assault against the American tradition of fenced-in yards. Advanced techniques of industrial building were experimented with, including the use of precast panels made of Nailcrete, a substance Atterbury devised that was nearly as strong as concrete and as nailable as white pine. While Atterbury pioneered construction techniques that he said were like "child's blocks raised to the Nth power,"[17] his designs at Forest Hills Gardens deliberately avoided any stylistic references to the machine and remained exultantly if nostalgically ethereal.

In a sense the nostalgia of the architecture was appropriate, for Forest Hills represents both a pinnacle and an end of a particular kind of suburb. The railroad suburbs were particularly successful in generating a special sense of place. Isolated in the countryside with one main link to the outside world, they were, like campuses, literally places apart. After World War I the dream of *rus in urbe*, which had combined with the construction of commuter railroad lines to produce dozens of remarkable suburban villages, was threatened by the meteoric rise of the automobile's popularity. The automobile, while fostering the democratization of suburbia at a hitherto unprecedented rate, also stretched the scale of the suburban dream to nightmare proportions. As a consequence, the suburb as a semi-independent village geographically bounded by comfortable walks to the train station that comprised its communal focus gradually gave way to a sprawling development pattern that could have a linear focus in the form of a highway. The car's impact on American life was seen by contemporary observers such as Hubert Towle, who noted in 1913 that within a very few years the automobile had evolved from a "transcendent plaything" to a sociological phenomenon of sufficient force to open up a new pattern of residential settlement.[18] In 1916 President Wilson signed the Federal Roads Act, initiating a national program of highway construction that opened the way to an unprecedented continental migration that would forever blur the distinction between city and country and transform large parts of America into a continuous suburb.

At first, planners and architects viewed the role of the car in suburban developments as a natural continuation of the increased flexibility that trolleys had over railroads. Few recognized the inherent difference between the fixed routes of

In designing houses for the residential enclave of Llewellyn Park in West Orange, New Jersey, Alexander Jackson Davis employed a naturalistic approach based on the ideas of landscape architect Andrew Jackson Downing. His Byerly-Kerr House (1868), pictured here, is typical of what is sometimes referred to as the American Style, with deep eaves and generous verandas that achieve a modest, picturesque effect.

Right: Castlewood was designed by Davis in the midst of the Ramble in Llewellyn Park. A mock-Gothic castle with two massive towers and a long cloister connecting the main house to the stone stables, it evoked an imaginary past — an American dream of the English Middle Ages as it never was.

rail systems, on the one hand, and the infinite capriciousness of individually owned and maintained automobiles. As a result, new suburbs such as Radburn, New Jersey, of 1927, attempted to discipline the automobile to the centralized planning principles of the railroad era.

At Radburn, dubbed a "Town for the Motor Age," the car was seen as the enemy of the suburban ideal. The planners, Clarence Stein and Henry Wright, contrived strategies to minimize its intrusion into Arcadia. Looking back for inspiration to Llewellyn Park, they called for the creation of forever-green open spaces — parkways without roads — as the focus of community design. At Radburn, the idea of the Ramble or Olmsted's Long Common was treated as a traffic-free park, a slice of the country brought right up to suburban front doors. Stein and Wright saw in these broad greenswards a place where families and neighborhood children could all play, safely isolated from the street.

Radburn was built ten miles outside New York City, just over the George Washington Bridge. Borrowing an idea from Olmsted's Central Park, Radburn's traffic was separated. A system of pedestrian walkways permitted children to go to school without ever having to cross automobile traffic. A key design idea was to have the fronts of the houses face the parklike greenswards and garage and service doors face tight cul-de-sacs that would be little more than service alleys. But while the greenswards and cul-de-sacs are the best-known features of the so-called Radburn plan, the hierarchical organization of the overall village supplied a necessary urban counterbalance to the more deliberately bucolic aspects of the single-family housing sectors. The commercial center was also architecturally more lively. It included a railroad station in the local vernacular — Dutch Colonial with a gambrel roof — a pyramidally roofed gasoline station in the form of a gatehouse, a shopping center with offices above, designed by Andrew J. Thomas, and a number of apartment houses nearby.

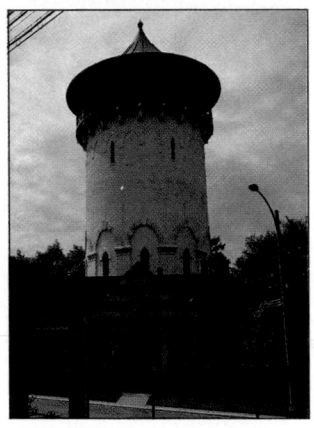

Olmsted and Vaux's plans for Riverside (*top*), a model community nine miles outside Chicago, transformed unattractive, flood-prone prairie land into an inviting suburb with parks and curving streets. While financial troubles plagued Riverside's growth, a town center did eventually grow up around the railway station, which included such public works buildings as the turreted water tower (*bottom*) that became a landmark for the community.

At first, Radburn was viewed as a planning triumph. Only its architecture was found by some to be a disappointment. The bland Georgian-style houses were not inspiring. But later critics have come to criticize even the Radburn plan. For example, Alden Christie, a young architect who grew up in Radburn, questioned its superarticulation and its provisions for open space:

The layout of the dwellings in the superblocks creates a network of intensely developed spaces which abruptly evaporate into a shapeless common, too vaguely defined to suggest an extension or expansion of private yards, too wide to command a directional tendency towards a focal point, too sparsely landscaped to invite the refuge from the tight complex of houses. . . . The dwelling complexes surrounding the open green in effect are drawn away from it. The automobile has been made such a dominant feature that life is more oriented towards the peripheral access road . . . than towards the common.[19]

For, in fact, Radburn has not worked out the way Stein and Wright had hoped. The automotive cul-de-sacs have proved more appealing focuses of activity than the greenswards. Children prefer to play among the routine activities of daily life. Adults prefer to drive to neighbors' houses. Except for rare occasions of neighborly ceremony, the back door functions as the front door might, with cups of sugar exchanged at the same place where roller skates and bicycles are stored and dinner guests arrive in their cars.

Radburn had little immediate impact on suburban development. This was more a consequence of bad timing than of inherent weaknesses in its planning. Only a quarter of the original town was built before the Depression bankrupted its sponsors. But in the long run its attempt to moderate the hegemony of the automobile in suburbia has been widely influential. From "high art" schemes such as Frank Lloyd Wright's Broadacre City, discussed below, to countless less idealistic speculative developments, to the very notion of cluster zoning, so pervasive today, Radburn helped demonstrate that a town for the motor age could be designed with both the motorcar and a bucolic quality of life in mind.

Radburn, and the ideas of Clarence Stein in particular, were also cited as inspiration for a series of New Towns undertaken by the federal government during the Depression. According to President Roosevelt, one-third of all Americans during the Depression were ill fed and ill housed. Roosevelt's Brain Trusters created the Suburban Resettlement Program, devising a series of suburban communities set in permanent green parks — greenbelts, they were called — at the edges of the major cities. The most fully realized of these is Greenbelt, Maryland, ten miles from downtown Washington, D.C., in what was open country when the town was laid out in 1935. The planning process was supervised by Rexford Guy Tugwell, a New Deal Brain Truster. One of his primary objectives was to obtain the maximum amount of sun for each of the houses. Unfortunately such ideal solar orientation could be achieved only at the expense of the traditional hierarchical organization of a town.

The houses didn't front each other across streets or commonly shared parks but instead faced neighbors' back yards or whatever lay in the path of optimal solar exposure. Streets were merely the conduits for traffic, not the social focus of neighborhood life. As a strict response to solar orientation forced the abandonment of traditional hierarchies, the ideal of individual houses gave way to a guiding visual impression of abstract, impersonal, mass "housing."

Tugwell's ideal, which owed a lot to the German housing projects of the 1920s, abandoned the inspiration of preindustrial village life — the key to nearly a century of suburban planning — for a site-planning strategy that claimed to be scientific and rational and an architectural aesthetic that exulted in the utilitarian and the functional. The architecture of Greenbelt was as bleak as its planning was misguided. As designed by Douglas D. Ellington and R. J. Wadsworth, the houses were stripped of all overtly historicizing emblems: there were no gables, turrets, or pedimented porches or the visual richness that comes from combining brick, stone, and stucco. While the Suburban Resettlement communities did provide essential housing, they were built without any passion for architecture's subtleties and without any respect for its past. The greenbelt towns represented the grim realities of the present moment. Built on an extremely tight government budget, they not only gave planning a bad name but also gave Clarence Stein, upon whose ideas the towns were in large measure based, a nervous breakdown. (Stein recovered after the Second World War and, based on his own experiences, wrote a highly instructive book on suburban planning, *Toward New Towns in America*.)[20] Although government-sponsored greenbelt towns were soon abandoned as a planning ideal, they were symptomatic of a decentralized and regional view that would characterize subsequent suburban development.

The mobility of the car along with other developments in communications, including the radio, movies, and, later, television, culminated in a way of life that combined unprecedented individual freedom of movement and choice with equally strong unprecedented tendencies toward social conformity and privatization. By the late twenties, "superhighways," with limited access and grade separation at intersections, began to spread their tentacles across the nation. A revolutionary change in settlement patterns and mode of transport quite naturally emerged in the following decades.[21] In 1941, when the Bureau of Public Roads prepared a survey of the nation's daily commuting patterns, 2,100 communities with populations ranging from 2,500 to 50,000 had dispensed with interurban mass transportation systems and depended almost entirely on the private automobile for travel within their own boundaries.[22] In the thirties and forties, it seemed increasingly that the highway planner and the city planner were one and the same and that architects and old-style town planners like Vaux and Olmsted had little to contribute as the Depression drowned American architecture and urban planning in social realism and do-goodism. One architect, however, Frank Lloyd Wright, turned his attention to adapting the suburb to the regional

Pullman, Illinois, occupied four thousand acres south of Chicago. This 1881 illustration shows the model town where George Pullman's railroad car construction plant was to be located, surrounded by housing for plant workers.

Pullman was the first fully functioning instantly created town in America. Its founder believed in the commercial value of beauty and included in the plan the Lake Drive Clock Tower (*top*), the handsome Hotel Florence (*center*), named for Pullman's daughter, and row houses (*bottom*) for the factory workers.

Right. A 250-foot-long, 90-foot-high arcade housed a theater and library under a grand glass canopy.

scale of the automobile in order to resuscitate the dream of an American Arcadia. Wright's Broadacre City, an infinitely extendable paradigm for suburban development and the century's most synoptic suburban proposal, was hatched against the background of the economic failure of the metropolitan suburbs and the bleakness of European-inspired Modernist community design typified by the greenbelt towns. In his numerous plans for Broadacre City, Wright, more than any planner of his time, grasped the opportunities twentieth-century technology provided. Wright understood that, thanks to automobiles and the highway system, the entire continent could be suburbanized, farm and city homogenized into one even-textured development pattern as the final fulfillment of the Jeffersonian dream of a continuously gridded, continuously — but sparsely — settled agrarian paradise. For Wright, the suburb could now be located "nowhere yet everywhere."[23] Freed from fixed centers mandated by the location of railroad stations, Wright devised a gridded network of superhighways parceling out communities whose property was also gridded so that every family would own at least one tillable acre of land. There, modern office and factory workers would exchange the oppressive vitality of city life for the rural life, which labor-saving devices had rendered a far more liberating, if duller, experience than Jefferson had ever imagined. Wright envisioned a new settlement pattern that would take full advantage of developing systems of transportation, including family-owned aerial machines, which he called gyros, forever dispensing with the need for concentrated development.

In contrast to the orthogonality of Wright's highway grid, individual one-acre plots were to be circular, freed from the conforming demands of conventional street patterns, so that the orientation of the single-family house could be a matter of individual choice. For those citizens of Broadacre who might cling to urban ways, Wright adapted his design for the unbuilt New York skyscraper apartment houses, the St. Mark's Towers of 1929. He also proposed small, four-unit apartment clusters, based on the cloverleaf design of highway engineering. One of these, the Suntop Homes, was built outside Philadelphia at Ardmore. Few low-cost houses ever had such elaborate interior plans. In an intricate Chinese box–like package of rooms, four separate but connected homes, all sharing a central chimney and plumbing core, were oriented away from each other. Back yard life was replaced by rooftop terraces where the country family could turn its back on prying neighborly eyes. There would be no borrowing of sugar there.

But the meat and potatoes of Wright's Broadacre dream was a series of modest single-family house types, which he called Usonian "automatics," based on the number of cars required by a family. Within the endless sea of mobility that Wright recognized as an inescapable fact of the American landscape and of American life, he designed houses that enclosed a series of flexible spaces open to one another. Even the kitchen was open to adjacent living and dining space and renamed the "workspace." The hearth at the center of each house was the sole icon of stability. Wright's Usonian houses, with their insistently horizontal low-pitched roofs and broad, sheltering carports, predicted the essential ranch house of post–World War II development, though their finishes, detail, and design sophistication were never replicated. These warm, cozy, natural wood and red brick houses were, as Vincent Scully has written, "finished like a kind of lush hunting lodge . . . combining Europe and autochthonous America in their forms . . . [the] houses were indeed a dream of a timeless suburban peace, an Indian-summer architecture, a last harvest of the land."[24]

Broadacre posed a fundamental contradiction. The chief deficiency in the creed of decentralization was that when everybody moves to the country, all the benefits of the country disappear. Wright argued that in Broadacre City, "the country is not spoiled, because quality in building comes into the picture to save it from destruction. You can build an organic house anywhere and it will not spoil anything; so you could build an organic city out in the country and not harm the country."[25] But architecture can only go so far and as the reality of Sunbelt suburbia spread, Wright's theme of "the disappearing city" was joined by one of the disappearing country as well.

The danger of transforming the countryside into a uniformly developed, uncentered residential area was first and most strikingly demonstrated by William J. Levitt. Capitalizing on the surge of house-seeking GIs after World War II, Levitt transformed thousands of acres of open country into sprawling housing developments. The entrepreneurial Levitt seized the opportunity, understood by Wright and explored during the New Deal by idealistic planners, to build affordable homes by using mass production on a vast scale. Built uniformly in row upon row of a street grid, Levitt's developments were not towns but land subdivisions. Jobs and services were provided by the nearby city; with no railroad station, there was no logical location for a town or village center. Besides, in an era of electronic communications, inhabitants would not need to congregate anywhere. They could use the telephone and watch the television. Daily journeys from house to regional highway were accomplished in the asocial environment of the automobile's interior. In a sense, Levitt's towns perfectly mirrored the Depression- and war-weary American's desire for insular, self-sufficient family life; such community life as was desired was focused on the schools, recreational areas, and the shopping centers.

Zeroing in on the vast, flat Long Island farmland that lay just beyond New York City's limits, Levitt developed his first "town" in 1948. Levittown, Long Island, grew grid block by grid block to almost twenty thousand homes by 1951. Though over the years Levitt's houses came to be increasingly suggestive of historical styles — the one-and-a-half-storey "Cape Cod," the single-storey Western "ranch" house, the two-storey "Colonial" — the single-storey houses built initially owed much to Frank Lloyd Wright. In an earlier stage of suburban house evolution, the garage had replaced the stable at the back of the house. Levitt, taking a cue from Wright, moved the garage to the front, with a long, low profile parallel to the street, acknowledging the garage's symbolic importance by placing it next to the front door. The cars were only a step away from the bedroom as well, confirming the widely held suspicion of Europeans that a vast number of Americans would almost prefer to sleep in their cars than in their own beds. Like Wright's Usonian houses, early Levitt houses had an openness in the arrangement of spaces and a symbolically important core at the center. Not only was the fireplace built in, but Levitt sold every house with its own built-in TV set, on which Levittowners could view the adventures of other recent urban fugitives such as Lucille Ball and Desi Arnaz, who moved to the 'burbs at just about the same time that Levitt reached the zenith of his influence.

What a strange moment that postwar era was. Five hundred years of history

Overleaf. Typical of many residential enclaves planned by Julius Pitzman in St. Louis, Portland Place (1889) was graced with a distinctive set of gates and a gatehouse. These elements were meant to add to residents' sense of escape from the surrounding urban context.

were turned over and for the first time since the Middle Ages, an entire generation was convinced that the city denied freedom and that the countryside was liberating. In return for freeing the family from the oppressive city, Levittowns would re-imprison the woman in the home, often returning her from the factory and office, where she had performed vital services during the war, to the same status she had possessed in the days of the early pioneers. With her husband commuting to work, the wife became the mistress of an endless community meeting in her kitchen; the pilot of a vast supply line, she controlled the destiny of frozen food, deep-fried chicken, and back yard barbecues. Her only release would be her task as family chauffeur, driving her children on their endless comings and goings, backward and forward across the sprawling subdivisions.

In Wright's Broadacre City, highways were either lined with trees or rimmed by uncorrupted pasture and an occasional "organic" gas station. As long as suburban drivers stayed on the picturesque parkways of the prewar era, such as those Robert Moses looped across Long Island, they could enjoy an approximation of Wright's ideal. With the great spurt of suburban development after World War II and the consequent sprawl of anonymous, uncentered, residential areas like Levittown, the parkways were choked with traffic, and secondary roadways evolved into the spatially amorphous commercial "strip." Much of both the lyrical American landscape and the compact Main Streets of prewar suburbia, with their dense side walls of shops and office blocks, was subsumed by it. The dehumanized engineering schemes of new interstates guided a nation literally driving itself to distraction. Much of the lyrical American landscape soon gave way to a sleazy if vital trashitecture. McDonald's twin arches, parodying Saarinen's great Gateway Arch at St. Louis that celebrated the opening of the American West, were only the tip of a blindingly illuminated iceberg, whose vulgarity and energy rose to catch the eye of the constantly moving automobiling American. The architecture of the strip provided a collision of instant symbols to which no region of American history was immune; in New England, Colonial Georgian was redesigned to showcase fried clams at Howard Johnson's, while in the Southwest the resonating Angelus of the monastic mission bell tolled for fast-food tacos.

Although Wright never built Broadacre City, and his dream, as realized through the ubiquitous presence of subdivided suburbia, turned out to be quite nightmarish, America's self-appointed prophet of decentralization picked up and hit the road, embodying the sense of mobility and escape that he felt were central to the American experience. In the annual hegiras of his entire architectural entourage from Wisconsin, where he summered, to Arizona, where he wintered, Wright saw at first hand the vast Depression-era migration from the Midwest to the West. But unlike the jalopy used by the Joads in John Steinbeck's *Grapes of Wrath*, Wright and his followers crisscrossed the continent in an elegant caravan of Cords, Auburns, and Dusenbergs all custom colored Cherokee red. For Wright, the only desirable form of communal life was in the country, not in the city. For his desert home, Taliesin West, Wright chose a remote desert site on Maricopa Mesa near Scottsdale, twenty-six miles northeast of Phoenix. At least when he bought the eight hundred acres of land from the Government Land Office in 1937, the desert was empty as far as the eye could see to the Superstition Mountains. In his book *The Natural House*, published in 1954, Wright stated, "Clients have asked me: 'How far should we go out, Mr. Wright?' I say: 'Just ten times as far as you think

Frank Lloyd Wright developed numerous plans for Broadacre City, a paradigm for suburban development that included modest, single-family houses such as the one pictured here. Although his planned community was never built, the low-pitched roofs and broad carports of his designs predicted the ranch house of post–World War II development projects.

A Small House with "Lots of Room in It"

By Frank Lloyd Wright

NINTH DESIGN IN THE JOURNAL'S NEW SERIES OF MODEL SUBURBAN HOUSES AT MODERATE COST

you ought to go!' So my suggestion would be to go just as far as you can go — and go soon and go fast."[26] Wright heeded his own advice, but by the 1950s he had become the victim of his own prophecies. Americans, whether or not they had ever heard of him, followed Wright's counsel to drive onto the freeway and move to the country, and the miniature haciendas of suburban Phoenix had reached his Paradise Valley doorstep.

Wright fought the development. Nature, the only architectural force he considered equal to his own genius, was being violated. Taliesin West, Wright's "look over the rim of the world,"[27] had become a baleful glance over suburbia. In 1951 Wright fought the power lines bringing electricity to run the air conditioners of burgeoning Greater Phoenix. The lines both interfered with Wright's view and portended further suburban development to come; Wright threatened that if the power lines didn't come down, he and his acolytes would decamp, thus depriving Arizona of its best-known resident. But the lines stayed and so did Wright, although there was enough rankling bitterness for the state later to threaten Wright with prosecution if he failed to obtain an architectural license, while Wright would attack the state's political leaders as "pole-and-wire men," denouncing their plans for a new state capitol and offering his own in 1957.[28]

Yet who was Wright to complain? Wasn't the inevitable result of his sermons against the city that Usonia's last frontiers would be filled by Wright's fellow exurbanite pioneers?

But whatever its architectural and sociological failures during the postwar

Above. To meet housing demands of returning GIs after World War II, entrepreneur William Levitt developed subdivisions such as Levittown, Pennsylvania. The houses, such as the ones pictured in this newspaper ad, were bastardized, mass-produced versions of architectural styles, designed to fulfill Americans' postwar desire for insular, self-sufficient family life.

William Levitt's first "town" was developed on Long Island in 1948 and grew to almost twenty thousand homes by 1951. The town's early single-storey houses, seen in this photograph, owed much to Frank Lloyd Wright's designs for Broadacre.

period, the tug of suburbia remains strong. In New York's South Bronx, a ready-made suburbia rises in an urban wasteland, representing a decisive popular vote against the towering cliffs of postwar public housing projects. Factory-produced ranch houses, trucked in from Pennsylvania, are "installed" in three days — affordable, accessible symbols of the American dream. To knock the point home, one new street bears the name Suburban Place. Whatever the ideals of the planners who designed the original high-rise tower-in-the-park apartment blocks as an approximation of suburban amenities in a skyborn life liberated by fresh air and light, the grim reality of public housing now seems a sad and utterly bankrupt solution to the basic needs for family life. Impersonal elevators and corridors leading to bleak, boxlike apartments cut off occupants from the sights and sounds of street life and, most important, from their children at play. The South Bronx as a suburb. Why not? Despite the implausibility, the suburban ranch houses there stand in telling counterpoint to the anonymity of the high-rise projects. They seem to argue by their very physicality, so redolent with associations of Jeffersonian agrarianism, that the house is its family's temple. Most important, Charlotte Gardens — named after the devastated street that in the late 1970s became a symbol of the nation's urban blight and shame — borrows not only suburbia's architecture but also its principal economic reality: home ownership. Too bad the houses are so ordinary and the site planning so ill considered. Yet however odd the project's architectural pretensions and ideological stance may seem to some, the single-family house in a suburban setting nonetheless may represent our best hope for a way out of the dilemma of urban disintegration. For in America owning a house and a yard of one's own seems perennially to summon much of what we like to conceive as the national character: self-sufficiency, care and nurture of personal property, and engagement in community affairs.

The planned suburb itself is a glory of American life. It constitutes one of the most significant contributions to American urbanism as it serves to make real our most extravagant and lyrical fantasies. But in even the most lovingly crafted plan for suburban development, the pressures of the workaday world create compromises. Thus, despite their visual and social charm, the old village centers of the railroad suburbs were no match for the convenience and variety of choice available along the highway strip. But the original dreams for suburbs — natural beauty and gracious civility, the collective idealization of individuality within the context of social conformity — retain their appeal. As we will see in the next chapter, it is on holiday, as at no other time, that America releases its collective architectural libido, creating exuberant expressions of the builder's art. So, too, have some of our most perfectly crafted, architecturally consistent, continually venerated images of the bucolic ideal been created. In resort villages, Americans have rendered the dream landscapes of seaside and mountaintop Arcadias habitable and rentable for each of us able to pay the price. Ever since industrialization provided the middle class with sufficient prosperity and leisure time to travel, Americans have taken the suburb with them on vacation.

Oak Bluffs on Martha's Vineyard, an island four miles off the coast of Massachusetts, began as a rural retreat for religious camp meetings in 1835. Fifteen years later, the original configuration of nine tents arranged in a semicircle around a shed and a preacher's stand had grown to an elaborate tent city focused on a big top capable of housing two thousand worshipers. Post–Civil War prosperity

With no special centers of community and commercial life and with the single-family automobile the primary environment, the commercial strip, like this one in Las Vegas, Nevada, arose as a natural consequence of free enterprise and Americans' automotive mobility.

swelled the Vineyard crowds, bringing at least as many sun worshipers as religious revivalists. To meet the demand for resort accommodations, a group of local businessmen and retired sea captains bought an adjacent parcel and in 1880 hired Robert Copeland, a self-described "landscape artist," from Boston to lay out a permanent village that would link the tent city and the sea. It had a 125-room hotel, a Unitarian chapel, and an arcaded shopping center, all designed by the architect S. F. Pratt. Copeland's plan, no doubt influenced by Davis and Olmsted, included naturalistically curving roads, neighborhood parks, and a grassy boulevard leading from the village center to the water, where a broad crescent of houses embraced a seven-acre park. An American version of the great English seaside resorts, Oak Bluffs replaced the continuous rows of terraced housing typical of Brighton and Hove with individual freestanding dream cottages whose porches and turrets and jigsaw ornament were a perfect backdrop for summer afternoons by the sea.

Meanwhile, the tents of the Methodist campground were developed by gradual steps into tiny versions of the resort's houses. Indeed, the Methodists went further than the businessmen in sponsoring the imaginative carpenter-builders to produce elaborate fantasies with their jigsaw ornamentation. Each house gave the appearance of an individual family church, with wide doors and narthex-porches that offered the passers-by a lively tableau of family life ennobled by religion. Forty-five different jigsaw patterns were used to decorate the cottages, yet the overall effect was quite coherent because the ornamental invention was limited to the facade and the same basic house type was used throughout. Despite their exuberant detail, the cottages' dollhouse scale clearly expressed their secondary status in the community. At one and a half storeys high and approximately fourteen feet wide, the houses were not significantly larger than the

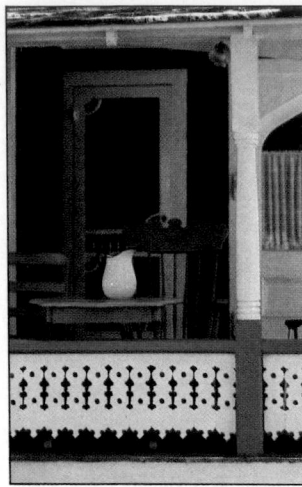

An American version of the great English seaside resorts, Oak Bluffs on Martha's Vineyard began as a rural retreat for religious meetings in 1835. The wide doors, porches, and elaborate jigsaw ornamentation of its cottages, seen in a photograph from the 1870s (*right*), gave them the appearance of individual family churches. *Above:* a present-day detail of a typical jigsaw pattern.

tents they replaced and were clearly subordinate to the central tabernacle, which was rebuilt in cast iron in 1879. As large in scale as the cottages were small, the tabernacle was a shrine dedicated to a fierce morality, rising one hundred feet to a wooden cupola and forming the symbolic as well as visual focus of the religious resort community.

If at its best a suburb creates a social center as well as a collection of houses, then the resort suburb fabricated by Pierre Lorillard III in 1885 might be called one of the nation's most idealistic. Finding himself unexpectedly excluded from the list of the Four Hundred socially elect, Lorillard fled the established summer resort of the group, Newport, Rhode Island, to create his own exclusive but informal resort community. Lorillard intended Tuxedo Park, which was located in the Ramapo Mountains, only forty minutes by train from New York City, to be visited in the late spring and early autumn between the social seasons of New York and Newport. Not exactly a screaming populist, Lorillard developed Tuxedo for two hundred families. Like George Pullman, Lorillard had originally intended to maintain ownership of all the houses in his community, renting them to friends. But even when his friends persuaded him to sell, ownership was restricted to members of the Tuxedo Club, whose Two Hundred were described by one observer as "a guide to Who is especially Who in the Four Hundred."[29] Lorillard had succeeded in establishing his community as the cutting edge of snobbery. The laws of American etiquette were laid down there as well by Emily Price Post, a resident of Tuxedo and the daughter of its principal architect. Even the style of the short dinner jacket without tails introduced by Lorillard's son has come to be adopted everywhere, bearing the name of Lorillard's retreat.

To underscore the informality of his natural retreat, Lorillard, with the assistance of James Smith Haring and Ernest W. Bowditch, devised a scheme that incorporated a network of looping roads related to the land's natural contours and relied on natural vistas, including views of Tuxedo Lake, for the visual impact. The architecture at Tuxedo Park was, like the plan, intended to harmonize with the site and was modest in scale and character. Like other great railroad suburbs — Riverside and Forest Hills, for example — the community had a "front door," the railroad station. The stone lodge and gatehouse opposite the station were designed by Bruce Price, Tuxedo's leading architect in the early years, who described them as looking "like a frontispiece to an English novel."[30] Price's houses, intended primarily for young, rich couples, were small and articulated to harmonize with the surrounding landscape; the cottages were constructed of roughhewn stone, brick, and wood shingles stained varying shades of russets and grays. In many of the cottages, the interior space was articulated by centrally located fireplace masses whose monumental scale and primitive symbolic power of the hearth were to have a profound influence on Frank Lloyd Wright.

By the turn of the century, Tuxedo Park was on its way to becoming a year-round suburb of New York. As a result, the character of the preserve changed radically. The rustic resort suburb became the site for a dazzling array of extravagant mansions designed by some of the leading firms of the day, including McKim, Mead & White, Walker & Gillette, and Warren & Wetmore. Medieval manor houses and châteaux that seemed to have been transported directly from the Loire stood next to sprawling houses that eclectically married Tudor and Georgian vocabularies. Out of the hands of a single visionary, and with the pressure to invest one's year-round residence with more than conformity to a larger planning scheme, the expression of a jointly held fantasy gave way to that of individual voices.

If Tuxedo Park and its original cohesiveness fell prey to real world pressures, the resort suburbs of southern Florida have always been protected by climate and geography as unadulterated backdrops for vacations.

With fast rail travel and the proliferation of automobile travel, southern Florida of the 1920s was the scene of some of the most innovative large-scale town planning as well as some of the wildest real estate speculation in the United States. So popular did it become, as the next chapter will show, that in 1925 the architectural and political commentator Herbert Croly called Florida a "national suburb and winter resort . . . intended not for exceptionally wealthy people but for the average small town American who in the past has considered himself unable to afford such luxury."[31]

Coral Gables was Florida's most architecturally ambitious, and certainly its most fully realized, resort suburb. Located at the edge of Miami, Coral Gables was founded in 1921 by George E. Merrick, who had made his fortune by supplying citrus fruit to Miami's expanding hotel industry. Setting out to build a "suburb where castles in Spain are made real,"[32] Merrick sent several of the architects and artists he hired to Europe to study the Mediterranean architecture that was to serve as the model for his town, although he was probably also influenced by local precedents, such as James Deering's limpid Mediterranean dream house, Vizcaya.

The plan of Coral Gables was developed by Merrick's uncle, Denman Fink, who served as artistic consultant and designer, and Phineas Paist, who served as architect. Frank Button, who had worked on the design of Lincoln Park in Chicago and the garden at Vizcaya, served as landscape consultant. The outstanding features of the Coral Gables plan were its series of canals, complete with gondolas, that flowed through the town, providing, as Merrick's advertisements boasted, "more than 40 miles of waterfront,"[33] and the imposing entrance gates and plazas that gave spatial definition to an otherwise monotonous, flat site. Merrick deemed it essential that a dreamlike environment, evoking another time and place, be established. He therefore proposed to enclose his suburb with a wall punctuated by seven entrances. While only a small part of the wall and four gateways were realized, as with the private places of St. Louis, the entrances that were built definitively established a sense of a private, special place apart. The Alhambra Gate resembled the entrance to a Spanish farm; the Prado Entrance, which led to Coral Gables's most elegant residential street, the Country Club Prado, was an appropriately grand composition with pylons surrounding an ellipse that contained a stepped fountain and reflecting pool; the partially completed La Puerta del Sol, now known as the Douglas Entrance, was set within an apartment complex that formed the wall of the city and included a tower from which prospective buyers could view the suburb.

Initially, Merrick had proposed to build the entire town out of the local oolitic limestone, but when that proved too expensive and too slow, he employed stucco. The stucco could not only be "antiqued," using techniques including beating it with chains and spraying it with buttermilk or even cow dung, but it also lent itself to a variety of building forms and styles. It was used to create magical domestic spaces, public plazas, and city gates evocative of those of Spain. Most of the houses in Coral Gables were designed in that style, with many designed by Denman Fink's cousin H. George Fink, who traveled in Spain with Merrick in 1924. But Merrick also built individual villages within the suburb based on exotic architectural themes, such as the French Provincial village and the French City village, the latter of which — designed by the fashionable New York architect Mott Schmidt — is a remarkable cluster of houses that illustrate a variety of techniques appropriate to provide high-density housing with the amenities and character of the archetypal single-family suburban house. Also included were a Dutch South African village and a Chinese village. A Persian village was planned but never realized. Given Florida's semijungle, perhaps the most exotic village of all was built in the North American Colonial style, with houses sited on wide streets lined by deciduous trees. Many of the houses overlooked a golf course, synthesizing the time-honored suburban planning device of the greensward with the American suburban ideal of leisure and convenience. In the Colonial village it is but a quick trip across the back yard from the bedroom or kitchen to the links.

Perhaps the most ingenious element in Coral Gables was the transformation of an abandoned pit, from which much of the oolitic limestone used to build the suburb's early houses had been quarried, into the Venetian Pool, a swim club for residents. Marrying the practical and the fantastic, the Venetian Pool was equipped with caves, a waterfall, an island, diving boards suspended from towering rock formations, and even a sandy beach. All of this was served by a Mediterranean-style casino where vine-covered loggias provided shade from the hot sun. Billed by the town's promoters as "the world's most beautiful swimming hole,"[34] the Venetian Pool provided Coral Gables with not only a recreational center but also a setting for spectacular promotional stunts. Merrick's army of three thousand salesmen and fleet of seventy-six buses would regularly transport, courtesy of the corporation, prospective buyers from Southern cities as well as from New York, Chicago, and even San Francisco to Coral Gables, where they were entertained at the Venetian Pool by the likes of Paul Whiteman's band and Jackie Ott the Aqua Tot.

Coral Gables also incorporated a host of resort facilities, including an indoor sports complex named the Coliseum, the Coral Gables Inn, and the Miami-Biltmore Hotel, which was known as the Dowager Queen of Coral Gables. Designed by the nationally known hotel architects Schultze & Weaver, the Miami-Biltmore's twenty-six-storey tower was modeled on the Giralda Tower in Seville, Spain. In a typically American transformation, the hotel lorded over Coral Gables in much the same way as its ecclesiastical prototype dominated its surroundings. In planning the most comprehensive resort suburb ever, Merrick even provided land for a university, the University of Miami, which would lend the town prestige as well as provide a more nearly year-round base for its economy. Despite the high expectations of the developers, however, the school was nearly ended by the demise of the Florida economy. Construction of its principal building, begun in 1926, was not completed until 1950.

But despite curtailment in building, Merrick's community was sufficiently completed to create and maintain a special sense. Its success is in large part due to the adoption and adaptation of key elements of enduring suburban planning. The suggestion of a wall and its honorific gates set the place apart. Each neighborhood cluster has a similar sense of identity through coherent, but not monotonous, architectural consistency. The idea of a public greensward, so effective at organizing a community since the days of Llewellyn Park's design, is used at Coral Gables — but does double duty as a golf course. Similarly, the hotels provide the community focus that usually occurs in the town center.

In 1925, just before the bottom fell out of the Florida boom, Addison Mizner, the flamboyant and high-living architect whose work at Palm Beach will be seen in the following chapter, sought to create, like Merrick, an entirely new town. Although inspired in part by Merrick's romantic, middle-class suburb at Coral Gables, Mizner aimed higher, conceiving Boca Raton as a supersuburb for the super rich. By far the most lavish, ostentatious, but also logically planned of the Florida schemes, Addison Mizner's romantic-sounding suburb, whose Spanish name meant "rat's mouth," was to be ideal, yet not idealistic.

Mizner maintained design approval of all major construction projects and laid out the suburb to be at once artistic and lucrative. Most of the planning conformed to the typical southern Florida scheme of squared blocks containing twenty-five- and thirty-five-foot lots. Parcels of these lots were conceived as distinct subdivisions, given their own names like Old Floresta and Spanish Village, and presumably developed with some suggestion of an architecturally consistent character. The land farthest from the ocean, however, which in most developments was the least valuable, was ingeniously transformed into a highly desirable subdivision called Ritz-Carlton Park, with Olmsted-like winding streets lined by generous lots surrounding golf courses.

Everything about Mizner's version was grand. He designed the town's principal east-west street, El Camino Real, to be a two-and-a-half-mile-long, 160-foot-wide, twenty-lane highway. Beginning on the beach at the site of a projected grand hotel, the roadway crossed the Intracoastal Highway on a Venetian-style bridge that Mizner designed to incorporate a tower apartment for the keeper; after passing through the hotel's golf course, it became the development's principal commercial and business street. This portion of the thoroughfare, modeled after Rio de Janeiro's famed Avenida Beira Mar, was bisected by a central canal. Motor-powered gondolas were imported from Italy to ply the waterway. While El Camino Real may have been one of the world's widest roads, it was also among the shortest. Boomtime blueprints showed the roadway rolling past gleaming new towns; Mizner completed slightly less than half a mile of it; the road quickly dwindled to two lanes and died out in the swamp.

The list of Boca Raton's projected facilities was exhaustive: the town was to be serviced by its own airport, and, in addition to golf courses, was to contain a polo field, a yacht basin, and a floating cabaret. In a more sober vein, it would have a church dedicated to the developer's mother. Although Mizner claimed that his resort suburb would be "the world's most architecturally beautiful playground,"[35] Boca Raton also incorporated small houses, a subdivision for workers, and an industrial district.

At first Boca Raton land sales produced massive traffic jams and pandemonium in the realty offices. On the record-breaking opening day, two million dollars worth of lots were sold. But uncontrolled hucksterism and the devastating hurricane of 1926 brought Florida's real estate boom to an abrupt end as it dashed any hope of completing Mizner's scheme. Boca Raton, perhaps a dream too far, was barely realized in actuality. Only fragments of the plan were built. The Cloister Inn officially opened in February 1926, a virtuosic example of Mizner's imagination and flair. It synthesized a variety of architectural vocabularies, all at least vaguely Mediterranean in origin, juxtaposing elements such as Romanesque arches and a late Gothic tower. To give the building the appearance of having been built over time, walls were constructed and reconstructed, patched, smoked, and otherwise "antiqued" in ways even Hollywood would envy. Yet the Cloister Inn was much more than a movie set; Mizner's design lifted function to the level of fantasy. Also completed were a portion of El Camino Real, some of the houses designed in the Old Floresta and Spanish Village subdivisions, and the development company's Administration Building, which Mizner modeled after El Greco's home in Toledo. The Boca Raton City Hall was completed toward the end of 1926, but Mizner's original scheme was significantly diminished in size because the town, which counted on real estate tax revenue for building projects, could not afford to construct it as proposed.

And after Addison Mizner's death in 1932 much of his scheme for Boca Raton, including the airport, polo field, golf courses, yacht basins, and Spanish-style shopping complexes, was realized, but not to his designs. Yet the architectural

Boca Raton was Addison Mizner's dream for a logically planned resort-suburb in Florida that would cater to the super rich. Although little of his scheme was built as he designed it, his Cloister Inn (*right*) opened in February of 1926. Vaguely Mediterranean in its overall effect, the building provides an example of Mizner's flair for the fantastical.

spirit, if not the actual fact of his designs, indelibly left their mark.

The spirit of the architect — the daring of one visionary seeking to raise an entirely new community on a wild site — is a spirit that has infused our best suburbs, from that of Llewellyn Haskell to that of Pierre Lorillard. It is a spirit found all too rarely, especially of late in southern Florida. Once the site of inventive community planning, now grim condominium developments predominate. These "condo villages" possess few, if any, traditional town facilities, such as an easily accessible commercial center, and are thoroughly drained of all sense of place. Living in such a development one could, like being in a fast-food restaurant, be *anywhere*.

In the late 1970s, one developer sought to build a resort community that would be architecturally and urbanistically richer than the sprawling condos that litter Florida's landscape. Robert Davis owned eighty acres of land in the Florida panhandle with a half mile of beach fronting the Gulf of Mexico. The site was just about the right size for a profitable condominium development, but it was also right for a small town. Davis chose the latter, calling his town Seaside. He seeks to create a community that has the mix of land use, building types, and architectural styles which define towns that have developed organically over time while also establishing an architecturally coherent sense of place. To this end, he has worked with two young architect-planners, Andreas Duany and Elizabeth Plater-Zyberk, to devise a master plan and zoning code, which were completed in 1983, for the town that they project will be substantially built within ten to fifteen years.

A town center, with shops, offices, workshops, and a conference center that doubles as a town hall, will focus on two connected public squares. The squares,

At the Seaside resort community, now being developed on the Florida panhandle, architects are encouraged to design residential houses with observation towers (*above*), to provide views of the Gulf of Mexico and give the low-lying town a dynamic skyline.

For the design of Seaside, developer Robert Davis enlisted the aid of architects to create a visually coherent town. This watercolor plan, by the firm of Andres Duany & Elizabeth Plater-Zyberk, shows the town center, which focuses on two connected public squares that slope gently to the water. Streets are laid out in a modified grid that incorporates curves and diagonals.

Pictured here is one of the community beach pavilions in Seaside. Most Gulf shore developers crowd condominiums at the water's edge, thereby neglecting less desirable inland lots. Robert Davis's plan works in reverse: by lining the waterfront with these pavilions, he affords inland residents equal and easy access to the beaches.

which slope down to the water, will be defined along their edges by buildings with continuous ground-floor arcades. Streets, ranging from wide tree-lined avenues to narrow alleys, are laid out in a modified grid that incorporates diagonals and curves but that maintains spatial clarity. A principal street, lined with large lots radiating out from the town center to the tennis club at the edge of the development, is zoned for private houses, small apartment buildings, and inns. These buildings will each incorporate a continuous porch in its street façade based on the prototype of the Greek Revival mansion of the antebellum South. Six other streets terminate at the bluff overlooking the beach, where a pavilion will serve as a beachside changing room as well as a small social center. The deck of one such pavilion that has been constructed has been partially enclosed by wood lattice and is already serving as a place where neighbors sit, talk, and enjoy the Gulf breezes. Beyond the pavilions, which will each have a different but stylistically consistent design, a boardwalk will provide a public promenade along the beach. While the town is clearly oriented to the automobile, it does not surrender to it; many of the streets are unpaved, the provision of on-street parking minimizes the need for intrusive parking lots, and pedestrian walkways on both sides of every street as well as through blocks encourage walking.

After conducting a study of small Southern towns, the planners concluded that a vital and authentic town character could not be established by a single architect. Seaside's public buildings are being designed by numerous architects with diverse backgrounds who are sensitive to the regional vernacular. Private buildings are commissioned by individual citizen-buyers but are subject to the building code, which encourages, and in some cases requires, the inclusion of elements of regional architecture, such as front porches, white picket fences, painted wood siding, and roofs made of wood shingles or metal and sloped at a specified low angle. The code also encourages outbuildings, such as guest houses and freestanding observation towers, which provide landlocked residents with Gulf views as well as give the low-lying town a dynamic "skyline." While some houses built or planned at Seaside to date are quite large for a small beach town, exceeding three thousand square feet, most are modest in size. Apartments built over stores in the center of town and bed and breakfast lodgings are planned as part of a community intended to attract a socioeconomically diverse population. Seaside's slogan is "A New Town. The Old Ways." While the houses may evoke memories of simple summertime life before air conditioning, condos, and time-sharing plans, Seaside is not a nostalgic pipe dream. It is a very real attempt to realize the full potential of urban design in an Arcadian setting in part by learning from the successes of the planned American suburb.

The suburban model, whether realized in a remote vacation spot or in the midst of a major city, is central to the development of communities that serve the needs of their inhabitants. While at first glance the suburb seems to have hastened the demise of our older cities and doomed our undeveloped countryside, it may well hold the key to their futures. Once we free ourselves from the belief that the suburb is merely a metropolitan by-product and from our conception of the suburb as the exclusive property of the rich, it can be recaptured as a tool for both inner-city and rural developments. The construction of typical subdivision ranch houses in the devastated South Bronx is a naive first step, but it is a sure sign that we are beginning once again to come to grips with who we are.

5　Resorts: Paradise Regained

Typically, resorts constitute a permanent, habitable dreamworld which we can escape into and depart from at will — a dreamworld we can share with others. Resorts provide us with the opportunity, however fleeting, to realize the ultimate fantasy of inventing and exploring new roles for ourselves: at a resort, the clerk or the truck driver can become the daredevil or the social sophisticate, the denizen of the concrete jungle, an explorer of the forest primeval. And as resorts seem to free their patrons from the constraining conventions of the workaday world, so does their design free their architects. Just as one can see normally buttoned-down men and women reveal their every physical and psychological nuance during a summer afternoon at the beach, one can see national architectural preferences, free at last from so many economic and societal constraints, intensely expressed in resort architecture.

　　The greatest American resorts have gone beyond conventional exercises in escape; resorts have functioned as stage sets upon which the nation has enacted a mythic version of its past. Whether going "back to nature" to celebrate the majesty of the continent itself, concocting a modern-dress version of life in Europe's royal courts, or elevating the nation's history to pageantry, the architecture of our resorts has provided us with some of the most public expressions of our collective identity. Moreover, Americans have learned to live together in a community at their resorts. In a democracy where strict social traditions and codes of behavior do not apply, the resort has provided an image of communitarian stability that the "real" world fails to provide. Whether at a grand hotel, a summer colony, or a theme village, Americans on holiday have dealt themselves strong lessons in social behavior, often under the benignly dictatorial hand of a hotelier or self-appointed tastemaker. Isolated resort hotels, which at first glance seem little more than good-time places, prove on closer examination to be much more. Americans never fully liberate themselves from the constraints of the Puritan work ethic; not surprisingly, they take even their pleasures very seriously.

　　Beginning in the eighteenth century, Saratoga, 186 miles north of New York City, attracted visitors including George Washington, who tried to invest in Saratoga's Congress Spring in 1783. But the inelegant bathhouses, where the tubs resembled hog troughs, and the primitive accommodations did little to encourage tourists other than the most hypochondriacal. It was not until the installation of a steam-engine passenger train in 1833, which spared vacationers an arduous overland stagecoach route from Albany, that Saratoga took off as a resort. What

The El Tovar (1901) provided all of the amenities of a great American resort. Perched on the southern rim of the Grand Canyon in Arizona, it achieved through its use of local limestone, logs, and shingles an overall effect that was complementary to its natural surroundings.

Steam-locomotive passenger trains made the American wilderness accessible to tourists from all walks of life. In 1833, the Mt. McGregor and Lake George Railroad helped to establish Saratoga, 186 miles north of New York City, as a popular vacation resort.

had begun as a retreat for the sick became a social center. In the nineteenth century, Saratoga and other American resorts provided the country with an escape from the competitiveness of business and the private nature of family life; resorts were a democratized escape into the pleasures of "high society."

The railroads brought large numbers of vacationers from all walks of life. To accommodate the influx, the modest inns of an earlier era were expanded or replaced by a number of enormous hotels. In 1864 Putnam's establishment burgeoned into the vast Union Hotel, incorporating a whole city block, the center of which was developed as a green, elm-shaded park. The complex comprised building wings and freestanding structures containing baths, clubhouses, a dining hall seating a thousand guests, an opera house, a church, rooms, and cottages. But it was the Union's entrance that expressed and established an architectural and social mainstay of American resort architecture. The Union faced Broadway, the town's main thoroughfare, with a 450-foot-long colonnaded veranda.

Across the nation, resort hotels incorporated verandas like that at the Union Hotel, which evoked the promenade deck of a riverboat or ocean liner. Boatlike resort hotels provided Americans with a comforting sense of place amidst the vast continental sea as they evoked the treacherous ocean journey made by the nation's first settlers — but of course the mythic ocean crossings of nineteenth-century

Americans on vacation were strictly "first class." While a few hotels, like the Prospect House (ca. 1870) and others built near Niagara Falls, catered to a younger romantic crowd, serving as love boats for honeymooners, most of the land-locked luxury liners were family oriented, their grand porticos dedicated to the everyday rituals of resort life — conversation, promenading, and people-watching. For the wealthiest Americans of the late nineteenth and early twentieth centuries, verandas of great hotels were parade grounds on a perpetual itinerary of American resorts and European capitals. The always-traveling rich turned virtually the entire continent into a resort, escaping its less agreeable weather by passing through a succession of geographically discrete seasons.

The Grand Hotel on Mackinac Island offered Midwesterners the pleasures of an ocean liner without the inconveniences. Like so many early resorts, the original appeal of Mackinac Island, a six-square-mile handkerchief of land at the confluence of Lakes Michigan and Huron, was to health seekers. Beginning in the 1850s, most of the first vacationers to visit Mackinac were attracted by the island's spring waters. But in 1887, when the Grand Hotel was completed by a consortium of railroad companies, the island became a magnet for families who wanted little more than to escape from the brutal Midwestern summer heat and enjoy each other's company. If verandas were the parade grounds of turn-of-the-century resorts, then the Grand's claim to celebrity was incontrovertible. The porch of the Grand — some 880 feet long — is by far the world's longest. The austerity of a colonnade of that length is offset by the steamboat-like curves it takes as it wraps around the ends of the building. Indeed, a stay at the Grand must have had much of the appeal of a luxury passenger ship. After a sumptuous midday meal, guests could retire to the porch, where, safely seated in rocking chairs, they could enjoy an unparalleled view. At no other hotel in America could guests see the sun rise over one Great Lake and set over another, convincingly giving the viewer the impression of being hundreds of miles out to sea. The Grand combined the democracy of a small town with the allure of a private club or exclusive resort enclave. On its enormous veranda, ordinary men and women sat or strolled beside famous guests, including Presidents Grover Cleveland, William Howard Taft, and both Roosevelts.

The Grand Hotel at Saratoga boasted a 450-foot colonnaded veranda at the entrance, which allowed guests to gather comfortably shielded from the sun and indulge in conversation, promenading, and people-watching — the everyday rituals of resort life.

The opening of San Diego's Del Coronado in 1888 marked a high point in the history of American resort architecture. The elegant dining room (*above*) featured a vaulted ceiling of sugar pine that rose to a height of 33 feet. The room was built without columns to provide unobstructed views of the ocean and the bay. An 1893 photograph of the hotel's main entrance (*right*) shows the elaborate use of wraparound verandas, arcaded balconies, and turreted towers.

The passion for spending "seasons" anywhere but at home that had inspired the construction of the Grand Hotel on Mackinac Island also encouraged the railroad companies to build great resort hotels far from the East's and Midwest's industrial and commercial capitals. The end of the transcontinental lines in California became a favored setting for new grand hotels, which would take advantage of the Golden State's romantic landscape and mild climate. In 1885 Elisha S. Babcock and H. L. Story set out to build a grand hotel in San Diego, which had been made easily accessible to Midwesterners with the completion of the southern transcontinental link the previous year. While the Del Coronado never fulfilled its developers' intention to build the world's largest hotel, it rose in less than eleven months to open in 1888 as a wooden phantasmagoria that constituted a high point in the history of American resort architecture.

The Del Coronado's architects, James and Merrit Reid, incorporated many elements and materials common to Eastern hotels: verandas, arcaded balconies, turreted towers rendered in wood framing with shingled roofs — even the hotel's staff was from the East. Yet the Del, as the Reids' hotel was known, acknowledged the region's Spanish Colonial heritage in its exterior colors, with white walls and a striking red roof. Its organization was derived from the same source. The hotel was built around a courtyard that could shelter a lush garden from the ocean's salt-air breezes. As built, the one-acre courtyard was densely filled with plants as well as exotic birds and monkeys, fostering the myth of California as an earth-bound paradise. The hotel's public rooms included a Ladies' Billiard Parlor, of which the management was particularly proud, and a dining room and a circular ballroom that were among the most memorable ever built. The dining room, which could seat one thousand, contained an elegant and complexly constructed vaulted ceiling made of sugar pine. Built only with pegs, not nails, the room's construction allowed the 156-foot-long, 62-foot-wide, and 33-foot-high space to be free of columns that would block the sweeping views of the ocean and the bay. But the most spectacular space was without doubt the conical ballroom, which could hold twelve hundred dancers seemingly suspended over the Pacific.

While the proprietors of the Del sought to import urbanity to the West, it was as retreats from urbanity — as escapes into the wilderness — that many of the greatest Western resorts were built. The first wilderness resorts were built in the East. Beginning early in the nineteenth century, the work of painters like Thomas Cole of the Hudson River School as well as the writings of Emerson and Thoreau emphasized the uplifting inspiration to be found in the contemplation of untamed nature. Indeed, by mid-century such activity was advocated as being as restorative to the spirit as natural springs were to the body. Among the most persuasive advocates of wilderness retreat was William H. H. Murray, later known as "Adirondack Murray," a minister who spoke not only of the spiritual value of hiking, hunting, and fishing but also of the landscape's spiritual aspect. His *Adventures in the Wilderness* of 1869 prompted a mass migration to the Adirondacks that came to be called "Murray's Rush." Many who were moved to follow his advice came to be known as "Murray's Fools" when injuries and deaths piled up among those totally unsuited to the arduousness of wilderness life. Nevertheless, the idea of retreating to a primitive setting took hold of Americans.

The Adirondack Mountains became the first wilderness area made convenient for tourism, with the completion of Thomas Durant's Adirondack Railroad in 1871.

Durant's son, William, was the premier developer and promoter of the land he and his father owned in the area, establishing whole townships and promoting the region as an important resort area. Hotels were developed on the shores of the region's many lakes, providing profits, tourist destinations, and the social structure and amenities deemed important even in the wilderness. But it was in the development of lakefront acreage into "camps" — private compounds in the woods — that Durant helped establish both a way of life and an original architectural style.

Durant began Camp Pine Knot in 1879, on a peninsula projecting into Raquette Lake, as a summer retreat for his family and a sort of advertisement for the potential of the area as a vacation spot. While lumber was readily available from nearby sawmills, Durant employed log construction, using trees felled on the grounds, and emphasized the exposed ribs that carried roofs and the corbeling of projecting beams that supported upper stories. Unpeeled limbs and branches of cedar and spruce were used in ornamental porch railings and gable screens. Durant continued the rustic aesthetic into the interiors, constructing monumental fireplaces from stones found on the site, using birch bark to cover walls and ceilings, and using branches and roots to create intricately dovetailed furniture as complex and imaginative as any since the Rococo of eighteenth-century France. By the time Durant sold Camp Pine Knot to Collis P. Huntington, builder of the Central Pacific and Southern Pacific railroads, in 1895, the compound consisted of more than twenty different luxuriously appointed buildings — including cottages, open-air and enclosed dining halls, kitchens, and a recreation hall — arranged in an informal plan, like tents or temporary housing.

A pioneering and striking example of what has come to be called the Adirondack Style, Camp Pine Knot was made up of buildings that were seemingly simple log cabins and suggested the rude huts of the early settlers. Nonetheless, they provided all the modern comforts of home and looked like the kind of house that pioneer woodsmen and mountain guides might have built if they'd had the cash. Both in its planning and in its architecture, the Adirondack Style represents a uniquely American invention. Romantic evocations of a pioneer past or a hermit's retreat, the camps built in the Adirondacks were like no buildings seen before. Their accommodation of creature comforts within the charmingly rugged cabins was ingeniously devised. The very notion of the camps was a manifestation of the American character, offering the privacy many ostensibly had come to the mountains to find while providing a welcome sense of community.

A year after heavy debts had forced him to sell Pine Knot, Durant began to build an even grander year-round house, Sagamore Lodge, on the shores of Shedd Lake, which Durant renamed Sagamore Lake. The lodge, while also built of logs rustically joined, is an imposing three-and-a-half-storey house set a mile away from its service buildings. It established a new Adirondack standard in its size, in the grandeur of its rustic forms, such as its great stone fireplaces, and in its luxurious appointments. However, Durant's ambitions once again exceeded his assets and, faced with imminent bankruptcy, he sold Sagamore to Alfred Gwynne Vanderbilt in 1901. Vanderbilt expanded the compound to even greater proportions and purchased a private Pullman coach car, the Wayfarer, to make the journey from New York more comfortable. After Vanderbilt went down with the *Lusitania* in 1915, his widow expanded Sagamore. To the lodge and outbuildings

William Durant, pictured above, was responsible for the first land development projects in the Adirondack Mountains and for establishing the region as an important resort area. He began construction of Camp Pine Knot, one of several private compounds, in 1879.

erected by Durant, she added new cottages and ancillary buildings until she had created two village-size compounds on the property, one for family and guests, the other for staff and support services. The forty-six bedrooms and twenty-three bathrooms provided in the family's compound — which included the capacious original lodge — could easily accommodate ninety-nine guests.

The cleverly named Kamp Kill Kare, on nearby Lake Kora, was even more magnificent. Originally laid out in the 1890s by Durant, the estate was purchased by Alfred Vanderbilt in 1913 and sold the next year to Francis P. Garvan, a wealthy New York City lawyer. In 1915 Garvan commissioned John Russell Pope — the leading Classical architect of his generation, whose buildings include the Temple of the Scottish Rite in Washington, D.C. (1910), the National Gallery of Art (1938–41), and the Jefferson Memorial (1939–43) — to expand the house extensively. Pope's design gave Kamp Kill Kare a monumentally scaled gate tower, marking the entrance to a courtyard defined by the camp's roughhewn granite service buildings. The split-log-clad main lodge was an immense complex of separate buildings linked together, over time, to form a multilevel gabled, dormered, and verandaed structure more than three hundred feet long that descended the sloping terrain to the shores of the lake. Inside, many of the vast rooms were spanned by massive timber trusses and dominated by monumentally scaled stone hearths and rustic-style furniture built of gnarled tree roots, limbs, and trunks. A double-height ceiling was required in a main bedroom to house a bed whose headboard was formed of artfully composed saplings stripped of their bark and leaves.

The most spectacular Adirondack camp was without question a sixty-eight-building complex called Topridge, the work of a totally untrained, untutored local builder, Ben Muncil, Jr. In 1920 the oft-married Mrs. Marjorie Merriweather Post

Camp Pine Knot consisted of more than twenty buildings situated on a peninsula projecting into Raquette Lake. The group of cottages shown here was typical of the site's numerous camps, which were built in what has come to be known as the Adirondack Style.

The buildings at Camp Pine Knot were arranged in an informal plan, suggesting tents or temporary housing. *Left:* The original open-air summer kitchen (ca. 1889) is notable for its log-beam construction. *Right:* Lakefront boathouses served as a welcoming terminal for disembarking guests.

Close Hutton Davies May, who skillfully transformed her father's breakfast cereal company into the vast General Foods Corporation, decided to build on St. Regis Lake. She delivered her New York architect's plans to Muncil, who, though he freely admitted he wasn't educated enough to follow the drawings, immediately recognized that the buildings would not suit their site. Muncil offered to design a camp that he *could* build and that he felt was contextually appropriate. The result was Topridge, an extraordinary harmony of seemingly effortless design, remarkably in tune not only with the landscape of the Upper St. Regis area but also with Mrs. Post's dream of a luxurious life in the wilderness. Arriving by plane or limousine at the lake, guests boarded a twenty-six-passenger yacht for a sail to the camp's private dock. The boathouse was itself an extraordinary evocation of Classical forms, with columns made of roots, limbs, and twigs supporting low shingled roofs. A funicular transported guests from waterside to the main house.

The relatively modest appearance of Topridge Lodge's rough wood exterior was no preparation for the splendid opulence that awaited inside, where soaring space was bounded by elaborate detail. Up a stairway with treads of halved logs and rails of stripped saplings, one entered a living room eighty feet wide, one hundred feet long, and thirty feet tall. Massive timber beams supported the ceiling, among and from which were originally hung native Indian kayaks and chandeliers made of intertwined antlers. Off the living room lay the dining room, in which thirty people could be served under a stucco and log ceiling. To provide a full view of Regis Mountain, Mrs. Post ordered a special plate glass window, which was floated to the site by barge from Utica. It took fifteen men to install the window, and years later, when broken by the sonic boom of an air force jet flying overhead, it proved irreplaceable.

The vast Adirondack camps offered men and women of wealth a way to escape into a carefully groomed, lavishly serviced version of the wilderness. The combination of wilderness and comfort pioneered in the Adirondacks reached its culmination in the resort hotels built in government-maintained national parks. In 1872, President Ulysses S. Grant established Yellowstone as the first national park, in an unprecedented instance of large-scale wilderness preservation enacted in the public interest. The park was first administered by the United States Army and later by the National Park Service, established in 1916 during Woodrow Wilson's administration. Yellowstone was very difficult to reach until 1888, when railroad service was established. A steady stream of tourists then found their way into the

Right. Kamp Kill Kare was designed for the Alfred Vanderbilt family by John Russell Pope. The main lodge included large stone fireplaces and rustic furniture. In one main bedroom, a double-height ceiling was necessary to accommodate a headboard made of saplings .

From its raw limbs and rugged line to the simple ornamentality of its porch latticework, Knollwood (*left*) typifies the rustic charm of the Adirondack Style.

wilderness area, turning the park into what the English author Rudyard Kipling, who visited it in 1889 on his first trip to the United States, described as a "ghastly vulgarity . . . oozing, rampant Bessemer-steel self-sufficiency and ignorance."[1]

From its opening, tourists have seemed particularly drawn to Yellowstone National Park and its Old Faithful geyser, the wilderness area's spectacular and instantly identifiable natural feature. Hotels were built at the park as early as 1871, but for more than thirty years the only hotel located close to Old Faithful was the appropriately named Shack Hotel. But in 1902 the Great Northern Railway, having completed a line terminating within thirty miles of Old Faithful the previous year, hired the architect Robert C. Reamer to design a deluxe hotel at the foot of the geyser. Reamer, a self-educated architect from Ohio, was still in his twenties when he received the Yellowstone commission through a fortuitous introduction to the president of the Yellowstone Park Company. Reamer's design followed Frederick Law Olmsted's 1865 injunction to the State of California against the construction of any facilities in the Yosemite Valley that "would unnecessarily obscure, distort, or detract from the dignity of the scenery."[2] Taking his cues from the Adirondack camps of Durant and Muncil, Reamer designed his Old Faithful Inn to rise on its site, two hundred yards from the geyser, like a small mountain of stone, logs, and shingles, capped by a sweeping gabled roof. Inside and out, rustic details — including roof brackets made of stripped branches and a cathedral-like eighty-five-foot-high lobby vaulted with rafters made from whole tree trunks — rendering at enormous scale a romanticized version of the frontiersman's rude cabin.

Reamer designed another hotel at Yellowstone, the Canyon Hotel, overlooking the park's immense chasm. The hotel was built in 1910–11, with workmen laboring through the fierce winter to complete the project for the summer season. A broad hipped roof covered the hotel's main section, which contained the dining room, some guest rooms, and service rooms. On the interior, a cascade of stairs led from the lobby to a great central lounge, the glazed end walls of which projected beyond the main building mass to create a sort of sun parlor at one end of the hall. Overhead, polished blond wood trusses were but the most outstanding example of the building's smooth-planed, carefully joined wood construction, which stood in sharp contrast to the Old Faithful Inn's rustic logs.

For those who sought even more spectacular canyon vistas, the El Tovar hotel (1901) was perched breathtakingly close to the southern rim of the mile-deep Grand Canyon in Arizona. The hotel was named for Don Pedro de Tovar, a sixteenth-century Spanish scout who learned about the canyon from the native Hopi Indians. The canyon was ignored by pioneers and settlers for nearly three centuries until Major John Wesley Powell came upon it while traveling the rapids of the Colorado River in 1869. In 1901 the Atchison Topeka & Santa Fe Railroad completed a branch to the canyon from its Chicago–Los Angeles main line, opening the site up for tourists. The El Tovar, built by the railroad and designed by the company's chief architect, Charles Whittlesey of Chicago, incorporated a base and chimneys of local limestone and upper walls faced with logs and shingles in a scheme that, according to the architect, was based on a "Norwegian villa." But despite the somewhat discordant European stylistic reference, Whittlesey created a remarkably appropriate hotel, using a muted palette on the exteriors and Navajo rugs and artifacts, animal trophies, and landscape paintings by Thomas Moran, the artist whose paintings of the West had done so much to stimulate the national parks movement thirty years before, to decorate the interior.

Adjacent to the El Tovar was the Hopi House, built in 1905 by the railroad concessionaire Fred Harvey. Known as the Lucullus of the West, Harvey managed many hotels in the Southwest, staffed by "Harvey girls," who were known for their courtesy and their trim, starched uniforms. Although the hotel's design, attributed to Mary Elizabeth Jane Colter, an architect for the Fred Harvey Company, was closely based on the Hopi pueblo at Orailu, Arizona, the management adopted a culturally pluralistic point of view: the gift shop featured handicrafts made by the Hopi who lived in the building as well as the Navajo who lived in traditional hogans nearby.

In 1913, when the Great Northern Railroad was extended to the entrance of Glacier National Park in Montana, near the Canadian border, the architectural firm of Cutter & Malmgram from Spokane, Washington, designed the Lewis Glacier Hotel, later called Lake McDonald Lodge. Capitalizing on the site's spectacular alpine qualities, a resemblance not lost on many turn-of-the-century tourists, the architects developed a scheme that resembled a Swiss resort, incorporating clapboard siding, bracketed hipped roofs, and log railings. Another hotel in the park, built the same year and designed by the architect Thomas D. McMahon of St. Paul, Minnesota, was named the Glacier Park Hotel but called Oom-Coo-La-Mush-Taw, or Big Tree Lodge, by the local Indians. Nowhere in America could the contradictory nature of a luxury resort that was also an escape into the wilds of nature be more fully experienced than at the Glacier Park Hotel, a behemoth that was at once grandly Classical and artfully rustic. At the main entrance, a symmetrical gate of tree trunks supporting shingled gable roofs surmounted by American flags dwarfed the automobiles that passed through it. The sprawling four-storey wooden hotel, which contained an arcade of tree-trunk columns, sat on a meticulously manicured lawn, crisscrossed with paths edged by formal flower beds. The precise landscaping provided a counterpoint to the primeval forest as well as to the cluster of tepees in front of the hotel that Indians inhabited — at least from nine to five — providing "authentic" local color. The hotel's spectacularly proportioned lobby exhibited a similar synthesis of the natural and the Classical, the familiar and the exotic. One of the greatest rooms ever realized in an American hotel, its sixty-foot height was framed by sixty bark-covered tree trunks, brought in from Oregon and Washington, each between thirty-six and forty-two inches in diameter, forty feet long, and from five hundred to eight hundred years old. At the top of each natural column, horizontal logs suggesting volute scrolls returned the Ionic order to its origins in the wooden architecture of Greece's pre-Periclean era, while bearskins, animal heads and skulls, rugs woven by Navajo Indians from the distant Southwest, and a frieze painted by local Blackfoot Indians depicting the history of their tribe returned the tourists to their mythic native roots. In the evening, visitors could don formal attire and dine in the hotel's restaurant underneath a multipanel mural that portrayed the park they had just seen, now framed by totem poles. Waitresses dressed in alpine-style costumes served hearty American cuisine on Chinese blue-willow-patterned tableware, while guests chewed to the rhythms of tom-toms beaten by local Amerindians. After dinner, tea and coffee were served in the lobby, beneath hanging Japanese lanterns, from a cart manned by a Japanese couple wearing native dress.

The dream of a life in nature began to coalesce with a romantic view of the pre-industrial American past in the 1870s. Americans not only discovered the pleasures of wilderness retreat but rediscovered the restorative value of the old, bypassed Colonial villages as well. This launched what could be seen as America's second Colonial era, in which the old villages were given a new lease on life by colonists who came not from England to escape religious persecution but from New York, Boston, or Charleston, South Carolina, to escape the heat. For the first time, the nation confidently viewed its manmade past in positive terms, reflecting that it had been liberated from its negative self-image as a cultural colony of Europe to achieve an unprecedented level of maturity and independence as a civilization. At last America was old enough to have its own past worthy of veneration. Colonial houses, weatherbeaten and rundown, were seen as natural, even organic, rather than manmade, possessing an admirable simplicity of form and directness of expression. Certainly, by comparison with the post–Civil War era's aggressively individualistic, often overblown domestic architecture, the nation's early domestic architecture seemed imbued with a higher and deeper set of values. While these houses had been little more than rude huts for the early settlers — huts that prosperous Colonists quickly abandoned — to the romantic citybound citizens of the Gilded Age they were the architectural component of an Arcadian ideal that regarded the American continent, not as a harsh landscape held at bay or as a domain for plunder, but as a divinely inspired garden, as if the Creation and the birth of landscape architecture had been simultaneous.

After the Civil War, many artists seeking to escape industrial America turned to the old, largely bypassed seaside villages of New England as subjects for their

8808. DINING ROOM, OLD FAITHFUL INN, YELLOWSTONE PARK.

Old Faithful, dining room. July 22/07

8810 THE LOBBY, OLD FAITHFUL INN, YELLOWSTONE PARK

The lobby. Old Faithful

Robert C. Reamer was hired in 1902 to design a deluxe hotel in Yellowstone National Park at the foot of the Old Faithful geyser. The Old Faithful Inn (*right*) was constructed in the Adirondack Style, of stone, logs, and shingles, and capped with a sweeping gabled roof.

Above, top: The lobby was vaulted with rafters made from whole tree trunks. Carved wood balconies encircled the room, with a monumental stone hearth in the center. *Bottom:* Logs on the dining room walls and ceiling created the feeling of a log cabin on a grand scale.

183   RESORTS

The Glacier Park Hotel in Montana was built in 1913. The lobby was a synthesis of grandly Classical and artfully rustic elements, including sixty tree trunk "columns," each at least five hundred years old. The decor included Native American rugs, bearskins, and animal heads and skulls.

paintings and to the raw power of the uncharted West. When Winslow Homer, Childe Hassam, and Thomas Moran discovered the village of East Hampton in 1874, its historic town green and pond, its windmills, and its 160-foot-wide elm-lined, grass-covered Main Street seemed the perfect place to re-create an earlier and less complicated phase of American civilization — and, as luck would have it, the sleepy village was only six miles from a railroad station and two and a half hours by train and ferry from Manhattan. In 1874, amidst the town's venerable artifacts, Moran built a new-old house for himself and his wife, the artist Mary Nimmo, that combined modern functional requirements with the character of the old shingled architecture. Moran and his younger colleague, Albert Herter, the muralist, took the love of nature to the furthest shores of reason, relaunching, on an East Hampton lake, the gondola that the poet Robert Browning had sailed in Venice, retaining as gondolier a local Amerindian.

The artists were quickly followed by ministers and professionals and businessmen — the new middle class, in short. While at first the ironically dubbed "Summer colonists" were usually content to board in existing houses or stay at small inns, many were anxious to put down roots, initiating an era of house-building in which the new summer residents to a remarkable extent subsumed themselves and their architecture into the genius of the place. It was in the development of resort architecture in long-settled areas of the northern Atlantic states that an intriguing, widely imitable style evolved. As documented and named by historian Vincent Scully, the Shingle Style represents an unprecedented historical synthesis of historical American architectural forms, picturesque composition, and the exuberance of resort design, which is even today widely studied and influential. The proving ground of its architectural development was Newport, Rhode Island.

In the eighteenth century, Newport had been an important port and a principal manufacturing center in the Colonies. British occupation during the Revolutionary War seriously crippled the town, however, and its population declined significantly. Around 1830 the town was developed as a summer resort by plantation owners from the southern United States and Cuba escaping the pestilent summer heat. With hotel accommodations at Newport scarce, summer visitors often built inexpensive structures intended to last for only one or two seasons. By the 1850s permanent houses began to be built in what was clearly being established as a resort. Following the Civil War, a richer, Northern clientele ushered in a new era in the town's architecture and social life. Newport was valued less as a beauty spot than as an opportunely located piece of real estate between New York and Boston — a convenient location for social adventure.

While no affluent resorters chose the existing Colonial town as a place to settle, the architects they commissioned, led by Henry Hobson Richardson, were drawn to qualities of the early buildings of Newport, to their architectural purity and simplicity and the coziness and shelter their exterior forms and interior details suggested. The result was a summer resort and a new architectural style evocative of a distinctive sense of place. The architects of the Shingle Style were accomplished professionals, well schooled in the forms and planning techniques of many historical styles. Their innovation begun at Newport was to harness the grand principles of architectural composition and planning to not entirely original but distinctly native forms. While the freely composed, picturesque domesticity of the so-called Queen Anne Revival developing simultaneously in England is related to the Shingle Style, the American work is wholly its own in its evocation of Colonial building forms. The Shingle Style work of Richardson and his followers has a crispness of line resulting from the simple and direct expression of their wood-frame construction and their tightly fitted sheathing of clapboard or shingle. The effect was of the taut skin enclosing the generously proportioned interior spaces. The Shingle Style devised by architects to fulfill the expansive programs of their prosperous clients was exuberant and picturesque, resulting in a complex and powerfully original building style. The discovery of America's architectural past was seen as a sign of the nation's cultural coming of age and a way to reaffirm the Union after the divisive Civil War. The Boston architect Robert Swain Peabody wrote in the *American Architect and Building News* in 1877, "With our centennial year have we not discovered that we too have a past worthy of study? . . . our Colonial work is our only native source of antiquarian study and inspiration."[3]

Richardson's Watts Sherman House, completed on Shepard Avenue in 1876, was the first major expression of the Shingle Style. Built of stone, half-timbering, and shingles, the house incorporated an asymmetrical composition in which the main roof line ran longitudinally but the principal façade was distinguished by a broad subsidiary gable supporting a centered porte-cochère. While in some ways it was quite English, reflecting the influence of the architect Richard Norman Shaw, in others it was distinctly American, with a unified, sweeping horizontality, interrupted only by chimneys, that expressed the possibilities for the internal

Overleaf. Southside, the grandest example of McKim, Mead & White's Shingle Style houses in Newport, Rhode Island, was designed with a profusion of porches, gables, loggias, chimneys, and dormers, all wrapped in a skin of varying shingle patterns. The elaborate plaster panel set in the central bay was composed of seashells, glass, and old rope.

continuity of space that central heating, a native innovation, made possible. Richardson's nascent dialogue with the nation's architectural past was particularly evident in the house's interior, where a centrally located hall containing a massive fireplace ran the full depth of the house and was flanked by rooms with more specific functions: dining room, library, and drawing room. The great hall evoked the central, hearth-centered rooms of Colonial saltboxes, which served to powerfully shelter their inhabitants, providing both a physical and a symbolic place on the uncharted continent.[4] Between 1879 and 1881, the architect Stanford White, who had worked for Richardson beginning in 1872 at the age of nineteen, redecorated three of the main rooms and added a wing to the house, transforming its basically rectangular organization into an "L." Historians have credited the young White with much of the house's original detailing, but whatever his initial contribution, his subsequently executed interiors clearly pushed the house toward the unabashedly opulent.

In the late 1870s and early 1880s, the rapidly expanding resort increasingly took on the character of a suburban village, with a rather densely developed collection of freestanding houses and a commercial center on Bellevue Avenue, the thoroughfare that connected the historical town center with the new "cottages" of the summer colony. An accident of social history gave the resort a social center that provided a focus for the lively sports-oriented community and, coincidentally, was one of the consummate architectural creations of the Shingle Style. According to legend, James Gordon Bennett, Jr., the playboy heir to the New York *Herald* fortune, had challenged a visiting British army officer to ride a horse through Newport's most prestigious club, the Newport Reading Room. The officer obliged, and Bennett was barred from the club. Piqued, Bennett set out to establish the Newport Casino, a livelier center for summertime frolics. He commissioned McKim, Mead & White to design the Casino, which opened in 1881. To Bennett's satisfaction, it quickly became *the* club in Newport.

Built on Bellevue Avenue, near the heart of the summer crowd's shopping district, the Casino's facilities were designed for sport and the social whirl. While tennis was the Casino's specialty, there were also shops, dining rooms, a theater, and a bandstand. The Casino's impact was profound, a design breakthrough for the young firm. A compositional tour de force, the Casino combined Classical Roman planning with motifs and materials from both vernacular American and French architecture. An adroit exercise in urbanism, it addressed the town with a public façade of shops. Inside, the club's activities were sheltered by a Roman courtyard. The far end of the court was defined by the curving arms of broad latticework porches, beyond which lay the tennis courts. Facing the avenue, McKim's ordered, symmetrical composition of modest red brick storefronts was surmounted by a second storey sheathed in shingles and subtly superimposed gable-ends of contrasting shingle patterns and painted wood. At the central bay, a second-storey porch over a brick archway marked the entrance. Within the entrance passageway, access was given to the upper storeys and to the courtyard beyond. The court's broad porches, called piazzas, created a continuous protected walkway from which strollers could observe croquet and lawn tennis matches. As articulated by White, the piazzas were partially enclosed volumes that provided shelter from the summer sun. Here, even the exotic Orient was incorporated, as the delicate Japanese-style woodwork and lathe-turned spindle screens transformed them into kaleidoscopes of shade and shadow. The building block that screened the court from Bellevue was combined with lateral wings defining the sides of the court, a tower of French inspiration, and numerous gables to create a seemingly haphazard but careful composition of elements that was a dignified and exuberant setting for resort life.

The Casino and the seminal Watts Sherman House served as springboards for a series of remarkable houses in Newport designed by McKim, Mead & White: the Isaac Bell, Jr., House, known as Edna Villa (1881–83), the Colman House (1882–83), and the Tilton House (1881–82), with its lively exterior decoration in which the stucco of half-timbered walls was embedded with pebbles and bits of glass, seemingly tossed up from the sea. The grandest of the firm's Shingle Style houses, Southside, was completed in 1883 for Robert Goelet, on Narragansett Avenue, facing the ocean. A sprawling composition, incorporating a profusion of porches, gables, loggias, chimneys, and dormers, the house was a sensitive interplay of void and volume. Symmetries among various building parts — two projecting gabled porches on the ocean side, for example — were established and then enlivened by the interruptions of other asymmetrically located building parts, apparently independently located towers and gables which were themselves intricately composed. Each building element was wrapped in a skin of varying shingle patterns, with excisions of windows and porches neatly framed in painted wood. Providing a contrast to the diverse wooden shingle patterns, the central bay on the ocean side of the house contained one of White's most elaborate plaster panels, which included not only seashells and glass but old rope as well. The house's first-floor interior was organized around a great hall dominated by a massive fireplace, while above, galleries created a sense of movement on several different levels and allowed sea breezes to blow freely through the house.

The Shingle Style represented the pinnacle of an era in Newport — an age of innocence. It was formed of a dream of a uniquely American yet broadly synthetic architecture. It was a noble vision — perhaps too noble to be sustained.

Around 1890 a far more presumptuous mood overtook the American gentry, who aspired to create a social class on a par with Europe's aristocracy, with a summer base in Newport. For them America's architectural past, no matter how romanticized, did not seem sufficiently grand. It was immediately adjacent to Robert Goelet's Southside that his brother Ogden, a wealthy New York real estate developer, initiated a change in architectural aspirations with his palatial Ochre Court of 1888. Its evocation of Europe's architectural past ignited a domestic building explosion that would last for nearly thirty years. It set the era's standard not only for opulence but for scale. Goelet's architect, Richard Morris Hunt, designed a free but rather severe interpretation of sixteenth-century French Renaissance elements, which he would later bring to an apogee in North Carolina at Biltmore. Inside, Ochre Court revealed a rigidly academic plan, featuring a three-storey-high entrance hall, which incorporated a variety of styles and many objects and architectural fragments that Goelet had collected in Europe.

Although Ogden Goelet started the game at Newport, the unofficial winners were the Vanderbilts, who, perhaps more than any other family, personified the spirit of the resort's palace-building era. In 1892 William Vanderbilt commissioned Hunt to design a palace in Newport as a thirty-ninth-birthday gift for his wife, Alva, who proved to be one of the architect's most demanding clients. Costing two million dollars to build and nine million to furnish, Marble House, as the mansion was called, was a remarkable portrait of the Vanderbilts. While it evoked the second-century Roman Temple of Bacchus at Baalbeck, it was a more direct synthesis of two somewhat less improbable sources: Jacques-Ange Gabriel's Petit Trianon at Versailles and James Hoban's White House in Washington, D.C. What could be more fitting for William and Alva Vanderbilt, who had as much power as the kings of France, and certainly a lot more money than the American presidents? The two-storey principal façade was a Classical, symmetrical composition, in the center of which a portico was carried by four huge Corinthian columns; on all sides, the exterior was divided into bays separated by fluted Corinthian pilasters. A large entablature and a balustrade concealed the nearly flat roof, which covered an attic storey. To underscore that what was suitable for the king of France was suitable for William Vanderbilt, Hunt's design for the massive bronze and steel entrance grille adopted Louis XIV's monogram and emblem, the head of the boy Apollo emanating sun rays, and incorporated his client's initials, "W. V." It was one thing for Vanderbilt to think he was the Sun King, but it took an architect to give him an appropriate, believable setting. So grateful was Vanderbilt to Hunt that he had the architect memorialized in a medallion.

The cool, ultrarestrained façades of Marble House were a perfect foil for the extravagant and inventive interiors. With the exception of the anachronistic Gothic Room, which reflected the nation's dwindling fascination with a romanticized medieval past, the opulent interiors were inspired by Parisian Second Empire designs. Marble House's ballroom, the Gold Room, a veritable hall of mirrors, was one of the most sumptuously decorated interiors of any building, public or private, ever realized in America. Throughout the house, the carvings depicted sea motifs

The Casino was designed by McKim, Mead & White to serve as Newport's sports and social center. Here, turn-of-the-century spectators enjoy a game of lawn tennis, shaded by the broad, partially enclosed porches known as piazzas.

This drawing, first published in an 1885 issue of *Harper's Weekly*, shows a detail of the delicate, Japanese-style woodwork that adorned the piazzas of the Casino.

Overleaf. William Vanderbilt's summer mansion in Newport, known as Marble House, was designed by Richard Morris Hunt in 1892. The two-storey principal façade is a Classical, symmetrical composition of Corinthian columns and fluted pilasters, with a large entablature and a balustrade concealing the nearly flat third-storey roof.

and sea creatures, both real and mythical, reminding the occupants of the monumental house, so divorced from its surroundings and nature as a whole, that the Atlantic Ocean lay just beyond the doorstep.

In 1895 Mrs. Vanderbilt was divorced and soon married August Belmont. As a wedding present, Belmont deeded her his recently completed Newport mansion, Belcourt. The stylistic eclecticism of this era of Newport's history is apparent in Mrs. Vanderbilt Belmont's two "cottages." Designed by the same architect at nearly the same time for sites nearly opposite each other on Bellevue Avenue, Belcourt was modeled on the hunting lodges of Louis XIII and built of roughly finished stone and brick. Planned around a large central courtyard, the design combined French, Italian, and English elements. The main first-floor reception room was originally a passageway that was open to the outside, allowing horse-drawn carriages to drive into the house and directly up to the grand staircase. A French Gothic ballroom and a Neo-Classical oval dining room were the settings for the Belmonts' frequent formal parties; even lunch at Belcourt was served by servants dressed in breeches, silk stockings, and powdered wigs. Belmont, an avid sportsman, had instructed Hunt to provide suitable quarters for his horses. Their stables occupied most of the ground floor. Two of his favorite horses were allowed upstairs — stuffed, next to medieval suits of armor in one of the sumptuous main rooms. Following the death of her husband, who collapsed at a costume party in 1908 while dressed in knight's armor, Mrs. Belmont moved back to Marble House, which she had managed to keep in her divorce settlement. In 1912, Alva Belmont undertook one more building project, commissioning Hunt's sons, whose partnership succeeded their father's firm, to design an Oriental garden pavilion at the edge of the fifty-foot cliffs overlooking the Atlantic Ocean just beyond the mansion. Traveling to China to do research, the Hunts returned to translate their client's dream into a synthesis of various Chinese styles, strengthened by American construction techniques in order to withstand Newport's harsh weather conditions. The teahouse's principal feature was a boldly proportioned terra-cotta tiled roof whose radically upswept eave-ends were decorated with twenty-three hammered-copper figures, including two large sculpted serpent-fish at the ridge. The teahouse lacked only one essential ingredient — a place to boil the water for tea. To solve that problem, Mrs. Belmont reputedly built a miniature railway, connecting the pavilion to the main house, on which food and hot drinks could be transported in a warming oven.

The teahouse was officially opened on July 25, 1914, as part of a Chinese costume ball. But a week earlier Marble House and its teahouse had served as the setting for a national conference of suffragettes sponsored by Mrs. Belmont, an ardent supporter of the movement. When one of her fellow suffragettes became discouraged, the indefatigable Alva told her, "Brace up, my dear. Just pray to God. *She* will help you."[5]

Despite their grandeur, Ochre Court, Belcourt, and Marble House were all overshadowed by The Breakers. In October 1885, William Vanderbilt's older brother Cornelius Vanderbilt II purchased The Breakers, built by Pierre Lorillard III, a rambling Shingle Style house on Ochre Point designed by Peabody & Stearns (1877). In 1892, it burned to the ground, and Vanderbilt hired his brother's architect, Hunt, to build a marble palace. Still called The Breakers, it was based on the sixteenth-century palazzos of Genoa and Turin. Despite its formality and

NEVVPORT.R.I.

RES

Wᴹ.K.V

NCE

BILT ESQ⁵

SCALE ½ INCH = 1 FOOT

enormity, it was conceived of as a summer place, with extensive loggias, arcades, and terraces. The principal façade was organized in a three-part scheme, with the central bay incorporating a porte-cochère. However, the ocean-facing east façade, with its double-level loggia balanced by flanking towers, was the most impressive.

The Breakers' interiors were as sparkling as diamonds and as cold as the North Atlantic. A cerulean blue ceiling floated over a forty-five-foot-high entrance hall, which functioned as a lobby does in a grand hotel. Directly across the hall from the main entrance, large windows opened onto the lower loggia and provided sweeping views of the ocean. Hunt commissioned the Parisian architect Richard Bouwens Van der Boyen to articulate the interior of the double-height state dining room. Bouwens pulled out all the stops to create a lavishly crafted, complex design, controlled by a gilded cornice supported by twelve red alabaster columns and topped with gilded bronze Corinthian capitals. Lest anyone get the impression that the Vanderbilts were materialistic parvenus, an inscription in antiquated French on the library's sixteenth-century mantelpiece, which had been imported from the Château d'Arnay-le-Duc, translated: "Little do I care for riches, and do not miss them, since only cleverness prevails in the end."

Returning to Newport in 1904, after twenty-nine years abroad, Henry James deplored the transformation of the resort by the Vanderbilts and their peers. For James, even nature had been corrupted by wealth: at Newport, one could hear "something like the chink of money itself in the murmur of the breezy little waves."[6] As for the mansions themselves, James concluded that Newport had become "a mere breeding ground for white elephants."[7]

Newport's implacable and majestic mansions stand today, most of them unoccupied and many preserved as museums. Newport has become a trip back in time — one of America's great theme parks — where busloads of tourists momentarily share an aristocratic fantasy as they crawl all over "cottages" like Cornelius Vanderbilt's Breakers, marveling at the luxury and gasping at the excess. Today, as in its heyday, Newport thrills us as it appalls. The essayist Joan Didion has characterized the turn-of-the-century rich who made Newport the nation's most exclusive enclave as curiously self-defeating: "More than anyone else in the society, these men had apparently dreamed the dream and made it work. And what they did then was to build a place which seems to illustrate, as in a child's primer, that the production ethic led step by step to unhappiness, to restrictiveness." For Didion, "To stand in the dining room of 'The Breakers' is to imagine fleeing from it, pleading migraine."[8] But it is not the near-ridiculous dream of a would-be American aristocracy that is compelling; it is a simpler dream that is expressed and almost universally shared — that from circumstances of modesty, fortunes can be made, enjoyed, and flaunted.

While Newport may now seem more a museum than a resort, the nation's largest resort area, the state of Florida, is still thriving. With its exotic flora and fauna — coconuts and flamingos and alligators — Florida is our premier tropical paradise, offering an enticing synthesis of the exotic, the comfortable, and the convenient. It affords the imagined glamour and license of the tropics, which has come to represent our very notion of a vacation in a jungle setting that evokes man's prehistory.

It is appropriate that the development in Florida of planned and profitable resort areas began in St. Augustine, which was also the first established town in North America. Its transformation from a sleepy backwater was the work of a fifty-three-year-old freewheeling entrepreneur named Henry Morrison Flagler. Flagler had made his fortune in a business partnership with Samuel Andrews and John D. Rockefeller, which later became the Standard Oil Company. In 1885, two years after Flagler's honeymoon trip to St. Augustine had entailed an arduous ninety-hour train ride, he returned, finding that the rail system in Florida had vastly improved since his last trip and a luxury hotel was under construction in St. Augustine. Ever the entrepreneur, Flagler decided to do more in Florida than grow old.

Flagler dreamed of a grand resort hotel to be named for the sixteenth-century Spanish explorer Ponce de León, who had searched in Florida for the fabled Fountain of Youth. Flagler's hotel would promise rejuvenation under Florida's sunny skies. To design his hotel, Flagler hired the firm of two inexperienced New York architects who had trained at the École des Beaux-Arts: twenty-six-year-old John M. Carrère and twenty-eight-year-old Thomas Hastings, whose father had been the Flagler family's minister and close friend. The Ponce de Leon marked an auspicious start for the young architects, who had followed study in Paris with brief apprenticeships in the office of McKim, Mead & White before setting out on their own in 1884. The Ponce de Leon, opened in 1888, was an oasis of convenience in the midst of a town that had slumbered for fifty years.

Neither Flagler nor his architects appear to have been the least interested in St. Augustine's existing Colonial architecture. Instead Carrère & Hastings took exuberantly detailed fantasy drawn from elements of the architecture of old Spain and the Arabic influences introduced into that country by the Moors and grafted them onto the efficient organization of academic French planning. Florida offered little in the way of building materials. Most of the local coquina stone was too soft, but when ground into gravel and mixed with cement and water it formed a superb concrete that Carrère & Hastings exploited to great advantage, creating one of the first large poured concrete structures in the country. Its four-foot-thick exterior walls kept interiors cool in the hot season and warm in the dead of winter. The hotel's principal façade, built close to the street, incorporated an arched gateway flanked by arcaded verandas. Trimmed with brick and terra cotta and surmounted by red tile roofs, the verandas enclosed a large, landscaped interior court. Two towers topped by conical roofs served the functional purpose of housing water tanks for fire protection as they lent a romantic silhouette to the flat landscape.

After the Ponce de Leon opened, Flagler boasted that St. Augustine was a winter Newport. But unlike Newport, which emerged from its Colonial chrysalis to become a resort town slowly, through the efforts of numerous individuals, St. Augustine blossomed instantly and was shaped almost exclusively by Flagler. It was he who initiated the trend away from isolated hotels or collections of private mansions in favor of completely planned resort villages. Reaping the profits from his successful hotels didn't satisfy his devotion to rebuilding St. Augustine as his own dream village. In 1888 he built the Mediterranean-style Grace United Methodist Church, also designed by Carrère & Hastings. Two years later, he erected the First Presbyterian Church as a memorial to his daughter, who died in childbirth. A Venetian Renaissance-style building, again designed by Carrère & Hastings, the church was surmounted by a graceful dome and a classical lantern,

The Gold Room at Marble House is an opulent display of gilded carvings, mirrors, marble, and sparkling chandeliers. False doors were installed to maintain the symmetry of the room.

Mrs. Alva Vanderbilt Belmont and her daughter Consuelo Vanderbilt, the Duchess of Marlborough, attend a national suffragette conference held at Belcourt, Mrs. Belmont's second Newport mansion, in 1914.

which, when seen together with the adjacent Ponce de Leon, evoked the skyline of a Mediterranean city. Flagler also financed the construction of a hospital, a city hall, a school, houses, paved streets, water works, sewers, and electrical lines.

To facilitate the construction of his hotels in St. Augustine, Flagler purchased and improved the Jacksonville, St. Augustine, and Halifax rail line, which coincidentally was critical to the development of southern Florida, forging railroad connections to the north. In 1892 Flagler obtained a charter from the state of Florida authorizing the construction of tracks as far south as Miami, and it was then that he began to build his first railroad from scratch.

By 1892 the Flagler line reached beyond Daytona to a point across Lake Worth from Palm Beach. As soon as his railroad reached Palm Beach, Flagler built another hotel, the Royal Poinciana, named for a summer flower that, ironically, few visitors would ever see in full bloom. Facing the eastern bank of Lake Worth and backing onto the Atlantic Ocean, the Royal Poinciana Hotel, designed by McDonald & McGuire and completed in 1894, was a sprawling six-storey wooden structure. While without specific historical models, it was not without pretension. The hotel's principal façade featured a broad veranda supported by Ionic columns. Surmounting the temple front of the main entrance, a cupola rose above the rows of dormer windows that punctuated the hotel's long roof. Exterior clapboards were painted a bright yellow, known as "Flagler yellow," while the verandas, balconies, window frames, and decorative trim were all white. Inside, the rooms abounded in green and white wicker. A large rotunda served as the nucleus of the hotel's three-mile-long network of corridors, many of which were as wide as city streets, and some, in fact, were lined with fashionable stores. Flagler's guests could lounge along the verandas and corridors, watching one another promenade, or they could ride about the grounds and through the long halls in single- and double-seated "Afro-mobiles," wicker carts pedaled by black hotel employees.

At first most visitors to Palm Beach were invalids from the North, and Flagler's hotel became known as a huge infirmary for "sick Yankees." But Flagler, a shrewd observer of high society and a publicity wizard, soon changed its image and its patronage. He insured that the hotel became known for both its cuisine and its service. A staff of fourteen hundred employees included one waiter for every four diners, a chambermaid for every few rooms, and a bellboy in every hall. The hotel's elaborate social activities included teas in the Coconut Grove Room and formal balls, highlighted by an annual Washington's Birthday Ball, which officially marked the end of "the season" and was as extravagant as some of those held in Newport in summer.

The Royal Poinciana attracted the upper crust, but it also provided the perfect setting for parvenu social climbers. In 1916, Ring Lardner, the baseball umpire and sportswriter turned humorist, wrote of "Gullible's Travels" to Palm Beach in search of "the high *polloi*."[9] Gullible found the hotel's dining room so vast that "from one end of it to the other is a toll call, and if a man that was settin' at the table farthest from the kitchen ordered roast lamb he'd get mutton."[10] After more than a week of trying, unsuccessfully, to meet the elite, Gullible's "Missus" is approached in the hallway by *the* Mrs. Potter from Chicago: "'Are you on this floor?' she says. The Missus shook like a leaf. 'Yes,' says she, so low you couldn't hardly hear her. 'Please see that they's some towels put in 559,' says *the* Mrs. Potter from Chicago."[11]

Flagler died in 1914 at the age of eighty-three, having realized his dream of transforming the underdeveloped state of Florida into the nation's winter playground. Yet five years after Flagler's death, through the efforts of two men, Palm Beach would be completely remade, becoming more opulent, more glamorous, and vastly more architecturally significant than anything Flagler had ever imagined. The enterprising pair who transformed Palm Beach into a world-class resort were two high-style oddballs: Paris Singer, one of Isaac Merritt Singer's twenty-five children and an heir to the vast sewing machine fortune, and Addison Mizner, an architect and adventurer from California.

Mizner, whose work at Boca Raton was seen in the last chapter, ranks with Richard Morris Hunt and Stanford White as one of America's great "society" architects. But, unlike Hunt and White, Mizner has not been taken seriously by his fellow architects. His reputation has been tarnished by his wit and sharp tongue and his own ceaseless efforts to create the persona of an inspired flâneur. Yet not only did Mizner conduct serious architectural research and design individual buildings of great inventiveness and vitality — work that was admired by Frank Lloyd Wright — but he masterminded one transformation of Palm Beach into the quintessential twentieth-century resort village. Far exceeding Flagler's pioneering efforts to create a resort village at St. Augustine, Mizner succeeded in building an architecturally coherent place in which Americans could escape from the drudgery of daily life — any American with a fistful of dollars, that is. Palm Beach became an American Venice. But Mizner went further than simply building a great resort; together with Singer, he taught vacationers how to enjoy themselves, how to make each holiday in the sun a romp in the Fountain of Youth.

Mizner's architectural training consisted of a three-year apprenticeship with the prominent San Francisco architect Willis Polk and extended travel in Central America and Spain. While his charm and quick wit won him entrée into and a few commissions from the social elite of the Northeast, it was not until he was commissioned to design Paris Singer's hospital and convalescent home, originally named the Touchstone Convalescents Club, in Palm Beach that his architectural career began in earnest.

Upon arriving in Palm Beach, Mizner found that the existing "Northern architecture didn't register. . . . There was one New England Colonial house that was placed in the midst of the coconut trees and it was an abortion."[12] Despite wartime shortages and a severe lack of skilled help, within seven months of commencing the design of Singer's hospital, Mizner had transformed Joe's Alligator Farm, a mosquito-infested quagmire, into a complex of stucco buildings with balconies, porches, and red tile roofs, which would have looked as appropriate on the shores of the Mediterranean as it did on the banks of Lake Worth.

Mizner envisioned a building style that would combine a variety of Mediterranean architectural vocabularies into a synthesis suited to the climate and landscape of Florida. Furthermore, he sought to create buildings that appeared to have grown organically over time and looked as if they were "based on Romanesque ruins that had been rebuilt by the triumphant Saracens, added to by a variety of conquerors bringing in new styles from the Gothic to the Baroque, and picturesquely cracked up by everything from battering rams to artillery duels between Wellington and Napoleon's marshals."[13]

The main clubhouse in the Touchstone Convalescents Home, which Mizner would in fact continue to alter for years, fulfilled the architect's intention. To create a strong skyline in the flat landscape, he punctuated the building's asymmetrical principal façade with a tower, which housed a modest apartment for himself and a triplex apartment for Singer. The rear façade referred to ecclesiastical architecture with a two-tiered domed tower that explicitly resembled the campanile of a Spanish church. The lobby of the clubhouse was decorated with two-thousand-year-old Tunisian tiles that Singer had collected over a twenty-year period. Mizner informed reporters from the Palm Beach *Post* that because Palm Beach was the Tunis of the American empire, it was quite appropriate to employ relics of Roman splendor.[14] According to Alva Johnston, Mizner's biographer, a group of Islamic visitors once entered the lobby and assumed prayer positions in front of the tiles.[15] Mizner also introduced several features at the club that later became trademarks of his Palm Beach houses, including a cantilevered spiral staircase that seemingly floated without support and the use of the native worm-eaten cypress wood, known as "pecky cypress," for ceiling beams. Previously thought of as worthless, the wood harmonized with the interiors of rooms such as the dining hall, which housed antique wood wall panels taken from a Spanish church, achieving Mizner's aim of simulating what he described as "the silent touches of time."[16] Most important, the club set the precedent for nearly open plans in which rooms flowed into landscaped terraces and patios, exploiting Florida's year-round warm weather to create spaces that were at once poetic, fanciful, and grand.

While Singer claimed that his motives in building the hospital and convalescent home were exclusively altruistic and patriotic, not entrepreneurial, he

The Chinese teahouse was built on the Vanderbilt estate just behind Marble House, overlooking the Atlantic Ocean. It synthesized various Chinese styles and lacked only one essential ingredient — a place to boil water for tea.

Overleaf. All Newport mansions were overshadowed by the grandeur of The Breakers, Cornelius Vanderbilt II's summer palace on Ochre Point in Newport. The east façade, shown here, was the most impressive, with a two-level loggia balanced by flanking towers. The estate is bordered by the Cliff Walk, a three-mile trail along the ocean.

had, within two months of beginning construction, changed the convalescent home's name to the Everglades Club and begun selling house lots along the ocean in what was known as the Singer Addition. Admission to the health facility was significantly different from that at hospitals Singer had built in Europe: only army and naval officers who could afford to pay for room and board were permitted to sign up; even the shell-shocked had to be interviewed. Singer sent out as many as three hundred thousand invitations for membership, but by the time the club was completed in January 1919, the war was over and most officers chose to recover at home. But the Everglades Club prevailed, not as a high-class hospital, but as a highly exclusive social club restricted to three hundred members, who, like Singer, had discovered Palm Beach when they had been cut off by the war from their usual seaside vacation spots along the Riviera. The club immediately replaced the formal, stuffy, but much more democratic Flagler hotels as the social center of Palm Beach. Singer and Mizner's resort had apparently sparked the imagination of the entire community: within four weeks of the club's completion, Mizner received four house commissions, and in the next six years dozens more would follow.

During the construction of the Everglades Club, World War I shipping embargoes had prevented Mizner from importing handmade roof tiles. Finding domestically manufactured tiles unacceptable, he ordered clay from Georgia and hired workmen to make tiles according to the Spanish method, using a wooden form shaped roughly like a man's thigh. He bought kiln facilities to fire the tiles

The Ponce de Leon in St. Augustine, Florida, one of the country's first large poured concrete structures, combined Mediterranean influences with Classical planning. Its principal façade incorporated an arched gateway flanked by arcaded verandas.

from Singer and in 1919 established Las Manos — Spanish for "handcrafted." Located in West Palm Beach, the plant constituted the first division of Mizner Industries, which later produced a wide array of objects and building materials suited to historically referential architecture, including light fixtures, andirons, gates, grilles, pottery, stained glass windows, pecky cypress beams internally supported by steel, cast-stone ornaments, bricks, and blocks of coquina rock quarried near Islamorada in the Florida Keys. Mizner Industries also produced antique furniture reproductions, made of the finest woods and built with hand-cut joints. "Antiques" were instantly created by scraping the reproductions with broken bottles or beating them with chains to make them appear old.

The results of Mizner's efforts were remarkably convincing. Alexander P. Moore, once the United States Ambassador to Spain, remarked after seeing one of Mizner's Palm Beach houses, "It's more Spanish than anything I ever saw in Spain."[17] But Mizner never claimed to adhere strictly to Spanish precedent. He freely adapted the mode to suit his clients' needs and the local conditions, stating that he had inverted the archetypal Spanish courtyard house plan, putting "plenty of openings on the outside walls to let the sunshine and air into the house and . . . make people feel that they were living out-of-doors. The patio was retained so that people did not lose the openness inside the Spanish plan."[18] Having turned the Spanish house "inside out like a glove,"[19] Mizner further blurred the distinction between inside and outside by the generous use of wide balconies, glazed cloisterways, and open-loggia rooms that anticipated the popular "Florida room." The use of these elements allowed a large portion of a house to be only a single room deep, with rooms often having two or more exposures to capitalize on the cooling effects of cross ventilation. Centrally located courtyards also constituted protected environments shielded from harsh ocean winds, where delicate ornamental plants could thrive in lush gardens. Westward-facing French doors or large windows provided sunset views, while cloisters placed along the western façade shaded principal rooms during the hottest part of the day. Kitchens were often located in separate wings to the northwest so that prevailing breezes would remove heat and odors.

Mizner was commissioned to design his first private residence in Palm Beach by the undisputed grand dame of Palm Beach society, Mrs. Eva Cromwell Stotesbury. Completed in 1920, the Stotesbury house, El Mirasol, set the standard for all Palm Beach mansions and served as a prototype for Mizner's subsequent domestic work. A picturesque composition of stucco and red tile roofs, the house was entered on a floor below the principal rooms. A grand staircase led up to a cloistered hallway bordered by loggias opening onto patios. In the grand living room, three French doors opened onto the patio, while three others led to a terrace overlooking the ocean, establishing an open feeling that contrasted with the sense of solidity created by a massive fireplace and the richly articulated wood-paneled ceiling. Lavishly landscaped grounds contained an orange grove, an aviary, and a small zoo. In keeping with the characteristically American tendency to be simultaneously extravagant and practical, Mr. Stotesbury insisted that the grounds include a vegetable garden and a chicken house.

In 1922, William Gray Warden, whose father had founded the Atlantic Refining Company and, in 1874, joined the Standard Oil Trust, commissioned Mizner to design a villa facing the ocean. Although cost was certainly not a problem, Warden requested a small, unpretentious house, while Mrs. Warden preferred something rather more imposing. Mizner later said that to please them both he sketched the house at half the scale of the neighboring houses, telling only Mrs. Warden of his gimmick. When Mr. Warden requested a detailed set of elevations, Mizner, protecting his secret, answered, "Elevations! Why, Bill, you look intelligent at times; how could I send you elevations when the house isn't finished yet."[20] While in fact both Wardens inspected the house during construction and were pleased, Mizner, who relished good gossip, often repeated the story of how he had satisfied the Wardens, helping to establish the myth that he never drew elevations or plans before the completion of a project. Throughout the 1920s, Palm Beach buzzed with stories of the architect's alleged unorthodoxies

Left. The large interior court of the Ponce de Leon was landscaped with lush gardens and fountains. *Right.* Guests ride in wicker carts among the gardens of the Royal Poinciana Hotel in Palm Beach, Florida, at the turn of the century.

Addison Mizner envisioned a building style suitable to the climate and landscape of Florida that would combine a variety of Mediterranean architectural vocabularies. In this photograph, circa 1920, he holds a model with arched colonnades, characteristic of that style.

The value of attention — and even of some notoriety — was never lost on Mizner.

The Warden house's principal façade presented a rather austere asymmetrical composition. Thirty-two rooms were arranged in a U-shape, bordering a 100-by-85-foot patio open to the west, with a cloistered arcade serving to link the two principal wings. A stone staircase in the entrance hall led to the main rooms, which were located on the second floor, including a bachelor suite of guest rooms directly accessible from the patio by a spiral staircase.

In the many private houses he designed subsequently, Mizner refined his architectural vocabulary drawn from the many traditions of Hispanic architecture. Mizner Industries was outfitted to produce standardized window frames for his projects, making complicated figures such as pointed and trefoil arched windows readily available. But Mizner's houses were never replicas, as he continued to develop his synthesis of Mediterranean elements in designs that appeared to have grown over time, a style he extended to the urban scale.

Mizner's vision for Palm Beach extended far beyond dream houses and hotels, no matter how glamorous. In 1923 he began to shape an architecturally distinctive commercial center. On Worth Avenue across from the Everglades Club, he created a Mediterranean-style building to house his design studios and Mizner Industries' headquarters, as well as street-level display space for his pottery and antiques businesses. Until this time, with the exception of the club and its stores, Worth Avenue had been residential. Mizner's new commercial building signaled its transformation into one of the world's most fashionable shopping streets.

The following year Mizner built another shopping complex, which was stylistically consistent with the first. A street for pedestrians, the Via Mizner twisted between the two buildings; it was lined with small shops and restaurants and punctuated by plazas incorporating fountains and gardens. Here the delicious spatial sequences of old Spanish towns like Granada were invoked to create an intimate world of movement and surprise that perfectly counterpointed the grandeur of Worth Avenue. It solidified Palm Beach's architectural identity. Mizner had masterfully demonstrated that the consistent application of a Mediterranean architectural vocabulary on a large scale could establish a sense of community without monotony. He created large-scale public and private buildings that were dignified yet sufficiently inventive to play up the romantic attributes of the same tradition, achieving charming, intimate public spaces. The Via Mizner proved immediately successful and was followed in 1925 by the construction of another similarly delineated pedestrian street to the west; acknowledging Paris Singer's financial backing, Mizner named it Via Parigi.

A flight of steps led from the Via Mizner to the architect's apartment-villa, in which the dining room contained wood panels from a room at the University of Salamanca in which Ferdinand and Isabella were reputed to have commissioned Christopher Columbus and set in motion the Spanish Inquisition. On the floor above, a studio-library incorporated a mirador from which Mizner could survey the entire resort town that was in large part his own creation.

Mizner's own house was an advertisement for his architecture and the products of Mizner Industries. He reproduced the Ferdinand and Isabella dining room in "woodite," a pulpy composite of wood shavings, plaster of Paris, and fibrous material. The Gedney House in the neighboring village of Manalpan boasted the woodite version. A seaside farmhouse, it grouped its wings around a

The Everglades Club in Palm Beach featured a cantilevered spiral staircase (*above*) that seemed to float without support. It was to become one of Mizner's trademarks in later buildings. The elaborately tiled bathroom (*right*) was part of a triplex apartment that Mizner designed for the club's owner, Paris Singer.

west-facing courtyard, yet, instead of arcades and vestigially Moorish fenestration, Mizner surrounded the court with loggias and balconies supported by heavy, unpainted wood posts and beams.

Singer and Mizner's dream for Palm Beach elevated the resort from its somewhat mundane architectural origins to the status of a permanent stage set for the public and private games of the rich and the not-so-rich. Hunt's Newport was the perfect setting for historical costume drama, Mizner's Palm Beach perfectly suited modern drawing room comedy. Mizner's architecture had created a new style — a romanticized synthesis of Hispanic architectural traditions — and established a model of stylistic consistency in commercial as well as private buildings. Its example was soon followed all across Florida, as virtually the entire state became a resort suburb of Northeastern and Midwestern cities. Seasonal commuters breathed life into countless Florida towns and villages, transforming the sleepy swampland into a subdivisible version of the paradise that Ponce de León had dreamed about almost four hundred years before. Thousands migrated to amuse themselves in the balmy Florida climate, where they could frolic with the assurance that they were never farther than a comfortable twenty-four-hour train trip to offices back home.

While Palm Beach was without doubt Florida's premier resort, resorts farther south began to vie with it as early as 1896, when Flagler's Florida East Coast Railroad reached Miami. In 1913 a two-and-a-half-mile wooden bridge connected the mainland to the mangrove swamp now known as Miami Beach, an island separating Biscayne Bay from the Atlantic Ocean. Two years later, when Miami Beach was incorporated as a city, its choicest real estate was newly created ground literally pumped up from the bottom of Biscayne Bay. Carl Fisher, who had partially financed the bridge in exchange for two hundred acres of the island, began selling land that he often couldn't scoop up fast enough: auctioneers selling property would often point to the mangrove swamp and describe a lot's location in only the vaguest terms — because it was in fact still under water. In the early twenties, senators, socialites, and the plain rich flocked to Fisher's fleet of grand hotels: the Flamingo (Price & McLanahan, 1921), the Nautilus (Schultze & Weaver, 1924), and the King Cole (Kiehnel & Elliot, 1925). The fast crowd piloted powerboats, swam at Fisher's Roman Pools, and gambled in the Spanish Village, a stuccoed mock-up built in 1925 as an artists' colony by N. B. T. Roney, who in the same year completed one of Miami Beach's grandest hotels, the Roney Plaza, which was designed by Schultze & Weaver and, like their Biltmore Hotel in nearby Coral Gables, was surmounted by a tower modeled after the Giralda Tower in Seville. The real estate boom was further catalyzed by vacationers who built their own beachfront estates, lured by the state of Florida's shameless 1924 constitutional amendment prohibiting both income and inheritance taxes.

By 1925, word of the Florida real estate boom had trickled down to the middle class, whose cars lined the Dixie Highway bumper to bumper. For a generation that grew up with the rags-to-riches stories of Horatio Alger, the lure of Florida real estate was intense and the competition for property in Miami, where at the height of the boom land prices could triple in a single day, led to widespread fraud. While affluent tourists continued to migrate south in the late twenties and even during the first years of the Great Depression, the real estate market began to decline as a result of rampant hucksterism and the devastating hurricane of September 1926. As a result, building activity ceased for a decade. In 1928 Henry S. Villard described a new, sobered Miami, where "lonely, white-way lights stand guard over miles of cement sidewalks . . . grass and palmetto take the place of homes that were to be. . . . Whole sections of outlying subdivisions are composed of unoccupied homes, through which one speeds on broad thoroughfares as if traversing a city in the grip of death."[21]

When Miami Beach began to build again in the late 1930s, it abandoned the

Beginning in the mid-1930s, small, Modernist hotels were built in Miami Beach, and the Florida coastline was suddenly transformed into a two-week paradise for the middle class. The designs of the Marlin Hotel (*left*) and the Collins Park Hotel (*right*) mimicked the streamlined aesthetic of ocean liners, with rounded corners and flat roofs emphasizing their horizontality.

historical allusionism and grandiose scale of the 1920s Mediterranean Revival. No longer a magnet for the super rich who went for the season, Miami Beach thrived as a two-week paradise for the middle class. Small, Modernist-style hotels faced Ocean Park and the broad beach beyond. Their designs generally mimicked the streamlined aesthetic of ocean liners, with rounded corners, racing stripes, eyebrow canopies over the windows, and flat roofs to emphasize the buildings' horizontality. Porthole windows, pipe railings, sun decks, and flagstaff finials brought the glamour of transatlantic ocean liners like the *Normandie* and *Île de France* to tropical dry dock. In his design for the Cardozo Hotel (1939), Henry Hohauser applied windowless portholes as ornament for the top storey, and at the Nevon Hotel (1940), he put functioning octagonal portholes at both sides of the entrance. The Senator Hotel (1939), designed by L. Murray Dixon, was a humorous mixture, which included porthole openings, a swimming pool guarded by pipe railings, and a freestanding fountain in the shape of a pelican, which spewed water into a catch basin shaped like a seashell at the main entrance.

By the early forties, Miami Beach seemed ready to recover some of its earlier architectural dignity. Igor Polevitzky and T. Trip Russel's Shelborne Hotel (1941) was a spirited synthesis drawn from the best European and South American Modernist work. A Russian-born architect trained in Philadelphia at the University of Pennsylvania, Polevitzky revealed himself a master of the new machine aesthetic. Gone were the porthole windows and curving façade of his firm's earlier Albion Hotel (1940). Here was a sophisticated design with strip windows and sharp right-angle corners that suggested the vitality and purity of technology. But purity and technological determinism were probably not what sun-starved holiday seekers craved. No one understood this more clearly than the architect who fashioned a new aesthetic identity for Miami — Morris Lapidus.

Born in Odessa, Russia, in 1903, Lapidus grew up in New York City, spending summer vacations at the farm-hotels in the Catskill Mountains that he later admitted were the basis for his concept of resort luxury. Abandoning his childhood ambition of becoming an actor, he studied architecture at Columbia University with the intention of entering the field of set design but failed to find employment in the theater. He worked briefly as a draftsman for the firm of Warren & Wetmore in New York before developing a national career designing storefronts and their interiors, in which he pioneered the use of bright colors, lights, and sweeping

During the thirties, the Mediterranean Revival buildings of Miami Beach were abandoned for a new, sleek style. Art Deco details such as round windows (*left*) and scalloped trim (*right*) became common elements of design.

Architect Morris Lapidus understood the vacationer's needs and strove to instill his Florida designs with elements of fantasy. Here he stands in the lightwell of the Americana Hotel in Bal Harbor. The Fontainebleau (*right*) is his massive twelve-storey curved slab in Miami Beach. The French Baroque garden in front seems to be the only evidence of a hotel design that he termed "modern French château."

curvilinear forms to stimulate retail activity. At a time when most architects followed Mies van der Rohe's oracular pronouncement that "less is more" and stripped their buildings to conform to an ascetic, universal, machine-inspired antidecorative style, Lapidus unabashedly decorated his work to imbue projects with fantasy and excitement.

In 1948 his career as a designer of hotels began when he was hired to serve as interior designer and associate architect for the Sans Souci hotel in Miami Beach. Lapidus would later recall,

I could enlarge upon all the theories that I had been developing about human nature and the emotional hunger that the average man had for visual excitement and personal adornment. . . . I did not have to sell shirts or panties or coats or hats. . . . I was convinced that just as a store had to be designed to make people want to buy what the merchant had to sell, so a hotel had something to sell also. What was that something? A home away from home? Absolutely not! Who wants a homey feeling on a vacation? . . . forget the office, the house, the kids, the bills. Anything but that good old homey feeling that the old hotels used to sell.[22]

The Sans Souci's interior incorporated many of the features Lapidus had exploited in his store designs. He had observed that people liked to meander more than walk in straight lines, so the lobby curved and the carpets were cut as asymmetrical "woggles" that evoked Salvador Dali's surrealistic shapes. Lapidus's "proven moth theory"[23] that people will always move toward light led him to lure customers to the dining room, cocktail lounge, and nightclub with brightly lit entrances. Lapidus's other signature elements were "bean poles," in this case supporting wire-mesh planters meant to be bird cages, and "cheese holes," cove-lit hollows in the ceiling.

Often following the instructions of his clients, Lapidus filled his Miami Beach hotels with references to European and American historical styles, which he interpreted in refreshing, if unorthodox, ways. Lapidus understood his clientele; he knew that the new batch of Florida vacationers, a newly rich middle class, wanted the grand scale and stylistic dandyism of Carl Fisher's salad days, but souped up and dressed down to suit a more informal lifestyle. To Lapidus, a resort hotel was not so much a theater as a Hollywood sound stage: "People are looking for illusions; they don't want the world's realities. . . . Where are their tastes formulated? Do they study it in school? Do they go to museums? Do they travel in Europe? Only one place — the movies. They go to the movies. The hell with everything else."[24]

At the Hotel Fontainebleau (1954), Lapidus reached his zenith. Responding to his client's request for a "modern French château" style, Lapidus invented a vision of an architectural past that never existed, squeezing a massive twelve-storey curved slab onto a sliver of Miami Beach sand. The "Frenchness" of the hotel was most apparent in a French Baroque garden — Americanized with flowers blooming in red, white, and blue — and the occasional decorative adornment. Lapidus's design synthesized these elements into an environment like none known before. With its undulating form, so strikingly in contrast to the ordinary

At the opulent Eden Roc hotel in Miami Beach, architect Morris Lapidus used standard elements of Classical architecture in an unconventional way. In the lobby, shown here, the fluted columns had neither bases nor capitals and functioned only as purely decorative light fixtures.

buildings of the workaday world, its landscaping, and, most powerfully, its interiors, Lapidus's design fulfilled and helped define expectations of a glamorous resort. Never mind that this resort château closely resembled a low-income housing project in Brazil designed by one of that country's leading Modernists (Eduardo Alfonso Reidy's Pedregulho housing development, Rio de Janeiro, 1950), it was the decoration and not the mass that would create the mood.

The Fontainebleau's interior transformed guests into movie stars as they glided through the pink, slate, and gold lobby over a bow-tie-patterned floor, inspired by Lapidus's own sartorial trademark. A marble staircase swirled past a blown-up Piranesi print to nowhere in particular: "The stairway . . . was the influence of Busby Berkeley," Lapidus has recently recalled. It didn't "go anyplace . . . [but] the people really loved walking up and down." Luxuriating in his triumph as a designer of permanent stage sets, Lapidus was pleased by the comment of Hollywood director Joseph L. Mankiewicz: "You know, Mr. Lapidus, I would shoot a picture right in this lobby. I wouldn't change a thing. I wouldn't even bring lights in."[25] Hollywood eventually caught up with Lapidus by filming a sequence of *Goldfinger* (1964) at the Fontainebleau.

Harry Mufson, who had been Ben Novak's partner in the Sans Souci hotel, vowed to outshine his estranged partner's Fontainebleau by building an even more luxurious hotel, called the Eden Roc, on the beachfront immediately to the north. Mufson hired Lapidus as his architect, enraging Novak, who declared the Fontainebleau off-limits to his former architect as he had done years before to his former partner. Mufson told Lapidus that he wanted crystal and marble assembled with the same "European" glamour as at the "French Provincial" edifice next door. Lapidus showed him photographs of Italian Renaissance palazzos. Mufson liked them, but disliked the "heavy ornament."[26] When Lapidus asked his client if he objected to the Baroque influence, Mufson replied, "I don't care if it's Baroque or Brooklyn, but give me something that will knock them flat on their backsides when they walk in."[27] The commission took Lapidus on his first trip to Europe, during which he bought bronze and marble statues in Florence and crystal chandeliers and glass in Venice, which he shipped to Florida to add to the Eden Roc's screamingly deluxe appointments.

At the Eden Roc, Lapidus's unorthodox interpretation of standard elements of Classical architecture appeared in the marble staircase, where balusters were of such delicate metal construction that they seemed ghostlike between the massive stairs and the bold banister they supported. The lobby's rotunda, the focus of the hotel, relied on architectural phantoms as well. The fluted columns that defined the center of the room had neither base nor capital. With the thin square bearing columns they encased illuminated at the top, they were revealed as grand, purely decorative light fixtures. While never eclipsing the Fontainebleau, the Eden Roc joined it as representative of the best Miami Beach had to offer in service and vacation fantasy.

In his design for the Americana Hotel (1956), located in Bal Harbor, two miles north of Miami Beach, Lapidus abandoned the European past, looking south of the border for inspiration instead. Lapidus had previously utilized the basic forms of Brazilian Modernist architecture, but at the Americana, all twenty-one countries in the Western Hemisphere were represented in native materials and decorative motifs, including even unexotic Canada, symbolized by a maple-paneled dining room articulated with maple leaf patterns. The Carioca lounge had a swirling mosaic floor reminiscent of Brazil's plazas, while the Gaucho Room had walls covered with leather tile and decorated with bullhead ornaments. Lapidus's signature grand staircase was here walled on the outside by terra-cotta-colored Mayan-inspired carvings in sand-molded concrete and circled the hotel's focal point, a lushly planted forty-foot-high terrarium open to the sun and rain and home to baby alligators — second best to the monkeys that the architect had originally intended.

While most of the public loved Lapidus's work, fellow architects loathed it. He had, they charged, betrayed Modernism, applying decoration with a thorough disregard for structural considerations. All Lapidus's efforts to entertain, to create, as he stated, "a tasteful three-ring circus,"[28] seemed to most architects and critics to be at best misguided and at worst evidence that he had thoroughly sold out. Ada Louise Huxtable, the architecture critic for the *New York Times,* assessing Lapidus's work, wrote that "one man's joy is another man's hell. I have never felt more joyless than in Miami . . . I was depressed in direct ratio of aesthetic illiteracy and hokey pretensions to the shoddiness of the execution. I got a terrible case of the Fountainblues."[29] But Lapidus's genius for reinterpreting disparate architectural elements and for creating what has been called "an architecture of joy" has of late attracted some supporters. And it is undeniable that within the seeming glibness of hotels like the Fontainebleau stands a powerful embodiment of the same American dreams of escape and glamour that have inspired the resort builders since Saratoga to design some of the most original and inventive architecture produced in this country.

Florida's architecture of escape — into the Mediterranean vision of Mizner or the Hollywood musical and costume drama mélange of Lapidus — has reached a climax of sorts in the creation of one of the most inspired dream merchants, Walt Disney. In 1965, ten years after he had opened Disneyland in Anaheim, California, Disney, at the age of sixty-four, bought 27,433 acres fifteen miles south of Orlando, Florida, and immodestly declared his plans for the property "the greatest thing to happen to the state of Florida since Ponce de León."[30] Where the first Disneyland in Anaheim had merely entertained, the new park would also instruct. The first site in Walt Disney's "World," as he dubbed it, was Main Street, U.S.A., a one-eighth-mile-long time trip down Memory Lane, lined with carefully detailed gingerbread buildings set at the turn of the century. It is the result of meticulous research and craft: the buildings were five-eighths to seven-eighths full size, a movie-set technique that made them friendlier to children while enhancing the common perception of adults that everything is smaller than they had remembered. Although it was essentially a re-creation of his hometown, Marceline, Missouri, where in his youth the street was muddy and the vistas marred by ugly telephone poles, it was now paved with resilient asphalt, the telephone and utility wires buried underground. Main Street is the heart of Walt Disney World and it is the key to the secret of the Disney vision. It represents a point in time when America seemed to have been simpler, clearer, and more coherent.

But to walk down Main Street costs money. As Charles Moore wryly observed in 1965 about Disney's first Main Street, "You have to pay [Disney] for the public life."[31] And yet, you have a good time. It's amazing. It's a shared experience. It's

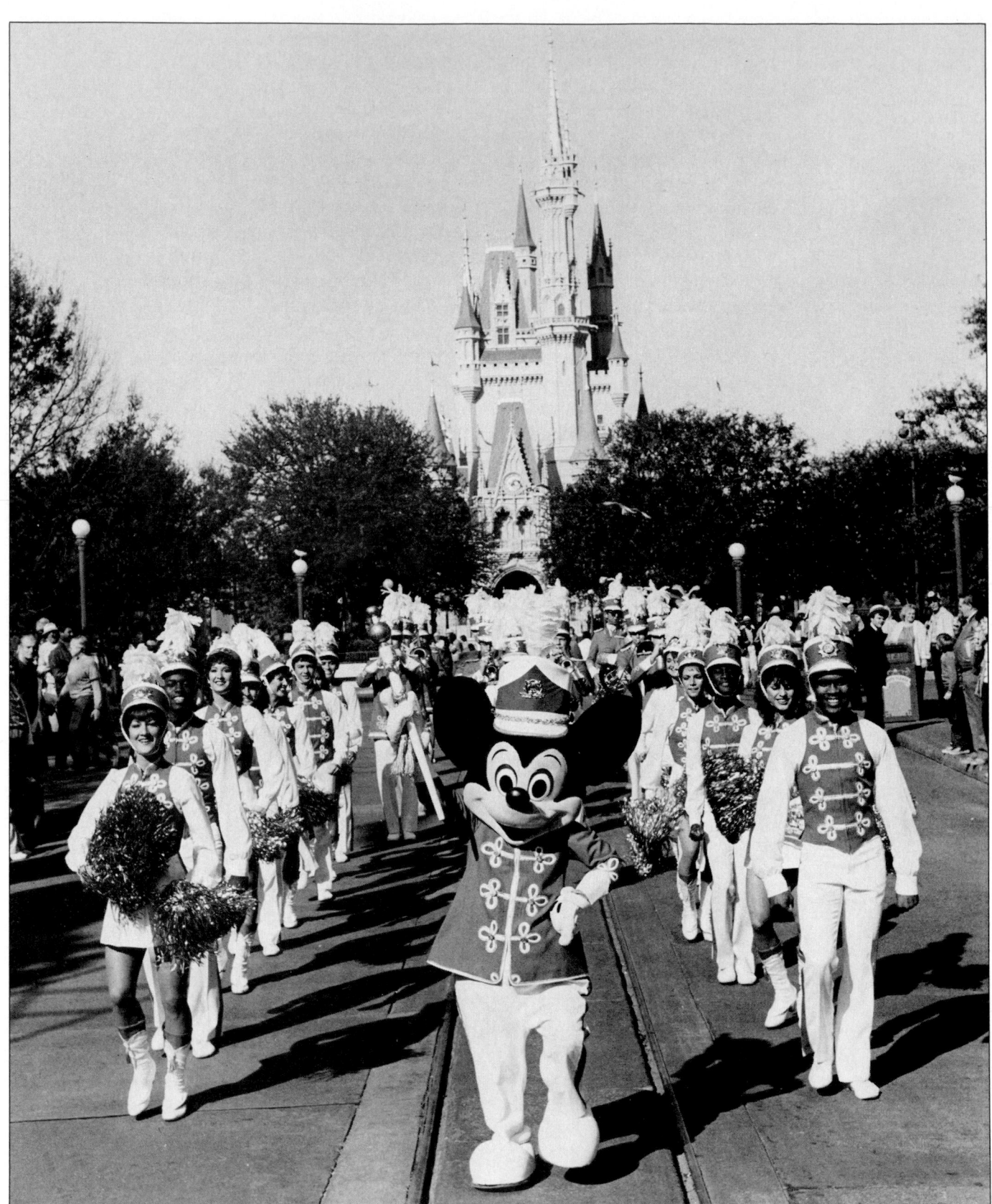

what resorts are about. And Disney, more than anyone else in our time, captured the resort experience for a wide audience.

As in any great theatrical enterprise, backstage at Disney World is almost as fascinating as what appears on the stage itself. The technology of the underground area that Disney and his so-called imagineers devised is remarkable. In a lesson for any modern city planner, a network of subterranean roads connects all the pavilions, allowing the workers to move around unseen by the guests. Sewage is treated by a tertiary plant that recycles the effluent to water and fertilizes the experimental farms and forests, and garbage is sucked through pneumatic tubes to a smokeless incinerator. And everywhere the rides, which combine entertainment with pragmatic transportation, are powered by clean energy: monorails, paddle steamers (not operated by steam), and electronic carts.

Disney World is a complete resort, where the dream never ends so long as the guest pays the bills. When a day of traveling around Disney World draws to a close, guests can retire via monorail to one of two Disney-controlled resort hotels. The Contemporary, a fifteen-storey concrete A-frame, penetrated by the monorail, contains a vast ten-storey atrium fittingly called the Grand Canyon Concourse surrounded by one thousand prefabricated fourteen-foot-wide module-rooms, which fetishize the impersonality of modern life. The other Disney World hotel, the Polynesian, is made out of the same modules, now slipped not into a megastructural A-frame but beneath the fake-thatch roofs of nine low longhouses. At this manmade island paradise, water flows over rocky precipices to create quiet pools for swimming, and, in case of rain, a tropical waterfall can be found indoors.

Another monorail loop deposits visitors at EPCOT, the Experimental Prototype Community of Tomorrow, where visitors are asked to become Mousketeers of the future. But here the Disney magic disappears. It turns out to be more like a permanent world's fair than the research station twenty-five years ahead of its time that Disney had hoped it would be. Visitors arrive at the Geosphere, an eighteen-storey geodesic dome that mirrors Buckminster Fuller's vision of the future presented at Montreal's Expo '67. Arranged in a horseshoe around the Geosphere, pavilions sponsored by America's leading corporations are no more inspired.

Across the lagoon from EPCOT, the World Showcase offers a journey to major cities around the globe. Each nation is housed in a building that exemplifies its architecture. Historical accuracy is not the issue; Disney's designers exploited the scenographic techniques learned in Hollywood to present scaled-down and scrubbed-up versions of the world's most familiar and symbolic buildings. In "Italy," the Doge's Palace and San Marco Campanile are in reverse position and the cathedral is left out altogether. In "France," the Eiffel Tower is shrunk to fit an exaggerated distant perspective. At the World Showcase, Disney offers us architecture on the comparative method: idealized versions of the world's great architecture that can be seen in a single glance serve to instruct and inspire. Disney's dream of teaching as he entertained has been accomplished, but ironically his lessons come from the past rather than the future. The unintentional lesson of EPCOT and Disney World as a whole is that the present is an impossible escape, the idealized future even more so. It is only by looking back to the past that the future is fully revealed.

6 The Great Places Within

Much more than the seat of government, the United States Capitol is our national pantheon, at once a theater for the public drama of political life and a secular church dedicated to the dream of continental empire. President Abraham Lincoln, who fully understood the symbolic power of the Capitol's Rotunda, commanded that work continue on the unfinished dome above it despite the exigencies of the Civil War, stating that "when people see the dome rising it will be a sign that we intend the union to go on."[1]

While some have argued that mass democracy has rendered the grand gestures of monumental public architecture obsolete, such clearly has not been the case in America. From its inception, American democracy has sought to legitimize itself as a stable, enduring form of governance by housing its functions in buildings formed out of the trappings of the palaces and cathedrals of the past. Absent a state religion or ruling aristocracy, the American struggle has been to lift the facts of everyday life — the ordinary activities of government and commerce — to the symbolic level of divine power. Absent the traditional institutions that shaped Europe's public places by framing squares and piazzas with cathedrals and palaces, America inverted the hierarchies of Europe: the public square itself became the glorious room inside the walls, rendering the Capitol's Rotunda at once a pantheon and a piazza — a national village square.

Just as its design reconstituted the outdoor stage of European public life in an interior room, the Capitol transformed the palatial hierarchies of corridor and room into great halls, interior streets, in effect, where the public and its legislators could mingle, converging in the Rotunda, which became the national crossroads of democratic power.

Yet, as the history of the Capitol's construction documents, American attitudes have been ambivalent toward symbolic public architecture. From its inception in 1792, the Capitol was a battleground for the vying forces of executive and legislative power and architectural ego. On Thomas Jefferson's advice, President George Washington decided that the design for the Capitol should be chosen through a competition. The bare-boned programmatic requirements gave the competitors enormous leeway, yet the crop of designs submitted by the July 15 deadline were condemned as dull and derivative by the president and the three district commissioners who formed the jury. Not until April 1793 did they find an acceptable entry, from the Philadelphia physician and amateur architect Dr. William Thornton. His design, while it lacked the chaste temple form of Jefferson's

In his elegant 1905 modernization of the lobby of Burnham & Root's Rookery building in Chicago, Frank Lloyd Wright replaced the Art Nouveau lighting fixtures with huge potted plants, added elaborate gold and ivory decorations, and formalized the lyrical, lacy railings with a bold geometric design.

Virginia State Capitol in Richmond, still impressed Washington and Jefferson as appropriately Classical, and hence American. Behind a simple Ionic temple front, Thornton inserted a low, pantheonic dome enclosing a rotunda — a room not called for in the competition's guidelines.

From the first the construction of the Capitol did little to instill confidence in the new government's capacity to realize the nation's political destiny in a convincing symbolic architecture. The competition's runner-up, Stephen Hallet, a professional architect, was given the compensatory role of supervising architect, a position he used to lay the building's foundations according to his own specifications rather than Thornton's. Thornton managed to have him dismissed, and the unending subsequent delays make President Washington's letter to the commissioners seem a plaintive cry: "It may be relied on, it is the progress of that building [the Capitol] that is to inspire or depress the public confidence."[2] Depressed it was, because Thornton fought every succeeding supervisory architect except himself during his brief tenure in the position, and his struggles, combined with congressional niggardliness, left the Capitol far from complete when the government installed itself in Washington in 1800.

When Benjamin H. Latrobe, an architect born and trained in England, took over in 1803, he set to work completing the House and Senate wings and began to plan the dome that was to rise between them, over the maze of foundations left by Thornton and his enemies. Championed by President Jefferson, Latrobe overcame most of Thornton's obstructions — even successfully suing him for libel — to reconstruct the Capitol according to his passion for Classical precedent, tempered by his admission that the "forms and the distribution of Roman & Greek Buildings which remain, are in general, inapplicable to the objects & uses of our public buildings."[3] Though he characterized himself as a willing "slavish copyist"[4] of the

This eighteenth-century engraving shows the Piazza del Campo in Siena. The public squares of Europe were framed with monumental cathedrals and palaces.

ISOMETRICAL VIEW OF THE PRINCIPAL FLOOR PLAN
UNITED STATES CAPITAL WITH THE EXTENSION.

Above. In the Classical plan for the United States Capitol, the Senate Chamber and House of Representatives flank the great central Rotunda, with grand corridors providing areas for public interaction.

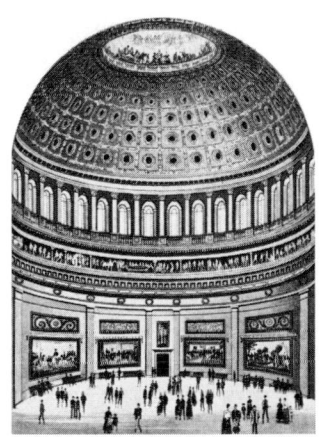

The Rotunda is both pantheon and piazza — a national village square. This 1891 lithograph shows the Rotunda's four historical paintings by John Trumbull.

Greeks, Latrobe went so far as to invent American versions of the Classical orders, with acanthus leaves giving way to corn, tobacco, and cotton as decorations on the column capitals.

After he was dismissed in 1812, Latrobe's greatest opportunity followed on the heels of catastrophe. The British burned the unfinished Capitol during the War of 1812, and in 1815 Latrobe was recalled to restore and complete the ruin. He recast the Senate and House wings and, most significant, established the design of the connecting rotunda before he was again forced out by commissioners jealous of his power, who saw to it that the new president, James Monroe, was angered at the pace of the reconstruction.

In 1818 the Boston architect Charles Bulfinch was called in. Bulfinch negotiated the quiet path of compromise. He stayed close to Latrobe's design, altering it only in extreme instances, such as when Congress threatened to chop the Rotunda into committee rooms if Bulfinch couldn't place them elsewhere in the plan. The integrity of the Rotunda was preserved, but the dome above it was higher than either Latrobe's original design or Bulfinch's wishes. Presenting a variety of schemes for the dome to the Cabinet, Bulfinch recalled their preference for the highest one, and there was "even a wish expressed that it might be raised higher still in a Gothic form."[5] The dome, which Bulfinch tried again to lower after the ribs were in place, was finished in 1828, still higher than he wanted, yet as a plain, wooden hemisphere sheathed in copper, free of Gothic forms.

But the dome's modest height of fifty-five feet above the Rotunda's walls could not satisfy the emotional demands of a democratic empire spreading clear across the continent to California. Nor could the Capitol itself encompass the swelling bureaucracies required to administer the country. In 1851, just after the

A statue of Abraham Lincoln stands in the Rotunda. The cast-iron dome that caps the room was modeled on St. Peter's in Rome and weighs approximately nine million pounds.

nation succeeded in realizing its continental destiny by admitting California as a state, Thomas Ustick Walter's plans for the Capitol's expansion, which included a new dome, were adopted. Walter's dome was an immense structure, modeled on St. Peter's in Rome, rising 285 feet. Despite its historical inspiration, it employed the latest technology, replacing masonry with cast iron.

On December 2, 1863, as the Civil War raged only a few miles away, President Lincoln presided over a ceremony celebrating the placement of Thomas Crawford's Statue of Freedom atop the new dome. Accompanied by a thirty-five-gun salute, intended not only to mark the occasion but also to hearten the languishing Union troops, many of them stricken with smallpox in their encampment on the Mall, Lincoln's grand ceremony was soon to be undercut by the tragedy of his assassination. He was laid out in state in the Rotunda, for decades a room without purpose, which now achieved its first full measure of significance.

With the Civil War's conclusion, America set out to reconstruct itself. At last it had a complete past of its own to idealize. Now the Rotunda would become a shrine to that past, within which the decentralized and ravaged country might seem whole. The panels between the Doric pilasters already included Colonel John Trumbull's four historical paintings of the Revolutionary era as well as other artists' views of other high-water marks of America's Colonial past, including the landing of the Pilgrims and the vanquishing of the Indians. American history-in-the-round recommenced above the cornice in a frieze by Constantino Brumidi, depicting *The Discovery and Settlement of the New World*. Brumidi also contributed the decoration of the canopy, *The Apotheosis of George Washington*, the florid grandiosity of which inspired Mark Twain to write that a visitor to the Rotunda exposed himself to "the delirium tremens of art."[6] Here at last, after seventy-four years of struggle, was a room magnificent enough to provide convincing evidence of the nation's capacity to govern and glorify; here at last was the building Jefferson had hoped for when he asked Latrobe for something "worthy of the first temple dedicated to the sovereignty of the people."[7]

The Capitol's newfound status reverberated across the country. While before the Civil War the individual states had pursued a variety of aesthetic directions, they now modeled their capitols closely on Washington's. Set between the states' bicameral legislatures, their rotundas focused the noble and not so noble machinations of government. Among the most obvious imitators were the Illinois State Capitol (1868–88) by J. C. Cochrane and Alfred H. Piquenard, Indiana's State Capitol (1878–88) by Elijah Myers, and the Texas State Capitol (1882–88), also by Myers, a pink granite leviathan that was the largest of state capitols.

What these capitols achieved in size and bravura they lacked in refinement. But Rhode Island, the smallest yet one of the richest states, memorialized its role as one of the founding thirteen by building a grandly Roman marble palace that brought to scholarly perfection the forms that had evolved in Washington for over seventy years. The Rhode Island State House (1892–1905) and its commanding site emulated the Capitol in Washington. McKim, Mead & White's design powerfully redefined the ideal of the state capitol, surpassing the domes and temple fronts of Illinois, Indiana, and Texas in its scholarly synthesis of ancient and modern Classical precedents. At the Rhode Island State House, the identical wings of the Senate and the House, with low domical skylights inspired by Latrobe's, flank the projecting entrance portico, surmounted by the loggia of the symbolic center of

The Rhode Island State House, designed by McKim, Mead & White, is a Roman marble palace that beautifully synthesizes ancient and modern Classical elements.

executive power, the Governor's Reception Room. The high central dome, which architecturally unites the three sources of governmental authority, is an interpretation of Michelangelo and Della Porta's St. Peter's in Rome, Wren's St. Paul's Cathedral in London, and Soufflot's Panthéon in Paris. Its scale was made more impressive by the figure of the Independent Man at its top and the tourelles at its sides. Entering the building from the center of either of its long sides, the visitor is pulled through lobbies, up flights of marble stairs, directly into the rotunda, which is in effect an ennobled stair landing, a crossroads in time and space. At right angles, two more flights of stairs ascend to the second storey, in opposite directions to the House and Senate chambers. Directly beneath the dome, the state seal is inlaid in brass, and, above, the four spandrels are decorated with painted medallions of four allegorical deities, Literature, Education, Justice, and Commerce. Higher, in the dome's drum, is a mural depicting the first settlement of Providence. Under this dome's grand historical panorama, the day-to-day deals that oil the wheels of government are made, putting the windy, high-minded speechifying where it probably belongs, in the wings.

The construction of enormous, unprecedentedly expensive state capitols as well as city halls, county courthouses, and other representative public buildings reverberated with federal ideals as well as federal boondoggles. In our own time, the fear of public criticism of governmental extravagance, together with an aesthetic contempt for the historical architectural symbols of government, has led to the construction of public architecture that is occasionally grand but, usually, symbolically incomprehensible. Kallmann, McKinnell & Knowles's Boston City Hall (1963–69) has no dome, no rotunda, no colonnade, no pediment. For precedents, it looks to two twentieth-century architectural monuments by Le Corbusier: La Tourette, a French monastery, and the Assembly Building at Chandigarh, the capital of India's Punjab state. An exercise in grandiloquent gestures rendered in brutalist concrete, it does, however, contain an impressive five-storey lobby that is an interior extension of the overscaled red brick plaza outside. The lobby space is public, the setting for occasional musical performances and exhibitions, but its unornamented surfaces and fragmented configuration diminish its impact as a room. Boston's City Hall does not celebrate the glories of the past nor does it convey a sense of boundless optimism about the future; rather, it confronts us with the all too harsh reality of the present.

I. M. Pei's Dallas City Hall (1975–78) is also designed around a large hall, with its gravitationally unnerving, outward-canting mass promising little solace beyond shade. Inside, its hundred-foot-high, toplit Great Court, reached by a two-storey escalator, is surrounded by balconies green with plantings, a setting that at least adds drama if not traditional symbolic resonance to the government services frequented by the public. But it offers too little in the way of symbolic reference: the space and the walls that bound it are wonderful for what they are — clean, well-lighted spaces. But they lack the symbolic dimension that unites the modest county courthouse or town hall of the nineteenth century to the grand places of public administration and enterprise, most notably the Capitol in Washington.

Ironically, while Boston and Dallas have forgone the traditional representations of governmental authority that Classicism conveys, the corporate world has never been particularly embarrassed by the possibilities inherent in a show of power using Classical architecture. Perhaps the shyness of the public

Above. The outward-canting exterior mass of I. M. Pei's modern Dallas City Hall provides shade for passers-by but no reference to the architectural traditions of earlier public administration buildings. Inside, the Great Court (*right*) provides a clean, well-lit space surrounded by balconies planted with greenery.

sector and the enthusiasm of the private realm are as they should be, given President Calvin Coolidge's supposition that "the business of America is business." Not surprisingly, then, that as governments house themselves in anonymous office blocks or ambiguous monuments, a major corporation, General Foods, should choose as the model for its world headquarters a building not so very different from Bulfinch's version of the Capitol. Clad in brilliant white vinyl–clad panels — the same aluminum siding that sheathes millions of suburban ranch houses — Kevin Roche and John Dinkeloo's General Foods Headquarters (1983), in Rye, New York, sits high on a manmade podium of parked automobiles. Climaxing the sprawling floors of offices, a ninety-five-foot-high rotunda rises above the entrance. Lacking a grand theme to symbolize, Roche Dinkeloo's central rotunda is a corporate living room that relies on shape and size to impress visitors and inspire employees. It includes a grand double staircase, galleries whose balustrades drip with greenery, and a show of mirrors, from the planters to the dome's glittery finish, that visually dematerialize the building's structure. Roche has spoken less about the brash symbolism of the building's exterior than the communality of the interior. "I am very interested in the idea of the corporate headquarters as a house . . . the community space in an office building corresponds to the living and dining area of the house."[8] The atrium is a dining room — a four-hundred-seat cafeteria — and a living room, for the guests who come on the public tours and for the employees within a firmly hierarchical house. The atrium's seventh-floor gallery of Roche Dinkeloo's twisted rotunda offers a lesson in who is calling the shots. Executives occupy the pantheonic heights, exuberantly identifying their role with that of the gods and heroes normally depicted in the murals and friezes encircling the drum of a dome.

Given the national split personality, dedicated to both the Hamiltonian realities of moneymaking and the Jeffersonian idealism of a self-sufficient agrarian Arcadia, it is not surprising that General Foods, seeking to express the American-ness of its business enterprise, assumes the mantle of Classicism. Almost since the dawn of the Republic, private wealth has not only aggrandized its position with Classical architecture, it has also provided the majority of the public settings — the piazzas, arcades, palm courts, atria — that enable most Americans to escape from the privacy and the loneliness of the home and the farm and share, at least for a while, public life. Many of our great public meeting places have been created and maintained by commercial enterprises. In fact, in a land of "private affluence and public squalor," to use John Kenneth Galbraith's phrase, the Capitol is an anomaly.

No architect mastered the closed system of a skylit sanctuary dedicated to the work ethic better than Frank Lloyd Wright, who created a research and administration center for the Johnson Wax Company in Racine, Wisconsin. The complex of the main building (1936–39) and tower (1950), almost a city within the city, turns its back on the drab Midwestern downtown to create a hermetically sealed interior world. Here space was rendered virtually tangible; the employees almost float in a toplit windowless room. Punctuated by lily-pad-like columns that blossom into disks beneath the roof of bundled glass tubes, the room has a subaqueous quality that gives new meaning to the phrase "typing pool." The Johnson Wax Building renders the eight-hour workday more an escape into a dreamlike ideality than a daily chore.

Entered through a carport whose cavelike opening is the only break in the complex's brick screen walls, the visitor continues to the garage, which has its own lily-pad columns, or walks through a transitional passage to the main workroom. The original building supplemented the day-to-day work space with an auditorium and squash courts, and after 1950 the complex included a fourteen-storey laboratory tower, where new techniques for making shoes and floors shinier are explored. It rises as a campanile for the wax empire's city as well as the city of Racine. The laboratory tower is as maniacally introverted as the atrium, with its translucent walls wrapped in glass tubes that block any outward view.

The same year that the Johnson Wax laboratory tower was completed, Wright's first great office building was demolished. The red brick Larkin

The General Foods Headquarters in Rye, New York, designed by Kevin Roche and John Dinkeloo, evoked Classical models in an unembarrassed show of power.

Right. The interior of the main building at the Johnson Wax Company's research and administration center in Racine, Wisconsin, represents Frank Lloyd Wright's ideal of communality in a controlled environment sealed off from the outside world. The large, windowless room is punctuated by lily-pad columns that blossom into disks beneath a roof of bundled glass tubes, giving the space a dreamlike quality.

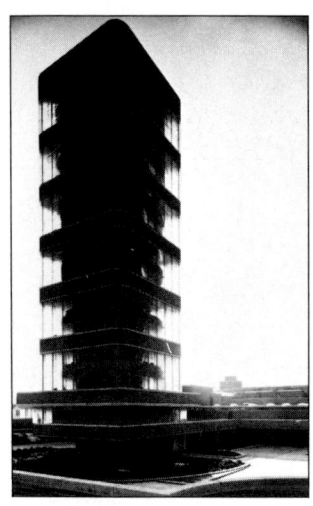

In 1950 Wright added a fourteen-storey laboratory tower to the Johnson Wax Company's complex. Its translucent walls are wrapped in glass tubes that obstruct any outward views.

Administration Building (1903–6), in Buffalo, New York, had pioneered the ideals of communality and environmental control that Wright had used in the Johnson Wax buildings. Across the street from the Larkin Soap and Mail Order Company's factories, the Administration Building confronted Buffalo's bleak industrial landscape with a tough, clifflike exterior held in at the corners by four massive, hollow piers that contained the staircases as well as the vertical ducts that provided fresh air year round. From this hard, bright, exterior world, the employee would, as Vincent Scully has written, travel

toward interior dimness beyond which, to the left, somewhat more light could be perceived filtering down between the central piers. These then rise up towards their rich capitals in a climactic spatial expansion, lighted from above as in Roman buildings and creating, as those also did, an idealized interior space cut off from the world outside.[9]

The building was organized around an atrium. On the main floor, Larkin Company employees sat at long desks directly beneath the skylight; above them, the rest of the staff was arranged around this great hall in galleries, from which they could view the humming human machine they collectively constituted. They couldn't look outside because the windows were above eye level, sitting or standing, and the deep banks of file cabinets were beneath them. When weary of the view of their fellow employees or the distant sky framed by the clerestory, they could raise their eyes to the hortatory inscription of the Golden Rule at the top floor where the restaurant was located: "Whatsoever ye would that others should do unto you, Do you even so unto them" — a fitting admonition in a building that resembled a church of work.

Wright's glazed interiors were private communal worlds sealed off from the city. The climate-controlled public square for the entire city was the shopping arcade. The Cleveland Arcade (1888–90) reveled in giantism and structural expression, surpassing the scale of the greatest European arcade, the Galleria Vittorio Emmanuele II (1865–67), in Milan. The architects, John Eisenmann and George H. Smith, designed a five-level, glass-roofed street, 290 feet long, 60 feet wide, and 104 feet high. The lower two floors, each a main floor because of a 12-foot change in level between the two outside avenues, contained space for a hundred shops, while the galleried floors above were chiefly for professional and office use. Decoration was spare, limited to the wrought iron railings and lighting fixtures. In addition, fifty-four gargoyles, holding incandescent bulbs in their mouths, marked the ends of the roof's trussed arches.

Arcades had been built in Paris as early as 1799 and in London in 1816, but these were chiefly midblock passages squeezing through buildings to connect important institutions, like the Passage des Panoramas (1810) and Passages de l'Opéra (1822) in Paris and the Royal Opera Arcade (1816–18) in London. American arcades, by contrast, were not merely a commercial distraction on the way to the theater but the focus of large commercial blocks, in effect prototypical shopping malls.

The Providence Arcade (1827–29) in Rhode Island's capital, the only one of the four American arcades built in the 1820s to survive into this century, exemplifies the American transformation of the arcade more than any other: a temple of consumerism, it shelters a stadiumlike arrangement of tiered shops that at once glorifies the consumer and puts his or her every act of consumption onstage.

James C. Bucklin, the younger partner in the Providence firm of Russell Warren & William Tallman, traveled to Philadelphia and New York in 1826 to sketch America's first two arcades, both designed by John Haviland in the 1820s. The original elevations he and his partners submitted to the builder, Cyrus Butler, matched the arched entryways of the earlier designs. In the end, however, Warren, who would become best known for his lavish private residences in Bristol, and Bucklin, who would build many Providence landmarks and maintain his Providence office until 1890, collaborated on a design in which the façades on both Westminster and Weybosset streets were dominated by six smooth, monolithic, twenty-two-foot-high granite columns, the largest stone columns in the New World at the time, topped by Ionic capitals, modeled on the temple on the Ilissus at Athens. On the Westminster Street side, a Classical Greek pediment rose above the colonnade while, on Weybosset Street, Warren and Bucklin terminated the elevation in horizontal stone panels. Significantly, the Arcade was not squeezed in between existing buildings but set at the edge of the existing business district, an independent icon that nonetheless served as a focus for the future growth its blank side walls anticipated. The aspirations for monumentality that led residents to call the structure "Butler's folly" didn't hinder the technological currency of the design, as clearly visible behind the columns as the freestanding stairways that led to the upper tiers of shops, beneath the pitched roof of glass. Commercially, the Arcade was folly, only reaching ninety percent occupancy in 1870, after it had stood for decades waiting for Providence's business district to catch up with it. As a symbol

The Larkin Administration Building in Buffalo, New York, built in 1903–6 and demolished in 1950, was Wright's first great office building design. Organized around a large, skylit atrium, the building resembled a church of work.

of civic life, however, it was a great success, and its popularity staved off the wrecking ball in 1944, when an office building threatened to replace it.

By the 1970s, the Arcade had undergone three unsympathetic twentieth-century renovations, and its status had skidded downward from temple of consumerism to dingy passageway. The successful transformation in 1974–78 of Alexander Parris's 1824–26 Quincy Market in Boston (Benjamin Thompson & Associates) inspired Providence to revitalize the Arcade as a downtown center of restaurants, shops, and professional offices. The Providence architectural firm of Irving Haynes & Associates brought the Arcade up to contemporary standards of environmental control by adding glass curtain walls to both ends to enclose the stairwells; and the Arcade Company, whose executives had learned their lessons as former employees of the Rouse Company, which had developed Boston's Quincy Market, orchestrated the precise mix of tenants so that rites of the temple, which reopened in 1980, are once again honored.

The contemporary shopping mall is a community center for suburbanites, giving them a version of the great interior public places that their urban ancestors enjoyed. The suburban mall, however, unlike its urban antecedents, has no necessary relation to an existing town; all that is needed is a crossroads, preferably between two superhighways, and plenty of space for parking.

Some malls have succeeded as simulacra of town centers. Best known as a palace of fabulous consumption, Houston's Galleria is the air-conditioned heart of a complex of hotels and offices in a section of suburban-scaled Houston that was prairie thirty years ago. As originally designed in 1969–72 by the St. Louis firm of Hellmuth, Obata & Kassabaum, the Galleria consists of stores, shops, and restaurants grouped on three levels along a six-hundred-foot skylit arcade loosely modeled after the vaulted enclosures of nineteenth-century arcades. But while the prototypes merely enclose a few blocks of public street, Houston's is a self-contained world virtually unto itself. Sealed off from the larger network of city streets, the Galleria's main street describes to the average consumer a short but pricey journey from a Neiman-Marcus department store at one end to a Lord & Taylor at the other, with hotels and office buildings along the way. To the wider world, the Galleria development presents a blank façade facing a parking lot. Only the internal street raises the blank, anonymous, warehouselike boxy forms to the level of architecture.

Inside the Galleria, hot, humid, congested Houston simply doesn't exist. Castigated by critic Paul Goldberger as a "canned city,"[10] it not only shares precious little but skylights with the earlier arcades but also with its namesake, the Galleria Vittorio Emmanuele II in Milan. The Galleria offers climate control Texas style, with an 80-by-170-foot ice-skating rink that encourages shoppers to believe that every day in Houston is like Christmas at Rockefeller Center. Admirers of the fit and wealthy can also look up through the skylight to the rooftop jogging track, where dues-paying members of the University Club exercise. Stores like Tiffany and Cartier conspire in the belief that everything that's wonderful can happen indoors: an easily digested meal, yet less satisfying than the movable feast that a city street can be.

In the 1960s and 1970s, the advocates of mall development argued, with some justification, that the downtown street had ceased to exist in America's cities. In fact, municipal planners across the country, faced by decaying city cores, were exercising their political and economic power to bring the mall downtown. In some respects, the new inner-city malls were merely returning the type to where it had begun.

The Tabor Center in Denver is a complex of one hotel and two office towers connected by a 500-foot-long, 75-foot-high glazed gallery of shops. It is a Providence Arcade for the postmodern age. Built on the site of a former urban gathering place, the Daniels & Fisher Department Store, whose twenty-one-storey tower (Frederick G. Sterner, 1911) was retained as a campanile, it presides over the glass and granite shopping basilica, designed in 1984 by the Urban Design Group of Tulsa, Oklahoma. Approached from the street by escalators, the glass-roofed and -walled galleria space exemplifies the arcade's twin characteristics: it is an enclosed street and a great public room.

In the nineteenth century, American urbanites flocked to the urbane predecessor of the contemporary shopping mall, the department store. It was a perfectly controlled indoor world where the wares and services of the interiorized street were organized under a single management. The origins of the department store arguably began in Cincinnati, where in 1829, only a year after the Providence Arcade was dedicated, Mrs. Frances Trollope, an imperious Englishwoman, set up a new kind of shop, which she called the Bazaar. Mrs. Trollope, who would later write a scathing assessment of what she experienced in her *Domestic Manners of the Americans* (1832), decided to bring high culture to the wilds and profit to herself by opening the Bazaar, which she dedicated to trade, business, and culture. Its twenty-four-foot-high dome, which lived up to the store's Middle Eastern name by the placement of a Turkish crescent at its top, enclosed a four-storey rotunda meant to organize multiple functions under one symbolic roof. A commercial failure from the start, it had become, by the 1861 visit of Mrs. Trollope's son, the novelist Anthony, "a 'Physico-medical Institute' . . . under the dominion of a quack doctor on one side, and of a college of rights-of-women female medical professors on the other."[11]

Much more successful as both a commercial and architectural prototype, Alexander Turney Stewart's department store, known as the Marble Palace, opened in New York in 1846. Built on the "penny side" of Broadway, on the northeast corner of Chambers Street, the store was designed by John B. Snook and Joseph Trench. Its impressive façade of Corinthian columns, with unprecedentedly large plate glass display windows between them, easily lured rich customers from the exclusive shops opposite as did Stewart's policy of advertising his prices and holding to them, freeing customers from the embarrassing uncertainties of bargaining and selecting items beyond their means. Stewart's had the dignity of a dome rising ninety feet above the main hall, associating it with the public monuments of New York's City Hall (1802–11), which was just across the street, and the Merchants' Exchange (1838–42), farther downtown.

No American department store of the mid–nineteenth century was as spatially grand as the Parisian department store Bon Marché (1869–80), which was, as Émile Zola described it, "la cathédrale du commerce moderne."[12] Yet by the end of the century, America once again led the way. Marshall Field's department store in Chicago incorporated the lessons of Stewart's and Bon Marché in its presentation of shopping as theater and fair. Its first incarnation was under the direction of Potter Palmer, who went to Chicago in 1852 after having worked for Stewart in

The Galleria Vittorio
Emmanuele II in Milan,
built in 1865–67, is the
greatest of all European
arcades and a prototype for
the modern shopping mall.
The facade and arched
entryway (*above*) led to
interior streets (*right*) lined
with restaurants and shops
beneath a vaulted glass
roof.

New York. In 1863, Palmer built a marble palace for shopping on State Street, which he leased to his former partners, Marshall Field and Levi Leiter. The Great Fire toppled that one, and its replacement, a six-storey edifice, burned to the ground in 1877. The eight-storey, stone-faced monument that replaced it, decorated with Classical details and heroic statuary, became Marshall Field's in 1882 with the withdrawal of Leiter. Almost a city within a city, Marshall Field's was a woman's world where the management devoted themselves to "giving the lady what she wants." The store manager, Gordon Selfridge, and the merchant prince himself, Marshall Field, presided over the artful display; far from disdaining to talk with customers, they considered their own personalities integral to the store's identity.

In 1893, Daniel H. Burnham's Old Annex extended the store the length of Washington Street in a tough, palazzo design similar to Marshall Field's wholesale store by Henry Hobson Richardson, completed six years before. A decade later, Burnham extended the store the length of State Street, this time with a Classical façade that included a portico of colossal, monolithic Ionic columns. They rendered the 1878 building absurd, and in 1906 it was demolished to make way for the main store as it stands today, a commanding block-long façade of stone and glass that rests on a base of large shop windows punctuated by two-storey pilasters. Chicago's street grid was raised to three dimensions inside, articulated in piazzalike light wells that were lavish, dizzyingly vertical interior rooms. A mosaic dome of iridescent glass rose five storeys above one galleried piazza; the north well rose thirteen storeys to a skylight. To further articulate the grid, customers were courted by luxurious specialty shops. Fifty elevators made sure that pampered customers and fresh stock kept circulating; as a national magazine observed in 1907, Marshall Field's was "more than a store. It was an exposition, a school of courtesy, a museum of modern commerce."[13]

On the strength of his ongoing success at Field's, Burnham was summoned to Philadelphia, where between 1902 and 1910 he provided John Wanamaker, who had an extremely successful but architecturally undistinguished department store, with a twelve-storey palazzo that Burnham described as "the most monumental commercial structure erected anywhere in the world."[14] Burnham's enthusiasm was matched by that of the store's founder, and the December 30, 1911, dedication ceremony, held long after the building was finished in order to coincide with the store's fiftieth anniversary, included President William H. Taft on its roster of luminaries as well as an array of Chicago dignitaries who chartered a private train to travel to Philadelphia for the occasion.

The monument they celebrated epitomized the potential of the department store to constitute a dreamworld where one could spend an entire day, not only shopping for every kind of item, but meeting friends, listening to a concert, or dining in the luxurious Crystal Dining Room, which seated 350 customers in the self-satisfied atmosphere of a private club. In the five-storey Grand Court, a monumental atrium framed by balconies supported by a profusion of fluted columns, piers, and pilasters, the world's largest organ, brought from the 1904 St. Louis World's Fair, supplied music at a volume equal to the architecture.

Merchants like Field and Wanamaker, who orchestrated the transformation of the utilitarian dry goods store into a palace of consumption, were canny enough to realize that labor-saving devices combined with cheap domestic help were

Right. The Arcade in Providence, Rhode Island, sheltered a stadiumlike arrangement of tiered shops under a pitched roof of glass. It is the only American arcade built in the 1820s still standing today.

The Arcade was a temple of consumerism set at the edge of Providence's business district. Its two principal façades were dominated by twelve monolithic granite columns, modeled on a Greek temple.

enabling affluent women, long relegated to the domestic hearth, to assume a major role in the urban drama. Politicians and lawyers could act out their public roles in the templelike settings of statehouse and courthouse, merchants and bankers could pursue their tasks in equally impressive surroundings, and now, with the department store, women could play their part in a setting that was the equivalent and more. All that was lacking to complete the scenario was a place where men and women could socialize together in public: this was provided by the grand hotel, a distinctly American invention.

The very word "hotel" is an American coinage by which the idea of an inn or tavern was elevated to the status of the French *hôtel particulier*, a nobleman's house, or *hôtel de ville*, a city hall. As early as 1827, the *National Intelligencer* in Washington, D.C., editorialized on the phenomenon of the American hotels, calling them "the palaces of the People." More than a resting place for travelers, they have traditionally served as the preeminent social meeting ground of American cities. The great suites of rooms are the sites of the balls, receptions, and dinners of the local populace. Quite frequently in nascent urban areas, with municipal government too weak, poor, or disinclined to invest in monuments to the town's dream of its future, it was the hotel that came to shelter and symbolize a growing city. Anthony Trollope remarked upon the phenomenon in North America:

In the States of America the first sign of an incipient settlement is a hotel five stories high, with an office, a bar, a cloak-room, three gentlemen's parlours, two ladies' parlours, a ladies' entrance, and two hundred bedrooms. . . . Whence are to come the sleepers in those two hundred bedrooms, and who is to pay for the gaudy sofas . . . ? In all other countries the expectations would extend itself simply to travelers; to travelers or to strangers sojourning in the land. But this is by no means the case as to these speculations in America. When the new hotel rises up in the wilderness, it is presumed that people will come there with the express object of inhabiting it. The hotel itself will create a population . . . as the railways do.[15]

Pictured here is Chicago's Marshall Field's department store in its final and current form. Burnham remodeled the original 1878 building in 1903, adding the Classical facade with massive Ionic columns. Considered an anachronism, the building was torn down in 1906 and replaced with a gridded structure of stone and glass.

The Tremont House in Boston (1827–29) was the first to fully shed the humble image of the inn and replace it with that of a luxurious hotel that could be a municipal asset and a source of civic pride. There was no doubt in the minds of its builders that the Tremont had an important public role in the life of the city and the nation. Its cornerstone was laid on July 4, a date that became traditional among hotel builders. When the Tremont opened on October 16, 1829, it held a great banquet that included such public luminaries as Senator Daniel Webster. Designed by Isaiah Rogers, it sheltered grand public rooms behind a Classical four-storey façade so obviously monumental that it needed no sign to announce its presence. Inside, the luxury of private rooms with locking doors, free soap, and gas lights was matched by the grandeur of the public spaces. The Tremont contained large dining rooms and a reading room that resembled a nascent public library. Its suite of grand interior spaces also included a rotunda, which evoked the authority and idealism of the national democracy. The Tremont's rotunda served as an office and organized the circulation between the public and private rooms and the glazed corridors that led to the renowned, innovative battery of modern water closets. Like traditional inns, there was a courtyard at the center of the hotel, but rather than being a stable yard, it was a garden planted with rosebushes — a precursor of the great central interior courts that became fairly standard features of grand American hotels once the technology of their enclosure had been mastered, as it was by Rogers in New York's Astor House (1834–36).

In 1875 San Francisco, though hardly a wilderness, was not much of a metropolis either. Its Palace Hotel, however, designed by John Gaynor, covered two and a half acres, creating an instant, enclosed city in advance of that which was to rise around it. Financed by five million dollars of Comstock Lode wealth, it represented San Francisco's aspirations to being one of the world's great metropolises, and though it would be years before the 850 luxury rooms could be filled, the public rooms inside achieved a new standard for any future "palace of the people." The Great Court, nearly 150 feet long and 50 feet wide, was surrounded by seven storeys of galleries and crowned with a glass roof. Heated by huge bronze braziers, it was planted with palms and other exotic plants and fountains. A new type of lobby — a "palm court" — it provided a setting for twice-daily band concerts, skylit by day and illuminated by multicolored gas lights at night. San Francisco's Champagne Society could drive their carriages directly into the court; as they alighted, it was as if on a stage with tiers of spectators gazing from behind the gilt and marble-columned galleries above.

The Palace Hotel inspired a host of imitators in other young cities. The presence of a grand hotel in the raw city of Denver displayed the same cosmopolitan yearnings as San Francisco's monument. Designed by Frank E. Edbrooke, originally from Chicago, the Brown Palace Hotel (1889–92) loomed above its small residential neighbors. Clad in red granite and sandstone, it resembled an Italian Renaissance palazzo squeezed onto a triangular site and stretched to nine storeys. Inside, the Brown Palace flaunted wealth like the newly rich prospectors, miners, and cattlemen who filled its rooms. The hotel boasted an atrium walled in onyx and bronze beneath a stained glass skylight. The interior world of the atrium, sealed off from Colorado's harsh weather and the rough-and-ready street life of Denver, was Edbrooke's triumph and soon became the social center for the silver-rich city. From the main floor piers rose two storeys to low-springing elliptical arches. As if it were butter on toast, Mexican onyx was slathered on the walls as well as on piers, arches, a massive fireplace, and even the clerk's desk; in fact, more onyx was used than in any previous building, exhausting an entire quarry. Above the lobby's arches rose six storeys of uniform galleries, with copper-plated iron railings and Classical columns of steel. The local scene was represented in the medallion carvings of Rocky Mountain animals placed between the arched windows of the seventh floor. On the eighth floor, in the two-storey dining room, the onyx wainscoting and the upper course of stained glass windows framed a panoramic view of the Rocky Mountains. Once an outpost of Eastern gentility, today the Brown Palace endures as a bastion of the Old West.

John Portman's Detroit Plaza Hotel, completed in 1977, is the seventy-three-storey cylindrical centerpiece of the Renaissance Center. Built to revitalize downtown Detroit, which had been ravaged by the 1967 riots, the complex is cut off from city life by more than a ridiculously wide street. Virtually inaccessible by foot, it is above ground level on a fourteen-acre concrete podium, whose medievalizing, battlemented, fortresslike form betrays the center's hopeful name. At the center of the urbanistically catastrophic complex, however, overscaled interiors do at least begin to reclaim the tradition of great places within. Portman supplies the harried jet age businessman with a thrill a minute. The public spaces of the Ren Cen, as the project is less than affectionately known, consist of a kinetic maze of ramps, escalators, and "pods" accessible by spiral staircases and exposed elevators. To wander from the neutral "people scoops"[16] of corridors to the multilevel histrionics of the eight-storey atrium is to stumble forward into the future of Buck Rogers's twenty-fifth century and backward into the fantastic past

The Great Court of San Francisco's Palace Hotel (*above*), seven storeys high and crowned with a glass roof, introduced a new type of hotel lobby: the palm court. Arriving guests would drive their carriages into the enormous, plant-filled lobby, while others watched from the gilt and marble-columned galleries or from the surrounding arcades (*right*).

The Auditorium Building, designed by Louis Sullivan, functioned as the center of Chicago's cultural life for forty years. The bar (*above*) was one of the city's favorite meeting places. Its walls were tinted shades of brown to harmonize with the massive carved oak columns.

Overleaf. The Auditorium Theater is a magnificent blend of light, color, and pattern. Sullivan married function to form in the intricately crafted decorative grilles that filtered a constant supply of fresh air and in the lamps that emphasized the outlines of the gold-leafed elliptical arches supporting the vault and ceiling. It has been hailed as the world's greatest room for music.

of Tarzan's jungle, while to ride on its elevators is to travel from Degree Zero to Alphaville.

While the Renaissance Center is not so much a refuge as a refusal, many of the greatest American places within have been both escapes from and celebrations of urban vitality and dynamism. When Ferdinand Wythe Peck, a prominent Chicago businessman, set out to build a moneymaking opera house in 1889, the result was a new kind of building. Hiring the firm of Dankmar Adler and Louis Sullivan, Peck built a superstructure that even more than the grand hotel could qualify as a city within a city. The Auditorium Building was a marvel of complexity and convenience. It was one of the first large buildings to be wired for electricity, it was thoroughly fireproof, and it was equipped with thirteen elevators. A visitor could spend his entire day inside it, conducting business in the office section, attending an opera or a concert, drinking and dining in the numerous restaurants of the hotel, and, after all this, ascending to a bedroom floor to enjoy a night's rest in one of its four hundred guest rooms.

The masonry exterior was a bit stolid in design, although the massive ten-storey block was enlivened by a campanile that rose to a height of 270 feet, at the top of which Adler & Sullivan located its offices. The first designs had been much more ornate, covered with what Frank Lloyd Wright later called "effluorescent terra cotta."[17] Yet while Sullivan ultimately simplified the façades, he let loose his ornamental vision in the interior. The Auditorium Theater, in particular, was developed as a fantasia of light, color, and pattern. Encased within the office block, the 4,237-seat theater was the largest of its kind in the world and had perfect lines of sight and sound enhanced by Adler's acoustical engineering genius. Sullivan married function to form in the intricately crafted decorative grilles that filtered a constant supply of fresh air — warmed in winter by steam coils and cooled in summer over tons of ice. Even the electric carbon filament lamps served Sullivan's decorative scheme, placed to emphasize the outlines of the gold-leafed elliptical arches that supported the vault and ceiling. Sullivan didn't limit himself to abstract patterns. He also commissioned murals of the natural world, representing the "Symphony of Nature." The room was instantly beloved by audiences as well as the world's leading singers and musicians, such as the incomparable Australian diva Dame Nellie Melba, who was so thrilled by the hall that she wished to "fold it up and take it with me everywhere, to open up for every performance I give."[18]

The hotel portion of the building, although lacking the usual skylit atrium, offered the most luxurious public rooms in Chicago. Guests passed through an entrance lobby in which every surface was subject to Sullivan's curling organic forms, from the mosaic floor to the cast-iron railings and the ceiling's massive stenciled beams. Ascending the stairway that rose through a great archway, hotel visitors arrived at the main reception room, decorated in green and gold. Its floor was covered in the foliate patterns of a Wilton carpet and its windows hung with claret-colored draperies. Beyond lay a loggia overlooking Lake Michigan.

The history of the loggia speaks volumes about why the industrialists of the late nineteenth century put so much of their energy and fortune into building sealed, perfect environments for work, commerce, and entertainment. By the 1870s, the Capitol in Washington had perforce become a world apart from the belching engines of the railroads that Congress had permitted to crisscross the

Top. New York's Grand Central Terminal, seen in a 1931 photograph. *Bottom.* A cross-section drawing of the proposed station shows the various levels of the tracks and waiting rooms and the efficient system of ramps that connect them.

Mall; in most downtowns, the streets were thronged not only with citizens of every social class and national origin but also with horses, carts, carriages, trolleys, and even, sometimes, belching steam locomotives. The Auditorium Building insulated Chicagoans from the packed street of the business district, from the screeching trains of its elevated Loop, from the vast railyards that lined the shore of Lake Michigan. The loggia, originally designed as a grand porch open to the lakefront, almost immediately had to be enclosed in glass to protect the guests from the sooty exhaust of the coal-burning trains thundering along the shore and to further sustain its function as a cultural oasis. The Auditorium was a city within a city that offered the environmental and social control unattainable in the real metropolis outside.

In addition to the main auditorium, there was a small recital hall and a café and adjacent bar on the first floor. The latter became one of Chicago's most famous meeting places, with walls tinted in shades of brown that harmonized with the fat, intricately carved, fumed oak columns. Perhaps the most impressive public room in the building was the dining hall on the tenth floor. Like a giant attic, this room consisted of a curved vault that began at floor level, punctuated by stained glass skylights. Painted white and stenciled in light gold, the vault was cut through by

Light pours through the semicircular windows of the Grand Concourse of Grand Central Terminal. The towering steel-frame piers were covered with stone to support the immense entablature, and the vaulted ceiling was painted with the constellations of the zodiac.

archways on one side that afforded a broad, elevated view of Lake Michigan.

For forty years the Auditorium Building functioned as the center of Chicago's cultural life, until the Chicago Auditorium Association went bankrupt. Despite Peck's dream of commerce subsidizing culture, the Auditorium had never been in the black. It had cost too much to build, and in the end it was saved because it cost too much to demolish. In 1941, the city of Chicago turned the building into a Servicemen's Center, converting the auditorium itself into a bowling alley. In 1946, it fell upon the newly founded Roosevelt University to restore the complex. During its tenure, significant portions of the building, including the theater, have been meticulously restored, although some of the elegant public rooms have been sacrificed to the more mundane requirements of the university. The Auditorium Theater, which reopened in 1967, remains, as Sullivan's disciple Frank Lloyd Wright described it, "the greatest room for music and opera in the world — bar none."[19]

Even more than the Auditorium Building, the great urban railroad stations took up the ideal of re-creating, in miniature, a version of the city as a whole. Railroad stations were important manifestations of the national commitment to democracy, for while protection from the harsh realities of the city was offered by hotels and theaters for those with the leisure time and financial wherewithal, the railroad station was a place where anyone could go. As Whitney Warren, one of the architects of New York's Grand Central Terminal (1903–13), put it: "The up-to-date station resembles a bazaar."[20] The station that Warren helped to design certainly did: its Grand Concourse and arcades were the focus of a thirty-block real estate project that included a post office, a YMCA, private clubs, two hotels, and numerous office buildings.

Grand Central was a triumph not only of design and planning but of technological progress. The chief engineer of the New York Central, William J. Wilgus, formulated the fullest exploitation of electrified trackage. Tracks, usually open or partially covered to allow the steam to escape, could now be placed within fully closed tunnels, allowing the railroad to lease the air rights to the land above the tracks for development and thus earn revenues for the company. As a result Park Avenue, once a neighborhood blighted by belching steam engines, could be transformed into a broad, landscaped boulevard at last worthy of its name.

Wilgus also contributed the "bunk-bed" two-tiered system of tracks that divided the terminal into suburban and express levels. The architects Charles A. Reed and Allen H. Stem of St. Paul, Minnesota, responsible for the elegant and efficient system of ramps between the two levels, had originally been commissioned to design the entire station, but it was the New York architects Whitney Warren and Charles D. Wetmore who executed the final design after Warren persuaded his cousin, William K. Vanderbilt, chairman of the New York Central, that Reed and Stem might relinquish their leading role.

Under Warren & Wetmore's guidance, Grand Central Terminal evolved into the bazaar of the city efficient. Not only its planning but also its design marked it as a consummately urban megastructure. In Warren & Wetmore's design, the grand façade is lifted above the level of an elevated roadway that rings the building. The

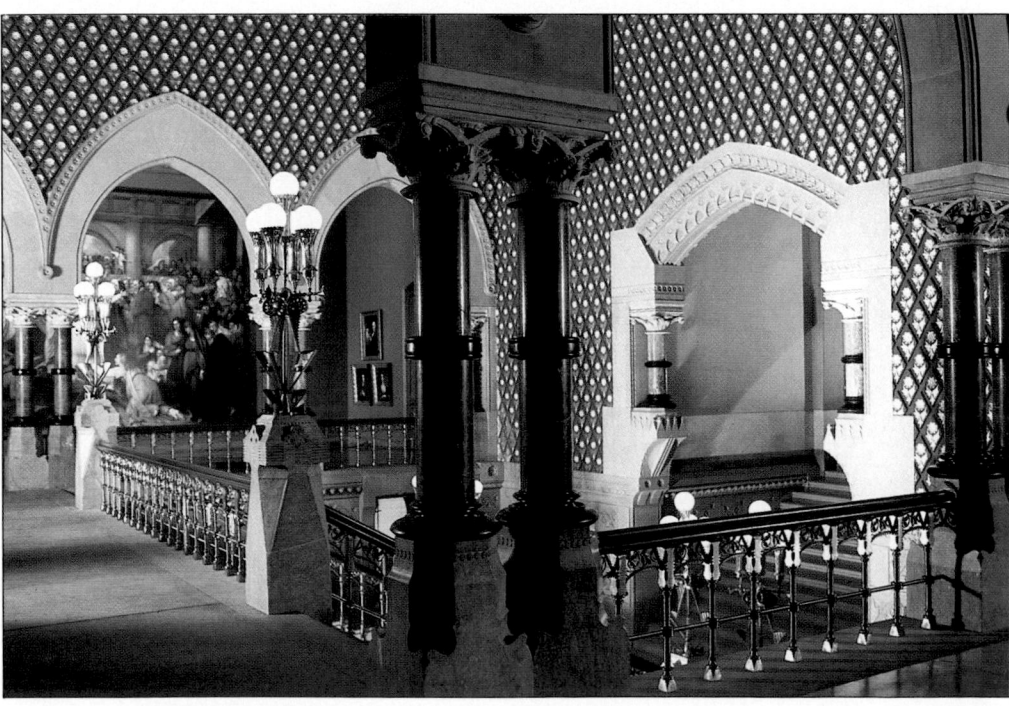

Frank Furness's 1876 design for the Pennsylvania Academy of Art achieved a broad synthesis of architectural styles. At the top of a four-storey stairwell, the exhibition galleries combined pistonlike columns, Gothic arches, and repetitive wall patterns in a dialogue between culture, art, and architecture that challenges the twentieth-century notion that art is best displayed in nondescript surroundings.

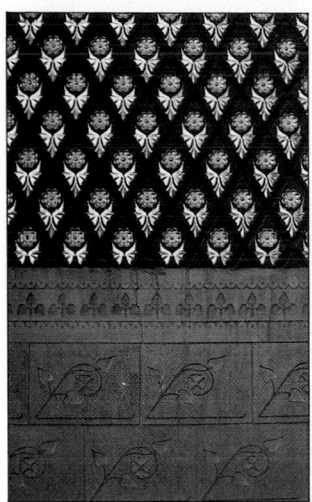

The worlds of nature and mechanics were combined on the walls of the Pennsylvania Academy's exhibition galleries in the stamped-out floral pattern detailed here. Throughout the museum, art and industry were symbolically united in the building's design.

drama of circulation triumphs, with cars rushing overhead and storefronts at street level below. At the same time, the seemingly overblown scale of the arches allows the architecture to hold its own as an urban monument above the traffic and also gives promise of the interior's size.

For the passengers entering the terminal from the street, the dramatic architectural sequence surpassed that of even the most monumental office and hotel lobbies. From Forty-second Street, the spacious, low entrance portals swept into the bright vertical release of the main waiting room and then down farther to the cavernous main concourse. The best view of the concourse was to be seen from the head of an intricately planned marble staircase that descended from a broad interior terrace to its bustling floor below.

The Grand Concourse was New York's Piazza San Marco. Here the circulatory thrill of the city was ensconced in a magnificent Classical shell. The masonry walls were stripped to their essentials. The steel frames of the towering piers that punctuate the walk were clad in stone to ironically support an immense entablature. Light poured through semicircular windows set above the entablature in rows of four on the north and south sides, while on the east and west, light entered through immense arched windows. The ceiling, which had once been planned with skylights, was a blue vault painted with the constellations of the zodiac, drawn as though one were looking down from the heavens rather than up to them. Although the railroad's advertising trumpeted that "every facility is progressively arranged so that no step need be retraced, no time lost,"[21] the main concourse nonetheless invited one to linger beneath its starry sky. It seemed to raise the comings and goings of travelers to the level of romantic rites of passage, luring urbanites to the station to gawk, meet, or simply use it as a covered street, the nexus of the greater theater of New York.

In the 1960s, Grand Central's capacious concourse, deemed a waste of space, was threatened with demolition. Its designation as a landmark by New York City in 1967 was challenged by real estate interests, who took the case all the way to the Supreme Court, which ruled on behalf of preservation. Today, we are once again building great places within. At the western edge of New York's lower Manhattan business district, Cesar Pelli's design for the World Financial Center, a development for thirty thousand employees within the larger context of Battery Park City, has a glazed living room for the city at its core that functions as a crossroads for the thousands who walk from the World Trade Center's transportation hub to the offices of the center's four towers. Pelli's nobly proportioned Winter Garden, at once evoking a greenhouse and a commercial arcade, also suggests New York's best-known crossroads, the Grand Concourse of Grand Central Terminal. Like it, the Winter Garden is both a place of passage and a place of repose where one can sit down, have a drink or a cup of coffee, or just contemplate the sweeping Hudson River vista. It is also like an Italian piazza, in some ways like San Marco in Venice, covered in glass and air-conditioned to suit the extremes of the American climate.

Pelli's task has been to find an architectural scale and language as powerful as Grand Central Terminal's to express the idea of a public living room. The floor is of patterned marble and the walls are granite, with sixteen Washingtonian palm trees from California rising to the glass dome. Entered from above on steps that serve as a viewing platform for the whole space, like Grand Central's Concourse, it is a

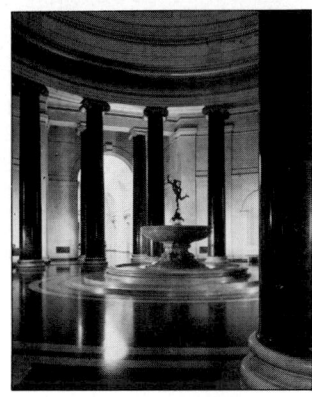

Top. The East Building of the National Gallery features diagonal skylights that cut across the lines of the main structure.

The National Gallery's rotunda (*bottom*) is a Classical temple of art. Its spatial clarity contrasts with the frenetic central court of the East Building (*right*).

place to see and be seen. The steps are a promenade and a public stage, like a spillway flowing from the mountain range of Wall Street's skyscrapers toward the Hudson River and the western landscape beyond. The palm trees offer an exquisite irony all their own: they suggest that the Sunbelt, the booming region of the 1970s that once posed a threat to New York's dominance, has been encapsulated in a glazed court by the Hudson.

Pelli's Winter Garden recalls the glory of nineteenth-century urbanism and its recognition that great enclosed places were an essential element of a livable city. The office building and the department store were symbols of our material achievements. To satisfy cultural ambitions, Americans built great places within dedicated to art.

In 1876, Philadelphia's Pennsylvania Academy of Art, founded in 1805, built new headquarters that adopted a radical design by the architectural firm of Furness & Hewitt. Frank Furness, the dominant designer of the partnership, attempted a broad-reaching synthesis, gathering together under a Gothic mantle a score of architectural traditions and a passionate structural expressionism that symbolically united art and industry as no building had ever before.

As requested by the Academy, Furness installed the collection's *Winged Victory* over the main entrance, a clear symbol of its values and traditions. From that point on, no stylistic holds were barred, as Furness let loose a stylistical synoptic polychromed façade that included a grand Gothic window, a Greek frieze, Moorish crenelations, and Byzantine tiles laid up in emulation of an American

Indian rug pattern. The entrance led through a low vestibule into a toplit four-storey stairwell that surpassed the exterior in its architectonic density. Because the Academy's studios and lecture halls were on the building's ground floor, every visitor to the exhibition galleries had to ascend the stairs in what amounted to an initiation into the dreamworld of art. Above, the vault of the sky was represented in a ceiling painted cerulean blue and studded with silver stars. The worlds of nature and mechanics were combined in repetitively stamped-out floral patterns on the walls, in the pistonlike columns with black rings around their centers, and in bronze lighting standards configured like cruelly conceived, robotic crustaceans.

In the 1950s, the Academy "modernized" its galleries, sealing its ornate columns in plywood to provide neutral rooms. For an era that preferred its art hermetically sealed from the external world, Furness's materialistic dialogue between culture, art, and architecture seemed an embarrassment. Uncovered during the restoration of the Academy for the Bicentennial, the columns, like the entire Academy, once again powerfully challenge the twentieth-century notion that art is best displayed in nondescript surroundings.

Furness's use of the Gothic elevated a visit to the Academy to a ritual comparable to a religious pilgrimage. But if Furness's building was a church of art, other museums were Classical temples to art. The ideal for a temple to art was established in 1893 at Chicago's Columbian Exposition, where Charles Atwood's Fine Arts Museum posed Classicism as an irrevocable civic ideal. In New York, Richard Morris Hunt and Richard Howland Hunt designed an imperial façade for an addition to the Metropolitan Museum (1895–1902), while in Brooklyn the firm of McKim, Mead & White planned a pedimented, domed, and statue-bedizened Classical palace for the Brooklyn Museum (1897–1924). The concept of the museum as a Classical temple culminated in John Russell Pope's National Gallery (1937–41), which surpassed its predecessors in the austere dignity of its design and in its standard of functional perfection. The blank exterior walls of Tennessee marble are relieved only by an Ionic portico. Immediately inside, the great pantheonic rotunda, 100 feet high and 100 feet wide, contains twenty-four green-black marble columns that support a coffered limestone dome. The pinnacle of the dome is pierced by a glass oculus that directs a shaft of light onto the sixteenth-century bronze sculpture *Mercury*, by Giovanni Bologna, which stands at the center of the rotunda. Two long, spacious, toplit, marble-lined corridors, leading to the display galleries, are punctuated by glazed garden courts. Although actually windowless boxes, through the use of lighting, fountains, and proportions, the courts give visitors the refreshing feeling of being outdoors. The great corridor is like a street in a Classical city. Its pavement, its walls, are all architectural in the fullest sense, yet done simply, the moldings stripped to their essence, never intruding on the works of art, while the courts become the city's *piazzi*.

The National Gallery is itself a work of art, yet the building doesn't compete for attention with the canvases and sculptures it holds. Not only ideal in its spatial clarity and majestic vistas, the scheme is ideal in accommodating the Gallery's crowds of visitors. It is almost like a machine for viewing art. Replete with the latest technological advances in lighting, air conditioning, and humidity control, it is a vessel for our cultural experience made perfect through the mastery of Pope and his Classical dream.

When the National Gallery made plans to expand, it commissioned I. M. Pei

The Garden Court at the Museum of Modern Art in New York is the architectural focus of the addition designed by Cesar Pelli.

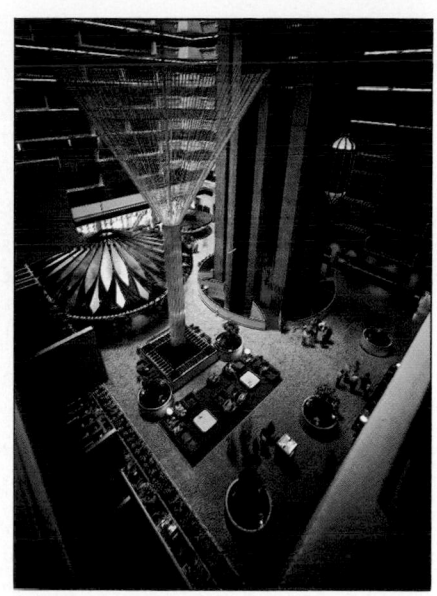

With little relation to its urban context, the contemporary inner-city shopping mall is a world unto itself. *Left:* The Houston Galleria's ice-skating rink leaves the humid, congested city behind. *Center:* The overscale interior of Detroit's Renaissance Center, with its skylit, histrionic atrium, is entirely sealed off from the surrounding urban blight. *Right:* The lobby of the Peachtree Plaza in Atlanta is filled with fantasy elements.

to design a building that would capture the representational power of its traditional space in the language of Modernism. Pei's design utilized the same pink-hued Tennessee marble and a cornice line which approximates that of the older building, but there the similarities end. The exterior's abstract geometry is symptomatic of the architecture of the late 1960s and early 1970s. Some have said that Pei's building suffers from a kind of disease of the 1970s — acute diagonalysis of form — which has cut it off from the traditions of Pope's design and the surrounding public buildings of Washington, D.C. Speaking of his design for the East Building (1978), Pei has said, "To make the visit a pleasant one . . . we built a circus."[22] In this case, the "big top," a triangular cluster of twenty-five tetrahedronal skylights, encloses a seventy-foot-high atrium that contains a spectacle of circulation, a monumental atrium reminiscent to many of a suburban shopping mall. Pei filled the East Building's large central core with escalators, ramps, and balconies, which lead to small galleries off to the side. Dazzlingly finished and washed in light, the court is undeniably impressive, so much so that it overwhelms even the large pieces of art commissioned for the space. Alexander Calder's enormous mobile suspended within seems like mere decoration. Its circus animals are trapped in a circular performance just as the viewers are trapped by the confusion of movement around them. They are left to wonder where the art is, or perhaps to look for the shops in what has been called the Mellon Mall after its patron, Paul Mellon, son of Andrew Mellon, the National Gallery's founder.

At its heart, the East Building overturns the traditional concept expressed by Pope's Classical building of the museum as a temple dedicated to the contemplation of art. Pei's building is all complication, diagonal organization, circulation, and nonrepresentation. The journey between the two buildings that now compose the National Gallery is far more complex than the mere few hundred feet and forty years that separate. The contrast is nowhere more poignantly felt than in the handling of the zones between them — a plaza at ground level and a concourse underground. The cobblestone plaza, perhaps intended to evoke a town square or the entrance court of a palace, is strewn with

The State of Illinois Building, designed by Helmut Jahn, is a colored-glass structure containing a rotunda 160 feet in diameter and rising seventeen storeys to a glass ceiling. Here, we look down to the geometrically patterned concourse floor.

menacing, shardlike, glass tetrahedrons that are skylights for the passage below. This subterranean concourse contains only a "people-mover" transporting visitors between the wings, a procession without hierarchy. Without the Classical elements of Pope's corridors, the connecting passageway alludes only to the banal realities of life in the jet age, providing an all too appropriate way to enter what the English critic Colin Amery has described as an "artistic terminal building."[23]

The triumph of the idea of a museum as a transportation hub rather than a

Cesar Pelli's model of the World Financial Center in lower Manhattan has the glazed Winter Garden building at its core, surrounded by four towers. A place of passage and repose, it evokes both a greenhouse and a commercial arcade.

place for contemplating art took place with the completion of the newest addition to the Museum of Modern Art in New York. The original building, commissioned and constructed at the same time as Pope's National Gallery, was designed to represent the spirit and achievement of Modernism. In terms of interior space, the results were austere, fairly cold, and neutral, unadorned volumes. The Miesian west wing (1951) and the larger, somewhat less doctrinaire east wing (1964) by Philip Johnson carried out the spirit if not the letter of the original design, but in the new addition (1977–84), designed by Cesar Pelli, such Miesian formalism was abandoned. Whether inspired by Pei or the mall-making Gruen Associates, at which he was a design partner, Pelli has built his addition seemingly as an articulation of circulation for circulation's sake. Crouched at the base of a tower of condominiums built to finance the expansion and renovation, the museum's architectural focus is the glazed "Garden Court" — little more than a hall for escalators. Hilton Kramer, the art critic and editor of *The New Criterion,* has condemned the "irksome sense of bustle and commotion" of the Garden Court and adds that "it is a space remarkably inhospitable to the exhibition of works of art. . . . Owing to the unremitting volume and intensity of the circumambient light, even sculptures as powerful as Gaston Lachaise's 'Floating Figure' (1927) and Alberto Giacometti's 'Large Head' (1960) are reduced to silhouettes."[24]

While in the nineteenth century commercial buildings tried to aggrandize themselves by incorporating the public grandeur of the architecture of the temple and the palace, in the twentieth, public buildings like art museums have often taken commercial and technological expediency as their guidelines. As early as the Pennsylvania Academy, modernity became the subject of the museum's design, and while Furness held on to the grand gestures of spatial progression and historical symbolism, he employed a mechanical morphology. At the Museum of Modern Art, the traditions of monumental public space were entirely abandoned, while at the National Gallery, Pei struggled to recapture the representational power of traditional space using the language of Modernism. Unfortunately the results, far from inspiring wonder at the unfamiliar, have assumed the all too familiar appearance of the suburban shopping mall.

Frank Lloyd Wright's Marin County Civic Center, designed in 1957 but completed in 1969, brings the story full circle. At Marin the commercial arcade and the public rotunda merge in a convincing synthesis. The center is consummately suburban in its ideology, set in open country next to the freeway. The site was perfectly suited to Wright's anti-urban, Jefferson-inspired philosophy of decentralization, which he had articulated in his proposal for Broadacre City.

Frank Lloyd Wright's design for the Marin County Civic Center merges American themes and ideals. The Administration Building's 560-foot commercial arcade terminates at the public library rotunda and a towering pylon that might be both a totem pole and the mast of this "ship of state." Set in the open country next to the freeway, the complex satisfies the requirements of the motor age while referring back to Jeffersonian ideals of Arcadia.

The Marin County Civic Center stretches in bold, seemingly limitless horizontals, marrying architecture and nature in a wonderful dialogue that reaches for inspiration to ancient Roman architecture, as had Jefferson. But Wright's scheme is strictly a part of contemporary America as well. More than any other architect of his time, Wright understood the ramifications of the nation's obsessive automobility. Wright's building at once celebrates the car and provides a refuge from it. Inside the building, Wright has lifted the street into the air, putting it at the center of the building and roofing it in glass. Wanting government to be user friendly, Wright organized his Civic Center like a suburban shopping mall where citizens can shop for services along the Administration Building's 560-foot-long toplit corridors. Like stores, the offices are open for view. Like the Lawn of Jefferson's University of Virginia, Wright's interior street is thickly planted and is terminated with a library rotunda suggesting that the state's highest function may well be educational. Arched windows frame views of the landscape; their several storeys suggest, against Marin County's green-brown hills, the grace of an aqueduct traversing the Roman campagna. The aquatic theme is carried out in the startling watery blue color of the roof as well as in the details such as porthole window openings, which suggest that the building may also be a colossal ship of state, a safe anchorage for citizens amidst the smaller craft that tack back and forth along the freeway. References to commercial architecture, to ancient Rome, to Jefferson, are pinned in place by the bold form of a mast that recalls the ancient totemic architecture of pre-white America. A 217-foot pylon, the mast rises from the deck, part Native American totem pole, part ocean liner smokestack, and part flagpole, concealing the boiler's stacks. At Marin, Frank Lloyd Wright, our most brilliant and complex architect, disciplined Roman grandeur to the democracy of the motor age. At Marin, he brought together the two principal types of American interior space: the dome of the pantheon and the arcade of the market. At Marin, Wright reconciled the twin impulses of the American character: the need to get away, to escape, to hit the road, with the need to establish roots, to weave an architectural mythology out of the facts and dreams of our national past.

7 Proud Towers

The skyscraper tower, rising free of the city, is the single most potent and widely recognized architectural expression of American pride. More than any other building type, the skyscraper, with its romantic synthesis of utilitarian office space and aesthetically powerful, historically derived form, emblematizes the American genius of marrying materialism to idealism. One hundred years ago, the church was the tallest building in most American towns and cities, dominating the skyline as it did in Europe. St. Michael's in Charleston (1752–61), St. Paul's in New York (1764–66; tower, steeple, and porch, 1796), and the Old North Church in Boston (1723) of Paul Revere fame were echoed in small towns across America.

Richard Upjohn's Gothic-style Trinity Church, built in 1846, was the tallest building in New York City until 1892, when it lost its preeminence to a new kind of tower building, the skyscraper, dedicated not to God but to Mammon. When George B. Post's Pulitzer Building thrust its mass to 309 feet, 25 feet higher than Trinity Church, not only the physical form but also the symbolic content of American urbanism was revolutionized. The Pulitzer Building was a full-blown provocation: American capitalism had found its artistic voice.

Yet the formal lessons of traditional church designs were not lost on those who undertook to build tall buildings: it was not the technology or even mere height that made a tall building a proud tower; what was needed was a permanent independence of form, a striking silhouette, and most of all an aspirational quality. A true skyscraper must be a fully modeled tower, rising from a decisive base to an equally decisive pinnaclelike conclusion at its top. Gothic, Classic, or whatever in its formal vocabulary, a skyscraper, wrote the architect Louis Sullivan in 1896, must be "every inch a proud and soaring thing."[1]

America was the first nation to grow up in the industrial age. Unlike Europe, America had no existing stock of buildings or even a building type to emulate that could satisfy its need for warehouses to store goods, offices to store workers, and department stores to display goods for sale. In the mid–nineteenth century, a whole new category of building — the loft — was invented to fill the city's grid with flexible, leasable commercial space. The introduction of metal construction made it possible to build larger interior spaces with fewer columns than ever before; the invention of mechanical elevators made it possible to pile them up virtually to the heavens, disregarding traditional architectural distinctions between the bottom, middle, and top of a building in an endlessly repetitious vertical grid that mirrored the gridiron of streets that defined many American cities.

Houston's banded office building fills the sky behind the Fourth Church of Christ, Scientist. Here, as in most large American cities, corporate towers have shouldered in on the steeples that once commanded the skyline.

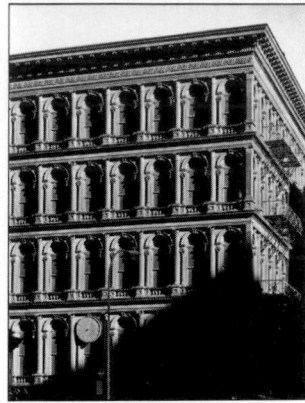

The Haughwout Building still stands in lower Manhattan as a landmark example of the modular castings designed by Daniel D. Badger's Architectural Iron Works.

Right. This 1865 lithograph of Badger's Architectural Iron Works, which appeared in the company's catalogue, shows the business of cast-iron production in full swing. The iron foundry is in the basement, the hoisting and assembling shops on the balconies above.

When the first passenger elevator with a safety device was installed in New York's modular, cast-iron-paneled Haughwout Store in 1857, it destroyed forever the traditional hierarchy of functions by making the fifth floor as rentable as the first. Architecture was at last free from the constraints of leg power and from the upward limits of masonry construction. But feats of technology were not and are not enough to make the story of America's tall buildings so compelling. Rather, it is the transformation by American entrepreneurs and their architects of buildings intended for ordinary, commercial purposes into lyrical architecture that reveals

The expansive auditorium of Adler & Sullivan's Schiller Building in Chicago is an example of their appreciation for the "poetry of height."

the nation's fundamental idealism, even in what appears its most brutally acquisitive acts. For the building of lofts quickly became the building of commercial palaces, and today the Haughwout Building endures as a perfect fusion of the American dream — an idealized pastiche of Renaissance Italy bolted together with the up-to-the-minute Yankee ingenuity of Daniel Badger's Architectural Iron Works founded a decade before. Cast-iron construction established the principle of repetitive rhythms as a natural expression of prefabricated construction, as well as the idea that traditional styles could take on new life when translated into new materials rendered on a vast new scale. Cast-iron modules from New York's foundries filled the grids of American cities such as Chicago, St. Louis, and Galveston, as well as New York, with commercial palaces.

Fueled by Civil War profits and technical innovations, including the shift from steam-powered to electric-powered elevators and the replacement of cast iron, with its comparatively low melting point, by more resilient steel, loft palaces grew taller. At 230 feet, the Western Union Building in New York broke the record for commercial buildings in 1875, only to be surpassed by the 260-foot Tribune Building in the same year. But it was in Chicago rather than in New York that the economic advantages of great height and skeletal construction were first understood. After Chicago's devastating fire of 1871, the Boston investors financing its reconstruction were quick to realize that tall buildings housing more rentable space per site would yield a greater profit. Since the East Coast financiers were interested in profits, not symbolism, the tall buildings that rose in Chicago were merely taller versions of the cast-iron palaces of New York and St. Louis. Tall they were; but proud, soaring evocations of corporate life they were not. In fact, the pragmatic Eastern investors encouraged their architects to fill up their sites with regularly gridded lofts and to encase these "blocks" as simply and cheaply as possible by stripping away all inessential ornament and relying on the expressiveness of the minimally sheathed structural frame. The result, widely celebrated for its bare-bones minimalism by a later generation of antihistoricizing Modernists, has been labeled the Chicago Style.

One Chicago architect, Louis Sullivan, understood the symbolic possibilities of articulating the height, rather than just the mass, of the loft building. Fresh from a sojourn at the École des Beaux-Arts in Paris and a stint as a draftsman in Frank Furness's Philadelphia office, Sullivan surveyed Chicago two years after the fire and found the city "magnificent and wild: A crude extravaganza: An intoxicating rawness: A sense of big things to be done."[2] For Sullivan, the dull repetitiousness of loft building façades violated the traditional principles of architectural composition and robbed them of any celebratory quality. Henry Hobson Richardson's Marshall Field Warehouse (1885–87) was the first to embody Sullivan's anthropomorphic concept of a loft building. The Field Warehouse was a monumental mass as carefully articulated as a traditional palace. It rose seven storeys and spanned a city block with its simple, unornamented façades, which contained graduated sequences of window arches. The Marshall Field Warehouse powerfully demonstrated that a loft building could be a work of art. Sullivan praised it as "a monument . . . to the power and progress of its age." Here was "a man," Sullivan stated, "that walks on two legs instead of four."[3]

Sullivan saw the anthropomorphic verticality of Richardson's design as evolutionary and strove to give the commercial blocks he designed an even greater poetry of height. Longing to go beyond the money-making exigencies of the Chicago Style, Sullivan paved the way for skyscrapers to become the industrial age equivalent of the spires of the medieval world. The Wainwright Building (1890–91) was his first bold step toward building the "proud and soaring things" by which he would later define tall buildings in his seminal essay of 1896 "The Tall Office Building Artistically Considered." Rather than being content with an inexpressive stack of floors, or a literal expression of the structural grid, Sullivan articulated the distinctions between base and capital, pushing the spandrels back to let the piers ascend uninterruptedly to a portholed attic and boldly projecting cornice. A brick and terra-cotta essay in verticality, it was built not in Chicago but in St. Louis. In the Bayard Building (1898), his only building in New York City, Sullivan went much further, with the piers rising in perfect register to an arcade of angels, whose arms stretched out as though to the heavens. The Bayard Building was a work of almost religious aspiration, a true spiritual ancestor to the soaring skyscrapers to come. Sullivan, who is often interpreted as a leading proponent of the straightforward structural expression that characterized the Chicago Style, actually believed quite the opposite. As we saw in chapter 1, he clearly articulated his aesthetic goals for the skyscraper: "Problem: How shall we impart to this sterile pile, this crude, harsh, brutal agglomeration, this stark, staring exclamation of eternal strife, the graciousness of those higher forms of sensibility and culture that rest on the lower and fiercer passions? How shall we proclaim from the dizzy height of this strange, weird, modern housetop the peaceful evangel of sentiment, of beauty, the cult of a higher life?"[4] Ironically, Sullivan and his partner, Dankmar Adler, built only one building in their home city of Chicago. Although more

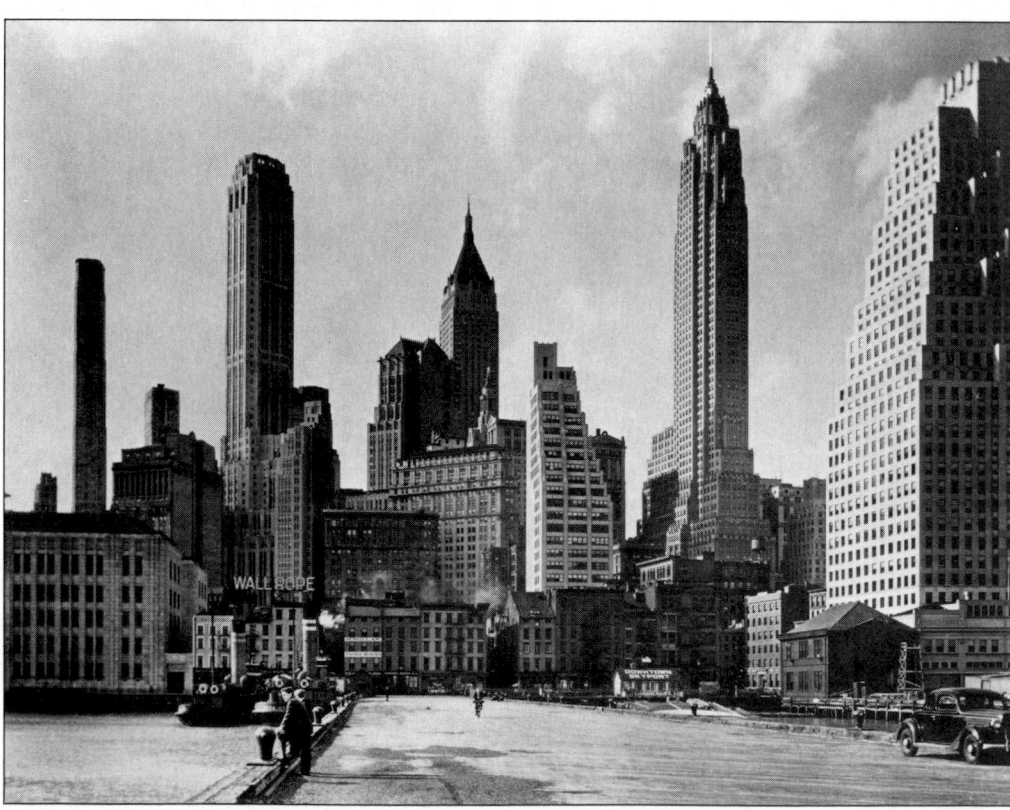

Berenice Abbott photographed the sprouting skyline of lower Manhattan while working for the 1936 Federal Arts Project "Changing New York." The city's downtown business district, confined by water on three sides, found release in its full-throttle vertical growth.

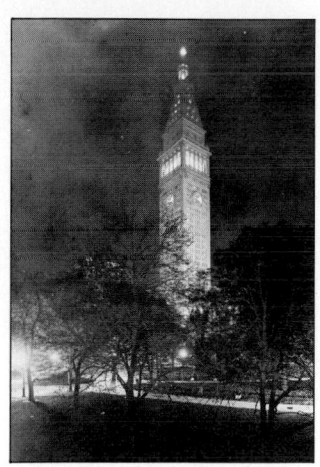

In 1909 Metropolitan Life unveiled its high-rise in Madison Park as a symbol of corporate stability. The model for the tower was the campanile of St. Mark's Cathedral in Venice.

prosaic in its vertical expression than Sullivan's tall buildings in St. Louis, New York, and Buffalo, the Schiller Building (1891–92), with its massing of a central seventeen-storey tower, two flanking nine-storey wings, and a fourteen-storey tower at the stem of the "T," was one of the first setback skyscrapers, allowing more light into all its offices and breaking from the solid block of buildings.

As Sullivan's work suggested, it was not the technology of tall buildings but the idea of soaring verticality that gave the skyscraper its rationale and its magic. In physical terms, the idea of the skyscraper was very simple, almost elemental: a tower that rose upward in such a way that it was forever freestanding. As such, the skyscraper would forever guarantee its inhabitants light, air, and views and so become a commercial symbol that overwhelmed the scale of the church steeple and thrilled us with a sense of power and romance.

But the most dramatic steps were taken in New York, whose business district at the tip of Manhattan quickly became overcrowded. The fact of Manhattan's geography — it is an island — and the need of businesses to congregate forced the city to expand upward rather than outward, retaining the closeness of village life at an unprecedented scale. In a dozen years beginning in 1892, the tip of Manhattan became a city of steel-framed towers sheathed in masonry. At first New York's skyscrapers were such in name only, merely extremely tall versions of the typical loft building that had filled in the city's grid. It was a Chicagoan, Daniel Burnham, who showed New York the way to the true skyscraper type on its home ground. Burnham's Flatiron Building (1902) was the first to come close to the ideal skyscraper — an inhabited tower standing forever free. Burnham, who had come to dominate Chicago's architecture after going past his former rival Sullivan, achieved at the Flatiron Building an even bolder resolution of the design problems of a tall office building. In 1892 he and his partner, John Wellborn Root, had come close to perfecting the skyscraper form in their sixteen-storey Monadnock Building, which, with its 1893 addition by Holabird & Roche, completely filled up a narrow block. But the Monadnock was the world's tallest stone building, and in the Flatiron he returned to a steel structural frame, sheathing it in terra cotta and stone. An accident of New York's street plan — the very prominent but irregular triangular site caused by the intersection of the Colonial road, Broadway, and the gridiron of the city's 1811 plan — created a parcel that was surrounded by streets and faced Madison Square Park, insuring that it would be forever free of encumbrances on all sides. It was ironic, but predictable, that this new triumph was built not in stolid, practical Chicago, but in flashy, newspaper- and magazine-oriented, hucksterish New York. Officially called the Fuller Building after the prominent firm of building contractors who built and owned it, the name "Flatiron Building" was a joking reference to the building's shape.

The Flatiron Building was the sensation of its time, joining the Statue of Liberty and the Brooklyn Bridge as one of the foremost postcard souvenirs of the city. From downtown, it appeared at first glance yet another enormous palazzo, but as one looked back on it from Madison Square it revealed itself as a towering column. For photographer Alfred Stieglitz, it was "like the bow of a monster ocean steamer — a picture of a new America still in the making."[5] It also had a different aesthetic effect, as its wind-cutting wedge was said to bare the ankles of the fashionable women on Fifth Avenue at Twenty-third Street. The legend is that police called out "twenty-three skidoo" to shoo away the male gawkers.

The Flatiron Building revolutionized the institution of the office building. No longer was the design problem confined to maximizing profit through maximizing height and rentable square footage. The tall building would now be something more than a real estate venture; it would be a permanent symbol of corporate pride, monumental and religious in its ambitions.

The twenty-two-storey Flatiron Building became an instant challenge to the Metropolitan Life Insurance Company's ten-storey office building (1893) across the street. After the financial collapse of 1893, insurance companies sought to regain the public's confidence through architecture that symbolized enduring stability. For Metropolitan Life, the architect Napoleon Le Brun chose as his aesthetic model the campanile of Venice's St. Mark's Cathedral, unperturbed that the original had collapsed seven years before. In materialist terms, the Metropolitan Life Tower (1909) could be seen as a fifty-one-storey filing cabinet for office workers; but Le Brun's use of historical analogy transformed the design from a steel-framed, stone-dressed technological feat into a highly visible, highly evocative, monumental public building that was a veritable pillar of strength. In fact, the Metropolitan Life Tower was a conscious effort to outstrip the prominence and usurp some of the glory of its near neighbor, Stanford White's Madison Square Garden (1890), whose tower was a version of Seville's Giralda Tower. But the Metropolitan tower was a working monument, filled with office workers. It was not a colossal rooftop folly; it was a grandiose corporate symbol.

Unable to resist the growing prestige and big bucks of skyscraper commissions, Ernest Flagg, who had first argued against and refused to design buildings over one hundred feet, devised a formula for building high without violating his principles. Towers, he argued, could rise to unlimited heights, provided they never occupied more than a quarter of their site. The opportunity to demonstrate his theory came with the six-hundred-foot-high Singer Tower, finished in 1908. Flagg designed it to rise above the ten-storey Singer Headquarters Building, which he had completed only nine years before. The tower was a slender lattice of steel, with a skin of glass and metal panels between corners sheathed in brick and limestone, crowned by a spectacularly mansarded rooftop lantern. Its observatory soon replaced the Brooklyn Bridge as New York's most popular suicide leap. But of more social significance to the happier man and woman on the street was the Singer Building's grand lobby. It was a place to meet, to date, a delightful sun-washed indoor concourse of shops and restaurants. A flash of light in the city's canyon, it married the preoccupation with monumental interior space to symbolic tower design.

If the Singer Tower and its lobby called on the public buildings of Europe for their inspiration, Cass Gilbert aspired to the ecclesiastical grandeur of the Gothic cathedral. In the Woolworth Building (1913), Gilbert transformed the office building into what the popular reverend S. Parkes Cadman dubbed a "Cathedral of Commerce."[6] Like a church, it was built on the nickels and dimes of its parishioners, except that Woolworth's worshipers dropped their money in cash registers rather than church collection plates.

Frank Woolworth, the self-made multimillionaire whose chain-store fortune had begun thirty-five years before in Utica, New York, was determined to build the most beautiful, the grandest, the biggest, but above all the tallest building in the world. Woolworth kept the scope of his ambition secret for a time, at first

The triangular site of Daniel Burnham's Flatiron Building dictated the unusual shape of the twenty-two-storey skyscraper and insured that it would remain forever free of surrounding structures.

AUGUST 29, 1907   OCTOBER 12, 1907   DECEMBER 26 1907

This fold-out postcard of 1907 features Ernest Flagg's Singer Tower in different stages of construction. Never an advocate of thick, sky-blocking buildings, Flagg designed a slender steel tower with a skin of glass and metal panels between brick and limestone corners. The tower was set atop the existing Singer Headquarters Building.

Right. The large windows and two-storey arched entryway at the base of the Singer Building admitted light into the grand lobby, creating an inviting, airy interior space for visitors to its shops and restaurants.

approving plans for a 692-foot tower, but keeping 100 extra feet up his sleeve. His bankers refused to finance the project, and his builder, Louis J. Horowitz, president of the Thompson-Starrett Company, predicted a financial nightmare of unrented office space. But Woolworth went ahead anyway. He could do without his bankers: he paid for the building with thirteen million dollars cash. He explained to Horowitz how he would reap profits from the building: "He confessed that the Woolworth Building was going to be like a giant signboard to advertise around the world his spreading chain of five-and-ten-cent stores. On that basis, of course, his splendid building was a sound investment."[7]

Cass Gilbert, Woolworth's architect, devised a Gothic structure whose soaring verticality brilliantly articulated what Sullivan had identified as the essence of skyscraper design. Gilbert derived his inspiration not from the age of cathedrals but from the nineteenth-century Gothic Revival, so that he could somewhat disingenuously maintain that he drew on exclusively secular models.[8] Nonetheless, the cathedral analogy was pretty explicit: the lobby was a vaulted nave, its transepts providing convenient side-street entrances, its triforium gallery lined with shops and banks. The basement level was a crypt for restaurants and supplied access to subway trains. And its tower was a spire as sublimely articulated as that of Chartres — but huge, with buttresses and finials pushing up and up sixty storeys toward the sky.

Those who had said that Woolworth would squander his fortune on building unrentable office space must have stood in amazement on its opening night in 1913, whether they were one of the eight hundred guests invited to the darkened banquet hall on the twenty-seventh floor or among those thousands in the crowd standing in the street below who watched as eighty thousand electric lights, lit by a

signal from President Wilson in the White House, made it blazingly clear that Frank Woolworth had created one of the great corporate symbols of his time. F. Hopkins Smith, the engineer-novelist-artist who was master of ceremonies, declared at the banquet that the building had "the lines of a great cathedral, its spire pointing to God."[9]

True skyscrapers like the Singer and Woolworth buildings did not begin the process of blight that has been associated with high-rise construction in cities. On the contrary, they pointed the way to a new, rational, even liberating urbanism in which light and air would be guaranteed to all. To many citizens and architects increasingly concerned about the canyonization of Manhattan, the skyscraper form was seen as a way out, a way to achieve density while preserving light and air. Besides, skyscrapers were a perfect expression of the optimism and self-confidence of fin-de-siècle America, the at-home architectural equivalent of the big sticks Theodore Roosevelt's imperialists were carrying abroad. The popular press took up the skyscraper as the building block of a new urbanism, an idea first adumbrated by Louis Sullivan in the architectural press in 1891. His "Skyscraper City" drawings and corresponding article on "The High-Building Question" show slim towers rising from massive city blocks, not unlike Sullivan's Schiller Building design, here defining the skyline of an entire city and accommodated by avenues scaled for terrific volumes of traffic.[10] Sullivan saw the skyscraper as a way of satisfying the developers' desire to extract the most profit possible from their office blocks while providing the public with the benefits of light and air in an era before air conditioning or reliable artificial light.

Moses King, the guidebook publisher, had similar if more fanciful hopes for the evolving skyscraper city. In 1908 he and his draftsman, H. M. Pettit, fantasized a New York abounding in stone-clad skyscrapers topped by roof-garden restaurants; aerial bridges crossed wide canyons filled with multiple layers of traffic, while the sky churned with airplanes, balloons, and dirigibles. King's dream probably frightened more people than it excited, and by 1916 New York was sufficiently concerned about the threat posed by tall buildings that it enacted the first zoning law in an attempt to encourage the best features of the skyscraper city — freestanding towers — while preventing the formation of any more preternaturally dark canyons like those of downtown Manhattan. Recognizing that a tall office block deprived its neighbors of light and air (and consequently tenants), the new law required upper storeys to be set back in calculated stages. Above the setbacks, a tower could rise, just as Flagg had proposed, to any height if it occupied no more than a quarter of its site. Flagg's Singer Tower and Gilbert's Woolworth Building, like Sullivan's drawings, anticipated and influenced the law.

Hugh Ferriss was the Piranesi of the new post-zoning skyscraper metropolitanism. With Harvey Wiley Corbett, he drew a city of freestanding towers (1926); for Raymond Hood he sketched skyscraper apartment houses that formed the towers of bridges spanning New York's rivers. In drawing upon drawing, Ferriss poured forth a vision of a new Babylon of massive, swaggering office pyramids and towers, spires, and needles bathed in sunlight by day and incandescent with electricity by night. Ferriss dreamed of a city of energy at the brink of frenzy, with rivers of fast-moving traffic and surging pedestrian throngs reflected against glistening pavements fresh from rain. Newspapers, magazines, and films carried the message of the new skyscraper universe to virtually every

A uniformed operator attends the elevators in the lobby of the Woolworth Building (1913). Architect Cass Gilbert employed the Gothic Revival style to create a "Cathedral of Commerce."

corner of the globe. Ferriss's vision was thrilling but also terrifying; his ideal city, described in his book *Metropolis of Tomorrow,* featured thousand-foot towers, but they were at least set at wide intervals. Such a vision was truly futuristic: even in the mid-twenties, the average building height in New York was six storeys. *Metropolis of Tomorrow* was published in 1929, the year of the stock market crash that turned Ferriss's giddy and optimistic dream into a frightening nightmare. But by then the sinister side of Ferriss's vision had already revealed itself to the German director Fritz Lang, who, after visiting New York in 1924, interpreted its skyscraper urbanism two years later in his film *Metropolis.* Lang showed skyscrapers as the containers of a dark, unnatural world of dehumanized automatons, above which was a paradise of roof gardens, like those Ferriss had drawn, reserved for the very rich, spoiled children who had no contact with the worker-zombies slaving away a hundred storeys below.

Not surprisingly, American filmmakers took a less critical tack. David Butler opened his 1930 film *Just Imagine,* a mediocre musical comedy, with Maureen O'Sullivan and John Garrick cruising in an air car through a spectacular vision of New York in 1980. Busby Berkeley turned the skyscrapers of midtown Manhattan into a dancing chorus for the title song of the 1933 film *42nd Street,* while in the "Lullaby of Broadway" sequence of his *Gold Diggers of 1935,* he portrayed New York's skyscraper world as both glamorous and sinister. An army of tap dancers, led by Rosita and Ramon, advance on singer Wini Shaw and swell Dick Powell, the sole patrons of an enormous skyscraper-nightclub, drawing them into their frenzy. Shaw tries to escape by running to a glass door opening onto a small balcony. She stumbles and falls from the tower to her death.

Over and over again the movies portrayed the skyscraper as safe only for a new breed. Los Angeles's real, towering City Hall, by Austin, Parkinson & Martin (1928), became known to millions of American moviegoers as the home office of a mild-mannered reporter for the *Daily Planet.* From its tower, Clark Kent's alter ego could fly into the subconscious of the world as Superman, the only man fully at home with the townscape of the new skyscraper urbanism.

Whatever their dangers for people who couldn't fly, skyscrapers had become an American obsession, and even those building types that were traditionally horizontal, such as schools, universities, and state capitols, took up the vertical ideal. As early as 1915, when Peabody & Stearns's soaring sixteen-storey Classical tower was set atop Ammi B. Young's Custom House in Boston (1837), it had become clear that even the traditional symbol of government, the domed interior space, was no longer sacrosanct. On the almost endlessly horizontal prairie, Bertram Grosvenor Goodhue synthesized the tower and dome to create what is this century's most compelling governmental structure, the Nebraska State Capitol (1920–32). At the University of Texas, the Old Main Building (Frederick Ernest Ruffini, 1882–98) was pulled down to make way for Paul Cret's monumental library (1931–37), a tower of books piled thirty storeys high and crowned by a tempietto.

No tower was more madcap than Day & Klauder's Cathedral of Learning, commissioned by the University of Pittsburgh (1928–31). A marriage of wisdom, wampum, and inspired hokum, this splendid Gothic stepped-back stone tower included seventeen classrooms in different national styles, as well as an eighteenth-century library from Damascus and a Greek Revival ballroom from a

With big buildings came big dreams of urban planning. In this sketch by Hugh Ferriss for Raymond Hood, soaring apartment towers perch atop massive bridges.

Pittsburgh mansion. Le Corbusier, the French architect and urbanist, singled out the Pittsburgh edifice for his Modernist contempt, illustrating it in *La Ville Radieuse* (1935) with the caption "An American university (who would believe it?). What child's play!"[11]

Perhaps the most startling application of the new skyscraper type was to churches. As early as 1904, the tables of status and chronology began to turn when Barney & Chapman, responding to the need to accommodate social and athletic functions well beyond those of the traditional parish church on a tight urban site, designed the first skyscraper church, the Broadway Tabernacle in New York, piling offices and classrooms into the tower. Bertram Goodhue went much further in his unrealized Convocation Tower (1921), a lyrically lofty office tower incorporating a vast church as its base and a copper flèche at the top, eighty storeys above Madison Square. In Chicago, Holabird & Roche designed the Chicago Temple Building (1922–23) to house the central offices and various chapels of the Methodist Episcopal Church. Above the flat roof of the twenty-one-storey main block, an eight-storey Gothic spire rose to 568 feet above street level. Allen & Collens's design for John D. Rockefeller's Baptist cathedral, the Riverside Church (1930), had a nave surmounted by a tower modeled after the south tower at Chartres. But Riverside's tower was taller and far more massive, twenty storeys framed in steel and filled with offices.

The greatest proof of the extent of the skyscraper craze was probably that Americans, and especially New Yorkers, were not only willing to work, govern, and exercise in them, they were eager to live in them as well. Irwin Chanin, the flamboyant developer, produced two double-towered skyscraper apartment buildings on New York's Central Park West, the Majestic (1930) and the Century (1931), which were joined by Emery Roth's San Remo (1930) and Margon & Holder's Eldorado (1931) to create one of the world's most memorable skyline silhouettes. The Waldorf-Astoria Hotel (Schultze & Weaver, 1931) also raised twin towers against the sky, but its complex midriff, constituting in effect a broad, massive city within the city, and its base, straddling the tracks of the New York Central Railroad, were even more significant. Guests could arrive at an entrance for those with their own motorcars or one for those with their own railroad car. The pedestrian visitor passed beneath a figure representing the Spirit of Achievement — the Spirit of Money might have been more appropriate for a luxury hotel opened during the bleakest years of the Depression — to a grand foyer, to continue on to the walnut and marble splendor of Peacock Alley, or to the ballroom, larger than any other in Manhattan at 130 by 135 feet, or to ascend to the eighteenth-floor Starlight Room, whose ceiling rolled back to reveal the sky.

Yet beyond the unexpected uses of the skyscraper type for noncommercial buildings and the presumed economic advantages of skyscraper building, the paramount ambition of any New York tower builder was to build *higher* than his competitors. Beating your way to the top was the great game in architecture as much as it was in bootlegging or on Broadway. The trophy for the world's tallest building had been passed up and down the streets of Manhattan since the turn of the century, when the Singer Tower's 600-foot crest downtown was the world's tallest for only one year (1908–9), preempted by the Metropolitan Life campanile on Madison Square, soaring 100 feet higher, which in turn gave up its statistical distinction to the 792-foot-tall Woolworth Building in 1913. The Cathedral of Commerce held on until 1930, although it was seriously challenged in 1926 by John Larkin's proposal for a 110-storey, 1,208-foot-high tower. Scoffed at as infeasible, although it included innovative solutions to the problem of minimizing the potentially rentable floor space consumed by elevator shafts, Larkin's proposal was never built. But its Midtown site was prophetic of the shift to a second business center in Manhattan, where the next generation of skyscrapers would be built close to the center of New York's consuming pleasures of fashionable apartments and hotels, theater and shopping, as well as to the railroad stations that cemented

Below, left. German film director Fritz Lang portrayed the potential horror of urbanization gone wild in his 1926 classic *Metropolis.* Here laborers reduced to automatons file into the gloomy bottom levels of monolithic skyscrapers. *Right.* For the title song of the 1933 film *42nd Street,* Busby Berkeley turned Manhattan's skyscrapers into a toe-tapping chorus line.

New York's status as downtown to the nation. Although the Chanin Building (Sloan & Robertson, 1929), built for Irwin Chanin, was lower than the Woolworth Building or Metropolitan Life Tower, it rose as the tallest, most magnificent tower in Midtown. Despite all its Jazz Age modernity, it was soon overshadowed by the two archetypal skyscrapers, the Empire State and Chrysler buildings, winner and runner-up in the race for height and enduring appeal in the drama of skyscraper urbanism.

Before the Empire State Building overtook them both, William Van Alen's Chrysler Building (1930) in Midtown and H. Craig Severance's Bank of the Manhattan Company Building (1929) on Wall Street jostled for position as tallest. When Severance and Van Alen, who had recently dissolved their architectural partnership, each announced that his new building would be the world's tallest, the race for height became a bitter and widely publicized personal rivalry. The buildings themselves were also altered by the competition. Walter Chrysler ordered Van Alen to shorten his design by ten floors, but during construction he recognized the potential publicity value and reversed his decision. Van Alen added more floors, only to discover that Severance, working in association with Yasuo Matsui, had added a lantern atop his design. Just to be sure, Severance added a 50-foot flagpole as well. But Van Alen was determined to capture the title. He kept a 185-foot spire hidden within the building's fire shaft until Severance completed his 71-storey, 927-foot-high building. Then Van Alen's spire, which he called the "vertex,"[12] was put in place. He later recalled, "The signal was given and the spire gradually emerged from the top of the dome like a butterfly from its cocoon, and in about ninety minutes was securely riveted in position, the highest piece of stationary steel in the world."[13]

Left. The Chrysler Building remains the most enduring advertisement for a commercial product: the tower is embellished with motifs enlarged from Chrysler car designs, including winged radiator caps, steel hubcaps, and brick running boards.

Right. Chrome eagle-gargoyles, overscale versions of the hood ornaments on the company's cars, were placed at the sixty-first floor.

In this photograph from the 1933 movie *King Kong*, the giant ape has climbed atop the Empire State Building with heroine Fay Wray to escape the frenzy of New York. The world's tallest building became a symbol of the city's self-destructive lust for architectural thrills.

Van Alen's Chrysler Building went beyond the Woolworth Building in its expression of pride. While the Woolworth cloaked commercialism in its religious associations, the Chrysler flaunted it right on the façade. Surely the greatest and most enduring advertisement for a product ever, the Chrysler Building still hypes its builder and the company he founded long after ownership has passed on to others. Chrysler's amazing expressionistic crown was Gothic and gaudy, just as the tower was practical and modern, banding together a conventional pattern of windows to create the streamline effects by horizontality.

The office tower itself was embellished with ornamental motifs enlarged from the late-twenties range of Chrysler car designs. At the thirty-first floor, four enormous winged radiator caps cornered a frieze of steel hubcaps and running boards rendered in black brick. At the sixty-first floor, four chrome eagle-gargoyles, monstrously overscaled versions of the hood ornaments on Chrysler's cars, hovered over the traffic in the streets below, intimidating everyone but the fearless, publicity-seeking photographer Margaret Bourke-White, who crawled out to the building's edge to capture thrilling views of the skyscraper city from its zenith and front-page headlines for herself.

The Chrysler Building combined the brash energy of Detroit during its heyday with an undercurrent of mordant gloom — a perhaps subconscious expression of the feeling that the era of untrammeled corporate capitalism that it celebrated was about to crash resoundingly. The entrances to the grand lobby were framed in polished black Georgia marble to create coffinlike portals; at the top, the observation gallery looked like a set lifted straight out of *The Cabinet of Dr. Caligari*. Even so, skyscraper-crazy New Yorkers were more thrilled than frightened.

Lewis H. Hine took this photograph of a worker resting on a steel girder during construction of the Empire State Building. In the background we see the spire of the Chrysler Building, soon to be surpassed as the world's tallest tower.

Far right. From its inception, the Empire State Building was promoted as a landmark of civic and national grandeur. Completed in 1931, it achieved a truly modern synthesis of technology and romance.

Chrysler's immediate challenge was the Empire State Building. Conceived in boomtime but built after the stock market crash, in 1930–31, it rose on the site of the first Waldorf-Astoria Hotel, once New York's most fashionable meeting place. Constructed at a record-breaking pace in thirteen months, the Empire State Building soared past the 1,048-foot-high Chrysler Building to 1,250 feet. Aware that theirs was the tallest building in the world, the owners had insisted that the building be topped with a 200-foot mooring mast for dirigibles, an impractical vision worthy of King's *Views of New York* and achieved only once, four months after the building opened in 1931, when a privately owned dirigible managed to dock for three minutes.

More important to the developers of the building was the symbolism of the spire. From its inception, the Empire State Building, actually a purely speculative venture, was promoted as a monument of civic and even national grandeur. The developer, John J. Raskob, who had managed former New York governor Al Smith's 1928 presidential campaign, hired the popular politician as president of the Empire State Company, and on May 1, 1931, President Herbert Hoover flipped a switch at the White House to light the newly completed skyscraper.

Compared to the narrative complexity of earlier skyscrapers such as the Woolworth Building, the Empire State Building's interior and exterior were exaltingly simple in their message. The one-hundred-foot-long, three-storey-high navelike vestibule of stainless steel, marble, and glass terminated in a map of the New York metropolitan area and was surmounted by a portrait of the building itself, thereby dedicating the building to its place as it celebrated its towering mass as a worthy object of veneration — a transcendent symbol in its own right, cosmically tied to the earth by radio waves emanating from its peak. The tower within the tower also relieved one of the principal ironies of building skyscrapers in Manhattan's grid: when the man on the street came close enough for an unencumbered view, he could only see a foreshortened image; inside the Empire State's lobby, he could master a full-length silhouette. The architects of the Cities Services Building (1930–32), Clinton & Russell, took this reorienting gesture further by using a model of their tower to frame the building's portal.

Shreve, Lamb & Harmon's Empire State design, a paradigm of symmetrical massing, was remarkable for its central shaft, 725 feet of unvarying fenestration and wall that contemporary critic Douglas Haskell described as having "something positively brutal in the monotony, but something inevitable and hypnotic too." Haskell theorized that the Empire State Building was exciting because of its contradictions: "It was caught at the exact moment of transition — between metal and stone, between the ideal of 'monumental mass' and that of airy volume, between handicraft and machine design."[14] Here was a commercial architecture that went beyond the ballyhoo of Chrysler to achieve a genuine modern synthesis of technology and romance — an incomparably sublime mass of masonry monumentalized in heroic height.

For its visitors, the building was hypnotically brutal less because of its unornamented shaft than because of the violent shift from the street to the observation deck, where for an hour or two visitors could become the gilded citizens of Hugh Ferriss's vision, looking down from a lofty perch of perfect peace onto the teeming city of traffic and shadows a quarter mile below. Though the Empire State Building was "user friendly," with lobbies and shops at ground level and observation decks at its peaks, it was terrifying as well, a fact that the pulp novels and movies of the day exploited to the fullest. In the movie *King Kong* (1933), New York City's insatiable appetite for new sensations brings Kong to the Broadway stage, where the bright lights provoke his destructive rampage. Kong embodies the terrors inherent in Manhattan's everyday frenzy by grabbing Fay Wray through her hotel room window, wrecking an elevated train, and climbing the Empire State Building, ultimate symbol of New York's lust for architectural thrills. In the end, the skyscraper city's own greed has released the force that would destroy it, an animal almost as big and surely as proud as the towers themselves. At the moment when the economy crashed and all the civilization it had supported seemed dangerously close to crashing along with it, only Fay and the airplanes, flying free of the dangerous city — the symbolic alliance of beauty and mechanical strength — could save the city from itself.

The sexual excitement of the era's race for height, brilliantly captured on film by *King Kong*'s creators, has also been celebrated recently by the painter Madelon Vriesendorp, whose *Flagrant délit* depicts an illicit assignation between two lovers, Madame Chrysler and Monsieur Empire State. The couple has been caught in bed by a priggish interloper, perhaps Madame's husband, Rockefeller Center's RCA Building, whose cold light of puritanical sobriety shines on the uncovered lovers.

If the crownless slab of the RCA Building (1934) looks like a drab husband in Vriesendorp's painting, it is because as architecture it plays the husband's more complex role. Raymond Hood's design for the RCA Building is at once tower and slab, commercial money maker and symbolic capitol of Rockefeller Center. It is also the culmination of Hood's meteoric rise to prominence as the leading poet-pragmatist of the skyscraper era. Only seven years before beginning work on Rockefeller Center, Hood was a virtually unknown architect, who had never built anything larger than a Greenwich Village speakeasy and whose income was largely derived from the design of radiator covers. His 1922 victory in the international competition for the Chicago Tribune Tower, when he was forty-one years old, made Hood famous overnight. In the next decade, Hood built four more skyscrapers and, more than any other architect of his generation, succeeded in reconciling the ideals of a public architecture that aspired to an ennobling aestheticism with the pragmatism of a commercial era. By 1934, the year the RCA Building was completed, Hood was dead. Dead also were the economy and culture that had allowed him to realize his genius.

In 1922, the *Tribune*'s owner, the outspokenly bombastic editor-publisher Colonel Robert R. McCormick, issued an international call for a tower to memorialize his newspaper's seventy-fifth anniversary. The publisher's architectural ambitions were straightforward and characteristically brash — "to erect the most beautiful and distinct office building in the world is the desire of the *Tribune*"[15] — and not only architects but also the citizens of the "Hog Butcher to the World" were expected to take part in the excitement. From the opening of the competition in June 1922 until a month after its closing in January 1923, the Sunday *Tribune* ran "a series of pages in Rotogravure and Coloroto . . . giving examples of architectural achievement through the ages."[16]

The *Tribune*, which considered itself one of Chicago's foremost institutions, deliberately chose a site where the headquarters would inevitably take on a larger urban role, playing a part in the grand scheme that Daniel Burnham and Edward

Rooftop gardens were a part of Raymond Hood's early vision for urban place-making at Rockefeller Center. Once constructed, the gardens were somewhat less elaborate than the original scheme. *Right:* The final plan, as seen in this John Weinrich drawing, included formal gardens atop the British Empire Building (*above*) and the Maison Française.

Left. The soaring RCA Building stands at the core of Rockefeller Center in New York City. Architect Raymond Hood left the building unadorned except for its base and lobby, relying on the height of the crownless slab to convey the structure's status as commercial moneymaker and symbolic capital of Rockefeller Center.

Bennett proposed as part of the Chicago Plan of 1909 to carry Michigan Avenue north across the Chicago River. In 1918 Burnham and Bennett's proposal was further refined by Andrew Rebori, who designed a gateway plaza flanking Michigan Avenue between twin towers.[17] Yet before the bridge was finished, Graham, Anderson, Probst & White, the firm that succeeded Daniel Burnham's, had filled the site of Rebori's proposed west tower with the Wrigley Building (1921), a complexly massed structure with a tower, modeled on the Giralda Tower in Seville, rising as a freestanding column from a bent slab of white terra cotta.

Nonetheless, together with its extension of 1923–24, the Wrigley Building demonstrated to Chicagoans that the tall building could shape monumental public spaces. Hood's tower came much closer to the Rebori scheme, treating the *Tribune* headquarters as a campanile anchoring a corner of the plaza.

The 1922 *Tribune* competition was not only the first important international architectural competition after World War I but also one of the first American competitions sponsored by a corporation rather than a government agency or a cultural institution. As such it was an important milestone in the growing institutionalization of corporate capitalism. The foreign entries included the German Modernist architect Walter Gropius's design, arguably the boldest misunderstanding of McCormick's vision and American attitudes toward technology and corporate capitalism. A blunt essay in structural expression, with only the most tentative gestures to aesthetics, which took the form of a few gratuitous balconies that provided a De Stijlesque asymmetry, Gropius's factorylike scheme flew in the face of McCormick's symbolic intentions. It also failed to take into account that Americans, who lived their daily lives in close relationship to machines, did not see them as symbols in and of themselves but as instrumentalities of symbolism. Of the European submissions, none was more to the point or more beautiful than that of the Finnish architect Eliel Saarinen, whose lyrical, historically inexplicit but vaguely Gothic stepped-back tower was heralded by critics and many architects, including Louis Sullivan, whose essay "The

Paul Manship's gilded Prometheus adorns the sunken plaza at Rockefeller Center. It quickly became one of the world's most memorable places, with outdoor dining in summer and ice-skating in winter. The RCA Building stands behind the plaza.

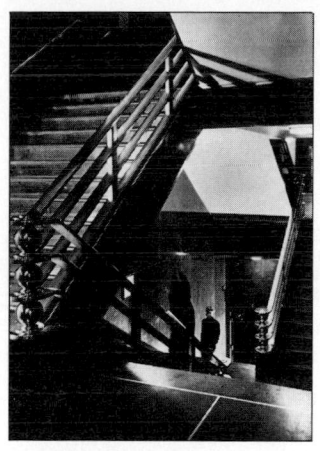

The wide staircase at the heart of the RCA Building lobby provided access to the upper levels, where the NBC studios were housed, and led to a well-lit concourse below.

The height and scale of the elaborately appointed lobby of the RCA Building was accentuated with rows of marble piers and a pattern of large concentric boxes on the floor. The mural by José Maria Sert is to the right, above the reception desk.

Chicago Tribune Competition" established the standard interpretation of Howells & Hood's scheme as "traditional" and Saarinen's as "modern," a somewhat flawed analysis given the structural and functional sophistication of the winning design and the historicizing detail of the runner-up. Although many of the European designs were startlingly innovative, anticipating the minimalism of post–World War II office building design, a number of them were laughable, including a German proposal for a tower crowned by a massive head of an American Indian with a tomahawk. But the most ironic and revealing commentary on American commercial architecture was a tall Doric column rising proudly from its pedestal, offered by Adolf Loos, an Austrian who had worked in Chicago in the 1890s. At once an homage to the skyscraper as column, a celebration of American ballyhoo, and a witty comment on newspapers and their *column*ists, Loos's scheme, though at the time taken as a joke, has come to seem a profound and knowing comment on the symbolic function of the American skyscraper.

Many of the American entries were less than inspiring, including Albert Randolph Ross and John Sloan's octagonal tower topped by a seven-storey statue of a Roman tribune. Several of the entries, however, did inspire skyscraper architects in the next decade, including Bertram G. Goodhue's, which stripped his 1921 Convocation Tower proposal of its clerical garb, flattened its decoration into the wall, and rose sheer from its stone-clad base to a central twenty-storey shaft, whose uninterrupted brick piers emphasized its verticality.

This 1933 photograph shows Mexican artist Diego Rivera with his wife, Frieda Kahlo, in front of his unfinished mural for the RCA Building lobby. Rivera was a Marxist. When it was discovered that he had included a portrait of Lenin in his painting, he was paid off and the mural was destroyed.

Loosely derived from the medieval "Butter Tower" at Rouen, Howells & Hood's Tribune Tower incorporated many advanced technological ideas, including chamfered corners glazed to emphasize the separateness of the masonry from the structure. But its expression was fundamentally traditional, as befit the wishes of McCormick, who was convinced that the greatness of his headquarters building, like that of the newspaper it served, depended on a sense of the living past. As the building went into construction, McCormick had fragments of the world's great architecture embedded in the base for all passers-by to see: a bit of the Great Wall of China, a chip of marble from the Taj Mahal, a piece of Chartres. Like so many restaurant ashtrays or hotel towels appropriated by globe-trotting Americans, each was a trophy allegedly smuggled from the sites McCormick visited during his world travels.

Hood came into his own as an innovator after winning the Tribune Tower competition, when the American Radiator and Standard Sanitary Company acknowledged their former radiator cover designer's newfound fame by commissioning him to design an office tower for a site opposite Bryant Park in

Manhattan. Though the massing of the building resembled that of the Tribune Tower, the profile of the tower, its subtle setbacks and its abstract gilded rooftop, and its dramatically black brick superstructure conspired to give the Neo-Gothicism of the earlier building a new lease on life. Hood was forthright about his sources, and in a statement of faith in eclecticism acknowledged his debt to his rivals, Saarinen, Goodhue, and Corbett, "who gave impetus to the study of [the skyscraper problem] and reproductions of whose drawings were scattered over our tables as we worked, [giving] us a lift over many rough places."[18]

The American Radiator Building (1924) was probably Hood's ideal commercial skyscraper, a design that mated Saarinen's abstract Gothicism to an innately American sense that the true symbolic function of a skyscraper was to represent, that is to advertise, the corporation it housed. Hood's decision to sheath the building in black brick enhanced the building's sense of mass. He reasoned that windows, normally seen as a monotonous pattern of black voids in the walls of towers clad in lighter materials, would virtually disappear when framed by black brick, allowing the building to be seen as a solid monument. Yet Hood lightened the building's grim monumentality by gilding the top with gold. During the day, the golden pinnacles and crown glittered above the stark black brick shaft, while at night the crest glowed with light, suggesting to some observers that Hood intended the design as a symbol of the furnaces and radiators sold by its owner.

Howells & Hood followed their Tribune collaboration with a design for the offices and printing plant of the *New York Daily News*. America's first mass-circulation tabloid, the *News* was led by Captain Joseph Medill Patterson, a campaigning populist and first cousin of Colonel McCormick of the *Chicago Tribune*. Stylistically, the Daily News Building (1930) was halfway between their overtly Gothic Chicago Tribune Tower and the technological expressionism of Gropius's proposal. The News Building's alternating pattern of vertical windows and brick piers was Gothic in spirit, yet Hood eliminated the decorative crown and chose instead to carry his unadorned ribbed cliffs from the sidewalk to the sky, justifying his design on functionalist grounds although he valued the walls' sweep of unending verticality enough to extend the façade ten feet beyond the upper storey to hide the building's ungainly rooftop services.[19]

Hood avoided applied ornament except for a narrow band at street level and a

Late in 1931, fifteen thousand dollars was set aside to embellish the public spaces of Rockefeller Center. Decorations included a sculpted panel by Isamu Noguchi entitled *News* (*left*), above the door of the Associated Press Building, and a gold-leaf figure of Mercury (*right*), representing commerce, on the British Empire Building.

striking two-storey-high granite frontispiece at the entrance that depicted the grandeur of the skyscraper city of New York (with the News Building at the center) and images of workers pursuing various trades, surrounding a quotation from Abraham Lincoln: "He made so many of them."[20] At the center of the glistening black entrance lobby, like the control tower of a Buck Rogers spaceship keeping pace with the earth itself, Hood placed an enormous globe, fifty feet in diameter, which told the time of day around the world to remind visitors that the scope of the *News* went beyond the skyscraper city to include the entire planet.

For the publishers McGraw-Hill, Hood did an abrupt about-face, exchanging the verticality of his former designs for one with horizontal bands of windows and blue-green tile, which was immediately seen as a somewhat superficial manifestation of European Modernism. More to the point, it showed both Hood's restless eclecticism and his commercial pragmatism. The McGraw-Hill Building (1932) was an ideally flexible loft for the widely divergent functions of a large publishing and printing operation, and its glazed terra-cotta skin was easy to maintain. But Hood also recognized the complexity of the skyscraper tower's "function." The building's color and the sign at the top — the owner's name wittily emblazoned in Broadway capitals — were calculated efforts at shock value, which, along with the crest's tombstone massing, dismayed architectural critics but succeeded as corporate advertising. In the interior, Hood showed a similar skill at using Modernism to his own ends. If the lobby was less dramatic than the Daily News Building's, it was far more vivacious. Its insistent multicolored stripping provoked the historian Vincent Scully to proclaim after his first visit that at last he knew what the inside of a juke box looked like.

Hood's designs for American Radiator, the *Daily News,* and McGraw-Hill were all individual events, responsive to the overall skyscraper city of Manhattan but, because of their sites, not capable of creating urban places as the Tribune Tower had in Chicago. With his last design, Rockefeller Center (1931–40), Hood would be given the chance to design the ultimate expression of America's skyscraper urbanism, in a project that called on his instincts for monumentality, corporate brio, and amenable urban place-making. It was a visionary scheme: born in the boom years of the twenties as a cultural center that would house a new Metropolitan Opera House, it evolved into a commercial venture in the Depression years of the thirties.

Many of Hood's proposals for Rockefeller Center never went further than beautiful renderings: skywalks between towers connecting rooftop gardens, which recalled his and Ferriss's visions of skyscraper cities as the modern version of the hanging gardens of Babylon; a low elliptical tower, which was lampooned by newspaper critics as an oil can symbolic of the source of Rockefeller's fortune. Yet Rockefeller Center as built was the manifestation of the dream Hood shared with the prophetic artists of the twenties: a city of proud towers defining great urban spaces, of vibrant congestion disciplined to the order of Classical composition.

Once again, Hood would draw on the work of Eliel Saarinen. Following the critical success of his Chicago Tribune entry, Saarinen was invited to the United States and in the next year (1923) completed a proposal for the Chicago lakefront which included a massive stepped-back skyscraper as an axial focus and urban place-maker, flanked by square, blocky Chicago Frame buildings and fronted by a landscaped plaza. Four years later, Hood presented his City of Towers proposal in

In 1935 people thronged to see entertainers such as Lydia and Joresco perform at the Rainbow Room, a mirrored palace for drinking, dining, and dancing on the sixty-fifth floor of Rockefeller Center's RCA Building.

The craze for bigger and better skyscrapers was at its peak when the Waldorf-Astoria Hotel was built in 1931. This 1937 drawing shows the allocation of space, which allowed the complex to function as a city within the city, catering to the rich and famous. The twin towers were built for permanent residency.

① SUBURBAN LEVEL
② HEATING
③ LIGHTING
④ VENTILATING
⑤ N.Y. CENTRAL TRACKS
⑥ EXPRESS LEVEL
⑦ EMPLOYEES LOCKERS
⑧ STORAGE
⑨ BANK
⑩ KITCHEN
⑪ BAKERY
⑫ SHOPS
⑬ DRIVEWAY
⑭ MEN'S BAR
⑮ GALLERY
⑯ FOYER
⑰ KITCHENS
⑱ PEACOCK ALLEY
⑲ LOBBY
⑳ LOCKERS
㉑ SHOPS
㉒ BARBER SHOP
㉓ EXECUTIVE OFFICE
㉔ ASTOR GALLERY

㉕ SILVER GALLERY
㉖ EAST COURT
㉗ EAST GALLERY
㉘ BALL ROOM
㉙ WEST GALLERY
㉚ WEST COURT
㉛ SERVICE
㉜ TERRACE
㉝ SERT ROOM
㉞ RADIO & TELEVISION
㉟ CENTER COURT
㊱ LIGHTING
㊲ TRANSIENT
㊳ TRANSIENT
㊴ JANSEN SUITE
㊵ STARLIGHT ROOF
㊶ PALM BAR
㊷ CANADIAN CLUB
㊸ CANADIAN CLUB
㊹ JUNIOR LEAGUE
㊺ TOWER SUITES
㊻ TOWER SUITES
㊼ PARK AVENUE
㊽ 50TH STREET
㊾ LEXINGTON AVENUE

THE WALDORF-ASTORIA
PARK AVENUE 49TH TO 50TH STREET NEW YORK CITY

which instead of one there were dozens of gargantuan towers, but wide enough apart to equal the emblematic power of Saarinen's design. In 1929 Hood contributed to a less purely visionary project, Terminal Park in Chicago, in association with Ralph Walker and the firm of Holabird & Root. Hood and his colleagues proposed a vast complex of stepped slabs rising toward blocky towers at the center, which would form, as an aggregate, a kind of city within the city. The project, never realized, called for a road mall running east-west, intersected by a cross street near the lakefront. Four exceptionally tall towers flanked this intersection, echeloning along crossed diagonal axes. In the cluster of towers at the core, the Terminal Park proposal related directly to one of Hood's earliest designs for Rockefeller Center, which he called "The Fling," never expecting his colleagues to consider it seriously. Like Terminal Park, its cluster of towers read as one enormous structure on the scale of Hood's City of Towers fantasy, here cleft asunder by intersecting streets.

Rockefeller Center's final design rejected the terrifying giantism of Terminal Park and The Fling, defining its central square with one enormous skyscraper rather than four and putting two buildings at its flanks, a scheme closer to Saarinen's 1923 proposal than was Terminal Park six years later.

Less than the city within the city it has frequently been labeled, Rockefeller Center was a monumental fragment, an urban place blown up to metropolitan scale: the soaring slab of the seventy-storey RCA Building was its focal pylon, closing the vista granted by the Channel Gardens, a green sliver of ceremonial axiality wedged between as much hollowed-out masonry as corporate greed could get away with. The rooftop gardens, neither as luxuriant as in Hood's vision nor linked by skybridges, included formal gardens atop the British Empire and Maison Française buildings and, to sustain the international theme, the Gardens of the Nations — fragments of Spain, Japan, France, Italy, and England on a New York roof. Refreshing the eyes of office workers, the gardens treated them to a spectacle of water and greenery as well as Rockettes at their leisure between acts at Radio City Music Hall. While subway-bound crowds were less well tended, they were given well-lit, shop-lined concourses to walk through. At the foot of the pylon lay the grottolike sunken plaza. Lined with restaurants and shops, the plaza quickly became one of the world's most memorable public places, with outdoor dining in summer and ice-skating in winter. How ironic that amidst the economic collapse of the 1930s Rockefeller Center should provide the preeminent demonstration that American capitalism could achieve lasting monuments comparable to those of monarchical Europe. By the 1960s, Rockefeller Center, as Vincent Scully has observed, continued to function as "one of the few surviving public spaces in America that look as if they were designed and used by people who knew what stable wealth was and were not ashamed to admit it. Flags snap, high heels tap: a little sex and aggression, the city's delights. Jefferson would have hated it all."[21]

The flat-topped slab of the RCA Building, finished in 1934, when compared to the decorative tower of the first RCA Victor Building, completed only three years before by Cross & Cross, shows how rapidly skyscraper design evolved and how quickly a corporation was willing to move its headquarters to acquire a more impressive, stylistically up-to-date edifice. The earlier building rose from a stocky base to a thin tower topped by prickly finials, whose zigzag forms quite possibly were intended to represent the vibrating Victrola needles that helped to make the company's fortune.

The new RCA Building reserved its decoration for the base and lobby, where it took up far more metaphysical concerns than Victrola needles to sustain Rockefeller Center's feeling of grand theater for workers and visitors. The development's builders were determined to give it an aura of cultural grandeur, even though the impetus for the project — a new home for the Metropolitan Opera — was abandoned a month after the 1929 crash. Hartley Burr Alexander, a professor of philosophy at the University of Nebraska, who had already developed an artistic program for the Nebraska State Capitol, was hired by Rockefeller to

Overleaf. The glass-skinned exterior of the Citicorp Building in New York reflects not only its immediate surroundings but the style of urban architecture that had become prevalent by the late 1970s.

The 1960 movie *The Apartment* featured Jack Lemmon as a victim of the modernized corporate world. The office in which he worked represented the anonymous nature of the International Style.

articulate a theme that would serve as a program for the artists who would be called upon to embellish the buildings. Alexander's first proposal, "Homo fabor, Man the Builder,"[22] was rejected and his next one, "Frontiers of Civilization," also fizzled, but both ideas were incorporated into the final mouth-filling decision: "New Frontiers and the March of Civilization." A team of artists were employed to render this theme, including Paul Manship, whose gaudily gilded Prometheus became an internationally beloved symbol.

A mural by Diego Rivera, the Mexican Marxist painter, was destroyed before it could be seen by the public. Rivera had been hired to paint the main lobby of the RCA Building with a gracelessly phrased theme: "Man at the Crossroads Looking with Uncertainty but with Hope and High Vision to the Choosing of a Course Heading to a New and Better Future." Whatever possessed John D. Rockefeller, Jr.'s son, the twenty-four-year-old Nelson, to suggest a Marxist surpasses logical examination. The best explanation is that of the senior Rockefeller, who dryly commented that "as for Rivera . . . he seems to have become very popular just now and will probably be a good drawing card."[23] Rivera's mural was destroyed and he was paid off when it was discovered that it included á portrait of Lenin. José Maria Sert, the fashionable Spanish artist, painted a less controversial but no less ideological work on the theme of "American Progress: The Triumph of Man's Accomplishments Through Physical and Mental Labor," which depicts Rockefeller Center itself as the leading symbol of that triumph and Abraham Lincoln and Ralph Waldo Emerson, not Lenin, as its guides.

At the heart of the RCA Building's lobby, broad stairs led to the NBC studios, where the famed "Studio H" brought the musicianship of Toscanini to millions. Elevators sped Gothamites to a sixty-fifth-floor mirrored drinking, dining, and dancing palace, the Rainbow Room, the real-life inspiration for the celluloid settings of countless musical supper clubs, such as the Club Raymond in *Swing Time* (1936), where Fred Astaire and Ginger Rogers waltzed across the silver screen. Above, on the building's roof, broad as the deck of an ocean liner, tourists could confront visitors at the top of the Empire State Building almost eyeball to eyeball, like suburban neighbors exchanging pleasantries over a back yard fence. The canyons of Manhattan were, for a moment at least, brought down to the scale of Main Street.

Rockefeller Center is a monument to its principal designer, Raymond Hood. His vision was projected so coherently that, despite the Depression, his collaborators were able to bring it to its full conclusion by 1939, ten years after work began.

When the economy began to surge after World War II, America's skyscraper dream seemed drained of energy. Tall buildings were no longer proud towers but just high-rises. City pride seemed to give way to suburb pride. The glamour of city life and city building succumbed to the opportunism of real estate speculators with much narrower visions than the builders of Rockefeller Center and the Empire State Building. Office buildings became commodities, warehouses for workers no different in conception from the refrigerators that the icebox coldness of their steel and glass exteriors suggested. The office blocks of postwar America rose as so many rentable floors of anonymous space in so many dumb boxes. They became the perfect embodiment of the hegemony of the man in the gray flannel suit. This anonymity was more than a change in architectural taste or even a failure of aesthetic and corporate nerve; it revealed America's disenchantment with cities. Corporations abandoned the cities and the skyscraper ideal, moving their offices to suburban sites whose Arcadian neutrality was only too convincingly reinforced by their architecture. In the suburbs, the office building, as we have seen, camouflaged itself in the aesthetics of the factory and the aura of the academical village. With the action shifted to the suburbs and the once-open country, the cities' increasing dullness was memorialized in the black glass office towers that replaced the rich dream façades of the prewar generation. The subject of the new buildings was not architecture as a representation of the American dream — not America as a new Rome or a glorified Victrola needle — but merely the task of building, the weary effort of it all, just the facts of technology and the corporate bureaucracy that oiled the economy.

Worse still, beloved landmarks only thirty or forty years old began to fall. Morgan, Walls & Clement's vividly polychromed 371-foot-high black and gold Richfield Building (1929) — a building that brought the glamour of Hood's American Radiator Building to Los Angeles — was toppled in 1968 to give way to the twin monoliths of ARCO Plaza. More shocking still, Ernest Flagg's Singer Tower in lower Manhattan, once the world's tallest and still one of its most beautiful skyscrapers, was torn down in 1967 to make way for the black-framed behemoth of Skidmore, Owings & Merrill's headquarters for U.S. Steel (1974). Not a tear was shed for the old masterpiece or for the city forced to absorb its brutish replacement. American architecture had turned its back on its own unique achievements. It not only gave up the search for a usable past, it even gave up caring about the differences between places: New York, Houston, Dallas, Phoenix, and Los Angeles began to look alike; and as the world of multinational capitalism began to emerge, cities worldwide began to look alike — and less than notably like Houston. Singapore, Hong Kong, and West Berlin were rebuilt in the architectural equivalent of the linguists' pet dream, a language that no one can speak because its roots are theoretical rather than cultural. Architectural Esperanto, correctly labeled the International Style, succeeded all too well in its vision of a universal, uniform approach to building design, not only creating all places pretty much the same but also transforming streets and avenues — the very arteries that rendered the old, pre-Modernist cities vital — into Norman Mailer's "empty landscapes of psychosis." Architects and developers, breaking their contract with the city and its people to create and maintain a sense of place, doomed the public to a blank-walled townscape without grace, to buildings without memory or meaning.

Pride of place was out; so too was pride of craft. The bigger the brick, the quicker the buck. Most buildings of this corporate International Style confirmed the growing fear that modern civilization was becoming a mere by-product of the corporations. To them we were all organization men and women, increasingly doomed to resemble automatons in the new computer world — a vision amusingly but tellingly parodied in films such as *The Apartment* (1960) and raised to sensational heights in *Blade Runner* (1982). By the 1970s, architecture had lost not only its dream but also a sense of its own past, resulting in an utter denial of the street-level life and the harmony of towers imagined and built in the 1930s by Raymond Hood. The dream had turned sour. The dark side of skyscrapers prophesied by Lang in *Metropolis* had come.

Just what had gone wrong? As we saw in chapter 1, the idealists of the

Modern movement in Europe were indirectly responsible for America's dull towers and the collapse of American urbanism. Antonio Sant'Elia's dream-vision drawings of an American city revealed a contempt for the traditional city and a passion for the same cruel new world of speed and violence that his Futurist contemporary Filippo Tommaso Marinetti had celebrated in the Futurist Manifesto of 1909 and reasserted in "War, the World's Only Hygiene" (1911–15):

Nothing is more beautiful than the steel frame of a house in construction. To a finished house we prefer the framework of a house in construction whose girders are the color of danger — landing platforms for airplanes. . . . The steel skeleton with its rhythms of blocks and pulleys, of harness and hearts, and from time to time — yes, let it happen — the harrowing cry and heavy thud of a fallen construction worker, great drop of blood in the pavement.[24]

Sant'Elia, whose taste also ran to gruesome dynamism, wrote:

We must reinvent and rebuild *ex novo* our Modern city like an immense and tumultuous shipyard, active, mobile, and everywhere dynamic, and the modern building like a gigantic machine. . . . The house of cement, iron, and glass . . . extraordinarily brutish in its mechanistic simplicity . . . must rise from the brick of a tumultuous abyss: the street which, itself, will no longer lie like a doormat at the level of the thresholds, but plunge storeys deep into the earth, gathering up the traffic of the metropolis.[25]

Sant'Elia's was perhaps the first dream of American architecture and life ever dreamed by a European architect; it was also the most misconceived and ultimately the most destructive.

Behind Sant'Elia's dream also lay Louis Sullivan's 1891 vision of a skyscraper city and King's *Views of New York,* as well as the intricate, multilevel complexities of

The bland, boxlike buildings that appeared on the American urban landscape after World War II had their roots in the European Modern movement of the early twentieth century. In 1914 Italian architect Antonio Sant'Elia sketched his dream of the American city (*above*), with buildings resembling giant machines. This vision was later interpreted by Le Corbusier in his design of La Ville Radieuse (*right*), an ideal city of uniform, unornamented towers rising from a gridlike plain.

Grand Central Station, a widely published engineering wonder of the day. Sant'Elia's architectural career was cut short by World War I: appropriately enlisting in a motorcycle brigade, he died in an attack at Monfalcone in 1916. But his dream was not lost; part of it, its fleshy materialism, lived on in America in the urbanism of Ferriss, Corbett, and Hood, each of whom romanticized not only the skyscraper but also the churning gorges of traffic below. But its underlying premise, its bones, picked clean of the dreamlike historicism of American practice, was given a new, sleek treatment by Le Corbusier, the Swiss Calvinist architect, painter, and polemicist. Le Corbusier's avowed ideals of managerial and technological efficiency translated into uniform design were complemented by those of Ludwig Mies van der Rohe, whose aphorism "Less is more" neatly boxed the Modernist ideal.

While Hood, Corbett, and Ferriss dreamed of a new Babylonian urbanism, rich with historical reference and detail, a sublime mixture of terrifyingly high skybridges and serenely beautiful roof gardens, Le Corbusier sketched a world relentlessly locked into a shadowless present. His dream encased the bureaucrats of business and commerce in huge unornamented and uniform office blocks, which he dubbed "Cartesian" out of respect for the French logician. Le Corbusier's towers were to be reserved for the new managerial elite, who after their working day traveled high-speed roadways to be decanted into stacked duplexes around the edges of the park. Like his contemporary T. S. Eliot, Le Corbusier emulated this managerial elite, transforming himself into the bowler-hatted man in the black suit that Charlie Chaplin would parody. To Le Corbusier the American skyscrapers were too little and too close. He saw his city of the future spaced out wide, with towers rising from a gridded plain. The shadows and slow-moving traffic of the traditional street were eliminated, the sordid intimacy of a chance encounter on a sidewalk replaced by the impersonal telephone.

Le Corbusier never built an entire ideal city anywhere, but he saw his urbanism, if not his luminous architecture, realized in the high-rise projects that typified postwar housing in American cities. Here the very unmanagerial poor were forced to live in buildings modeled on the abstract towers Le Corbusier had imagined for the corporate bureaucracy. Meanwhile, the middle class, the managerial elite, free to exercise its preferences, escaped to single-family houses in the suburbs.

Even more so, Mies van der Rohe laid his stamp on the character of America's apartment and office buildings in the postwar era. The vision of Mies preceded Le Corbusier's. Amidst the havoc, destruction, and disillusionment of post–World War I Germany, Mies had dreamed of crystalline office towers composed of layer upon layer of universal space, gridded by steel, girdled by walls of glass. His architecture, even more than Walter Gropius's Tribune competition design two years later, appeared to be completely neutral, epitomizing a belief that the modern world would benefit from its liberation from the historical tyranny of the establishment that had conspired behind the stone walls of palaces. Close examination of Mies's buildings suggests that the liberation would take three forms: transparent glass walls would render the machinations of government and corporations visible to all; buildings physically composed as uniform extrusions with no discernible top and bottom would suggest an antigravitational force and eliminate any representation of hierarchy; and shapes as contradictory to prevailing urban patterns as possible would destroy the age-old notion of solid buildings defining open spaces in cities, without which mass political meetings and military demonstrations would be impossible.

But by the time Mies got to build tall buildings in the United States, twenty-five years later, he would, like Le Corbusier, first see his ideal realized mostly for apartment houses and not for office buildings. Mies, however, controlled the design and built for the elite, who, unlike the poor stacked in their Le Corbusier–inspired towers, could decide for themselves whether or not to live as part of a visionary's ideal. Mies's own choice of domicile in Chicago speaks volumes: he

Disillusionment following World War I gave rise to visions of an ideal world, free from the tyranny of traditional political and social structures. For Ludwig Mies van der Rohe (*above*), this vision took the form of Modernist buildings of steel columns and glass walls.

Right. Mies's Lake Shore Drive Apartments in Chicago are an example of his crystalline dream compromised. Forced to adjust his aesthetic to American building techniques and capabilities, the towers incorporated less glass than his earlier plans had called for.

lived in a brick and stone building of the 1920s, in an apartment with high ceilings, rich moldings, and big, untinted windows, through which he could clearly see his magnificently sculpted Lake Shore Drive Apartments (1952) yet not have to endure their interiors, rendered murky by acres of glass tinted to make them habitable. Radical as Mies's Chicago apartments were, they were not really as glassy as his projects of 1919–21. American building technology was not able to keep up with Mies's crystalline dream, so that when he immigrated to Chicago in 1938, he was forced to develop a new aesthetic of building, based on American techniques as they were rather than as he'd imagined them. Translating Sullivan's terra-cotta

With the Seagram Building in New York, Mies demonstrated that less could indeed be more. It stands as a proud corporate monument, set back from Park Avenue by the broad plaza in front. Its curtain wall of glass is framed by bronzed metal mullions, which lend the building a visual solidity.

ideal of a tower where the "function *created* or organized its form"[26] into steel, aluminum, and glass, Mies evolved a far more solid and ultimately traditional language of composition and began to reunite the humanistic ideals of Classicism with contemporary building techniques.

Like Burnham half a century before, Mies found his greatest opportunity as a skyscraper architect not in Chicago but in New York, where he built the Seagram Building in 1958, demonstrating a purity of vision that showed up the era's typical corporate Modernism for the tinsel it was and revealed how his own work had suffered for lack of amply funded patronage. The Seagram Building is perhaps the only Modernist skyscraper to succeed as a corporate monument. Compared to this proud tower of buccaneer capitalism, all of the glassy boxes of corporate Modernism seem little more than disposable gift wrapping. As no other building of its type before or since, the Seagram celebrates the grid with which the real estate investor had bought and sold America. It reinvents the classical Sullivanian approach in terms of metal and glass. Without terra-cotta ornament but with "God in the details," it returns us to Sullivan's anthropomorphic skyscraper ideal that a building should stand on two legs, not four. The result was not a seemingly insubstantial glass tower but a mordant design of tinted glass panels, deeply framed in mullions of bronze. The Seagram Building demonstrated that the corollary to Mies's claim that less is more was that where building budgets are concerned, more is more.

The initiative had come from Phyllis Lambert, the daughter of Samuel Bronfman, Seagram's president. Lambert took charge of the situation after reading in a Paris newspaper that her father was about to hire Charles Luckman, an American architect once employed as the president of Lever Brothers soap company. Assisted by Philip Johnson, then Director of Architecture at the Museum of Modern Art, Lambert interviewed a number of architects, including Frank Lloyd Wright, who said he would see Lambert's father only if fifty thousand dollars was deposited in his Wisconsin bank. Lambert and Johnson settled on Mies, which was not surprising given that Johnson had been advocating Mies's vision for thirty years.

Mies did not disappoint. His solution was a profound if not particularly sympathetic statement about the city. Breaking with the wall of Park Avenue — a pattern much less convincingly initiated under Luckman's direction by Skidmore, Owings & Merrill at Lever House (1952) — Mies created a broad plaza, itself an expression of corporate grandeur, that freed his design to rise more independent of its urban context than any twenties skyscraper, including Hood's RCA Building. The curtain wall of glass was framed behind a precise composition of bronzed metal mullions, which, while it ostensibly stiffened the glass wall, was really there to give the design visual solidity. The plaza was an austere stage for the tower, relieved only by two reflecting pools and some trees. Though Mies provided no benches and no hot-dog vendor, New Yorkers adopted it as a new square, flocking there to eat lunch, sun themselves, and stroll. Perhaps it was just absence of any other place to go that drew people to it; more likely it was the tower's grace and its seeming inevitability of form, as well as the Sullivanian humanism of the design, that lured them. The Seagram Building took the two-footed stance of a man, if not a very warm-blooded one. It came to symbolize the cool elegance, even indifference, of the mid-century urban gentleman — so much so that in Stephen

The forty-two-storey Cathedral of Learning (*top*) at the University of Pittsburgh, designed by Day & Klauder in 1926, was a source of stylistic inspiration for PPG Place (*bottom*), by Johnson and Burgee. At PPG Place the architects achieved a synthesis of old and new, creating a Gothic tower in glass — and a brazen display of the Pittsburgh Plate Glass Company's best-known product.

Sondheim's musical *Company* (1970), the suave, unmarried Bobby is compared to it: "You know what comes to my mind when I see him? The Seagram Building. Isn't that funny?"[27]

By the late sixties, technology had caught up with Mies's post–World War I dream of crystalline towers for a managerial elite. Its ironic fulfillment came in the glazed packing crates of corporate bureaucracy that loom above the plains in the Sun Belt cities, those icily impersonal cubes dominating the downtown skylines and reflecting onto the sidewalks below the blazing heat of cities like Fort Worth and Dallas. What had been imagined as a liberating ideal of enlightened efficiency in two generations had become mindless.

American urbanism had become so laid back as to appear virtually kicked over. Cities seemed lifeless and incapable of self-preservation. All that Raymond Hood had stood for at Rockefeller Center had been contradicted. The dream of an American Babylon of gardens and towers and walkways full of people was fast fading into one of corporate ghost towns, impersonal work places that never came alive. The architectural excitement of the 1920s seemed as remote as ancient Babylon itself.

"Less" had revealed itself a bore; Mies's leading corporate disciples, Skidmore, Owings & Merrill, had spread his work quickly and glibly across the country. To younger architects, the Seagram Building, with its echoes, however faint, of humanism mixed with swaggering corporate capitalism, was an end, not a beginning: fittingly, a young Austrian architect, Hans Hollein, like his predecessor Adolf Loos in the 1922 Tribune Tower competition two generations before, captured the essence of the skyscraper for his own generation. Visiting the United States as a student, Hollein revolted against the strictures of Mies's educational program at the Illinois Institute of Technology and found freedom at the Berkeley campus of the University of California. Back in Vienna, Hollein presented as one of his first and best-known projects a design that decorated the bland box of the Chase Manhattan Bank (Skidmore, Owings & Merrill, 1960) with a Classical pediment, thereby issuing a call for architects to recapture the symbolic possibilities of great height and symbolic resonance.

Only one major architect appeared to understand Hollein's point. Philip Johnson, at one time a devout advocate of Mies's architecture and his associate on the Seagram Building, working with John Burgee, began to issue a series of daring designs for tall buildings, including Pennzoil Place (1974–76), Transco Tower (1983), and RepublicBank Center (1984), all in Houston, as well as the AT&T Building in New York (1978–84) and PPG Place in Pittsburgh (1985), which, as discussed in chapter 1, rekindled the confident spirit of the 1920s, once again deserving the name skyscrapers.

The first of these buildings by Johnson and Burgee was designed for the Investors Diversified Services company in Minneapolis and completed in 1973. The scheme turned to Mies's earliest skyscraper design, his 1921 proposal of a prismatic all-glass tower, and combined it with the confident skyscraper urbanism of American architecture in the 1920s. It realized not only the technology of Mies's 1921 proposal but also the expressionist magic that Mies had imagined, with corners seemingly dissolving into their own reflections. The IDS Center also recalled the urbanism of the great lobbies of nineteenth-century office buildings such as the Rookery in Chicago and such downtown shopping centers as the

This recent photograph of lower Manhattan highlights the evolution of the skyscraper, with the Gothic splendor of the Woolworth Building, 1913 (*center*), standing in stark contrast to the Modern towers of the World Trade Center, 1976 (*right*). In the foreground is a typical New York City apartment house.

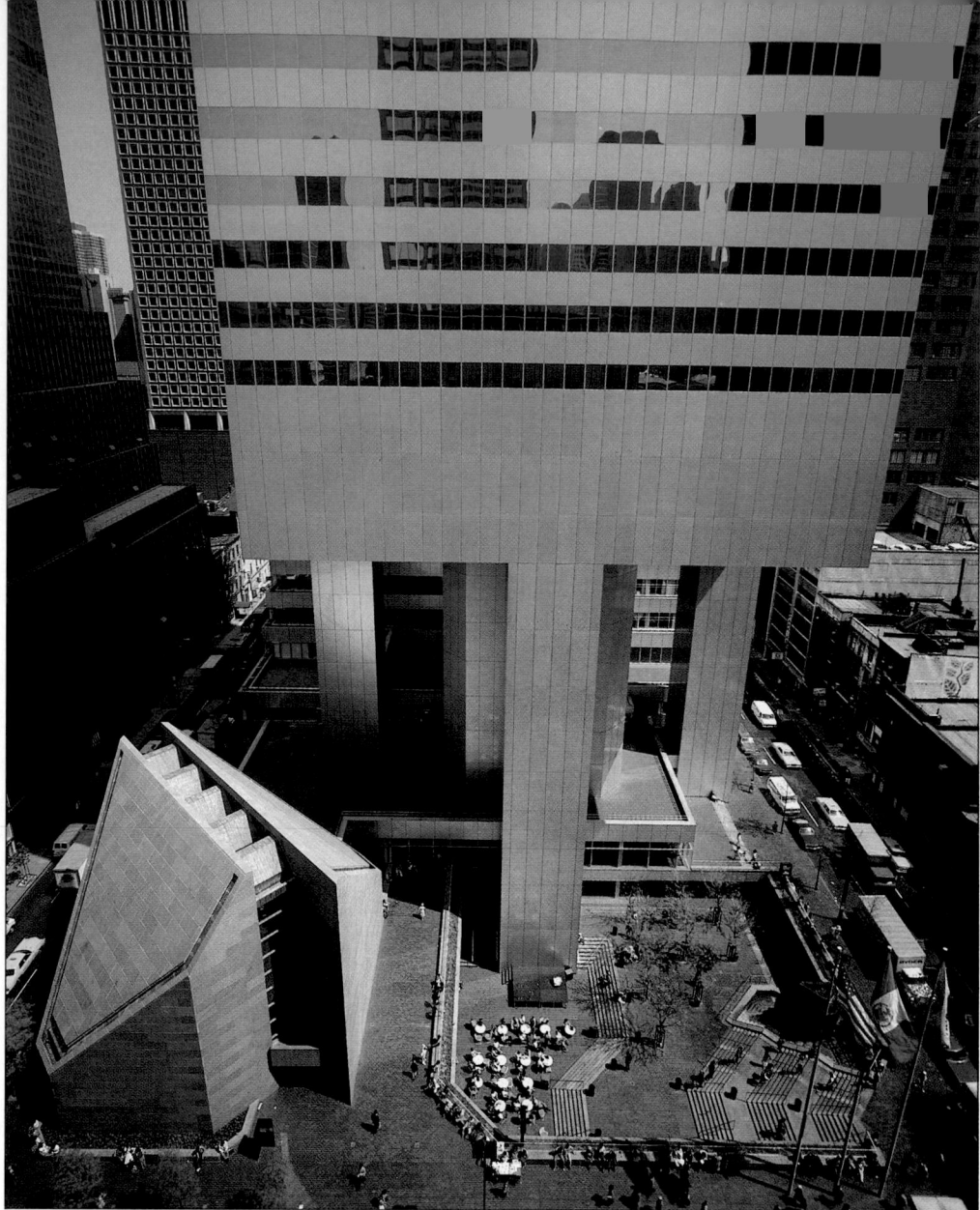

Cleveland Arcade in Johnson's native city. Johnson created a glazed atrium, a vast public room on two levels that serves as an indoor town square protected from Minneapolis's harsh winters and connected to the surrounding city through a network of enclosed pedestrian bridges called "skyways" that realize Ferriss's visions of a skyscraper urbanism, if not quite at the same dizzying heights.

Johnson and Burgee's skyscrapers have prompted a Renaissance in American skyscraper architecture. Michael Graves's Humana Tower (1985) in Louisville, Kentucky, marries idiosyncratic Classicism to complex abstract geometries. The building occupies its entire site, posing as a public institution and suggesting monumentality, as does Johnson and Burgee's AT&T Building, by gesture rather than by extreme height or daunting plazas. Although only twenty-six storeys high, the Humana Tower invokes the thrilling outdoor pleasure of skyscraper living imagined by Hood and Ferriss by placing a truss-supported garden balcony along the twenty-fourth floor, overlooking Main Street and the Ohio River beyond.

Even Skidmore, Owings & Merrill, past master of the anonymous box, has increasingly abandoned its engineering aesthetic in favor of individualistic designs

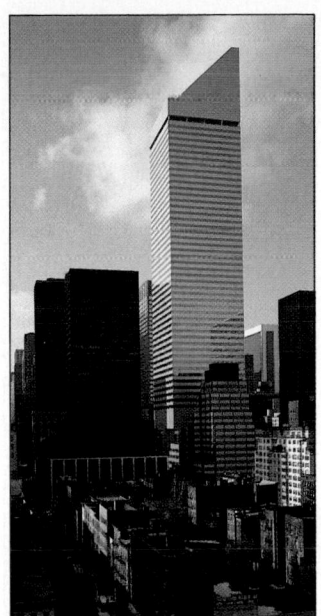

Originally intended to harness solar power, the distinctive ski-slope top of the Citicorp Building was retained as a glistening advertisement for the bank.

harking back to the spirit and forms of the 1920s skyscraper era. As early as 1974 in Chicago, it abandoned the corseted structuralism of the John Hancock Center (1970) for the stepped-back masses of the Sears Tower (1974), touted as an engineering marvel of bundled tubes but most remarkable for its profile, evoking New York's 1920s skyline. At 1,454 feet, it was also the world's tallest building, reinitiating the race for height of a half century before and proving that height could again be exciting — a point unfortunately lost on the Sears Tower's competitor, the supremely mute World Trade Center (Minoru Yamasaki & Associates, 1976), a twin-tower complex that does, however, succeed as a work of megalomaniacal minimalist sculpture. Closer to the ground, Skidmore, Owings & Merrill has shown a new skill in designing towers that create rather than destroy urban places. The fifty-storey LTV Center in Dallas (1985) was built in a section of town that the city's leaders were determined to fill with the brontosaurus of the prairie — the pedestrian. LTV Center is meant to serve as both campanile and town square in the new Arts District, and the tower's soaring bays and pyramidal top are the background to a two-storey shopping pavilion and plaza below.

Though aspects of these contemporary skyscrapers may push the frontiers of technology a bit, it is their success as art, as corporate art, if you will, that is critical. For in the end it is the look of the building that matters. Not that its features are independent of function, but that they go beyond function toward poetry. The great ski slope–like diagonally pitched roof of the Citicorp Building in New York (Hugh Stubbins & Associates, 1977) was originally built to harness solar power — probably a preposterous notion. When the technical problems rendered the feature impossible, the roof line was retained as a glistening, skyline-enhancing advertisement for the bank.

Back on the street — beneath the Citicorp's stainless steel–clad legs — rests the abstracted form of St. Peter's Church, which sold its site to the bank with the idea that it could return as part of the new building. But St. Peter's cringes beneath the giant, a pathetic heir to churches whose steeples once constituted proud towers defining the American skyline.

For it is not height but pride — the ability to appear tall — that inspires. The ever so modestly tall tower of Bertram Goodhue's Los Angeles Public Library (1925), a symbol of a city's dedication to learning, still holds its own amidst the bland venality of the postwar city. And in New York, where all this began, Trinity Church still keeps watch over the skyscraper city — a warning to all who would confuse size with glory, a warning that it is not height but its poetic possibilities that inspire and endure.

8 The Garden and the Grid

The story of American urbanism, like that of American architecture, is the story of beginning anew. American cities are based on old ideas of planning, but they also have the distinction of having begun de novo, from nothing, new. Though the nation has grown from less than 4 million in 1776 to 50 million in 1880 to more than 230 million today, it is the vast open space of the continent that remains the quintessential fact of American architecture and urbanism. That vastness has from the first opened the possibility of continual renewal: if one place grows old or dull, get away, hit the road, begin again. It has provided opportunity and, increasingly with the passage of time, a terrible responsibility as well: can America come to terms with its growing antiquity? Can it renew itself, not by beginning again and again and again, but by rediscovering and revitalizing its own urban tradition, a tradition that combines the practicality of the grid with the ideality of the garden?

The founders of Colonial America's early cities believed in the city as a place of reason, a marriage of circumstance, belief, and the liberating logic of plane geometry. Yet Americans have always been ambivalent about cities; as summed up in that old saying: it's a nice place to visit, but I wouldn't want to live there. That ambivalence can be found even in Thomas Jefferson, who dreamed of an agrarian democracy and condemned large cities as "pestilential to the *morals*, the *health*, and the *liberties* of man,"[1] yet considered urban growth inevitable and insisted that the new nation's cities be as rationally planned as possible. To Jefferson, this meant a gridiron of streets and open squares, a pattern that had been held up as an ideal in America since the earliest Colonial settlement.

The grid was at once practical and idealistic. By the seventh century B.C., the ancient Greeks planned their colonial cities along straightforward orthogonal lines in order to organize urban life and secure property values far away from the traditional centers of culture and power. It was also the ancient Greeks who first imbued the grid with idealism. Philosophers like Hippodamus came to describe the grid as an embodiment of a universal logic that transcended daily reality, a cosmic order rendered tangible. As a result, cities like Miletus, rebuilt in the fifth century B.C., were laid out according to geometric principles rather than topographic considerations. The Romans adopted the grid, both as a military necessity and as an ideal representation of urban order in which the ease of physical mobility reflected the social mobility granted in the most heterogeneous, urbanized empire the world had yet seen.

The resurgence of Classical culture in the Renaissance included the

In the painstaking restoration of Colonial Williamsburg, Virginia, some elements were idealized: for example, the beautiful new gardens were probably more elaborate than the simple, functional ones planted by eighteenth-century colonists. The Governor's Palace stands in the background.

Since ancient times, the grid has represented an ideal of urban planning. Europeans hoped to extend that ideal to their new settlements in the Colonies. In this unrealized 1660 plan for New Amsterdam — now Manhattan — rectangular city lots and a typical plaza are enclosed by a fortress wall.

rediscovery of the Classical city. By the sixteenth century, the concept of the grid as an urban ideal had spread throughout Europe. Colonization offered modern European nations the opportunity to realize their urbanistic ideals in the construction of new settlements. For instance, the directors of the Dutch West India Company in Holland drew up a neat, symmetrical plan for their American colony, New Amsterdam, in 1625. It called for rectangular city lots within a pentagonal fortress and rectangular farming lots outside the walls. But the colonists who actually settled on the tip of Manhattan Island largely ignored the plan, building a city like the one they knew back home. Boston, founded five years later as the principal city of the Massachusetts Bay Colony, also developed without geometric imperatives. A hilly peninsula, it lacked the level ground that could easily accommodate a grid. Boston grew into an irregular pattern of crooked streets and squares, its outlines determined by the shoreline, marshes, and hills. Colonial New York and Boston, however, were destined to be the exception rather than the rule, because America, founded in the Age of Reason on the principles of that era, for the most part was laid out rationally.

Ironically, it was at first not the emphasis on efficient commerce — later a hallmark of American life — that was expressed in its urban settlement patterns but rather obedience to authority. The Spanish priests and soldiers who came to settle the new continent were more closely tied to royal authority than the farmers and tradesmen of New Amsterdam. They adhered to the Laws of the Indies, an edict of 1573 which mandated that towns be designed to emphasize government authority as well as facilitate trade. These towns, including San Antonio (1730) and Los Angeles (1781), built at the farthest outposts of the Spanish Empire, incorporated a regular grid of orthogonal blocks, extending the physical and intellectual discipline of geometry into the wilderness. A rectangular plaza, ideally 600 by 400 feet, was the town center. There the institutions of church, government, and commerce were each represented in commanding buildings. The Laws of the Indies demanded that the uniformity of the plaza be sustained beyond the central area "for the sake of the beauty of the town."[2] This idealistic, aesthetic vision of the city derived from Leon Battista Alberti's *De re aedificatoria*. Written in Rome between 1443 and 1452 and published posthumously in 1485, Alberti's treatise advocated the rebirth of the ancient city plans as an antidote to the organically evolved medieval reality, which he condemned as irrational.

To plan towns in New France, Jean Baptiste le Moyne, sieur de Bienville, governor of the French colony, instituted formal, gridded schemes. First establishing Colonial rule in Fort Louis on Mobile Bay in 1702, Bienville planned Mobile in 1711 and New Orleans in 1722 around central parade grounds, or *places d'armes*, with gridded streets to each side. In Mobile the fort, containing the governor's house and guardhouse, intruded on the rectangular *place*, but in New Orleans the place opened directly onto the quay, its three other sides formed by the town's principal buildings. The church, at the center of the inland side, overlooking the square and the river beyond, also marked the town's central axis, cut through the three blocks behind the church.

Boston's plan, with its pragmatic and organic irregularities, was not typical of English settlements, which as often as not brought the same Renaissance ideal of a disciplined, rational Classicism to the New World. But the English also brought with them another Classical vision, that of an idyllic, heavenly life in a garden — Arcadia. For them, the cities in the New World held the promise of being rationally planned utopian communities that embraced both the grid and the garden. To

San Antonio was typical of Spanish settlements in the New World. Arranged around a central plaza (*above*) were commanding church, government, and commerce buildings that formed a backdrop to citizens' activities (*right*).

The grid plan of Savannah, Georgia, embodied the democratic principles of its founder, James Oglethorpe. In this 1734 drawing, the main street leads from the banks of the river to the settlement's outer edge. Open squares at regular intervals provide easy access to the town's common areas.

the settlers of New Haven, Connecticut, the new town was to be an earthly representation of the city of God. New Haven was the first English city in America laid out according to abstract laws of geometry. Its nine-square gridiron plan of 1638 was a near-perfect geometric figure, shifted slightly off alignment with the cardinal points in order to fit between the area's two roughly perpendicular rivers. According to tradition, it was devised by John Brockett. The plan may have represented humanist metaphysics, or a literal interpretation of the description of the New Jerusalem in Revelations: "And the city lieth foursquare, and the length is as the breadth."[3] The central open area in New Haven's grid was occupied by a common, or green, a feature that would become the most formal expression of public life in most New England settlements. Three churches and the Connecticut State House were set within its borders. Buildings devoted to commerce, municipal government, and education, as represented by Yale College, as well as houses surrounded the green.

In 1681, William Penn used a gridiron plan to lay out Philadelphia. He went beyond the idealism of the New Haven plan to anticipate the commercial realities of a Colonial capital: the grid provided easily divisible real estate. It also inhibited the catastrophic spread of fire and disease that had been fostered by the narrow, crooked street patterns of Europe's medieval cities. But Penn's use of the grid went beyond purely practical considerations to mandate the partial preservation of a rural landscape. In a letter to the settlers of Philadelphia, Penn described the placement of houses within a grid: "Let every house be placed, if the person pleases, in the middle of its plat, as to the breadth way of it, so there may be ground on each side for gardens or orchards, or fields, that it may be a green country town, which will never be burnt, and always be wholesome."[4] In the finished plan of 1683, Penn included a central square, and four others symmetrically disposed, to assure that even if the settlers did not "please" to set their houses in open lots, some feeling of a "green country town" would always be part of the city.

William Penn's 1681 plan for Philadelphia preserved part of the rural landscape. This 1767 drawing shows (*left to right*) the House of Employment, the Almshouse, and the Pennsylvania Hospital, with the city beyond.

This sketch of New Orleans, circa 1722, shows its central square, which opened directly onto the quay and was bordered on its other three sides by the town's principal buildings.

Savannah, founded by James Oglethorpe in 1733, may be the most idealistic and democratic representation of a gridded town ever designed in America. The town's grid straddled a main thoroughfare leading from the banks of the Savannah to the far edge of the settlement. The thoroughfare was regularly interrupted by open squares, which in time were landscaped as parks, making Savannah's common areas more accessible than those of other towns. Additionally, there were lots set aside for churches and stores and an outlying common in which each family was given a five-acre plot to cultivate. Oglethorpe, a member of the House of Commons who had chaired a committee investigating the conditions of London's jails, planned the city as a new lease on life for the inmates of debtors' prison and other British citizens ostracized from society. A town founded on democratic ideals, Savannah ironically became a center for the nation's slave trade.

The Colonial governor of Virginia, Francis Nicholson, planned Williamsburg as the colony's capital city in 1699. He may have been directly inspired by the designs of Christopher Wren, who, as Royal Surveyor, was responsible for all English Colonial buildings of consequence. In 1698, Nicholson had orchestrated the move of the Virginia capital from the swampy lands of Jamestown, where the capitol had burned down, to the healthier climate of Williamsburg, where he had helped to found the College of William and Mary in 1690. Nicholson's first plan for the city reputedly used the initials of the reigning British sovereigns, William and Mary, in a pattern of diagonal streets, some traces of which may be detected in the roads that lead from the opposite sides of the college. As the town was finally built, however, diagonals were dispensed with in favor of a strongly cross-axial arrangement that made Williamsburg the grandest American Colonial town by far. Nicholson planned the city to resemble an English Baroque garden, organized for processions of aristocratic leisure as well as for the symbolic and pragmatic functions of state and commerce. The principal thoroughfare, the ninety-foot-wide Duke of Gloucester Street, led straight from the College of William and Mary to the capitol at the opposite end. The church, the militia, and the judiciary, each

The strong cross-axial design of Williamsburg, seen at the center of this early map, made it the grandest of Colonial towns. The wide main thoroughfare ran from the College of William and Mary at one end to the Capitol at the other, with church, military, and judicial buildings clustered around the central square.

in its own structure, were clustered around Market Square, midway between the headquarters of higher learning and elective government.

The Governor's Palace sat at the end of an imperially scaled cross axis, a mall twice the width of Duke of Gloucester Street. Set at right angles to the main axis of the town in command of the grand mall, the Governor's Palace is firmly ensconced as the head of the town; its two arms are implied, invisible diagonals that extend to the capitol and the college. But while the governor's position as the fulcrum of Colonial life is implied, the palace's discrete distance from the main thoroughfare of daily life suggested that the iron fist of monarchical power was sheathed beneath the velvet glove of daily bureaucratic and educational pursuits.

When Virginia had joined with the twelve other colonies to form a new nation, a capital city was required for the now united states. The site for such an enterprise was the subject of a long dispute. During the Revolutionary War, the Continental Congress shifted between Philadelphia, Baltimore, Lancaster, and York. After the cessation of hostilities in 1783, the weak national government was even more peripatetic, by turns temporarily headquartered in Philadelphia, Princeton, Annapolis, Trenton, and New York. It was ultimately decided that the capital of a new nation should be a new city. The agricultural South, fearing political domination by the more urban, mercantile North, agreed to support Alexander Hamilton's economic plans in exchange for locating the national capital in its own region. President Washington, who was given the task of choosing a location for the new city, selected a site at the confluence of the Potomac and Anacostia rivers. The area within the borders of the site was made independent of all the states and called the District of Columbia. Thomas Jefferson, who, with Washington, decided on the procedure for planning the capital, prepared a straightforward gridiron plan. Major Pierre L'Enfant, however, found the proposal inadequate to the task and countered with a grander scheme. A French-born artist-engineer who had served in the Revolutionary War, L'Enfant was hired to assist in surveying the site for the new capital. He envisioned the District of Columbia as the capital of a continental empire that would at once foster commerce and symbolize the nation's manifest destiny. For L'Enfant, the new capital would be a workable expression of civic art.

In his youth, as the son of a court painter, L'Enfant had explored André Le Nôtre's gardens at Versailles, studying the axes, vistas, and diagonals of its monumental parterres. Later, as an art student in Paris, L'Enfant had become familiar with one of Le Nôtre's other grand gardens, the Tuileries, which lay adjacent to the Louvre and was an oasis of spatial and geometric clarity amid the twisting medieval intricacies of the streets of old Paris. Having trained as a painter and engineer, he set out to see more of the world, serving in the American army during the Revolutionary War.

L'Enfant's ambitious design for the capital, first presented to President Washington in June 1791 and revised throughout the following summer, described a rationally organized city larger than Paris. More than a plan for orderly land development, it was a roadmap of American government, outlining in time and space the separation of powers that is the fundamental proposition of the United States Constitution. At a time when the English Houses of Parliament did not meet in a building of their own and the French government was compressed into the Palace of Versailles, L'Enfant proposed separate buildings for the Congress and the President, connected by a diagonal avenue, rendering explicit the armatures of power suggested by Nicholson's plan for Williamsburg. Provision was made for separate buildings housing a national church and a national university and public squares dedicated to each of the fifteen states (Vermont and Maine were now allied with the original thirteen). L'Enfant's plan took advantage of the topography to further articulate the governmental hierarchies: the Capitol was sited at the top of a hill, where it could command a view of the Virginia hills beyond what L'Enfant identified as a "Grand Avenue," a 1½-mile-long, 400-foot-wide boulevard — the Mall. In L'Enfant's plan, it stretched to a monument placed at the intersection of the axis from the president's house.

L'Enfant's plan relied on a gridded system of streets overlaid by diagonal avenues, which he saw not merely in symbolic or artistic terms but as means for connecting "each part of the city . . . by making the real distance less from place to place; by giving to them reciprocity of sight and by making them thus seemingly connected, promote a rapid settlement over the whole extent, rendering those even of the most remote parts an addition to the principal."[5] Diagonals did little to speed the development of the District, which came to be known as the City of Washington in September 1791. Though ideal for ceremonies and processions, such as the inaugural parade from the Capitol to the White House, they were the source of traffic congestion and created awkward building sites that discouraged property development. In all fairness, Washington's failure to achieve success as a mercantile center was probably due less to L'Enfant's plan than to an environmental catastrophe. The deforestation and settlement of the Potomac River upstream made the river silt up downstream, turning the city's riverfront into a marsh, effectively foreclosing the capital's future as a great port.

While the complex geometries of the District of Columbia inspired an occasional town planner such as Judge Augustus Woodward, who in 1805 proposed an intricate honeycomb plan for Detroit, most American cities were gridded along strictly pragmatic lines. Even the two leading Eastern cities that had initially evolved in a more organic manner with irregular medieval plans — Boston and New York — met the demands of their burgeoning populations with new districts of gridded streets. In the 1740s, the northern slope of Boston's Beacon Hill was cut up into rectangular lots, and in the 1850s, when the city expanded into the marshlands of adjacent Back Bay, the grid was also employed.

New York City went even further in 1811, adopting a relentless gridiron plan that blanketed the island with block upon block subdivided into 25-by-100-foot building lots. The plan provided for only four small parks. But the phenomenal economic growth that squeezed residences and businesses onto the narrow lots and resulted in unprecedented congestion led William Cullen Bryant, the poet and editor-in-chief of the *New York Evening Post,* to spearhead a movement for the creation of a large urban park. The campaign resulted in a brilliant solution: Central Park. As discussed in chapter 4, Frederick Law Olmsted and Calvert Vaux's 1858 design for Central Park transformed what had once been deemed unusable land — a muddy, garbage-strewn site littered with squatter's shacks — into an Arcadian dreamworld of meandering walks, hills, and dales cut through by a grand axial mall. Until the creation of Central Park, the only landscaped public areas in the nation were New England commons and an occasional parade ground, like the Battery in New York and in Charleston. Central Park was both a village green magnified to metropolitan scale and ingenious compensation for a city whose relentless gridded plan offered neither romantic nor classical vistas.

The vastness and seemingly infinite visual drama of the American continent had blinded its citizens to the pleasures of a simple, natural landscape close to home. Olmsted demonstrated that a carefully but naturalistically manipulated landscape within the city could seem at once urban and rural and add a measure of civility to daily life. Central Park did not, however, fulfill Olmsted's vision. He sought nothing less than a complete revision of American urbanism that would balance the works of nature with those of man, that would marry the garden to the grid. Brooklyn's rivalry with New York (which it would become part of only in 1898) moved its leaders to hire Olmsted and Vaux to create Prospect Park. In their

The 1893 World's Columbian Exposition on the South Side of Chicago celebrated the four hundredth anniversary of Columbus's discovery of the New World as well as the cultural achievements of a nation perceived as the rightful heir to the Classical world. This poster included a small plan of the fairgrounds as laid out by Frederick Law Olmsted.

report of 1866, Olmsted and Vaux looked beyond the park's boundaries, proposing that adjoining land be set aside for museums and other institutional structures and, more prophetically, calling for "suburban connections," which they would soon dub "park ways."[6] Olmsted proposed Ocean Parkway, which connected Prospect Park with Coney Island, as a curved road "bordered by a small belt of trees and shrubbery."[7] In the end, however, real estate pragmatism prevailed and it was laid out as a landscaped boulevard running a straight five miles to the sea.

Overleaf. With its "urban" areas relieved by parks and landscaped boulevards, the Chicago fair was designed as an urbanistic and architectural paradigm. The monumental Court of Honor is at the left.

The Chicago exposition was a collaborative project among leading architects. Hailed as initiating the American Renaissance, the fair revolutionized the course of American architecture. In this photograph from July 1892, the Manufacturers and Liberal Arts Building is under construction.

Olmsted was able to further advance his concept of metropolitanism — where town and country, buildings and parks, were combined in a mutually supportive system — in Chicago, the nineteenth century's most relentlessly commercial city. As discussed in chapter 4, Olmsted and Vaux designed the suburb of Riverside, nine miles from downtown, in 1868. Two years later they proposed a coordinated park system for Chicago that led to the creation of Washington and Jackson parks. The Great Fire of 1871 stymied construction efforts, and Olmsted's elaborate park plans were only partially realized. Jackson Park, however, was built and became the site of the World's Columbian Exposition in 1893, where Americans were entertained as they were offered a radical solution to the nation's urban problems.

Celebrating the four-hundredth anniversary of Columbus's discovery of the New World, the 1893 exposition was a watershed in the development of American culture. The fair set out to announce that America had come of age as a civilization by showing the world that it was the rightful heir of the Classical world — the new Rome — and the last great hope of Western humanism. In 1890 the House of Representatives chose Chicago over New York as the fair's location. National and local commissions were created to guide its planning. Chicago's corporation, comprising prominent businessmen, hired America's foremost landscape designer, Frederick Law Olmsted, to advise on a location in Chicago and to lay out the fairgrounds. Olmsted recommended a lakefront site north of the Loop, but when the railroad company refused to provide transportation, he reluctantly accepted the southern portion of Jackson Park, which consisted of marshland still not improved twenty years after his proposal of 1870.

Working with his associate Henry Codman and the architectural partnership of Daniel H. Burnham and John Wellborn Root, Olmsted devised an overall plan that powerfully translated the fair's ideal into a physical reality. Designed as a miniature version of the national landscape, the plan created gridded "urban" areas, naturalistic parks, and landscaped boulevards connecting the two. A system of canals completed Olmsted's vision.

The World's Columbian Exposition was the first effectively planned complex of public buildings built in America since the Jeffersonian era. To a generation of urban Americans raised amidst the confusion and congestion of the nation's rapidly industrialized cities, it powerfully demonstrated the potential of the American city to constitute a monumental work of art. But the fair's planners and architects intended it as more than an urbanistic and architectural paradigm. To express the nation's immense cultural ambitions, the Columbian Exposition broke with the precedent of previous fairs, which had emphasized industrial innovations, to define its role as an artistic and cultural event. Despite the realities of the squalid Chicago slums only a few miles away, the fair was to become, if only for a single summer, a transcendent representation of America's promise, an alabaster city undimmed by human tears.

Burnham and Root, designers of many of Chicago's commercial monuments, including the Rookery (1885–88) and the Monadnock (1889–92) buildings, were put

Louis Sullivan's Transportation Building, facing the lagoon, was less strictly Classical than most of the fair's buildings, with decoration related to the Art Nouveau style. Here we see the building's Golden Door. Ironically, Sullivan was a harsh critic of the fair's architecture in later years.

in charge of the fair. The pair in turn went to the East to seek the help of the leading architects, painters, and sculptors of New York and Boston. At first most Eastern architects were slow to accept the idea that a fair's impermanent buildings could be important architecture, but Burnham's invitations were finally accepted after he convinced them that the exposition could determine the future of American architecture. From New York came Richard Morris Hunt, McKim, Mead & White, and George B. Post and from Boston, Peabody & Stearns. Although many of Chicago's leading practitioners participated in the fair, including Louis Sullivan, it was the Eastern architects who saw in Burnham's initiative the potential to build a daringly monumental city of white Classical buildings that, complementing Olmsted's plan, would express the nation's readiness to realize its aesthetic potential. They seized the opportunity and ultimately revolutionized the course of contemporary American architecture. To the architects and to their collaborating artists, the fair quickly came to be viewed as the initiation of an American Renaissance, a Classical revival comparable to that which occurred in Renaissance Florence. As the sculptor Augustus Saint-Gaudens, who completed the fair's committee as its chief art consultant, somewhat smugly put it after a planning session, "Do you realize this is the greatest meeting of artists since the fifteenth century?"[8]

The fairgrounds were dominated by the Court of Honor, a complex of white Classical buildings arranged around a 350-foot-wide, 1,100-foot-long basin. The scheme clearly recalled the plan of the Universal Exposition, held in 1889 on the Champ-de-Mars in Paris, in which a formal court was dominated by the Eiffel Tower. (The latter, a work of pure engineering, was held in contempt by many who for that very reason deemed it exceptionally ugly.) In Chicago, the Columbian Exposition's Court of Honor was dominated by a basin. At its head was the Administration Building, designed by Richard Morris Hunt. Composed of four Doric corner pavilions and a lofty, open, Ionic colonnade, Hunt's design culminated in a 250-foot-high dome. The Administration Building stood in deliberate contrast to the technological bravura of Gustave Eiffel's tower. While Eiffel had celebrated the ambition of the French to forge an industrial culture, Hunt asserted the cultural ambitions of a nation where the power of science and industry were everywhere evident. In Paris, the bare-bones aesthetic of the display halls devoted to industrial exhibits had been designed to reflect the objects they housed. In Chicago, science and engineering displays were lifted to the level of art objects by their placement in a museumlike setting.

The buildings surrounding the basin were consistent in height and all incorporated porticos, which together created a nearly continuous colonnade. The buildings' spectacular, detailed Classicism was realized in staff, a mixture of jute, cement, and plaster, which was also employed to create sculpture, ubiquitous throughout the fairgrounds. The thematic climax of the sculptural efforts was reached with the Columbian Fountain, designed by the sculptor Frederick MacMonnies, at the western end of the basin directly in front of the Administration Building. Perhaps the most telling representation of America's rekindled sense of itself as the guardian of the Classical tradition, the fountain represented the female figure of Columbia commanding a barge rowed — presumably across the Atlantic from Europe — by allegorical representations of Art, Science, Industry, and Agriculture.

The Court of Honor was but a part of Olmsted's micrometropolis. It was complemented by a large, lushly landscaped Lagoon, in the middle of which was a wooded island. This manmade island had been dredged up from Lake Michigan's bottom and planted with willow trees, cattails, and pond lilies found at more remote lakes and rivers in rural Illinois and Wisconsin. Olmsted had intended the island to be free of public buildings, but it became the site of the ultimate in architectural exotica, a Japanese temple, the Ho-O-Den. The pavilion's traditional wood craftsmanship would inspire a generation of Midwestern architects, led by Frank Lloyd Wright, who adopted its open plan and spreading roof lines to help shape their vision of an appropriate house for the sweeping prairie landscapes of the Midwest. The island was also the location of Burnham's office, which provided him with an ideal vantage point from which to observe the construction of his Classical city. It positioned Burnham metaphorically as the pioneer in his wilderness cabin, fulfilling the nation's manifest destiny by building a Classical dreamworld in Arcadia.

To complement the Lagoon's naturalism, the buildings surrounding it tended to be stylistically eclectic and lyrical in detail. The most compelling design was Louis Sullivan's Transportation Building, a Classically composed pavilion overlaid with polychromatically rendered arches and domes. Also facing the Lagoon was a pavilion that acknowledged the increasingly important public role of American women. The arcaded Woman's Building resembled an Italian Renaissance villa and was the only structure designed by a woman architect, Sophia G. Hayden. A twenty-one-year-old graduate of MIT, Hayden would design one more building before a nervous collapse ended her architectural career, even though she lived to be an octogenarian.

The Court of Honor and the Lagoon were only half of the exposition. The fair was what America was: a synthesis of civicism and commerce, culture and ballyhoo, high ideals and down-to-earth pragmatism. The Midway Plaisance, a ⅞-mile-long "panhandle" of land penetrating the Chicago grid westward from the lake, was full of rides and attractions and unabashedly dedicated to delighting the audience for a buck. In contrast to the lofty ideals of the fair's Classical architecture, the Midway's buildings tended more to preindustrial vernacular: nostalgic and picturesque reconstructions of Vienna's old town and Irish, Samoan, Dahomeyan, and pre-European American villages. Among the favorite attractions was the "hootchy-kootchy dance" of undulating bellies at the "Streets of Cairo." The exhibit's scenography was designed by Henry Ives Cobb, who didn't disdain a detour into low art despite being the architect of important fair buildings. Presiding over it all was George Ferris's 250-foot-diameter wheel, which rotated visitors in thirty-six plush wood-veneered cars. Intended to rival the Eiffel Tower — but shunted to the Midway as an amusement — it offered the only vantage point from which the fair's complex, synoptic metropolitanism could be taken in at once and viewed in contrast to the relentless uniformity of Chicago's gridiron. From the Ferris wheel's thrilling height of 264 feet, visitors were able to clearly comprehend the fair's challenge: Could the smoky city be transformed into a White City? Could America rise to its self-proclaimed dream as a new Rome?

To a few, the fair's Classicism reflected a cultural bankruptcy and absence of originality, a compulsion to mindlessly replicate ancient models. With the wisdom that only hindsight can yield, Louis Sullivan pronounced in 1924 that the "damage

This lithograph of the Chicago exposition's Administration Building, by Richard Morris Hunt, shows the four Doric corner pavilions and its 250-foot-high dome.

wrought by the World's Fair will last for half a century . . . if not longer."[9] But to most Americans, intellectuals and average people alike, the fair meant just the opposite; America could pick up where Europe had left off. The fair was, in its selective use of history, a bold, optimistic blend of Rome and Venice, Thoreau's Walden and a small-town carnival on the Fourth of July.

The World's Columbian Exposition succeeded because it was both garden and grid. Clearly the American public was compelled by the White City's example. Twenty-seven million visitors came to the Chicago fair, an enormous figure given that the national population was only seventy million. Hamlin Garland, a journalist who crusaded against the hardships of tenement life in Eastern cities and farm life in his native Middle West, wrote to his parents on their Dakota farm to "sell the cook stove if necessary and come. . . . You must see this Fair."[10]

A succession of international expositions across the country in the next two decades — in Omaha (1898), Buffalo (1901), St. Louis (1904), San Francisco (1915), and San Diego (1916) — extended not only the coherent urbanism established with Chicago's White City but also its proclamation to the world that America was capable of creating the architectural as well as the political and economic dimensions of global empire. Chicago's Columbian Exposition, however, remained the most significant of the international fairs in America. It left behind more than its immediate legacy of parks and museums, constituting one of the first examples of American culture influencing Europe. French observers visiting the fair were generally critical of its revivalist architecture, claiming to admire only Sullivan's Transportation Building, whose decoration related to the incipient Art Nouveau style; nevertheless, seven years later, when the French put on their next fair, the Universal Exposition held in Paris in 1900, they clearly emulated the Classical splendors of the White City. At home, the Chicago fair inspired an American vision of the metropolis as a collaborative art project: a City Beautiful. The monumental architecture, formal courts, sculpture, and greenery typical of fairgrounds inspired Americans to rebuild their cities. Praising the contemporary example of the fair, public-spirited citizens were intent on reforming the sociological and physical structure of urban life: gardens were once again to bloom in the unsympathetic real estate of the grid.

In Chicago, the first direct benefit of the Columbian Exposition was Burnham's plan for the further development of Jackson Park. Burnham soon proposed the expansion of another waterfront site, Grant Park, next to downtown Chicago. In 1896, the desirability of a park on Lake Michigan, bordering Chicago's Loop, was hard to imagine. The city's sewage poured into the lake from the mouth of the Chicago River. Burnham, however, realized that his city would be transformed by the completion of the Chicago Sanitary and Ship Canal, an immense construction project begun in 1892. Opened in 1900, the canal was a bold solution to the city's sewage problem and also provided a trade link for barge traffic. To do this, it reversed the Chicago River's flow: once the river had sluggishly debouched into Lake Michigan; now, in a perhaps too literal recapitulation of American settlement, the flotsam and jetsam of industrialization was once again sent west, flowing from Lake Michigan to the Mississippi Basin. Requiring more excavation than the Panama Canal, this engineering marvel designed by Rudolph Hering held aesthetic possibilities for Burnham, who saw it

George Ferris's enormous wheel was built to rival the Eiffel Tower as a technological feat, but it was relegated to a Midway amusement. Its plush cars carried visitors to a height of 264 feet, where they had a panoramic view of the micrometropolis.

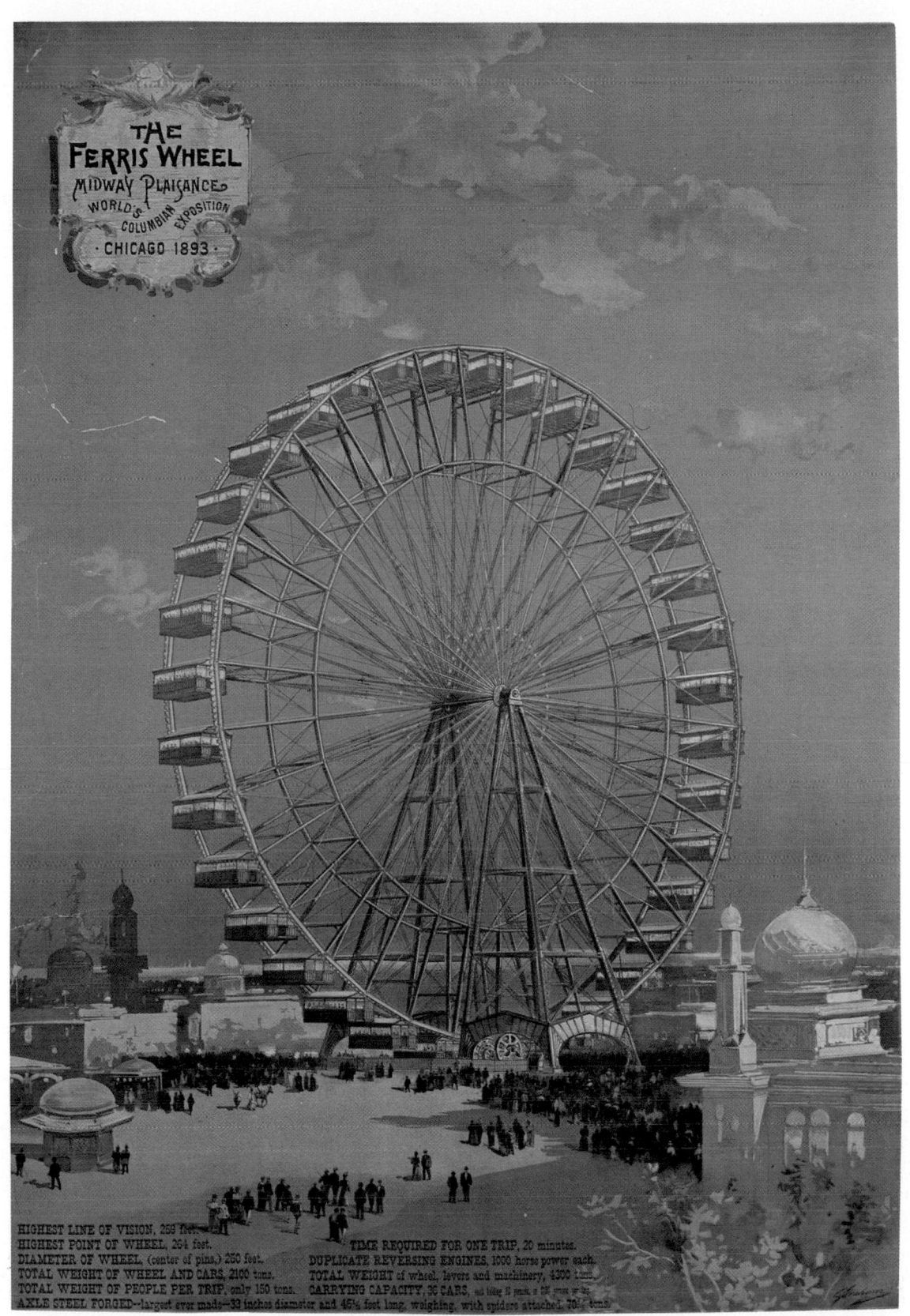

as a work of historically synoptic urban art. He foresaw that the lake could become Chicago's Adriatic and the river its Seine, lined with a quaylike two-level boulevard.

Seven years after the canal's completion, Chicago began to be redesigned as a new Paris. In 1906 the Merchants' Club, a group of civic-minded young men, called upon Burnham to revive the cooperative spirit of the World's Columbian Exposition in practical terms by establishing a citywide plan for parks, regional transportation, street systems, zoning, and architectural development. The following year, the Merchants' Club was absorbed into the powerful businessmen's organization the Commercial Club, which financed the venture. Working with Edward H. Bennett, Burnham devoted two years to the project and produced a proposal whose lasting effect on Chicago includes the schematic design of a regional highway system, twenty-three and a half miles of park along Lake Michigan, the development of Grant Park as a cultural center for the city, the improvement of the riverfront with the two-tiered Wacker Drive, and the widening of North Michigan Avenue into what became known as the Miracle Mile.

While its authors stressed pragmatism as the basis of their designs, the *Plan*, published in a lush edition of 1,650 copies, including fifty color illustrations by Jules Guérin, made an unequivocal play for beauty as the expression of civic pride. Paris, whose quays and boulevards were the touchstones of Burnham's notion of civic beauty, was continually invoked in the design. Further, among many of the unbuilt portions of the plan — indeed, at the very heart of it — was an enormous civic center that would have put the nation's capital to shame. The Civic Center Plaza, east of the Chicago River at the end of a broadened Congress Avenue, was to be the hub of a wheel of avenues radiating out into the suburbs. The City Hall's

Both pragmatic and beautiful, Burnham's plan for Chicago's downtown waterfront mirrored the 1893 fair's idea of the city as civic art. This rendering by Jules Guérin illustrates the impressive system of bridges and waterways that allowed for barge traffic.

towering dome was to dominate the plaza, whose absolute center was marked by an obelisk. Congress Avenue was to be lined by monumental buildings, including a railroad station at its terminal point and the Field Museum of Natural History in Grant Park. South of the park stretched pleasure grounds incorporating the islands and lagoons Burnham proposed for the waterfront, which were illustrated by Guérin as a golden-hued scene of racing shells and sleek pleasure boats. Burnham and his successors would never approximate in Chicago the power he had exercised over the Columbian Exposition. In Washington, D.C., however, working with McKim and Saint-Gaudens, Burnham came closest to building a permanent incarnation of his idealized White City. It would become an alabaster city for all time.

In 1900 Washington, D.C., was a city of 218,000 citizens and had the street plan, if not much else, that L'Enfant had designated. During the nineteenth century, the diagrammatic clarity of L'Enfant's plan had been compromised by politically motivated ad hoc decisions, the exigencies of soil conditions, and shifting taste. For decades the city had been mocked for its unfulfilled grandiosity. In 1842 Charles Dickens wrote after a visit: "It is sometimes called the City of Magnificent Distances, but it might with greater propriety be termed the 'City of Magnificent Intentions'; for it is only on taking a bird's-eye view of it from the top of the Capitol, that one can at all comprehend the vast designs of its projector, an aspiring Frenchman."[11] In 1860 Henry Adams, returning from Europe to serve as an assistant to his father, newly elected to Congress, found the city unchanged from ten years earlier: "the same rude colony was camped in the same forest, with the same unfinished Greek temples for workrooms, and sloughs for roads."[12]

In 1836, when President Andrew Jackson authorized the construction of Robert Mills's Treasury Building, he compromised the symbolic legibility of L'Enfant's plan as well as the beauty of one of its principal vistas by interrupting the axis of Pennsylvania Avenue, which connected the Mall with the Capitol. Eleven years later, James Renwick further compromised the spacious if unrealized Mall of L'Enfant's plan with his Smithsonian Institution, a red sandstone castle that not only intruded on its space but also introduced a restless, idiosyncratic Gothicism to Washington's hitherto rational Classical world. In 1851 Andrew Jackson Downing proposed that the Mall be developed with romantic rambles, curving walks, and naturalistic groves. Part of Downing's scheme was carried out in front of the Smithsonian. The Washington Monument, begun in 1848, like the Treasury Building was designed by Robert Mills and played equal havoc with L'Enfant's geometries. Marshy ground conditions required that it be built a hundred yards off the intersecting axes drawn from the White House and the Capitol.

Yet the picturesque naturalism of Downing's landscape plan for the Capitol and the Mall as well as the monument, which remained an incomplete 150-foot stump for decades, was a minor infringement on the dignity of L'Enfant's "Grand Avenue" compared to the intrusion of railroad tracks that crisscrossed it. In 1855 the Washington and Alexandria Railroad extended its track to the foot of Capitol Hill, and in 1872 an act of Congress permitted the Baltimore and Potomac Railroad, a subsidiary of the Pennsylvania Railroad, to lay its tracks across the Mall to a stone, Gothic-style railroad station. The power of the railroads to violate the established plan for the national capital roused increasing discontent as district

Above. Pierre L'Enfant's eighteenth-century plan for Washington, D.C., relied on a gridded system of streets overlaid by diagonal avenues that connected all parts of the city. For L'Enfant, the plan symbolized the nation's manifest destiny, its order articulating the hierarchies of government.

This "Bird's-Eye View of Washington, D.C., and the Vicinity," published in *Harper's Weekly* in January 1862, shows the placement of forts and railroad tracks. In the nineteenth century, the intrusion of the railroad compromised L'Enfant's design.

commissioners repeatedly succumbed to the railroads' refusal to move the tracks and terminal. In February 1901 Congress passed and President McKinley approved a bill that provided, among other things, for fourteen acres of the Mall to be used for a huge railroad station. According to the plan, train sheds would project into the Mall and tracks raised on a six-hundred-foot-wide embankment would cross it diagonally. L'Enfant's dream was all but forgotten. Even Senator James McMillan, who would soon reverse himself and spearhead a drive to recapture L'Enfant's plan, defended the bill: "Indeed so far as sightliness is concerned, the proposed changes will add greatly to the beauty of that portion of the Mall."[13]

Virtually every citizens' group immediately voiced its outrage and the Board of Trade reiterated its ten-year opposition to any infringement on the city's public parks. On the strength of the plans presented at the American Institute of Architects' 1900 congress, the subject of which had been the restoration of Washington, Senator McMillan was persuaded to enlist the support of his congressional colleagues in establishing a Senate Parks Commission. On the advice of the AIA, the Senate appointed to the commission Frederick Law Olmsted, Jr., who had presented the scheme that most strictly adhered to L'Enfant's original design at the architects' congress, and Daniel Burnham. Burnham added two of his colleagues from the Chicago exposition, Charles F. McKim and Augustus Saint-Gaudens.

An 1852 rendering of the Capitol portrays the placement of principal sites in L'Enfant's plan. The diagonal boulevards, while ideal for processionals, hindered traffic and property development.

In 1902 the Senate Parks Commission presented a plan for the reconstruction of Washington that would restore and modify L'Enfant's design. The city's roadways were altered and the Mall extended to the Potomac, aligning the principal sites. No longer simply an avenue, the Mall became a national front lawn 300 feet wide.

While the commissioners acknowledged the fundamental value of L'Enfant's intentions, they recognized that Washington's inevitable destiny as a large modern city demanded more than just an archaeological reconstruction of the original design. In seeking to extend and modify L'Enfant's eighteenth-century plan, the commission turned for inspiration to the formal gardens of Virginia's Colonial estates and to the largely ignored city of Williamsburg, where they discovered what they believed to be the prototype for L'Enfant's design: "the Capitol at one end of the broad parkway, the College of William and Mary at the other end of the main axis, and the Governor's Palace at the head of the cross-axis, a location similar to that of the White House."[14] Williamsburg's scale, however, was inadequate to that of a metropolis, which Washington, D.C., ever a commercial failure, could now hope to become thanks to the growth of government. Not surprisingly, the commissioners visited the most advanced cities in Europe as well. Burnham and his colleagues, with the exception of the ailing Saint-Gaudens and the addition of Charles Moore, clerk of McMillan's Committee on the District of Columbia and later spokesman for the commission, traveled to Paris, Rome, Venice, Budapest, Frankfurt, Berlin, and London. They explored the gardens that L'Enfant had known: Versailles, Vaux-le-Vicomte, the Tuileries, and the renewed city of Paris, which Baron Haussmann, like L'Enfant, had designed according to aesthetic principles similar to those of Le Nôtre's Versailles. In short, the commissioners made a pilgrimage to both the sources and the latest examples of the Classical tradition. While in London, Burnham learned that the greatest obstacle to the reimposition of L'Enfant's plan — the existing and proposed railroad tracks and station on the Mall — had been removed. The Pennsylvania Railroad had recently acquired control of the Baltimore and Ohio line, and its president, Alexander J. Cassatt, was willing to consider a Union Station. The B&O line had been given a site north of the Capitol for a new station, and Cassatt proposed to build it there if the U.S. Congress agreed to defray the expenses of burrowing a railroad tunnel beneath Capitol Hill. The existing tracks and depot would be removed, and Washington would gain an imperially scaled portal three blocks from the Capitol.

In January 1902 the commission presented its plan at the Corcoran Gallery of Art. The impressive array of models, renderings, and perspectives won over the press and Congress. The Mall's function as the symbolic expression of national unity was unequivocally articulated. The reconstituted Mall was not to be the avenue that L'Enfant had proposed but a *tapis vert* three hundred feet wide — a national front lawn extending from the Capitol beyond the Washington Monument to the Potomac — a suggestion of McKim, who felt that in order to tease the obelisk of the Washington Monument into alignment, the Mall's axis would need to go beyond it. At the culmination of the extended Mall, McKim, son of an ardent abolitionist preacher, proposed a memorial to Abraham Lincoln. The romantic groves planted by Downing where deer had wandered were to be chopped down to give way to geometrical bosks planted in marching order west to the Potomac. At the foot of Capitol Hill, a Union Square filled with equestrian statues of Generals Grant, Sherman, and Sheridan would become America's Place de la Concorde. The cross axis from the White House would also be lengthened and its importance enhanced by the construction, south of the Washington Monument, of a pantheon dedicated to the authors of the Constitution or a memorial to a national hero, which it became when the site was dedicated to Jefferson's memory. The triangle between the Mall and Pennsylvania Avenue would become a complex of Classical government buildings, while the Mall would be not simply a national front lawn but a kind of high-minded Main Street, lined with museums and other cultural institutions. Capitol Hill was to become an acropolis, where the vaguely Classical Library of Congress, designed by Smithmeyer & Pelz with Edward Pearce Casey (1873–97), would become part of a monumental frame containing the Supreme Court, which L'Enfant had not deemed important enough to command an independent status in his scheme, and palatial office buildings for the members of the Senate and the House of Representatives.

Senator McMillan's concern that Washington's park system be improved was answered by the younger Olmsted, who as the architect of Boston's Metropolitan Park District had realized his father's vision of parkways serving as green lungs and purifying arteries for a unified metropolitan region embracing both city and suburb. Rock Creek, the debris-strewn boundary between Georgetown and the rest of the city, would be transformed into a winding park and roadway extending to the northern section of the city and on to Potomac Park along the river. Parklands bordered the Potomac north through Maryland to Virginia, and a parkway followed the river's curves south to Mount Vernon, rendering it, in fact, what it was becoming in its many reproductions — the ultimate suburban American dream house, accessible from the city's center by means of a picturesque, but public, front drive scaled to the motorcar. At the eastern edge of the District, the banks of the Anacostia River were preserved as parkland, which laced through the city and a dozen miles beyond into the country.

The renewal of L'Enfant's vision corresponded to a renewed sense of national unity. America's global imperialism and the passage of time had combined to heal the divisiveness of the Civil War. This was rendered absolutely clear by the diagonal avenue that was carried across the Potomac River to connect the Lincoln Memorial with the former mansion of Robert E. Lee, Arlington House, which looked down upon it from a high hill in the middle of what had become the Arlington Cemetery. Lee already had a Classical shrine; Lincoln would soon get his on the Washington side.

The first demonstration of the Classical architecture that the commissioners advocated for the reconstructed capital was Union Station (1903–8), designed by Commissioner Burnham's own firm. The new station gave witness that the architecture of the impermanent White City in Chicago could be made real and lasting in Washington. The design, which derived from Charles Atwood's station at the 1893 exposition, consisted of a central pavilion with three monumental arches flanked by long, arcaded wings extending to arched pavilions. Immediately in front of the station, three flagstaffs, 110 feet high and surmounted by huge eagles, stood beside Lorado Taft's Columbus Memorial Fountain in a vast semicircular plaza, 600 by 1,200 feet, planned as a setting grandiose enough for the military parades and festivals of the newest world power.

Across Massachusetts Avenue, the City Post Office (1914) was also designed by Burnham. Its three-storey Ionic colonnade, with projecting entrance pavilions at each end, complemented the station. The most impressive Classical architectural grouping in Washington, D.C., however, was not devoted to mail or trains or

Frederick Law Olmsted, Jr.'s design for Washington adhered closely to L'Enfant's original plan. As a member of the Parks Commission, Olmsted traveled to Europe to study the gardens that had inspired L'Enfant.

bureaucracy but rather was the purely symbolic architecture on the Mall, the single most brilliant example of which is, quite appropriately, Henry Bacon's Lincoln Memorial (1915–22). Rising from a circular lawn at the end of a two-thousand-foot-long reflecting pool stretching from the Washington Monument, which neatly slices the Capitol's dome in the view from the memorial's steps, the Lincoln Memorial is a marble temple loosely based on the Parthenon. With the entrance on the long side, it consists of thirty-six Doric columns, representing the thirty-six states at the time of Lincoln's death, rising not to a pediment but to an attic inscribed with the names of the Civil War–era states in a frieze between wreaths in bas-relief. The forty-eight states of 1915 are represented by festoons in the attic parapet above. The memorial is elevated fourteen feet by a granite plinth and is approached by a flight of steps leading to the temple's cella, where Daniel Chester French's nineteen-foot-high marble statue of Lincoln, seated, gazes out to the Washington Monument and the Capitol. Bathed in light filtered partially through thin marble panels, the hall opens on the north and south through Ionic columns to anterooms that contain bronze plaques inscribed with the texts of the Gettysburg Address and Lincoln's Second Inaugural Address.

Bacon's design was widely praised and President Harding presented the architect with the Gold Medal of the American Institute of Architects upon the memorial's dedication on May 30, 1922. The following year, the memorial was the site of a great spectacle: the AIA staged a torchlit evening pageant honoring Bacon. Chief Justice Taft and President Harding arrived at the ceremonies by car, but the architect was rowed down the reflecting pool in a barge.

Not everyone has greeted the Lincoln Memorial with acclaim. Lewis Mumford loathed its imperialist associations:

The America that Lincoln was bred in, the homespun and humane and humorous America that he wished to preserve, has nothing in common with the sedulously classic monument that was erected to his memory. Who lives in that shrine, I wonder — Lincoln or the men who conceived it; the leader who beheld the mournful victory of the Civil War, or the generation that took pleasure in the mean triumph of the Spanish-American Exploit.[15]

For American blacks, the Classical style of the Lincoln Memorial has understandably engendered the most ambivalent responses. The architectural associations of Classicism include the ancient civilizations of Rome and Greece. Not only models of democracy to which our founding fathers often turned for counsel, they were also elitist, slave-owning societies. And within our nation's own architectural history, some associations are troubling. As Max Bond, a black architect and educator, has said, "For black people in America, Classicism as a symbol of the Southern courthouses has not always been benign."[16] As it happens, however, the memorial has assumed important symbolic stature by virtue of its use as a stage in several critical events in the ongoing battle for racial equality. Marian Anderson, who had been barred by virtue of her race from singing at Constitution Hall, was invited by Eleanor Roosevelt to sing on its steps before seventy-five thousand listeners on Easter Sunday 1939, turning the concert and its setting into a symbol of the struggle for racial justice. On August 28, 1963, to commemorate the hundredth anniversary of Lincoln's Emancipation Proclamation, Martin Luther King, Jr., led his March on Washington to the memorial,

Overleaf. Maya Ying Lin's Vietnam Memorial on the Mall was chosen in a national competition in 1981. The names of those who died in the war are inscribed on an open V-shaped wall, sunk into the ground. The memorial's somber aspect in the midst of the capital's gleaming monumentality provokes reflection on a painful and turbulent era.

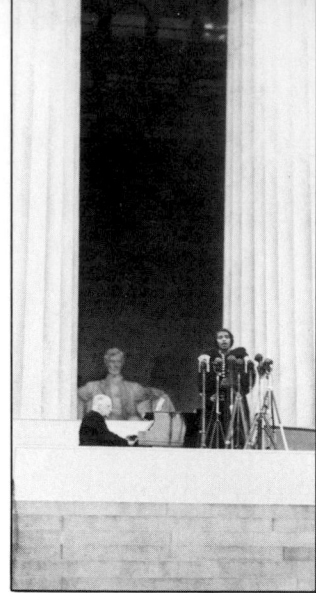

At the invitation of Eleanor Roosevelt, Marian Anderson sang at the Lincoln Memorial in Washington on Easter Sunday 1939.

proclaiming to the more than two hundred thousand people gathered at its steps, "I have a dream that one day . . . black men and white men, Jews and Gentiles, Protestants and Catholics, will be able to join hands and sing in the words of the old Negro spiritual, 'Free at last, free at last, thank God Almighty, we are free at last.'"

King's decision to lead his march on the Mall also reflected the grand space's potential to serve as the country's forum, an equivalent of the village green of a Colonial New England town. But most important, as Max Bond has observed, the decision to hold the march on the Mall and to gather at the steps of the great Classical monument "was to really appropriate in some ways . . . the symbols of state power, to move them to say that this also belongs to us and we can take possession of it in some spiritual sense."[17] The march rekindled the tradition of public demonstrations of consensus as it initiated a turbulent new era in American history. A new sense of civic activism generated throughout the 1960s can be accurately said to have started on the Mall, realizing what L'Enfant and Jefferson may well have hoped for it — a forum worthy of a democratic empire. The Mall served as the site of both the Vietnam Moratorium demonstration in 1969, the largest protest of the antiwar movement, and a memorial to that war's dead. Chosen in a national competition in 1981, the memorial, designed by Maya Ying Lin, is an open V-shaped wall burrowed into the earth upon which are inscribed the names of all those who died in the war. The monument's seemingly contradictory antimonumentality was denounced by veterans like Tom Carhart, who argued that "in a city of soaring white monuments, we get a black ditch in the ground."[18] Yet if Mumford felt the Classical styling of the Lincoln Memorial inappropriately expressive of imperialism, perhaps Lin's design is an appropriate monument. Its seeming negativism provokes reflection on a painful and turbulent war and era; its place on the Mall, the nation's forum, guarantees that those reflections be institutionalized as part of our collective past and present.

While work on the Mall in this century has restored L'Enfant's grand axis from the Capitol to the Potomac, no equivalent success has been met in strengthening the diagonal of power between the Capitol and the White House. Pennsylvania Avenue has never lived up to its role as the nation's most symbolically important street. While one side was gradually filled with important public buildings, the other was a ragtag collection of shops and offices. When President Kennedy made his inaugural journey in 1961, he pledged to rebuild the avenue. After a succession of commissions and two decades of planning, Pennsylvania Avenue's commercial side is being rebuilt. Unfortunately, the architects of many of the new commercial buildings don't seem particularly interested in reflecting the grandeur of official Washington across the street, and the new buildings look as though they could have been built anywhere.

As a priority of the avenue's reconstruction, the Pennsylvania Avenue Development Corporation called for the construction of a national square at Fifteenth Street to form a forecourt for the Treasury Building, which had done so much to destroy the clarity of L'Enfant's plan. The most distinguished part of the square is Venturi, Rauch & Scott Brown's Western Plaza, which celebrates L'Enfant and his dream city. The plaza consists of white marble and black granite panels outlining L'Enfant's original plan, with inscriptions and graphics representing the sites of major buildings and a lawn representing the Mall. The inscriptions are quotations from the great and near-great who have sojourned in Washington. At the place of the Capitol, a letter from Thomas Jefferson to Benjamin Latrobe is quoted; revealing his vision for the new nation, Jefferson describes the Capitol as "the first temple dedicated to the sovereignty of the people, embellishing with Athenian taste the course of a nation looking far beyond the range of Athenian destinies." Also embedded in the plaza is Ernest Kroll's less poetic but perhaps more telling characterization of Washington as "neither Rome nor home." The architects' original 1979 proposal was even more interesting. It called for three-dimensional scale models of the White House and the Capitol as well as two eighty-six-foot-high pylons that would recapture the vista reputedly confounded by Jackson. The final design, completed in 1981, was carried out in two dimensions, a victim of the Pennsylvania Avenue Development Corporation's caution.

While the struggle by citizens and elected officials to achieve L'Enfant's dream city on the Potomac has been long and circuitous and the ultimate victory hard won, the concentrated efforts of individuals of vision and determination has sometimes accomplished ambitious urban development in a much shorter time. In September 1959, during his first year as governor of New York, Nelson Rockefeller played host to Crown Princess Beatrix of the Netherlands. Escorting Dutch royalty in the gubernatorial limousine, Rockefeller became acutely aware that his capital city of Albany — which the Dutch had founded as Fort Orange — looked squalid. With the characteristic bravura of the super rich, Rockefeller decided to raze the offending urban blight and to erect the most beautiful capital in the world — at the public's expense. In its scale, materials, and aspirations, the Governor Nelson A. Rockefeller Empire State Plaza (dedicated in 1973, completed in 1979) matches the national capital's Mall. Rockefeller, never fully confident that he would be elected president, did his best to bring Washington's architectural grandeur to New York.

Rockefeller had enormous influence over the plaza's design. Together with his favorite architect, Wallace K. Harrison, who had worked on Rockefeller Center, the governor contrived to transform a ninety-eight-acre site into a grandly formal civic center, filled with abstract architecture that mimicked the materials and siting of Washington, D.C., but deleted direct references to historic architectural styles. Neither the pure Classicism of the nation's capital nor the eclectic synthesis of Albany's existing public buildings was suggested in the new buildings' designs. Empire State Plaza was to be a Modernist monument to the future.

Rockefeller's Mall, adorned with basins and fountains and bordered by *allées* of trees and buildings, stretched south from the late-nineteenth-century New York State Capitol to the Cultural Education Center, housing the state library and museum. The Mall's principal elements were four identical twenty-two-storey office towers, a forty-four-storey version, and a Meeting Center in the odd form of a concrete egg on a pedestal.

Monumental though the Mall and its architectural hedging may have been in scale, they were only half the story. The plaza and its buildings were built atop a six-storey plinth containing parking, services, and a grand concourse, an indoor shopping mall. When this superscaled government center was completed, the price tag for the 40,000 tons of marble, 232,000 tons of steel, and 900,000 cubic yards of concrete was a mere $2 billion, four times the original estimate. Rockefeller circumvented voter approval by having the County of Albany float the bonds, then leasing the whole development to the state, a scheme developed by Albany's mayor, Erastus Corning II, who had been promised in return housing for some of the nine thousand poor blacks displaced by the Mall. At the dedication, on November 21, 1973, Rockefeller declared that "mean structures breed small vision. But great architecture reflects mankind at its true worth."[19] Yet for all its grandeur, the Albany Mall was afflicted by mean vision. The replacement housing intended for five hundred families, the cost of which had escalated from $10 million to $20 million, was trimmed as fat from the $2 billion budget of the Mall. Urbanist Jane Jacobs saw the project in simple terms: as "planning insanity."[20] On its podium, the Mall almost sails out onto the Hudson, a magnificent aircraft carrier, a post–World War II ship of state, cast adrift from a dream of the past or place.

It exemplifies a seemingly contradictory but fairly common phenomenon in American architecture and planning. Our best-known public places have often been the result of private dreams. Whether paid for by private capital or the public purse, they have been created by individuals of enormous will and fortune who have contrived to transform the towns and cities they lived in to conform to their personal visions of America. These visions have usually been the opposite of Rockefeller's, looking not toward the future but to a pre-nineteenth-century world untroubled by the disintegrating forces of industrialism. Yet it was industry, amply lining these citizens' very private purses, that made their civic gestures possible.

One such American vision was realized by the Ames family, who transformed the grim, motley, industrial village of North Easton, Massachusetts, into a dignified town by endowing it with parks and public architecture. The founder of the dynasty, Oliver Ames, was the son of a local shovelmaker who made a fortune and a local industry by mass-producing what his father had made by hand. As a consequence, North Easton developed as little more than shovel shops, cottages

The Empire State Plaza in Albany, New York, was Governor Nelson Rockefeller's vision of urban grandeur. It included four identical soaring office towers. The old New York State Capitol is visible in the background.

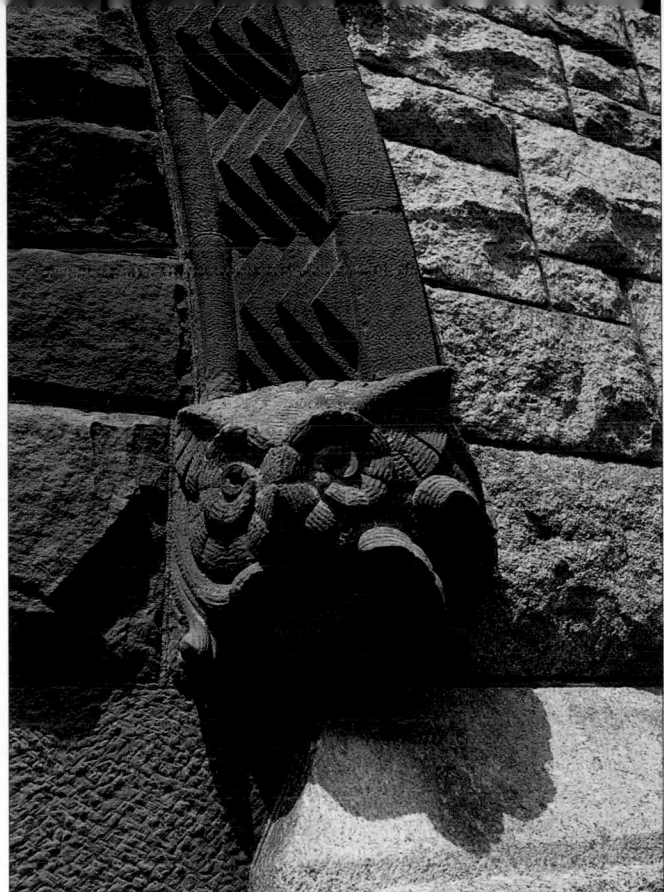

North Easton, Massachusetts, was developed with the industrial fortune of the Ames family. The Romanesque town hall (*above*), designed by Henry Hobson Richardson, had low "Syrian" granite arches. Gargoyles were carved into the brownstone trim (*right*).

for workers, and a few large houses for the members of the factory-owning family. Ames's grandsons were industrial age squires, and once they dramatically expanded the family fortune, they decided to spend some of it on embellishing their feudal domain. Oakes Angier Ames ran the shovel company, which controlled railroads and mines, and his cousin Frederick Lothrop Ames was New England's leading capitalist and the largest landowner in Cambridge and Boston. They began their aesthetic transformation of the town slowly, first with their own houses. Oakes built a Gothic villa in 1854, and in 1859 Frederick hired Boston architect George Snell to design a château in the Second Empire style. The family's role as the builders of the town's public monuments began after the death of Frederick's father, Oliver Ames II, who had stipulated the construction of a memorial library in his will. Frederick hired Henry Hobson Richardson, the Boston architect who had become famous by winning the Trinity Church competition in 1872 and who was, like his patron, a Harvard graduate.

While Richardson's work drew upon French Romanesque architecture, it also captured the flinty toughness of old mercantile Boston, which was being rapidly swallowed up by post–Civil War progress. In North Easton, Richardson helped the cousins realize a personal past that they had never known.

The robust, rusticated masonry of the Oliver Ames Free Library (1877–83) rose on a site between North Easton's Main Street and the Queset River. The entrance was through what was Richardson's first "Syrian" arch — a bold arch sprung almost from the ground — a forbidding portal set within the almost windowless granite walls of the first storey. The brownstone trim, carved into geometric banding and gargoyles, was probably the work of Richardson's assistant Stanford White, who would go on to collaborate with Charles McKim in the Shingle Style masterpieces of Newport. The archway was a powerful prelude to an interior

Robert Moses's design for Jones Beach on Long Island placed a water tower campanile at its center. Parking lots were set far back from the beach, which was bordered by bathhouses and gardens.

glowing with golden light. A barrel vault made of polished butternut crowned the basilical hall. The side aisles brimmed with the stacks of books.

In 1879 Richardson was commissioned by Oakes Angier Ames and his two brothers to erect a Town Hall as a memorial to their father, Oakes Ames. The site was a rocky ledge at the bend in the town's Main Street, south of the new library. Richardson united the two buildings stylistically, once again employing low-springing Syrian arches, here as a granite arcade on the first storey. Richardson abruptly changed to brick for the second storey of the façade, and above that a steep hipped roof of orange tile rose to a balustrade.

As the core of a coherent Main Street for North Easton, the Town Hall and the library formed a subtle ensemble. Frederick Law Olmsted provided the central focus the town needed by creating a town square out of the triangular plot of ground across the street from the Town Hall. Olmsted designed "a rustic walk . . . laid out with seats and shade trees"[21] — the perfect setting for viewing the new edifice and a civic center for the community.

The center of the town thus identified and aggrandized, Richardson worked in his last projects for North Easton to create appropriate portals — one for the community, one for the community's benefactor. Frederick L. Ames commissioned a gatehouse for his private estate, Langwater. The result was a fortress of rough boulders pierced by a Syrian archway. Two years later, Ames supplied North Easton with a public gateway, a railroad station, whose salient feature was a porte-cochère supported by Syrian arches, which faced Ames's nearby estate. With these two projects, the Ameses completed their creation of a personally commissioned environment that proved in its architectural originality and excellence to be a satisfying memorial to their dynastic achievements and a gift to the citizens of North Easton.

The impact of individuals who have felt a personal commitment to the public

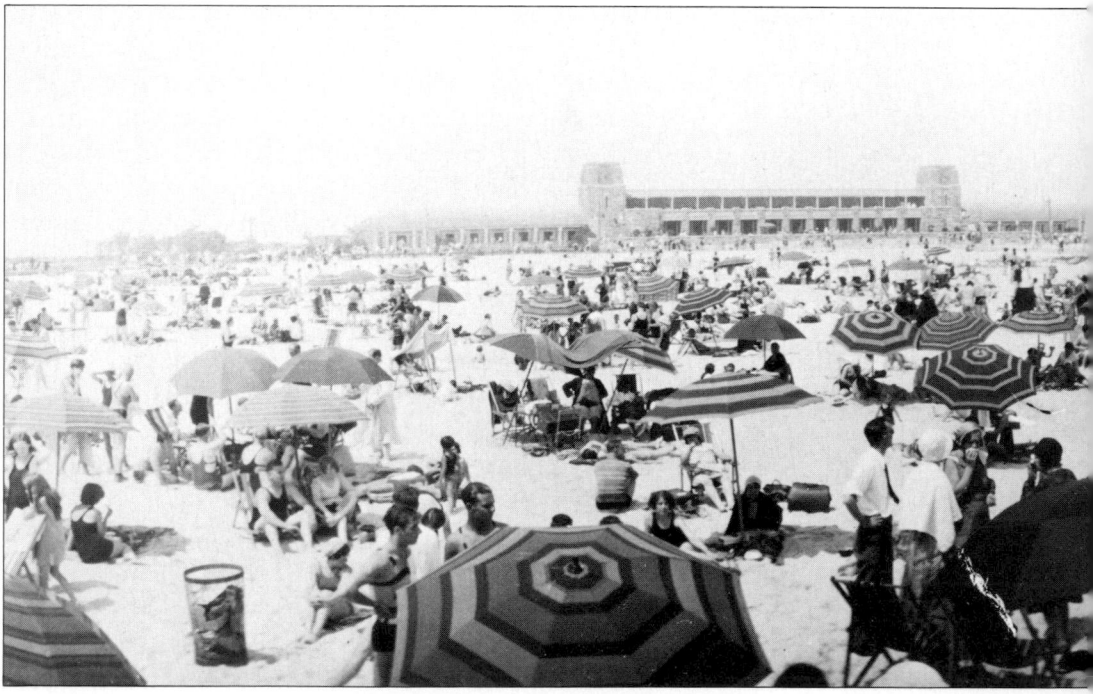

Jones Beach was opened to the public in 1929. Located only twenty-five miles from Times Square, it quickly became a favorite spot for those seeking refuge from the city's relentless summer heat.

environment has proven even more important in this century than the last. Robert Moses is one such individual. As New York's State Park Commissioner, Moses stretched his job description to a magnitude rivaling that of a president. Recognizing the potential impact of the automobile on patterns of development, he decided in the 1920s that he would orchestrate the transformation of New York City from a nineteenth-century metropolis into a twentieth-century megalopolis. America's middle class had already acquired the automobiles that would allow them to spread out beyond the dense inner city. Moses would give them places to go and the roads to get them there.

Robert Moses was a man of Jeffersonian ideals and Hamiltonian strategies. A rich boy, he grew up in New Haven and New York and was educated at Yale and Oxford before returning to his city in 1913 to receive a Ph.D. in political science from Columbia. Moses's first job, with the New York Bureau of Municipal Research, was followed by another stint as a civic reformer in a nonprofit organization, the New York State Association.

Moses's fundamental dream was simple. A new motoring middle class, given liberty, at least on Sundays, by Ford's Tin Lizzie, was discovering that the countryside near the metropolis — the beaches, the fields, the forests — was largely closed to them by No Trespassing signs. Moses set out to provide this public access to country and shorefront property comparable to that enjoyed by the very rich. His vision of what a park should be was daring in its scope and its ambition, and he laid it out before the public in the fall of 1922 in *A State Park Plan for New York.* Whereas Olmsted had seen parks as "breathing spaces" for city dwellers taking contemplative, Emersonian walks, Moses saw parks as places for more varied and strenuous activities. He planned parks in which the urban middle class could play all the sports that they had never before had the time, place, or money to pursue. Further, he intended the parks to be accessible by parkways, so that the drive from the city would extend the visitors' pleasure in the out-of-doors to include travel time. The press gave immediate acclaim to Moses's proposal, but there were two principal questions: where would the parks be, and who had the political power to build them? Moses found answers to both questions.

He had discovered the area for the first parks the summer before he wrote the plan. In 1922 Moses and his wife rented a house in Babylon, on Long Island's South Shore. Commuting between New York and Babylon, Moses observed from the train window an almost continuous chain of ponds, lakes, and forest belonging to New York City's water companies. He envisioned this area as a system of parks linked by landscaped motor parkways. And from his summer house he could see across Great South Bay to the nearly empty strand of Jones Beach, whose western tip was only twenty-five miles from Times Square. Jones Beach would become New York's Lido, connected back to the mainland by causeways.

The linchpin of his parks proposal was Jones Beach. It was threatened, however, by the recalcitrance of the citizens of Hempstead and Oyster Bay. But Moses, appointed State Park Commissioner by Governor Al Smith in 1924, proved that he had the political power and savvy to make his dream a reality. The eastern half of Jones Beach belonged to Babylon, and the fishermen there had no intention of giving up their portion of the strand. Moses, however, discovered that a nineteenth-century legal oversight had left the town of Babylon without ownership of the bottom of Great South Bay, the source of the baymen's livelihood and the town's tax income. Moses told the town board that they could keep the bay bottom if he got the beach. They agreed, and the town held a referendum on giving up the beach, which the town board made an easy victory by allowing the votes of the town's newest citizens, several hundred State Highway Commission employees.

Moses had won the political battle, but the geological one was still unsettled. Jones Beach was only two feet above sea level, and during storms, sections of it disappeared under the water. To create stable parkland, seventeen miles of sandbar were raised twelve feet higher, with sand scooped up from the bottom of Great South Bay. When the fine white sand refused to stay in place, Moses employed an army of workers to hand-plant millions of clumps of dune grass.

In 1929, seven years after he had first conceived it, the Jones Beach State Park opened to the public. In its first month of operation, 325,000 people drove along the landscaped parkways to what was surely the world's most glorious public beach. And the crowds kept coming, even after Moses's imposition of a fifty-cent parking fee flew in the face of the American tradition of free public parks. With sixty-two parking lots linked to the beach by highway underpasses and scrupulously landscaped gardens, Moses had realized on a metropolitan scale what Olmsted had imagined in his plans for Brooklyn years before.

Moses chose to monumentalize the park's water tower as a symbol of his dream and its realization. His engineers proposed a ruthlessly utilitarian, spindly-legged metal tower. His architect, Herbert Magoon, suggested a lighthouse. Moses suggested a streamlined version of the campanile at San Marco and got it. He was determined that Jones Beach remain a family resort — by which he meant a very proper middle-class place. He banished the typical seaside honky-tonk, constructing buildings like the vaguely Venetian East Bathhouse in a palette of tawny Barbizon brick and Briar Hill sandstone harmonized with the sand and ocean, and created miles of boardwalk with neither the rides nor the arcade amusements that typified Brooklyn's Coney Island. Moses's boardwalk was modeled after the promenade deck of a great luxury liner, from which one could look at the sea or watch fellow passengers pursuing such elevated pleasures as shuffleboard or handball. An exhibition saltwater pool was available for the public's use between scheduled events. Every detail was shipshape. Trashcans were placed in ship's funnels and water fountain handles were fashioned as pilot wheels. Freshly varnished nautical railings rimmed the "deck," while the lampposts supported ship's lanterns. Flagpole masts incorporated yardarms and halyards adorned with bright semaphore signals, and the nautical theme was driven into the ground in slate inlays of seahorses, anchors, and lobsters.

Moses's techniques for keeping out the underclass were less than subtle. He blocked proposals to run a spur line from the Long Island Railroad to Jones Beach so that the urban poor, who typically did not own cars, could not get there easily by train. Buses were discouraged by their requiring permits to enter state parks and, later, by Moses's instructions to build the bridges across his parkways too low for them to pass under. But Moses got things done and, on the whole, his projects delivered real pleasure to a world starved by the Depression, especially in the fulfillment of his dream of parks for urbanites in every section of New York State. His success did not go unrecognized, for, from his position as Parks Commissioner, Moses's power and titles expanded until he had been entrusted with masterminding the city's highway system and the housing projects of urban renewal.

While Moses grasped Olmsted's perception that parkland could be a by-product of highway construction, he failed to understand the car's potential for urban destruction. He girdled Manhattan with great highways that cut its citizens off from their own waterfront and turned the city into an immense traffic machine. The magnificent engineering of his highways didn't compensate for the fate of neighborhoods like Sunset Park in Brooklyn, which had its core ripped out by the Gowanus Parkway, opened in 1941. Moses's cataclysmic style of planning, razing neighborhoods for freeways and planting groves of virtually identical housing towers, "saved" the city by destroying it.

Moses's Jones Beach was an unparalleled public playground just a short drive from the heart of the city. But the real problem in American urbanism has been to build cities that combine the garden and the grid. Ironically, it is the Colonial town of Williamsburg, Virginia, that offers one of the most compelling models for contemporary urban planning. The restoration of Colonial Williamsburg was begun in 1926 by John D. Rockefeller. Rockefeller and his architects had their work cut out for them. The splendid eighteenth-century capital had degenerated into a typical Southern backwater. The town's glorious heritage of Colonial architecture was obscured by power lines, gas stations, and Victorian "improvements" to the original façades. But to W. A. R. Goodwin, rector of the Bruton Parish Church in Williamsburg, the town was an American Pompeii. At first, the Reverend Goodwin undertook a successful one-man campaign to restore the interior of his church, which was completed in 1907. After fifteen years away from Williamsburg, Dr. Goodwin returned in 1923 to be a professor and the director of the endowment campaign for the College of William and Mary. He now dreamed of restoring the college and the entire Colonial town.

To make his dream a reality, Goodwin went to Rockefeller, the man who had

restored Rheims Cathedral and the Palace of Versailles. Rockefeller, groomed to run Standard Oil and the rest of his family's businesses, had abandoned it all for philanthropy in 1910, following the publication of Ida Tarbell's muckraking articles that revealed the ruthless greed of the family firm. Rockefeller had spent most of his life giving away half a billion dollars, and the Reverend Goodwin was determined to direct some of that to Williamsburg. After two years he finally lured Rockefeller from New York. As part of a school vacation trip with three of their sons, Rockefeller and his wife, Abby, agreed to visit Williamsburg. Goodwin waited by the side of the road for the black Lincoln touring car to drive down the dusty, rutted road. A knowledgeable architectural scholar, Goodwin guided the Rockefellers through the sleepy town, painting vivid pictures of the Colonial splendor buried behind and beneath the Victorian overlays. A year later Rockefeller agreed to fund the restoration, and within ten years Williamsburg had been transformed into a living museum.

Rockefeller and his team of consultants approached the task with enthusiasm and care. Everything had to be just right. For instance, during the reconstruction of the Red Lion Inn, new evidence was found indicating that it was about four feet off its original foundation. Rockefeller had the whole structure dismantled and moved to the correct location. Altogether, 572 post-Colonial wooden buildings were torn down, 19 were relocated on a new site outside the restored city, 88 were restored, and 188 were reconstructed on their old foundations.

Today, some consider the restored city too pretty, inaccurately genteel. Much of the painting, for example, in terms of hues and the manner in which they are combined, does not conform to recent paint analyses of original samplings. Historically, outbuildings were often not painted at all. The pathways would have been made of materials such as broken crockery, chicken bones, and oyster shells rather than the brick presently in place.[22] Further, the gardens that were planted as part of the restoration are more ornate than those of eighteenth-century Virginians. The historian Charles B. Hosmer, Jr., has written that "there was a conscious refusal to accept the conclusions of research reports that implied Colonial gardens had been simple, functional, and even somewhat bare. Perhaps the tendency to such refusal became a form of patriotism as the Great Depression generation searched for a stable past to alleviate the stresses of an uncertain present."[23]

However idealized, Williamsburg's past is an eminently usable one. Leon Krier, the architect and theorist who has astonished the architectural community by arguing that today's cities should be built according to preindustrial European models, agrees with the American architect and urbanist Jaquelin Robertson, who has said that Williamsburg is the best new town of the twentieth century. To Krier, Williamsburg is an antidote to "Modernist planning [which] tends to put all public buildings in one spot and all housing in the other." Krier believes that "there is a very close mix of public and private functions."[24] The artifacts, houses, and the town plan are the backdrop for a restored urban drama. The tourist can use the past: walk up a Colonial street, eat at a Colonial inn, shop at the Colonial shops, and spend the night in a Colonial house. At Williamsburg one can simultaneously escape into history and escape from it.

The motto of the Colonial Williamsburg Foundation is: "That the Future may learn from the Past." Remarkably, Williamsburg has proved itself not only a

With close attention to historical accuracy, the restoration of Colonial Williamsburg transformed the town into a living museum. Here a tavern sign in the shape of a boar casts its shadow against the carefully crafted wood siding.

compelling history lesson but a textbook for the future. Yet, as Krier has pointed out, "architects to this day refuse to learn from Williamsburg, which is unfortunate because Williamsburg was built to resist the vulgarization of the industrial environment."[25] Williamsburg calls attention to the pleasures of fine materials meticulously crafted. Its carefully restored and re-created buildings introduce the forms of Colonial architecture to a public most familiar with the awkward versions built in the suburbs. Most radical of all, Williamsburg's streets teach automobiling Americans how to walk in a town. Rockefeller, who resided intermittently at Bassett Hall, an eighteenth-century frame house just a few blocks from Duke of Gloucester Street, stated that "you can't appreciate Williamsburg unless you walk through the town."[26] But visitors weren't obliged to walk until 1962, when a seasonal interdiction against cars on Duke of Gloucester Street was imposed, to be extended to a year-round basis ten years later.

Williamsburg was both a revival of the eighteenth century's ideological urbanism and a reversal of the nineteenth century's more programmatic approach. Williamsburg's research proposed an old ideal for the twentieth century: a gridded, axial, planned alternative to the arbitrary, winding residential streets and commercial strips of suburbia. The gridiron town of the nineteenth century had needed green lungs — which the great parks and model suburban villages had provided; the auto age suburban subdivisions needed representative public spaces where the business of government and commercial and social interactions could take place.

On Long Island, while small towns were rapidly being absorbed into the suburban stew of Levittown-style tract developments facilitated by Moses's highways, one man of vision, the shoe tycoon Ward Melville, set out to rebuild the town where he lived, Stony Brook, New York, as an American place that could defy anonymity. During the 1930s, with the nation's democratic traditions threatened by world war, Melville dreamed of the sort of well-planned country town in which those traditions had been born. Taking his cue from the Williamsburg restoration, Melville not only recaptured Stony Brook's neglected Colonial past but also made it fully functional as a twentieth-century suburban village. Aided by the architect Richard Haviland Smythe, Melville restored existing buildings, removing those that were inconsistent with his dream and erecting new ones in appropriate Colonial styles. The crescent-shaped center of Melville's new village, completed in 1941, contained a post office, a courthouse, and a firehouse. A true town center, it was the opposite of the ubiquitous strip that plagued postwar suburban development. At Stony Brook, services like deliveries and trash collection for the blocks of attached shops were consigned to the rear of the blocks. With the messy services behind, the principal street could devote itself to pedestrians, who enjoyed an intimate, quiet village environment.

Melville's new village faced Long Island Sound across an archetypal New England green whose lovely trees were not ancient survivors but fully grown nursery specimens, shipped in to instantly create a sense of the past. Yet Stony Brook is no theme park. It is a place that works, but a place that casts a gentle spell of the timeless traditions as it fulfills the requirements of everyday life in urban America. Even the garbage cans bear a message, quoting Abraham Lincoln: "I like to see a man proud of the place in which he lives."

Stony Brook is more than a livable community. It is an urgently needed lesson

As part of the Williamsburg project, the College of William and Mary was restored to its original splendor. Here we see the entrance to the college.

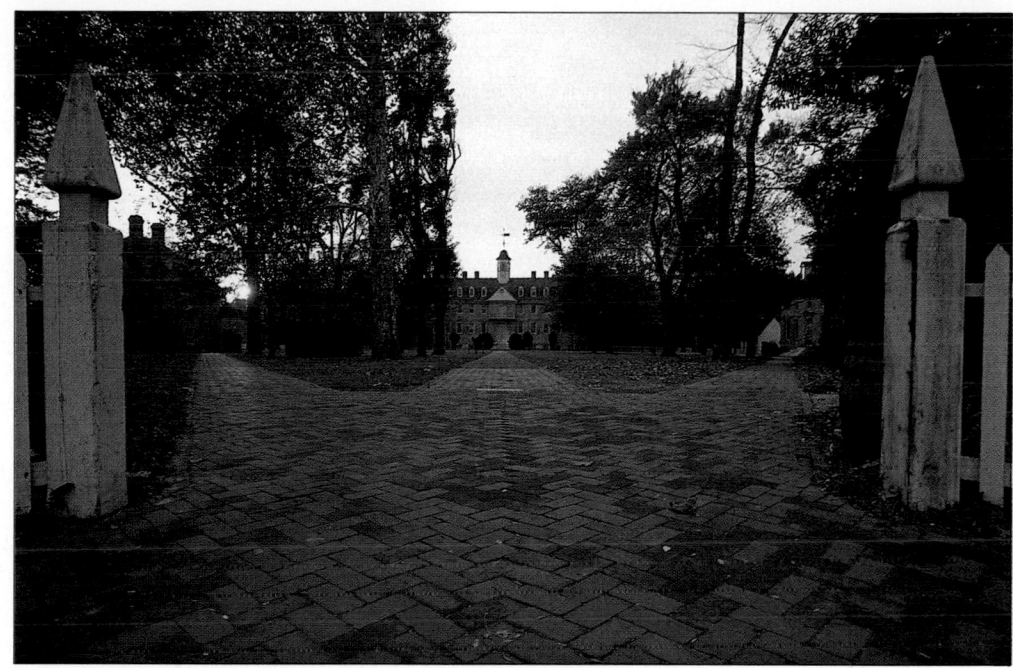

in the importance of finding a usable past. It is not simply enough to remember; we must choose the best our history has to offer if we are to realize the dreams of the founding fathers, who saw America as the last best hope of civilization. As Lewis Mumford has written,

The future of our civilization depends upon our ability to select and control our heritage from the past, to alter our present attitudes and habits, and to project fresh forms into which our energies may be freely poured. On our ability to re-introduce old elements, as the humanists of the late Middle Ages brought back the classic literature and uncovered the Roman monuments, or to introduce new elements, as the inventors and engineers of the last century brought in physical science and the machine-tool technology, our position as creators depends.[27]

At Stony Brook, this interpretation of the American dream ends where it began — in the East, facing Long Island Sound, where, as F. Scott Fitzgerald wrote in *The Great Gatsby*, one can marvel at the "old island . . . that flowered for Dutch sailors' eyes — a fresh, green breast of the new world." The American dream has not been a blind leap into the future but a determined march: at our best, our march forward has been directed by the lessons of what went before, and only when we have broken our contract with the past, with our best sense of what is noble and right, have we stumbled: we stumbled in the South Bronxes of our inner cities; we stumbled in Vietnam. When we stumble again, let us hope we do not fall down once and for all. Like Fitzgerald's Jay Gatsby, I believe "in the green light, the orgiastic future that year by year recedes before us." It eluded us at the dawn of our Republic, it eludes us now, "but that's no matter — to-morrow we will run faster, stretch out our arms farther. . . . And one fine morning —

"So we beat on, boats against the current, borne back ceaselessly into the past."[28]

Acknowledgments

In the beginning there was the idea — and it wasn't my idea. It was the idea of Herbert Schmertz, vice president of public affairs at Mobil, who proposed that I shape and present a personal view of American architecture in a television series. That was in October 1982; by August 1984 we were filming — a prodigious feat of organization and testimony to Mobil's enthusiastic support.

Once the initial concept was formulated, Herb Schmertz turned the day-to-day operation over to Sandra Ruch, Mobil's manager for cultural programs and promotion, whose unflagging enthusiasm for the project and superb organizational skills have never failed to turn an obstacle into an advantage. Sandra and I selected Malone Gill Productions to produce the programs. In the early stages, Adrian Malone was helpful in putting the story into cinematographic terms; but as the project grew more complex and the schedule grew more hectic, Michael Gill took over as executive producer, bringing with him Stephany Marks as producer. Part Ahab, part Billy Budd, Stephany kept the ship afloat with a firm hand and a genial wit, preventing many cases of cabin fever from erupting into mutiny. As location coordinator, Fran Kambitsis steered us into ports not normally hospitable to film crews. Michael Gill's decision to bring Murray Grigor into the process as director was nothing short of inspired.

I first met W. A. Murray Grigor in 1975 in Los Angeles, where I was delivering a lecture at UCLA. Murray was working on a film about Frank Lloyd Wright, and Professor Thomas Hines, his adviser for that film and our mutual friend, introduced us. I later got to know Murray's architectural films — *Mackintosh* (1967), *Hand of Adam* (1975), *The Architecture of Frank Lloyd Wright* (1983) — as well as his witty send-up *Scotch Myths — The Movie* (1981). I believe Murray is architecture's most sympathetic cinematographic interpreter.

As much to the point as our shared love of architecture is our near-mad mutual chemistry. Grigor and I are two peas in a pod: the same age; four initials each to our names; two A. M.'s; and we both talk faster than anyone else — only Murray's verbal rushes are accompanied by a gentle Scot's burr. Can you imagine the two of us, while racing across the country scouting locations, trying to talk our way out of a speeding ticket in, of all places, Manhattan, Kansas? Gilbert and Sullivan, maybe. Or Laurel and Hardy.

Almost from the first, Tom Mellins has been my invaluable collaborator on this project, developing the ideas, translating the jottings into sentences and paragraphs, balancing and meshing the literary and production demands and the requirements of film and book production. Once the filming began, and with it the book, Ray Gastil joined our team and he, too, has contributed mightily to the spoken and written words. Susan Morris was Murray's discovery and we would have been nowhere without her: ferret and friend, she has been Mrs. Danvers to our Rebecca, Gracie Allen to our George Burns.

Signe Warner, Janet Silver, Mason Andrews, Catherine Bergart, and Luise Erdmann contributed their editorial skills to the book; David Fishman performed prodigious feats of word processing and much more — he is erudite and literate and should be counted among our editorial collaborators. The enthusiastic support of Nan Talese, editor-in-chief at Houghton Mifflin, and Connie Roosevelt, editor at American Heritage, got the project over many a rough patch. Sabra Moore's photo research for the book was a perfect complement to Susan Morris's work for the television films. Steven M. L. Aronson, another of the four-name band, gave me superb advice at the outset.

To me the phrase "the movies" had been just about the most romantic in the English language — that is, before I got to make not one but eight of them. Now I know that the romance is in the eye of the beholder; making movies is hard work. Like architecture, cinematic creation is a patient search: for the right weather, the right sun angle, the right luggage, the right hotel . . . Most important, it is the search for the right combination of talents and temperaments to create a "crew" who will work together for the best interests of art and sanity.

Two members of the crew deserve my special personal thanks: Robin Schwartz, who not only kept my tie straight and my complexion rosy but also kept me amused in the endless hours between takes; and Terry Hopkins, whose steady hand and gimlet eye combined with an absolutely unflappable demeanor to make him the superb cameraman he is. While Robin tried to make me look beautiful on camera but ultimately was hampered by poor material, Terry, as directed by Murray Grigor, managed to make even the urban wastelands of the South Bronx and the trashitecture of the highway look Arcadian. Limitations of space prevent me from acknowledging individually every member of the Malone Gill "Pride of Place" crew, which included:

EXECUTIVE PRODUCER
Michael Gill

PRODUCERS
Murray Grigor
Stephany Marks

DIRECTOR
Murray Grigor

DIRECTOR FOR WEST COAST/
DIRECTOR OF PHOTOGRAPHY
FOR MIDWEST
Rob Orr

DIRECTOR OF PHOTOGRAPHY
Terry Hopkins

DIRECTOR OF RESEARCH/
PRODUCTION SUPERVISOR
Susan Morris

SCRIPT COLLABORATOR
Thomas Mellins

NARRATION COLLABORATOR
Raymond Gastil

LOCATION COORDINATOR
Fran Kambitsis

ASSOCIATE PRODUCER
Penelope Pigott

PRODUCTION COORDINATOR
Peter Cohen

PRODUCTION OFFICE
ASSISTANT
Howard Coe

PRODUCTION MANAGERS
Martin Bluford
Jim Sterne
Karen Goodman
Pamela Baker Elder
Stephen Kern

LIGHTING GAFFER
Scott Ramsey

CAMERA ASSISTANTS
Jeffrey Victor
David McGowan

SOUND RECORDISTS
Roger Phenix
Peter Agoos
Ronald Yoshida
Phil Koch

GRIPS/ELECTRICIANS
Don Angst
John Merriman

WARDROBE CONSULTANT
Nan Cibula

MAKEUP/WARDROBE
Robin Schwartz
Rona Lamont

Notes

29. Ibid., p. 212.
30. Johnson, interview with the author, October 6, 1984.
31. Ibid.
32. Scully, interview with the author, September 25, 1984.
33. Norman Mailer, "Mailer vs. Scully," *Architectural Forum* 120 (April 1964): 96–97.
34. Robert Venturi, *Complexity and Contradiction in Architecture* (New York: The Museum of Modern Art, 1966), p. 46.
35. Graves, in Pilar Viladas, "Ex Libris," *Progressive Architecture* 6, no. 65 (June 1984): 70.
36. Hines, in Carleton Knight III, "Significant Clients: Gerald Hines," *Architecture* 73 (April 1984): 49.
37. Liedtke, ibid.

2. ACADEMICAL VILLAGES

1. Jefferson, May 6, 1810 (Jefferson Papers, Library of Congress), in Mary N. Woods, "Thomas Jefferson and the University of Virginia, Planning the Academic Village," *Journal of the Society of Architectural Historians* 44 (October 1985): 269.
2. Jefferson to Latrobe, June 12, 1817, in Fiske Kimball, *Thomas Jefferson, Architect* (New York: Da Capo Press, 1916; 1968), p. 190.
3. Montgomery Schuyler, "A Review of the Work of Charles Coolidge Haight," *Architectural Record* 17 (July 1899); rpt. in Great American Architects Series no. 6, p. 8.
4. Schuyler, "Architecture of American Colleges. Part IV: New York City Colleges," *Architectural Record* 27 (June 1919): 448–49.
5. Princeton trustees, in Alexander Leitch, *A Princeton Companion* (Princeton, N.J.: Princeton University Press, 1978), p. 75.
6. Leitch, *Princeton Companion*, p. 74; Paul Venable Turner, *Campus: An American Planning Tradition* (Cambridge, Mass.: MIT Press, 1984), p. 47.
7. Ralph Adams Cram, "Princeton Architecture," *The American Architect* 96 (July 21, 1909): 24.
8. Comment on Austin's library, in Reuben A. Holden, *Yale: A Pictorial History* (New Haven, Conn.: Yale University Press, 1967), figs. 42–44.
9. Thomas Hastings and Everett V. Weeks's Corinthian portico and cenotaph were added to the commons in 1927 to memorialize the World War I dead.
10. Edwin Oviatt (editor of the *Yale Alumni Weekly*), in George Nichols, "The Memorial Quadrangle of Yale University and the Harkness Memorial Tower," *Architecture* 44 (October 1921): 293.
11. Turner, *Campus*, p. 59.
12. George Bancroft, in the *National Intelligencer* in James Russell Soley, *Historical Sketch of the United States Naval Academy* (Washington, D.C.: U.S. Government Printing Office, 1876), p. 66; cited in Jack Sweetman, *The U.S. Naval Academy: An Illustrated History* (Annapolis, Md.: Naval Institute Press, 1979), p. 23.
13. "Report of Professor Charles W. Larned upon the Reorganization of the Plant of the United States Military Academy, Accompanied by Estimates, Maps, and Drawings," December 21, 1901 (USMA Archives), pp. 4–5; cited in Richard Oliver, *Bertram Grosvenor Goodhue* (New York: Architectural History Foundation, 1983), p. 45.
14. *Journal of the American Institute of Architects* 1, no. 3 (March 1913): 117–18.
15. Cram, "Have I a 'Philosophy of Design'?" *Pencil Points* 13 (November 1932): 730.
16. See Stephen Fox, "The General Plan of the William M. Rice Institute and Its Architectural Development," Architecture at Rice Monograph 29 (Houston: School of Architecture, Rice University, 1980), pp. 55, 87.
17. Anderson, in Turner, *Campus*, p. 150.
18. Werner Hegemann and Elbert Peets, *The American Vitruvius: An Architect's Handbook of Civic Art* (New York: The Architectural Book Publishing Co., 1922), p. 114; cited in Turner, *Campus*, p. 202.
19. Mies, in Werner Blaser, *Mies van der Rohe* (New York: Praeger, 1965), p. 80.
20. Charles Jencks, interview with the author, September 6, 1984.
21. Mies, "Burohaus," *il G* (Berlin), June 3, 1923; "Baukunst und Zeitwille," *Der Querschnitt* 4 (1924).
22. Wright, in a seminar at the University of California at Berkeley, April 27, 1957; cited in *The Master Architect: Conversations with Frank Lloyd Wright*, ed. Patrick J. Meehan (New York: John Wiley and Sons, 1984), p. 202.
23. Wright, in film footage, July 6, 1957 (Sherman Grinberg Film Libraries, New York).

1. THE SEARCH FOR A USABLE PAST

1. Le Corbusier, *Towards a New Architecture*, trans. Frederick Etchells (London: The Architectural Press; Praeger, 1946), p. 58.
2. Louis Sullivan, "The Tall Office Building Artistically Considered," in *Kindergarten Chats and Other Writings* (New York: George Wittenborn, 1947), pp. 208, 202.
3. William Bradford, *Of Plymouth Plantation, 1620–1647* (New York: Modern Library, 1981), p. 70.
4. John Donne, "Annual Sermon of the Reverend John Donne, Chaplain of the London Company, to the Members of That Company, 1622," Jamestown Festival Park, Virginia, plaque.
5. Perry Miller, *Nature's Nation* (Cambridge, Mass.: Harvard University Press, 1967), p. 3.
6. Henry James, *The American Scene* (Bloomington: Indiana University Press, 1968), p. 336.
7. Jefferson to John Page, May 4, 1786, in *The Life and Selected Writings of Thomas Jefferson*, ed. Adriene Koch and William Peden (New York: Modern Library, 1944), p. 392.
8. Andrea Palladio, *The Four Books of Architecture* (1738; New York: Dover, 1965), p. 46.
9. Marquis de Chastellux, quoted in William H. Pierson, Jr., *American Buildings and Their Architects: The Colonial and Neo-Classical Styles* (Garden City, N.Y.: Doubleday, 1970), p. 289.
10. Jefferson, *Notes on Virginia*, in *Life and Selected Writings*, p. 269.
11. Directors of Public Buildings in Virginia, in Fiske Kimball, *Thomas Jefferson, Architect* (New York: Da Capo Press, 1916; 1968), p. 40.
12. Jefferson to William Short, 1789, in *The Writings of Thomas Jefferson*, ed. Paul Leicester Ford, 10 vols. (New York: G. P. Putnam's Sons, 1903), 5:186; cited in Kimball, *Jefferson, Architect*, p. 43.
13. Kimball, *Jefferson, Architect*, p. 41.
14. Jefferson to Maria Cosway, in Desmond Guinness and Julius Trousdale Sadler, Jr., *Mr. Jefferson, Architect* (New York: Viking Press, 1973), p. 71.
15. Pierson, *American Buildings*, p. 297.
16. Jaquelin Robertson, interview with the author, October 31, 1984.
17. Jefferson, in William Howard Adams, *Monticello* (New York: Abbeville Press, 1983), p. 34.
18. Frank Lloyd Wright, *An Autobiography* (1932; New York: Horizon Press, 1977), p. 192.
19. Vincent Scully, *Frank Lloyd Wright* (New York: George Braziller, 1960), p. 22.
20. Wright, *An Autobiography*, p. 195.
21. Philip Johnson, *Philip Johnson: Writings* (New York: Oxford University Press, 1979), p. 197.
22. Ibid., p. 198.
23. Cass Gilbert, in Brooks Emeny, *Theodate Pope Riddle and the Founding of Avon Old Farms* (Farmington, Conn.: Avon Old Farms School, 1977), p. 8.
24. Riddle, ibid., p. 14.
25. Johnson, interview with the author, October 6, 1984.
26. Ibid.
27. Ibid.
28. Wright, in Johnson, *Writings*, p. 193.

24. Francis Crick and Graeme Mitchison, "The Function of Dream Sleep," *Nature* 304 (July 1983): 112.
25. Eero Saarinen, *Eero Saarinen on His Work*, ed. Aline B. Saarinen, rev. ed. (New Haven, Conn.: Yale University Press, 1968), p. 88.
26. Ibid.
27. Vincent Scully, interview with the author, September 25, 1984.
28. Jencks, *The Language of Post-Modern Architecture*, 4th rev. ed. (New York: Rizzoli, 1984), p. 125.
29. Moore, in David Littlejohn, *Architect: The Life and Work of Charles W. Moore* (New York: Holt, Rinehart, and Winston, A William Abrahams Book, 1984), p. 230.
30. Frank Gehry, interview with the author, December 8, 1984.
31. Gehry, in Pilar Viladas, "Form Follows Ferment," *Progressive Architecture* 65 (February 1985): 67.

3. DREAM HOUSES

1. Robert Venturi, Denise Scott Brown, Steven Izenour, *Signs of Life: Symbols in the American City* (Millerton, N.Y.: Aperture, Inc., 1976), n.p.
2. Peter Eisenman, interview with the author, May 9, 1985.
3. Lewis Mumford, *The Golden Day: A Study in American Literature and Culture* (Boston: Beacon Press, 1957), pp. 25–26.
4. Samuel Clemens (Mark Twain), *Alta, California*, September 6, 1868.
5. Clemens, in Joseph J. Thorndike, Jr., *The Magnificent Builders and Their Dream Houses* (New York: American Heritage, 1978), p. 208.
6. Stowe and Beecher, in Dolores Hayden, *Redesigning the American Dream: The Future of Housing, Work, and Family Life* (New York, W. W. Norton, 1984), p. 23.
7. *American Architect and Building News* 11 (October 22, 1881): 192; 1 (October 21, 1876): 340.
8. Clemens to Mrs. Clemens, March 20, 1895, *The Letters of Mark Twain*, ed. Dixon Wector (New York: Harper and Brothers, 1949), p. 312.
9. Clemens, *Travelers Record*, January 1877, Mark Twain Memorial Collection, Hartford, Conn.
10. Clemens to Rev. Joseph Twichell, January 1897, *Mark Twain's Letters*, comp. Albert Bigelow Paine, 2 vols. (New York: Harper and Brothers, 1917), 2:641.
11. Sleeper, in Samuel Chamberlain and Paul Hollister, *Beauport at Gloucester* (New York: Hastings House, 1951), p. 2.
12. Mumford, *The Golden Day*, p. 107.
13. Olmsted, in Paul R. Baker, *Richard Morris Hunt* (Cambridge, Mass.: MIT Press, 1980), p. 414.
14. Ibid.
15. Olmsted, "Letter to the Editor," *Lyceum Magazine* 2 (December 1891): 6.
16. Hunt, in Baker, *Richard Morris Hunt*, p. 414.
17. Pinchot, in George W. S. Trow, "Annals of Discourse: The Harvard Black Rock Forest," *The New Yorker*, June 18, 1984, p. 44.
18. James, in Leon Edel, *Henry James: The Master, 1901–1916* (Philadelphia: Lippincott, 1972), pp. 270–71.
19. James, in Clara Barbara Kozol, "Creator and Collector: The Unpublished Letters of Henry James to Isabella Stewart Gardner" (Ph.D. diss., Columbia University, 1973), p. 17.
20. James, *The Notebooks of Henry James*, ed. F. O. Matthiessen and Kenneth B. Murdock (New York: Horizon Press, 1967), p. 207.
21. *Town Topics*, in Cleveland Amory, *The Proper Bostonians* (New York: E. P. Dutton, 1947), p. 130.
22. Van Wyck Brooks, *New England: Indian Summer, 1865–1915* (New York, E. P. Dutton, 1940), p. 331.
23. Ibid., p. 207.
24. James, *The Outcry*, in *The Complete Henry James*, ed. Edel (Philadelphia: Lippincott, 1949), p. 778.
25. Mary Berenson, in *Mary Berenson: A Self-Portrait from Her Letters and Diaries*, ed. Barbara Strachey and Jayne Samuels (New York: W. W. Norton, 1983), p. 237.
26. Critic's comment on Sargent's portrait of Gardner, in Amory, *Proper Bostonians*, frontispiece.
27. James, in Douglass Shand Tucci, *Built in Boston: City and Suburb, 1800–1950* (Boston: New York Graphic Society, 1978), p. 154.
28. Chalfin, in *Vizcaya* (Miami: Martori Enterprises II, 1984), p. 93.

29. Nell Dorr in conversation with Gish, in James T. Maher, *The Twilight of Splendor: Chronicles of the Age of American Palaces* (Boston: Little, Brown, 1975), pp. 208–9.
30. Hoffman, in Maher, *Twilight of Splendor*, p. 166.
31. Hearst, quoted by Walter Steilberg, typescript of an oral history conducted by Sally Woodbridge, 1972, for the Julia Morgan Architectural History Project, Regional Oral History Office, The Bancroft Library, University of California, Berkeley; cited in Thomas R. Aidala and Curtis Bruce, *Hearst Castle: San Simeon* (New York: Hudson Hills Press, 1981), p. 39.
32. David Gebhard and Robert Winter, *A Guide to Architecture in Los Angeles and Southern California* (Salt Lake City: A Peregrine South Book, 1982), p. 597.
33. Hearst, in Merrill Folson, *Great American Mansions and Their Stories* (New York: Hastings House, 1963), p. 123.
34. Millicent Hearst, in Thorndike, *Magnificent Builders*, p. 333.
35. Morgan and Hearst, ibid., p. 329.
36. Hearst, in Aidala and Bruce, *Hearst Castle*, p. 175.
37. Brooks, *Lulu in Hollywood* (New York: Knopf, 1983), p. 40.
38. Barnsdall, in Norman Bel Geddes, *Miracle in the Evening* (Garden City, N.Y.: Doubleday, 1960), p. 156.
39. Vincent Scully, *American Architecture and Urbanism* (New York: Praeger, 1969), p. 157.
40. Barnsdall citing Wright, in F. Lawrence, "Eminence to Be Made Rare Beauty Spot," *Los Angeles Examiner*, July 6, 1919; cited in Kathryn Smith, "Frank Lloyd Wright, Hollyhock House and Olive Hill, 1914–1924," *Journal of the Society of Architectural Historians* 38 (March 1979): 20.
41. Frank Lloyd Wright, *An Autobiography*, 2nd rev. ed. (New York: Duell, Sloan & Pearce, 1943), p. 228.

4. SUBURBS

1. From "Little Boxes," words and music by Malvina Reynolds, copyright 1962 by Schroder Music Co., ASCAP.
2. Denise Scott Brown, "Suburban Space, Scale, and Symbols," *Via* 3 (Graduate School of Fine Arts, University of Pennsylvania, 1977); see also Brown et al., *Signs of Life: Symbols in the American City* (New York: Aperture, Inc., 1976).
3. Andrew Jackson Downing, "Public Cemeteries and Public Gardens," *The Horticulturist* (July 1849); rpt. in Downing, *Rural Essays*, ed. George William Curtis (New York: G. P. Putnam, 1853), pp. 154–55.
4. Cornelia W. Walter, *Mount Auburn Illustrated* (New York: R. Martin, 1847), p. 14.
5. Frederick Law Olmsted, *Walks and Talks of an American Farmer in England*, 2 vols. (New York: Dix, Edwards, 1852), 1:79.
6. Ibid., p. 81.
7. Olmsted, "The Beginning of Central Park: A Fragment of Autobiography" (1877), in *Landscape into Cityscape: Frederick Law Olmsted's Plans for a Greater New York City*, ed. Albert Fein (New York: Van Nostrand Reinhold, 1967), p. 61.
8. "Llewellyn Park: Country Homes for City People," undated promotional pamphlet; see also advertisement in the *Orange Journal*, May 16, 1857, to November 28, 1863, and March 24 to April 14, 1866.
9. Riverside observer, in Harold M. Mayer and Richard C. Wade, *Chicago: Growth of a Metropolis* (Chicago: University of Chicago Press, 1969), p. 184.
10. Olmsted, Vaux & Company, "Preliminary Report Upon the Proposed Suburban Village at Riverside, Near Chicago" (New York, 1866), p. 17.
11. Comment on Pullman, in Stanley Buder, *Pullman: An Experiment in Industrial Order and Community Planning, 1880–1930* (New York: Oxford University Press, 1967), p. 21.
12. Pullman Palace Car Company brochure, in Daniel J. Boorstin, *The Americans: The Democratic Experience* (New York: Vintage Books, 1974), p. 282.
13. London reporter, in Mayer and Wade, *Chicago*, p. 190.
14. Ely, in Boorstin, *The Americans*, p. 283.
15. Hanna, in Thomas Beer, *Hanna* (New York: Knopf, 1929), pp. 132–33.
16. Forest Hills Gardens prospectus, in Christopher Tunnard, "The Romantic Suburb in America," *Magazine of Art* 40 (May 1947): 187.
17. Atterbury, in David P. Handlin, *The American Home: Architecture and Society, 1815–1915* (Boston: Little, Brown, 1979), p. 286.
18. Hubert Ladd Towle, "The Automobile and Its Mission," *Scribner's Magazine* (February 1919): 149.

19. Alden Christie, "Radburn Reconsidered," *Connection* 7 (May 25, 1964): 38.
20. Clarence Stein, *Toward New Towns in America* (Cambridge, Mass.: MIT Press, 1957).
21. See Wyatt B. Brumitt, "The Superhighway," *American City* 40 (January 1929): 85–87; Fritz Malcher, "Abolishing Street Traffic Intersections Without Grade Separation," *American City* 41 (September 1929): 89–92, part II (October 1929): 101–5; and "Townless Highways," *American City* 42 (May 1930): 94–96.
22. See Mel C. Scott, *American City Planning Since 1890* (Berkeley: University of California Press, 1969), p. 540.
23. Frank Lloyd Wright, *An Autobiography*, 2nd rev. ed. (New York: Duell, Sloan & Pearce, 1943), p. 320.
24. Vincent Scully, *American Architecture and Urbanism* (New York: Praeger, 1969), p. 173.
25. Wright, "London Lectures" (1939), in John Sergeant, *Frank Lloyd Wright's Usonian Houses* (New York: Whitney Library of Design, 1976), p. 134.
26. Wright, *The Natural House* (New York: Horizon Press, 1954), p. 135.
27. Wright, *An Autobiography*, p. 252.
28. Robert C. Twombly, *Frank Lloyd Wright, An Interpretive Biography* (New York: Harper and Row, 1973), p. 263.
29. Tuxedo Club observer, in Cleveland Amory, *The Last Resorts* (New York: Harper and Brothers, 1948), p. 84.
30. Price, ibid.
31. Herbert Croly, "Notes and Comments: A National Winter Suburb," *Architectural Record* (December 1925): 605.
32. George E. Merrick, "The Story of Coral Gables," promotional brochure, no date, p. 4.
33. Advertisement for Coral Gables, in Hampton Dunn, *Florida Sketches* (Miami: E. A. Seemann, 1974), p. 23.
34. Advertisement for Coral Gables, in Donald W. Curl, *Mizner's Florida: American Resort Architecture* (Cambridge, Mass.: MIT Press, 1984), p. 138.

5. RESORTS

1. Rudyard Kipling, *American Notes* (New York: Manhattan Press, n.d. [ca. 1890]), p. 130.
2. Olmsted, in Phyllis Meyers, "The Park Service as Client: I," *Architecture* 73 (December 1984): 42.
3. Robert Swain Peabody, "Georgian Homes of New England," *American Architect and Building News* 2 (October 20, 1877): 338–39.
4. Richardson's scholarly interest in Colonial America's medieval architectural roots was reflected in the editorial orientation of the *New York Sketchbook of Architecture*, which he founded in 1874 and for which he served as editor. (The critic Montgomery Schuyler, however, noted that the bulk of the editorial responsibility was delegated to the twenty-seven-year-old Charles Follen McKim, who had briefly worked as a draftsman in Richardson's firm.) The first published photograph of an American Colonial house appeared in 1874 in the premier volume of the journal. Tellingly, the photograph, of the Bishop Berkeley House (1728) near Newport, focused not on the nearly symmetrical principal façade but on the rear of the house's long sloping gable, the composition of which set the tone for the emerging Shingle Style.
5. Alva Belmont, in Cleveland Amory, *The Last Resorts* (New York: Harper and Brothers, 1948), p. 212.
6. Henry James, *The Ivory Tower* (Fairfield, Conn.: Augustus M. Kelley, 1976, Scribners Reprint Series [New York: Charles Scribner & Sons, 1917]), p. 23.
7. James, *The American Scene*, ed. Leon Edel (Bloomington: Indiana University Press, 1968), p. 224.
8. Joan Didion, *Slouching Towards Bethlehem* (New York: Pocket Books, 1961), pp. 211–12.
9. Ring W. Lardner, "Gullible's Travels," *Saturday Evening Post* 189 (August 19, 1916): 3.
10. Ibid., p. 38.
11. Ibid., p. 34.
12. Mizner, in John Taylor Boyd, Jr., "The Florida House," *Arts and Decoration* 32 (January 1930): 39.
13. Mizner, in Barbara D. Hoffstat, *Landmark Architecture of Palm Beach*, rev. ed. (Pittsburgh: Ober Park Associates, 1980), p. 11.
14. *Palm Beach Post*, July 24, 1918.
15. Alva Johnston, "Profiles: The Palm Beach Architect. II: The Boom," *The New Yorker*, November 29, 1952, p. 60.
16. Mizner, ibid., pp. 65–66.
17. Moore, in Johnston, "Profiles: The Palm Beach Architect. I: Construction First, Blueprints Afterwards," *The New Yorker*, November 22, 1952, p. 46.
18. Mizner, in Boyd, "The Florida House," p. 38.
19. Mizner, in Ida Tarbell, *Florida Architecture of Addison Mizner* (New York: William Helburn, 1928), n.p.
20. Addison Mizner, *Autobiography* (Historical Society of Palm Beach County, typescript), pp. 71–72.
21. Henry S. Villard, "Florida Aftermath," *The Nation* 126 (June 6, 1928): 636.
22. Morris Lapidus, *Architecture of Joy* (Miami: E. A. Seemann, 1979), p. 129.
23. Ibid., p. 132.
24. Lapidus, in John Margolies, "Now, Once and for All, Know Why I Did It," *Progressive Architecture* 51 (September 1970): 120.
25. Lapidus, interview with the author, January 13, 1985.
26. Mufson, in Lapidus, *Architecture of Joy*, p. 164.
27. Mufson, quoted by Lapidus, interview with the author, January 13, 1985.
28. Lapidus, in Jeffrey Limerick, Nancy Ferguson, and Richard Oliver, *America's Grand Resort Hotels* (New York: Pantheon, 1979), p. 245.
29. Ada Louise Huxtable, "Show Offers 'Joy' of Hotel Architecture," *New York Times*, October 15, 1970, p. 60.
30. Disney, November 15, 1965, press conference, in Royston Landau, "Mickey Mouse, the Great Dictator: The Disney Game as a Control System," *Architectural Design* 43 (September 1973): 591.
31. Charles Moore, "You Have to Pay for the Public Life," *Perspecta* 9/10 (1965): 65.

6. THE GREAT PLACES WITHIN

1. Lincoln, in Lois Craig et al., *The Federal Presence: Architecture, Politics, and Symbols in United States Government Buildings* (Cambridge, Mass.: MIT Press, 1977), p. 31.
2. Washington to the district commissioners, ibid.
3. Latrobe to Jefferson, May 21, 1807, in Talbot Hamlin, *Benjamin Henry Latrobe* (New York: Oxford University Press, 1955), p. 274.
4. Ibid.
5. Bulfinch, in Harold Kirker, *The Architecture of Charles Bulfinch* (Cambridge, Mass.: Harvard University Press, 1969), p. 328.
6. Mark Twain and Charles Dudley Warner, *The Gilded Age: A Tale of Today*, 2 vols. (1873; New York: Harper and Brothers, Author's National Edition, 1901), 1:265.
7. Jefferson to Latrobe, July 12, 1812, in Craig et al., *The Federal Presence*, p. 38.
8. Roche, in Mildred F. Schmertz, "General Foods Corporation Headquarters," *Architectural Record* 172 (September 1984): 106.
9. Vincent Scully, *Frank Lloyd Wright* (New York: George Braziller, 1960), p. 20.
10. Paul Goldberger, interview with the author, March 12, 1985.
11. Anthony Trollope, *North America* (New York: Knopf, 1951), pp. 372–73.
12. Émile Zola, *Au bonheur des dames (Ladies' Delight)* (1883), cited in Gunther Barth, *City People: The Rise of Modern City Culture in Nineteenth-Century America* (New York: Oxford University Press, 1980), p. 116.
13. Quoted in Harold M. Mayer and Richard C. Wade, *Chicago: Growth of a Metropolis* (Chicago: University of Chicago Press, 1969), p. 218.
14. Burnham to Fred W. Upham, December 21, 1911, in Thomas S. Hines, *Burnham of Chicago: Architect and Planner* (New York: Oxford University Press, 1974), p. 303.
15. Trollope, *North America*, pp. 483–84.
16. John Portman and Jonathon Barnett, *The Architect as Developer* (New York: McGraw-Hill, 1976), p. 74.
17. Frank Lloyd Wright, *Genius and the Mobocracy* (New York: Duell, Sloan & Pearce, 1949), p. 48.
18. Melba, in *The Auditorium Building* (Chicago: Roosevelt University, n.d.), pp. 11–12.
19. Wright, ibid., p. 1.
20. Warren, in "The Great Railway Terminal of the Future," *New York Times*, February 9, 1913, VI, 9.
21. Advertisement for Grand Central Terminal, rpt. in John R. Stilgoe, *Metropolitan Corridor: Railroads and the American Scene* (New Haven, Conn.: Yale University Press, 1983), p. 42.

22. Pei, in Russell Lynes, "National Gallery's New Building Is Triangular Triumph," *Smithsonian* 9 (June 1978): 47.

23. Colin Amery, "Inside the NGA," *Architectural Review* 165 (January 1979): 22.

24. Hilton Kramer, "MoMA Reopened: The Museum of Modern Art in the Postmodern Era," *The New Criterion* (Special issue, 1984): 5.

7. PROUD TOWERS

1. Louis H. Sullivan, "The Tall Office Building Artistically Considered," first published in *Lippincott's* 57 (March 1896): 403–9; rpt. in Sullivan, *Kindergarten Chats and Other Writings* (New York, George Wittenborn, 1947), p. 206.

2. Sullivan, *The Autobiography of an Idea* (New York: Dover, 1924; 1956), p. 200.

3. Sullivan, *Kindergarten Chats*, pp. 30, 29.

4. Sullivan, "The Tall Office Building Artistically Considered," p. 202.

5. Stieglitz, in Dorothy Norman, *Alfred Stieglitz: An American Seer* (New York: Aperture, 1973), p. 45.

6. Cadman, in *The Cathedral of Commerce: Woolworth Building, New York* (New York: Broadway Park Place, 1917; 1921), introduction.

7. Louis J. Horowitz and Boyden Sparkes, *The Towers of New York* (New York: Simon & Schuster, 1937); cited in Seymour I. Toll, *Zoned America* (New York: Grossman, 1969), p. 61.

8. See Donald Martin Reynolds, *The Architecture of New York City: Histories and Views of Important Structures, Sites, and Symbols* (New York: Macmillan, 1984), p. 179.

9. Smith, in Toll, *Zoned America*, p. 63.

10. See Sullivan, "The High-Building Question," *Graphic* 5 (December 19, 1891): 405; rpt. in Donald Hoffman, "The Setback Skyscraper City of 1891: An Unknown Essay of Louis H. Sullivan," *Journal of the Society of Architectural Historians* 29, no. 2 (May 1970): 181–87.

11. Le Corbusier, *La Ville Radieuse* (Paris: Vincent Fréal, 1964), p. 129, caption.

12. See Reynolds, *Architecture of New York City*, p. 235.

13. William Van Alen, "The Structure and Metal Work of the Chrysler Building," *Architectural Forum* 53 (October 1930): 493–98.

14. Douglas Haskell, "The Empire State Building," *Creative Art* 8 (April 1931): 242–44.

15. Chicago Tribune Tower Competition, vol. 1 (Rizzoli, 1980), rpt. of "The International Competition for a New Administration Building for the Chicago Tribune, 1922."

16. Ibid., p. 6.

17. See "The North Michigan Avenue, Chicago, Development," *The American Architect* 114 (December 11, 1919): 691–99, plates 179–85. Rebori was the managing architect of the Architects' Committee, North Michigan Avenue Development.

18. Raymond M. Hood, "The American Radiator Company Building, New York," *The American Architect* 124 (November 19, 1924): 468.

19. See Hood, "The News Building," *Architectural Forum* 58, no. 5 (November 1930): 531.

20. Lincoln's entire quotation was: "God must have loved the common man, he made so many of them." Cited in "Monument on 42nd Street," *The News* (New York: News Syndicated Company, 1969), pp. 178–87.

21. Vincent Scully, *American Architecture and Urbanism* (New York: Praeger, 1969), p. 154.

22. See Hartley Burr Alexander, "Rockefeller City: Thematic Synopsis," May 1932, Rockefeller Family Archives; in Alan Balfour, *Rockefeller Center* (New York: McGraw-Hill, 1978), p. 137.

23. John D. Rockefeller, Jr., to Raymond Hood, October 12, 1932, Rockefeller Family Archives; cited in Balfour, *Rockefeller Center*, p. 152.

24. Filippo Tommaso Marinetti, *Selected Writings*, ed. R. W. Flint, trans. Flint and Arthur A. Coppobelli (New York: Farrar, Straus & Giroux, 1971), pp. 81–82.

25. Antonio Sant'Elia, with Ugo Nebbia, in Kenneth Frampton and Yukio Futagawa, *Modern Architecture, 1851–1919* (New York: Rizzoli, 1983), p. 192.

26. Sullivan, *Autobiography of an Idea*, p. 290.

27. Stephen Sondheim (book by George Furth), *Company* (New York: Random House, 1970), act II, sc. i, p. 81.

8. THE GARDEN AND THE GRID

1. *Works of Thomas Jefferson*, ed. P. L. Ford, 10 vols. (New York: G. P. Putnam's Sons, 1896), 7:458–59; cited in Christopher Tunnard, *The City of Man*, 2nd ed. (New York: Charles Scribner's Sons, 1970), p. 34.

2. The Laws of the Indies (1513), trans. Zelia Nuttall, "Royal Ordinances Concerning the Laying Out of New Towns," *Hispanic American Historical Review* 5 (1922): 249–54; cited in John W. Reps, *Town Planning in Frontier America* (Princeton, N.J.: Princeton University Press, 1969), p. 45.

3. King James, Authorized Version, Rev. 21:16.

4. William Penn, "Instructions . . . to . . . my Commissioners for the Settling of the . . . Colony . . . ," in Samuel Hazard, *Annals of Pennsylvania* (Philadelphia, 1850); cited in Reps, *Town Planning*, p. 208.

5. Undated report by L'Enfant to Washington, ibid., p. 319.

6. Frederick Law Olmsted and Calvert Vaux, "Preliminary Report to the Commissioners for Laying Out a Park in Brooklyn" (1866) and "Report of the Landscape Architects and Superintendents to the President of the Board of Commissioners of Prospect Park, Brooklyn (1868); rpt. in *Landscape into Cityscape: Frederick Law Olmsted's Plans for a Greater New York City*, ed. Albert Fein (New York: Van Nostrand Reinhold, 1967), pp. 126, 131.

7. Olmsted and Vaux, "Preliminary Report," p. 126.

8. Saint-Gaudens, in Charles Moore, *Daniel H. Burnham: Architect Planner of Cities*, 2 vols. (Boston: Houghton Mifflin, 1921), 1:47.

9. Louis Sullivan, *The Autobiography of an Idea* (New York: Press of the American Institute of Architects, 1924), p. 325.

10. Hamlin Garland, *Son of the Middle Border* (New York: Macmillan, 1917; 1962), p. 389.

11. Charles Dickens, *American Notes and Pictures from Italy* (1842; New York: Oxford University Press, 1957), p. 116.

12. Henry Adams, *The Education of Henry Adams* (1918; Boston: Houghton Mifflin, 1974), p. 99.

13. McMillan, in Constance McLaughlin Green, *Washington: A History of the Capital, 1800–1950*, 2 vols. (Princeton, N.J.: Princeton University Press, 1962), 2:54.

14. Senate Parks Commission, in Moore, *Burnham*, 1:144–45.

15. Lewis Mumford, *Sticks and Stones* (New York: Boni and Liveright, 1924), pp. 141–42.

16. Max Bond, interview with the author, October 24, 1984.

17. Ibid.

18. Tom Carhart, in Christopher Buckley, "The Wall," *Esquire*, September 1985, p. 92.

19. Nelson Rockefeller, in Joseph E. Persico, *The Imperial Rockefeller* (New York: Simon & Schuster, 1982), p. 204.

20. Jacobs, in Michael Kramer and Sam Roberts, *An Investigative Biography of Nelson Rockefeller* (New York: Basic Books, 1976), p. 158.

21. Robert F. Brown, "The Aesthetic Transformation of an Industrial Community," *Winterthur Portfolio* 12 (1977): 47.

22. Michael Olmert, "The New, No-Frills Williamsburg," *Historic Preservation* 37 (October 1985): 27–33.

23. Charles B. Hosmer, Jr., "The Colonial Revival in the Public Eye: Williamsburg and the Early Garden Restoration," in Alan Axelrod, ed., *The Colonial Revival in America* (New York: W. W. Norton, 1985), p. 53.

24. Leon Krier, interview with the author, October 24, 1984.

25. Ibid.

26. Rockefeller, in Parke Rouse, Jr., "When Williamsburg Woke Up" (Williamsburg, Va.: privately printed, 1977).

27. Mumford, *Sticks and Stones*, pp. 195–96.

28. F. Scott Fitzgerald, *The Great Gatsby* (New York: Charles Scribner's Sons, 1925), p. 218.

Picture Credits

Credits for illustrations from top to bottom are separated by semicolons; from left to right, by dashes.

HALF-TITLE PAGE: Culver Pictures
TITLE PAGE: B. R. Jawitz/The Image Bank
EPIGRAPH: Andy Carr/Photo Researchers, Inc.

CHAPTER ONE Opening page: Scott Ramsey. 2, 3: Culver Pictures. 5: J. D. Levine/Yale University; Joseph W. Molitar. 6, 7: Darius Kinsey Collection, Whatcom Museum of History & Art, Bellingham, Washington. 8: John Lewis Stage/The Image Bank (both). 10: Murray Grigor. 11: Murray Grigor; Howard Johnson Company; CBS. 13: Massachusetts Historical Society. 14: New York Public Library. 14, 15: Scott Ramsey. 16: Frank Lloyd Wright Foundation. 17: George Roos, Courtesy of Avery Architectural and Fine Arts Library, Columbia University. 18: Myron Davis, *Life* Magazine © 1946, Time Inc. 19: Ezra Stoller/ESTO © 1945. 20, 21: Hedrich Blessing. 22: Hill-Stead Museum. 23: Avon Old Farms School — Murray Grigor. 26, 27: Ezra Stoller Associates. 28: DOTY/*Life* Magazine © 1949, Time Inc. 29: George Leavens. 31: Norman McGrath; Murray Grigor. 32: Chuck Place/The Image Bank. 33: ESTO Photographics, Inc. 34: ESTO Photographics, Inc. 36, 37: Arthur Meyerson/The Image Bank. 38: Norman McGrath.

CHAPTER TWO 40: J. Miller/Photo Researchers, Inc. 42: Vassar College. 44, 45: Robert Llewellyn. 46: Elliott Erwitt/Magnum Photos, Inc. 47: Elliott Erwitt/Magnum Photos, Inc. 49: Culver Pictures. 50: Culver Pictures. 50, 51: Culver Pictures. 54: Margot Granitsas/Photo Researchers, Inc. 55: Michael de Camp/The Image Bank. 56: The New-York Historical Society. 58: Culver Pictures. 59: Culver Pictures (both). 60: Patti McConville/The Image Bank. 61: Steve Dunwell/The Image Bank. 62: Steve Dunwell/The Image Bank; Richard Longstreath; Charles Erickson/Yale University. 66: Richard Longstreath. 67: Patti McConville/The Image Bank. 68: Robert A. Isaacs/Photo Researchers, Inc. 69: Weinberg-Clark/The Image Bank; Mike Schneps/The Image Bank. 70: Yukio Futagawa. 71: Yukio Futagawa. 72: Detroit Public Library. 76, 77: Melanie Kaestner/Zephyr Pictures. 78: Susan Zehl/Cold Spring Harbor Research Laboratory Archives (both). 80: Eero Saarinen Papers, Yale University Library. 82: Tim Street-Porter.

CHAPTER THREE 84: Karen Halverson. 86: C. Vergara/Photo Researchers, Inc. (both). 87: Day Williams/Photo Researchers, Inc. — C. Vergara/Photo Researchers, Inc. 88: Mark Twain Memorial, Hartford. 89: Alexander O. Boulton. 90: Alexander O. Boulton. 91: Alexander O. Boulton (both). 92: Mark Twain Memorial, Hartford. 95: Karen Halverson. 96: Karen Halverson (all). 97: Karen Halverson. 98: Biltmore House (both). 99: Biltmore House & Gardens. 100: Biltmore House. 102: Isabella Stewart Gardner Museum, Boston (all). 104: Isabella Stewart Gardner Museum, Boston. 105: Isabella Stewart Gardner Museum, Boston. 106: R. A. M. Stern (both). 107: R. A. M. Stern. 108: Robert Isear/Photo Researchers, Inc. 110: Culver Pictures. 111: James Abbee. 112, 113: René Burri/Magnum Photos, Inc. 115: Hiroji Kuboto/Magnum Photos, Inc. 118: Julius Shulman. 119: Courtesy of Friends of Hollyhock House. 120: Virginia Ernst Kazor. 120, 121: Virginia Ernst Kazor.

CHAPTER FOUR 124: Childs Gallery, Boston. 126: Metropolitan Museum of Art, Harris Brisbane Dick Fund, 1924. 126, 127: Stuart Klipper. 130: Dr. George Gerster/Photo Researchers, Inc.; Tom McHugh/Photo Researchers, Inc.; Allen Green/Photo Researchers, Inc. 130, 131: Tom McHugh/Photo Researchers, Inc. 132: Ed Stoecklein, Courtesy of R. A. M. Stern. 133: R. A. M. Stern. 134: Culver Pictures — Library of Congress. 135: Rare Book Division, New York Public Library. 136: Museum of the City of New York (both). 136, 137: Collection of Mr. & Mrs. Martin Goodman. 140, 141: Norman McGrath. 141: The New-York Historical Society. 144: Tom Crane/Antiques Magazine. 145: Tom Crane/Antiques Magazine. 146: Riverside Historical Commission; R. A. M. Stern. 147: Chicago Historical Society. 148: Chicago Historical Society; Paul Petraitis; Library of Congress. 148, 149: Chicago Historical Society. 152, 153: Missouri Historical Society. 155: Frank Lloyd Wright Foundation. 156, 157: Culver Pictures. 157: L. H. C. Newsclipping File. 159: Allen Green/Photo Researchers, Inc. 160: Scott Ramsey — Dukes County Historical Society, Edgartown. 165: Bob Gelberg/Photo Researchers, Inc. 166: Steven Brook Studios; Steven Brook Studios, Courtesy of Andres Duany & Elizabeth Plater-Zyberk, Architects. 167: Steven Brook Studios.

CHAPTER FIVE 168: Fossil Films & Photos. 170: Culver Pictures. 171: Culver Pictures. 172: Wayne Andrews. 172, 173: Culver Pictures. 176: Adirondack Museum; Culver Pictures. 177: Culver Pictures (both). 178: Harvey Kaiser. 179: Richard J. Linke, Adirondack Museum. 182: Fossil Films & Photos (both). 182, 183: Culver Pictures. 184: Brown Brothers. 186, 187: Wayne Andrews. 190: Newport Historical Society. 191: *Harper's Weekly*, 1885. 192, 193: ATA Foundation, Photo by John Tennant. 196: United Press International — The Preservation Society of Newport County. 199: House & Garden Photo/The Preservation Society of Newport County. 200, 201: The Preservation Society of Newport County. 202: Culver Pictures. 203: Library of Congress (both). 204: Courtesy of Donald W. Curl. 205: Murray Grigor — Walter Smalling, Jr. 206: Dade Heritage Trust (both). 207: Dade Heritage Trust (both). 208: John Margolies (both). 209: Ezra Stoller/ESTO © 1956. 212: Walt Disney Productions.

CHAPTER SIX 214: Hedrich Blessing. 216: Museo Civico, Siena-Grassi. 217: Library of Congress/Collection of the Architect of the Capitol; Library of Congress. 218: Robert Llewellyn. 219: Courtesy of The New-York Historical Society. 221: Balthazar Korab Ltd. — Robert Lautman, Courtesy of I. M. Pei & Partners. 223: Kevin Roche/John Dinkeloo & Associates. 224: Ezra Stoller/ESTO © 1950; Wayne Andrews. 225: © The Frank Lloyd Wright Foundation 1963, Courtesy of the Frank Lloyd Wright Memorial Foundation. 228: Culver Pictures. 228, 229: Culver Pictures. 231: Goodspard Collection, Worcester Art Museum; Courtesy of The Rhode Island Historical Society. 232: Culver Pictures. 234: Culver Pictures (both). 235: David R. Philips Collection, Chicago Architectural Photography Company. 236, 237: Hedrich Blessing. 238: Culver Pictures (both). 239: Culver Pictures. 240: Murray Grigor. 241: Murray Grigor. 242: James A. Sugar/Black Star; National Gallery of Art, Washington, D.C. 243: James A. Sugar/Black Star. 244: Cervin Robinson © 1984/Cesar Pelli & Associates. 245: Balthazar Korab Ltd. (all). 246: George Heinrich. 247: Wolfgang Hoyt Esto/ESTO Photographics, Inc. 248, 249: © The Frank Lloyd Wright Foundation 1959, Courtesy of the Frank Lloyd Wright Memorial Foundation.

CHAPTER SEVEN 250: Mike Schneps/The Image Bank. 252: Cervin Robinson © 1985; Library of Congress. 252: Richard Nickel. 254: Berenice Abbott/Museum of the City of New York. 255: Culver Pictures. 256: Elliott Erwitt/Magnum Photos. 258: Museum of the City of New York. 259: Museum of the City of New York. 261: F. W. Woolworth Co. 262: George Roos, Courtesy of Avery Architectural & Fine Arts Library, Columbia University. 263: The Museum of Modern Art Film Stills Archive (both). 264: Norman McGrath. 265: Norman McGrath. 266: The Museum of Modern Art Film Stills Archive; Lewis W. Hine/George Eastman House. 267: Culver Pictures. 270: Norman McGrath. 271: Wurts Photo, Museum of the City of New York; Rockefeller Center, Inc. 272: Wurts Photo, Museum of the City of New York. 273: Wurts Photo, Museum of the City of New York (both). 274: Rockefeller Center, Inc. 275: René Burn/Magnum Photos — Norman McGrath. 276: Rockefeller Center Management Corporation. 278: Lucas Monroe Collection, Museum of the City of New York. 280, 281: Marc Romanelli/The Image Bank. 282: The Museum of Modern Art Film Stills Archive. 284: Ghizzonidi Scotti; New York Public Library. 286: Hedrich Blessing (both). 287: Ezra Stoller Associates. 289: Scott Ramsey; C. Vergara/Photo Researchers, Inc. 290, 291: Mitchell Funk/The Image Bank. 292: Norman McGrath. 293: Norman McGrath.

CHAPTER EIGHT 294: John Lewis Stage/The Image Bank. 296: New York Public Library/Stokes Collection. 297: Archivo General de Indias, Sevilla; Witte Museum. 298: Methodist Collection of Drew University, Madison, New Jersey. 298, 299: New York Public Library/Stokes Collection. 299: Louis Falquet/Bibliothèque Nationale, Dépôt des Cartes et Plans de Marine, Paris. 300: Princeton University Library, The Berthier Papers. 303: Library of Congress. 304, 305: Culver Pictures. 306: Chicago Historical Society. 307: Culver Pictures. 309: Culver Pictures. 311: Chicago Historical Society. 312: © 1909, The Commercial Club of Chicago. 314, 315: *Harper's Weekly*, January 4, 1862. 315: Library of Congress. 316: Library of Congress. 317: Jim Pickerell/Black Star. 319: Library of Congress/Collection of the Architect of the Capitol. 320, 321: Christopher Morris/Black Star. 322: United Press International. 324: Alvis Upitis/The Image Bank. 325: R. A. M. Stern (both). 326: Culver Pictures. 326, 327: Culver Pictures. 330: John Lewis Stage/The Image Bank. 333: John Lewis Stage/The Image Bank.

Index